CHILTON'S
AUTO REPAIR MANUAL 1985

Domestic and Canadian Cars from 1978 through 1985

Editorial Director	Alan F. Turner
Executive Editor	Kerry A. Freeman, S.A.E.
Senior Editor	Richard J. Rivele, S.A.E.
Project Coordinator	Martin Gunther
Editorial Staff	John M. Baxter
	A. Lindsay Brooke
	Tony Molla
	W. Calvin Settle, Jr.
	Ron Webb
Production Manager	John J. Cantwell
Manager, Editing and Design	Dean F. Morgantini, S.A.E.
Production Coordinator	Robin S. Miller
Mechanical Artists	Margaret A. Stoner
	Cynthia Fiore
	William Gaskins
OFFICERS	
President	Lawrence A. Fornasieri
Vice President & General Manager	John P. Kushnerick

CHILTON BOOK COMPANY
Chilton Way, Radnor, PA 19089

Manufactured in USA
© 1984 by Chilton Book Company
ISBN 0-8019-7470-4
Library of Congress Card No. 76-648878
ISSN No 0069-3634
234567890 321098765

CAR MODELS

CONTENTS

CAR SECTIONS

UNIT REPAIR SECTIONS

INDEX

R & I: Removal and Installation

Pontiac RWD	GM "A" & "X" Body	GM "C" Body	GM "E" & "K" Body	GM "F" Body	GM "H" Body	GM "J" Body	GM "P" Body	GM "T" Body	Sprint	
11	12	13	14	15	16	17	18	19	20	
C500	C528	C573	C603	C644	C679	C708	C744	C774	C802	Alternator R & I
U39	U39	U39	U39	U39	U39	U39	U39	U39	—	Alternator Overhaul
C511	C553	C581	C608	C659	C689	C726	C753	C791	—	Auto Transmission R & I
U395	U395	U395	U395	U395	U395	U395	U395	U395	—	Service
C511	C555	C582	C608	C660	C691	C727	C754	C792	—	Axle Shaft
C513	C557	C583	C614	C662	C691	C730	C756	C793	—	Ball Joints
C515	C558	C586	C616	C665	C694	C736	C761	C794	C809	Brakes
C507	C548	C580	C606	C655	C686	C721	C751	C788	—	Camshaft
C502	C531	C575	C603	C646	C681	C712	—	C777	—	Carburetor R & I
U59	U59	U59	U59	U59	U59	U59	U59	U59	—	Specifications & Overhaul
C509	C551	—	—	C657	C687	C724	C753	C789	—	Clutch
—	C562	C589	—	—	—	C733	C763	C796	—	Combination Switch
—	C555	C582	C609	—	—	C727	C754	—	—	CV–Joint
C506	C544	C577	C604	C655	C686	C718	C750	C785	—	Cylinder Head
C503	C531	C577	C604	—	—	—	—	C779	—	Diesel Injection
U13	U13	U13	U13	—	—	—	—	U13	—	Diesel Service
C511	—	—	—	C660	C690	—	—	—	—	Differential
C501	C528	C574	C604	C644	C679	C709	C745	C775	C804	Distributor R & I
U219	U219	U219	U219	U219	U219	U219	U219	U219	—	Overhaul
C511	C555	C582	C608	C660	C691	C727	C754	C792	C808	Drive Axles
C511	C555	—	—	C659	C690	—	—	C791	—	Driveshaft
C500	C528	C574	C603	C644	C679	C709	C744	C775	—	Electronic Ignition
C501	C528	C574	C604	C644	C679	C709	C745	C775	C804	Distributor R & I
C501	C529	C575	C603	C646	C680	C710	C745	C776	—	Timing Adjustment
U219	U219	U219	U219	U219	U219	U219	U219	U219	—	Testing & Overhaul
C504	C535	C576	U259	C650	C683	C713	C747	C781	C807	Emission Controls
C503	C533	C575	C603	C649	C683	C712	C746	C780	C805	Engine Cooling
C504	C535	C577	C604	C650	C684	C713	C747	C781	C808	Engine R & I
U307	U307	U307	U307	U307	U307	U307	U307	U307	—	Engine Rebuilding
C505	C540	C579	C605	C650	C685	C720	C749	C784	—	Exhaust Manifold
C489	C525	C570	C597	C631	C676	C705	C742	C772	C802	Firing Order
C507	C545	C577	C606	C655	C686	C720	C750	C786	—	Front Cover
U499	U499	U499	U499	U499	U499	U499	U499	U499	—	Front End Alignment
C500	C527	C573	C603	C644	C679	C707	C743	C774	C801	Specifications
C512	C556	C583	C612	C661	C675	C728	C756	C792	C809	Front Suspension
C502	C530	C575	C603	C648	C681	C712	C746	C777	—	Fuel Filter
—	C531	C575	C603	C647	—	C712	C746	—	—	Fuel Injection
C501	C530	C575	C603	C647	C681	C710	C745	C777	C805	Fuel Pump
C519	C568	—	C620	C671	C701	C740	C768	C799	C814	Fuse Box
C520	C566	—	C621	C670	C699	C740	C767	C798	—	Heater
C502	C530	C575	C603	C646	C682	C712	—	C778	—	Idle Speed and Mixture
C517	C563	C589	C617	C667	C696	C734	C764	C799	—	Ignition Lock and Switch
C501	C529	C575	C603	C646	C680	C710	C745	C776	—	Ignition Timing
C518	C565	—	C618	C668	C697	C737	C765	C797	C814	Instrument Cluster
C504	C539	C577	C605	C651	C685	C719	C749	C783	—	Intake Manifold
C513	C557	C584	C614	C662	C692	C731	C758	C793	—	Lower Control Arm
—	C556	C582	—	—	—	C728	C759	—	—	MacPherson Strut R & I

(Continued on next page)

INDEX

	AMC	Chrysler FWD	Chrysler RWD	Ford FWD	Ford RWD	Buick RWD	Cadillac RWD	Corvette	Chevrolet RWD	Oldsmobile RWD
	1	2	3	4	5	6	7	8	9	10
MacPherson Strut Overhaul	—	—	U449	U449	U449	U449	—	—	—	—
Maintenance	U2	U2	U2	U2	U2	U2	U2	U2	U2	U2
Manual Steering Gear	C51	C98	C138	C183	C268	—	—	C393	C434	C475
Manual Transaxle R & I	—	—	C130	C177	—	—	—	—	—	—
Manual Transaxle Overhaul	—	—	U327	U327	—	—	—	—	—	—
Manual Transmission R & I	C38	C86	C130	—	C245	C317	—	C381	C425	C470
Manual Trans. Overhaul	U327	U327	—	—	U327	U327	—	U327	U327	U327
Master Cylinder R & I	C51	C97	—	C182	C267	C322	C359	C392	C432	C475
Master Cylinder Overhaul	U463	U463	U463	U463	U463	U463	U463	U463	U463	U463
Neutral Safety Switch	U395	U395	U395	U395	U395	U395	U395	U395	U395	U395
Oil Pan R & I Engine	C34	C83	C128	C174	C238	C315	C352	C378	C423	C469
Transmission	U395	U395	U395	U395	U395	U395	U395	U395	U395	U395
Oil Pump	C35	C84	C129	C174	C242	C315	C351	C378	C424	C469
Parking Brake Adj.	C51	C97	C138	C182	C268	C322	C358	C392	C432	C475
Piston and Connecting Rod	C33	C83	C128	C174	C242	C314	C351	C377	C423	C469
Power Steering Gear	C52	C98	C138	C183	C269	C323	C360	C393	C434	C475
Power Steering Pump	C52	C98	C139	—	C270	C323	C360	C393	C433	C476
Radiator	C16	C74	C119	C160	C221	C308	C343	C376	C416	C462
Radio	C55	C101	C143	C186	C278	C325	C363	C395	C437	C478
Rear Axle	C45	C90	—	C179	C252	C318	C353	C382	C427	C471
Rear Main Oil Seal	C35	C84	C129	C177	C243	C316	C352	C378	C424	C469
Rear Suspension	C50	C95	C136	C181	C259	C321	C357	C387	C430	C474
Regulator	C11	C68	C116	C152	C211	C305	—	—	C413	C457
Rocker Shafts/Arms	C25	C77	C121	C167	C230	C313	C346	C377	C419	C465
Serial Numbers	C2	C60	C112	C148	C193	C288	C330	C368	C401	C443
Shock Absorbers	C46,C50	C91,C95	C136	—	C261	C321	C354	C384	C428	C472
Specifications	C4	C62	C111	C148	C195	C289	C331	C369	C402	C444
Springs Front	C46	—	C136	C180	C254	C320	C355	C384	C428	C473
Springs Rear	C50	C95	C137	C181	C259	C321	C357	C388	C431	C474
Starter	C11	C68	C116	C152	C211	C305	C337	C373	C413	C457
Steering	C51	C98	C138	C183	C268	C323	C359	C392	C433	C475
Thermostat	C18	C75	C119	C160	C221	C308	C343	C377	C416	C463
Timing Belt	C30	—	C124	C170	C234	—	—	—	—	—
Timing Belt/Chain Cover	C28	C80	C124	C172	C234	C313	C349	C377	C421	C466
Timing Belt/Chain	C30	C80	C124	C172	C234	C313	C349	C377	C422	C467
Troubleshooting	U509	U509	U509	U509	U509	U509	U509	U509	U509	U509
Turbocharger	—	—	U215	C167	C228	C309	—	—	—	—
Turn Signal Switch	C53	C98	C139	C184	C272	C324	C359	C394	C434	C476
U–Joints	C45	U435	—	—	C252	C318	C353	C382	C427	C471
Upper Control Arm	C47	C94	—	—	C254	C319	C356	C386	C430	C473
Valve Adjustment	C25	C78	C121	C167	C229	C313	C346	C378	C418	C465
Vehicle Indentification	C1	C57	C109	C147	C189	C285	C329	C367	C399	C441
Water Pump	C17	C74	C119	C160	C221	C308	C343	C377	C416	C463
Wheel Alignment	U499	U499	U499	U499	U499	U499	U499	U499	U499	U499
Adjustment	U499	U499	U499	U499	U499	U499	U499	U499	U499	U499
Specifications	C9	C67	C115	C151	C707	C304	C336	C372	C412	C457
Wheel Bearings (Front)	C48	C94	—	—	C258	C321	C356	C386	C428	C473
Wheel Bearings (Rear)	C45	C90	C137	C179	C252	C318	C353	C390	C427	C471
Wheel Cylinders	U463	U463	U463	U463	U463	U463	U463	U463	U463	U463
Windshield Wipers	C54	C101	C142	C186	C272	C325	C363	C395	C437	C477

R & I: Removal and Installation

HOW TO USE THIS MANUAL

This manual is arranged in two sections:

Car Section

Car Sections are grouped by manufacturer and arranged in alphabetical order. The text and illustrations that comprise the service procedures in each Car Section are arranged in the following order of systems and components: Charging, Starting, Ignition, Fuel, and Cooling Systems; Emission Controls, Engine, Clutch, Manual Transmission, Automatic Transmission, Driveshaft and U-Joints, Rear Axle, Jacking and Hoisting, Front Suspension, Rear Suspension, Brakes, Steering, Instrument Panel, Windshield Wipers, Radio, and Heater. Specifications are always located at the front of each section. All illustrations are located as close as possible to the pertinent text. Procedures are for all models in the particular section unless specifically noted otherwise.

Unit Repair Section

The Unit Repair Section contains troubleshooting and overhaul procedures for the major components and systems of your car, and is intended to be used in conjunction with the Car Sections. For example, if your car's engine is misfiring and you do not know the cause, use the "Troubleshooting" portion of the Unit Repair Section to find the cause and its remedy. If the cause should prove to be defective piston rings which are allowing oil to foul the spark plugs, the remedy is to overhaul the engine. Turn to the proper Car Section to find the procedure for removing the engine from the car. After you have removed the engine, turn to "Engine Rebuilding" in the Unit Repair Section and follow the steps listed there to overhaul the engine.

Most Unit Repair Sections are arranged by brands, manufacturers, or types of components rather than models of cars, and all overhaul procedures begin with the component removed from the car. The reason for this division of material is economic. The steps involved in overhauling an engine, for example, are virtually the same for all engines, but the operation of removing the engine from the car varies greatly from model to model. By combining where possible and separating where necessary, we are able to publish the maximum amount of information.

Locating Information

The Table of Contents, at the front of the book, lists the beginning of each Car and Unit Repair Section in the manual. The Car Sections are grouped by manufacturer. There is also an alphabetical listing of names of cars, so that you can find the right section quickly, even if you are not sure of the manufacturer. Car Section pages are prefixed with the letter "C." Unit Repair Section pages are prefixed with the letter "U."

To find the page number for a particular Car Section, you need only look in the Table of Contents. Once you have found the proper section, you may wish to find where specific procedures are located in that section. Turn to the Index on the following page and read across the top of the grid until you reach the number that corresponds to the car section. When the proper column has been found, read down the side column to the procedure in question. The intersection of the two columns will provide the page number for the procedure.

Safety Notice

Proper service and repair procedures are vital to the safe, reliable operation of all motor vehicles, as well as the personal safety of those performing repairs. This manual outlines procedures for servicing and repairing vehicles using safe effective methods. The procedures contain many NOTES, CAUTIONS and WARNINGS which should be followed along with standard safety procedures to eliminate the possibility of personal injury or improper service which could damage the vehicle or compromise its safety.

It is important to note that repair procedures and techniques, tools and parts for servicing motor vehicles, as well as the skill and experience of the individual performing the work may vary widely. It is not possible to anticipate all of the conceivable ways or conditions under which vehicles may be serviced, or to provide cautions as to all of the possible hazards that may result. Standard and accepted safety precautions and equipment should be used when handling toxic or flammable fluids, and safety goggles or other protection should be used during cutting, grinding, chiseling, prying, or any other process that can cause material removal or projectiles.

Some procedures require the use of tools specially designed for a specific purpose. Before substituting another tool or procedure, you must be completely satisfied that neither your personal safety nor the performance of the vehicle will be endangered.

Part Numbers

Part numbers listed in this book are not recommendations by Chilton for any product by brand name. They are references that can be used with interchange manuals and aftermarket supplier catalogs to locate each brand supplier's discrete part number.

American Motors
AMX, Concord, Eagle, SX-4
Gremlin, Matador, Pacer, Spirit

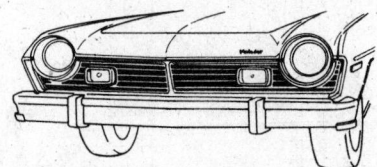

1978 Matador Coupe

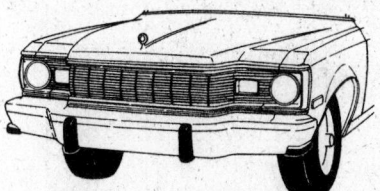

1978 Matador Sedan, Wagon

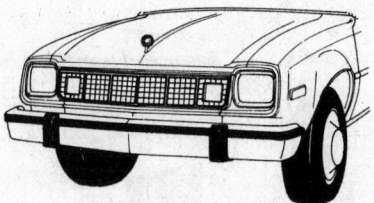

1978 Concord

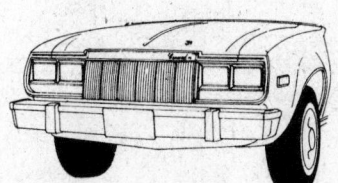

1979 Concord

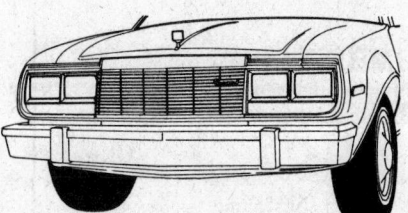

1980 Concord

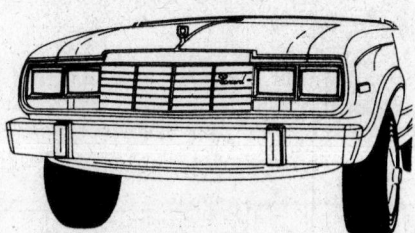

1981–83 Concord

1978 AMX

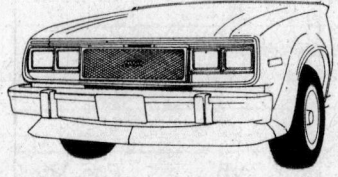

1979 AMX

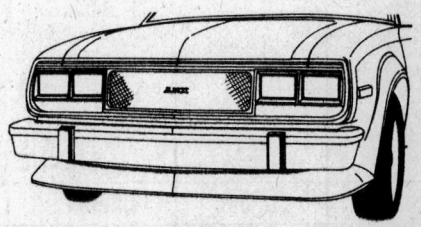

1980 AMX

C1

AMERICAN MOTORS

1978 Gremlin

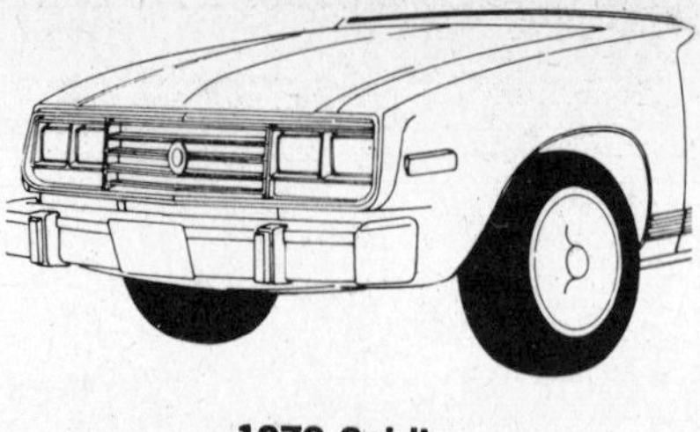

1979 Spirit

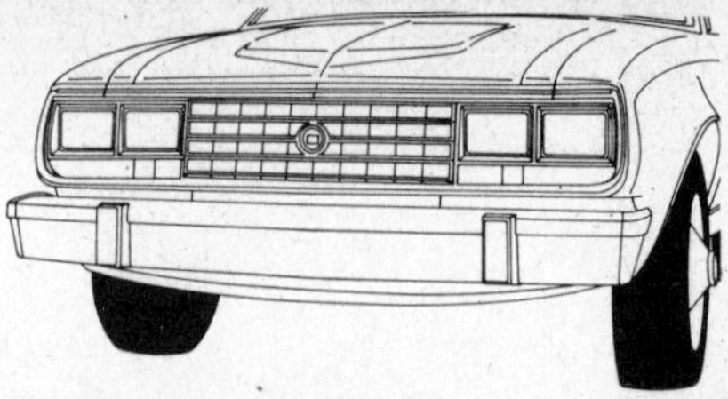

1980 Spirit

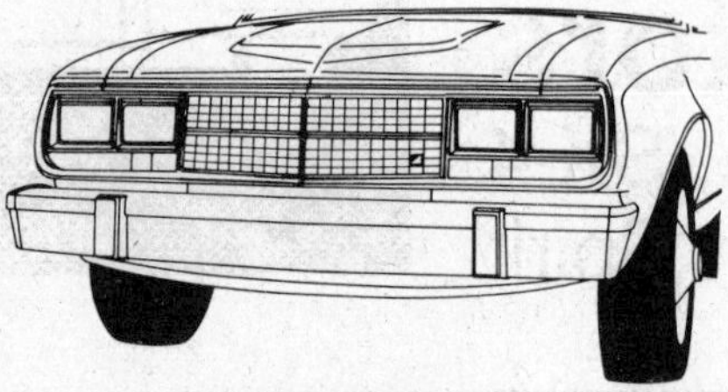

1981–83 Spirit

1978 Pacer

1979 Pacer

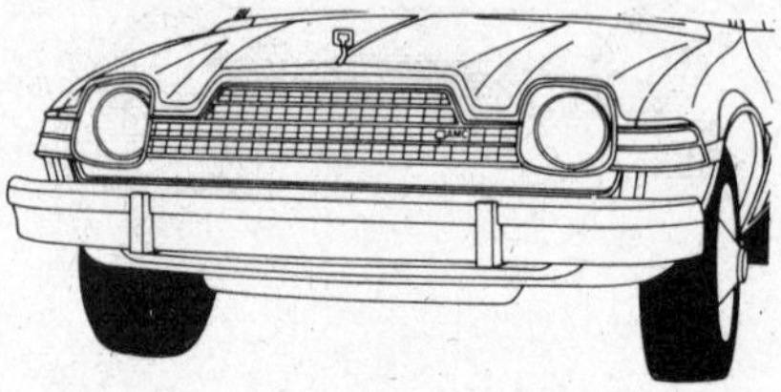

1980 Pacer

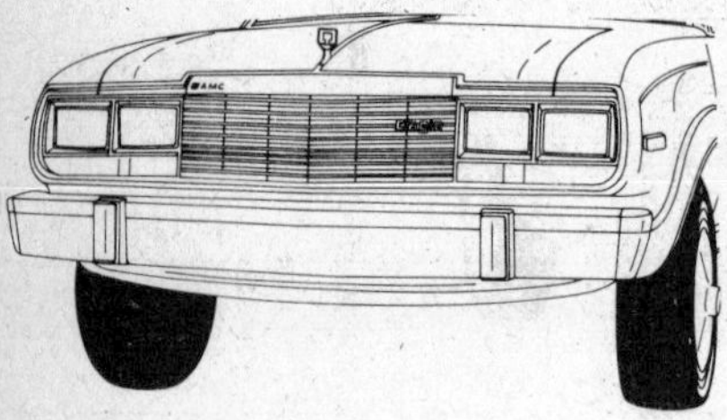

1980 Eagle

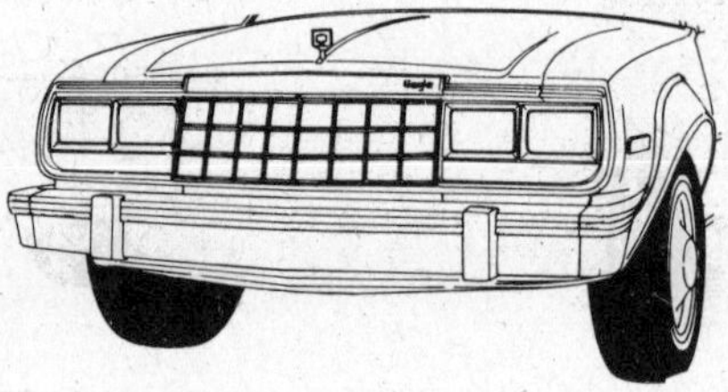

1981–85 Eagle

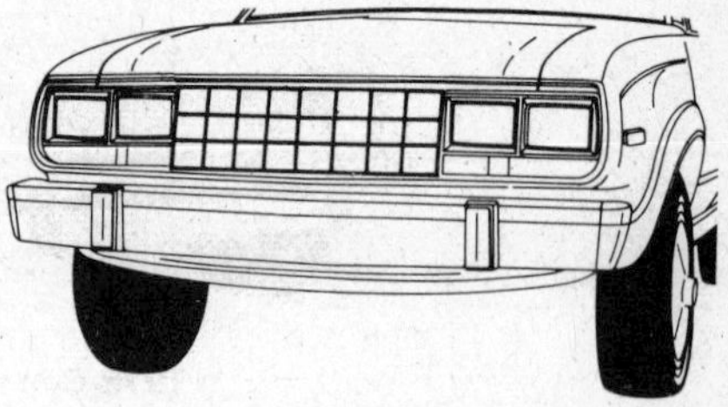

1981–85 Eagle SX-4

VEHICLE IDENTIFICATION NUMBER (VIN)

It is important for servicing and ordering parts to be certain of the vehicle and engine identification. The VIN (vehicle identification number) is a 13 or 17 digit number visible through the windshield on the driver's side of the dash and contains the vehicle and engine identification codes. It can be interpreted as follows:

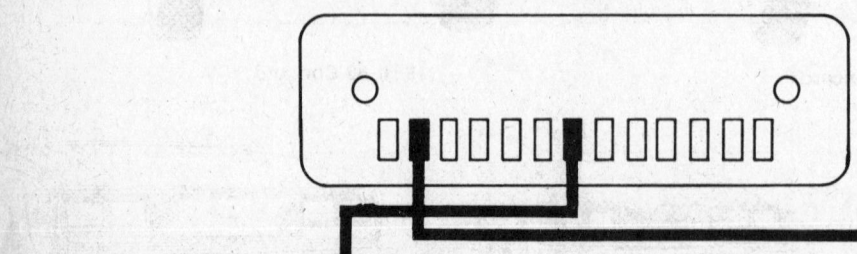

ENGINE CODE						MODEL YEAR CODE	
Code	Cu. In.	Liters	Cyl.	Carb.	Eng. Mfg.	Code	Year
G	121	2.0	4	2	VW	8	1978

ENGINE CODE						MODEL YEAR CODE	
Code	Cu. In.	Liters	Cyl.	Carb.	Eng. Mfg.	Code	Year
B	151	2.5	4	2	Pontiac	9	1979
E	232	3.8	6	1	AMC	0	1980
A	258	4.2	6	1	AMC		
C	258	4.2	6	2	AMC		
H	304	5.0	8	2	AMC		
N	360	5.9	8	2	AMC		

The thirteen digit Vehicle Identification Number can be used to determine engine application and model year. The second digit indicates model year, and the seventh digit indicates engine code.

VEHICLE IDENTIFICATION NUMBER (VIN)

It is important for servicing and ordering parts to be certain of the vehicle and engine identification. The VIN (vehicle identification number) is a 13 or 17 digit number visible through the windshield on the driver's side of the dash and contains the vehicle and engine identification codes. It can be interpreted as follows:

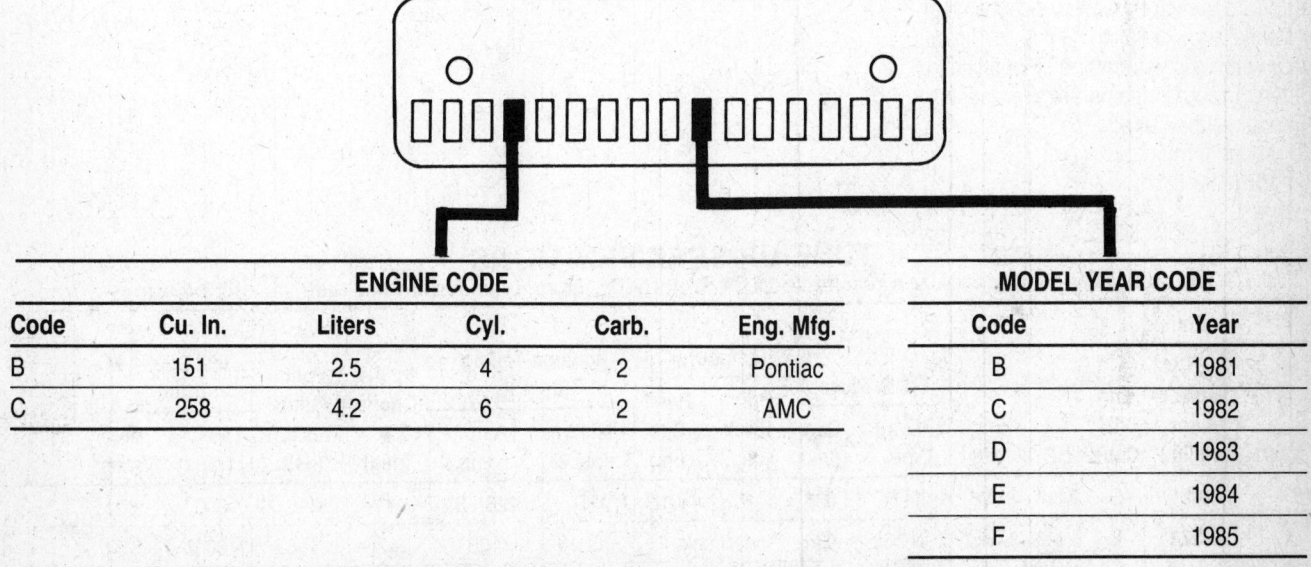

ENGINE CODE						MODEL YEAR CODE	
Code	Cu. In.	Liters	Cyl.	Carb.	Eng. Mfg.	Code	Year
B	151	2.5	4	2	Pontiac	B	1981
C	258	4.2	6	2	AMC	C	1982
						D	1983
						E	1984
						F	1985

The seventeen digit Vehicle Identification Number can be used to determine engine identification and model year. The tenth digit indicates model year, and the fourth digit indicates engine code.

GENERAL ENGINE SPECIFICATIONS

Year	Eng V.I.N. Code	Engine No. Cyl. Displacement Cu. In.	ENG. Mfg.	Carburetor Type	Horsepower @ rpm ■	Torque @ rpm (ft lbs) ■	Bore and Stroke (in.)	Compression Ratio	Oil Pressure @ 2000 rpm
'78	G	4-121	VW	2 bbl	80 @ 5000	105 @ 2800	3.410 × 3.320	8.1:1	28.5①
	E	6-232	AMC	1 bbl	90 @ 3400	168 @ 1600	3.750 × 3.500	8.0:1	46
	A	6-258	AMC	1 bbl	100 @ 3400	200 @ 1600	3.750 × 3.900	8.0:1	46
	C	6-258	AMC	2 bbl	120 @ 3600	201 @ 1800	3.750 × 3.900	8.0:1	46
	H	8-304	AMC	2 bbl	130 @ 3200	238 @ 2000	3.750 × 3.440	8.4:1	46
	N	8-360	AMC	2 bbl	140 @ 3350	278 @ 2000	4.080 × 3.440	8.25:1	46

GENERAL ENGINE SPECIFICATIONS

Year	Eng V.I.N. Code	Engine No. Cyl. Displacement Cu. In.	ENG. Mfg.	Carburetor Type	Horsepower @ rpm ■	Torque @ rpm (ft lbs) ■	Bore and Stroke (in.)	Compression Ratio	Oil Pressure @ 2000 rpm
'79	G	4-121	VW	2 bbl	80 @ 5000	105 @ 2800	3.410 × 3.320	8.1:1	28.5①
	E	6-232	AMC	1 bbl	90 @ 3400	168 @ 1600	3.750 × 3.500	8.0:1	46
	A	6-258	AMC	1 bbl	100 @ 3400	200 @ 1600	3.750 × 3.900	8.0:1	46
	C	6-258	AMC	2 bbl	110 @ 3200	210 @ 1800	3.750 × 3.900	8.3:1	46
	H	8-304	AMC	2 bbl	125 @ 3200	220 @ 2400	3.750 × 3.440	8.4:1	46
'80–'82	B	4-151	Pontiac	2 bbl	99 @ 4000	134 @ 2400	4.000 × 3.000	8.2:1②	36–41
	C	6-258	AMC	2 bbl	110 @ 3200	210 @ 1800	3.750 × 3.900	8.3:1	46
'83	B	4-151	Pontiac	2 bbl	99 @ 4000	134 @ 2400	4.000 × 3.000	8.3:1	36–41
	C	6-258	AMC	2 bbl	110 @ 3200	210 @ 1800	3.750 × 3.900	8.3:1	46
'84–'85	U	4-150	AMC	1 bbl	83 @ 4200	116 @ 2600	3.876 × 3.188	9.2:1	40
	C	6-258	AMC	2 bbl	110 @ 3200	210 @ 1800	3.750 × 3.900	8.3:1	46

■ Horsepower and torque are SAE net figures. They are measured at the rear of the transmission with all accessories installed and operating. Since the figures vary when a given engine is installed in different models, some are representative rather than exact.
① At sending unit
② 1981–82 8.3:1

TUNE-UP SPECIFICATIONS

(When analyzing compression test results, look for uniformity among cylinders rather than specific pressures.)

Year	Engine No. Cyl. Displacement (cu. in.)	Eng VIN Code	HP	Eng Mfg	Spark Plugs Orig. Type	Gap (in.)	Distributor Point Dwell (deg)	Point Gap (in.)	Ignition Timing (deg) ▲ Man. Trans. ●	Auto. Trans.	Valves Intake Opens ■ (deg)	Fuel Pump Pressure (psi)	Idle Speed ● (rpm) ▲ Man Trans	Auto Trans*
'78	4-121	G	2 bbl	VW	N-8L	.035	47	.018	12B	12B(8B)	41¾	4–6	900	800
	6-232	E	1 bbl	AMC	N-13L	.035	electronic		8B	10B	12	4–5	600	550
	6-258	A	1 bbl	AMC	N-13L	.035	electronic		(6B)①	(8B)①	12	4–5	600(850)	550(700)
	6-258	C	2 bbl	AMC	N-13L	.035	electronic		6B	8B	14½	4–5	600	600
	8-304	H	2 bbl	AMC	N-12Y	.035	electronic		—	10B(5B)①	14¾	5–6½	—	600(700)
	8-360	N	2 bbl	AMC	N-12Y	.035	electronic		—	10B	14¾	5–6½	—	600(650)
'79	4-121	G	2 bbl	VW	N-8L	.035	47	.018	12B②	12B(8B)	41¾	4–6	900	800
	6-232	E	1 bbl	AMC	N-13L	.035	electronic		8B	10B	12	4–5	600	550
	6-258	A	1 bbl	AMC	N-13L	.035	electronic			8B	12	4–5		700
	6-258	C	2 bbl	AMC	N-13L	.035	electronic		4B	8B	12	4–5	700	600
	8-304	H	2 bbl	AMC	N-12Y	.035	electronic		5B	8B	14¾	5–6½	800	600
'80	4-151	B	2 bbl	Pontiac	R44TSX	.060	electronic		10B(12B)	12B(10B)	33	6½–8	900	700
	6-258	C	2 bbl	AMC	N14LY④	.035	electronic		6B	10B③	14½	4–5	700	600
'81–'82	4-151	B	2 bbl	Pontiac	R44TSX	.060	electronic		10B⑤	12B③	25	6½–8	900	700
	6-258	C	2 bbl	AMC	RFN-14LY	.033	electronic		⑥	⑦	9	5–6½	700	600

TUNE-UP SPECIFICATIONS

(When analyzing compression test results, look for uniformity among cylinders rather than specific pressures.)

Year	No. Cyl. Displacement (cu. in.)	Eng VIN Code	HP	Eng Mfg	Spark Plugs Orig. Type	Gap (in.)	Distributor Point Dwell (deg)	Point Gap (in.)	Ignition Timing (deg) ▲ Man. Trans. ●	Auto. Trans.	Valves Intake Opens ■ (deg)	Fuel Pump Pressure (psi)	Idle Speed ● (rpm) ▲ Man Trans	Auto Trans*
'83	4-151	B	2 bbl	Pontiac	R44TSX	.060	electronic		10B⑤	12B③	25	6½–8	900	700
	6-258	C	2 bbl	AMC	RFN14LY	.033	electronic		⑥	⑦	9	5–6½	700	600
'84–'85	4-150	U	1 bbl	AMC	RFN14LY	.035	electronic		12B	12B	27B	6½–8	750	750
	6-258	C	2bbl	AMC	RFN14LY	.033	electronic		⑥	⑦	9	5–6½	700	600

▲ If underhood emissions decal differs, always use the specifications on the decal.
* With transmission in Drive
● Figure in parentheses indicates California engine
■ All figures before Top Dead Center
B Before Top Dead Center
TDC Top Dead Center (zero degrees)
— Not applicable
① High Altitude—10B

② 16B for models with code EH on upper right corner of emission information label.
③ 8B—Eagle for Calif. and all Pacer
④ N13L—Eagle
⑤ Eagle except for Calif.—11B
⑥ Concord, Spirit—6B
 Eagle except Calif.—8B
 Eagle Calif.—4B High Alt.—15B
⑦ Concord, Spirit—6B
 Eagle Except Calif.—8B
 Eagle Calif.—6B High Alt.—15B

FIRING ORDER

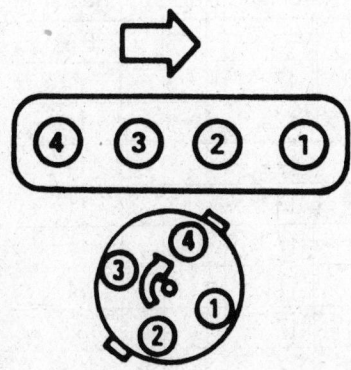

AMC 150-4 cylinder firing order: 4-3-2-1

AMC 151 4-cyl.
Engine firing order: 1-3-4-2
Distributor rotation: clockwise

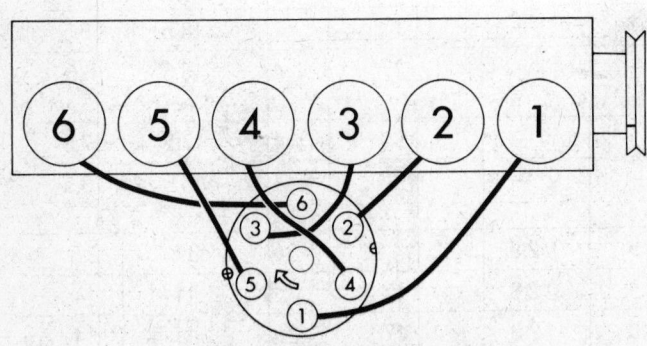

AMC 232, 258 6-cyl. 1978 and later
Engine firing order 1-5-3-6-2-4
Distributor rotation: clockwise

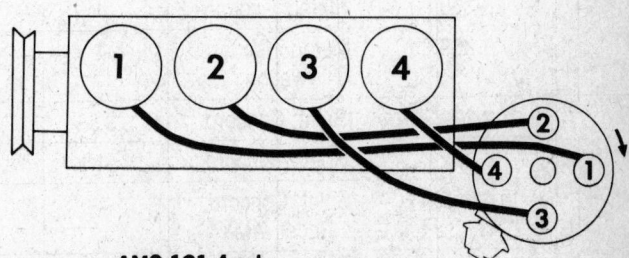

AMC 121 4-cyl.
Engine firing order: 1-3-4-2
Distributor rotation: clockwise

FIRING ORDERS

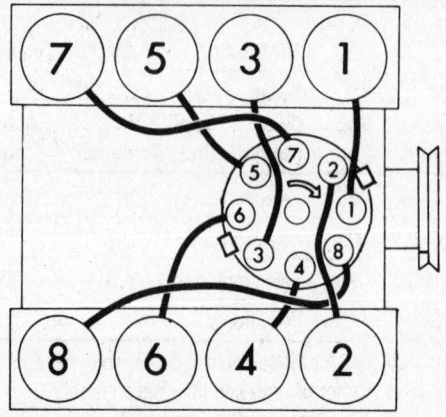

AMC 304, 360, 401 V8
Engine firing order: 1-8-4-3-6-5-7-2
Distributor rotation: clockwise

CAPACITIES

Year	Engine No. Cyl. Displacement (cu. in.)	Model	Engine Crankcase Add 1 Qt. For New Filter	Transmission (Pts. To Refill After Draining) Manual 3-Speed	4-Speed	Automatic	Drive Axle (pts)	Cooling System (qts) With Heater	With A/C
'78	4-121	Gremlin	3.5	—	2.4①	14.2	3	6.5	—
	6-232	Gremlin	4	3.5②	3.5	17	3	11	14
	6-232	Hornet, Concord	4	3.5②	3.5	17	3	11	11.5③
	6-232	Pacer	4	3.5②	3.5	17	3	14	14
	6-258	Gremlin	4	3.5②	3.5	17	3	11	14
	6-258	Hornet, Concord	4	3.5②	3.5	17	3	11	11.5③
	6-258	Pacer	4	3.5②	3.5	17	3	14	14
	6-258	Matador coupe	4	—	—	17	4	13.5	13.5
	6-258	Matador sedan, wagon	4	—	—	17	4	11.5	11.5
	8-304	Hornet, Concord, Pacer	4	—	—	17	4	16④	16④
	8-304	Matador coupe	4	—	—	17	4	18.5	18.5
	8-304	Matador sedan, wagon	4	—	—	17	4	16.5	16.5
	8-360	Matador coupe	4	—	—	19⑤	4	17.5	17.5
	8-360	Matador sedan, wagon	4	—	—	19⑤	4	15.5	15.5
'79	4-121	Spirit, Concord	3.5	2.5	2.8	14.2	3⑥	6.5	6.5
	6-232	Spirit, Concord	4	2.5	2.8	17	3⑥	11	14
	6-258	Spirit, Concord, Pacer, AMX	4	2.5	2.8	17	3⑥	11	14
	8-304	Spirit, Concord, Pacer, AMX	4	2.5	2.8	17	3⑥	18	18

CAPACITIES

Year	Engine No. Cyl. Displacement (cu. in.)	Model	Engine Crankcase Add 1 Qt. For New Filter	Transmission (Pts. To Refill After Draining) Manual 3-Speed	Transmission 4-Speed	Automatic	Drive Axle (pts)	Cooling System (qts) With Heater	Cooling System With A/C
'80	4-151	Spirit, Concord	3.5⑦	—	3.3	17	3	6.5	6.5
	6-258	Spirit, Concord Pacer, AMX	4	—	3.3	17	3	11⑧	11⑧
	6-258	Eagle	4	—	3.3⑨	17⑨	3⑩	11	14
'81–'83	4-151	Spirit, Concord	3.0	—	3.5⑪	14.2	3	6.5	6.5
	4-151	Eagle	3.0	—	3.5⑪	14.2	3⑩	6.5	6.5
'81–'85	6-258	Spirit, Concord	4.0	—	3.5⑪	17.0	3	11	14
	6-258	Eagle	4.0	—	3.5⑪	17.0	3⑩	14	14
'84–'85	4-150	Eagle	4.0	—	7.4	15.8	2.5	10.0	10.0

① 2.8—1978
② 3 pts—1978
③ 14.0—1978
④ 18.0—1978
⑤ 16.4—1978
⑥ 8.875 ring gear—4 pts

⑦ Add ½ qt. for new filter
⑧ 14.5 qts. in Pacer
⑨ Transfer case: 3.0 pts. until March 1980; 4.0 pts. thereafter
⑩ 2.5—front axle

⑪ 82 and later:
T4 Spirit-Concord; 4.0 pts.
T4 Eagle; 3.5 pts.
T5 Spirit-Concord; 4.5 pts.
T5 Eagle; 4.0 pts.
— Not applicable

VALVE SPECIFICATIONS

Year	Engine No. Cyl. Displacement (cu in.)	Seat Angle (deg) ■	Face Angle (deg) ●	Outer Spring Test Pressure (lbs @ in.)	Spring Installed Height (in.)	Stem to Guide Clearance (in.) Intake	Stem to Guide Clearance Exhaust	Stem Diameter (in.) Intake	Stem Diameter Exhaust
'78	4-121	45.75	45.33	160 @ 1.319②	1.7③	.0012–.0026	.0015–.0030	.3529	.3525
	6-232, 258	44.5	44	195 @ 1.411①	1¹³⁄₁₆	.0010–.0030	.0010–.002	.3720	.3722
	8-304, 360	44.5	44	213 @ 1.356	1¹³⁄₁₆	.0010–.0030	.0010–.0027	.3720	.3722
'79	4-121	44.75	45.33	160 @ 1.319②	1.7③	.0012–.0026	.0015–.0030	.3529	.3525
	6,232,258, 8,304	44.5	44	195 @ 1.411①	1¹³⁄₁₆	.0010–.0030	.0010–.0027	.3720	.3722
'80–'82	4-151	46	45	176 @ 1.254	④	.0010–.0027	.0010–.0027	.3423	.3423
	6-258	44.5	44	195 @ 1.411	1¹³⁄₁₆	.0010–.0030	.0010–.0030	.3720	.3720
'83	4-151	46	45	176 @ 1.254	1	.0010–.0027	.0010–.0027	.3423	.3423
	6-258	44.5	44	195 @ 1.411	1¹³⁄₁₆	.0010–.0030	.0010–.0030	.3720	.3720
'84–'85	4-150	45	44	212 @ 1.203	1¹¹⁄₃₂	.0010–.0030	.0010–.0030	.3115	.3115
	6-258	44.5	44	195 @ 1.411	1¹³⁄₁₆	.0010–.0030	.0010–.0030	.3720	.3720

● Exhaust valve face angles are shown. All intake valve face angles are 29°, except 121 and 151 cu. in. engines.
■ Exhaust valve seat angles are shown. All intake valve seat angles are 30°, except 121 and 151 cu. in. engines
① 204 @ 1.39 in. for 2 bbl—258
② Intake—166 @ 1.299
③ Inner spring—1.49 in.
④ Intake: 2.057 in.; exhaust: 1.730 in.

CRANKSHAFT AND CONNECTING ROD SPECIFICATIONS

(All measurements are given in inches)

Year	Engine	Crankshaft			Thrust on No.	Connecting Rod		
		Main Brg. Journal Dia	Main Brg. Oil Clearance	Shaft End-Play		Journal Diameter	Oil Clearance	Side Clearance
'78–'79	4-121	2.5177–2.5185	.0010–.0030	.0040–.0080	3	1.8880–1.8890	.0010–.0020	.002–.012
'78–'79	6-All	2.4986–2.5001	.0003–.0024	.0020–.0070	3	2.0934–2.0955	.0010–.0020	.005–.014
'78–'79	8-All	2.7474–2.7489①	.0003–.0020	.0030–.0080	3	③	.0010–.0030	.006–.018
'80–'83	4-151	2.2988	.0005–.0022	.0035–.0085	5	2.000	.0005–.0026	.017
'80–'85	6-258	2.4986–2.5001	.0010–.0030	.0015–.0065	3	2.0934–2.0955	.0010–.0030	.005–.014
'84–'85	4-150	2.4996–2.5001	.0010–.0025	.0015–.0060	2	2.0934–2.0955	.0010–.0030	.010–.019

① No. 5—2.7464–2.7479
② Rear main 1976—.002–.003; 1977 and later—.001–.003
③ All 304, 360—2.0934–2.0955; 401—2.2464–2.2485

CAMSHAFT SPECIFICATIONS

(All measurements in inches)

Engine	Journal Diameter					Bearing Clearance	Lobe Lift		Camshaft End Play
	1	2	3	4	5		Intake	Exhaust	
4-121	1.2579 1.2569	1.0220– 1.0212	1.0220– 1.0212	1.0220– 1.0212	1.0220– 1.0212	#1 .004–.002 2–5 .003–.002	.396 .396	.366	.0019–.0061
4-151	1.8690	1.8690	1.8690	—	—	.0007–.0027	.398	.398	.0015–.0050
6-232, 258	2.0290– 2.0300	2.0190– 2.0200	2.0090– 2.0100	1.9990– 2.0000	—	.001–.003	.254①	.254①	0
8-304, 360	2.1195– 2.1205	2.0895– 2.0905	2.0595– 2.0605	2.0295– 2.0305	1.9995– 2.0005	.001–.003	.266	.266	0
4-150	2.0290– 2.0300	2.0190– 2.0200	2.0009– 2.0100	1.9990– 2.0000	—	.001–.003	.265	.265	0

① 258 2-bbl: .248

TORQUE SPECIFICATIONS

(All specifications in ft. lb.)

Year	Engine	Cylinder Head Bolts	Connecting Rod Bearing Bolts	Main Bearing Bolts	Crank Pulley Bolt	Flywheel Bolts	Manifold	
							Intake	Exhaust
'78–79	4-121	65 cold 80 hot	41	58 47 rear	181	65	18	18
'78–80	6-232, 258	95–115	30–35	75–85	70–90	95–120	18–28	18–28
'81–85	6-258	80–90	30–35	75–85	70–90	95–115	18–28	18–28
'78–79	8-304, 360	100–120	30–35	90–105	80–100	95–120	37–47	20–30①
'80–83	4-151	80–103	27–33	62–68	157–163	65–71	34–40	36–42
'84–'85	4-150	80–90	30–35	75–85	75–85	50–65	20–25	20–25

① ⅜ inch bolts: 25
⁵⁄₁₆ inch bolts: 15

PISTON AND RING SPECIFICATIONS

(All measurements are given in inches. To convert inches to metric units, refer to the Metric Information section.)

Year	Engine Type/ Disp.	Piston-to-Bore Clearance	Ring Gap			Ring Side Clearance		
			Top Compression	Bottom Compression	Oil Control	Top Compression	Bottom Compression	Oil Control
'78–'79	4-121	.0007–.0017	.010–.020	.010–.020	.010–.016	.0012–.0024	.0012–.0024	.0012–.0024
'80–'83	4-151	.0025–.0033	.010–.022	.010–.028	.015–.055	.0030	.0030	.0000
'78–'80	6-232, 258	.0009–.0017	.010–.020	.010–.020	.010–.025	.0015–.0030	.0015–.0030	.0011–.0080
'81–'85	6-258	.0009–.0017	.010–.020	.010–.020	.010–.025	.0017–.0032	.0017–.0032	.0010–.0080
'78–'79	8-304	.0010–.0018	.010–.020	.010–.020	.010–.025	.0015–.0035	.0015–.0030	.0011–.0080
'78	8-360	.0012–.0020①	.010–.020	.010–.020	.015–.045	.0015–.0030	.0015–.0035	.0000–.0070
'84–'85	4-150	.0009–.0017	.010–.020	.010–.020	.010–.025	.0017–.0032	.0017–.0032	.0010–.0080

① Police 360—.0016–.0024

WHEEL ALIGNMENT SPECIFICATIONS

Year	Model	Caster		Camber		Toe-in (in.)	Steering Axis Inclin. (deg)	Wheel Pivot Ratio	
		Range (deg)	Pref Setting (deg)	Range (deg)	Pref Setting (deg)			Inner Wheel (deg)	Outer Wheel (deg)
'78	Concord, Gremlin, Matador	0–2P	1P	①	②	1/16 to 3/16	7¾	25	22
	Pacer	1P–3P	2P	①	②	1/16 to 3/16	7¾	25	22
'79–'80	AMX	0–2½P	1P	0–¾P	¼P	1/16 to 3/16	7¾	2	22
	Spirit, Concord	0–2½P	1P	0–¾P	¼P	1/16 to 3/16	7¾	25	22
	Pacer	1P–3½P	2P	0–¾P	¼P	1/16 to 3/16	7¾	25	22
'80	Eagle	3P–5P	4P	⅜N–⅜P	0	1/16 to 3/16③	11½	N.A.	N.A.
'81–'83	Spirit, Concord	0–2½P	1P	④	②	1/16 to 3/16	7¾	—	—
'81–'85	Eagle	2P–3P	2½P	⅛N–⅝P	⅜P	1/16 to 3/16③⑤	11½	N.A.	N.A.

N Negative
P Positive
N.A. Not Available
— Specifications not available at time of publication
① Left: ⅛P to ⅝P; Right: 0 to ½P
② Left: ⅜P; Right: ⅛P
③ Toe-out
④ Left: ¾P to ⅛P; Right: ½P to ①P
⑤ 1982 Eagles 1/16 toe-out, 1/16 toe in

FUSIBLE LINKS

Location	Color	Circuit Protected	Years Used				
			1978	1979	1980–81	1982–83	1984–85
Starter relay battery terminal to main wire harness	Red	Complete wiring	X	X	X	X	X
Horn relay battery terminal to main wire harness	Pink	Horn circuit	X	X	X	X	X
Starter relay battery terminal to rear window defogger switch	Red	Rear window defogger, (1980–85 headlights)	X	X	X	X	X
1-3 ignition switch terminal (single wire splits into two)*	Yellow	Tailgate motor and/or side window motors and throttle stop solenoid	X				
Battery terminal of solenoid to lamp	Pink	Engine compartment lamp	X	X			
Battery terminal of solenoid to A/C blower motor relay	Red	A/C blower motor	X				
S terminal of ignition switch to wiring harness	Green	Feed to starter solenoid S terminal	X				
Battery terminal of starter to harness	Pink	Rally Package Ammeter	X	X	X	X	
Block terminal to harness	Pink	Rally Package Ammeter	X				
Harness to dash conn.	Red	Headlight switch		X	X	X	
Battery terminal of starter solenoid to main wiring	Red	Ign./power option eng. comp. lamp, deck lid release					X
Battery terminal of start solenoid to main wiring	Red	Power Options					X
Alternator to battery terminal of starter solenoid	Red	Alternator output wire					X

GASOLINE TANK CAPACITIES
(Gals.)

Model	'78	'79	'80	'81	'82	'83	'84	'85
Gremlin 4 cyl.	15	—	—	—	—	—	—	—
Gremlin 6 cyl.	21	—	—	—	—	—	—	—
Hornet, Concord	22	22	22	22	22	22	—	—
Matador	25	—	—	—	—	—	—	—
Matador Wagon	21	—	—	—	—	—	—	—
Pacer	20	21	21	—	—	—	—	—
Spirit 4 cyl.	—	13	21	21	21	21	—	—
Spirit 6 & 8 cyl.	—	21	21	21	21	21	—	—
Eagle	—	—	22	22	①	①	①	①

① 21 gal: 97.19 wheel base
   22 gal: 109.27 wheel base

CHARGING SYSTEM

Delco-Remy, Motorcraft or Motorola alternators are used, depending on engine. A Bosch unit replaced the Motorcraft in 1979. Most 1980 models, except Eagles with heated rear windows and fog lights, use Delco-Remy alternators; the Eagles use the Bosch unit. Most 1981 and later models use Delco-Remy alternators.

For information on alternator and regulator repair and troubleshooting, please refer to "Charging and Starting" in the Unit Repair Section.

NOTE: Voltage regulators that are built into the alternator require alternator disassembly for replacement.

External Regulator

REMOVAL

Disconnect the negative battery cable. Disconnect plug to the regulator. Remove the metal screws which hold the regulator in place, and lift off the regulator.

Alternator

REMOVAL & INSTALLATION

1. Disconnect battery cables, negative cable first.
2. Disconnect and label the alternator wires or plug, then loosen adjusting bolt.
3. Remove the V-belt, mounting bolts and alternator.
4. To install, reverse removal procedure.
5. There are several methods used for tightening the belt. Some alternator brackets have a hole through which you can insert a bar to pry out on the front alternator housing, others have a hole into which you can insert a ½ in. square socket drive to pull out on the alternator, and others have a square boss around the adjusting bolt which takes a 1 in. open end wrench. If there are none of these systems, use a bar to pry against the *front alternator housing*. The longest run of belt should deflect about ½ in. under moderate thumb pressure.

STARTING SYSTEM

American Motors cars, except for the 151-4, are equipped with an integral positive engagement drive starter, and a separate starter relay. Cars equipped with the 151-4 engine do not have a separate relay.

For additional information on starters, please refer to "Charging and Starting" in the Unit Repair section.

Starter

REMOVAL & INSTALLATION

Disconnect the negative battery cable first, then the battery and solenoid lead at the starter, if used. From underneath the car, remove the bolts which hold the starter to the bellhousing (and starter-to-engine brace on the 151). Remove the starter. Before installing the starter, make sure the mounting surfaces are free from burrs and dirt. Install the starter onto the housing together with any shims, and tighten the bolts to 18 ft. lbs. on sixes and V8s; on the 121, tighten the larger bolt to 54 ft. lbs., the smaller bolt to 33 ft. lbs. Tighten the bolts to 17 ft. lbs. on the 151. Clean the battery and solenoid terminal(s), install the cable(s).

IGNITION SYSTEM

A breaker point ignition system is used on all 121-4 cylinder engines.
1978 and later American Motors 4(150), 6 and V8 engine cars have a Solid State Ignition (SSI) system. 1980 and later 4 cylinder 151 cu. in. engines use the Delco-Remy High Energy Ignition (HEI) system.

For additional information on the ignition system, please refer to "Electronic Ignition Systems" in the Unit Repair section.

Distributor

REMOVAL

1. Bring the engine's No. 1 piston to TDC. Remove the distributor cap, mark the position of the rotor relative to the distributor body and mark the body relative to the block. Remove the carburetor air cleaner if necessary, then remove the distributor primary wire and the distributor vacuum lines. Tag any disconnected wires or hoses for installation.
2. Remove the hold-down bolt and take the distributor up out of the block.

NOTE: Don't turn the engine while the distributor is out. This would complicate reinstalling the distributor.

3. The procedure for installation varies depending on whether or not the engine was turned while the distributor was out.

INSTALLATION

Engine Not Turned

1. Turn the rotor about one-eighth turn past the mark indicating its original position.
2. Align the distributor locating marks on the distributor body and the block, and push the unit into place. The rotor should turn back to the mark as the unit seats and the gear meshes. Wiggle the rotor slightly to start the gear in mesh as necessary.
3. Tighten the hold-down bolt and reconnect the primary wire and the vacuum line. Replace the cap.
4. Check the ignition timing. Theoretically, the timing shouldn't have changed if the distributor was reinstalled exactly in its original position, but it is always best to make sure.

Engine Turned

This procedure is necessary to install a new distributor or if the engine has been turned while the distributor was out.
1. Place the No. 1 cylinder in firing position by turning the engine with a finger held over the No. 1 spark plug hole. No. 1 spark plug is the left front one on a V8, and the front one on a 4 or 6 cylinder. When compression is felt, turn the engine to align the TDC mark on the timing pointer with the notch on the crankshaft pulley.
2. Align the metal end of the rotor with the No. 1 spark plug wire in the distributor cap.
3. Turn the distributor body counterclockwise about one-eighth turn and set it into place in the engine. Wiggle the rotor slightly to start the gear in mesh as necessary.
4. The distributor should now be positioned so that the rotor is still pointing to the No. 1 wire location on the cap.
5. Tighten the hold-down bolt and reconnect the primary wire and the vacuum line. Replace the cap.
6. Check the ignition timing.

BREAKER POINTS AND CONDENSER REPLACEMENT, DWELL ANGLE ADJUSTMENT

121-4 Cylinder Engine

Replace the condenser each time the point set is replaced, although this is not always necessary, it is easy to do at this time and the cost is negligible. Whenever you adjust or replace the breaker points, the ignition timing must be checked and, if necessary, adjusted. No special equipment other than a feeler gauge is required for point replacement or adjustment, but a dwell meter is strongly advised, as it gives a far more accurate reading.

1. Use a small screwdriver to unclip the distributor cap latches. Remove the cap. You might have to unclip or detach some or all of the plug wires to remove the cap. Mark the wires for proper installation.
2. Clean the cap inside and out with a clean rag. Check for cracks and carbon paths. A carbon path shows up as a dark line, usually from one of the cap sockets or in-

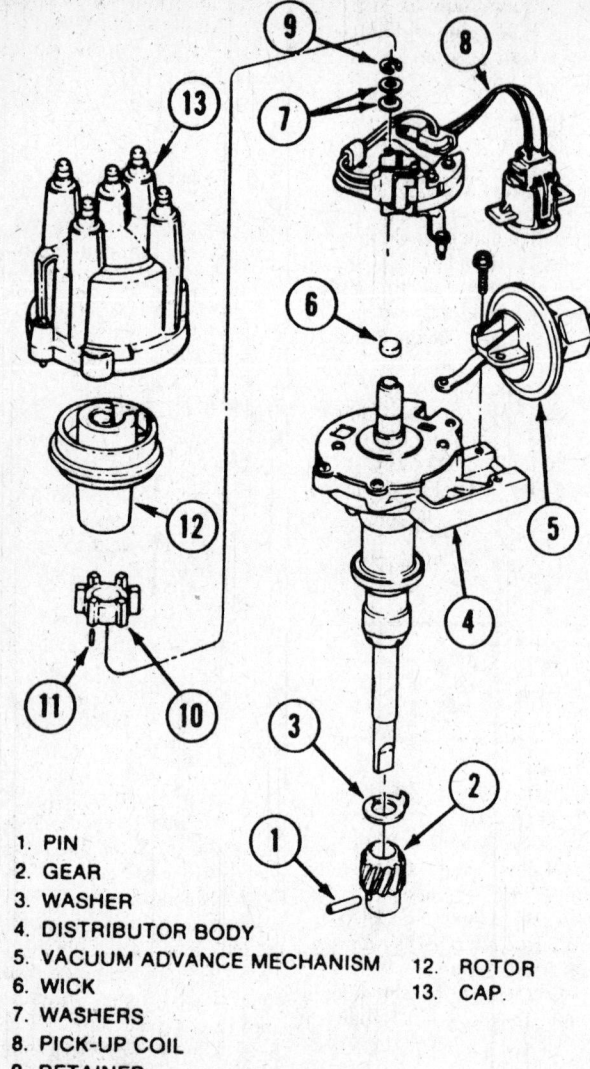

1. PIN
2. GEAR
3. WASHER
4. DISTRIBUTOR BODY
5. VACUUM ADVANCE MECHANISM
6. WICK
7. WASHERS
8. PICK-UP COIL
9. RETAINER
10. TRIGGER WHEEL
11. PIN
12. ROTOR
13. CAP.

150-4 cylinder distributor

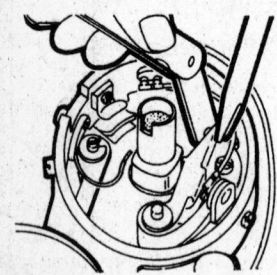

Point adjustment, 4 cylinder
(© American Motors Corp.)

side terminals to a ground. Check the condition of the carbon button inside the center of the cap and the inside terminals. Replace the cap as necessary.

3. Pull the rotor up and off the shaft. Clean off the metal outer tip if it is burned or corroded. Don't file it. Replace the rotor

as necessary or if one came with your tune-up kit.

4. If there is any pitting on the breaker point contact surfaces, the points should be replaced.

5. Pull off the two wire terminals from the point assembly. One wire comes from the condenser and the other comes from within the distributor. The terminals are usually held in place by spring tension only. There might be a clamp screw securing the terminals on some older versions. Loosen the point set hold-down screw(s). Be very careful not to drop any of these little screws inside the distributor. If this happens, the distributor will probably have to be removed to get at the screw. If the hold-down screw is lost elsewhere, it must be replaced with one that is no longer than the original to avoid interference with the distributor workings. Remove the point set, even if it is to be reused.

6. If the points are to be reused, clean them with a few strokes of a special point file. This is done with the points removed to prevent tiny metal filings getting into the distributor.

7. Remove the condenser and connector as an assembly from the side of the distributor. Don't lose the screw.

8. If possible replace the distributor cam lubricator at every tune-up. Most ignition point sets will have the cam lubricator wick as part of the kit, or a plastic tube of high melting-point grease will be included. Use the grease sparingly on the distributor cam.

9. Install the new condenser.

10. Replace the point set. Leave the screw slightly loose. Install the two wire terminals, making sure that the wires won't interfere with anything. Tighten the condenser.

11. Check that the contacts meet squarely. If they don't, bend the tab supporting the fixed contact to match contact surfaces.

12. Turn the engine until a high point on the cam that opens the points contacts the rubbing block on the point arm. You can turn the engine with a wrench or socket on the crankshaft pulley nut. Turn the crankshaft only in the direction of normal rotation.

Another alternative is to bump the starter switch or use a remote starter switch.

13. There is a screwdriver slot near the contacts. Insert a screwdriver and lever the points open or closed until they appear to be at about the gap specified in the "Tune-Up Specifications."

14. Insert the correct size feeler gauge and adjust the gap until you can push the gauge in and out between the contacts with a slight drag, but without disturbing the point arm. Check by trying the gauges 0.001–0.002 larger and smaller than the setting size. The larger one should disturb the point arm, while the smaller one should not drag at all. Tighten the point set hold-down screw. Recheck the gap, because it often changes when the screw is tightened.

15. After all the point adjustments are complete, pull a white business card through (between) the contacts to remove any traces of oil. Oil causes rapid contact burning.

16. If a dwell meter is available, check the dwell. The dwell meter hookup is shown in the "Engine Troubleshooting" Section.

Dwell can be checked with the engine running or cranking. Decrease dwell by increasing the point gap; increase by decreasing the gap. Dwell angle is simply the number of degrees of distributor shaft rotation during which the points stay closed. Theoretically, if the point gap is correct, the dwell should also be correct or nearly so. Adjustment with a dwell meter produces more exact results since it is a dynamic adjustment. If dwell varies more than 3 degrees from idle speed to 1,750 engine rpm, the distributor is worn.

17. To adjust dwell, trial-and-error point adjustments are required.

18. If the engine won't start, check:

a. That all the spark plug wires are in place.

b. That the rotor has been installed.

c. That the two (or three) wires inside the distributor are connected.

d. That the points open and close when the engine turns.

e. That the gap is correct, and the hold-down screw is tight.

19. After the first 200 miles or so on a new set of points, the point gap often closes up due to initial rubbing block wear. For best performance, recheck the dwell (or gap) at this time.

20. Since changing the gap affects the ignition point setting, the timing should be checked and adjusted as necessary after each point replacement or adjustment.

IGNITION TIMING ADJUSTMENT

A scale located on the timing chain cover and a notch milled into the vibration damper are used as references to set ignition timing.

NOTE: Connect a tachometer to the BID or SSI ignition system in the conventional way; to the negative (distributor) side of the coil and to a ground. HEI distributor caps have a "Tach" terminal. Some tachometers may not work with a BID, SSI, or HEI ignition system and there is a possibility that some could be damaged. Check with the manufacturer of the tachometer to make sure it can be used.

1. Disconnect the vacuum hose(s), at the distributor vacuum unit. Plug the vacuum line(s) to prevent leakage.

2. Connect a timing light and a tachometer in accordance with the manufacturer's instructions. If the timing light has an advance control, be sure it is off.

3. Start the engine. Adjust the carburetor curb idle screw so the engine idles at the specified curb idle speed at operating temperature. If there is a throttle stop solenoid, disconnect it electrically. Aim the timing light at the pointer marks.

4. Adjust the timing by loosening the distributor clamp nut and rotating the distributor. Set the timing to the proper specification.

NOTE: On some models, a white paint mark is applied to the scale for the specified, initial timing setting. Do not mistake this mark for TDC.

5. Check the timing again after tightening the distributor clamp.

6. Connect the vacuum hose(s) and set the idle speed to specifications.

FUEL SYSTEM

Fuel Pump

REMOVAL & INSTALLATION
All Engines

1. Disconnect the inlet and outlet fuel lines, and any vacuum lines.

2. Remove the two fuel pump body attaching nuts and lockwashers.

3. Pull the pump and gasket free of the engine. Make sure the mating surfaces of the fuel pump and the engine are clean.

4. Cement a new gasket to the mounting flange of the fuel pump.

5. Position the fuel pump on the engine block so that the lever of the fuel pump rests on the fuel pump cam of the camshaft.

6. Secure the fuel pump to the block with the two capscrews and lockwashers.

7. Connect the intake and outlet fuel lines to the fuel pump, and any vacuum lines.

NOTE: When installing the pump on 121-4 cylinder engines, be sure that the pushrod is properly positioned against the actuating lever, or the pump may be damaged when the screws are tightened. On the six and eight cylinder engines, be sure that the actuating lever is positioned on top of the camshaft eccentric.

Fuel Filter

REMOVAL & INSTALLATION

American Motors uses an in-line fuel filter in the line from the carburetor to the fuel pump on all engines except the 151. All models (except the 151) also have a vapor return line from the filter to the tank.

1. Remove the air cleaner as necessary.

2. Put an absorbent rag under the filter to catch spillage.

3. Remove the hose clamps.

4. Remove the filter and short attaching hoses.

5. Assemble the new filter and hoses. If the filter has a return line, position the line at the top.

NOTE: The original equipment type hose clamps can't be reused with much success. It is much better to replace them with screw type clamps. If there is an arrow on the new filter, it must point toward the carburetor. Four barrel models also have a check valve with flow indicating arrows.

6. Fit the filter in place, tighten the clamps, start the engine, and check for leaks. Discard the rag safely.

The 151 uses a replaceable filter located within the carburetor body, at the fuel inlet fitting. To replace:

1. Place an absorbent cloth under the inlet fitting at the carburetor.

2. Unscrew the fuel inlet nut.

3. The filter will be pushed out part way by a spring located behind the filter. Remove the filter.

4. Install the new filter with the hole in the filter facing the inlet fitting. Install a new gasket on the fitting. Tighten to 18 ft. lbs.

Carburetor

REMOVAL & INSTALLATION

1. Remove the air cleaner.

2. Disconnect the fuel and vacuum lines. It might be a good idea to tag them to avoid confusion when the time comes to put them back.

3. Disconnect the choke rod.

4. Disconnect the accelerator linkage.

5. Disconnect the automatic transmission linkage.

6. Unbolt and remove the carburetor.

7. Remove the base gasket.

8. Before installation, make sure that the carburetor and manifold sealing surfaces are clean.

9. Install a new carburetor base gasket.

10. Install the carburetor and start the fuel and vacuum lines.

11. Bolt down the carburetor evenly.

12. Tighten the fuel and vacuum lines.

13. Connect the accelerator and automatic transmission linkage. If the transmission linkage was disturbed, refer to the Unit Repair section on Automatic Transmissions.

14. Connect the choke rod.

15. Install the air cleaner. Adjust the idle speed and mixture.

ADJUSTMENTS (IDLE SPEED AND MIXTURE)

1978–79

SIX CYLINDER AND V8

Special carburetors, incorporating an altitude compensating circuit to increase the air flow are used on cars that are sold for use at elevations above 4,000 feet. The single barrel YF-1 is manually adjusted for altitutde, while the two barrel 2150-2 has an automatic compensator system, controlled by an aneroid, which is sensitive to atmospheric pressures. At high altitudes, where the atmospheric pressure is lower, the aneroid expands and opens an altitude compensating valve, allowing extra air to enter the carburetor and lean out the fuel-air mixture.

NOTE: The aneroid is factory calibrated and is not adjustable. With a change of altitude operation, ignition timing and carburetor adjustments must be reset on all models.

NOTE: This adjustment is performed with the air cleaner installed. Do not allow the engine to idle more than three minutes at a time. If the idle/mixture adjustment is not completed by the end of three minutes, run the engine for one minute at 2,000 rpm. Return to the specified rpm and continue the adjustment.

1. Adjust the idle screw(s) to the full rich stop(s). Note the position of the screw head slot inside the limiter cap slots.

2. Carefully remove the idle limiter cap(s) by installing a sheet metal screw in the center of the cap and turning clockwise. Discard the old caps. Return the screws to their original positions.

3. Install a tachometer on the engine.

4. Start the engine, and allow it to reach normal operating temperature.

5. Adjust the idle speed to 30 rpm above the specified idle speed. See the "Tune-Up Specifications" chart.

NOTE: On most engines the idle speed is adjusted with the throttle stop solenoid. Use the following procedure for idle speed adjustment. When setting idle speed, put the manual transmission in Neutral and the automatic transmission in Drive.

a. With the solenoid wire connected, turn the nut on the solenoid plunger, idle speed adjusting screw, or the hex screw on the solenoid carriage in or out to obtain specified idle rpm.

b. Tighten the solenoid lock nut, if so equipped.

c. Disconnect the solenoid wire and adjust curb idle speed screw to obtain 500 rpm.

d. Connect the solenoid wire.

--- **CAUTION** ---

On the Carter BBD 2bbl., the curb idle and fast idle screws are side by side; it is easy to get the wrong one when setting idle speed on cars without a throttle stop solenoid. The screw for idle speed is the longer of the two.

6. Starting from the full rich stop position, as noted in step 1, turn the mixture screw(s) clockwise (leaner) until the engine loses speed.

7. Turn the mixture screw(s) counterclockwise until the highest rpm reading is obtained.

NOTE: On engines with two mixture screws, turn both of the screws an equal number of turns unless the engine demands otherwise.

8. If the idle speed has changed more than 30 rpm during the mixture adjustment, reset the idle to 30 rpm above the specified

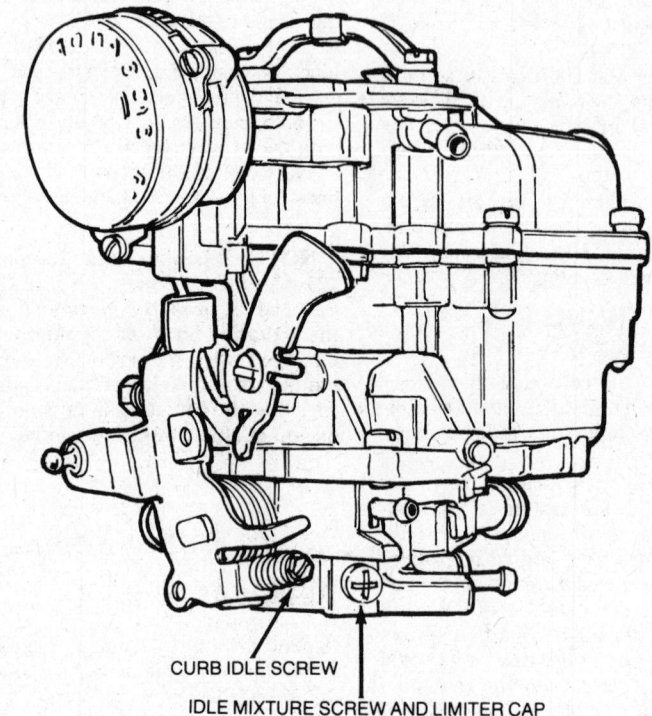

CURB IDLE SCREW

IDLE MIXTURE SCREW AND LIMITER CAP

Carter YF carburetor adjustments

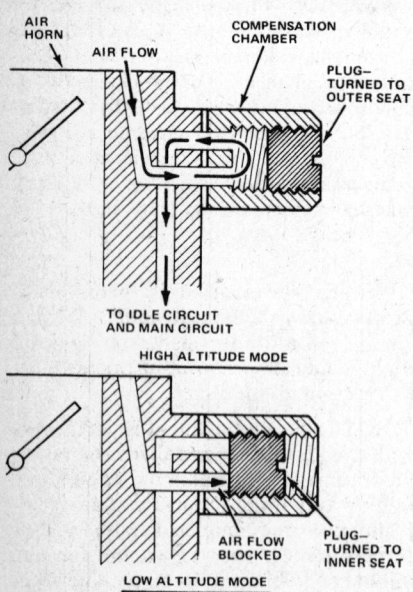

AIR HORN

AIR FLOW

COMPENSATION CHAMBER

PLUG— TURNED TO OUTER SEAT

TO IDLE CIRCUIT AND MAIN CIRCUIT

HIGH ALTITUDE MODE

AIR FLOW BLOCKED

PLUG— TURNED TO INNER SEAT

LOW ALTITUDE MODE

6 Cylinder altitude compensator plug operation and adjustment
(© American Motors Corp.)

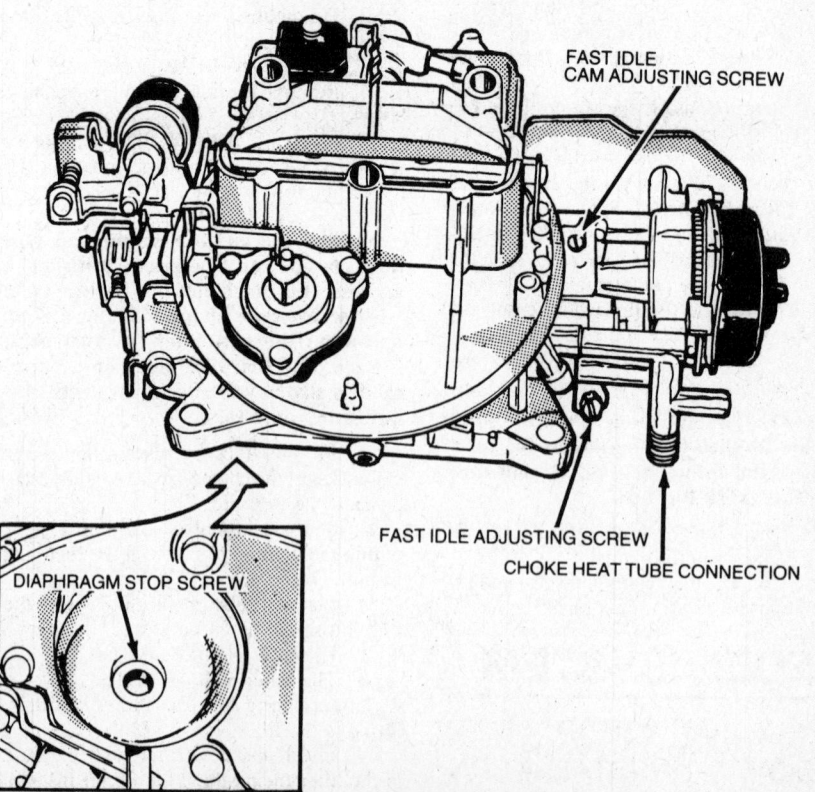

FAST IDLE CAM ADJUSTING SCREW

DIAPHRAGM STOP SCREW

FAST IDLE ADJUSTING SCREW

CHOKE HEAT TUBE CONNECTION

Autolite/Motorcraft 2100 carburetor adjustments

idle rpm as indicated in the "Tune-Up Specifications" chart.

9. Turn the mixture adjustment screw(s) clockwise until the rpm drops as follows:

1978–79	Six cylinder	
	manual	50 rpm
	Matador–manual	25 rpm
	automatic	25 rpm
1978	Six cylinder	
	automatic	
	Matador	75 rpm
1978–79	Six cylinder	
	automatic,	
	high altitude	25 rpm
1978–79	Six cylinder	
	manual,	
	high altitude	50 rpm
1978–79	Six cylinder	
	two barrel	
	automatic	25 rpm
1978–79	Six cylinder	
	two barrel	
	manual	50 rpm
1978–78	V8	
	automatic	20 rpm
1979	V8	
	automatic	40 rpm

10. Install new blue service idle limiter cap(s) over the idle mixture screw(s) with the limiter cap tang(s) positioned against the full rich stop(s). Be careful not to disturb the idle mixture setting while installing the cap(s). Press the cap(s) firmly into place.

121-4 CYLINDER

The four cylinder engine uses a staged, two barrel carburetor. The primary barrel is smaller than the secondary barrel, and mechanical linkage progressively opens the secondary barrel.

Idle speed and mixture setting procedures are as follows:

NOTE: To compensate for temperature and fuel variations, while performing idle mixture adjustments, don't idle the engine over three minutes at a time. If settings are not completed within three minutes, operate the engine at 2,000 rpm for one minute. Repeat as necessary until the proper adjustments are attained.

1. Note position of the screw head slot in the limiter cap.

2. Remove the limiter cap by installing a sheet metal screw in the center of the cap and turning the screw clockwise.

3. Reset the idle screw to its approximate original position.

4. Attach a tachometer. Start engine, and warm to operating temperature.

5. A throttle stop solenoid is used to adjust curb idle. With the solenoid wire connected, turn the adjusting screw of the solenoid in or out to obtain the specified setting of 30 rpm above the specified rpm.

6. Disconnect the solenoid wire and adjust the solenoid off idle adjusting screw to obtain 500 rpm. Connect the solenoid wire.

7. Turn the mixture screw clockwise (lean) until a loss of rpm is indicated.

8. Turn the mixture screw counter-clockwise until the highest rpm reading is obtained at the best lean idle setting.

9. As a final adjustment, turn the mixture screw clockwise (leaner) until the specified drop in engine rpm is obtained.

10. Install a replacement limiter cap on the idle mixture screw, with the tab positioned inside the slot on the carburetor body, while being careful not to move the mixture screw.

Idle drop specifications for 1978 are 120 rpm, except for high altitude manual transmission models (75 rpm). For 1979 models they are 120 for manual transmissions, and 45 for automatic transmissions.

1980 and Later

SIX CYLINDER

On all 1980 and later models, mixture is not adjustable because it is controlled by a Micro Computer Unit.

1. Connect a tachometer. Start the engine and allow it to reach normal operating temperature. The air cleaner should be installed, automatic transmissions in drive.

2. Turn the idle screw in or out to obtain the specified idle speed (see the Tune-Up Specifications chart or the car's underhood sticker).

3. If the carburetor is equipped with a solenoid:

a. Loosen the locknut on the solenoid plunger, if present. Turn the idle speed adjusting nut on the plunger, or the hex screw on the carriage to obtain the specified speed. Tighten the locknut, if present.

b. Disconnect the solenoid wire and adjust the curb idle screw to obtain 500 rpm (in Neutral). Reconnect the wire unless the carburetor has a dashpot.

4. If the carburetor has a dashpot, allow the engine to idle while fully depressing the dashpot stem. Measure the clearance between the stem and the lever. It should be 0.093 in. Adjust by loosening the locknut and turning the dashpot. Connect the solenoid wire.

150-4 CYLINDER

1. Start engine, and run to normal operating temperature.

2. Disconnect vacuum hose from Sole-Vac vacuum actuator, and plug the hole.

3. Adjust curb-idle speed with the ¼ in. hex head screw at the end of the Sole-Vac unit: automatic transmissions on Drive, to 700 rpm; manual transmissions on Neutral, to 750 rpm.

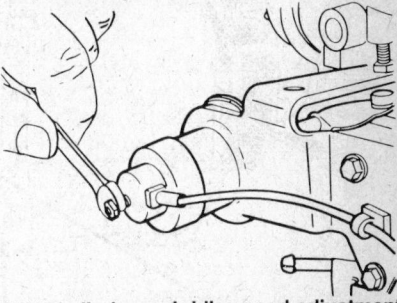

150-4 cylinder curb-idle speed adjustment

4. Unplug vacuum actuator hole, and reconnect the hose.

151-4 CYLINDER

The air cleaner should be removed and associated vacuum hoses plugged, choke open, a/c compressor clutch wire disconnected (if so equipped), and the deceleration valve supply hose plugged.

1. Disconnect and plug the purge hose at the charcoal canister.

2. If equipped with a feedback system, connect a dwell meter to the single light blue wire which is taped to the mixture control solenoid wires at the carburetor. Set the meter on the six cylinder scale.

3. Connect a tachometer. There is a green wire above the heater fan motor for easy tachometer connection. Start the engine and allow it to reach normal operating temperature. On feedback models, the dwell meter should be fluctuating; the oscillation should be within 10 to 15 degrees of needle movement. If not, the feedback system is not operating correctly and must be repaired.

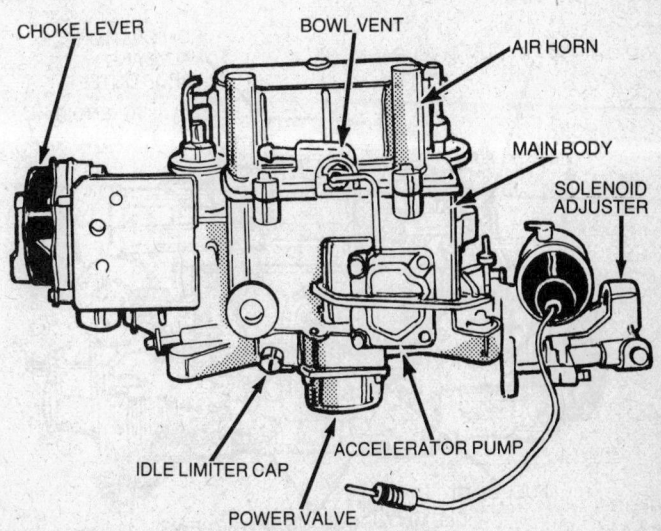

2100 2-bbl carburetor assembly

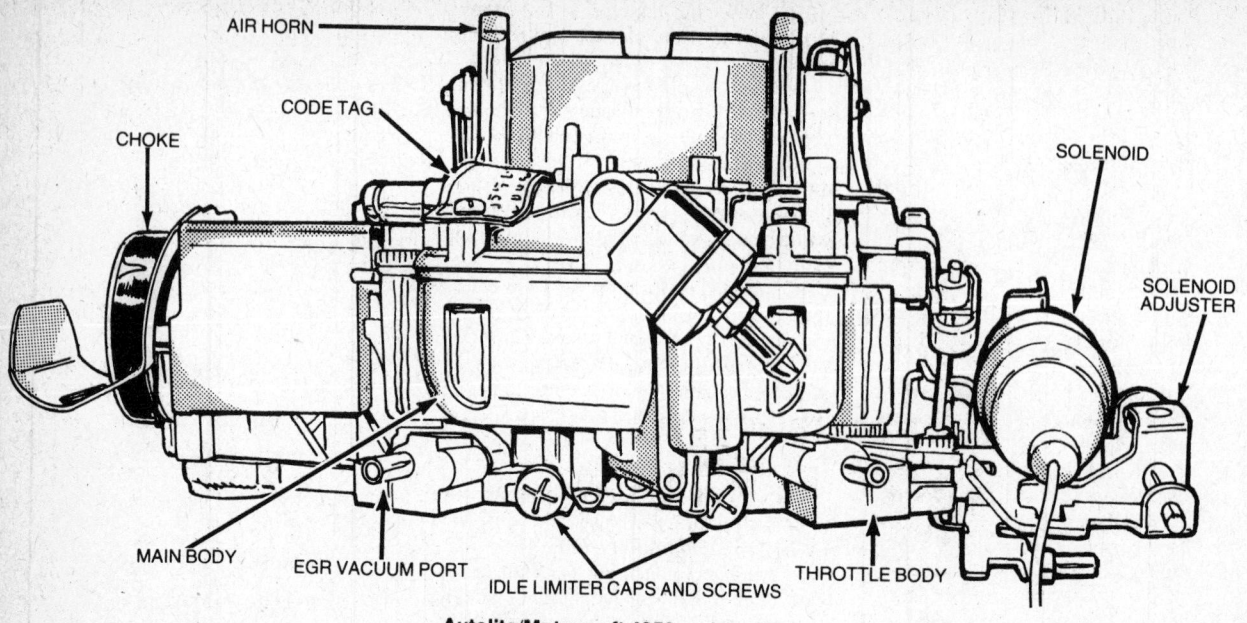

AIR HORN

CODE TAG

CHOKE

SOLENOID

SOLENOID ADJUSTER

MAIN BODY

EGR VACUUM PORT

IDLE LIMITER CAPS AND SCREWS

THROTTLE BODY

Autolite/Motorcraft 4350 carburetor

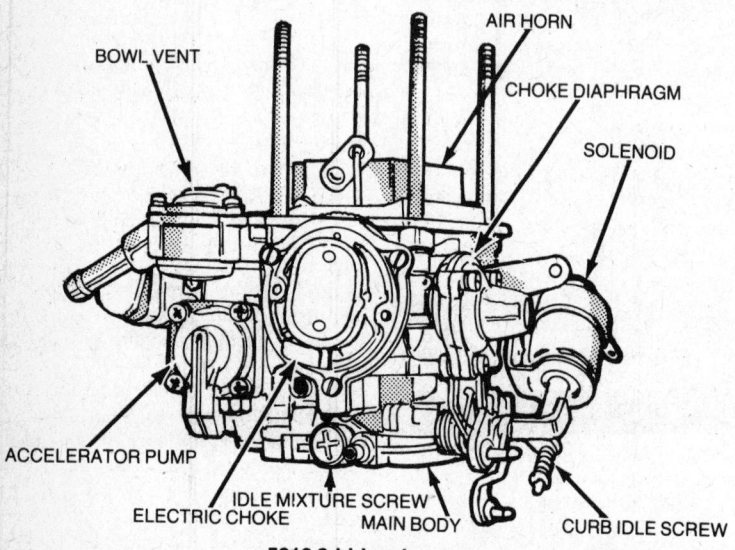

BOWL VENT

AIR HORN

CHOKE DIAPHRAGM

SOLENOID

ACCELERATOR PUMP

IDLE MIXTURE SCREW

ELECTRIC CHOKE

MAIN BODY

CURB IDLE SCREW

5210 2-bbl carburetor

CHOKE VACUUM DIAPHRAGM

ROLLOVER CHECK VALVE AND VAPOR OUTLET

CHOKE HOUSING

SOLENOID

FUEL INLET

IDLE MIXTURE ADJUSTING SCREWS

BBD 2-bbl carburetor

4. Set the parking brake, shift automatic transmissions to Drive; if equipped with air conditioning, turn it on. Open the throttle to extend the solenoid plunger. Set idle speed by turning the solenoid idle screw. Turn off the A/C, if so equipped.

5. Disconnect the anti-dieseling solenoid wire. Use the curb-idle screw to adjust idle to specifications. Connect the solenoid wire.

COOLING SYSTEM

Radiator

REMOVAL & INSTALLATION

1. Raise the hood and remove the radiator cap. Be sure the engine is cold.

2. Drain the radiator. If the coolant appears to be clean, drain it into a clean container and save it for re-use.

3. Remove the upper and lower radiator hoses. Disconnect the coolant recovery hose, if so equipped.

4. On four cylinder models, remove the ambient air intake from the radiator support.

5. On four cylinder air-conditioned models, remove the charcoal canister and the bracket.

6. Remove the fan shroud, if so equipped. On models equipped with an electric cooling fan; disconnect the motor and sensor wiring harnesses, remove the motor, fan and support: or remove as an assembly with the radiator.

7. On automatic transmission models, disconnect and plug the fluid cooler lines. Remove battery on Pacers for access.

8. Remove the radiator attaching screws and bolts and lift out the radiator.

9. To install radiator, reverse the sequence above.

Water Pump

REMOVAL & INSTALLATION

121-4 Cylinder Engine

1. Drain the cooling system. Disconnect the negative cable from the battery. Remove the fan shroud.

2. Rotate the crankshaft until the camshaft and crankshaft are at TDC for number one cylinder.

3. If equipped with power steering, loosen the pump and remove the belt. Loosen the air conditioner idler pulley and remove the belt, if so equipped.

4. Loosen the alternator and air pump.

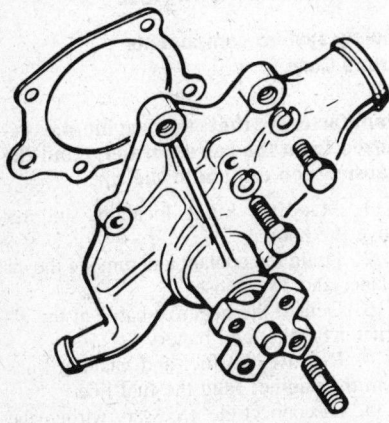

150-4 cylinder water pump and gasket

5. Remove the fan, spacer, and pulley.

6. Remove the belt guard and air pump bracket.

7. Remove the camshaft and drive belt idler pulley.

8. Disconnect all the hoses from the pump except the hose from the thermostat.

9. Remove the water pump attaching bolts and pull the pump out of the hose from the thermostat.

10. Clean the gasket from the block, install a new gasket on the pump or block.

11. Insert the pump into the thermostat hose, install the pump attaching bolts and torque the small bolts to 7 ft. lbs. and the large bolts to 16 ft. lbs.

12. Reassemble in the reverse order, align the timing belt, apply tension to alternator, air pump, power steering (if equipped), belts.

13. Install coolant, operate engine for 3 to 5 minutes with the heater on to check for leaks and correct fluid level.

150-4 Cylinder Engine

1. Disconnect all hoses at the pump.

2. Remove the drive belts.

3. Remove the fan shroud attaching screws.

4. Unbolt the fan and fan drive assembly, and remove along with the shroud. On some models it may be easier to turn the shroud ½ turn, to remove it.

5. Unbolt and remove the pump.

CAUTION

Engines built for sale in California having a single, serpentine drive belt and viscous fan drive, have a reverse rotating pump and drive. These components are identified by the word REVERSE stamped on the drive cover and inner side of the fan, and REV cast into the water pump body.

Never interchange standard rotating parts with these.

6. Installation is in the reverse order of removal. Always use a new gasket coated with sealer. Torque the water pump bolts to 13 ft. lbs., the fan bolts to 18 ft. lbs.

151-4 Cylinder Engine

1. Drain the cooling system.

2. Remove all drive belts.

3. Remove the fan and pump pulley.

4. Unbolt and remove the pump from the engine.

5. Clean the gasket surfaces, coat the new gasket with non-hardening type sealer and position the gasket on the block.

6. Coat the threaded areas of the bolts with waterproof sealer and install the pump. Torque the bolts to 25 ft. lbs.

7. Install the pulley and fan.

8. Install the drive belts. The belts should be adjusted so that a ½ in. deflection is present when they are depressed mid-point along their longest straight run.

6 Cylinder

1. Drain the cooling system. Disconnect the negative cable from the battery.

2. Unfasten the radiator and the heater hoses at the pump.

3. Loosen the adjustment bolts from the alternator and the power steering pump, if so equipped. Remove the V-belts.

4. Unfasten the fan ring securing belts. Remove the fan and pump pulley assembly. Withdraw the fan ring (or shroud).

5. Remove the securing bolts from the water pump. Withdraw the pump along with its gasket.

Installation is in the reverse order of removal. Always use a new pump gasket. Bleed the radiator by running the engine and opening the heater control valve. Run the engine long enough to open the thermostat. Check the coolant level.

The water pump securing bolts should be tightened to 10–15 ft. lbs.

V8

1. Drain the cooling system at the radiator. Remove the upper hose from the radiator. Disconnect the negative cable from the battery.

2. Remove the air cleaner.

3. Remove the fan shroud. Remove the drive belts, the fan, and hub assembly by withdrawing the attaching bolts.

4. If the car is equipped with power steering or an air pump, unbolt the pump, and move it aside (hoses attached).

5. Loosen the bolts attaching the alternator bracket. Leave one bolt in position, so that the alternator may be swung to one side. Do not disconnect the wires.

6. Disconnect the heater hose at the water pump.

7. On cars equipped with A/C, disconnect the compressor bracket, and set it and

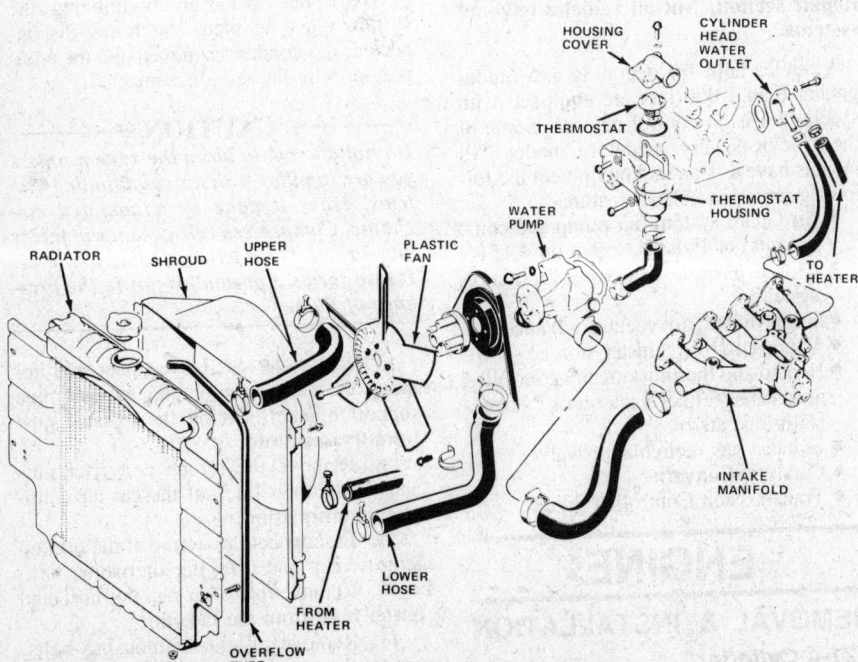

Water pump and hose routing, 121-4 cylinder (© American Motors Corp.)

RADIATOR SHROUD UPPER HOSE PLASTIC FAN WATER PUMP HOUSING COVER CYLINDER HEAD WATER OUTLET THERMOSTAT THERMOSTAT HOUSING TO HEATER INTAKE MANIFOLD FROM HEATER LOWER HOSE OVERFLOW TUBE

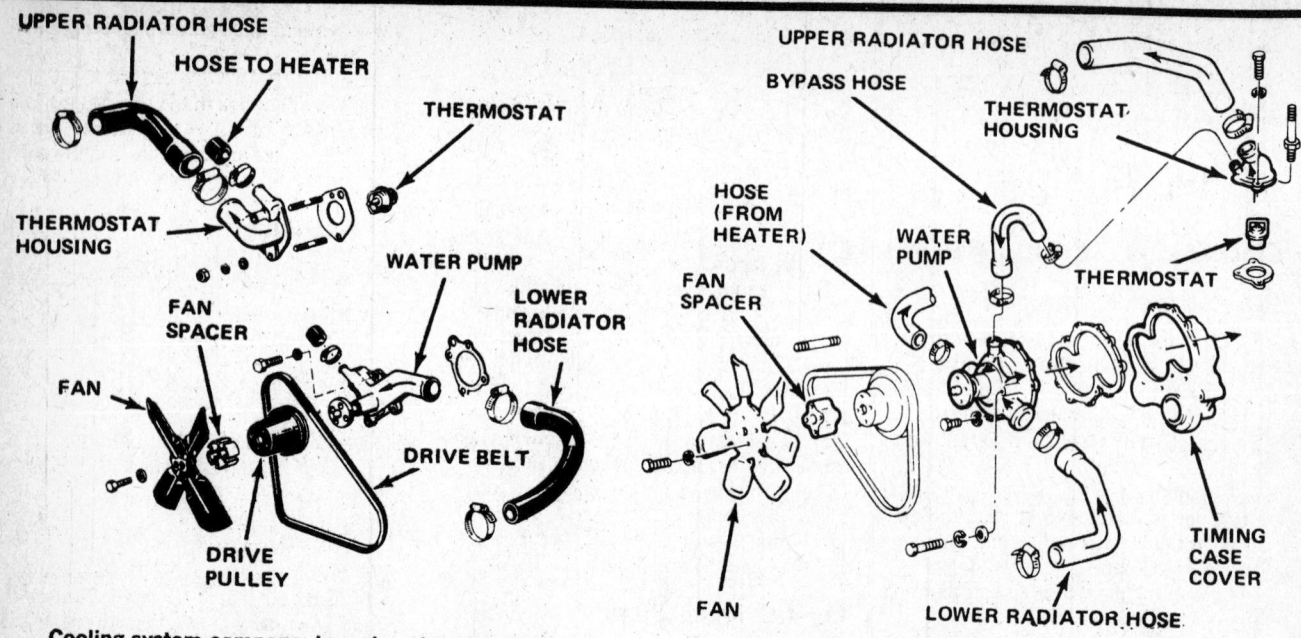

Cooling system components and coolant flow for 6 cylinder engines (© American Motors Corp)

Eight cylinder cooling system components (© American Motors Corp.)

the compressor out of the way. Do not discharge the air conditioning system.

8. Remove the by-pass and the lower radiator hoses from the pump.

9. Remove the pump, and clean the gasket areas.

Installation is in the reverse order of removal. Always install a new pump gasket. Tighten the pump bolts to 18 ft. lbs. Bleed the cooling system by starting the engine and opening the heater valve. Leave it open until the thermostat opens. Check the coolant level.

Thermostat

REMOVAL & INSTALLATION

The thermostat is located in the water outlet housing at the top or front of the cylinder head; in the hose, itself, or on V8 models in front of the manifold.

Drain the coolant to a point below the thermostat. Disconnect the upper radiator hose and/or remove the bolts which hold the water outlet neck to the engine. Remove the thermostat.

When installing the thermostat, make certain the pellet or coil spring is facing the engine. Thermostats are marked on the outer flange with the proper installing direction. Replace the gasket between the thermostat and the housing cover.

The bleed hole on the thermostats used on six cylinder engines must be installed up (at 12 o'clock), to prevent "burping" caused by trapped air.

CAUTION
Tightening the housing bolts unevenly, or with the thermostat cocked in its recess, will cause the housing to crack.

Refill the cooling system, and run the engine for a while with the heater on to bleed the system of air. Recheck the coolant level.

EMISSION CONTROLS

NOTE: For a description and service procedures for the following emission control systems, please refer to the "Emission Control" section of the Unit Repair section. Not all vehicles have all systems.

Vehicles built for operating at altitudes greater than 4,000 feet are equipped with special emission control devices. Some of these devices vary model to model. All models have as standard equipment the following emission control features.

- Air Guard system (air pump and components) or Pulsair system on 4-151
- Closed positive crankcase ventilation system
- Single diaphragm vacuum advance unit
- Vapor control, canister storage
- Heated and thermostatically controlled air cleaner (either vacuum or mechanically operated)
- Exhaust gas recirculation valve
- Catalytic Converter
- Transmission Controlled Spark

ENGINE

REMOVAL & INSTALLATION
121-4 Cylinder
NOTE: It is recommended by the

manufacturer that the engine be removed from the car separately, and the transmission remain in the car.

1. Mark the hinge locations and remove the hood.

2. Drain the coolant and remove the air cleaner and TAC hose.

3. Detach the negative cable at the alternator bracket and battery.

4. Remove the fuel and vacuum lines from the engine. Plug the fuel line.

5. Disconnect the necessary wiring, the throttle cable, and automatic transmission throttle valve linkage.

6. If your car has air conditioning, the system must be bled, the hoses disconnected, the condenser moved and the compressor wire harness disconnected.

CAUTION
Do not attempt to bleed the system unless you are familiar with air conditioning systems. Have it done by a qualified mechanic. Compressed refrigerant will freeze any surface it contacts, including your eyes. It also forms a poisonous gas in the presence of flame.

---

7. Raise the car, disconnect and remove the starter motor and exhaust pipe support bracket. Unbolt the exhaust pipe from the manifold.

8. Remove the torque converter nuts and fluid cooler lines, if the car has automatic transmission.

9. Disconnect the wiring at the backup lamp switch and from the alternator.

10. Remove the lower radiator hose and heater hose from the radiator.

11. Remove all the bellhousing bolts, except the top center bolt.

12. Lower the car and remove the top

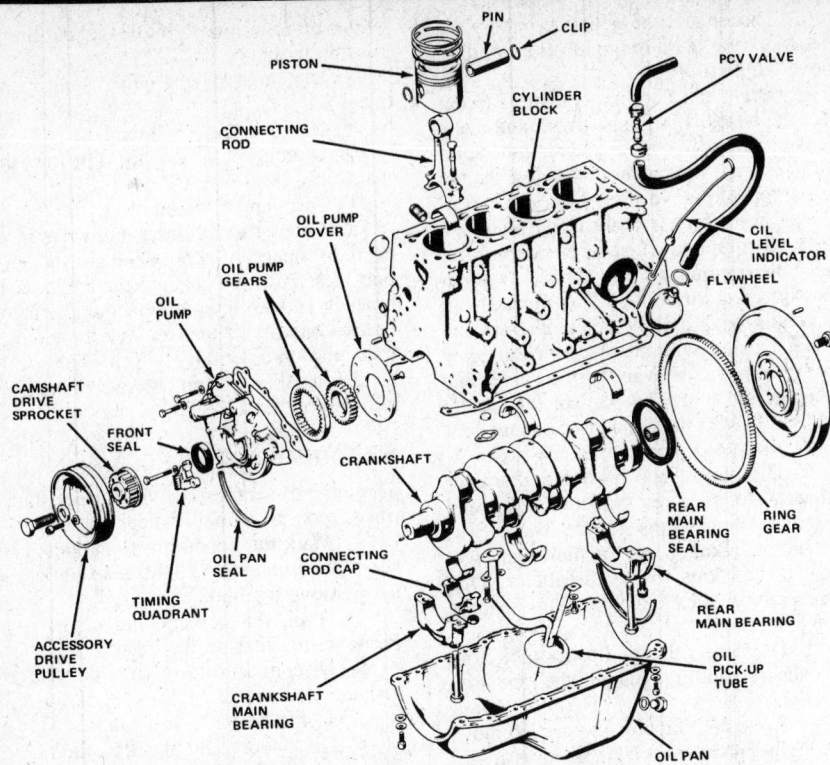

Exploded view of the 121-4 cylinder block (© American Motors Corp.)

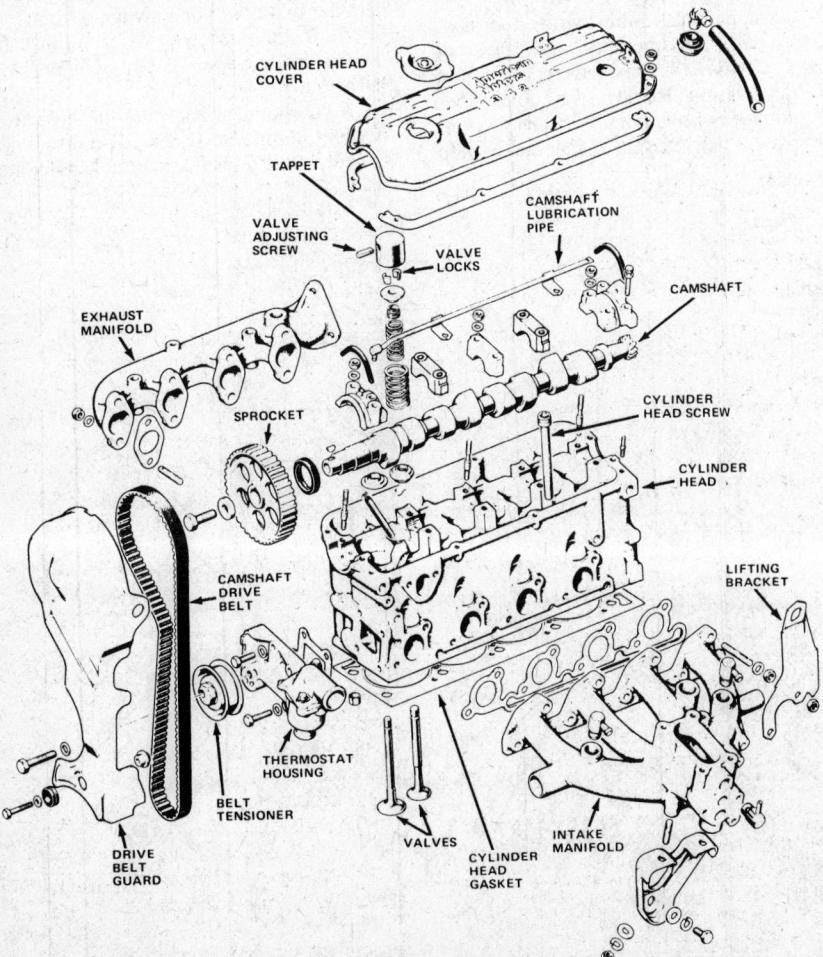

Exploded view of the 121-4 cylinder head (© American Motors Corp.)

radiator hose and the cold air induction manifold at the radiator.

13. Remove the radiator screws, move the radiator one inch to the left, rotate, and lift the radiator and shroud assembly out of the car. With air conditioning, first remove the condenser attaching bolts and move the condenser away from the radiator.

14. Remove any other heater hoses and wiring that are still attached to the car.

15. With power steering, disconnect the hoses from the steering gear. Remove the transmission filler tube support screws with automatic transmission.

16. Remove the engine support cushion nuts on both sides of the engine, and attach a lifting device.

17. With the engine partially raised, support the transmission and remove the center bolt from the transmission bellhousing. Carefully remove the engine from the car.

18. The installation procedure is in the reverse order of removal.

NOTE: When mating the engine to the transmission bellhousing, install three bolts for a more secure mounting until the engine is bolted into place.

150-4 Cylinder

1. Disconnect the battery cables.
2. Remove the air cleaner.
3. Remove the hood.

--- **CAUTION** ---

If the engine has been recently operated, use care to prevent scalding by hot coolant. The system is pressurized.

4. Drain the radiator.
5. Remove the lower radiator hose.
6. Remove the upper radiator hose and coolant recovery hose.
7. Remove the fan shroud and disconnect the transmission fluid cooler tubing (automatic transmission).
8. Remove the radiator/condenser (if equipped with A/C).
9. Remove the fan assembly and install a 5/16 × 1/2 inch SAE capscrew through the fan pulley into the water pump flange, to maintain the pulley and water pump in alignment when the crankshaft is rotated.
10. Disconnect the heater hoses.
11. Disconnect the throttle linkages, cruise control cable (if so equipped) and throttle valve rod.
12. Disconnect the wires from the starter motor solenoid and disconnect CEC System wire harness connector.
13. Disconnect the fuel pipe from the fuel pump.
14. If equipped with air conditioning, remove the service valves and cap the compressor ports.
15. Disconnect the fuel return hose from the fuel filter.
16. Remove the power brake vacuum check valve from the booster, if so equipped.

17. If equipped with power steering:

a. disconnect the power steering hoses from the fittings at the steering gear

b. drain the pump reservoir

c. cap the fittings on the hoses and steering gear to prevent foreign objects from entering the system

18. Identify, tag and disconnect all necessary wire connectors and vacuum hoses.

19. Raise the vehicle.

20. Remove the starter motor.

21. Disconnect the exhaust pipe from the manifold.

22. Remove the flywheel/converter housing access cover. On models with automatic transmission, mark the converter and drive plate location and remove the converter-to-drive plate bolts.

23. Remove the upper flywheel/converter housing bolts and loosen the bottom bolts.

24. Remove the engine mount cushion-to-engine compartment bracket bolts.

25. Attach a lifting device to the engine.

26. Raise the engine off the front supports.

27. Place a support stand under the converter (or flywheel) housing.

28. Remove the remaining converter (or flywheel) housing bolts.

29. Lift the engine out of the engine compartment.

30. Installation is in the reverse order of removal.

151-4 Cylinder

The engine and transmission are removed as an assembly.

1. Disconnect the negative battery cable. Mark the hood hinge locations and remove the hood.

2. Drain the cooling system. Disconnect the hoses. If equipped with automatic transmission, disconnect and plug the coolant lines from the radiator. Remove the fan and shroud; remove the radiator. Disconnect the heater hose from the intake manifold.

3. If equipped with power steering, remove the pump and set it aside, without disconnecting any hoses. If equipped with air conditioning, unbolt the compressor and move it aside without disconnecting any hoses. Remove the evaporator-to-dryer line from the sill clips, but do not disconnect the line. Unbolt the condenser and move it aside, without disconnecting any hoses.

4. Disconnect and label the alternator harness, starter wires, vacuum hoses and electrical connections to the carburetor, carburetor linkage, and vacuum and electrical connections to the distributor. Disconnect the coolant and oil pressure sending unit wires.

5. Disconnect the oil dipstick tube from the exhaust manifold, and pull the tube from the block.

6. Raise and support the car. Remove the engine mount nuts from the crossmember. Remove the ground cable at the left mount bracket.

7. Support assembly with floorjack. Loosen the crossmember and lower it slightly. Remove the speedometer cable from the transmission. Remove the cooler tubes if equipped with automatic transmission. Remove the transmission linkage and backup

light switch wiring. Remove the rear transmission mount.

8. Matchmark the driveshaft and remove.

9. Remove the crossmember.

10. Disconnect the exhaust pipe from the manifold.

11. Disconnect the fuel line

12. Check that all hoses and wires have been disconnected. Lower the car and support jack. Attach a chain to the engine rear bracket, and the air conditioner or alternator bracket, and raise and remove the engine/transmission assembly.

13. Installation is in the reverse order of removal.

6 Cylinder and V8

The engine is removed without the transmission on all models except the Pacer.

1. Mark the hood hinge locations, disconnect the underhood light, if so equipped, and remove the hood.

2. Drain the coolant and engine oil. Remove the filter on the Pacer.

3. Disconnect and remove the battery and air cleaner. On Pacers, first run the wipers to the center of the windshield.

4. Disconnect and tag the alternator, ignition coil, distributor, temperature and oil sender wiring. On Pacers, also disconnect the brake warning switch wiring.

5. If equipped with TCS, remove the switch bracket and vacuum solenoid wire harness.

6. Disconnect and plug the hose from the fuel pump. On Pacers, also disconnect the automatic transmission fluid cooler line.

1. Drive plate and ring gear (automatic trans)
2. Oil filter
3. Push rod cover and bolts
4. Piston
5. Piston ring
6. Piston pin
7. Connecting rod
8. Connecting rod bolt
9. Dowel
10. Oil level indicator and tube
11. Block drain
12. Flywheel and ring gear (manual trans)
13. Dowel
14. Cylinder block
15. Pilot and/or converter bushing
16. Rear oil seal
17. Crankshaft
18. Block core plug
19. Timing gear oil nozzle
20. Main bearings
21. Main bearing caps
22. Connecting rod bearing cap
23. Connecting rod bearing
24. Crankshaft gear
25. Timing gear cover (front)
26. Timing gear cover oil seal
27. Crankshaft pulley hub
28. Crankshaft pulley
29. Crankshaft pulley hub bolt
30. Crankshaft pulley bolt
31. Crankshaft timing gear
32. Camshaft thrust plate screw
33. Camshaft thrust plate
34. Camshaft
35. Camshaft bearing
36. Oil pump driveshaft retainer plate, gasket and bolt

Exploded view of the 151-4 cylinder block (© American Motors Corp.)

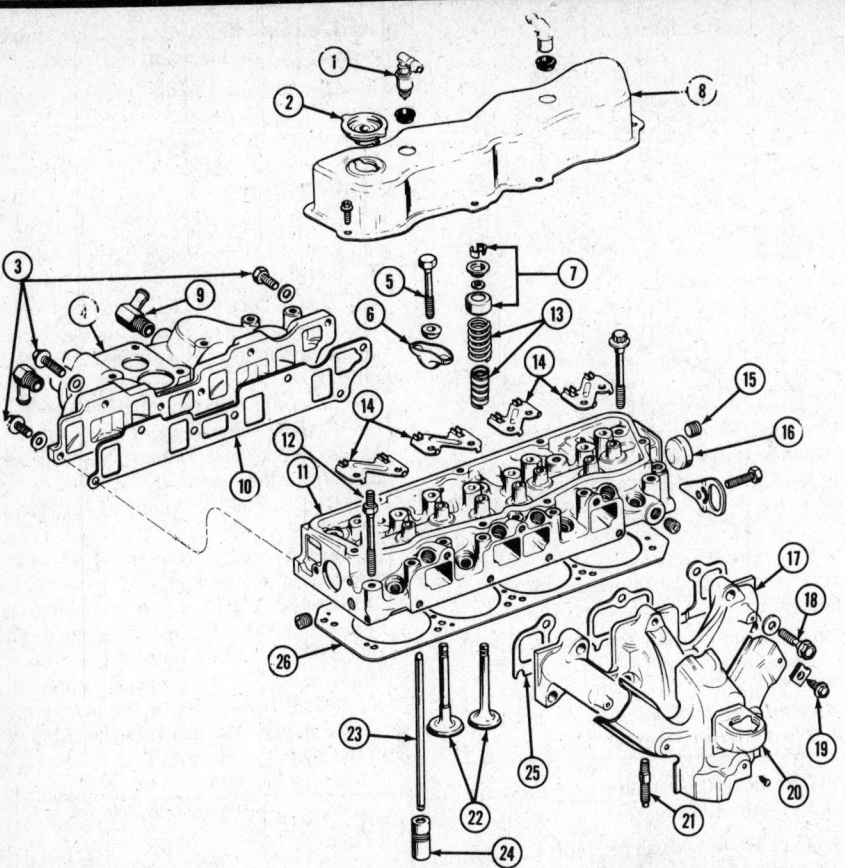

1. PCV valve
2. Oil filler cap
3. Intake manifold attaching bolts
4. Intake manifold
5. Rocker arm capscrew
6. Rocker arm
7. Valve spring retainer assembly
8. Cylinder head cover (rocker cover)
9. Coolant hose fitting
10. Intake manifold gasket
11. Cylinder head
12. Cylinder head stud bolt
13. Valve spring
14. Push rod guide
15. Cylinder head plug
16. Cylinder head core plug
17. Exhaust manifold
18. Exhaust manifold bolt
19. Oil level indicator tube attaching screw
20. Exhaust manifold heat shroud (heat shield)
21. Exhaust manifold to exhaust pipe stud
22. Valves
23. Push rod
24. Tappet
25. Exhaust manifold gasket
26. Cylinder head gasket

Exploded view of the 151-4 cylinder head (© American Motors Corp.)

7. Disconnect the engine ground strap at the block and the starter cable at the starter. Remove the right front engine support cushion-to-bracket bolt.

8. If your car has air conditioning, the system must be bled, the hoses disconnected, and the compressor removed.

──── CAUTION ────

Do not perform this operation if you are unfamiliar with A/C systems. Have the system bled by a qualified mechanic. Compressed refrigerant will freeze any surface it contacts, including your eyes. It also forms a poisonous gas in the presence of flame.

Bleed the refrigerant from the system. Remove the service valves, cap the compressor ports and the service valves, and disconnect the clutch wire. On Pacers, also disconnect the receiver outlet at the coupling, and remove the receiver and condenser assembly.

9. Disconnect the return hose from the fuel filter, TAC hose from the manifold, carburetor vent hose, heater or A/C vacuum hose and/or power brake hose at intake manifold, and power brake vacuum check valve from booster, if so equipped.

10. Disconnect the throttle cable and throttle valve rod, if so equipped.

11. Disconnect the radiator and heater hoses from the engine, automatic transmission cooler lines from the radiator, radiator shroud, fan, and spacer, and remove the radiator.

12. Install a 5/16 × 1/2 in. bolt through the fan pulley into the water pump flange to maintain alignment (all but Pacer).

13. With power steering, disconnect the hoses, drain the reservoir, and cap the fittings. With power brakes, remove the vacuum check valve from the booster.

14. On Pacers only, remove the carburetor and plug the fitting, remove the valve cover(s), and remove the vibration damper.

15. With automatic transmission, remove the filler tube.

16. Jack and support the front of the car. Remove the starter.

17. With automatic transmission on all except the Pacer, remove the converter cover, converter bolts (rotate the crankshaft for access), and the exhaust pipe-to-transmission linkage support.

With manual transmission on all but the Pacer, remove the clutch cover, bellcrank inner support bolts and springs, the bellcrank, outer bellcrank-to-strut retainer, and disconnect the back-up lamp wire harness at the firewall for access later.

On Pacers, disconnect the transmission and clutch linkage, speedometer cable at the transmission, remove the driveshaft (plug the transmission), and support the transmission with a jack. Remove the rear crossmember.

18. Attach the lifting device and support the engine. Remove the engine mount bolts.

19. Disconnect the exhaust pipe from the manifold.

20. On all but the Pacer, remove the upper converter or clutch housing bolts and loosen the lower bolts. Raise the car and move the jackstands to the jack pad area. Remove the A/C idler pulley and bracket, if so equipped. Lift the engine off the front supports, support the transmission, remove the lower transmission cover attaching bolts, and lift the engine out of the car.

On Pacers, lift the engine slightly and remove the front support cushions. Remove the transmission support, raise the front of the car so that the bottom of the bumper is three feet from the floor, and partially remove the engine/transmission assembly until the rear of the cylinder head clears the cowl. Lower the car and remove the engine.

21. On installations with manual transmission, insert the transmission shaft into the clutch spline and align the clutch housing to the engine. Install and tighten the lower housing bolts. On installations with automatic transmission, align the converter housing to the engine and loosely install the bottom housing bolts. Then install the next higher bolts and tighten all four bolts. With both transmissions, next remove the transmission support, lower the engine onto the mounts, and install the mounting bolts. The remainder of the installation is in the reverse order of removal.

On Pacers, raise the car with a jack as in Step 20. Lower the engine/transmission assembly into the compartment. Raise the transmission into position with a jack and install the rear crossmember. Install the front engine support cushions. The remainder of the installation is in the reverse order of removal.

Intake Manifold

REMOVAL & INSTALLATION

121-4 Cylinder

1. Drain the cooling system.

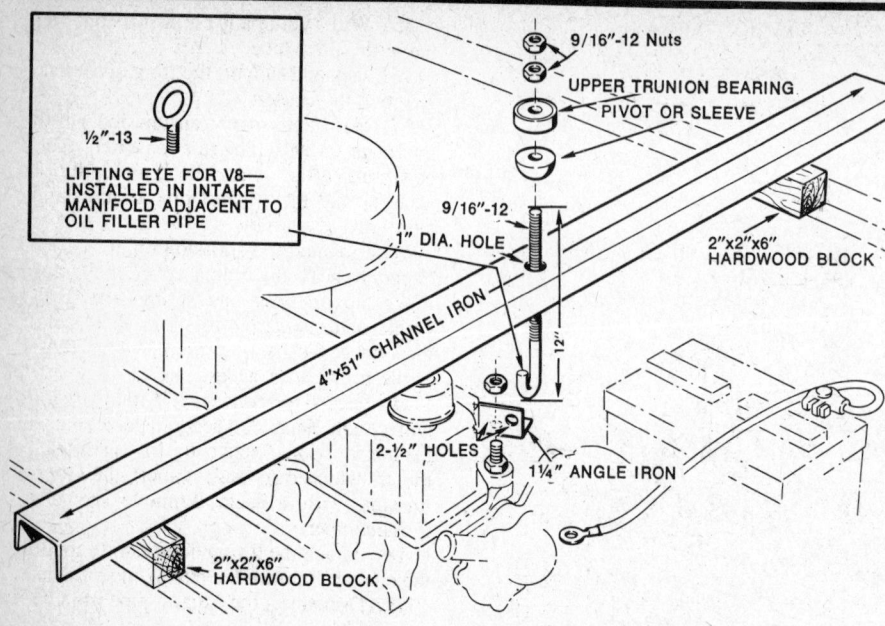

9/16"-12 Nuts
UPPER TRUNION BEARING
PIVOT OR SLEEVE

1/2"-13 →
LIFTING EYE FOR V8—
INSTALLED IN INTAKE
MANIFOLD ADJACENT TO
OIL FILLER PIPE

9/16"-12
1" DIA. HOLE
2"x2"x6"
HARDWOOD BLOCK
4"x51" CHANNEL IRON
12"
2-1/2" HOLES
1 1/4" ANGLE IRON
2"x2"x6"
HARDWOOD BLOCK

Lifting fixture can be fabricated as illustrated to facilitate oil pan and motor mount removal

2. Remove the EGR tube at the exhaust manifold and remove the air cleaner assembly.

3. Disconnect the fuel and vacuum lines, and plug the main fuel line to avoid gasoline leakage.

4. Remove the accelerator cable and the air hose from the diverter valve.

5. Remove the fuel pump and the power brake cylinder vacuum hose. Loosen the air conditioner compressor mounting bracket, if so equipped. Do not discharge the system.

6. Remove the water inlet and outlet hoses from the manifold and the PCV hose at the block.

7. Remove the wires from the carburetor, accessories, and from the ignition coil.

8. Remove the manifold bracket lower screw, loosen and remove the manifold nuts, and remove the manifold and lift bracket from the engine.

9. Remove the gasket and clean the mating surfaces on the manifold and the cylinder head.

10. To reinstall the intake manifold reverse disassembly procedure. When installing the manifold, don't tighten the manifold retaining nuts until the EGR tube is connected to the exhaust manifold. Then tighten the retaining nuts to 18 ft. lbs. torque and the bracket lower screw to 30 ft. lbs. When the installation is completed, operate the engine for 3–5 minutes and check for leaks.

150-4 Cylinder

NOTE: It is necessary to remove the carburetor from the intake manifold before the manifold is removed. After removing the carburetor from the intake manifold, it may be set to one side with vacuum hoses still attached.

── CAUTION ──
If the engine has been recently operated,

use care to prevent scalding by hot coolant. The system is pressurized.

1. Remove the radiator cap and drain-cock to drain the coolant.

NOTE: Do not waste reusable coolant. If the coolant is acceptable for reuse, drain into a clean container.

2. Remove the air cleaner. Disconnect the fuel pipe, carburetor air horn vent hose, idle speed control vacuum hose, and wire connector.

3. Disconnect the coolant hoses from the intake manifold.

4. Disconnect the throttle cable from the bellcrank.

5. Disconnect the PCV valve vacuum hose from the intake manifold.

6. Remove the vacuum advance CTO valve vacuum hoses.

7. Disconnect the feedback system coolant temperature sender wire connector (located on the intake manifold).

8. Disconnect the vacuum hose from the EGR valve.

9. Disconnect the intake manifold electric heater wire connector.

10. Remove the power steering mounting bracket, if so equipped.

11. Detach the power steering pump and set aside, if so equipped.

12. Do not remove the hoses.

13. Disconnect the throttle valve linkage, if equipped with automatic transmission.

14. Disconnect the EGR valve tube from the intake manifold.

15. Remove the intake manifold attaching screws, nuts and clamps. Remove the intake manifold. Discard the gasket.

16. Clean the mating surfaces of the manifold and cylinder head.

NOTE: If the manifold is being re-

placed, ensure all fittings, etc. are transferred to the replacement manifold.

17. Installation is in the reverse order of removal. Torque manifold bolts to 23 ft. lbs.

151-4 Cylinder

1. Remove the air cleaner. Drain the cooling system. Disconnect the heater hose from the intake manifold.

2. Disconnect and label the fuel line, all vacuum lines and electrical connectors from the carburetor, insulator and the intake manifold.

3. Disconnect the throttle linkage.

4. Remove the carburetor and insulator.

5. Remove the alternator rear support bracket from the manifold.

6. Remove the A/C compressor, if so equipped.

7. Remove the intake manifold bolts and remove the manifold.

8. To install, place a new gasket against the cylinder head, then install the manifold in place by starting all bolts finger-tight.

9. Torque the intake manifold bolts to 25 ft. lbs. in two stages, using the torque sequence shown. The rest of the installation is in the reverse order of removal.

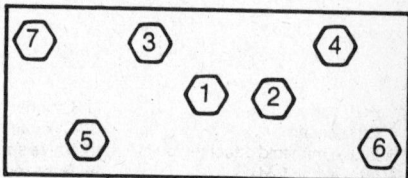

151-4 cylinder intake manifold bolt torque sequence

6 Cylinder

The intake manifold is mounted on the left-hand side of the engine and bolted to the cylinder head. A gasket is used between the intake manifold and the head; none is required for the exhaust manifold.

1. Remove the air cleaner. Disconnect the fuel line, vent hose, and solenoid wire, if so equipped.

2. Disconnect the accelerator cable from the accelerator bellcrank.

3. Disconnect the PCV vacuum hose from the intake manifold and the TCS solenoid and bracket, if so equipped.

4. Remove the spark CTO switch and EGR valve (or exhaust back-pressure sensor) vacuum lines from each of these components.

5. Disconnect the hoses from the air pump and the injection manifold check valve. Disconnect the vacuum line from the diverter valve and remove the diverter valve with hoses, if so equipped.

6. Remove the air pump and power steering bracket (if so equipped) and remove the air pump. Move the power steering pump aside, out of the way, without disconnecting the hoses.

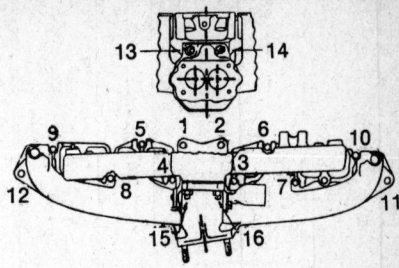

1 CYLINDER HEAD
2 ROCKER ARMS
3 BRIDGE
4 PIVOT
5 PUSHROD
6 INTAKE MANIFOLD
7 EXHAUST MANIFOLD
8 CYL. HEAD BOLTS
9 CYLINDER HEAD
10 CYL. HEAD GASKET
11 INTAKE MANIF. GASKET

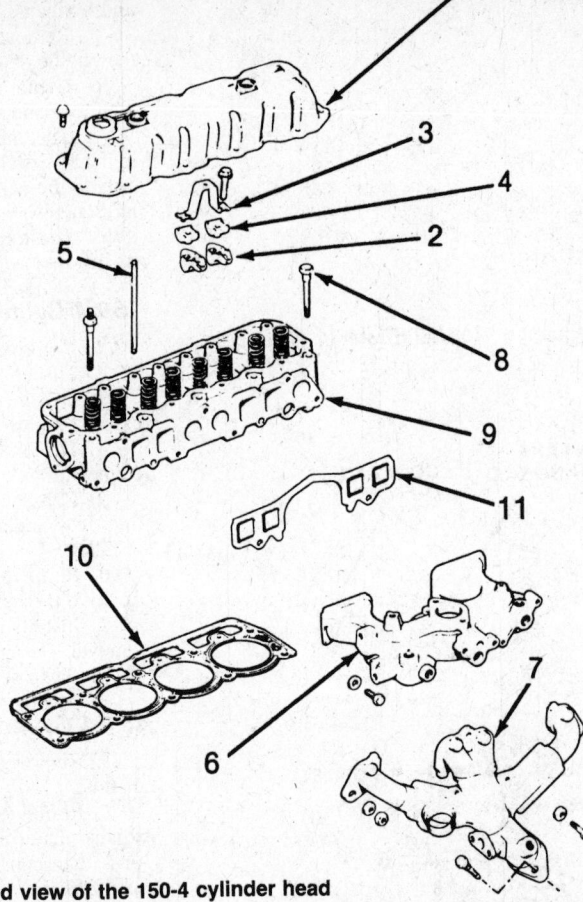

Exploded view of the 150-4 cylinder head

6 Cylinder intake and exhaust manifold torque sequence

and tighten the manifold attaching bolts and nuts in the proper sequence to the specified torque.

4. Install the remaining components in the reverse order of removal. Adjust the automatic transmission throttle linkage, if so equipped. Adjust the drive belt(s) tension.

V8 Engine

The cast iron manifold completely encloses and seals the tappet valley between the cylinder heads. The manifold contains water passages, a crankcase vent passage, exhaust crossover, induction, and in some cases EGR passages. A one-piece metal gasket seals the intake manifold to cylinder head joint, also serves as an oil splash baffle. The left-hand carburetor bores supply cylinders No. 1, 7, 4 and 6; the right-hand bores supply cylinders No. 3, 5, 2 and 8.

1. Drain the cooling system.

2. Remove the air cleaner assembly from the carburetor.

3. Mark and remove the spark plug wires.

4. Remove the spark plug wire guides from the rocker cover, ignition coil and by-pass valve brackets.

5. Disconnect the radiator upper hose and the by-pass hoses from their fittings on the intake manifold. Disconnect the temperature gauge sending unit electrical lead.

6. Remove the ignition coil and bracket. Set the coil/bracket assembly out of the way.

7. Remove the TCS solenoid if so equipped, from the right-hand valve cover. Remove the A/C compressor bracket, if so equipped. Do not discharge the system, just move the compressor aside with lines attached.

8. Disconnect any of the emission control wiring or hoses as necessary. Disconnect the heater hose from the rear of the intake manifold.

9. Disconnect the throttle linkage and fuel and vacuum lines from the carburetor.

10. On the cars equipped with air injection, remove the by-pass (diverter) valve bracket. Set the valve assembly (with hoses) out of the way, forward of the engine.

11. If the car is equipped with "Cruise Command" (automatic speed control), remove the vacuum servo mounting bracket and set the servo assembly aside.

12. Remove the carburetor assembly from the manifold.

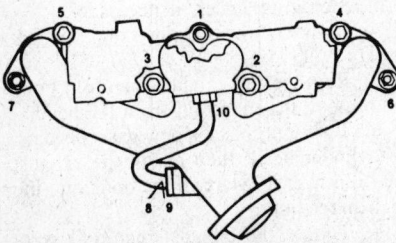

150-4 cylinder intake manifold bolt tightening sequence. Tightening torque is 23 ft. lbs.

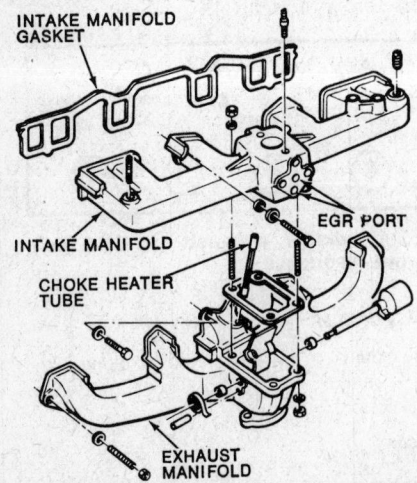

INTAKE MANIFOLD GASKET
INTAKE MANIFOLD
CHOKE HEATER TUBE
EGR PORT
EXHAUST MANIFOLD

Typical 6 cylinder intake and exhaust manifold

7. Remove the air conditioning drive belt idler assembly from the cylinder head, if so equipped. On some models it is necessary to remove the A/C compressor. Do not discharge the A/C system; just lay the compressor aside.

8. Disconnect the throttle valve linkage if equipped with automatic transmission.

9. Disconnect the exhaust pipe from the manifold.

10. On some 1981 and later models, an oxygen sensor is screwed in the exhaust manifold just above the exhaust pipe connection. Disconnect the wire and remove the sensor, if so equipped.

11. Remove the manifold attaching bolts, nuts, and clamps and remove the intake and exhaust manifolds as an assembly. Discard the gasket. The two manifolds are separated at the heat riser. Discard the asbestos gasket if manifolds are separated. The asbestos gasket is not used on 1980 and later models.

To install the intake and exhaust manifolds:

1. Clean all of the mating surfaces on the cylinder head and the manifolds.

2. Assemble the two manifolds together with a new gasket (through 1979) and tighten the heat riser retaining nuts to 5 ft. lbs.

3. Position the manifold on the engine, together with a new intake manifold gasket,

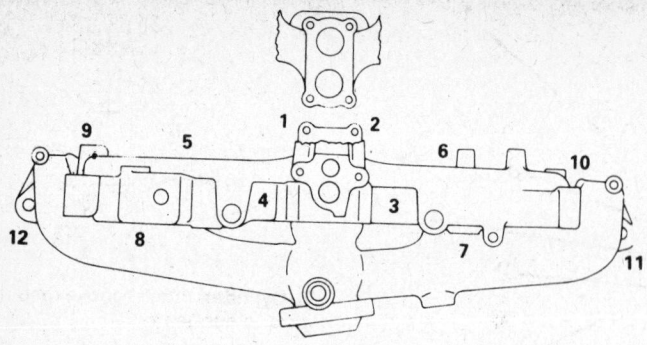

6 cyl. intake and exhaust manifold torque sequence—1981 and later (© American Motors Corp.)

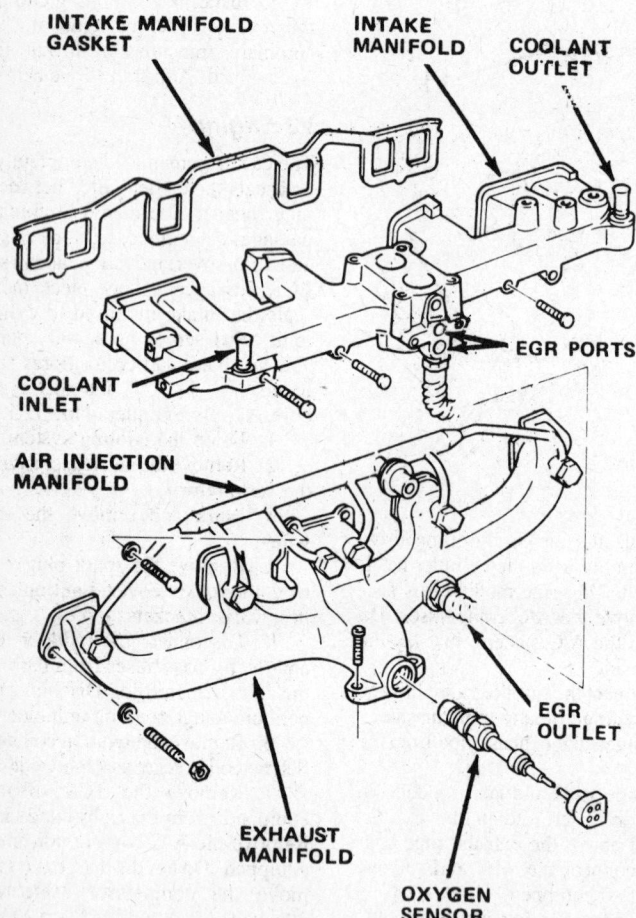

6 cyl. intake and exhaust manifold—1981 and later (© American Motors Corp.)

13. Remove the intake manifold assembly complete with gasket and end seals.

Always use a new gasket when installing the intake manifold. Use a good commercial sealer on both sides of the metal gasket and on the rubber end seals. Align the gasket at the rear first, then at the front.

The rest of the installation procedure is in the reverse order of removal. Torque the manifold bolts evenly to the specified torque, working from the center out.

Exhaust Manifold
REMOVAL & INSTALLATION
121-4 Cylinder

1. Remove the TAC cold air induction manifold assembly and components.
2. Disconnect the EGR tube from the manifold.
3. Remove the exhaust pipe from the manifold.

4. Remove the manifold retaining nuts and washers.
5. Remove the manifold and gasket from the engine.
6. Clean the mating surfaces of the manifold and the head.
7. The installation of the manifold is in the reverse order of disassembly. Do not tighten the exhaust manifold nuts until the EGR tube is attached to the exhaust manifold, then torque the manifold nuts to 18 ft. lbs.

150-4 Cylinder

1. Remove the intake manifold.
2. Disconnect the EGR valve tube.
3. Disconnect the exhaust pipe from the exhaust manifold.
4. Disconnect the oxygen sensor wire connector.
5. Remove the sensor from the manifold if a replacement manifold is to be installed.
6. Remove the nuts from the end studs. Remove the exhaust manifold.
7. Installation is in the reverse order of removal. Torque manifold nuts to 23 ft. lbs., oxygen sensor to 35 ft. lbs.

151-4 Cylinder

1. Remove the air cleaner and the hot air tube.
2. Remove the Pulsair system from the exhaust manifold.
3. Disconnect the exhaust pipe from the manifold at the flange. Spray the bolts first with penetrating sealer, if necessary.
4. Remove the engine oil dipstick bracket bolt.
5. Remove the exhaust manifold bolts and remove the manifold from the head.
6. To install, place a new gasket against the cylinder head, then install the exhaust manifold over it. Start all the bolts into the head finger-tight.
7. Torque the exhaust manifold bolts to 37 ft. lbs. in two stages, using the torque sequence illustrated.
8. Complete the installation in the reverse order of removal.

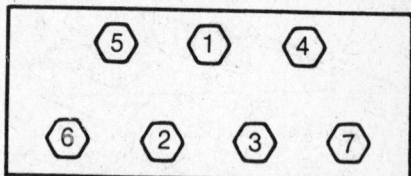

151-4 cylinder exhaust manifold bolt torque sequence

6 Cylinder

The exhaust manifold is removed along with the intake manifold; see previous instructions.

V8 Engine

NOTE: The mating surfaces of both the exhaust manifold and the cylinder

head are machined smooth, thus eliminating any need for a gasket between them.

1. Disconnect the wires from the spark plugs after marking them for firing order.

2. On models equipped with air injection, disconnect the air delivery hoses from the injection manifold. Remove the injection manifold and nozzles from the exhaust manifold.

3. Disconnect the exhaust pipe from the exhaust manifold flange.

4. Remove the bolts and washers used to retain the manifold.

5. Remove the shields from the spark plugs. On 1978 and later Concords only, before removing the right side manifold, remove the transmission filler tube bolt and tube. Use a new O-ring when installing the tube.

6. Remove the exhaust manifold from the cylinder head.

7. Clean the machined surfaces of the manifold and head. Installation is in the reverse order of removal.

Valve System

ADJUSTMENT

121-4 Cylinder

The valves are operated by an overhead-cam, driven by a toothed rubber belt, connected to the crankshaft. The cam lobes contact "bucket" type tappets, which are set over the valve and valve springs, and force the valve and springs to move downward, moving the valve from its seat on the cylinder head. Both intake and exhaust valves are manually adjusted by a wedge type screw angled into the tappet, perpendicular to the valve stem. A flat area is milled onto the screw, which contacts the valve stem end. The threaded area locks to a threaded area within the tappet. Each turn changes the clearance .002 in. When tappet adjustment is made, the flat side of the adjusting screw must be toward the valve stem end at the completion of the adjustment. Refer to the "Tune-Up Specifications" chart for hot valve clearances. Cold assembly clearances are 0.004–0.007, intake; and 0.014–0.017, exhaust.

NOTE: Valve adjustment must be made with the engine at normal operating temperature.

1. Remove the TAC hose, the cylinder head cover, the spark plug wires and distributor cap.

2. Rotate the crankshaft to bring the number one cylinder to TDC (the beginning of its firing stroke). The position of the distributor rotor will assist in determining the TDC position.

NOTE: There is a mark on the edge of the distributor housing at number one terminal position. Do not attempt to rotate the engine by turning the camshaft.

Turn the crankshaft in the direction of normal rotation to avoid damage to the timing belt.

3. With number one cylinder on TDC of its firing stroke, the clearance of the exhaust valves on cylinders number one and three, and of the intake valves on cylinders number one and two, can be checked.

NOTE: The front valve in each pair per cylinder is the intake valve. If the clearance requires adjustment, a special tool is required to move the adjusting screw.

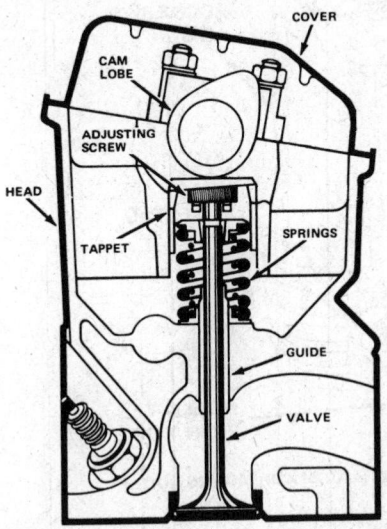

121-4 cylinder valve train (© American Motors Corp.)

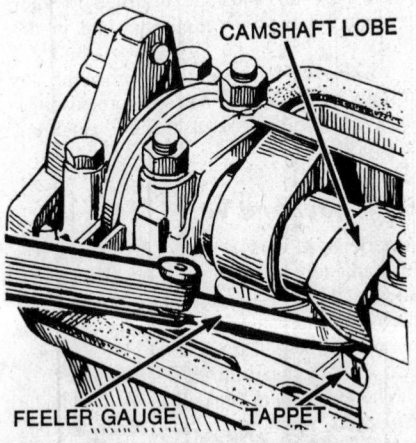

121-4 cylinder valve clearance measurement (© American Motors Corp.)

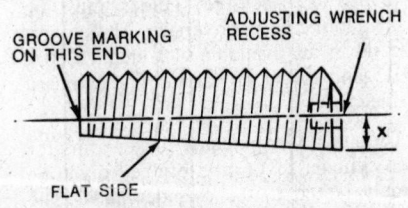

121-4 cylinder valve tappet adjusting screw (© American Motors Corp.)

4. Adjust the screw by turning one complete turn until it clicks, and continue until the proper clearance is obtained.

5. After adjusting the clearance, use the special AMC gauge J-26860 to check the position of the screw in the tappet. If the gauge indicates the adjusting screw is turned too far into the tappet, the screw must be replaced. Five sizes of screws are available, identified by grooves on the end of the screws.

NOTE: If the adjusting screws must be replaced, the tappets must be removed from the head. Note which tappets must be removed, then continue the adjustment procedure. When all eight adjustments are made, remove those tappets requiring screw replacement. Refer to camshaft removal and installation.

6. Rotate the crankshaft 360 degrees. The distributor rotor should be 180 degrees opposite the mark on the distributor housing.

7. The clearance can now be checked on the exhaust valves for cylinders two and four, and the intake valve on cylinders three and four.

8. Reinstall the head cover, using a new gasket.

9. Reinstall the distributor cap and spark plug wiring. Reinstall the TAC flexible hose.

MECHANICAL VALVE LIFTER CLEARANCE

Engine	Intake (Hot) In.	Exhaust (Hot) In.
121-4	.006–.009	.016–.019

150 and 151-4 Cylinder

The 150 and the 151 use hydraulic lifters, eliminating periodic valve adjustments. The 151 cylinder head has integral valve guides. Oversized valves are available in 0.003 and 0.005 in. sizes. To fit these, the valve guide bores must be enlarged with a reamer.

As an alternate procedure, some automotive machine shops fit replacement valve guides which accept the standard size valves.

Rocker Assembly

REMOVAL & INSTALLATION

150-4 Cylinder

1. Remove the valve cover.

2. Remove the capscrews at each bridge and pivot assembly.

3. Alternately loosen the capscrews one turn at a time to avoid damaging the bridge.

4. Remove the bridges, pivots and corresponding pair of rocker arms.

5. Installation is in the reverse order of removal. Tighten capscrews to 19 ft. lbs.

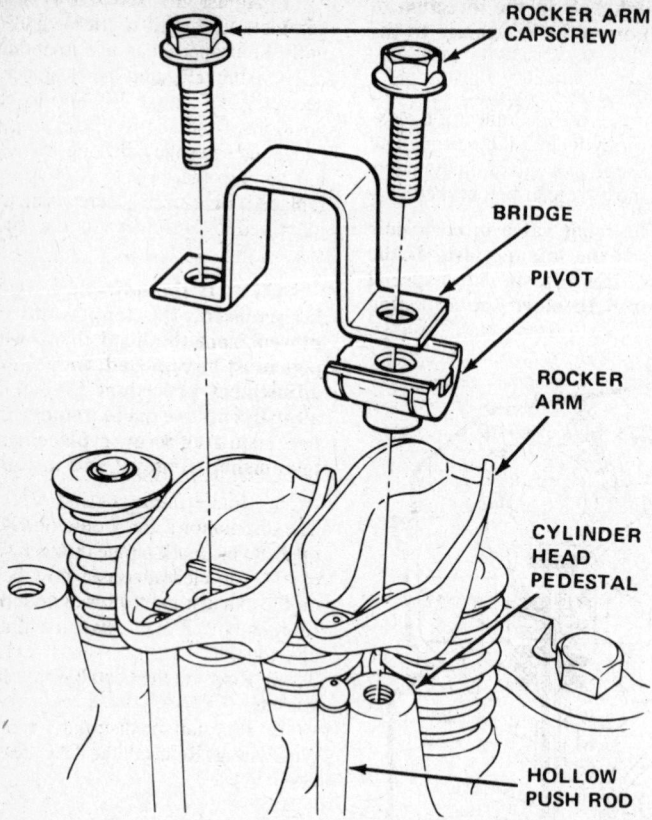

Rocker arm assembly—258-6 cylinder (© American Motors Corp.)

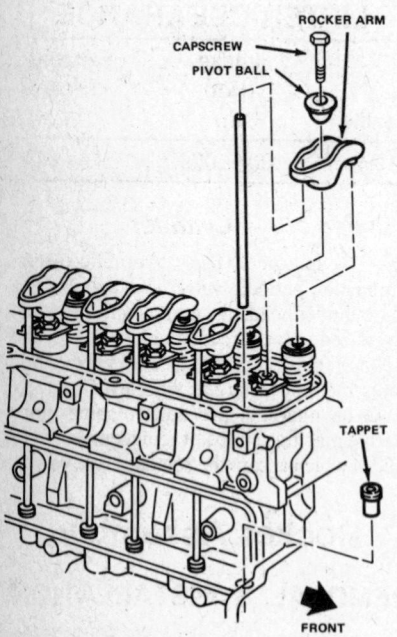

Rocker arm assembly—151-4 cylinder
(© American Motors Corp.)

151-4 Cylinder

1. Remove the valve cover.
2. Remove the rocker arm nut and rocker arm ball.
3. Lift the rocker arm off the stud. Al-

ways keep the rocker arm assemblies together and assemble them on the same stud.
4. Remove the pushrod from its bore. Make sure the rods are returned to their original bores, with the same end in the block.
5. Reverse the removal procedure to install. Lubricate all parts before installation. Tighten the rocker arm ball retaining nut to 20 ft. lbs.

6 Cylinder and V8

American Motors 6 and V8 engines use hydraulic tappets; thus, no mechanical valve adjustment is necessary. Special tappets to permit higher sustained rpm are used in police engines. The valve guides are integral with the head on all engines.

The valve stem oil deflectors should be replaced whenever valve service is performed.

American Motors engines do not have replaceable valve guides. If stem-to-guide clearance is excessive, guides must be reamed to the proper oversize. Three over-size valves are available with stems 0.003, 0.015 and 0.030 in. larger than standard diameter.

The intake and exhaust rocker arms for each cylinder pivot on a bridged pivot assembly bolted to the cylinder head. The pushrods are hollow to supply lubrication to the rocker arms. The pushrods act as guides to keep the rocker arms in align-

ment, so it is not abnormal for pushrods to rub slightly on the cylinder head.

NOTE: Be careful when ordering new valve train components, not to get parts for the wrong year.

1. Remove any accessories which are in the way and remove the valve cover, complete with gasket.
2. Unscrew the rocker arm capscrews evenly to avoid breaking the bridge.
3. Remove the pivot assemblies, rocker arms, and pushrods.

NOTE: Be sure to keep all parts in the same order in which they were removed.

4. Clean all parts in solvent. Blow all oil passages in the rocker arms and pushrods dry with compressed air.

Replace any deeply pitted rocker arms and scuffed or worn pushrods. If the pushrod is worn from lack of oil, replace it, its valve lifter and rocker arm, as well.

Installation is performed in the following order:

1. Insert the pushrods in their bores. Be sure to center the bottom of each rod in the plunger cap of the hydraulic valve lifter.
2. Install the rocker arms, pivot assemblies and capscrews. Tighten the capscrews evenly 19 ft. lbs. on all engines.

NOTE: Be sure that the pushrods, pivot assemblies, and capscrews are returned to exactly the same places from which they were removed.

3. Wipe the gasket surface clean.
a. If a silicone sealer is being used, wipe the surface with an oily rag and apply a 1/8 in. bead of silicone along the sealing surface. Before the silicone begins to harden, install the cover, being careful not to touch the silicone to the rocker arms. Apply a small amount of sealer to each screw hole and tighten the screws to specifications.
b. When using a gasket, cement the gasket in several places with a quick-drying adhesive. Correctly position the cover and gasket on the engine and install the attaching screws.
4. Install whatever was removed to gain access to the valve covers.

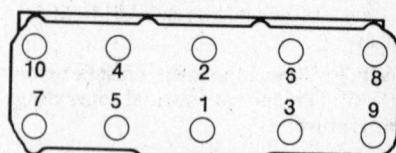

Head bolt torque sequence, 121-4 cylinder (© American Motors Corp.)

Cylinder Head
REMOVAL & INSTALLATION
——— CAUTION ———
To prevent cylinder head warping don't loosen the head bolts until the engine is thoroughly cool. Do not remove block drain

plugs or loosen radiator draincock with the system hot and under pressure, as serious burns from coolant can occur.

If the head sticks, operate the starter to loosen it by compression or rap it upward with a soft hammer. Do not force anything between the head and the block.

Cylinder head bolts should be retorqued after the first 500 miles or so, unless a special AMC gasket is used. The special gasket doesn't require retorquing.

— CAUTION —

Make sure to blow any coolant out of the cylinder head bolt holes before reassembly to prevent inaccurate torque readings.

121-4 Cylinder

1. Drain the coolant from the system and disconnect the negative cable from the battery.

2. Remove the air cleaner assembly, vacuum hoses and flexible hoses from the cylinder head area.

3. Remove the radiator hoses, radiator bypass hose and the heater hoses.

4. Remove the accessory drive belts, camshaft drive belt cover, and the camshaft drive belt. Loosen the compressor mounting bracket if equipped with A/C.

5. Remove the fan belt, fan blades, spacer and pulley. Remove the air pump and the alternator pivot bolt. Do not disconnect the wire harness from the alternator.

6. Remove the air pump front bracket, and the exhaust pipe from the manifold. Remove the air hose from the diverter valve, and remove the EGR tube-to-bellhousing screw.

7. Disconnect the remaining wires to the electrical units of the cylinder head, marking the wires for connection during assembly.

8. Remove the fuel line at the bottom of the intake manifold, and remove the screw from the bottom of the manifold bracket.

9. Disconnect the power brake vacuum hose. Remove the remaining fuel vapor control hoses, PCV hoses, and the remaining vacuum lines.

10. Disconnect the accelerator cable.

11. Remove the coolant inlet and outlet hoses from the intake manifold.

12. Remove the cylinder head cover. Loosen and remove the head bolts. Loosen the bolts in the reverse order of the tightening sequence, in two passes. Remove the cylinder head, manifolds and carburetor as a unit.

13. Clean the machined surfaces of the cylinder head and the engine block. With a straight edge and feeler gauge check the flatness of the mating surfaces. There should not be a distortion of over 0.002 in. on both surfaces.

14. After servicing the cylinder head and/or the block assembly as necessary, prepare the mating surfaces by cleaning thoroughly. Install a new head gasket, and place the

head on the block with the aid of locating dowels. Torque the cylinder head bolts in three stages, to 65 ft. lbs., following the cylinder head torque sequence illustration.

15. Complete cylinder head replacement by following the reverse procedure of disassembly. Temporarily install the head cover. Start the engine and allow it to warm up for five minutes.

16. When the engine has warmed up to operating temperature, stop the engine and remove the top engine cover.

17. Following the head torque sequence, loosen the first head bolt ⅛ of a turn and re-torque the bolt to 80 ft. lbs. Proceed to the second bolt and repeat the procedure for each head bolt until all the bolts have been re-torqued to the new specification.

18. Replace the head cover and complete the assembly of the lines, tubes, wires, and air cleaner assembly.

19. Check the engine for leakage.

150-4 Cylinder

1. Disconnect the battery cables.

— CAUTION —

Do not perform this procedure on a hot engine.

2. Drain the coolant and disconnect the hoses at the thermostat housing.

3. Remove the air cleaner.

4. Remove the valve cover.

5. Remove the rocker arms, bridge and pivot assemblies. Remove the push rods.

NOTE: Retain the push rods, bridge, pivot and rocker arms in the same order as removed to facilitate installation into their original positions.

6. Disconnect the power steering pump bracket. Set the pump and bracket aside. Do not disconnect the hoses.

7. Remove the intake and exhaust manifolds from the cylinder head.

8. If equipped with air conditioning, perform the following:

   a. remove the air conditioner compressor drive belt

   b. loosen the alternator drive belt

   c. remove the A/C compressor/alternator bracket-to-cylinder head mounting screw

NOTE: The serpentine drive belt tension is released by loosening the alternator.

   d. remove the bolts from the A/C compressor (if so equipped) and alternator mounting bracket, and set the compressor aside

9. Disconnect the ignition wires and remove the spark plugs.

10. Disconnect the temperature sending unit wire connector.

11. Remove the cylinder head bolts, cylinder head and gasket.

12. Thoroughly clean the machined surfaces of the cylinder head and block. Remove all gasket material and cement.

13. Installation is in the reverse order of removal, with the following recommendations.

— CAUTION —

Do not apply sealing compound to the cylinder head and block machined surfaces. Do not allow the sealing compound to enter the cylinder bores.

14. Apply an even coat of Perfect Seal sealing compound, or equivalent, to both sides of the replacement cylinder head gasket and position the gasket on the cylinder block with word TOP facing upward.

15. Torque the head bolts to 85 ft. lbs. in the sequence illustrated.

151-4 Cylinder

1. Disconnect the negative battery cable. Drain the cooling system.

2. Disconnect the accelerator cable at the bellcrank, and the manifold vacuum and fuel lines at the carburetor.

3. Remove the intake and exhaust manifolds.

4. Remove the alternator and power steering pump. Unbolt the A/C compressor, if so equipped and move it aside—without disconnecting any lines.

5. Disconnect all electrical connectors at the head.

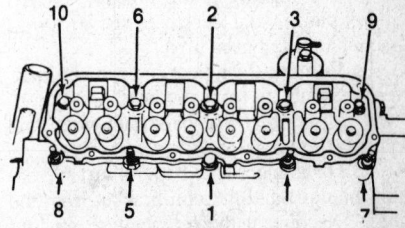

150-4 cylinder head bolt tightening sequence. Tightening torque is 85 ft. lbs.

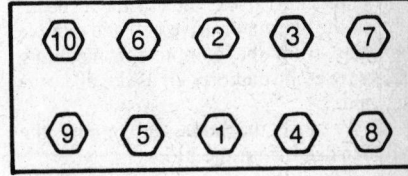

151-4 cylinder head bolt torque sequence

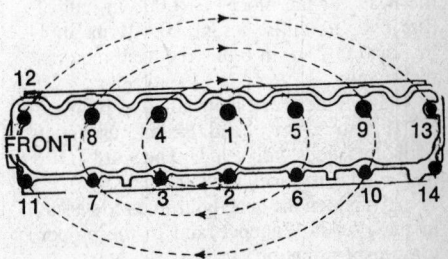

Cylinder head torque sequence for all 6 cylinder engines

6. Disconnect the radiator and heater hoses, and the battery ground strap.

7. Remove the spark plugs.

8. Remove the rocker arm cover, rocker arms, and push rods. Keep all parts in order.

9. Unbolt and remove the cylinder head.

10. Clean the gasket surfaces thoroughly.

11. Install a new gasket over the dowels, and then position the cylinder head.

12. Coat the head bolt threads with sealer and install finger-tight.

13. Tighten the bolts in sequence, in three equal steps, to the specified torque.

14. Install all parts in the reverse order of removal.

6 Cylinder

NOTE: On Pacers, run the wipers to the center of the windshield to ease valve cover removal.

1. Drain the cooling system. Disconnect throttle linkage, fuel lines, water hoses, spark plug wires and vacuum line. Remove the air cleaner, PCV hose, and the temperature sender.

2. Remove the valve cover and its gasket. Remove the rocker arm assembly and the pushrods. With bridged pivots, loosen each bolt alternately, one turn at a time, to avoid damage. Keep the pushrods in order. If equipped with power steering, remove the power steering pump bracket and Air Guard pump, and set them aside. Don't disconnect the hoses.

3. Remove the intake and exhaust manifold assemblies from the head.

4. Disconnect the spark plug wires, and remove the plugs.

5. Disconnect the battery ground cable, the coil, and the coil bracket from the head. Disconnect the temperature sending unit wire.

6. If the vehicle is equipped with air conditioning, remove the drive belt idler pulley bracket from the cylinder head. Loosen the alternator drive belt and remove the bolts from the compressor mounting bracket. Set the compressor aside, all hoses attached.

7. Remove the bolts and remove the cylinder head from the block.

8. Clean the gasket surfaces of both the head and the block. Remove the carbon deposits from the top of each piston, and from the combustion chambers.

9. Check the head for straightness. If the head (or the block) is 0.008 in. out of true over its entire length, 0.001 in. in 1 in., or 0.002 in. in 6 in., the head requires resurfacing.

The cylinder head is installed as follows:

1. Use a new head gasket, and coat both of its sides with sealer. The word TOP, on the gasket, faces upward.

2. Tighten the head bolts in three stages, in the proper sequence and to the proper torque specification.

3. Complete the installation in the reverse order of removal. Refill the cooling system when completed.

V8 Engine

1. Drain the cooling system.

2. Remove the cylinder head cover and gasket.

3. Remove the rocker arm assemblies. Loosen the capscrews on the bridged pivots alternately, to avoid damaging the bridges.

4. Remove the pushrods.

NOTE: Keep the rocker arms and push rods in order. They must be returned to their original places at assembly.

5. Remove the ignition wires and spark plugs.

6. Remove the intake and exhaust manifolds.

7. Loosen all drive belts.

8. Remove the a/c compressor mounting bracket, if so equipped. Remove the alternator support brace.

9. Remove the air pump and power steering mounting bracket, if so equipped.

10. Remove the cylinder head retaining bolts in the reverse order of the installation sequence, and in two stages.

11. Remove the cylinder head and gasket. To install:

12. Apply a coat of sealer to both sides of the new head gasket. Position the gasket on the block with the word TOP facing up.

13. Install the cylinder head and gasket.

14. Tighten the cylinder bolts to 80 ft. lbs., following the torquing sequence chart. Following the sequence chart again, torque the bolts to 110 ft. lbs.

Complete the installation procedure in the reverse order of removal.

Vibration Damper

REMOVAL

4, 6 and 8 Cylinder Engines

Remove the radiator core, all drive belts, and the fan. Remove the nut from the center of the pulley. The best way to do this is to affix a heavy wrench and rap it with a substantial hammer. It may be necessary to lock up the engine at the flywheel to prevent crankshaft rotation. The nut must be unscrewed in the opposite direction of normal engine rotation. Using a puller, remove the pulley from the front of the crankshaft.

Vibration damper removal

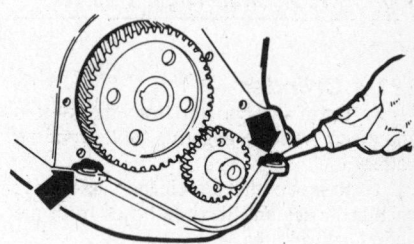

Sealer application prior to front cover installation, 4-151

INSTALLATION

1. With key in crankshaft keyway, align damper hub keyway with crankshaft key and tap damper onto crankshaft.

2. Install damper retaining bolt and washer, and tighten bolt to specifications.

3. Install crankshaft pulley and retaining bolts, and tighten to specifications.

4. Install drive belt(s) and tighten to specified tension.

Timing Case Cover

REMOVAL & INSTALLATION

151-4 Cylinder

1. Remove the crankshaft hub.

2. Remove the oil pan-to-front cover screws.

3. Remove the front cover-to-block screws.

4. Pull the cover slightly forward, just enough to allow cutting of the oil pan front seal flush with the block on both sides.

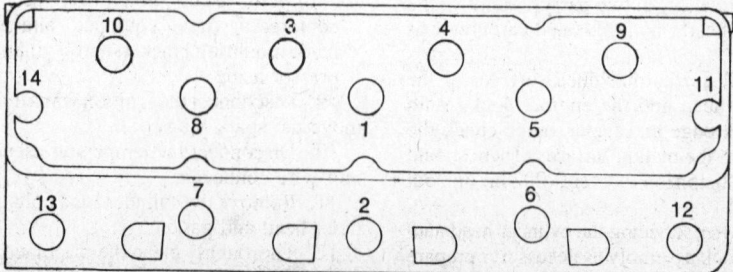

Cylinder head torque sequence for all V8 engines

5. Remove the front cover and attached portion of the pan seal.

6. Clean the gasket surfaces thoroughly.

7. Cut the tabs from the new oil pan front seal.

8. Install the seal on the front cover, pressing the tips into the holes provided.

9. Coat the new gasket with sealer and position it on the front cover.

10. Apply a ⅛ in. bead of silicone sealer to the joint formed at the oil pan and block.

11. Align the front cover seal with a centering tool and install the front cover. Tighten the screws to 7.5 ft. lbs. Install the crankshaft hub.

150-4 Cylinder, 232 and 258-6 Cylinder

1. Remove all V-belts, fan and pulley.
2. Remove vibration damper.
3. Remove oil pan-to-cover bolts and cover-to-block bolts.
4. Raise cover and pull oil pan front seal up far enough to extract the tabs from the holes in cover.

────────── **CAUTION** ──────────

If this isn't done, the oil pan will have to be removed to get the seals into place.

5. Remove cover gasket from block; cut off seal tab flush with front face of block.

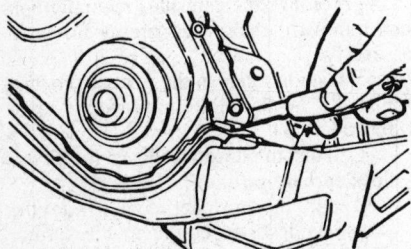

Cutting the pan gasket on the 4 cylinder engine

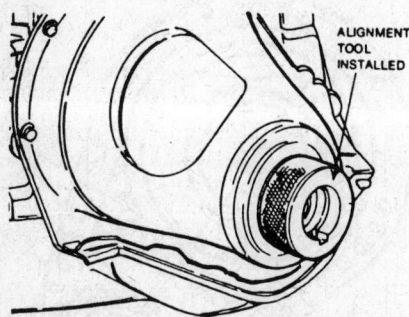

151-4 cylinder timing case cover alignment tool in place

6. Clean all mating surfaces and remove oil seal.

7. Install a new front oil seal.

8. Install a new neoprene seal in front oil pan, cutting off protruding tabs to match original. Use sealer on the end tabs and the gasket surfaces.

9. Position cover on block and install

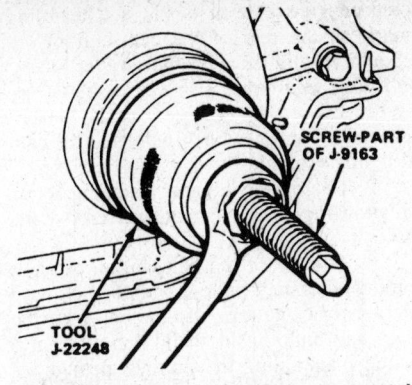

6 cylinder engine timing case cover seal installation

bolts. Align the front cover with a centering tool. Tighten cover bolts to 4–6 ft. lbs.; four lower bolts to 10–12 ft. lbs. Remove the centering tool.

10. Install vibration damper, tightening the bolt to the specified torque.

NOTE: Front oil seal can be installed with cover in place only if proper tool or equivalent is available.

V8 Engine

The die-cast timing cover incorporates an oil seal at the vibration damper hub. Oil seals are installed from the front, and can be replaced using a special AMC tool, without removing the cover.

1. Drain coolant and remove hoses from water pump.

2. Remove distributor, fuel pump, alternator drive belt, accessory drive belts, fan and hub assembly, alternator and bracket, and back idler pulley.

3. Remove the vibration damper bolts, then pull off the damper.

4. Remove air conditioner compressor and power steering pump, if so equipped, and swing them out of the way *without* disconnecting hoses.

5. Remove the two front oil pan bolts from beneath the car, then remove the cover bolts.

NOTE: The timing case cover attaching bolts are of different lengths and must be replaced in their original locations.

6. Remove cover from block, then clean all parts and mating surfaces and remove oil seal.

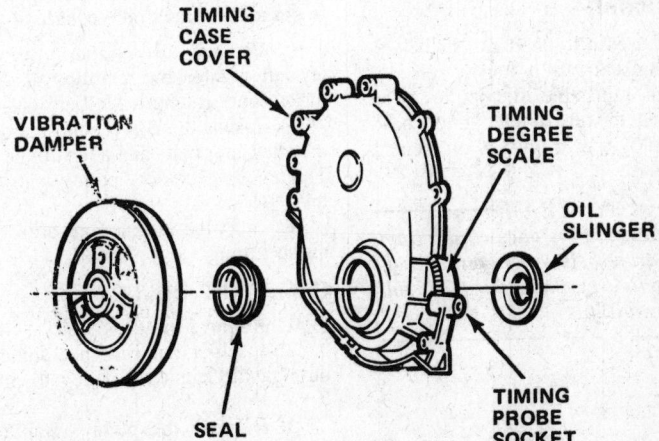

Timing case cover assembly—258-6 cylinder (© American Motors Corp.)

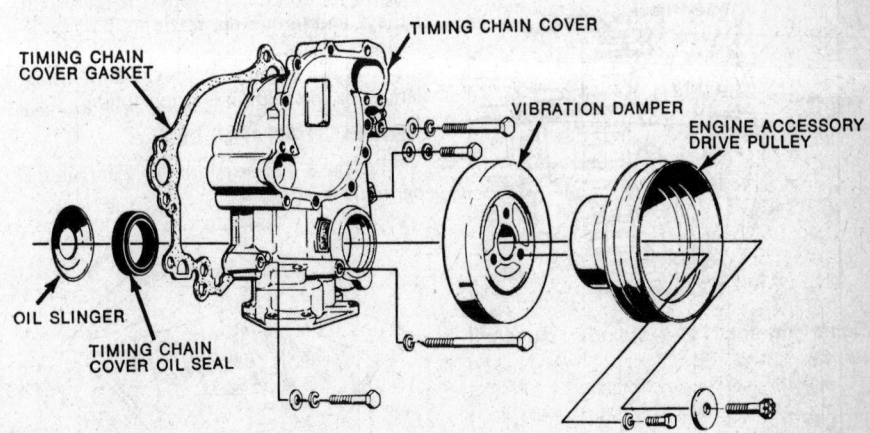

V8 timing chain cover assembly through 1976. 1977 and later are similar except for seal location (© American Motors Corp.)

7. Coat new seal lips with petroleum jelly and seal surface with sealer, then drive the seal into the cover bore until it seats against the cover face.

8. Remove lower dowel pin from cylinder block; this must be replaced when cover is in position, but before bolts are installed.

9. Cut the oil pan gasket flush with the block on both sides of the oil pan.

10. Cut corresponding pieces of gasket from another oil pan gasket and cement them to cover. Install neoprene oil pan front seal into cover and align gasket tabs with pan seal.

11. Apply sealant to gaskets, then position cover. Install oil pan bolts and tighten evenly until cover lines up with upper dowel pin.

12. Install lower dowel pin, then cover-to-block bolts; tighten to 20–30 ft. lbs.

13. Install all removed pieces and adjust ignition timing.

Cam Drive

REMOVAL & INSTALLATION

121-4 Cylinder

This engine uses a toothed rubber belt to drive the camshaft. Belt tension is controlled by an adjustable idler pulley. The distributor is at the rear of the cylinder head and is driven by a gear pressed on the rear of the camshaft.

—————— CAUTION ——————

Do not turn the engine backwards. Damage to the drive belt teeth could result. Turn the engine by the crankshaft bolt, not the camshaft.

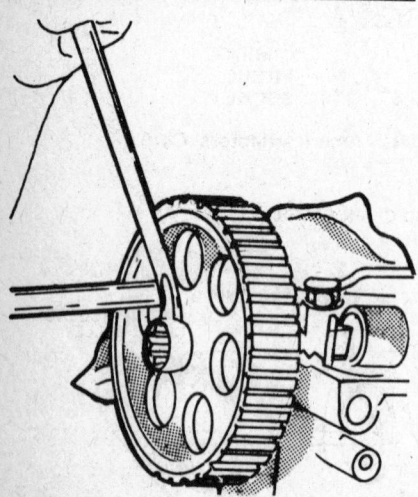

Removing the 121-4 cylinder camshaft pulley

BELT

1. Rotate the crankshaft in the normal direction of rotation, until the timing mark on the pulley is pointing to the zero position on the degree scale on the block. The timing mark on the rear of the camshaft pulley should be aligned with the pointer on the cylinder head cover.

2. Loosen the accessory pulley attaching bolts. Remove the V belts and the cam drive belt shield.

3. Loosen the adjuster retaining screw to allow the belt to slacken and remove the belt.

4. To replace the belt, install the belt on the crankshaft pulley, and position it on the tensioner pulley. Slip the belt over the camshaft pulley using hand pressure only, while maintaining the pulleys at their respective timing marks.

NOTE: Do not pry the belt with metal tools. The belt drive surface can be damaged and premature belt failure can result.

5. Turn the offset adjusting nut on the tensioning pulley counterclockwise to increase the belt tension. The belt is properly tensioned when the drive side of the belt can be twisted 90 degrees with finger pressure.

NOTE: When checking belt tension, apply tension on the crankshaft with a wrench, in a counterclockwise direction, to get all the slack on one side of the belt.

6. With pressure on the tensioning pulley nut, tighten the retaining nut to 29 ft. lbs. torque. Recheck the belt tension.

7. Install the drive belt shield. Install the alternator belts and adjust their tension. Tighten the accessory pulley bolts to 15 ft. lbs.

8. Start the engine and adjust the ignition timing.

CAMSHAFT PULLEY

1. Remove the drive belt.

2. Insert a bar or other suitable tool through the camshaft pulley to prevent it from turning.

3. Remove the pulley retaining bolt. Remove the pulley, woodruff key, and washer from the camshaft.

4. To replace the pulley reverse the disassembly procedure. Hold the camshaft pulley, and torque the retaining bolt to 58 ft. lbs.

5. Refer to Belt Removal and Installation for installation and tensioning.

CRANKSHAFT PULLEY

1. Raise and support the front of the car with stands.

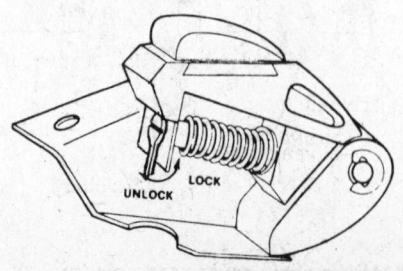

150-4 cylinder timing chain tensioner

2. Remove the camshaft drive belt.

3. Remove the accessory drive pulley from the crankshaft pulley using a No. 40 Torx head bit to remove the pulley screws.

4. The sprocket retaining bolt can be loosened and removed from the crankshaft. Hold the pulley from turning while the bolt is loosened.

5. Remove the pulley from the crankshaft.

6. Install the pulley so that the indexing hole in the pulley takes the pin on the crankshaft.

7. Hold the pulley from turning. Install the retaining bolt and torque to 181 ft. lbs.

8. Install the drive belt. See Belt Removal and Installation for tensioning.

9. Replace the belt guard. Replace the accessory drive pulley and torque the attaching bolts to 15 ft. lbs.

10. Complete the assembly in the reverse order of disassembly. Start the engine and reset the ignition timing.

150-4 Cylinder

1. Remove the timing case cover as previously outlined.

2. Rotate the crankshaft until the zero timing mark on the crankshaft sprocket is closest to and on center line with the mark on the cam sprocket.

3. Remove the oil slinger from the crankshaft.

4. Remove the camshaft retaining bolt and remove the sprockets and chain as an assembly.

5. Installation is in the reverse order of removal, with the following recommendations:

   a. Turn the tensioner lever to the unlock (down) position.

   b. Pull the tensioner block toward the tensioner lever to compress the spring. Hold the block and turn the tensioner lever to the lock (up) position.

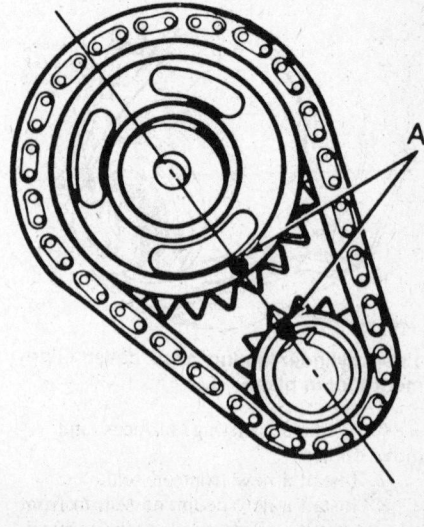

150-4 cylinder timing mark (A) alignment

151-4 Cylinder

The 151 uses timing gears instead of a chain and sprockets or a belt. The cam timing gear is pressed onto the camshaft. The camshaft must be removed to remove the gear, which must be pressed off the camshaft. See the camshaft removal procedure for details. The replacement cam gear must be pressed onto the camshaft. To replace the gear, first place the gear spacer ring and thrust plate over the end of the camshaft, then install the woodruff key. Press the camshaft gear onto the cam until it bottoms against the gear spacer ring. End clearance of the thrust plate must be 0.0015–0.0050 in. If less than 0.0015 in., the spacer ring must be replaced. If more than 0.0050 in., the thrust plate must be replaced.

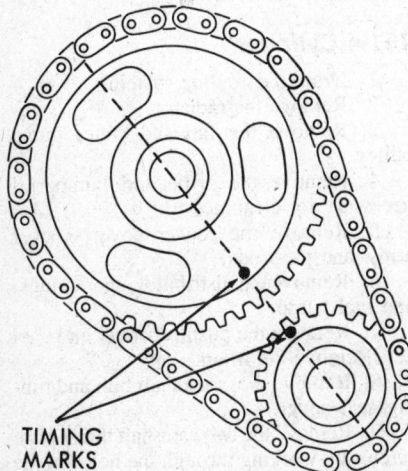

Six-cylinder timing chain and sprockets

6 Cylinder

1. Remove the drive belt(s).
2. Remove the engine fan and hub assembly.
3. Remove the vibration damper pulley and remove the vibration damper.
4. Remove the timing case cover. Remove the seal from the timing case cover, because the seal should be replaced every time the cover is removed from the engine.
5. Remove the camshaft sprocket retaining bolt and washer.
6. Turn the crankshaft until the 0 timing mark on the crankshaft sprocket is closest to and on a centerline with the timing pointer of the camshaft sprocket.
7. Remove the crankshaft sprocket, camshaft sprocket and timing chain as an assembly. Disassemble the chain and sprockets.
To install:
8. Assemble the timing chain, crankshaft sprocket, and camshaft sprocket with the timing marks aligned.
9. Install the assembly to the crankshaft and camshaft.
10. Install the camshaft sprocket retain-

ing bolt and washer and tighten the bolt to 50 ft. lbs.
11. To ensure the correct installation of the timing chain, locate the timing mark of the camshaft sprocket at about the 1 o'clock position. This should place the timing mark on the crankshaft sprocket where the sprocket teeth mesh with the chain. There must be 15 timing chain pins between the timing marks of both sprockets.

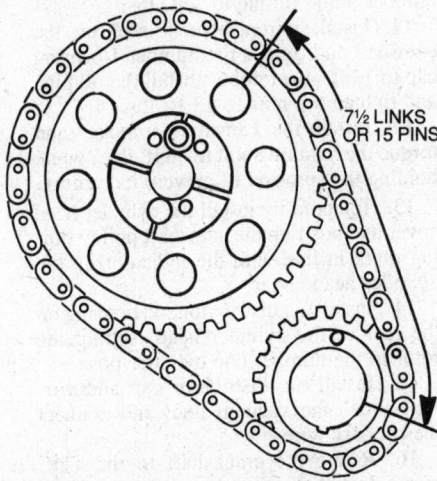

Correct timing chain installation—6 cylinder

V8 Engine

1. Remove the timing case cover and gasket.
2. Remove the crankshaft oil slinger.
3. Remove the camshaft sprocket retaining bolt and washer.
4. Remove the distributor drive gear and the fuel pump eccentric.
5. Turn the crankshaft until the 0 timing mark on the crankshaft sprocket is closest to and on a center line with the 0 timing mark on the camshaft sprocket.

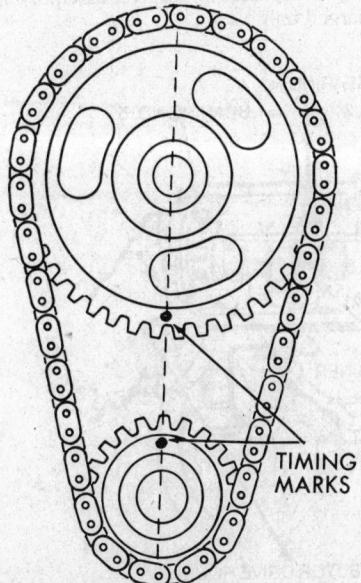

V8 timing chain and sprockets

6. Remove the crankshaft sprocket, camshaft sprocket and the timing chain as an assembly.
To install:
7. Assemble the timing chain, and the two sprockets with the timing marks aligned vertically and install the assembly onto the crankshaft and camshaft.
8. Install the fuel pump eccentric and the distributor drive gear. The fuel pump eccentric is installed with the word REAR toward the camshaft sprocket.
9. Install the camshaft sprocket, washer, and retaining bolt, tightening the bolt to 30 ft. lbs.
10. To ensure the timing chain is installed correctly, turn the crankshaft until the timing mark on the camshaft sprocket is placed horizontally at the 3 o'clock position. Starting with the timing chain pin directly opposite the camshaft sprocket timing mark, count the number of pins down to the timing mark on the crankshaft sprocket. There should be 20 pins between the two timing marks. The crankshaft timing mark must be between the 20th and 21st pin.
11. Install the crankshaft oil slinger.
12. Install the timing case cover together with a new gasket and seal.

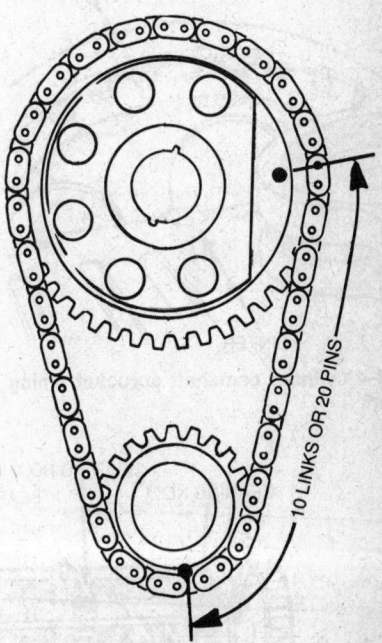

Correct timing chain installation—V8

Camshaft

REMOVAL & INSTALLATION

121-4 Cylinder

1. Remove the air cleaner assembly, and the distributor cap with the wires attached.
2. Remove the accessory belts, and the belt guard. Loosen and remove the camshaft drive belt.

3. Remove the distributor and housing assembly from the rear of the cylinder head.

4. Remove the cylinder head cover, and the camshaft pulley from the camshaft.

NOTE: Use a tool to prevent the sprocket from turning while removing the retaining bolt, and protect the head surface by wrapping a cloth around the end of the tool.

5. Remove the bolts from number 5 camshaft bearing cap (rear cap), and then remove the retaining nuts from caps 1, 3, and 5. Next remove the nuts from bearing caps number 2 and 4, backing off each nut ½ turn at a time to relieve tension on the camshaft. Remove the oil pipe retainers from the bolts on bearing caps number 2 and 4.

6. Remove all the camshaft bearing caps from the cylinder head. Keep them in order.

7. Remove the camshaft from the cylinder head.

NOTE: The distributor drive gear should be removed from the camshaft with a puller. It can be replaced by driving the gear on the camshaft with the use of a block of wood and a hammer. Note the gear location before removal.

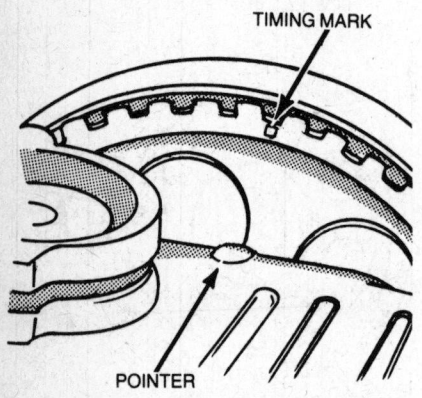

121-4 cylinder camshaft sprocket timing mark

8. The tappets may be removed for service by lifting them out of their bores in the cylinder head.

9. On installation, lubricate the camshaft lobes and bearing surfaces and install the shaft into the cylinder head. Install the camshaft bearing caps on their respective seats, and install the retaining nuts on caps number 2 and 4, tightening to 13 ft. lbs.

10. Torque number 3 and 5 retaining nuts to 13 ft. lbs. Install the bolts in bearing cap number 5 and torque to 7 ft. lbs.

11. Install a replacement seal on the camshaft and tighten the number 1 bearing cap to 13 ft. lbs. torque. Install the oil pipe and tighten the nuts to 13 ft. lbs.

12. Install the camshaft sprocket and torque the retaining bolt to 58 ft. lbs., while holding the sprocket to prevent its turning.

13. Temporarily install the cylinder head cover and position the camshaft pulley timing mark in line with the indicator on the cylinder head cover.

14. Install the distributor and housing on the rear of the cylinder head, setting the rotor to the number one cylinder position.

15. Install the distributor cap and wiring, attach the vacuum line, and connect the primary wire.

16. Rotate the crankshaft to the TDC mark. Install the camshaft drive belt and adjust. Refer to Belt Removal and Installation.

17. Reassemble the drive belt guard, replace the accessory belts and adjust.

18. Remove the cylinder head cover and adjust the tappet-to-camshaft clearance.

19. Install the cylinder head cover and complete the assembly. Start the engine and adjust the ignition timing.

150-4 Cylinder

1. Drain and remove radiator.

2. If so equipped, remove air conditioning condenser and receiver assembly as a charged unit.

3. Remove fuel pump, distributor and ignition wires.

4. Remove cylinder head cover and gasket.

5. Remove rocker arms, bridged pivot assemblies and pushrods. Be sure to replace these parts in the same order as removed.

6. Remove cylinder head and gasket and lifters.

7. Remove timing case cover.

8. Remove timing chain and sprockets as one assembly, being careful to rotate the crankshaft until the timing mark on the crankshaft sprocket is lined up with the timing pointer on the camshaft sprocket.

9. Remove the front bumper or grill as required.

10. Carefully remove the camshaft from the engine.

11. Installation is in the reverse order of removal.

151-4 Cylinder

1. Drain the cooling system.

2. Remove the radiator.

3. Remove the fan and water pump pulley.

4. Remove the grille and bumper if necessary for clearance.

5. Remove the rocker cover, rocker arms, and pushrods.

6. Remove the distributor, spark plugs, and fuel pump.

7. Remove the pushrod cover and gasket. Remove the lifters.

8. Remove the crankshaft hub and timing gear cover.

9. Remove the two camshaft thrust plate screws by working through the holes in the gear.

10. Remove the camshaft and gear assembly by pulling it through the front of the block. Take care not to damage the bearings.

11. Install in the reverse order. Torque the thrust plate screws to 75 inch lbs.

232 and 258-6 Cylinder

1. Drain the cooling system and remove the radiator. Remove the hood (Pacers only).

2. If the car is equipped with air conditioning, remove the condenser and the receiver unit as a *charged assembly*, only.

NOTE: Do not discharge the A/C system.

3. Remove the valve cover and gasket.

4. Remove the rocker arm assembly and the cylinder head. Remove the pushrods and tappets.

NOTE: Pushrods and tappets should be kept in the proper order. They must be returned to their original places during assembly.

5. Remove the drivebelt(s), fan assembly, accessory pulley(s), vibration damper, and the timing chain cover.

6. Remove the fuel pump. Remove the

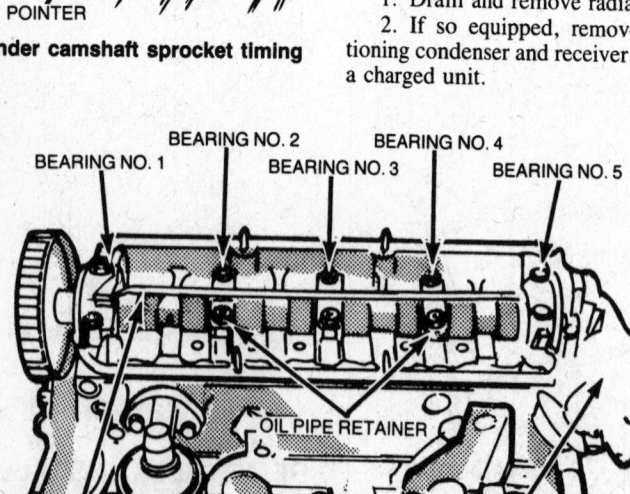

121-4 cylinder camshaft and bearings

distributor assembly, including spark plug wires.

7. Turn the crankshaft until the "0" timing mark on the crankshaft sprocket is nearest to, on a centerline with, and aligns with the timing pointer on the camshaft sprocket.

8. Remove the sprockets and the timing chain as an assembly.

9. Remove the front bumper and/or grille as necessary. Withdraw the camshaft through the opening. On the Pacer, unbolt the front engine mounts from the crossmember and raise the engine.

10. Inspect the bearing journals, distributor drive, cam lobes, and tappets for wear or damage. Replace parts, as required.

Camshaft installation is performed in the following order:

1. Use a generous amount of an engine oil supplement on the camshaft. Install it in the block, using care not to damage any surfaces. On the Pacer, lower the engine and connect the engine mounts.

2. Install the timing chain and sprocket assembly.

3. Install the timing chain cover and a new oil seal.

4. Install the vibration damper and the accessory drive pulley(s).

5. Install the engine fan assembly and the drive belt(s). Tighten the belts to the proper tension.

6. Install the fuel pump.

7. With the number one piston at TDC of its compression stroke, fit the distributor so that the rotor is aligned with the No. one terminal on the cap (distributor fully seated on the block). Install the cap and the spark plug wires.

8. Install the tappets, cylinder head, its gasket, valve train (pushrods in the same order, as removed), valve cover and its gasket.

NOTE: All valve train components must be lubricated with engine oil supplement. The supplement must remain in the engine for at least the first 1,000 miles. It does not require draining until the next regular oil change.

9. Install the air conditioner receiver and condenser, without discharging any coolant, if so equipped.

10. Install the radiator and top up the cooling system.

11. Install the front bumper and/or grille. Bolt down the Pacer engine mounts and install the hood.

12. Check ignition timing and reset as required.

V8 Engine

1. Disconnect the negative battery cable.

2. Drain the radiator and both banks of the cylinder block. Remove the radiator, the hoses, and the thermostat housing. Remove the air conditioning condenser and receiver assembly as a charged unit, if so equipped.

3. Remove the distributor, complete with spark plug wires and the coil from the intake manifold.

4. Remove the intake manifold as a complete assembly.

5. Take off the valve cover and take out the valve train, including the hydraulic tappets.

NOTE: Keep the valve train components in proper order. They must be returned to their original places during assembly.

6. Remove the power steering pump from its bracket, without disconnecting the hoses. Set it out of the way.

7. Remove the fan assembly and then the fuel pump. Disconnect heater hose at the water pump.

8. Unbolt the alternator bracket and set it out of the way, complete with the alternator. Do not disconnect the alternator wiring.

9. Remove the crankshaft pulley and the vibration damper.

10. Remove the timing case cover. With the timing marks in vertical alignment, remove the front cover, distributor/oil pump drive gear, fuel pump eccentric, sprockets, and the timing chain.

11. Remove the hood latch upper support bracket attachment screws. Move the bracket, as necessary, to permit removal of the camshaft. Remove the bumper and grille if necessary.

12. Use care during camshaft removal, so that the journal bearings are not damaged.

13. Inspect all parts for wear and damage. Replace them as required.

Install the camshaft in the reverse order of removal. Install the timing chain and cover. Adjust the belt tension, and fill up the cooling system.

NOTE: Lubricate the camshaft tappets, and the valve train with an engine oil supplement. Add the remaining supplement to the crankcase, and leave it in the engine for at least the first 1000 miles. It does not require draining until the next regular oil change.

Pistons and Connecting Rods

IDENTIFICATION & POSITIONING

The piston and rod assemblies are installed from the top, and the dimple, notch, or dot, marked on the top of the piston, goes toward the front. On the 121-4 cylinder, the rod and piston assemblies must be marked on disassembly; the projections on the connecting rods must face the front of the engine. On the 151-4 cylinder, the raised notch side of the rod (near the bearing end) must be 180° opposite the notch in the piston. On the six cylinder, the connecting rod numbers must go toward the camshaft; on

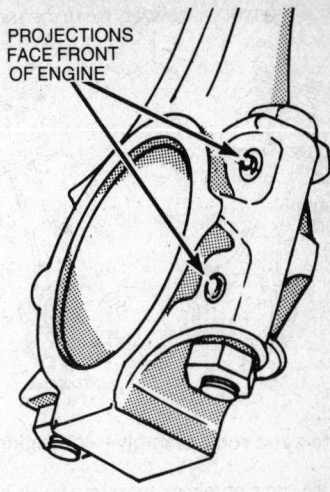

Connecting rod installation, 121-4

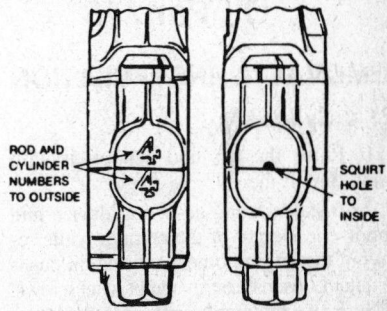

151-4 cylinder connecting rod and cylinder numbers, and squirt hole

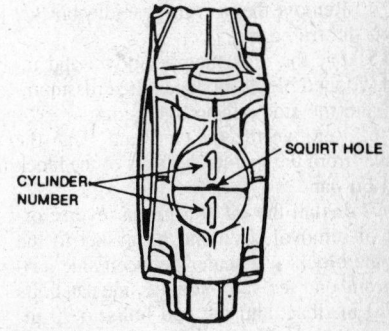

236-6 and 258-6 cylinder connecting rod numbering

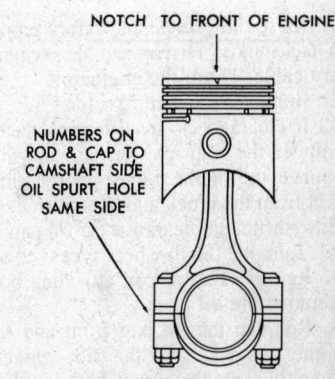

Piston and rod assembly 6 cylinder engine

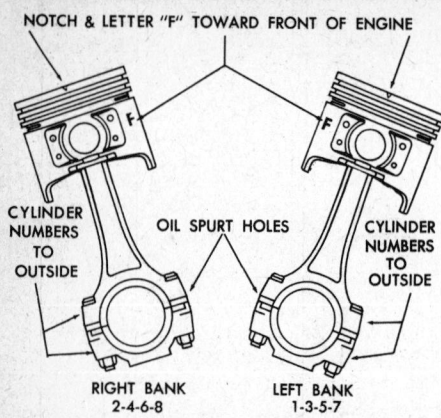

NOTCH & LETTER "F" TOWARD FRONT OF ENGINE

CYLINDER NUMBERS TO OUTSIDE

OIL SPURT HOLES

CYLINDER NUMBERS TO OUTSIDE

RIGHT BANK 2-4-6-8

LEFT BANK 1-3-5-7

Piston and rod assembly—V8 engines

the V8, the numbers must go toward the outside of the engine.

Oil Pan

REMOVAL & INSTALLATION

121-4 Cylinder

1. Raise the car and support it with stands. Drain the oil.

2. Install an engine-lifting device and support the weight of the engine, while removing the engine bracket-to-mount cushion nuts. Loosen the strut and bracket screws.

3. Raise the engine approximately two inches and remove the crossmember-to-sill attaching parts.

4. Remove the steering gear idler bracket from the frame rail.

5. Pry the crossmember down and insert wooden blocks between the crossmember and the side sill on both sides.

6. Remove the oil pan, and clean the gasket from the mating surfaces of the block and oil pan.

7. Install the oil pan in the reverse order of removal. Cement the gasket to the engine block; use sealer between side gaskets and end seals; tighten the side pan bolts to 70 in. lbs., and the end bolts to 90 in. lbs.

150-4 Cylinder

1. Raise the vehicle and safely support it on jackstands. Disconnect the negative battery cable. Drain the engine oil.

2. Remove the starter motor.

3. If clearance is insufficient, place a jack under the transmission bell housing. Disconnect the engine right support cushion bracket from the block and raise the engine to allow sufficient clearance for oil pan removal. Remove the flywheel access cover.

4. Remove the oil pan attaching bolts and remove the oil pan.

5. Remove the oil pan front and rear neoprene oil seals and the side gaskets. Thoroughly clean the gasket surfaces of the oil pan and the engine block. Remove all of the sludge and dirt from the oil pan sump.

6. Apply a generous amount of RTV silicone to the end tabs of a new oil pan front seal and install the seal onto the timing case cover.

7. Cement new oil pan side gaskets into position on the engine block and apply a generous amount of RTV silicone to the side gasket contacting surface of the seal end tabs.

8. Install the seal in the recess of the rear main bearing cap, making sure that it is fully seated.

9. Coat the oil pan contacting surface of the front and rear oil pan seals with engine oil.

10. Install the oil pan and assemble the engine mount in the reverse order of removal.

151-4 Cylinder

1. Follow Steps 1 through 6 of the 121-4 cylinder procedure.

2. To install the pan, thoroughly clean all the gasket mating surfaces.

3. Install a new rear oil pan gasket in the rear main bearing cap. Apply a small quantity of RTV silicone sealer into the depressions where the rear pan gasket engages the block.

4. Install a new front oil pan gasket onto the timing gear cover. Press the tips into the holes in the cover.

5. Install the side gaskets onto the block, not the oil pan. Retain them with a thin film of grease. Apply a ¼ in. long bead of RTV silicone sealer to the split lines of the front and side gaskets; the bead should be ⅛ in. wide.

6. Install the oil pan onto the engine. The timing cover bolts should be installed last. They are installed at an angle; the holes will line up after the rest of the pan bolts have been snugged down. The bolts should be tightened to 6 ft. lbs. all around. The remainder of the installation is in the reverse order of removal.

6 Cylinder and V8 EXCEPT PACER

1. Turn the steering wheel to full left-lock. Support the engine with a hoist. Raise and support the car at the side sills. Dis-

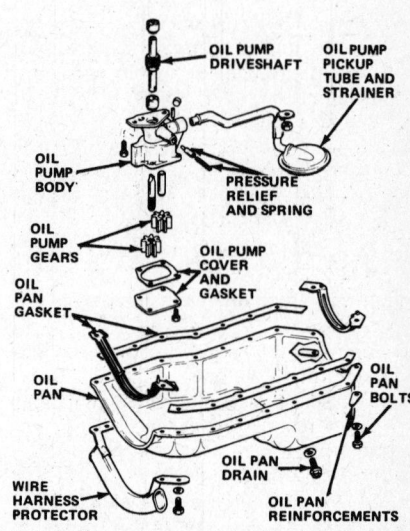

OIL PUMP DRIVESHAFT

OIL PUMP PICKUP TUBE AND STRAINER

OIL PUMP BODY

PRESSURE RELIEF AND SPRING

OIL PUMP GEARS

OIL PUMP COVER AND GASKET

OIL PAN GASKET

OIL PAN

OIL PAN BOLTS

OIL PAN DRAIN

WIRE HARNESS PROTECTOR

OIL PAN REINFORCEMENTS

Oil pump and pan, 4-151 (© American Motors Corp.)

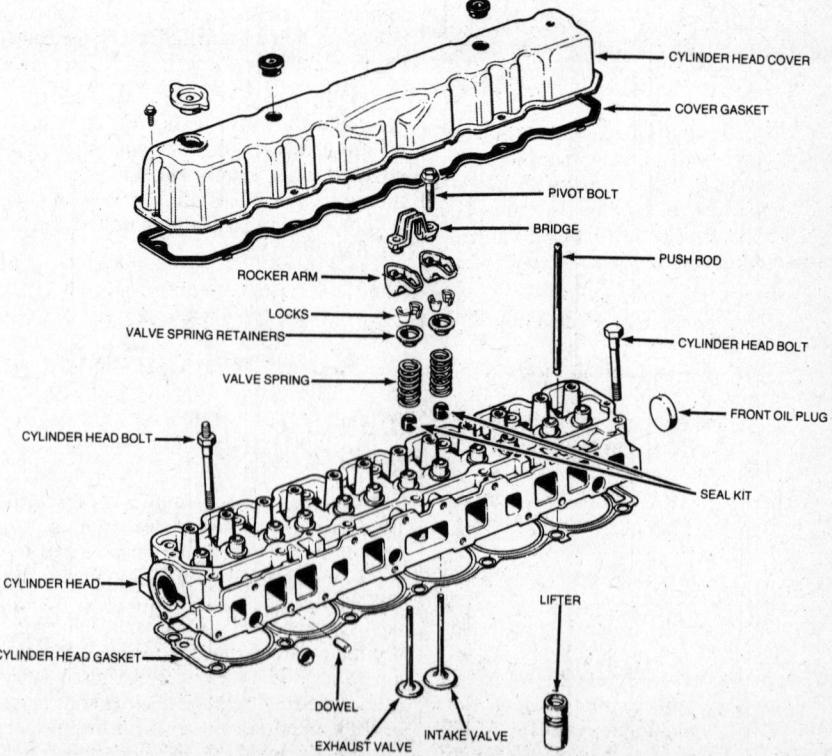

CYLINDER HEAD COVER

COVER GASKET

PIVOT BOLT

BRIDGE

PUSH ROD

ROCKER ARM

LOCKS

VALVE SPRING RETAINERS

CYLINDER HEAD BOLT

VALVE SPRING

FRONT OIL PLUG

CYLINDER HEAD BOLT

SEAL KIT

LIFTER

CYLINDER HEAD

CYLINDER HEAD GASKET

DOWEL

EXHAUST VALVE

INTAKE VALVE

Exploded view of the 258-6 cylinder head (© American Motors Corp.)

connect the negative battery cable and engine ground strap cable.

2. Unbolt the steering idler arm at the side sill, and the engine cushions at the brackets.

3. Remove the sway bar, if so equipped. Remove the front crossmember-to-side sill bolts and pull the crossmember down. Remove the right engine bracket. Loosen but do not remove the strut rods at the lower control arm.

4. Drain the engine oil.

5. Remove the starter.

6. Remove the oil pan bolts and pan. Remove the front and rear seals, and clean the gasket surfaces.

7. Install the new pan-to-timing cover front seal, and apply sealer to end tabs. Cement new pan side gaskets to the block, and apply sealer to the ends of the gasket.

8. Coat the inside surface of the new rear seal with soap, and apply sealer to end tabs. Install the seal in the rear main cap.

9. Coat front and rear seal contact surfaces with engine oil, and install the pan. The remainder of the installation is in the reverse order of removal.

PACER

1. Drain the engine oil.

2. Install an engine-lifting device and support the weight of the engine.

3. Disconnect the steering shaft flexible joint and hold it aside with a length of wire.

4. Raise and support the car.

5. Remove the front engine support through bolts.

6. Disconnect the front brake lines at the wheel cylinders.

7. Disconnect the upper ball joints from the spindles. Make sure the shock absorbers are attached securely.

8. Remove the upper control arm and move it aside.

9. Support the front crossmember with a jack.

10. Remove the nuts from the front crossmember rear mounts and swing the crossmember down and forward.

11. Follow Steps 5–9 of the preceding six cylinder and V8 procedure.

12. Install and assemble the remaining components in the reverse order of removal, tightening the 1/4 in. oil pan screws to 7 ft. lbs., the 5/16 in. oil pan screws to 11 ft. lbs., the crossmember attaching nuts to 50 ft. lbs., the upper control arm cross shaft bolt and nut to 60 ft. lbs., and the engine mount and steering shaft nuts to 25 ft. lbs. Fill the crankcase with oil and bleed the brakes.

Oil Pump

REMOVAL & INSTALLATION

CAUTION
Whenever the oil pump cover is removed or the pump disassembled, the pump must be primed by filling the spaces around the gears with petroleum jelly. Do not use grease.

121-4 Cylinder

The oil pump is on the lower front of the engine block. It consists of two gears with meshing teeth, one with internal teeth and the other with external teeth. Oil pressure is controlled by a pressure relief valve and spring assembly. The inner gear is driven by the crankshaft at twice the speed of distributor driven oil pumps. To service the oil pump assembly, removal is necessary. Proceed as follows.

1. Remove the fan shroud.

2. Raise the car and support it on stands.

3. Loosen the crankshaft pulley screws, but don't remove them.

4. Loosen and remove the power steering pump belt, air conditioner belt and alternator belt.

5. Remove the crankshaft pulley. Attach a crankshaft sprocket wrench using all of the pulley screws and remove the crankshaft screw.

6. Remove the camshaft drive sprocket from the crankshaft.

7. Remove the oil pump screws and the front oil pan screws and remove the oil pump by prying in the slots with a large screwdriver.

8. Replace the gasket and the crankshaft seal. Trim the edges of the gasket.

9. Rotate the crankshaft so the oil pump lugs are either vertical or horizontal.

10. Cut off the oil pan gasket flush with the front of the block.

11. Align the gears of the oil pump with the crankshaft lugs and carefully tap the pump on as far as possible.

12. Apply silicone sealant to the edges of the pump and the oil pan and to the pump sealing surfaces. Tighten the screws to 87 in. lbs.

13. Install the crankshaft seal with a seal installing tool.

14. Install the camshaft drive sprocket and the crankshaft accessory drive pulley, making sure the pins align with the holes. Install the crankshaft screw.

15. Install the camshaft drive belt, belt guard, accessory drive belts and the fan shroud. Start the engine and check for leaks or low oil pressure, and adjust the timing.

CAUTION
An oil filter with a built-in bypass valve must be used on the 121–4 cylinder engine.

150-4 Cylinder

1. Drain the oil and remove the oil pan.

2. Remove the oil pump retaining screws and separate the oil pump and gasket from the engine block.

3. Install in the reverse order of the above procedure.

151-4 Cylinder

1. Remove engine oil pan. (See "121-4" procedure.)

2. Remove the two bolts and one nut, and carefully lower the pump.

3. Reinstall in reverse order. To ensure immediate oil pressure on start-up, the oil pump gear cavity can be packed with petroleum jelly.

6 Cylinder

The oil pump is driven by the distributor drive shaft. Oil pump replacement does not, however, affect distributor timing because the drive gear remains in mesh with the camshaft gear.

1. Drain the oil and remove the oil pan.

2. Remove the oil pump attaching screws. Remove the pump and gasket from the engine block.

Installation is in the reverse order of removal. Prime the pump before installation; use a new cover gasket.

V8

The oil pump is located in, and is part of, the timing cover. The pump is driven by the distributor drive shaft. Oil pump replacement does not, however, affect distributor timing.

1. Remove the retaining bolts and separate the oil pump cover, complete with filter and gasket, from the timing cover.

2. The drive gear and shaft, and the idler gear will slide out of the timing cover after removal of the pump cover.

3. Prime the pump before installation, and use a new gasket.

Rear Main Bearing Oil Seal

REMOVAL & INSTALLATION

121-4 Cylinder

The rear main bearing oil seal consists of a single piece of formed neoprene with a single lip. To replace the seal, proceed as follows.

1. Remove the transmission assembly. If manual transmission, remove the pressure plate and flywheel.

2. Remove the crankshaft seal from its seat in the block, while exercising care not to scratch the seal contacting area of the crankshaft.

3. Lubricate the seal lip with engine oil, and install the seal into the recess of the engine block so it bottoms. The seal should be about 1/32 inch below the surface of the block.

4. Reinstall the flywheel and components. Reinstall the transmission assembly, adjust as necessary, start the engine and check for oil leakage.

150 and 151-4 Cylinder Engines

The rear main oil seal is a one piece unit, and

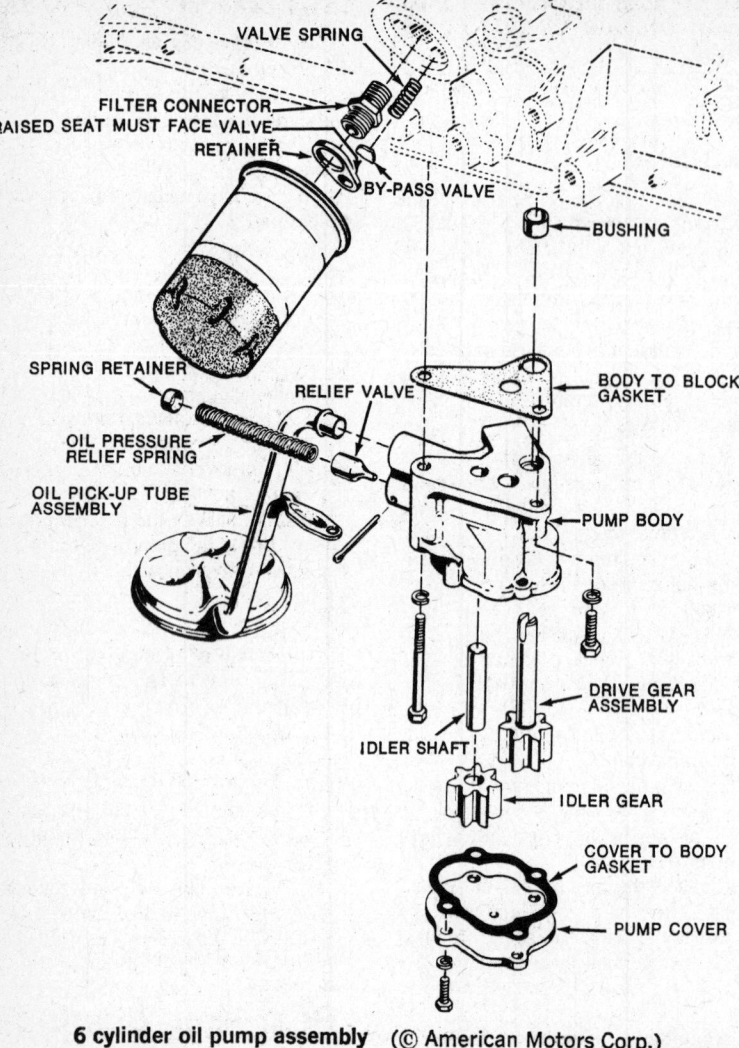

6 cylinder oil pump assembly (© American Motors Corp.)

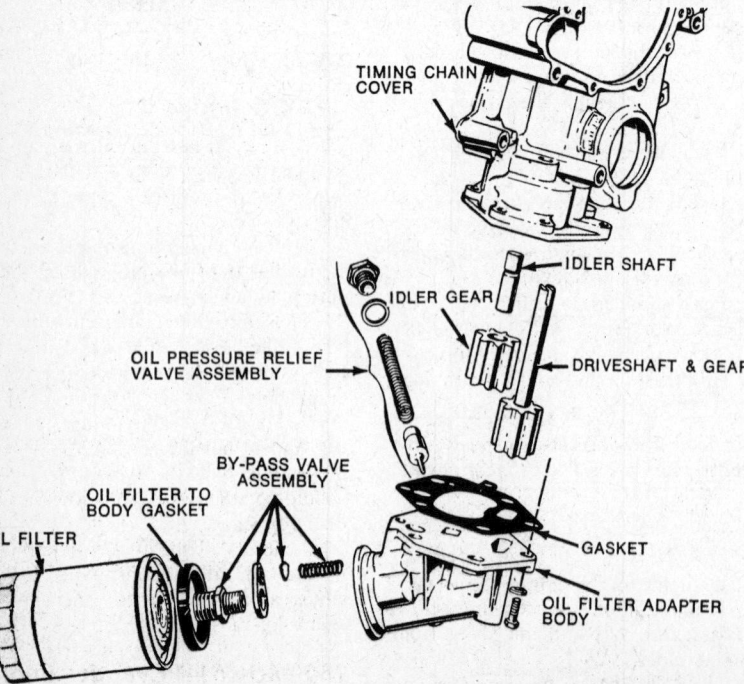

V8 oil pump assembly (© American Motors Corp)

is removed or installed without removal of the oil pan or crankshaft.

1. Remove the transmission, flywheel or torque converter bellhousing, and the flywheel or flex plate.

2. Remove the rear main oil seal with a small prying tool. Be extremely careful not to scratch the crankshaft.

3. Oil the lips of the new seal with clean engine oil. Install the new seal by hand onto the rear crankshaft flange. The helical lip side of the seal should face the engine. Make sure the seal is firmly and evenly installed.

4. Replace the flywheel or flexplate, bellhousing and transmission.

6 Cylinder and V8

1. Remove oil pan, as previously described.

2. Scrape clean all gasket surfaces, then remove rear main cap.

3. Discard lower portion of seal. Clean the main bearing cap thoroughly and loosen all remaining bearing capscrews.

4. Using a brass drift and a hammer, tap the upper seal out until it can be grasped by pliers and pulled out completely.

5. Coat the lip of the new upper seal with SAE 40 engine oil.

6. Install upper seal portion with the lip facing the front.

7. Coat both sides of the lower seal end tabs with sealant.

NOTE: Do not apply sealer to the cylinder block mating surfaces of the cap.

8. Coat the back surface of new lower seal with soap, the lip with SAE 40 engine oil. Install lower seal firmly into main cap.

9. Coat both chamfered edges of rear main cap with sealant, install bearing inserts (if removed) and tighten all cap bolts to 100 ft. lbs. on V-8s, and to 80 ft. lbs. on six cylinder engines.

10. Install the pan.

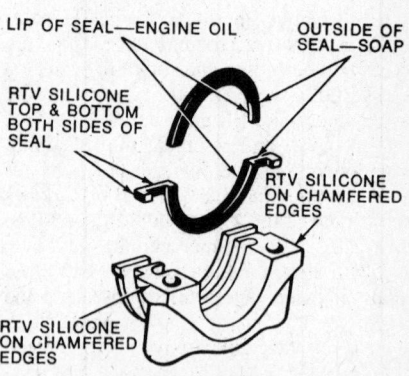

Rear main bearing installation details, 6 cylinder and V8 (© American Motors Corp.)

CLUTCH

NOTE: Pedal travel decrease due to normal wear of the lining can be com-

pensated for by adjusting the clutch pedal free-play, except for 1981 and later models, which have a hydraulically actuated clutch with no provision for adjustment.

PEDAL FREE-PLAY ADJUSTMENT

6 and V8 Engines

Adjust the free-play of the clutch pedal to ⅞–1⅛ in. This is done by changing the length of the link between the throwout lever rod and the bellcrank assembly.

121-4 Cylinder

The clutch pedal free-play is adjusted by varying the length of the control cable. The preferred free-play is 1⅛ inch.

1. To adjust the cable, loosen the cable locknut at the rear of the cable and pull the cable forward until the free-play is eliminated from the throwout lever.

2. Rotate the adjuster nut toward the rear of the cable until the nut tabs contact the clutch housing.

3. Release the cable housing and turn the adjuster nut until the tabs engage the slots on the clutch housing.

4. Tighten the clutch cable locknut. Recheck clutch pedal free-play.

REMOVAL & INSTALLATION

121-4 Cylinder

1. Remove the transmission.

2. Mark the clutch cover and flywheel for reassembly. Remove the cover and driven plate by loosening the bolts alternately and in several stages to avoid cover distortion.

Inspect the flywheel surface for heat cracks, scoring, or blue heat marks. Check the flywheel capscrews for proper torque.

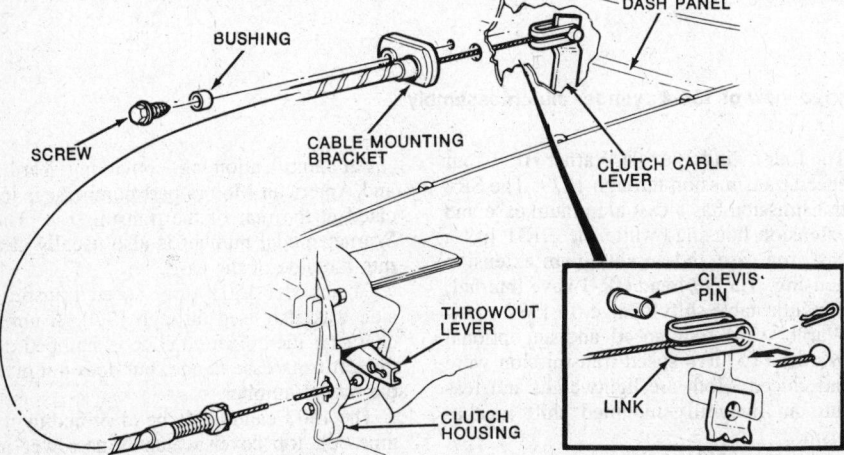

Four cylinder clutch cable linkage, through 1979 (© American Motors Corp.)

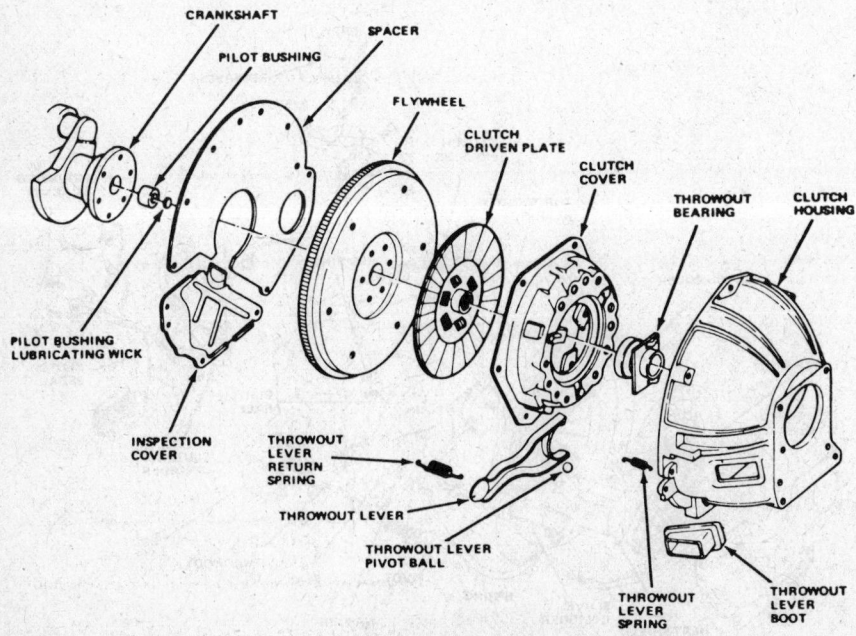

Typical 6 cylinder and V8 clutch assembly

It will be necessary to lock-up the flywheel ring gear with a block or flywheel-holding clamp tool before tightening these capscrews.

To install:

3. Align the driven plate and the cover on the flywheel with the marks made during removal and install the cover bolts finger-tight. Make sure the cover is engaged with the flywheel dowel pins.

4. Using a clutch alignment tool, align the driven plate. Tighten the cover bolts to 23 ft. lbs.

5. Install the transmission and the clutch housing. It may be necessary to raise the front of the engine on the 121.

6. On the 121 engine, position the rear crossmember on the side sills and finger-tighten the bolts. Install the transmission-to-crossmember bolts. Tighten the crossmember nuts.

The remainder of the installation is in the reverse order of removal. Be sure, when installing the gearshift lever that the shift rail insert is facing straight down and that the offset on the side of the lever fork is facing the right side of the extension housing.

150-4 Cylinder

1. Remove the transmission/transfer case assembly as described in the Unit Repair section.

2. Mark the position of the clutch pressure plate in relation to the flywheel, for installation.

3. Loosen the pressure plate bolts evenly, a little at a time each! Failure to loosen the bolts evenly, in rotation, will cause warping of the pressure plate.

4. When all spring tension is relieved from the pressure plate, back-out the bolts and remove the pressure plate and driven plate.

5. If the pilot bushing is equipped with a lubricating wick, remove it and soak it in clean engine oil.

6. Installation is in the reverse order of removal. Tighten the pressure plate bolts evenly, in rotation, in three or four different steps, to 23 ft. lbs.

151-4 Cylinder

1. Remove the starter, disconnect the slave cylinder spring at the throwout lever, and remove the transmission.

2. Remove the clutch housing-to-engine bolts. Remove the housing.

3. Remove the throwout bearing.

4. Matchmark the clutch cover and flywheel for installation. Loosen the clutch cover bolts alternately and evenly, to avoid distortion, and remove the clutch cover and disc.

5. Inspect the parts for signs of overheating (blue color), scoring, or abnormal wear. Overheated parts should be replaced. Deep scoring or wear may require replacement of the disc and cover, and refacing or replacement of the flywheel.

6. If the same cover is being used, place the disc and cover on the flywheel, aligning

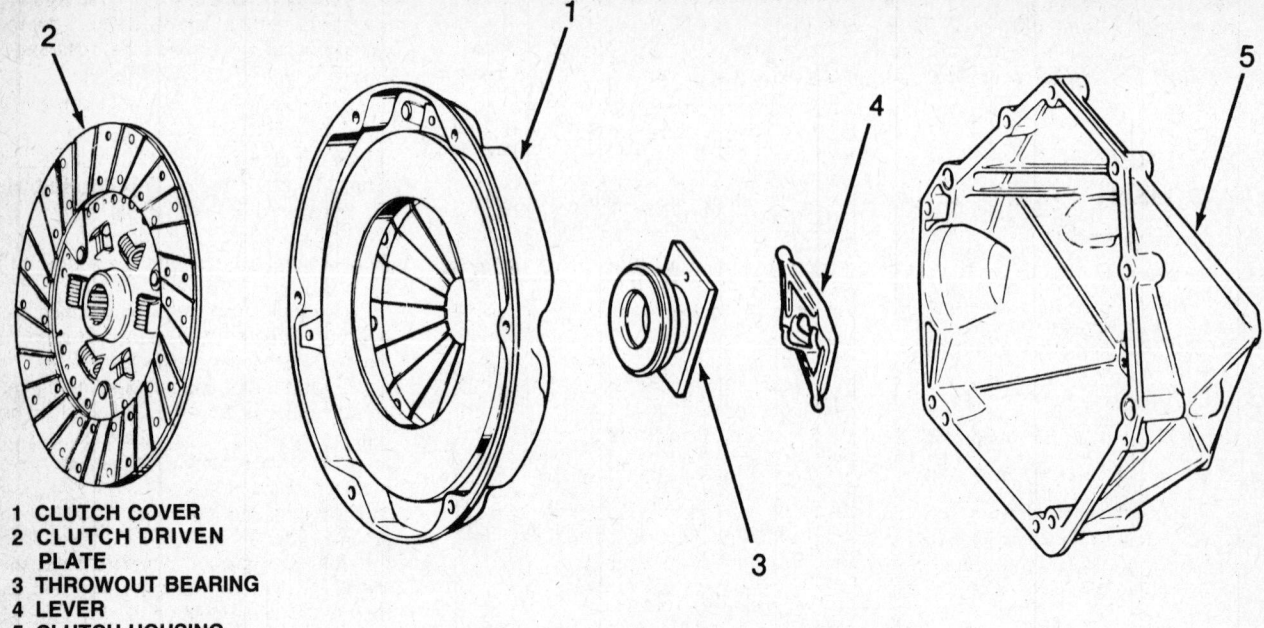

1 CLUTCH COVER
2 CLUTCH DRIVEN PLATE
3 THROWOUT BEARING
4 LEVER
5 CLUTCH HOUSING

Exploded view of 150-4 cylinder clutch assembly

the marks made previously. Be sure the cover is engaged with the dowel pins. Install the cover bolts finger-tight.

7. Align the disc with an alignment tool.

8. Tighten the cover bolts alternately and evenly to 23 ft. lbs. Remove the alignment tool.

9. Install the throwout bearing, clutch housing, and transmission. The housing-to-engine bolts and transmission-to-housing bolts should be tightened to 54 ft. lbs.

6 Cylinder and V8

1. Remove the transmission, starter motor and throwout bearing.

2. Disconnect the clutch linkage at the housing and remove the housing.

3. Mark the clutch cover and flywheel for reassembly.

4. Remove the clutch cover and the driven plate by loosening the bolts alternately and in several stages.

5. Remove the pilot bushing lubricating wick and soak the wick in engine oil.

6. Inspect the parts for signs of overheating (blue color), distortion, scoring, or wear. Overheated or deeply scored or worn parts should be replaced. Light wear may be cleaned up by sanding or refacing.

Installation is in the reverse order of removal. Use an alignment tool to position the driven plate on the flywheel. Tighten the cover bolts alternately and in several stages.

MANUAL TRANSMISSION

A lightweight Warner SR4 four-speed is used in all 1980-81 six cylinder models.

The four cylinder uses a Warner HR-1 four speed transmission through 1979. The SR4 transmission has a cast aluminum case and extension housing, while the HR-1 has a cast iron case and an aluminum extension housing. The SR4 and HR-1 have internal, non-adjustable shift linkage. In 1982 a new Warner (T4) four speed and an optional Warner (T5) five speed transmission were introduced. Both are lightweight and feature an integrally mounted shift mechanism.

NOTE: SR4 and HR-1 transmissions have metric fasteners in most threaded holes.

An identification tag, containing Warner and American Motors part numbers, is located at the rear of the transmission. The Warner model number is also usually cast into the side of the case.

The model 150T three-speed transmission was also used through 1979. A nine-character identification code is stamped on the left front case flange, but does not give the model number.

The 150 can readily be identified by its nine-bolt top cover which is narrower in the front. Unlike the Warner transmissions, it does not have a drain plug; lubricant is drained by removing the lower extension

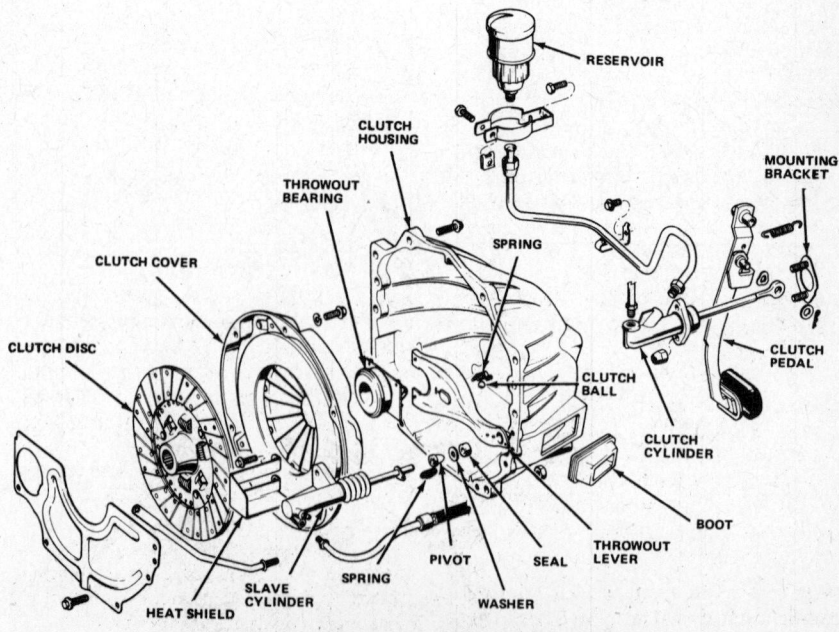

Exploded view of 151-4 cylinder clutch assembly

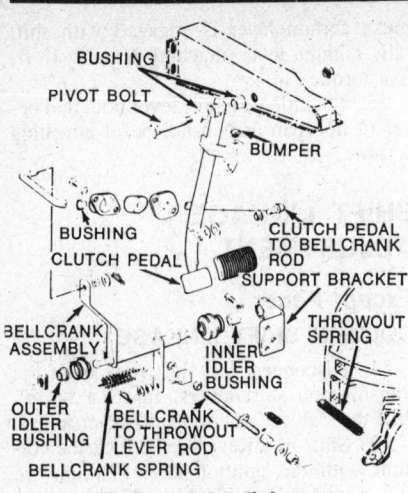

BUSHING
PIVOT BOLT
BUMPER
BUSHING
CLUTCH PEDAL
CLUTCH PEDAL TO BELLCRANK ROD
SUPPORT BRACKET
BELLCRANK ASSEMBLY
INNER IDLER BUSHING
THROWOUT SPRING
OUTER IDLER BUSHING
BELLCRANK TO THROWOUT LEVER ROD
BELLCRANK SPRING

Typical clutch linkage
(© American Motors Corp.)

housing bolt. Warner three-speeds have a rectangular top cover, usually with four or six bolts.

For all manual transmission overhaul procedures, please refer to "Manual Transmission Overhaul" in the Unit Repair section.

REMOVAL & INSTALLATION

Except Eagle

NOTE: Open the hood to avoid damage when the rear crossmember is removed. If the overdrive and transmission are to be separated, first engage then disengage the overdrive with the clutch pedal depressed and the engine running.

1. Matchmark the driveshaft and rear axle yoke for correct installation. Split the rear universal joint and slide the driveshaft off the back of the transmission. Support the transmission with a jack.

2. Detach the column shift mechanism linkage to the transmission, and disconnect the clutch linkage and speedometer cable; disconnect the back-up light switch wiring and TCS switch wiring.

On a floorshift, remove the shift lever. Remove the boot and unbolt the lever. Detach the column reverse lockup rod. Pull the lever and gauge out together. Support the engine.

3. Disconnect the overdrive wiring. Remove the rear transmission support cushion bolts. Also remove the starter on four cylinder models.

4. On Pacers with overdrive, remove the cotter pin from the parking brake equalizer, and disconnect the front cable from the equalizer. Remove the cable adjuster and hooks from the floorpan bracket and lower the equalizer and rear brake cables to provide clearance. Also, remove the ground strap from the floorpan.

NOTE: On V8 models with dual exhaust or dual catalytic converters, exhaust pipes must be disconnected from

manifolds and lowered to gain working clearance.

5. On HR1s, remove the throwout lever protective boot and disengage the clutch cable from the lever. Also remove the inspection cover at the front of the clutch housing.

6. Remove the transmission support crossmember except on Pacers; remove the crossmember with the transmission on those models. Remove the two lower studs which hold the transmission to the bell housing and replace these two studs with two long pilot studs on 150Ts and SR4s. On the HR1, remove the catalytic converter support bracket attaching bolts from the transmission rear support.

7. Remove the two top studs and slide the transmission assembly along the pilot studs and out of the car. On HR1s, support the engine and remove the clutch housing to engine bolts and remove the clutch and transmission as an assembly.

Installation is as follows:

1. Fill the slots in the inner groove of the throwout bearing with high temperature grease and soak the crankshaft pilot bushing wick in engine oil. Fit the throwout bearing and the sleeve assembly into the clutch fork. Center the bearing over the clutch lever. Shift 150Ts and SR4s into first gear.

2. On the 150Ts and SR4s, instead of the two lower clutch housing capscrews install two pilot studs.

3. Carefully slide the transmission into place. Be careful not to damage the clutch driven plate splines while mating them with the transmission input shaft. It may be necessary to raise the front of the engine for the HR1.

4. Install the upper screws, which attach the case to the housing. Remove the two pilot studs and install the two lower cap screws.

5. If the car is equipped with a floor shift, install the shift lever retainer and shift rods, if removed.

6. Attach the speedometer cable, connect the back-up light switch wires and the transmission controlled spark (TCS) wire, if so equipped. On the HR1, connect the clutch cable and adjust as necessary. Also install the inspection cover and the catalytic converter bracket bolts.

7. Raise the transmission. Attach the rear crossmember and support to the transmission. Fasten the crossmember to the side sills and finger-tighten the bolts. Install and tighten the crossmember-to-support bolts. Tighten the crossmember stud nuts. Install the parking brake cables and ground strap on Pacer.

8. Attach the exhaust pipes to the exhaust manifolds, on V8 engines, if they were removed.

9. Install the front U-joint yoke on the transmission. Do the same for the rear U-joint at the differential. Be sure the alignment marks made earlier line up.

10. Connect the shift rods on the column

shift transmissions and the reverse lockup rod on the floorshift transmissions. Check the transmission oil level and add lubricant, as needed.

11. Remove the supports and lower the car.

12. If the car has a floorshift transmission, install the shift lever.

13. Adjust the shift linkage, if it was disturbed.

1980–81 Eagle

1. Shift transmission into neutral.

2. Remove screws attaching gearshift lever bezel and boot to floorpan.

3. Slide bezel and boot upward on gearshift lever to provide access to lever attaching bolts.

4. Remove bolts attaching gearshift lever to lever mounting cover on transmission adapter housing and remove gearshift lever.

5. Remove bolts attaching gearshift lever mounting cover to transmission adapter and remove mounting cover to provide access to transfer case upper mounting stud nut in transmission adapter housing.

6. Remove nut from transfer case upper mounting stud located inside transmission adapter housing.

7. Raise automobile.

8. Remove skid plate.

9. Remove speedometer adapter retainer bolt and remove retainer, adapter, and cable. Discard adapter O-ring and plug adapter opening in transfer case to prevent excessive oil spillage.

NOTE: Mark the position of the speedometer adapter for assembly alignment reference before removing it.

10. Mark propeller shafts and axle yokes for assembly alignment reference and disconnect propeller shafts at transfer case.

11. Disconnect backup lamp switch wire.

12. Place support stand under engine.

13. Support transmission and transfer case using transmission jack.

14. Remove rear crossmember.

15. Remove catalytic converter bracket from transfer case.

16. Remove bolts attaching transmission to clutch housing.

17. Remove transmission and transfer case as an assembly.

18. Remove nuts from transfer case mounting studs and remove transmission from transfer case.

19. Install transmission on transfer case. Install and tighten all transfer case mounting stud nuts to 26 ft. lbs. torque.

20. Support transmission-transfer case assembly on transmission jack.

21. Align transmission clutch shaft with throwout bearing and clutch disc splines and seat transmission against clutch housing.

22. Install and tighten transmission-to-clutch housing attaching bolts to 55 ft. lbs. torque.

23. Connect propeller shafts to transfer case yokes. Tighten clamp strap bolts to 15 ft. lbs. torque.

24. Install rear crossmember. Tighten crossmember attaching bolts to 30 ft. lbs. torque.

25. Connect backup lamp switch wire.

26. Install replacement O-ring on speedometer adapter and install adapter and cable, and retainer. Tighten retainer bolt to 100 inch lbs. torque.

CAUTION

Do not attempt to reuse the original adapter O-ring. The ring is designed to swell in service to improve its sealing qualities and could be cut or torn during installation if reuse is attempted.

---

27. Attach catalytic converter bracket to transfer case. Tighten retaining nuts to 26 ft. lbs. torque.

28. Check and correct lubricant levels in transmission and transfer case, if necessary.

29. Install skid plate. Tighten skid plate attaching bolts to 30 ft. lbs. torque.

30. Remove stand used to support engine, and remove transmission jack, if not removed previously.

31. Lower automobile.

32. Clean mating surfaces of gearshift lever mounting cover and transmission adapter housing.

33. Apply RTV-type sealant to gearshift lever mounting cover and install cover on transmission adapter housing. Tighten cover bolts to 13 ft. lbs. torque.

34. Install gearshift lever on mounting cover. Be sure lever is engaged with shift rail before tightening lever attaching bolts. Tighten lever attaching bolts to 18 ft. lbs. torque.

35. Position gearshift lever boot and bezel in floorpan and install bezel attaching screws.

1982–84 Eagle

1. Shift transmission into neutral.

2. Remove screws attaching gearshift lever bezel and boot to floorpan.

3. Slide bezel and boot upward on gearshift lever to provide access to lever attaching bolts.

4. Remove bolts attaching gearshift lever to lever mounting cover on transmission adapter housing and remove gearshift lever.

5. Remove bolts attaching gearshift lever mounting cover to transmission adapter and remove mounting cover to provide access to transfer case upper mounting stud nut in transmission adapter housing.

6. Remove nut from transfer case upper mounting stud located inside transmission adapter housing.

7. Raise automobile.

8. Remove skid plate.

9. Remove speedometer adapter retainer bolt and remove retainer, adapter, and cable. Discard adapter O-ring and plug adapter opening in transfer case to prevent excessive oil spillage.

NOTE: Matchmark the position of the

speedometer adapter for assembly alignment, before removing it.

10. Matchmark propeller shafts and axle yokes for assembly alignment, and disconnect propeller shafts at transfer case.

11. Disconnect backup lamp switch wire.

12. Place support stand under engine.

13. Support transmission and transfer case using transmission jack.

14. Remove rear crossmember.

15. Remove catalytic converter bracket from transfer case, and brace rod from bracket.

16. Remove bolts attaching transmission to clutch housing.

17. Remove transmission and transfer case as an assembly.

18. Remove nuts from transfer case mounting studs and remove transmission from transfer case.

19. Install transmission on transfer case. Install and tighten all transfer case mounting stud nuts to 26 ft. lbs. torque.

20. Support transmission-transfer case assembly on transmission jack.

21. Align transmission clutch shaft without throwout bearing and clutch disc splines and seat transmission against clutch housing.

22. Install and tighten transmission-to-clutch housing attaching bolts to 55 ft. lbs. torque.

23. Connect propeller shafts to transfer case yokes. Tighten clamp strap bolts to 15 ft. lbs. torque.

24. Install brace rod and rear crossmember. Tighten attaching bolts to 30 ft. lbs. torque.

25. Connect backup lamp switch wire.

26. Install replacement O-ring on speedometer adapter and install adapter and cable, and retainer. Tighten retainer bolt to 100 inch lbs. torque.

CAUTION

Do not attempt to reuse the original adapter O-ring. The ring is designed to swell in service to improve its sealing qualities and could be cut or torn during installation if reuse is attempted.

---

27. Attach catalytic converter bracket to transfer case. Tighten skid plate attaching bolts to 30 ft. lbs. torque.

28. Check and correct lubricant levels in transmission and transfer case, if necessary.

29. Install skid plate. Tighten skid plate attaching bolts to 30 ft. lbs. torque.

30. Remove stand used to support engine, and remove transmission jack, if not removed previously.

31. Lower automobile.

32. Clean mating surfaces of gearshift lever mounting cover and of transmission adapter housing.

33. Apply RTV-type sealant to gearshift lever mounting cover, install cover bolts and torque to 13 ft. lbs. torque.

34. Install gearshift lever on mounting cover. Before tightening lever attaching bolts

make certain lever is engaged with shift rail. Tighten lever attaching bolts to 18 ft. lbs. torque.

35. Position gearshift lever boot and bezel in floorpan and install bezel attaching screws.

SHIFT LINKAGE ADJUSTMENT

Except Pacer
COLUMN SHIFT LINKAGE

1. Disconnect the shift rods from the transmission shift levers. Insert a 3/16 in. drill through the column shift lever holes.

2. Shift into Reverse and lock the column with the ignition key. Position the transmission First/Reverse shift lever in Reverse.

3. Adjust the shift-rod trunnion to a free-pin-fit in the transmission shift lever. Tighten the trunnion locknuts.

4. Unlock the column and move the gearshift to Neutral. Both of the transmission shift levers should be in the Neutral detent.

5. Repeat step three for the Second/Third shift rod trunnion.

6. Remove the drill from the column levers. Shift through all gears and check for a free crossover into Neutral.

7. Shift into Reverse and lock the column. The column should lock without any binding.

THREE-SPEED FLOORSHIFT

1. Place the transmission shift levers in their Neutral positions.

2. Loosen the Second-Third lever adjuster.

3. Keeping the First-Reverse shift rod and transmission lever in the Neutral position, align the Second-Third rod so the shift notch is exactly aligned with the First-Reverse shift notch. Tighten the adjuster.

4. Operate the linkage and check for full engagement of all gears, and for a smooth crossover from First to Second.

5. If there is a Reverse lockup rod to the steering column, loosen both of the locknuts about 1/2 in. each. Shift into Reverse and lock the column. You may have to rotate the lever at the bottom of the column up into the locked position. Tighten the lower locknut until it contacts the trunnion. Tighten the upper locknut while holding the trunnion centered. Unlock the column and shift through the gears. Shift into Reverse and lock the binding.

Pacer
COLUMN SHIFT LINKAGE

1. Detach the shift rods from the shift levers. Insert a 3/16 in. drill through the column shift lever holes.

2. Shift into Reverse and lock the column with the ignition key. Position the First/Reverse shift lever in Reverse.

3. Adjust the shift rod trunnion to a

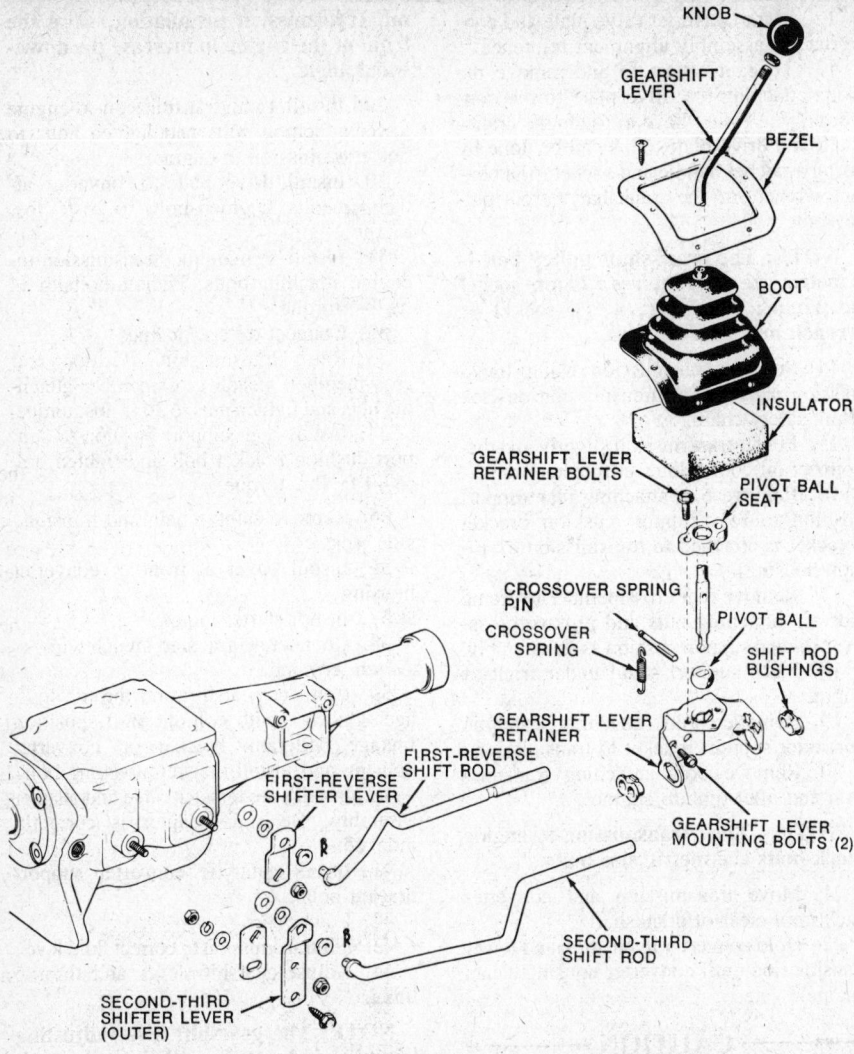

KNOB

GEARSHIFT
LEVER

BEZEL

BOOT

INSULATOR

GEARSHIFT LEVER
RETAINER BOLTS

PIVOT BALL
SEAT

CROSSOVER SPRING
PIN

PIVOT BALL

CROSSOVER
SPRING

SHIFT ROD
BUSHINGS

GEARSHIFT LEVER
RETAINER

FIRST-REVERSE
SHIFT ROD

FIRST-REVERSE
SHIFTER LEVER

GEARSHIFT LEVER
MOUNTING BOLTS (2)

SECOND-THIRD
SHIFT ROD

SECOND-THIRD
SHIFTER LEVER
(OUTER)

Three-speed floorshift linkage (© American Motors Corp.)

free-pin-fit in the outer shift lever. Tighten the trunnion locknuts.

4. Unlock the column and move the gearshift to Neutral. Both of the transmission outer shift levers should be in the Neutral detent.

5. Repeat Step 3 for the Second/Third shift rod trunnion.

6. Withdraw the drill from the column levers. Shift through all gears and check for a free crossover into Neutral.

7. Shift into Reverse and lock the column. The column should lock without any binding.

FLOOR SHIFT LINKAGE

1. Place the transmission shift levers in Neutral.

2. Loosen the Second/Third transmission lever attaching nut and adjusting bolt.

3. With the First/Reverse shift rod in the Neutral position, align the Second/Third shift rod so that its notch is exactly aligned with the notch in the First-Reverse shift rod.

4. Tighten the adjustment bolt and attaching nut.

5. Shift through all of the gears, being particularly careful to check for binding in the First-to-Second shift.

6. To adjust the back-up light switch, loosen the jam nuts, then slide the switch forward or backward, as necessary. Tighten the jam nuts.

Pacer Overdrive

The Laycock de Normanville overdrive unit for the Pacer is an electro-hydraulic-actuated, planetary gear-type, mounted on a special adapter at the rear of the transmission.

When the overdrive is in the direct drive position (overdrive switched off), and the car is driven forward, power from the transmission mainshaft is transmitted through the freewheel rollers and unidirectional clutch to the overdrive output shaft. When the car is backing up or during periods of engine braking, torque is transmitted through the clutch sliding member which is held by spring pressure against the tapered portion of the output shaft. When the overdrive is actuated, the clutch sliding member is pressed by hydraulic pressure against the brake disc (ring), which locks the sun wheel.

As a result, the output shaft of the overdrive rotates at a higher speed than the mainshaft, thereby accomplishing a 30% reduction in engine speed in relation to vehicle speed.

The overdrive is actuated by a switch located beneath the steering wheel. This switch energizes a solenoid on the overdrive unit, via a switch on the transmission. The switch cuts in only when the third gear is engaged. The solenoid has two windings: a heavy CONTROL winding and a lower-current, HOLD winding. When actuated, the CONTROL winding opens the overdrive control valve, whereupon the control winding is cut off and the valve is held in the open position by the HOLD winding. The control valve regulates the pressurized oil flow from the cam-operated pump to the hydraulic pistons which operate the overdrive clutch sliding member.

REMOVAL AND INSTALLATION

To facilitate removal, the vehicle should first be driven in Third gear with the overdrive engaged; it should then be coasted for a few seconds with the overdrive disengaged and the clutch pedal depressed. Transmission removal sequence is as follows.

1. Remove the transmission from the vehicle as previously outlined in the "Transmission Removal and Installation" section.

2. Disconnect the solenoid cables.

3. If the overdrive unit has not already been drained, remove the six bolts and the overdrive oil pan.

--- CAUTION ---

Be careful to avoid spilling hot transmission fluid on the skin.

4. Remove the bolts which keep the overdrive unit mounted on the transmission intermediate flange. Pull the unit straight to the rear until it clears the transmission mainshaft.

5. Reverse the above procedure to install. Install the overdrive oil pan with a new gasket. After installation of the transmission and overdrive assembly, fill the transmission to the proper level with the correct lubricant. This also fills the overdrive. Drive the car 6–9 miles, then check

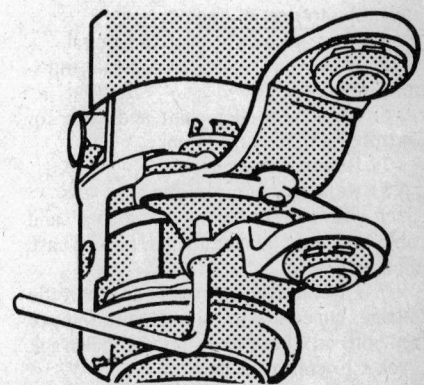

Aligning shift levers on column shift models

the transmission's oil level, and add as necessary.

AUTOMATIC TRANSMISSION

AUTOMATIC TRANSMISSION IDENTIFICATION

Year	Engine	Transmission
'78–'79	4-121	Chrysler 904
	6-232	Chrysler 904
	6-258	Chrysler 904①
	8-304	Chrysler 998①
	8-360	Chrysler 727
	8-401	Chrysler 727
'80–'85	4-150	Chrysler 904②
	4-151	Chrysler 904②
	6-258	Chrysler 904③
	6-258 (Eagle)	Chrysler 998

① 727 available as an option on 6-258 and 8-304, except Pacer
② Standard ratio
③ Wide ratio

REMOVAL & INSTALLATION

121-4 Cylinder Engine

1. Open hood.

— CAUTION —

The hood must remain open to avoid damaging the hood and air cleaner when the rear crossmember is removed.

2. Disconnect fan shroud.
3. Remove bolt attaching transmission filler tube to rear of engine.
4. Place gearshift lever in Neutral.
5. Raise and support car. Drain transmission fluid.
6. Mark propeller shaft and yoke for assembly alignment reference.
7. Remove propeller shaft.
8. Remove starter motor.
9. Remove speedometer adapter and cable assembly. Cover adapter bore in case after removal.
10. Disconnect gearshift and throttle linkage. On cars with column shift, remove the bolt attaching the linkage bellcrank bracket to converter housing.
11. Remove cover at front of converter housing.

12. Mark converter drive plate and converter for assembly alignment reference.
13. To gain access to and remove the bolts attaching the drive plate to the converter, you'll first have to rotate the crankshaft and drive plate. This can be done by using a ratchet handle and socket, or a box-end wrench, on the crankshaft's front pulley bolt.

NOTE: The crankshaft pulley bolt is a metric size and requires a 24 mm socket or wrench. However, a 15/16 socket or wrench may also be used.

14. Support transmission using transmission jack. Retain transmission on jack using safety chain.
15. Lower transmission slightly and disconnect oil cooler lines at transmission.
16. Remove bolt attaching rear support cushion to rear support cushion bracket (bracket is attached to transmission extension housing).
17. Remove rear crossmember-to-frame side sill attaching nuts and remove crossmember and support cushion as an assembly.
18. Place support stand under front of engine.
19. Remove bolts attaching catalytic converter support bracket to transmission.
20. Remove bolts attaching transmission and filler tube to engine.

NOTE: The transmission-to-engine block bolts are metric size bolts.

21. Move transmission and converter back until clear of crankshaft.
22. Hold converter in position and lower transmission until converter housing clears engine.

— CAUTION —

If the transmission was removed to correct a malfunction that generated sludge or heavy accumulations of metal or friction material particles, the oil cooler and cooler lines must be thoroughly flushed and the torque converter replaced. Do not attempt to flush the converter if it is contaminated.

23. If torque converter was removed, insert Pump Aligning Tool J-24033 into pump rotor and engage tool slots with pump rotor drive lugs.
24. Rotate aligning tool until hole in tool is vertical, then remove tool.
25. Rotate converter until pump drive slots in converter hub are vertical.
26. Carefully insert converter hub into oil pump. Be sure drive lugs of pump inner rotor are completely engaged with drive slots in converter hub.
27. Raise transmission and align converter with drive plate. Refer to alignment marks made during removal.
28. Move transmission forward and raise, lower, or tilt transmission to align converter housing pilot holes with dowels in engine block.

NOTE: If the downward angle at the rear of the engine is not sufficient to per-

mit transmission installation, raise the front of the engine to increase the downward angle.

29. Install two, transmission-to-engine lower attaching bolts and tighten bolts to pull transmission to engine.
30. Install drive plate-to-converter attaching bolts. Tighten bolts to 26 ft. lbs. torque.
31. Install remaining transmission-to-engine attaching bolts. Tighten bolts to 54 ft. lbs. torque.
32. Connect oil cooler lines.
33. Raise transmission, position rear crossmember, install crossmember attaching nuts and tighten nuts to 30 ft. lbs. torque.
34. Install rear support cushion-to-support cushion bracket bolt and tighten bolt to 49 ft. lbs. torque.
35. Remove safety chain and transmission jack.
36. Install cover at front of converter housing.
37. Install starter motor.
38. Connect neutral start switch wires to switch terminal.
39. Connect gearshift and throttle linkage. On cars with column shift, position linkage bellcrank bracket on converter housing and install bracket attaching bolt.
40. Install speedometer cable and adapter assembly. Be sure adapter is correctly indexed.
41. Install catalytic converter support bracket bolts.
42. Lower car.
43. Fill transmission to correct fluid level.
44. Adjust gearshift lever and throttle linkage.

NOTE: The gearshift lever adjusting trunnion is located on the steering column shift lever.

45. Road test car to check transmission operation.

4 Cylinder Engines

1. Open hood.

— CAUTION —

The hood must remain open to avoid damaging the hood and air cleaner when the rear crossmember is removed.

2. Disconnect fan shroud.
3. Remove bolt attaching transmission fill tube to engine.
4. Place gearshift lever in Neutral.
5. Raise and support car. Drain transmission fluid.
6. Mark propeller shaft and yoke for assembly alignment reference. On Eagle models, also remove skid plate.
7. Remove propeller shafts.
8. On Eagle models, disconnect exhaust system at exhaust manifold, loosen exhaust system hangers and move exhaust system as necessary to gain work space.
9. Remove starter motor. On Eagle models, also remove stiffening braces.

10. Remove speedometer adapter and cable assembly. Cover adapter bore after removal.

11. Disconnect gearshift and throttle linkage. On automobiles with column shift, remove bolt that mounts the linkage bellcrank bracket on the converter housing.

12. Remove cover at front of converter housing.

13. Mark converter drive plate and converter for assembly alignment reference.

14. To gain excess to and remove the bolts attaching the drive plate to the converter, you'll first have to rotate the crankshaft and drive plate. This can be done by using a ratchet handle and socket, or a box-end wrench, on the crankshaft's front pulley bolt.

NOTE: The crankshaft pulley bolt is a metric size bolt.

15. Support transmission using transmission jack. Retain transmission on jack using safety chain.

──────── CAUTION ────────

On Eagle models, both the transmission and transfer case must be properly supported on the transmission jack and retained with safety chain.

16. Disconnect oil cooler lines at transmission.

17. Remove bolt attaching rear support cushion to rear support cushion bracket (bracket is attached to transmission extension housing).

18. Remove rear crossmember attaching nuts and remove crossmember and support cushion as an assembly.

19. Place support stand under front of engine.

20. Remove bolts attaching catalytic converter support bracket to transmission, if so equipped.

21. Remove fill tube.

22. Remove bolts attaching transmission to engine.

NOTE: The transmission-to-engine block bolts are metric size bolts.

23. Move transmission (and transfer case, if so equipped) and converter back until clear of crankshaft.

24. Hold converter in position and lower transmission until transmission converter housing clears engine.

──────── CAUTION ────────

If the transmission was removed to correct a malfunction that generated sludge or heavy accumulations of metal or friction material particles, the oil cooler and cooler lines must be thoroughly flushed and the torque converter replaced. Do not attempt to flush the converter if it is contaminated.

25. If torque converter was removed, insert Pump Aligning Tool J-24033 into pump rotor and engage tool slots with pump rotor drive lugs.

26. Rotate aligning tool until hole in tool is vertical, then remove tool.

27. Rotate converter until pump drive slots in converter hub are vertical.

28. Carefully insert converter hub into oil pump. Be sure drive lugs of pump inner rotor are completely engaged with drive slots in converter hub.

29. Raise transmission and align converter with drive plate. Refer to alignment marks made during removal.

──────── CAUTION ────────

On Eagle models, both the transmission and transfer case must be supported on a transmission jack and retained with safety chain.

30. Move transmission forward and raise, lower, or tilt transmission to align transmission converter housing dowel holes with dowels in engine block.

NOTE: If the downward angle at the rear of the engine is not sufficient to permit transmission installation, raise the front of the engine to increase the downward angle.

31. Install two transmission-to-engine lower attaching bolts and tighten bolts evenly to pull transmission to engine.

32. Install drive plate-to-converter attaching bolts. Tighten bolts to 40 ft. lbs. torque.

NOTE: Coat threads of drive plate-to-converter attaching bolts with Loctite 271 or equivalent.

33. Install remaining transmission-to-engine attaching bolts. Tighten bolts to 54 ft. lbs. torque.

34. Connect oil cooler lines.

35. Install propeller shaft using reference marks made during assembly.

36. Install rear crossmember and support cushion. Tighten attaching nuts to 30 ft. lbs. torque.

37. Install rear support cushion-to-support bracket bolt. Tighten bolt to 48 ft. lbs. torque.

38. Remove safety chain and transmission jack.

39. Install converter housing inspection cover.

40. Install starter motor. On Eagle models also install stiffening brace and skid plate.

41. Connect neutral start switch wires to switch terminal.

42. Connect gearshift and throttle linkage. On automobiles with column shift, position linkage bellcrank bracket on converter housing and install bracket attaching bolt.

43. Install speedometer cable and adapter assembly. Be sure adapter is correctly indexed.

44. Connect catalytic converter, if so equipped. On Eagle models, add correct quantity of transfer case lubricant.

45. Lower automobile.

46. Fill transmission to correct fluid level.

47. Check and adjust gearshift lever and throttle linkage if necessary.

NOTE: The gearshift lever adjusting trunnion is located at the lower end of the steering column.

48. Road test automobile to check transmission operation.

6 and V8 Engines

1. Disconnect fan shroud, if so equipped.

2. Disconnect transmission fill tube at upper bracket.

3. Open hood.

──────── CAUTION ────────

It is necessary that the hood be open to avoid damaging the hood and air cleaner when the rear crossmember is removed.

4. Raise and support car. Drain transmission fluid.

5. Remove inspection cover from converter housing.

6. On Spirit and Concord, remove screw attaching exhaust pipe clamp to exhaust pipe support bracket and slide clamp off bracket.

7. Remove transmission fill tube.

8. Remove starter. On Eagle models, also remove stiffening braces.

9. Mark propeller shaft(s) and yoke(s) for assembly alignment reference.

10. Remove propeller shaft(s).

11. On Eagle models, disconnect exhaust pipe and move it aside for working clearance.

12. Remove speedometer adapter and cable assembly. Discard adapter and cable seals, they are not reuseable. Cover adapter bore after removal.

13. Disconnect gearshift and throttle linkage.

14. Disconnect wires at neutral start switch.

15. Mark converter drive plate and converter for assembly alignment reference.

16. To gain access to and remove the bolts attaching the drive plate to the converter, you'll first have to rotate the crankshaft and drive plate. This can be done by using a ratchet handle and socket, or a box-end wrench, on the crankshaft's front pulley bolt.

17. On Eagle models, remove skid plate and stiffening brace.

18. Support transmission (and transfer case on Eagle models) using transmission jack. Retain transmission on jack using safety chain.

19. Disconnect oil cooler lines at transmission.

20. Remove bolts attaching rear support cushion to transmission.

21. Remove rear crossmember.

22. Remove bolts attaching transmission to engine.

23. Move transmission and converter back to clear crankshaft.

24. Hold converter in position and lower assembly until converter housing clears engine.

25. If torque converter was removed, insert Pump Aligning Tool J-24033 in pump rotor until rotor drive lugs engage slots in tool.

26. Rotate tool until drilled hole in tool is vertical and remove tool.

27. Rotate converter until pump drive slots in converter hub are vertical and carefully insert converter hub into pump. Be sure drive lugs of pump inner rotor are properly engaged in drive slots of converter hub.

28. Raise transmission (and transfer case on Eagle models) and align converter with drive plate. Refer to assembly alignment marks.

29. Move transmission forward.

30. Raise, lower, or tilt transmission to align converter housing pilot holes with dowels in engine.

31. Install two transmission lower attaching bolts and tighten bolts evenly to pull transmission to engine.

32. Install drive plate-to-converter attaching bolts.

33. Install remaining transmission attaching bolts and tighten all bolts to 28 ft. lbs. torque.

34. Connect oil cooler lines.

35. Install rear support cushion on transmission, if removed.

36. Install rear crossmember.

37. Remove safety chain and transmission jack.

38. Install inspection cover.

39. On Spirit and Concord, install exhaust pipe clamp on support bracket.

40. Install starter. On Eagle models, also install stiffening braces.

41. Connect wires to neutral start switch.

42. Connect gearshift and throttle linkage.

43. Install speedometer cable and adapter assembly. Be sure adapter is correctly indexed.

44. On Eagle models, connect exhaust pipes, attach stiffening brace and install skid plate.

45. Install propeller shaft(s). Refer to alignment marks made during removal. On Eagle models, add correct quantity of transfer case lubricant.

46. Lower automobile.

47. Fill transmission to correct level.

48. Check and adjust gearshift and throttle linkage, if necessary.

49. Road-test automobile to check transmission operation.

For further details on linkage and band adjustments, please refer to "Automatic Transmissions" in the Unit Repair section.

Transfer Case

For all transfer case overhaul procedures, please refer to "Transfer Cases" in the Unit Repair section.

REMOVAL & INSTALLATION

Manual Transmission

NOTE: Steps 1–6, below, pertain to models with the SR-4 transmission only.

1. Shift transmission into Neutral.

2. Remove screws attaching gearshift lever bezel to floorpan or console, if so equipped.

3. Slide bezel and boot upward on gearshift lever to provide access to lever attaching bolts.

4. Remove bolts attaching gearshift lever to lever mounting cover on transmission adapter housing and remove lever.

5. Remove bolts attaching gearshift lever mounting cover to transmission adapter housing and remove cover.

6. Remove nut from transfer case mounting stud located inside transmission adapter housing.

7. Raise and support automobile.

8. Remove skid plate and rear brace rod at transfer case.

9. Remove speedometer adapter retainer attaching bolt and remove retainer, adapter, and cable. Plug adapter opening in transfer case to prevent excessive oil spillage.

NOTE: Mark the position of the speedometer adapter for assembly reference before removing it.

10. Mark propeller shafts and axle yokes for assembly alignment reference and disconnect propeller shafts at transfer case.

11. On models so equipped, remove transfer case shift motor vacuum harness.

12. Support transfer case with transmission jack.

13. Remove nuts from transfer case mounting studs and remove transfer case.

14. Align transmission output and transfer case input shafts and install transfer case on transmission adapter housing.

15. Install and tighten transfer case mounting stud nuts to 33 ft. lbs. torque.

16. Remove jack used to support transfer case.

17. Align and connect propeller shafts to axle yokes. Tighten clamp strap bolts to 15 ft. lbs. torque.

18. Install replacement O-ring on speedometer adapter and install adapter and cable and retainer. Tighten retainer bolt to 100 inch lbs. torque.

19. Install skid plate and rear brace rod. Torque retaining bolts to 30 ft. lbs. torque.

20. On models so equipped, install transfer case shift motor vacuum harness.

21. Check and correct lubricant levels in transmission and transfer case, if necessary.

22. Lower automobile.

23. Install nut on transfer case mounting stud located inside transmission adapter housing. Tighten nut to 33 ft. lbs. torque.

24. Install gearshift lever mounting cover on transmission adapter housing.

25. Install gearshift lever on mounting cover. Be sure lever is engaged with shift rail before tightening lever attaching bolts.

26. Position gearshift lever boot and bezel on floorpan or console, if so equipped, and install bezel attaching screws.

Automatic Transmission

1. Raise and support automobile.

2. Support engine and transmission with support stand or transmission jack.

3. Disconnect catalytic converter support bracket at adapter housing.

4. Remove skid plate and rear brace rod at transfer case.

5. Remove speedometer cable and adapter from transfer case. Discard adapter O-ring, it is not reusable.

6. Matchmark propeller shafts and transfer case yokes for assembly reference.

7. Disconnect propeller shafts at yokes. Secure shafts to underside of automobile.

8. Disconnect gearshift and throttle linkage at transmission.

9. Lower the rear crossmember.

10. Remove all transfer case-to-adapter housing stud nuts and remove transfer case.

11. Install transfer case on adapter housing. Be careful not to damage output shaft splines during installation.

12. Install transfer case-to-adapter housing stud nuts. Tighten nuts to 33 ft. lbs. torque.

13. Install rear crossmember. Tighten crossmember attaching nuts to 30 ft. lbs. torque.

14. Install rear brace rod.

15. Remove transmission jack or support stand.

16. Connect gearshift and throttle linkage to transmission.

17. Connect propeller shafts. Tighten clamp strap bolts to 15 ft. lbs. torque.

18. Install new O-ring on speedometer adapter and install adapter and cable in transfer case.

NOTE: Do not attempt to reuse the old adapter O-ring. O-ring is designed to "swell" in service to provide improved sealing qualities and could be cut or torn if reinstallation is attempted.

19. Install skid plate and stiffening brace, if so equipped. Tighten retaining bolts to 30 ft. lbs.

20. Connect catalytic converter support bracket to adapter housing.

21. Check transfer case lubricant level and transmission linkage adjustments to make certain they are correct.

22. Lower automobile.

FRONT AXLE

AXLE, SHAFT, SHAFT SEAL AND BEARING

The procedure for replacing the axle shafts and seals on four-wheel drive models calls for removal of the axle first.

1. Raise and support the front of the car. Install protectors over the halfshaft boots. Remove the halfshaft-to-axle flange bolts, and tie the halfshafts out of the way.

2. Matchmark the driveshaft and the axle yoke. Remove the driveshaft.

3. Support the axle on stands. Remove the five axle-to-engine mounting bolts.

4. Lower the axle partway and remove the vent hose. Remove the axle.

5. Remove the differential cover and drain the oil. Remove the axle shaft "C" clips.

6. Remove the axle shafts.

7. Carefully remove the shaft seal.

8. Two different bearings are used: the left side uses a ball bearing, and the right side uses a needle bearing. The ball bearing should be removed using a brass drift and a hammer; the needle bearing should be removed using a needle bearing removal tool.

NOTE: If the proper bearing removal tool is not available, remove the differential and remove the needle bearing using a $^{15}/_{16}$ inch socket and a three foot ratchet extension.

9. Install the bearings, using drivers of the appropriate type and size.

10. Oil the lips of the new seal and install into the housing using a driver of the correct size.

11. Install the axle shafts and "C" clips.

12. Apply a bead of silicone seal to the differential cover and install the cover.

13. Fill the axle with 2.5 pints of 85W-90 GL-5 gear oil.

14. Move the axle into place under the car. Raise it sufficiently to connect the vent hose, then raise it fully into place and install the mounting bolts. Tighten to 50 ft. lbs.

15. Install the driveshaft, aligning the marks made during removal. Install the halfshaft-to-axle flange bolts, and tighten to 45 ft. lbs.

REAR AXLE

Two sizes of differential assemblies are used on American Motors cars; $7^9/_{16}$ in. and $8^7/_8$ in. ring gear units. A Twin-Grip limited slip differential is available as an option on both units.

A letter code used to identify the axle ratio will be found on most differentials, stamped on the right axle tube housing boss, on the rear side, adjacent to the dowel hole. Some earlier cars have either a metal tag attached to one of the bolts of the differential housing cover or the code letter is stamped on the right differential housing cover flange. It may be necessary to remove the cover from the differential to locate the letter. The codes and the axle ratios are listed in dealer parts books and shop manuals.

NOTE: The $7^9/_{16}$ in. axle can be identified by the cover mounted filler plug, and the $8^7/_8$ in. axle by the front filler on the housing.

AXLE SHAFT, BEARING AND SEAL

1. The hub and drum are separate units and are removed after the wheel is removed. The hub and axle shaft are serrated together on the taper. An axle shaft key assures proper alignment during assembly.

2. With the wheel on the ground and the parking brake applied, remove and discard the axle shaft nut cotter pin and remove the nut. Raise the car and remove the wheel. Release the parking brakes and remove the drum.

3. Attach a puller to the rear hub and remove the hub. The use of a "Knock-out" puller should be discouraged, since it may result in damage to the axle shaft or wheel bearings.

4. Disconnect the parking brake cable at the equalizer.

5. Disconnect the brake tube at the wheel cylinder and remove the brake support plate assembly, oil seal, and axle shims. Note that the axle shims are located on the left side only.

6. Using a screw type puller, remove the axle shaft and bearings from the axle housing.

---- CAUTION ----

On Twin-Grip axles, rotating the differential with one shaft removed will misalign the side gear splines, preventing installation of the replacement shaft.

7. Remove the axle shaft inner oil seal and install new seals at assembly.

8. The bearing is a press fit and should be removed with an arbor press.

9. The axle shaft bearings have no provision for lubrication after assembly. Before installing the bearings, they should be packed with a good quality wheel bearing lubricant.

10. Press the axle shaft bearings onto the axle shaft with the small diameter of the cone toward the outer (tapered) end of the shaft.

11. Soak the inner axle shaft seal in light lubricating oil. Coat the outer surface of the seal retainer with sealant.

12. Install the inner oil seal.

13. Install the axle shafts, indexing the splined end with the differential side gears.

14. Install the outer bearing cup.

15. Install the brake support plate. Sealant should be applied to the axle housing flange and to the brake support mounting plate.

16. Install the original shims, oil seal and brake support plate. Torque the nuts to 30–35 ft. lbs.

NOTE: The oil seal and retainer go between the axle housing flange and the brake support plate on 9 in. brakes or $7^9/_{16}$ axle. On 10 in. brakes or $8^7/_8$ axle, they go on the outside of the brake support plate.

17. To adjust the axle shaft end-play, strike the axle shafts with a lead mallet to seat the bearings. Install a dial indicator on the brake support plate and check the play while pushing and pulling the axle shaft. End-play should be 0.004–0.008 in., with 0.006 in. desirable. Add shims to the left side only to decrease the play and remove shims to increase the play.

18. Slide the hub onto the axle shafts by aligning the serrations and the keyway on the hub with the axle shaft key.

19. Replace the hub and drum, install the wheel, lower the car onto the floor and tighten the axle shaft nut to 250 ft. lbs. If the cotter pin hole is not aligned with a castellation on the nut, tighten the nut to the next castellation.

NOTE: A new hub must be installed whenever a new axle shaft is installed. Install two thrust washers on the shaft. Tighten the new hub onto the shaft until the hub is 1.19 in. from the end of the shaft on $7^9/_{16}$ in. differentials, and 1.31 in. on $8^7/_8$ in. models. Remove the nut and remove one thrust washer. Install the nut and torque to 250 ft. lbs. New hubs do not have serrations on the axle shaft mating surface. The serrations are cut when the hub is installed onto the axle shaft.

20. Connect the parking brake cable at the equalizer.

21. Connect the brake tube at the wheel cylinder and bleed the brakes.

DRIVESHAFT AND U-JOINTS

A one piece tubular driveshaft is used with a yoke at each end, to position the cross-and-roller type universal joints.

NOTE: The driveshaft is a balanced unit; care must be used in handling. Do not bend or distort the tube or yokes, or vibration will result.

Driveshaft
REMOVAL & INSTALLATION
All Models Except Eagle

1. Matchmark and disassemble rear U-

joint by removing nuts. Retention is by U-bolts or straps, depending on model.

2. Drop rear of driveshaft and slide front yoke out of transmission.

3. To install, reverse removal procedure, tightening U-joint nuts to 15 ft. lbs.

Eagle

Both driveshafts are secured at the transfer case end and the axle yoke end by straps. The straps are retained by Torx® head bolts.

1. Shift into Neutral. Raise and support the car.

2. Matchmark the driveshaft(s) at the transfer case and axle yoke for alignment reference.

3. Remove the retaining straps with a Torx® bit tool of the proper size. Remove the driveshaft(s).

4. To install, align the matchmarks made during removal to assure proper balance. Seat the universal joints in the yokes and install the straps, tightening to 17 ft. lbs.

UNIVERSAL JOINT OVERHAUL

For all U-Joint overhaul procedures, please refer to "U-Joint/CV-Joint Overhaul" in the Unit Repair section.

JACKING, HOISTING

1. Jack car, at front, under lower support arms and, at rear, under rear axle housing or on the side rocker flanges.

2. To lift, contact car at rear lift pads marked LIFT just forward of rear wheels (at the rear spring hangers on Gremlin, Spirit, Hornet, Concord, Eagle and Pacer). Front lift points are on underbody sill just to the rear of strut rod-to-sill mounting bracket. On Pacer, the front lift points are located on the front wheelwell sill.

FRONT SUSPENSION

The front suspension on all models except Pacer is an independent, linked-type with the coil springs located between seats in the wheelwell panels and seats in the upper control arms. Rubber insulators between the springs and seats reduce noise transmission to the body.

Direct acting, telescopic shock absorbers are located inside the coil springs and the control arms are attached to the body via rubber bushings.

The suspension system is a double ball joint design, both upper and lower control arms each having one joint.

On all models, strut rods serve to support the lower control arms. Stabilizer bars are used on some models.

The Pacer front suspension is different from all other AMC cars. The coil spring is mounted between the two control arms; it is seated at the bottom on the lower control arm and at the top in the suspension/engine mount crossmember. The crossmember is isolated from the rest of the body structure by rubber mounting points. The shock absorbers are mounted within the coil springs. The steering knuckle is attached to the upper and lower control arms by upper and lower ball joints. A front stabilizer bar is optional.

NOTE: The front end alignment must be checked after any disassembly procedure.

Shock Absorber

REPLACEMENT

NOTE: When installing new shock absorbers, purge them of air by extending them in their normal position and compressing them while inverted. Do this several times. It is normal for new shock absorbers to be more resistant to extension than to compression.

Except Pacer

1. Remove the two lower shock absorber attaching nuts. Remove the washers and the grommets.

2. Remove the upper mounting bracket nuts and bolts.

3. Remove the bracket, complete with shock.

4. Remove the upper attaching nut and separate the shock from the mounting bracket.

5. For adjustable shocks: To adjust the shock, compress the piston completely. Holding the upper part of the shock, turn the shock until the lower arrow is aligned with the desired setting. A click will be heard when the desired setting is reached.

Install the shock as follows:

1. Fit the grommets, washers, upper mounting bracket and nut on the shock, in the reverse order of removal. Tighten the nut to 8 ft. lbs.

2. Fully extend the shock and install two grommets on the lower mounting studs.

3. Lower the shock through the hole in the wheelwell. Fit the lower attachment studs through the lower spring seat.

4. Install the grommets, washers, and nuts. Tighten the nuts to 15 ft. lbs.

5. Secure the upper mounting bracket with its attachment nuts and bolts. Tighten them to 20 ft. lbs.

Pacer

1. Remove the shock absorber upper locknut.

2. Raise the car and remove the nuts from the lower shock absorber mounting studs.

3. Remove the shock along with the lower grommet and jounce bumper retainer from the shock absorber piston rod.

4. Install the retainer on the new shock and the lower grommet on the piston rod.

5. Extend the piston to full length and insert the shock through the lower control arm.

6. Install the locknuts on the lower mounting studs and lower the car.

7. Install the grommet, retainer, and locknut on the piston rod, making sure the grommet seats properly in the hole in the crossmember.

Spring

REMOVAL & INSTALLATION

Except Pacer

Remove the shock absorber. Install a spring compressor through the upper spring seat opening and bolt it to the lower spring seat using the lower shock absorber mounting holes. Remove the lower spring seat pivot retaining nuts, then tighten the compressor tool to compress the spring about 1 in.

Jack up the front of the car and support it on axle stands at the subframe (allowing the control arms to hang free). Remove the front wheel and pull the lower spring seat out and away from the car, then slowly release the spring tension and remove the coil spring and lower spring seat.

To install, place the spring compressor through the coil spring and tape the rubber spring cushion to the small-diameter end of the spring (upper). Place the lower spring seat against the spring with the end of the coil against the formed shoulder in the seat. The shoulder and coil end face inward, toward the engine, when the spring is installed.

Place the spring up against the upper seat, then align the lower spring seat pivot so the retaining studs will enter the holes in the upper control arm. Compress the coil spring and install the spring, then install the wheel and tire and lower the car to the floor (to place weight on suspension). Install and tighten lower spring seat spindle retaining nuts and tighten them to 35 ft. lbs. Remove the spring compressor and install the shock absorber.

Pacer

1. Disconnect the upper end of the shock absorber.

2. Raise the front end of the car and support it.

3. Disconnect the lower end of the shock absorber and remove it.

4. Disconnect the stabilizer bar at the lower control arm, if so equipped.

5. Remove the wheel, and caliper and rotor. Do not allow the brake hose to support the weight of the caliper; use a length of wire to suspend the caliper from the frame.

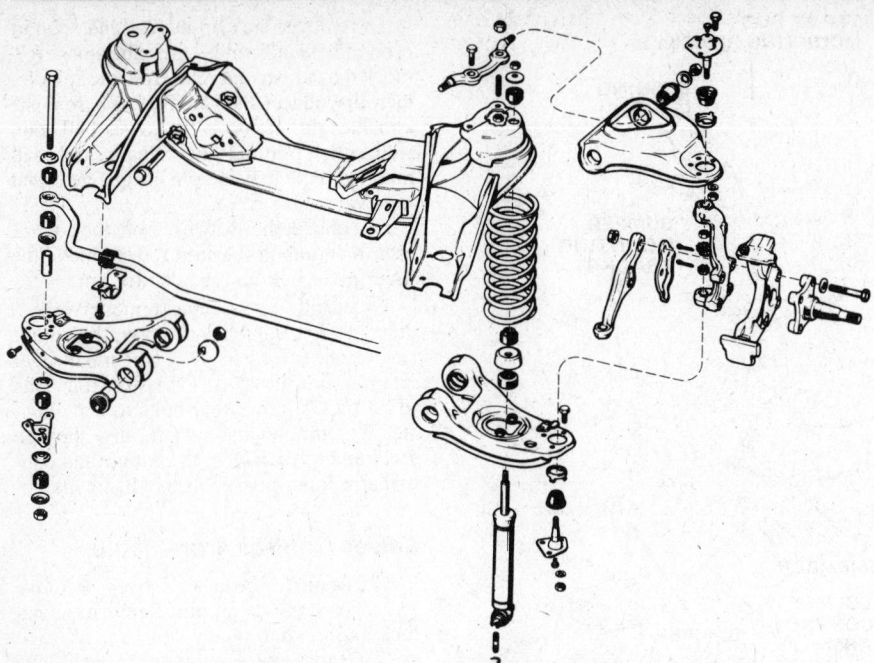

Exploded view of the Pacer front suspension

the coil spring approximately 2 in. using the procedure under "Front Spring Removal and Installation".

Jack up the front of the car and support the body on jackstands placed under the subframes (allow the control arms to hang free). Remove the wheel and the upper ball joint cotter pin and retaining nut. Separate the ball joint stud from the steering knuckle using a ball joint removal tool. Remove the inner pivot bolts, then remove the control arm.

To install, reverse the removal procedure. Do not tighten the pivot bolt nuts until the full weight of the car is on the wheels. The ball joint stud nut must be tightened to 75 ft. lbs., the lower spring seat pivot retaining nuts to 35 ft. lbs., and the control arm inner pivot bolts to 80 ft. lbs.

Upper Control Arm—Pacer

1. Raise and support the front of the vehicle.
2. Remove the wheel and tire.
3. Remove the cotter pin, locknut, and retaining nuts from the upper ball joint stud.
4. Loosen the stud from the steering knuckle with a ball joint removal tool.

6. Remove the two bolts that attach the steering arm to the steering knuckle and move the steering arm aside.

7. Use a spring compressor to compress the coil spring.

8. Remove the cotter pin and nut from the lower ball joint stud and disengage the stud from the steering knuckle with a puller.

9. Move the steering knuckle, steering spindle, and support plate, or anchor plate assembly aside, to provide working clearance. Do not allow the brake hose to support the weight of these components. Use wire to hang the components from the upper control arm.

10. Move the lower control arm aside and remove the spring.

To install the front coil spring:

11. Position the upper end of the spring in the spring seat of the front crossmember. Align the cut-off end of the bottom coil with the formed shoulder in the spring seat. The top coil is flat and does not use an insulator. Use a floor jack or jackstand to support the spring until the spring compressor is installed. Install the spring compressor.

12. Assemble the remaining components of the front suspension in the reverse order of removal. Tighten the ball joint stud nut to 75 ft. lbs., the steering arm-to-knuckle attaching bolts to 55 ft. lbs., the shock absorber lower mounting nuts to 20 ft. lbs., and the stabilizer bar locknut to 8 ft. lbs.

Control Arm

REMOVAL & INSTALLATION

Upper Control Arm—Except Pacer

Remove the shock absorber and compress

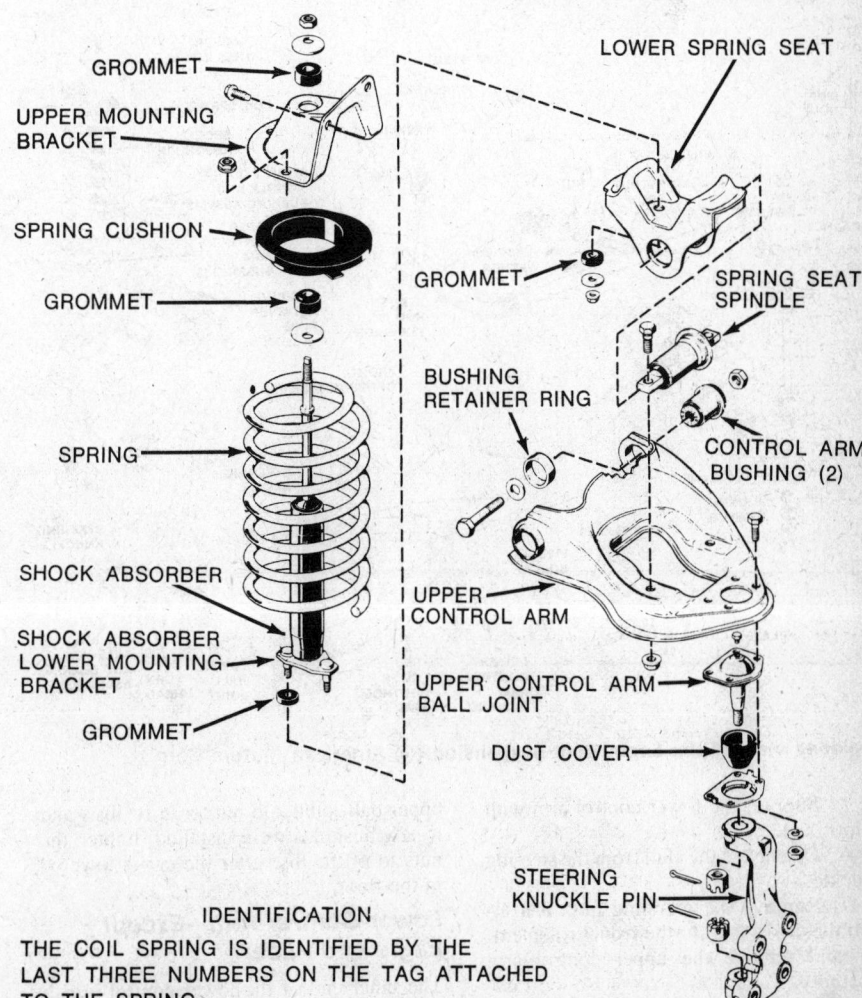

IDENTIFICATION

THE COIL SPRING IS IDENTIFIED BY THE LAST THREE NUMBERS ON THE TAG ATTACHED TO THE SPRING

Upper control arm and shock absorber—except Eagle and Pacer (© American Motors Corp.)

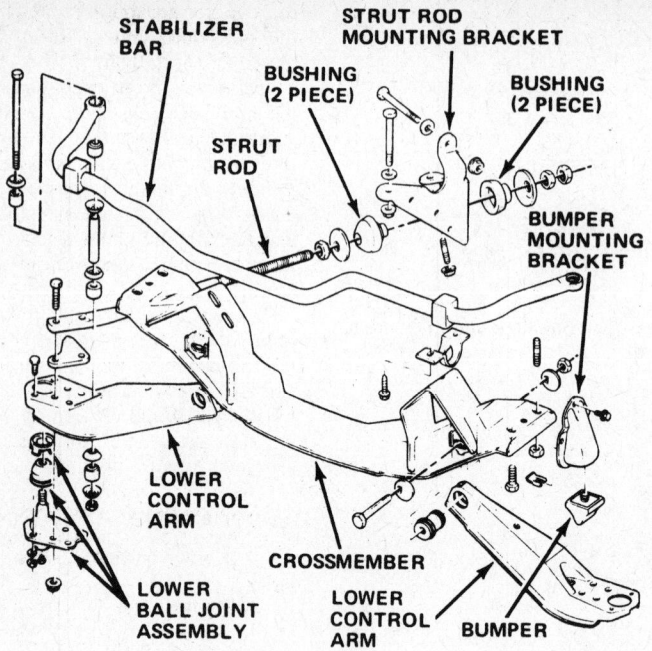

Lower control arm and details—except Eagle and Pacer (© American Motors Corp.)

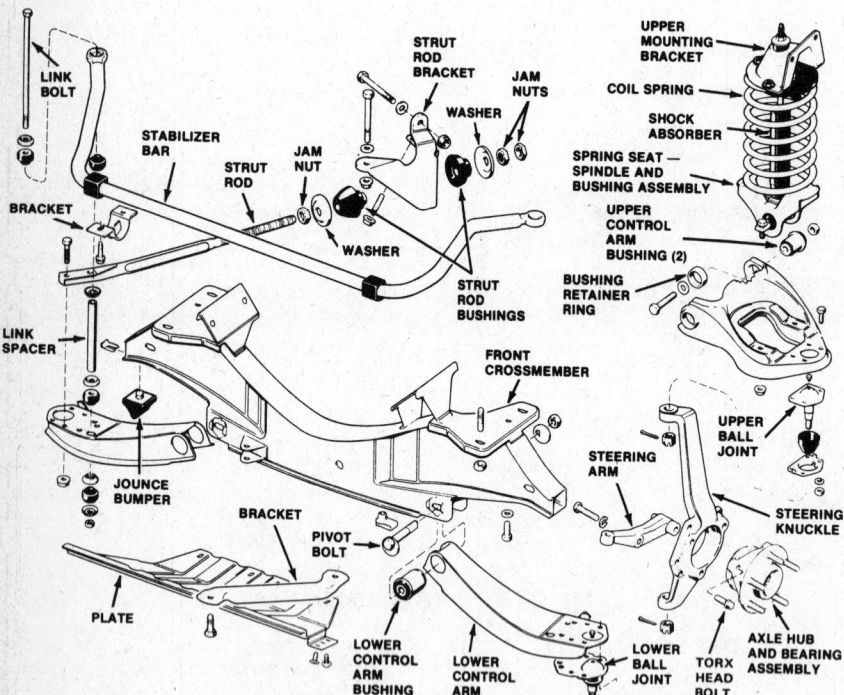

Exploded view of the Eagle front suspension (© American Motors Corp.)

To remove, jack up the car and support it on axle stands under the subframes. Remove the caliper and rotor from the spindle, then disconnect the steering arm from the knuckle pin. Remove the lower ball joint stud cotter pin and nut. Separate the ball joint from the knuckle pin using a ball joint removal tool.

Disconnect the sway bar from the control arm, then unbolt the strut rod. Remove the inner pivot bolt and the control arm.

To install, reverse the removal procedure; do not tighten inner pivot bolt until car weight is on wheels. Tighten ball joint retaining nut to 75 ft. lbs., strut rod bolts to 75 ft. lbs., sway bar bolts to 8 ft. lbs., steering arm bolts to 65 ft. lbs. through 1979 and to 55 ft. lbs. thereafter, and control arm inner pivot bolt to 110 ft. lbs.

Lower Control Arm—Eagle

1. Remove the wheel cover. Remove and discard the cotter pin. Remove the nut lock and the hub pin.

2. Raise and support the front of the car. Remove the wheel. Remove the brake caliper from the knuckle and suspend it from the body by a length of wire; do not allow it to hang by the hose. Remove the rotor.

3. Remove the lower ball joint cotter pin and retaining nut. Discard the cotter pin.

4. Separate the ball joint stud from the steering knuckle using a ball joint removal tool.

5. Remove the halfshaft flange bolts and remove the halfshaft.

6. Remove the strut rod-to-control arm bolts. Disconnect the stabilizer bar from the arm.

7. Remove the inner pivot bolt and remove the control arm.

8. To install, place the control arm into position and install the inner pivot bolt, but do not tighten the pivot bolt yet.

9. Install the ball joint stud into the steering knuckle. Install the nut and tighten to 75 ft. lbs. Continue to tighten until the holes align, and install a new cotter pin.

10. Connect the stabilizer bar to the arm; tighten the bolts to 7 ft. lbs. Install the strut rod; tighten the bolts to 75 ft. lbs.

11. Install the halfshaft-to-axle flange bolts; tighten to 45 ft. lbs.

12. Place a jack under the lower control arm. Raise the jack carefully to compress the spring slightly. Tighten the control arm pivot bolt to 110 ft. lbs.

13. Install the rotor, caliper, and hub nut. Tighten the hub nut to 180 ft. lbs. Install the nut lock and a new cotter pin.

14. Install the wheel. Check and adjust the front end alignment as necessary.

Lower Control Arm—Pacer

1. Disconnect the upper end of the shock absorber, raise the front end of the car and disconnect the lower end of the shock absorber, then remove the shock absorber.

5. Support the lower control arm with a floor jack.

6. Disengage the stud from the steering knuckle.

7. Remove the retaining nuts that attach the cross-shaft to the front crossmember and remove the upper control arm assembly.

8. Install the upper control arm in the reverse order of removal, tightening the cross-shaft retaining nuts to 80 ft. lbs., the

upper ball joint stud nut to 75 ft. lbs., and if new bushings were installed, tighten the nuts to 60 ft. lbs. after the car is lowered to the floor.

Lower Control Arm—Except Eagle and Pacer

The inner end of the lower control arm is attached to a removable crossmember. The outer end is attached to the steering knuckle pin and ball joint assembly.

2. Disconnect the stabilizer bar at the lower control arm, if so equipped.

3. Remove the wheel, brake drum, or caliper and rotor. Do not allow the brake hose to support the weight of the caliper. Use wire to support it from the frame.

4. Remove the two bolts attaching the steering arm to the steering knuckle and move the steering arm aside.

5. Install a spring compressor and compress the spring.

6. Remove the cotter pin and nut from the lower ball joint stud. Remove the ball joint from the steering knuckle using a ball joint removal tool.

7. Move the steering knuckle assembly out of the way. Support the assembly with wire from the upper control arm.

8. Remove the two pivot bolts that attach the lower arm to the front crossmember and remove the lower control arm.

9. Install the lower control arm in the reverse order of removal, tightening the ball joint stud nut to 75 ft. lbs., the steering arm attaching bolts to 55 ft. lbs., the shock absorber lower attaching nuts to 20 ft. lbs., the stabilizer bar locknut to 8 ft. lbs., and lastly, after the car has been lowered to the ground with the wheel and tire installed, tighten the lower control arm pivot bolts to 110 ft. lbs.

Ball Joints

INSPECTION

Except Pacer

NOTE: Before checking the upper ball joint, make certain the front wheel bearings are adjusted to specifications.

1. Jack up the front of the car and place jackstands under the frame side sills.

NOTE: The control arms must hang free if an accurate reading is to be obtained.

2. Check the lower ball joints by grasping the lower portion of the wheel and pulling it in and out.

3. If there is noticeable lateral free-play, the lower ball joint is worn and must be replaced.

NOTE: On Eagles the lower ball joints and control arms must be replaced as assemblies.

4. To check the condition of the upper ball joint, place a dial indicator with its plunger against the tire scrub bead (just outside the whitewall).

5. Move the upper portion of the wheel and tire toward the car's center, while watching the dial indicator.

6. Move the wheel and tire back out while watching the indicator.

7. The upper ball joint should be replaced if its *total* movement is greater than 0.160 in.

NOTE: On 1980 Eagles the upper ball joints and control arms must be replaced

as assemblies. On 1981 and later Eagles the upper ball joints are replaceable separately.

Pacer

1. Check that the front wheel bearings are adjusted properly.

2. Remove the lubrication plug from the lower ball joint. Insert a straight piece of stiff wire until it contacts the ball. Mark the wire even with the edge of the plug hole.

3. Measure from the end of the wire to the mark. If it exceeds 7/16 in., the ball joint should be replaced.

4. Place a jack under the lower control arm and lift the wheel off the floor.

5. Push the top of the tire in and out. If there is any looseness, replace the upper ball joint.

6. Pry the upper control arm up and down. If there is any looseness, replace the upper ball joint.

REMOVAL & INSTALLATION

NOTE: On Eagles, do not attempt to replace the ball joints separately. If the ball joints are worn, the control arms and ball joints must be replaced as complete assemblies.

Lower Ball Joint

1. On all vehicles except Pacer, place a 2 × 4 × 5 in. block of wood on the side sill so that it supports the control arm.

2. Jack up the front end of the car and place jackstands underneath the frame side sills to support the body.

3. Remove the wheel, the caliper and rotor.

4. Disconnect the lower control arm strut rod, on models other than Pacer. Disconnect the stabilizer bar, if so equipped.

5. Separate the steering arm from the steering knuckle.

6. Remove the ball stud retaining nut, after removing its cotter pin.

7. Install a ball joint removal tool, then loosen the ball stud in the knuckle pin. Leave the tool in place on the stud.

8. Place a jackstand under the lower control arm.

9. Chisel the heads off the rivets which secure the ball joint to the control arm. Use a punch to remove the rivets.

10. Remove the tool from the ball stud.

11. Remove the ball stud from the knuckle pin and remove the joint from the control arm.

Installation of a new lower ball joint is as follows:

1. Position the new ball joint so that its securing holes align with the rivet holes in the control arm.

2. Loosely install the special 5/16 in. bolts used to secure the ball joint.

----------- **CAUTION** -----------
Use only the hardened 5/16 in. bolts sup-

plied with the ball joint replacement kit; standard bolts are not strong enough.

3. Install the steering strut and stop on the lower control arm. Tighten their bolts to 75 ft. lbs.

4. Tighten the 5/16 in. ball joint securing bolts to 25 ft. lbs.

5. Apply chassis grease to the steering stops and fit the knuckle pin and retaining nut on the ball stud; tighten the nut to 75 ft. lbs. Install a new cotter pin.

6. Complete the installation procedure in the reverse order of removal, then check front end alignment.

Upper Ball Joint

1. Perform Steps 1–3 of the "Lower Ball Joint Removal" procedure.

NOTE: On 1981 and later Eagle models temporarily reinstall two lug nuts to retain each brake rotor. This eliminates repositioning rotors and calipers prior to reassembly.

2. Next, perform Steps 6–9 of the "Lower Ball Joint Removal" procedure to the upper ball joint.

3. Separate the upper ball joint from the control arm.

4. Remove the ball joint puller from the knuckle pin.

Installation of a new upper ball joint is as follows:

1. Perform Steps 1–2 of the "Lower Ball Joint Installation" procedure.

2. Skip Step 3 and go on to Steps 4–5 of the "Lower Ball Joint Installation" procedure.

3. Complete the installation in the reverse order of removal and check front end alignment.

Wheel Bearings

Four wheel drive models have sealed, non-adjustable front hubs and bearings. There are darkened areas surrounding the bearing races in the hubs. These darkened areas are the result of a heat treatment process, they do not signify defects.

INSPECTION

Check to see that the inner cones of the bearings are free to "creep" on the spindle. Polish and lubricate the spindle to allow "creeping" movement and to keep rust from forming.

ADJUSTMENT

1. With the tire and wheel removed and the car supported by a suitable and safe means, remove the dust cover from the spindle.

2. Remove the cotter pin and nut retainer.

3. Rotate the wheel while tightening the spindle nut to 20–25 ft. lbs.

4. Loosen the spindle nut ⅓ of a turn.

5. Rotate the wheel while tightening the spindle nut to 6 in. lbs.

6. Fit the nut retainer over the spindle and align the slots in it with the cotter pin hole. Insert the cotter pin.

7. Install the dust cover.

REAR SUSPENSION

All Pacer, Spirit, Concord, Eagle, AMX and Gremlin models use a four or five-leaf semi-elliptic spring, and live axle rear suspension. Shock absorbers are mounted at their lower ends to studs and are bayonet or stud type at their upper ends. Upper shock nuts are accessible by removing cover plates or by removing trunk floormat on some models, or by removing underbody brackets bolted to the trunk pan on others, such as on the Pacer and Concord.

The rear suspension on Matador models is a four-trailing arm, coil spring type. The two lower control arms are attached to the differential housing and to a rear crossmember. Rubber bushings are used on the lower arms and on the crossmember ends of the upper arms. The lower end of the upper arms are attached to the outer ends of the axle tubes and to the body side sills; while the two upper control arms are attached to pressed-in bushings in ears on the differential case. Shock absorbers are accessible at their upper ends by removing cover plates in the body or by removing brackets from underneath the car.

Shock Absorber

REPLACEMENT

NOTE: When installing new shocks purge them of air by repeatedly extending them in their normal position and compressing them while inverted. It is normal for new shocks to be more resistant to extension than to compression.

1. Support the rear axle with jacks or a lift; this allows the weight of the car to compress the rear spring.

2. Remove the lower shock attachment.

3. Remove the access plate on the rear underbody panel, and remove the upper securing nut. It may be necessary to hold the top of the shock while unfastening the nut.

NOTE: Some models do not have an access plate. On these cars, remove the upper attachment plate complete as an assembly, from under the car.

4. Remove the shock from under the car.

5. Installation is in the reverse order of removal.

SPRING

REMOVAL & INSTALLATION
Except Matador

1. Raise the car. Support the rear axle with jacks, or a lift, to take the load off the rear springs.

2. Disconnect the rear shock from the lower mounting stud.

3. Disconnect the axle U-bolts.

4. Remove the nut from the bolt which attaches the eye of the spring to the front mount. Remove the bolt.

5. On all models except Pacer, remove the nuts from the rear shackle. Remove the shackle.

6. On the Pacer, remove the nuts from the rear hanger bracket on the frame side sill and remove the spring. Remove the shackle nuts and the shackle after the spring is removed.

7. Installation is in the reverse order of removal.

Matador

1. Raise the rear of the car and support the rear axle with jacks or a lift to take the load off the rear springs.

2. Disconnect the shock from the axle tube. Lower the axle to the fullest extent of its travel (limited by the control arms). Detach the upper control arms at the axle.

3. Pull down the axle tube to completely release the spring.

4. Reverse the above to install the spring. Keeping the weight of the car on the springs,

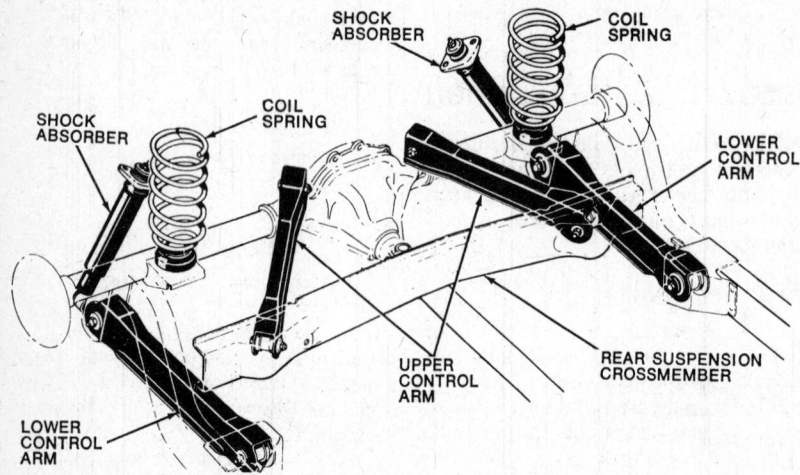

Typical coil spring rear suspension (© American Motors Corp.)

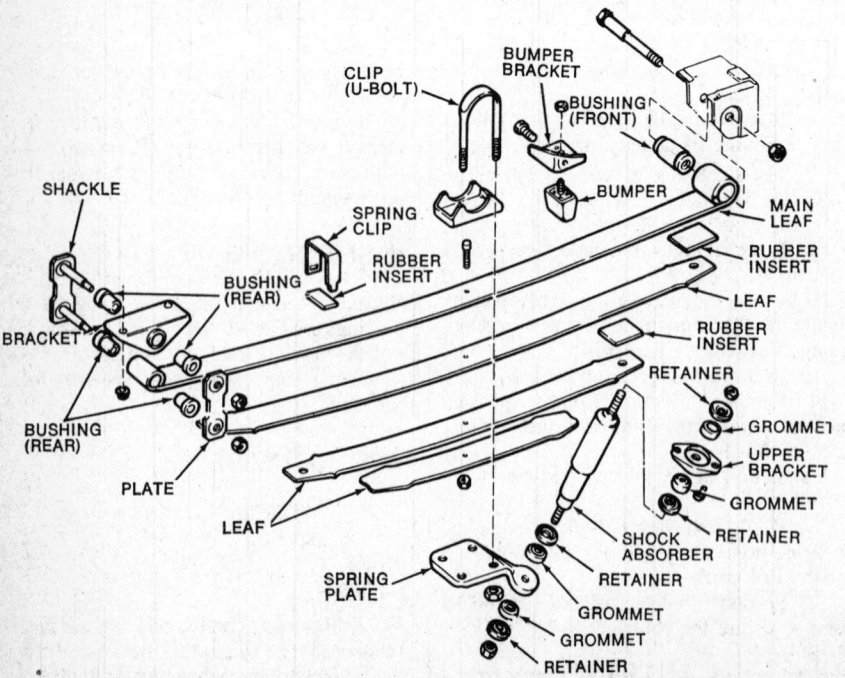

Typical leaf spring rear suspension (© American Motors Corp.)

torque the control arm pivot bolts to 45–80 ft. lbs.

BRAKES

All American Motors cars are equipped with tandem (dual reservoir) master cylinders. This allows one set of brakes to operate, should the other set fail. A switch in the system, connected to a warning light on the instrument panel, indicates a difference in pressure between the front and rear brake lines, thus signaling the failure of one brake system. Repair procedures for both the master cylinder and the switch are found in the Unit Repair Section.

All drum brakes have automatic brake adjusters. These compensate for lining wear, by operating when the brakes are applied while the car is backing up. The automatic adjusting mechanism functions through the star wheel.

For additional brake system repair and service procedures, please refer to "Brakes" in the Unit Repair section.

Master Cylinder

REMOVAL & INSTALLATION

1. Disconnect the front and rear brake lines from the master cylinder. Both outlets must be plugged, to prevent fluid loss.

2. Remove the nuts which attach the master cylinder to the firewall or the power brake booster, if so equipped. On Pacers, remove the mounting bracket and the boot retainer plate.

3. On cars without power brakes, disconnect the pedal push-rod at the brake pedal.

4. Remove the master cylinder from the car.

Installation is in the reverse order of removal. Remember to bleed the brake system once the master cylinder has been installed. (See the Unit Repair section.)

Power Brake Unit

REMOVAL & INSTALLATION

Disconnect the power brake clevis pin from the power unit operating rod at the linkage under the hood, or from the brake pedal inside the car, depending on which type is being serviced. Remove the vacuum hose from the check valve. Separate the master cylinder from the power unit. Do not disconnect the hydraulic lines from the master cylinder. Remove the power unit mounting bolts, and lift the unit from the car. Installation is in the reverse order of removal.

Parking Brake

ADJUSTMENT

1. To adjust the drum brakes, apply the

brakes several times while backing up. Make one forward application for each reverse application to equalize the adjustment. Fully apply the parking brake about 10 times. Set the pedal on the first notch from the released position.

2. Block the front wheels and raise the rear wheels.

3. Tighten the cable at the equalizer so the wheels can just barely be turned forward. Be sure to hold the end of the cable screw to prevent the cable from turning.

4. Release the parking brake and check for rear brake drag. The wheels should rotate freely with the parking brake off.

STEERING

All models except the Pacer use Ackerman-type articulated linkage to interconnect the steering gear and front wheels. Pacers use rack and pinion steering with integral linkage to the front wheels.

Tie-Rod End

REMOVAL & INSTALLATION

1. Raise and support the front of the car.

2. Remove the cotter pin and retaining nut from the tie-rod end stud.

3. Mark the position of the tie-rod end adjuster tube and inner tie-rod, for reference.

4. Loosen the adjuster tube clamps.

5. Disconnect the tie-rod end from the steering arm with a puller.

6. Remove the tie-rod end from the adjuster tube.

7. Install the replacement tie-rod end in the adjuster tube, and insert the end stud in the steering arm. Tighten the nut to 35 ft. lbs., and install a new cotter pin. Do not loosen the nuts to align. Adjust the toe-in and tighten the clamps.

Manual Steering Gear

REMOVAL & INSTALLATION
Except Pacer

1. Remove flexible coupling bolts.

2. Remove Pitman arm, using puller J-5566-04 or equivalent.

3. Remove steering gear mounting screws and lower the steering gear.

4. Center steering gear with index mark up. Mark on shaft of flange must be aligned at assembly.

5. Insert the flexible coupling bolts into shaft flange. Tighten nuts to 20 ft. lbs. torque and pinch bolt to 30 ft. lbs.

6. Tighten gear mounting screws to 65 ft. lbs. and Pitman arm nut to 115 ft. lbs.

NOTE: After tightening Pitman shaft nut, stake thread at nut with a center punch to insure nut retention.

NOTE: Whenever the steering gear assembly is removed for replacement or overhaul, or the mounting bolts are loosened for any reason, the steering column MUST be realigned to the gear assembly. Slight misalignment of the steering column may cause increased steering effort and additional wear to the steering components.

Pacer

1. Unlock steering column.

2. Raise and support front of car.

3. Remove screws attaching reinforcement brace to front crossmember and left engine support bracket and remove brace.

4. Remove flexible coupling pinch bolt and disengage flexible coupling from steering gear pinion shaft.

5. Remove cotter pins and nuts from tie rod ends.

6. Disconnect tie-rod ends using tool J-26951.

7. Remove bolts attaching steering gear mounting clamp to right side of front crossmember.

NOTE: Before removing bolts, loosen them slightly to minimize clamp distortion.

8. Remove steering gear housing-to-cross-member nuts. Using a blunt punch remove bolts, washers, sleeves, and grommets.

9. Rotate bottom of gear housing toward front of car until pinion shaft is approximately parallel with skid plate. Slide gear assembly toward right side of car until housing and tube clear mounting plate and remove steering gear assembly.

10. Assemble grommets, sleeves, and washers and install on steering gear. Sleeves will hold grommets in place during assembly.

11. Position steering gear assembly on crossmember. Install tube and housing from right side of car. During installation, keep pinion shaft approximately parallel with mounting plate.

12. Install mounting clamp-to-crossmember attaching bolts. Hand-tighten bolts only.

13. Install steering gear housing-to-crossmember attaching bolts, washers, and nuts and tighten to 60 ft. lbs. torque.

14. Tighten mounting clamp-to-crossmember attaching bolts to 50 ft. lbs. torque.

15. Connect tie rod ends to steering arms. Tighten nuts to 50 ft. lbs. torque and install replacement cotter pins.

16. Align flat spline on pinion shaft with flat on flexible coupling and install coupling on shaft. Install pinchbolt and tighten to 30 ft. lbs. torque.

17. Install bolts attaching reinforcement brace to front crossmember and engine support bracket. Torque bolts to 30 ft. lbs.

18. Remove supports and lower car.

19. Check and correct toe-in adjustment, if necessary.

Power Steering Gear

REMOVAL & INSTALLATION

Except Pacer

1. Place wheels in straight-ahead position.
2. Position drain pan under steering gear.
3. Disconnect hoses at gear. Raise and secure hoses above pump fluid level to prevent excessive oil spillage and cap ends of hoses to keep out dirt.
4. Remove flexible coupling-to-intermediate shaft attaching nuts.
5. Raise automobile on hoist.

NOTE: On Eagle models, remove:

    a. skid plate, if so equipped;
    b. left side crossmember-to-still support brace;
    c. stabilizer bar brackets from frame.

6. Paint alignment marks on Pitman arm and Pitman shaft for assembly reference.
7. Remove Pitman arm using Puller Tool J-5566-04 or equivalent.
8. Remove steering gear mounting bolts and remove steering gear.
9. Center steering gear. Turn stub shaft (using flexible coupling) from stop-to-stop and count total number of turns; then turn back from either stop one-half total number of turns to center gear. At this point, flat on stub shaft should be facing upward.
10. Align flexible coupling and intermediate shaft flange.
11. Install gear mounting bolts in gear, install spacer on gear, and mount gear on frame side-sill. Tighten gear mounting bolts to 65 ft. lbs. torque.
12. Install and tighten flexible coupling nuts to 25 ft. lbs. torque.
13. Install Pitman arm. Index arm to shaft using alignment marks made during removal.
14. Install Pitman arm nut. Tighten nut to 115 ft. lbs. torque and stake nut to Pitman shaft in one place.

───── CAUTION ─────
The Pitman arm nut must be staked to the shaft to retain it properly.

NOTE: On Eagle models, install:

    a. stabilizer bar brackets;
    b. left side crossmember-to-sill support brace;
    c. skid plate, if so equipped.

15. Lower automobile.
16. Align flexible coupling, if necessary.
17. Connect hoses to gear and tighten fittings to 25 ft. lbs. torque.
18. Fill pump reservoir with power steering fluid and bleed air from system.

Pacer

1. Unlock steering column.
2. Raise and support front of car.

3. Remove screws attaching reinforcement brace to front crossmember and left engine support bracket and remove brace.
4. Disconnect stabilizer bar at left-side lower control arm, if so equipped.
5. Remove bolts attaching stabilizer bar mounting clamps to frame rail brackets and move bar away from front crossmember.
6. Place support under stabilizer bar to prevent damaging the bolt attaching the bar to the right-side lower control arm.
7. Remove left-side frame rail clamp brackets.
8. Position drain pan under steering gear housing and disconnect power steering hoses at gear housing. Cap hoses and plug gear housing to keep dirt out.
9. Remove flexible coupling pinchbolt and disengage flexible coupling from steering gear pinion shaft.
10. Remove and discard cotter pins from tie rod end retaining nuts.
11. Disconnect tie rod ends using tool J-26951.
12. Remove bolts attaching steering gear mounting clamp to crossmember.

───── CAUTION ─────
Before removing the bolts, loosen them slightly to minimize clamp distortion.

13. Remove steering gear housing-to-crossmember attaching bolt nuts.
14. Using a blunt punch remove bolts, washers, sleeves and grommets from steering gear housing.
15. Rotate bottom of gear housing toward front of car until pinion shaft is approximately parallel with skid plate. Slide gear assembly toward right side of car until housing and tube clear mounting plate and remove steering gear assembly.
16. Assemble and install grommets, sleeves, and washers on steering gear. Sleeves will hold grommets in place during assembly.
17. Position steering gear assembly on crossmember. Install gear from driver side of car.

NOTE: When installing the gear, keep the pinion shaft approximately parallel to the mounting plate.

18. Install mounting clamp bolts, and hand-tighten them only.
19. Install steering gear housing-to-crossmember attaching bolts, washers, and nuts and tighten to 60 ft. lbs. torque.
20. Tighten mounting clamp bolts to 48 ft. lbs. torque.
21. Connect tie rod ends to steering arms. Tighten tie rod end retaining nuts to 50 ft. lbs. torque and install replacement cotter pins.
22. Align flat spline of steering gear pinion shaft with index flat of flexible coupling and install coupling on pinion shaft. Install pinchbolt and tighten to 30 ft. lbs. torque.
23. Install bolts attaching reinforcement brace to front crossmember and engine support bracket. Tighten bolts to 30 ft. lbs. torque.

24. Connect power steering hoses to gear housing. Be sure that hoses do not touch brace or crossmember.
25. Install left-side frame rail clamp brackets.
26. Position stabilizer bar on frame rail brackets and install mounting clamp bolts. Hand tighten bolts only.
27. Install bolts, washers, and grommets attaching stabilizer bar to left-side lower control arm.
28. Tighten stabilizer bar mounting clamp bolts to 18 ft. lbs. torque.
29. Remove supports and lower car.
30. Fill power steering pump reservoir with power steering fluid.
31. Operate engine until fluid reaches normal operating temperature. Turn wheel right and left several times (do not hold wheel against steering stops). Stop engine and check fluid level. Add fluid as necessary.

Power Steering Pump

REMOVAL & INSTALLATION

1. Remove the fan belt.
2. Place a container under the pump to catch fluid. Remove the fuel vapor storage canister and six-cylinder air cleaner, if necessary.
3. Disconnect the hoses and cap the outlets, so the power steering unit does not lose fluid. Remove the air pump belt.
4. On sixes with air conditioning, loosen the idler pulley adjusting bolt and idler pulley, air pump adjusting strap mounting bolt and remove the compressor drive belt from the idler pulley. Loosen the two nuts that attach the upper leg of the aluminum idler pulley mounting bracket to the cylinder head and remove the bolt that attaches the lower leg of the mounting bracket to the engine front cover.
5. On sixes, remove the nut from the air pump mounting stud, remove the power steering pump to engine front cover front adapter plate (do not unbolt the adapter plate from the pump), remove the long adjusting bolt that passes through the adapter plate, and remove the bolt hidden behind the flange in the rear adapter plate. Remove the pump, adapter plate and mounting bracket together.

On V8s, remove the two pump mounting stud nuts at the rear of the two-piece mounting bracket and remove the drive belt from the pump pulley. Remove the pump support strap bolts and the front half of the pump mounting bracket. Remove the nut from the stud holding the front half of the pump bracket. Remove the pump and the front half of the mounting bracket.

On four cylinder models, remove the adjuster locknuts and washers which retain the pump and pivot bracket on the mounting bracket. All of the pump mounting bolts are metric, except for the 9/16 in. adjuster locknuts. Move the pump and remove the belt. Remove the bolts which connect the front bracket to the rear bracket and engine block, and remove the pump complete with the pivot and front brackets.

6. After installation, fill the system with Dexron or AMC power steering fluid. Bleed the system of air by raising the front of the car, and by turning the wheels from side to side several times, without hitting the stops. Check the level frequently.

Steering Wheel

REMOVAL & INSTALLATION

1. Disconnect the battery and remove the horn button by one of the following methods:

    a. center button—lift upward.

    b. trim cover—from the back side of the steering wheel remove the screws which hold the cover on. On "rimblow" wheels, remove the center contact.

2. Remove the steering wheel center nut and washer. Before removing the wheel, note the position of the index marks on the wheel and the steering shaft. If none are present, paint an alignment mark on the shaft and wheel.

3. Remove the wheel with a puller. Installation is in the reverse order of removal. Tighten the steering wheel nut to 20 ft. lbs.

NOTE: Some shafts have metric threads. These can be identified by a groove in the shaft splines. Metric nuts are coded blue.

——————— CAUTION ———————

Do not hammer on the end of the steering shaft; hammering could shear the plastic retainers which maintain the rigidity of the energy-absorbing steering column.

TURN SIGNAL SWITCH, HAZARD SIGNAL AND LOCK CYLINDER

1. Disconnect the ground cable from the battery. On cars with tilt steering wheels, place the column in the straight position. Remove the steering wheel.

2. Loosen the anti-theft cover attaching screws and remove the cover from the column. Do not hammer on the shaft. Do not remove the screws from the cover; they are attached to it with plastic retainers.

3. To remove the lockplate, a special compressing tool is required. This tool is an inverted U-shape with a hole for the shaft. The shaft nut is used to force it down. Depress the lockplate and pry the snap-ring from the groove in the steering shaft. Remove the tool, snap-ring, plate, turn signal cam, upper bearing preload spring, and the thrust washer from the shaft.

4. Place the turn signal lever in the Right turn position and remove it.

5. Depress the hazard warning switch button and remove it by rotating it coun-

terclockwise. Remove the package tray (if so equipped) and the lower trim panel.

6. Disconnect the wire harness connector block at its mounting bracket, which is located on the right side of the lower column. Remove the steering column mounting bracket attaching bolts. Remove the turn signal switch wiring harness protector from the bottom of the column.

NOTE: To ease the removal and replacement of the directional switch harness, tape the harness connector to the wire harness. This will prevent snagging while removing the wiring harness assembly through the steering column. Prepare the new turn signal switch harness in the same manner to ease installation.

7. If the car (Gremlin, Concord, and Spirit only) is equipped with a column-mounted automatic transmission selector, use a paper clip to depress the locktab that holds the shift quadrant light wire in the connector block.

8. Remove the switch attaching screws. Withdraw the switch and wire harness from the column.

9. Insert the key into the lock cylinder and turn the key to the ON position. Remove the warning buzzer switch and the contacts as an assembly using needlenose pliers. Take care not to let the contacts fall into the column.

10. Turn the key to the LOCK position and compress the lock cylinder retaining tab. Remove the lock cylinder. If the tab is not visible through the slot, knock the casting flash out of the slot.

To install:

1. Hold the lock cylinder sleeve and turn the lock cylinder counterclockwise until it contacts the stop.

2. Align the lock cylinder key with the keyway in the housing and slip the cylinder into the housing.

3. Lightly depress the cylinder against the sector, while turning it counterclockwise, until the cylinder and sector are engaged.

4. Depress the cylinder until the retaining tab engages, and the lock cylinder is secured.

5. In installing the turn signal switch, don't screw it in place until you are sure the actuating lever pivot is properly seated and aligned in the top of the housing boss.

6. Install the turn signal lever and check the operation of the switch.

7. Install the thrust washer, spring and turn-signal cancelling cam on the steering shaft.

8. Align the lockplate and steering shaft splines, and position the lockplate so the turn signal camshaft protrudes from the "dogleg" opening in the lockplate.

9. Use snap-ring pliers to install the snap-ring on the end of the steering shaft.

10. Secure the anti-theft cover with its screws.

11. Install the button on the hazard warning switch. Install the steering wheel as detailed above.

IGNITION SWITCH

The ignition switch on all models is mounted on the lower steering column tube and is

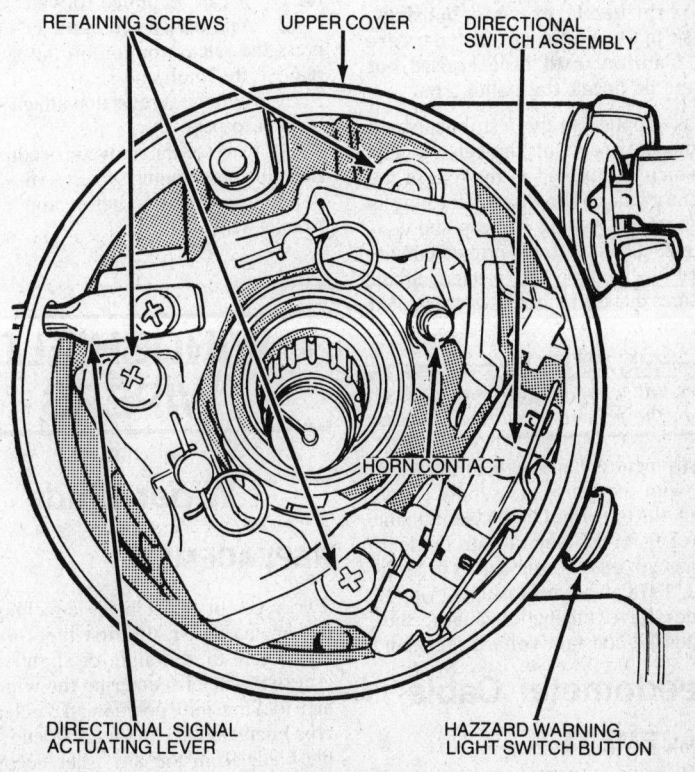

Turn signal switch

connected to the lock cylinder via a lock rod.

1. Place the key in OFF-LOCK position.
2. Remove switch mounting screws.
3. Disconnect the lock rod, remove harness connector and switch.
4. To install on the standard column, move the switch slide as far as it will go to the left (toward the wheel). On the tilt-column, push the slide to the extreme right.
5. Position the lock rod into the hole on the switch slide.
6. Install the switch on the steering column. Be sure that the slide stays in its detent.
7. On the tilt-column, do not tighten the mounting screws. Instead, push the switch down the column, away from the steering wheel. This will remove any slack from the lock rod.
8. Tighten the switch mounting screws.

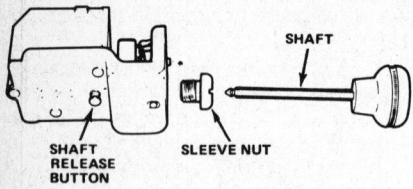

Light switch assembly
(© American Motors Corp.)

INSTRUMENT PANEL

NOTE: To remove the various units from the instrument panel it is necessary to remove the bezels, overlays, housings, and crash pads. Numerous fasteners are hidden. Caution must be exercised not to damage or break the panel trim.

Current is supplied to the instruments and the instrument panel lights through a printed circuit which is attached to the rear of the instrument cluster. The disconnect plug is part of the panel wiring harness and connects to pins attached to the printed circuit. A keyway located on the printed circuit board insures that the plug is always mounted correctly.

— **CAUTION** —
Never pry under the plug to remove it, or damage to the printed circuit will result.

An instrument voltage regulator is wired in series with the gauges to supply a constant five volts to them. On the Gremlin the voltage regulator is integral with the temperature gauge; on other models it is a separate unit. 1978 and later Concords, Spirits and Eagles have magnetic gauges, thus eliminating the constant voltage regulator.

Speedometer Cable

REPLACEMENT

Two types of fasteners are used to attach the cable to the speedometer. One type has a knurled round captive nut, which is screwed to the rear of the speedometer housing. By depressing the plastic finger, the lug is raised, and the cable is released.

NOTE: The negative battery cable should be detached before any repairs behind the instrument panel are attempted.

1. Disconnect the speedometer cable from the transmission and the underbody routing brackets.
2. Disconnect the negative battery cable.
3. Remove the package tray, if so equipped.
4. If the speedometer cable connection at the rear of the speedometer can not be reached from under the dash, remove the instrument cluster bezel.
5. Remove the headlight switch overlay cover, if necessary for clearance.
6. Unscrew the speedometer cable, and remove the cable and the grommet from the dash panel.

Installation is in the reverse order of removal.

Headlight Switch

REPLACEMENT

Light switches are similar in all models. Some variation occurs in the shape and position of the nut mounting the switch on the dash.

1. Disconnect battery and remove the switch overlay cover attaching screws so the cover can be pulled forward.
2. With the switch in the ON position, press the release button on the switch and remove the knob and shaft.
3. Remove screws that attach switch or bracket to panel.
4. Reverse the above procedure for installation, positioning switch so that the shaft is lined up properly before tightening the bracket screws.

WINDSHIELD WIPERS

Wiper Blade

REPLACEMENT

Two types of wiper blade attaching methods are used. On the first type, the blade is attached to a straight or slightly curved arm, with the arm entering the wiper blade and locking into position. To release this type, depress the locking tab and remove the blade from the arm. The second type of blade is attached to a pin at a right angle

to the arm. To release the pin, a tool is inserted into the wiper blade saddle to depress the spring clip and release the pin.

Motor

REMOVAL & INSTALLATION

Gremlin, Concord, Matador Sedan and Wagon, Eagle and Spirit

1. Remove the wiper arms and blades.
2. Remove the screws holding the motor adapter plate on the dash panel.
3. Separate the wiper wiring harness connector at the motor.
4. Pull the motor and linkage out of the opening to expose the drive link-to-crank stud retaining clip. Raise up the lock tab of the clip with a screwdriver and slide the clip off the stud. Remove the wiper motor assembly.
5. Install the windshield wiper motor in the reverse order of removal.

Matador Coupe

1. Remove the wiper arm/blade assemblies.
2. Open the hood and remove the cowl screen from the cowl opening.
3. Separate the linkage drive arm from the motor arm crankpin, by unfastening the retaining clip.
4. Disconnect the two multiconnectors from the motor.
5. Remove the wiper motor securing screws and withdraw the motor from the opening.

NOTE: If the output arm hangs up on the firewall panel during motor removal, rotate the arm clockwise by hand, so that it clears the panel opening.

Installation is performed in the reverse order of removal. Prior to installation, make sure that the output arm is in the PARK position. Tighten the motor securing screws to 90–120 in. lbs.

Pacer

1. Remove the vacuum canister bracket and canister, if so equipped.
2. Disconnect the linkage drive arm from the motor output arm crankpin by removing the retaining clip.
3. On vehicles equipped with air conditioning:
   a. Remove the two nuts on the left side of the heater housing.
   b. Remove the one nut on the right side of the heater housing.
   c. Remove the screw from the heater housing support.
4. On vehicles not equipped with air conditioning:
   a. Remove the two nuts and one screw on the left side of the heater housing.
   b. Remove the one nut on the right side of the heater housing.

c. Remove the screw from the heater housing support. Pull the heater housing forward.

5. Remove the wiper motor mounting plate attaching screws and remove the wiper motor assembly from the cowl.

6. Disconnect the two wire connectors from the wiper motor.

7. Remove the wiper motor attaching screws and remove the wiper motor.

8. Install the wiper motor following the reverse order of removal.

RADIO

The following precautions should be observed when working on a car radio:

1. Always observe the proper polarity of the power connections; i.e., positive (+) goes to the power source and negative (−) to ground (negative ground electrical system).

2. Never run the radio without a speaker; damage to the output transistors will result. If a replacement (or additional) speaker is used, be sure that it is of the correct impedance (ohms) for the radio. The proper impedance is stamped on the case of American Motors radios.

3. If a new antenna or antenna cable is used, adjust the antenna trimmer for the best reception of a weak AM station around 1400kc; the trimmer is located behind or above the tuning knob or in the radio case near the antenna lead. On tape player radios, it is in the cartridge slot.

REMOVAL & INSTALLATION

Matador

1. Disconnect the negative battery cable. Remove the knobs from the radio and unfasten the control shafts retaining nuts.

2. Remove the bezel securing screws, and remove the bezel.

3. Loosen, but do not remove, the upper radio securing screw.

4. Raise the rear of the radio to separate its bracket from the upper securing screw.

5. Pull the radio forward slightly, and disconnect all of the leads from it. Remove the radio.

To install radio, follow the removal sequence above, in reverse order. Adjust the antenna trimmer.

Gremlin, Concord, Spirit and Eagle

1. Disconnect the battery ground cable.

2. Pull off the radio knobs and remove shaft retaining nuts.

3. Remove the bezel retaining screws and remove the bezel. On models with A/C, remove the center housing of the instrument panel.

4. Disconnect the speaker, antenna, and power leads, and remove the radio.
Installation sequence is the reverse of the above.

Pacer

1. Disconnect the negative battery cable.

2. Remove the radio knobs, attaching nuts, cluster bezel, and overlay cover.

3. Loosen the radio-to-instrument panel attaching screw.

4. Lift the rear of the radio and pull forward slightly. Disconnect the electrical connections and the antenna and remove the radio.

5. Installation sequence is the reverse of the above.

HEATER

NOTE: It is recommended, unless you are trained in air conditioning servicing procedures, that you do not disconnect any of the air conditioning refrigerant lines.

Heater Core

REMOVAL & INSTALLATION

Matador

1. Disconnect the negative battery cable.

2. Drain about 2 quarts of coolant from the cooling system.

3. Disconnect the heater hoses from the heater core in the engine compartment and plug the core tubes.

4. On air conditioned cars, disconnect the blend-air damper cable at the heater core housing and remove the fuse panel. On non A/C cars, disconnect the blend-air damper door and fresh air door cables.

5. Remove the lower instrument finish panel and remove the glove box door and liner.

6. Remove the right windshield pillar and corner finish mouldings for access to the upper right heater core housing mounting screws.

7. On air conditioned cars, remove the vacuum motor hoses.

8. Remove the remaining heater core housing attaching screws.

9. On air conditioned cars, remove the capscrew fastening the instrument panel to the right body pillar. Pull the right side of the instrument panel slightly rearward.

10. Remove the heater core housing and heater core. Remove the heater core from the housing.

11. Install the heater core and housing in the reverse order of removal.

Gremlin, Concord, Spirit, and Eagle

1. Disconnect the negative battery cable and drain 2 qts. of coolant.

2. Disconnect heater hoses and plug hoses and core fittings.

3. Disconnect blower wires and remove motor and fan assembly.

4. Remove the housing attaching nut from the stud in the engine compartment.

5. Remove package shelf, if so equipped.

6. Disconnect wire at resistor, located below glove box.

7. Remove instrument panel center bezel, air outlet and duct, on A/C models.

8. Disconnect air and defroster cables from damper levers.

9. Remove right-side windshield pillar molding, the instrument panel upper sheet metal screws and the capscrew at the right door post.

10. Remove the right cowl trim panel and door sill plate.

11. Remove right kick panel and heater housing attaching screws.

12. Pull right side of instrument panel outward slightly and remove housing.

13. Remove core, defroster and blower housing.

14. Remove core from housing.
Installation is in the reverse order of removal.

Pacer

1. Disconnect the negative battery cable. Drain about 2 quarts of coolant from the radiator.

2. Disconnect the heater hoses from the heater core tubes and install plugs in the heater hoses and core tubes.

3. Remove the vacuum hoses from the heater core housing cover clip and move the lines aside. With A/C, disconnect the outside air door vacuum hose from the vacuum motor.

4. Remove the heater core housing cover screws and disconnect the air blend door cable.

5. Disconnect the overcenter spring from the cover and remove the cover.

6. Remove the heater core-to-housing attaching screws and remove the heater core.

7. Install the heater core in the reverse order of removal.

Heater Blower

REMOVAL & INSTALLATION

Gremlin, Concord, Spirit and Eagle

1. Drain about 2 quarts of coolant from the radiator.

2. Disconnect the heater hoses from the heater core tubes and plug the core tubes.

3. Disconnect blower wires.

4. Remove retaining nut from cover and remove motor and fan assembly.

5. To install, reverse removal procedure.

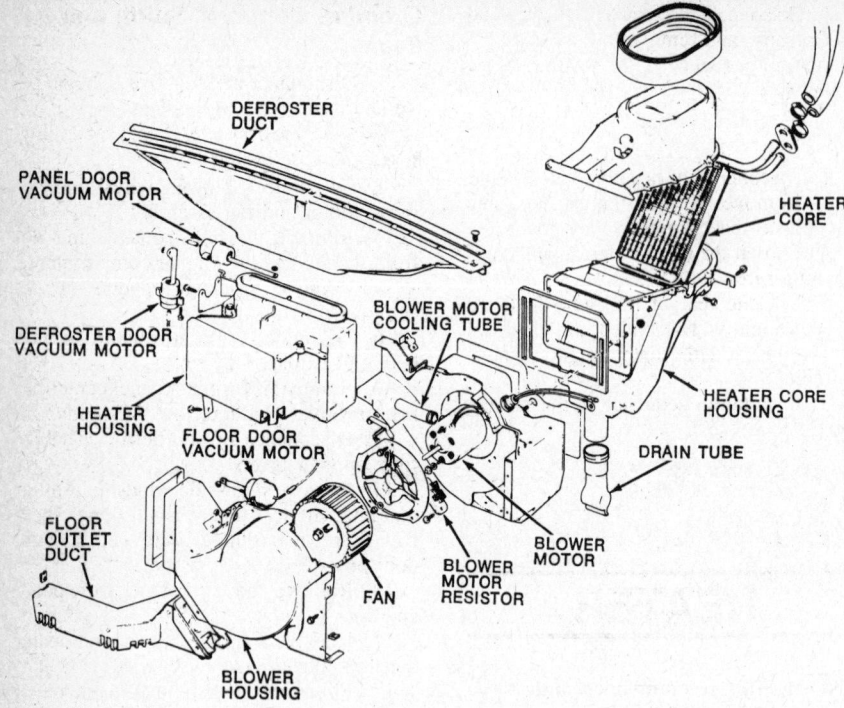

Pacer heater assembly (without air conditioning) (© American Motors Corp.)

Matador

1. Working from the engine compartment side of the firewall, disconnect the blower motor leads. Remove the motor cooling hose, if so equipped.
2. Remove the screws which secure the blower motor mounting plate on the blower motor housing.
3. Remove the motor, mounting plate, and fan as an assembly.
Installation is in the reverse order of removal.

Pacer Without A/C

1. Disconnect the negative battery cable.
2. Remove the right side windshield finish moulding.
3. Remove the instrument panel crash pad.
4. Remove the right scuff plate and cowl trim panel.
5. Remove the lower instrument panel-to-right A-pillar attaching screws.
6. Pull the instrument panel to the rear and replace the lower attaching screw in the right A-pillar. Allow the instrument panel to rest on the screw.
7. Remove the heater core housing attaching nuts and screw.
8. Remove the vacuum hoses from the heater core housing clip and set the lines aside.

9. Disconnect the blend-air door cable from the heater core housing.
10. Pull the heater core housing forward and set atop the upper control arm.
11. Remove the blower motor ground wire. Remove the blower motor housing attaching screw.
12. Disconnect the wires at the blower motor resistor.
13. Remove the blower motor housing brace.
14. Loosen the heater housing-to-dash panel attaching nuts.
15. Pull the blower housing to the rear and downward.
16. Disconnect the vacuum hoses from the vacuum motors.
17. Remove the blower housing.
18. Remove the blower housing cover.
19. Disconnect the white blower wire inside the housing.
20. Remove the blower motor mounting plate-to-housing screws and remove the blower motor assembly.
21. Remove the blower fan from the motor shaft and remove the mounting plate from the motor housing.
22. Install the blower motor in the reverse order of removal.

Pacer With A/C

1. Disconnect the negative battery cable.

2. Remove the right scuff plate and cowl trim panel.
3. Remove the radio overlay cover.
4. Remove the instrument panel crash pad.
5. Remove the instrument panel-to-right A-pillar attaching screws.
6. Remove the two upper instrument panel-to-lower instrument panel attaching screws above the glove box.
7. Disconnect the blend-air door cable from the heater core housing.
8. Remove the housing brace-to-floor-pan screw.
9. Disconnect the wire at the blower motor resistor.
10. Disconnect the vacuum hoses from the vacuum motors.
11. Remove the heater core housing attaching nuts and screw.
12. Remove the vacuum hoses from the housing clip and set the lines aside.
13. Pull the heater core housing forward and set it atop the upper control arm.
14. Remove the floor outlet duct.
15. Disconnect the wires from the blower motor relay.
16. Remove the blower housing attaching screw located in the engine compartment on the firewall.
17. Loosen the evaporator housing-to-firewall panel attaching nuts.
18. Remove the blower housing to firewall attaching screw.
19. Pull the blower housing to the rear and downward.
20. Pull the right side of the instrument panel to the rear and remove the blower housing from under the panel.
21. Remove the floor door vacuum motor attaching screws and motor to gain access to the blower housing cover attaching screws.
22. Remove the blower housing cover attaching screws and remove the cover.
23. Remove the blower motor mounting plate and remove the blower motor assembly.
24. Remove the blower fan from the motor shaft and the mounting plate from the body of the motor.
25. Install the motor in the reverse order of removal.

FUSE BOX LOCATION

- Pacer: On the left of the glove box
- 1978 Gremlin: Next to the parking brake mechanism
- 1978 Except Pacer and Gremlin: In the glove box
- 1979–85 All models: Next to the parking brake mechanism

Chrysler Corp.
Rear Wheel Drive

Chrysler: Cordoba, Fifth Avenue
Imperial, LeBaron, Newport, New Yorker
Dodge: Aspen, Charger, Magnum XE,
Mirada, Monaco, Royal Monaco, St. Regis
Plymouth: Caravelle,
Fury, Gran Fury, Volare

YEAR IDENTIFICATION

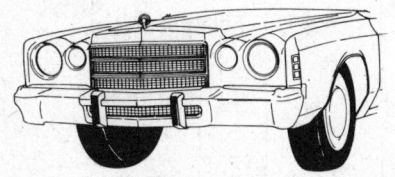

1978 Charger

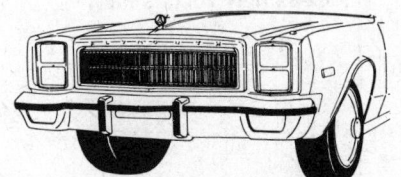

1978 Plymouth Gran Fury

1980 Gran Fury

1981 Gran Fury

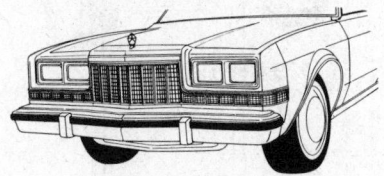

1982–85 Gran Fury

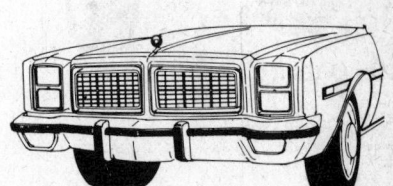

1978 Royal Monaco

1979 St. Regis

1980 St. Regis

1981 St. Regis

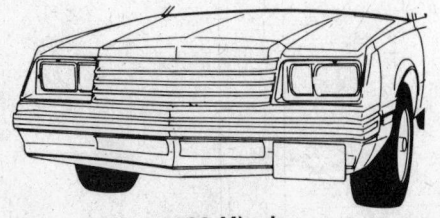

1980 Mirada

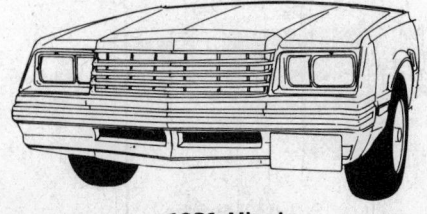

1981 Mirada

1981-83 Mirada

C57

YEAR IDENTIFICATION

1978 New Yorker

1979 New Yorker

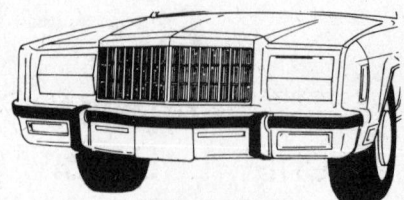

1980 New Yorker

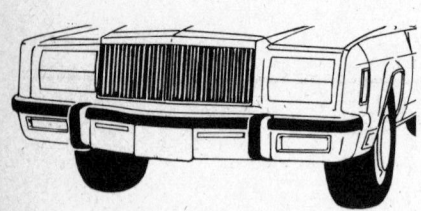

1981 New Yorker

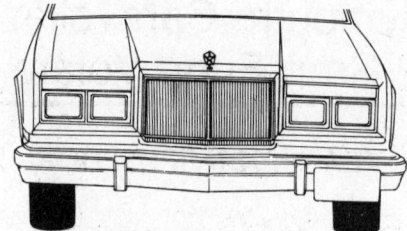

1982-83 New Yorker, 5th Ave.

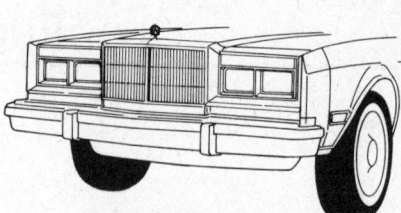

1984–85 Fifth Avenue

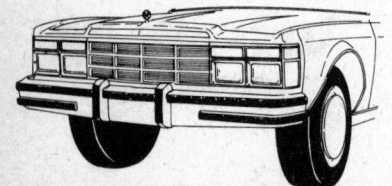

1978 Chrysler Le Baron

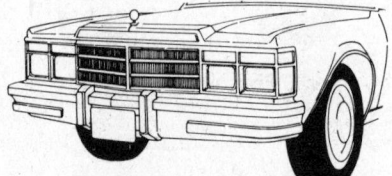

1979 Chrysler LeBaron

1980 LeBaron

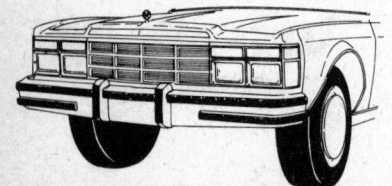

1981 LeBaron

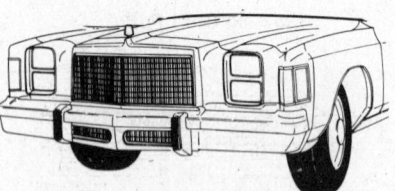

1978 Cordoba

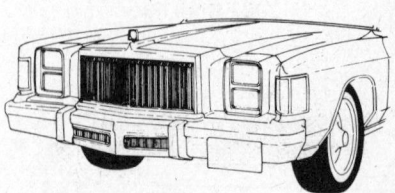

1979 Cordoba

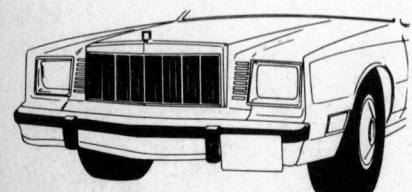

1980 Cordoba

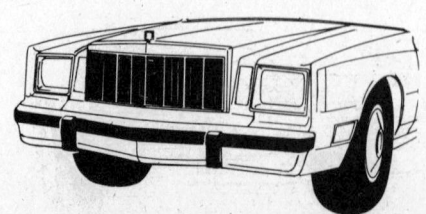

1981-83 Cordoba

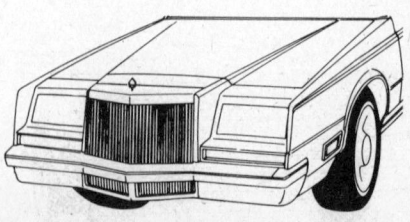

1981-83 Imperial

YEAR IDENTIFICATION

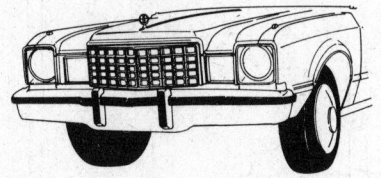

1978 Volare

1979 Volare

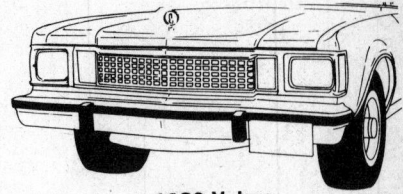

1980 Volare

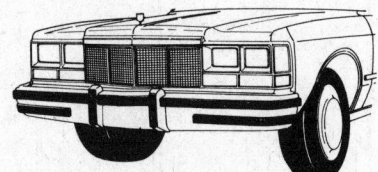

1978 Dodge Diplomat

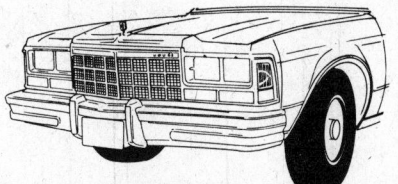

1979 Dodge Diplomat

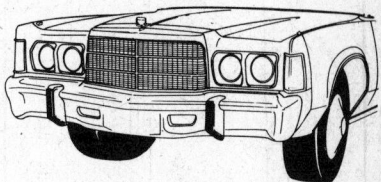

1978 Newport

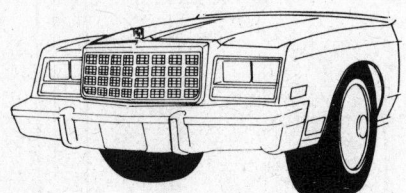

1979 Newport

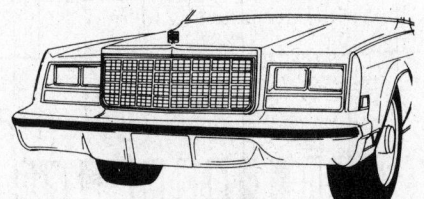

1980 Newport

1981 Newport

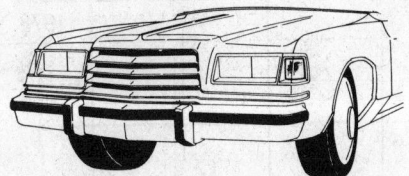

1978 Magnum XE

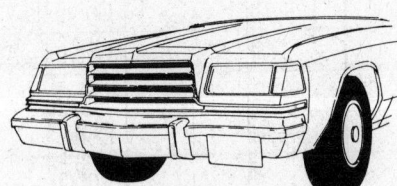

1979 Magnum XE

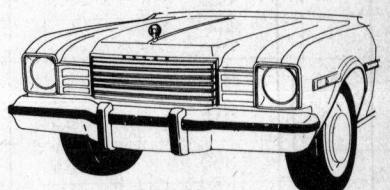

1978 Aspen

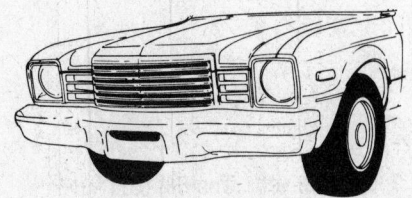

1979 Aspen

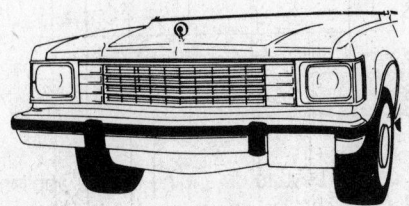

1980 Aspen

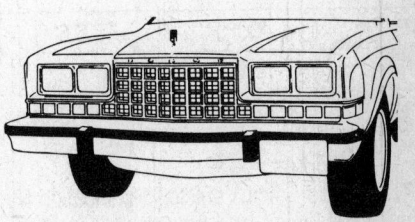

1980 Diplomat

YEAR IDENTIFICATION

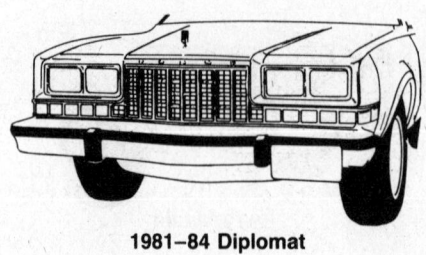

1981–84 Diplomat

VEHICLE IDENTIFICATION NUMBER (VIN)

It is important for servicing and ordering parts to be certain of the vehicle and engine identification. The VIN (vehicle identification number) is a 13 or 17 digit number visible through the windshield on the driver's side of the dash and contains the vehicle and engine identification codes. It can be interpreted as follows:

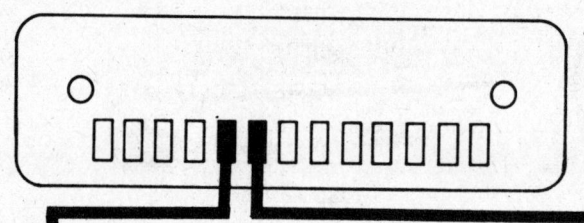

		Engine Code					Model Year Code	
Code	Cu. In.	Liters	Cyl.	Carb.(Bbl.)	Eng.Mfg.		Code	Year
C	225	3.7	6	1	Chrys.		8	1978
D	225	3.7	6	2	Chrys.		9	1979
G	318	5.2	8	2	Chrys.		A	1980
H	318	5.2	8	4	Chrys.			
K	360	5.9	8	2	Chrys.			
L	360HP①	5.9	8	4	Chrys.			
J	360	5.9	8	4	Chrys.			
N	400	6.6	8	4	Chrys.			
P	400HP①	6.6	8	4	Chrys.			
T	440	7.2	8	4	Chrys.			
U	440HP①	7.2	8	4	Chrys.			

The thirteen digit Vehicle Identification Number can be used to determine engine application and model year. The 6th digit indicates the model year, and the 5th digit identifies the factory installed engine.
① High Performance

VEHICLE IDENTIFICATION NUMBER (VIN)

It is important for servicing and ordering parts to be certain of the vehicle and engine identification. The VIN (vehicle identification number) is a 13 or 17 digit number visible through the windshield on the driver's side of the dash and contains the vehicle and engine identification codes. It can be interpreted as follows:

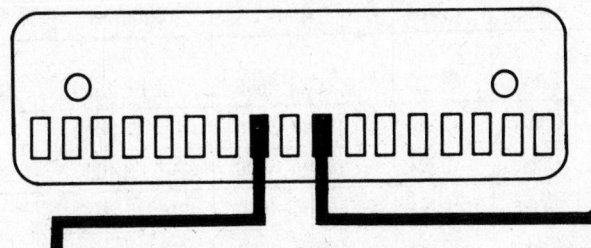

Engine Code							Model Year Code	
Code	Cu. In.	Liters	Cyl.	Carb.(Bbl.)	Eng.Mfg.		Code	Year
E	225	3.7	6	1	Chrys.		B	1981
H	225	3.7	6	1	Chrys.		C	1982
F	225	3.7	6	1 H.D.	Chrys.		D	1983
J	225	3.7	6	1 H.D.	Chrys.		E	1984
G	225	3.7	6	2①	Chrys.		F	1985
K	225	3.7	6	2①	Chrys.			
H	225	3.7	6	2 H.D.①	Chrys.			
L	225	3.7	6	2 H.D.①	Chrys.			
K	318	5.2	8	2	Chrys.			
P	318	5.2	8	2	Chrys.			
L	318	5.2	8	2 H.D.	Chrys.			
J	318	5.2	8	EFI	Chrys.			
N	318	5.2	8	EFI	Chrys.			
R	318	5.2	8	4	Chrys.			
M	318	5.2	8	4	Chrys.			
N	318	5.2	8	4 H.D.	Chrys.			
S	318	5.2	8	4 H.D.	Chrys.			

H.D. = Heavy Duty
EFI = Electronic Fuel Injection
① = Canada Only
The seventeen digit Vehicle Identification Number can be used to determine engine application and model year. The seventeen digit code supercedes the thirteen digit code which ended in 1980. The 10th digit indicates the model year, and the 8th digit identifies the factory installed engine.
EFI Electronic Fuel Injection

GENERAL ENGINE SPECIFICATIONS

Year	Eng. V.I.N. Code	Engine No. Cyl. Displacement (Cu. In.)	Eng. Mfg.	Carburetor Type	Horsepower @ rpm■	Torque @ rpm (ft lbs)■	Bore x Stroke (in.)	Compression Ratio	Oil Pressure @ 2000 rpm
'78	C	6-225	Chrys.	1 bbl	90 @ 3600	160 @ 1600	3.406 × 4.125	8.4:1	55
	D	6-225	Chrys.	2 bbl	110 @ 3600	180 @ 2000	3.406 × 4.125	8.4:1	55
	G	8-318	Chrys.	2 bbl	140 @ 4000	245 @ 1600	3.910 × 3.310	8.5:1	55
	H	8-318 Calif.	Chrys.	4 bbl	155 @ 4000	245 @ 1600	3.910 × 3.310	8.5:1	55
	K	8-360	Chrys.	2 bbl	155 @ 3600	270 @ 2400	4.000 × 3.580	8.4:1	55
	L	8-360 HP	Chrys.	4 bbl	170 @ 4000	270 @ 1600	4.000 × 3.580	8.4:1	55
	J	8-360	Chrys.	4 bbl	160 @ 3600	265 @ 1600	4.000 × 3.580	8.0:1	55
	N	8-400③	Chrys.	4 bbl	190 @ 3600	305 @ 3200	4.340 × 3.380	8.2:1	30–80
	T	8-440③	Chrys.	4 bbl	195 @ 3600	320 @ 2000	4.320 × 3.750	8.2:1	30–80
	T,U	8-440②③	Chrys.	4 bbl	185 @ 3600	310 @ 2400	4.320 × 3.750	8.2:1	30–80
'79	C	6-225	Chrys.	1 bbl	90 @ 3600	160 @ 1600	3.406 × 4.125	8.4:1	55
	C	6-225 ESC Calif.	Chrys.	1 bbl	90 @ 3600	160 @ 1600	3.406 × 4.125	8.4:1	55
	D	6-225	Chrys.	2 bbl	110 @ 3600	180 @ 2000	3.406 × 4.125	8.4:1	55
	G	8-318 ESC	Chrys.	2 bbl	140 @ 4000	245 @ 1600	3.910 × 3.310	8.5:1	55
	H	8-318 ESC Calif.	Chrys.	4 bbl	155 @ 4000	245 @ 1600	3.910 × 3.310	8.5:1	55
	K	8-360 ESC	Chrys.	2 bbl	155 @ 3600	270 @ 2400	4.000 × 3.580	8.4:1	55
	J	8-360 ESC Calif.	Chrys.	4 bbl	160 @ 3600	265 @ 1600	4.000 × 3.580	8.4:1	55
	L	8-360 ESC HP	Chrys.	4 bbl	170 @ 4000	270 @ 1600	4.000 × 3.580	8.0:1	55
	J,L	8-360	Chrys.	EFM	160 @ 3600	265 @ 1600	4.000 × 3.580	8.4:1	30–80
'80	C	6-225	Chrys.	1 bbl	90 @ 3600	160 @ 1600	3.406 × 4.125	8.4:1	55
	G	8-318	Chrys.	2 bbl	120 @ 3600	245 @ 2000	3.910 × 3.310	8.5:1	55
	H	8-318②	Chrys.	4 bbl	155 @ 4000	240 @ 2000	3.910 × 3.310	8.5:1	55
	L	8-360 ESC	Chrys.	4 bbl	185 @ 4000	275 @ 2000	4.000 × 3.580	8.0:1	55
'81–'83	E	6-225	Chrys.	1 bbl	85 @ 3600	165 @ 1600	3.406 × 4.125	8.4:1	55
	E	6-225 Calif.	Chrys.	1 bbl	90 @ 3600	165 @ 1200	3.406 × 4.125	8.4:1	55
	K	8-318	Chrys.	2 bbl	130 @ 4000	235 @ 1600	3.910 × 3.310	8.6:1	55
	M	8-318 Calif.	Chrys.	4 bbl	165 @ 4000	240 @ 2000	3.910 × 3.310	8.5:1	55
	J	8-318	Chrys.	EFI	140 @ 4000	245 @ 2000	3.910 × 3.310	8.5:1	55
'84–'85	P	8-318	Chrys.	2 bbl	130 @ 4000	235 @ 1600	3.910 × 3.310	8.6:1	55
	R	8-318	Chrys.	4 bbl	165 @ 4000	240 @ 2000	3.910 × 3.310	8.5:1	55
	S	8-318 HD	Chrys.	4 bbl	165 @ 4000	240 @ 2000	3.910 × 3.310	8.5:1	55

■Horsepower and torque are SAE net figures. They are measured at the rear of the transmission with all accessories installed and operating. Since the figures vary when a given engine is installed in different models, some figures are representative rather than exact.

HP High Performance
HD Heavy Duty
ESC Electronic Spark Control
EFI Electronic Fuel Injection
EFM Electronic Fuel Metering
① Applies to Lean Burn 318 engines
② California and high altitude
③ Lean Burn

TUNE-UP SPECIFICATIONS

(When analyzing compression test results, look for uniformity among cylinders rather than specific pressures.)

Year	Eng. V.I.N. Code	No. Cyl. Displacement (cu.in.)	Carb. (bbl.)	Spark Plugs Orig. Type	Gap (in.)	Distributor Point Dwell (deg)	Point Gap (in.)	Ignition Timing (deg)▲ Man Trans●	Auto Trans	Valves Intake Opens ■(deg)	Fuel Pump Pressure (psi)	Idle Speed (rpm)▲ Man Trans●	Auto Trans
'78	C	6-225	1	RBL-16Y	.035	Electronic		12B(8B)	12B(8B)	16	3½–5	700(750)	700(750)
	D	6-225	2	RBL-16Y	.035	Electronic		12B(10B)	12B(10B)	16	3½–5	700(750)	700(750)
	G	8-318	2	RN-12Y	.035	Electronic		16B	16B	10	5¾–7¼	700(750)	700(750)
	H	8-318①	4	RN-12Y	.035	Electronic		—	10B	10	5¾–7¼	700(750)	700(750)
	K	8-360①	2	RN-12Y	.035	Electronic		—	20B	18	5¾–7¼	—	750
	L,J	8-360HP	4	RN-12Y	.035	Electronic		—	16B(6/8B)	18	5¾–7¼	—	750
	N	8-400①	4	OJ-13Y	.035	Electronic		—	20B	18	5–7	—	750
	T	8-440①	4	OJ-13Y	.035	Electronic		—	12B(8B)	18	5¾–7¼	—	750
	U	8-440①	4	OJ-11Y	.035	Electronic		—	16B(8B)	18	6–7½	—	750
'79	C	6-225	1	RBL-16Y	.035	Electronic		12B(8B)	12B (8B)	16	3½–5	700(750)	700(750)
	D	6-225	2	RBL-16Y	.035	Electronic		12B	12B	16	3½–5	700(750)	700(750)
	G	8-318	2	RN-12Y	.035	Electronic		—	16B	10	5–7	—	750
	H	8-318	4	RN-12Y	.035	Electronic		—	16B	10	5–7	750	750
	K	8-360	2	RN-12Y	.035	Electronic		—	16B	18	5–7	—	750
	L,J	8-360HP	4	RN-12Y	.035	Electronic		—	16B	18	5–7	750	750
'80	C	6-225	1	P-560 PR	.035	Electronic		12B	12B	16	3½–5	725	725(750)
	D	6-225	2	P-560 PR	.035	Electronic		—	12B	16	3½–5	725	725②
	G	8-318	2	P-65 PR	.035	Electronic		—	12B	10	5–7	—	700
	H	8-318	4	P-65 PR	.035	Electronic		—	10B②(16B)	10	5–7	—	750②(700)
	K	8-360	2	P-65 PR	.035	Electronic		—	16B	18	5–7	—	750
	L	8-360	4	P-65 PR	.035	Electronic		—	16B	18	5–7	—	750
'81	E	6-225	1	P-560 PR4Y	.048	Electronic		—	12B③	6	4.0–5.5	—	600
	J	8-318	EFI	P-68 ER	.048	Electronic		—	12B	10	15.2–19.4	—	580
	K	8-318	2	P-65 PR4Y	.048④	Electronic		—	16B	10	5.75–7.25	—	600
	M	8-318	4	P-65 PR4Y	.048	Electronic		—	16B	10	5.75–7.25	—	600
'82	E,F,G,H	6-225	1 & 2	560PR	.035	Electronic		—	⑤	6	4.0–5.5	—	750
	J	8-318	EFI	65PR	.048	Electronic		—	⑤	10	5.75–11.5	—	600
	K,L,M,N	8-318	2 & 4	RN-12YC	.035	Electronic		—	⑤	10	5.75–7.25	—	700
'83	H,J,K,L	6-225	1 & 2	RBL-16Y	.035	Electronic		—	⑤	6	4.0–5.5	—	750
	N,P,R,S	8-318	2 & 4	RN-12Y	.035	Electronic		—	⑤	10	5.75–7.25	—	700
'84–'85	P,R,S	8-318	2 & 4	RN-127	.035	Electronic		—	⑤	10	5.75–7.25	—	700

NOTE: The underhood specifications sticker often reflects tune-up specification changes made in production. Sticker figures must be used if they disagree with those in this chart.

Part numbers in this chart are not recommendations by Chilton for any product by brand name.

▲See text for procedure
■All figures Before Top Dead Center
●Figure in parentheses indicates California engine
HP High Performance
EFI Electronic Fuel Injection
B Before TDC
① Lean Burn

② Canada
③ California 16B
④ Late Production .035—See underhood sticker
⑤ See underhood sticker

FIRING ORDERS

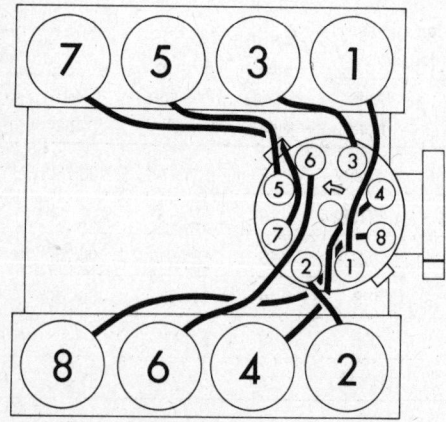

Chrysler Corp.: 400, 440 V8 Engine firing
order:1-8-4-3-6-5-7-2 Distributor rotation:
counterclockwise

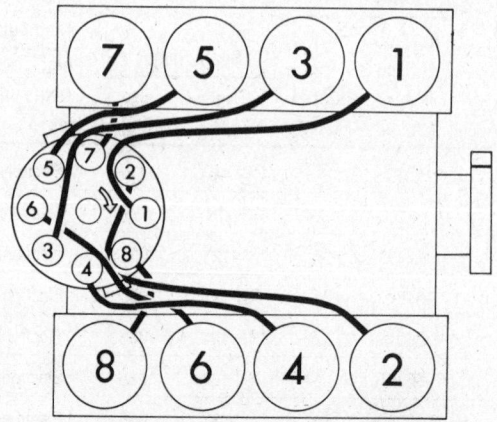

CHRYSLER CORP. 318, 360 V8 Engine firing order: 1-8-4-3-6-5-7-2
Distributor rotation: clockwise

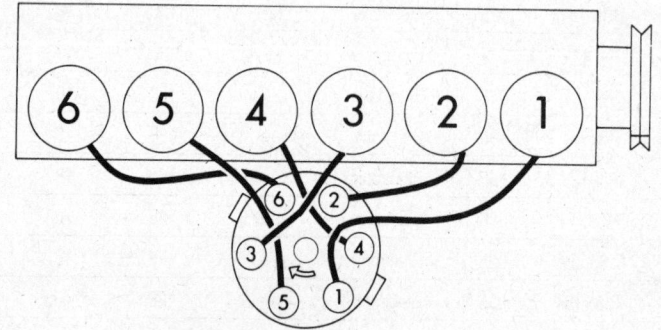

CHRYSLER CORP. 6-cyl.
Engine firing order: 1-5-3-6-2-4
Distributor rotation: clockwise

MECHANICAL VALVE
LIFTER CLEARANCE

Year	Engine	Intake (Hot) In.	Exhaust (Hot) In.
'78–'80	Six cylinder	.010	.020

NOTE: 1981 and later slant six engines are
equipped with hydraulic valve tappets, which
eliminate the need for periodic valve lash
adjustment.

CAPACITIES

Year	Engine No. Cyl. Displacement (Cu. In.)	Engine Crankcase Add 1 Qt For New Filter	Transmission Pts to Refill After Draining			Drive Axle (pts)	Gasoline Tank (gals)	Cooling System (qts)	
			Manual		Automatic			With Heater	With A/C
			3-Speed	4-Speed					
'78	6-225	4	4.75	7.0④	17⑪	2.1⑥	18⑤⑩	12	14
	8-318	4	4.75	7.0④	17⑪	2.1⑥	20⑩	16	17.5
	8-360	4	—	—	17⑪	4.5	20⑩	16	17.5
	8-400	4	—	—	16.5⑪	4.5	25.5⑤	16.5	16.5
	8-400HP	4	—	—	19.0⑪	4.5	20.5	16.5	16.5
	8-440	4	—	—	16.5⑪	4.5	26.5⑬	16.0	16.5
'79	6-225	4	4.75	7.0④	17⑧⑭	③	18⑩⑫	11.5	12.5
	8-318	4	—	—	17⑧⑭	③	19.5	15①	16.5
	8-360	4	—	—	17⑧⑭	③	19.5	15	15
'80–'85	6-225	4	4.75	7.0④	17⑧⑭	③	18⑫	11.5	14.5②
	8-318	4	—	—	17⑧⑭	③	18.0⑮	15.0⑦	16.5⑨
	8-360	4	—	—	17⑧⑭	③	18.0⑮	16.0	16.0

① Calif.—16.5
② 15 qts on Cordoba, Mirada
③ 7¼" axle—2.1 pts., 8¼" axle—4.4 pts., 9¼" axle—4.5 pts.
④ Aspen/Volare
⑤ 20 gal. on wagon
⑥ 4.4 pts for station wagon or High Altitude models.
⑦ 15.5 qts. on Imperial
⑧ A904 trans.; 15.9 pts.—A727 trans.
⑨ 17.5 on Imperial and heavy duty coding systems
⑩ 19.5 gal. on Diplomat, LeBaron; 25.5 gal. on Fury, Monaco, Royal Monaco, Charger, Gran Fury; 26.5 gal on Cordoba, Newport, New Yorker
⑪ 7.3–7.8 pts. if converter isn't drained.
⑫ 19.5 on Aspen/Volare wagon; 21 gal. on 1979 and later Cordoba, Mirada, Gran Fury, St. Regis and Magnum
⑬ 24 gal. on wagons; 25.5 gal. Cordoba
⑭ 16.3 pts. on Aspen/Volare with A904 trans.; 15.9 pts. on A727 trans.
⑮ 21 gal. on '78–'79 Cordoba/Newport and '78–'81 New Yorker, Dodge/Plymouth full size. 19.5 gal. on 1980 Dodge/Plymouth midsize.

VALVE SPECIFICATIONS

Year	Engine No. Cyl. Displacement (cu in.)	Seat Angle (deg)	Face Angle (deg)	Spring Test Pressure (lbs @ in.)	Spring Installed Height (in.)	Stem to Guide Clearance (in.) Intake	Stem to Guide Clearance (in.) Exhaust	Stem Diameter (in.) Intake	Stem Diameter (in.) Exhaust
'78	6-225	45	①	143 @ 1.31	1²¹⁄₃₂	.0010–.0030	.0020–.0040	.3725	.3715
	8-318	45	①	177 @ 1.31	1²¹⁄₃₂	.0010–.0030	.0020–.0040	.3725	.3715
	8-360	45	①	177 @ 1.31	1²¹⁄₃₂	.0010–.0030	.0020–.0040	.3725	.3715
	8-360HP	45	①	193 @ 1.25	1²¹⁄₃₂	.0015–.0035	.0025–.0045	.3720	.3710
	8-400	45	45	200 @ 1.44	1⁵³⁄₆₄	.0011–.0028	⑦	.3726	⑧
	8-440	45	45①	200 @ 1.44	1⁵³⁄₆₄	.0011–.0028	⑦	.3726	⑧
'79–85	6-225	45	①	143 @ 1.31	1²¹⁄₃₂	.0010–.0030	.0020–.0040	.3725	.3715
	8-318	45	45	177 @ 1.31②	1¹¹⁄₁₆⑨	.0010–.0030③	.0020–.0040④	.3725⑤	.3715⑥
	8-360	45	45	177 @ 1.31	1²¹⁄₃₂	.0010–.0030	.0020–.0040	.3725	.3715
	8-360HP	45	45	193 @ 1.25	1²¹⁄₃₂	.0015–.0035	.0025–.0045	.3720	.3710

HP High Performance
① Intake 45°, Exhaust 43°
② 318 EFM—193@1.25
③ 318 EFM—.0015–.0035
④ 318 EFM—.0025–.0045
⑤ 318 EFM—.3720
⑥ 318 EFM—.3710
⑦ Hot end—.0027–.0037; cold end—.0010–.0027
⑧ Hot end—.3712; cold end—.3722
⑨ 318 HP—1²¹⁄₃₂

CRANKSHAFT AND CONNECTING ROD SPECIFICATIONS

(All measurements are given in inches)

Year	Engine No. Cyl. Displacement (cu in.)	Crankshaft Main Brg. Journal Dia	Crankshaft Main Brg. Oil Clearance	Crankshaft Shaft End-Play	Crankshaft Thrust on No.	Connecting Rod Journal Diameter	Connecting Rod Oil Clearance	Connecting Rod Side* Clearance
'78–'80	6-225	2.7495–2.7505	.0005–.0020	.002–.009	3	2.1865–2.1875	.0005–.0025	.006–.025
'81–'85	6-225	2.7495–2.7505	.0010–.0025	.0035–.0095	3	2.1865–2.1875	.0010–.0025	.007–.013
'78–'85	8-318	2.4995–2.5005	.0005–.0020①	.002–.010	3	2.1240–2.1250	.0005–.0025	.006–.014
'78–'81	8-360	2.8095–2.8105	.0005–.0020①	.002–.009	3	2.1240–2.1250	.0005–.0025	.006–.014
'78	8-400	2.6245–2.6255	.0005–.0020	.002–.009	3	2.3750–2.3760	.0005–.0025	.009–.017
'78	8-440	2.7495–2.7505	.0005–.0020	.002–.009	3	2.3750–2.3760	.0005–.0025	.009–.017

*Total for two rods on V8s
① 1980 and later: #1—.0005–.0015; #2, #3, #4, #5—.0005–.0020

PISTON AND RING SPECIFICATIONS

(All measurements given in inches)

Year	Engine No. Cyl. Displacement (cu. in.)	Ring Gap Top Compression	Ring Gap Bottom Compression	Ring Gap Oil Control	Ring Side Clearance Top Compression	Ring Side Clearance Bottom Compression	Ring Side Clearance Oil Control	Piston Clearance③ Piston-to-Bore Clearance
'78–'85	6-225, 8-318, 8-360	.010–.020	.010–.020	.015–.055	.0015–.0030①	.0015–.0030①	.0002–.0050	0.0005–0.0015②
'78	8-400, 8-440	.013–.023	.013–.023	.015–.055	.0015–.0030	.0015–.0030	.0002–.005	.0003–.0013

① .0015–.0040 in. on 1979–84 318, 360 V8s
② .0010–.0020 in. on 1978–81 360 V8 w/4 bbl
③ At top of skirt

TORQUE SPECIFICATIONS

(All readings in ft lbs)

Year	Engine No. Cyl. Displacement (cu. in.)	Cylinder Head Bolts	Rod Bearing Bolts	Main Bearing Bolts	Crankshaft Damper Bolt	Flywheel to Crankshaft Bolts	Manifold Intake	Manifold Exhaust
'78–'84	6-225	70	45	85	Press fit	55	①	10
'78–'84	8-318, 360	95③④	45	85	100	55	45⑤	15/20②
'78	8-400, 440	70	45	85	135	55	45	30

① Intake to exhaust manifold bolts—17 ft. lbs., studs—20 ft. lbs.
② Nuts/screws
③ 95—1977
④ For '78–'83 318 engines, see step #15 under "Cylinder Head Removal, V8" in text
⑤ 40—1980–'83

WHEEL ALIGNMENT SPECIFICATIONS

Year	Model	Caster Range (deg)	Caster Pref Setting (deg)	Camber Range (deg)	Camber Pref Setting (deg)	Toe-in (in.)	Steering Axis Inclin. (deg.)	Wheel Pivot Ratio Inner Wheel	Wheel Pivot Ratio Outer Wheel
'78–'79	Aspen, Volare Diplomat, LeBaron	1½P to 3¾P	2½P	②	①	1/16 to ¼	8	20	18
'78	M.S.—Monaco, Fury, Charger,	1¾N to ¾P	¼N	④	④	1/16 to ¼	8.0	20.0	18.0
	Magnum P.S.—Monaco, Fury, Charger,	½N to 2P	¾P	④	④	1/16 to ¼	8.0	20.0	18.0
	Magnum P.S.—Gran Fury, Royal Monaco	½N to 2P	¾P	④	④	1/16 to ¼	9.0	20.0	18.3
'79	St. Regis Magnum XE	½N to 2P	¾P	④	④	1/16 to ¼	8.0	20.0	18.0
'78–'79	Cordoba	½N to 2P	¾P	④	½P③	1/16 to ¼	8	20	19.0
'78	Chrysler	½N to 2P	¾P	④	½P③	1/16 to ¼	9	20	18.3
'79	Chrysler	½N to 2P	¾P	④	½P③	1/16 to ¼	8	20	18.3
'80–'81	Chrysler	¼N to 2¼P	1P	¼N–1¼P	½P	⅛ ± 1/16	8	20	18.0
'80–'85	Aspen, Volare, Diplomat, Gran Fury, Newport, 5th Avenue	1¼P to 3¾P	2½P ± 1	¼N–1¼P	½P ± ½	⅛ ± 1/16	8	20	18

N Negative
P Positive
M.S. Manual Steering
P.S. Power Steering
① Left wheel—½P; Right wheel—¼P
② Left wheel—0 to 1P; Right wheel—¼N to ¾P
③ ¼P on right side
④ Left side—0 to 1P; ½P preferred
  Right side—¼N to +¾P; ¼P preferred

FRONT END HEIGHT

Year	Model	Front End Height (± ⅛ in.)

FRONT END HEIGHT

Year	Model	Front End Height (± ⅛ in.)
'78–'79	Aspen, Volare, Diplomat, LeBaron	10¼
	Monaco, Fury, Charger, Magnum, St. Regis	10¾
	Wagon	11¼
	Gran Fury, Royal Monaco	10⅛
	Chrysler, Imperial, Cordoba①	10⅛
'80–'81	Chrysler, St. Regis, Gran Fury	16¾ ② ③
'80–'85	Aspen, Volare, 5th Avenue	12½ ② ③

① '79 models 10¾
② ± ¼ in.
③ Measured from the head of the suspension crossmember front isolator bolt to ground

CHARGING SYSTEM

For further information on the charging system, please refer to "Charging and Starting in the Unit Repair" section.

Alternator

REMOVAL & INSTALLATION

1. Disconnect battery ground cable.
2. Disconnect BAT and FLD leads from alternator. Disconnect the ground wire.
3. Remove alternator by removing two mounting bolts and belt tensioner bracket bolt.
4. To reinstall, reverse above. Tighten the belt so it can be depressed about ½ in. by moderate thumb pressure in the center of the longest span between pulleys. Some alternator brackets have a square hole into which you can insert a ½ in. square socket drive to tension the belt.

NOTE: Never attempt to polarize an alternator, or short the regulator.

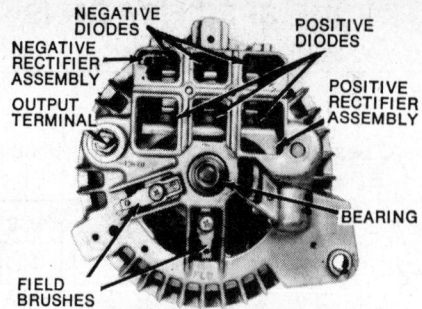

Rear view of the alternator
(© Chrysler Corp)

Regulator

REMOVAL & INSTALLATION

All models have a solid-state (silicon transistor) voltage regulator which is not adjustable. The regulator is in the engine compartment and clearly labeled.

1. Release the spring clips and pull off the regulator wiring plug.
2. Unbolt and remove the regulator.
3. Installation is in the reverse order of removal. Be sure that the spring clips engage the wiring plug and that the unit has a good ground.

STARTING SYSTEM

All models are equipped with a reduction-gear starter, with a 3.5:1 or 2:1 reduction gear set. Both types have solenoids which are mounted on the starter assembly.

For further information on the starting system, please refer to "Charging and Starting" in the Unit Repair section.

Starter

REMOVAL & INSTALLATION

1. Disconnect the ground cable at the battery.
2. Remove the cable from the starter.
3. Disconnect the solenoid leads at their solenoid terminals.
4. Remove the starter securing nut and bolt and remove the starter from the engine flywheel housing. On some models with automatic transmissions, the oil cooler tube bracket will interfere with starter removal. In this case, remove the starter securing nut and bolt, slide the cooler tube bracket off the stud, and then remove the starter.
5. Installation is in the reverse order of the preceding. Be sure that the starter and flywheel housing mating surfaces are free of dirt and oil. Position the starter to flywheel housing seal. When tightening the bolt and nut, hold the starter away from the engine to ensure proper alignment.

IGNITION SYSTEM

Electronic ignition is standard on all models. The only regular ignition system maintenance required is inspection of the wiring and replacement of spark plugs (check timing on occasion only).

For further details on the Chrysler ignition system, please refer to "Electronic Ignition Systems" in the Unit Repair section.

NOTE: Dwell/tachometer hookup with electronic ignition is the same as with conventional point-type systems. One tachometer lead connects to the negative primary coil terminal and the other to ground. Some meters will not work at all with this system.

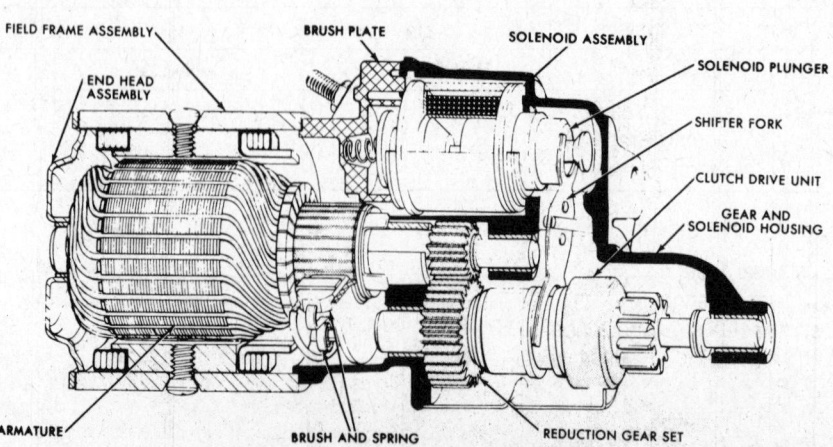

Starter motor details (© Chrysler Corp.)

Distributor

REMOVAL

1. Disconnect the vacuum advance line at the distributor.

2. Disconnect the lead wire at the harness connector.

3. Unfasten the distributor cap retaining clips and lift off the cap.

4. On six cylinder models, rotate the engine until the distributor rotor is pointing toward the cylinder block. Matchmark the distributor body and the engine block to indicate the position of the body in the block. Scribe a mark on the edge of the distributor housing to indicate the position of the rotor on the distributor. These marks can be used as guides when installing the distributor in a correctly timed engine.

5. Remove the distributor hold-down clamp screw and clamp.

6. Carefully lift the distributor out of the block. On six cylinder models, the shaft will rotate slightly as the distributor is removed.

INSTALLATION

If the crankshaft has not been rotated while the distributor was removed from the engine, installation is in the reverse order of the removal procedure. (See Step 2 or 3 of the procedure below.) Use the reference marks that were made before removal to correctly position the distributor in the block. Before connecting the vacuum advance line adjust the ignition timing.

If the crankshaft has been rotated or otherwise disturbed (as during engine rebuilding) after the distributor was removed, proceed as follows to install the distributor.

1. Bring the No. 1 piston to top dead center (TDC) by removing the No. 1 spark plug and inserting a finger into the hole, while rotating the crankshaft. Compression pressure can be felt as the No. 1 piston approaches TDC. The TDC timing mark (O) on the crankshaft vibration damper should now be opposite the indicator on the timing chain case. Make sure that you don't have No. 6 piston at TDC.

2. On six cylinder engines, note the position of the distributor cap (which should be connected to the engine by the spark plug cables). Hold the distributor so that the rotor will be in position just ahead of the distributor cap terminal for the No. 1 spark plug when the distributor is installed. Now lower the distributor into its engine block opening, and mesh the distributor gear with the camshaft drive gear. Be sure that the rubber O-ring seal is in the groove in the distributor shank. When the distributor is properly seated, the rotor should be under the No. 1 distributor cap terminal. Proceed with Step 4.

3. For eight cylinder engines: Clean the top of the engine block around the distributor opening, to ensure a good seal between the distributor base and the block. Note the position of the distributor cap (which should be connected to the engine by the spark plug cables). Hold the distributor so that the rotor will be in position directly under the distributor cap terminal for the No. 1 spark plug when the distributor is installed (rotor pointing to the No. 1 cylinder firing position). Now lower the distributor into its engine block opening, engaging the tongue of the distributor shaft with the slot in the distributor and oil pump drive gear. Proceed with Step 4.

4. Install the distributor hold-down clamp and tighten its retaining screw finger-tight.

5. Install the distributor cap. Connect the primary wire to the coil, or the lead wire to the harness.

6. Check and adjust the ignition timing.

7. Connect the vacuum advance line to the distributor.

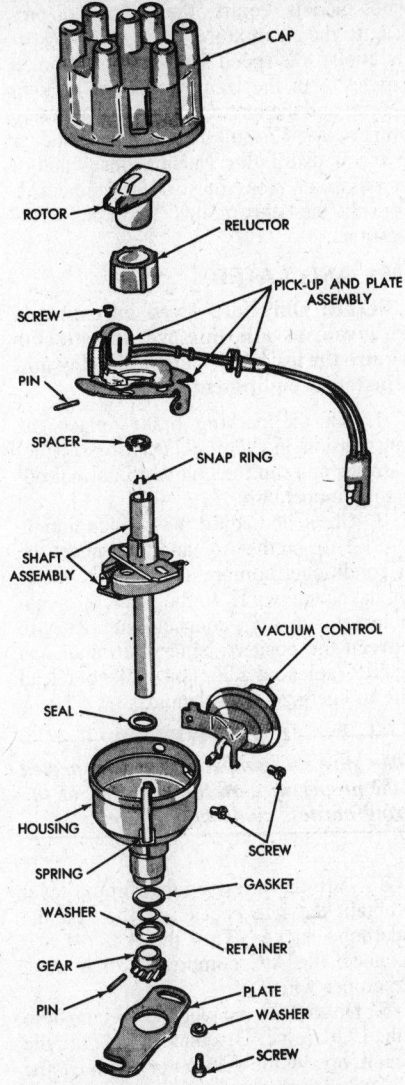

Six cylinder single pick-up distributor exploded view. Dual pick-up has twin pick-ups on plate assembly

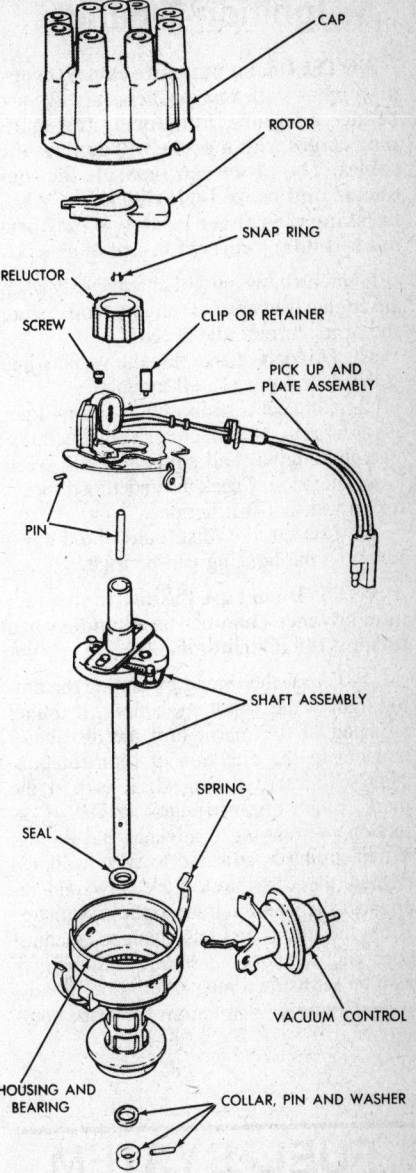

Exploded view of the V8 electronic ignition distributor. (© Chrysler Corp.)

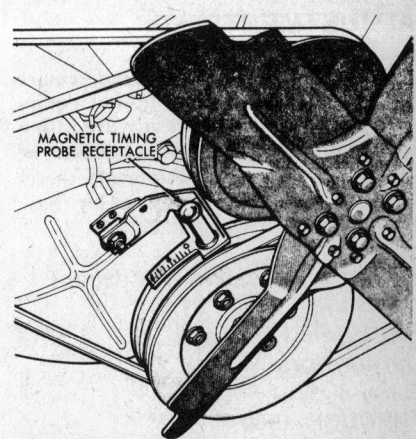

Magnetic timing probe provision, six cylinder. V8 similar (© Chrysler Corp.)

Ignition Timing

NOTE: Do not puncture cables, boots, or nipples with test probes—always use proper adaptors. Puncturing the spark plug cables with a probe will damage the cables. The probe can separate the conductor and cause high resistance. Also, breaking the rubber insulation may permit secondary current to arc to ground.

Ignition timing must be checked only when the engine is at normal running temperature and at its correct idle speed.

1. Disconnect and plug the vacuum line at the distributor (on all models).

2. Connect a stroboscopic timing light according to manufacturer's instructions, start the engine, and adjust the idle speed to specification. Check the underhood sticker for any further instructions.

3. Loosen the distributor hold-down screw so the housing can be rotated.

NOTE: Do not use the distributor vacuum advance chamber as a handle when turning the distributor.

4. Check the timing by aiming the timing light at the vibration damper. If timing is ahead of the mark, turn the distributor housing in the direction of rotor-rotation. This will retard timing. If it is past the mark, rotate the distributor against its direction of rotation to advance the timing. When timing is adjusted to specifications, tighten the distributor lockscrew and reconnect the vacuum hose to the distributor. If engine idle speed has changed, readjust curb idle. *Do not reset timing.* Timing may also be set using a magnetic probe. Follow manufacturers' instructions for probe hookup.

FUEL SYSTEM

Idle Speed and Mixture

ADJUSTMENTS

NOTE: These procedures all require the use of sophisticated testing equipment to ensure that the results are within legal limits. These adjustments cannot be made without such equipment; therefore, the procedures are given for those with access to the equipment.

All Carbureted Engines except the Holley Model 6145, Electronic Feedback Carburetors

THROUGH 1980

The factory recommended procedure for idle mixture adjustment on 1978 and later 49 states models requires the addition of propane to the air mixture, in addition to special tools. Idle speed can be adjusted on all engines with the transmission in Park or Neutral and the engine at normal operating temperature. Consult the underhood sticker to see if distributor vacuum hoses and/or air pump air tubes must be disconnected. Consult the illustrations for idle screw locations.

1981 AND LATER

NOTE: Only idle speed adjustments are given, as idle mixture adjustments require the use of special monitoring and adjustment equipment.

1. Set the parking brake, place the transmission in Neutral. Turn off all accessories and run the engine to normal operating temperature.

2. Check and adjust the ignition timing.

3. Turn on the A/C and disconnect the air conditioner compressor by disconnecting its clutch wire. If the vehicle is not equipped with A/C, connect a jumper wire between the positive battery terminal and the SIS (solenoid idle stop) solenoid lead wire to energize the solenoid.

—— CAUTION ——

Make sure the jumper wire is connected to the proper wire on the solenoid, or the wiring harness could be damaged.

4. Turn the screw on the throttle lever to obtain the idle speed specified on the underhood sticker. Turn the A/C off and reconnect the A/C compressor or remove the jumper wire.

5. Disconnect and plug the vacuum hose to the EGR valve. Disconnect and plug the vacuum hose at the distributor. Remove the PCV valve from the valve cover and allow the valve to draw underhood air. Disconnect and plug the $\frac{3}{16}$ in. diameter control hose at the evaporative canister.

6. Allow the engine to run for two minutes, then read the rpm. If the rpm is not the same as the curb idle rpm specified on the label, turn the idle speed screw on the solenoid until the specified curb idle speed is reached.

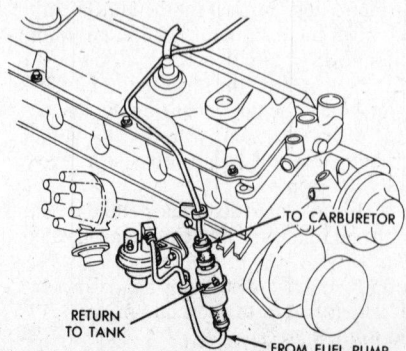

Fuel pump and filter location, six cylinder (© Chrysler Corp.)

Holley 6145 Electronic Feedback Carburetors

NOTE: Adjustment of the idle air-fuel mixture on these carburetors can be made only under certain circumstances. Adjustment should only be considered if an idle defect still exists after normal diagnosis has revealed no other faulty condition, such as faulty hose connections, incorrect idle speed, etc. There are two main procedures that must be completed before the idle speed can actually be adjusted: the solenoid idle stop and idle set RPM must both be adjusted.

SOLENOID IDLE STOP ADJUSTMENT

1. Adjust ignition timing to specifications. Disconnect and plug the vacuum hose at the EGR valve. Connect a jumper wire between the carburetor switch and a good ground.

2. Disconnect and plug the $\frac{3}{16}$ in. diameter control hose at the canister.

NOTE: The air cleaner cannot be removed, but may be propped up to provide access to the carburetor.

3. Remove the PCV valve from the cylinder rocker cover and allow the valve to draw underhood air. Connect a tachometer to the engine.

4. Turn on the air conditioning (if so equipped) and set the blower on low. Disconnect the air conditioning clutch wire.

5. On non-air conditioned models, connect a jumper wire between the battery positive post and the solenoid idle stop lead wire.

—— CAUTION ——

Use care in jumping to the proper wire on the solenoid. Applying battery voltage to other than the correct wire will damage the wiring harness.

6. Open the throttle slightly to allow the solenoid plunger to extend.

7. Remove the adjusting screw and spring from the solenoid. Insert a $\frac{1}{8}$ in. Allen wrench into the solenoid and adjust to the correct engine speed.

8. Turn off air conditioning and replace clutch wire, or remove jumper wire. Replace solenoid screw and spring. Proceed to idle set RPM adjustment.

IDLE SET RPM ADJUSTMENT

1. Remove the exhaust manifold heat shield for access to the O_2 sensor.

2. Disconnect the engine harness lead from the O_2 sensor, and ground the engine harness lead.

—— CAUTION ——

Use care so no pulling force is put on the wire attached to the O_2 sensor. The "bullet" connector to be disconnected is about 4 in. from the sensor. The exhaust manifold is very hot during this procedure.

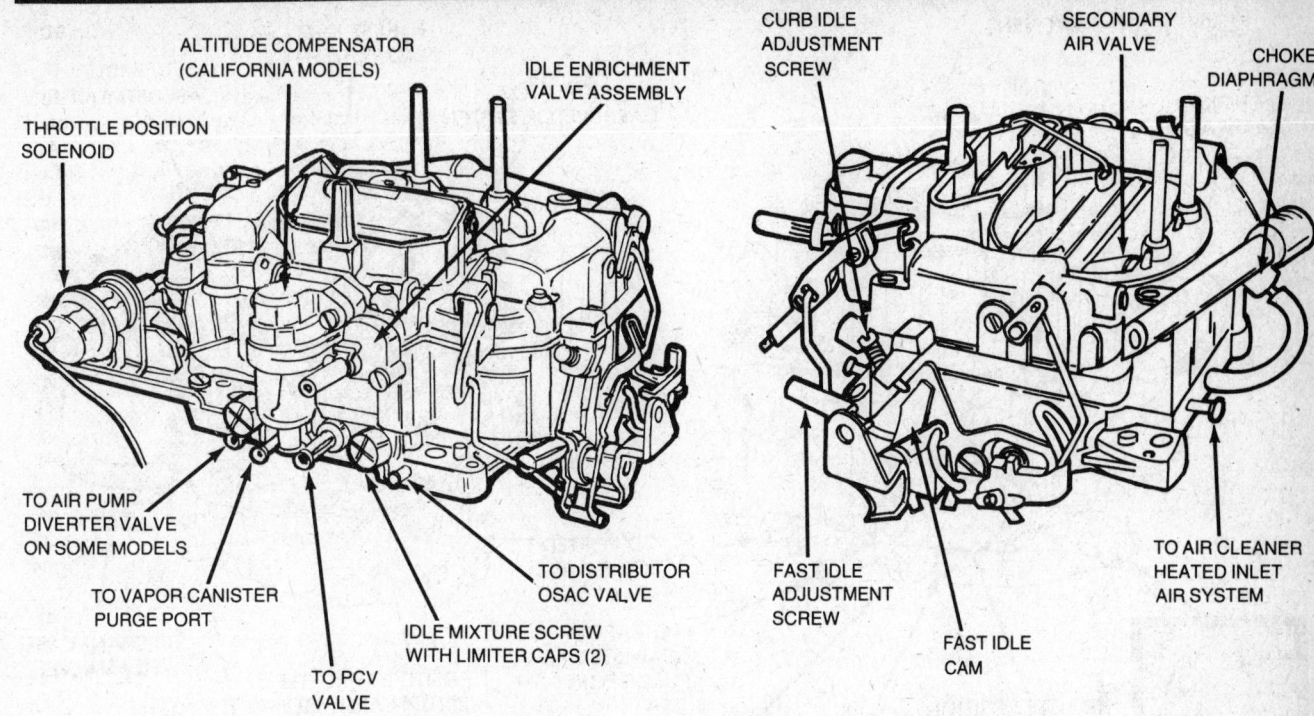

THROTTLE POSITION SOLENOID

ALTITUDE COMPENSATOR (CALIFORNIA MODELS)

IDLE ENRICHMENT VALVE ASSEMBLY

CURB IDLE ADJUSTMENT SCREW

SECONDARY AIR VALVE

CHOKE DIAPHRAGM

TO AIR PUMP DIVERTER VALVE ON SOME MODELS

TO VAPOR CANISTER PURGE PORT

TO PCV VALVE

IDLE MIXTURE SCREW WITH LIMITER CAPS (2)

TO DISTRIBUTOR OSAC VALVE

FAST IDLE ADJUSTMENT SCREW

FAST IDLE CAM

TO AIR CLEANER HEATED INLET AIR SYSTEM

Carter Thermo-Quad® carburetor vacuum hose connections and carburetor adjustments (© Chrysler Corp.)

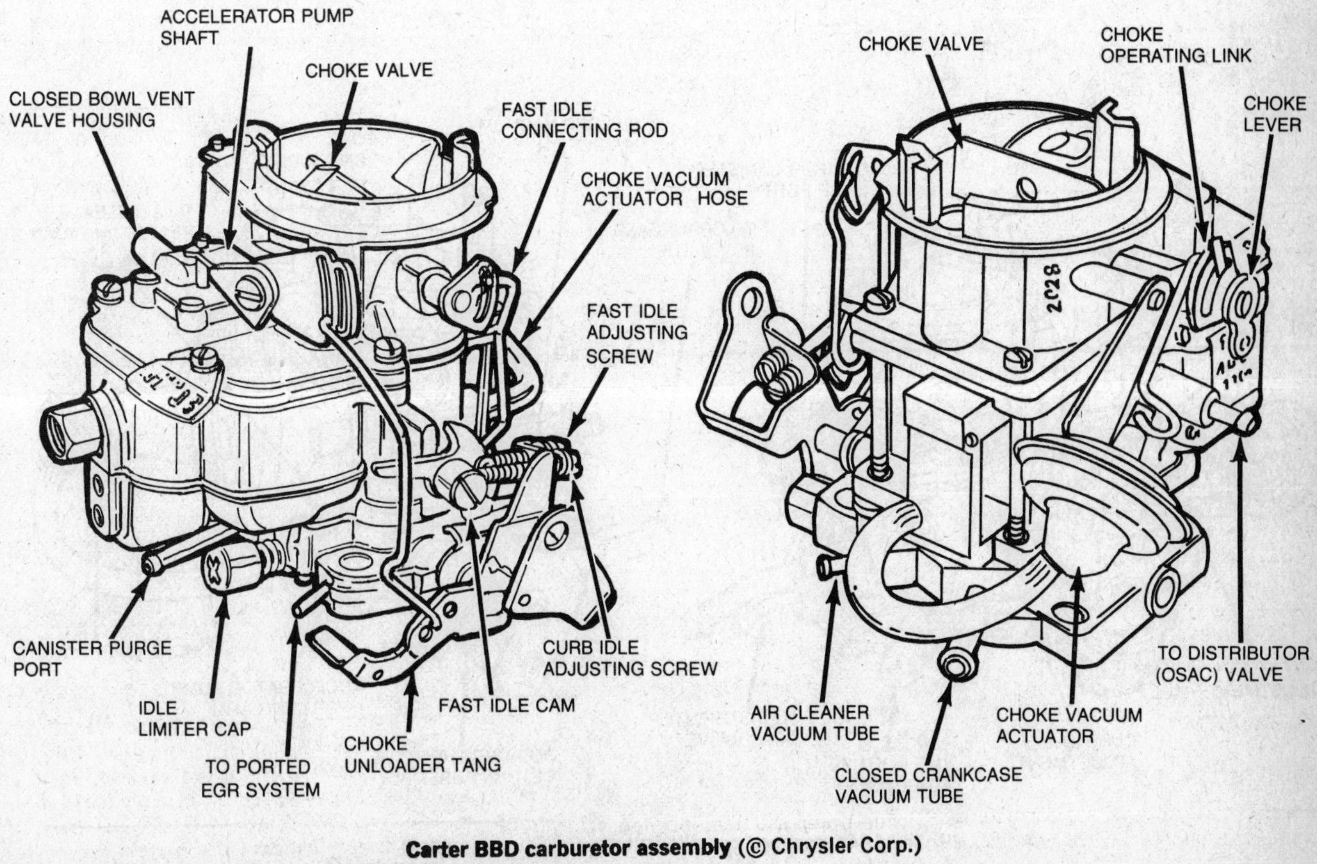

ACCELERATOR PUMP SHAFT

CHOKE VALVE

CLOSED BOWL VENT VALVE HOUSING

FAST IDLE CONNECTING ROD

CHOKE VACUUM ACTUATOR HOSE

FAST IDLE ADJUSTING SCREW

CANISTER PURGE PORT

IDLE LIMITER CAP

TO PORTED EGR SYSTEM

CHOKE UNLOADER TANG

FAST IDLE CAM

CURB IDLE ADJUSTING SCREW

CHOKE VALVE

CHOKE OPERATING LINK

CHOKE LEVER

TO DISTRIBUTOR (OSAC) VALVE

AIR CLEANER VACUUM TUBE

CLOSED CRANKCASE VACUUM TUBE

CHOKE VACUUM ACTUATOR

Carter BBD carburetor assembly (© Chrysler Corp.)

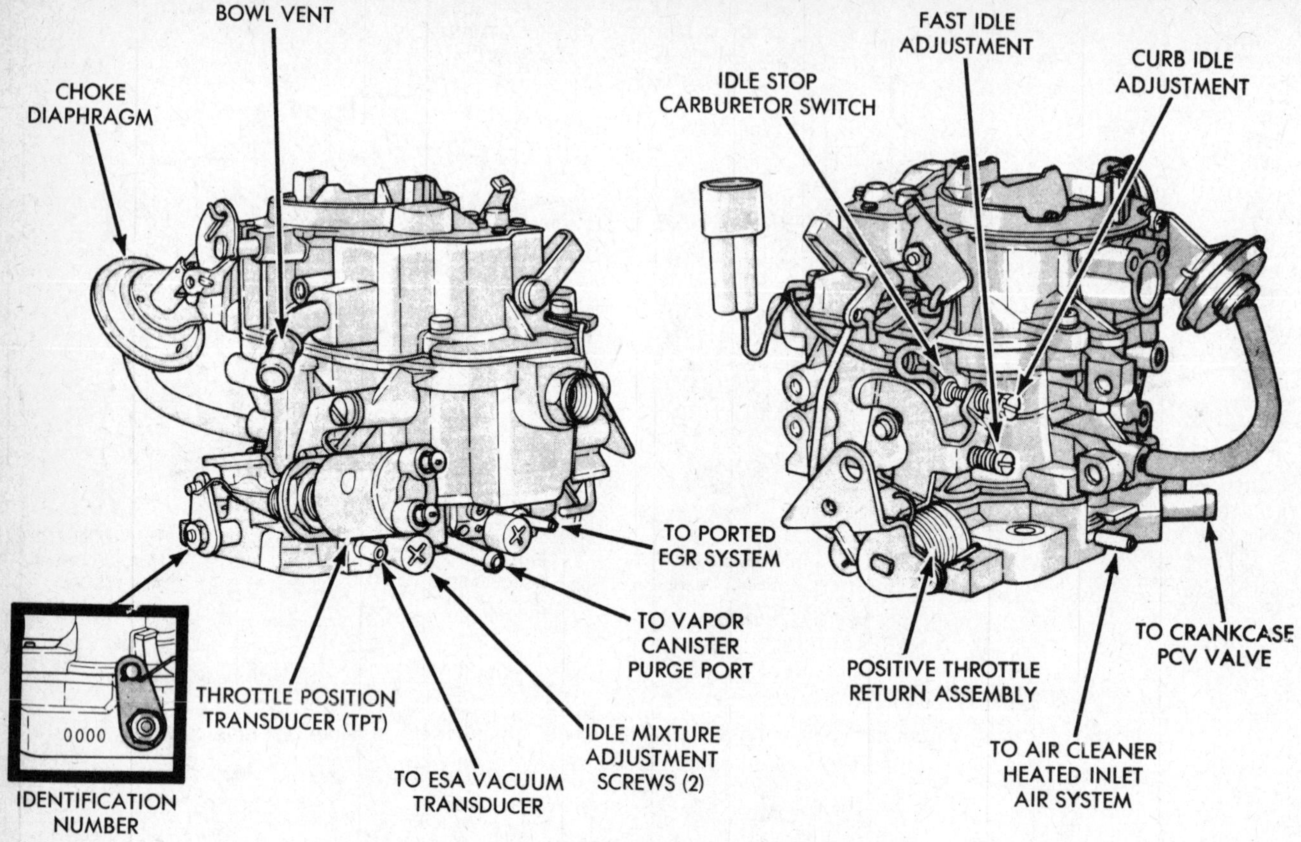

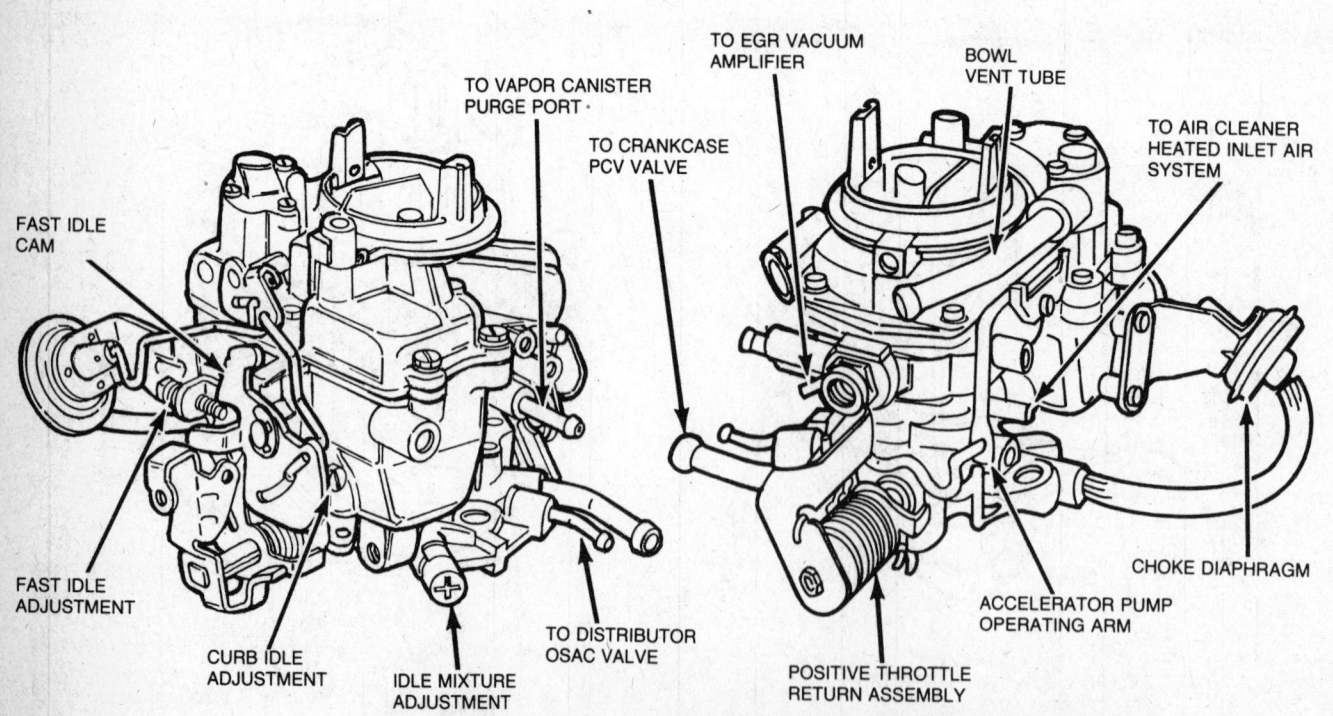

BOWL VENT

CHOKE
DIAPHRAGM

FAST IDLE
ADJUSTMENT

CURB IDLE
ADJUSTMENT

IDLE STOP
CARBURETOR SWITCH

TO PORTED
EGR SYSTEM

TO VAPOR
CANISTER
PURGE PORT

POSITIVE THROTTLE
RETURN ASSEMBLY

TO CRANKCASE
PCV VALVE

THROTTLE POSITION
TRANSDUCER (TPT)

IDLE MIXTURE
ADJUSTMENT
SCREWS (2)

TO AIR CLEANER
HEATED INLET
AIR SYSTEM

TO ESA VACUUM
TRANSDUCER

IDENTIFICATION
NUMBER

0000

Holley 2280 carburetor assembly (© Chrysler Corp.)

TO VAPOR CANISTER
PURGE PORT

TO EGR VACUUM
AMPLIFIER

BOWL
VENT TUBE

TO AIR CLEANER
HEATED INLET AIR
SYSTEM

TO CRANKCASE
PCV VALVE

FAST IDLE
CAM

FAST IDLE
ADJUSTMENT

CURB IDLE
ADJUSTMENT

IDLE MIXTURE
ADJUSTMENT

TO DISTRIBUTOR
OSAC VALVE

POSITIVE THROTTLE
RETURN ASSEMBLY

ACCELERATOR PUMP
OPERATING ARM

CHOKE DIAPHRAGM

Holley 1945 carburetor adjustments (© Chrysler Corp)

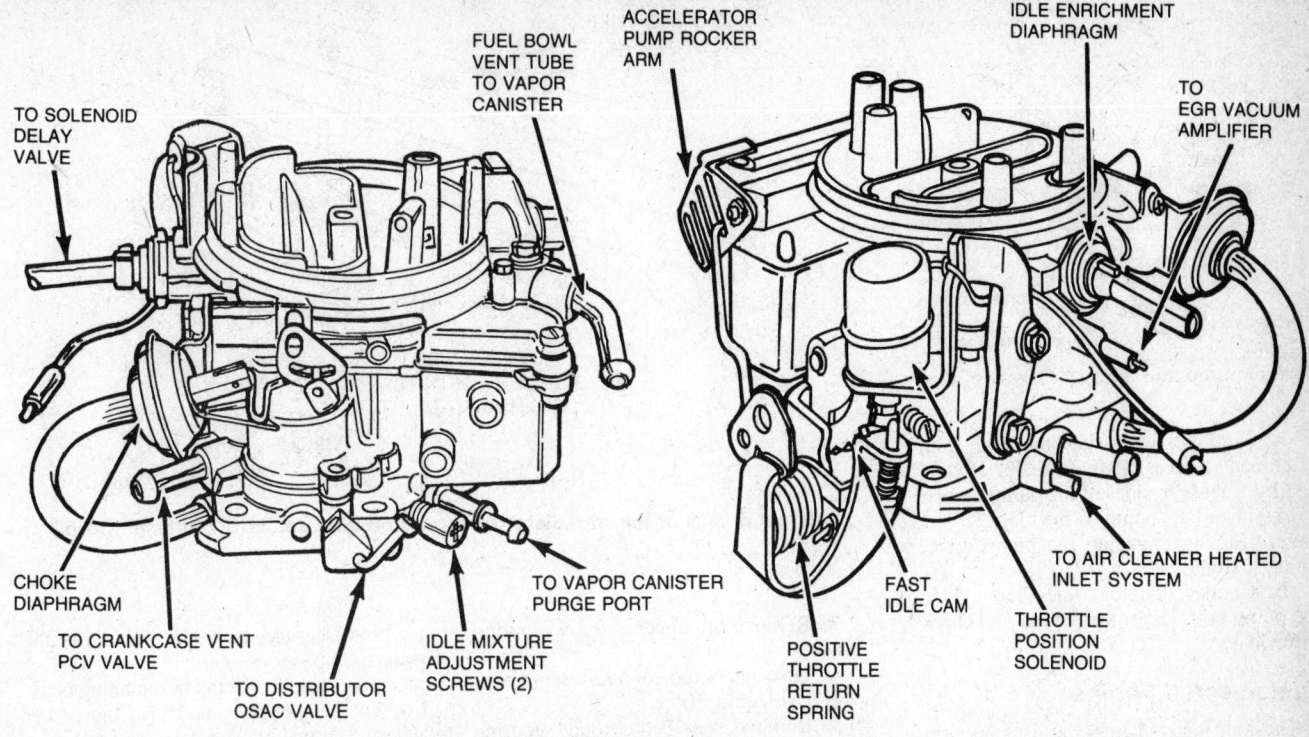

TO SOLENOID DELAY VALVE

FUEL BOWL VENT TUBE TO VAPOR CANISTER

ACCELERATOR PUMP ROCKER ARM

IDLE ENRICHMENT DIAPHRAGM

TO EGR VACUUM AMPLIFIER

CHOKE DIAPHRAGM

TO CRANKCASE VENT PCV VALVE

TO DISTRIBUTOR OSAC VALVE

IDLE MIXTURE ADJUSTMENT SCREWS (2)

TO VAPOR CANISTER PURGE PORT

POSITIVE THROTTLE RETURN SPRING

FAST IDLE CAM

THROTTLE POSITION SOLENOID

TO AIR CLEANER HEATED INLET SYSTEM

Holley 2245 carburetor assembly (© Chrysler Corp.)

3. Remove and plug the vacuum line at the vacuum transducer on the Spark Control Computer. Connect an auxiliary vacuum supply to the vacuum transducer and apply 16 in. of vacuum.

4. Let the engine run for two minutes to allow the effect of disconnecting the O_2 sensor to take place.

5. Adjust the idle set screw on the solenoid to obtain the correct idle set rpm. Proceed to the fast idle speed adjustment.

FAST IDLE SPEED ADJUSTMENT

1. Open throttle slightly and place the fast idle speed screw on the second highest step of the fast idle cam.

2. With the choke fully open, adjust the fast idle speed screw to obtain the correct fast idle rpm.

3. Return to idle, then reposition the adjusting screw on the second highest step of the fast idle cam to verify fast idle speed. Readjust if necessary.

4. Return to idle and turn off the engine. Unplug and reconnect the vacuum hoses at the EGR valve and canister. Reconnect the vacuum line at the Spark Control Computer. Install the exhaust manifold heat shield. Remove the tachometer, reinstall the PCV valve, reconnect the O_2 sensor, and remove the ground wire.

NOTE: The idle speed with the engine in normal operating condition (everything connected) may vary from set speeds. Do not readjust.

EFI Fuel Injected Engine

Idle speed is automatically adjusted by the AIS (automatic idle speed) system. If the system goes awry, it must be reset using the special Chrysler EFI Tester. EFI system mixture calibration verification requires a CO analyzer as well as the EFI Tester.

For more information, see the Fuel Injection Unit Repair Section.

Fuel Filter

REMOVAL & INSTALLATION

Carbureted Engines

Locate the filter in the fuel line between the fuel pump and the carburetor. Using hose-clamp pliers, remove the attaching clamps and pull the filter off. Reverse this procedure for installation. Be sure the arrow on the filter is pointing toward the carburetor (direction of fuel flow). Replace the filter every 30,000 miles.

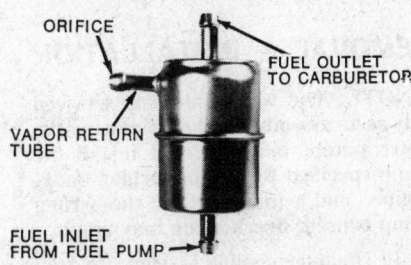

ORIFICE

FUEL OUTLET TO CARBURETOR

VAPOR RETURN TUBE

FUEL INLET FROM FUEL PUMP

The combination filter and vapor separator found on some models (© Chrysler Corp.)

NOTE: Some filters have a third line, the purpose of which is to prevent vapor lock by allowing fuel vapors to return to the tank.

Fuel Injected Engine

The fuel injected Imperial is equipped with parallel fuel filters mounted in the delivery line between the fuel tank and the throttle body on the engine. The filters are mounted side by side on a common bracket. Replace both filters when servicing.

Fuel Pump

REMOVAL & INSTALLATION

Carbureted Engines

The fuel pumps used on the 225-6, 400-8 and 440-8 engines are driven by a small cam eccentric cast into the main camshaft. On the 318 and 360 V8 engines, the pump is driven by a pressed steel eccentric cam secured on the gear end of the camshaft. On the 225-6 cylinder, 318 and 360 V8 engines, the pump is driven directly by the pump rocker arm pressing on the cam eccentric. On the 400 and 440 big block V8s, there is a pushrod located between the pump rocker arm and the driving eccentric.

1. Wipe the pump exterior to remove all dirt and oil.

2. Taking note of positions, remove the pump fuel lines.

3. Remove the bolts securing the pump to the block and remove the pump.

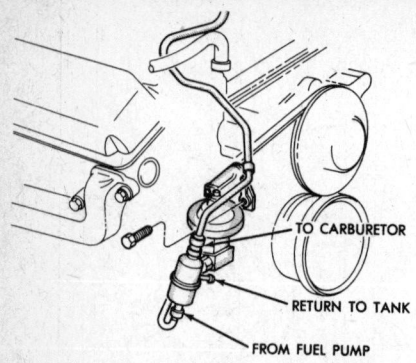

V8 fuel pump and filter (© Chrysler Corp.)

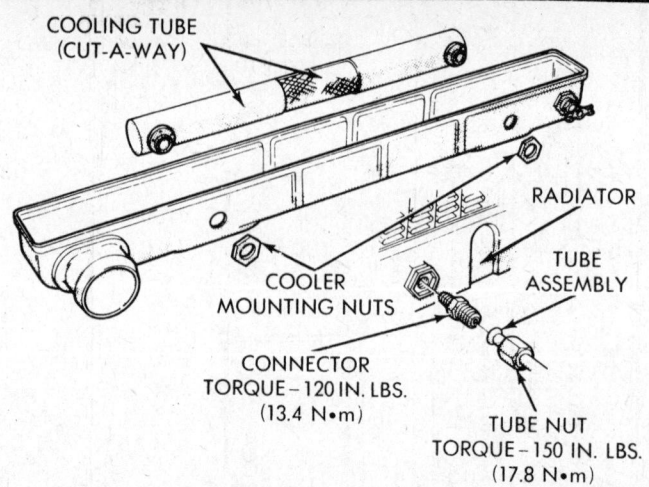

Internal details of the in-radiator transmission fluid cooler (© Chrysler Corp.)

4. Remove all gasket material from machined surfaces. Using a sealer of good quality, coat both sides of the pump gasket.

5. Install the pump on the block. If you have difficulty engaging the pump drive, rotate it slightly.

6. Connect the fuel lines and tighten the pump bolts. Start the engine and check it for leaks.

Fuel Injected Engine

The fuel injected Imperial uses an electrical fuel pump mounted in the fuel tank. There is also a fuel control pump mounted in the throttle body. See the Fuel Injection Unit Repair Section for a description of the fuel injection system.

COOLING SYSTEM

There are three levels of cooling: standard, air conditioning, and maximum cooling. Radiator size varies with the engine and cooling level. Other variable items are fan size, fan shrouds, thermostatically controlled fluid fan drives, and external automatic transmission fluid coolers. The maximum cooling system is usually used only in trailer-towing packages.

NOTE: Chrysler recommends that only ethylene glycol type anti-freeze mixed with water be used.

Radiator

REMOVAL & INSTALLATION

1. Drain the cooling system by opening draincock. When the reserve tank is empty, remove the radiator cap to hasten the draining.

2. On cars with automatic transmissions, disconnect the fluid cooler lines at the radiator bottom tank. To avoid fluid loss or dirt contamination, plug the cooler lines.

3. Remove the upper and lower radiator hoses.

4. Disconnect the coolant reserve tank hoses if so equipped.

5. Remove the fan shroud securing screws and separate the shroud from the radiator. Move the shroud toward the engine as far as possible to obtain maximum clearance for removing the radiator.

6. Remove the radiator mounting screws.

7. Lift the radiator out of the engine compartment.

CAUTION

Extreme care should be taken during removal not to damage the radiator cooling fins or water tubes

---

8. Reverse the procedure to install the radiator. Fill cooling systems without a coolant reserve tank to 1¼ in. below the filler neck with the correct water and antifreeze mixture. With cooling systems that have a reserve tank, fill the radiator and the reserve tank to the indicated level. Warm up the engine with the heater on and check the coolant level. On cars with automatic transmissions, check the transmission fluid level after warm-up and add fluid as required.

Water Pump

REMOVAL & INSTALLATION

NOTE: The water pump is serviced only as an assembly. When replacing the water pump, make sure to install the pump specified for the particular body, engine, and equipment. If the wrong pump is used, overheating may result.

1. Drain the cooling system.

2. Remove the fan shroud securing screws and move the shroud out of the way.

3. It may be necessary to remove the radiator, on some models, to obtain the

working clearance necessary to remove the water pump.

4. Loosen the alternator mounting bolts. Loosen the mounting bolts for the power steering pump, idler pulley, air conditioning compressor, and air pump (if so equipped). Remove all the accessory belts.

5. Remove the fan, spacer or fluid drive, and the pulley.

CAUTION

With fluid-coupled fan drives, to prevent silicone fluid from leaking do not set the drive unit down with its shaft pointing downward.

---

6. On some models, it may be necessary to remove the alternator or compressor mounting bracket bolts from the water pump to swing the alternator or compressor out of the way. Keep the compressor in an upright position.

7. On 318 and 360 engines, unbolt the power steering pump and set it aside leaving the hoses connected. Also remove the air pump and brackets, if so equipped.

8. Detach the hoses from the water pump. Remove the bolts which secure the water pump body to its engine block housing. Remove the water pump and discard the gasket.

9. Install the bypass hose to the pump with the second clamp temporarily in the center of the hose. Using a new gasket and sealer install the water pump on its housing. Torque its mounting bolts to 30 ft lbs.

10. Rotate the pump shaft by hand to make sure it rotates freely. Refit the alternator or compressor mounting bracket on the pump if either was removed. Install the lower radiator hose and heater bypass hoses. Install the pulley, spacer or fluid drive, and the fan. Torque their retaining nuts to 15 ft lbs.

11. Refit all the accessory drive belts. Adjust them to get about ½ in. of play

under moderate thumb pressure on the longest run of belt between pulleys.

12. Install the radiator if it was removed.

13. Install the fan shroud. Fill the cooling system without a coolant reserve tank to 1¼ in. below the filler neck with correct water and antifreeze mixture. With systems having a reserve tank, fill the radiator and fill the tank to the indicated level. Warm up the engine with the heater on and inspect the water pump for any leaks. Check the coolant level and add as required.

Thermostat

REMOVAL & INSTALLATION

All engines use a 195°F thermostat.

1. Drain the cooling system to below the level of the thermostat.

2. Remove the housing bolts and take out the thermostat and housing.

3. To install the thermostat, use a new gasket. On V8s, be sure that the pellet end is facing the engine. Six cylinder models must have the vent hole facing up.

4. Refill the system. Let the engine warm up with the heater on and recheck the level.

EMISSION CONTROLS

See the Emission Control Systems Unit Repair Section for details on the following systems:

- *Positive Crankcase Ventilation*
- *Evaporative Control System*
- *Air Injection System (Air Pump)*
- *Air Aspirator System*
- *Exhaust Gas Recirculation*
- *Electrically Assisted Choke*
- *OSAC Valve*
- *Catalytic Converter*
- *Coolant Controlled Engine Vacuum Switch (CCEVS)*
- *Coolant Control Idle Enrichment (CCIE) System*
- *Lean Burn/Electronic Spark Control System*
- *Feedback Carburetors*
- *Electronic Fuel Injection*

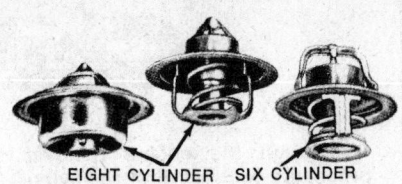

The spring side (arrow) is inserted into the engine when installing a thermostat (© Chrysler Corp.)

ENGINE

The standard equipment engine in most Chrysler Corporation rear wheel drive cars is the 225 Slant Six. Although this engine has a long stroke, it presents a low profile because the entire block is canted 30 degrees to the right. An optional two barrel carburetor was available through 1980. These models utilize mechanical tappets that can be adjusted; 1981 and later models have hydraulic lifters which need no periodic adjustment.

The 318 and 360 cu. in. engines are Chrysler's "A" block series of V8s. All of the V8s utilize hydraulic tappets.

Chrysler's "B" block series consists of the 400 and 440 cu in. engines. Actually, these may be divided into two types: the 400 low-block engine and a 440 high-block. The difference is a larger, deeper block on the 440 to accommodate a longer stroke crank. In addition, main journal diameter, connecting rod length, pushrod length, and intake manifolds are different. Otherwise, these engines are similar and many of their parts will interchange.

SPECIAL ENGINE MARKINGS

Oversize and undersize engine components, such as crankshaft and connecting rod journals, cylinder bores, tappets, and valve stems are identified by various marks. These marks may be located on top front engine pads, following the serial number, or on the crankshaft counterweights. In addition, some engines may have oversize

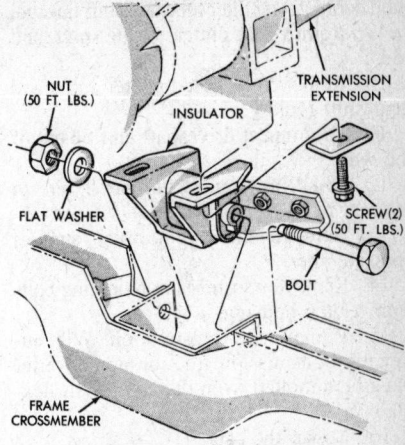

Typical rear engine mount (© Chrysler Corp.)

valve stem markings stamped on cylinder head ends. For explanation of the meanings of the various markings, consult a dealer parts book.

--- CAUTION ---

The fuel system on the 318 EFI engine retains pressure after the engine is shut down. Fuel will be sprayed when fuel lines are opened; take appropriate precautions, do not smoke, and perform service operations with the engine cold.

REMOVAL & INSTALLATION

Six Cylinder Engines

1. Scribe the hood hinge outlines on the underside of the hood, then remove the hood.

2. Drain the cooling system, remove the battery and the carburetor air cleaner.

3. Remove radiator and heater hoses, then the radiator. Remove PCV and evaporative control system.

4. Remove the outlet vent pipe from the cylinder head cover.

5. Disconnect fuel lines, linkage and wiring to the engine.

6. Disconnect exhaust pipe at exhaust manifold.

7. Raise car on hoist.

8. If equipped with automatic transmission, it must be drained. Remove the

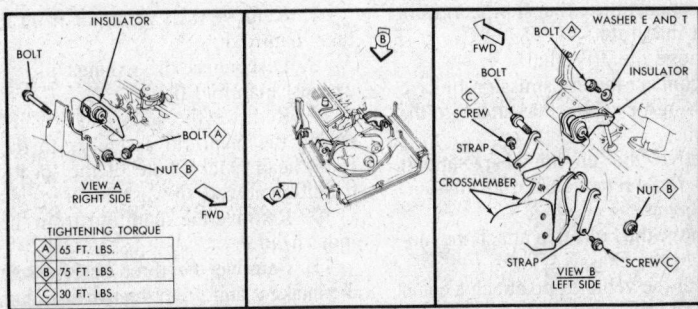

Engine front mounts, Slant Six, all models (© Chrysler Corp.)

fluid cooler lines, filler tube and shift linkage.

9. Remove the clutch torque shaft, and rods.

10. Remove the speedometer cable and gear shift rods.

11. Disconnect driveshaft and tie out of the way.

12. Install an engine support fixture to the rear of the engine.

13. Remove the engine rear support crossmember.

14. Remove transmission mounting bolts from clutch housing.

15. Remove the transmission. With automatic transmission, the torque converter must be unbolted from the crankshaft flexplate first.

16. Lower the car.

17. Position engine lifting fixture onto the engine, and attach chain hoist to the fixture eyebolt.

18. Remove the engine support fixture.

19. Remove the engine front mounting bolts.

20. Lift the engine out of the engine compartment and lower it onto a substantial work stand.

21. To install the engine, reverse the above procedure.

V8 Engines

1. Scribe the outline of the hood hinge brackets on the bottom of the hood and remove the hood.

2. Drain the cooling system and remove the radiator.

3. Remove the battery.

4. Remove the fuel line from the fuel pump on the carbureted engine, and plug the line. On the fuel injected engine, disconnect and plug both the fuel feed and return lines.

5. Remove all wires and hoses that attach to the engine.

6. If equipped with air conditioning and/or power steering, remove the unit from the engine and position it out of the way without disconnecting the lines.

7. Attach lifting sling to the engine.

8. Raise the vehicle on a hoist and install an engine support fixture to support the rear of the engine.

9. On automatic transmission models, drain the transmission and converter. On manual transmission models, disconnect the clutch torque shaft from the engine.

10. Disconnect the exhaust pipe(s) from the exhaust manifold(s).

11. Remove the driveshaft.

12. Disconnect the transmission linkage and any wiring or cables that attach to the transmission.

13. Remove the engine rear support crossmember and remove the transmission. See Time Saver.

14. Remove the bolts that attach the motor mounts to the chassis.

15. Lower the vehicle and attach a chain hoist or other lifting device to the engine.

16. Raise the engine, and carefully re-

Although the engine removal procedure requires first removing the transmission, the transmission can be left in the chassis.

If the car is equipped with an automatic transmission, remove the inspection plate from the bellhousing. Attach a remote starter switch to the engine and crank the engine until you have access to the converter-to-driveplate attaching nuts. Remove the nuts, then remove the starter. If the car has a manual transmission, disconnect the clutch torque shaft from the engine block and the clutch linkage from the adjustment rod.

Remove the automatic transmission filler tube. Support the transmission from below and remove the transmission-to-engine or transmission-to clutch bell housing attaching bolts. Place a block of wood on the floor jack lifting pad and position the jack under the transmission. As the engine is lifted out of

the car, raise and lower the jack as necessary so the angle of the transmission follows the angle of the engine as nearly as possible. Use care, as the transmission will probably be tilting on the jack pad.

When installing the engine into a car with an automatic transmission, remember that the crankshaft flange bolt circle, the inner and outer circle of holes in the driveplate, and the four tapped holes in the front face of the converter all have one hole offset. The torque converter must be mounted to the driveplate in its original location to insure proper engine-to-converter balance.

When installing an engine into a car with a manual transmission, it may be necessary to turn the crankshaft pulley slightly, with the transmission in gear, to mesh the transmission input shaft spline with the clutch disc inner hub.

move it from the engine compartment.

17. Reverse above procedure to install the engine.

Combination Manifolds

REMOVAL & INSTALLATION

Six Cylinder

1. Remove the air cleaner.

2. Disconnect the vacuum control tube at the carburetor.

3. Disconnect the fuel line at the carburetor.

4. Disconnect the crankcase ventilation tube at the carburetor.

5. Disconnect the automatic choke rod at the carburetor and remove the choke from the intake manifold.

6. Disconnect the throttle linkage at the carburetor.

7. Remove the carburetor from the intake manifold.

8. Disconnect the exhaust pipe at the exhaust manifold flange.

9. Remove the nuts and washers securing the manifold assembly to the cylinder head. Make note of the location of the different types of washers for installation.

10. Remove the manifold from the cylinder head.

11. Remove the three screws securing the intake manifold to the exhaust manifold.

12. Separate the intake and exhaust manifolds and discard the gasket.

13. Clean all gasket surfaces with solvent and blow them dry with compressed air.

14. Check the mating surfaces of the manifolds with a straightedge. Surfaces should be flat within .008 in. per foot.

15. To install, first install a new gasket between the two manifolds.

16. Install the three long screws securing the two manifolds. Do not tighten the screws yet.

17. Position the manifold assembly on the cylinder head, using a new gasket with sealer on both sides.

18. Install the triangular washers and nuts on the upper studs and on the four lower studs opposite number 2 and 5 cylinders. The eight triangular washers should be positioned squarely on the machined surfaces of both intake and exhaust manifold retaining pads. These washers must be installed with the cup side against the manifold. Install the nuts and washers only when the engine is cold.

19. Install the steel conical washers with the cup (concave) side to the manifold, one on the center upper stud and two on the center lower studs. Install the brass washers at each end, with the flat side to the manifold. Install the nuts with the flat side away from the washers. Snug up the nuts.

20. Tighten the intake-to-exhaust manifold screws to 20 ft. lbs., starting with the inner stud. Tighten the manifold-to-head screws and nuts to 18 ft. lbs.

21. Attach the exhaust pipe-to-manifold

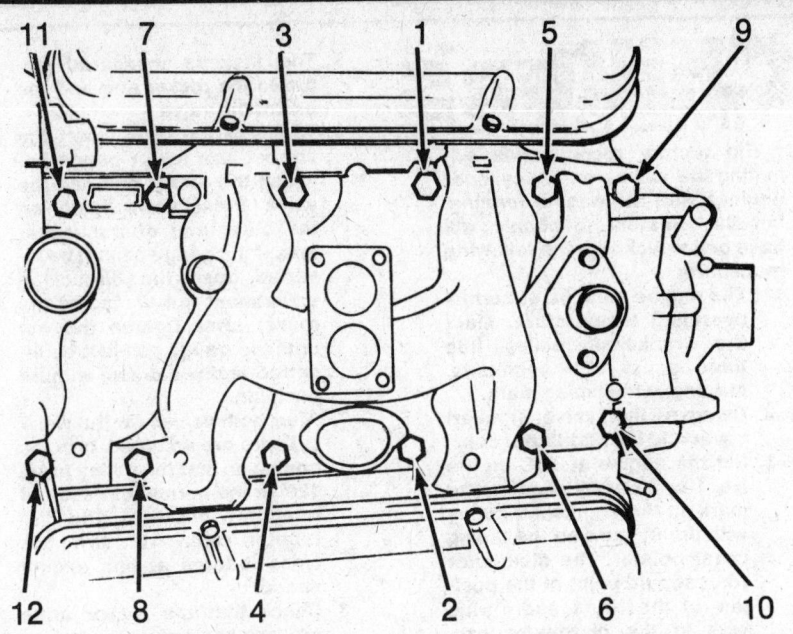

Intake manifold tightening sequence for V8 engines. 400 and 440 V8s do not have bolts 9, 10, 11, and 12 (© Chrysler Corp)

flange, using a new gasket and tighten the nuts to 35 ft. lbs.

22. Install the carburetor and connect the automatic choke rod and throttle linkage. Assemble the crankcase ventilation hose, vacuum control tube, and fuel line to the carburetor. Install the carburetor air cleaner, and connect the closed breather cap hose to the air cleaner inlet tube.

Intake Manifold

REMOVAL & INSTALLATION

V8 Engines

1. Drain the cooling system. Disconnect the negative battery cable.
2. Remove the alternator, the air cleaner and disconnect the fuel line(s) from the carburetor or throttle body.
3. Disconnect all vacuum lines and throttle linkage that attach to the carburetor or throttle body, and intake manifold.
4. Disconnect the spark plug wires from the plugs and remove the distributor cap and wires as an assembly.
5. Disconnect the wires from the coil and the temperature sending unit.
6. Disconnect the heater hose and bypass hose from the intake manifold.
7. Remove the intake manifold attaching bolts and remove the manifold, carburetor, or throttle body, and coil from the engine as an assembly.
8. Clean all gasket mounting surfaces and firmly cement new gaskets to the engine.

NOTE: Do not use sealer on the composition side gaskets used on 360 engines.

9. Reverse the procedure to install.

Torque the bolts to 45 ft. lbs. in three passes, in the sequence shown.

Exhaust Manifold

REMOVAL & INSTALLATION

V8 Engines

Disconnect the exhaust manifold at the pipe flange. Access to these bolts is from underneath the vehicle. If so equipped, disconnect the Air Injection nozzles and carburetor heated air stove. Disconnect any components of the EGR system which are in the way. Remove the exhaust manifold

by removing the securing bolts and washers. To reach these bolts, it may be necessary to jack the engine slightly off its front mounts. When the exhaust manifold is removed, sometimes the securing studs will come out with the nuts. If this occurs, studs must be replaced with the aid of sealing compound on the coarse thread ends. If this is not done, water leaks may develop at the studs. To install the exhaust manifold, reverse the removal procedure. On the center branch of the 318 and 360 manifold, no conical washers are used.

Valve System

All valves used in Chrysler engines are arranged in line in the cylinder head; they ride in guides that are integrally cast with the head. Service valves with oversize stems are available; therefore, valve guides may be reamed if necessary.

Rocker Shaft

REMOVAL & INSTALLATION

Six Cylinder Engines

1. Remove the closed ventilation system.
2. Remove the evaporative control system.
3. Remove the valve cover with its gasket.
4. Take out the rocker arm and shaft assembly securing bolts and remove the rocker arm and shaft.
5. Reverse the above for installation. The oil hole on the end of the shaft must be on the top and point toward the front of the engine to provide proper lubrication to the rocker arms. The special bolt goes to the rear. Torque the rocker arm bolts to 25 ft. lbs. and be sure to adjust the valves. See Time Saver.

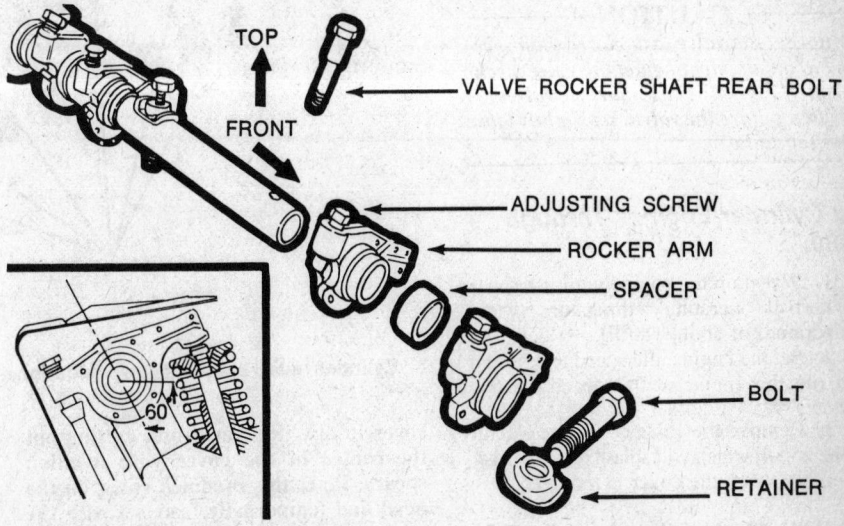

Slant Six rocker shaft details (© Chrysler Corp.)

NOTE: On vehicle models through 1985, use 0.012 in. for intake, and 0.028 in. for exhaust. These settings are to be used only for reassembly; adjust the valves to the normal hot setting (.010 intake, .020 exhaust) as soon as the engine has been warmed up.

V8 Engines

The stamped steel rocker arms are arranged on one rocker arm shaft per cylinder head. To remove the rocker arms and shaft:

1. Disconnect the spark plug wires.
2. Disconnect the closed ventilation and evaporative control system.
3. Remove the valve covers with their gaskets.
4. Remove the rocker shaft bolts and retainers, and lift off the rocker arm assembly.
5. Reverse the above procedure to install. The notch on the end of both rocker shafts on the 318 and 360 should point to the engine centerline and toward the front of the engine on the left cylinder head, or toward the rear on the right cylinder head. On the 400 and 440, the rocker arm lubrication holes must point down and toward the valves. Torque the rocker shaft bolts to 17 ft. lbs. on the 318 and 360, and 25 ft. lbs. on the 400 and 440.

VALVE ADJUSTMENT

This adjustment is required only on six cylinder engines, through 1980. The pre-1981 sixes use solid lifters and adjustable rocker arms. All V8s and 1981 and later 6 cylinders use hydraulic lifters and non-adjustable rocker arms; the lifters take up lash automatically and no adjustment is possible. After engine reassembly, these lifters adjust themselves shortly after oil pressure builds up.

Valve lash should be adjusted whenever there is excessive noise from the valve mechanism.

— **CAUTION** —

Do not set the valve lash closer than specified in an attempt to quiet the valve mechanism. This will cause burned valves. It is better to have the valves set slightly loose than too tight.

Six Cylinder Engines Through 1980

1. Warm up the engine until it reaches its normal operating temperature (water temperature of about 180°F).
2. Set the engine idle speed to 550 rpm and run the engine at this speed for five minutes.
3. Remove the valve cover. Be careful of the hot oil which will splash off the rocker assembly when the cover is removed.

NOTE: Much of the oil splash can be avoided by purchasing a Slant Six rocker

TIME SAVER

The factory recommends adjusting the valves on six cylinder engines with the engine running, but the amateur mechanic will have better luck with the following procedure:

1. The engine must be at normal operating temperature. Mark the crankshaft pulley into three equal 120° segments, starting at the timing mark.
2. Remove the valve (rocker) cover and the distributor cap.
3. Set the engine at TDC on the No. 1 cylinder by aligning the mark on the crankshaft pulley with the 0° mark on the timing cover pointer. The distributor rotor should point at the position of the No. 1 spark plug wire in the distributor cap. Both rocker arms on No. 1 cylinder should be free to move slightly. If all this isn't the case, you have No. 6 cylinder at TDC and will have to turn the engine 360° in the normal direction of rotation.
4. The cylinders are numbered from front to rear. The intake and exhaust valves are in the following sequence, starting at the front: E-I, E-I, E-I, I-E, I-E, I-E. Note that intake and exhaust valves have different settings.
5. The lash is measured between the rocker arm and the end of the valve.
6. To check the lash, insert the correct size feeler gauge between the rocker arm and the valve. Press down lightly on the other end of the rocker arm. If the gauge cannot be inserted, loosen the self-locking adjustment nut on top of the rocker arm. Tighten the nut until the gauge can just be inserted and withdrawn without buckling.
7. After both valves for the No. 1 cylinder are adjusted, turn the engine so that the pulley turns 120° in the normal direction of rotation (clockwise). The distributor rotor will turn 60°, since it turns at half engine speed.
8. Check that the rocker arms are free and adjust the valves for the next cylinder in the firing order, No. 5. The firing order is 1-5-3-6-2-4.
9. Turn the engine 120° to adjust each of the remaining cylinders in the firing order. When you are done the engine will have made two complete revolutions (720°) and the rotor one complete revolution (360°).
10. Replace the rocker cover with a new gasket. Replace the distributor cap. Start the engine and check for leaks.

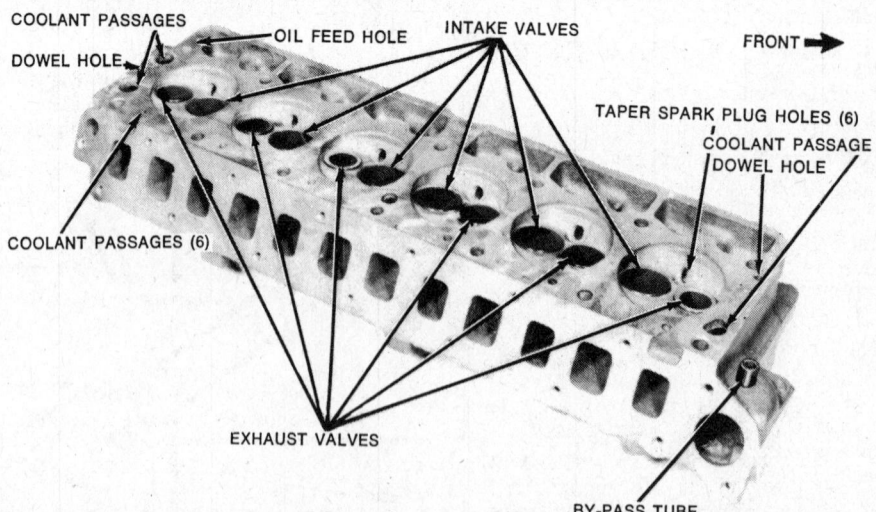

Cylinder head, showing valve sequence—six cylinder engines (© Chrysler Corp)

cover in any junkyard, and cutting out the center of the cover with aviation shears. Place this modified cover on the head and temporarily fasten it with the rocker cover bolts. Proceed with the adjustment through the hole you've cut out.

The remaining sides will keep most of the oil splash on the rocker assembly. When the valves are adjusted, remove this cover and replace with the original.

4. Using the proper thickness feeler

gauge, measure the clearance between the valve stem tip and the end of the rocker arm adjusting screw at each valve. If necessary, loosen the locknut on each rocker arm and turn the adjusting screw (while the feeler gauge is still inserted) to obtain the correct valve clearance.

5. After all of the valves have been checked and adjusted, stop the engine and replace the valve cover, using a new gasket between the cover and cylinder head. If much oil was lost during the valve adjustment procedure, check the oil level in the crankcase.

Cylinder Head

─────── **CAUTION** ───────

Don't loosen the head bolts until the engine is thoroughly cool, to prevent warping the head. If the head sticks to the block, operate the starter to loosen it by compression, or rap it upward with a soft rubber hammer. Do not force anything between the head and the block. Cylinder head bolts should be retorqued after the first 500 miles, unless a special gasket is used.

REMOVAL & INSTALLATION

Six Cylinder Engines

1. Drain the cooling system.
2. Remove carburetor air cleaner and fuel lines.
3. Disconnect accelerator linkage.
4. Remove all of the vacuum lines from the carburetor.
5. Carefully disconnect spark plug wires by pulling straight, in line with plug.
6. Disconnect heater hose and clamp holding the by-pass hose.
7. Disconnect the heat indicator sending unit wire.
8. Disconnect exhaust pipe at the exhaust manifold flange. If so equipped, disconnect the diverter valve vacuum line from the intake manifold; also remove the air injection assembly (if applicable).
9. Remove the outlet vent tube, evaporative control system, and cylinder head cover.
10. Remove the rocker arms and shaft.
11. Remove the pushrods and keep them in order.

NOTE: It is a good idea to set the pushrods in order (as they are removed from the engine) in a piece of lumber that has been drilled. The twelve pushrods can be labeled by writing the cylinder number and ''In'' and ''Ex'' under each hole in the lumber.

12. Remove the head bolts and lift off the cylinder head. The cylinder head is removed with the intake and exhaust manifolds as an assembly.
   To install:
1. Clean carbon from the combustion

area. Clean all gasket surfaces of both head and cylinder block. Install spark plugs.

2. If there is any cause to suspect leakage, check all surfaces with a straightedge. If out-of-flatness exceeds 0.00075 times the span length in any direction, replace head or machine head gasket surface. For example, on a 12 in. span the maximum allowable out of flat is 12 × 0.00075 or 0.009 in.

3. Apply a reliable sealer to the new gasket and install the gasket and cylinder head.

4. Install the 14 cylinder head bolts. Starting at the top center, tighten all cylinder head bolts to specification, in three steps.

5. Inspect all push rods for bends or wear. Replace if necessary.

6. Insert the pushrods, small ends down into the tappets.

7. Install rocker arms and shaft assembly with flat or oil hole on the end of the shaft on top and pointing toward the front of the engine. This is necessary to provide lubrication to the rocker assemblies. Torque the attaching bolts to 25 ft. lbs. Make a temporary cold valve adjustment on models through 1980.

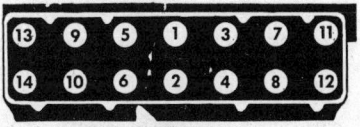

6 cylinder

Frequently valves become bent or warped or their seats become blocked with carbon or other material. Left unattended, this can cause burnt valves, damaged cylinder heads and other expensive troubles. To detect leaking valves early, perform this test whenever the cylinder head is removed.
1. **After removing head, replace sparkplugs. Removing sparkplugs before removing heads eliminates breakage.**
2. **Place head on bench with valves, springs, retainers and keys installed and combustion chambers up.**
3. **Pour enough safe solvent in each combustion chamber to completely cover both valves. Watch combustion chambers for two minutes for any leakage.**

NOTE: Valve settings are 0.012 in. for intake, and 0.028 in. for exhaust. These settings are to be used only for reassembly; adjust the valves to the normal hot setting (.010 intake, .020 exhaust) as soon as the engine has been warmed up.

8. Connect the heater hose and by-pass hose clamp.

9. Connect the heat indicator sending-unit wire, the accelerator linkage and the spark plug wires. If applicable, install vacuum control tube at the carburetor, the air injection assembly, and the diverter valve.

10. Install carburetor vacuum line(s).

11. Connect exhaust pipe to the exhaust manifold.

12. Install the fuel line and carburetor air cleaner.

13. Refill the cooling system.

14. Start the engine, and let run until operating temperatures have been reached.

15. Adjust valve tappet clearance on models through 1980. The adjusting screw in the pushrod end of the rocker arm should have a minimum of 3 ft. lbs. (36 in. lbs.) tension as it is turned. If less, replace the adjusting screw and the rocker arm.

16. Place the new cylinder head cover gasket in position, and install cylinder head cover.

17. Install outlet vent tube, and evaporative control system (if applicable).

V8 Engines

1. Drain cooling system and disconnect battery.

2. Remove alternator, air cleaner and fuel line.

3. Disconnect accelerator linkage.

4. Remove vacuum hose(s) from the carburetor or throttle body.

5. Remove distributor cap and wires. If removing heads in vehicle, remove plugs to prevent breaking them.

6. Disconnect coil wires, temperature sending wire, heater hoses, and by-pass hose.

7. Remove closed ventilation system (PCV), evaporative control system, if so equipped, and remove valve covers.

8. Remove intake manifold, ignition coil, and carburetor or throttle body as an assembly. Remove the tappet chamber cover, if used.

9. Remove exhaust manifolds.

10. Remove rocker arm and shaft assemblies. Remove pushrods and identify to ensure installation in original locations.

11. Remove the head bolts from each cylinder head, and lift off heads.

12. Clean all surfaces.

13. If there is any reason to suspect leakage between a cylinder block and its head, inspect all surfaces with straight edge. If out of flatness exceeds 0.00075 times span length in any direction, replace head or machine mating surface. For example, if span length is 12 in., maximum out of flatness is 12 × 0.00075, or 0.009 in.

14. On all but some 1979 and 1980 and later 318 engines, installation is in the re-

318 and 360 V8

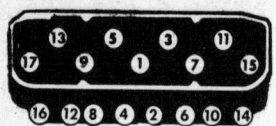

400 and 440 V8

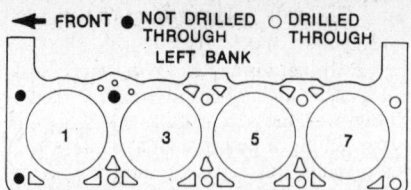

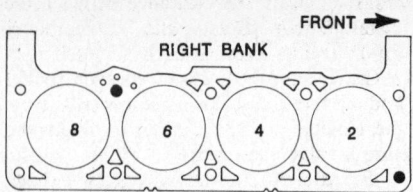

Sealant must be applied to the drilled through head bolt threads on some 1979 and all 1980 and later 318 cu in. engines (© Chrysler Corp.)

verse order of removal. Be sure to use sealer and torque the cylinder head bolts to 105 ft. lbs., in three stages.

15. On some 1979 and all 1980 and later 318 engines, the blocks have certain head bolt holes which are open to the water jacket; seven in the left bank and eight in the right bank. A sealant, preferably P/N 4057989, must be applied to the threads of these bolts to prevent coolant leakage. Clean away old sealer before applying new. The 1979 318 engines of this type begin with numbers 9M3180702 or 4104230-318. Another way to tell is to insert a screwdriver into block head bolt holes indicated in the illustration. If it goes into the holes at least two inches, the bolt threads must be sealed. On these engines, head bolt torque has been reduced to 95 ft lbs. The safest procedure, and the one Chrysler recommends starting in 1981, is to apply sealer to all bolt threads.

NOTE: 318 cylinder heads were changed during the 1979 model year; 360 heads were changed during the 1977 model year. A new type gasket must be used with the new heads.

Timing Chain and Cover

REPLACEMENT

Six Cylinder Engines

1. Drain the cooling system and disconnect the battery.
2. Remove the radiator and fan.
3. With a puller, remove the vibration damper.
4. Loosen the oil pan bolts to allow clearance and remove the timing case cover and gasket.
5. Remove the camshaft sprocket bolt.
6. Remove the timing chain with the camshaft sprocket.
7. On installation: Turn the crankshaft to line up the timing mark on the crankshaft sprocket with the centerline of the camshaft (without the chain).
8. Install the camshaft sprocket and chain. Align the timing marks.

9. Torque the camshaft sprocket bolt to 35 ft. lbs.
10. Apply a ⅛ in. bead of sealer to the junction of the rubber and cork oil pan seals.
11. Reinstall the timing case cover with a new gasket and torque the bolts to 17 ft. lbs. Retighten the engine oil pan to 17 ft. lbs.
12. Press the vibration damper back on.
13. Replace the radiator and hoses.
14. Refill the cooling system.

V8 Engines

1. Disconnect the battery and drain the cooling system. Remove the water pump. Remove the power steering pump attaching bolts and move the pump aside, if so equipped. Move the air conditioning compressor aside, if so equipped.
2. Remove the vibration damper pulley. Unbolt and remove the vibration damper with a puller. On 318 and 360 engines, remove the fuel lines and fuel pump (carbureted engine), then loosen the oil pan bolts and remove the front bolt on each side.
3. Remove the timing gear cover and the crankshaft oil slinger.
4. On 318 and 360 engines, remove the camshaft sprocket lockbolt, securing cup washer, and fuel pump eccentric. Remove the timing chain with both sprockets. On 400 and 440 engines, remove the camshaft sprocket lockbolt and remove the timing chain with the camshaft and crankshaft sprockets.

5. To begin the installation procedure, place the camshaft and crankshaft sprockets on a flat surface, with the timing indicators on an imaginary centerline through both sprocket bores. Place the timing chain around both sprockets. Be sure the timing marks are in alignment.

--- CAUTION ---

When installing the timing chain, have an assistant support the camshaft with a screwdriver to prevent it from knocking out the cup plug in the rear of the engine block. Remove the distributor and the oil pump/distributor drive gear. Position the screwdriver against the rear side of the cam gear and be careful not to damage the cam lobes.

6. Turn the crankshaft and camshaft to align them with the keyway location in the crankshaft sprocket and the keyway or dowel hole in the camshaft sprocket.
7. Lift the sprockets and timing chain while keeping the sprockets tight against the chain in the correct position. Slide both sprockets evenly onto their respective shafts.
8. Use a straightedge to measure the alignment of the sprocket timing marks. They must be perfectly aligned.
9. On 318 and 360 engines, install the fuel pump eccentric, cup washer, and camshaft sprocket lockbolt, and torque to 35 ft.

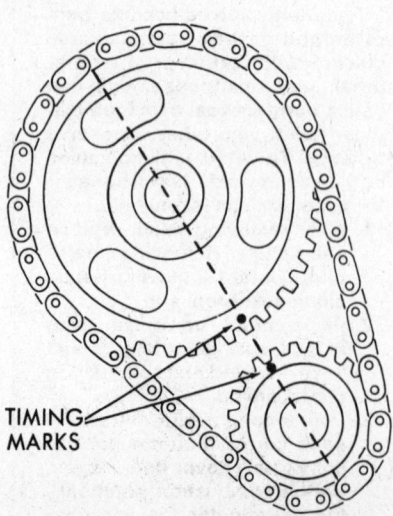

Alignment of timing marks—6 cylinder

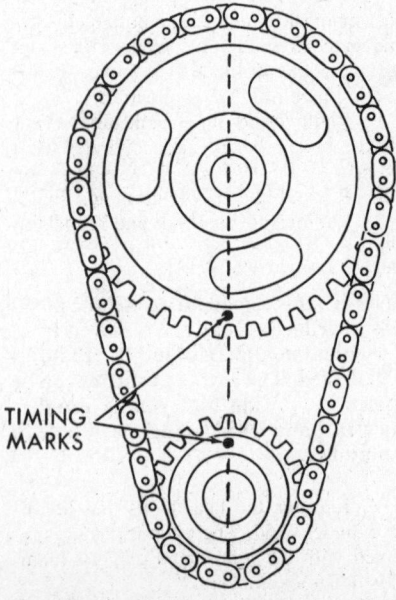

Alignment of timing marks—V8

lbs. If camshaft end play exceeds 0.010 in., install a new thrust plate. It should be 0.002–0.006 in. with the new plate.

On 400 and 440 V8s, install the washer and camshaft sprocket lockbolt and torque the lockbolt to 50 ft. lbs. Check to make sure the rear face of the camshaft sprocket is flush with the camshaft end.

Timing Cover Seal

REPLACEMENT

NOTE: A seal remover and installer tool is required to prevent seal damage.

Six Cylinder Engines

1. Disconnect the battery and drain the cooling system.
2. Remove the radiator and fan assembly.
3. Remove the power steering crankshaft pulley.
4. Using a special Chrysler tool (part No. C-3732A) or a puller, remove the vibration damper.
5. Pry the seal out, *being careful not to damage the sealing surface of the cover*.
6. Install the new seal by installing the threaded shaft of the seal installer tool into the threads of the crankshaft and by placing the seal in the opening with the seal spring toward the inside of the engine.
7. Using an installing adapter, place the thrust bearing and nut on the shaft and tighten until the tool is flush with the timing chain cover.
8. Lubricate the seal lip with Lubriplate®, then install the vibration damper.
9. Install the power steering crankshaft pulley.
10. Install radiator and fan assembly, fill the cooling system and connect the battery.

V8 Engines

1. Disconnect the battery and loosen the belts from the crankshaft pulley.
2. Remove the radiator shroud retaining screws and remove the shroud and fan.
3. Remove the crankshaft pulley and vibration damper bolt and washer from the end of the crankshaft.
4. Install the bar from Chrysler tool No. C-3688 and the screw from Chrysler tool No. C-3732A and pull the vibration damper from the end of the crankshaft.
5. Carefully pry the seal out without scratching the sealing surface of the cover.
6. Refer to Steps 6–8 of the six cylinder procedure.
7. Install the retaining bolts and washer. Torque to 135 ft. lbs.
8. Install the pulley on the vibration damper and torque to 200 in. lbs.
9. Install the fan, shroud and belts.
10. Connect the battery.

Camshaft

REMOVAL & INSTALLATION

NOTE: Whenever a new camshaft and/or new tappets are installed, the manufacturer recommends that one qt. of their crankcase conditioner, or equivalent, be added to the engine oil to aid break-in. This oil mixture should be left in the engine for a minimum of 500 miles. Chrysler recommends that the engine be removed from the vehicle before removing the camshaft. However, in some cases it may be possible to remove the camshaft from the engine, with the engine still in the car, by removing the radiator

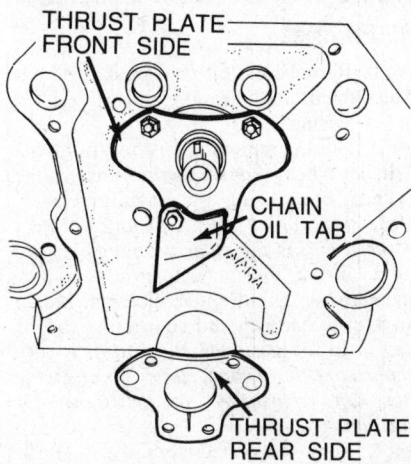

Timing chain oil tab installation, V8s (© Chrysler Corp.)

and grille, and sliding the camshaft out through the front of the vehicle.

Six Cylinder

1. Remove the cylinder head, timing gear cover, camshaft sprocket, and timing chain.
2. Remove the valve tappets, keeping them in order to ensure installation in their original locations.

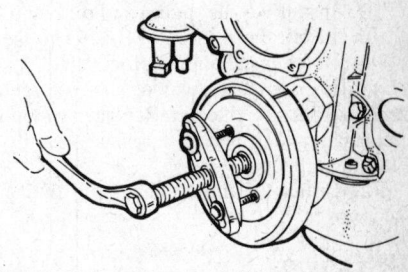

Removing vibration damper assembly, 318 V8. Slant Six similar (© Chrysler Corp.)

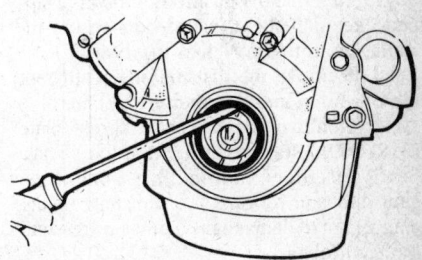

Oil seal removal, V8s Six cylinder similar (© Chrysler Corp.)

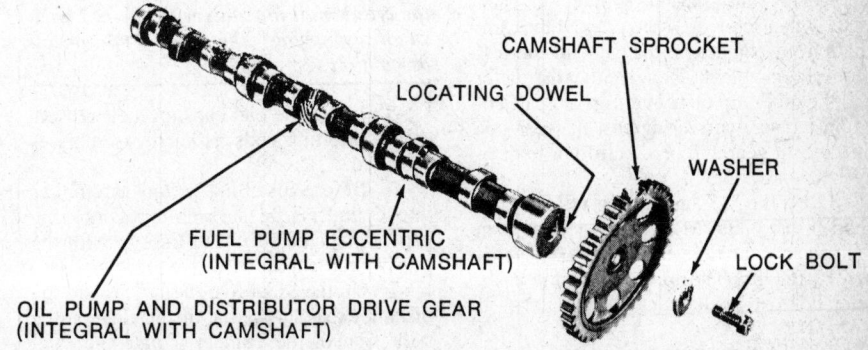

Camshaft and sprocket assembly—six cylinder (© Chrysler Corp.)

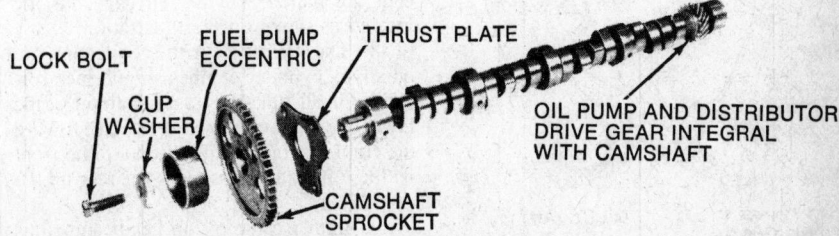

Camshaft and sprocket assembly—V8 through 360 cu. in. (© Chrysler Corp)

3. Remove the crankshaft sprocket.

4. Remove the distributor and the oil pump.

5. Remove the fuel pump.

6. Fit a long bolt into the front of the camshaft to facilitate camshaft removal.

7. Remove the camshaft, being careful not to damage the cam bearings with the cam lobes.

8. Lubricate the camshaft lobes and bearing journals with camshaft lubricant. Insert the camshaft into the engine block.

9. Install the fuel pump and oil pump.

10. Install the distributor. (Refer to the "Distributor Installation" procedure.)

11. Inspect the crowns of all the tappet faces with a straightedge. Replace any tappets that have dished or worn surfaces. Install the tappets.

12. Install the timing chain and timing gear cover.

V8 Engines

1. Remove the valve covers, intake manifold, timing gear cover, camshaft and crankshaft sprocket, and the timing chain.

2. Remove the pushrods and valve tappets, keeping them in order to ensure installation in their original locations.

3. Remove the distributor and lift out the oil pump and distributor driveshaft.

4. Remove the camshaft thrust plate (318, 360). Note the location of the oil tab.

5. Fit a long bolt into the front of the camshaft and remove the camshaft, being careful not to damage the cam bearings with the cam lobes.

6. Lubricate the camshaft lobes and bearing journals with camshaft lubricant. Insert the camshaft into the engine block within 2 in. of its final position in the block.

7. Have an assistant support the camshaft with a screwdriver to prevent the camshaft from contacting the plug in the rear of the engine block. Remove the distributor and the oil pump/distributor drive gear. Position the screwdriver against the rear side of the cam gear and be careful not to damage the cam lobes.

8. On the 318 and 360, install the camshaft thrust plate. Make sure the tang is in the lower right hole in the plate. Tighten to 210 in. lbs. The top edge of the chain oil tab must be flat against the plate. If

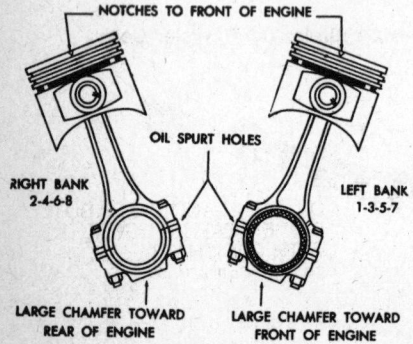

V8 piston and connecting rod assembly

camshaft end play exceeds 0.010 in., install a new thrust plate. Play should be 0.002–0.006 in. with the new plate.

9. Install the oil pump and the distributor driveshaft. Install the distributor. (Refer to the "Distributor Installation" procedure.)

10. Inspect the crown of all the tappet faces with a straightedge. Replace any tappets that have dished or worn surfaces. Install the tappets.

11. Install the timing chain, cover, and cylinder heads.

Pistons and Connecting Rods

REMOVAL & INSTALLATION

All Engines

1. Remove the oil pan, intake and exhaust manifolds, head(s) and all related hoses, wiring, etc.

2. Before removing pistons from the cylinder block, remove the top ridge of the cylinder bores using a good ridge reamer. *Make sure the tops of the pistons are kept covered during the ridge reaming.*

3. Inspect the connecting rods and big-end caps for cylinder identification. Match mark each end cap and connecting rod, if necessary for later identification. *It is very important to have connecting rods and their end caps reinstalled in their original positions.*

4. Remove connecting rod cap. Push each piston and rod assembly out of the cylinder bore with a wooden hammer handle.

—————— **CAUTION** ——————

Use extreme care not to nick or scratch the crankshaft journals with the rod bolts when removing the rod and piston assemblies.

5. Install the end caps on their repsective connecting rods as each assembly is removed.

6. Before installing piston assemblies into cylinders, be sure compression ring gaps are staggered not to line up with the oil ring rail gaps.

7. On the Slant Six engines, rotate the oil ring expander so that the ends are at the right side of the engine. Rotate the steel rails so the gaps are approximately opposite and positioned above the wrist pin holes. On the V8s, make sure the oil ring expander ends are butted and the rail gap ends are located as shown in the illustration.

8. The squirt hole in the connecting rod on all six cylinder engines should face forward. On all V8s, the larger chamfer of the lower connecting rod bore must face toward the crankpin journal fillet (toward the front on the left bank and toward the rear on the right bank).

9. Immerse the piston heads and rings in clean engine oil. Slide the ring compressor over the piston and tighten. Make

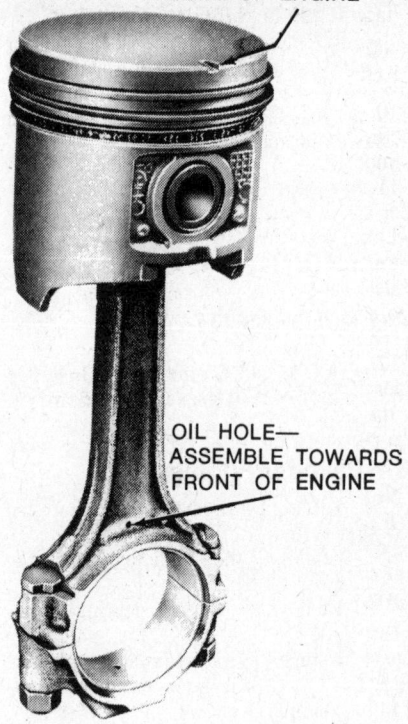

Piston and connecting rod assembly— 1978 and later six cylinder

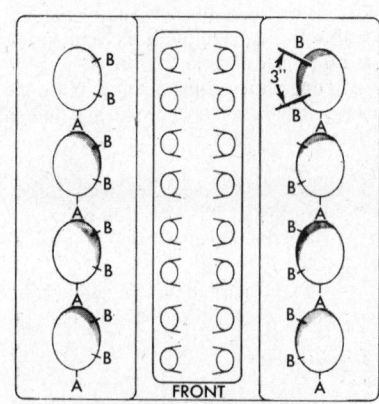

Correct piston ring arrangement in cylinder bores, V8s. Slant Six similar (© Chrysler Corp.)

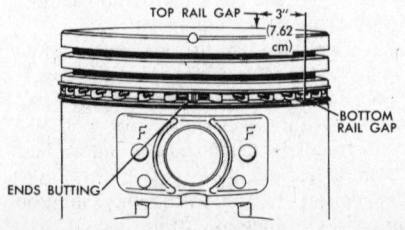

Proper oil ring installation (© Chrysler Corp.)

sure each cylinder bore is clean, then wipe a thin coat of clean engine oil over the entire surface of each bore.

NOTE: The position of the rings must not change during this operation.

10. Rotate the crankshaft so the connecting rod journal is on the center of the cylinder bore.

11. Cut lengths of rubber tubing to fit over the big-end bolts on each connecting rod. The tubing will protect the crankshaft journals when the piston assemblies are installed. Insert the rod and piston assemblies into each cylinder bore and guide the rod over the crank journal.

12. Tap each piston down into the cylinder bore using a wooden hammer handle. At the same time, guide the connecting rod into position on the crankshaft journal.

NOTE: It helps having two people install piston assemblies: one to make sure the connecting rod mates with the crank journal and the other to tap the piston down into the cylinder.

13. Install the rod cap, and torque the nuts to 45 ft. lbs. Repeat the procedure for the rest of the cylinders.

14. Reassemble pistons and connecting rods in the reverse order of removal.

Oil Pan

REMOVAL & INSTALLATION
Six Cylinder

1. Disconnect the battery and drain the radiator. Disconnect the upper and lower radiator hoses, and remove the oil dipstick.

2. Remove the radiator shroud attaching screws and place it rearward on the engine.

3. Jack up the vehicle and drain the oil. Remove the engine-to-transmission bracket, the exhaust pipe, and the torque converter inspection shield if equipped with automatic transmission.

4. Remove the steering center link from the steering and idler arms.

5. Position a jack stand at the right front corner of the engine oil pan. Be sure not to support the engine at the crankshaft pulley or vibration damper.

6. Remove the front engine mount bolts. Raise the engine about 1½–2 in.

7. Remove the oil pan bolts, rotate the engine crankshaft to clear the counterweights, and remove the oil pan.

8. Using a new pan gasket set, apply sealer to the four junctions of the gaskets, install the oil pan and torque it to 200 inch lbs. Make sure the pickup screen contacts the bottom of the pan.

9. Lower the engine into its original position and install the front engine mount bolts. Torque to 75 ft. lbs.

10. Connect the steering and idler arms to the center link. Torque to 175 ft. lbs.;

be sure to install the cotter pins. Install the torque converter cover, exhaust pipe, and support bracket.

11. Install the radiator hoses, if removed, and replace the fan shroud.

12. Fill the cooling system, install the dipstick, replace the oil, and check for leaks. Connect the battery and start the vehicle. Run for five minutes with the heater on, then check again for leaks.

318 and 360 V8—All Models

1. Disconnect the battery and remove the dipstick. On 360 HP 4-bbl engines, disconnect the radiator fan shroud and set it back over the fan.

2. Jack up the vehicle and drain the oil. Remove the torque converter-to-engine left housing strut, if so equipped.

3. Disconnect the steering center link from the steering and idler arms on all cars except 1978–82 Aspen, Volare, LeBaron to 1981, Chrysler and Diplomat and 1980–84 Cordoba, Mirada, 1981–83 Imperial and 1982–84 New Yorker, 5th Avenue and Gran Fury.

4. Disconnect the exhaust pipes from the manifolds on all cars except 360 HP 4-bbl models and secure them out of the way. On the models mentioned in Step 3, remove the starter, starter mounting stud (if so equipped), and the torque converter inspection plate, if equipped with automatic transmission.

5. Visually check to see if there is sufficient clearance to reach all of the oil pan bolts. If there is not, it will be necessary to raise the engine about 1½–2 in. Do this by loosening the motor mounts and jacking or hoisting the engine until the bolts become accessible. Be sure to raise the engine only the minimum amount necessary to reach these bolts. Remove the distributor cap for clearance. Remove the oil pan bolts, rotate

the engine crankshaft to clear the counterweights, and remove the pan with a twisting motion. On some models, you may have to unbolt the transmission till the pan clears. On 360 HP engines, first raise the transmission to clear the rear of the pan, then raise the front of the engine to remove the pan.

6. When installing the oil pan, be sure the oil strainer will be parallel to and will contact the pan bottom. Use a new gasket and apply sealer to the junctions of the cork and rubber gaskets. The side gaskets should overlap the rear seal. On 360s, be sure the notches in the side gaskets are at the rear. Torque the pan bolts to 200 in. lbs.

7. If it was necessary to jack the engine from its mounts, return it to its proper position at this time. Tighten the engine mount bolts to 75 ft. lbs.

8. Install the engine-to-converter housing strut (if so equipped).

9. From this point, reverse the removal procedure.

400 and 440 V8

1. Disconnect the battery and remove the dipstick.

2. Jack up the vehicle and remove the center steering link from the steering and idler arms.

3. Disconnect the exhaust pipes from the manifolds and secure them out of the way.

4. If there is not sufficient clearance for the oil pan to clear the exhaust pipe, remove the clamp attaching the exhaust pipe to the extension and remove the exhaust pipe.

5. Drain the oil.

6. Remove the dust shield from the torque converter.

7. Remove the oil pan bolts. On some models, it may be necessary to jack the engine off its mounts (1½–2 in.) to reach

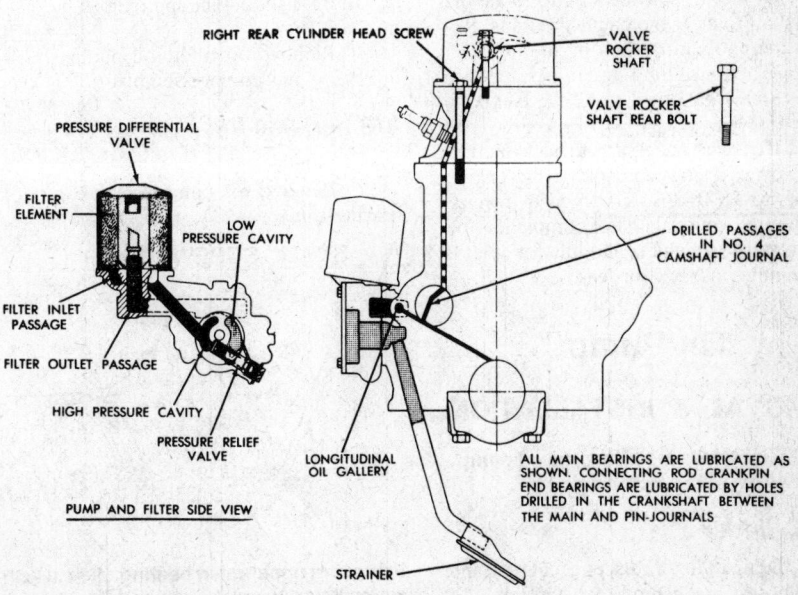

Six-cylinder lubrication system (© Chrysler Corp.)

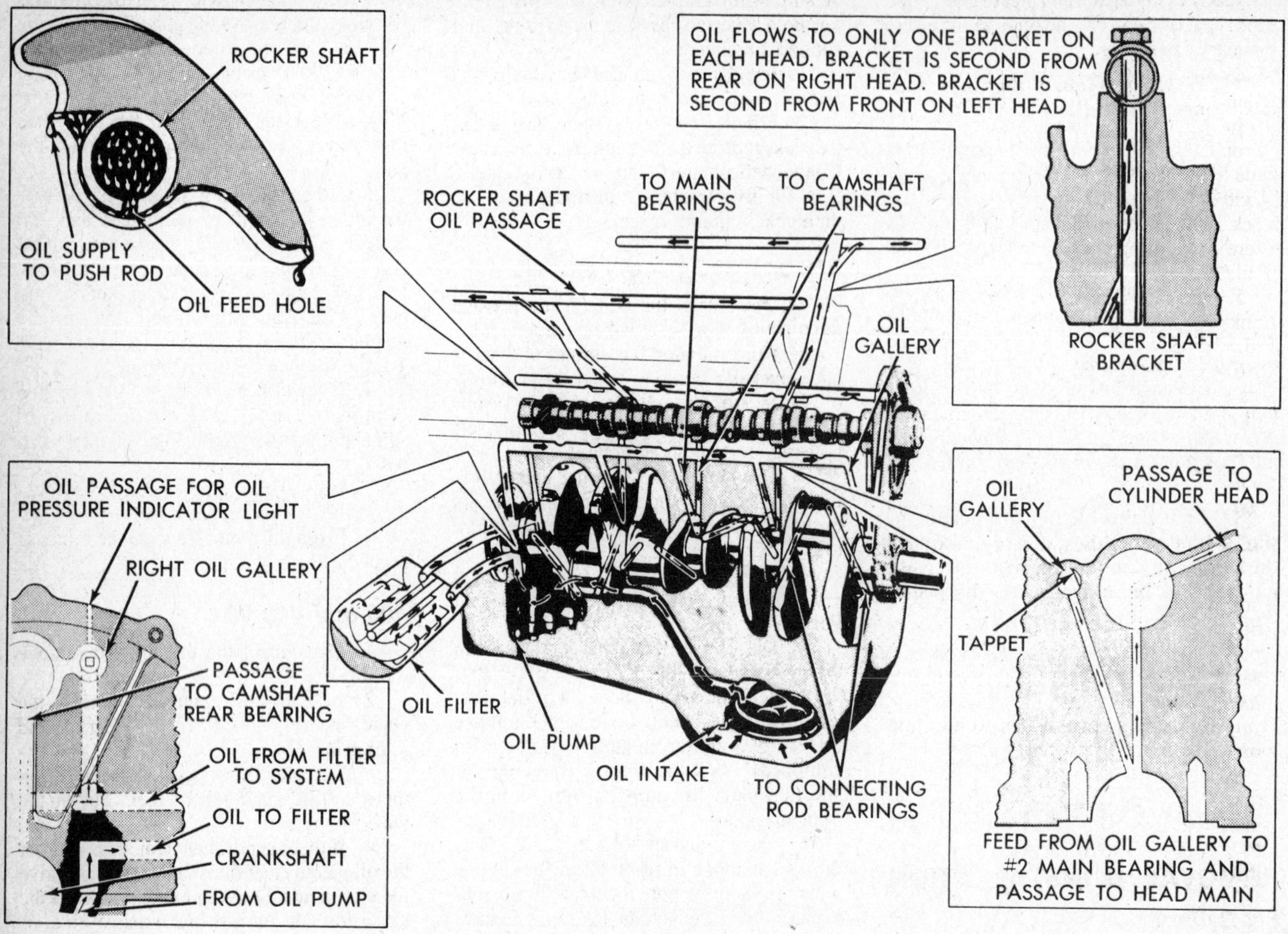

ROCKER SHAFT

OIL SUPPLY TO PUSH ROD

OIL FEED HOLE

OIL FLOWS TO ONLY ONE BRACKET ON EACH HEAD. BRACKET IS SECOND FROM REAR ON RIGHT HEAD. BRACKET IS SECOND FROM FRONT ON LEFT HEAD

ROCKER SHAFT OIL PASSAGE

TO MAIN BEARINGS

TO CAMSHAFT BEARINGS

OIL GALLERY

ROCKER SHAFT BRACKET

OIL PASSAGE FOR OIL PRESSURE INDICATOR LIGHT

RIGHT OIL GALLERY

PASSAGE TO CAMSHAFT REAR BEARING

OIL FROM FILTER TO SYSTEM

OIL TO FILTER

CRANKSHAFT

FROM OIL PUMP

OIL FILTER

OIL PUMP

OIL INTAKE

TO CONNECTING ROD BEARINGS

OIL GALLERY

PASSAGE TO CYLINDER HEAD

TAPPET

FEED FROM OIL GALLERY TO #2 MAIN BEARING AND PASSAGE TO HEAD MAIN

V8 (through 360 cu. in.) lubrication system (© Chrysler Corp.)

the oil pan bolts. Do this by loosening the motor mounts and jacking or hoisting the engine. Raise the engine only the minimum amount required to reach the bolts. When removing the oil pan, be sure to rotate the crankshaft to clear the counterweights. Remove the pan with a twisting motion.

8. When installing the oil pan, be sure to use a new gasket. Torque the pan bolts to 200 in. lbs.

9. If it was necessary to jack the engine, lower it now and torque the engine mounts to 75 ft. lbs. To proceed, reverse the order of removal. After completion, be sure to start the vehicle and idle for at least five minutes. Check for leaks.

Oil Pump

REMOVAL & INSTALLATION

NOTE: Before installing the oil pump, prime it by filling with engine oil.

Six Cylinder

1. Drain radiator, disconnect upper and lower hoses, and remove fan shroud.
2. Raise vehicle on hoist, support front of engine with jackstand placed under right front corner of oil pan, and remove engine mount bolts. Do not support engine at crankshaft pulley or vibration damper.

3. Raise the engine approximately 1½–2 in.

4. Remove oil filter, oil pump attaching bolts, and pump assembly.

318 and 360 V8

1. Remove oil pan.
2. Remove oil pump from rear main bearing cap.

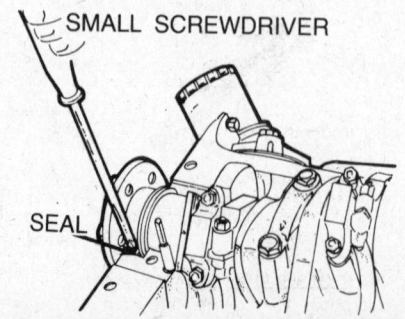

SMALL SCREWDRIVER

SEAL

Removing upper main bearing oil seal with screwdriver. View showed with engine out of car. (© Chrysler Corp.)

400 and 440 V8

1. The oil pump is located on the bottom side of the engine block, at the filter.
2. Removal consists of taking out the attaching bolts and removing the pump and filter as an assembly.
3. To install the pump, reverse the removal procedure.

Rear Main Seal

REPLACEMENT

Service replacement seals are of split, rubber-type composition. This type of seal makes it possible to replace the upper half of the rear main oil seal without removing the engine from the car, or the crankshaft from the engine. When installing rubber seals, they must be replaced as a set and cannot be combined with the rope type rear main seal. The following procedure is for removing the rope type seal and replacing it with the rubber type seal.

1. Remove the oil pan.
2. Remove the rear seal retainer and the rear main bearing cap.

3. Remove the lower rope seal by carefully prying from the side with a small screwdriver.

4. To remove the upper rope seal, drive up on either exposed end of the seal with a 6 in. piece of ³⁄₁₆ in. brazing rod. When the opposite end of the seal starts to protrude from the block, have an assistant grasp it with pliers and gently pull it from the block while the opposite end is being driven. There are also screw type extractor tools available.

5. Wipe crankshaft clean and lightly oil crankshaft and new seal before installing seal.

6. If necessary, loosen all main bearing caps slightly to lower the crankshaft. This will ease installation.

—— CAUTION ——

Do not allow the crankshaft to drop enough to let the main bearings become displaced on the crankshaft.

7. Hold the seal tightly against the crankshaft with thumb pressure (with paint stripe to the rear) and install the seal in the block groove. Rotate the crankshaft if necessary while installing the seal in the groove. *Make sure the sharp edges on the block groove do not cut or nick the rear of the seal.*

8. Install lower half of seal (with paint stripe to the rear) into the lower seal retainer. On 318s only, insert the cap seals into the slots in the bearing cap; the one with the yellow paint goes on the right side.

Be sure the narrow edge is facing up. Pull outward on the small end of the seal until its edge lines up with the shoulder. On 360s only, apply a dot of sealer to the main bearing cap surface adjacent to the seal. *Do not use sealer on any other engine.* On all engines, lightly oil the seal lips before installation.

9. Install rear main bearing cap.

10. Tighten all main bearing caps to 85 ft. lbs.

NOTE: Before tightening the main bearing caps, make sure all main bearings are located in their proper positions.

CLUTCH

All models utilize a single, dry-plate clutch operated by a pedal suspended under the dash. All models are equipped with a return spring; some models have centrifugal rollers assembled between the pressure plate and cover.

NOTE: It is normal for the centrifugal rollers to rattle before the cover is installed.

REMOVAL

1. Remove the transmission.
2. Remove the clutch housing pan.
3. Disconnect the fork return spring from the clutch housing and release fork.
4. Remove the spring washer fastening the fork rod to the torque shaft lever pin. Remove the pin from the rod and release the fork.
5. Remove the sleeve assembly and clutch release bearing from the clutch release fork. Remove the release fork and boot from the clutch housing.
6. Punch-mark the clutch cover and flywheel so they may be installed in the same relative positions.
7. Loosen the clutch cover attaching screws one or two turns at-a-time, in rotation, to avoid bending the cover.
8. Remove the clutch assembly. Be careful not to contaminate the clutch with grease or oil.

INSTALLATION

1. Lightly lubricate the drive pinion bushing in the end of the crankshaft. Use

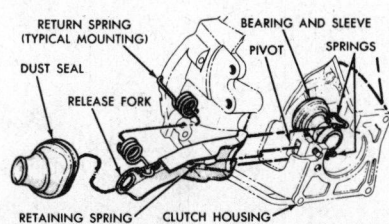

Clutch release fork, bearing and sleeve
(© Chrysler Corp)

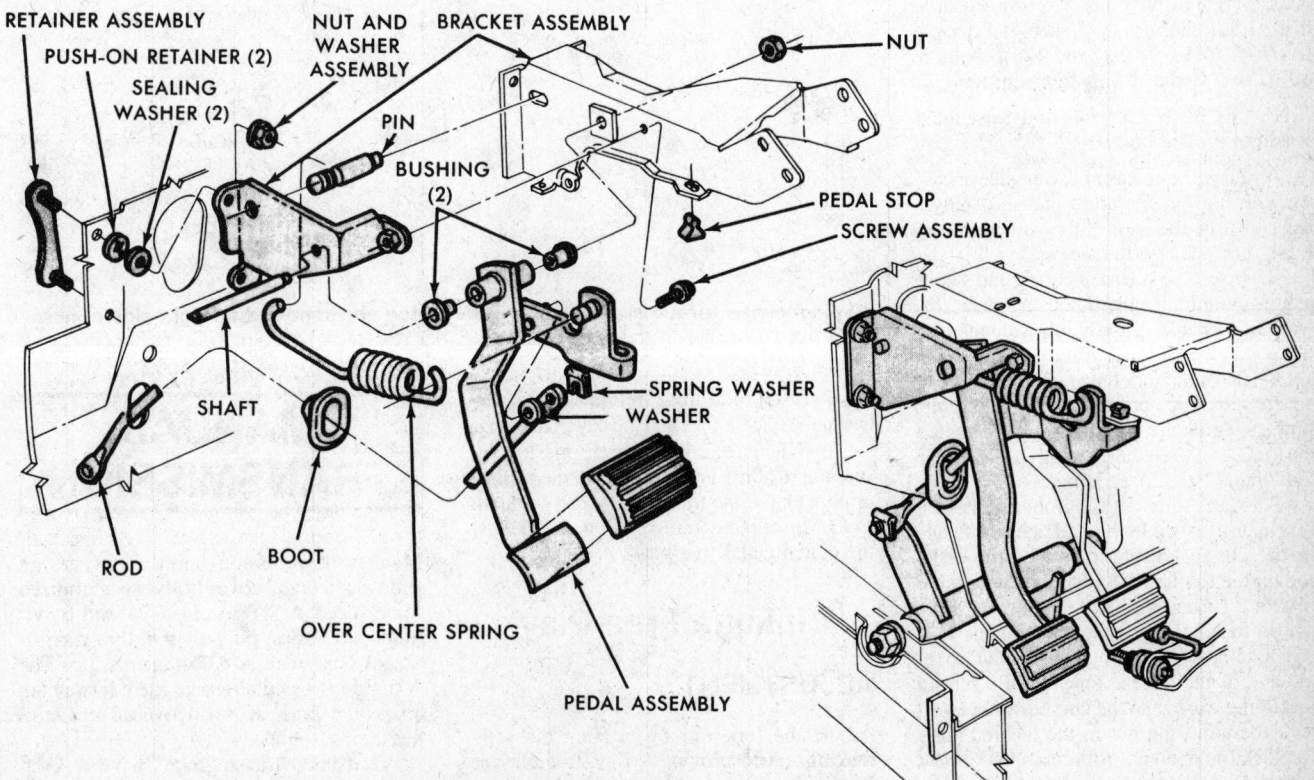

Clutch pedal and linkage for Aspen, Diplomat, Lebaron and Volare

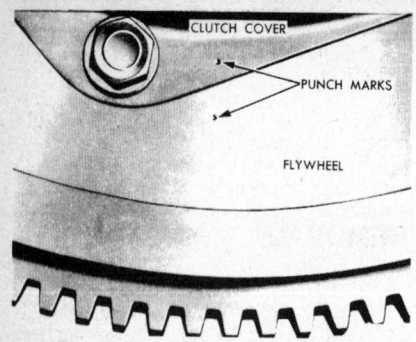

Marking clutch and flywheel (© Chrysler Corp.)

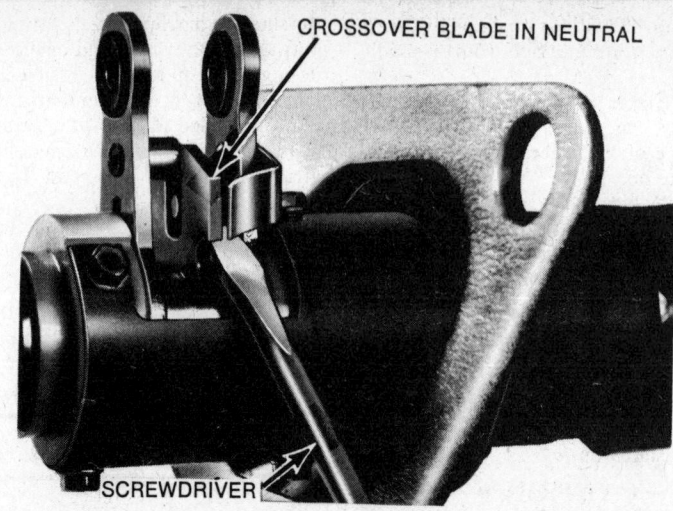

Holding cross-over blades in neutral (© Chrysler Corp)

about ½ teaspoonful of long-life chassis grease. Lubricant should be inserted in the cavity in front of the bushing. Also coat the inner surface of the bushing with a light film of grease.

2. Thoroughly clean the surfaces of the flywheel and pressure plate with fine sandpaper. All oil or grease must be removed at this time.

3. Position the clutch disc, pressure plate and cover in the mounting position. Springs on disc damper must be facing away from the flywheel. *Do not touch the disc facing at any time, and especially avoid disc contact with oil or grease.* Insert a clutch disc aligning arbor or suitable substitute (such as a spare transmission input shaft) through the disc hub and into the bushing.

4. Align the punch marks that were made at removal. Install the clutch cover bolts, but do not tighten them.

5. Tighten all bolts a few turns at-a-time in an alternate sequence. Torque ⁵⁄₁₆ in. bolts to 17 ft. lbs. and ³⁄₈ in. bolts to 30 ft. lbs. Remove the alignment tool.

NOTE: 11 in. clutches don't use lock-washers on the bolts.

6. Pack the release bearing sleeve cavity with high temperature grease. Apply a light film of the same lubricant to the release fork pads on the sleeve.

7. Insert the release bearing and sleeve assembly into the clutch housing as far forward as possible. Lightly lubricate the fork fingers and retaining spring.

8. Insert the fork fingers under the clutch sleeve retaining springs, while at the same time engaging the fork retaining spring into the fork pivot. Retaining springs on the sleeve must have lateral freedom.

9. Make sure that the groove in the seal is properly seated in the seal opening flange in the clutch housing. Replace the pedal rod on the torque shaft lever pin and secure it with a spring washer.

10. Insert the threaded end of the fork rod assembly in the opening provided in the end of the release fork rod. Be sure to install the washer so the curved surface will lock the adjusting nut in the tapered hole. Replace the eye end of the fork rod on the torque shaft lever pin and lock it with a spring washer.

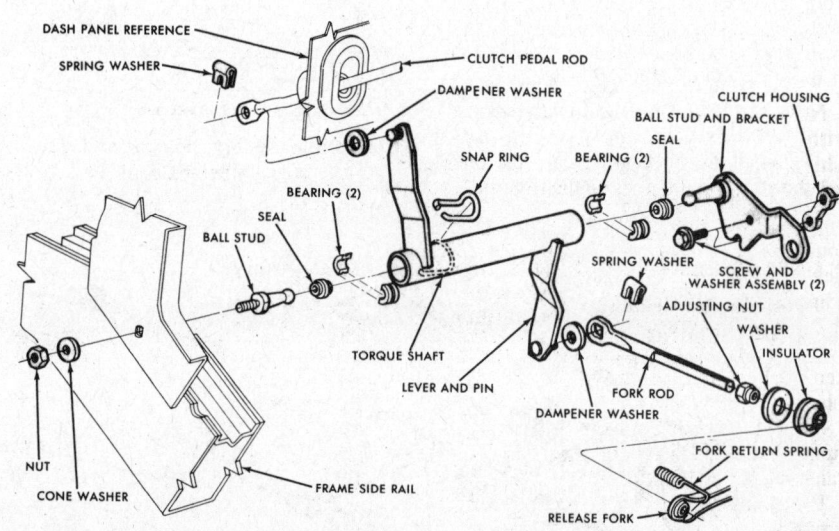

Typical clutch torque shaft linkage. Note clutch adjusting nut on right side of illustration (© Chrysler Corp.)

11. Install the fork return spring between the release fork and the clutch housing.

12. When installing the transmission, be sure not to allow grease to get on the splines or pilot end of the transmission drive pinion.

13. Install the transmission and adjust the clutch pedal free-play.

Linkage Free-Play

ADJUSTMENT

Adjust the fork rod by rotating the self-locking nut to provide ⁵⁄₃₂ in. free-play at the fork end. This adjustment will result in the proper 1 in. free-play at the clutch pedal.

MANUAL TRANSMISSION

Manual transmission applications are as follows: a side cover fully synchronized three-speed A-230 used on V8 and 6-cylinder models; a side cover fully synchronized four-speed A-833 transmission. The A-833 four-speed has been offered with both sixes and V8s, with an overdrive fourth gear, since 1976.

All manual transmissions have a serial number stamped on a pad on the right side of the case. The third, fourth, and fifth digits are the transmission model number.

For manual transmission overhaul procedures, please refer to "Manual Transmission Overhaul" in the Unit Repair section.

REMOVAL & INSTALLATION

1. Jack up the car, and safely support it with jackstands.
2. Drain the transmission fluid.
3. Remove the shift rods from the transmission levers.
4. After marking both parts for reassembly, detach the driveshaft and the rear universal joint. Carefully pull the shaft yoke out of the transmission extension housing.

─── CAUTION ───

Don't nick or scratch the ground surface on the sliding spline yoke.

5. Disconnect the speedometer cable, transmission controlled spark switch, and back-up light switch. On the A-390, disconnect the gearshift operating levers. Remove the console, if necessary, and unbolt the shifter from the extension housing on floor-shift models. The shift lever unbolts from the shifter, except on later four-speed overdrive models. On these, insert a 0.014 in. feeler gauge alongside the driver's side of the lever and pull the lever out.

NOTE: Some earlier models equipped with the A-833 have exhaust systems which will have to be partially removed for clearance.

6. Unfasten the transmission extension housing from the center crossmember and jack up the engine and transmission about 1 in.
7. Remove the center crossmember.
8. Support the transmission on a jack. Remove the bolts which secure the transmission to the clutch housing.
9. Slide the transmission back until the input shaft clears the clutch disc. Lower the transmission and remove it from the car.
10. Installation is in the reverse order of removal. Lubricate the input shaft pilot bearing in the flywheel and the bearing retainer pilot (for the clutch release sleeve). Do not lubricate the clutch splines or the clutch release levers.
11. Position the transmission so the drive pinion is centered in the clutch housing bore. Push the transmission forward until the pinion shaft enters the clutch disc. Place the transmission in gear. Twist the output shaft until the splines are in alignment. Push the transmission forward until it is seated against the clutch housing.

─── CAUTION ───

As soon as the transmission pinion is inside the clutch, the transmission unit must be supported with a jack or like support, so that the weight is not placed on the input shaft. While the transmission is being held in position by the jack, the bolts and mounts can be attached.

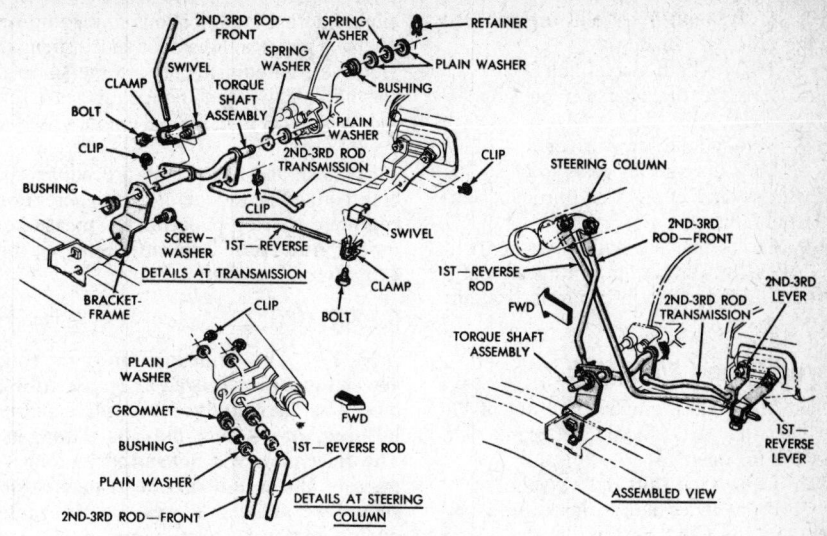

Typical three-speed column shift linkage (© Chrysler Corp)

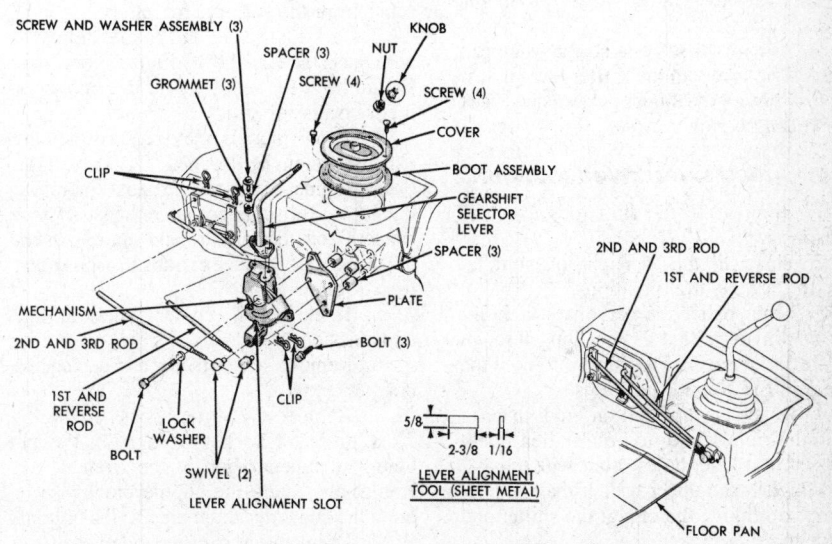

Typical three-speed floor shift linkage (© Chrysler Corp.)

12. Replace the transmission housing bolts. Torque them to 50 ft. lbs. With a drift align the crossmember bolt holes and install the bolts. Torque them to 40–50 ft. lbs. Remove the engine support fixture. Tighten the engine mount-to-crossmember bolt. Install the gearshift linkage, and make adjustments. Connect the driveshaft and universal joints. Connect the exhaust system and fill the transmission with lubricant.

LINKAGE ADJUSTMENT

Column Shift

1. Loosen both shift rod swivels at the ends of the two long rods from the column.
2. Make sure the transmission levers are in the Neutral or middle positions.
3. Move the column shift lever into Neutral to line up the locating slots in the

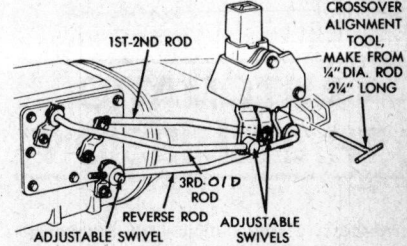

Three speed overdrive shift linkage adjustment

bottom of the steering column shift housing and the bearing housing. Install a tool into the slot to hold the lever in place.

4. Place a screwdriver between the crossover blade (between the two column levers) and the second-third (the upper one)

lever so that both lever pins are engaged by the crossover blade.

5. Tighten both swivel bolts.

6. Remove the gearshift housing locating tool.

7. Remove the screwdriver.

8. Shift through all gears to check the adjustment and cross-over (through Neutral) smoothness.

9. Check that the ignition switch will lock with the shift lever in Reverse only, without applying any pressure to the shift lever.

Three-Speed Floorshift

1. Make an alignment tool out of ¹⁄₁₆ in. thick metal. It should be ⅝ in. wide and 2⅜ in. long.

2. Detach the shift rod swivels.

3. From under the car, insert the alignment tool through the shifter levers and the shifter to hold the levers in the Neutral positions.

4. Place both shift levers on the transmission side cover in the Neutral or middle position.

5. Adjust the swivels so that they can be installed freely in the shifter lever holes.

6. Remove the alignment tool and check the shifting action.

Four-Speed Overdrive Floorshift

1. Remove all the shift rods from the transmission shift levers.

2. Place all the transmission shift levers in their Neutral positions.

3. From under the car, insert a ¼ in. rod or drill bit about 2¼ in. long through the shifter levers and the shifter to hold the levers in the Neutral positions.

4. Rotate the threaded shift rods to make them the right length to be installed freely in the shifter lever holes. Start with the 1–2 rod which is the upper rod. It may be necessary to remove the clip at the shifter end to rotate this rod.

5. Remove the aligning tool and check the shifting action.

slight internal modifications in the number of clutch plates and discs for added strength. However, all adjustments are the same as for the A-904. Fleet, police, and taxi service 6 cylinder and 318 V8 engines use the A-727 also.

Removal and installation procedures for both Torqueflite models are given here. **For complete service procedures, please refer to "Automatic Transmissions" in the Unit Repair section.**

REMOVAL

NOTE: The transmission and converter must be removed as an assembly; otherwise, the converter drive plate, pump bushing, or oil seal may be damaged. The drive plate will not support a load—none of the weight of the transmission should be allowed to rest on the plate during removal. Also, removal and installation will vary slightly from this procedure by car and by model.

1. Disconnect the negative (ground) cable from the battery, for safety.

2. Jack up the car and safely support it with jackstands. The hydraulic floor jack should be at the ready to aid in removal of the transmission unit.

3. Some models may require that the exhaust system be dropped. Disconnect the exhaust pipe from the exhaust manifold flange, and disconnect all exhaust system hangers from the car. Drop the entire system.

4. Remove engine to transmission struts, if so equipped.

5. Remove oil cooler lines at the transmission.

6. Remove starter motor and cooler line bracket.

7. Remove converter access cover.

8. Using a socket wrench on the vibration dampener bolt at the front of the crankshaft, rotate the engine clockwise to bring the converter drain plug to the bottom.

9. Drain the converter and loosen the pan to drain the transmission.

10. Matchmark the converter and drive plate to aid in later installation. The crankshaft flange bolt circle, inner and outer circle of holes in the drive plate, and the four tapped holes in the front face of the converter all have one hole offset so these parts will be installed in their original positions. This maintains balance of the engine and converter.

11. Rotate the engine clockwise with the socket wrench on the vibration dampener bolt to position the bolts attaching the torque converter to the drive plate, and remove them.

12. Match mark the parts for reassembly, then disconnect the drive shaft at the rear universal joint. Carefully pull the shaft assembly out of the extension housing.

13. Disconnect the wire connector from the back up light and neutral starting switch.

14. Disconnect the gearshift rod and torque shaft assembly from the transmission.

NOTE: When you disassemble the linkage rods from the levers that use plastic grommets as retainers, the grommets should be replaced with new ones. Use a small pry bar to pry the rod from the grommet in the lever, then cut away the old grommet. Use pliers to snap the new grommet into the lever, and the rod into the grommet.

15. Disconnect the throttle rod from the lever at the left side of the transmission. Remove the linkage bellcrank from the transmission if so equipped.

16. Remove the oil filler tube and speedometer cable.

17. Support the rear of the engine safely with blocks or jackstands.

18. Raise the transmission slightly with the hydraulic jack to relieve the load on the supports.

19. Remove the bolts securing the transmission mount to the crossmember and the crossmember to the frame, then remove the crossmember.

AUTOMATIC TRANSMISSION

Two different Torqueflite transmission models are used in all models. The model may be identified by the part number, which is stamped on a pad on the left side of the case pan flange. The A-727 transmission has a more gradual slope to the converter housing than does the A-904. Generally speaking, all 6 cylinder and 318 V8 engines for normal use are equipped with a model A-904 Torque-flite, while all larger V8s use the model A-727. Most late model V8s use an A-904 LA transmission, which includes

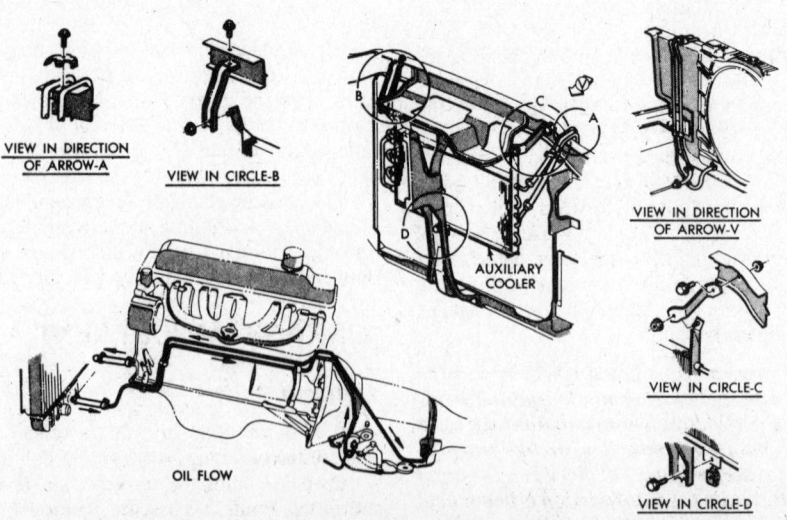

Oil flow—transmission oil coolers, Slant Six engine (© Chrysler Corp.)

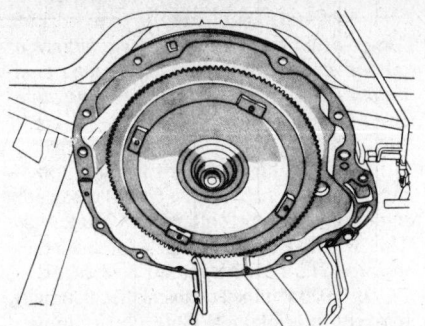

Attach a C-clamp to automatic transmission bell housing to keep torque converter in place when removing engine (© Chrysler Corp.)

DRAIN PLUG

1/8 INCH HOLE

Converter and drive plate markings (© Chrysler Corp.)

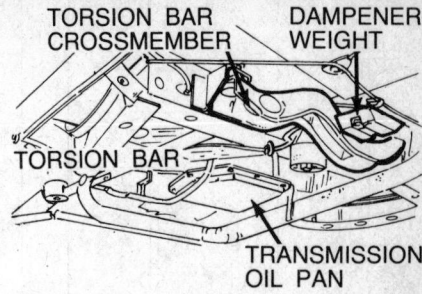

TORSION BAR CROSSMEMBER

DAMPENER WEIGHT

TORSION BAR

TRANSMISSION OIL PAN

Rear torsion bar crossmember assembly, showing dampener weight (© Chrysler Corp.)

NOTE: Cars with longitudinal torsion bars (in line with the chassis) have a torsion bar anchor crossmember, which remains in place, requiring a careful downward tilt of the front of the transmission as it is being removed. If a vibration dampening weight is bolted to the rear of the extension housing (the long tapered housing on the rear of the transmission), it must be removed to provide additional clearance. These cars also have access holes through the crossmembers for the three bolts which retain the weight mounting bracket on the extension housing.

20. Remove all bellhousing bolts.
21. Carefully work the transmission and converter assembly rearward, off the engine block dowels, and disengage the converter hub from the end of the crankshaft.

NOTE: Attach a small C-clamp to the edge of the bellhousing to hold converter in place during transmission removal.

22. Lower transmission and remove assembly from under the car.

INSTALLATION

NOTE: The transmission and converter must be installed as an assembly; otherwise, the converter drive plate, pump bushing, and oil seal will be damaged. The drive plate will not support a load, so none of the weight of the transmission should be allowed to rest on the plate during installation.

1. Coat the converter hub hole in the crankshaft with multi-purpose grease. Place the transmission and converter assembly on a hydraulic floor jack and position the assembly under the car for installation. Raise or tilt as necessary until the transmission is aligned with the engine.
2. Rotate the converter so the mark on

the converter (made during removal) will align with the mark on the drive plate. The offset holes in the plate are located next to a 1/8 in. hole in the inner circle of the plate. Carefully work the transmission assembly forward over the engine block dowels with the converter hub entering the crankshaft opening.

3. After the transmission is in position, install the converter housing bolts and tighten to 28 ft. lbs. If so equipped, install the vibration dampener weight on the rear of the extension housing.
4. Install the crossmember onto the frame and lower transmission, in order to fasten the mount on the extension housing to the crossmember.
5. The jack or stands supporting the transmission may now be removed.
6. Install the oil filter tube and speedometer cable.
7. Connect the throttle rod to the transmission lever.
8. Connect the gearshift rod and torque shaft assembly to the transmission lever and frame.
9. Place the wire connector on the combination back-up light and Neutral/Park starter switch.
10. Carefully guide the sliding yoke into the extension housing and on the output splines. Align the marks made at removal, then connect the driveshaft to the rear axle pinion shaft yoke.
11. Rotate the engine clockwise as needed to install the converter to drive plate bolts, matching the marks made at removal. Tighten to 22.5 ft. lbs.
12. Install the converter access cover.
13. Install the starter motor and cooler line bracket. Tighten the cooler lines to the transmission fittings.
14. Install the engine-to-transmission struts, if so equipped.
15. Replace the exhaust system if it was distrubed for clearance.
16. Adjust shift and throttle linkage. Refill the transmission with Dexron® II type automatic transmission fluid.

DRIVESHAFT AND U-JOINTS

The driveshaft is a one-piece tubular shaft with two universal joints, one at each end. The front joint yoke serves as a slip yoke on the transmission output shaft. The rear universal joint is of the type that must be disassembled to be removed.

REMOVAL & INSTALLATION

You can avoid loss of lubricant from the rear of the transmission by raising the rear of the car before removing the driveshaft. In any case, keep, a clean rag handy to plug the end of the extension housing when the driveshaft is removed.

1. Match-mark the driveshaft, U-joint and pinion flange before disassembly. These marks must be realigned during reassembly to maintain the balance of the driveline. Failure to align them may result in excessive vibration.
2. Remove both of the clamps from the differential pinion yoke and slide the driveshaft forward slightly to disengage the U-joint from the pinion yoke. Tape the two loose U-joint bearings together to prevent them from falling off.

—— **CAUTION** ——
Do not disturb the bearing assembly retaining strap. Never allow the driveshaft to hang from either of the U-joints. Always support the unattached end of the shaft to prevent damage to the joints.

3. Lower the rear end of the driveshaft and gently slide the front yoke/driveshaft assembly rearward, disengaging the assembly from the transmission output shaft. Be careful not to damage the splines or the surface on which the output shaft seal rides.
4. Check the transmission output shaft seal for signs of leakage.

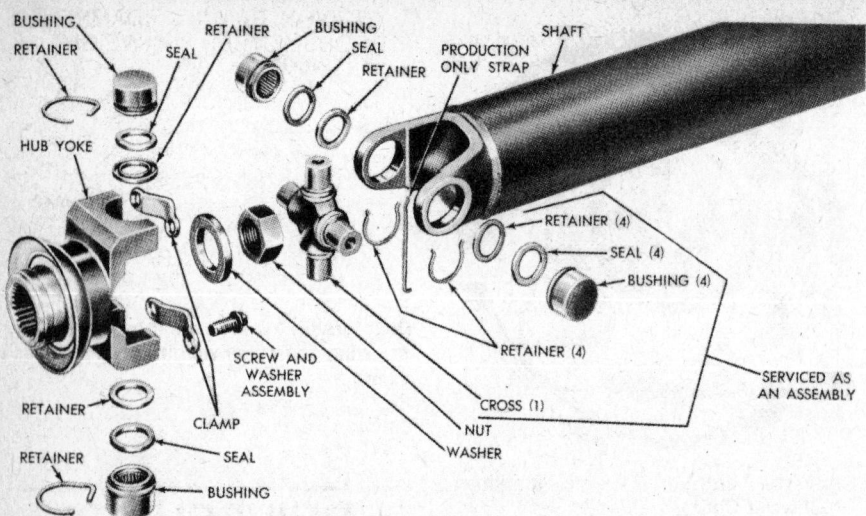

Rear driveshaft universal joint assembly—remove the two clamps to remove driveshaft (© Chrysler Corp.)

5. Installation is in the reverse order of removal. Be sure to align the matchmarks. The torque for the clamp bolts is 14 ft. lbs.

U-JOINT OVERHAUL

For all U-Joint overhaul procedures, please refer to "U-Joint/CV-Joint Overhaul" in the Unit Repair section.

REAR AXLE

Four different rear axle assemblies have been used. A 7¼ in. (ring gear diameter) unitized carrier axle is used with all six cylinder applications and on some late production 318 V8 models. An 8¼ in. or 9¼ in. unitized carrier axle is installed in most models with 318, or 360 V8s.

These axles can be visually identified as follows:

The 1978–79 7¼ in. axle has a 9 bolt rear cover with a filler plug. The 1980–83 7¼ in. has 10 bolts and an oval shape. The 8¼ in. has a 10 bolt rear cover without a filler plug; 1978 on there is a filler plug in the cover. The 9¼ in. has a 12 bolt cover.

Some cars are equipped with the Sure-Grip limited slip differential. Identification of the Sure-Grip rear axle can be made easily by lifting both rear wheels off the ground and turning them. If both rear wheels turn in the same direction simultaneously, the car has the Sure-Grip axle.

All axles have a ratio identification tag under one of the cover or carrier bolts.

Axle Shaft, Bearing, and Seal

REMOVAL & INSTALLATION

Because the axle shafts are slightly different from one rear axle assembly to another, individual service procedures are required for each axle shaft assembly. Two very important points to remember when servicing any rear axle assembly are:

1. Always elevate *both* rear wheels when performing any rear axle service, or when using the engine or other means to rotate the axle.

2. On cars equipped with a Sure-Grip differential, you must never rotate one axle shaft without rotating the other. If it is necessary to rotate one of the axle shafts, *both* shafts must be in position and both must be rotated. Otherwise, alignment of the axle shafts will be very difficult.

NOTE: This procedure also covers axle shaft end-play adjustment, on those axles on which it is possible.

7¼ in. Axle

NOTE: Whenever this axle assembly is serviced, both the brake support plate gaskets and the inner axle shaft oil seal must be renewed. There is no provision for adjusting axle shaft end-play.

1. Support the rear of the car and remove the rear wheels.

2. Detach the clips which secure the brake drum to the axle shaft studs and remove the brake drum.

3. Disconnect the brake lines at the wheel cylinders and block off the lines.

4. Through the access hole in the axle shaft flange, remove the axle shaft retaining nuts.

5. Attach a puller or slide hammer to the axle shaft flange and remove the axle shaft.

6. Remove the brake assembly from the axle housing.

7. Remove the axle shaft oil seal from the axle housing.

Never use a torch or other heat source as an aid in removing any axle shaft components as this will result in serious damage to the axle assembly.

8. Place the axle shaft housing retaining collar in a vise. With a chisel, cut deeply into the retaining collar at 90° intervals. This will loosen it enough so it can be removed. The bearing can be pressed off.

9. To assemble and install the axle shaft, replace the retainer plate, bearing, and bearing retainer collar on the axle shaft, using a press.

10. Insert new axle shaft oil seals in the axle housing and lightly grease the outside diameter of the bearing.

11. Replace the foam gasket on the studs of the axle housing and install the brake support plate assembly on the axle housing studs. Refit the outer gasket.

12. Very carefully slide the axle shaft assembly through the oil seal and engage the splines of the differential side gear. Using a non-metallic hammer, lightly tap the end of the axle shaft to position the axle shaft bearing in the recess of the axle housing. Install the retainer plate over the axle housing studs and torque the securing nuts to 35 ft. lbs.

13. Reconnect the brake lines to the wheel cylinders and bleed the hydraulic system.

14. Install the brake drum and retaining clips.

15. Refit the rear wheels and lower the car.

8¼ and 9¼ in. Axles

NOTE: There is no provision for adjusting axle shaft endplay on this axle.

1. Raise the vehicle and remove the wheels.

2. Clean all dirt from the housing cover and remove the cover to drain the lubricant.

3. Remove the brake drum.

4. Rotate the differential case until the differential pinion shaft lockscrew can be

Removal of differential pinion shaft lock screw on the 8¼ in. rear axle (© Chrysler Corp.)

removed. Remove the lockscrew and pinion shaft.

5. Push the axle shaft toward the center of the vehicle and remove the C-lock from the groove on the axle shaft.

6. Pull the axle shaft from the housing, being careful not to damage the bearing which remains in the housing.

------ **CAUTION** ------

During Sure-Grip axle shaft removal and installation, DO NOT rotate an axle shaft unless both are in position. Rotation of one shaft without the other in place may result in misalignment of the two spline segments with which the axle shaft spline engages, and will mean difficult realignment procedures when the shaft is installed.

7. Inspect the axle shaft bearings and replace any doubtful parts. Whenever the axle shaft is replaced, the bearings should also be replaced.

8. Remove the axle shaft seal from the bore in the housing, using the button end of the axle shaft.

9. Using a slide hammer, remove the axle shaft bearing from the housing. Do not reuse the bearing or the seal; always install a new axle shaft seal.

10. Check the bearing shoulder in the axle housing for imperfections. These should be smoothed out with a fine file or polish.

11. Clean the axle shaft bearing cavity.

12. Install the axle shaft bearing in the cavity. Be sure that the bearing is not cocked and that it is seated firmly against the shoulder.

13. Install the axle shaft bearing seal. It should be seated beyond the end of the flange face.

14. Insert the axle shaft, making sure the splines do not damage the seal. Be sure the splines are properly engaged with the differential side gear splines.

15. Install the C-locks in the grooves on the axle shafts. Pull the shafts outward so the C-locks seat in the counterbore of the differential side gears.

16. Install the differential pinion shaft through the case and pinions. Install the lockscrew and secure it in position.

17. Clean the housing and gasket surfaces. Install the cover and a new gasket.

NOTE: Replacement gaskets may not be available for differential covers. In this case, the use of MOPAR Silicone Rubber sealant or equivalent is recommended.

Be sure to replace the rear axle ratio identification tag under one of the cover bolts. Refill the axle with lubricant. The proper lubricant level is ⅛–¼ in. below the filler plug hole on axles with the filler plug in the axle housing, and at the filler plug hole to ½ in. below on axles with the filler plug in the cover (1978 and later). MOPAR Hypoid lubricant and Friction Modifier additive must be used in Sure-Grip limited slip units.

18. Install the brake drum and wheel.
19. Lower the vehicle.

JACKING, HOISTING

Jack car at front control arms and at rear under axle housing.

To lift at frame use adapters, so that contact will be made at points shown. Lifting pads must extend beyond sides of supporting structure.

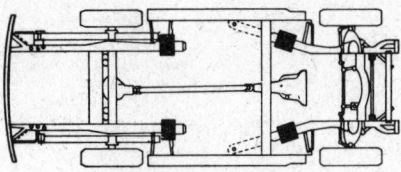

Positioning lift adapter
(© Chrysler Corp)

FRONT SUSPENSION

All Chrysler vehicles in this section utilize a torsion bar type front suspension. Aspen,

Volare, Diplomat, LeBaron to 1981, Mirada, 1981–83 Imperial, 1980–83 Cordoba and 1982 New Yorker (and 1983–84 New Yorker Fifth Avenue) and Gran Fury have transverse torsion bars; all others have longitudinal (parallel to the frame) bars. Compression type lower ball joints are located in the steering knuckles. When servicing the front suspension, it should be kept in mind that *rubber bushings must not be lubricated.* Any front suspension part that contains rubber should be tightened with full vehicle weight on the suspension.

Shock Absorber

REMOVAL & REPLACEMENT

1. Jack the vehicle until the wheels clear the ground. Support the car with jackstands. Remove the front wheels. Remove the washer and nut from shock absorber upper end. Be sure to note the positions of all small parts.

2. Remove the shock absorber lower attaching bolt or nut. Allow the control arm to lower itself.

3. Fully compress the shock absorber by pushing upward. Pull the shock firmly and remove it from the vehicle.

4. Check the shock absorber bushings; if they are worn, cracked, or scored, replace them. Remove and install the bushings with a press, or using a drift and a

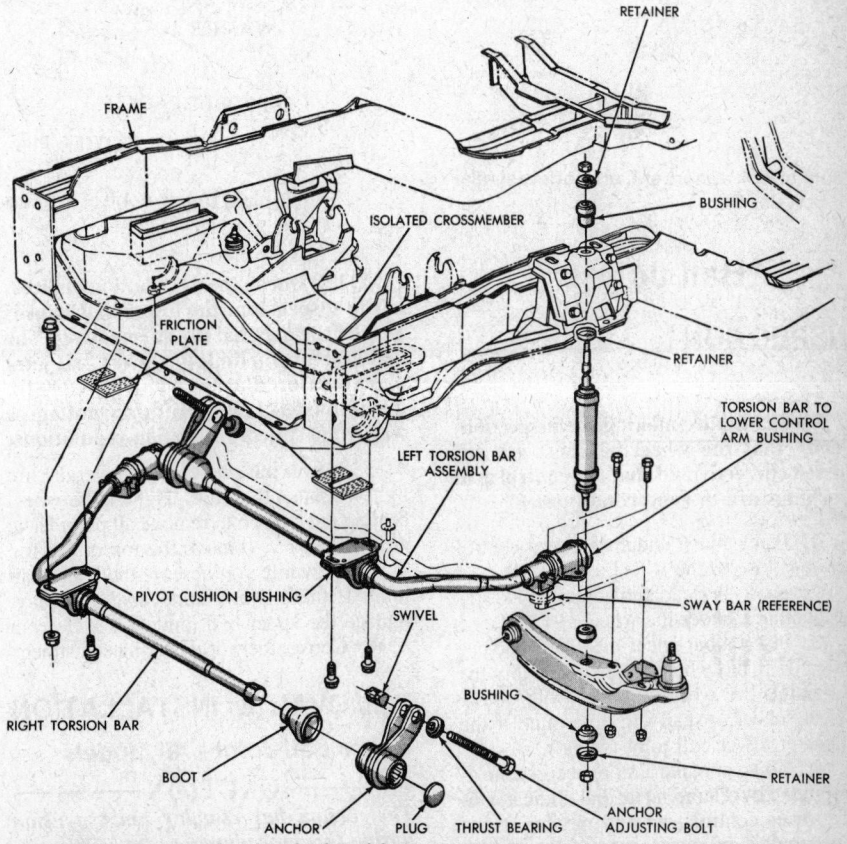

Transverse torsion bar isolated front suspension system (© Chrysler Corp.)

hammer. To ease installation, lubricate with soapy water.

NOTE: Do not use oil to ease installation.

5. Purge the new shock of air by repeatedly extending it in its normal position and compressing it while inverted. It is normal to have more resistance to extension than to compression. Fully compress the new shock absorber. Insert the mount through the upper bushing and install the retainer and nut. Torque the nut to 25 ft. lbs. Be sure all the retainers are installed with the concave side in contact with rubber.

6. Position and align the lower mount of shock absorber. Install the bolt (from the rear) or nut and finger-tighten it. Lower the vehicle and torque the nut to 35 ft. lbs. with the full weight of the vehicle on the wheels.

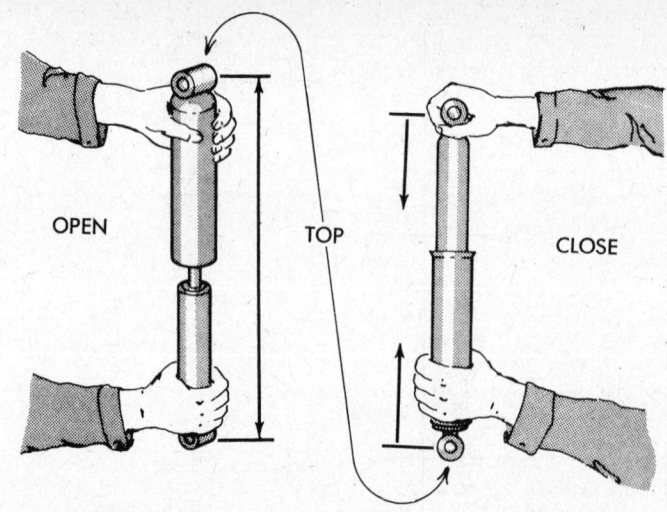

Purging new shock absorbers of air (© Chrysler Corp.)

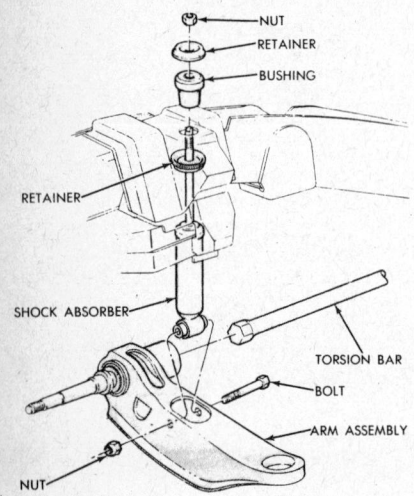

Front shock absorbers, all models similar (©Chrysler Corp.)

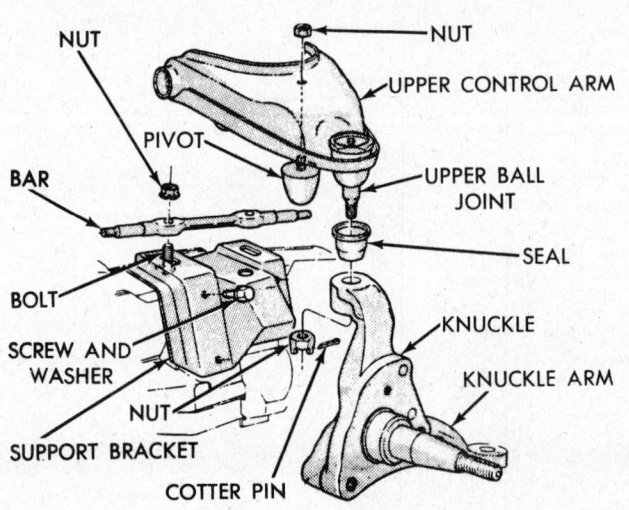

Typical upper control arm and steering knuckle (© Chrysler Corp.)

Ball Joints

INSPECTION

NOTE: Before making the inspection, verify that the wheel bearings are adjusted correctly and that the control arm bushings are in good condition.

1. Place a jack under the lower control arm as close to the wheel as possible.
2. Raise the car until there is 1–2 in. of clearance under the wheel.
3. Insert a bar under the wheel and pry upward. If the wheel raises noticeably the ball joints are worn. While prying on the wheel, check visually to determine if the upper or lower ball joint is worn.
4. You can make a more accurate measurement by clamping a dial indicator to the lower control arm and measuring the lower ball joint stud movement.

NOTE: Due to the distribution of forces in the suspension, the lower ball joint is usually the one that needs replacing. The manufacturer's limit for lower ball joint play, measured at the joint, is 0.030 in. for all models. This limit may not agree with your state's inspection regulations.

5. Lower the jack enough to let the tire lightly contact the floor. Tighten the wheel bearing nut enough to remove all play. Have an assistant try to move the top of the tire in and out while you observe the upper ball joint. If there is any noticeable side play, replace the upper ball joint.
6. Correct the wheel bearing adjustment.

REMOVAL & INSTALLATION
Upper Ball Joint—All Models

———— **CAUTION** ————
The torsion bar remains under tension during this procedure.

NOTE: Turn the ignition key to the OFF or unlocked position.

1. Raise the car by placing a jackstand under the lower control arm as close to the wheel as possible. Remove the wheel.
2. Remove the nut that attaches the upper ball joint to the steering knuckle. Slide a ball joint remover tool onto the lower ball joint stud, allowing the tool to rest on the knuckle arm. Set the tool securely against the upper stud. Apply pressure to the upper stud by tightening the tool and strike the knuckle sharply to loosen the stud. *Never strike the ball joint stud.*

NOTE: The brake caliper may have to be removed for clearance.

3. Unscrew the upper ball joint from the upper control arm and remove it from the vehicle.
4. Position a new ball joint on the upper control arm and screw the joint into the arm. Be careful not to cross thread the joint

in the arm. Torque it to 125 ft. lbs.

5. Position a new seal on the ball joint stud and install the seal in the ball joint making sure the seal is fully seated on the ball joint housing.

6. Position the ball joint stud in the steering knuckle and install the retaining nut. Torque the nut to 100 ft. lbs. Install a new cotter pin.

7. Lubricate the ball joint. Adjust the wheel alignment.

Lower Ball Joint—Aspen, Volare, Diplomat, LeBaron to 1981, Mirada, 1980–83 Cordoba, 1981–83 Imperial, 1982 New Yorker, 1983–85 New Yorker Fifth Avenue, and Gran Fury

NOTE: Turn the ignition key to the OFF or unlocked position.

1. Remove the lower control arm rebound bumper.

2. Raise the vehicle so the front suspension drops to the downward limit of its travel. Position jackstands beneath the front frame for extra support.

Remove the lower ball joint with the illustrated tool. Don't try to free the ball joint completely with tool alone: see text (© Chrysler Corp.)

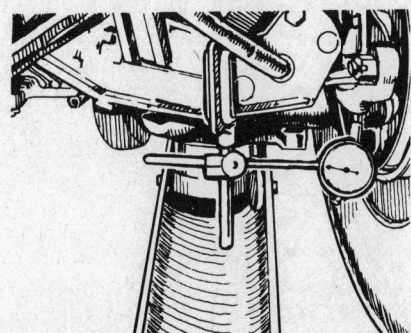

Measuring lower ball joint play; see text for specifications (© Chrysler Corp)

3. Remove the wheel and tire assembly.

4. Remove the brake caliper from its mounts and tie it up out of the way so there is no strain on the flexible brake hose.

5. Remove the hub and rotor assembly, splash shield, and lower shock absorber mounting nut and bolt.

6. Unload the torsion bar by rotating the adjusting bolt counterclockwise.

7. Remove the lower ball joint stud cotter pin and nut. Use a ball joint removal tool to press the ball joint out. *Never strike the ball joint stud.*

8. Press the ball joint out of the lower control arm.

9. Press the new ball joint into the lower control arm.

10. Place a new seal over the ball joint. Press the retainer portion of the seal down over the ball joint housing until it locks into position.

11. Insert the ball joint stud through the opening in the knuckle arm and install the stud retaining nut. Tighten to 100 ft. lbs. Install the cotter pin and lubricate the ball joint.

12. Load the torsion bar by rotating the adjusting bolt clockwise.

13. Install the shock absorber nut and bolt, the splash shield, hub and rotor assembly, and brake caliper. Install the wheel and tire assembly.

14. Adjust the front wheel bearings. Remove the jackstands and lower the car. In-

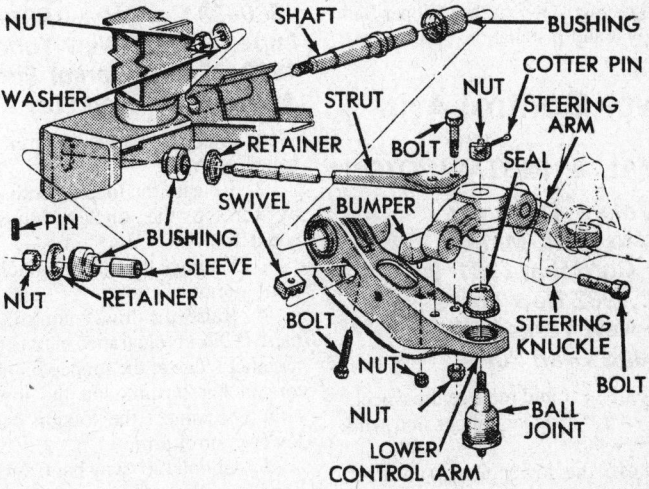

Typical lower control arm

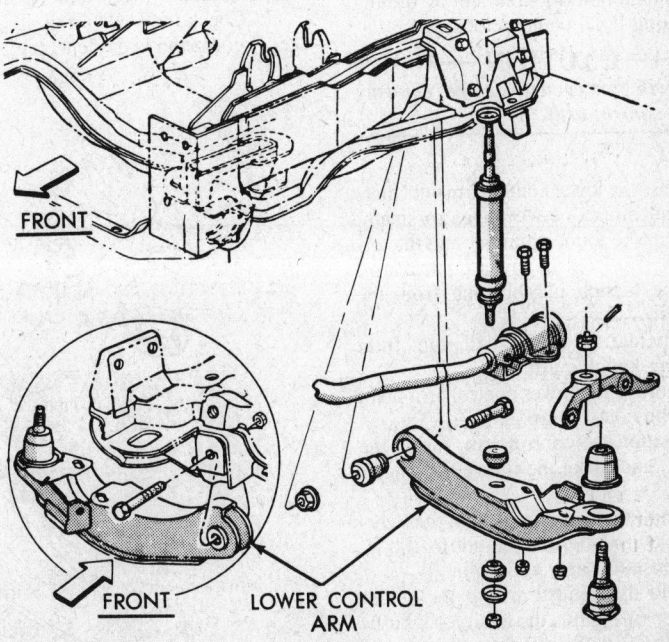

Aspen, 1980 and later Cordoba, Diplomat, LeBaron to 1981, 1981 and later Imperial, Mirada, Volare, 1982 New Yorker, 1983–84 New Yorker 5th Avenue, 1982 and later Gran Fury lower control arm details (© Chrysler Corp.)

stall the rebound bumper. Adjust the front suspension height and alignment.

Upper Control Arm

REMOVAL & INSTALLATION

1. Follow Steps 1–2 of the "Upper Ball Joint Removal and Installation" procedures.
2. On Aspen, Volare, Diplomat, LeBaron, Mirada, 1980–83 Cordoba, 1981–83 Imperial, 1982 New Yorker, 1983–85 New Yorker Fifth Avenue and Gran Fury, remove the rubber splash shield and remove the pivot shaft nuts. It will be easier to reset the alignment if you mark the original pivot bar location. Remove the control arm and pivot shaft assembly.
3. Follow Steps 3–7 of the "Upper Ball Joint Removal and Installation" procedures.

Lower Control Arm

REMOVAL & INSTALLATION

Aspen, Volare, Diplomat, LeBaron to 1981, Mirada, 1980–83 Cordoba, 1981–83 Imperial, 1982 New Yorker, 1983–85 New Yorker Fifth Avenue and Gran Fury

1. Raise the car and remove the wheel.
2. Remove the brake caliper and wire it up.
3. Remove the lower shock absorber attachment.
4. Remove the hub, rotor and splash shield.
5. Unload both torsion bars by turning the adjusting bolts counterclockwise.

—————— CAUTION ——————
Unload both bars even if you are removing only one control arm.

6. Raise the lower control arm until there is 2⅞ in. clearance between the crossmember ledge at the jounce bumper and the torsion bar bushing on the lower control arm. Unbolt the torsion bar bushing from the control arm.
7. Separate the lower ball joint from the steering knuckle arm.
8. Remove the lower control arm pivot bolt and the control arm.
9. Position the control arm, install the pivot bolt, and make the flange nut finger-tight.
10. Install the ball joint stud in the steering knuckle arm, tighten the nut to 100 ft. lbs., and install a new cotter pin.
11. Hold the control arm at the height used in Step 6. Tighten the torsion bar bushing bolts to 70 ft. lbs. Tighten the control arm pivot bolt to 75 ft. lbs.
12. Replace the shock absorber and tighten the lower nut to 35 ft. lbs.

13. Replace the brake assembly. Tighten the caliper bolts to 15 ft. lbs.
14. Turn the adjusting screws clockwise to load the torsion bars.
15. Lower the car and adjust suspension height and wheel alignment.

Torsion Bar

REMOVAL & INSTALLATION

The torsion bars are not interchangeable from right to left. Longitudinal bars are marked with an R or an L, according to their location.

Aspen, Volare, Diplomat, LeBaron to 1981, Mirada, 1980–83 Cordoba, 1981–83 Imperial, 1982 New Yorker, 1983–85 New Yorker Fifth Avenue and Gran Fury

1. Raise the car so the front suspension hangs down.
2. Release the load on both torsion bars by turning the anchor adjusting bolts counterclockwise.
3. Remove the adjusting bolt on the bar to be removed.
4. Raise the lower control arms until there is 2⅞ in. clearance between the crossmember ledge at the jounce bumper and the torsion bar bushing on the lower control arm. Disconnect the torsion bar from the lower control arm.
5. Unbolt the sway bar from the control arm.
6. Unbolt the torsion bar pivot bushing from the crossmember. Remove the bar and anchor assembly from the crossmember.
7. Check the seals on the bar for damage. If corrosion is evident, replace the bar

assembly. Touch up any paint nicks or scratches. Check the adjusting bolt and swivel for corrosion or damage. Replace them if necessary.
8. Slide the balloon seal over the end of the bar with the cupped end toward the hex.
9. Coat the hex end of the bar with high-temperature waterproof grease.
10. Install the hex end of the bar into the anchor bracket. The ears of the bracket should be nearly straight up.
11. Install the bar anchor bracket assembly into the crossmember anchor retainer. Install the adjusting bolt and bearing. Attach the pivot bushing to the crossmember, finger-tight.
12. Support the lower control arms at the height specified in Step 4, and install the torsion bar bushing to lower control arm bolts. Tighten control arm bolts to 70 ft. lbs.
13. Check that the anchor bracket is fully seated in the crossmember. Tighten the pivot bushing bolts to 85 ft. lbs.

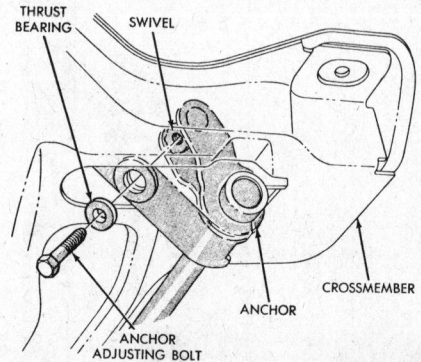

Torsion bar anchor bolt, all longitudinal torsion bar cars (© Chrysler Corp.)

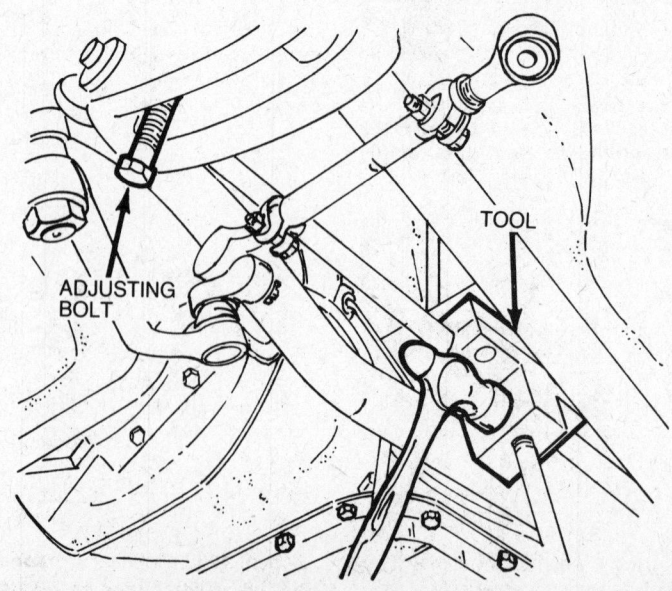

Torsion bar removal (© Chrysler Corp.)

14. Put the balloon seal over the anchor bracket.

15. Install a new sway bar end bolt and tighten to 50 ft. lbs.

16. Load the bars by turning the adjusting bolts clockwise. Lower the car and adjust the front end height.

Wheel Bearing

ADJUSTMENT

1. Jack up or hoist the car, so that the front wheels are off the floor.

2. Remove the hub caps, grease cup, cotter pin and nut lock.

3. Back off on the adjusting nut.

4. Check for free wheel rotation.

5. While rotating the wheel, tighten the wheel bearing adjustment nut to 240–300 in. lbs.

6. Loosen the nut, then retighten the nut finger-tight.

7. Position the nut lock so that one pair of slots is in line with the cotter pin hole and install the cotter pin. This adjustment should give 0.001–0.003 in. end play.

8. Install the rest of the items removed. Repeat the procedure for the other wheel and lower the car.

REAR SUSPENSION

All models utilize rear springs of the semi-elliptical leaf-type. They are engineered to operate with little or no camber under conditions of small or no load. Heavy-duty springs are offered as an option on most models. They serve to increase the stability of the vehicle under conditions of heavy load. All vehicles with leaf springs are constructed with zinc interleaves between the normal leaves. They have the purpose of reducing spring corrosion and lengthening spring life.

Shock Absorber

REMOVAL & INSTALLATION

1. Jack the vehicle under the axle assembly so as to relieve load from the shock absorbers.

2. Remove the nut attaching the shock to the spring mounting plate. To avoid damage to the shock, grip the base of the shock below the base-to-reservoir weld while loosening the retaining nut.

3. At the upper mount, remove the shock attaching bolt or nut and the shock.

4. Purge the new shock of air by repeatedly extending it in its normal position and compressing it while inverted. It is normal to have more resistance to extension than to compression. To install the shock, position it so the upper bolt or nut may be replaced. Hand-tighten only.

5. Align the shock with the spring mounting plate and install the bolt or nut. Hand-tighten only.

6. Lower the vehicle and tighten the shock absorber mounting bolts. Torques are 50 ft. lbs. at the bottom, except for Aspen, Volare, Diplomat, LeBaron, Mirada, 1980–83 Cordoba, 1981–83 Imperial, 1982 New Yorker, 1983–85 New Yorker Fifth Avenue and Gran Fury stud nuts, which are 35 ft. lbs. Top bolt torques are 70 ft. lbs.

Spring

REMOVAL & INSTALLATION

1. Jack up the vehicle and remove the wheels. Position jackstands under the axle so as to relieve weight from the rear springs.

2. Disconnect the rear shock absorbers at the bottom. Lower the axle assembly to allow the rear springs to hang free. Disconnect the rear sway bar links, if so equipped.

3. Remove the U-bolt nuts and remove the bolts and spring plates. Remove the nuts securing the front spring hanger to the body mounting bracket.

4. Remove the rear spring hanger bolts and allow the spring to drop enough to allow the front spring hanger bolts to be removed.

5. Remove the front pivot bolt from the front spring hanger.

6. Remove the shackle nuts and shackle from the rear of the spring.

7. To begin installation, assemble the shackle and bushings in the rear of the spring and hanger. Start the shackle bolt nut. Do not lubricate rubber bushings to ease installation. Do not tighten the bolt nut.

8. Align the front spring hanger with the front spring eye and insert the pivot bolt and nut. Do not tighten them.

9. Install the rear spring hanger-to-body bracket and torque the bolts to 30 ft. lbs. For 1979–84 cars, torque to 35 ft. lbs.

10. With the aid of a helper, raise the spring and insert the bolts in the spring hanger mounting bracket holes. Install the nuts and torque them to 30 ft. lbs. For 1979–83 cars, torque to 35 ft. lbs.

11. Position the axle assembly so it is correctly aligned with the spring center bolt.

12. Position the center bolt over the lower spring plate. Insert the U-bolt and nut. Tighten the U-bolts to 45 ft. lbs. (40 ft. lbs. with 2½ in. diameter axle tube). Connect the rear shock absorbers.

13. Lower the vehicle. On 1978 models, torque the pivot bolts to 125 ft. lbs., and to 105 ft. lbs. on 1979–83 models. Tighten the shackle nuts to 40 ft. lbs. (all 1978), or 35 ft. lbs. (all 1979–84).

BRAKES

A dual (tandem) aluminum master cylinder has been used by Chrysler since 1978. This master cylinder features a removable dual chambered reservoir and a factory anodized body which resists wear and corrosion. The tandem type cylinder provides braking even if one section of the system should develop a leak or fail. A cast iron tandem master cylinder was used through the 1978 model year.

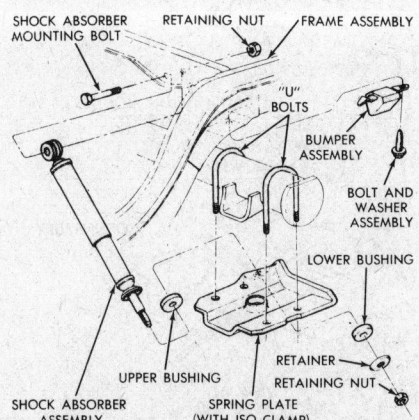

Typical rear shock mounting (© Chrysler Corp.)

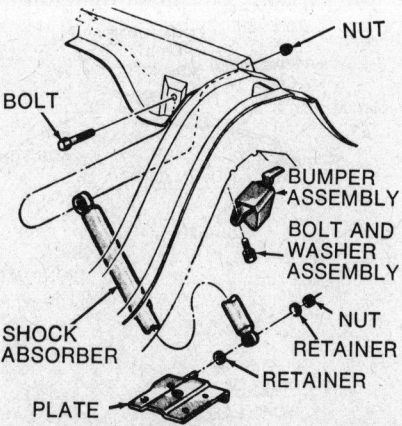

Rear shock absorber installation—Charger, Fury, 1978 and later Monaco

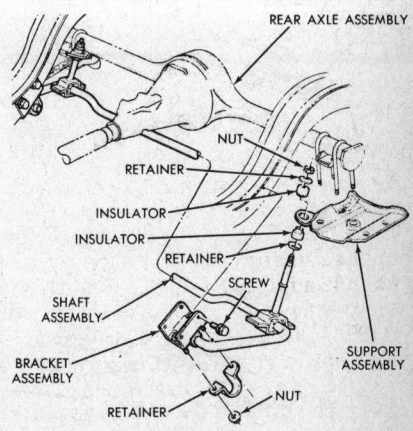

Rear swaybar mounting (© Chrysler Corp.)

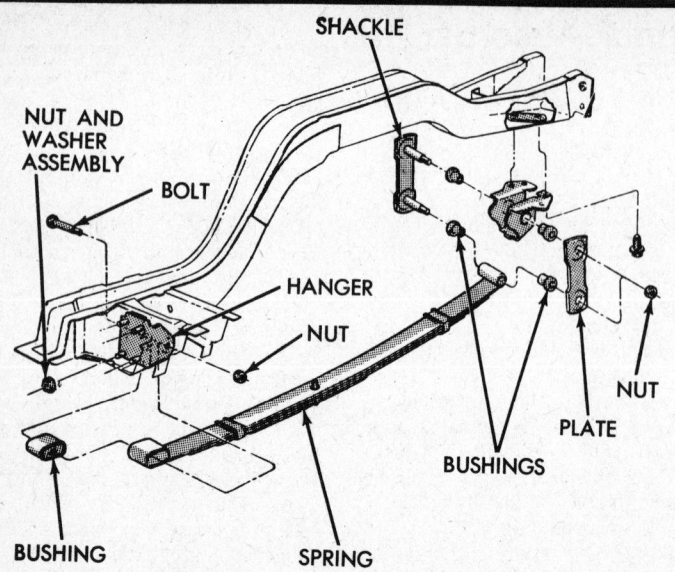

NUT AND WASHER ASSEMBLY

SHACKLE

BOLT

HANGER

NUT

BOLT

PLATE

NUT

BUSHINGS

BUSHING

SPRING

Rear Spring details for Aspen, 1980 and later Cordoba, Diplomat, LeBaron to 1981, 1981 and later Imperial, Mirada, Volare, 1982 New Yorker 5th Avenue, 1983 and later New Yorker 5th Avenue and 1982 and later Gran Fury (© Chrysler Corp.)

All front disc brakes are self-adjusting. All rear drum brakes are self-adjusting, but can also be manually adjusted.

Front disc brakes are standard on all models.

NOTE: Disc brake squeal can be minimized by installing pads with riveted linings in place of the original equipment pads with bonded linings.

NOTE: For brake service procedures refer to the ''Brake Section'' in the Unit Repair Section of this manual.

Master Cylinder

REMOVAL & INSTALLATION

1. Disconnect the brake lines from the master cylinder. Plug the brake line outlets to prevent fluid loss.

2. Remove the nuts that attach the master cylinder to the cowl panel or brake booster.

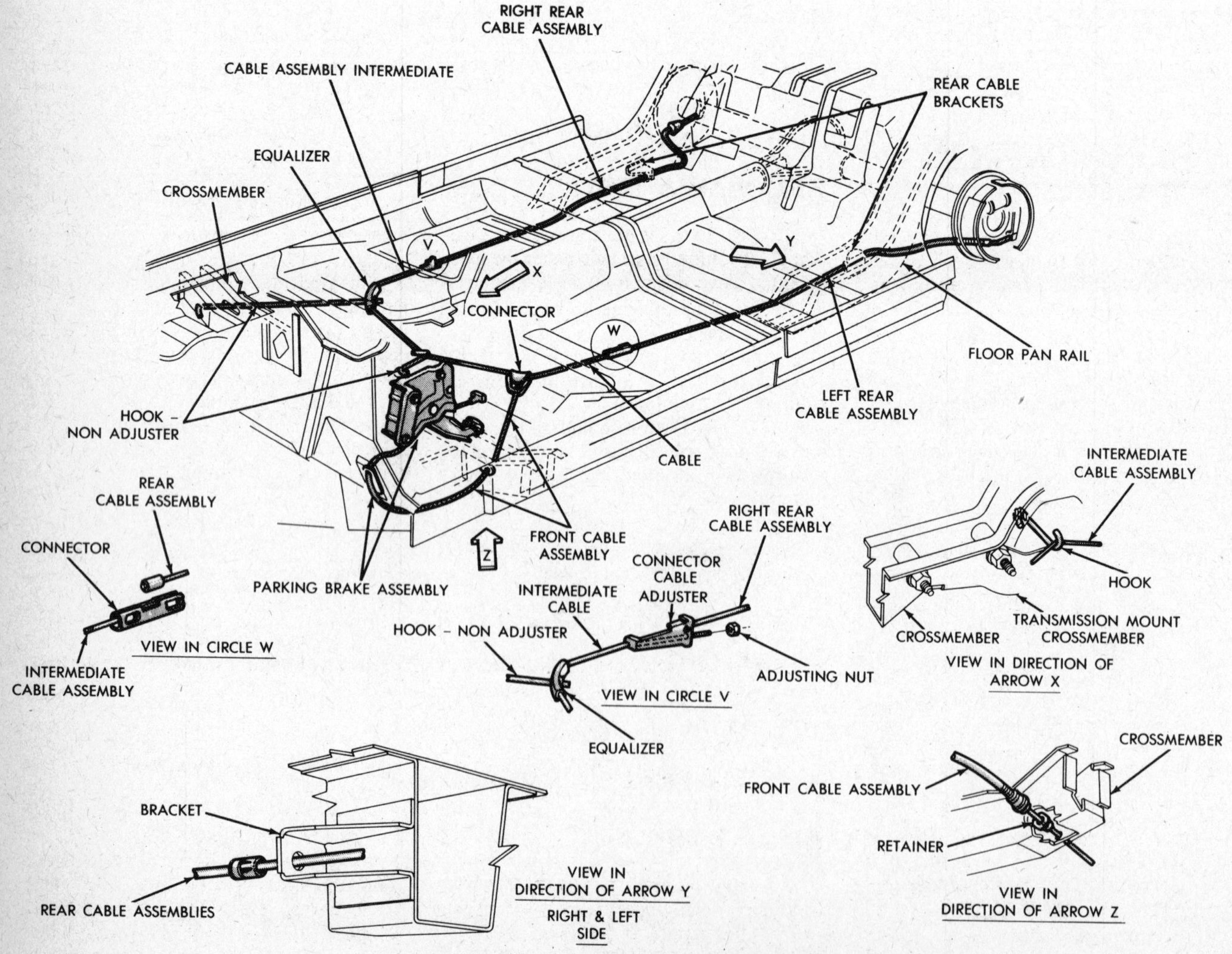

RIGHT REAR CABLE ASSEMBLY

CABLE ASSEMBLY INTERMEDIATE

REAR CABLE BRACKETS

EQUALIZER

CROSSMEMBER

V

X

CONNECTOR

Y

W

FLOOR PAN RAIL

HOOK – NON ADJUSTER

LEFT REAR CABLE ASSEMBLY

CABLE

Z

INTERMEDIATE CABLE ASSEMBLY

REAR CABLE ASSEMBLY

CONNECTOR

INTERMEDIATE CABLE ASSEMBLY

VIEW IN CIRCLE W

PARKING BRAKE ASSEMBLY

FRONT CABLE ASSEMBLY

RIGHT REAR CABLE ASSEMBLY

CONNECTOR CABLE ADJUSTER

HOOK

TRANSMISSION MOUNT CROSSMEMBER

CROSSMEMBER

VIEW IN DIRECTION OF ARROW X

INTERMEDIATE CABLE

HOOK – NON ADJUSTER

ADJUSTING NUT

VIEW IN CIRCLE V

EQUALIZER

CROSSMEMBER

FRONT CABLE ASSEMBLY

BRACKET

REAR CABLE ASSEMBLIES

VIEW IN DIRECTION OF ARROW Y
RIGHT & LEFT SIDE

RETAINER

VIEW IN DIRECTION OF ARROW Z

Parking brake cable routing, typical (© Chrysler Corp.)

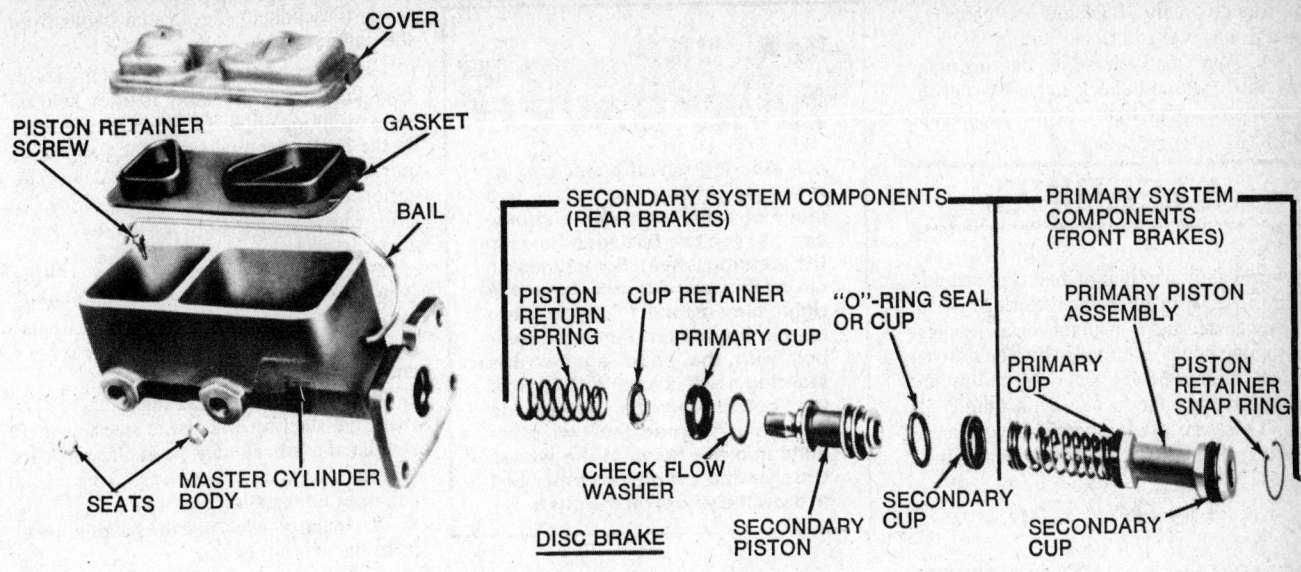

Cast iron dual type master cylinder (disc brakes) (© Chrysler Corp.)

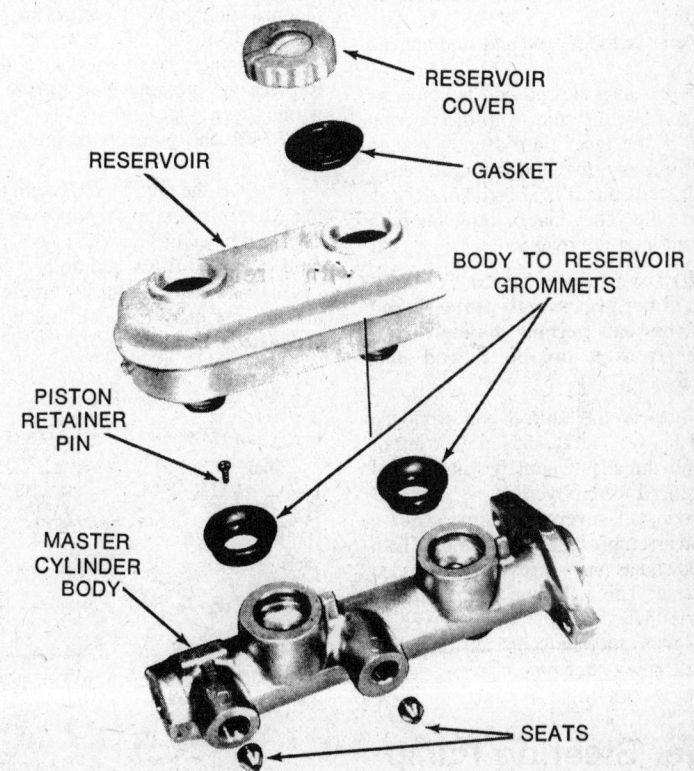

Aluminum master cylinder—primary and secondary system components similar to cast iron cylinder (© Chrysler Corp.)

3. On models with non-power brakes, disconnect the pushrod from the brake pedal. On non-power brake models, disconnect the stop light switch bracket and pull the brake pedal back hard enough to separate the push rod from the master cylinder piston. This will destroy the pushrod grommet; it must be replaced. Lubricate the new one with a drop of water on installation.

4. Slide the master cylinder straight out and off the cowl panel or brake booster.

5. Reverse above procedure to install and bleed brake system.

Power Brake Booster

REMOVAL & INSTALLATION

1. Remove the nuts that attach the master cylinder to the brake booster and position the master cylinder out of the way without disconnecting the lines. Use care not to kink the brake lines.

2. Disconnect the vacuum hose from the brake booster.

3. Working under the dash, remove the nut and bolt that attaches the brake booster pushrod to the brake pedal. Use a small screwdriver to expand the retainer clip and remove the clip from the brake pedal pin. Discard the clip. Unbolt and remove the lower pivot bolt and nut.

4. Remove the brake booster attaching nuts and washers.

5. Remove booster assembly from the vehicle.

6. Reverse above procedure to install. Use a new retainer clip on models so equipped.

Parking Brake

ADJUSTMENT

1. Apply the brakes several times while backing up to adjust the rear drum brakes. Release the parking brake lever and clean and lubricate the parking brake cable adjusting nut and threads. Loosen the cable adjusting nut. Raise the rear of the car and support it safely.

2. Insert a screwdriver through the brake adjusting hole and rotate the star wheel until a slight drag is felt while rotating the wheels. Back-off the star wheel until no drag is felt.

3. Tighten the cable adjusting nut until a slight drag is felt in the rear wheels when the rear wheels are rotated. Loosen the cable adjusting nut until the rear wheels can

be rotated freely. Back off the cable adjusting nut two additional turns.

4. Apply and release the parking brake several times and check to verify that the rear wheels rotate freely, without any brake drag.

STEERING

A worm and recirculating ball type steering gear is used with the manual steering system.

Power steering is available on all models. Hydraulic power is provided by a belt-driven pump. Some power steering pumps are equipped from the factory with fluid coolers. These are used on vehicles with high-performance engines and/or special axle ratios.

Tie-Rod End

REMOVAL & INSTALLATION

1. Loosen the tie-rod adjuster sleeve clamp nuts.
2. Remove the tie-rod end stud nut and cotter pin.
3. If the outer tie-rod end is being removed, remove the stud from the steering knuckle. If the inner tie-rod end is being removed, remove the stud from the center link. The studs on all the tie-rod ends fit in a tapered hole. They can be removed with a ball joint stud removal tool.

NOTE: Use extreme care not to damage the rubber grease seals at the tie-rod ends. If the seals become damaged they must be removed and the tie-rod ends inspected.

4. Unscrew the tie-rod end from the threaded sleeve. The threads may be left or right hand threads. Count the number of turns required to remove it.
5. To install, reverse the above. Grease the tie-rod assembly before reassembly. Turn the tie-rod end as many turns as were needed to remove it. This will give approximately correct toe-in.
6. Tighten the stud nuts to 40 ft. lbs. and install new cotter pins.
7. Set the toe-in.

Power Steering Pump

REMOVAL & INSTALLATION

1. Back off the pump mounting and locking bolts, and remove the pump drive belt.
2. Disconnect all hoses at the pump.
3. Remove the pump bolts and pump with the bracket.
4. To install the pump, place the pump in position and install the mounting bolts.
5. Install the pump drive belt and adjust. There should be no more than ½ in. of play, under moderate thumb pressure, on the longest run of belt. Some pump

brackets have a ½ in. square hole for use in tensioning the belt. Torque the mounting bolts to 30 ft. lbs.
6. Connect the pressure and return hoses. Replace the pressure hose O-ring, if there is one.
7. Fill the pump with power steering fluid.
8. Start the engine and rotate the steering wheel from stop to stop several times. This will bleed the system. Check the pump fluid level and fill as required.
9. Be certain the hoses are away from the exhaust manifolds and are not kinked or twisted.

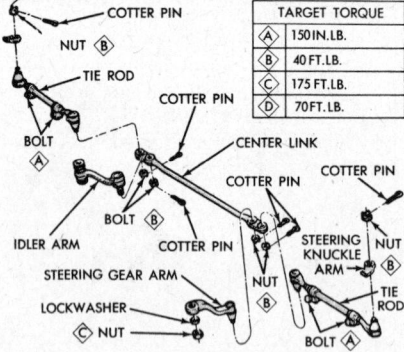

TARGET TORQUE	
Ⓐ	150 IN. LB.
Ⓑ	40 FT. LB.
Ⓒ	175 FT. LB.
Ⓓ	70 FT. LB.

Steering linkage, all models similar (© Chrysler Corp.)

Steering Wheel

REMOVAL & INSTALLATION

— CAUTION —
All models are equipped with collapsible steering columns. A sharp blow or excessive pressure on the column will cause it to collapse. Do not hammer on the steering wheel or center nut.

1. Disconnect the ground cable from the battery.
2. Remove the padded center assembly. This center assembly is often held on only by spring clips. There are usually holes in the back of the wheel so the pad can be pushed off. However, on some deluxe interiors it is held on by screws behind the arms of the wheel. Remove the horn wire, if necessary.
3. On the tilt and telescoping steering column through 1978, remove the locking lever knob by releasing the clip on its underside. Remove the locking lever screws and the lever.
4. Remove the large center nut. Matchmark the steering wheel and steering shaft so that the wheel may be replaced in its original position. In most cases, the wheel can only be installed one way.
5. Using a puller, pull the steering wheel from the steering shaft.
6. Reverse the procedure to install the wheel. When placing the wheel on the shaft, make sure the tires are straight ahead and the matchmarks are aligned. Tighten the nut to 60 ft. lbs.

Turn Signal/Hazard Switch

REMOVAL & INSTALLATION

1. Disconnect the battery ground cable.
2. Remove the steering wheel.
3. Remove the steering column cover. On some models it will be necessary to remove the lower instrument panel bezel.
4. With tilting steering wheel, remove the shift position indicator, unbolt the steering column from the lower instrument panel reinforcement and the mounting bracket from the column, and remove the column wiring trough.

— CAUTION —
Support the steering column to prevent damage.

5. With standard column, unsnap the wiring trough from the column.
6. Position the automatic transmission column shift lever fully clockwise. Set the tilting steering wheel at its midpoint.
7. Disconnect the harness wire connector.
8. Remove the turn signal lever screw and the lever. If the car has speed control, just let the lever hang; don't remove it.
9. Remove the upper bearing retainer screws.
10. Pull the switch gently from the column while guiding the wires through the column opening.
11. Installation is in the reverse order of removal. Tighten the mounting bracket-to-steering column bolts to 10 ft. lbs. and the bracket bolts to 9 ft. lbs.

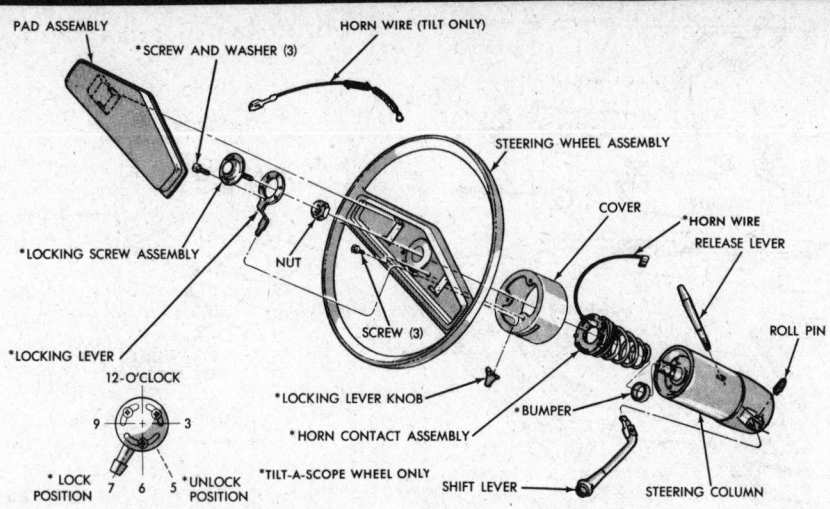

Typical steering wheel details (© Chrysler Corp.)

Ignition Switch and/or Ignition Lock Cylinder

REMOVAL & INSTALLATION

Standard Steering Column

1. Disconnect the negative battery cable and remove the steering wheel.

2. On vehicles equipped with a column shift, pry the lever out of the grommet with a screwdriver.

3. Remove the steering shaft lower coupling at the wormshaft roll pin.

4. Disconnect the wiring connectors at the steering column jacket. Disconnect the horn wire.

5. Disconnect the turn signal lever by removing the retaining bolt located in the column housing, next to the steering column.

6. Disconnect the transmission indicator pointer from the shifter housing. Remove the nuts attaching the steering column bracket to the instrument panel support.

7. Remove the column through the passenger compartment.

8. Remove the ignition buzzer switch retaining screw and lift out the switch.

9. Remove the two retaining screws and the lock lever guide plate to expose the lock cylinder release hole.

10. Place the cylinder in the "Lock" position and remove the key.

11. Insert a small screwdriver into the release hole and push it in to release the spring loaded lock retainer. Pull the lock cylinder out of the housing at the same time.

12. Remove the retaining screws and the ignition switch assembly. Pull the lock lever and spring assembly out of the housing.

13. Reverse the above for installation.

Tilt Steering Column

1. Disconnect the negative battery cable.
2. Remove the steering wheel.
3. Remove the three attaching screws and the shaft lock cover.

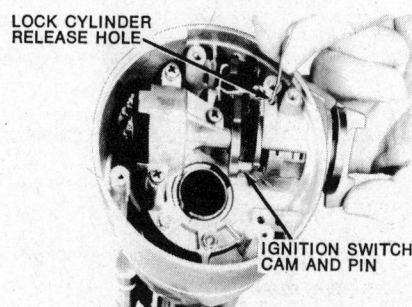

Lock cylinder removal (© Chrysler Corp)

4. Remove the screws that attach the tilt control lever and the turn signal lever to the steering column and remove the levers.

5. Push the hazard warning knob in and unscrew the knob from the turn signal switch. Remove the ignition key lamp assembly.

6. Using a suitable tool, depress the lockplate to gain access to the lockplate retaining snap-ring. Remove the snap-ring from the steering shaft.

7. Remove the lockplate, cancelling cam, and spring.

8. Remove the three turn signal switch attaching screws, place the shift lever in the LOW position, and pull the switch and wires as far upward as possible.

9. With the ignition lock cylinder in the ACCESSORY position, insert a small screwdriver into the lock release slot in the housing cover.

10. Press down with the screwdriver to release the spring latch at bottom of the slot and pull the lock cylinder from the housing.

The following steps are for ignition switch replacement only.

11. Remove the three screws that attach the upper steering column housing to the steering column and remove the housing.

12. Install the column tilt control lever and move the column to the full UP position.

13. Insert a screwdriver into the slot in the spring retainer and press the retainer in

approximately 3/16 in. Turn the retainer approximately 1/8 turn to the left until the ears align with the grooves in the housing. Remove the spring retainer, spring, and guide.

14. Push the steering shaft inward to enable removal of the inner race and seat. Remove the race and seat.

15. Make sure the ignition switch is in the ACCESSORY position, then remove the wire connector from the ignition switch and remove the screws that attach the ignition switch to the outside of the steering column.

16. Lift the ignition switch from the column and twist it to disengage the switch actuating rod from the rack. Remove the switch.

17. To install the ignition lock cylinder, insert the cylinder into the housing with the cylinder in the lock position and the key removed.

18. Move the cylinder into the housing until it contacts the switch actuator. Move the switch actuator rod up and down to align the parts. When the parts are aligned the cylinder will move inward and lock into place.

The following steps are for ignition switch installation only.

19. With the ignition switch in the ACCESSORY position, insert the actuating rod into the steering column.

20. Twist the switch and rod assembly as required to engage the actuating rod with the rack. Make sure the ignition lock cylinder is in the correct position.

21. Install the ignition switch mounting screws, but do not tighten them.

22. Move the ignition switch downward away from the steering wheel and tighten the switch mounting screws. Make sure the ignition switch has not moved out of the lock detent.

23. Attach the switch wiring connector.

INSTRUMENT PANEL

To service the instrument cluster, the cluster bezel must be removed. On some models, it will be necessary to remove the instrument panel upper cover and the sub-bezel to gain access to the speedometer cable and the electrical wire connectors that must be disconnected before the cluster can be removed. Care should be exercised not to force the finish panels when removing or installing, or breakage can occur. The speedometer cable is attached to the speedometer housing by a spring clip, which locks into a groove on the speedometer cable. To release the cable, depress the spring clip arm to disengage it from the groove, and pull the cable away from the speedometer housing.

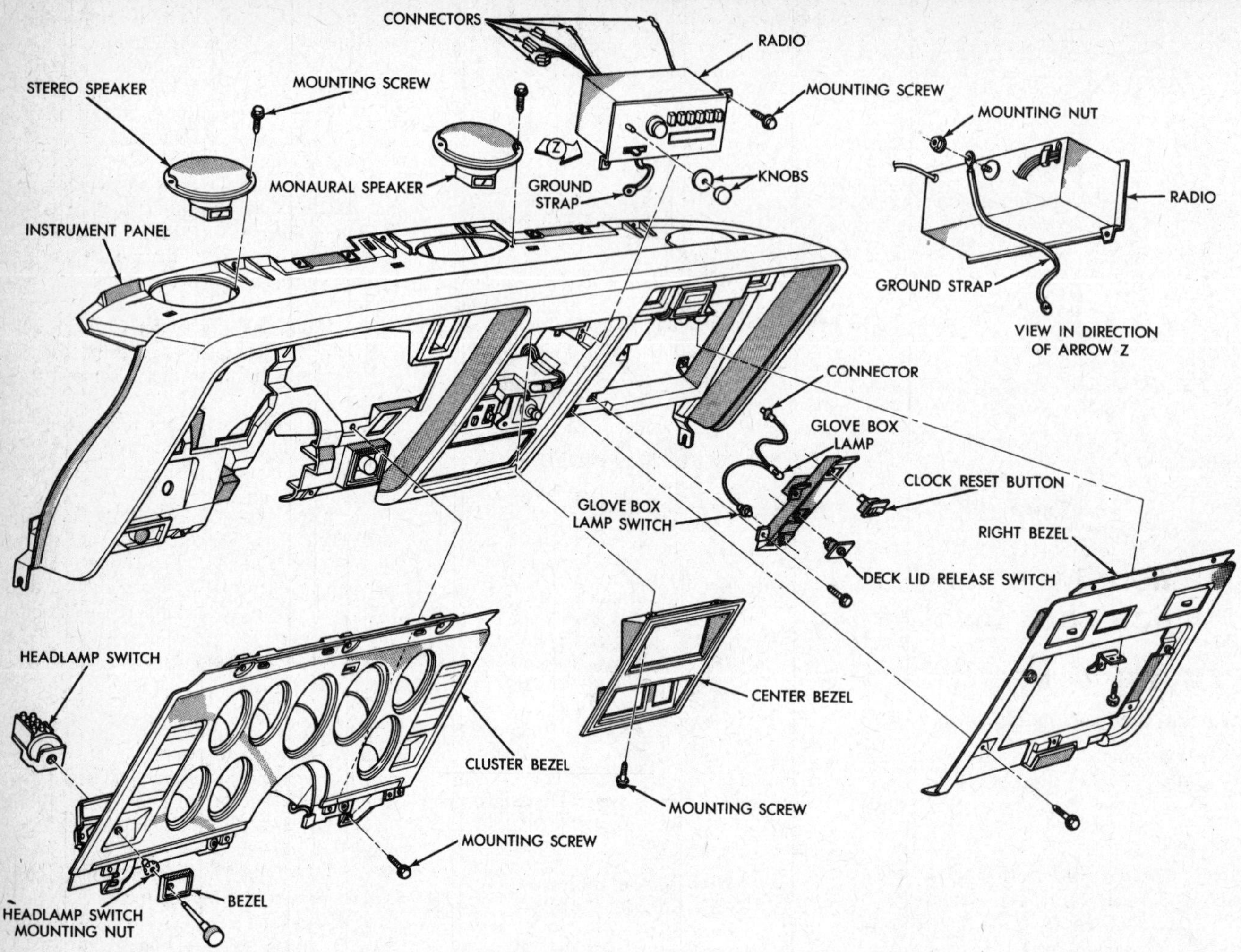

Instrument panel cluster, bezels, switches and radio, typical. **Most models similar layout** (© Chrysler Corp.)

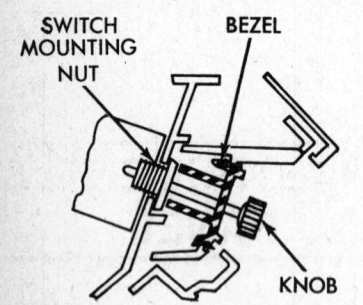

Headlight switch mounting (© Chrysler Corp.)

Headlight Switch

REMOVAL & INSTALLATION

Aspen, Volare, Diplomat, LeBaron to 1981, Mirada, 1981–83 Imperial, 1980–83 Cordoba, 1982 New Yorker, 1983–85 New Yorker Fifth Avenue and Gran Fury

1. Remove the instrument cluster bezel on the Aspen, Volare, Diplomat, LeBaron, and 1982 New Yorker, 1983–84 New Yorker Fifth Avenue and Gran Fury by removing the four screws along the lower edge, placing the automatic transmission selector in 1, and pulling out to detach the top edge clips. Remove the intermittent wipe and power antenna assembly on the Mirada, 1980–83 Cordoba, and 1981–83 Imperial.

2. Remove the switch module assembly mounting screws, pull the assembly out, and let it hang on the Aspen, Volare, Diplomat, LeBaron, 1982 New Yorker, 1983–84 New Yorker Fifth Avenue and Gran Fury.

3. Depress the switch stem, release the button on the switch, and pull out the knob and stem.

4. Remove the bezel on the Imperial, Mirada and Cordoba. Insert a Phillips screwdriver through a stem opening in the switch bezel and remove the switch mounting nut.

5. Disconnect the switch wiring connector. Remove the switch.

6. Reverse the procedure for installation, making sure the stem locks into place.

Charger, 1978 Monaco, Magnum

1. Disconnect the battery ground cable. Remove the instrument cluster upper bezel by removing the screws and pulling out at the top.

2. Remove the escutcheon mounting screw.

3. Remove the screws holding the switch mounting plate on the cluster housing.

4. Pull the switch assembly from the cluster housing and disconnect the wires.

5. Depress the switch stem release button and pull the knob and stem from the switch.

6. Remove the switch mounting nut and remove the switch from the plate.

7. Reverse the above procedure for installation.

1979–81 St. Regis, Gran Fury

NOTE: It may be necessary to remove the intermittent wipe and power antenna module assembly to gain access to the switch.

1. Reaching under the dash, depress the headlight switch stem release button and pull the knob and stem from the switch.

2. Remove the instrument cluster lower bezel.

3. Disconnect the antenna, speaker, and electrical leads.

4. Remove the nut holding the radio to the support bracket. The nut is at the back of the radio and on the side of tape player/radios.

5. Remove the screws holding the radio on the cluster housing from the front.

6. Remove the radio.

7. Reverse the procedure for installation.

CHARGER

1. Disconnect the battery ground cable.

2. Remove the ashtray.

3. Remove the right radio mounting screw from the right cluster leg. You can reach the screw through the lower left corner of the ashtray housing.

4. Loosen the support bracket nut on the right side of the radio.

5. Pull the knobs off. Remove the mounting nuts from the panel.

6. Detach the antenna, speaker, and power wires.

7. Remove the radio. Reverse the procedure for installation.

Fury, Magnum, 1978 Monaco

1. Disconnect the battery ground cable.

2. Remove the instrument cluster lower bezel by removing the right remote control mirror mounting nut, removing the mounting screws, and pull it off.

3. Disconnect the power, speaker, and antenna leads.

4. Remove the nut holding the radio to the support bracket at the rear. On tape player/radios, it is on the side.

5. Remove the radio mounting screws from the front of the panel.

6. Remove the radio from the front of the panel. Reverse the above procedure for installation.

HEATER

Heater Assembly

REMOVAL & INSTALLATION

Without A/C

Heater assembly removal is required in order to service the blower motor or heater core on cars without A/C.

Aspen, Volare, Diplomat, LeBaron to 1981 and 1982 New Yorker, 1983–85 New Yorker Fifth Avenue and Gran Fury

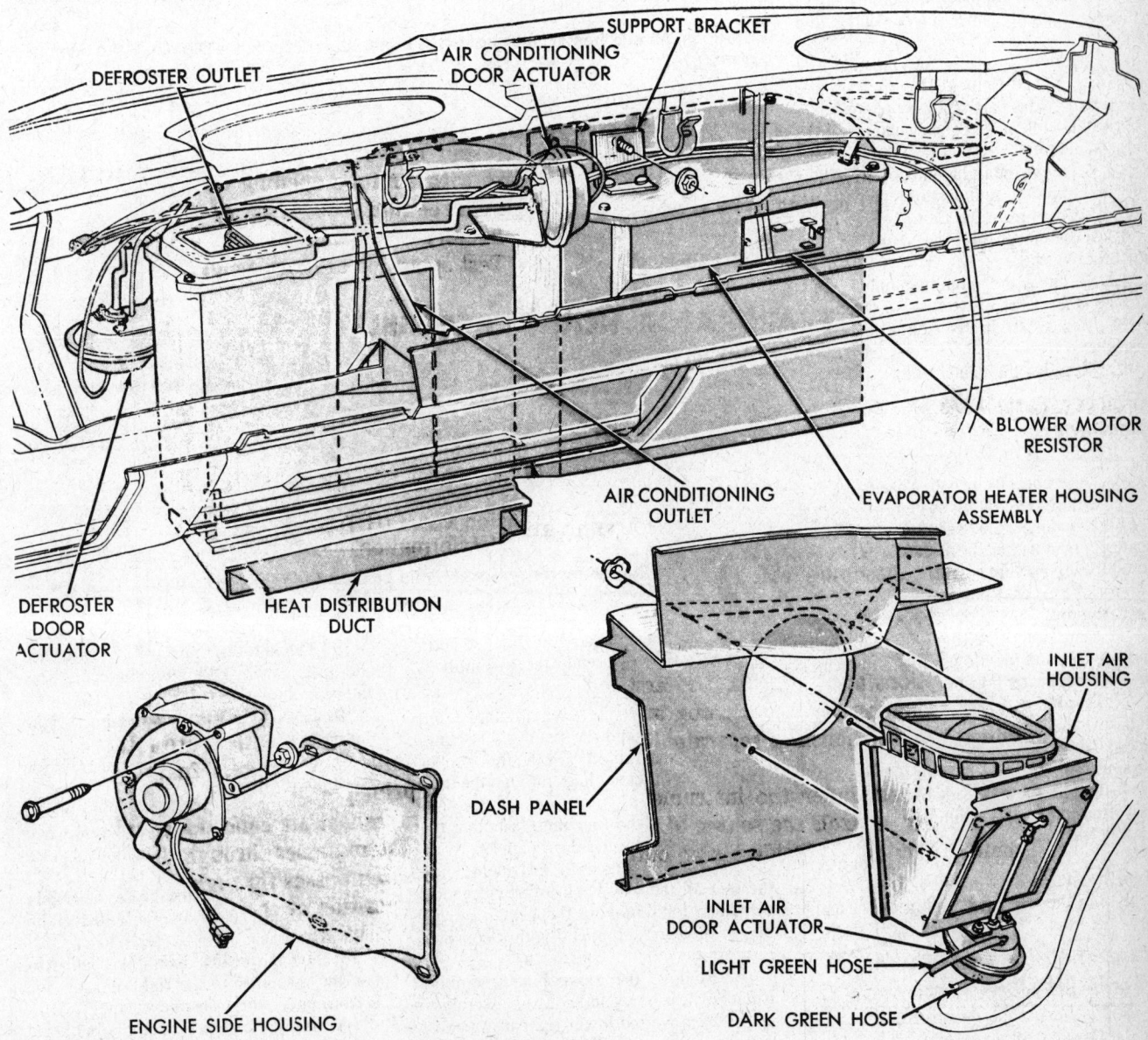

DEFROSTER OUTLET — AIR CONDITIONING DOOR ACTUATOR — SUPPORT BRACKET — BLOWER MOTOR RESISTOR — AIR CONDITIONING OUTLET — EVAPORATOR HEATER HOUSING ASSEMBLY — DEFROSTER DOOR ACTUATOR — HEAT DISTRIBUTION DUCT — DASH PANEL — INLET AIR HOUSING — INLET AIR DOOR ACTUATOR — LIGHT GREEN HOSE — DARK GREEN HOSE — ENGINE SIDE HOUSING

— CAUTION —
This is a major disassembly operation.

1. Disconnect the battery ground cable and drain the coolant.
2. Disconnect the heater hoses at the firewall. Plug the core tubes to prevent spillage.
3. Slide the front seat all the way back.
4. Remove the core tube firewall seals and retainer.
5. Remove the instrument cluster bezel by removing the four screws along the lower edge, placing the automatic transmission selector in 1, and pulling out to detach the upper edge clips.
6. Remove the instrument panel upper cover by removing the mounting screws at the top inner surface of the glove box, at the brow above the instrument cluster, at the left end cap mounting, at the right side of the pad brow, and in the defroster outlets.
7. Remove the steering column cover (the instrument panel piece under the column).
8. Remove the right intermediate side cowl trim panel. Remove the lower instrument panel (the part with the glove box). Remove the instrument panel center to lower reinforcement.
9. Remove the right vent control cable, the temperature, and heating mode door control cables from the unit.
10. Disconnect the blower motor resistor block wiring.
11. Remove the mounting nuts on the engine side of the firewall.
12. Remove the heater support-to-plenum bracket.
13. Remove the heater unit.

Charger, Fury; 1978 Monaco, Magnum

1. Disconnect the negative battery cable.
2. Drain the cooling system.
3. Disconnect the heater hoses from the heater core tubes at the firewall. Plug the core tubes to prevent spilling coolant on the interior of the car. Remove the blower motor vent tube.
4. Remove the three mounting nuts from the studs around the blower motor, the one nut from the heater housing near the center.
5. Disconnect the antenna lead wire from the radio and position it out of the way.
6. Remove the screw that attaches the housing to the support rod for the plenum. It is located on the right-side of the housing, above the outside air opening.
7. Disconnect the air door cables.
8. Disconnect the wires from the blower motor resistor.
9. Tip the heater assembly down and out.

MIRADA, 1980–83 CORDOBA, 1981–83 IMPERIAL

1. Disconnect the negative battery cable. Drain the cooling system.
2. Disconnect the heater hoses to the

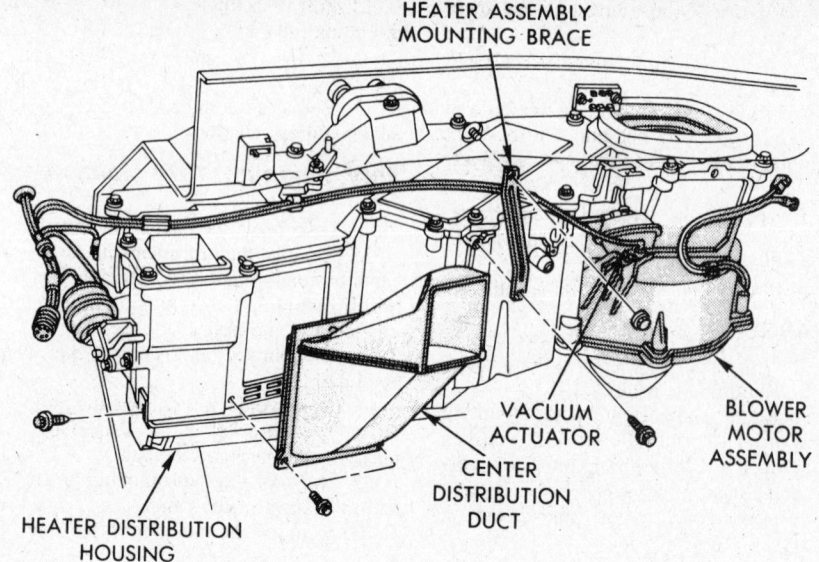

Cordoba, Mirada heater assembly, 1983 and later. Gran Fury, Diplomat, 5th Avenue similar

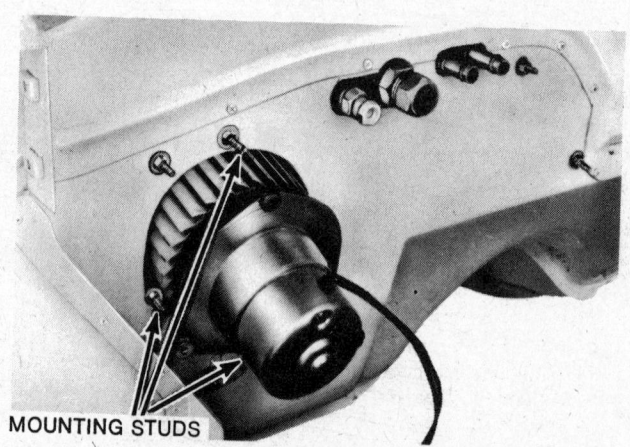

Blower motor removal—mid size cars (© Chrysler Corp)

engine. Plug both heater core tubes so coolant won't spill out when the assembly is removed.

3. Disconnect the vacuum lines from the water valve and the manifold vacuum tree (see illustration). Push the rubber grommet and vacuum lines through the dash panel.
4. Remove the four nuts fastening the heater assembly to the dash panel.
5. In the passenger compartment, slide the seat all the way back to provide good clearance for removing the heater assembly. If the car is equipped with a console, remove it.
6. Remove the glove box assembly. Remove the ash tray and housing assembly.
7. Remove the lower right trim panel, and the right cowl. Remove the top panel cover.

8. Tag and disconnect the blower feed and ground wires. Remove the center distribution duct.
9. Disconnect the vacuum harness from the harness extension.
10. Remove the heater distribution housing.
11. Depress the tab on the flag of the temperature control cable, and remove it from the receiver on the heater housing (see illustration).
12. While holding the heater assembly up, remove the heater assembly-to-plenum mounting brace.
13. Pull the heater assembly back. Rotate the assembly to the right and remove it from under the instrument panel.
14. Install the heater assembly in the reverse order of removal. After connecting the negative battery cable and refilling the

cooling system, check the operation of the heater and controls.

Blower Motor

REMOVAL & INSTALLATION

Without A/C

ASPEN, VOLARE, DIPLOMAT, LEBARON TO 1981, 1982 NEW YORKER, 1983–85 NEW YORKER FIFTH AVENUE AND GRAN FURY

1. Remove the heater assembly from the car.
2. Remove the retainer clips and separate the housing halves.
3. Remove the screw attaching the seal retainer, and seal around the core tubes. Remove the core tube support clamp.
4. Slide the core out.
5. Remove the blower vent tube and the blower mounting nuts. Remove the blower motor.

MIRADA, 1980–83 CORDOBA, 1981–83 IMPERIAL

1. Disconnect the negative battery cable.
2. Disconnect motor electrical connections.
3. Remove screws fastening blower motor assembly-to-heater housing and remove motor.

Heater Core

REMOVAL & INSTALLATION

Without A/C

CHRYSLER THROUGH 1978

The blower motor is mounted to the housing under the right front fender, between the inner fender shield and the fender. The inner fender shield must be removed to service the blower motor.

1979–81 CHRYSLER NEWPORT, NEW YORKER, 1979 CORDOBA AND MAGNUM

1. Disconnect the battery ground cable.
2. Remove the glove box.
3. Disconnect the blower motor wires.
4. Remove the heater assembly to plenum brace.
5. Remove the screws holding the blower motor on the heater housing. Remove the blower motor.
6. Reverse the procedure for installation.

1978 Cordoba

1. Disconnect the battery ground cable.
2. Remove the entire heater assembly from the car, as outlined under Heater Core Removal and Installation, Non-Air Conditioned Models.
3. Disconnect the blower motor lead from the resistor block, and the ground wire from the mounting plate.

4. Remove the 6 sheet metal screws and clips retaining the blower mount on the housing. Separate the mount and blower from the housing.
5. Remove the blower wheel from the motor shaft.
6. Remove the two retaining nuts, and separate the motor from its mount.
7. Reverse the above procedure to install.

Charger, Fury; 1978 Monaco, Magnum

1. Remove the heater assembly.
2. Disconnect the wiring from the blower motor-to-heater assembly.
3. Remove the motor cooler tube.
4. Remove the heater back plate assembly from the heater.
5. Remove the fan from the motor shaft.
6. Remove the blower motor from the back plate.

ASPEN, VOLARE, DIPLOMAT, LEBARON TO 1981, 1982 NEW YORKER, 1983–85 NEW YORKER FIFTH AVENUE, AND GRAN FURY

This procedure is the same as that for "Heater Blower Motor Removal".

MIRADA, 1980–83 CORDOBA, 1981–83 IMPERIAL

1. Remove heater assembly from car.
2. Remove retaining screws in top cover, remove cover and remove the heater core.

1978 Chrysler

1. Disconnect the battery ground cable and drain the coolant.
2. Detach the heater hoses at the firewall and plug the core tubes.
3. Slide the front seat back. Remove the instrument panel lower cover.
4. Unplug the antenna from the radio. Disconnect the upper level ventilation actuator vacuum line.
5. Remove the screw holding the upper level vent ducts on the heater housing, and the screw holding the bracket on the instrument panel. Swing back the duct.
6. Disconnect the blower motor resistor connectors at the lower right end of the housing.
7. Detach the mode cable from the mode door crank on the front of the housing.
8. Remove the bottom retaining nut and swing the support bracket out of the way.
9. On the engine side, remove the five nuts.
10. Tip the housing out from under the instrument panel.
11. Detach the temperature control cable at the top.
12. Remove the core tube locating screw between the tubes. Remove the six nuts holding the front and rear housings together. Remove the four core retaining screws and separate the housings. Slide the core out.
13. Reverse the above procedure for installation.

1979–81 CHRYSLER NEWPORT, NEW YORKER

1. Disconnect the battery ground cable. Drain the coolant.
2. Disconnect the heater hoses and plug the core tubes. Disconnect the vacuum lines from the water valve and the manifold vacuum tee and push the lines through the dash panel.
3. Remove the four nuts holding the heater assembly on the firewall.
4. Slide the front seat all the way back. Remove the console, if any.
5. Remove the heater controls and disconnect the vacuum harness from the harness extension.
6. Remove the ash tray and housing, and the glove box.
7. Disconnect the right lap cooler tube from the lap cooler and remove the trim bezel. Remove the right cowl trim pad.
8. Disconnect the blower motor wires.
9. Detach the temperature control cable from the heater housing by depressing the tab on the flag of the cable.
10. Remove the heater distribution housing.
11. Hold the assembly up and remove the mounting brace to the plenum.
12. Pull the assembly back and rotate it to the right and out from under the instrument panel. Remove the top cover for access to the heater core.
13. Reverse the above procedure for installation.

1979 CORDOBA

1. Refer to Steps 1–4 of the "1979–81 Chrysler Newport" section.
2. Remove the glove box. Remove the ash tray housing assembly.
3. Remove the right lap cooler duct from the lap cooler and remove the lower right trim panel.
4. Remove the right cowl trim pad.
5. Disconnect the blower motor wiring.
6. Remove the center distribution duct.
7. Disconnect the vacuum harness from the harness extension.
8. Refer to Steps 10–13 of the "1979–81 Chrysler Newport" section.

CORDOBA THROUGH 1978

1. Disconnect the battery ground cable and drain the coolant.
2. Disconnect the heater hoses at the firewall and plug the core tubes. Remove the blower motor vent tube.
3. Remove the three mounting nuts around the blower motor and the one near the center.
4. Remove the lower instrument panel bezel, glove box, and glove box door.
5. Unplug the antenna from the radio.
6. Remove the screw from the housing-to-plenum support rod on the right side above the outside air opening.
7. Detach the two air door cables and the blower motor resistor wires.
8. Tip the unit out from under the instrument panel.

9. Remove the front cover screws. Cut the plenum to housing air seal in two places where the front cover separates the cover from the housing.

10. Remove the core tube retaining screw between the tubes. Remove the heater core.

11. Reverse the above procedure for installation. Seal the plenum air seal with rubber cement.

Charger, Fury; 1978 Monaco, Magnum

1. Remove the heater assembly.

2. Remove the screws that attach the front cover to the heater housing.

3. Cut the sponge rubber plenum-to-housing air seal in two places, where the front cover separates the cover from the housing.

4. Remove the one core tube retaining screw from behind the heater housing, between the heater core tubes.

5. Remove the sponge rubber gaskets from the heater core tubes. Remove the heater core from the heater housing.

1979 MAGNUM

1. Remove the heater assembly.

2. Remove the top cover of the heater assembly housing.

3. Remove the heater core fastening screw and lift out the core.

Blower Motor

REMOVAL & INSTALLATION

With A/C

ASPEN, VOLARE, DIPLOMAT, LEBARON TO 1981, MIRADA, 1981–83 IMPERIAL AND 1980–83 CORDOBA AND 1982 NEW YORKER, 1983–85 NEW YORKER FIFTH AVENUE AND GRAN FURY

The blower motor is removed from inside the car.

1. Disconnect the blower motor wiring.

2. Remove the blower motor mounting nuts from the bottom of the recirculation housing.

3. Separate the lower blower motor housing from the upper housing.

4. Remove the mounting plate screws and remove the mounting plate and blower motor.

Charger, Fury; 1978 Monaco, Magnum

1. Working inside the engine compartment, disconnect the feed wire and ground wire. Remove the air tube (if so equipped).

2. Remove the mounting screws located on the outer surface of the mounting plate.

3. Remove the mounting plate, blower motor, and fan as an assembly.

4. To install the motor, if the motor

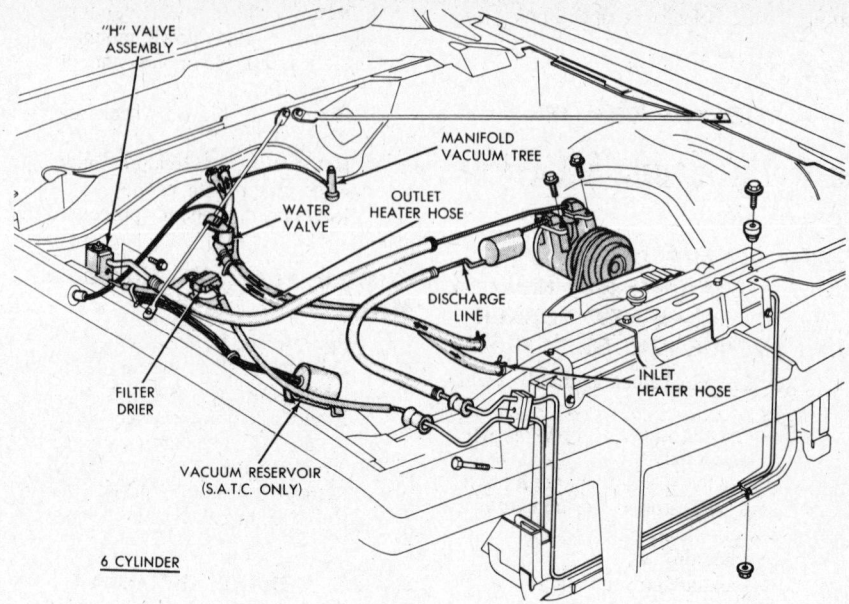

1979-81 Chrysler six cylinder air conditioner hose layout—note position of "H" valve (same location for V8s) © Chrysler Corp.

was removed from its mounting plate, be sure mounting grommets are installed at the attaching bolts. In addition, be sure the blower wheel is free and does not rub.

5. Install the blower motor assembly on the evaporator casing with the air tube opening toward the bottom. Install its retaining screws.

6. Install the air tube, ground, and feed wires.

7. Check blower motor operation.

1978 Chrysler

1. The blower motor is mounted on the engine side housing, under the right front fender, between the inner fender shield and the fender. To service the motor, it is necessary to remove the inner fender panel by removing its securing bolts. If the car is equipped with a power antenna, it is necessary to disconnect it before the inner fender panel is removed.

2. For all models, disconnect the battery and feed wires, and remove the air tube (if so equipped). Remove its mounting bolts and remove the blower assembly.

3. Installation is in the reverse order of removal.

1979–81 CHRYSLER NEWPORT, NEW YORKER, 1979 CORDOBA, 1979 MAGNUM

This procedure is the same as for non-air conditioned cars.

1978 Cordoba

1. Disconnect the feed wire at its connector. Remove the air tube.

2. Remove the three nuts retaining the blower mount on the firewall (from the engine side.)

3. Lift out the blower motor and fan assembly.

4. Reverse the above procedure to install.

Heater Core

REMOVAL & INSTALLATION

With A/C

ASPEN, VOLARE, DIPLOMAT, LEBARON TO 1981, 1982 NEW YORKER, 1983–85 NEW YORKER FIFTH AVENUE AND GRAN FURY

—— CAUTION ——

This procedure requires evacuation of the air conditioner refrigerant which is dangerous when released from the system. Do not attempt this yourself unless you are familiar with air conditioning service. This is also a major disassembly operation.

1. Discharge the air conditioning system.

2. Disconnect the battery ground cable, drain the coolant, remove the air cleaner, and disconnect the heater hoses. Plug the core tubes to prevent spillage.

3. Remove the H-type expansion valve.

4. Slide the front seat all the way back.

5. Remove the instrument cluster bezel assembly by removing the four screws along the lower edge, placing the automatic transmission selector in 1, and pulling out to detach the upper edge clips.

6. Remove the instrument panel upper cover by removing the mounting screws at the top inner surface of the glove box, at the brow above the instrument cluster, at the left end cap mounting, at the right side

of the pad brow, and in the defroster outlets.

7. Remove the steering column cover (the instrument panel piece under the column).

8. Remove the right intermediate side cowl trim panel. Remove the lower instrument panel (the part with the glove box). Remove the instrument panel center to lower reinforcement.

9. Remove the floor console, if any.

10. Remove the right center air distribution duct. Detach the locking tab on the defroster duct.

11. Disconnect the temperature control cable from the housing. Disconnect the blower motor resistor block wiring.

12. In the engine compartment, detach the vacuum lines from the water valve and tee. Detach the wiring from the evaporator housing. Remove the vacuum lines from the inlet air housing and disconnect the vacuum harness coupling.

13. Remove the drain tube in the engine compartment. Remove the mounting nuts from the firewall.

14. Remove the hanger strap from the rear of the evaporator and plenum stud.

15. Roll the unit back so the pipes clear and remove it.

16. Remove the blend air door lever from the shaft. Remove the screws and lift off the top cover. Lift the heater core out.

17. Reverse the procedure for installation. Sweep, leak test, and charge the air conditioning system. Refill the cooling system.

MIRADA, 1980–83 CORDOBA, 1981–82 IMPERIAL

Procedures are similar to "1979–81 Chrysler Newport, New Yorker" procedures in the Chrysler Section.

1978 Chrysler

NOTE: This procedure requires evacuation of the refrigerant in the air conditioning system. Therefore, it should not be attempted by persons not having the special tools and training required to perform the job safely.

1. Purge the system of refrigerant.

2. Disconnect the battery ground cable. Drain the coolant.

3. Remove the air cleaner and disconnect the heater hoses. Plug the core tubes.

4. Remove the 5/16 in. bolt in the center of the plumbing sealing plate.

5. Pull the refrigerant line assembly toward the front of the car.

6. Remove the two 1/4-20 Allen screws and remove the H valve.

7. Slide the front seat back, out of the way. Remove the lap cooler and lower instrument panel cover.

8. Remove the A/C distribution duct.

9. Unplug the antenna lead from the radio.

10. Disconnect the wires and vacuum lines from unit.

11. Remove the drain tube. With automatic temperature control (ATC), remove the electrical connections and vacuum connector from the servo. Disconnect the amplifier wires. Disconnect the wires and vacuum hoses from the master and compressor switches. Disconnect the aspirator tube.

12. Remove the temperature control cable from the clip on the unit.

13. Remove the retaining nut from the support bracket.

14. Remove the six retaining nuts from the studs in the engine compartment.

15. Remove the housing from under the instrument panel, and place it on a work table.

16. Remove the mode door and the blend air door levers from the shaft. Remove the screws and lift off the top cover.

17. Remove the 4 retaining screws and the 3 screws for the core tube seal. Lift out the core.

18. Reverse the above procedure to install.

1979–81 CHRYSLER NEWPORT, NEW YORKER

NOTE: This procedure requires evacuation of the refrigerant in the air conditioning system. Therefore, it should not be attempted by persons not having the special tools and training required to perform the job safely.

1. Discharge the air conditioning system completely.

2. Disconnect the battery ground cable. Drain the coolant.

3. Disconnect the heater hoses and plug the core tubes.

4. Remove the air conditioning system H-valve. Cap all openings.

5. Remove the condensation drain tube.

6. Disconnect the vacuum lines in the engine compartment and push the rubber grommet and vacuum lines through the firewall.

7. Remove the four nuts holding the heater assembly on the firewall.

8. Slide the front seat all the way back. Remove the console, if any.

9. Remove the heater/air conditioning controls and disconnect the vacuum harness from the harness extension.

10. Remove the ash tray and housing, and the glove box.

11. Disconnect the right lap cooler tube from the lap cooler and remove the trim bezel. Remove the right cowl trim pad.

12. Disconnect the blower motor wires.

13. Detach the temperature control or bimetal sensor cable from the evaporator/heater housing.

14. Remove the heater distribution housing.

15. Remove the center distribution duct.

16. Remove the mode door actuator or vacuum servo from the lower left corner of the housing.

17. Remove the automatic temperature control system in-car air hose from the compensator.

18. Hold the assembly up and remove the mounting brace to the plenum.

19. Pull the assembly back and rotate it to the right and out from under the instrument panel. Remove the top cover for access to the heater core.

20. Place the assembly on a workbench, remove the cover screws and lift off the top cover.

21. Remove the screw which holds the evaporator coil on the housing and lift out the coil.

22. Remove the screw which holds the heater coil on the housing and lift out the core.

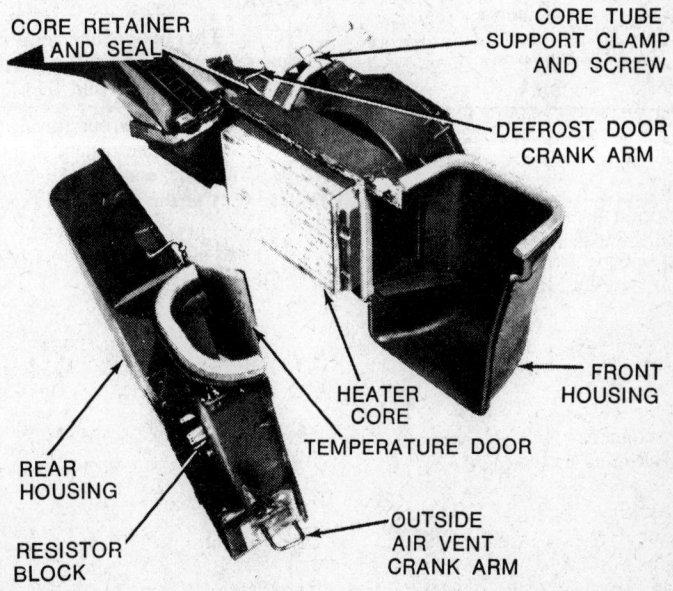

Heater core removal—Aspen, Volare, Diplomat, LeBaron, 1982 New Yorker, 1983 and later New Yorker 5th Avenue, 1982 and later Gran Fury (© Chrysler Corp.)

23. Reverse the above procedure for installation.

1978 Cordoba

1. Disconnect the battery ground cable.
2. Remove the air cleaner.
3. Drain the cooling system and disconnect the heater hoses. Plug the core tubes.
4. Discharge the refrigerant from the air conditioning.
5. Disconnect the refrigerant line at the H valve and cover the plumbing sealing plate. Remove the expansion valve and cover both sealing surfaces of the expansion valve and the evaporator sealing plate.
6. Disconnect the blower motor wires and remove the cooling tube.
7. Remove the glove box and ash tray.
8. Working on the lower edge of the instrument panel, remove the appearance shield and the right lap cooler duct.
9. Remove the cowl panel from the right front passenger side.
10. Remove the A/C door actuator from its mounting bracket and shift the actuator forward, on top of the unit.
11. Remove the wiring from the seat belt interlock and let it hang from the glove box opening. Disconnect the wiring from the blower motor and the antenna from the radio.
12. Remove the radio.
13. Disconnect the vacuum harness from the extension of the control.
14. Remove the nuts from the housing mounting studs and remove the rubber drain tube.
15. Move the front seat all the way back and remove the support bracket from the rear unit to the plenum.
16. Pull the unit back so the pipes clear the dash panel. Rotate the unit so the right end comes out from under the instrument panel first.
17. Place the unit on a workbench and carefully remove the plenum air seal.
18. Disconnect the vacuum hose from the air door actuator. Remove the air seal from the heater core tubes.
19. Remove the 18 clamps holding the front and rear covers together and separate the housings.
20. Remove the 4 screws from the evaporator coil access plate and remove the plate.
21. Remove the evaporator coil from the front housing.

22. Carefully lift the left half of the housing seal from the rear cover. Do not remove the entire seal as the lower portion is a water seal.
23. Remove the core retaining screws and lift the core from the housing.
24. Reverse the above procedure to install.

1979 Cordoba and 1979 Magnum

Refer to Steps 1–12, excluding Step 9, of the "1979–81 Chrysler Newport, New Yorker" section.
13. Remove the center distribution duct.
14. Disconnect the vacuum harness from the harness extension.
15. Remove the heater distribution housing.
16. Remove the temperature control cable from the heater assembly housing.
17. Remove the Hi/Lo door actuator from the lower left corner of the evaporative heater assembly housing. On models with Semi-Automatic Temperature Control, also remove the vacuum servo actuator.
18. Hold the assembly up and remove the mounting brace to the plenum.
19. Pull the assembly back and rotate it to the right and out from under the instrument panel. Remove the top cover for access to the heater core.
20. Place the assembly on a workbench, remove the screws and lift off the top cover.
21. Remove the screw which holds the evaporative coil on the housing and lift out the coil.
22. Remove the heater core fastening screw, and remove the heater core from the housing.

Charger, Fury; 1978 Monaco, Magnum

NOTE: This procedure requires evacuation of the air conditioning system which requires special tools and training.

1. Remove the carburetor air cleaner.
2. Disconnect the battery ground cable.
3. Drain the coolant. Disconnect the heater hoses at the firewall. Plug the core tubes.
4. Discharge the air conditioning system.

5. Disconnect the refrigerant line assembly at the H-valve. Cover the plumbing sealing plate. Remove the expansion valve attached to the evaporator and cover the evaporator sealing plate and both sealing surfaces of the expansion valve.
6. Disconnect the blower motor wires and remove the blower motor cooling tube.
7. Remove the glove box, the ashtray, and housing.
8. Remove the appearance shield and right lap cooler duct from the lower edge of the instrument panel.
9. Remove the right front passenger side cowl panel.
10. Remove the air distribution duct.
11. Remove the air conditioner mode door vacuum actuator from its mounting bracket and shift the actuator forward 90 degrees.
12. Remove the wiring from the seat belt interlock control unit and leave it hanging from the glove box opening.
13. Disconnect the blower motor resistor wires and the radio antenna wire.
14. Remove the radio.
15. Disconnect the vacuum housing from the extension to the control.
16. Remove the nuts from the housing mounting studs in the engine compartment.
17. Remove the rubber drain tube.
18. Adjust the front seat all the way back.
19. Remove the support bracket from the rear unit to the plenum.
20. Pull the unit back so it clears the firewall. Rotate it out from under the instrument panel, right end first.
21. Remove the plenum air seal. Disconnect the inlet air door vacuum actuator hose. Remove the air seal from the heater and evaporator core tubes. Remove the clamps and screws holding the housing together and separate them.
22. Remove the screws from the evaporator coil access plate and remove the plate for access to the two evaporator coil mounting screws. Remove the screws holding the evaporator coil on the front cover and remove the coil.
23. Carefully lift the left half of the housing seal from the rear cover; do not remove the entire seal.
24. Remove the two core retaining screws from the mounting plates and the one between the core tubes. Lift the core out of the housing.
25. Reverse the above procedure for installation.

Chrysler Corp. Front Wheel Drive

TC3, 024, Aries, Charger, Daytona, Horizon, Dodge 400, Dodge 600, E Class, Lancer, Laser, LeBaron, LeBaron GTS, New Yorker, Omni, Reliant, Turismo,

YEAR IDENTIFICATION

1978-79 Omni

1980 Omni

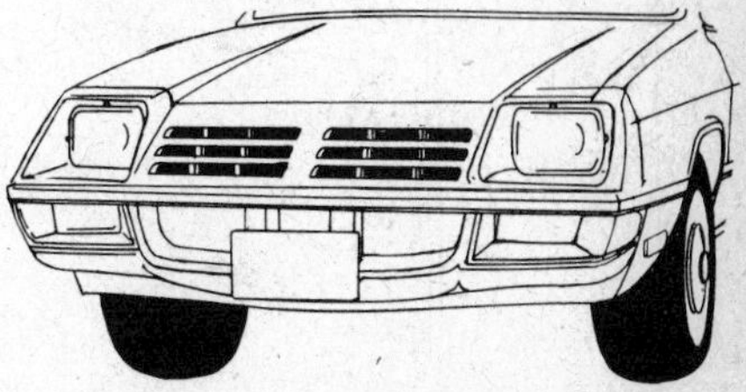

1980 –83 Omni 024, Charger 2.2

1981 Omni

1982–83 Omni

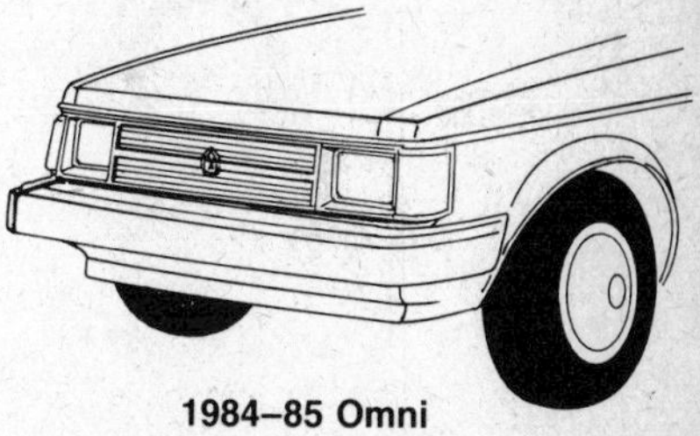

1984–85 Omni

1985 Omni GLH

1978-80 Horizon

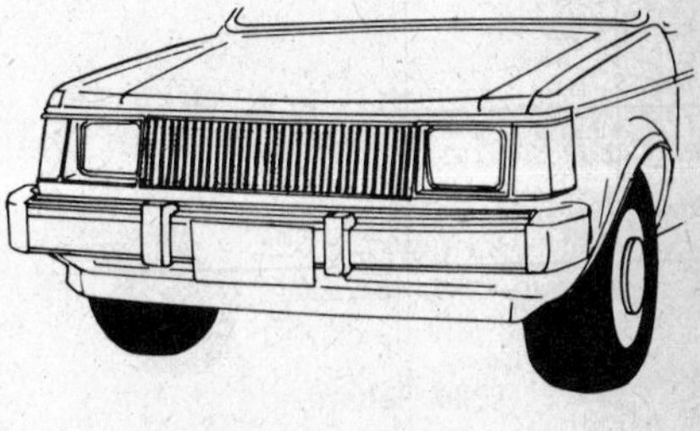

1981 Horizon

1982–83 Horizon

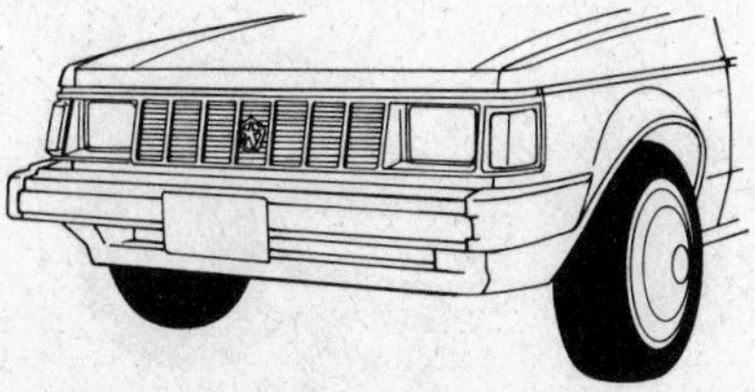

1984–85 Horizon

1980 Horizon TC3

YEAR IDENTIFICATION

1981 Horizon TC3

1984 Turismo/Charger

1985 Turismo Duster

1985 Turismo 2.2

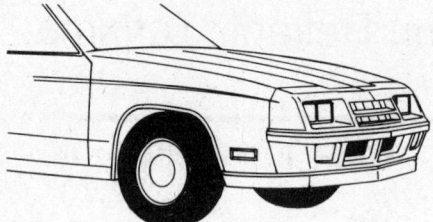

1985 Charger 2.2

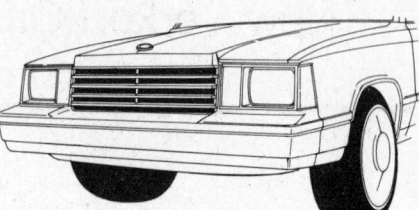

1981–83 Aires

1984 Aries

1985 Aries

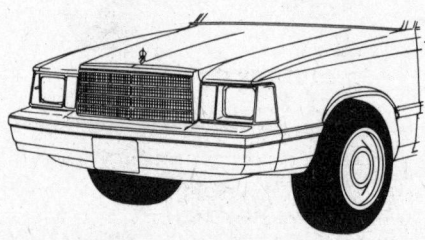

1981–83 Reliant

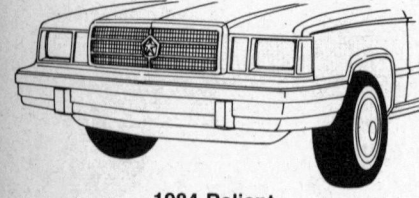

1984 Reliant

1985 Reliant

1984–85 LeBaron, E Class

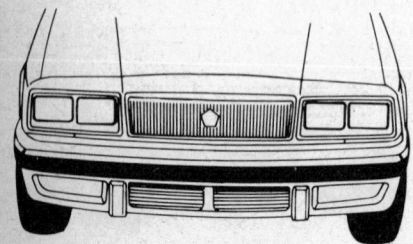

1985 LeBaron GTS

1984–85 Shelby Charger

1984–85 Daytona

YEAR IDENTIFICATION

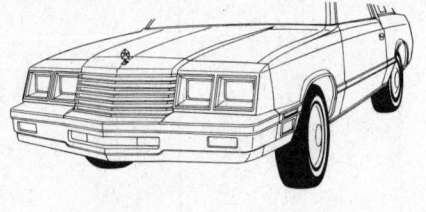

1982–85 Dodge 400, 600

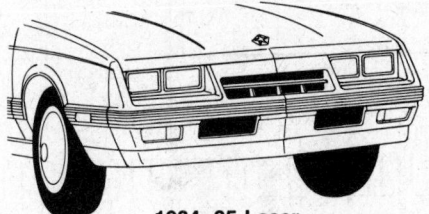

1984–85 Laser

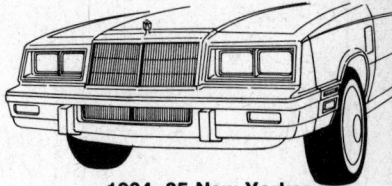

1984–85 New Yorker

1985 Caravelle

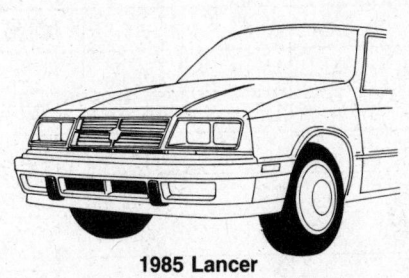

1985 Lancer

GENERAL ENGINE SPECIFICATIONS

Year	Eng. V.I.N. Code	Engine No. Cyl. Displ. Cu. In.	Eng. Mfg.	Carb. Type	Horsepower at rpm ■	Torque (ftlb.) at rpm ■	Bore X Stroke (in.)	Compression Ratio	Oil Pressure (psi) at 2000 rpm
'83	A	4–98	Peugeot	2 bbl.	64 @ 4800	83 @ 3200	3.07 × 3.46	8.8:1	58–87①
'84–'85	A	4-98	Peugeot	2 bbl.	64 @ 4800	87 @ 2800	3.07 × 3.46	8.8:1	58–87①
'78–'80	A	4-105	VW	2 bbl.	75 @ 5600	90 @ 3200	3.13 × 3.40	8.2:1	60–90
'81–'82	A	4-105	VW	2 bbl.	63 @ 4800	83 @ 3200	3.13 × 3.40	8.2:1	60–90
'83	B	4-105	VW	2 bbl.	63 @ 4800	83 @ 2400	3.13 × 3.40	8.2:1	60–90
'81–'82	B	4-135	Chrysler	2 bbl.	84 @ 4800	111 @ 2800	3.44 × 3.62	8.5:1	50
'83	C	4-135	Chrysler	2 bbl.	94 @ 5200	117 @ 3200	3.44 × 3.62	9.0:1	50
'84–'85	C	4-135	Chrysler	2 bbl.	96 @ 5200	119 @ 3200	3.44 × 3.62	9.0:1	50
'85	②	4-135	Chrysler	2 bbl.	110 @ 5600	129 @ 3600	3.44 × 3.62	9.6:1	50
'83–'85	D	4-135	Chrysler	EFI	99 @ 5600	121 @ 3200	3.44 × 3.62	9.0:1	50
'84–'85	E	4-135	Chrysler	Turbo	146 @ 5200	168 @ 3600	3.44 × 3.62	8.0:1	50
'81–'82	D	4-156	Mitsubishi	2 bbl.	92 @ 4500	131 @ 2500	3.59 × 3.86	8.2:1	58③
'83	G	4-156	Mitsubishi	2 bbl.	93 @ 5600	132 @ 2800	3.59 × 3.86	8.2:1	58③
'84–'85	G	4-156	Mitsubishi	2 bbl.	101 @ 5600	140 @ 2800	3.59 × 3.86	8.7:1	58③

■ Horsepower and torque are SAE net, with all accessories installed and operating. Figure may vary from model-to-model and is intended to be representative rather than exact.

① @ 3000 rpm
② Eng code not available at time of publication
③ @ 2500 rpm

VEHICLE IDENTIFICATION NUMBER (VIN)

It is important for servicing and ordering parts to be certain of the vehicle and engine identification. The VIN (vehicle identification number) is a 13 or 17 digit number visible through the windshield on the driver's side of the dash, and contains the vehicle and engine identification codes. It can be interpreted as follows:

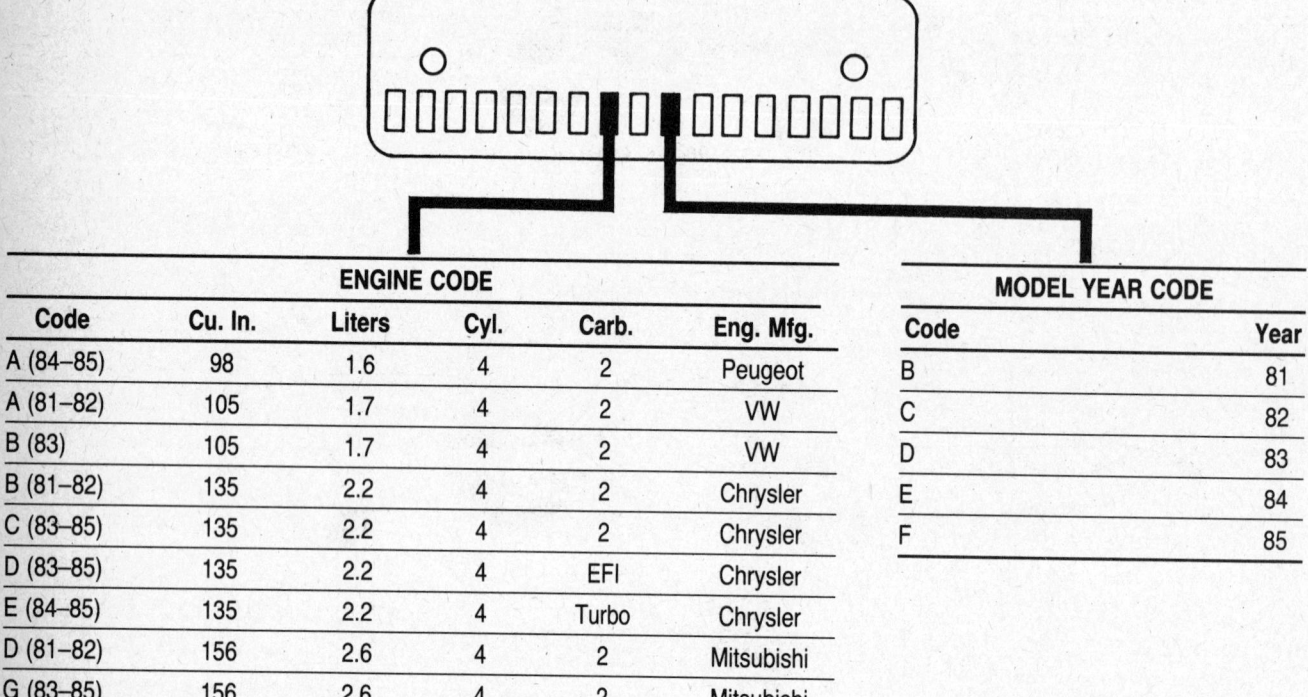

ENGINE CODE						MODEL YEAR CODE	
Code	Cu. In.	Liters	Cyl.	Carb.	Eng. Mfg.	Code	Year
A (84–85)	98	1.6	4	2	Peugeot	B	81
A (81–82)	105	1.7	4	2	VW	C	82
B (83)	105	1.7	4	2	VW	D	83
B (81–82)	135	2.2	4	2	Chrysler	E	84
C (83–85)	135	2.2	4	2	Chrysler	F	85
D (83–85)	135	2.2	4	EFI	Chrysler		
E (84–85)	135	2.2	4	Turbo	Chrysler		
D (81–82)	156	2.6	4	2	Mitsubishi		
G (83–85)	156	2.6	4	2	Mitsubishi		

The seventeen digit Vehicle Identification Number can be used to determine engine application and model year. The tenth indicates the model year, and the eighth digit identifies engine displacement.

VEHICLE IDENTIFICATION NUMBER (VIN)

It is important for servicing and ordering parts to be certain of the vehicle and engine identification. The VIN (vehicle identification number) is a 13 or 17 digit number visible through the windshield on the driver's side of the dash, and contains the vehicle and engine identification codes. It can be interpreted as follows:

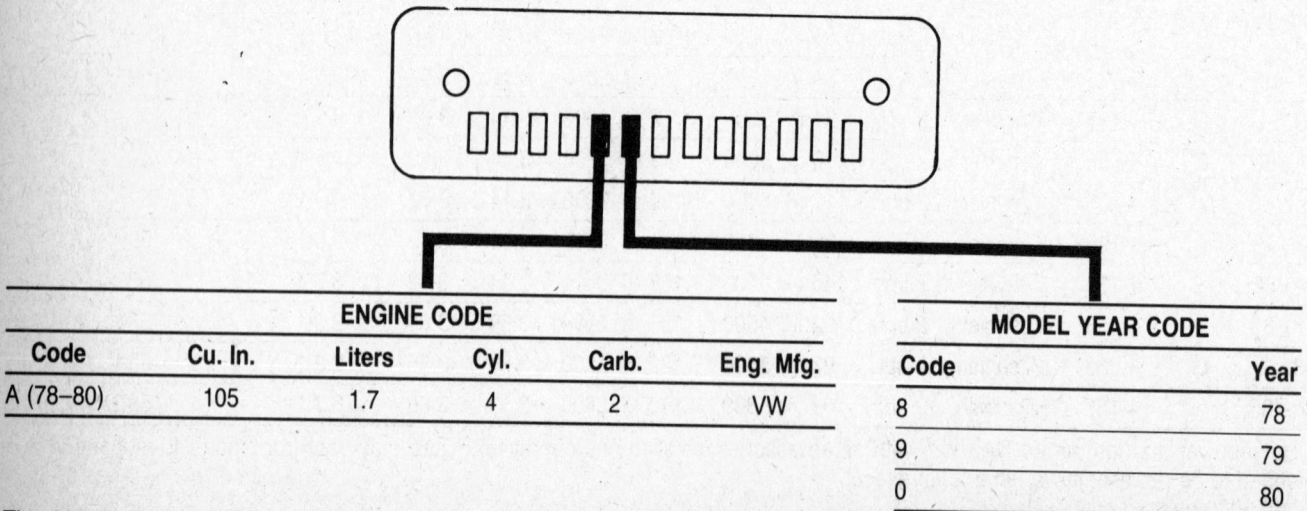

ENGINE CODE						MODEL YEAR CODE	
Code	Cu. In.	Liters	Cyl.	Carb.	Eng. Mfg.	Code	Year
A (78–80)	105	1.7	4	2	VW	8	78
						9	79
						0	80

The thirteen digit Vehicle Identification Number can be used to determine engine application and model year. The sixth digit indicates the model year, and the fifth digit indicates engine displacement.

TUNE-UP SPECIFICATIONS

Year	Eng. V.I.N. Code	No. Cyl. Displ. Cu. In.	Eng. Mfg.	h.p.	Spark Plugs Orig. Type	Gap (in.)	Ignition Timing (deg.) ▲ Man. Trans.	Auto Trans.	Intake Valve Opens (deg.)■	Fuel Pump Pressure (psi)	Idle Speed (rpm) ▲ Man. Trans.	Auto Trans.	Valve Lash (in.) ▲ Intake	Exhaust
'84–'85	A	4–98	Peugeot	64	RN12YC	.035	12B	12B	16	4.5–6.0	850	1000	.012C	.014C
'78	A	4–105	VW	75	RN-12Y	.035	15B	15B	23	4.5–6.0	900	900	.008–.012H	.016–.020H
'79	A	4–105	VW	75	RN-12Y	.035	15B	15B	14	4.4–5.8	900	900	.008–.012H	.016–.020H
'80	A	4–105	VW	75	RN-12Y	.035	15B	15B	14	4.4–5.8	900	900	.008–.012H	.016–.020H
'81–'82	A	4–105	VW	63	P65-PR4	.048②	12B④	10B	14	4.5–6.0	900	900	.008–.012H	.016–.020H
'83	A	4–105	VW	63	65PR	.035	20B	12B	14	4.4–5.8	900	900	.008–.012H	.016–.020H
'81–'82	B	4–135	Chrysler	84	P65-PR4	.035	10B	10B	12	4.5–6.0	900	900	Hyd.	Hyd.
'84–'85	C	4–135	Chrysler	All	RN12YC	.035	10B	10B	12	4.5–6.0	900	900	Hyd.	Hyd.
'84–'85	E	4–135	Chrysler	146	RN12YC	.035	12B	12B	12	73–122	900	800	Hyd.	Hyd.
'81–'82	D	4–156	Mitsubishi	92	P65-PR4	.041③	7B	7B	25	4.5–6.0	800①	800①	.006H	.010H
'83–'85	G	4–156	Mitsubishi	92	RN11YC4	.041③	7B	7B	25	4.5–6.0	800①	800①	.006H	.010H

NOTE: The underhood specifications sticker often reflects tune-up specification changes made in production. Sticker figures must be used if they disagree with those in this chart. Part numbers in this chart are not recommendations by Chilton for any product by brand name.

▲See text for procedure   H Hot   ②.035-Canada
■Before top dead center   C Cold   ③.030-Canada
Hyd. Hydraulic   ①750 rpm-Canada   ④1982–20B

FIRING ORDERS

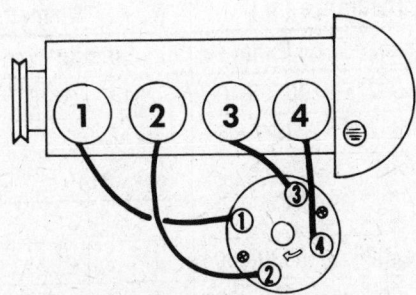

Chrysler Corp. 1.7L 1978 and later
Engine Firing Order: 1-3-4-2
Distributor Rotation: Clockwise

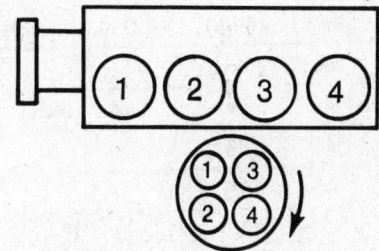

Chrysler Corp. 2.2L
Engine Firing Order: 1-3-4-2
Distributor Rotation: Clockwise

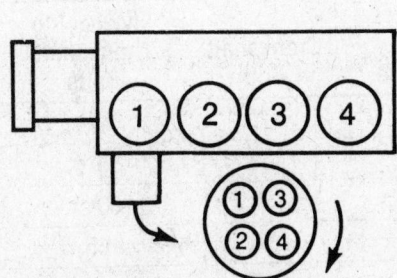

Chrysler Corp. (Mitsubishi) 2.6L
Engine Firing Order: 1-3-4-2
Distributor Rotation: Clockwise

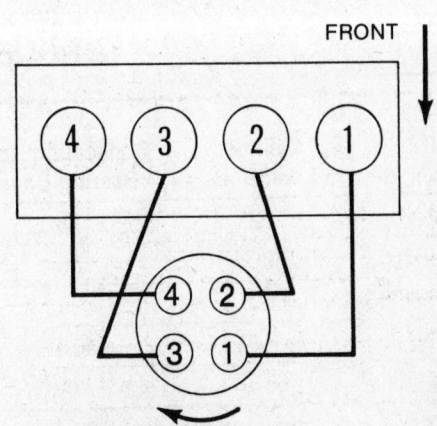

FRONT

Chrysler Corp: 1.6L
Engine Firing Order: 1-3-4-2
Distributor Rotation: Clockwise

C113

CAPACITIES

Year	Engine	Crankcase Incl. Filter	Pints To Refill After Draining		Final Drive (pts.)	Fuel Tank (gal.)	Cooling System (qts.)	
			Manual	Automatic			With Heater	With A/C
'84–'85	4–98	3.5	③	16②	—	13	7.0	—
'78–'80	4–105	4	2.65	13.0②	2.4	13	6.0①	6.0①
'81–'82	4–105	4	2.60	14.5②	2.4	13	6.0	6.0
'83	4–105	4	③	16.75②	2.4	13	6.0	6.0
'81–'82	4–135	4	2.60	15.0②	2.4	13	7.5	7.5
'83–'85	4–135	4④	③	17.75②	2.4	13	9	9
'81–'82	4–156	5	3.75	15.0②	2.4	13	8.5	8.5
'83–'85	4–156	5	③	17.75②	2.4	13	9	9

NOTE: If the starter motor is located on the radiator side of the engine the car is equipped with an A-412 manual transaxle; Use GL-4 Hypoid Lubricant. If the starter motor is located on the firewall side of the engine the car is equipped with an A-460 manual transaxle; Use only Dexron II lubricant.

① 1978 models with A/C: 6.5 qts., without A/C: 8.0 qts.
② Includes torque converter. Approx. 6 pts without draining converter.
③ 4 speed: 3.75–use Dexron® II lubricant
   5 speed: 4.55–use Dexron® II lubricant
④ '84–'85 2.2 Turbo engines: 5 qts. (Effective 4-24-84 Chrysler Corp. increased the oil capacity from 4 to 5 qts.)

VALVE SPECIFICATIONS

Year	Engine	Seat Angle (deg.)	Face Angle (deg.)	Spring Test Pressure (lb in.)	Spring Installed Height (in.)	Steam-To-Guide Clearance (in.)		Stem Diameter (in.)	
						Intake	Exhause	Intake	Exhaust
'84–'85	4–98	45	45	—	—	.0015–.00275	.00225–.0035	.3140–.3146	.3132–.3138
'78–'82	4–105	45	①	②	③	.020 max.	.027 max.	.3140	.3130
'81–'82	4–105	45	45	②	③	.0028	.0035	.314	.313
'81–'82	4–135	45	45.5	175 @ 1.22	1.65	.001–.003	.002–.004	.312–.313	.311–.312
'83–'85	4–135	45	45	175 @ 1.22	1.65	.0009–.0026	.0030–.0047	.3124	.3103
'82	4–156	43.75	45.25	34.1 @ 1.18	1.59	.001–.002	.002–.003	.315	.315
'83–'85	4–156	45	45	61 @ 1.59	1.59	.0012–.0024	.0020–.0035	.315	.315

① Intake 45°33′
   Exhaust: 43°33′
② outer: 101 @ .878
   inner: 49 @ .720
③ outer: 1.28
   inner: 1.13

TORQUE SPECIFICATIONS
(ft lbs.)

Year	Engine	Cylinder Head Bolts	Connecting Rod Bearing Bolts	Main Bearing Bolts	Crankshaft Bolt	Flywheel to Crankshaft Bolts	Camshaft Cap Bolts
'84–'85	4–98	52	28	48	110	—	—
'78	4–105	60①	25	47	58	55②	14
'79–'84	4–105	60①	35	47	58	60②	168④
'81–'85	4–135	③	40①	50	50	65	165④
'82–'85	4–156	69⑤	34	58	87	—	160④

① plus ¼ turn more
② 50 with auto. trans.
③ For torque sequence - 30, 45, 45 + ¼ turn more
④ Inch lbs.
⑤ Cold

CRANKSHAFT AND CONNECTING ROD SPECIFICATIONS
(All specifications in inches)

Year	Engine	Main Brg. Journal Dia.	Main Brg. Oil Clearance	Crankshaft End Play	Thrust on No.	Connecting Rod Journal Dia.	Rod Bearing Oil Clearance	Rod Bearing Side Clearance
'84–'85	4–98	2.048	.0009–.0031	.0035–.011	—	—	.001–.0025	.006–.009
'78–'82	4-105	2.124–2.128	.0008–.0030	.003–.007	3	1.809–1.813	.0011–.0034	.015
'83	4–105	2.1236–2.1244	.0008–.0030	.003–.007	3	1.809–1.813	.0011–.0034	.014
'81–'82	4–135	2.362–2.363	.0004–.0026	.002–.007	3	1.968–1.969	.0004–.0026	.005–.013
'84–'85	4–135	2.362–2.363	.0003–.0031	.002–.007	3	1.968–1.969	.0008–.0034	.005–.013
'82	4–156	2.3622	.0008–.0028	.002–.007	3	2.0866	.0008–.0028	.004–.010
'83–'85	4–156	2.3622	.0008–.0028	.002–.007	3	2.0866	.0008–.0028	.004–.010

PISTON, RING AND PIN SPECIFICATIONS
(All specifications in inches)

Year	Engine	Piston Clearance	Ring Gap			Ring Side Clearance			Pin Clearance In Piston
			Top Compression	Bottom Compression	Oil Control	Top Compression	Bottom Compression	Oil Control	
'84–'85	4–98	.0016–.0020	.012–.018	.012–.018	—	.0018–.0028	.0018–.0020	.010–.016	—
'78–'79	4–105	.0011–.0270	.012–.018	.012–.018	.010–.016	.0008–.0020	.0008–.0020	.0008–.0200	.00004–.00035
'80–'83	4–105	.0005–.0015	.012–.018	.012–.018	.016–.055	.0016–.0028	.008–.0020	.008–.0020	.00004–.00035
'81–'85	4–135	.0005–.0240	.011–.021	.011–.021	.015–.055	.0015–.0031	.0015–.0037	—	.00024–.00075
'82–'85	4–156	.0008–.0016	.01–.018	.01–.018	.0078–.035	.0024–.0039	.0008–.0024	—	.00020–.00035

WHEEL ALIGNMENT SPECIFICATIONS
(Caster is not adjustable)

Year	Front Camber		Rear Chamber		Toe-Out (in.)	
	Range (deg.)	Preferred	Range (deg.)	Preferred	Front	Rear
'78 Omni, Horizon	½N to ¾P	5/16P	1½N to ½N	1N	⅛ out to 0	5/32 out to 1/32 in
'79–'80 Omni, Horizon	⅕N to ⅘P	⅓P	1½N to ½N	1N	5/32 out to ⅛ in	5/32 out to 1/32 in
'81–'82 Omni, Horizon	¼N to ¾P	5/16P	1½N to ¾N	½	7/32 out to ⅛ in	5/32 out to 11/32 in
'81–'82 Aries, Reliant	¼N to ¾P	5/16P	1N-0	½	7/32 out to ⅛ in	3/16 out to 3/16 in
'82 LeBaron, Dodge 400	1/10N to 7/10N	3/10N	1N-0	½	3/20 out to 1/10 in	3/16 out to 3/16 in
'83–'85 All Models	¼N to ¾P	5/16P	①	½ all	7/32 out to ⅛ in	②

① Omni, Horizon 1½N to ¼N
  Aries, Reliant 1N to 0P
  LeBaron, 400

② Omni, Horizon 3/32 in
  Aries, Reliant 3/16 out to 3/16 in
  LeBaron, 400

CHARGING SYSTEM

A conventional alternator is used. An electronic voltage regulator regulates the vehicle electrical system voltage, by limiting the output voltage generated by the alternator. The regulator has no moving parts, and requires no adjustment. Various models are equipped with the voltage regulator built into the alternator. Regulator replacement requires the disassembly of the alternator.

For further information on the charging system, please refer to "Charging and Starting" in the Unit Repair section.

Alternator

REMOVAL & INSTALLATION

1.6, 1.7 and 2.2 Engines

1. Disconnect the battery ground cable.
2. Disconnect the wires from the alternator.
3. Support the alternator, remove the mounting bolts, and lift out the unit.
4. Reverse the procedure for installation. On models through 1982, proper belt tension on the alternator should be set with the special tool shown. Do not use thumb pressure on these belts. The adjustment should be made from below the car after removing the splash shield on all models, and the horn on California models. Adjust the tension to 70 ft. lbs. (new) or 50 ft. lbs. (used). Some 1983 and later models are equipped with a four groove belt, deflection should be ¼-⅜ in.

2.6 Engines

1. Disconnect the battery ground cable.
2. Disconnect and tag the wires from the alternator.
3. Remove the alternator brace bolt and support bolt nut. Disconnect the belt.
4. Remove the support bolt and the alternator.
5. To install, reverse the removal procedure. Clearance between the alternator leg and front case should be less than 0.008 in. Shims are available to adjust the clearance. Adjust the belt tension to ¼-⅜ in. deflection under thumb pressure.

Regulator

REMOVAL & INSTALLATION

1.6, 1.7 and 2.2 Engines

1. Disconnect the battery ground cable.
2. Disconnect the wires from the regulator.

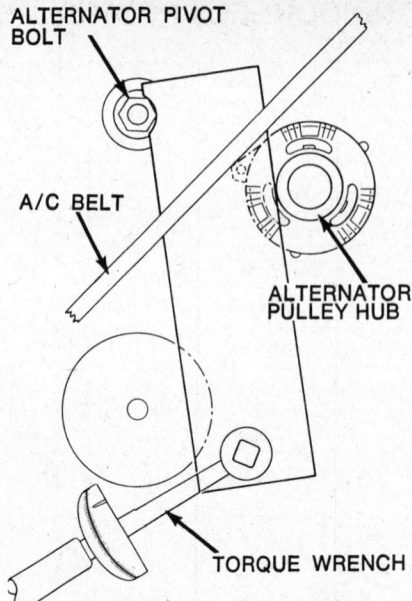

Adjusting the alternator belt tension on models with 1.7 engine.

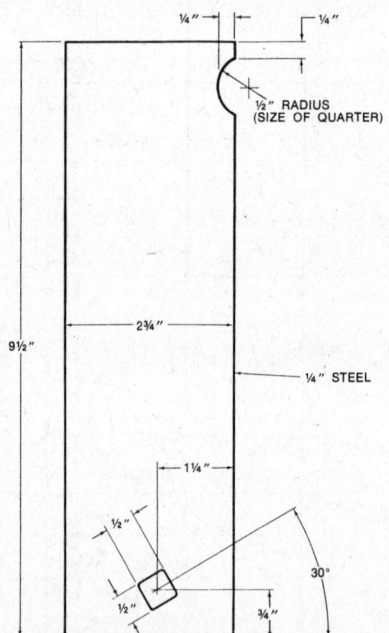

This special tool can be fabricated and must be used to adjust the alternator belt tension on 1.7 engines (© Chrysler Corp.)

3. Remove the two sheet metal screws that fasten the regulator to the right side fender skirt.
4. Installation is in the reverse order of removal.

2.6 Engines

NOTE: Some 2.6 engines may use a Chrysler built external regulator with the Chrysler built alternator. If so, refer to the above procedures for regulator removal.

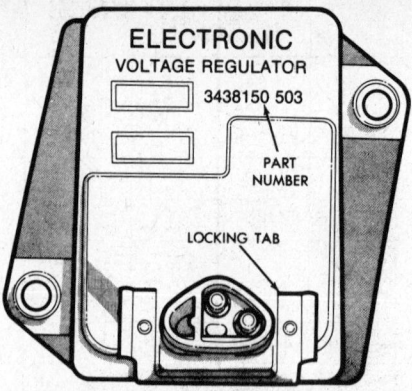

Voltage regulator (© Chrysler Corp.)

Most 2.6 engines are equipped with a Mitsubishi-built alternator that contains a built-in regulator. See the alternator replacement procedures for removal and installation.

STARTING SYSTEM

Three different makes of starters are used: Bosch, Mitsubishi and Nippondenso. Removal and installation procedures are the same for all units. The solenoid is mounted on the starter motor.

For further information on the starting system, please refer to "Charging and Starting" in the Unit Repair section.

REMOVAL & INSTALLATION

1. Disconnect the battery ground cable.
2. Disconnect the wires from the starter and solenoid.
3. Support the starter, remove the bolts, and lift the unit out from the flywheel housing.
4. Installation is in the reverse order of removal.

IGNITION SYSTEM

Models using 1.7 and 2.2 engines, except the 1980 1.7 Federal engines, are equipped with a computer controlled Hall-Effect ignition system. The 1980 1.7 Federal engine uses a Hall-Effect distributor that is not computer controlled.

NOTE: 1980 and later 1.7 and 2.2 equipped cars use a prong type connector at the distributor end of the spark plug cable. The distributor cap must be removed from the distributor and the prongs squeezed together on the inside of the cap before the cable can be removed.

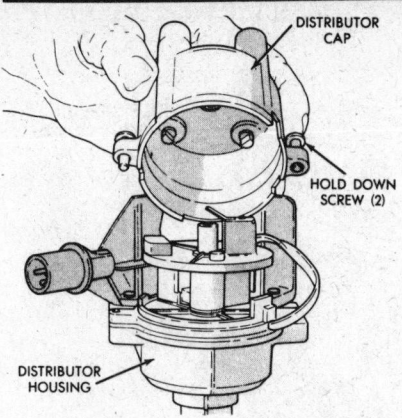

Distributor (© Chrysler Corp.)

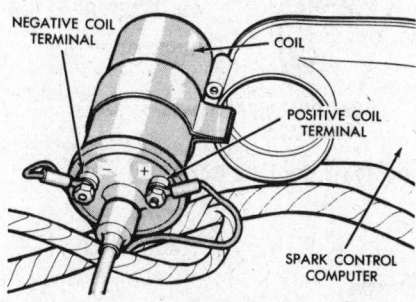

Ignition coil (© Chrysler Corp.)

All engines use electronic ignition, eliminating the point/condenser system. But the electronic ignition on 1.6 and 2.6 engines is slightly different from that used on 1.7 and 2.2 engines.

For additional information on the ignition system, please refer to "Electronic Ignition Systems" in the Unit Repair section.

DISTRIBUTOR REMOVAL

1. Disconnect the distributor pickup lead wire at the harness connector.
2. Remove the distributor cap.
3. Rotate the engine crankshaft (in the direction of normal rotation) until No. 1 cylinder is at TDC on the compression stroke. Make a mark on the block where the rotor points for installation reference.
4. Remove the distributor hold-down screw.
5. Carefully lift the distributor from the engine. The shaft will rotate slightly as the distributor is removed.

DISTRIBUTOR INSTALLATION

1. If the engine has been cranked over while the distributor was removed, rotate the crankshaft until the number one piston is at TDC on the compression stroke. This will be indicated by the O mark on the flywheel or crank pulley aligning with the

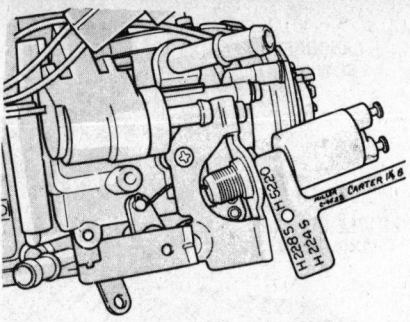

Throttle position transducer adjustment (© Chrysler Corp.)

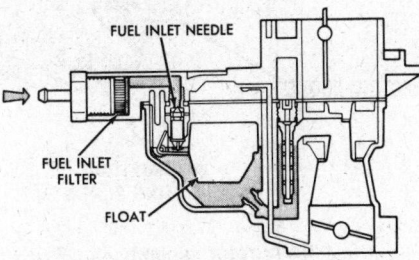

Fuel inlet system (© Chrysler Corp.)

pointer on the clutch housing or engine front cover. Position the rotor just ahead of the No. 1 terminal of the cap and lower the distributor into the engine. With the distributor fully seated, the rotor should be directly under the No. 1 terminal.

2. If the engine was not disturbed while the distributor was out, lower the distributor into the engine, engaging the gears and making sure that the gasket is properly seated in the block. The rotor should line up with the mark made before removal.
3. Tighten the hold-down screw and connect the wires.
4. Check and, if necessary, adjust the ignition timing.

IGNITION TIMING

The ignition is timed on No. 1 cylinder, the left-hand side, facing the car. The exception is the 1.6 engine, where the No. 1 cylinder is on the right side (flywheel end).

1. Connect a timing light according to the manufacturer's instructions.
2. Run the engine to normal operating temperature.
3. Make sure the idle speed is correct.
4. Loosen the distributor hold-down screw just enough so the distributor can be rotated.
5. Ground the carburetor switch.
6. Remove the timing hole access cover (1.7 and 2.2 engines) and aim the timing light at the hole in the clutch housing. The 2.6 engine timing marks are on the crankshaft pulley and front cover. Carefully rotate the distributor until the timing marks are aligned.
7. Tighten the distributor and recheck the timing.

8. Check, and if necessary adjust, the idle speed.

FUEL SYSTEM

The fuel system consists of the fuel tank, fuel pump, fuel filter, carburetor, fuel lines and vacuum lines.

Fuel Pump

REMOVAL & INSTALLATION

A mechanical fuel pump is located on the left side of the engine. Right front on 1.6 engines. To remove the pump, disconnect the fuel and vapor lines and remove the attaching bolts. Installation is in the reverse of removal. Always use a new gasket when installing the pump and make certain the gasket surfaces are clean. On 2.6 engines, coat both sides of the insulator and gasket with sealer.

Fuel Filter

REMOVAL & INSTALLATION

Two filters are used. One is part of the fuel pickup in the fuel tank. The other is a sealed paper unit (on 1.6, 1.7 and 2.2 engines) located in the carburetor inlet, or an in-line filter is used (on 2.6 engines). The tank unit does not usually need replacing, but can be replaced if necessary. The carburetor filter should be replaced periodically. To replace the inlet filter, place a rag or container under the inlet and disconnect the fuel line. Unscrew the inlet fitting. The filter has a spring behind it, so take care not to lose it. Replacement is in the reverse order of removal.

The inline filter can be removed by placing a rag under the filter and removing the clamps. Pull the filter out of the lines and discard it. Install a new filter, noting the direction of fuel flow, usually indicated by an arrow.

Carburetor

REMOVAL & INSTALLATION

1. Disconnect the negative battery cable.
2. Remove the air cleaner.
3. Disconnect the accelerator linkage.
4. Disconnect the transmission detent cable.
5. Disconnect the cruise control, if so equipped.
6. Disconnect the fuel line, at the carburetor.
7. Disconnect all necessary vacuum lines. Number them for easy reinstallation.
8. Remove the attaching bolts, then the carburetor.
9. Installation is in the reverse order of removal.

IDLE SPEED ADJUSTMENT

1.6, 1.7, and 2.2 Engines

1. Set the parking brake and place the transmission in Neutral.

2. Turn off all the lights and accessories.

3. Connect a tachometer to the engine following the manufacturer's instructions.

4. Start the engine and allow it to reach normal operating temperature.

5. Disconnect and plug the vacuum hoses to the EGR valve and the distributor.

6. Unplug the connector at the radiator fan and install a jumper so the fan will run continuously.

7. On 1981 and later models equipped with the fuel control computer, connect a jumper wire between the carburetor switch and the ground.

8. Remove the PCV from the rubber molded connector and disconnect the purge hose to the vapor canister at the carburetor end. Leave both open to underhood air (through 1980). On 1981 and later models plug the 3/16 in. diameter control hose at the canister.

9. Read the RPM indicated on the tachometer. If the RPM is not the same as the idle set rpm specified on the emissions label, turn the idle speed screw (on top of the solenoid) to correct it.

10. Unplug and connect all hoses and reconnect all wires.

NOTE: Do not attempt to adjust the mixture screw. This procedure requires the use of a bottle of propane and a propane metering valve. If a mixture problem is suspected it is recommended that the adjustment be made by a qualified repair shop.

2.6 Engine

1. Set the parking brake and place the transmission in Neutral.

2. Turn off all the lights and accessories and disconnect the cooling fan.

3. Connect a tachometer to the engine, following the manufacturer's instructions.

4. Start the engine and allow it to reach normal operating temperature.

5. Check the timing and adjust if necessary.

6. Remove the timing light and read the rpm indicated on the tachometer. If it not the same as the curb idle specified on the emission label adjust the idle speed adjusting screw. The screw is accessible through the hole in the choke cover plate using a long, narrow screwdriver at a 45° angle inward.

7. After adjusting the curb idle speed, press the A/C button ON. With the compressor running, set the engine speed to 900 rpm by turning the idle up adjusting screw. The idle up adjusting screw is accessible through a hole in the choke cover plate using a long, narrow shaft screwdriver at a 45° angle downward.

8. Turn the engine off, disconnect the tachometer and reconnect the cooling fan.

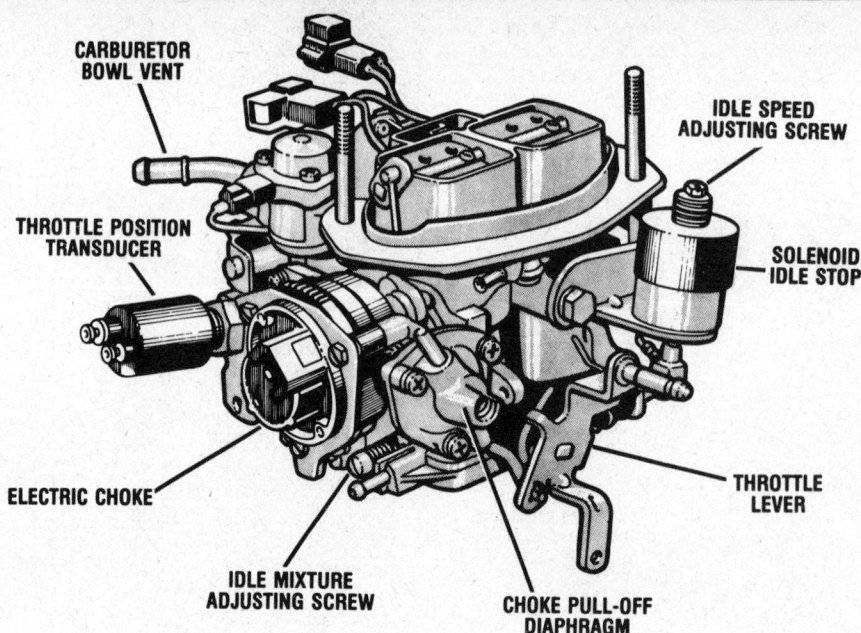

Carburetor assembly—1.7 and 2.2 engine (© Chrysler Corp.)

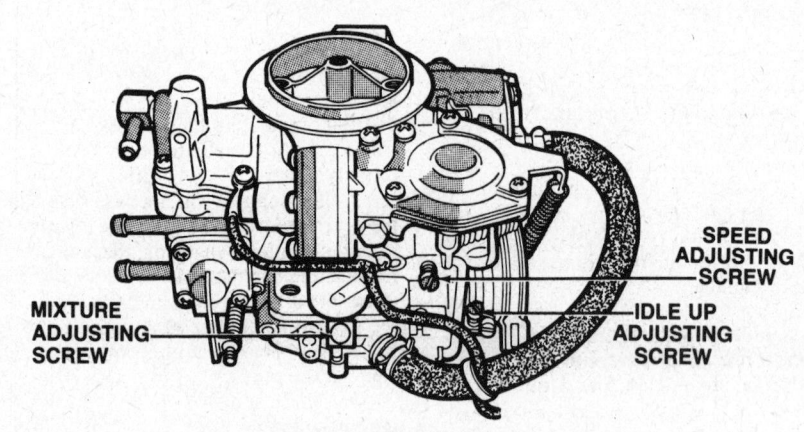

Carburetor adjustment screws—2.6 engine

MIXTURE ADJUSTMENT

Chrysler recommends the use of a propane enrichment procedure to adjust the mixture. The equipment needed for this procedure is not readily available to the general public.

Fuel Injection

Two types of electronic (computer regulated) fuel injection systems are used: a single-point injection system and a multi-point injection system. In both systems, a digital pre-programmed computer (Logic Module) responds to changing operating conditions by regulating ignition timing, air-fuel ratio, emission control devices and idle speed; in both systems sensors and switches are used to provide the input necessary for the Logic Module and to regulate the fuel injection.

In the single-point fuel injection system a Throttle Body Assembly is mounted on top of the intake manifold, instead of a carburetor. This assembly houses the fuel injector, pressure regulator, throttle position sensor, and the automatic idle speed motor. In the multi-point system, the throttle body houses the throttle position sensor and the automatic idle speed motor. This system is called "multi-point" because it uses a separate fuel injector for each cylinder.

For further information on the fuel injection system, please refer to "Fuel Injection" in the Unit Repair section.

COOLING SYSTEM

The cooling system consists of a radiator, overflow tank, water pump, thermostat, coolant temperature switch, electric fan and radiator fan switch. The electric fan is used for cooling the transversely mounted engine. A radiator bypass system is used for faster warmup.

Radiator

REMOVAL & INSTALLATION

1. Move the temperature selector to full ON.
2. Open the radiator drain cock.
3. When the coolant reserve tank is empty, remove the radiator cap.
4. Remove the hoses.
5. If equipped with automatic transmission, disconnect and plug the fluid cooler lines.
6. Remove the upper and lower mounting brackets.
7. Remove the shroud.
8. Remove the fan motor attaching bolts.
9. Remove the top radiator attaching bolts.
10. Remove the bottom radiator attaching bolts.
11. Lift radiator from engine compartment.
12. Installation is in the reverse order of removal.

Water Pump

REMOVAL & INSTALLATION

1.6 Engine

1. Remove radiator cap and drain cooling system through water pump drain plug.
2. Disconnect pump to block coolant hose at the pump.
3. Loosen alternator/water pump drive belt.
4. Remove four pump-to-crankcase extension screws and remove assembly.
5. Installation is in the reverse order of removal. Torque the pump extension bolts to 9 ft. lbs., the pump drain plug to 13 ft. lbs.

1.7 Engine

1. Drain the cooling system.
2. Without discharging the system, move the compressor from the engine brackets and set aside.
3. Completely remove the alternator.
4. Remove the water pump pulley.
5. If so equipped, disconnect the diverter valve hose at the diverter valve, remove the front and rear air pump bracket.
6. Remove the alternator bracket attached to the water pump.
7. Disconnect the lower radiator hose and the by-pass hose.
8. Loosen the timing belt cover bolt and the two top water pump bolts and remove the water pump.
9. Installation is in the reverse order of

removal, be sure the rubber O-ring is properly installed before mounting the water pump. It is important that the following torque sequence be followed. Tighten the two upper water pump attaching bolts to 250 inch lbs. Next, tighten the two front air pump brackets to the water pump bolts, one to 250 inch lbs. and one to 40 ft. lbs. Next, install the air pump and tighten the two bolts to 24 ft. lbs. Next, tighten the two rear air pump brackets and the lower water pump to engine bolts to 250 inch lbs.

2.2 Engine

1. Drain the cooling system.
2. Remove the upper radiator hose.
3. Without discharging the system, remove the air conditioning compressor from the engine brackets and set to one side.
4. Remove the alternator and move to one side.
5. Disconnect the lower radiator hose and the bypass hose and remove the water pump by removing the pump-to-engine retaining screws.
6. Installation is in the reverse order of removal. Tighten the top three retaining screws to 250 inch lbs. and the lower screw to 40 ft. lbs.

2.6 Engine

1. Drain the cooling system.
2. Remove the radiator hose, by-pass hose and heater hose from the water pump.
3. Remove the drive pulley shield.
4. Remove the locking screw and pivot screws.
5. Remove the drive belt and water pump from the engine.
6. Installation is in the reverse order of removal. After adjusting the belt tension tighten the locking screw and pivot screws to 204 inch lbs. Tighten the drive pulley shield to 105 inch lbs.

Thermostat

REMOVAL & INSTALLATION

1. Drain the cooling system to a level below the thermostat.
2. Remove the hoses from the thermostat housing.

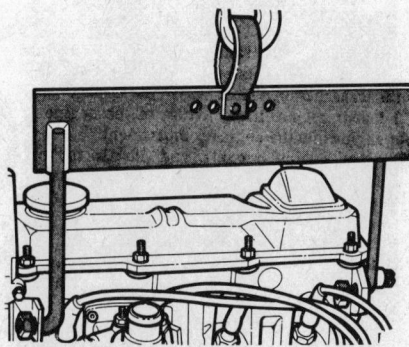

Lifting fixture (© Chrysler Corp.)

3. Remove the thermostat housing.
4. Remove the thermostat, and discard the gasket. Thoroughly clean the surfces that will take the new gasket.
5. Using a new gasket, position the thermostat and install the housing and bolts. Make sure the thermostat is seated squarely in place.
6. Refill the cooling system.

EMISSION CONTROL SYSTEMS

Several different systems are used on each car, but not all systems are found on any one car. Most require no service and those which may require service also require sophisticated equipment for testing purposes.

For further information on the Emission control system, please refer to "Emission Controls" in the Unit Repair section.

ENGINE

Four engines are used depending on year and model:

1.6L (98 cu.in.): Introduced in 1984, the 1.6 engine is of overhead valve design with adjustable rocker arms. The cast iron camshaft rides in three babbit alloy type bearings and is driven by the crankshaft via a two-row rocker chain. The engine uses a forged steel crankshaft supported by five main bearings. The engine block is cast iron, with a "Siamese" bore design, in which pairs of combustion chambers share a common wall between themselves, featuring a shorter engine block. The cylinder head is aluminum.

1.7L (105 cu. in.): The 1.7 engine is of the overhead cam design. The block is cast iron and the cylinder head is aluminum. A five main bearing, forged steel crankshaft is used. The camshaft is belt driven.

2.2L (135 cu. in.): The 2.2 engine is very similar to the 1.7 engine. The difference being the use of hydraulic valve lash adjusters (instead of shims) to adjust valve clearance, and an increase in the bore an stroke.

2.6L (156 cu. in.): The 2.6 engine feat an overhead camshaft mounted in ar minum cylinder head, a jet valve (l beside the intake valve of each c providing for better combustion) lent shaft system (to reduce vibration).

ENGINE REMOVAL

NOTE: The engine a

must be removed together, or the transmission should be completely removed from the car first. The following is for engine/transmission assembly removal

1. Disconnect the battery.
2. Mark the hood hinge outline and remove the hood.
3. Drain the cooling system.
4. Remove the radiator hoses and remove the radiator and shroud assembly.
5. Remove the air cleaner and hoses.
6. The air conditioning-compressor generally does not have to be disconnected. Remove it from its bracket and position it out of the way. Securing it with wire is the best method.
7. Remove the power steering pump mounting bolts and set the pump to one side, if so equipped.
8. Disconnect and label all wiring from the engine, alternator and carburetor.
9. Disconnect the fuel line, heater hoses and accelerator linkage.
10. Disconnect the air pump lines.
11. Remove the alternator.
12. Disconnect the clutch and speedometer cables.
13. Raise the vehicle and support it on jackstands.

NOTE: See driveshaft section before attempting removal.

14. Disconnect the driveshafts from the transmission and support them with wires.
15. Disconnect the exhaust pipe.
16. Remove the air pump.
17. Disconnect the transmission linkage.
18. Lower the vehicle.
19. Attach a lifting fixture and a shop crane to the engine. Raise the engine slightly to take up the weight and disconnect the engine mounts in this order: front. right, left. Lift the engine from the car.

ENGINE INSTALLATION

1. Lower the engine into place and loosely install all mounting bolts. When all mounts have been hand tightened, torque each to 40 ft. lbs.
2. Remove the lifting fixture and raise the vehicle, supporting it on jackstands.
3. Connect the driveshafts. Torque the bolts to 35 ft. lbs.
4. Connect the transmission linkage, install the air pump, connect the exhaust pipe and lower the vehicle.
5. Connect the clutch and speedometer cables.
6. Install the alternator.
7. Install the air pump lines.
8. Connect the fuel line, heater hoses and accelerator linkage.
9. Connect all wiring.
10. Reinstall power steering pump, if previously removed.
11. Mount the air conditioning compressor.
12. Install the air cleaner.
13. Install the radiator and hoses.

14. Fill the cooling system.
15. Install the hood.
16. Connect the battery.
17. Start the engine and run it to normal operating temperature.
18. Check the timing and adjust if necessary. Adjust the carburetor idle speed and mixture, and the transmission linkage.

Intake Manifold

REMOVAL & INSTALLATION
1.6, 1.7 and 2.2 Engines

1. Drain the cooling system.
2. Remove the air cleaner and hoses.
3. Remove all wiring and any hoses connected to the carburetor and manifold.
4. Disconnect the accelerator linkage and shift linkage (if so equipped).
5. Remove the intake-to-exhaust manifold bolts.
6. Remove the manifold-to-head bolts and lift out the intake manifold.
7. Clean all gasket surfaces and install the intake manifold using new gaskets.
8. Connect all hoses and wires, and install the air cleaner.
9. Connect the accelerator linkage and shift linkage (if so equipped).

2.6 Engine

1. Disconnect the battery.
2. Drain the cooling system and disconnect the hoses from the water pump to the intake manifold.

3. Disconnect the carburetor air horn and move to one side.
4. Disconnect the vacuum hoses and throttle linkage from the carburetor.
5. Disconnect the fuel inlet line at the fuel filter.
6. Remove the fuel filter and fuel pump and move to one side.
7. Remove the intake manifold retaining nuts and washers and remove the manifold.
8. Installation is in the reverse order of removal. Tighten the retaining nuts to 150 in. lbs.

Exhaust Manifold

REMOVAL & INSTALLATION
1.6, 1.7 and 2.2 Engines

1. Follow the intake manifold removal procedure above.
2. Disconnect the exhaust pipe or the converter and exhaust pipe.
3. Unbolt and remove the exhaust manifold.
4. Clean the gasket surfaces, and using a new gasket, install the manifold.

2.6 Engines

1. Disconnect the battery.
2. Drain the cooling system.
3. Remove the air cleaner.
4. Remove the belt from the power steering pump.
5. Raise the vehicle and make sure it is supported safely.

1.6L engine

6. Remove the exhaust pipe from the manifold.

7. Disconnect the air injection tube assembly from the exhaust manifold and lower the vehicle.

8. Remove the power steering pump assembly and move to one side.

9. Remove the heat cowl from the exhaust manifold.

10. Remove the exhaust manifold retaining nuts and remove the assembly from the vehicle.

11. Remove the carburetor air heater from the manifold.

12. Separate the exhaust manifold from the catalytic converter by removing the retaining screws.

13. Installation is in the reverse order of removal. Use a new gasket between the exhaust manifold and the front catalytic converter and torque the mounting screws to 24 ft. lbs. Use a new manifold gasket and coat the cylinder head side lightly with sealer. Torque the manifold center mounting nuts to 150 inch lbs. then torque the outer mounting nuts to 150 inch lbs.

VALVE ADJUSTMENT

1.7 Engine Only

Valve adjustment is not required as a matter of routine maintenance. It is, however, necessary to check the valve clearance after head repairs. Adjusting clearance is a matter of substituting discs located in the top of the cam follower. The discs are available in 0.05mm increments from 3.00mm–4.25mm. One disc is located in each follower. A special tool is required for disc removal and installation. Cold clearance should be 0.15-0.25mm (0.006-0.010in.) intake and 0.35-0.45mm (0.014-0.018in.) exhaust; warm clearance is 0.20-0.30mm (0.008-0.012in.) intake and 0.40-0.50mm (0.016-0.020in.) exhaust.

CHECKING/ADJUSTING VALVE CLEARANCE

1.6 Engine

NOTE: Valve clearance must be set with the piston at TDC on the compression stroke with the engine COLD.

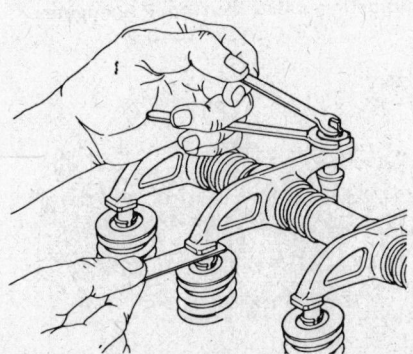

1.6 engine—adjusting valve clearance

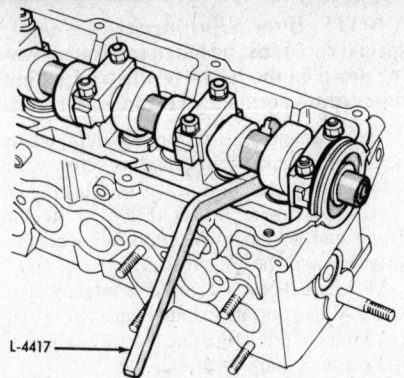

Adjusting valve clearance on 1.7 engines
(© Chrysler Corp.)

1. Turn crankshaft and watch movement of exhaust valves. When one is closing—moving upward—continue turning slowly until the inlet valve on the same cylinder just starts to open. This is the "valve rocking" position. The piston in the opposite cylinder is then at TDC on compression, and its valve clearance can be checked and adjusted.

Example, to check valve clearances on number one cylinder, position valves on (pared) cylinder number four in rocking position, as follows:

a. Observe rockers on (pared) cylinder number four. Turn crankshaft until exhaust valve rocker is moving upward (valve closing)—keep turning slowly until intake valve rocker just starts to move down (valve opening)—stop.

b. Check both valve clearances on number one cylinder.

2. After checking both valve clearances, rotate the crankshaft one half turn, the next cylinder in the firing order should have its valves "rocking" and the pared cylinder can be adjusted.

Valves 'Rocking' on Cylinder Number	Adjust Valves on Cylinder Number
4	1
2	3
1	4
3	2

3. Adjust valves as needed.
Intake 0.010 in.
Exhaust 0.012 in.

1.7 Engine

The valves should be checked with the engine warm and be checked in the firing order 1-3-4-2.

1. Run the engine to normal operating temperature.

2. Remove the valve cover.

3. Use a socket wrench on the crankshaft pulley, or bump the engine around until the camshaft lobes of No. 1 cylinder are positioned as shown. Due to the design of the camshaft lobes, it is not necessary that the lobes be pointing directly away (perpendicular) to the adjusting disc.

— **CAUTION** —
Do not turn the engine using the camshaft pulley, and only turn the engine in the direction of normal rotation.

4. Using a feeler gauge, check the valve clearance between the camshaft lobe and the valve adjusting disc.

5. If the measured clearance is not as specified, this can be corrected by replacing the valve adjusting disc with another of the proper size.

6. To remove the disc:

a. Depress the cam follower with Tool L-4417. This tool is necessary to remove the disc without damaging the camshaft or cylinder head.

b. Remove the valve adjusting disc with a magnet.

c. Calculate the thickness of a new disc and install one of the proper size. Be sure the number indicating the thickness of the disc (mm) faces down when installed.

d. Recheck the valve clearance.

VALVE ADJUSTING DISCS

Thickness (mm)	Part Number
3.00	5240946
3.05	5240945
3.10	5240944
3.15	5240943
3.20	5240942
3.25	5240941
3.30	5240573
3.35	5240574
3.40	5240575
3.45	5240576
3.50	5240577
3.55	5240578
3.60	5240579
3.65	5240580
3.70	5240581
3.75	5240582
3.80	5240583
3.85	5240584
3.90	5240585
3.95	5240586
4.00	5240587
4.05	5240588
4.10	5240589
4.15	5240590
4.20	5240591
4.25	5240592

7. Recheck or adjust all other valves in the same manner.

NOTE: When the camshaft is in position to check the valves of No. 1 cylinder, cylinders No. 3 and 4 can also be checked or adjusted. It is only necessary to turn the engine one time to position the camshaft to check No. 2 cylinder.

8. Reinstall the valve cover.

2.2 Engine

The 2.2 liter engine uses hydraulic lash adjusters. No periodic adjustment or checking is necessary

2.6 Engine

The 2.6 engine has a jet valve located beside the intake valve of each cylinder.

NOTE: When adjusting valve clearances, the jet valve must be adjusted before the intake valve.

1. Start the engine and allow it to reach normal operating temperature.

2. Stop the engine and remove the air cleaner and its hoses. Remove any other cables, hoses, wires, etc., which are attached to the valve cover, and remove the valve cover.

3. Disconnect the high tension coil-to-distributor wire at the coil.

4. Watch the rocker arms for No. 1 cylinder and rotate the crankshaft until the exhaust valve is closing and the intake valve has just started to open. At this point, No. 4 cylinder will be at Top Dead Center (TDC) commencing its firing stroke.

5. Loosen the locknut on cylinder No. 4 intake valve and back off the intake valve adjusting screw 2 or more turns.

6. Loosen the locknut on the jet valve adjusting screw.

7. Turn the jet valve adjusting screw counter-clockwise and insert a 0.006 in. feeler gauge between the jet valve stem and the adjusting screw.

8. Tighten the adjusting screw until it touches the feeler gauge.

Take care not to press on the valve while adjusting because the jet valve spring is very weak.

NOTE: If the adjusting screw is tight, special care must be taken to avoid pressing down on the jet valve when adjusting the clearance or a false reading will result.

9. Tighten the locknut securely while holding the rocker arm adjusting screw with a screwdriver to prevent it from turning.

10. Make sure that a 0.006 in. feeler gauge can be easily inserted between the jet valve and the rocker arm.

11. Adjust No. 4 cylinder's intake valve to 0.006 in., and its exhaust valve to 0.010 in. Tighten the adjusting screw locknuts and recheck each clearance.

12. Perform step 4 in conjunction with the chart below to set up the remaining three cylinders for valve adjustments.

Exhaust Valve Closing	Adjust
No. 1 Cylinder	No. 4 Cylinder Valves
No. 2 Cylinder	No. 3 Cylinder Valves
No. 3 Cylinder	No. 2 Cylinder Valves
No. 4 Cylinder	No. 1 Cylinder Valves

13. Replace the valve cover and all other components. Run the engine and check for oil leaks at the valve cover.

Cylinder Head

REMOVAL & INSTALLATION

1.6 Engine

NOTE: The cylinder head must be cold before removing to avoid distortion.

1. Remove the valve cover and any necessary vacuum lines. Drain cooling system.

2. Release cylinder head bolts evenly, beginning at the ends and working toward

the center. Brackets supporting rocker assembly are located on dowels and retained by the head bolts. Only brackets 2 and 4 are pinned to the rocker arm shafts.

3. Tie end brackets and remove rockers as an assembly.

4. Remove push rods and identify so they can be installed in the same positions.

5. Remove cylinder head.

6. Installation is in the reverse order of removal. When reinstalling the head, tighten the bolts progressively to 52 ft. lbs. Run the engine to operating temperature. Allow it to cool to normal air temperature. Retorque the head bolts as needed.

NOTE: Always use a new head gasket upon reinstallation.

1.7 Engine

The cylinder head should be cold before removal.

1. Disconnect the battery.
2. Drain the cooling system.
3. Remove the air cleaner assembly.
4. Disconnect all lines, hoses and wires from the head, manifold and carburetor.
5. Disconnect the accelerator linkage.
6. Remove the distributor cap.
7. Disconnect the exhaust pipe.
8. Remove the carburetor.
9. Remove the intake and exhaust manifolds.
10. Remove the upper portion of the front cover.

Adjusting valve lash on 2.6 engines
(© Chrysler Corp.)

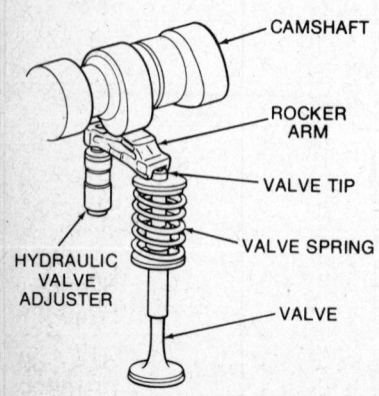

Hydraulic valve adjuster used on 2.2 engine (© Chrysler Corp.)

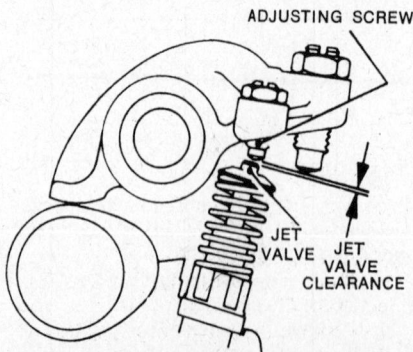

Adjusting the jet valve on 2.6 engines
(© Chrysler Corp.)

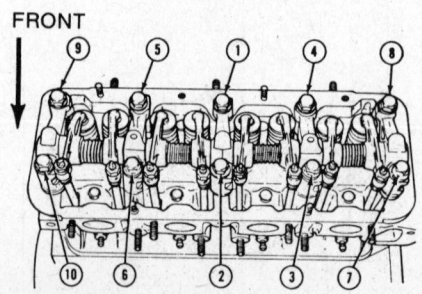

1.6 engine—head bolt tightening sequence

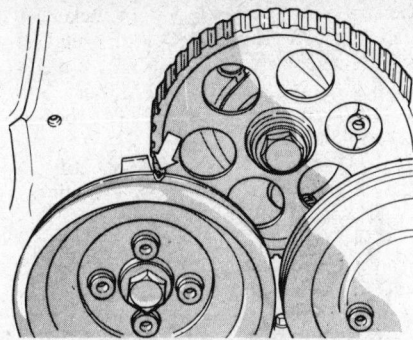

Crankshaft and intermediate gear alignment on 1.7 engines (© Chrysler Corp.)

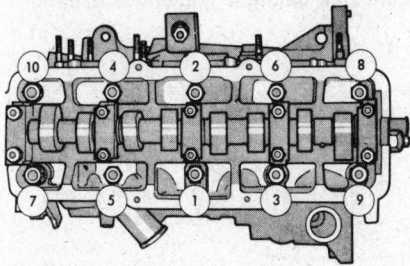

Cylinder head bolt tightening sequence on 1.7 (© Chrysler Corp.)

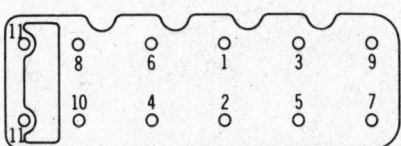

Cylinder head torque sequence—2.6 engines (© Chrysler Corp.)

11. Turn the engine by hand until all gear timing marks are aligned.

12. Loosen the drive belt tensioner and slip the belt off the camshaft gear

NOTE: The camshaft timing mark on the 1.7 engine is on the back of the gear and is properly positioned when it is in line with the left corner of the camshaft cover at the head.

13. If equipped with air conditioning, remove the compressor from the mounting brackets and support it out of the way with wires. Remove the mounting brackets from the head.

14. Remove the valve cover, gaskets and seals.

15. Remove head bolts in the reverse order of the tightening sequence.

16. Lift off the head and discard the gasket.

17. Installation is in the reverse order of removal. Make certain all gasket surfaces are thoroughly cleaned and are free of deep nicks or scratches. Always use new gaskets and seals. The word "OBEN" (top) on the 1.7 engine head gasket faces up. Never reuse a gasket or seal, even if it looks good. When positioning the head on the block, insert bolts 8 and 10 (see illustration) to align the head. Tighten bolts in the order shown to

specifications. Make sure all timing marks are aligned before installing the drive belt. The drive belt is correctly tensioned when it can be twisted 90° with the thumb and index finger, midway between the camshaft and the intermediate shaft.

2.2 Engine

———— CAUTION ————

Do not perform this operation on a warm engine. Remove the head bolts in the reverse order of the installation sequence shown. Loosen evenly in several steps. Do not attempt to slide the cylinder head off the block. Lift the head straight up and off the engine block.

1. Disconnect the negative battery cable and drain the cooling system.

2. Remove the air cleaner assembly. Mark the various hoses for installation identification.

3. Disconnect all lines, hoses, wiring harnesses, etc. from the manifold, carburetor and cylinder head.

4. Disconnect the accelerator linkage. Remove the carburetor. Disconnect the converter and exhaust pipe. Remove the intake and exhaust mainfolds.

5. Remove the upper part of the timing case (front cover).

6. Turn the engine by hand until all gear timing marks line up (engine at TDC, No. 1 piston).

7. Loosen the drive belt tensioner and slip the timing belt off the camshaft gear.

8. If the car is equipped with air conditioning, remove the compressor and mounting brackets, and place out of the way. Do not disconnect any of the compressor lines unless the system is safely bled of freon.

9. Remove the valve cover, gaskets and seals. Remove the head bolts in the reverse order of the tightening sequence.

10. Lift off the cylinder head, clean all gasket surfaces.

11. Installation is in the reverse order of removal. Refer to the timing belt replacement section to check camshaft timing. Make sure all gasket surfaces are cleaned and free of deep nicks or scratches. Always install new gaskets and seals. Tighten bolts in the order shown in the illustration. Make sure all timing marks are aligned before installing the drive belt. The drive belt is correctly tensioned when it can be twisted 90° with the thumb and index finger, midway between the cam and intermediate shafts.

2.6 Engine

———— CAUTION ————

Do not perform this operation on a warm engine. Remove the head bolts in the sequence shown, in several steps. Loosen the head bolts evenly, not one at a time. Do not attempt to slide the cylinder head off the block, as it is located with dowel pins. Lift the head straight up and off the block.

NOTE: In order to remove the engine front cover, you need to support the engine, and to first remove the motor mount.

1. Disconnect the battery and drain the cooling system. Disconnect the upper radiator hose.

2. Remove the breather hoses and the purge hose.

3. Remove the air cleaner and the fuel line.

4. Remove the vacuum hose at the distributor and purge the control valve.

5. Tag the ignition wires for reinstallation, and disconnect them from the spark plugs.

6. Remove the distributor cap and distributor by removing the retainer nut and pulling the unit out.

7. Disconnect the heater hose at the intake manifold.

8. Disconnect the water temperature gauge unit wire.

9. Place No. 1 piston in the TDC position to take pressure off the fuel pump rocker arm. Disconnect the fuel hoses and plug the line leading to the gas tank to prevent fuel leakage.

10. Remove the fuel pump mounting nuts or bolts and remove the pump assembly. Remove the insulator and gaskets.

11. Disconnect the exhaust pipe at the exhaust manifold flange.

12. Remove the rocker cover.

13. Remove its breather and semi-circular seal.

14. After slightly loosening the camshaft sprocket bolt, turn the crankshaft until No. 1 piston is at TDC on compression stroke (both valves closed).

NOTE: Never turn the engine over using the camshaft bolt; it puts undue strain on the chain and other components.

15. Remove the camshaft sprocket bolt and distributor drive gear. Remove the camshaft sprocket and allow it to rest in the chain on the holder below.

16. Remove the cylinder head bolts in the reverse of the bolt tightening sequence shown. Head bolts should be loosened in two or three stages to prevent head warpage.

17. Remove the cylinder head and cylinder head gasket.

Installation is performed in the following manner.

18. Clean all gasket surfaces of cylinder block and cylinder head.

19. Install a new cylinder head gasket. Install the cylinder head assembly.

NOTE: Do not apply sealant to the head gasket and do not reuse an old head gasket.

NOTE: The head gasket has the number "54" stamped at the front of the upper surface.

20. Install the ten cylinder head bolts. Starting at top center, tighten all cylinder head bolts to specifications.

21. Tighten the two front bolts to 11-15 ft. lbs.

22. Verify that No. 1 cylinder is at TDC. Align the dowel pin in the end of the camshaft sprocket with the groove in the top of the front camshaft bearing cap and install the camshaft sprocket and chain while pulling up on the sprocket.

23. Install the distributor drive gear and the sprocket bolt.

24. Turn the crankshaft about 90° back, and tighten the camshaft sprocket bolt back to 37-43 ft. lbs.

Very slowly turn the engine over two times to make sure the valve timing is correct. If the engine locks at a certain point in these two revolutions, the valve timing is not correct. Repeat steps 22-24.

━━━ CAUTION ━━━

At this point, do not turn the engine over using the starter. If the valve timing is off, several of the valves could be bent.

25. Install the breather and semicircular seal on the cylinder head after applying sealant to surface contact points. Install the rocker cover with a new gasket.

26. Connect the exhaust pipe to the exhaust manifold flange. Tighten the bolts to 11-18 ft. lbs.

27. Put No. 1 cylinder at TDC and install the fuel pump with a new gasket and insulator. Connect all hoses.

28. Connect the water temperature gauge unit wire. Connect the heater hose to the intake manifold.

29. Install the distributor and spark plug cables.

30. Connect the vacuum hose to the distributor and purge the control valve. Connect the upper radiator hose and fill the cooling system with coolant.

Timing Cover and Belt

REMOVAL & INSTALLATION

1.7 Engine

1. Disconnect the battery.
2. Remove the air compressor, alternator, power steering pump and drive belts and set to one side.
3. Raise the vehicle and remove the splash fender shield.
4. Remove the idler pulley assembly.
5. Remove the crankshaft pulley.
6. Remove the lower timing belt cover.
7. Lower the vehicle and place a jack under the engine.
8. Remove the right engine mounting bolt and raise the engine slightly.
9. Loosen the timing belt tensioner and remove the timing belt.
10. To install, turn the crankshaft and intermediate sprockets until both markings on the sprockets are aligned.
11. Turn the camshaft sprocket until the mark on the sprocket is in line with the cylinder head cover.
12. Install the timing belt and adjust the tension.

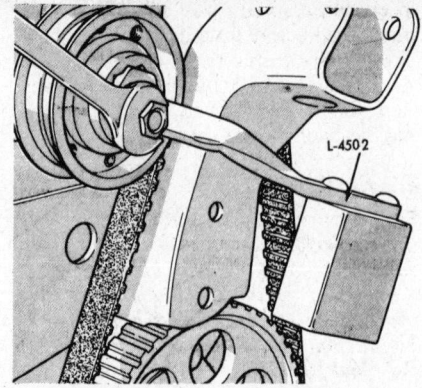

Adjusting drive belt tension—1.7 engine   Camshaft timing alignment; 2.2L engine

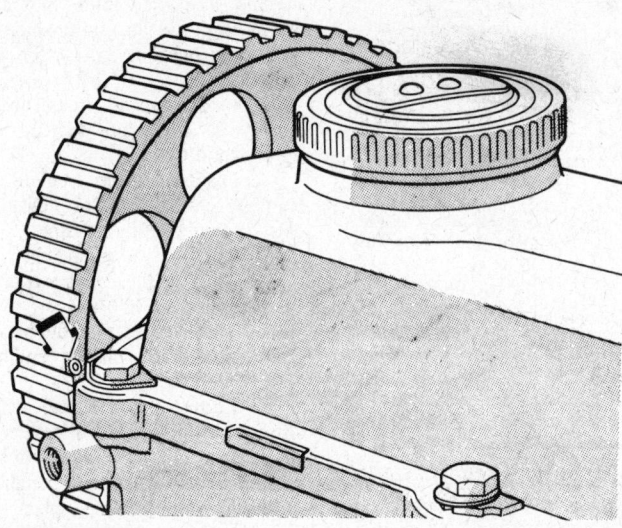

Camshaft gear positioning on 1.7 engines (© Chrysler Corp.)

13. Remove the spark plugs and rotate the crankshaft to TDC position.

14. Place a belt tension tool No. L-4502 horizontally on the large hex of the timing belt tensioner pulley and loosen the tensioner lock nut.

15. Reset the belt tension tool L-4502 index, if necessary, to have axis within 15° of horozontal.

16. Turn the engine clockwise from TDC two crank revolutions to TDC.

17. Tighten the locknut to 32 ft. lbs.

NOTE: If a whirring noise is heard from the timing belt with the engine running the belt is too tight.

18. The rest of the installation is in the reverse order of removal.

2.2 Engine

1. Remove the timing belt cover.
2. While holding the large hex on the tension pulley, loosen the pulley nut.
3. Remove the belt from the tensioner.
4. Slide the belt off the three toothed pulleys.
5. Using the larger bolt on the crankshaft pulley, turn the engine until the No.

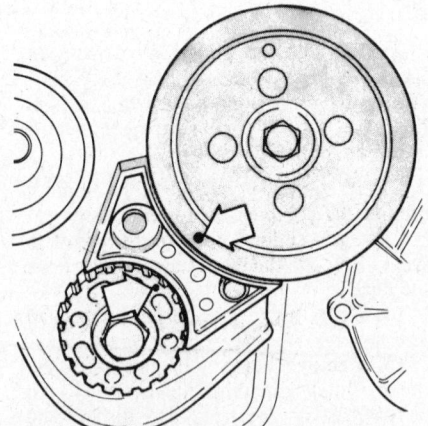

Crankshaft and intermediate shaft timing marks; 2.2L engine

1 cylinder is at TDC of the compression stroke. At this point the valves for the No. 1 cylinder will be closed and the timing mark will be aligned with the pointer on the flywheel housing. Make sure the dots on the cam sprocket and cylinder head are aligned.

6. Verify that the V-notch in the crankshaft pulley aligns with the dot mark on the intermediate shaft.

CAUTION

If the timing marks are not perfectly aligned, poor engine performance and engine damage will result.

7. Install the belt on the pulleys.

8. Adjust the tensioner by turning the large tensioner hex to the right. Tension is correct when the belt can be twisted 90° with the thumb and forefinger, midway between the camshaft and intermediate pulleys.

9. Tighten the tensioner locknut to 32 ft. lbs.

10. Install the timing belt cover and check the ignition timing.

Timing Chain, Cover, "Silent Shafts" and Tensioner

REMOVAL & INSTALLATION

1.6 Engine

TIMING COVER SEAL

1. Remove the air pump and alternator belts.

2. Raise vehicle and remove right inner splash shield.

3. Remove crankshaft pulley bolt, washer and pulley.

4. Install seal remover Tool C-748 over crankshaft nose and turn tightly into seal.

5. Tighten thrust screw to remove seal. (With timing cover removed from engine, tap the side of the thurst screw to "upset" and remove the seal).

6. Installation is in the reverse order of removal. Use seal installation tool C-4761 when installing the new seal. Tighten crankshaft pulley bolt to 110 ft. lbs.

TIMING COVER/CHAIN

NOTE: Follow steps 1-3 of the previous procedure.

1. Drain the cooling system through water pump drain plug. Remove water pump to timing cover hose.

2. Raise slightly and carefully support engine (timing cover end).

3. Remove bolts securing engine mount bracket to timing cover and block.

4. Remove crankcase extension to cover and cover to block screws. Two cover block screws pass through tubular locating dowels. Make sure dowels do not fall into crankcase extension during cover removal. Remove timing cover.

5. Rotate camshaft sprocket so that one (of three) bolt heads is located at the top of a centerline drawn through the camshaft and crankshaft sprockets.

6. With torque wrench and socket installed on the top bolt head, apply torque

in the direction of crankshaft rotation to take up slack; 30 ft. lbs. cylinder head installed, or 15 ft. lbs. cylinder head removed. Do not allow crankshaft to rotate during this procedure.

7. Holding a ruler even with the edge of a chain link, apply the same torque specified above, in the reverse direction and note amount of chain movement. If chain movement exceeds (⅛ in), install new chain.

8. Remove the timing gear bolts, timing gear, and chain.

9. Installation is in the reverse order of removal. Align the timing marks. Torque the camshaft sprocket bolts to 113 in. lbs.

2.6 Engines

NOTE: All 2.6 engines are equipped with two "Silent Shafts" which cancel the vertical vibrating force of the engine and the secondary vibrating forces, which include the sideways rocking of the engine due to the turning direction of the crankshaft and other rolling parts. The shafts are linked by a duplex chain and are driven by the crankshaft. The silent shaft chain assembly is mounted in front of the timing chain assembly, therefore the silent shaft chain assembly must be removed first, to reach the timing chain.

1. Remove the battery cables.

2. Drain the radiator and remove it from the vehicle.

3. Remove the cylinder head.

4. Remove the cooling fan, spacer, water pump pulley and belt.

5. Remove the alternator and water pump.

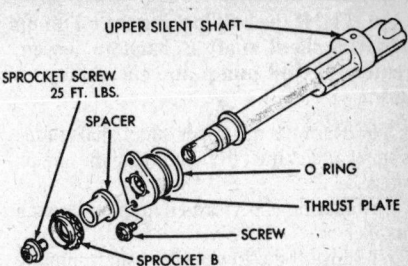

Upper "Silent Shaft" components on 2.6 engines

6. Raise the front of the vehicle and support it on jack stands.

7. Remove the oil pan and screen. Remove the crankshaft pulley.

8. Remove the chain case cover.

9. From the "Silent Shaft" chain system remove the three chain guides: side (A), top (B), bottom (C).

10. Remove the locking bolts from the upper and lower chain sprockets.

11. Remove the crankshaft sprocket, the upper and lower Silent Shaft sprockets, and the chain. You can now reach the timing chain.

12. Remove the crankshaft and camshaft sprockets and the timing chain.

13. Remove the camshaft sprocket holder and the chain guides, both left and right.

14. Remove the chain tensioner.

15. Remove the sleeve from the oil pump. Remove the oil pump by first removing the bolt locking the oil pump driven gear and the lower silent shaft, then remove the oil pump mounting bolts. Remove the silent shaft from the engine block.

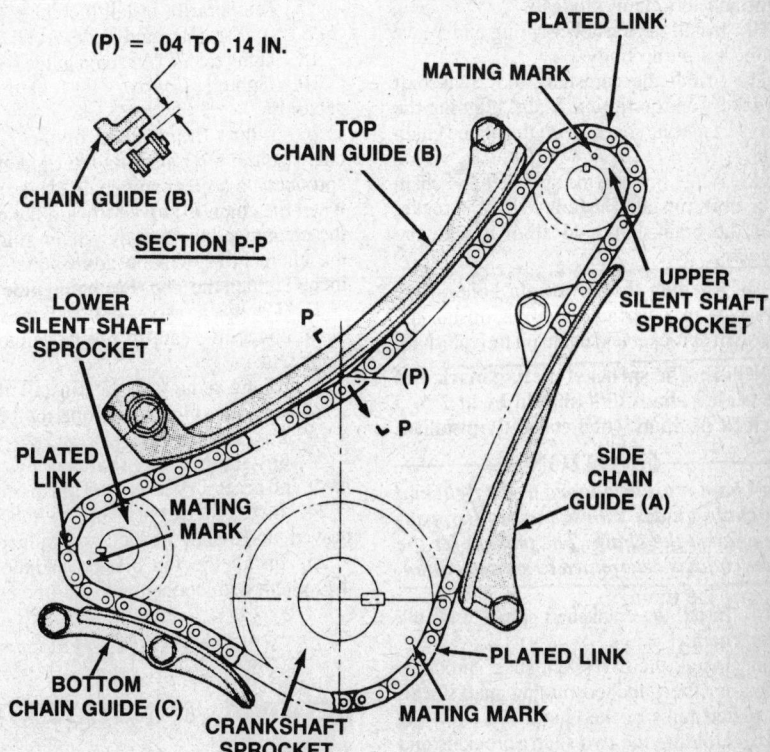

"Silent Shaft" balancing system on 2.6 engines

NOTE: If the bolt locking the oil pump and the silent shaft is hard to loosen, remove the oil pump and the shaft as a unit.

16. Remove the upper silent shaft thrust washer and extract the shaft from the engine block.

Installation is performed in the following manner:

1. Install the lower silent shaft into the engine block.

2. Install the oil pump assembly. Do not lose the woodruff key from the end of the silent shaft. Torque the oil pump mounting bolts 6–7 ft. lbs.

3. Tighten the silent shaft and the oil pump driven gear mounting bolt.

NOTE: The silent shaft and the oil pump can be installed as a unit, if necessary.

4. Install the upper silent shaft into the engine block.

5. Install a new "O" ring on the thrust plate and install the unit into the engine block, using a pair of bolts without heads, as alignment guides.

—— **CAUTION** ——

If the thrust plate is turned to align the bolt holes, the "O" ring may be damaged.

6. Remove the guide bolts and install the regular bolts into the thrust plate and tighten securely.

7. Rotate the crankshaft to bring No. 1 piston to TDC.

8. Install the cylinder head.

9. Install the sprocket holder and the right and left chain guides.

10. Install the tensioner spring and sleeve on the oil pump body.

11. Install the camshaft and crankshaft sprockets on the timing chain, aligning the sprocket mating marks with the plated chain links.

12. While holding the sprocket and chain as a unit, install the crankshaft sprocket over the crankshaft and align it with the keyway.

13. Keeping the dowel pin hole on the camshaft in a vertical position, install the camshaft sprocket and chain on the camshaft.

NOTE: The sprocket mating mark and the plated chain link should be at 2 to 3 O'clock position when correctly installed.

—— **CAUTION** ——

The chain must be aligned in the right and left chain guides with the tensioner pushing against the chain. The tension for the inner chain is determined by spring tension.

14. Install the crankshaft sprocket for the outer chain.

15. Install the two silent shaft sprockets and align the punched mating marks with the plated links of the chain.

16. Holding the two shaft sprockets and chain, install the outer chain in alignment with the mark on the crankshaft sprocket.

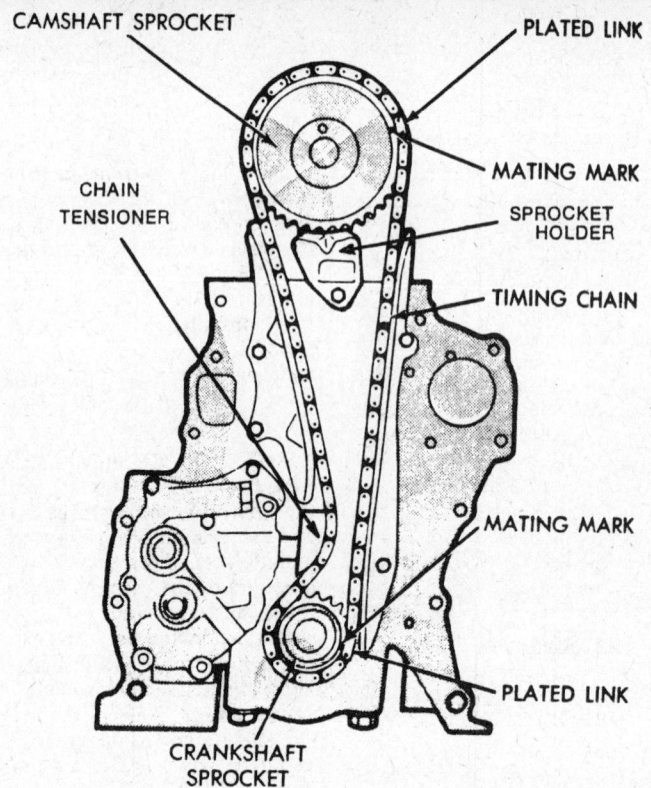

Timing chain installation on 2.6 engines. Align the plated links with the mating marks on the camshaft and crankshaft sprockets

Install the shaft sprockets on the silent shaft and the oil pump driver gear. Install the lock bolts and recheck the alignment of the mating marks and the plated links.

17. Temporarily install the chain guides, *Side* (A), *Top* (B), and *Bottom* (C).

18. Tighten *Side* (A) chain guide securely.

19. Tighten *Bottom* (B) chain guide securely.

20. Adjust the position of the *Top* (B) chain guide, after shaking the right and left sprockets to collect any chain slack, so that when the chain is moved toward the center, the clearance between the chain guide and the chain links will be approximately %4 inch. Tighten the *Top* (B) chain guide bolts.

21. Using a new gasket install the timing chain cover. Be careful not to damage the front seal.

22. Using a new gasket install the oil screen and the oil pan. Torque the bolts to 4.5–5.5 ft. lbs.

23. Install the crankshaft pulley, alternator and accessory belts, and the distributor.

24. Install the oil pressure switch, if removed, and install the battery ground cable.

25. Install the fan blades, radiator, fill the system with coolant and start the engine.

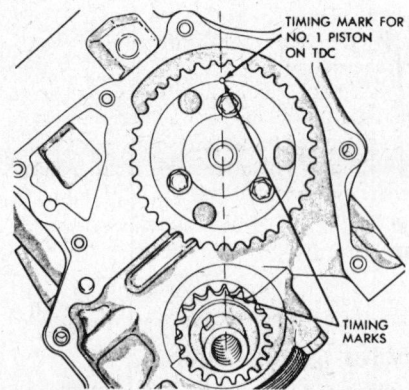

1.6 engine—align camshaft and crankshaft sprockets

Camshaft

REMOVAL & INSTALLATION

1.6 Engine

1. Remove the oil pump.

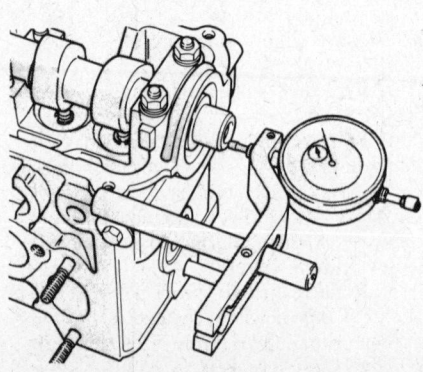

Checking camshaft end-play
(© Chrysler Corp.)

2. Remove distributor and drive housing. Mark crankcase in relation to drive slot.

3. Remove distributor drive from driveshaft spindle with magnet.

4. Remove shaft drive gear circlip.

NOTE: Insert s shot towel in the cavity around the gear to insure that the circlip does not fall into the crankcase during removal or installation.

5. Tap driveshaft toward pump side of crankcase until gear is free from the spline. Remove the gear.

6. Remove driveshaft from the pump side of the crankcase.

7. Remove fuel pump and tappets. Identify tappets to ensure installation in original positions.

8. Remove camshaft thrust plate.

9. Carefully remove camshaft.

10. Installation is in the reverse order of removal.

Tighten thrust plate bolts to 132 inch. lbs. Check camshaft end play (0.004-0.008).

NOTE: When installing new camshaft or tappets, add one pint of Chrysler Crankcase Conditioner, Part Number 3419130, or equivalent, to engine oil. Retain oil mixture for a minimum of 500 miles. When replacing camshaft, use a straight edge to check all tappet faces for wear. Replace tappets with negative crown or dishing.

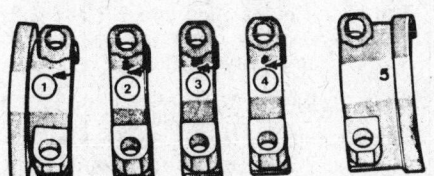

Installation positions of camshaft bearing caps

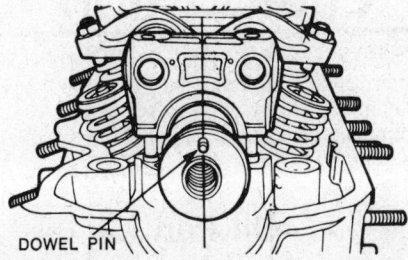

Install the camshaft on 2.6 engines by aligning the dowel pin with the notch in the top of the front bearing cap (© Chrysler Corp.)

1.7 Engine

1. Remove the timing belt cover.
2. Remove the timing belt.
3. Remove the air cleaner assembly.
4. Remove the valve cover.
5. Remove the No. 1, 3, and 5 camshaft bearing caps.
6. Loosen caps No. 2 and 4 diagonally and in increments.

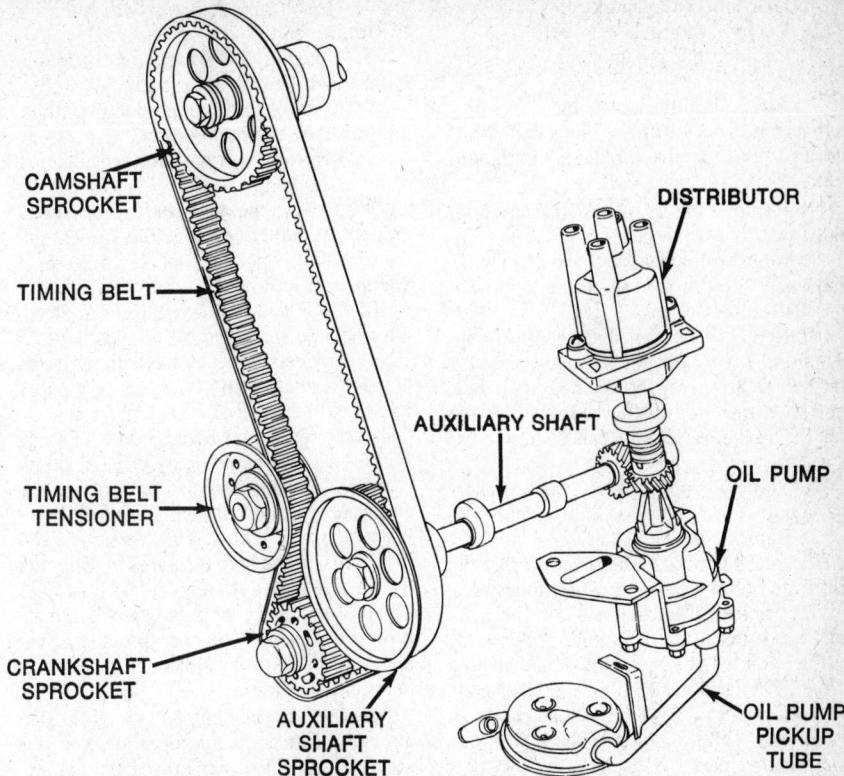

Timing belt, auxiliary shaft, and oil pump and distributor drive details, 2.2L (135.0 cu. in.) engine

7. Lift the camshaft out.

8. Lubricate the camshaft journals and lobes with engine assembly lubricant, and position the camshaft in the cylinder head.

9. Install a new oil seal.

10. Install bearing caps No. 1, 3, and 5, and torque the nuts to 14 ft. lbs.

11. Install the No. 2 and 4 caps, and diagonally torque the nuts to 14 ft. lbs.

— CAUTION —
All bearing caps are slightly offset. They should be installed so the numbers on the caps read right side up from the driver's seat.

12. Position a dial indicator so that the feeler touches the front end of the camshaft. Check for end play. Play should not exceed 0.006 in.

13. Place a new seal on the No. 1 bearing cap. If necessary, replace the end plug in the cylinder head.

14. Follow the procedures under Timing Belt Removal and Installation for belt installation and timing.

15. Check the valve clearance and ignition timing.

2.2L Engine

1. Remove the timing belt.
2. Mark the rocker arms for installation identification.
3. Loosen the camshaft bearing capnuts several turns each.

4. Using a wooden or rubber mallet, rap the rear of the camshaft a few times to break it loose.

5. Remove the capnuts and caps, being very careful that the camshaft does not cock. Cocking the camshaft could cause irreparable damage to the bearings.

6. Check all oil holes for blockage.

7. Install the bearing caps with No. 1 at the timing belt end, and No., 5 at the transmission end. Camshaft bearing caps are numbered and have arrows facing forward. Cap nut torque is 14 ft. lbs.

8. Apply RTV silicone gasket material as to No. 1 and No. 5 bearing caps.

9. Install the bearing caps BEFORE the seals are installed.

10. To complete camshaft installation, follow the reverse of the removal procedure.

Camshaft Endplay Check

1. Move the camshaft as far forward as possible.

2. Install a dial indicator as shown in the accompanying illustration.

3. Zero the indicator, push the camshaft backward, then forward as far as possible and record the play. Maximum play should be 0.006 in.

2.6 Engines

1. Remove the breather hoses and purge hose.

2. Remove the air cleaner and fuel line.

3. Remove the fuel pump. Remove the distributor.

4. Disconnect the spark plug cables.

5. Remove the rocker cover.

6. Remove the breather and semi-circular seal.

7. After slightly loosening the camshaft sprocket bolt, turn the crankshaft until No. 1 piston is at TDC on the compression stroke (both valves closed).

8. Remove the camshaft sprocket bolt and distributor drive gear.

9. Remove the camshaft sprocket with chain and allow it to rest on the camshaft sprocket holder.

10. Remove the camshaft bearing cap tightening bolts. Do not remove the front and rear bearing cap bolts altogether, but keep them inserted in the bearing caps so that the rocker assembly can be removed as a unit.

11. Remove the rocker arms, rocker shafts and bearing caps as an assembly.

12. Remove the camshaft.

13. Installation is in the reverse order of removal. Lubricate the camshaft lobes and bearings and fit the camshaft into the cylinder head. Install the assembled rocker arm shaft assembly. The camshaft should be positioned so the dowel pin on the front end of the camshaft is in the 12 o'clock position and in line with the notch in the top of the front bearing cap.

Timing Gear

REMOVAL & INSTALLATION

1.7 Engine

The camshaft, intermediate shaft, and crankshaft pulleys are located by keys on their respective shafts and each is retained by a bolt. To remove any or all of the pulleys, first remove the timing belt cover and belt, then use the following procedure.

NOTE: When removing the crankshaft pulley, don't remove the four socket head bolts which retain the outer belt pulley on the timing belt pulley.

1. Remove the center bolt.

2. Gently pry the timing belt pulley off the shaft.

3. If the pulley is stubborn in coming off, use a gear puller. Don't hammer on the pulley.

4. Remove the pulley and key. The oil seal may now be carefully pried out. Special tools are available for this purpose. Install the new seal.

5. Install the pulley in the reverse order of removal.

6. Tighten the center bolt to 58 ft. lbs.

7. Install the timing belt, check valve timing, tension belt, and install the cover.

2.2 Engine

1. Raise and support the car on jackstands.

2. Remove the right inner splash shield.

3. Remove the crankshaft pulley.

4. Unbolt and remove both halves of the timing belt cover.

5. Take up the weight of the engine with a jack.

6. Remove the right engine mount bolt and raise the engine slightly.

7. Remove the timing belt tensioner and remove the belt.

8. Remove the crankshaft sprocket bolt, and with a puller, remove the sprocket.

9. Using special tool C-4679 or its equivalent, remove the crankshaft seal.

10. Unbolt and remove the camshaft and intermediate shaft sprockets.

11. To install the crankshaft seal, first polish the shaft with 400 grit emery paper. If the seal has a steel case, lightly coat the OD of the seal with Loctite Stud N' Bearing Mount ® or its equivalent. If the seal case is rubber coated, generously apply a soap and water solution to facilitate installation. Install the seal with a seal driver.

12. Install the sprockets making sure that the timing marks are aligned as illustrated. When installing the camshaft sprocket, make certain the arrows on the sprocket are in line with the No. 1 camshaft bearing cap-to-cylinder headline.

13. The small hole in the camshaft sprocket must be at the top and be in line with the vertical center line of the engine.

14. Rotate the engine two full revolutions and recheck timing mark positioning.

15. Install the belt.

16. Rotate the engine to the No. 1 piston TDC position.

17. Install the belt tensioner, and place tool C-4703 on the large hex nut.

18. Reset the belt tension so that the axis of the tool is about 15° off the horizontal.

19. Turn the engine clockwise two full revolutions to No. 1 TDC.

20. Tighten the tensioner locknut using a weighted wrench a shown in a previous illustration.

Torques: Timing belt cover bolts, 105 inch lbs.

Camshaft Sprocket bolt, 65 ft. lbs.
Crankshaft sprocket bolt, 50 ft. lbs.
Intermediate shaft sprocket bolt, 65 ft. lbs.

2.6 Engines

See the procedures under "Timing Chain, Cover and Silent Shafts."

PISTONS AND CONNECTING RODS

All Engines

The piston crown is marked with an arrow which must point toward the timing belt or chain end of the engine, when installed. On 1.7 and 2.2 engines, the connecting rod and cap are marked with rectangular forge marks which must be mated when assembled and which must be on the intermediate shaft side of the engine, when installed.

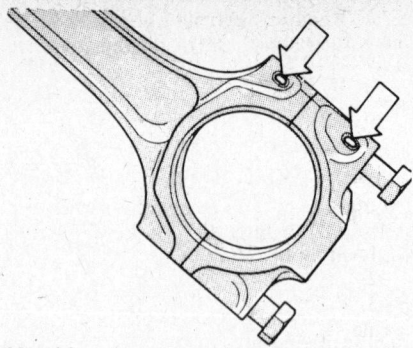

Matching the connecting rod with the cap on 1.7 engines (© Chrysler Corp.)

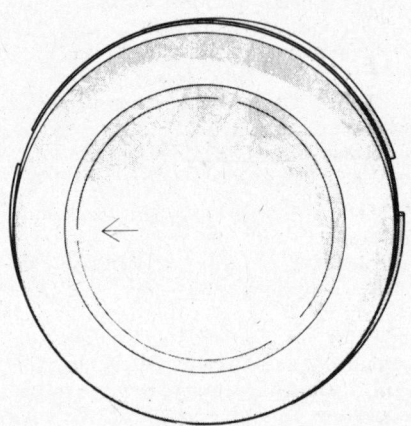

The piston is installed into 1.7 and 2.2 engines with the arrow facing forward (© Chrysler Corp.)

Pistons in the 1.6 engine are installed with the notch facing the flywheel (No. 1 & 3) 2 and 4 toward the timing cover.

LUBRICATION

Lubrication is conventional with a gear type pump. A pressure relief valve prevents extreme pressure from building up in the system.

Oil Pan

REMOVAL & INSTALLATION

1. Drain the oil pan.

2. Support the pan and remove the attaching bolts.

3. Lower the pan and discard the gaskets.

4. Clean all the gasket surfaces of the oil pan thoroughly and install the pan using gasket sealer and a new gasket.

5. Torque the pan bolts to 111 in. lbs. on 1.6 engine, 70 in. lbs. on the 1.7 engine, 200 in. lbs. on the 2.2 engine, and 60 in. lbs. on the 2.6 engine.

6. Refill the pan, start the engine, and check for leaks.

Oil Pump

REMOVAL & INSTALLATION

1.6, 1.7 and 2.2 Engines

1. Remove the oil pan.
2. Remove the pump mounting bolts.
3. Pull the pump down and out of the engine.
4. Installation is in the reverse order of removal. Torque the pump mounting bolts to 111 in. lbs. on the 1.6 engine, 14 ft. lbs. on the 1.7 engine, and 9 ft. lbs. on the 2.2 engine.

2.6 Engines

See Timing Chain, Cover, "Silent Shaft and Tensioner" removal and installation procedure covered earlier.

Rear Main Seal

REMOVAL & INSTALLATION

1.6 Engine

NOTE: Rear main seal removal is easier to accomplish if the engine is removed first.

1. Remove the engine from the car.
2. Remove the rear oil seal and housing.
3. Place the housing inner surface on two blocks of wood, allowing clearance for seal removal.
4. Using tool C-4759 or equivalent, remove the seal.
5. Installation is in the reverse order of removal. Torque rear oil seal housing bolts to 111 in. lbs.

NOTE: Special tool C-4759 or its equivalent is needed for this procedure. This tool can be used for removing or installing the seal.

1.7 and 2.2 Engines

The rear main seal is located in a housing on the rear of the block. To replace the seal the engine must be removed.

1. Remove the transaxle and flywheel.

— CAUTION —

Before removing the transaxle, align the dimple on the flywheel with the pointer on the flywheel housing. The transaxle will not mate with the engine during installation, unless this alignment is observed.

2. Very carefully, pry the old seal out of the support ring.
3. Coat the new seal with clean engine oil, and press it into place with tool L-4425 or equivalent (1.7 engine), and with tool L-4681 or equivalent (2.2 engine). Take great care not to scratch the seal or crankshaft.

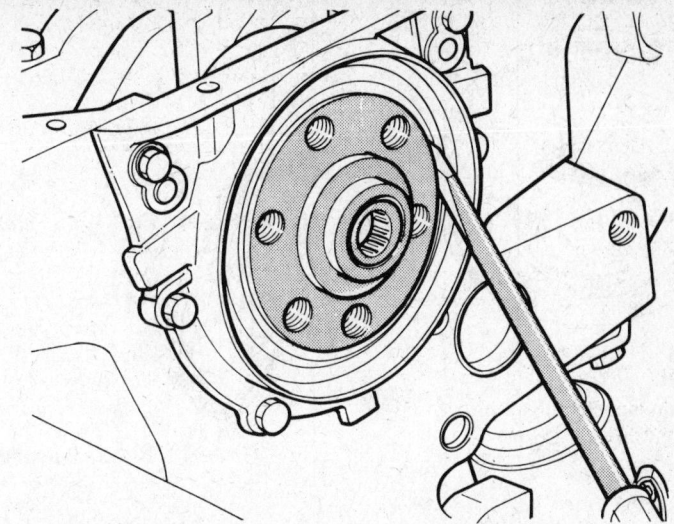

Removing the rear main oil seal on 1.7 engines (ⓒ Chrysler Corp.)

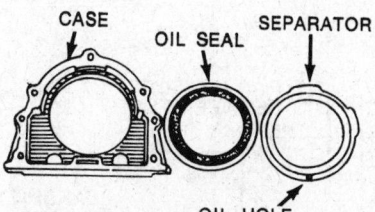

Rear main oil seal on 2.6 engines (ⓒ Chrysler Corp.)

4. Install the flywheel and transaxle.

2.6 Engines

The rear main oil seal is located in a housing on the rear of the block. To replace the seal, remove the transaxle and do the work from underneath the vehicle, or remove the engine and do the work on the bench.

1. Remove the housing from the block.
2. Remove the separator from the housing.
3. Pry out the old seal.
4. Lightly oil the replacement seal. The oil seal should be installed so the seal plate fits into the inner contact surface of the seal case. Install the separator with the oil holes facing down.

CLUTCH

— CAUTION —

When servicing clutch assemblies or components, do NOT create dust by sanding or by cleaning clutch parts with a dry brush or with compressed air. (A water dampened cloth should be used). The clutch disc contains "Asbestos Fibers" which can become airborne if dust is created during service operations. Breathing dust containing "Asbestos Fibers" may cause serious bodily harm.

The clutch is a simple dry disc unit, with no adjustment for wear provided in the clutch itself. Adjustment is made through an adjustable sleeve in the pedal linkage.

REPLACEMENT

NOTE: Chrysler recommends the use of special tool L-4533 for disc alignment on the A-412 manual transaxle clutch.

1. Remove the transaxle as described in the following section.
2. Loosen the flywheel-to-pressure plate bolts diagonally, one or two turns at a time to avoid warpage.
3. Remove the flywheel and clutch disc from the pressure plate.
4. Remove the retaining ring and release plate.
5. Diagonally loosen the pressure plate-to-crankshaft bolts. Mark all parts for reassembly.
6. Remove the bolts, spacer and pressure plate.
7. The flywheel and pressure plate surfaces should be cleaned thoroughly with a water dampened cloth.
8. Align marks and install the pressure plate, spacer and bolts. Coat the bolts with thread compound and torque them to 55 ft. lbs.
9. Install the release plate and retaining ring.
10. Using special tool L-4533 or its equivalent, install the clutch disc and flywheel on the pressure plate.

— CAUTION —

Make certain the drilled mark on the flywheel is at the top, so the two dowels on the flywheel align with the proper holes in the pressure plate.

11. Install the six flywheel bolts and tighten them to 14.5 ft. lbs. on A-412 manual transaxle equipped models, and to 21 ft. lbs. on A-460 equipped models.

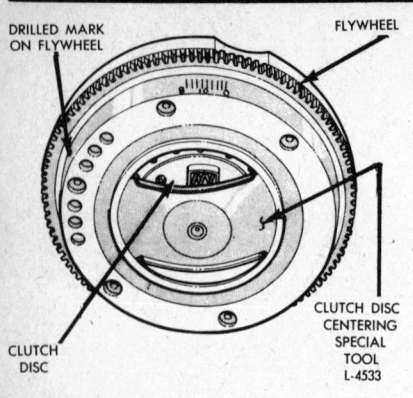

Using the special aligning tool
(© Chrysler Corp.)

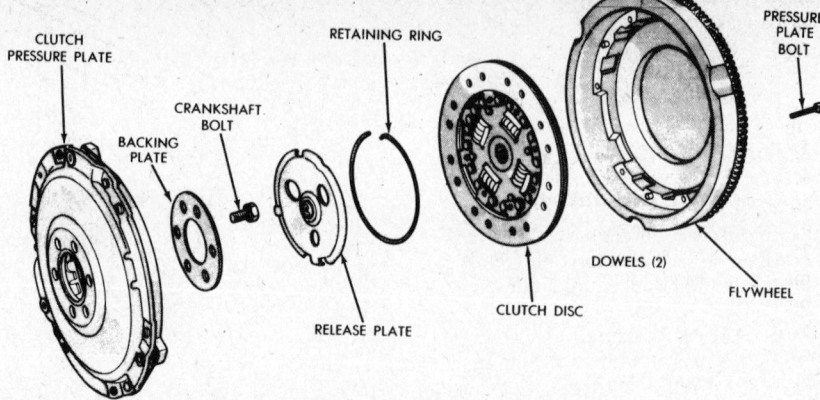

A-412 manual transaxle clutch—disassembled

12. Remove the aligning tool.
13. Install the transaxle.
14. Adjust the freeplay.

ADJUSTMENT

A-412 Transaxle

NOTE: The A-460, A-465, A525 transaxles are equipped with a self-adjusting clutch release mechanism.

1. Pull up on the clutch cable.
2. While holding the cable up, rotate the adjusting sleeve downward until a snug contact is made against the grommet.
3. Rotate the sleeve slightly to allow the end of the sleeve to seat in the rectangular hole in the grommet.

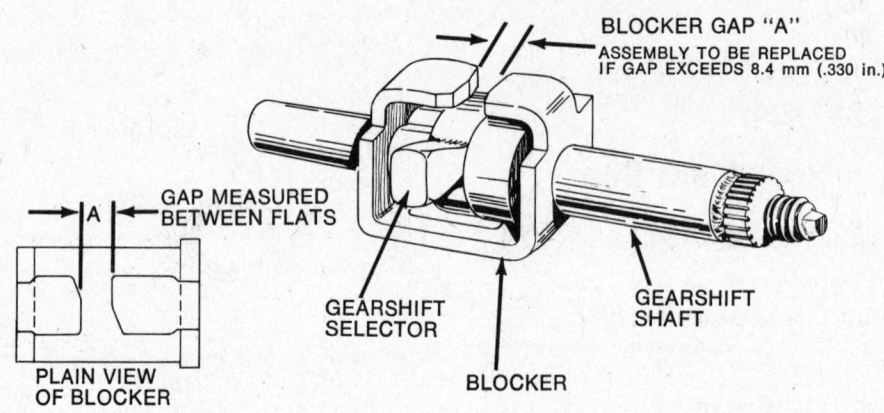

Checking the interlock blocker for failure on A-412 manual transaxles
(© Chrysler Corp.)

MANUAL TRANSAXLE

NOTE: It is possible for the A-412 manual transaxle to become locked in two gears at once. This will occur if the interlock blocker on the gearshift selector lever has spread apart. The result of operating like this will be clutch failure at the least, and driveline failure at the worst. To correctly diagnose the problem, the interlock should be checked using the following procedure:

For manual transaxle overhaul procedures, please refer to "Manual Transmission Overhaul" in the Unit Repair section.

1. Disconnect the shift linkage operating lever from the transaxle selector shaft.
2. Remove the transaxle detent spring assembly and selector shaft boot.
3. Remove the aluminum selector shaft plug.
4. Place the transaxle in Neutral and pull the selector shaft assembly out of the case.

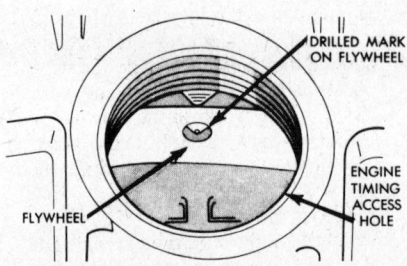

Drilled mark on 1.7 engine flywheels
(© Chrysler Corp.)

5. Measure the interlock blocker gap "A", as shown in the accompanying picture. If gap "A" exceeds .330 in. replace the gearshift selector shaft assembly.
6. Apply a thick coating of chassis grease to the selector shaft shoulder at the threaded end and carefully insert the shaft through the selector shaft oil seal. Reverse Steps 1-4 to install.
7. Adjust the shift linkage.

REMOVAL & INSTALLATION

NOTE: Whenever the differential cover is removed, a new gasket should be formed using RTV sealant.

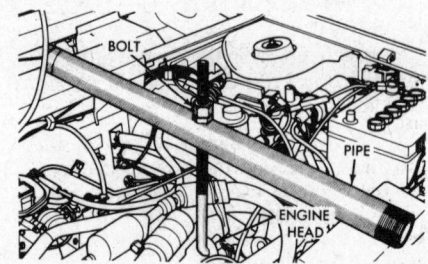

Engine support fixture
(© Chrysler Corp.)

A-412 Transaxle

1. Remove the engine timing mark access plug.
2. Rotate the engine to align the drilled mark on the flywheel with the pointer on the engine.
3. Disconnect the battery ground.
4. Disconnect the shift linkage rods.
5. Disconnect the starter and ground wires.
6. Disconnect the backup light switch wire.
7. Remove the starter.
8. Disconnect the clutch cable.
9. Disconnect the speedometer cable.

10. Support the weight of the engine from above, preferably with a shop hoist or a fabricated support fixture, as illustrated.

11. Raise and support the vehicle.

12. Disconnect the driveshafts and support them out of the way.

13. Remove the left splash shield.

14. Drain the transaxle.

15. Unbolt the left engine mount.

16. Remove the transaxle-to-engine bolts.

17. Slide the transaxle to the left until the mainshaft clears, then, carefully lower it from the car.

18. Installation is in the reverse order of removal.

19. Adjust the clutch cable.

20. Adjust the shift linkage.

21. Fill the transaxle.

A-460, A-465 and A-525 Transaxle

1. Disconnect the battery.

2. Install an engine lifting fixture on the engine.

3. Disconnect the shift linkage.

4. Remove both front wheels.

5. Remove the left front splash shield.

6. Follow the procedures under Driveshaft Removal and Installation in the next section.

7. The removal of the unit is the same as that for the automatic transaxle, except that no torque converter is used.

SHIFT LINKAGE ADJUSTMENT

A-412 Transaxle

1. Place the transmission in Neutral at the 3-4 position.

2. Loosen the shift tube clamp.

3. Place a ⅜ in. spacer between the shift tube flange and the yoke at the shift base.

4. Tighten the shift tube clamp and remove the spacer.

A-460/A-465/A-525 Transaxle

ROD OPERATED TYPE

1. Working over the left front fender, remove the lock pin from the transaxle selector shaft housing.

2. Reverse the lock pin (so long end is down) and insert lock pin into same threaded hole while pushing the selector shaft will align with the lock pin, allowing the lock pin to be screwed into the housing. This operation locks the selector shaft in the 1-2 neutral position.

3. Raise vehicle on hoist.

4. Loosen the clamp bolt that secures the gearshift tube to the gearshift connector.

5. Check to see that gearshift connector slides and turns freely in gearshift tube.

6. Position the shifter mechanism connector assembly so that the isolator is contacting the upstanding flange and the rib on the isolater is aligned fore and aft with the

hole in the block-out bracket. Hold the connector isolator in this position while tightening the clamp bolt on the gearshift tube

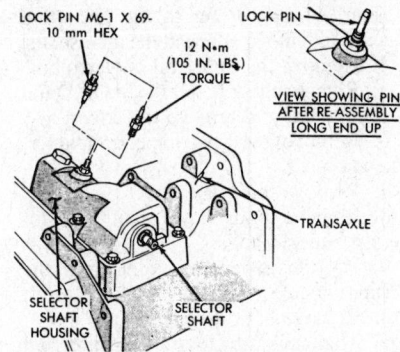

Transaxle pinned in the 1-2 neutral position to adjust gearshift linkage (rod or cable operated)

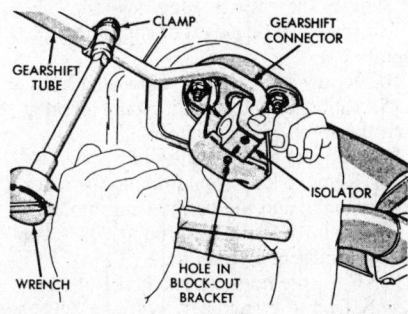

Adjusting gearshift linkage (rod operated)

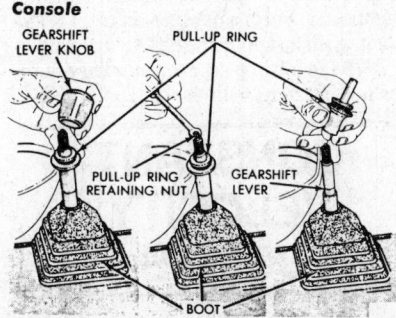

Gearshift knob, retaining nut and pull-up ring (Cable operated linkage)

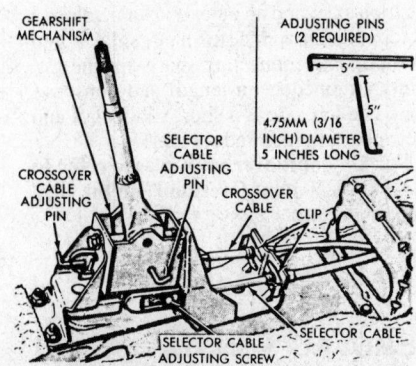

Fabricate (2) cable adjusting pins—all except Daytona and Laser

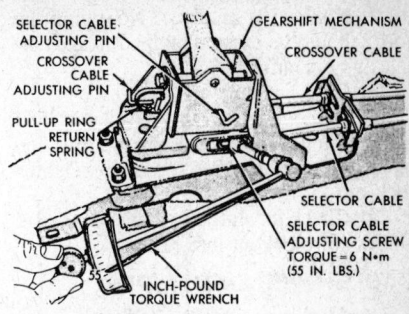

Adjusting the selector cable—all except Daytona and Laser

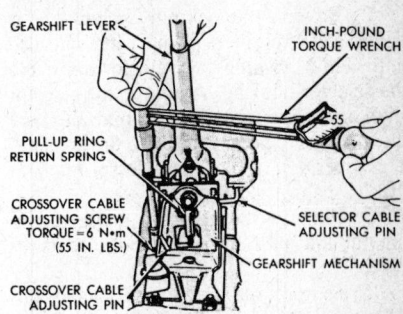

Adjusting the crossover cable—all except Daytona and Laser

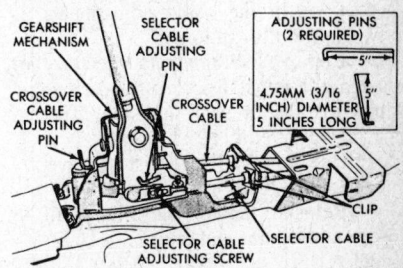

Fabricate (2) cable adjusting pins—Daytona and Laser

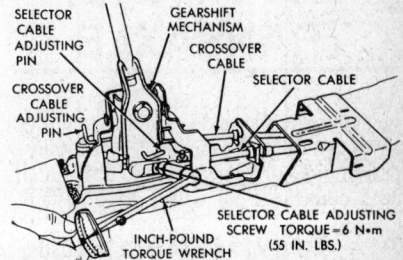

Adjusting the selector cable—Daytona and Laser

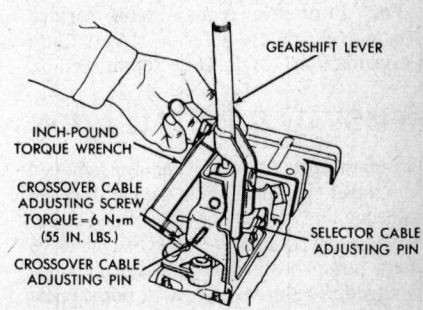

Adjusting the crossover cable—Daytona and Laser

to 19 N·m (170) in. lbs.). No significant force should be exerted on the linkage during this operation.

7. Lower vehicle to floor.

8. Remove lock pin from selector shaft housing and reinstall lock pin (so long end is up) in selector shaft housing. Tighten lock pin to 12 Nm (105 in. lbs.).

9. Check for shift into first and reverse. Check for blockout into reverse.

CABLE OPERATED TYPE

1. Working over the left front fender, remove the lock pin from the transaxle selector shaft housing.

2. Reverse the lock pin (so long end is down) and insert lock pin into same threaded hole while pushing the selector shift into the selector housing. A hole in the selector shaft will align with the lock pin, allowing the lock pin to be screwed into the housing. This operation locks the selector shaft in the 1-2 neutral position.

3. Remove the gearshift knob, retaining nut and, pull-up ring from the gearshift lever.

4. Remove the shift lever boot and console to expose the gearshift linkage.

5. Fabricate cable adjusting pins as shown in the illustration.

6. Perform the cable adjustments as shown in the illustrations.

7. Remove lock pin from selector shaft housing and reinstall lock pin (so long end is up) in selector shaft housing. Tighten lock pin to 12 Nm (105 in. lbs.).

8. Check for shift into first and reverse. Check for blockout into reverse.

9. Reinstall the console, boot, pull-up ring, retaining nut and knob.
Model A-460

AUTOMATIC TRANSAXLE

The automatic transaxle combines a torque converter, fully automatic 3-speed transmission, final drive gearing and differential into a compact front wheel drive system. Officially, they are designated as the A-404, A-413, A-415 and A-470 Torqueflite Automatic Transaxles.

For automatic transmission service procedures, please refer to "Automatic Transmissions" in the Unit Repair section.

REMOVAL & INSTALLATION

The automatic transaxle can be removed with the engine installed in the car, but, the transaxle and torque converter must be removed as an assembly. Otherwise the drive plate, pump bushing or oil seal could be damaged. The drive plate will not support a load—no weight should be allowed to bear on the drive plate.

1. Disconnect the negative battery cable.

2. Disconnect the throttle and shift linkage from the transaxle.

3. Raise and support the car. Remove the front wheels. Refer to the following sequence to remove or install the driveshafts.

4. Remove the upper oil cooler tube.

5. Remove the left splash shield. Drain the differential and remove the cover.

6. Remove the speedometer adapter, cable and gear.

7. Remove the sway bar.

8. Remove both lower ball joint-to-steering knuckle bolts.

9. Pry the lower ball joint from the steering knuckle.

10. Remove both driveshafts.

11. Matchmark the torque converter and drive plate. Remove the torque converter mounting bolts. Remove the access plug in the right splash shield to rotate the engine.

12. Remove the lower cooler tube and the wire to the neutral safety switch.

13. Install some means of supporting the engine.

14. Remove the upper bellhousing bolts.

15. Remove the engine mount bracket from the front crossmember.

16. Support the transmission.

17. Remove the front mount insulator through-bolts and the bellhousing mount.

18. Remove the long through-bolt from the left-hand engine mount.

19. Raise the transaxle, and carefully pry it away from the engine.

20. Installation is in the reverse order of removal. Fill the differential with Dexron ® automatic transmission fluid before lowering the car. Form a new gasket from RTV sealant when installing the differential cover. On 1978 models, be sure the auxiliary horn does not interfere with the oil cooler lines.

CONSTANT VELOCITY JOINTS

The driveshaft assemblies are three piece units. Each driveshaft has an inner sliding constant velocity (Tripode) joint bolted to the transaxle, and an outer constant velocity (Rzeppa) joint with a stub shaft splined into the hub. The connecting shafts for the CV joints are unequal in length and construction. The left side is a short solid shaft and the right is longer and tubular.

For CV-joint overhaul, please refer to "U-Joint/CV-Joint Overhaul" in the Unit Repair section.

Driveshaft

REMOVAL & INSTALLATION
A-412 Transaxle
NOTE: Whenever the differential cover

is removed, a new gasket should be formed from RTV sealant

1. With the vehicle on the floor and the brakes applied, loosen the hub nut.

NOTE: The hub and driveshafts are splined together and are retained by the hub nut which is torqued to at least 180 ft. lbs.

2. Raise and support the vehicle and remove the hub nut and washer.

NOTE: Always support both ends of the driveshaft during removal to prevent damage to the boots.

3. Disconnect the lower control arm ball joint stud nut from the steering knuckle.

4. Remove the Allenhead screws which fasten the CV-joint to the transmission flange.

5. Holding the CV-housing, push the outer joint and knuckle assembly outward while disengaging the inner housing from the flange face.

NOTE: The outer joint and shaft must be supported during disengagement of the inner joint.

Quickly turn the open end of the joint upward to retain as much lubricant as possible, then carefully pull the outer spline out of the hub. Cover the joint with a clean towel to prevent dirt contamination.

6. Before installation, make sure that any lost lubricant is replaced.

7. Clean the joint body and mating flange face.

8. Install the outer joint splined shaft into the hub. Do not secure with the nut and washer.

9. Position the inner joint in the transmission drive flange and secure it with *new* screws. Torque the screws to 37–40 ft. lbs.

10. Connect the lower control arm to the knuckle.

11. Install the outer joint and secure it with a *new* nut and washer. Torque the nut with the car on the ground and the brake set. Torque is 180 ft. lbs.

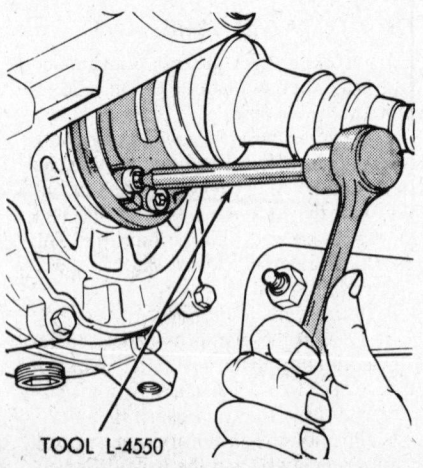

TOOL L-4550

Removing Allen head screws
(© Chrysler Corp.)

12. After attaching the driveshaft, if the inboard boot appears to be collapsed or deformed, vent the inner boot by inserting a round-tipped, small diameter rod between the boot and the shaft. As the venting occurs, boot will return to its original shape.

A-460, Five-speed and Automatic Transaxles

The inboard CV-joints on early production models may be retained by circlips in the differential side gears. On later production models, the shafts incorporate the use of a spring within the right and left inboard tripod joint assemblies and do not use a circlip.

To determine whether a spring loaded shaft is installed, place a pry bar between the transaxle extension housing (right shaft) and the face of the tripod joint housing, pry toward the outside of the vehicle, taking care not to damage the seal in the extension housing . If the joint can be moved at least ½ inch from the extension housing, the driveshaft is spring loaded and does not have a circlip retainer.

If complete removal of these driveshafts is required, the splines on the transaxle ends of both shafts can be easily pulled out without getting into the transaxle.

NOTE: On cars equipped with spring loaded shafts, exclude Steps 2, 4 and 5.

1. With the car on the ground, loosen the hub nut, which has been torqued to 200 ft. lbs.

2. Drain the transaxle differential and remove the cover. See preceding NOTE.

NOTE: Whenever the transaxle differential cover is removed, a new gasket should be formed from RTV sealant.

3. To remove the right-hand driveshaft, disconnect the speedometer cable and remove the cable and gear before removing the driveshaft.

4. Rotate the driveshaft to expose the circlip tangs. See NOTE.

5. Compress the circlip with needle nose pliers and push the shaft into the side gear cavity. See NOTE above.

6. Remove the clamp bolt from the ball stud and steering knuckle.

7. Separate the ball joint stud from the steering knuckle, by prying against the knuckle leg and control arm.

8. Separate the outer CV-joint splined shaft from the hub by holding the CV housing and moving the hub away. Do not pry on the slinger or outer CV-joint.

9. Support the shaft at the CV-joints, remove the six allen head screws (if so equipped) from the transaxle drive flange, and remove the shaft. Do not pull on the shaft.

NOTE: Removal of the left shaft may be made easier by inserting the blade of a thin prybar between the differential pinion shaft, and prying against the end face of the shaft.

10. Installation is in the reverse order of removal. Before installing the shaft be sure the circlip tangs are positioned against the flattened end of the shaft. A quick thrust will lock the circlip in the groove. With the wheels on the ground tighten the hub nut to 180 ft. lbs.

JACKING AND HOISTING

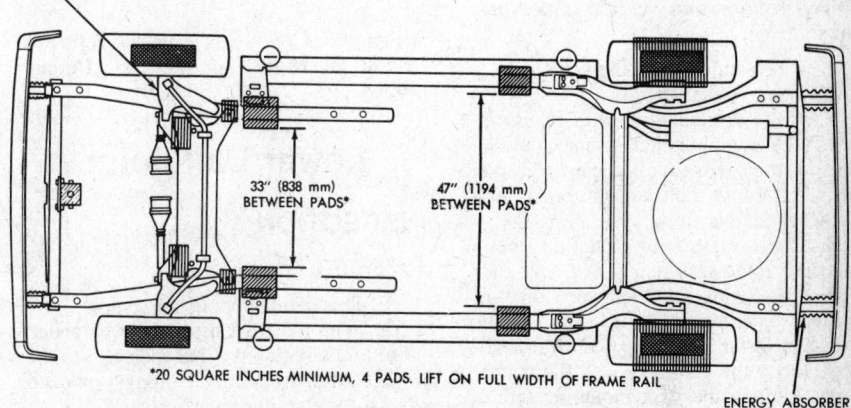

TWIN POST LIFT POINTS
FRAME CONTACT OR FLOOR JACK
DRIVE ON HOIST
O SCISSORS JACK (EMERGENCY) LOCATIONS
LIFTING, JACKING SUPPORT LOCATIONS

CONTROL ARM — CAUTION; DO NOT LIFT ON CONTROL ARMS

33" (838 mm) BETWEEN PADS*

47" (1194 mm) BETWEEN PADS*

*20 SQUARE INCHES MINIMUM, 4 PADS. LIFT ON FULL WIDTH OF FRAME RAIL

ENERGY ABSORBER

Jacking and hoisting locations—Omni and Horizon (© Chrysler Corp.)

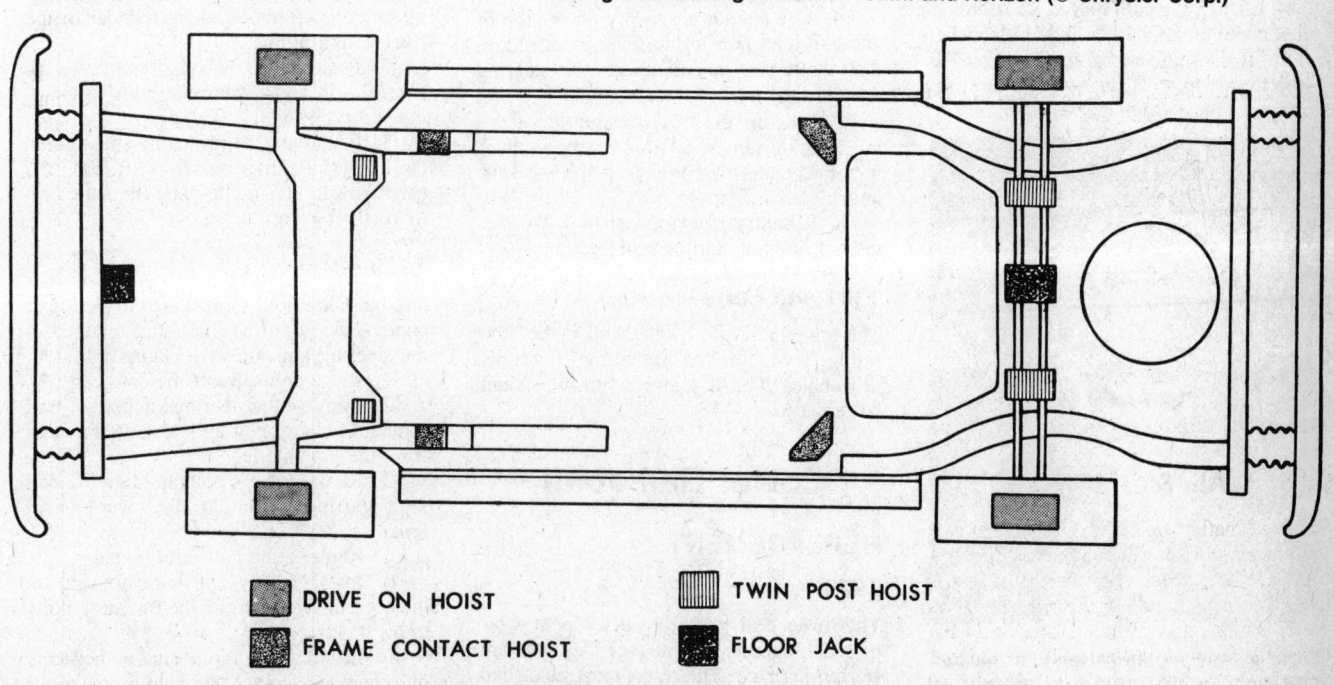

DRIVE ON HOIST

FRAME CONTACT HOIST

TWIN POST HOIST

FLOOR JACK

Jacking and hoisting locations—except Omni and Horizon

FRONT SUSPENSION

A MacPherson front suspension is used, with vertical shock absorbers attached to the upper fender reinforcement and the steering knuckle. Lower control arms, attached inboard to a cross-member and outboard to the steering knuckle through a ball joint, provide lower steering knuckle position. During steering manuevers, the upper strut and steering knuckle turn as an assembly.

Strut Damper

REMOVAL & INSTALLATION

NOTE: A new bonded mount assembly is used on late 1978 and later models, replacing the double nuts, bearing retainer, isolator and strut retainer previously used.

1. Raise and support the vehicle.
2. Remove the wheel.
3. If the original strut is to be assembled to the original knuckle, mark the cam adjusting bolt. Remove the cam adjusting bolt, the through bolt and the brake hose bracket retaining screw.
4. Remove the strut mounting screws and remove the strut.
5. Installation is in the reverse order of removal. Position the knuckle leg in the strut, and install the upper (cam) through-bolts. Index the cam bolt with the match-marks. Torque the strut mounting screws to 27 ft. lbs.; the brake hose bracket screw to 10 ft. lbs.; the cam bolt to 85 ft. lbs. on all except Omni/Charger and Horizon/Turismo, on Omni/Charger and Horizon/Turismo torque to 45 ft. lbs. plus ¼ turn, and toruqe the wheel nuts to 95 ft. lbs.

If the grease nipple (arrow) in the ball joint wobbles or turns, the ball joint is worn and should be replaced.

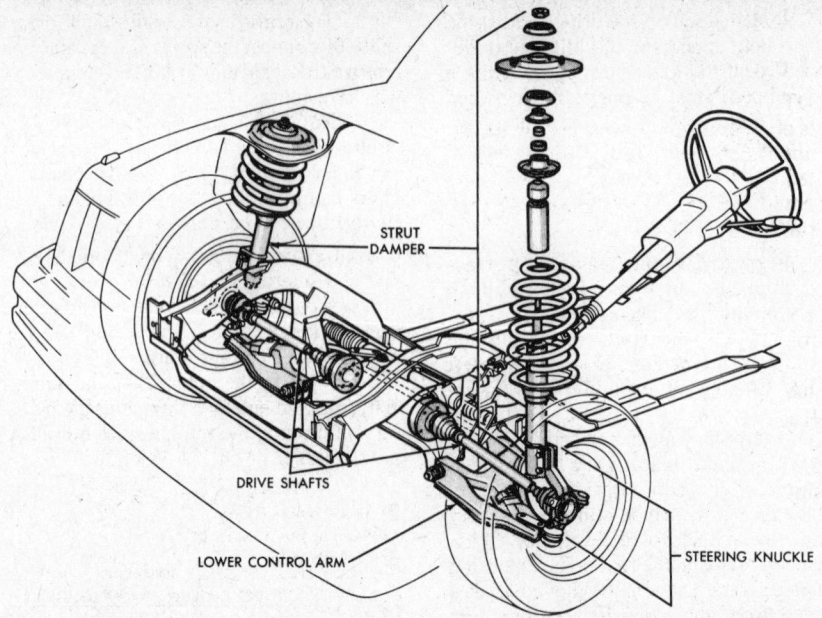

STRUT DAMPER

DRIVE SHAFTS

LOWER CONTROL ARM

STEERING KNUCKLE

Front suspension—Omni and Horizon shown; other models similar (© Chrysler Corp.)

For strut servicing, please refer to "Strut Overhaul" in the Unit Repair section.

Lower Ball Joint

INSPECTION

1978-80

1. Raise and support the vehicle.
2. With the suspension fully extended (at full travel) clamp a dial indicator to the lower control arm with the plunger indexed against the steering knuckle leg.
3. Zero the dial indicator.
4. Use a stout bar to pry on the top of the ball joint housing-to-lower control arm bolt with the bar tip under the steering knuckle leg.
5. Measure the axial travel of the steering knuckle leg in relation to the control arm by raising and lowering the steering knuckle as in Step 4.
6. If the travel is more than 0.050 in., the ball joint should be replaced.

1981 and Later

The lower ball joint is checked at the lube fitting. Try to turn the lube fitting. If it turns or wobbles, the ball joint is worn and should be replaced.

Lower Ball Joint

REPLACEMENT

1978

The lower ball joints are permanently lubricated, operate with no free play, and are riveted in place. The rivets must be drilled out and replaced with special bolts.

NOTE: To avoid damage to the control arm surface adjacent to the ball joint during drilling, the use of a center punch and a drill press are strongly recommended.

1. Remove the lower control arm.
2. Position the assembly with the ball joint up.
3. Center punch the rivets on the ball joint housing side.
4. Using a drill press with a 1/4 in. bit, drill out the center of the rivet.
5. Using a 1/2 in. bit, drill the center of the rivet until the bit makes contact with the ball joint housing.
6. Using a 3/8 in. bit, drill the center of the rivet. Remove the remainder of the rivet with a punch.
7. Position the new ball joint on the control arm and tighten the bolts to 60 ft. lbs.
8. Install the control arm and tighten the ball joint clamp bolt to 50 ft. lbs.; the pivot bolt to 105 ft. lbs. and the stub strut to 70 ft. lbs.

1979-80

The ball joint housing is bolted to the lower control arm with the joint stud retained in the steering knuckle by a clamp bolt.

1. Raise and support the car.
2. Remove the steering knuckle-to-ball joint stud clamp bolt and separate the stud from the knuckle leg.
3. Remove the 2 bolts holding the ball joint housing fastened to the lower control arm.
4. Remove the ball joint housing.
5. Install a new ball joint housing on the control arm. Torque the retaining bolts to 60 ft. lbs.
6. Install the ball joint stud in the steering knuckle. Tighten the clamp bolt to 50 ft. lbs.

7. Lower the car.

1981 and Later

NOTE: On some models the front ball joints are welded to the control arms and are not to be pressed out. Those that are welded must be serviced by complete replacement of the control arm and ball joint assembly.

1. Pry off the seal.
2. Position a receiving cup tool C-4699-2, or suitable tool, to support the lower control arm.
3. Install a 1-1/16 in. deep socket over the stud and against the joint upper housing.
4. Press the joint assembly from the arm.
5. To install, position the ball joint housing into the control arm cavity.

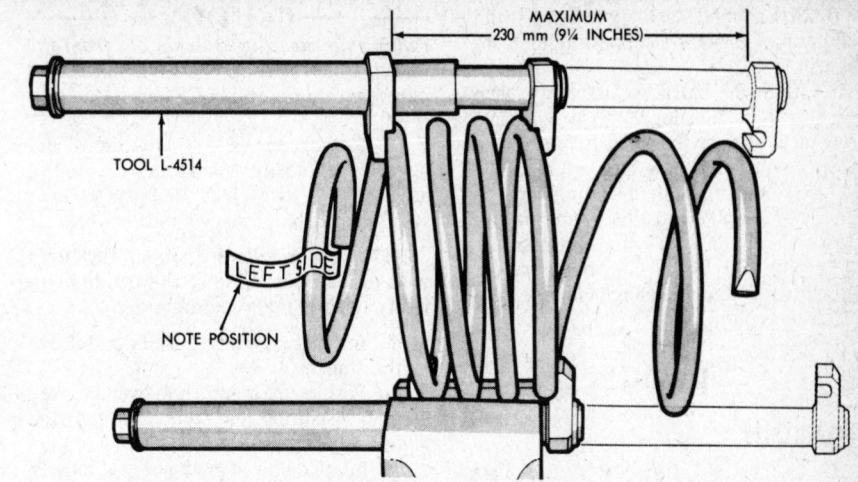

MAXIMUM 230 mm (9¼ INCHES)

TOOL L-4514

LEFT SIDE

NOTE POSITION

Strut spring is compressed by clamping evenly on four coils

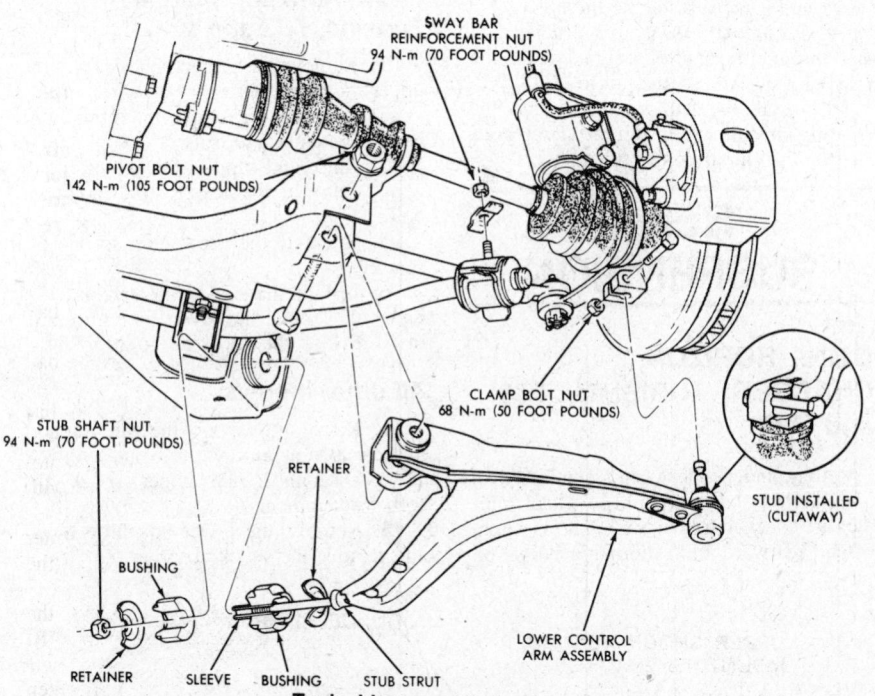

SWAY BAR REINFORCEMENT NUT 94 N-m (70 FOOT POUNDS)

PIVOT BOLT NUT 142 N-m (105 FOOT POUNDS)

STUB SHAFT NUT 94 N-m (70 FOOT POUNDS)

RETAINER

BUSHING

RETAINER   SLEEVE   BUSHING   STUB STRUT

CLAMP BOLT NUT 68 N-m (50 FOOT POUNDS)

STUD INSTALLED (CUTAWAY)

LOWER CONTROL ARM ASSEMBLY

Typical lower control arm

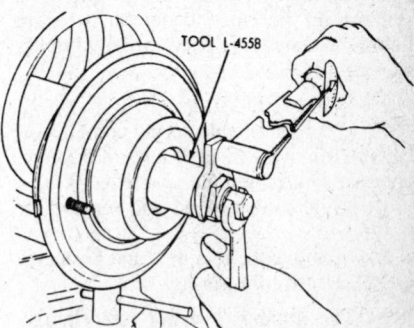

TOOL L-455B

Tighten strut rod nut to 60 ft. lbs.

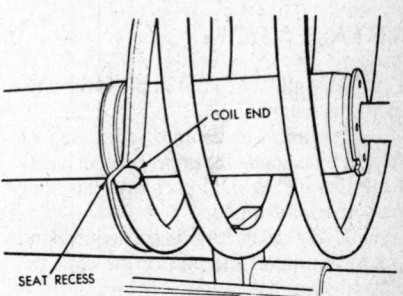

COIL END

SEAT RECESS

Strut coil lower end must be positioned in the recess of the lower spring retainer

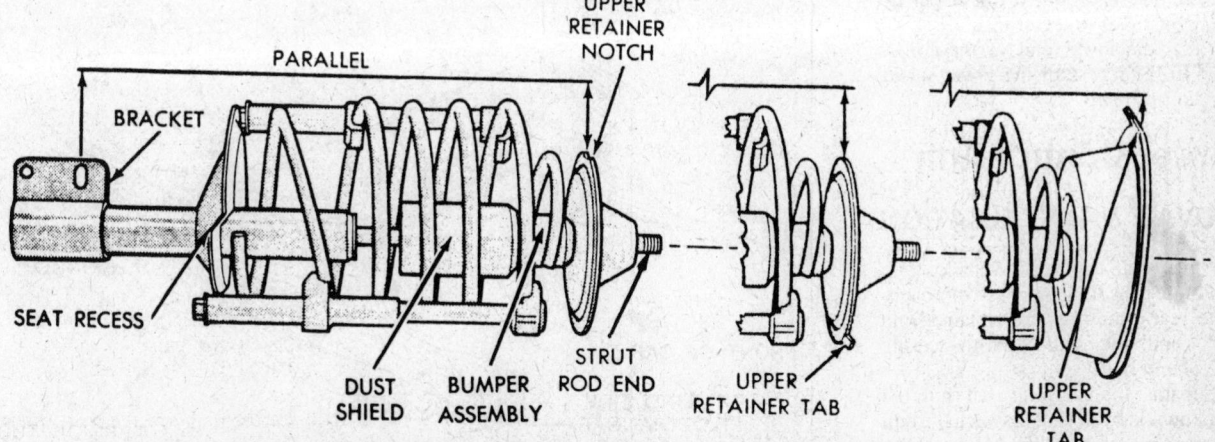

PARALLEL

UPPER RETAINER NOTCH

BRACKET

SEAT RECESS

DUST SHIELD

BUMPER ASSEMBLY

STRUT ROD END

UPPER RETAINER TAB

UPPER RETAINER TAB

Spring upper retainers may have a notch or tab that must be aligned parallel to strut lower bracket

6. Position the assembly in a press with installer tool C-4699-1 supporting the control arm.

7. Align the ball joint assembly, then press it until the housing ledge stops against the control arm cavity down flange.

8. To install a new seal, support the ball joint housing with installing tool C-4699-2, or suitable substitue, and position a new seal over the stud against the housing.

9. With a 1-1/2 in. socket, press the seal onto the joint housing with the seat against the control arm.

Spring

REMOVAL

NOTE: In disassembling strut dampers, carefully lay out partson a clean surface in the same order as they are being removed. This will simplify reassembly.

1. Remove the struts.
2. Using a reliable spring compressor, capture four coils into the jaws of the compressor, and tighten the jaws evenly.
3. Hold the strut rod and remove the rod nut.
4. Remove the retainers and bushings.
5. Remove the spring.

NOTE: Springs are not interchangeable from side to side.

INSTALLATION

1. Assemble the strut in the reverse order of disassembly.
2. Position the compressed spring on the strut by aligning the upper retainer notch, or tab, parallel to the lower strut-attaching bracket, as illustrated.
3. Using tool L-4558 or equivalent, tighten the nut at the end of the strut rod to 60 ft. lbs.
4. Carefully and evenly open the spring compressor to 9¼ in., and release the spring.
5. Make certain coil is seated properly at both ends, by checking that:
   a. the notch, or tab, of the upper retainer is parallel to the strut bracket.
   b. that the lower end of the coil is seated in the recess of the lower spring seat, as illustrated.

Lower Control Arm

REMOVAL & INSTALLATION

1. Raise and support the vehicle.
2. Remove the front inner pivot through-bolt, the rear stub strut nut, retainer and bushing, and the ball joint-to-steering knuckle clamp bolt.
3. Separate the ball joint stud from the steering knuckle by prying between the ball stud retainer on the knuckle and the lower control arm.

CAUTION
Pulling the steering knuckle out from the vehicle after releasing it from the ball joint can separate the inner CV joint.

---

4. Remove the sway bar-to-control arm nut and reinforcement and rotate the control arm over the sway bar. Remove the rear stub strut bushing, sleeve and retainer.

NOTE: The substitution of fasteners with other than those of the grade originally used is not recommended.

5. Install the retainer, bushing and sleeve on the stub strut.
6. Position the control arm over the sway bar and install the rear stub strut and front pivot into the crossmember.
7. Install the front pivot bolt and loosely install the nut.
8. Install the stub strut bushing and retainer and loosely assemble the nut.
9. Position the sway bar bracket and. stud through the control arm and install the retainer nut. Tighten the nut to 10 ft. lb.
10. Install the ball joint stud into the steering knuckle and install the clamp bolt. Torque the clamp bolt to 50 ft. lb.

REAR SUSPENSION

OMNI, HORIZON, CHARGER, TURISMO, TC3 and 024

A trailing, independent arm assembly, with integral sway bar is used. The wheel spindles are attached to two trailing arms which extend rearward from mounting points on the body where they are attached with shock absorbing, oval bushings. A crossmember is welded to the trailing arms, just to the rear of the bushings. A coil spring over shock absorber strut assembly, similar to the front suspension, is used.

ALL OTHER MODELS

These cars use a flexible beam axle with trailing links and coil springs. One shock absorber on each side is mounted outside the coil spring and attached to the body and the beam axle. Wheel spindles are bolted to the outer ends of the axle.

Shock Absorber Strut

REMOVAL & INSTALLATION

Omni, Horizon, Charger, Turismo, TC3 and 024

1. Remove the protective cap from the upper mounting nut.
2. Remove the upper mounting nut, isolator retainer and isolator.
3. Raise and support the vehicle.
4. Remove the lower strut mounting bolt.
5. Remove the strut and spring assembly.
6. Installation is in the reverse order of removal. Torque the lower mounting bolt to 40 ft. lbs.; the upper nut to 20 ft. lbs.

All other models

1. Raise and support the car. Support the rear axle assembly.
2. Disconnect the upper shock absorber attachments.
3. Remove the lower attaching bolts, and remove the shock absorber.

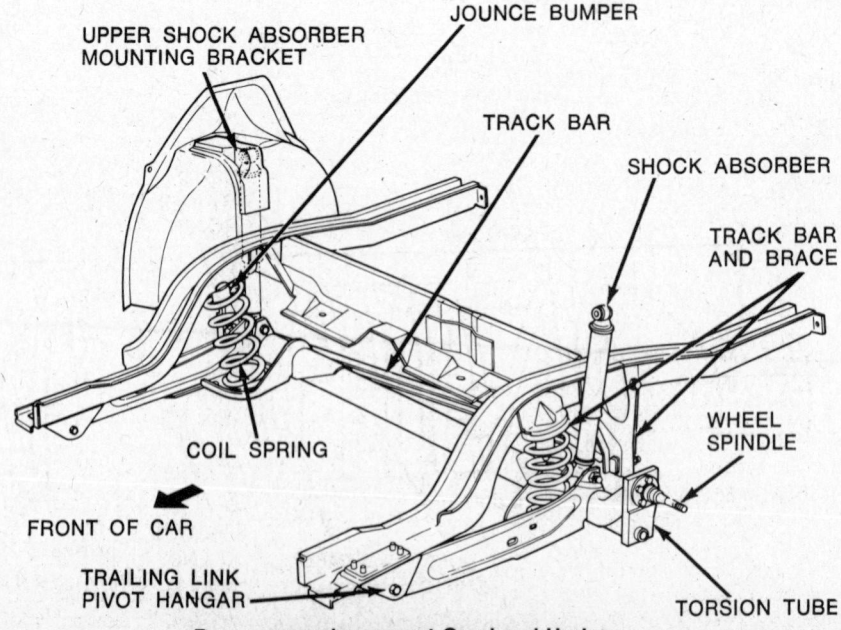

Rear suspension except Omni and Horizon

4. Purge the new shocks of air by compressing them while inverted and extending them in their normal position several times.

5. Installation is in the reverse order of removal.

Rear Spring

REMOVAL & INSTALLATION

Omni, Horizon, Charger, Turismo, TC3 and 024

The use of a coil spring compressor, such as Chrysler part #L-4514, is necessary.

1. Remove the strut and spring assembly as described earlier.

2. Install the spring compressor on the spring and place it in a vise.

——————— **CAUTION** ———————
Always grip 4 or 5 coils and never extend the retractors beyond 9 1/4 inches.

3. Tighten the retractors evenly until pressure is removed from the upper spring seat.

4. Loosen the retaining nut.

——————— **CAUTION** ———————
Be very careful when loosening the retaining nut. If the spring is not properly compressed, serious injury could result.

5. Remove the lower isolator, pushrod sleeve, and upper spring seat.

6. Carefully slip the strut from the spring.

7. Remove the bumper and dust shield from the strut.

8. Remove the lower spring seat.

9. Carefully and evenly, remove the compressor from the spring.

To installation:

1. Install the compressor on the spring, gripping four or five coils.

2. Compress the spring.

3. Install the lower spring seat, dust shield and bumper on the strut.

4. Slip the unit inside the coil spring and install the upper spring seat.

5. Make sure that the level surfaces on the seats are in position with the spring.

6. Install the sleeve on the pushrod and install the retaining nut. Torque the nut to 20 ft. lbs.

7. Install the lower isolator.

8. Install the strut and spring assembly.

All other models

1. Raise and support the car on a hoist. Do not use twin-post hoist. The swing arc of the axle may cause it to slip from the hoist when the bolts are removed. If a suitable hoist is not available, raise and support the car on jackstands, and use a jack under the axle.

2. Support the axle with a jack that can be raised and lowered.

3. Remove the brake hose attaching brackets (left and right) allowing the hoses

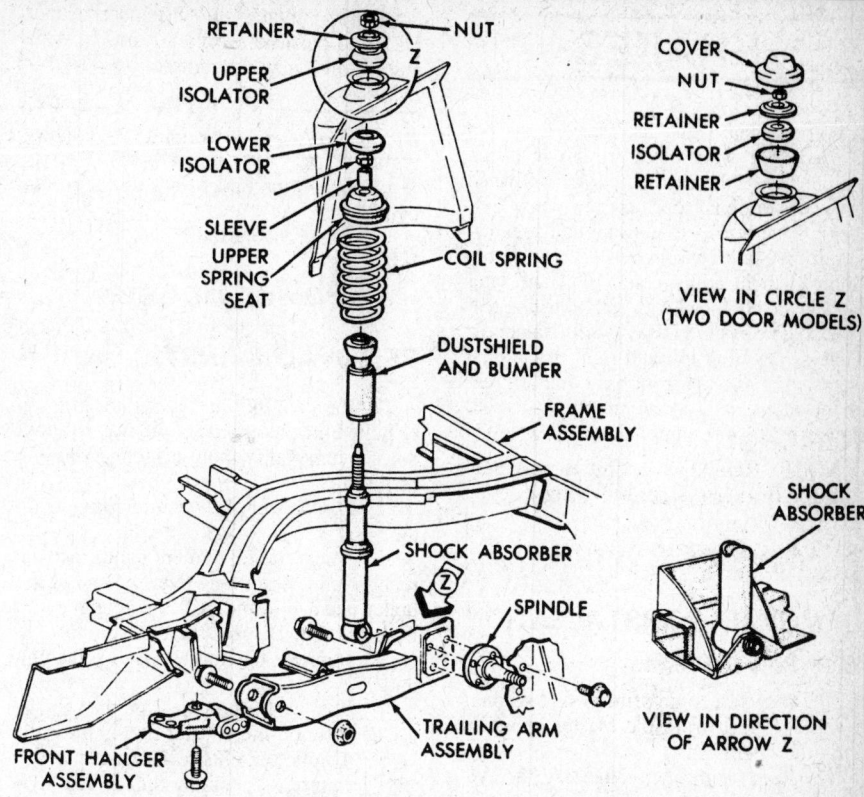

Semi-independent rear suspension system on Omni/Charger and Horizon/Turismo

to hang freely. Do not disconnect the hoses.

4. Remove both shock absorber lower attachments from the axle.

5. Lower the axle. Remove the spring and insulator.

6. To install, position the spring and insulator on the axle.

7. Install the shock absorber bolts and track bar. Install the brake line brackets.

REAR WHEEL BEARING ADJUSTMENT

1. Raise and support the car with the rear wheels off the floor.

2. Remove the wheel grease cap, cotter pin, nut-lock and bearing adjusting nut.

3. Remove the thrust washer and bearing.

4. Remove the drum from the spindle.

5. Thoroughly clean the old lubricant from the bearings and hub cavity. Inspect the bearing rollers for pitting or other signs of wear. Light discoloration is normal.

Clean the bearings in kerosene, mineral spirits or other suitable cleaning fluid. Do not dry them by spinning the bearings. Allow them to air dry.

6. Repack the bearings with high temperature multi-purpose EP grease, and add a small amount of new grease to the hub cavity. Be sure to force the lubricant between all rollers in the bearing.

7. Install the drum on the spindle after coating the polished spindle surfaces with wheel bearing lubricant.

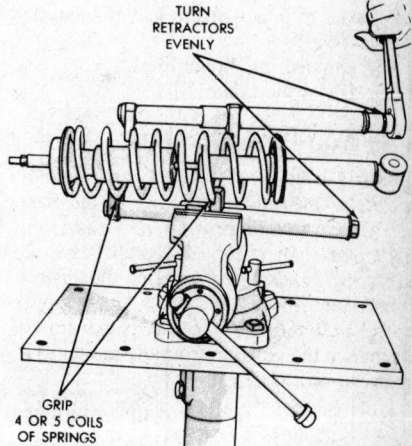

Compressing the rear spring on Omni and Horizon models (© Chrysler Corp.)

8. Install the outer bearing cone, thrust washer and adjusting nut.

9. Tighten the adjusting nut to 20-25 ft. lbs. while rotating the wheel.

10. Back off the adjusting nut to completely release the preload from the bearing.

11. Tighten the adjusting nut finger-tight.

12. Position the nut-lock with one pair of slots in line with the cotter pin hole. Install the cotter pin.

13. Clean and install the grease cap and wheel.

14. Lower the car.

BRAKES

A conventional front disc/rear drum setup is used. The front discs are single piston caliper types; the rear drums are activated by a conventional top mounted wheel cylinder. Disc brakes require no adjustments, the drum brakes through 1982 require periodic manual adjustment. 1983 and later models are equipped with self-adjusting rear brakes. The system is diagonally balanced. That is, the front left and right rear are on one system and the front right and left rear on the other. No proportioning valve is used. Power brakes are optional.

NOTE: Refer to the Unit Repair Section for brakes system servicing.

Master Cylinder

REMOVAL & INSTALLATION

With Power Brakes

1. Disconnect the primary and secondary brake lines from the master cylinder. Plug the openings.
2. Remove the nuts attaching the cylinder to the power brake booster.
3. Slide the master cylinder straight out, away from the booster.
4. Position the master cylinder over the studs on the booster, align the pushrod with the master cylinder piston and tighten the nuts to 16 ft. lbs.
5. Connect the brake lines.
6. Bleed the brakes.

With Non-Power Brakes

1. Disconnect the primary and secondary brake lines and install plugs in the master cylinder openings.
2. Disconnect the stoplight switch mounting bracket from under the instrument panel.
3. Pull the brake pedal backward to disengage the pushrod from the master cylinder piston.

NOTE: This will destroy the grommet.

4. Remove the master cylinder-to-firewall nuts.
5. Slide the master cylinder out and away from the firewall. Be sure to remove all pieces of the broken grommet.
6. Install the boot on the pushrod.
7. Install a new grommet on the pushrod.
8. Apply a soap and water solution to the grommet and slide it firmly into position in the primary piston socket. Move the pushrod from side to side to make sure it's seated.
9. From the engine side, press the pushrod through the master cylinder mounting plate and align the mounting studs with the holes in the cylinder.
10. Install the nuts and torque them to 16 ft. lbs.

11. From under the instrument panel, place the pushrod on the pin on the pedal and install a new retaining clip.

CAUTION
Be sure to lubricate the pin.

---

12. Install the brake lines on the master cylinder.
13. Bleed the system.

Power Booster

REMOVAL & INSTALLATION

1. Remove the master cylinder; it can be pulled far enough out of the way to allow booster removal without disconnecting the brake lines.
2. Disconnect the vacuum hose from the booster.
3. Under the instrument panel, pry the retainer clip center tang over the end of the brake pedal pin and pull the retainer clip from the pin. Discard the clip.
4. Remove the four booster attaching nuts.
5. Remove the booster from the vehicle.
6. Position the booster on the firewall.
7. Torque the nuts to 20 ft. lbs.
8. Carefully position the master cylinder on the booster.
9. Install the mounting nuts and torque them to 18 ft. lbs.
10. Connect the vacuum hose to the booster.
11. Coat the bearing surface of the pedal pin with chassis lube.
12. Connect the pushrod to the pedal pin and install a new clip.
13. Check the stoplight operation. With vacuum applied to the power brake unit and pressure applied to the pedal, the master cylinder should vent (force a jet of fluid through the front chamber vent port).

CAUTION
Do not attempt to disassemble the power brake unit, since the booster is serviced as a complete assembly only.

PARKING BRAKE ADJUSTMENT

1. Fully release the parking brake.
2. Locate the cable connector at the rear suspension crossmember and thoroughly clean the assembly.
3. Loosen the adjusting nut until there is slack in the cable.
4. Insert a brake adjusting spoon through the slot in the brake backing plate and rotate the starwheel so there is light shoe-to-drum contact.
5. Back-off the starwheel to allow free drum rotation.
6. Tighten the cable adjusting nut until a slight drag is felt at the wheels.
7. Loosen the cable adjusting nut until both rear wheels turn freely.

8. Back-off the nut two full turns.
9. Apply and release the parking brake several times to make sure the wheels rotate freely.

STEERING

The manual steering system consists of a tube which contains the toothed rack, a pinion, the rack slipper, and the rack slipper spring. Steering effort is transmitted to the steering arms by the tie-rods which are coupled to the ends of the rack, and the tie-rod ends. Connections between the ends of the rack and tie-rods are protected by bellows type oil seals which retain the gear lubricant.

The power steering system consists of four major parts: the power gear, power steering pump, pressure hose and the return hose. As with the manual system, the turning of the steering wheel is converted into linear travel through the meshing of helical pinion teeth with teeth on the rack. Power assist is provided by an open center, rotary type, three-way control valve which directs fluid to either side of the rack control piston.

Steering Gear

REMOVAL & INSTALLATION

All Models

NOTE: On all models, except Omni-Horizon the steering column must be removed.

1. Remove front wheels.
2. Remove tie rod ends, using a suitable puller.
3. Remove steering column assembly.

NOTE: The lower universal joint is removed with the steering gear.

On all models except Omni, Horizon, Charger, Turismo, TC3 and 024, follow procedure in Step 6, this exposes coupling pin so that it can be driven out. Also, remove anti-rotational link from crossmember, if so equipped, and remove air diverter valve bracket, if so equipped, from left side of crossmember.

4. On Omni-Horizon drive out lower roll pin attaching pinion shaft to lower universal joint.

NOTE: Use a back-up, to protect universal joint, while driving roll pin.

5. On Omni-Horizon support the front suspension crossmember with a hydraulic jack. Remove the two rear nuts attaching crossmember to frame. Loosen the two front bolts attaching crossmember to frame, and lower crossmember slightly for access to boot seal shields.

6. On all models except Omni, Horizon, Charger, Turismo, TC3 and 024, remove all four front suspension crossmember attaching bolts and lower front suspension crossmember, using transmission jack, so the steering gear can be removed from the crossmember.

7. Remove splash shields and boot seal shields.

8. Remove tubes to pump (power only).

9. Disconnect the tie rod ends from steering knuckles.

10. Remove bolts attaching gear to front suspension crossmember.

11. Remove gear from left side of vehicle.

12. Installation is in the reverse order of removal. The right rear crossmember bolt is a pilot bolt that correctly locates the crossmember. Tighten it first. Tighten all four crossmember bolts to 90 ft. lbs., and steering gear attaching bolts 250 ft. lbs.

Steering Column

REMOVAL & INSTALLATION

1. Disconnect the negative battery cable.

2. Disconnect all column wiring connectors.

3. Remove lower roll pin from upper universal joint.

4. Disconnect the column from the panel.

5. Installation is in the reverse order of removal.

Tie Rod End

REPLACEMENT

1. Loosen the jam nut which connects the tie-rod end to the knuckle. Mark the tie-rod position on the threads.

2. Using a ball joint separator, remove the tie-rod end from the knuckle.

3. Install a new tie-rod end in the reverse order of removal.

4. Check alignment.

Power Steering Pump

REMOVAL & INSTALLATION

NOTE: All power steering pump mounting nuts and bolts are metric

1. Disconnect the vapor separator hose from the carburetor and the two wires from the air conditioning clutch cycling switch, if so equipped.

2. Loosen the two drive belt adjustment bolts and nut at the rear of the pump and remove the belt from the pump pulley.

3. Raise the car on a hoist and remove the pressure hose locating bracket bolt at the crossmember.

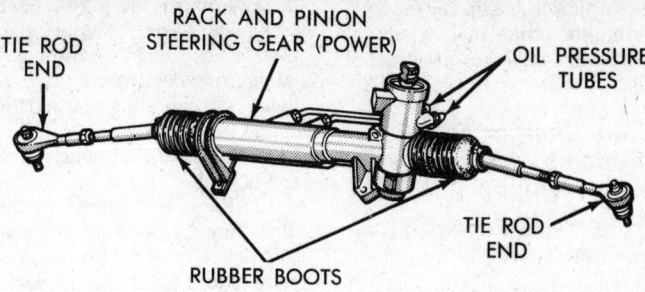

Power steering gear (© Chrysler Corp.)

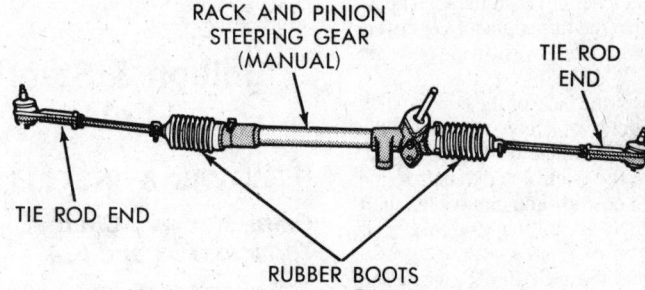

Manual steering gear (© Chrysler Corp.)

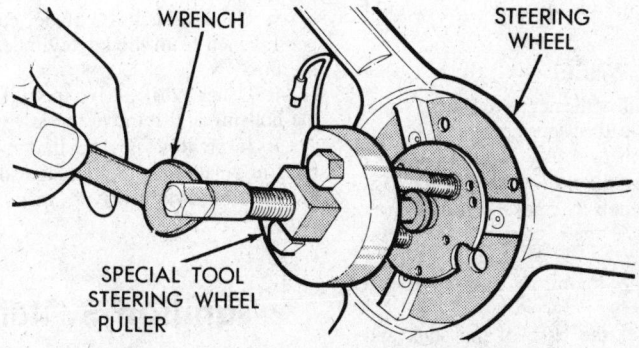

Steering wheel removal (© Chrysler Corp.)

4. Disconnect the pressure hose from the gear and drain the oil from the pump through the end of the hose.

5. Remove the right side splash shield that protects the drive belts.

6. Disconnect both hoses from the pump.

7. Remove the two rearmost bolts and loosen the one bolt that attaches the bracket.

8. Lower the car and remove the adjustment bolts and bracket from the front of the pump and the nut at the rear of the pump.

9. Move the bracket and carefully remove the pump.

10. To install, reverse the removal procedure. Adjust the belt to the correct tension, and fill the pump reservoir to the proper level with power steering fluid.

Steering Wheel

REMOVAL & INSTALLATION

1. Remove the horn button, or pad, and the horn switch.

2. Remove the steering wheel nut.

3. Using a steering wheel puller, remove the steering wheel.

4. Align the master serration in the wheel hub with the missing tooth on the shaft. Torque the shaft nut to 45 ft. lbs.

—— CAUTION ——
Do not torque the nut against the steering column lock, or damage will occur.

5. Replace the horn switch and button.

Turn Signal Switch

REMOVAL & INSTALLATION
Omni/Charger and Horizon/Turismo

1. Disconnect the electrical connector at column.

2. Remove the steering wheel as described earlier.

3. Remove the lower column cover.

4. Remove the wash/wipe switch.

5. Remove the wiring clip and the three screws securing the turn signal switch.

6. Installation is in the reverse order of removal.

Except Omni/Charger and Horizon/Turismo
WITHOUT TILT WHEEL

1. Disconnect the negative battery cable.
2. Remove the steering wheel as described earlier.
3. On vehicles equipped with intermittent wipe or intermittent wipe with speed control, remove the two screws that attach the turn signal lever cover to the lock housing and remove the turn signal lever cover.
4. Remove the wash/wipe switch assembly.
5. Uncover the base of the control stalk and remove the two screws that attach the control stalk sleeve to the wash/wipe switch.
6. Rotate the control stalk shaft to the full clockwise position and remove the shaft from the switch by pulling straight out of the switch.
7. Remove the turn signal switch and upper bearing retainer screws. Remove the retainer and lift the switch up and out.
8. Installation is in the reverse order of removal.

WITH TILT WHEEL

1. Disconnect the negative battery cable.
2. Remove the steering wheel as previously described.
3. Remove the tilt lever, push the hazard warning knob in, and unscrew it out.
4. Remove the ignition key lamp assembly.
5. Pull the knob off the wash/wipe switch assembly.
6. Uncover the base of the stalk and remove the two screws that attach the sleeve to the wash/wipe switch and remove the sleeve.
7. Rotate the shaft in the wiper switch to the full clockwise position and remove the shaft by pulling straight out of the wash/wipe switch.

8. Remove the plastic cover from the lock plate. Depress the lock plate with tool C-4156, or suitable substitute. Pry the retaining ring out of the groove. Remove the lock plate, canceling cam and upper bearing spring.
9. Remove the switch actuator screw and arm.
10. Remove the three mounting screws of the turn signal switch and place the gearshift lever bowl in low position. Wrap a piece of tape around the connector and wires to prevent snagging, then remove the switch and wires.
11. Installation is in the reverse order of removal.

Ignition & Steering Lock

REMOVAL & INSTALLATION

Omni, Horizon, Charger, Turismo, TC3 and 024

1. Remove the steering wheel.
2. Remove the upper and lower column covers.
3. Using a hacksaw blade, cut the upper 1/4 inch from the key cylinder retainer pin boss.
4. Using a drift, drive the roll pin from the housing and remove the key cylinder.
5. Insert the new cylinder into the housing, making sure it engages the lug on the ignition switch driver. Install the roll pin.

Ignition Switch

REMOVAL & INSTALLATION

Omni, Horizon, Charger, Turismo, TC3 and 024

1. Remove the connector from the switch.

2. Place the key in the LOCK position.
3. Remove the key.
4. Remove the two mounting screws from the switch and allow the switch and pushrod to drop below the jacket.
5. Rotate the switch 90 degrees to permit removal of the switch from the pushrod.
6. To install the switch, position the switch in LOCK (second detent from the top).
7. Place the switch at right angles to the column and insert the pushrod.
8. Align the switch on the bracket and install the screws.
9. With a light rearward load on the switch, tighten the screws. Check for proper operation.

Ignition Switch & Key Lock

REMOVAL & INSTALLATION

Except Omni/Charger and Horizon/Turismo
WITHOUT TILT WHEEL

1. Follow the turn signal switch removal procedure previously described.
2. Unclip the horn and key light ground wires.
3. Remove the retaining screw and move the ignition key lamp assembly out of the way.
4. Remove the four screws that attach the bearing housing to the lock housing.
5. Remove the snap ring from the upper end of the steering shaft.
6. Remove the bearing housing from the shaft.
7. Remove the lock plate spring and lock plate from the steering shaft.
8. Remove the ignition key, then remove the screw and lift out the buzzer/chime switch.
9. Remove the two screws attaching the ignition switch to the column jacket.
10. Remove the ignition switch by rotating the switch 90 degrees on the rod then slide switch off the rod.
11. Remove the two mounting screws from the dimmer switch and disengage the switch from the actuator rod.
12. Remove the two screws that mount the bellcrank and slide the bellcrank up in the lock housing until it can be disconnected from the ignition switch actuator rod.
13. To remove the lock cylinder and lock levers, place the cylinder in the LOCK position and remove the key.
14. Insert a small diameter screwdriver or similar tool into the lock cylinder release holes and push into the release spring loaded lock retainers. At the same time pull the lock cylinder out of the housing bore.
15. Grasp the lock lever and spring assembly and pull straight out of the housing.
16. If necessary the lock housing may be removed from the column jacket by removing the hex head retaining screws.

TURN SIGNAL SWITCH

RETAINING PLATE

Turn signal switch removal—Aries and Reliant

17. Installation is in the reverse order of removal. If the lock housing was removed tighten the lock housing screws to 90 in. lbs.

18. To install the dimmer switch, firmly seat the push rod into the switch. Compress the switch until two .093 in. drill shanks can be inserted into the alignment holes. Reposition the upper end of the push rod in the pocket of the wash/wipe switch. With a light rearward pressure on the switch, install the two screws.

19. Grease and assemble the two lock levers, lock lever spring and pin.

20. Install the lock lever assembly in the lock housing. Seat the pin firmly into the bottom of the slots and make sure the lock lever spring leg is firmly in place in the lock casting notch.

21. Install the ignition switch actuator rod from the bottom, through the oblong hole in the lock housing, and attach it to the bellcrank. Position the bellcrank assembly into the lock housing while pulling the ignition switch rod down the column, install the bellcrank onto its mounting surface. The gearshift lever should be in the "Park" position.

22. Place the ignition switch on the ignition switch actuator rod and rotate it 90 degrees to Lock the rod into position.

23. To install the ignition lock, turn the key to the lock position and remove the key. Insert the cylinder far enough into the housing to contact the switch actuator. Insert the key and press inward and rotate the cylinder. When the parts align, the cylinder will move inward and lock into the housing.

24. With the key cylinder in the lock position and the ignition switch in the lock position (second detent from top), tighten the ignition switch mounting screws.

25. Feed the buzzer/chime switch wires behind the wiring post and down through the space between the housing and the jacket. Remove the ignition key, position the switch in the housing and tighten the mounting screws. The ignition key should be removed.

26. Install the lock plate on the steering shaft.

27. Install the upper bearing spring, then the upper bearing housing.

28. Install the upper bearing snap ring on the steering shaft, locking the assembly in place.

29. Install the four screws attaching the bearing housing to the lock housing.

30. Install the key lamp and turn signal switch, following the procedure given previously.

Lock Cylinder

REMOVAL & INSTALLATION

Except Omni/Charger and Horizon/Turismo
WITH TILT WHEEL

1. Remove the turn signal switch as previously described.

2. Place the lock cylinder in the lock position.

3. Insert a thin tool into the slot next to the switch mounting screwboss (right hand slot), depress the spring latch at the bottom of the slot, and remove the lock.

4. Installation is in the reverse order of removal. Turn the ignition lock to the "Lock" position and remove the key. Insert the cylinder until the spring loaded retainer snaps into place.

Ignition Switch

REMOVAL & INSTALLATION

Except Omni/Charger and Horizon/Turismo
WITH TILT WHEEL

Due to the complexity of the ignition switch removal procedure and the necessity of special tools, it is recommended that the switch be replaced by a qualified repair shop.

INSTRUMENT PANEL

The fuel, temperature and oil pressure gauges work on the constant voltage principle through a common voltage limiter which pulses to provide intermittent current to the gauge system.

Cluster Assembly

REMOVAL & INSTALLATION

Omni, Horizon, Charger, Turismo, TC3 and 024

1. Remove the two lens assembly lower attaching retaining springs by pulling rearward with pliers.

2. Allow the lens assembly to drop as it is pulled rearward.

3. Remove the speedometer assembly by loosening two screws.

4. Remove the two wiring harness connectors.

5. Remove the two cluster attaching screws.

6. Pull the two upper spring retainers away from the panel.

7. If equipped with a clock, reach behind the panel and disconnect the wires.

8. Remove the cluster assembly.

9. Installation is in the reverse order of removal.

All other models

1. Place the gearshift lever in position "1".

2. Remove the instrument panel trim strip.

3. Remove the left upper and lower cluster bezel screws.

4. Remove the right lower cluster bezel screw and retaining clip.

5. Remove the instrument cluster bezel by snapping the bezel off the five retaining clips.

6. Remove the seven retaining screws and remove the upper right bezel.

7. Remove the four rear instrument panel top cover mounting screws.

8. Lift the rear edge of the panel top cover and remove the two screws attaching the upper trim strip retainer and cluster housing to the base panel.

9. Remove the trim strip retainer.

10. Remove the two screws attaching the cluster housing to the base panel of the lower cluster.

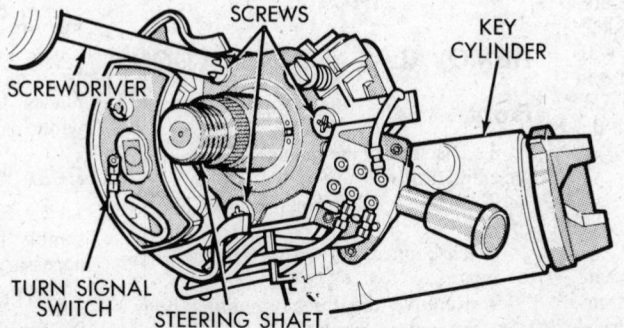

Turn signal switch removal—Omni and Horizon (© Chrysler Corp.)

11. Lift the rearward edge of the panel top cover and slide the cluster housing rearward.

12. Disconnect the right printed circuit board connector from behind the cluster housing.

13. Disconnect the speedometer cable connector.

14. Disconnect the left printed circuit connector.

15. Remove the cluster assembly.

16. Installation is in the reverse order of removal.

Headlight Switch

REMOVAL & INSTALLATION

Omni, Horizon, Charger, Turismo, TC3 and 024

1. Disconnect the battery ground.

2. Pull the headlight knob from the switch.

3. Unscrew the collar from the instrument panel side of the switch.

4. Push the switch through the panel, and let it drop; disconnect the wires.

5. Installation is in the reverse order of removal.

All other models

1. Remove the three screws that fasten the headlamp switch mounting plate to the base panel.

2. Pull the switch and plate rearward and disconnect the wiring connector.

3. Depress the button on the switch and remove the knob and stem.

4. Snap out the escutcheon, then remove the nut that attaches the switch to the mounting plate.

5. Installation is in the reverse order of removal.

SPEEDOMETER CABLE REPLACEMENT

1. Reach under the instrument panel and depress the spring clip that connects the cable to the speedometer head. Pull the cable back and away from the head.

2. If the core is broken, raise and support the vehicle and remove the cable retaining screw from the cable bracket. Carefully slide the cable out of the transaxle.

3. Coat the new core sparingly with speedometer cable lubricant and insert it in the cable. Install the cable at the transaxle, lower the car and connect the cable to the speedometer head.

Fusible Links

Fusible links are used to prevent major wire harness damage in the event of a short circuit or an overload condition in electrical circuits. Each fusible link is of a fixed value

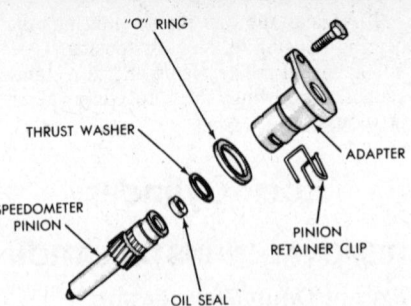

Transaxle end of the speedometer cable (© Chrysler Corp.)

for a specific electrical load and should a link fail, the cause of the failure must be determined and repaired prior to installing a new fusible link of the same value.

Circuit Breakers

Circuit breakers are used along with the fusible links to protect electrical system components such as headlamps, windshield wipers, electric windows, tailgate front switch and tailgate rear switch. The circuit breakers are located either in the switch, or are mounted on or near the lower lip of the instrument panel, to the right or left of the steering column.

Fuse Panels

The fuse panel is used to house the fuses that protect the individual or combined electrical circuits within the vehicle. The turn signal flasher, the hazard warning flasher and the seat belt warning buzzer/timer are located on the fuse panel for quick identification and replacement.

The fuses are usually identified by abbreviated circuit names or number, with the number of the rated fuse needed to protect the circuit printed below the fuse holder.

WINDSHIELD WIPER

Motor

REMOVAL & INSTALLATION

Front

1. Disconnect the linkage from the motor crank arm.

2. Remove the wiper motor plastic cover.

3. Disconnect the wiring harness from the motor.

4. Remove the three mounting bolts from the motor bracket and remove the motor.

5. Installation is in the reverse order of removal.

Rear (Omni and Horizon)

1. Open the tailgate.

2. Remove the wiper motor plastic cover.

3. Remove the blade and arm.

4. Remove the chrome nut and ring from the pivot shaft.

5. From inside the tailgate, remove the motor mounting screws.

6. Disconnect the main tailgate wiring harness from the motor pigtail wire.

7. Remove the motor.

8. Installation is in the reverse order of removal.

Rear (Except Omni and Horizon)

1. Remove the arm and blade assembly.

2. Open the tailgate.

3. Remove the motor cover and disconnect the wiring connector.

4. Remove the four bracket retaining screws, and remove the motor from the tailgate.

5. Installation is in the reverse order of removal.

WIPER BLADE REPLACEMENT

1. Lift the wiper arm away from the glass.

2. Depress the release lever on the bridge and remove the blade assembly from the arm.

3. Lift the tab and pinch the end bridge to release it from the center bridge.

4. Slide the end bridge from the blade element and the element from the opposite end bridge.

5. Assembly is in the reverse order of removal. Make sure the element locking tabs are securely locked in position.

WIPER ARM REMOVAL AND INSTALLATION

Front

1. Lift the arm so the latch can be pulled out to the holding position and release the arm. The arm will remain off the windshield in this position.

2. Remove the arm from the pivot using a rocking motion.

3. When installing, the motor should be in the park position and the tips of the blades 1½ in. above the bottom of the windshield moulding.

Rear

1. To remove the rear wiper arm assembly the use of special tool C-3982 is necessary.

NOTE: The use of a screwdriver is not recommended because it will distort and damage the arm.

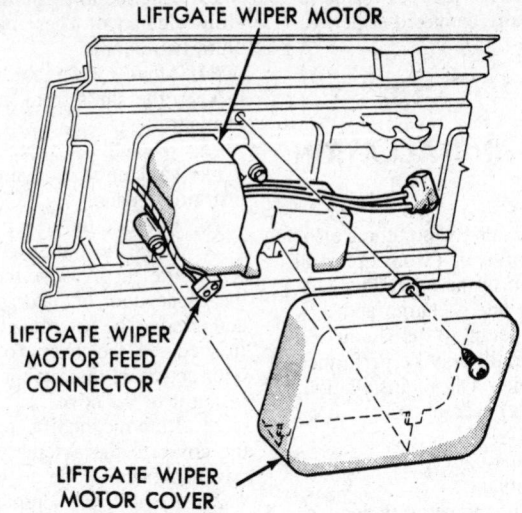

LIFTGATE WIPER MOTOR

LIFTGATE WIPER MOTOR FEED CONNECTOR

LIFTGATE WIPER MOTOR COVER

Rear wiper motor removal—Omni and Horizon (© Chrysler Corp.)

2. With the tool installed on the arm, lift the arm, then remove it from the output shaft.

3. To install, the wiper motor should be in the park position.

4. Install the arm so the tip of the blade is about 2 inches (Omni/Horizon), 1.3 inches (except Omni and Horizon) above the lower tailgate gasket.

RADIO

All radios are trimmed at the factory and should require no further adjustment. However, after a repair or if the antenna trim is to be verified, proceed as follows:

1. Turn radio on.

2. Manually tune the radio to a weak station between 1400 and 1600 KHz on AM.

3. Increase the volume and set the tone control to full treble (clockwise).

4. Viewing the radio from the front, the trimmer control is a slot-head located to the rear of the right side. Adjust it carefully by turning it back and forth with a screwdriver until maximum loudness is achieved.

REMOVAL & INSTALLATION

Omni, Horizon, Charger, Turismo, TC3 and 024

1. Remove the seven bezel attaching screws and open the glove compartment.

2. Remove the bezel, guiding the right end around the glove compartment and away from the panel.

3. Disconnect the radio ground strap and remove the two radio mounting screws.

4. Pull the radio from the panel and disconnect the wiring and antenna lead.

5. Installation is in the reverse order of removal.

All Other Models

1. Remove the center bezel.

2. If equipped with a mono-speaker, remove the instrument panel top cover, speaker, and disconnect the wires from the radio.

3. Remove the two screws attaching the radio to the base panel.

4. Pull the radio out through the front of the base panel, then disconnect the wiring harness, antenna lead and ground strap.

5. Installation is in the reverse order of removal.

HEATER

Heater Assembly

REMOVAL & INSTALLATION

Without A/C
Omni, Horizon, Charger, Turismo, TC3 and 024

1. Disconnect the battery and drain the cooling system.

2. Remove the center, outside air floor-vent housing.

3. Remove the ash tray.

4. Remove the two defroster duct adapter screws. The left one is reached through the ash tray opening.

5. Remove the defrost duct adapter and push the flexible hose up out of the way.

6. Disconnect the temperature control cable.

7. Disconnect the blower motor wiring connector. Remove blower motor assembly.

8. Disconnect the hoses from the heater core and plug the core openings.

9. Remove the two nuts holding the heater unit on the firewall.

10. Remove the glove compartment and door.

11. Remove the screw assembly support strap nut. Disconnect the strap from the plenum stud and lower the heater from the instrument panel.

12. Disconnect the control cable and remove the unit from the car.

13. Connect the control cable and raise the unit into position so the core tubes and mounting studs fit through their holes in the firewall.

14. Install the support strap and hand tighten the nut.

15. Install and tighten the two heater-to-firewall nuts.

16. Unplug and connect the core tubes.

17. Install the defroster duct adapter.

18. Install the ash tray.

19. Install the center, outside air floor-vent housing.

20. Install the glove compartment.

21. Refill the cooling system.

All Other Models

1. Disconnect the negative battery cable and drain the radiator.

2. Disconnect the blower motor wiring connector.

3. Reach under the unit, depress the tab on the mode door and temperature control cables, pull the flags from the receivers, and remove the self-adjust clip from the crank arm.

4. Remove the glove box assembly.

5. Disconnect the heater hoses to the unit on the engine side and seal the heater core tube openings and hoses.

6. Through the glove box opening remove the screw attaching the hanger strap to the heater assembly.

7. Remove the nut attaching the hanger strap to the dash panel and remove the hanger strap.

8. Remove the two nuts attaching the heater assembly to the dash panel. The nuts are on the engine side.

9. Pull out the bottom of the instrument panel and slide out the heater assembly.

10. Installation is in the reverse order of removal.

Blower Motor

REMOVAL & INSTALLATION
Without A/C

The blower motor is located under the instrument panel on the left side of the heater assembly.

1. Disconnect the motor wiring.

2. Remove the left outlet duct on some models.

3. Remove the motor retaining screws and remove the motor.

4. Installation is in the reverse order of removal.

Heater Core

REMOVAL & INSTALLATION

Without A/C
OMNI/CHARGER AND HORIZON/TURISMO

Omni, Horizon, Charger, Turismo, TC3 and 024

1. Remove the heater assembly as described earlier.
2. Remove the left outlet duct.
3. Remove the blower motor.
4. Remove the defroster duct adapter.
5. Remove the outside air and defroster door cover.
6. Remove the defroster door.
7. Remove the defroster door control rod.
8. Remove the core cover.
9. Lift the core out of the unit.
10. Installation is in the reverse order of removal.

All Other Models

1. Remove the heater assembly.
2. Remove the padding from around the heater core outlets and remove the upper core mounting screws.
3. Pry loose the retaining snaps from around the outer edge of the housing cover.

NOTE: If a retaining snap should break, the housing cover has provisions for mounting screws.

4. Remove the housing top cover.
5. Remove the bottom heater core mounting screw.
6. Slide the heater core out of the housing.
7. Installation is in the reverse order of removal.

Blower Motor

REMOVAL & INSTALLATION

A/C Cars

1. Disconnect the battery ground.
2. Remove the three screws fastening the glovebox to the instrument panel.
3. Disconnect the wiring from the blower and case.
4. Remove the blower vent tube from the case.
5. Loosen the recirculating door from its bracket and remove the actuator from the housing. Leave the vacuum lines attached.
6. Remove the seven screws attaching the recirculating housing to the A/C unit and remove the housing.
7. Remove the three mounting flange nuts and washers.
8. Remove the blower motor from the unit.

9. Installation is in the reverse order of removal. Replace any damaged sealer.

Heater Core

REMOVAL & INSTALLATION

A/C Cars

Removal of the Heater-Evaporator Unit is required for core removal. Two people will be required to perform the operation. Discharge, evacuation and recharge and leak testing of the refrigerant system is necessary. This work should only be performed by a trained technician. During installation, a small can of refrigerant oil will be necessary.

1. Disconnect the battery ground.
2. Drain the coolant.
3. Disconnect the temperature door cable from the heater-evaporator unit.
4. Disconnect the temperature door cable from the retaining clips.
5. Remove the glovebox.
6. Disconnect the vacuum harness from the control head.
7. Disconnect the blower motor lead and anti-diesel relay wire.
8. Remove the seven screws fastening the right trim bezel to the instrument panel. Starting at the right side, swing the bezel clear and remove it.
9. Remove the three screws on the bottom of the center distribution duct cover and slide the cover rearward and remove it.
10. Remove the center distribution duct.
11. Remove the defroster duct adapter.
12. Remove the H-type expansion valve, located on the right side of the firewall:

    a. remove the $^{15}/_{16}$ in. bolt in the center of the plumbing sealing plate.

    b. carefully pull the refrigerant lines toward the front of the car, taking care to avoid scratching the valve sealing surfaces.

    c. remove the two ¼-in. Allenhead capscrews and remove the valve.
13. Cap the pipe openings at once. Wrap the valve in a plastic bag.
14. Disconnect the hoses from the core tubes.
15. Disconnect the vacuum lines at the intake manifold and water valve.
16. Remove the unit-to-firewall retaining nuts.
17. Remove the panel support bracket.
18. Remove the right cowl lower panel.
19. Remove the instrument panel pivot bracket screw from the right side.
20. Remove the screws that fasten lower instrument panel to the steering column.
21. Pull back the carpet from under the unit as far as possible.
22. Remove the nut from the evaporator-heater unit-to-plenum mounting brace and blower motor ground cable. While supporting the unit, remove the brace from its stud.

23. Lift the unit, pulling it rearward to allow clearance. These operations may require two people.
24. Slowly lower the unit, taking care to keep the studs from hanging-up on the insulation.
25. When the unit reaches the floor, slide it rearward until it is out from under the instrument panel.
26. Remove the unit from the car.
27. Place the unit on a workbench. From within the car, remove the ¼-in. nut from the mode door actuator on the top cover and remove the two retaining clips from the front edge of the cover. To remove the mode door actuator, remove the two screws that fasten it to the cover.
28. Remove the fifteen screws attaching the cover to the assembly and lift off the cover. Lift the mode door out of the unit.
29. Remove the screw from the core retaining bracket and lift out the core.

To install:

30. Place the core in the unit and install the bracket.
31. Install the actuator arm.

——————— CAUTION ———————

When installing the unit in the car, care must be taken that the vacuum lines to the engine compartment do not hang-up on the accelerator or become trapped between the unit and the firewall. If this happens, kinked lines will result and the unit will have to be removed to free them. Proper routing of these lines will require two people. The portion of the vacuum harness which is routed through the steering column support MUST be positioned BEFORE the distribution housing is installed. The harness MUST be routed ABOVE the temperature control cable.

32. Place the unit on the floor, as far under the panel as possible.
33. Raise the unit carefully, at the same time pull the lower instrument panel rearward, as far as possible.
34. Position the unit in place and attach the brace to the stud.
35. Install the lower ground cable and attach the nut.
36. Install and tighten the unit-to-firewall nuts.
37. Reposition the carpet and install—but do not tighten—the right instrument panel pivot bracket screw.
38. Place a piece of sheet metal or thin cardboard against the evaporator-heater assembly to center the assembly duct seal.
39. Position the center distributor duct in place, making sure the upper left tab comes in through the left center A/C outlet opening and that each air take-off is properly inserted into its respective outlet.

NOTE: Make sure the radio wiring connector does not interfere with the duct.

40. Install and tighten the screw fastening the upper left tab of the center air distribution duct to the instrument panel.

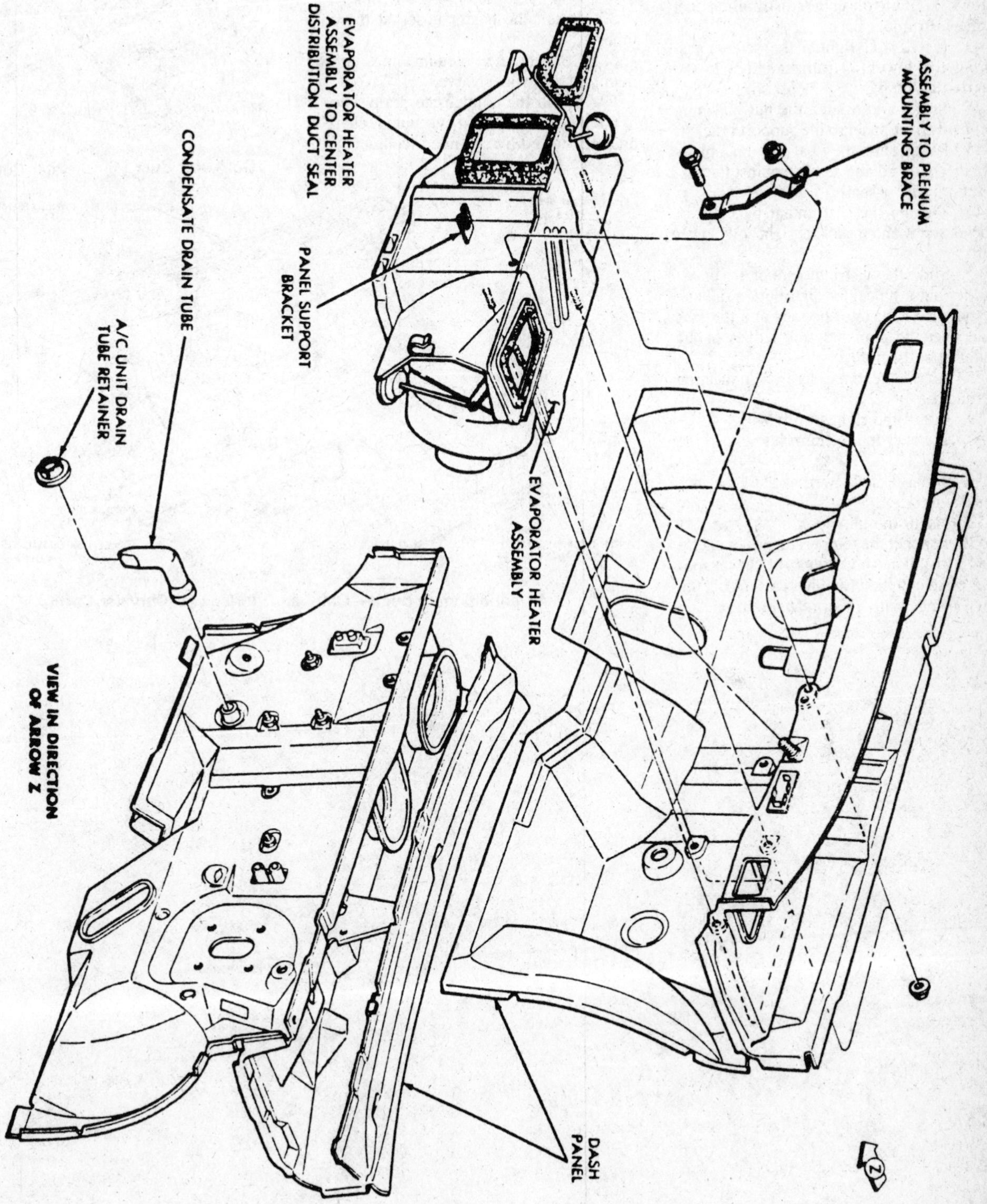

EVAPORATOR HEATER
ASSEMBLY TO CENTER
DISTRIBUTION DUCT SEAL

ASSEMBLY TO PLENUM
MOUNTING BRACE

CONDENSATE DRAIN TUBE

PANEL SUPPORT
BRACKET

A/C UNIT DRAIN
TUBE RETAINER

EVAPORATOR HEATER
ASSEMBLY

VIEW IN DIRECTION
OF ARROW Z

DASH
PANEL

Omni and Horizon heater-evaporator (© Chrysler Corp.)

41. Remove the sheet metal or cardboard from between the unit and the duct.

NOTE: Make sure the unit seal is properly aligned with the duct opening.

42. Install and tighten the two lower screws fastening the center distribution duct to the instrument panel.

43. Install and tighten the screws fastening the lower instrument panel to the steering column.

44. Install and tighten the nut fastening the instrument panel to the support bracket.

45. Make sure the seal on the unit is properly aligned and seated against the distribution duct assembly.

46. Tighten the instrument panel pivot bracket screw and install the right cowl lower trim.

47. Slide the distributor duct cover assembly onto the center distribution duct so the notches lock into the tabs and the tabs slide over the rear and side ledges of the center duct assembly.

48. Install the three screws connecting the ducting.

49. Install the right trim bezel.

50. Connect the vacuum harness to the control head.

51. Connect the blower lead and the anti-diesel wire.

52. Install the glovebox.

53. Connect the temperature door cable.

54. Install new O-rings on the evaporator plate and the plumbing plate. Coat the new O-rings with clean refrigerant oil.

55. Place the H-valve against the evaporator sealing plate surface and install the two ¼-in. through-bolts. Torque to 6–10 ft. lbs.

56. Carefully hold the refrigerant line connector against the valve and install the ⁵⁄₁₆-in. bolt. Torque to 14–20 ft. lbs.

57. Install the heater hoses at the core tubes.

58. Connect the vacuum lines at the manifold and water valve.

59. Install the condensate drain tube.

60. Have the system evacuated, charged and leak-tested by a trained technician.

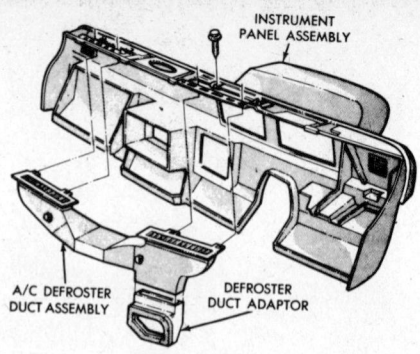

Defroster duct (© Chrysler Corp.)

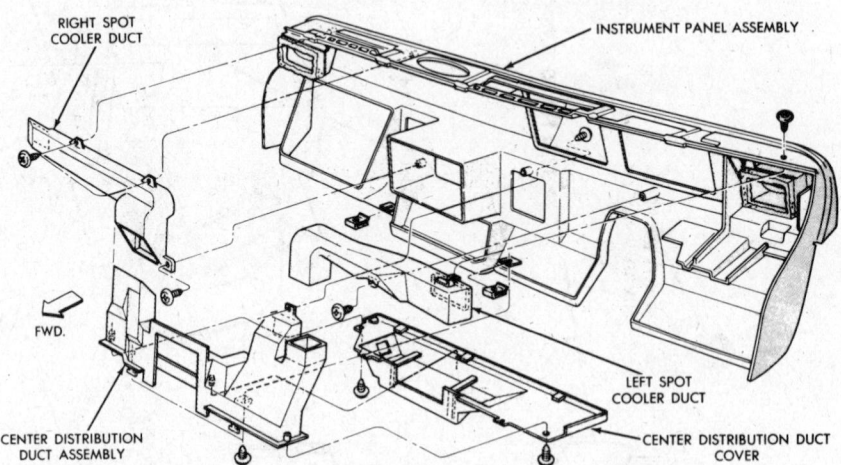

Air conditioning ducts—Omni and Horizon (© Chrysler Corp.)

Ford Motor Co. Front Wheel Drive
Escort, Lynx, EXP, LN7, Tempo, Topaz

YEAR IDENTIFICATION

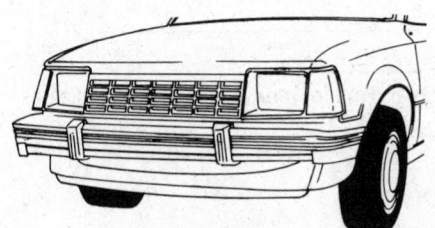

1981–82 Escort

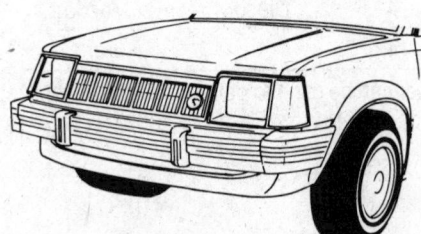

1981–82 Lynx

1981–82 LN7

1981–82 EXP

1983–85 Escort

1983–84 Lynx

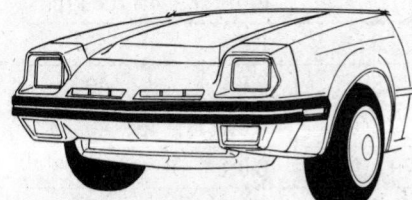

1983 EXP

1983 LN7

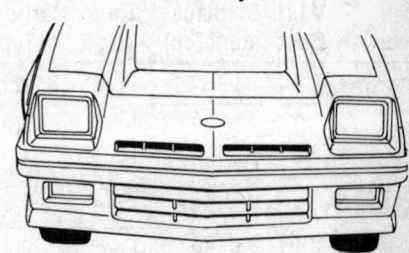

1984–85 EXP

1984 Tempo

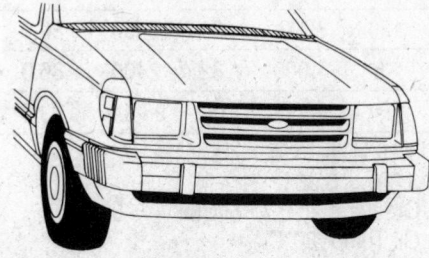

1985 Tempo

1984–85 Topaz

C147

VEHICLE IDENTIFICATION NUMBER (VIN)

It is important for servicing and ordering parts to be certain of the vehicle and engine identification. The VIN (vehicle identification number) is a 13 or 17 digit number visible through the windshield on the driver's side of the dash and contains the vehicle and engine identification codes. It can be interpreted as follows:

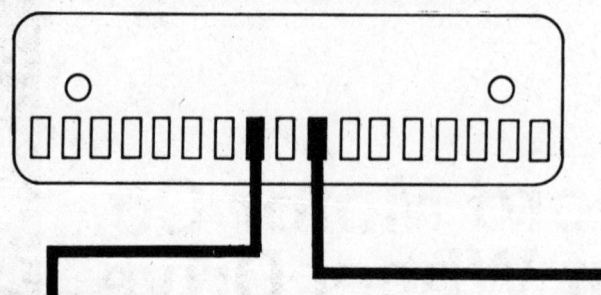

ENGINE CODE

Code	Cu. In.	Liters	Cyl.	Carb.	Eng. Mfg.
2	98	1.6	4	2	Ford
5	98	1.6	4	EFI	Ford
4	98	1.6 HO	4	2	Ford
H	121	2.0	4	Diesel	Mazda
R	140	2.3 HSC	4	1	Ford

MODEL YEAR CODE

Code	Year
B	'81
C	'82
D	'83
E	'84
F	'85

The seventeen digit Vehicle Identification Number can be used to determine engine application and model year. The tenth digit indicates model year, and the eighth digit identifies engine code.

GENERAL ENGINE SPECIFICATIONS

Year	Eng V.I.N. Code	Engine No. Cyl. Displacement (cc)	Eng Mfg	Carburetor Type	Horsepower @ rpm ■	Torque @ rpm (ft. lbs.) ■	Bore × Stroke (mm)	Compression Ratio	Oil Pressure @ 2000 rpm
'81	2	4-1597	Ford	2bbl	69 @ 5000	86 @ 3200	80.0 × 79.5①	8.8:1	40
'82	2	4-1597	Ford	2bbl	69 @ 5000	86 @ 3200	80.0 × 79.5①	8.8:1	40
	2	4-1597	Ford	2bbl	80 @ 5800	88 @ 3400	80.0 × 79.5①	9.0:1	40
'83–'85	2	4-1597	Ford	2bbl	70 @ 4600	89 @ 3000	80.0 × 79.5①	8.8:1	40
	4	4-1597	Ford	2bbl	80 @ 5800	88 @ 3400	80.0 × 79.5①	9.0:1	40
	5	4-1597	Ford	EFI	90 @ 5800	89 @ 3000	80.0 × 79.5①	9.0:1	40
	—	4-1597	Ford	Turbo	120 @ 5200	120 @ 3400	80.0 × 79.5①	8.0:1	35–65
	H	4-2000	Mazda	Diesel	52 @ 4000	82 @ 2400	86.0 × 86.0②	22.5:1	③
	R	4-2300	Ford	1bbl	84 @ 4600	118 @ 2600	93.5 × 84④	9.0:1	55–70

■Horsepower and torque are SAE net figures. They are measured at the rear of the transmission with all accessories installed and operating.

①3.15 × 3.13 in.
②3.39 × 3.39
③Greater than 0.7 KG/CM² @ 700 RPM
  Oil Temp. 80°C
④3.70 × 3.30

TUNE-UP SPECIFICATIONS

(When analyzing compression test results, look for uniformity among cylinders rather than specific pressures.)

Year	Engine Eng V.I.N. Code	Engine No. Cyl. Displacement cu in. (cc)	Eng Mfg	Spark Plugs Orig. Type ◆ ●	Spark Plugs Gap (in.)	Distributor	Distributor Point Dwell (deg)	Point Gap (in.)	Ignition Timing (deg) ▲ Man Trans ●	Ignition Timing (deg) ▲ Auto Trans	Valves Intake Opens ■ (deg)	Fuel Pump Pressure (psi)	Idle Speed (rpm) ▲ Man Trans	Idle Speed (rpm) ▲ Auto Trans
'81	2	4-97.6 (1597)	Ford	AGSP-32	.042–.046	Electronic			10B①	10B①	—	4–6	①	①
'82	2	4-97.6 (1597)	Ford	AWSF-32	.042–.046	Electronic			①	①	—	4–6	①	①
'83–'85	—	4-97.6 (1597)	Ford	AWSF-34②	.042–.046	Electronic			①	①	—	4–6③	①	①
'84–'85	R	4-140 (2300)	Ford	AWSF-62	.044	Electronic			10B	15B	—	5	①	①

NOTE: The underhood specifications sticker often reflects tune-up specification changes made in production. Sticker figures must be used if they disagree with those in this chart. Part numbers in this chart are not recommended by Chilton for any product by brand name.
▲See text for procedure
■All figures Before Top Dead Center
●Figure in parenthesis is for California
◆ See the Spark Plug Replacement Chart
B Before Top Dead Center
—Not applicable
①Calibration levels vary from model to model. Always refer to the underhood sticker for your cars requirements.
②EFI Models: AWSF24
③EFI pressure: 35–45 psi

FIRING ORDERS

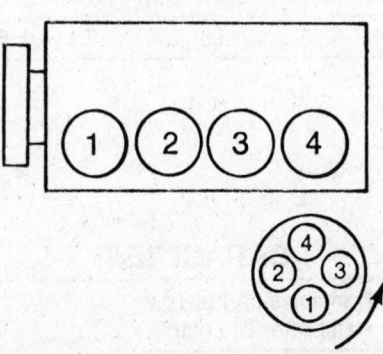

Ford Motor Co. 1600 cc and 2300 HSC 4-cyl. Engine Firing Order: 1-3-4-2
Distributor rotation: counterclockwise

VALVE SPECIFICATIONS

Year	Engine No. Cyl. Displacement (cc)	Seat Angle (deg)	Face Angle (deg)	Spring Test Pressure (lbs @ in.)	Spring Installed Height (in.)	Stem To Guide Clearance (in.) Intake	Stem To Guide Clearance (in.) Exhaust	Stem Diameter (in.) Intake	Stem Diameter (in.) Exhaust
'81	4-1597	45	45½	180 @ 1.09	1.46	.0008–.0027	.0015–.0032	.316	.315
'82	4-1597	45	45½	180 @ 1.09	1.46	.0010	.00210	.320	.310
'83–'85	4-1597	45	45½	200 @ 1.09①	1.480②	.0008–.0027	.0018–.0037	.316	.315
'84–'85	4-2000	45	45	—	1.7760	.0016–.0029	.0018–.0031	.3138	.3138
'84–'85	4-2300	45	45½	182 @ 1.10	1.49	.0018	.0023	.3415	.3411

①H.O and EFI Engines: 206 @ 1.09
②H.O and EFI Engines: 1.450–1.480

CRANKSHAFT AND CONNECTING ROD SPECIFICATIONS

(All measurements are given in inches)

Year	Engine No. Cyl. Displacement (cc)	Crankshaft				Connecting Rod		
		Main Brg. Journal Dia.	Main Brg. Oil Clearance	Shaft End-Play	Thrust on No.	Journal Diameter	Oil Clearance	Side Clearance
'81–'85	4-1597	2.2826–2.2834	.0008–.0015	.004–.008	3	1.885–1.886	.0002–.0003	.004–.011
'84–'85	4-2000	2.3598–2.3605	.0012–.0020	.0016	3	2.0055–2.0061	.0031	.0043–.0103
'84–'85	4-2300	2.2489–2.2490	.0008–.0024	.004–.008	3	2.1232–2.1240	.0008–.0015	.0035–.0105

PISTON AND RING SPECIFICATIONS

(All measurements are given in inches)

Year	Engine Displacement (cc)	Piston Clearance	Ring Gap			Ring Side Clearance		
			Top Compression	Bottom Compression	Oil Control	Top Compression	Bottom Compression	Oil Control
'81	1597	.0008–.0016	.012–.020	.012–.020	.016–.055	.001–.003	.002–.003	Snug
'82	1597	.0012–.0020	.012–.020	.012–.020	.016–.055	.001–.003	.002–.003	Snug
'83–'85	1597	.0018–.0026	.012–.020	.012–.020	.016–.055	.001–.003	.002–.003	Snug
'84–'85	2000	.0013–.0020	.0079–.0157	.0079–.0157	.0079–.0157	.0020–.0035	.0016–.0031	Snug
'84–'85	2300	.0013–.0021	.008–.016	.008–.016	.015–.055	.002–.004	.002–.004	Snug

CAPACITIES

Year	Engine No. Cyl. Displacement (cc)	Engine Crankcase Capacity Including Filter (qts.)	Transmission Pts To Refill After Draining		Drive Axle (pts)	Gasoline Tank (gals)	Cooling System (qts)	
			Manual	Automatic (Total Capacity)			With Heater	With A/C
'81–'85	4-1597	4.0	5.0①	②	③	④	6.7	8.1
'84–'85	4-2000	7.2⑤	①	—	③	⑥	8.1	8.1

①5 speed: 6.1
②Total dry capacity–converter, cooler and sump drained.
1981–82: 20 pts, 1983–85: 16.6 pts. Partial fluid change (pan sump only), add 8 pts, start engine and check level. Add necessary fluid until correct level is reached.
③Included in transmission capacity
④1981–'82: 10 gal. Standard
    11.3 gal. Extended range
1983–'85: 10 gal. FE models
    13 gal. Standard
    13 gal. EXP/LN7

⑤Capacity for complete system-pan capacity is 5.3 qts.
⑥1984: 14 gal; 1985; 15.2 gal.
⑦After filter replacement, add 4 qts of oil and run engine. Shut engine off and check oil level. Add ½ qt if necessary.

TORQUE SPECIFICATIONS
(All readings in ft. lbs.)

Year	Engine No. Cyl. Displacement (cc)	Cylinder Head Bolts	Rod Bearing Bolts	Main Bearing Bolts	Crankshaft Bolt	Flywheel to Crankshaft Bolts	Manifold	
							Intake	Exhaust
'81–'85	4-1597	①	19–25	67–80	74–90	59–69	12–15②	15–20
'84–'85	4-2000	①	51–54	61–65	115–123	130–137	12–16	16–19③
'84–'85	4-2300	81③	21–26	60–74	82–103	54–64	15–23	20–30③

① See head removal procedure for instructions
② Manifold stud nuts: 12–13 ft. lbs.
③ Tighten in two stages

CAMSHAFT SPECIFICATIONS
(All measurements are given in inches)

Year	Engine No. Cyl. Displacement (cc)	Lobe Lift	Valve Lift @ Zero Lash		Camshaft End Play	Journal-to-Bearing Clearance	Journal Diameter	Journal Out-of-Round Limit
			Intake	Exhaust				
'81–'85	4-1597	.229①	.377②	.377②	.0018–.006	.0008–.0028	③	.008
'84–'85	4-2000	—	—	—	.008–.0059	.001–.0026	1.2582–1.2589	—
'84–'85	4-2300	④	.392	.377	.009	.001–.003	⑤	.005

① HO and EFI: .240
② HO and EFI: .396
③ No. 1: 1.761–1.762
   No. 2: 1.771–1.772
   No. 3: 1.781–1.782
   No. 4: 1.791–1.792
   No. 5: 1.801–1.802
④ IN: .249
   EX: .239
⑤ Not Available

WHEEL ALIGNMENT SPECIFICATIONS

Year	Model	Caster		Camber		Toe-in (in.)	Steering Axis Inclin. (deg)
		Range (deg) ■ ▲	Pref Setting (deg)	Range (deg) ■	Pref Setting (deg)		
'81–'83	Escort, Lynx, EXP/LN7	9/16P to 2 1/16P	1 5/16P	—	—	1/32 to 7/32	—
		—	—	(Left) 1 13/32P to 2 29/32P	2 5/32P	—	14 21/32
		—	—	(Right) 3 1/32P to 2 15/32P	1 23/32P	—	15 3/32
'84–'85	Escort, Lynx, EXP	5/8P to 2 1/8P	1 2/3P	—	—	1/64 (in) to 7/32 (out)	—
				(Left) 1 3/8P to 2 7/8P	2 1/8P	—	14 21/32
				(Right) 15/16P to 2 7/16P	1 11/16P	—	15 3/32

WHEEL ALIGNMENT SPECIFICATIONS

Year	Model	Caster Range (deg) ■ ▲	Caster Pref Setting (deg)	Camber Range (deg) ■	Camber Pref Setting (deg)	Toe-in (in.)	Steering Axis Inclin. (deg)
'84–'85	Tempo, Topaz	9/16P to 2 1/16P	1 5/16P	—	—	1/32 (in) to 7/32 (out)	—
				(Left) 1 1/8P to 2 5/8P	1 7/8P	—	14 5/8
				(Right) 1 1/16P to 2 3/16P	1 1/2P	—	15 1/8

■ Caster and chamber are pre-set at the factory and cannot be adjusted

▲ Caster measurements must be made on the left side by turning left wheel through the prescribed angle of sweep and on the right side by turning right wheel through prescribed angle of sweep for the equipment being used. When using alignment equipment designed to measure caster on both the right and left side, turning only one wheel will result in a significant error in caster angle for the opposite side.

CHARGING SYSTEM

Alternator

REMOVAL & INSTALLATION

For alternator testing and diagnosis, refer to "Charging and Starting" in the Unit Repair section.

1. Disconnect the negative battery cable.
2. If equipped with a pulley cover shield, remove the shield at this time.
3. Loosen the alternator pivot bolt. Remove the adjustment bracket to alternator bolt (and nut, if equipped). Pivot the alternator to gain slack in the drive belt and remove the belt.
4. Disconnect and label (for correct installation) the alternator wiring.

NOTE: Some models use a push-on wiring connector on the field and stator connections. Pull or push straight when removing or installing, or damage to the connectors may occur.

5. Remove the pivot bolt and the alternator.
6. Install in the reverse order of removal. Adjust the drive belt tension so that there is approx. 1/4–1/2 in. deflection on the longest belt span between the pulleys. Reinstall the pulley shield, if equipped and connect the negative battery cable.

Regulator

REMOVAL & INSTALLATION

NOTE: Three different types of regulators are used, depending on model, engine, alternator output and type of dash mounted charging indicator used (light or ammeter). The regulators are 100 percent solid state and and are calibrated and preset by the manufacturer. No readjustment is required or possible on these regulators.

SERVICE

Whenever system components are being replaced the following precautions should be followed so that the charging system will work properly and the components will not be damaged.

1. Always use the proper alternator.
2. The electronic regulators are color coded for identification. Never install a different coded regulator for the one being replaced. General coding identification follows, if the regulator removed does not have the color mentioned, identify the output of the alternator and method of charging indication, then consult a parts department to obtain the correct regulator. A black coded regulator is used in systems which use a signal lamp for charging indication. Gray coded regulators are used with an ammeter gauge. Neutral coded regulators are used on models equipped with a diesel engine. The special regulator must be used on ve-

hicles equipped with a diesel engine to prevent glow plug failure.
3. Models using a charging lamp indicator are equipped with a 500 ohm resistor on the back of the instrument panel.

REMOVAL & INSTALLATION

1. Disconnect the negative battery cable.
2. Unplug the wiring harness from the regulator.
3. Remove the regulator mounting bolts.
4. Install in the reverse order.

STARTING SYSTEM

Starter

For all starter overhaul procedures, please refer to "Charging and Starting" in the Unit Repair section.

REMOVAL & INSTALLATION

1. Disconnect the negative battery cable.
2. Raise and safely support the front of the vehicle on jackstands. Disconnect the starter cable from the starter motor.
3. On models that are equipped with a manual transaxle, remove the three nuts that attach the roll restrictor brace to the starter

mounting studs at the transaxle. Remove the brace.

On models that are equipped with an automatic transaxle, remove the hose bracket mounted on the starter studs.

4. Remove the two bolts attaching the rear starter support bracket, remove the retaining nut from the rear of the starter motor and remove the support bracket.

5. On models equipped with a manual transaxle, remove the three starter mounting studs and the starter motor.

On models equipped with an automatic transaxle, remove the two starter mounting studs, mounting bolt and the starter motor.

6. Position the starter motor on the transaxle housing and install in the reverse order of removal. Tighten the mounting bolts or studs to 30–40 ft. lbs.

IGNITION SYSTEM

NOTE: Either a conventional Duraspark system, a Thickfilm Integrated (TFI) system, or a Thickfilm Integrated IV (TFI-IV) is used depending on year and model. Trouble-shooting and servicing of the systems are contained in the "Electronic Ignition Systems" Unit Repair section.

Distributor

REMOVAL & INSTALLATION

1.6 Engine

The camshaft-driven distributor is located at the top left end of the cylinder head. It is retained by two holddown bolts at the base of the distributor shaft housing.

1. Turn engine to No. 1 piston at TDC of the compression stroke. Disconnect negative battery cable. Disconnect the vacuum hose(s) from the advance unit. Disconnect the wiring harness at the distributor.

2. Remove the capscrews and remove the distributor cap.

3. Scribe a mark on the distributor body, showing the position of the ignition rotor. Scribe another mark on the distributor body and cylinder head, showing the position of the body in relation to the head. These marks can be used for reference when installing the distributor, as long as the engine remains undisturbed.

4. Remove the two distributor holddown bolts. Pull the distributor out of the head.

5. To install the distributor with the engine undisturbed, place the distributor in the cylinder head, seating the off-set tang of the drive coupling into the groove on the end of the camshaft. Install the two dis-

tributor holddown screws and tighten them so that the distributor can just barely be moved. Install the rotor (if removed), the distributor cap and all wiring, then set the ignition timing.

6. If the crankshaft was rotated while the distributor was removed, the engine must be brought to TDC (Top Dead Center) on the compression stroke of the No. 1 cylinder. Remove the No. 1 spark plug. Place your finger over the hole and rotate the crankshaft slowly (use a wrench on the crankshaft pulley bolt) in the direction of normal engine rotation, until engine compression is felt.

—————— CAUTION ——————
Turn the engine only in the direction of normal rotation. Backward rotation will cause the cam belt to slip or lose teeth, altering engine timing.

When engine compression is felt at the spark plug hole, indicating that the piston is approaching TDC, continue to turn the crankshaft until the timing mark on the pulley is aligned with the "0" mark (timing mark) on the engine front cover. Turn the distributor shaft until the ignition rotor is at the No. 1 firing position. Install the distributor into the cylinder head, as outlined in Step 5 of this procedure.

2.3 HSC Engine

The TFI-IV distributor is mounted on the side of the engine block. Some engines may

be equipped with a "security" type distributor hold down bolt which requires a special wrench for removal. The TFI-IV distributor incorporates a "Hall Effect" vane switch stator assembly and an integrally mounted thickfilm module. When the "Hall Effect" device is turned on and a pulse is produced, the EEC-IV electronics computes crankshaft position and engine demand to calibrate spark advance. Initial ignition timing adjustment/checking is necessary when the distributor has been removed. Repairs to the distributor are accomplished by distributor replacement.

1. Turn engine to No. 1 piston at TDC of the compression stroke. Disconnect the negative battery cable.

2. Disconnect the wiring harness at the distributor. Mark No. 1 spark plug wire cap terminal location on the distributor base. Remove the coil wire from cap.

3. Remove the distributor cap with plug wires attached and position out of the way. Remove the rotor.

4. Remove the distributor base hold down bolt and clamp. Slowly remove the distributor from the engine. Be careful not to disturb the intermediate driveshaft.

5. Install in reverse order after aligning the center blade of the rotor with the reference mark made on the distributor base for No. 1 plug wire terminal location.

6. If the engine was disturbed (turned) while the distributor was out, the engine will have to be reset at TDC before installation.

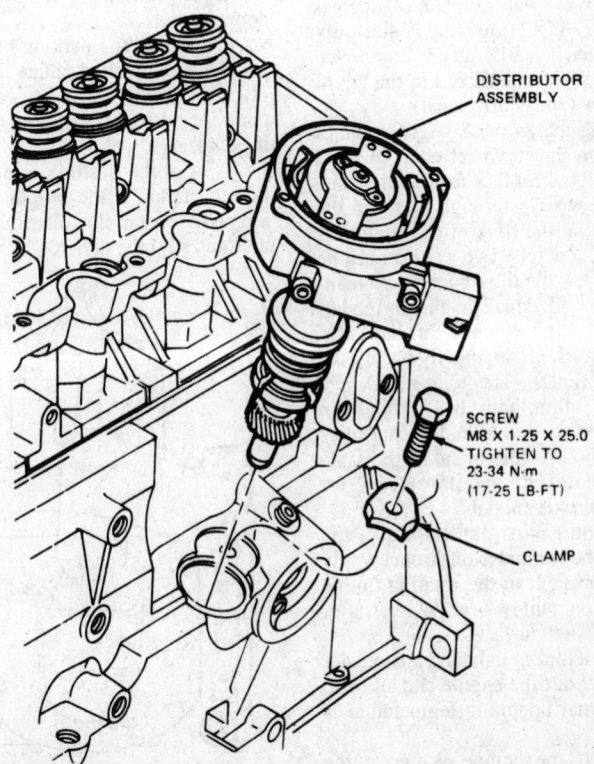

DISTRIBUTOR ASSEMBLY

SCREW
M8 X 1.25 X 25.0
TIGHTEN TO
23-34 N·m
(17-25 LB-FT)

CLAMP

Distributor mounting, 2.3 HSC engine (© Ford Motor Co.)

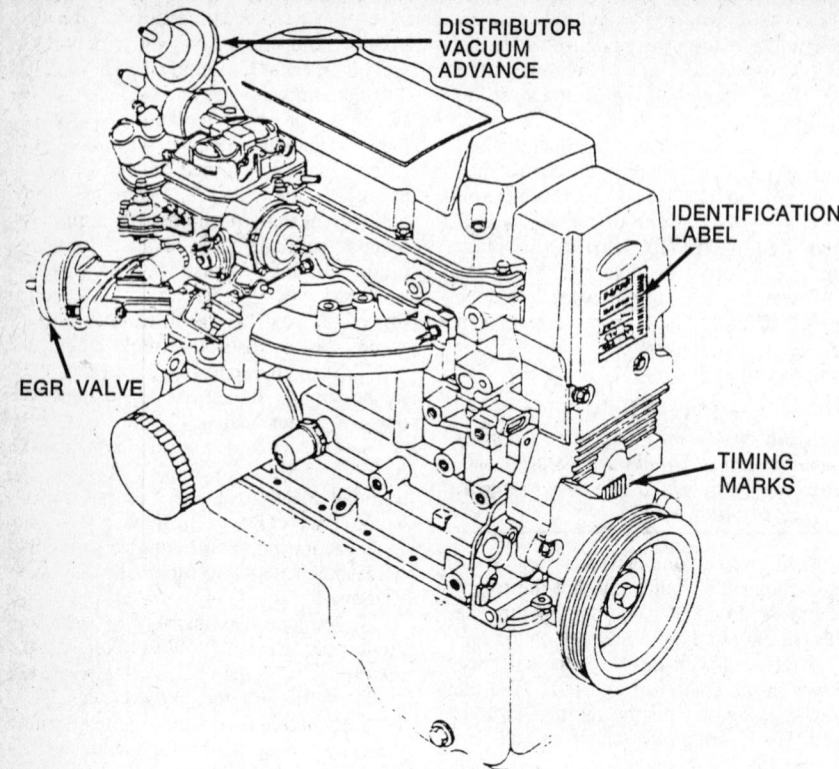

DISTRIBUTOR VACUUM ADVANCE

IDENTIFICATION LABEL

EGR VALVE

TIMING MARKS

Timing marks are molded into front cover on 1.6 engine (© Ford Motor Co.)

Ignition Timing

1. Timing marks on 1.6 engines consist of a notch on the crankshaft pulley and a graduated scale molded into the camshaft drive belt cover. The number of degrees before or after TDC (top dead center) represented by each mark can be interpreted according to the decal affixed to the top of the belt cover (emissions decal).

2. Timing marks on 2.3 HSC engines are located on the flywheel edge (manual transaxle) or flywheel face (automatic transaxle) and are visible through a slot in the transaxle case at the back of the engine. A cover plate retained by two screws must be removed to view the timing marks on manual cars. Each mark (small graduation) equals two degrees. Early automatic cars have timing marks punched on the flywheel, the marks are 5° apart. The required degree mark should align with the timing slot pointer. Unless the emission decal specifies otherwise, timing for manual transaxle models is 10° BTDC and 15° BTDC for automatic transaxle models.

3. Turn the engine until No. 1 piston is at TDC on the compression stroke. Apply white paint or chalk to the rotating timing mark (notch on pulley or flywheel) after cleaning the metal surface.

4. Attach a timing light and tachometer to the engine. Start the engine and allow to idle until normal operating temperature is reached.

5. Shut off the engine. Refer to the emissions decal for timing, engine rpm and

vacuum hose (if equipped) status information. Disconnect and plug the distributor vacuum line(s) if required. On models equipped with a 2.3 HSC engine, disconnect the ignition spout wire (circuit 36-yellow/light green dots) from the distributor connector.

6. Be sure the parking brake is applied and wheels blocked. Start the engine and place the transmission in gear specified on emissions decal. Check idle rpm and adjust if necessary.

7. Aim the flashing timing light at the timing marks. If the proper marks are not aligned, loosen the distributor holddown bolt/nut slightly and rotate the distributor

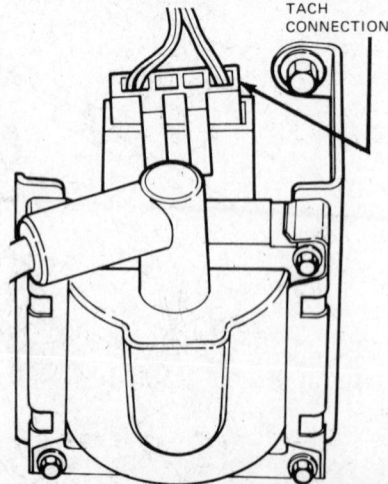

TACH CONNECTION

Tach connection, "E" coil

body until the marks are aligned. Tighten the holddown.

8. Recheck the ignition timing, readjust if necessary. Shut off the engine and reconnect vacuum hoses or spout connector. Start engine and readjust idle rpm if necessary.

Tachometer Hookup

Models equipped with a "conventional" type coil have an adapter on the top of the coil that provides a clip marked "Tach Test". On models (TFI) equipped with an "E" type coil, the tach connection is made at the back of the wire harness connector. A cut-out is provided and the tachometer lead wire alligator clip can be connected to the dark green/yellow dotted wire of the electrical harness plug.

GASOLINE FUEL SYSTEM

NOTE: Many models use push-connect fuel line fittings. Refer to the "Ford Rear Wheel Drive" section for removal and installation procedures.

Mechanical Fuel Pump

REMOVAL & INSTALLATION

1. Loosen the threaded fuel lines at the fuel pump slightly. Have a rag handy to absorb any gasoline spillage.

2. Loosen the fuel pump mounting bolts two turns and free the fuel pump from the engine.

3. Bump the engine around with the starter until reduced pressure (hold pump against the engine) is felt. The fuel pump drive lobe and push rod are now at their low point.

4. Remove fuel lines and vapor hose (if equipped). Remove the fuel pump mounting bolts and the fuel pump.

5. Remove fuel pump mounting gasket and clean the engine mounting surface.

6. Remove and check the pushrod. Replace if wear is apparent. Install the pushrod, new mounting gasket and fuel pump in the reverse order of removal. Fuel pump mounting bolts are torqued to 11–19 ft. lbs. Pushrod length should be: 1.6 engines = 3.88–3.90 in.; 2.3 HSC engine = 2.43 in.

Electric Fuel Pump

REMOVAL & INSTALLATION

NOTE: The fuel system on injected models is under pressure. Fuel system pressure must be relieved by connecting

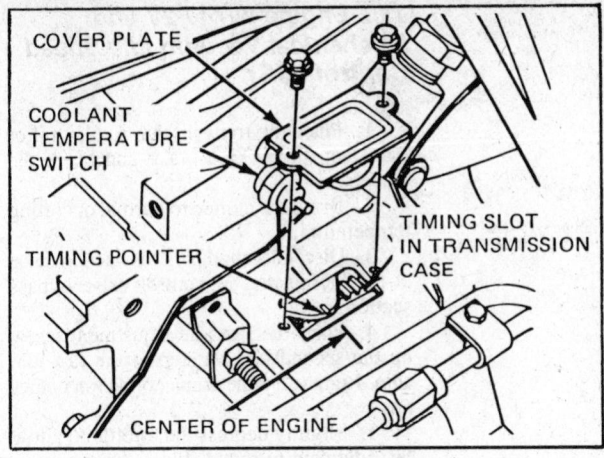

TIMING LOCATION FOR MTX

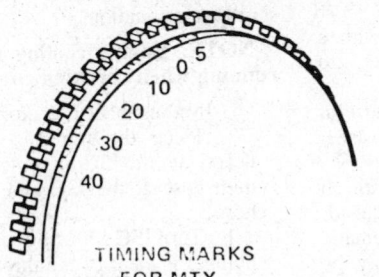

TIMING MARKS
FOR MTX

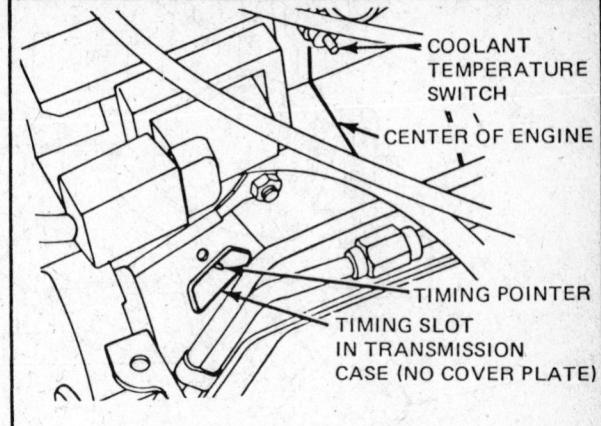

TIMING LOCATION FOR ATX

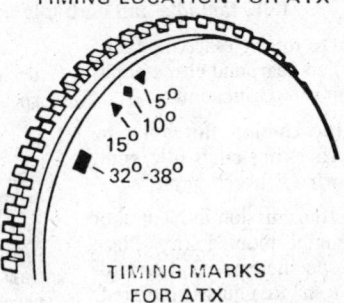

TIMING MARKS
FOR ATX

Timing marks; Tempo/Topaz

a service tool to the relief valve on the fuel rail before system service can be performed.

1. Relieve fuel system pressure. Raise and safely support the rear of the car on jackstands.

2. Remove the upper pump mounting bolt after disconnecting the parking brake cable from the mounting clip.

NOTE: Refer to the "Ford Rear Wheel Drive" section for details on disconnecting push type fuel line fitting connectors.

3. Disconnect the electrical connector from the pump. Disconnect the fuel line from the pump to injectors.

4. Disconnect and plug the fuel line from the gas tank. Remove the fuel pump.

5. Install in reverse order. Pressurize the system by turning the ignition key on and off several times, allowing the key to remain on for at least two seconds each time.

6. Start the engine and check for fuel leaks.

Fuel Filter

REMOVAL & INSTALLATION

NOTE: Before removing the fuel filter on models equipped with fuel injection, the fuel system pressure must be relieved.

1. If the fuel filter is located in the carburetor inlet and connected with rubber hose, remove clamps and inlet rubber hose. Unscrew the filter from the carburetor.

2. If the fuel filter is mounted in the carburetor inlet and connected with steel line, hold the filter nut with the proper size wrench and unscrew the inverted fitting nut on the steel line using a flare or suitable wrench. Remove the line and unscrew the filter.

NOTE: See the "Ford Rear Wheel Drive" section for details on disconnecting push type fuel line connectors.

3. If the fuel filter is connected to the carburetor with steel lines, hold the filter nuts with proper wrench and disconnect the steel lines with a flare or suitable wrench.

4. Install the fuel filter in the reverse order of removal.

Carburetors

REMOVAL & INSTALLATION

1. Remove the air cleaner assembly. Disconnect the throttle control cable and speed control (if equipped).

2. Disconnect the fuel line at the fuel filter or carburetor. Label (for identification and location) and disconnect all vacuum lines, wires, harnesses and linkage attached to the carburetor. Disconnect the TV linkage if the car is equipped with an automatic transaxle.

3. Remove the carburetor base mounting nuts and remove the carburetor.

4. Install in the reverse order. Start engine and allow to reach normal operating temperature. Adjust curb idle.

Overhaul

For further information, please refer to "Carburetors" in the Unit Repair section.

IDLE SPEED

Most carburetor mixture adjustments are factory set and are designed to reduce engine emissions. The following adjustments should be made only if absolutely necessary and should be checked on a machine as soon as possible to see if the emission level is OK.

NOTE: A tachometer must be used while making any idle rpm adjustments. Refer to the proceeding section for "tach" hook up instructions.

NOTE: Refer to emissions decal for idle speed and specific instructions.

1.6 Engine w/740-2V without Idle Speed Control

1. Place the transmission in Neutral or Park, set the parking brake and block the wheels.

2. Bring the engine to normal operating temperature.

3. Disconnect and plug the vacuum hose at the thermactor air control valve bypass section.

4. Place the fast idle adjustment screw on the second highest step of the fast idle cam. Run engine until cooling fan comes on.

5. Slightly depress the throttle to allow

C155

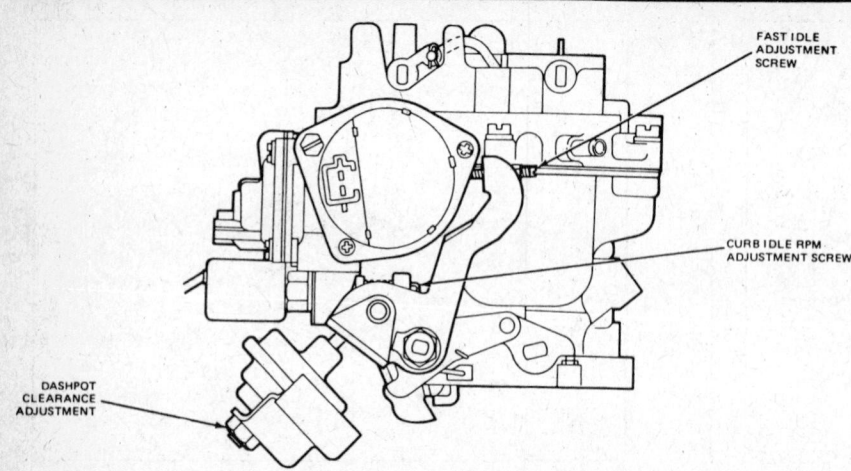

1.6L, fast idle and curb idle adjustment points

the fast idle cam to rotate. Place the transmission in specified gear, and check/adjust the curb idle rpm to specification.

NOTE: Engine cooling fan must be running when checking curb idle rpm. (Use a jumper wire if necessary).

6. Place the transmission in Neutral or Park. Rev the engine momentarily. Place transmission in specified position and re-check curb idle rpm. Readjust if required.

7. If the vehicle is equipped with a dashpot, check/adjust clearance to specification.

8. Remove the plug from the hose at the thermactor air control valve bypass section and reconnect.

9. If the vehicle is equipped with an automatic transmission and curb idle adjustment is more than 50 rpm, an automatic transmission linkage adjustment may be necessary.

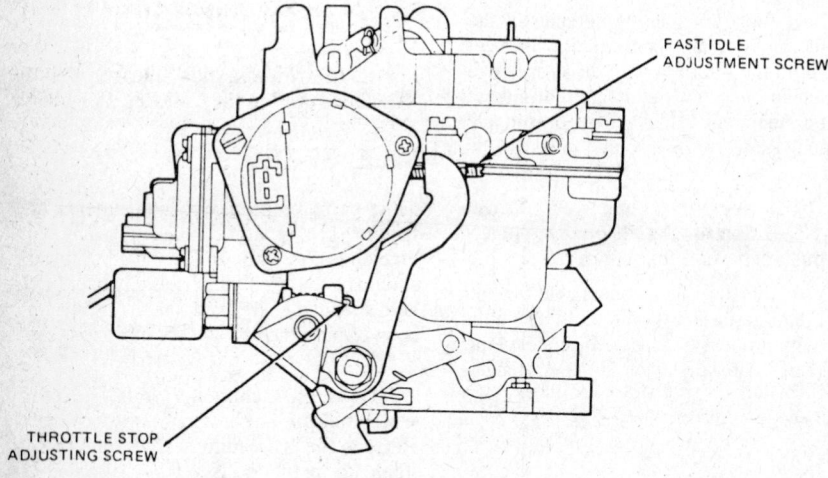

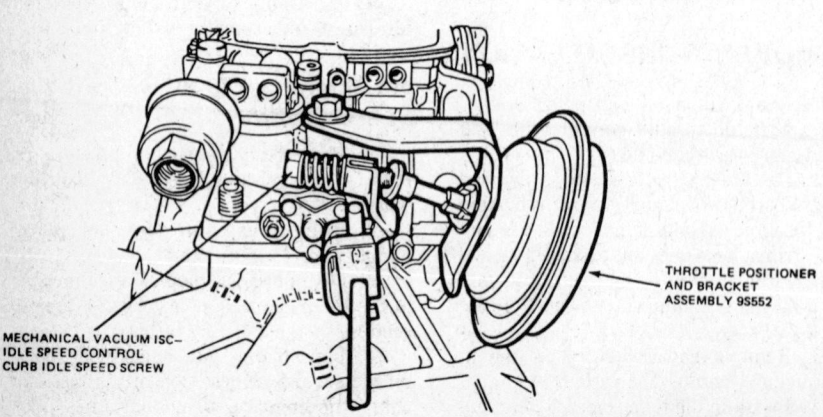

1.6L, with idle speed control (ISC) adjustment points

1.6L Engine w/740-2V and Mechanical Vacuum Idle Speed Control (ISC)

1. Place the transmission in Neutral or Park, set the parking brake and block the wheels.

2. Bring the engine to normal operating temperature.

3. Disconnect and plug the vacuum hose at the thermactor air control valve bypass section.

4. Place the fast idle adjustment screw on the second highest step of the fast idle cam. Run the engine until cooling fan comes on.

5. Slightly depress the throttle to allow fast idle cam to rotate. Place the transmission in Drive (fan on) and check curb idle rpm to specification.

NOTE: Engine cooling fan must be running when checking curb idle rpm.

6. If adjustment is required:
   a. Place the transmission in Park, deactivate the ISC by removing the vacuum hose at the ISC and plugging the hose.
   b. Turn ISC adjusting screw until ISC plunger is clear of the throttle lever.
   c. Place the transmission in Drive position, if rpm is not at the ISC retracted speed (fan on), adjust rpm by turning the throttle stop adjusting screw.
   d. Place the transmission in Park, remove plug from the ISC vacuum line and reconnect to ISC.
   e. Place transmission in Drive if rpm is not at the curb idle speed (fan on), adjust by turning the ISC adjustment screw.

7. Place transmission in Neutral or Park. Rev the engine momentarily. Place the transmission in specified position and re-check curb idle rpm. Readjust if required.

8. Remove the plug from the thermactor air control valve bypass section hose and reconnect.

9. If the vehicle is equipped with an automatic transmission and curb idle adjustment is more than 50 rpm, an automatic transmission linkage adjustment may be necessary.

1.6L Engine w/740-2V—Vacuum Operated Throttle Modulator (VOTM)

1. Place the transmission in Neutral or Park, set the parking brake and block the wheels.

2. Bring the engine to normal operating temperature.

3. To check/adjust VOTM rpm:
   • Place A/C heat sector in Heat position, blower switch on High.
   • Disconnect the vacuum hose from VOTM and plug, install a slave vacuum hose from the intake manifold vacuum to the VOTM.

4. Disconnect and plug the vacuum hose

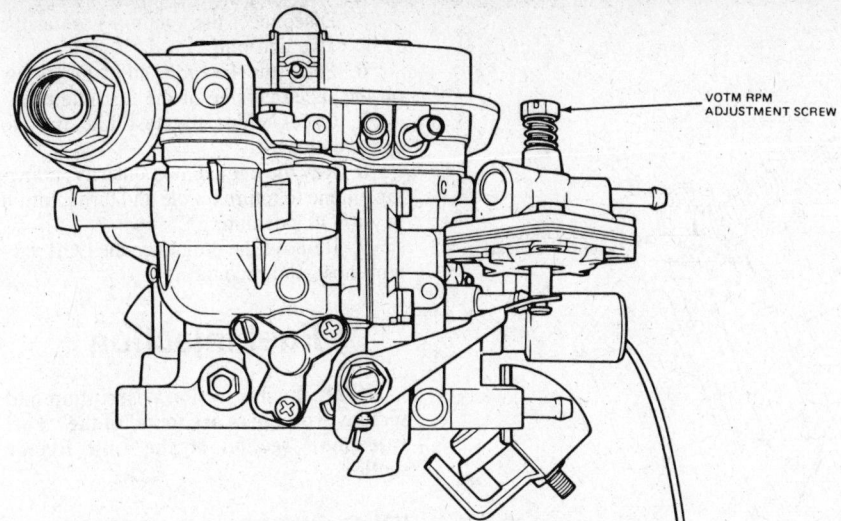

1.6L, VOTM idle adjustment point

at the thermactor air control valve - bypass section.

5. Run the engine until the engine cooling fan comes on.

6. Place the transmission in specified gear, and check/adjust VOTM rpm to specification.

NOTE: Engine cooling fan must be running when checking VOTM rpm. Adjust rpm by turning screw on VOTM.

7. Remove the slave vacuum hose. Remove the plug from the VOTM vacuum hose and reconnect the hose to the VOTM.

8. Return the intake manifold vacuum supply source to original location.

9. Remove the plug from the vacuum hose at the thermactor air control valve bypass section and reconnect.

Dashpot Clearance Adjustment—1.6 Engine

NOTE: If the carburetor is equipped with a dashpot, it must be adjusted if the curb idle speed is adjusted.

1. With the engine OFF, push the dashpot plunger in as far as possible and check the clearance between the plunger and the throttle lever pad.

NOTE: Refer to the emissions decal for proper dashpot clearance. If not available, set clearance to 0.138 ± 0.020 in.

2. Adjust the dashpot clearance by loosening the mounting locknut and rotating the dashpot.

----- **CAUTION** -----

If the locknut is very tight, remove the mounting bracket, hold it in a suitable device, so that it will not bend, and loosen the locknut. Reinstall bracket and dashpot.

3. After gaining the required clearance, tighten the locknut and recheck adjustment.

Fast Idle RPM—1.6 Engine

NOTE: Refer to the emissions decal for the required fast idle speed.

1. Place the transmission in Neutral or Park, set the parking brake and block the wheels.

2. Bring the engine to the normal operating temperature.

3. Disconnect the vacuum hose at the EGR and plug.

4. Place the fast idle adjustment screw on the second highest step of the fast idle cam. Run engine until cooling fan comes on.

5. Check/adjust fast idle rpm to specification. If adjustment is required, loosen locknut, adjust and retighten.

NOTE: Engine cooling fan must be running when checking fast idle rpm. (Use a jumper wire if necessary).

6. Remove the plug from the EGR hose and reconnect.

Air Conditioning/Throttle Kicker Adjustment—1.6 Engine

1. Place the transmission in Neutral or Park.

2. Bring engine to normal operating temperature.

3. Identify vacuum source to air bypass section of air supply control valve. If vacuum hose is connected to carburetor, disconnect and plug hose at air supply control valve. Install slave vacuum hose between intake manifold and air bypass connection on air supply control valve.

4. To check/adjust A/C or throttle kicker rpm:

• If vehicle is equipped with A/C, place selector to maximum cooling, blower switch on High. Disconnect A/C compressor clutch wire.

• If vehicle is equipped with kicker and no A/C, disconnect vacuum hose from kicker

and plug, install slave vacuum hose from intake manifold vacuum to kicker.

5. Run engine until engine cooling fan comes on.

6. Place transmission in specified gear and check/adjust A/C or throttle kicker rpm to specification.

NOTE: Engine cooling fan must be running when checking A/C or throttle kicker rpm. Adjust rpm by turning screw on kicker.

7. If slave vacuum hose was installed to check/adjust kicker rpm, remove slave vacuum hose. Remove plug from kicker vacuum hose and reconnect hose to kicker.

A/C or Throttle Kicker adjustment (© Ford Motor Co.)

8. Remove slave vacuum hose. Return intake manifold supply source to original condition. Remove plug from carburetor vacuum hose and reconnect to air bypass valve.

2.3L HSC Engine w/1949 and 6149 FB—Curb Idle RPM

NOTE: A/C—On RPM is non-adjustable. TSP-Off RPM is not required. Verify that TSP plunger extends with ignition key On.

1. Place the transaxle in Neutral or Park, set the parking brake and block the wheels.

2. Disconnect the throttle kicker vacuum line and plug.

3. Bring the engine to normal operating temperature. (Cooling fan should cycle).

4. Place the A/C selector in the Off position.

5. Place gear selector in specified position.

6. Activate the cooling fan by grounding the control wire with a jumper wire.

7. Check/adjust curb idle rpm. If adjustment is required, turn curb idle adjusting screw.

8. Place the transaxle in Neutral or Park. Rev the engine momentarily. Place the transaxle in specified position and recheck curb idle rpm. Readjust if required.

9. Reconnect the cooling fan wiring.

10. Turn the ignition key to the Off position.

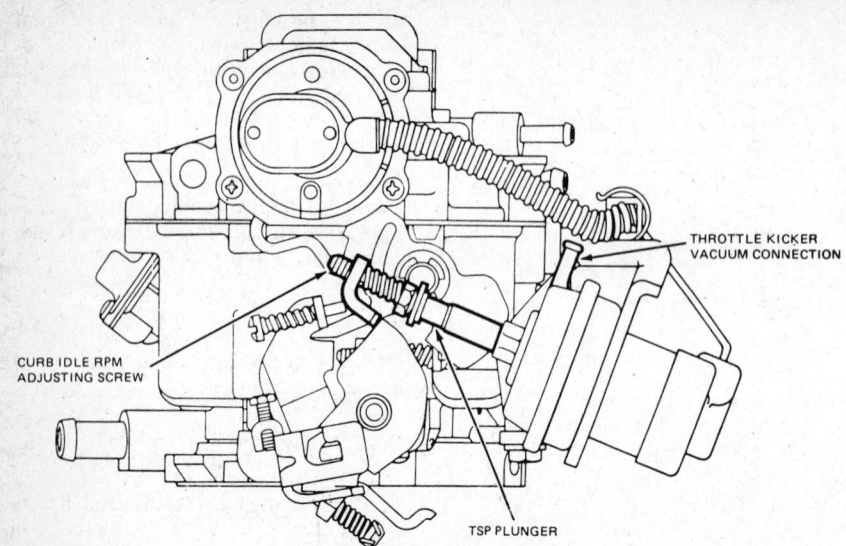

2.3HSC, fast idle adjustment

11. Reconnect the vacuum line to the throttle kicker.

12. If the vehicle is equipped with an automatic transaxle and curb idle adjustment exceeds 50 rpm, an automatic transaxle linkage adjustment may be necessary.

13. Remove all test equipment and reinstall the air cleaner assembly.

2.3L HSC Engine w/1949 and 6149 FB—TSP Off RPM

NOTE: This adjustment is not required as part of a normal engine idle RPM check/adjustment. If engine continues to run after ignition key is turned to Off position.

1. Place the transaxle in Neutral or Park, set the parking brake and block the wheels.

2. Bring the engine to normal operating temperature.

3. Disconnect the throttle kicker vacuum line and plug.

4. Place the A/C selector to Off position.

5. Disconnect the electrical lead to the TSP and verify that plunger collapses. Check/adjust engine RPM to specification (600 RPM).

6. Adjust the TSP Off RPM to specification.

7. Shut the engine off, reconnect TSP electrical lead and throttle kicker vacuum line.

2.3L HSC Engine w/1949 and 6149 FB—Fast Idle RPM

1. Place the transaxle in Neutral or Park, set the parking brake and block the wheels.

2. Bring the engine to normal operating temperature with the carburetor set on second step of fast idle cam.

3. Return the throttle to normal idle position.

4. Place the A/C selector in the Off position.

5. Disconnect the vacuum hose at the EGR valve and plug.

6. Place the fast idle adjusting screw on the specified step of the fast idle cam.

7. Check/adjust the fast idle rpm to specification.

8. Rev the engine momentarily, allowing engine to return to idle and turn ignition key to Off position.

9. Remove the plug from the EGR vacuum hose and reconnect.

Fuel Injection

NOTE: Fuel injection description and service procedures are found in the "Fuel Injection" section of the Unit Repair section.

IDLE SPEED ADJUSTMENT

1.6L Engine w/Electronic Fuel Injection (EFI)—Initial Engine RPM Adjustment (ISC Disconnected)

The purpose of this procedure is to provide a means of verifying the initial engine RPM setting with the ISC disconnected.

If engine idle RPM is not within specification after performing this procedure, it will be necessary to have 1.6L EFI EEC IV diagnostics performed.

NOTE: Curb idle RPM is controlled by the EEC IV processor and the Idle Speed Control (ISC) device (part of the fuel charging assembly).

1. Place the transmission in Neutral or Park, set the parking brake and block the wheel.

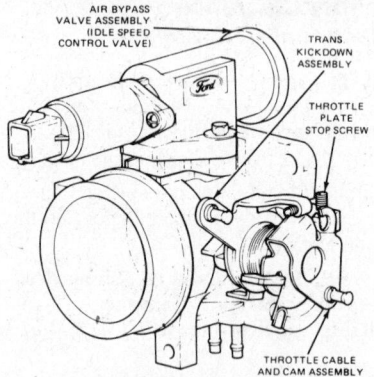

1.6L, models with EFI, adjustment point

2. Bring the engine to the normal operating temperature and shut engine off.

3. Disconnect vacuum connector at the EGR solenoid and plug both lines.

4. Disconnect the idle speed control (ISC) power lead.

5. Electric cooling fan must be on during the idle speed setting procedure.

6. Start the engine and operate at 2000 RPM for 60 seconds.

2.3HSC, curb idle adjustment

7. Place transmission in Neutral for M/T and Drive for A/T, check/adjust initial engine RPM within 120 seconds by adjusting throttle plate screw.

8. If idle adjustment is not completed within 120 second time limit, shut engine Off, retart and repeat Steps 6 and 7.

9. If the vehicle is equipped with an automatic transmission and initial engine RPM adjustment increases or decreases by more than 50 RPM, an automatic transmission linkage adjustment may be necessary.

10. Turn the engine Off and remove the plugs from the EGR vacuum lines at the EGR solenoid and reconnect.

11. Reconnect the speed control (ISC) power lead.

DIESEL FUEL SYSTEM

NOTE: Many models use push connect fuel line fittings. Refer to the Ford Rear Wheel Drive section for removal and installation procedures.

Fuel Filter

REMOVAL & INSTALLATION

1. Remove the spin-on filter by turning counterclockwise with hands or suitable tool, and discard filter.

2. Clean the filter mounting surfaces.

3. Coat the gasket of the new filter with clean diesel fuel.

4. Tighten the filter until the gasket touches the filter header, then tighten an additional ½ turn.

5. Air-Bleed the fuel system using the following procedure:

   a. Loosen the fuel filter air vent plug.

   b. Pump the priming pump on the top of the filter adapter.

   c. Continue pumping until clear fuel, free from air bubbles, flows from the air vent plug.

   d. Depress the priming pump and hold down while closing the air vent plug.

6. Start the engine and check for fuel leaks.

NOTE: To avoid fuel contamination do not add fuel directly to the new filter.

Fuel Injectors

REMOVAL & INSTALLATION

1. Remove the fuel injection pipe by loosening the union nut at the injector.

2. Remove the fuel leak pipe attaching nuts.

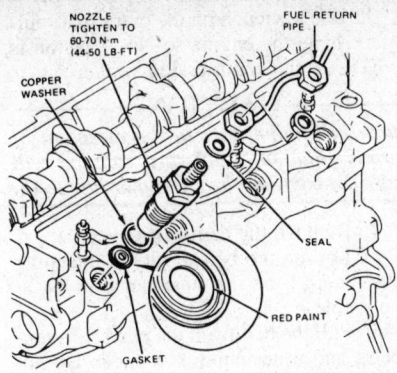

2.0 diesel, injector nozzle installation

3. Disconnect the fuel leak pipe.

4. Remove the fuel injector from the cylinder head.

5. Remove the copper washers and discard.

6. Installation is the reverse of removal. Use new copper washers and torque injector to 43–51 ft. lbs. Torque injection union nut to 18–22 ft. lbs.

NOTE: Other servicing of the diesel fuel system requires special tools and equipment. Servicing should be done by a mechanic experienced with diesels.

Idle Speed

ADJUSTMENT

1. Place the transmission in Neutral.

2. Bring the engine up to normal operating temperature. Stop engine.

3. Remove the timing hole cover. Clean the flywheel surface and install reflective tape.

4. Idle speed is measured with manual transmission in Neutral.

5. Check curb idle speed, using Rotunda 99-0001 or equivalent. Curb idle speed is specified on the Vehicle Emissions Control Information decal (VECI). Adjust to specification by loosening the locknut on the idle speed bolt. Turn the idle speed adjusting bolt clockwise to increase, or counterclockwise to decrease engine idle speed. Tighten the locknut.

6. Place transmission in Neutral. Rev engine momentarily and recheck the curb idle RPM. Readjust if necessary.

7. Turn A/C On. Check the idle speed. Adjust to specification by loosening nut on the A/C throttle kicker and rotating screw.

Glow Plugs

REMOVAL & INSTALLATION

1. Disconnect the battery ground cable from the battery, located in the luggage compartment.

2. Disconnect the glow plug harness from the glow plugs.

3. Using a 12mm deepwell socket, remove the glow plugs.

4. Install the glow plugs, using a 12mm deepwell socket. Tighten the glow plugs to 11–15 ft. lbs.

5. Connect the glow plug harness to the glow plugs. Tighten the nuts to 5–7 ft. lbs.

6. Connect the battery ground cable to the battery.

7. Check the glow plug system operation.

Injection Timing

ADJUSTMENT

NOTE: Engine coolant temperature must be above 80°C (176°F) before the injection timing can be checked and/or adjusted.

1. Disconnect the battery ground cable from the battery located in luggage compartment.

2. Remove the injection pump distributor head plug bolt and sealing washer.

3. Install Static Timing Gauge Adapter, Rotunda 14-0303 or equivalent with Metric Dial Indicator, so that indicator pointer is in contact with injection pump plunger.

4. Remove timing mark cover from transmission housing. Align timing mark (TDC) with pointer on the rear engine cover plate.

5. Rotate the crankshaft pulley slowly, counterclockwise until the dial indicator pointer stops moving (approximately 30°–50° BTDC).

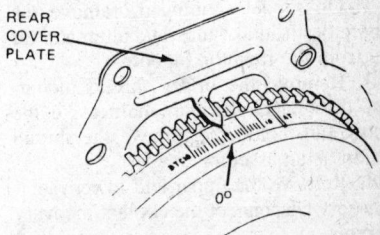

2.0 diesel, flywheel timing mark

6. Adjust dial indicator to Zero.

NOTE: Confirm that dial indicator pointer does not move from Zero by slightly rotating crankshaft left and right.

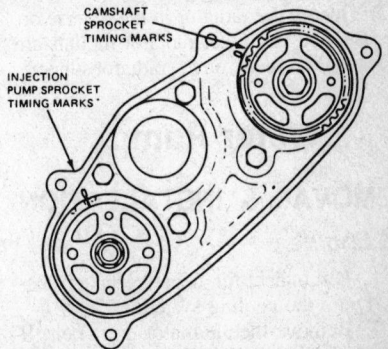

2.0 diesel, camshaft and injector pump timing marks

7. Turn crankshaft clockwise until crankshaft timing mark aligns with indicator pin. Dial indicator should read 1 + 0.02mm (0.04 + 0.0008 inch). If reading is not within specification, adjust as follows:

a. Loosen injection pump attaching bolt and nuts.

b. Rotate the injection pump toward the engine to advance timing and away from the engine to retard timing. Rotate the injection pump until the dial indicator reads 1 ± 0.02mm (0.04 ± 0.0008 inch).

c. Tighten the injection pump attaching nuts and bolt to 13–20 ft. lbs.

d. Repeat Steps 5, 6 and 7 to check that timing is adjusted correctly.

8. Remove the dial indicator and adapter and install the injection pump distributor head plug and tighten to 10–14.5 ft. lbs.

9. Connect the battery ground cable to the battery.

10. Run the engine, check and adjust idle rpm, if necessary. Check for fuel leaks.

COOLING SYSTEM

Radiator

REMOVAL & INSTALLATION

1. Disconnect the negative battery cable. Drain the cooling system.

2. On models equipped, remove the carburetor air intake tube and alternator air tube from the radiator support.

3. Remove the upper shroud mountings, disconnect the wire harness to the electric fan motor and remove the shroud and fan as an assembly.

4. Remove the upper and lower radiator hoses. Disconnect the coolant recovery reservoir.

5. On models equipped with an automatic transaxle, disconnect and plug the cooler lines.

6. Remove radiator mountings, tilt radiator toward engine and lift from engine compartment.

7. Install the radiator in the reverse order. Be sure the lower radiator mounts are positioned correctly on the radiator support.

Water Pump

REMOVAL & INSTALLATION

1.6 Engine

1. Disconnect the negative battery cable. Drain the cooling system.

2. Remove the alternator drive belt. If equipped with air conditioning or power steering, remove the drive belts.

3. Use a wrench on the crankshaft pulley to rotate the engine so No. 1 piston is on TDC of the compression stroke.

— CAUTION —

Turn the engine only in the direction of normal rotation. Backward rotation will cause the camshaft belt to slip or lose teeth.

4. Remove the cam belt cover.

5. Loosen the belt tensioner attaching bolts, then secure the tensioner over as far as possible.

6. Pull the belt from the camshaft, tensioner, and water pump sprockets. Do not remove it from, or allow it to change its position on, the crankshaft sprocket.

NOTE: Do not rotate the engine with the camshaft belt removed.

7. Remove the camshaft sprocket.

8. Remove the rear timing cover stud. Remove the heater return tube hose connection at the water pump inlet tube.

9. Remove the water pump inlet tube fasteners and the inlet tube and gasket.

10. Remove the water pump to cylinder block bolts and remove the water pump and its gasket.

11. To install, make sure the mating surfaces on the pump and the block are clean.

12. Using a new gasket and sealer, install the water pump and tighten the bolts to 5–7 ft. lbs. on models through 1982. 1983 and later models—30–40 ft. lbs. Make sure the pump impeller turns freely.

13. Install remaining parts in the reverse order of removal. Use new gaskets and sealer. Install the camshaft sprocket over the cam key. See below for procedure. Install new timing belt and adjust tension. See "Timing Belt Removal and Installation" for procedure.

2.0 Diesel Engine

1. Remove the front timing belt upper cover.

2. Loosen and remove the front timing belt, refer to timing belt in-vehicle services.

3. Drain the cooling system.

4. Raise the vehicle and support safely on jackstands.

5. Disconnect the lower radiator hose and heater hose from the water pump.

6. Disconnect the coolant tube from the thermostat housing and discard gasket.

7. Remove the three bolts attaching water pump to the crankcase. Remove the water pump. Discard gasket.

8. Clean the water pump and crankshaft gasket mating surfaces.

9. Install the water pump, using a new gasket. Tighten bolts to 23–34 ft. lbs.

10. Connect the coolant tube from the thermostat housing to the water pump using a new gasket. Tighten bolts to 5–7 ft. lbs.

11. Connect the heater hose and lower radiator hose to the water pump.

12. Lower vehicle.

13. Fill and bleed the cooling system.

14. Install and adjust the front timing belt.

15. Run the engine and check for coolant leaks.

16. Install the front timing belt upper cover.

2.3 HSC Engine

1. Disconnect the negative battery cable. Drain the cooling system.

2. Loosen the thermactor pump mounting and remove the drive belt. Disconnect and remove the hose clamp below the pump. Remove the thermactor pump bracket mounting bolts and remove the thermactor and bracket as an assembly.

3. Loosen the water pump drive belt idler pulley and remove the drive belt.

4. Disconnect the heater hose from the water pump.

5. Remove the water pump mounting bolts and the pump.

6. Clean the engine mounting surface. Apply gasket cement to both sides of the mounting gasket and position the gasket on the engine.

7. Install the pump in reverse order of removal. Torque the mounting bolts to 15–22 ft. lbs.

8. Add the proper coolant mixture, start the engine and check for leaks.

Thermostat

REMOVAL & INSTALLATION

1. Disconnect the negative battery cable. Drain the radiator until the coolant level is below the thermostat.

2. Disconnect the wire connector at the thermostat housing thermoswitch.

3. Loosen the top radiator hose clamp. Remove the thermostat housing mounting bolts and lift up the housing.

4. Remove the thermostat by turning counterclockwise.

5. Clean the thermostat housing and engine gasket mounting surfaces. Install new mounting gasket and fully insert the thermostat to compress the mounting gasket. Turn the thermostat clockwise to secure in housing.

6. Position the housing onto the engine. Install the mounting bolts and torque to 6–8 ft. lbs. on 1.6 engines and 12–18 ft. lbs. on 2.3 HSC engines.

7. The rest of the installation is in the reverse order of removal.

EMISSION CONTROLS

NOTE: Refer to "Emission Control" in the Unit Repair section for system servicing.

All engines are equipped with Ford's Thermactor (air pump) system, positive crankcase ventilation (PCV), exhaust gas recirculation (EGR), DuraSpark or TFI electronic ignition, a catalytic converter, a thermostatically-controlled air cleaner, and an evaporative emissions system (charcoal canister). The EEC IV system of electronic engine controls is used on fuel injected engines.

The belt-driven air pump injects clean air either into the exhaust manifold, or downstream into the catalytic converter, depending on engine conditions. The oxygen contained in the injected air supports continued combustion of the hot carbon monoxide (CO) and hydrocarbon (HC) gases, reducing their release into the atmosphere.

No external PCV valve is necessary on the PCV system. Instead, an internal baffle and an orifice control the flow of crankcase gases.

The back-pressure modulated EGR valve is mounted next to the carburetor on the intake manifold. Vacuum applied to the EGR diaphragm raises the pintle valve from its seat, allowing hot exhaust gases to be drawn into the intake manifold with the intake charge. The exhaust gases reduce peak combustion temperature; lower temperatures reduce the formation of oxides of nitrogen (NOx).

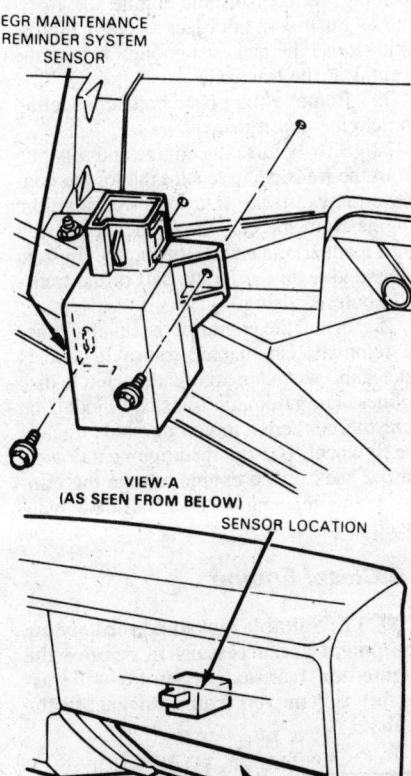

VIEW-A (AS SEEN FROM BELOW)

SENSOR LOCATION

VIEW-A GLOVE BOX

EGR sensor location. Replace the sensor to cancel the EGR service light in the dash (© Ford Motor Co.)

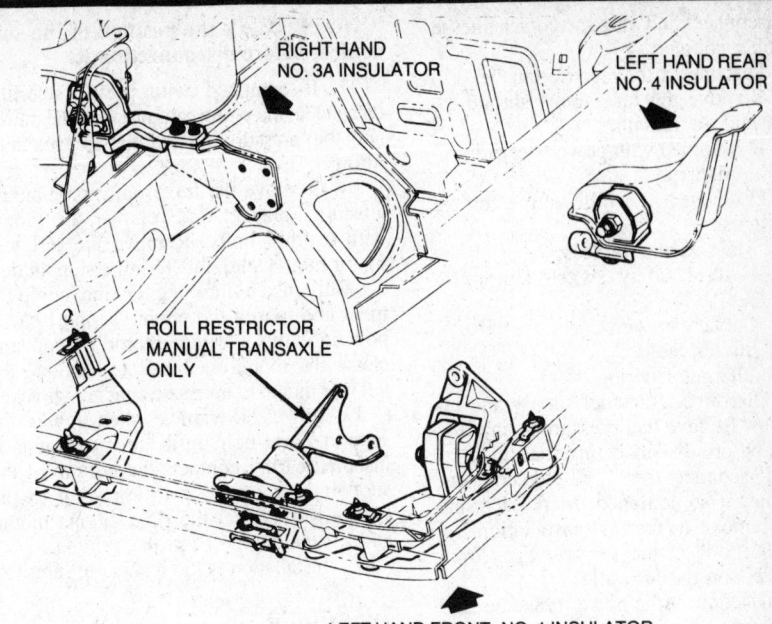

RIGHT HAND NO. 3A INSULATOR

LEFT HAND REAR NO. 4 INSULATOR

ROLL RESTRICTOR MANUAL TRANSAXLE ONLY

LEFT HAND FRONT NO. 1 INSULATOR

Engine/transaxle mounts; Escort/Lynx

The dual brick catalytic converter is mounted in the exhaust system, ahead of the muffler. Catalytic converters use noble metals (platinum and palladium) and great heat (1200°F) to catalytically oxidize HC and CO gases into H_2O and CO_2. The Thermactor system is used as a fresh air (and therefore, oxygen) supply.

The thermostatically-controlled air cleaner housing is able to draw fresh air from two sources: cool air from outside the car (behind the grille), or warm air obtained from a heat stove encircling the exhaust manifold. A warm air supply is desirable during cold engine operation, because it promotes better atomization of the air/fuel mixture, while cool air promotes better combustion in a hot engine.

Instead of venting gasoline vapors from the carburetor float bowl into the atmosphere, an evaporative emission system captures the vapors and stores them in a charcoal-filled canister, located ahead of the left front wheel arch. When the engine is running, a purge control solenoid allows fresh air to be drawn through the canister; the fresh air and vapors are then routed to the carburetor, to be mixed with the intake charge.

EGR MAINTENANCE REMINDER SYSTEM

Some vehicles are equipped with an EGR Maintenance Reminder System, that consists of a mileage sensor module, instrument panel warning light, and necessary wiring. This system provides a visual warning to indicate the EGR system needs service at 30,000 miles.

The mileage sensor is a blue plastic box mounted under the dash, behind the glove box.

The warning light is in the instrument panel to the left of the steering column.

NOTE: This light will remain on until the sensor module is replaced.

ENGINE

REMOVAL & INSTALLATION

1.6 Engine

NOTE: The following procedure is for engine and transaxle removal and installation as an assembly.

1. Mark the location of the hinges and remove the hood.
2. Remove the air cleaner, hot air tube and alternator fresh air intake tube.
3. Disconnect the battery cables, remove the battery and tray.
4. Drain the radiator, engine oil and transaxle fluid.
5. Remove the coil, the mounting bracket and the coil wire harness.
6. If the vehicle is equipped with air conditioning, remove the compressor from the engine with the refrigerant hoses still attached. Position compressor to the side.

— CAUTION —
Never loosen air conditioning refrigerant lines, as the escaping refrigerant is a deadly poison and can freeze exposed skin instantly.

7. Disconnect the upper and lower radiator hose.
8. Disconnect the heater hoses from the engine.
9. If equipped with an automatic trans-

axle disconnect and plug the cooler lines at the rubber coupler.

10. Disconnect the electric fan.

11. Remove the fan motor, shroud assembly and the radiator.

12. If equipped with power steering, remove the filler tube.

13. Disconnect the following electrical connections:

    a. Main wiring harness

    b. Neutral safety switch (automatic only)

    c. Choke cap wire

    d. Starter cable

    e. Alternator wiring

14. Disconnect the fuel supply and return lines. Relieve fuel pressure on injected models before disconnecting fuel lines.

15. Disconnect the (3) altitude compensator lines if so equipped. Mark each line as you remove it, for easy installation.

16. Disconnect the vacuum lines from the ''tree'' on the firewall.

17. Disconnect the power brake booster vacuum line.

18. Disconnect the cruise control if so equipped.

19. Disconnect all carburetor linkage.

20. Disconnect all engine vacuum lines. Mark each line as you remove it, for easy installation.

21. Disconnect the clutch cable if so equipped.

22. Remove the thermactor pump bracket bolt.

23. Install engine support T81P-6000-A or its equivalent. Using a short piece of chain, attach it to the engine using the 10 mm bolt holes at the transaxle, the exhaust manifold side of the head, and the thermactor bracket hole. Tighten the J-bolt. Place a piece of tape around the J-bolt threads where the bolt passes through the bottom of the support bar. This will act as a reference later.

24. Jack up the vehicle and support it with jack stands.

25. Remove the splash shields.

26. If equipped with a manual transaxle, remove the roll restrictor at the engine and body.

27. Remove the stabilizer bar.

28. Remove the lower control arm thru bolts at the body brackets.

29. Disconnect the left tie rod at the steering knuckle.

30. Disconnect the secondary air tube (catalyst) at the check valve.

31. Disconnect the exhaust system at the exhaust manifold and tail pipe.

32. Remove the right half-shaft from the transaxle. Some fluid will leak out when the shaft is removed.

33. Remove the left side half-shaft.

34. Install shipping plugs T81P-1177-B or equivalent in the differential seals.

35. Disconnect the speedometer cable.

36. If equipped with an automatic transaxle, disconnect the shift selector cable. On manual transaxles, disconnect the shift control rod.

NOTE: Mark the position of the shift control before disconnecting it.

37. If equipped with power steering, disconnect the pump return line at the pump, and the pressure line at the intermediate fitting.

38. Remove the left front motor mount attaching bracket and remove the mount with its thru bolts. Remove the left rear motor mount stud nut. Using a step ladder, carefully reach into the engine compartment and loosen the engine support bar J-bolt until the left rear motor mount stud clears the mounting bracket. Remove the left rear mount to transaxle attaching bracket.

39. Lower the vehicle, then tighten the support bar J-bolt until the piece of tape installed earlier contacts the bottom of the support bar. Attach a lifting sling to the engine, disconnect the right engine mount and lift the engine from the vehicle.

40. Installation is the reverse of removal.

1.6 Engine

NOTE: The following procedure is for engine only removal and installation.

1. Mark the position of the hinges on the hood underside and remove the hood.

2. Remove the air cleaner assembly. Remove the air feed duct and the heat tube. Remove the air duct to the alternator.

3. Disconnect the battery cables from the battery. Remove the battery. If equipped with air-conditioning, remove compressor with line still connected and position out of the way.

----- **CAUTION** -----

Never loosen refrigerant lines, as the escaping refrigerant is a deadly poison and can freeze exposed skin instantly.

4. Drain the cooling system. Remove the drive belts from the alternator and thermactor pump. Disconnect the thermactor air supply hose. Disconnect the wiring harness at the alternator. Remove alternator and thermactor.

5. Disconnect and remove the upper and lower radiator hoses. If equipped with an automatic transaxle, disconnect and plug the fluid cooler lines at the radiator.

6. Disconnect the heater hoses from the engine. Unplug the electric cooling fan wiring harness. Remove the fan and radiator shroud as an assembly.

7. Remove the radiator. Label and disconnect all vacuum lines, including power brake booster, from the engine. Label and disconnect all linkage, including kickdown linkage if automatic, and wiring harness connectors from the engine.

8. If equipped with fuel injection, discharge the system pressure. Remove supply and return fuel lines to the fuel pump. Plug the line from the gas tank.

9. Raise and safely support the car on jackstands. Remove the clamp from the heater supply and return tubes, remove the tubes.

10. Disconnect the battery cable from the starter motor. Remove brace or bracket from the back of the starter and remove the starter.

11. Disconnect the exhaust system from the exhaust manifold. Drain the engine oil.

12. Remove the brace in front of the bell housing (flywheel or converter) inspection cover. Remove the inspection cover.

13. Remove the crankshaft pulley. If equipped with a manual transaxle, remove the timing belt cover lower attaching bolts.

14. If equipped with an automatic transaxle, remove the torque converter to flywheel mounting nuts.

15. Remove the lower engine to transaxle attaching bolts.

16. Loosen the hose clamps on the bypass hose and remove the hose from the intake manifold.

17. Remove the bolt and nut attaching the right front mount insulator to the engine bracket.

18. Lower the car from the jackstands.

19. Attach an engine lifting sling to the engine. Connect a chain hoist to the lifting sling and remove all slack. Remove the through bolt from the right front engine mount and remove the insulator.

20. If the car is equipped with a manual transaxle, remove the timing belt cover upper mounting bolts and remove the cover.

21. Remove the right front insulator attaching bracket from the engine.

22. Position a floor jack under the transaxle. Raise the jack just enough to take the weight of the transaxle.

23. Remove the upper bolts connecting the engine and transaxle.

24. Slowly raise the engine and separate from the transaxle. Be sure the torque converter stays on the transaxle. Remove the engine from the car. On models equipped with manual transaxles, the engine must be separated from the input shaft of the transaxle before raising.

25. Install the engine in the reverse order of removal. On manual transaxle models take care when engaging the clutch disc splines. On automatic transaxle models be sure the converter mounting studs engage the flywheel. Be sure the alignment dowels on the back of the engine engage the transaxle and the engine and transaxle mate together flush.

2.0 Diesel Engine

NOTE: Suitable jackstands or hoisting equipment are necessary to remove the engine and transaxle assembly—the assembly is removed from underneath the vehicle.

----- **CAUTION** -----

The air conditioning system contains refrigerant (R-12) under high pressure. Use extreme care when discharging system. If the tools and know-how are not on hand, have the system discharged prior to start of engine removal.

1. Pressure plate alignment dowel
2. Flywheel
3. Crankshaft rear seal
4. Retainer attaching bolt
5. Seal retainer
6. Retainer gasket
7. Cylinder block
8. Engine lifting eye
9. Plug and gasket, monolithic timing
10. Coolant drain plug
11. Pump (oil) gasket
12. Oil pump
13. Pump (water) gasket
14. Water pump
15. Pump (water) attaching bolt
16. Timing belt—installed view
17. Tensioner spring
18. Tensioner bracket and idler
19. Tensioner attaching bolt
20. Timing belt cover

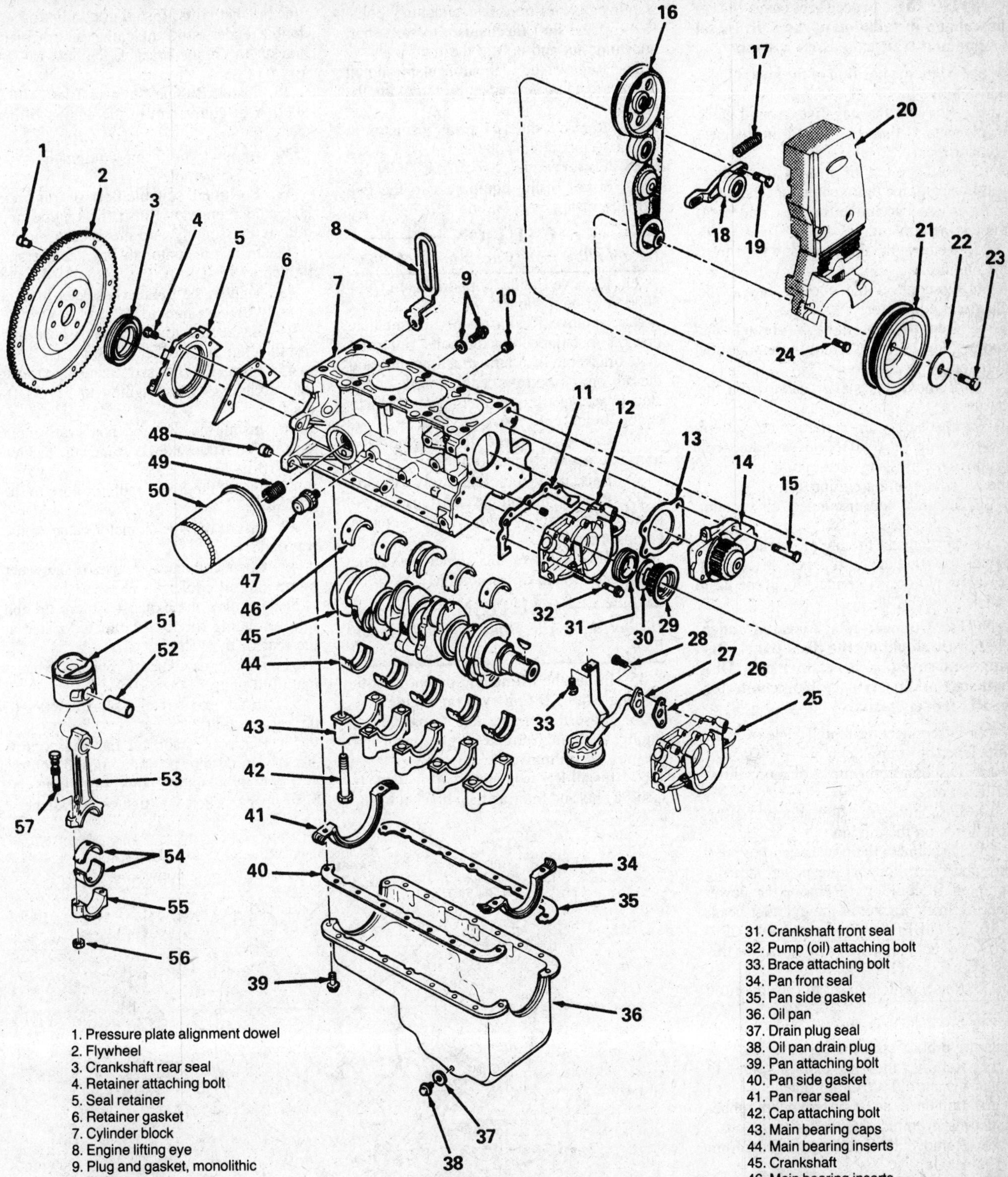

21. Crankshaft pulley
22. Pulley bolt washer
23. Pulley attaching bolt
24. Cover attaching bolt
25. Oil pump
26. Pick up tube gasket
27. Pick up and tube assembly
28. Pick up attaching bolt
29. Crankshaft gear
30. Timing belt guide

31. Crankshaft front seal
32. Pump (oil) attaching bolt
33. Brace attaching bolt
34. Pan front seal
35. Pan side gasket
36. Oil pan
37. Drain plug seal
38. Oil pan drain plug
39. Pan attaching bolt
40. Pan side gasket
41. Pan rear seal
42. Cap attaching bolt
43. Main bearing caps
44. Main bearing inserts
45. Crankshaft
46. Main bearing inserts
47. Oil pressure sending unit
48. Transmission alignment dowel
49. Oil filter adapter
50. Oil filter
51. Piston
52. Piston pin
53. Connecting rod
54. Connecting rod bearings
55. Connecting rod cap
56. Cap attaching nut
57. Cap attaching bolt

Engine block components exploded view (© Ford Motor Co.)

NOTE: These procedures cover the removal and installation of the 2.0L Diesel engine and transaxle as an assembly.

1. Mark the position of the hood hinges and remove the hood.
2. Remove the negative ground cable from battery that is located in luggage compartment.
3. Remove the air cleaner assembly.
4. Position a drain pan under the lower radiator hose. Remove the hose and drain the engine coolant.
5. Remove the upper radiator hose from the engine.
6. Disconnect the cooling fan at the electrical connector.
7. Remove the radiator shroud and cooling fan as an assembly. Remove the radiator.
8. Remove the starter cable from the starter.
9. Discharge air conditioning system (see opening CAUTION), if so equipped. Remove the pressure and suction lines from the air conditioning compressor.
10. Identify and disconnect all vacuum lines as necessary.
11. Disconnect the engine harness connectors (two) at the dash panel. Disconnect the glow plug relay connectors at the dash panel.

NOTE: Connectors are located under the plastic shield on the dash panel. Remove and save plastic retainer pins. Disconnect the alternator wiring connector on RH fender apron.

12. Disconnect the clutch cable from the shift lever on transaxle.
13. Disconnect the injection pump throttle linkage.
14. Disconnect the fuel supply and return hoses on the engine.
15. Disconnect the power steering pressure and return lines at the power steering pump, if so equipped. Remove the power steering lines bracket at the cylinder head.
16. Install Engine Support Tool D79P-8000-A or equivalent to existing engine lifting eye.
17. Raise vehicle and safely support on jackstands.
18. Remove the bolt attaching the exhaust pipe bracket to the oil pan.
19. Remove the two exhaust pipes to exhaust manifold attaching nuts.
20. Pull the exhaust system out of rubber insulating grommets and set aside.
21. Remove the speedometer cable from the transaxle.
22. Position a drain pan under the heater hoses. Remove one heater hose from the water pump inlet tube. Remove the other heater hose from the oil cooler.
23. Remove the bolts attaching the control arms to the body. Remove the stabilizer bar bracket retaining bolts and remove brackets.
24. Halfshaft assemblies must be removed from the transaxle at this time.
25. On MTX models, remove the shift stabilizer bar-to-transaxle attaching bolts. Remove the shift mechanism to shift shaft attaching nut and bolt at the transaxle.
26. Remove the LH rear insulator mount bracket from body bracket by removing the two nuts.
27. Remove the LH front insulator to transaxle mounting bolts.
28. Lower vehicle (see CAUTION below). Install lifting equipment to the two existing lifting eyes on engine.

— CAUTION —
Do not allow front wheels to touch floor.

29. Remove Engine Support Tool D79L-8000-A or equivalent.
30. Remove RH insulator intermediate bracket to engine bracket bolts, intermediate bracket to insulator attaching nuts and the nut on the bottom of the double ended stud attaching the intermediate bracket to engine bracket. Remove the bracket.
31. Carefully lower the engine and transaxle assembly to the floor.
32. Raise the vehicle and safely support.
33. Position the engine and transaxle assembly directly below the engine compartment.
34. Slowly lower the vehicle over the engine and transaxle assembly.

— CAUTION —
Do not allow the front wheels to touch floor.

35. Install the lifting equipment to both existing engine lifting eyes on engine:
36. Raise the engine and transaxle assembly up through engine compartment and position accordingly.
37. Install RH insulator intermediate attaching nuts and intermediate bracket to engine bracket bolts. Install nut on bottom of double ended stud attaching intermediate bracket to engine bracket. Tighten to 75–100 ft. lbs.
38. Install Engine Support Tool D79L-8000-A or equivalent to the engine lifting eye.
39. Remove the lifting equipment.
40. Raise vehicle.
41. Position a suitable floor or transaxle jack under engine. Raise the engine and transaxle assembly into mounted position.
42. Install insulator to bracket nut and tighten to 75–100 ft. lbs.
43. Tighten the LH rear insulator bracket to body bracket nuts to 75–100 ft. lbs.
44. Install the lower radiator hose and install retaining bracket and bolt.
45. Install the shift stabilizer bar to transaxle attaching bolt. Tighten to 23–35 ft. lbs.
46. Install the shift mechanism to input shift shaft (on transaxle) bolt and nut. Tighten to 7–10 ft. lbs.
47. Install the lower radiator hose to the radiator.
48. Install the speedometer cable to the transaxle.
49. Connect the heater hoses to the water pump and oil cooler.
50. Position the exhaust system up and into insulating rubber grommets located at the rear of the vehicle.
51. Install the exhaust pipe to exhaust manifold bolts.
52. Install the exhaust pipe bracket to the oil pan bolt.
53. Place the stabilizer bar and control arm assembly into position. Install control arm to body attaching bolts. Install the stabilizer bar brackets and tighten all fasteners.

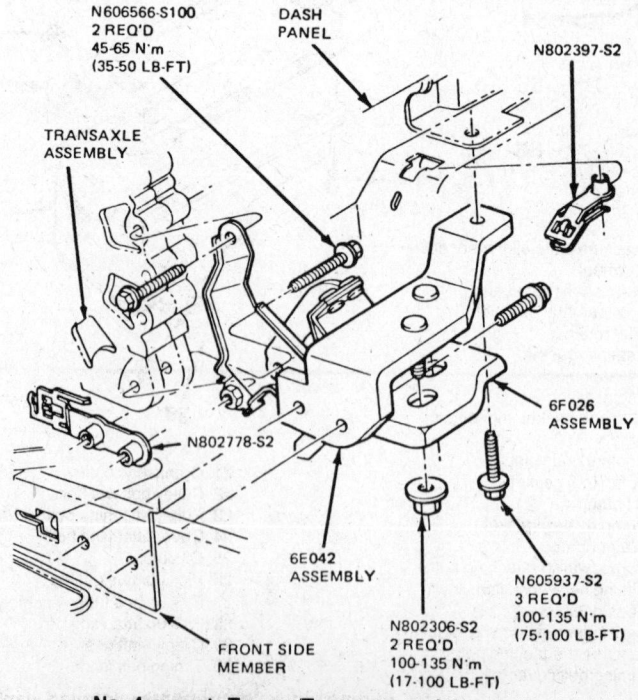

No. 4 mount; Tempo/Topaz manual 4 speed

54. Halfshaft assemblies must be installed at this time.

55. Lower the vehicle.

56. Remove the Engine Support Tool D79L-6000-A or equivalent.

57. Connect the alternator wiring at RH fender apron.

58. Connect the engine harness to main harness and glow plug relays at dash panel.

NOTE: Reinstall plastic shield.

59. Connect the vacuum lines.

60. Install the air conditioning discharge and suction lines to A/C compressor, if so equipped. Do not charge system at this time.

61. Connect the fuel supply and return lines to the injection pump.

62. Connect the injection pump throttle cable.

63. Install the power steering pressure and return lines. Install bracket.

64. Connect the clutch cable to shift lever on transaxle.

65. Connect the battery cable to starter.

66. Install the radiator shroud and coolant fan assembly. Tighten attaching bolts.

67. Connect the coolant fan electrical connector.

68. Install the upper radiator hose to engine.

69. Fill and bleed the cooling system.

70. Install the negative ground battery cable to battery.

71. Install the air cleaner assembly.

72. Install the hood.

73. Charge air conditioning system, if so equipped. System can be changed at a latter time if outside source is used.

74. Check and refill all fluid levels, (power steering, engine, MTX).

75. Start the vehicle. Check for leaks.

2.3 HSC Engine

NOTE: The following procedure is for engine and transaxle removal and installation as an assembly.

—— **CAUTION** ——

The engine and transaxle assembly are removed together as a unit from underneath the car. Provision must be made to safely raise and support the car for powertrain removal and installation.

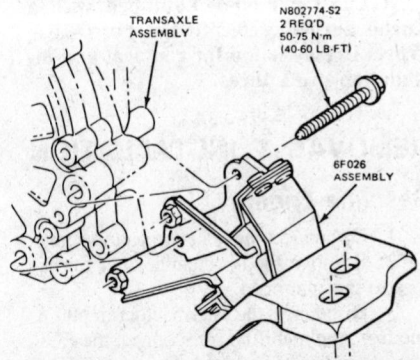

No. 4 mount; Tempo/Topaz 5 speed and automatic

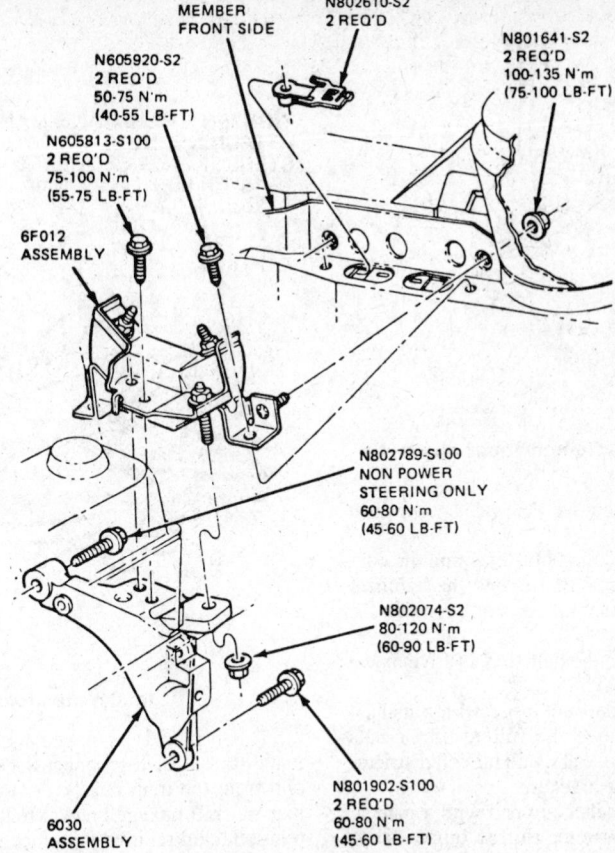

No. 3 mount; Tempo/Topaz

—— **CAUTION** ——

The air conditioning system (if equipped) must be discharged prior to engine removal. The refrigerant is contained under high pressure and is very dangerous when released. The system should be discharged by a knowledgeable person using the proper equipment.

1. Mark the position of the hinges on the underside of the hood and remove the hood.

2. Disconnect the battery cables from the battery, negative cable first. Remove the air cleaner assembly.

3. Remove the radiator cap and disconnect the lower radiator hose from the radiator to drain the cooling system.

4. Remove the upper and lower radiator hoses. On models equipped with an automatic transaxle, disconnect and plug the oil cooler lines from the rubber connectors at the radiator.

5. Disconnect and remove the coil from the cylinder head. Disconnect the cooling fan wiring harness. Remove the radiator shroud and electric fan as an assembly.

6. Be sure the air conditioning system is properly and safely discharged. Remove the hoses from the compressor. Label and disconnect all electrical harness connections, linkage and vacuum lines from the engine.

7. On automatic transaxle models disconnect the TV (throttle valve) linkage at the transaxle. On manual transaxle models disconnect the clutch cable from the lever at the transaxle.

8. Disconnect the fuel supply and return lines. Plug the fuel line from the gas tank. Disconnect the thermactor pump discharge hose at the pump.

9. Disconnect the power steering lines at the pump. Remove the hose support bracket from the cylinder head.

10. Install an engine support sling (Ford Tool T79L6000A, or equivalent), see the 1.6 removal and installation engine/transaxle assembly section for details.

11. Raise and safely support the car on jackstands.

12. Remove the starter cable from the starter motor terminal. Drain the engine oil and the transaxle lubricant.

13. Disconnect the hose from the catalytic converter. Remove the bolts retaining the exhaust pipe bracket to the oil pan.

14. Remove the exhaust pipe to exhaust manifold mounting nuts. Remove the pipes from the mounting bracket insulators and position out of the way.

15. Disconnect the speedometer cable from the transaxle. Remove the heater hoses from the water pump inlet and intake manifold connector.

16. Remove the water intake tube bracket from the engine block. Remove the two clamp attaching bolts from the bottom of

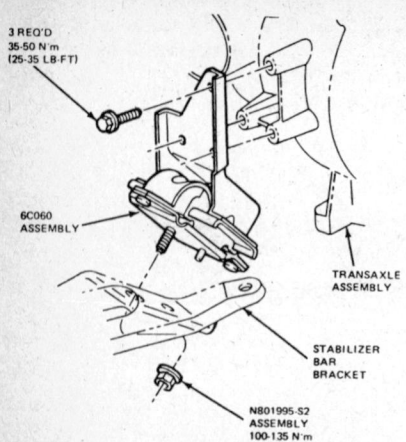

3 REQ'D
35-50 N·m
(25-35 LB-FT)

6C060
ASSEMBLY

TRANSAXLE
ASSEMBLY

STABILIZER
BAR
BRACKET

N801995-S2
ASSEMBLY
100-135 N·m

No. 1 mount; Tempo/Topaz automatic

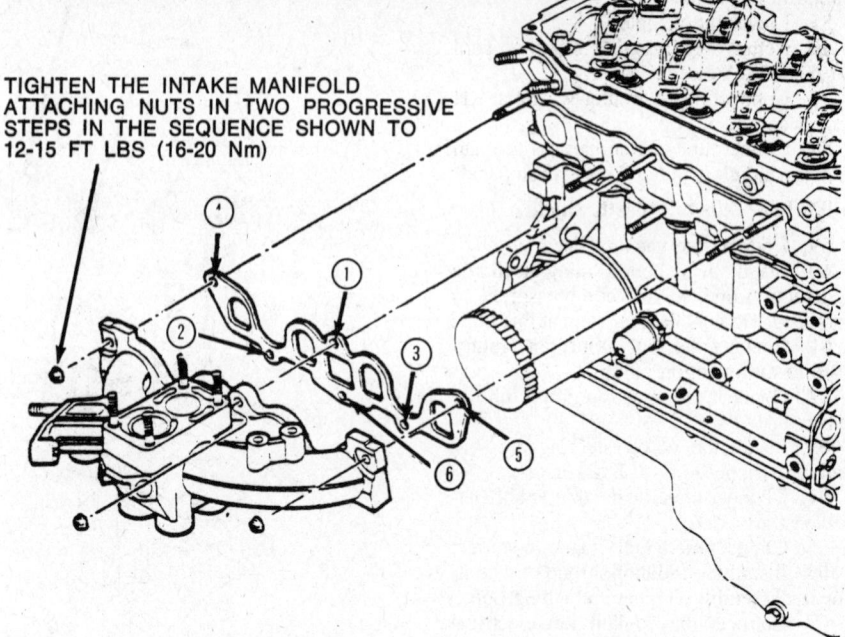

TIGHTEN THE INTAKE MANIFOLD
ATTACHING NUTS IN TWO PROGRESSIVE
STEPS IN THE SEQUENCE SHOWN TO
12-15 FT LBS (16-20 Nm)

Intake manifold torque sequence (© Ford Motor Co.)

the oil pan. Remove the water pump inlet tube.

17. Remove the bolts attaching the control arms to the body. Remove the stabilizer bar bracket retaining bolts and remove the brackets.

18. Remove the half shafts (drive axles) from the transaxle.

19. On models equipped with a manual transaxle, remove the roll restrictor nuts from the transaxle and pull the roll restrictor from mounting bracket.

20. On models equipped with a manual transaxle, remove the shift stabilizer bar to transaxle attaching bolts. Remove the shift mechanism to shift shaft attaching nut and bolt at the transaxle.

21. On models equipped with an automatic transaxle, disconnect the shift cable clip from the transaxle lever. Remove the manual shift linkage bracket bolts from the transaxle and remove the bracket.

22. Remove the left rear No. 4 insulator mount bracket from the body by removing the retaining nuts.

23. Remove the left front No. 1 insulator to transaxle mounting bolts.

24. Lower the car and support with stands so that the front wheels are just above the ground. Do not allow the wheels to touch the ground.

25. Connect an engine sling to the lifting brackets provided. Connect a hoist to the sling and apply slight tension. Remove the support sling (Step 10).

26. Remove the right hand insulator intermediate bracket to engine bracket bolts, intermediate bracket to insulator attaching nuts and the nut on the bottom of the double ended stud which attaches the intermediate bracket and engine bracket. Remove the bracket.

27. Lower the engine and transaxle assembly to the ground.

28. Raise and support the car at a height suitable from assembly to be removed.

29. Installation is in the reverse order.

Exhaust Manifold

NOTE: On models equipped with a Turbocharger, refer to the Ford Rear Wheel Drive section for removal and installation procedures.

REMOVAL & INSTALLATION

Gasoline Engine

1. Disconnect the negative battery cable.

2. Remove the air cleaner duct for access to the manifold.

3. Disconnect the Thermactor (air pump) line from the manifold. Disconnect the EGR tube. Remove heat shield. Disconnect sensor wire harness, if equipped. Unbolt the exhaust pipe from the manifold flange.

N620482-S2
3 REQ'D
35-60 N·m
(25-45 LB-FT)

N605800-S100
3 REQ'D
35-50 N·m
(25-35 LB-FT)

N801949-S2
ASSEMBLY
2 REQ'D
18-26 N·m
(13-19 LB-FT)

6B031
ASSEMBLY

6C060
ASSEMBLY

6F010
ASSEMBLY

N802310-S2
2 REQ'D

TRANSAXLE
ASSEMBLY

STABILIZER
BAR
BRACKET

N801995-S2
ASSEMBLY
100-135 N·m
(75-100 LB-FT)

N802310-S2

6B021

N801949-S2
ASSEMBLY
18-26 N·m
(13-19 LB-FT)

N605786-S2
18-26 N·m
(13-19 LB-FT)

FRONT
CROSSMEMBER

No. 1 mount; Tempo/Topaz 4 speed and 5 speed

4. Unbolt and remove the exhaust manifold.

5. Clean the manifold mating surfaces. Place a new gasket on the exhaust pipe-to-manifold flange.

6. Install the manifold. Tighten the bolts in a circular pattern, working from the center to the ends, in three progressive steps.

Diesel Engine

1. Remove the nuts attaching the muffler inlet pipe to the exhaust manifold.

2. Remove the bolts attaching the heat shield to the exhaust manifold.

3. Remove the nuts attaching the exhaust manifold to cylinder head and remove the exhaust manifold.

4. Install the exhaust manifold, using new gaskets, and tighten nuts to 16–20 ft. lbs.

5. Install the exhaust shield and tighten bolts to 12–16 ft. lbs.

6. Connect the muffler inlet pipe to the exhaust manifold and tighten the nuts to 25–35 ft. lbs.

7. Run the engine and check for exhaust leaks.

Intake Manifold

NOTE: On models with EFI, refer to the Ford Rear Wheel Drive section for removal and installation procedures.

REMOVAL & INSTALLATION

Gasoline Engine

1. Disconnect the negative battery terminal.

2. Remove the air cleaner housing.

3. Partially drain the cooling system and disconnect the heater hose from under the intake manifold.

4. Disconnect and label all vacuum and electrical connections.

5. Disconnect the fuel line and carburetor linkage.

6. Disconnect the EGR vacuum hose and supply tube.

7. On Escort & Lynx models, jack up the vehicle and support it with jack stands.

8. On Escort & Lynx models, remove the bottom (3) intake manifold nuts.

9. On Escort & Lynx models, remove the vehicle from the jack stands.

10. If equipped with automatic transmission disconnect the throttle valve linkage at the carburetor and remove the cable bracket attaching bolts.

11. If equipped with power steering (Escort/Lynx), remove the thermactor pump drive belt, the pump, the mounting bracket, and the by-pass hose.

12. Remove the fuel pump (Escort/Lynx). See the fuel pump removal procedure.

13. Remove the intake bolts, the manifold, and gasket.

NOTE: Do not lay the intake manifold flat as the gasket surfaces may be damaged.

14. Installation is the reverse of removal.

Diesel Engine

1. Disconnect the air inlet duct from the intake manifold and install the protective cap in the intake manifold, (part or Protective Cap Set T84P-9395-A or equivalent).

2. Disconnect the glow plug resistor electrical connector.

3. Disconnect the breather hose.

4. Drain the cooling system.

5. Disconnect the upper radiator hose at the thermostat housing.

6. Disconnect the two coolant hoses at the thermostat housing.

7. Disconnect the connectors to the temperature sensors in the thermostat housing.

8. Remove the bolts attaching the intake manifold to the cylinder head and remove the intake manifold.

9. Clean the intake manifold and cylinder head gasket mating surfaces.

10. Install the intake manifold, using a new gasket, and tighten the bolts to 12–16 ft. lbs.

11. Connect the temperature sensor connectors.

12. Connect the lower coolant hose to the thermostat housing and tighten the hose clamp.

13. Connect the upper coolant tube, using a new gasket and tighten bolts to 5–7 ft. lbs.

14. Connect the upper radiator hose to the thermostat housing.

15. Connect the breather hose.

16. Connect the glow plug resistor electrical connector.

17. Remove the protective cap and install the air inlet duct.

18. Fill and bleed the cooling system.

19. Run the engine and check for intake air leaks and coolant leaks.

Turbocharger

REMOVAL & INSTALLATION

NOTE: Refer to the Ford Rear Wheel Drive section for service details.

Rocker Arm

REMOVAL & INSTALLATION

Gasoline Engines

1. Disconnect the negative battery cable. Remove the air cleaner and air inlet duct. Disconnect and label all hoses and wires connected to or crossing the valve cover. Remove the cover.

2. On 1.6 engines, remove the rocker arm nuts and discard. On 2.3 HSC engines,

remove the rocker bolts and fulcrums. Remove the rocker arms. Keep all parts in order; they must be returned to their original positions.

3. Before installation, coat the valve tips and the rocker arm contact areas with Lubriplate® or the equivalent.

4. Rotate the engine until the lifter is on the base circle of the cam (valve closed).

—————— CAUTION ——————

On 1.6 engines, turn the engine only in the direction of normal rotation. Backward rotation will cause the camshaft belt to slip or lose teeth, altering valve timing and causing serious engine damage.

5. Install the rocker arm and new hex flange nuts or fulcrum and bolt. Be sure the lifter is on the base circle of the cam for each rocker arm as it is installed.

6. Clean the valve cover mating surfaces. Apply a bead of sealer to the cover flange and install the cover. Install all disconnected hoses and wires.

Valve Clearance

The intake and exhaust valves are driven by the camshaft, working through hydraulic lash adjusters and stamped rocker arms (1.6 engine) or through hydraulic lifters, pushrods and rocker arms (2.3 HSC engine). The hydraulic lash adjusters or lifters eliminate the need for periodic valve lash adjustment.

VALVE ADJUSTMENT

Diesel Engine

1. Warm up the engine to normal operating temperature.

2. Remove the cylinder head cover.

3. Loosen the head bolts in reverse order of the torque sequence.

4. Torque the head bolts in sequence to 80–85 ft. lbs.

5. Set No. 1 cylinder to TDC on the compression stroke and check the valve clearance of No. 1 and No. 2 intake and No. 1 and No. 3 exhaust valves. Adjust if necessary.

6. Rotate the crankshaft 360° and check the clearance of the No. 3 and No. 4 intake and No. 2 and No. 4 exhaust valves. Adjust if necessary.

7. Install the cylinder head cover.

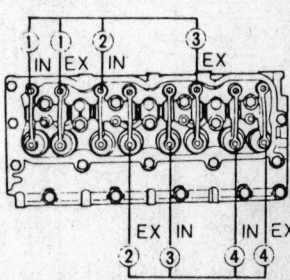

Valve adjustment sequence, diesel engine

Cylinder Head

REMOVAL & INSTALLATION

1.6 Engine

NOTE: The engine must be "overnight" cold before removing the cylinder head, to reduce the possibility of warpage or distortion.

— CAUTION —

Do not reuse the cylinder head retaining bolts. Use new bolts when installing head

1. Disconnect the negative battery cable.
2. Drain the cooling system, disconnect the heater hose under the intake manifold, and disconnect the radiator upper hose at the cylinder head.
3. Disconnect the wiring from the cooling fan switch, remove the air cleaner assembly, remove the PCV hose, and disconnect all interfering vacuum hoses after marking them for reassembly.
4. Remove the valve cover and disconnect all accessory drive belts. Remove the crankshaft pulley. Remove the timing belt cover.
5. Set the No. 1 cylinder to top dead center compression stroke. See distributor removal and installation procedure for details.
6. Remove the distributor cap and spark plug wires as an assembly.
7. Loosen both belt tensioner attaching bolts using special Ford tool T81P-6254-A

or the equivalent. Secure the belt tensioner as far left as possible. Remove the timing belt and discard.

NOTE: Once the tension on the timing belt has been released, the belt cannot be used again.

8. Disconnect the tube at the EGR valve, then remove the PVS hose connectors using tool T81P-8564-A or equivalent. Label the connectors and set aside.
9. Disconnect the choke wire, the fuel supply and return lines, the accelerator cable and speed control cable (if equipped). Disconnect the altitude compensator, if equipped, from the dash panel and place on the heater/AC air intake.

NOTE: Use caution not to damage the compensator.

10. Disconnect and remove the alternator.
11. If equipped with power steering, remove the thermactor pump drive belt, the pump and its bracket. If equipped with a turbocharger, refer to the Ford Mid-Size section for removal procedure. Refer to the Fuel Injection section for pressure discharge and removal instructions.
12. Raise the vehicle and disconnect the exhaust pipe from the manifold.
13. Lower the vehicle and remove the cylinder head bolts and washers. Discard the bolts, they cannot be used again.
14. Remove the cylinder head with the manifolds attached. Remove and discard the head gasket. Do not place the cylinder head with combustion chambers down or

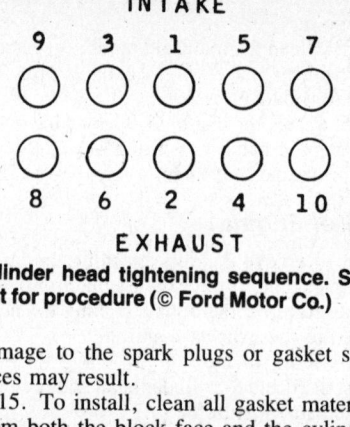

Cylinder head tightening sequence. See text for procedure (© Ford Motor Co.)

damage to the spark plugs or gasket surfaces may result.

15. To install, clean all gasket material from both the block face and the cylinder head, then rotate the crankshaft so that the No. 1 piston is 90° BTDC. In this position, the crankshaft pulley keyway is at 9 o'clock. Turn the camshaft so its keyway is at 6 o'clock. When installing the timing belt, turn the crankshaft keyway back to 12 o'clock but do not turn the camshaft from its 6 o'clock position. The crankshaft is turned 90° BTDC to prevent the valves from hitting the pistons when the cylinder head is installed.
16. Position the cylinder head gasket on the block and install the cylinder head using new bolts and washers. Tighten the bolts to 44 ft. lbs. in the sequence shown. After tightening, turn the bolts an additional 90° in the same sequence. Complete the bolt tightening by turning an additional 90° in the same sequence.
17. Remaining installation is the reverse of removal. See "Timing Belt Removal and Installation" for timing belt installation procedures. Fill the cooling system only with Ford Cooling System Fluid E1FZ-19549-A or Prestone II or the equivalent. Using the wrong type of coolant can damage the engine.

2.3 HSC Engine

1. Disconnect the negative battery cable. Drain the cooling system by disconnecting the lower radiator hose.
2. Disconnect the heater hose at the fitting under the intake manifold. Disconnect the upper radiator hose at the cylinder head connector.
3. Disconnect the electric cooling fan switch at the plastic connector. Remove the air cleaner assembly. Label and disconnect any vacuum lines that will interfere with cylinder head removal.
4. Disconnect all drive belts. Remove rocker arm cover. Remove the distributor cap and spark plug wires as an assembly.
5. Disconnect the EGR tube at EGR valve. Disconnect the choke wire from the choke.
6. Disconnect the fuel supply and return lines at the rubber connector. Disconnect the accelerator cable and speed control cable, if equipped. Loosen the bolts retaining the thermactor pump pulley.
7. Raise and safely support the front of

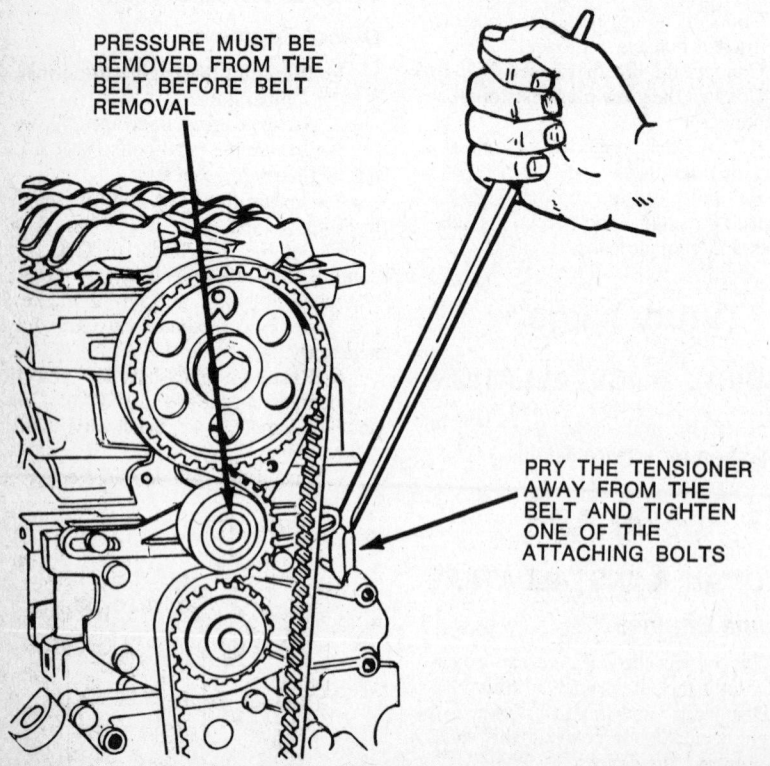

PRESSURE MUST BE REMOVED FROM THE BELT BEFORE BELT REMOVAL

PRY THE TENSIONER AWAY FROM THE BELT AND TIGHTEN ONE OF THE ATTACHING BOLTS

The timing belt tensioner must be released and moved away from the belt before the timing belt can be removed (© Ford Motor Co.)

the car. Disconnect the exhaust pipe from the exhaust manifold. Lower car.

8. Loosen the rocker arm bolts until the arms can pivot for pushrod removal. Remove the pushrods; keep the pushrods in order for installation in original position.

9. Remove the cylinder head bolts. Remove the cylinder head, gasket, thermactor pump, intake and exhaust manifolds as an assembly. Do not lay the cylinder head down flat before removing the spark plugs; take care not to damage the gasket surface.

10. Clean all gasket material from the head and block surfaces.

11. Position a new head gasket on the block surface, use sealer to retain the gasket.

12. To help with head installation alignment, purchase two head bolts and cut off the heads. Install the ''modified'' bolts at opposite corners of the block to act as guides.

13. Position the cylinder head over the guide bolts and lower onto the engine block.

14. Install head bolts, remove the guides and replace with regular bolts.

15. Tighten the head bolts to 53–59 ft. lbs. in two stages in the sequence shown.

16. The rest of the cylinder head installation is in the reverse order of removal.

Diesel Engine

1. Disconnect the battery ground cable from the battery, which is located in the luggage compartment.

2. Drain the cooling system.

3. Remove the camshaft cover, front and rear timing belt covers, and front and rear timing belts.

4. Raise the vehicle and safely support on jackstands.

5. Disconnect the muffler inlet pipe at the exhaust manifold. Lower the vehicle.

6. Disconnect the air inlet duct at the air cleaner and intake manifold. Install a protective cover.

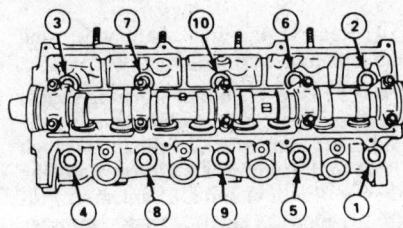

2.0 diesel, cylinder head bolt removal

7. Disconnect the electrical connectors and vacuum hoses to the temperature sensors located in the thermostat housing.

8. Disconnect the upper and lower coolant hoses, and the upper radiator hose at the thermostat housing.

9. Disconnect and remove the injection lines at the injection pump and nozzles. Cap all lines and fittings with Cap Protective Set T84P-9395-A or equivalent.

10. Disconnect the glow plug harness from the main engine harness.

11. Remove the cylinder head bolts in the sequence shown. Remove the cylinder head.

12. Remove the glow plugs. Then, remove pre-chamber cups from the cylinder head using a brass drift.

13. Clean the pre-chamber cups, prechambers in the cylinder head and the cylinder head and crankcase gasket mating surfaces.

14. Install the pre-chambers in the cylinder heads, making sure the locating pins are aligned with the slots provided.

15. Install the glow plugs and tighten to 11-15 ft lbs. Connect glow plug harness to the glow plugs. Tighten the nuts to 5-7 ft. lbs.

——— CAUTION ———

Carefully blow out the head bolt threads in the crankcase with compressed air. Failure to thoroughly clean the thread bores can result in incorrect cylinder head torque or possible cracking of the crankcase.

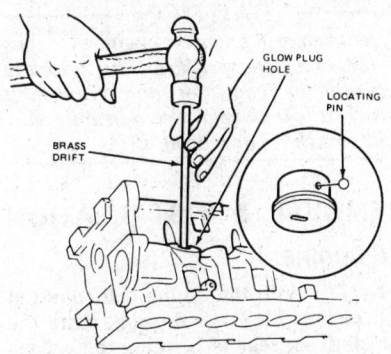

2.0 diesel, pre-chamber removal

16. Position a new cylinder head gasket on the crankcase making sure the cylinder head oil feed hole is not blocked.

17. Measure each cylinder head bolt dimension A. If the measurement is more than 114.5mm (4.51 inches), replace the head bolt.

——— CAUTION ———

Rotate the camshaft in the cylinder head until the cam lobes for No. 1 cylinder are at the base circle (both valves closed). Then, rotate the crankshaft clockwise until No. 1 piston is halfway up in the cylinder bore toward TDC. This is to prevent contact between the pistons and valves.

18. Install the cylinder head on the crankcase.

NOTE: Before installing the cylinder head bolts, paint a white reference dot on each one, and apply a light coat of engine oil on the bolt threads.

19. Tighten cylinder head bolts as follows:

a. Tighten bolts to 22 ft. lbs in the sequence shown.

b. Using the painted reference marks, tighten each bolt in sequence another 90 degrees to 105 degrees.

c. Repeat Step by turning the bolts another 90 degrees to 105 degrees.

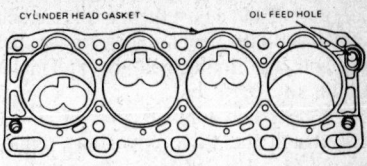

2.0 diesel, head gasket identification

20. Connect the glow plug harness to main engine harness.

21. Remove the protective caps and install injection lines to the injection pump and nozzles. Tighten capnuts to 18-22 ft. lbs.

22. Air bleed the system.

23. Connect the upper (with a new gasket) and lower coolant hoses, and the upper radiator hose to the thermostat housing. Tighten upper coolant hose bolts to 5-7 ft. lbs.

24. Connect the electrical connectors and the vacuum hoses to the temperature sensors in the thermostat housing.

25. Remove the protective cover and install the air inlet duct to the intake manifold and air cleaner.

26. Raise vehicle and support on jackstands. Connect the muffler inlet pipe to the exhaust manifold. Tighten nuts to 25-35 ft. lbs.

27. Lower the vehicle.

28. Install and adjust the front timing belt.

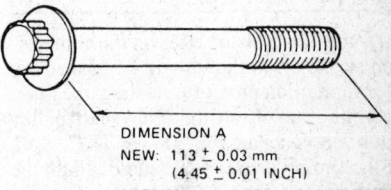

DIMENSION A
NEW: 113 ± 0.03 mm
(4.45 ± 0.01 INCH)
USED MAX.: 114.5 mm (4.51 INCHES)

2.0 diesel, head bolt measurement

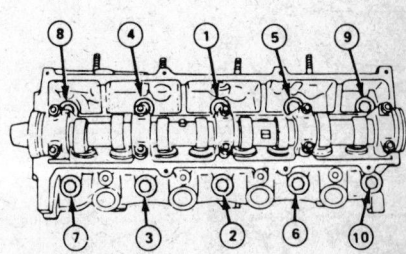

2.0 diesel, head bolt tightening sequence

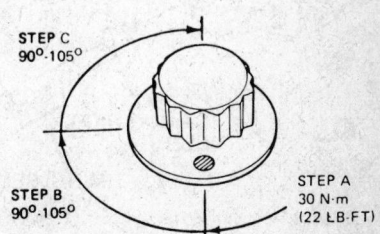

STEP C
90°-105°

STEP B
90°-105°

STEP A
30 N·m
(22 LB·FT)

2.0 diesel, head bolt tightening steps

29. Install and adjust the rear timing belt.

30. Install the front upper timing belt cover and rear timing belt cover. Tighten the bolts to 5-7 ft. lbs.

31. Check and adjust the valves as outlined. Install the valve cover and tighten the bolts to 5-7 ft. lbs.

32. Fill and bleed the cooling system.

33. Check and adjust the injection pump timing.

34. Connect battery ground cable to battery. Run engine and check for oil, fuel and coolant leaks.

Timing Belt

CHECKING ENGINE TIMING

1.6 Engine

Should the camshaft drive belt jump timing by a tooth or two, the engine could still run, although very poorly. To visually check for correct timing, remove the No. 1 spark plug and place your thumb over the hole. Use a wrench on the crankshaft pulley bolt to rotate the engine to TDC of the compression stroke for No. 1 cylinder.

— CAUTION —
Turn the crankshaft only in the direction of normal rotation. Backward rotation will cause the belt to slip or lose teeth, altering engine timing.

As the No. 1 piston rises on the compression stroke, your thumb will be pushed out by compression pressure. At the same time, the timing notch on the crankshaft pulley will be approaching the "0", or TDC, mark on the timing degree scale molded into the camshaft belt cover. Continue to turn the crankshaft until the pulley mark and "0"

mark are aligned, indicating that No. 1 cylinder is at TDC.

Remove the alternator drive belt, and the power steering pump and air conditioning compressor drive belts, if so equipped. Remove the camshaft belt cover.

The camshaft sprocket has a mark next to one of the holes. The cylinder head is similarly marked. These marks should be aligned, dot-to-dot, indicating that camshaft timing is correct.

NOTE: As a further check, the distributor cap can be removed; the ignition rotor should be pointing toward the No. 1 spark plug tower in the cap.

If the marks are aligned, the engine timing is correct. If not, the belt must be removed from the cam sprocket and the camshaft turned until its marks are aligned (crankshaft still at TDC).

— CAUTION —
Never attempt to rotate the engine by means of the camshaft sprocket. The 2:1 ratio between the camshaft and crankshaft sprockets will place a severe strain on the belt, stretching or tearing it.

REMOVAL & INSTALLATION

1.6 Engine

NOTE: With the timing belt removed and pistons at TDC, do not rotate the camshaft for fear of bending the valves. If the camshaft must be rotated, align the crankshaft pulley 90° BTDC. When actually installing the belt, the crankshaft pulley must be at TDC.

1. Disconnect the negative battery cable. Remove all accessory drive belts and remove the timing belt cover.

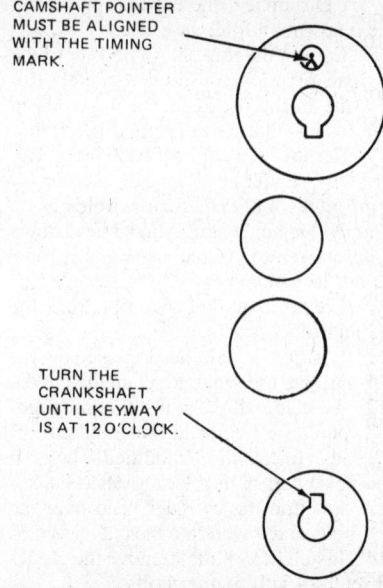

CAMSHAFT POINTER MUST BE ALIGNED WITH THE TIMING MARK.

TURN THE CRANKSHAFT UNTIL KEYWAY IS AT 12 O'CLOCK.

When installing the timing belt, the keyway on the crankshaft is at 12 o'clock, the camshaft pointer is aligned with the timing mark and the keyway on the camshaft is at 6 o'clock (© Ford Motor Co.)

NOTE: Align the timing mark on the camshaft sprocket with the timing mark on the cylinder head.

2. After aligning the camshaft timing marks, reinstall the timing belt cover and confirm that the timing mark on the crankshaft pulley aligns with the TDC mark on the front cover. Remove the timing belt cover.

3. Loosen both timing belt attaching bolts using tool T81P-6254-A or equivalent. Pry the tensioner away from the belt as far as possible and hold it in that position by tightening one of the tensioner attaching bolts.

4. Remove the crankshaft pulley and remove and discard the timing belt.

NOTE: Due to limited working space, special tools are required to remove the crankshaft pulley. Crankbelt wrench (Ford) tool number YA826 (to hold the pulley stationary) and a Crankshaft Pulley wrench (Ford) tool number T81P6312A or equivalent tools will make the job easier.

5. To install new belt, fit the timing belt over the gears in a counterclockwise direction starting at the crankshaft. Ensure that belt span between crankshaft and camshaft is kept tight as belt is installed over remaining gears.

6. Loosen belt tensioner attaching bolts and allow tensioner to extend against the belt.

7. Tighten one tensioner attaching bolt using special tool mentioned earlier or its equivalent.

8. Install the crankshaft pulley, drive plate and pulley attaching bolt.

9. Hold the crankshaft pulley station-

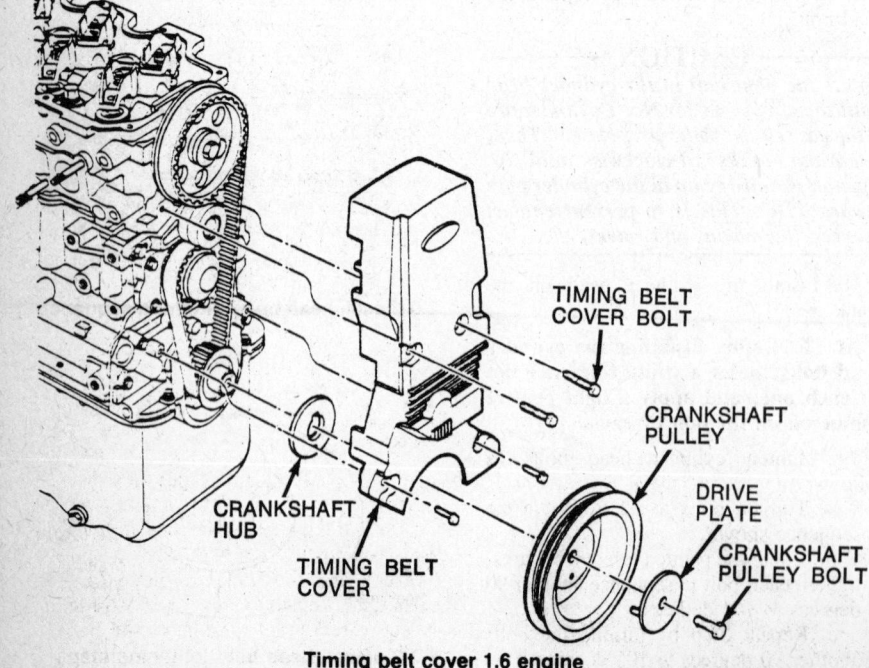

TIMING BELT COVER BOLT

CRANKSHAFT PULLEY

DRIVE PLATE

CRANKSHAFT PULLEY BOLT

CRANKSHAFT HUB

TIMING BELT COVER

Timing belt cover 1.6 engine

ary using tool YA-826 or equivalent and torque pulley bolt to 74–90 ft. lbs.

10. Disconnect the distributor coilwire and crank the engine for 30 seconds after reconnecting the negative battery cable. Disconnect the negative cable and realign marks. Check that the camshaft sprocket pointer is aligned with the TDC mark, and that the crankshaft is in the TDC position. If the timing marks do not align, remove the belt and reinstall.

11. Loosen belt tensioner attaching bolt (tightened in step 7) ¼ to ½ turn maximum, while holding the crankshaft stationary with wrench T81P6312A or equivalent.

12. While securing the crankshaft so that it cannot turn, turn the camshaft sprocket counterclockwise using Camshaft Holding Tool D81P6256A or equivalent, and a torque wrench. Tighten the belt tensioner attaching bolts when the torque wrench measures 27-32 ft. lbs for a new belt, or 10 ft. lbs, if an old belt was installed.

NOTE: Do not apply torque to the camshaft sprocket attaching bolt. Apply it to the hex on the sprocket.

13. Install the timing belt cover and remaining parts in reverse order of removal.

Timing Belt

IN CAR SERVICE

2.0 Diesel Engine

NOTE: This procedure is for Removal and Installation of the front timing belt for in-vehicle service of the water pump, camshaft, or cylinder head. The timing belt cannot be replaced with the engine installed in the vehicle.

1. Remove the front timing belt upper cover and the flywheel timing mark cover.

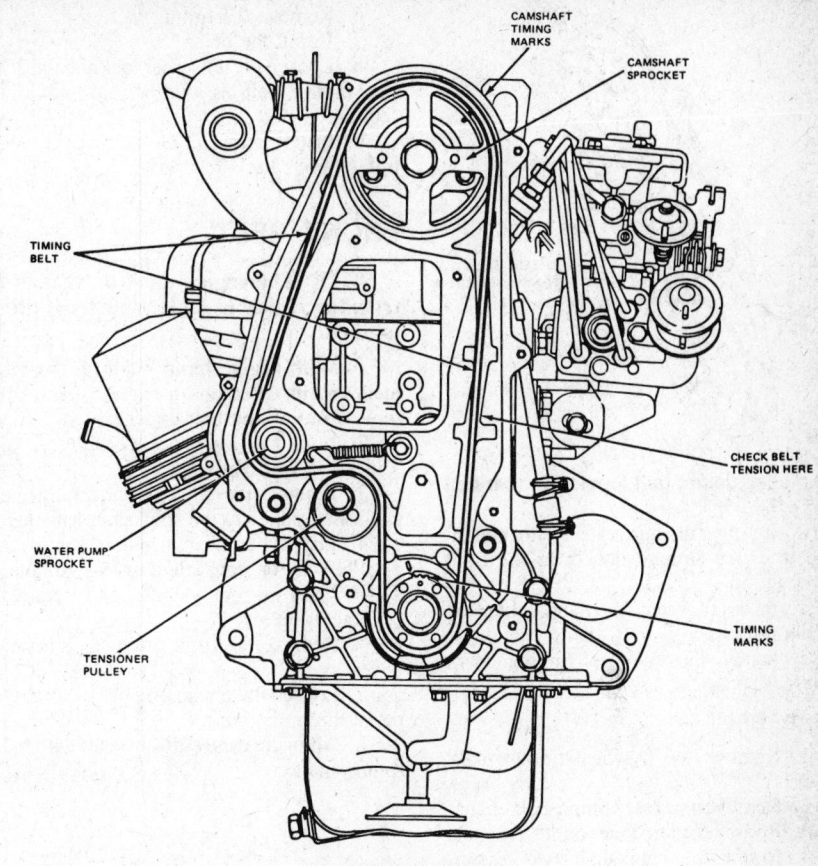

NOTE: TIMING BELT LOWER COVER REMOVED FOR CLARITY.

2.0 diesel, timing belt installation

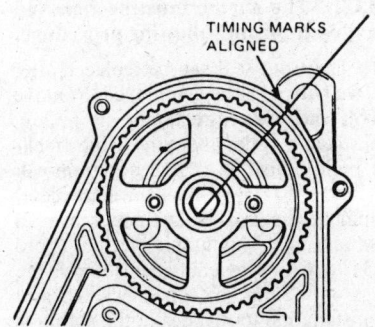

2.0 diesel, camshaft timing mark

2. Rotate engine clockwise until the timing marks on the flywheel and the front camshaft sprocket are aligned with their pointers.

3. Loosen tensioner pulley lockbolt and slide the timing belt off the water pump and camshaft sprockets.

4. The water pump and/or camshaft can now be serviced.

ADJUSTMENTS

2.0 Diesel Engine

Front Belt

1. Remove the flywheel timing mark cover.

2. Remove the front timing belt upper cover.

3. Remove the belt tension spring from the storage pocket in the front cover.

4. Install the tensioner spring in the belt tensioner lever and over the stud mounted on the front of the crankcase.

5. Loosen the tensioner pulley lockbolt.

6. Rotate the crankshaft pulley two revolutions clockwise until the flywheel TDC timing mark aligns with the pointer on the rear cover plate.

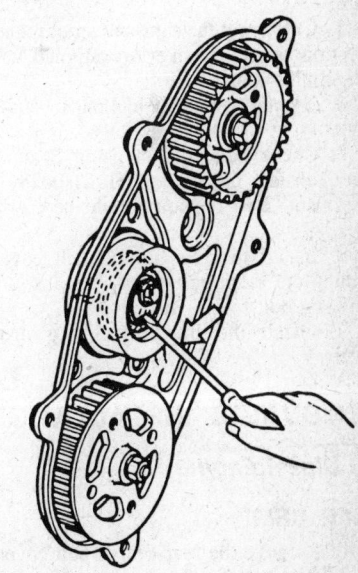

2.0 diesel, loosening tensioner pulley

7. Check the front camshaft sprocket to see that it is aligned with its timing mark.

8. Tighten the tensioner lockbolt to 23-34 ft. lbs.

9. Check the bolt tension using Rotunda Belt Tension Gauge model 21-0028 or equivalent. Belt tension should be 33-44 lbs.

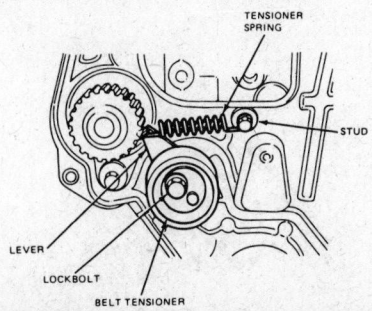

2.0 diesel, front timing belt tensioner spring installation

C171

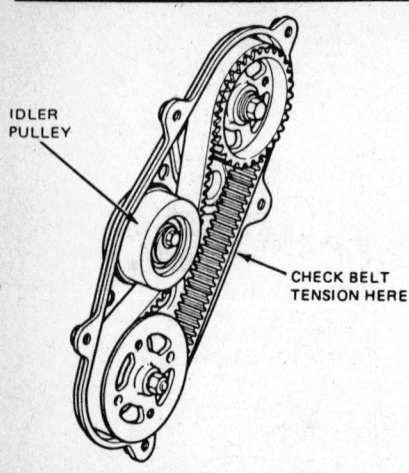

2.0 diesel, timing belt tensioner, rear belt

10. Remove the tensioner spring and install it in the storage pocket in the front cover.

11. Install the front cover and tighten the attaching bolts to 5–7 ft. lbs.

12. Install the flywheel timing mark cover.

REAR BELT

1. Remove the flywheel timing mark cover.

2. Remove the rear timing belt cover.

3. Loosen the tensioner pulley locknut.

4. Rotate the crankshaft two revolutions until the flywheel TDC timing mark aligns with the pointer on the rear cover plate.

5. Check that the camshaft sprocket and injection pump sprocket are aligned with their timing marks.

6. Tighten tensioner locknut to 15–20 ft. lbs.

7. Check belt tension using Rotunda Belt Tension Gauge model 21-0028 or equivalent. Belt tension should be 22–33 lbs.

8. Install the rear timing belt cover. Tighten the 6mm bolts to 5–7 ft. lbs. and the 8mm bolt to 12–16 ft. lbs.

9. Install the flywheel timing mark cover.

REMOVAL & INSTALLATION

2.0 Diesel Engine

REAR BELT

1. Remove the rear timing belt cover.

2. Remove the flywheel timing mark cover from clutch housing.

3. Rotate the crankshaft until the flywheel timing mark is at TDC on No. 1 cylinder.

4. Check that the injection pump and camshaft sprocket timing marks are aligned.

5. Loosen the tensioner locknut. With a screwdriver, or equivalent tool, inserted in the slot provided, rotate the tensioner clockwise to relieve belt tension. Tighten locknut snug.

6. Remove the timing belt.

7. Install the belt.

8. Loosen the tensioner locknut and adjust timing belt as outlined in previous section.

9. Install rear timing belt cover and tighten bolts to 5–7 ft. lbs.

FRONT BELT

NOTE: The engine must be removed from the vehicle to replace the front timing belt.

1. With engine removed from the vehicle and installed on an engine stand, remove front timing belt upper cover.

2. Install a Flywheel Holding Tool T84P6375A or equivalent.

3. Remove the six bolts attaching the crankshaft pulley to the crankshaft sprocket.

4. Install a crankshaft pulley Remover T58P6316D or equivalent using Adapter T74P6700B or equivalent, and remove crankshaft pulley.

5. Remove the front timing belt lower cover.

6. Loosen the tensioning pulley and remove the timing belt.

7. Align the camshaft sprocket with the timing mark.

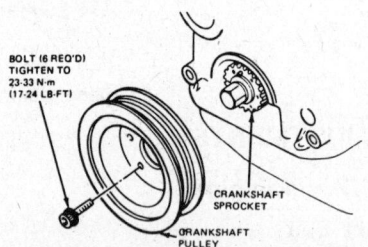

2.0 diesel, crankshaft pulley removal

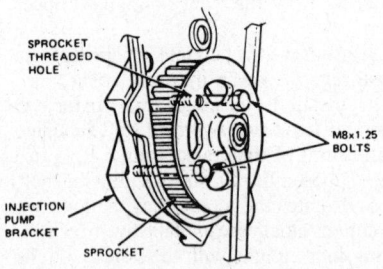

2.0 diesel, injector pump sprocket removal

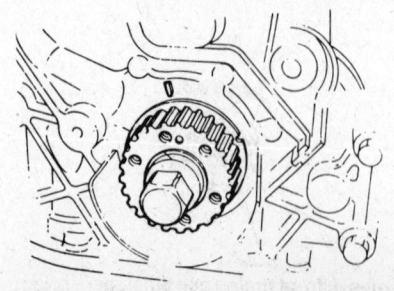

2.0 diesel, crankshaft pulley timing marks

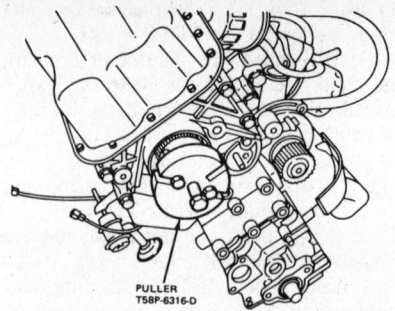

2.0 diesel, crankshaft sprocket removal

NOTE: Check the crankshaft sprocket to see that the timing marks are aligned.

8. Remove the tensioner spring from the pocket in the front timing belt upper cover and install it in the slot in the tensioner lever and over the stud in the crankcase.

9. Push the tensioner lever toward the water pump as far as it will travel and tighten lockbolt snug.

10. Install timing belt.

11. Adjust the timing belt tension as outlined in previous section.

12. Install the front timing belt lower cover and tighten bolts to 5–7 ft. lbs.

13. Install the crankshaft pulley and tighten bolts to 17–24 ft. lbs.

14. Install the front timing belt upper cover and tighten bolts to 5–7 ft. lbs.

Timing Cover, Oil Seal, Timing Chain and Gears

REMOVAL & INSTALLATION

2.3 HSC Engine

NOTE: The engine must be removed from the car for the following procedure.

1. The front seal can be replaced after the drive pulley has been removed. Remove the bolt and washer retaining the pulley. Use a suitable puller and remove the crankshaft pulley. Install a front seal remover tool (Ford #T74P6700A or the equivalent) and remove the seal. Coat a new seal with grease and install with suitable tool (Ford #T83T4676A or the equivalent). Drive the seal in until fully seated. Check the seal after installation to make sure the spring is in proper position around the seal. Install the crankshaft pulley, washer and bolt.

2. To remove the front cover, remove the crankshaft pulley as described above. Remove the front cover retaining bolts, pry the top of the cover away from the engine block and remove the cover.

3. Clean all gasket mounting surfaces. Check the play in the timing chain, replace chain if play is excessive. Check the timing chain tensioner blade for wear, if excessive replace the blade.

FRONT OF ENGINE

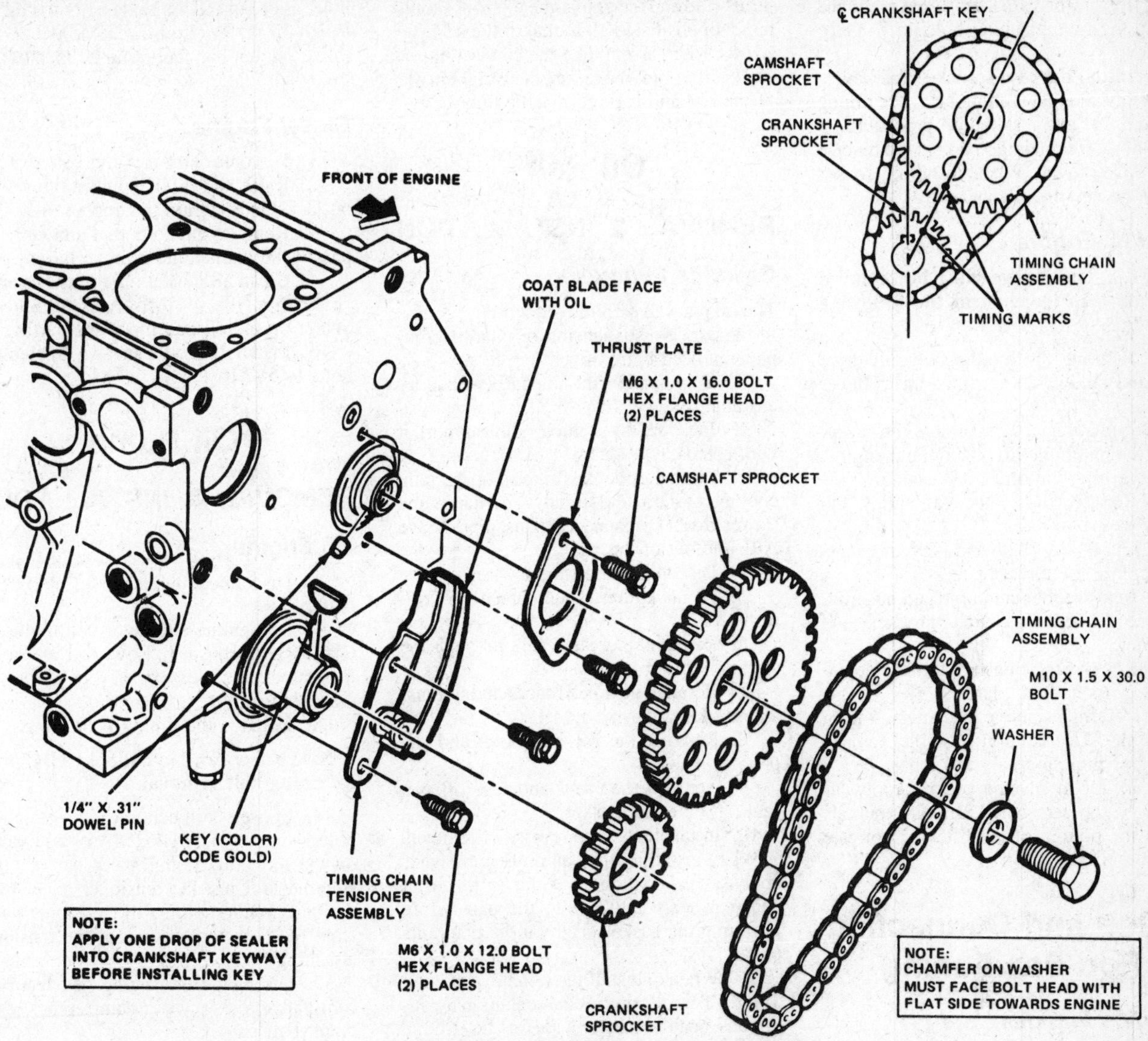

COAT BLADE FACE WITH OIL

THRUST PLATE

M6 X 1.0 X 16.0 BOLT HEX FLANGE HEAD (2) PLACES

CAMSHAFT SPROCKET

1/4" X .31" DOWEL PIN

KEY (COLOR) CODE GOLD)

TIMING CHAIN TENSIONER ASSEMBLY

M6 X 1.0 X 12.0 BOLT HEX FLANGE HEAD (2) PLACES

CRANKSHAFT SPROCKET

NOTE:
APPLY ONE DROP OF SEALER INTO CRANKSHAFT KEYWAY BEFORE INSTALLING KEY

¢ CRANKSHAFT KEY

CAMSHAFT SPROCKET

CRANKSHAFT SPROCKET

TIMING CHAIN ASSEMBLY

TIMING MARKS

TIMING CHAIN ASSEMBLY

M10 X 1.5 X 30.0 BOLT

WASHER

NOTE:
CHAMFER ON WASHER MUST FACE BOLT HEAD WITH FLAT SIDE TOWARDS ENGINE

2.3 HSC engine timing chain and gear assembly

4. Turn the engine until the timing marks on the crank and cam gears align.

5. Remove the camshaft gear attaching bolt and washer. Slide the two gears and chain forward and remove as an assembly.

6. Install in the reverse order. Make sure the timing marks on the camshaft and crank gears are in alignment. Check the timing chain damper, located in the front cover, for wear and replace damper if necessary. Lubricate gears, chain, tensioner blade and front cover oil seal before cover installation. Apply an oil resistant sealer to both sides of the front cover gasket.

Camshaft

REMOVAL & INSTALLATION

1.6 Engine

The camshaft can be removed with the engine in the car.

1. Remove the fuel pump and plunger. Set the engine to TDC on the compression stroke of No. 1 cylinder. Remove the negative battery cable.

2. Remove the alternator drive belt. Remove the power steering and air conditioning compressor drive belts, if equipped.

3. Remove the camshaft belt cover.

4. Remove the distributor.

5. Remove the rocker arms.

6. Remove the hydraulic valve lash adjusters. Keep the parts in order, as they must be returned to their original positions.

7. Remove and discard the timing belt.

8. Remove the camshaft sprocket and key.

9. Remove the camshaft thrust plate.

10. Remove the ignition coil and coil bracket.

11. Remove the camshaft through the back of the head towards the transaxle.

12. Before installing the camshaft, coat the bearing journals, cam lobe surfaces, seal and thrust plate groove with engine oil. Install the camshaft through the rear of the cylinder head. Rotate the camshaft during installation.

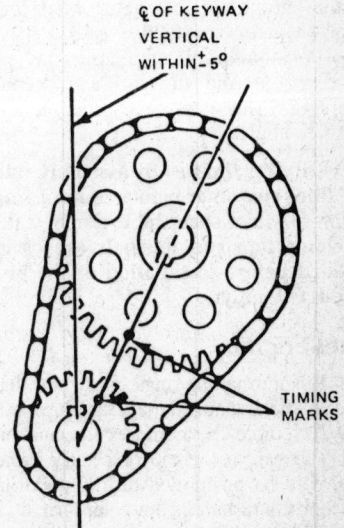

¢ OF KEYWAY VERTICAL WITHIN ± 5°

TIMING MARKS

Timing mark alignment 2.3 HSC engine

13. Install the camshaft thrust plate and tighten the two attaching bolts to 7–11 ft. lbs.

14. Install the cam sprocket and key.

15. Install a new timing belt. See timing belt removal and installation procedure.

16. Install remaining parts in the reverse order of removal. When installing rocker arms, use new hex flange nuts.

2.3 HSC Engine

NOTE: The engine must be removed from the car to perform the following procedure.

1. Remove the oil dipstick, all drive belts and pulleys and remove the cylinder head.

2. Use a magnet or suitable tool to remove the hydraulic lifters from the engine. Keep the lifters in order if reusable.

3. Remove the crankshaft pulley and timing case cover.

4. Check camshaft end play, if excessive replace the thrust plate.

5. Remove the fuel pump and pushrod. Remove the timing chain, sprockets and tensioner.

6. Remove the camshaft thrust plate retaining bolts and the plate.

7. Carefully remove the camshaft from the engine. Use caution to avoid damage to the bearings, journals and lobes.

8. Install in reverse order. Apply lubricant to the camshaft lobes and journals and to the bottom of the lifters. Lubricate all assemblies with oil.

Piston and Connecting Rod Positioning

Gasoline Engines

1. The "Front" markings on the connecting rod must align with the arrow on the piston crown.

2. "Front" and arrow markings must face the "front" of the engine when rods and pistons are reinstalled.

3. Position the oil ring gap to the rear of the piston and the top and second compression ring gaps at 180 degree and 90 degree angles.

NOTE: Dip the piston assembly into an oil filled container before compressing the rings. Make sure the cylinder walls and connecting rod journals are clean and oiled before installation of the piston/rod assembly.

Diesel Engine

1. When installing rings, make sure that the side with the stamped mark faces upward.

2. Assemble the compression and oil rings. The gap of the top ring and second ring should be positioned on the opposite side from the turbulent flow chamber.

3. The gap of the ring should not be directed toward the thrust side or counter-

thrust side and the gap of the top ring should be set opposite (180°) to that of the oil ring.

4. When assembling the connecting rod and bearing cap, make sure the weight marks of the rod and cap are matched correctly.

Oil Pan

REMOVAL & INSTALLATION

Gasoline Engines

The oil pan can be removed with the engine in the car. No suspension or chassis components need be removed.

1. Disconnect the negative battery terminal.

2. Jack up the vehicle and support it with stands.

3. Drain the oil. On Tempo/Topaz, drain cooling system and remove coolant tube (lower hose). Disconnect exhaust pipe. Move A/C line out of the way.

4. Disconnect the starter wires.

5. Remove the knee brace or roll restrictor.

6. Remove the starter bolts and the starter.

7. Remove the knee braces at the transaxle on Escort/Lynx models.

8. Remove the oil pan bolts and the pan.

9. Remove the front and rear oil pan seal, and the pan gasket.

10. Installation is the reverse of removal. When installing the pan on Escort/Lynx, apply a thin coating of sealer to the front and rear seals and also to the pan before installing the gasket. Tighten the pan bolts 6–8 ft. lbs.

11. When installing the pan on Tempo/Topaz, apply RTV sealant in a continuous bead 3/16 inch wide to the groove on the oil pan. Install pan and pan bolts. Tighten bolts enough to squeeze RTV sealant to a point where the two transaxle bolts

holes align. Install transaxle bolts and tighten to 30–39 ft. lbs. Loosen the bolts one-half turn. Tighten pan mounting bolts to 6–9 ft. lbs.

Diesel Engine

1. Disconnect the negative battery cable.

2. Raise and safely support the vehicle on jackstands. Drain the engine oil.

3. Remove the bolts that attach the oil pan to the engine and remove the oil pan.

4. Clean all gasket mounting surfaces.

5. Apply a 1/8 inch bead of Silicone Sealer on the oil pan mounting surface.

6. Install the oil pan and tighten the bolts to 5–7 ft. lbs.

Oil Pump

REMOVAL & INSTALLATION

1.6 Engine

1. Disconnect the negative cable at the battery.

2. Loosen the alternator bolt on the alternator adjusting arm. Lower the alternator to remove the accessory drivebelt from the crankshaft pulley.

3. Remove the timing belt cover.

NOTE: Set No. 1 cylinder at TDC prior to timing belt removal.

4. Loosen both belt tensioner attaching bolts using Tool T81P6254A or equivalent on the left bolt. Using a pry bar or other suitable tool pry the tensioner away from the belt. While holding the tensioner away from the belt, tighten one of the tensioner attaching bolts.

5. Disengage the timing belt from the camshaft sprocket, water pump sprocket and crankshaft sprocket.

6. Raise the vehicle and safely support on jackstands. Drain the crankcase.

7. Using a Crankshaft Pulley Wrench

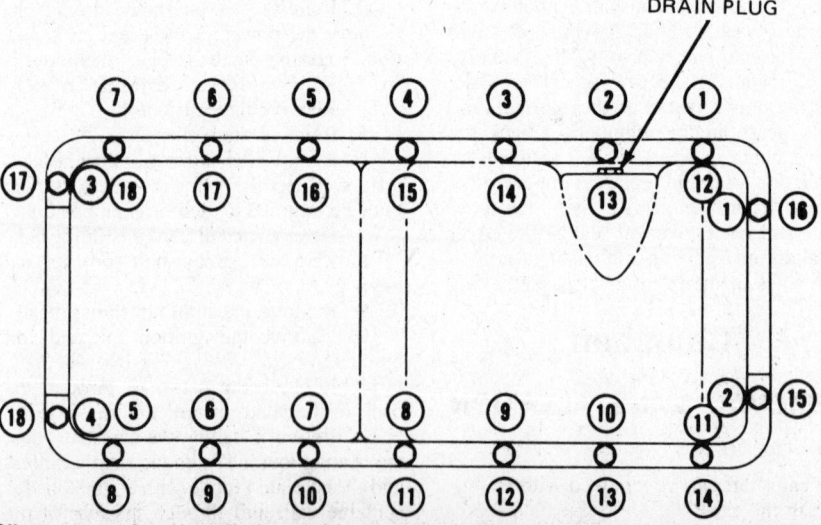

Oil pan removal and installation: tighten the bolts using the sequence inside the diagram, then retighten the bolts using the outside sequence (© Ford Motor Co.)

SECTION C

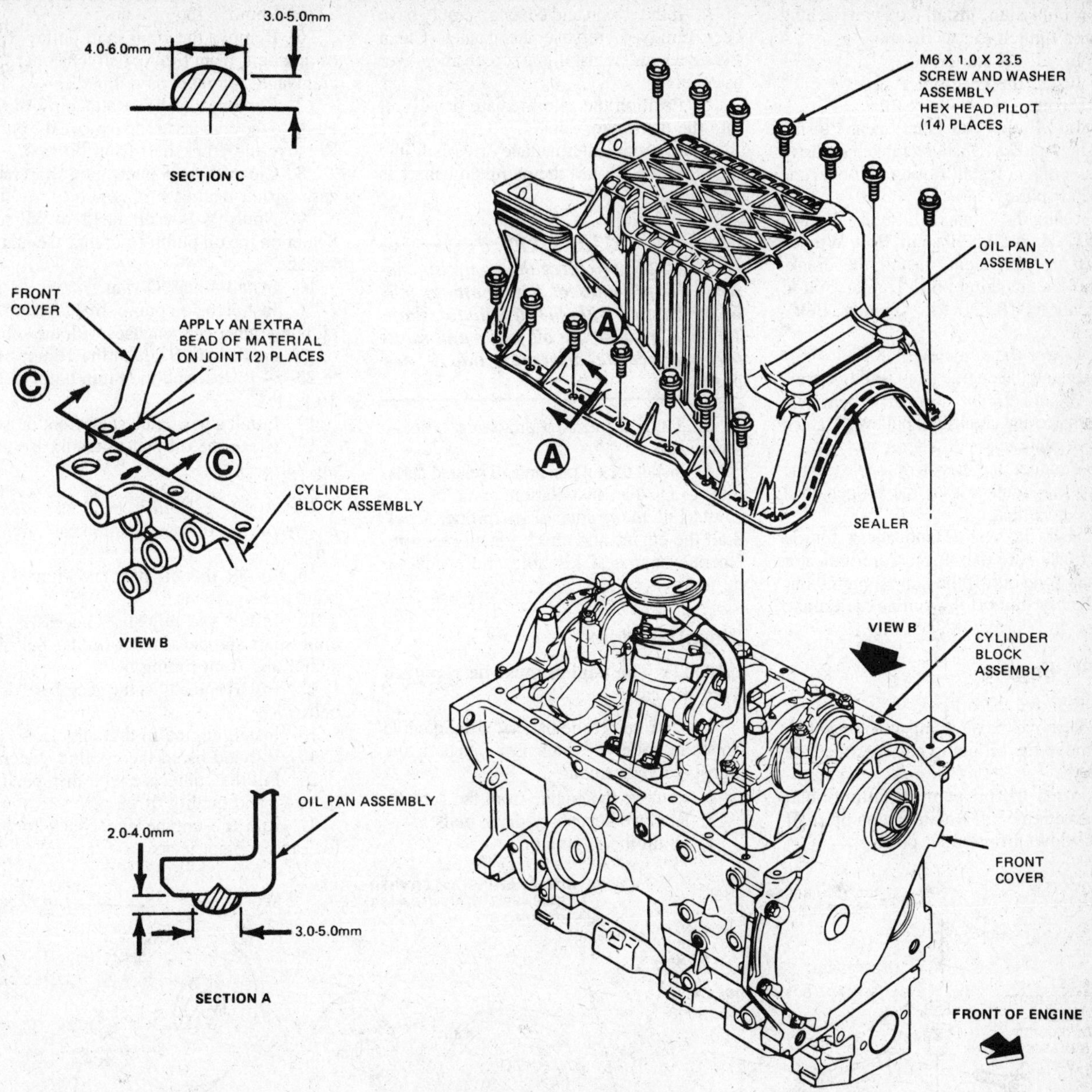

3.0-5.0mm

4.0-6.0mm

M6 X 1.0 X 23.5
SCREW AND WASHER
ASSEMBLY
HEX HEAD PILOT
(14) PLACES

OIL PAN
ASSEMBLY

FRONT
COVER

APPLY AN EXTRA
BEAD OF MATERIAL
ON JOINT (2) PLACES

CYLINDER
BLOCK ASSEMBLY

VIEW B

SEALER

VIEW B

CYLINDER
BLOCK
ASSEMBLY

OIL PAN ASSEMBLY

2.0-4.0mm

3.0-5.0mm

SECTION A

FRONT
COVER

FRONT OF ENGINE

Oil pan installation, 2.3 HSC engine

T81P6312A and Crankshaft Bolt Wrench YA-826 or equivalent, remove the crankshaft pulley attaching bolt.

8. Remove the timing belt.

9. Remove the crankshaft drive plate assembly. Remove the crankshaft pulley. Remove the crankshaft sprocket.

10. Disconnect the starter cable at the starter.

11. Remove the knee-brace from the engine.

12. Remove the starter.

13. Remove the rear section of the knee-brace and inspection plate at the transmission.

14. Remove the oil pan retaining bolts and oil pan. Remove the front and rear oil pan seals. Remove the oil pan side gaskets. Remove the oil pump attaching bolts, oil pump and gasket. Remove the oil pump seal.

15. Make sure the mating surfaces on the cylinder block and the oil pump are clean and free of gasket material.

16. Remove the oil pick-up tube and screen assembly from the pump for cleaning.

17. Lubricate the outside diameter of the oil pump seal with engine oil.

18. Install the oil pump seal using Seal Installer T81P6700A or equivalent.

19. Install the pick-up tube and screen assembly on the oil pump. Tighten attaching bolts to 6–9 ft. lbs.

20. Lubricate the oil pump seal lip with light engine oil.

21. Position the oil pump gasket over the locating dowels. Install attaching bolts and tighten to 5–7 ft. lbs.

22. Apply a bead of silcone sealer approximately 3.0mm wide at the corner of the front and rear oil pan seals, and at the seating point of the oil pump to the block

retainer joint.

23. Install the front oil pan seal by pressing firmly into the slot cut into the bottom of the pump.

24. Install the rear oil seal by pressing firmly into the slot cut into rear retainer assembly.

NOTE: Install the seal before the sealer has cured (within 10 minutes of application).

25. Apply adhesive sealer evenly to oil pan flange and to the oil pan side of the gaskets. Allow the adhesive to dry past the ''wet'' stage and then install the gaskets on the oil pan. Position the oil pan on the cylinder block.

26. Install oil pan attaching bolts. Tighten bolts in the proper sequence 6–8 ft. lbs.

27. Position the transmission inspection plate and the rear section of the knee-brace

on the tranmission. Install the two attaching bolts and tighten to specification.

28. Install the starter.

29. Install the knee-brace.

30. Connect the starter cable.

31. Install the crankshaft gear. Install crankshaft pulley. Install crankshaft drive plate assembly. Install timing belt over the crankshaft pulley.

32. Using the Crankshaft Pulley Wrench T81P6312A and Crankshaft Bolt Wrench YA-826 or equivalent, install the crank-shaft pulley attaching bolt. Tighten bolt to specification. (Refer to "Timing Belt" section).

33. Lower the vehicle.

34. Install the engine front timing cover.

35. Position the accessory drive belts over the alternator and crankshaft pulleys. Tighten the drive belts to specification.

36. Connect the negative cable at the battery. Fill crankcase to the proper level with the specified oil.

37. Start the engine and check for oil leaks. Make sure the oil pressure indicator lamp has gone out. If the lamp remains On, immediately shut off the engine, determine the case and correct the condition.

2.3HSC Engine

1. Remove the oil pan.

2. Remove the oil pump attaching bolts and remove the oil pump and intermediate driveshaft.

3. Prime the oil pump by filling inlet port with engine oil. Rotate the pump shaft until oil flows from outlet port.

4. If the screen and cover assembly have been removed, replace the gasket. Clean the screen and reinstall the screen and cover assembly.

5. Position the intermediate driveshaft into the distributor socket.

6. Insert the intermediate driveshaft into the oil pump. Install the pump and shaft as an assembly.

--- CAUTION ---

Do not attempt to force the pump into po-sition if it will not seat. The shaft hex may be misaligned with the distributor shaft. To align, remove the oil pump and rotate the intermediate driveshaft into a new position.

7. Tighten the two attaching bolts to specification.

8. Install the oil pan and all related parts, refer to Oil Pan Installation.

9. Fill the crankcase to proper level. Start the engine and check for oil pressure. Operate engine at fast idle and check for oil leaks.

Diesel Engine

NOTE: The engine must be removed from the car.

1. Disconnect the battery ground cable from the battery, which is located in the luggage compartment.

2. Remove the engine from the vehicle.

3. Remove accessory drive belts.

4. Drain the engine oil.

5. Remove the oil pan.

6. Remove the crankshaft pulley, front timing belt, front timing belt tensioner, and crankshaft sprocket as outlined.

7. Remove the bolts attaching the oil pump to the crankcase and remove the pump. Remove the crankshaft front oil seal.

8. Clean the oil pump and the crank-case gasket mating surfaces.

9. Apply a 1/8-inch bead of Silicone Sealer on the oil pump-to-crankcase mating surface.

10. Install a new O-ring.

11. Install the oil pump, making sure the oil pump inner gear engages with the splines on the crankshaft. Tighten the 10mm bolts to 23–34 ft. lbs. and the 8mm bolts to 12–16 ft. lbs.

12. Install a new crankshaft front oil seal.

13. Clean the oil pan-to-crankcase mat-ing surfaces.

14. Apply a 1/8-inch bead of Silicone Sealer on the oil-pan-to-crankcase mating surface.

15. Install the oil pan and tighten the bolts to 5–7 ft. lbs.

16. Install and adjust as necessary the crankshaft sprocket, front timing belt ten-sioner and front timing belt.

17. Install and adjust the accessory drive belts.

18. Install engine in the vehicle.

19. Fill and bleed the cooling system.

20. Fill the crankcase with the specified quantity and quality of oil.

21. Run the engine and check for oil, fuel and coolant leaks.

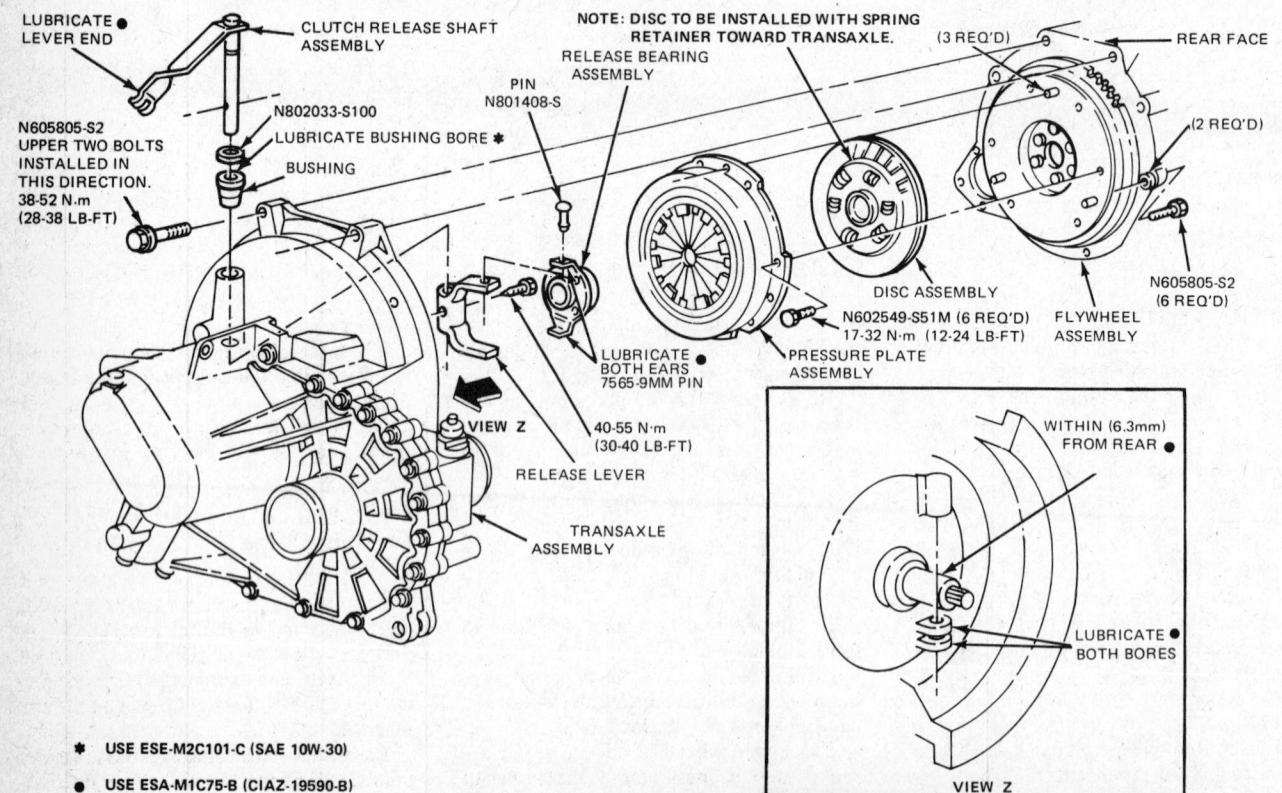

Typical clutch assembly installation

Rear Main Seal

REMOVAL & INSTALLATION

A one piece ring-type rear main oil seal is used.

NOTE: The engine must be removed prior to attempting this procedure.

1. Remove the transaxle.
2. Remove the rear cover plate.
3. Remove the flywheel or flexplate if so equipped.
4. Remove the rear main seal by carefully punching a hole in the seal and removing with a threaded slide hammer. Be extremely careful not to scratch the crankshaft or seal mating surface.
5. Coat the lips of the new seal with engine oil. Gently tap the seal into place.
6. Installation is the reverse of removal.

CLUTCH

REMOVAL & INSTALLATION

1. Remove the transaxle.
2. Mark the pressure plate assembly and the flywheel so that they can be assembled in the same position.
3. Loosen the attaching bolts one turn at a time, in sequence, until spring tension is relieved.
4. Support the pressure plate and remove the bolts. Remove the pressure plate and clutch disc.
5. Inspect the flywheel, clutch disc, pressure plate, throwout bearing, and the clutch fork for wear. Replace parts as required. If the flywheel shows any signs of overheating (blue discoloration) or if it is badly grooved or scored, it should be refaced or replaced.
6. Clean the pressure plate and flywheel surfaces thoroughly. Position the clutch disc and pressure plate into the in-

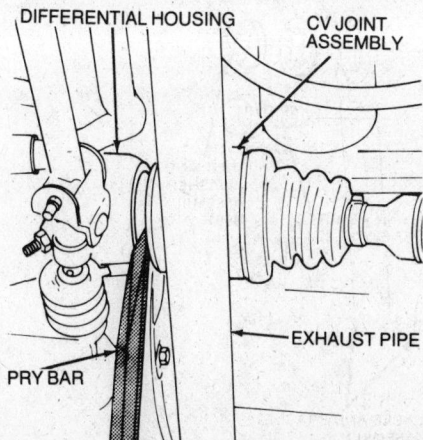

DIFFERENTIAL HOUSING
CV JOINT ASSEMBLY
EXHAUST PIPE
PRY BAR

Halfshaft removal (© Ford Motor Co.)

stalled position, aligning the marks made previously. Support them with a dummy shaft or clutch aligning tool.
7. Install the pressure plate-to-flywheel bolts. Tighten them gradually in a criss-cross pattern. Remove the alignment tool.
8. Lubricate the release bearing and install it in the fork.
9. Install the transaxle.

ADJUSTMENT

All models are equipped with automatically self-adjusting clutches. No separate free play adjustments are necessary.

MANUAL TRANSAXLE

REMOVAL & INSTALLATION

Escort/Lynx

1. Disconnect the negative battery terminal.
2. Remove the two transaxle to engine top mounting bolts.
3. Remove the clutch cable from the clutch release lever.
4. Raise the vehicle and support it on jack stands.
5. Remove the brake line routing clamps from the front wheels.
6. Remove the bolt that secures the lower control arm ball joint to the steering knuckle assembly, and pry the lower control arm away from the knuckle. When installing, a new nut and bolt must be used.

NOTE: The plastic shield installed behind the rotor contains a molded pocket for the lower control arm ball joint. When removing the control arm from the knuckle, bend the shield toward the rotor to provide clearance.

7. Pry the right inboard CV-joint from the transaxle, then remove the CV-joint and halfshaft by pulling outward on the steering knuckle; wire the CV-joint/halfshaft assembly out of the way. Wire the joint assembly in a level position to prevent it from expanding.

NOTE: When the CV-joint is pulled out of the transaxle fluid will leak out. Install shipping plugs T81P-1177-B or their equivalent to prevent the dislocation of the differential side gears.

8. Repeat the procedures and remove the left hand CV-joint/halfshaft from the transaxle.
9. Remove the stabilizer bar.
10. Disconnect the speedometer cable and back-up light.
11. Remove the (3) nuts from the starter mounting studs which hold the engine roll restrictor bracket.

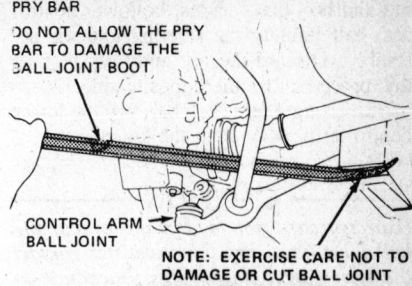

PRY BAR
DO NOT ALLOW THE PRY BAR TO DAMAGE THE BALL JOINT BOOT
CONTROL ARM BALL JOINT
NOTE: EXERCISE CARE NOT TO DAMAGE OR CUT BALL JOINT BOOT. PRY BAR MUST NOT CONTACT LOWER ARM.

Separating the steering knuckle from the ball joint (© Ford Motor Co.)

12. Remove the roll restrictor and the starter stud bolts.
13. Remove the stiffner brace.
14. Remove the shift mechanism crossover spring.
15. Remove the shift mechanism stabilizer bar.
16. Remove the shift mechanism.
17. Place a transmission jack under the transaxle.
18. Remove the rear transmission mounts.
19. Remove the front transmission mounts.
20. Lower the transaxle support jack until it clears the rear mount and support the engine with a jack, under the oil pan.
21. Remove the four remaining engine to transaxle bolts.
22. Remove the transaxle.

NOTE: The case may have sharp edges. Wear protective gloves when handling the transaxle.

23. Installation is the reverse of removal.

NOTE: When installing the CV-joint/halfshaft assemblies into the transaxle, install new circlips on the inner stub shafts, carefully install the assemblies into the transaxle to prevent damaging the oil seals, and insure that both joints are fully seated in the transaxle by lightly prying outward to confirm they are seated. If the circlips are not seated, the joints will move out of the transaxle.

Tempo/Topaz

1. Wedge a wood block approximately 7 inches long under the clutch pedal to hold the pedal up slightly beyond its normal position. Grasp the clutch cable and pull forward, disconnecting it from the clutch release shaft assembly. Remove the clutch casing from the rib on the top surface of the transaxle case.
2. Using a 13mm socket, remove the two top transaxle-to-engine mounting bolts. Using a 10mm socket, remove the air cleaner.
3. Raise and safely support the car. Remove the front stabilizer bar to control arm attaching nut and washer (drivers side). Discard the attaching nut. Remove the two front stabilizer bar mounting brackets. Discard the bolts.
4. Using a 15mm socket, remove the

nut and bolt that secures the lower control arm ball joint to the steering knuckle assembly. Discard the nut and bolt. Repeat this procedure on the opposite side.

5. Using a large pry bar, pry the lower control arm away from the knuckle.

--- CAUTION ---

Exercise care not to damage or cut the ball joint boot. Pry bar must not contact the lower arm. Repeat this procedure on the opposite side.

6. Using a large pry bar, pry the left inboard CV-joint assembly from the transaxle.

NOTE: Lubricant will drain from the seal at this time. Install shipping plugs (T81P-1177-B or equivalent). Two plugs are required (one for each seal). Remove the inboard CV-joint from the transaxle by grasping the left hand steering knuckle and swinging the knuckle and halfshaft outward from the transaxle.

--- CAUTION ---

Exercise care when using a pry bar to remove the CV-joint assembly. If not careful, damage to the differential oil seal may result.

7. If the CV-joint assembly cannot be pried from the transaxle, insert Differential Rotater Tool (T81P-4026-A or equivalent), through the left side and tap the joint out. Tool can be used from either side of transaxle.

8. Wire the halfshaft assembly in a near level position to prevent damage to the assembly during the remaining operations. Repeat this procedure on the opposite side.

9. Using a small prybar, remove the backup lamp switch connector from the transaxle back-up lamp switch.

10. Using a 15mm socket, remove the three nuts from the starter mounting studs which hold the engine roll restrictor bracket. Remove the engine roll restrictor.

11. Using a 13mm deep well socket, remove the three starter stud bolts.

12. Using a 10mm socket, remove the shift mechanism to shift shaft attaching nut and bolt and control selector indicator switch arm. Remove the shift shaft.

13. Using a 15mm socket, remove the shift mechanism stabilizer bar to transaxle attaching bolt. Remove the 7/32-in. sheet metal screw and the control selector indicator switch and bracket assembly.

14. Using a 22mm (7/8-in.) crows foot wrench, remove the speedometer cable from the transaxle.

15. Using a 13mm universal socket, remove the two stiffener brace attaching bolts from the oil pan to clutch bousing.

16. Position a suitable jack under the transaxle. Using an 18mm socket, remove the two nuts that secure the left hand rear No. 4 insulator to the body bracket.

17. Using a 13mm socket, remove the bolts that secure the left hand front No. 1 insulator to the body bracket. Lower the transaxle jack until the transaxle clears the rear insulator. Support the engine with a screw jack stand under the oil pan. Use a 2 × 4 inch piece of wood on top of the screw jack.

18. Using a 13mm socket, remove the four engine to transaxle attaching bolts. One of these bolts holds the ground strap and wiring loom stand off bracket.

19. Remove the transaxle from the rear face of the engine and lower transaxle from the vehicle.

20. Install in reverse order. WARNING: THE TRANSAXLE CASE CASTING MAY HAVE SHARP EDGES. WEAR PROTECTIVE GLOVES WHEN HANDLING THE TRANSAXLE ASSEMBLY.

OVERHUAL

For all overhual procedures, please refer to "Manual Transmission Overhual" in the Unit Repair section.

AUTOMATIC TRANSAXLE

For all automatic transaxle adjustment procedures, please refer to "Automatic Transmissions" in the Unit Repair section.

REMOVAL & INSTALLATION

Escort/Lynx

Removal of the automatic transaxle is basically the same as the standard transaxle with the following recommendations.

NOTE: Due to the ATX case configuration the right hand halfshaft assembly must be removed first. Special tool T81P-4026-A is then inserted into the transaxle to drive the left hand inboard CV joint assembly from the transaxle.

1. Remove the bolts attaching the managed air valve to the valve body.
2. Disconnect the neutral safety switch.
3. Disconnect the throttle valve linkage and the manual lever cable.
4. Remove both tie rod ends from the steering knuckles.
5. Remove the dust cover from the torque converter housing.
6. Remove the torque converter to flywheel attaching nuts.

NOTE: Turn the crankshaft pulley bolt to bring the attaching nuts to an accessible position.

7. Insert a screwdriver between the flywheel and torque converter, then carefully move the transaxle and converter away from the engine.

Tempo/Topaz

The engine and automatic transaxle must be removed as an assembly. Refer to "Engine Removal". Seperate the transaxle from the engine after removal from the car.

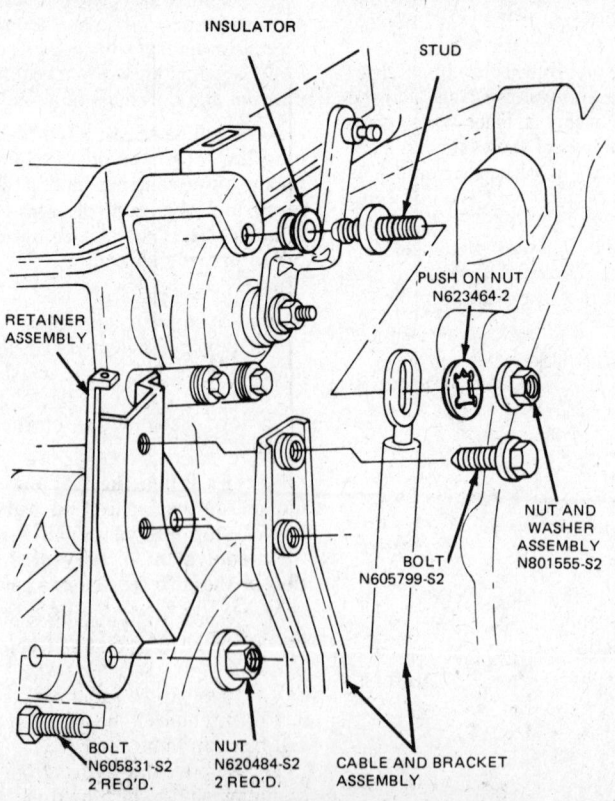

ATX shift control cable and bracket assembly

AXLE SHAFTS

REMOVAL & INSTALLATION

CAUTION

When removing both the left and right halfshafts special plug T81P-1177-B must be installed. Failure to use these plugs can result in dislocation of the differential side gears. Should these gears become misaligned the differential will have to be removed from the transaxle to re-align the gears.

When removing both the left and right half-shafts special plug T81P-1177-B must be installed. Failure to use these plugs can result in dislocation of the differential side gears. Should these gears become mis aligned the differential will have to be removed from the transaxle to re-align the gears.

The halfshaft removal procedure is the same for the ATX and MTX with the following exception.

Due to the case configuration on the ATX the right hand halfshaft assembly must be removed first. Driver #T81P-4026-A or equivalent is inserted into the transaxle to drive the left hand inboard CV joint assembly from the transaxle. If only the left hand halfshaft assembly is to be removed for service, remove the right hand halfshaft assembly from the transaxle only. After removal support it with a length of wire, then drive the left hand halfshaft assembly from the transaxle.

NOTE: Before attempting this procedure you must be sure to have a new hub nut and a new lower control arm to steering knuckle bolt and nut. Once these parts have been removed they must not be reused.

1. Remove the hub cap and loosen the hub nut.
2. Jack up the vehicle and support it with jack stands.
3. Remove the hub nut and washer.
4. Remove the bolt attaching the brake hose routing clip to the suspension strut.
5. Remove the ball joint to steering knuckle bolt and nut.
6. Separate the ball joint from the steering knuckle using a pry bar.

NOTE: The lower control arm ball joint fits into a pocket formed in the plastic disc brake rotor shield. This shield must be bent away from the ball joint while prying the ball joint out of the steering knuckle.

7. Remove the halfshaft from the differential housing, using a pry bar. Be careful not to damage any seals or boots.
8. Tie the end of the shaft out of the way with a piece of wire.
9. Separate the outboard CV joint from the hub using a puller.

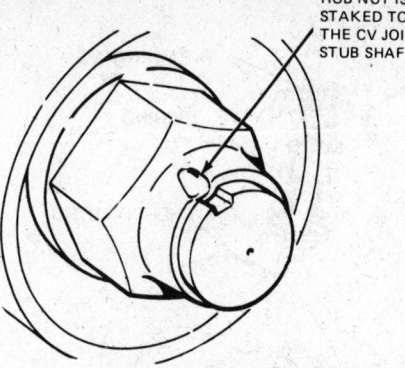

HUB NUT IS STAKED TO THE CV JOINT STUB SHAFT

Stake the front wheel axle nut

10. Installation is the reverse of removal with the following suggestions.
   a. Install a new circlip on the inboard CV joint stub shaft.
   b. Stake the new hub nut with a chisel, after torqueing nut to 180–200 ft. lbs.

Constant Velocity Joint

OVERHAUL

The CV joint components are matched during manufacture and cannot be interchanged with components from another CV joint. The joint can be disassembled for inspection and cleaning only: a damaged CV joint must be completely replaced.

REAR AXLE

Rear Wheel Bearings

REMOVAL, PACKING, INSTALLATION AND ADJUSTMENT

The rear wheel bearings are located in the brake drum hub. The inner wheel bearing is protected by a grease seal. A washer and spindle nut retain the hub/drum assembly and control the bearing endplay.

1. Remove wheel, dust cover, cotter pin nut and drum.
2. The outer bearing will be loose when the drum is removed and may be lifted out by hand. The inner bearing is retained by a grease seal. To remove the inner bearing, insert a wooden dowel or soft drift through the hub from the outer bearing side and carefully drive out the inner bearing and grease seal.
3. Clean the bearings, cups and hubs with a suitable solvent. Inspect the bearings and cups for damage or heat discoloring. Replace as a set if necessary. Always install a new grease seal.

4. If new bearings are to be used, use a three jawed slide-hammer puller to remove the cups from the drum hub. Install the new bearing cups using a suitable driver. Make sure they are fully seated in the hub.
5. Pack the bearings with a multi-purpose grease.
6. Coat the cups with a thin film of grease. Install the inner bearing and grease seal.
7. Coat the bearing surfaces of the spindle with a thin film of grease. Slowly and carefully slide the drum and hub over the spindle and brake shoes. Install the outer bearing over the spindle and into the hub.
8. Install the keyed flat washer and adjusting nut on the spindle.
9. Tighten the adjusting nut to between 17–25 ft. lbs.
10. Back-off the adjusting nut ½ turn. Then retighten it to between 10–15 ft. lbs.
11. Position the nut retainer on the nut and install the cotter pin. Do not tighten the nut to install the cotter pin.
12. Spread the ends of the cotter pin and bend them around the nut retainer. Install the center grease cap.
13. Install the tire and wheel assembly. Lower the car and tighten the wheel lugs.

JACKING

Contact points for jacking with either the jack supplied with the car, or with a floor jack are located on the side rocker flanges. When using a floor jack, the front of the car may be raised by positioning the jack under the front body rail behind the suspension arm-to-body bracket. The rear of the car may be raised by positioning the jack forward of the rear suspension rod on the bracket.

FRONT SUSPENSION

All models are equipped with a MacPherson strut front suspension with cast steering knuckles. The shock absorber strut assembly includes a rubber top mount and a coil spring insulator, mounted on the shock strut.

The entire strut assembly is attached to the top by two bolts. The lower end of the assembly is attached to the steering knuckle. A pinch joint is designed into the knuckle. The forged lower arm assembly is attached to the underbody side apron and steering knuckle. A stabilizer bar connects the outer end of the lower arm to the engine mount bracket. Caster and camber are preset and non-adjustable. The suspension fittings are

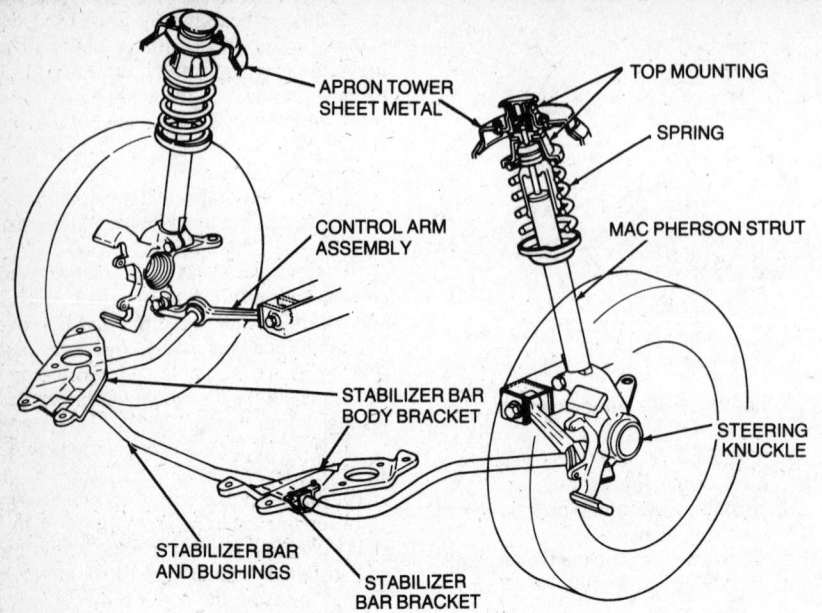

Front suspension components (© Ford Motor Co.)

Labels: APRON TOWER SHEET METAL, TOP MOUNTING, SPRING, CONTROL ARM ASSEMBLY, MAC PHERSON STRUT, STABILIZER BAR BODY BRACKET, STEERING KNUCKLE, STABILIZER BAR AND BUSHINGS, STABILIZER BAR BRACKET

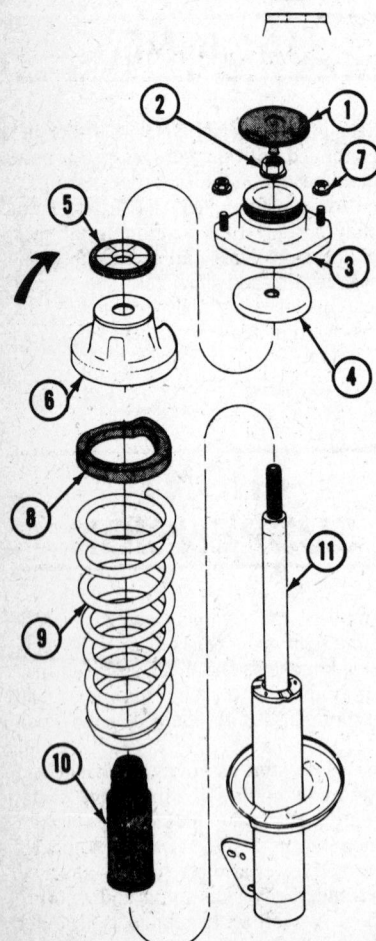

BEARING AND SEAL ASSY. MUST BE SEATED INTO THE SPRING SEAT

Exploded view of strut assembly (© Ford Motor Co.)

"lubed for life"; no grease fittings are provided.

Strut

REMOVAL & INSTALLATION

1. Jack up the vehicle and support it with jack stands.
2. Remove the front wheels. Remove caliper and rotor.
3. Remove the brake line flex hose clip from the strut.
4. Jack up the lower control arm and raise the strut as far as possible without lifting the vehicle from the jack stands.
5. Install a spring compressor on the spring.
6. Tighten the spring until there is approximately ⅛ inch between any two coils.

—— CAUTION ——
The spring must be compressed before the strut is removed to insure that excessive force is not applied to the constant velocity joints.

7. Remove the pinch bolt from the steering knuckle.
8. Loosen the two top mounting bolts, but do not remove them.
9. Lower the jack away from the control arm.
10. Use a suitable tool to spread the pinch joint.
11. Place a piece of 2 × 4 wood about 7½ inches long against the shoulder of the knuckle.
12. Insert a pry bar between the wooden block and the strut base. Separate the strut from the knuckle.
13. Remove the top mounting nuts.

14. Remove the strut and spring assembly.
15. Installation is the reverse of removal.

OVERHAUL

For all strut disassembly and overhaul procedures, please refer to "Strut Overhaul" in the Unit Repair section.

Control Arm and Ball Joint

REMOVAL & INSTALLATION

1. Loosen the wheel nuts, raise and support the car, and remove the wheel and tire.
2. Remove the ball joint stud pinch bolt from the steering knuckle.
3. Pull the control arm and ball joint down and away from the steering knuckle.
4. Remove the stabilizer bar-to-control arm nut.
5. Remove the control arm-to-chassis mounting bolt. Remove the control arm.
6. Installation is the reverse.

NOTE: Be sure the steering column is unlocked and do not use a hammer to separate the ball joint from the knuckle.

Front Wheel Bearings

Timken "Set-Right" front wheel bearings are used, which require no periodic lubrication or adjustment.

REAR SUSPENSION

The Escort, EXP, Lynx and LN7 feature a modified MacPherson strut independent rear suspension.

Each side consists of a shock strut, lower control arm, tie rod, forged spindle and a coil spring mounted on the control arm.

The shock strut consists of a rubber insulated top mount, one piece jounce bumper/dust shield and an integral shock absorber. The entire strut assembly is attached to the body side panel by a rubber insulated top mount assembly and nut. The lower end of the assembly is bolted to the spindle. The lower control arm attaches to the cross-member and to the spindle. A coil spring is located on the crossmember. The tie rod attaches to the frame rail and the spindle assembly.

The Tempo/Topaz use a true Mac-Pherson strut independent rear suspension. Each side consists of a shock absorber strut assembly, two parallel control arms per side, tie rod, forged spindle and a jounce bumper and bracket.

The shock absorber strut assembly includes a rubber isolated top mount, upper spring seat, coil spring insulator, coil spring and lower spring seat. The strut assembly is attached at the top by two studs, which retain the top mount of the strut to the inner body side panel. The lower end of the assembly is bolted to the spindle. The two stamped control arms attach to the underbody and spindle with nuts and bolts. A tie rod attaches to the underbody and to the forged spindle. The jounce bumper bracket attaches to the strut with the lower strut attaching bolts.

NOTE: Refer to the Unit Repair Section for strut servicing.

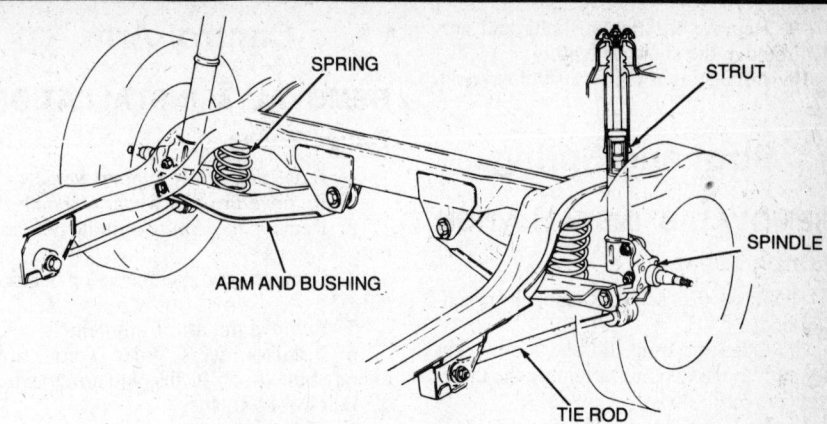

Rear suspension components Escort/Lynx

Coil Spring

REMOVAL & INSTALLATION
Escort/Lynx

1. Jack up the vehicle and support it with jackstands.

2. Place a jack under the control arm and raise the control arm enough to put tension on the spring.

NOTE: Be careful not to raise the car off the jackstands.

3. Remove the control arm bolt at the spindle.

4. Slowly lower the control arm until the spring can be removed.

5. Installation is the reverse of removal.

Shock Strut

REMOVAL & INSTALLATION
Escort/Lynx

1. Remove the rear compartment access panels.

NOTE: Four door models require the removal of the quarter panel trim.

2. Loosen, but do not remove the top strut nut.

NOTE: If the shock absorber is to be re-used do not grip the shock absorber shaft with pliers, as this will damage the shaft.

3. Jack up the vehicle and support it with jackstands.

4. Remove the rear tire.

5. Support the lower control arm with a jack.

6. Remove the clip retaining the brake hose to the shock and carefully move it out of the way.

7. Loosen the nuts and bolts retaining the shock to the spindle, but do not remove them.

8. Remove the top mounting nut.

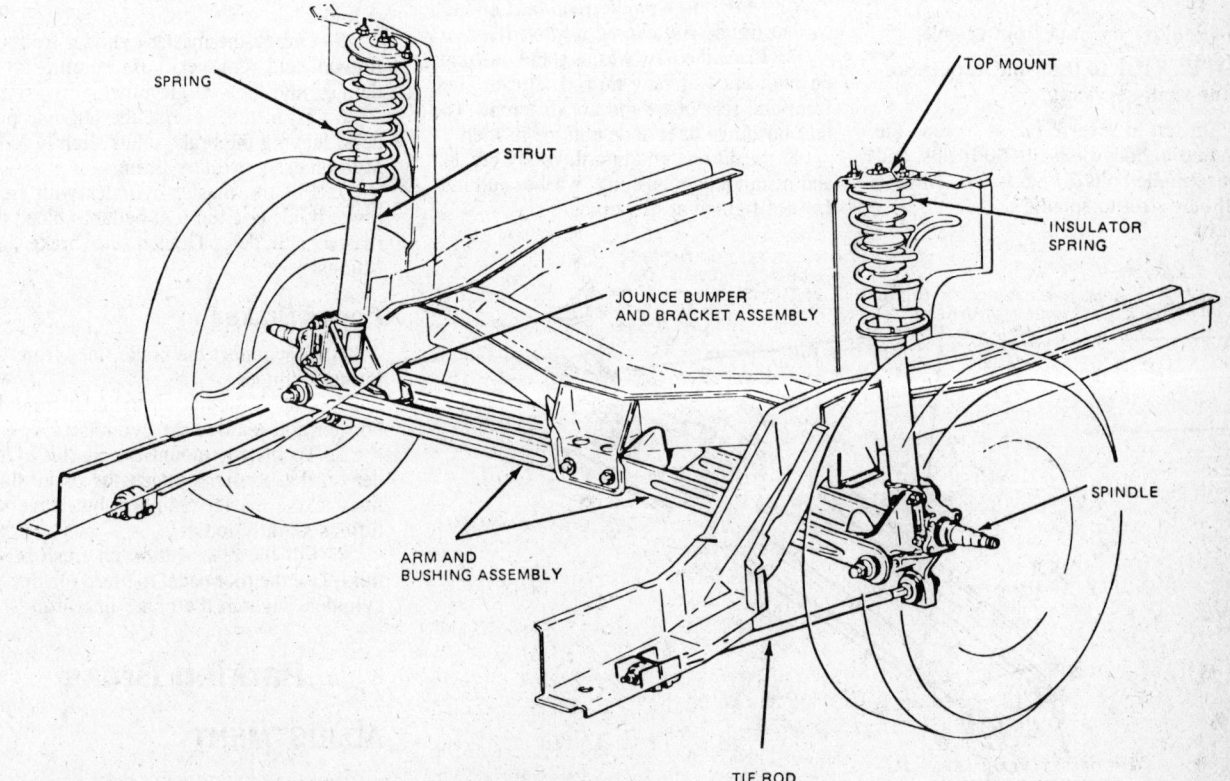

Rear-suspension; Tempo/Topaz

9. Remove the bottom bolts and nuts and remove the shock assembly.

10. Installation is the reverse of removal.

Strut and Spring

REMOVAL & INSTALLATION

Tempo/Topaz

1. Raise the jack only enough to contact body.

2. Open the trunk lid and loosen, but do not remove two nuts retaining the upper strut mount to body.

3. Raise the vehicle. Remove the wheel and tire.

4. Place a jackstand under the control arms to support the suspension.

——— CAUTION ———

Care should be taken when removing the strut that the rear brake flex hose is not stretched or the steel brake tube is not bent.

5. Remove the bolt attaching the brake hose bracket to the strut and carefully move it out of the way.

6. Remove the two bolts retaining the jounce bumper bracket and strut to the spindle.

7. Remove the jounce bumper bracket from the vehicle.

8. Remove the shock strut from the spindle.

9. Remove the two upper mount-to-body nuts.

10. Remove the strut from vehicle.

NOTE: Refer to the Unit Repair Section for strut servicing.

11. Install in reverse order. Torque the top mount to body bolts 20–30 ft. lbs. and strut to spindle bolts 70–96 ft. lbs. Always install new strut to spindle bolts.

Control Arm

REMOVAL & INSTALLATION

Tempo/Topaz

1. Raise and safely support vehicle.

2. Remove tire and wheel assembly.

3. Remove the arm-to-spindle bolt and nut.

4. Remove the center mounting bolt and nut.

5. Remove the arm from vehicle.

6. Install in reverse order. Torque arm to body bolt 40–55 ft. lbs. and arm to spindle bolt 60–86 ft. lbs.

Tie-Rod

REMOVAL & INSTALLATION

Tempo/Topaz

1. Raise the car only enough to contact the body. From inside the trunk loosen, but **Do not** remove, the two strut top mount-to-body nuts.

2. Raise the vehicle and place a jackstand under the suspension to support it. Remove wheel and tire assembly.

3. Remove the two top mount studs.

4. Remove the nut retaining tie-rod to the spindle. Remove the nut retaining tie-rod to body.

5. Lower the jackstand enough so that the upper strut mount studs are out of the holes in the body.

6. Move the spindle rearward enough so that the tie-rod can be removed.

7. Place the new washers and bushings on both ends of new tie-rod. Bushings at front and rear of tie-rod are different. The rear bushings have indentations in them.

8. Insert one end into the body bracket and install a new bushing, washer and nut. **Do not** tighten at this time.

9. Pull back on the spindle enough so that the tie rod end can be installed in the spindle.

10. Install a new bushing, washer and nut. **Do not** tighten at this time.

11. Raise the jackstand enough to hold the two strut mounting studs in place.

12. Install two new strut-to-body mount nuts. Tighten to 20–30 ft. lbs.

13. Raise the suspension to curb height and tighten the two tie-rod nuts to 52–74 ft. lbs.

14. Remove jackstand. Install the tire and wheel assembly. Lower the vehicle.

BRAKES

Master Cylinder

REMOVAL & INSTALLATION

Standard Brakes

1. Disconnect the negative battery terminal.

2. Working under the instrument panel, disconnect the master cylinder pushrod from the brake pedal.

3. Disconnect the stoplight switch and remove it.

4. Inside the engine compartment, disconnect the brake lines from the master cylinder.

5. Unbolt the master cylinder from the firewall and remove it. Be careful not to damage the firewall grommet.

6. To install, reverse the removal process, leaving the brake tubes slightly loose at the master cylinder fittings.

7. Fill the master cylinder with fresh brake fluid. Use the foot pedal to bleed the master cylinder. Tighten the brake line fittings.

Power Brakes

1. Disconnect the brake lines from the master cylinder.

2. Unbolt the master cylinder from the booster and remove the cylinder.

3. To install, mount the master cylinder on the booster. Attach the brake fluid lines to the master cylinder, but leave the fittings slightly loose.

4. Fill the reservoirs with fresh brake fluid. Use the foot pedal to bleed the master cylinder. Tighten the brake line fittings.

Parking Brake

ADJUSTMENT

1. Apply approximately 100 lbs. pedal effort to the hydraulic service brake three times, before adjusting the parking brake.

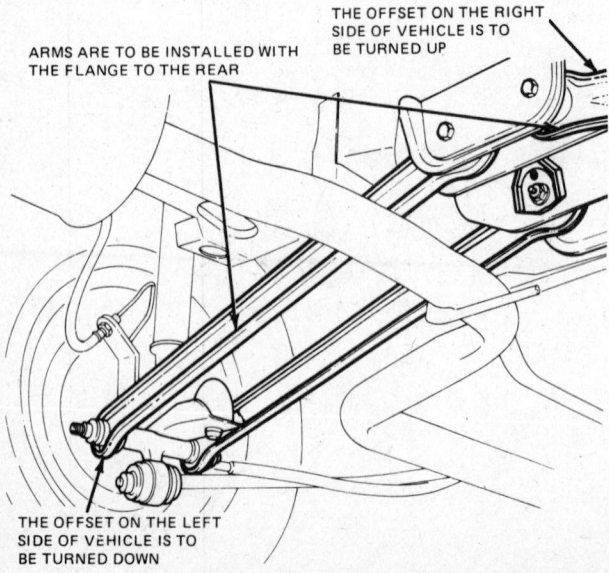

ARMS ARE TO BE INSTALLED WITH THE FLANGE TO THE REAR

THE OFFSET ON THE RIGHT SIDE OF VEHICLE IS TO BE TURNED UP

THE OFFSET ON THE LEFT SIDE OF VEHICLE IS TO BE TURNED DOWN

Rear control arm mounting, Tempo/Topaz

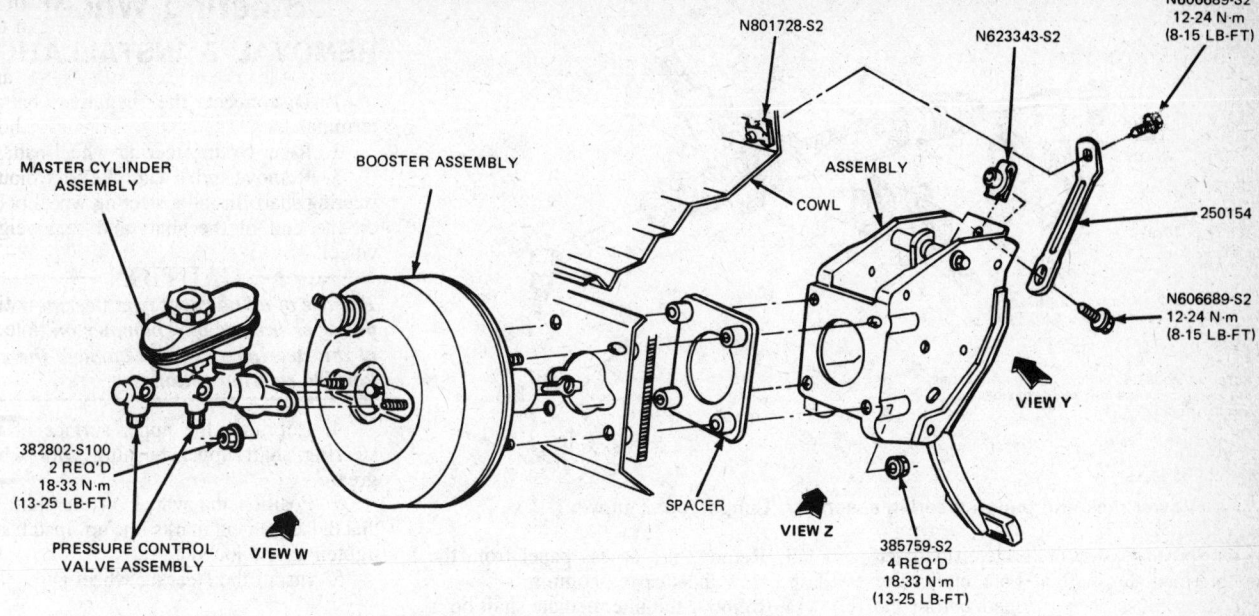

Typical master cylinder and power brake booster mounting

NOTE: On cars equipped with power brakes, the engine must be running before completing Step 1.

2. Place the transmission in neutral.

3. Jack up the rear of the vehicle and support it with jackstands.

4. Tighten the adjusting nut until the wheels drag slightly.

5. Pull the handle to the twelfth position (two from full application) and check the brake application.

6. Release the handle and loosen the adjuster only enough to eliminate brake drag.

7. Lower the vehicle and check the brake application.

Proportioning Valve

The proportioning valve regulates the rear brake system hydraulic pressure. It is located between the rear brake system inlet and outlet ports. There are no adjustments possible on this valve. If found to be defective it must be replaced.

STEERING

CAUTION

If the vehicle is equipped with a driver airbag restraint system, any required service should be performed by personnel trained on servicing the system so that accidental firing of the airbag will not occur.

Rack and pinion steering is offered in both manual and power-assisted versions. The steering system's outer tie-rod ends are "lubed-for-life"; no grease fittings are provided.

Tie-Rod End

REMOVAL & INSTALLATION

1. Remove and discard the cotter pin. Remove the nut at the spindle.

2. Separate the tie-rod end stud from the spindle using a puller.

3. Matchmark the position of the locknut with paint on the tie-rod if the tie-rod end is to be reused. Unscrew the locknut. Unscrew the tie-rod end from the rack arm, counting the number of turns required to remove it.

4. Install the new tie-rod end, screwing it on the same number of turns counted in Step 3. Attach the tie-rod end stud to the spindle. Install and tighten the nut. Install a new cotter pin.

5. Check and adjust the toe as necessary. Tighten the tie-rod end locknut.

Rack and Pinion Steering

REMOVAL & INSTALLATION
Escort/Lynx

1. Disconnect the negative battery cable from the battery. Jack up the front of the car and support it safely on jackstands.

2. Turn the ignition switch to the ON position. Remove the lower access (kick) panel from below the steering wheel.

3. Remove the intermediate shaft bolts at the gear input shaft and at the steering column shaft.

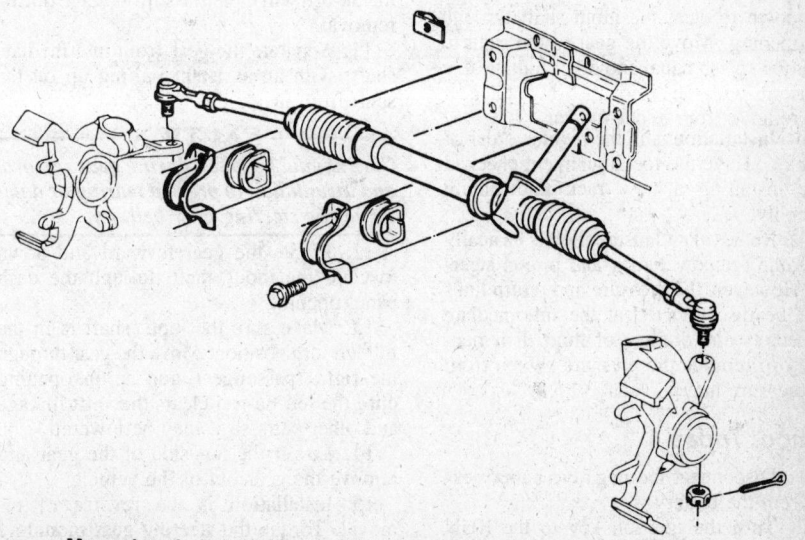

Manual rack and pinion steering mounting, Tempo/Topaz shown

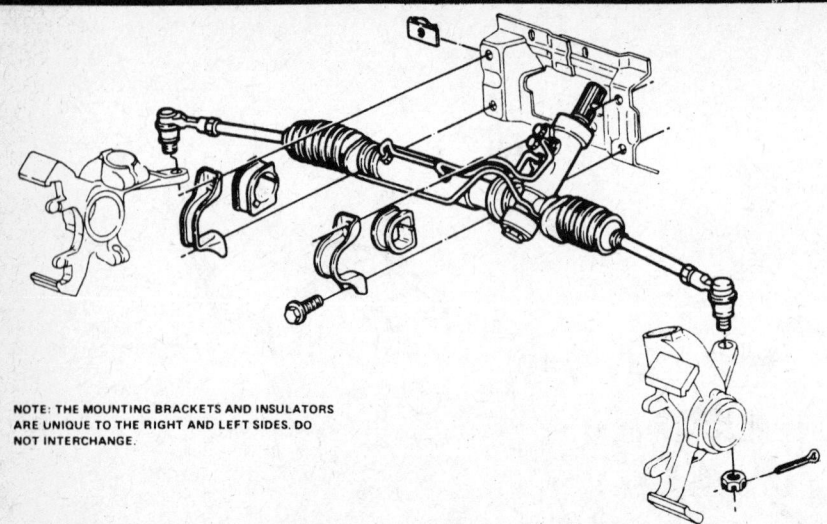

NOTE: THE MOUNTING BRACKETS AND INSULATORS ARE UNIQUE TO THE RIGHT AND LEFT SIDES. DO NOT INTERCHANGE.

Power rack and pinion steering assembly, Tempo/Topaz shown

4. Spread the slots of the clamp to loosen the intermediate shaft at both ends. The next steps must be performed before the intermediate shaft and gear input shaft can be separated.

5. Turn the steering wheel full left so the tie-rod will clear the shift linkage. Separate the outer tie rod ends from the steering knuckle by using a tie-rod end remover.

6. Remove the left tie-rod end from the tie-rod (wheel must be at full left position). Disconnect the speedometer cable from the transmission if the car is equipped with an automatic transaxle. Disconnect the secondary air tube at the check valve. Disconnect the exhaust pipe from the exhaust manifold and wire it out of the way to allow enough room to remove the steering gear.

7. Remove the exhaust hanger bracket from below the steering gear. Remove the steering gear mounting brackets and rubber mounting insulators.

8. Have someone help by holding the gear from the inside of the car. Separate the intermediate shaft from the input shaft.

9. Make sure the gear is still in the full left turn position. Rotate the gear forward and down to clear the input shaft through the opening. Move the gear to the right to clear the splash panel and other linkage that interferes with the removal. Lower the gear and remove from under the car.

10. Installation is in the reverse order of removal. Have the toe adjustment checked after installing a new rack and pinion assembly.

11. Removal and installation is basically the same for power rack and pinion steering. However, the pressure and return lines must be disconnected at the intermediate connectors and drained of fluid. It is necessary to remove the pressure switch from the pressure line.

Tempo, Topaz

1. Disconnect the negative battery cable from the battery.

2. Turn the ignition key to the RUN position.

3. Remove the access panel from the dash below the steering column.

4. Remove the intermediate shaft bolts at gear input shaft and at the steering column shaft.

5. With a wide blade tool, spread the slots enough to loosen intermediate shaft at both ends. The intermediate shaft and gear input shaft cannot be separated at this time.

6. From under vehicle, separate the tie-rod ends from steering knuckles, using Tool-3290-C and adapter T81P-3504-W or equivalent. Turn the right wheel to the full left turn position.

7. Disconnect the speedometer cable at transmission (automatic transmission only).

8. Disconnect the secondary air tube at the check valve. Disconnect the exhaust system at the exhaust manifold. Remove the exhaust system.

9. Remove the gear mounting brackets and insulators.

NOTE: Right and left hand brackets and insulators are not interchangeble side to side.

10. Turn the steering wheel full left so the tie-rod will clear the shift linkage during removal.

11. Separate the gear from intermediate shaft, with an assistant pulling up on the shaft from inside the vehicle.

CAUTION
Care should be taken during gear removal and installation to prevent tearing or damaging the steering gear bellows.

---

12. Rotate the gear forward and down to clear the input shaft through the dash panel opening.

13. Make sure the input shaft is in the full left turn position. Move the gear through the right (passenger) side apron opening until the left tie-rod clears the shift linkage and other parts so it may be lowered.

14. Lower the left side of the gear and remove the gear out of the vehicle.

15. Installation is the reverse of removal. Torque the steering gear mounting bolts to 48–55 ft. lbs.

Steering Wheel
REMOVAL & INSTALLATION

1. Disconnect the negative battery terminal.

2. Remove the steering wheel pad.

3. Remove and discard the nut from the steering shaft. Install a steering wheel puller on the end of the shaft and remove the wheel.

CAUTION
The use of a knock-off type steering wheel puller or the use of a hammer on the end of the steering shaft will damage the collapsible steering column.

---

4. Lubricate the upper surface of the steering shaft upper bushing with white grease.

5. Position the wheel on the shaft so that the alignment marks line up. Install and tighten a new locknut.

6. Install the steering wheel pad.

Turn Signal Switch, Windshield Wiper Switch
REMOVAL & INSTALLATION

These two switches are mounted on the steering column in the same manner.

1. Disconnect the negative battery terminal.

2. Remove the lower shroud screws and the shroud.

3. Remove the upper shroud.

4. Remove the lever by pulling and twisting straight out (windshield wiper switch only).

5. Peel back the foam cover from the appropriate switch.

6. Disconnect the electrical connectors.

7. Remove the two self tapping screws (hex head screws—wash/wipe switch) that attach the switch to the lock cylinder housing, and remove the switch.

NOTE: On vehicles equipped with cruise control, transfer the ground brush in the turn signal switch cancelling cam to the new switch.

8. Installation is the reverse of removal.

INSTRUMENT PANEL

Headlight Switch
REMOVAL & INSTALLATION

1. Disconnect the negative battery terminal.

2. Remove the left hand air vent control cable, and drop the cable and bracket down out of the way (cars without air conditioning only).

3. Remove the fuse panel bracket retaining screws and move the fuse panel assembly out of the way.

4. Pull the headlight knob out, to the on position.

5. Reach behind the dashboard and depress the release button on the switch housing, while at the same time pulling the knob and shaft from the switch.

6. Remove the retaining nut from the dashboard.

7. Pull the switch from the dash and remove the electrical connections.

8. Installation is the reverse of removal.

Instrument Cluster

REMOVAL & INSTALLATION

1. Disconnect the negative battery terminal.

2. Remove the bottom steering column cover.

3. Remove the steering column opening cover reinforcement screws.

NOTE: On cars equipped with speed control disconnect the wires from the amplified assembly.

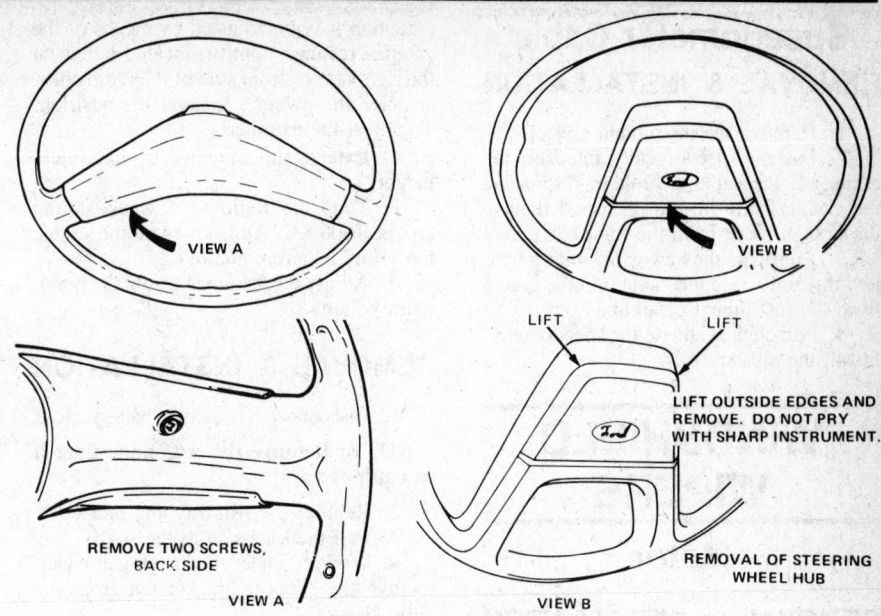

Steering wheel cover removal, Tempo/Topaz

4. Remove the steering column retaining screws from the steering column support bracket and lower the column.

5. Remove the column trim shrouds.

6. Disconnect all electrical connections from the column.

7. Remove the finish panel screws and the panel.

8. Remove the speedometer cable.

9. Remove the four cluster screws and remove the cluster.

10. Installation is the reverse of removal.

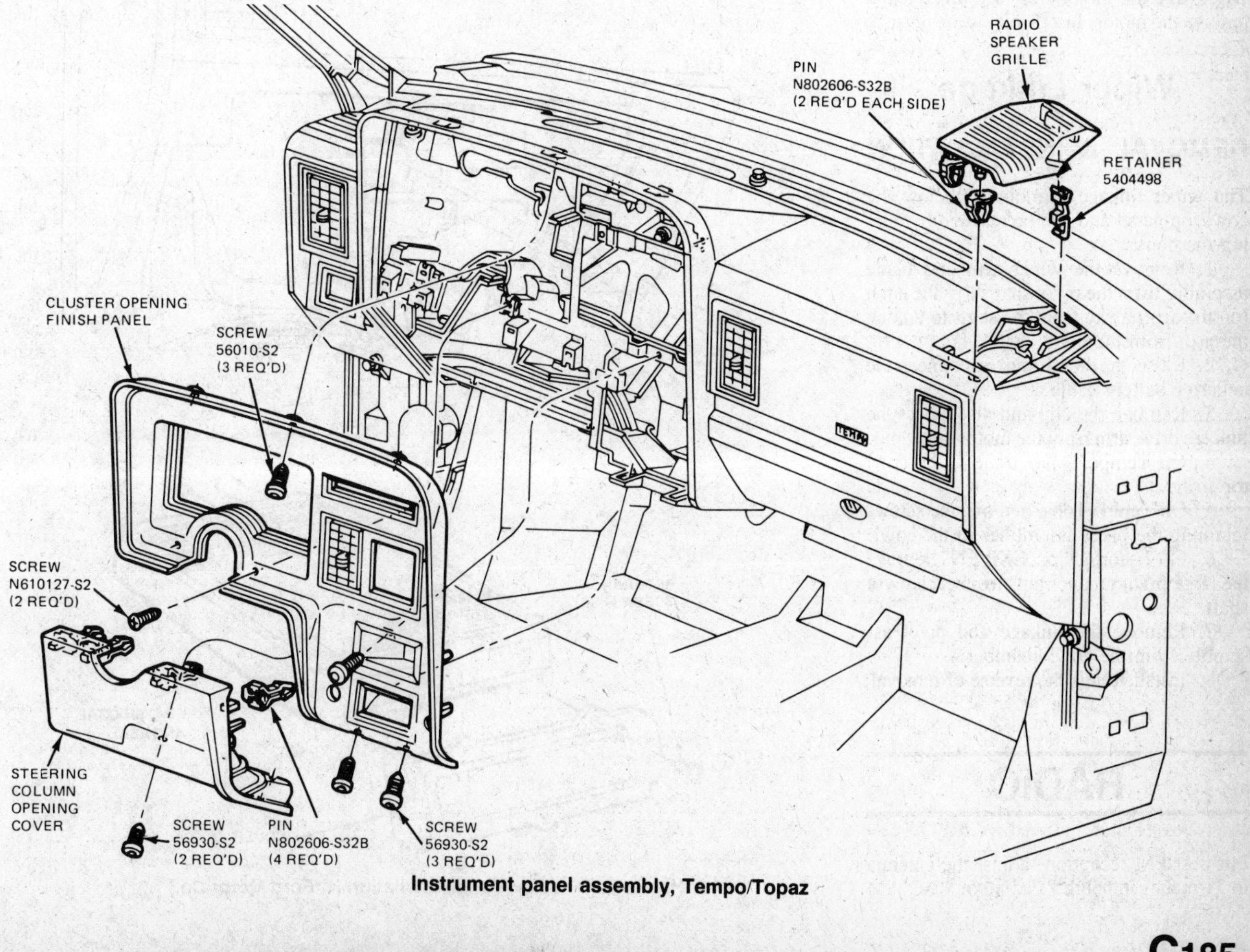

Instrument panel assembly, Tempo/Topaz

Speedometer Cable

REMOVAL & INSTALLATION

1. Remove the instrument cluster.
2. Pull the speedometer cable from the casing. If the cable is broken, disconnect the casing from the transaxle and remove the broken piece from the transaxle end.
3. Lubricate the new cable with graphite lubricant. Feed the cable into the casing from the instrument panel end.
4. Attach the cable to the speedometer. Install the cluster.

WINDSHIELD WIPERS

Motor

REMOVAL & INSTALLATION

The motor is located in the right rear corner of the engine compartment, in the cowl area above the firewall.

1. Disconnect the negative battery cable.
2. Remove the plastic cowl cover.
3. Disconnect the motor electrical connector.
4. Remove the motor attaching bolts. Disengage the motor from the linkage and remove the motor. Installation is the reverse.

Wiper Linkage

REMOVAL & INSTALLATION

The wiper linkage is mounted below the cowl top panel and can be reached by raising the hood.

1. Remove the wiper arm and blade assembly from the pivot shaft. Pry the latch (on the arm) away from the shaft to unlock the arm from the pivot shaft.
2. Raise the hood and disconnect the negative battery cable.
3. Remove the clip and disconnect the linkage drive arm from the motor crank pin.
4. On Tempo/Topaz remove the cowl top grille.
5. On Tempo/Topaz remove the screws retaining the pivot assemblies to the cowl.
6. On Escort/Lynx, EXP/LN7 remove the large pivot retainer nuts from each pivot shaft.
7. Remove the linkage and pivot assembly from the cowl chamber.
8. Installation is the reverse of removal.

RADIO

For best FM reception, adjust the antenna to 31 inches in height. Fading or weak AM reception may be adjusted by means of the antenna trimmer control, located either on the right rear or front side of the radio chassis. See the owner's manual for position. To adjust the trimmer:

1. Extend the antenna to maximum height.
2. Tune the radio to a weak station around 1600 KC. Adjust the volume so that the sound is barely audible.
3. Adjust the trimmer to obtain maximum volume.

REMOVAL & INSTALLATION

1. Disconnect the negative battery cable.

NOTE: Remove the A/C floor duct if so equipped.

2. Remove the ash tray and bracket.
3. Pull the knobs from the shafts.
4. Working under the instrument panel, remove the support bracket nut from the radio chassis.
5. Remove the shaft nuts and washers.
6. Drop the radio down from behind the instrument panel. Disconnect the power lead, antenna, and speaker wires. Remove the radio.
7. Installation is the reverse.

HEATER

Heater Core

REMOVAL & INSTALLATION

NOTE: In some cases removal of the instrument panel may be necessary.

Without A/C

1. Disconnect the negative battery cable.
2. Drain the coolant.
3. Disconnect the heater hoses from the core tubes at the firewall, inside the engine compartment. Plug the core tubes to prevent coolant spillage when the core is removed.

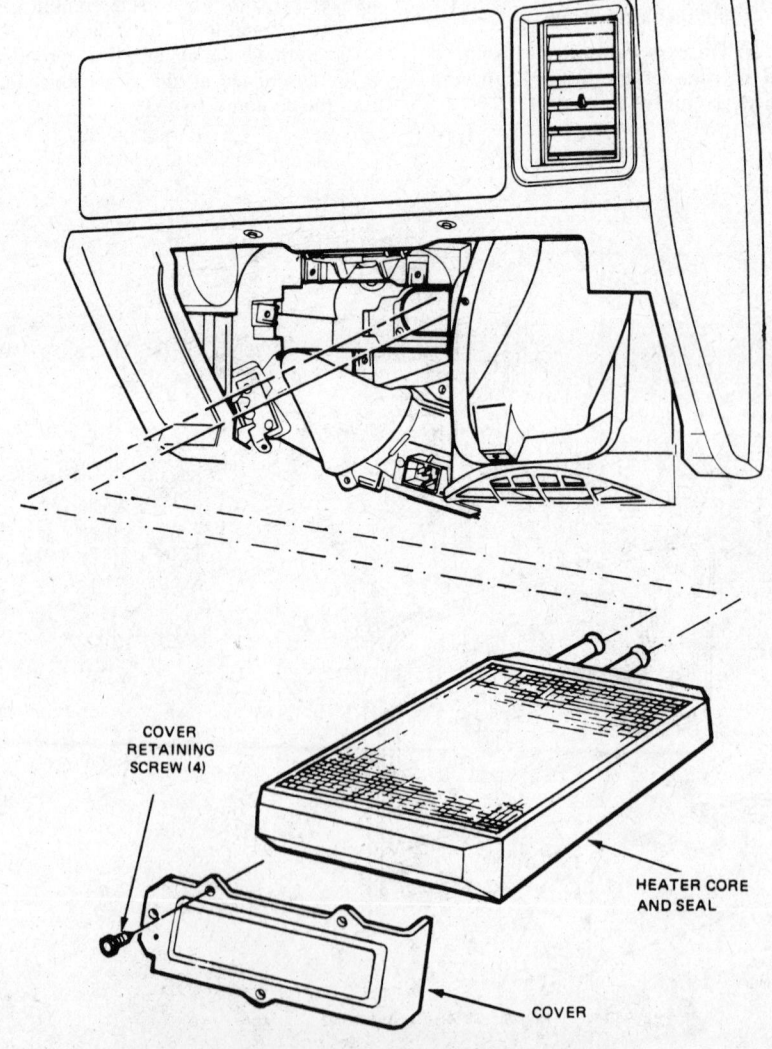

COVER
RETAINING
SCREW (4)

HEATER CORE
AND SEAL

COVER

Heater core removal and installation (© Ford Motor Co.)

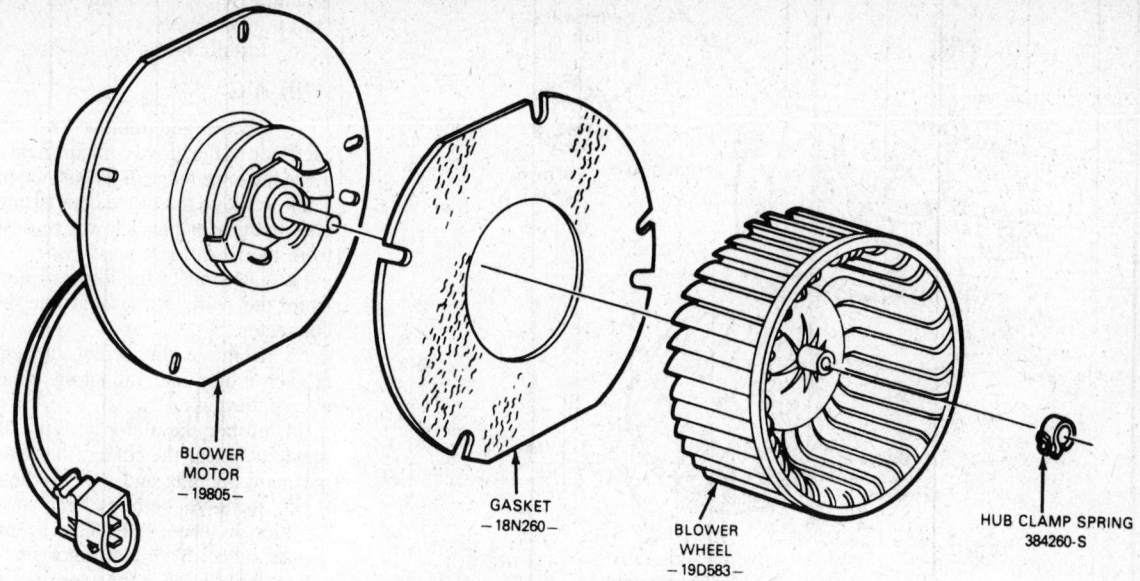

Blower motor and wheel disassembled

4. Open the glove compartment. Remove the glove compartment. Remove the glove compartment liner.

5. Remove the core access plate screws and remove the access plate.

6. Working under the hood, remove the two nuts attaching the heater assembly case to the dash panel.

7. Remove the core through the glove compartment opening. Installation is the reverse.

With A/C

1. Disconnect the negative battery cable and drain the cooling system.

2. Disconnect the heater hoses from the heater core.

3. Working inside the vehicle, remove the floor duct from the plenum (2 screws).

4. Remove the four screws attaching the heater core cover to the plenum, remove the cover and remove the heater core.

5. Installation is the reverse of removal.

Blower Motor

REMOVAL & INSTALLATION
Without A/C

1. Disconnect the negative battery cable.

2. Remove the glove compartment and lower instrument panel reinforcing rail.

3. Disconnect the blower electrical connectors.

4. Remove the blower motor-to-case

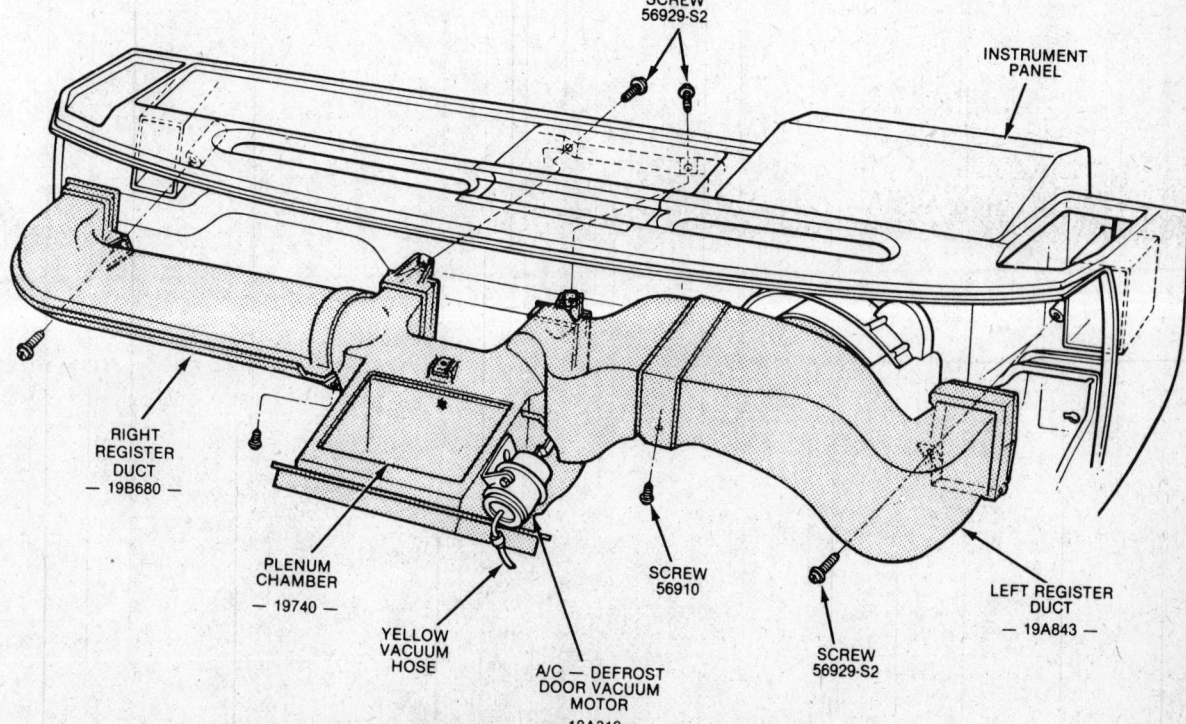

Removal of the plenum chamber and register ducts

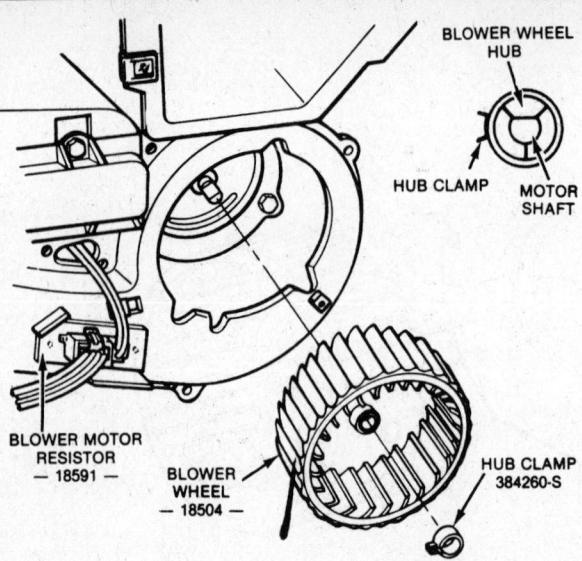

BLOWER WHEEL HUB

HUB CLAMP

MOTOR SHAFT

BLOWER MOTOR RESISTOR — 18591 —

BLOWER WHEEL — 18504 —

HUB CLAMP 384260-S

Blower motor and wheel removal

attaching screws. Remove the blower and fan as an assembly.

5. Installation is the reverse.

With A/C

1. Locate and remove two screws at each side of the glove compartment opening along the lower edge of the instrument panel. Then, remove the glove compartment door and instrument panel lower reinforcement from the instrument panel.

2. Disconnect the blower motor wires from the wire harness at the hardshell connector.

3. Remove the screws attaching the blower motor and mounting plate to the evaporator case.

4. Rotate the motor until the mounting plate flats clear the edge of the glove compartment opening and remove the motor.

5. Remove the hub clamp spring from the blower wheel hub. Then, remove the blower wheel from the motor shaft.

6. Installation is the reverse of removal.

Ford Motor Co.
Rear Wheel Drive
Ford, Lincoln, Mercury—All Models

YEAR IDENTIFICATION

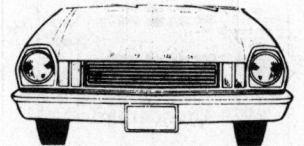

1978 Pinto

1979 Pinto

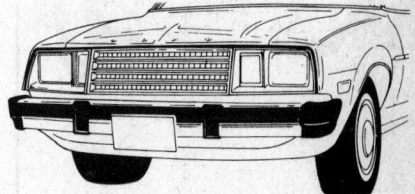

1980 Pinto

1978 Mustang II

1979 Mustang

1980–81 Mustang

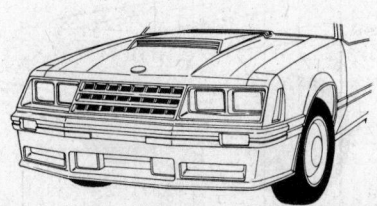

1982 Mustang

1983 Mustang

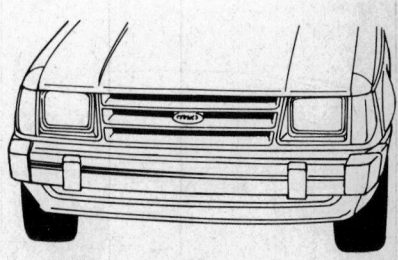

1984-85 Mustang

C189

1978–79 Fairmont

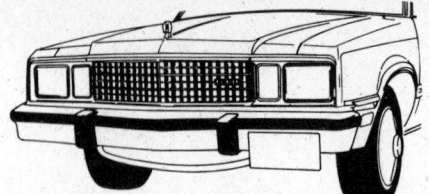

1980–81 Fairmont

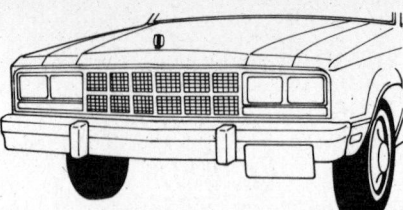

1980 Fairmont Futura

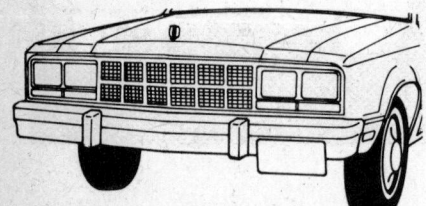

1981-83 Fairmont Futura

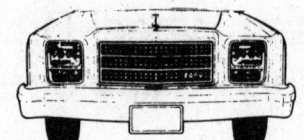

1978 Granada

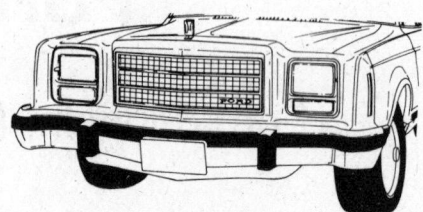

1979–80 Granada

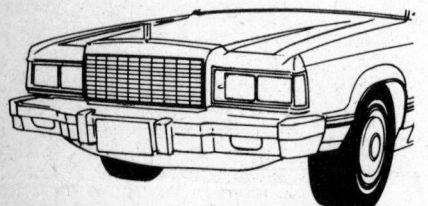

1981-82 Granada

1978 Thunderbird

1979 Thunderbird

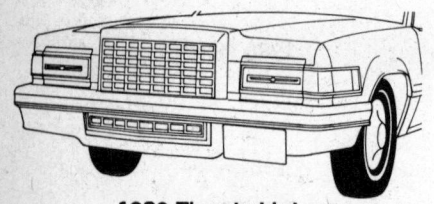

1980 Thunderbird

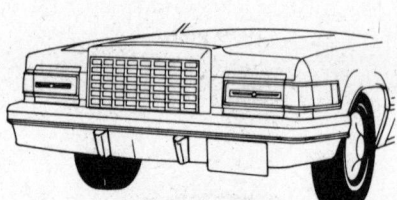

1981-82 Thunderbird

1983-85 Thunderbird

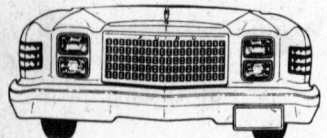

1978-79 LTD II

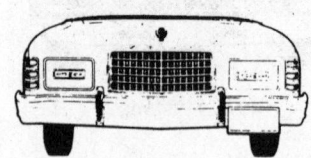

1978 LTD

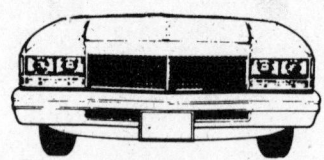

1979 LTD

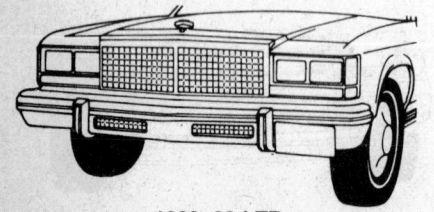

1980–82 LTD

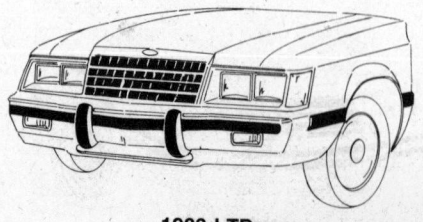

1983 LTD

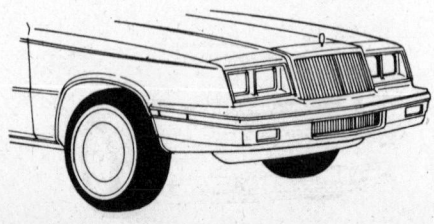

1984–85 LTD

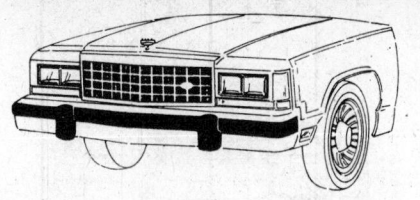

1983-85 Crown Victoria and Country Squire

1985 Mustang GT

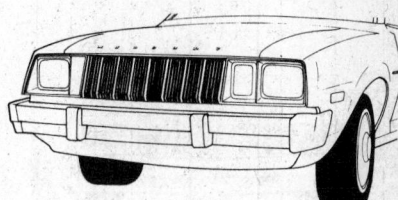

1985 Thunderbird Turbo Coupe

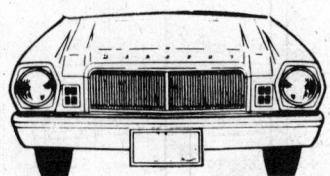

1978 Bobcat

1979 Bobcat

1980 Bobcat

1979 Capri

1980–82 Capri

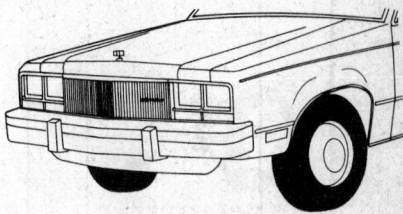

1983-85 Capri

1978–79 Zephyr

1980 Zephyr

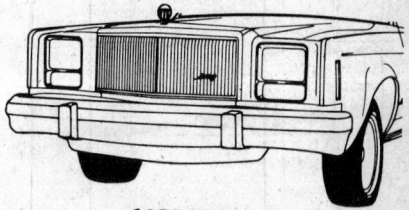

1981-83 Zephyr

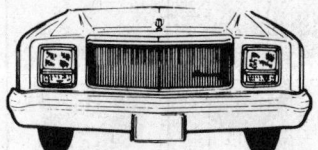

1978 Monarch

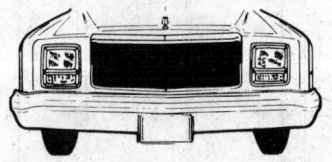

1979 Monarch

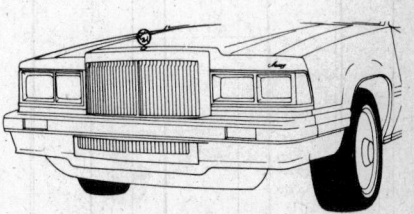

1980 Monarch

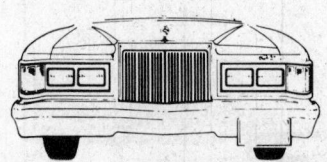

1978–79 Cougar

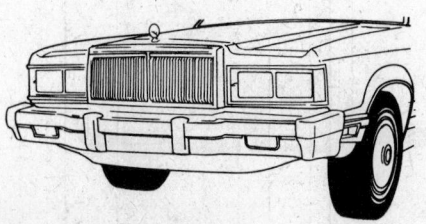

1981-82 Cougar

1980 Cougar XR-7

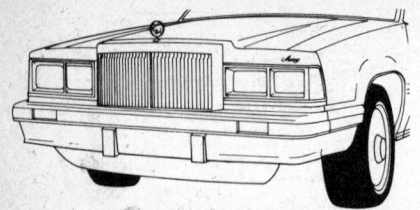

1981-82 Cougar XR-7

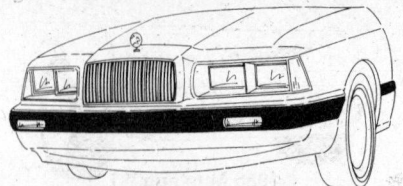

1983-85 Cougar

1978 Marquis

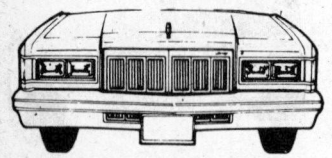

1979 Marquis

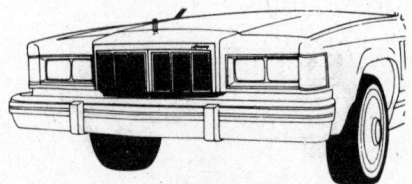

1980 Marquis

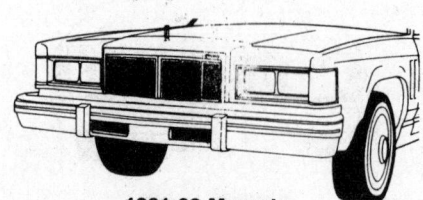

1981-82 Marquis

1983-85 Marquis

1983-85 Grand Marquis and Colony Park

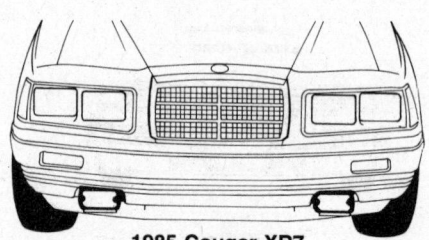

1985 Cougar XR7

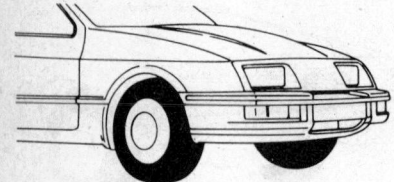

1985 Merkur XR4Ti

1978 Versailles

1979 Versailles

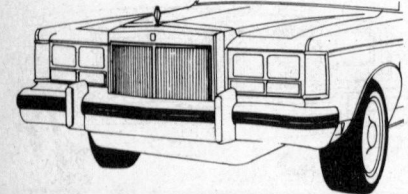

1980 Versailles

1978-79 Lincoln Continental

1980 Lincoln Continental

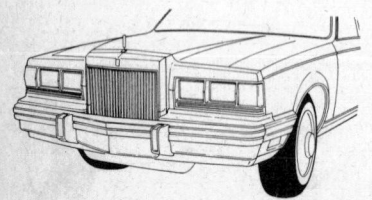

1982 Continental

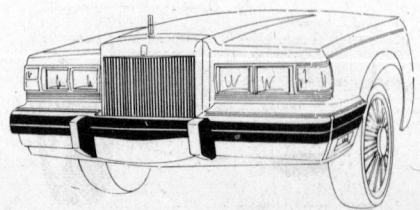

1983 Continental

1978-79 Continental Mark V

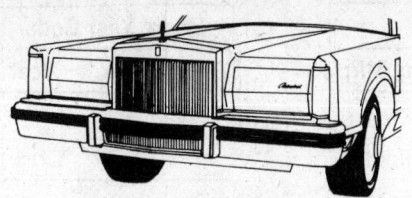

1980–82 Continental Mark VI

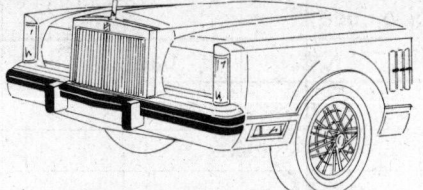

1983 Continental Mark VI

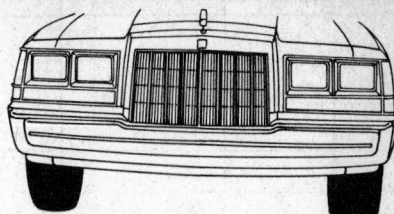

1984-85 Continental

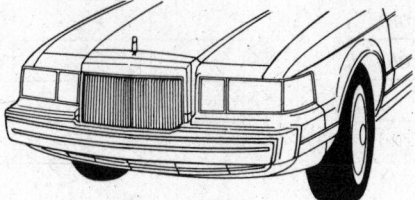

1984-85 Mark VII

1981-82 Lincoln Town Car

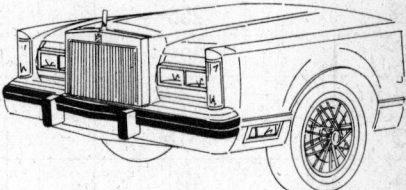

1983–84 Town Car

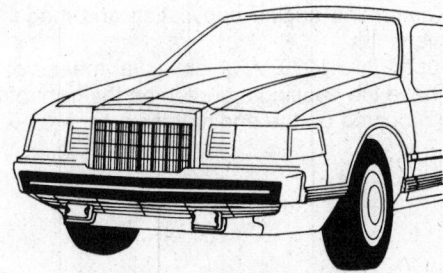

1985 Mark VII LSC

1985 Lincoln Town Car

VEHICLE IDENTIFICATION NUMBER (VIN)

It is important for servicing and ordering parts to be certain of the vehicle and engine identification. The VIN (vehicle identification number) is a 13 or 17 digit number visible through the windshield on the driver's side of the dash and contains the vehicle and engine identification codes. It can be interpreted as follows:

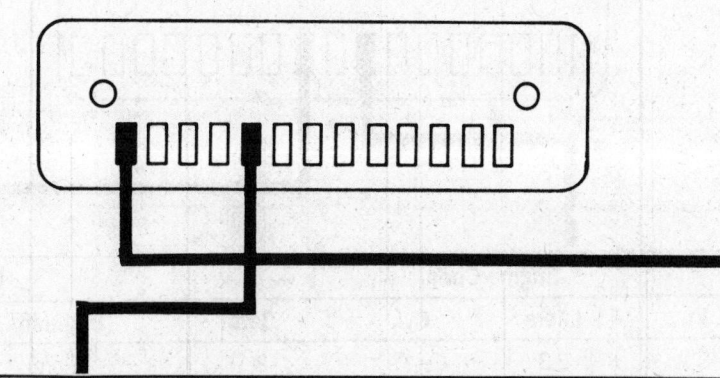

Engine Code						Model Year Code	
Code	Cu. In.	Liters	Cyl.	Carb.	Eng. Mfg.	Code	Year
Y	140	2.3	4	2	Ford	8	1978
W('79)	140	2.3	4	Turbo	Ford	9	1979
T('80)	140	2.3	4	Turbo	Ford	0	1980
A('80)	140	2.3	4	2	Ford		

FORD MOTOR CO. REAR WHEEL DRIVE

	Engine Code					Model Year Code	
Code	Cu. In.	Liters	Cyl.	Carb.	Eng. Mfg.	Code	Year
Z	170	2.8	6	2	Ford		
T	200	3.3	6	1	Ford		
B('80)	200	3.3	6	1	Ford		
L	250	4.1	6	1	Ford		
C('80)	250	4.1	6	1	Ford		
D	255	4.2	8	2(W)	Ford		
F	302	5.0	8	2①	Ford		
H②	351W	5.8	8	2③	Ford		
Q	351M	5.8	8	2	Ford		
S	400	6.6	8	2	Ford		
A	460	7.5	V8	4	Ford		
C	460PI	7.5	V8	4	Ford		

The thirteen digit Vehicle Identification Number can be used to determine engine application and model year. The first digit indicates model code, and the fifth digit indicates engine application.
NOTE: Windsor and Modified Cleveland 351 V8 engines were used thru 1979. A quick visual means of identification is the location of the thermostat housing water outlet. Windsor engines have the housing mounted on the front of the intake manifold, while the Modified Cleveland engine has the thermostat housing mounted on the engine block.
①EFI on various models in 1980
②G or E in 1980
③VV carburetor on various models in 1980
④A in Canada

VEHICLE IDENTIFICATION NUMBER (VIN)

It is important for servicing and ordering parts to be certain of the vehicle and engine identification. The VIN (vehicle identification number) is a 13 or 17 digit number visible through the windshield on the driver's side of the dash and contains the vehicle and engine identification codes. It can be interpreted as follows:

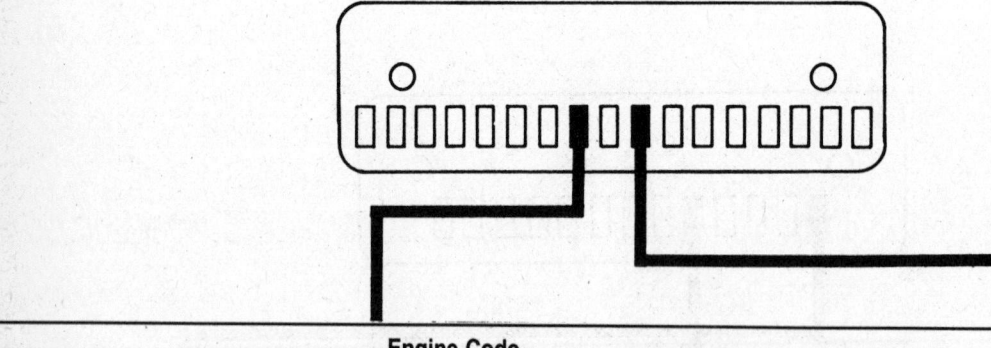

	Engine Code					Model Year Code	
Code	Cu. In.	Liters	Cyl.	Carb.	Eng. Mfg.	Code	Year
A	140	2.3	4	2(1)	Ford	B	1981
T	140	2.3	4	Turbo	Ford	C	1982
6	140	2.3	4	Propane	Ford	D	1983
W('83–'85)	140	2.3	4	Turbo	Ford	E	1984
B	200	3.3	6	1	Ford	F	1985
3	232	3.8	V6	①	Ford		
D	255	4.2	V8	2(VV)	Ford		

Engine Code						Model Year Code	
Code	Cu. In.	Liters	Cyl.	Carb.	Eng. Mfg.	Code	Year
F	302	5.0	V8	①	Ford		
M	302HO	5.0	V8	①	Ford		
G	351W	5.8	V8	①	Ford		
G	351HO	5.8	V8	①	Ford		

The seventeen digit Vehicle Identification Number can be used to determine engine application and model year. The tenth digit indicates the model year, and the eighth digit identifies the engine code.

①EFI, VV, 2 bbl. or 4 bbl. depending on model

TRANSMISSION CODES

1.	Three speed
2.	Five speed overdrive
4.	Four speed overdrive (SROD)
5.	Five speed
5.	Five speed overdrive (RAP)
6.	Four speed (Borg Warner)
7.	Four speed overdrive (RUG)
7.	Four speed (ET) (Hummer)
C.	C5 automatic
S.	JATCO automatic
T.	AOD (automatic overdrive)
U.	C6 automatic
V.	C3 automatic
W.	C4 automatic
X.	FMX automatic
Y.	Borg Warner automatic
Z.	C6 police automatic

Refer to the vehicle certification plate on the driver's door frame for transmission identification code.

GENERAL ENGINE SPECIFICATIONS

Year	Eng. V.I.N Code	Engine No. Cyl. Displacement (Cu. In.)	Eng. Mfg.	Carburetor Type	Horsepower @ rpm ■	Torque @ rpm (ft lbs) ■	Bore X Stroke (in.)	Compression Ratio	Oil Pressure @ 2000 rpm
'78	Y	4-140	Ford	2 bbl	88 @ 4800	118 @ 2800	3.781 × 3.126	9.0:1	50
	Z	6-170	Ford	2 bbl	90 @ 4200	143 @ 2200	3.660 × 2.700	8.7:1	40–55
	T	6-200	Ford	1 bbl	85 @ 3600	154 @ 1600	3.682 × 3.126	8.5:1	30–50
	L	6-250	Ford	1 bbl	97 @ 3200	210 @ 1400	3.682 × 3.910	8.5:1	40–60
	F	8-302	Ford	2 bbl	134 @ 3400	250 @ 1600	4.000 × 3.000	8.4:1	40–60
	F	8-302 Cal	Ford	2VV	133 @ 3600	243 @ 1600	4.000 × 3.000	8.1:1	40–60
	Q	8-351 M	Ford	2 bbl	152 @ 3600	278 @ 1800	4.000 × 3.500	8.0:1	50–75
	H	8-351 W	Ford	2 bbl	144 @ 3200	277 @ 1600	4.000 × 3.500	8.3:1	40–60
	S	8-400	Ford	2 bbl	166 @ 3800	319 @ 1800	4.000 × 4.000	8.0:1	50–75
	A	8-460	Ford	4 bbl	202 @ 4000	348 @ 2000	4.362 × 3.850	8.0:1	35–65
	C	8-460 PI	Ford	4 bbl	202 @ 4000	352 @ 1600	4.362 × 3.850	8.0:1	35–65

GENERAL ENGINE SPECIFICATIONS

Year	Eng. V.I.N Code	Engine No. Cyl. Displacement (Cu. In.)	Eng. Mfg.	Carburetor Type	Horsepower @ rpm ∎	Torque @ rpm (ft lbs) ∎	Bore X Stroke (in.)	Compression Ratio	Oil Pressure @ 2000 rpm
'79	Y	4-140	Ford	2 bbl	88 @ 4800	118 @ 2800	3.781 × 3.126	9.0:1	50
	W	4-140 T	Ford	2 bbl	147 @ 6000	143 @ 2800	3.781 × 3.126	9.0:1	55
	Z	6-170	Ford	2 bbl	109 @ 4800	142 @ 2800	3.660 × 2.700	8.7:1	40–60
	T	6-200	Ford	1 bbl	85 @ 3600	154 @ 1600	3.682 × 3.126	8.5:1	30–50
	L	6-250	Ford	1 bbl	97 @ 3200	210 @ 1400	3.682 × 3.910	8.6:1	50
	F	8-302	Ford	2 bbl	140 @ 3600	250 @ 1800	4.000 × 3.000	8.4:1	40–65
	F	8-302 Cal.	Ford	VV	134 @ 3600	243 @ 2200	4.000 × 3.000	8.1:1	40–65
	Q	8-351 M	Ford	2 bbl	152 @ 3600	270 @ 2200	4.000 × 3.500	8.0:1	51–75
	H	8-351 W	Ford	2 bbl	135 @ 3200	286 @ 1400	4.000 × 3.500	8.3:1	40–65
	S	8-400	Ford	2 bbl	159 @ 3800	315 @ 1800	4.000 × 4.000	8.0:1	50–75
'80	A	4-140 MT	Ford	2 bbl	88 @ 4800	118 @ 2800	3.781 × 3.126	9.0:1	50
	A	4-140 AT	Ford	2 bbl	90 @ 4800	125 @ 2600	3.781 × 3.126	9.0:1	50
	A	4-140 Cal	Ford	2 bbl	89 @ 4800	122 @ 2600	3.781 × 3.126	9.0:1	50
	T	4-140 T	Ford	2 bbl	135 @ 6000	143 @ 2800	3.781 × 3.126	9.0:1	55
	B	6-200 MT	Ford	1 bbl	91 @ 3800	160 @ 1600	3.682 × 3.126	8.6:1	30–50
	B	6-200 AT	Ford	1 bbl	94 @ 4000	157 @ 2000	3.682 × 3.126	8.6:1	30–50
	C	6-250 All	Ford	1 bbl	90 @ 3200	194 @ 1600	3.682 × 3.910	8.6:1	50
	D	8-255 49	Ford	2 bbl	119 @ 3800	194 @ 2200	3.680 × 3.000	8.8:1	40–60
	D	8-255 Cal	Ford	VV	119 @ 3800	194 @ 2200	3.680 × 3.000	8.8:1	40–60
	F	8-302	Ford	2 bbl	134 @ 3600	232 @ 1600	4.000 × 3.000	8.4:1	40–65
	F	8-302	Ford	VV	131 @ 3600	231 @ 1400	4.000 × 3.000	8.4:1	40–65
	H	8-351 W	Ford	VV	142 @ 3200	286 @ 1400	4.000 × 3.500	8.3:1	40–65
	H	8-351 W	Ford	2 bbl	138 @ 3200	260 @ 2200	4.000 × 3.500	8.3:1	40–65
	G	8-351	Ford	VV	140 @ 3400	265 @ 2000	4.000 × 3.500	8.3:1	40–65
'81	A	4-140	Ford	2 bbl	88 @ 4600	118 @ 2600	3.781 × 3.126	9.0:1	40–60
	B	6-200	Ford	1 bbl	88 @ 3800	154 @ 1400	3.680 × 3.130	8.6:1	30–50
	D	8-255	Ford	2 bbl	115 @ 3400	195 @ 2200	3.680 × 3.000	8.2:1	40–60
	D	8-255	Ford	VV	120 @ 3400	205 @ 2600	3.680 × 3.000	8.2:1	40–60
	F	8-302	Ford	2 bbl	130 @ 3400	235 @ 1600	4.000 × 3.000	8.4:1	40–60
	F	8-302	Ford	VV	130 @ 3400	235 @ 1800	4.000 × 3.000	8.4:1	40–60
	F	8-302	Ford	EFI	130 @ 3400	230 @ 2000	4.000 × 3.000	8.4:1	40–60
	G	8-351	Ford	VV	145 @ 3200	270 @ 1800	4.000 × 3.500	8.3:1	40–60
	G	8-351 HO	Ford	VV	165 @ 3600	285 @ 2200	4.000 × 3.500	8.3:1	40–60
'82	A	4-140	Ford	2 bbl	86 @ 4600	117 @ 2600	3.781 × 3.126	9.0:1	40–60
	B	6-200	Ford	1 bbl	87 @ 3800	154 @ 1400	3.680 × 3.130	8.6:1	30–50
	3	6-232	Ford	2 bbl	112 @ 4000	175 @ 2600	3.810 × 3.390	8.8:1	54–59
	3	6-232	Ford	VV	118 @ 4000	186 @ 2600	3.810 × 3.390	8.8:1	54–59
	D	8-255	Ford	2 bbl	122 @ 3400	209 @ 2400	3.680 × 3.000	8.2:1	40–60
	D	8-255	Ford	VV	120 @ 3400	205 @ 2600	3.680 × 3.000	8.2:1	40–60

GENERAL ENGINE SPECIFICATIONS

Year	Eng. V.I.N Code	Engine No. Cyl. Displacement (Cu. In.)	Eng. Mfg.	Carburetor Type	Horsepower @ rpm ■	Torque @ rpm (ft lbs) ■	Bore X Stroke (in.)	Compression Ratio	Oil Pressure @ 2000 rpm
	F	8-302	Ford	VV	132 @ 3400	236 @ 1800	4.000 × 3.000	8.4:1	40–60
	F	8-302	Ford	EFI	134 @ 3400	232 @ 3200	4.000 × 3.000	8.4:1	40–60
	G	8-351	Ford	2 bbl	140 @ 3400	265 @ 2000	4.000 × 3.500	8.3:1	40–60
'83	A	4-140	Ford	1 bbl	86 @ 4600	117 @ 2600	3.781 × 3.126	9.0:1	40–60
	X	6-200	Ford	1 bbl	87 @ 3800	154 @ 1400	3.680 × 3.130	8.6:1	30–50
	3	6-232	Ford	2 bbl	112 @ 4000	175 @ 2600	3.810 × 3.390	8.7:1	40–60
	F	8-302	Ford	EFI	130 @ 3200	240 @ 2000	4.000 × 3.000	8.4:1	40–60
	G	8-351	Ford	2 bbl	140 @ 3400	265 @ 2000	4.000 × 3.500	8.3:1	40–60
'84–'85	A	4-140	Ford	1 bbl	88 @ 4600	118 @ 2800	3.781 × 3.126	9.0:1	40–60
	W	4-140	Ford	EFI	145 @ 3800	180 @ 3600	3.781 × 3.126	8.0:1	40–60
	3	6-232	Ford	EFI	—	—	3.810 × 3.390	8.6:1	40–60
	3	6-232	Ford	2 bbl	—	—	3.810 × 3.390	8.6:1	40–60
	F	8-302	Ford	2 bbl	155 @ 3600	265 @ 2000	4.000 × 3.000	8.4:1	40–60
	F	8-302	Ford	EFI	140 @ 3200	250 @ 1600	4.000 × 3.000	8.4:1	40–60
	F	8-302	Ford	4 bbl	175 @ 4000	245 @ 2200	4.000 × 3.000	8.3:1	40–60
	G	8-351 HO	Ford	VV	180 @ 3600	285 @ 2400	4.000 × 3.500	8.3:1	40–60

■ Horsepower and torque are SAE net figures. They are measured at the rear of the transmission with all accessories installed and operating. Since the figures vary when a given engine is installed in different models, some are representative rather than exact.

W Windsor
M Modified Cleveland
PI Police Interceptor
VV Variable Venturi

T Turbocharged
MT Manual Transmission
AT Automatic Transmission
49 49 states only
Cal California only

TUNE-UP SPECIFICATIONS—PINTO/BOBCAT/MUSTANG II

(When analyzing compression test results, look for uniformity among cylinders rather than specific pressures.)

Year	Engine No. Cyl. Displacement cu in. (cc)	Spark Plugs Orig. Type	Spark Plugs Gap ● (in.)	Distributor Point Dwell (deg)	Distributor Point Gap (in.)	Ignition Timing (deg) ▲ Man Trans ●	Ignition Timing (deg) ▲ Auto Trans	Valves Intake Opens ■ (deg)	Fuel Pump Pressure (psi)	Idle Speed (rpm) ▲ Man Trans	Idle Speed (rpm) ▲ Auto Trans
'78	4-140 (2300)	AWRF-42	.034	Electronic		6B	20B	22	5½–6½	850①	800(750)①
	6-171 (2800)	AWSF-42	.034	Electronic		10B	12B(6B)	20	3½–5¾	700①	650⑤(600)①
	8-302 (4950)	ARF-52 (ARF-52-6)	.050 (.060)	Electronic		6B	4B(12B)	16	5½–6½	900①	700①
'79	4-140 (2300)	AWSF-42	.034	Electronic		6B	20B	22	5½–6½	850①	800(750)①
	6-171 (2800)	AWSF-42	.034	Electronic		NA	9B(6B)	28	3½–5½	NA	650(600)①
'80	4-140 (2300)	AWSF-42	.034	Electronic		6B	20B(12B)	22	5½–6½	850②	750②

NOTE: The underhood specifications sticker often reflects tune-up specification changes made in production. Sticker figures must be used if they disagree with those in this chart. Part numbers in this chart are not recommendations by Chilton for any product by brand name.

▲ See text for procedure
■ All figures Before Top Dead Center
● Figure in parentheses is for California
B Before Top Dead Center

— Not applicable
① See underhood sticker for TSP-OFF or A/C-OFF idle speeds
② TSP-off idle speed—550 rpm

FORD MOTOR CO. REAR WHEEL DRIVE

TUNE-UP SPECIFICATIONS—MID SIZE MODELS

(When analyzing compression test results, look for uniformity among cylinders rather than specific pressures.)

Year	Eng. V.I.N. Code	No. Cyl. Displacement (cu. in.)	Eng. mfg.	Spark Plugs Orig. Type	Gap ● (in.)	Distributor Point Dwell* (deg)	Point Gap (in.)	Ignition Timing (deg) ▲ Man Trans ●	Auto Trans	Valves Intake Opens ■ (deg)	Fuel Pump Pressure (psi)	Idle Speed (rpm) ▲ Man Trans ●	Auto Trans
'78	Y	4-140	Ford	AWRF-42	.034	Electronic		6B	20B	22	5½-6½	850	800
	T	6-200	Ford	BRF-82	.050 (.060)	Electronic		10B	10B(6B)	20	5½-6½	800	650
	L	6-250	Ford	BRF-82	.050	Electronic		4B	14B(6B)	18	5½-6½	800	600
	F	8-302	Ford	ARF-52 (ARF-52-6)	.050 (.060)	Electronic		10B	6B(12B)④	16	5½-6½	500	650
	H	8-351W	Ford	ARF-52 (ARF-52-6)	.050 (.060)	Electronic		—	14B	16	4-6	—	650
	Q	8-351M	Ford	ARF-52 (ARF-52-6)	.050 (.060)	Electronic		—	14B(16B)	19½	6½-7½	—	650
	S	8-400	Ford	ARF-52 (ARF-52-6)	.050 (.060)	Electronic		—	13B(16B)	17	6½-7½	—	650
'79	Y	4-140	Ford	AWSF-42	.034	Electronic		6B	20B	22	5½-6½	850	850(750)
	W	4-140T	Ford	AWSF-32	.034	Electronic		2B	—	22	6½-7½	900	—
	Z	6-170	Ford	AWSF-42	.034	Electronic		—	9B(6B)	28	3½-5½	—	650(600)
	T	6-200	Ford	BRF-82	.050 (.060)	Electronic		8B	10B	20	5½-6½	800	650
	L	6-250	Ford	BSF-82	.050	Electronic		4B	10B(6B)	18	5½-6½	800	600
	F	8-302	Ford	ASF-52 (ASF-52-6)	.050 (.060)	Electronic		12B	6B④	16	5½-6½	800	600
	H	8-351W	Ford	ASF-52	.050	Electronic		—	15B	23	6½-8	—	650
	Q	8-351M	Ford	ASF-52	.050	Electronic		—	12B(14B)	17⑤	6-8	—	600
'80	A	4-140	Ford	AWSF-42	.035	Electronic		6B	20B(12B)	22	5½-6½	850	750
	T	4-140T	Ford	AWSF-32	.050	Electronic		6B(2B)	8B(2B)	22	6½-7½	900	800(600)
	B	6-200	Ford	BRF-82	.050	Electronic		10B	12B	20	5½-6½	700⑥	550(600)⑦
	C	6-250	Ford	BSF-82	.050	Electronic		8B	10B	18	5½-6½	700	550
	D	8-255	Ford	ASF-42	.050	Electronic		8B	8B(6B)④	16	4-6	500	550(500)④
	F	8-302	Ford	ASF-52 (ASF-52-6)	.050 (.060)	Electronic		—	8B④	16	5½-6½	—	550④
'81	A	4-140	Ford	AWSF-42	.034	Electronic		6B	6B	22	5½-6½	700	700
	T	4-140T	Ford	AWSF-32	.034	Electronic		6B	8B	22	5½-6½	850	750(65
	B	6-200	Ford	BSF-92	.050	Electronic		10B	10B	20	5½-6½	700⑥	600(700)⑦
	D	8-255	Ford	ASF-52	.050	Electronic		10B	10B	16	5½-6½	700⑥	550⑦
	F	8-302	Ford	ASF-52	.050	Electronic		8B	8B	16	5½-6½	800	800
'82	A	4-140	Ford	AWSF-42	.034	Electronic		①	①	22	5½-6½	850	750
	B	6-200	Ford	BSF-92	.050	Electronic		①	①	20	6-8	700①	600(700)①
	3	6-232	Ford	AGSP-52	.044	Electronic		①	①	13	6-8	①	①
	F	8-302	Ford	ASF-52	.050	Electronic		—	①④	16	6-8⑧	①④	①④

TUNE-UP SPECIFICATIONS

(When analyzing compression test results, look for uniformity among cylinders rather than specific pressures.)

Year	Eng. V.I.N. Code	No. Cyl. Displacement (cu. in.)	Eng. mfg.	Spark Plugs Orig. Type	Spark Plugs Gap ● (in.)	Distributor Point Dwell* (deg)	Distributor Point Gap (in.)	Ignition Timing (deg) ▲ Man Trans ●	Ignition Timing (deg) ▲ Auto Trans	Valves Intake Opens ■ (deg)	Fuel Pump Pressure (psi)	Idle Speed (rpm) ▲ Man Trans ●	Idle Speed (rpm) ▲ Auto Trans
'83–'85	A	4-140	Ford	AWSF-44	.044	Electronic		①	①	22	5½–6½	850	800
	—	4-140P	Ford	AWSF-34	.034	Electronic		①	①	—	—	—	750
	W	4-140T	Ford	AWSF32C	.034	Electronic		①	①	—	—	①④	①④
	B	6-200	Ford	BSF-92	.050	Electronic		①	①	20	6–8	—	550
	3	6-232	Ford	AWSF-52⑪	.044	Electronic		①	①	13	6–8⑨	—	700(650)①
	F	8-302	Ford	ASF-42①⑫	.044	Electronic		①	①④	16	6–8⑧⑩	700①	550①

NOTE: The underhood specifications sticker often reflects tune-up specification changes. Sticker data must be used if they disagree with those shown in this chart.

NOTE: Part numbers listed in this chart are not recommendations by Chilton for any product by part number or brand name.

▲ See text for procedure

■ All figures are in degrees Before Top Dead Center

T Turbocharged

P Propane

① Calibrations vary depending upon model: refer to the underhood specifications sticker

② Electric fuel pump mounted in the gas tank

③ California models and Versailles use figures in parentheses

④ EEC equipped depending on model— Ignition timing, idle speed and mixture are non-adjustable.

⑤ California; 19½

⑥ 900 rpm w/AC

⑦ 700 rpm w/AC

⑧ EFI models; 39 psi

⑨ In tank pump 40–45

⑩ 6 low pressure pump 39 EFI pressure

⑪ CFI models: AWSF-54

⑫ '85–ASF52, HO–ASF42

MECHANICAL VALVE LIFTER CLEARANCE

Year	Engine	Intake In.	Exhaust In.
'78–'79	170 V6	.016 (cold)	.018 (cold)

TUNE-UP SPECIFICATIONS—FULL SIZE MODELS

(When analyzing compression test results, look for uniformity among cylinders rather than specific pressures.)

Year	No. Cyl. Displacement (cu. in.)	Eng. V.I.N. Code	hp	Eng MFG	Spark Plugs Orig. Type	Spark Plugs Gap ● (in.)	Distributor Point Dwell (deg)	Distributor Point Gap (in.)	Ignition Timing (deg) ▲ Man Trans ●	Ignition Timing (deg) ▲ Auto Trans	Valves Intake Opens ■ (deg)	Fuel Pump Pressure (psi)	Idle Speed (rpm) ▲ Man Trans*	Idle Speed (rpm) ▲ ● Auto Trans
'78	8-302	F	All	Ford	ARF-52 (ARF-52-6)	.050 (.060)	Electronic		—	14B	16	5½–6½	—	650
	8-351W	H	All	Ford	ARF-52 (ARF-52-6)	.050 (.060)	Electronic		—	4B	23	4–6	—	650
	8-351M	Q	All	Ford	ARF-52 (ARF-52-6)	.050 (.060)	Electronic		—	12B(16B)	19½	6½–7½	—	650
	8-400	S	All	Ford	ARF-52 (ARF-52-6)	.050 (.060)	Electronic		—	13B(16B)	17	6½–7½	—	650
	8-460	A	All	Ford	ARF-52 (ARF-52-6)	.050 (.060)	Electronic		—	10B	8	7½–8½	—	580
	8-460	C	Pl	Ford	ARF-52-6	.060	Electronic		—	16B	18	7½–8½	—	580
'79	8-302	F	All	Ford	ASF-52 (ASF-52-6)	.050 (.060)	Electronic		—	6B	16	5½–6½	—	550
	8-351 W	H	2 V	Ford	ASF-52 (ASF-52-6)	.050	Electronic		—	15B	23	6½–8	—	550
	8-351 W	H	VV	Ford	ASF-52	.050	Electronic		—	EEC	23	6½–8	—	550
	8-400	S	2 V	Ford	ASF-52 (ASF-52-6)	.050 .060	Electronic		—	14B	17	6.0–8.0	—	575(600)

TUNE-UP SPECIFICATIONS—FULL SIZE MODELS

(When analyzing compression test results, look for uniformity among cylinders rather than specific pressures.)

Year	Engine No. Cyl. Displacement (cu. in.)	Eng V.I.N. Code	hp	Eng MFG	Spark Plugs Orig. Type	Gap ● (in.)	Distributor Point Dwell (deg)	Point Gap (in.)	Ignition Timing (deg) ▲ Man Trans ●	Auto Trans	Valves Intake Opens ■ (deg)	Fuel Pump Pressure (psi)	Idle Speed (rpm) ▲ Man Trans*	Auto ● Trans
'80–'82	8-255	D	VV	Ford	ASF-52	.050	Electronic		—	① ②	16	6–8	—	500②
	8-302	F	VV	Ford	ASF-52	.050	Electronic		—	① ②	17	6½–8	—	550②
	8-302	F	EFI	Ford	ASF-52	.050	Electronic		—	① ②	17	39.2	—	550②
	8-351 W	H	VV	Ford	ASF-52	.050	Electronic		—	① ②	23	6½–8	—	550②
'83–'85	8-302	F	EFI	Ford	ASF-52	.050	Electronic		—	① ②	16	39.2	—	550②
	8-302	F	VV	Ford	ASF-52	.050	Electronic		—	① ②	16	6½–8	—	600②
	8-351	G	VV	Ford	ASF-52③	.050	Electronic		—	① ②	23	6½–8	—	600②

NOTE: The underhood specifications sticker often reflects tune-up specification changes made in production. Sticker figures must be used if they disagree with those in this chart.

▲ See text for procedure
● Figure in parentheses indicates California engine
■ All figures Before Top Dead Center
*In all cases where two idle speed figures are separated by a slash, the first is for idle speed with solenoid energized and the automatic transmission in Drive, while the second is for idle speed with solenoid disconnected and automatic transmission in Neutral.
Part numbers in this chart are not recommendations by Chilton for any product by brand name.

B Before Top Dead Center
M Modified Cleveland
PI Police Interceptor
W Windsor
EEC Electronic Engine Control. Ignition timing, idle speed and mixture are non-adjustable. See text for description.
VV Variable Venturi
— Not applicable
① See Underhood specifications Sticker
② Some models: EEC controls timing and idle speed.
③ '85—ASF-42 .044

FIRING ORDERS

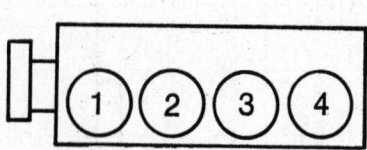

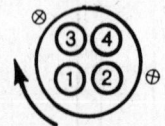

FORD MOTOR CO. 2300 cc 4-cyl.
Engine firing order: 1-3-4-2
Distributor rotation: clockwise

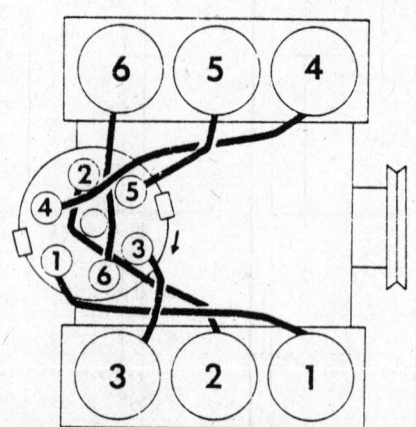

FORD MOTOR CO, 2800cc V6
Engine firing order: 1-4-2-5-3-6
Distributor rotation: Clockwise

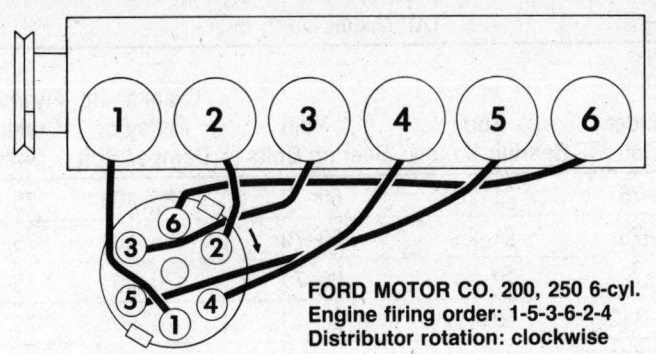

FORD MOTOR CO. 200, 250 6-cyl.
Engine firing order: 1-5-3-6-2-4
Distributor rotation: clockwise

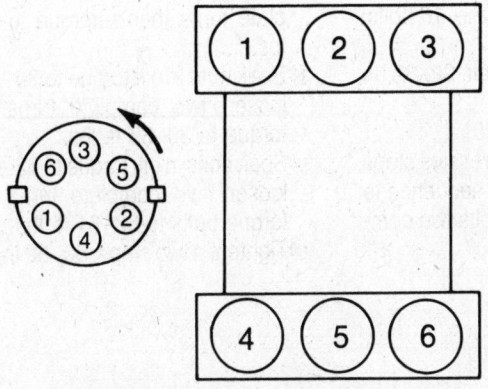

FORD MOTOR CO. 232 V6
Engine firing order: 1-4-2-5-3-6
Distributor rotation: counterclockwise

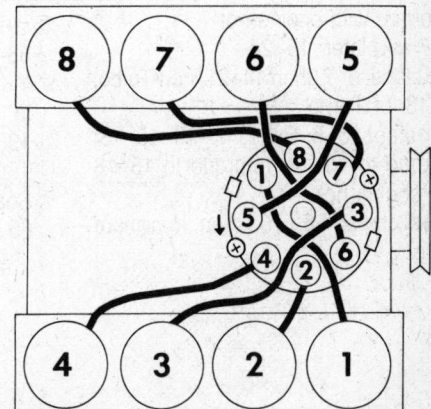

FORD MOTOR CO. 255,302 (exc. HO) 460
V8 Engine firing order: 1-5-4-2-6-3-7-8
Distributor rotation: counterclockwise

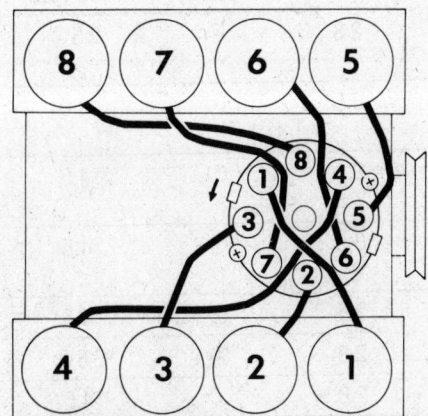

FORD MOTOR CO. 302HO, 351, 400 V8
Engine firing order: 1-3-7-2-6-5-4-8
Distributor rotation: counterclockwise

TORQUE SPECIFICATIONS
(All readings in ft. lbs.)

Year	Engine No. Cyl. Displacement (cu in.)	Cylinder Head Bolts⑨	Rod Bearing Bolts⑨	Main Bearing Bolts⑨	Crankshaft Pulley or Damper Bolt	Flywheel to Crankshaft Bolts⑨	Manifold Intake⑨	Manifold Exhaust⑨
'78–'85	6-200	70–75	21–26	60–70	85–100	75–85	—	13–18②
	6-250	70–75	21–26	60–70	85–100	75–85	—	13–18②
	8-255, 302	65–72	19–24	60–70	70–90	75–85	23–25①⑧	18–24
	8-351W	105–112	40–45	95–105	70–90	75–85	23–25①	18–24
	351M, 400	95–105⑤	40–45	⑥	70–90	75–85	⑦	18–24
	8-460	130–140	40–45	95–105	70–90	75–85	22–32	28–33
'78–'85	4-140	80–90⑬	30–36	80–90	100–120	54–64	③	16–23
'78–'79	V6-170	65–80	21–25	65–75	92–103	47–51	④	20–30
'82–'85	V6-232	⑩	⑪	⑫	85–100	75–85	18.4	15–22

① Retorque with engine hot
② 1977 and later: 18–24
③ Two steps: 5–7, then 14–21, non-Turbo, 13–18 for Turbo
④ Four steps: 3–6, 6–11, 11–15, 15–18; retorque to 15–18; retorque to 15–18 with engine hot
⑤ Three steps: 55, 75, then maximum figure
⑥ ½-in.—13 bolts: 95–105; ⅜—16 bolts: 35–45
⑦ ⁵⁄₁₆ in. bolt, 21–25; ⅜ in. bolt, 22–32, ¼ in. bolt, 6–9
⑧ 1981–82—255 V8—18–20
⑨ Tighten bolts in three progressive steps
⑩ Soak bolts in oil, torque in sequence to 65–81 ft. lbs., loosen all bolts two complete turns then retorque to 65–81 ft. lbs.
⑪ Soak nuts in oil, torque to 30–36 ft. lbs., loosen two complete turns then retorque to 30–36 ft. lbs.
⑫ Soak bolts in oil, torque to 62–81 ft. lbs., loosen two complete turns then retorque bolts to 62–81 ft. lbs.
⑬ Tighten in two steps: 50–60 then 80–90

CAPACITIES—PINTO/BOBCAT/MUSTANG II

Year	Engine No. Cyl. Displacement (Cu. In.)	Engine Crankcase Add 1 Qt For ■ New Filter	TRANSMISSION Pts To Refill After Draining 4-Speed Manual	TRANSMISSION Pts To Refill After Draining Automatic (Total capacity)	Drive Axle (pts)	Gasoline Tank (gals)	Cooling System (qts) With Heater	Cooling System (qts) With A/C
'78	4-140 (2300cc) Pinto, Bobcat	4.0	2.8	①	2.3②	13③	8.6	9.0
	4-140 (2300cc) Mustang II	4.0	3.5	①	3.0	13④	8.8	9.1
	6-171 (2800cc) Pinto, Bobcat	4.5	2.8	①	4.5	13③	8.5	9.2
	6-171 (2800cc) Mustang II	4.5	3.5	①	4.5	13④	8.5	9.0
	8-302 (4950)	4.0	3.5	①	4.5	13④	16.3	16.3
'79–'80	4-140 (2300cc)	4.0	2.8	①	2.5②	13③⑤	8.6	9.0
	6-171 (2800cc)	4.5	2.8	①	4.5	13③⑤	8.5	9.1

■ ½ quart for 2800
— Not applicable
① C3 trans.—16; C4 trans.—14
② 8.00 in. axle—4.5
③ 14 gals on station wagon
④ 16.5 gals with auxiliary tank in Mustang II
⑤ Optional on some 1979–80 models—11.7

CAPACITIES—MID SIZE MODELS

Year	Engine No. Cyl. Displacement (Cu. In.)	Engine Crankcase Add 1 Qt For New Filter	Transmission Pts to Refill After Draining			Drive Axle (pts)	Gasoline Tank (gals)	Cooling System (qts)	
			Manual		Automatic (Total Capacity)			With Heater	With A/C
			3-Speed	⅘-Speed					
'78–'80	Versailles								
	8-302	4	—	—	20.5③	5.0	19.2	14.6	14.6
	8-351W	4	—	—	20.5	5.0	19.2	15.7	15.7
'78–'80	Granada, Monarch								
	6-200	4	3.5	4.0④	—	4.0⑤	19.2⑥	9.9	9.9
	6-250	4	3.5	4.0④	17.0⑦	4.0⑤	19.2⑥	10.5	10.7
	8-255	4	3.5	4.0④	17.2	4.5	18.0	14.2	14.3
	8-302	4	3.5	4.0④	20.0⑧	4.0⑤	19.2⑥	14.6	14.6
	8-351	4	—	—	20.0	4.0⑤	19.2⑥	15.7	16.7
'78–'79	LTD II, Thunderbird, Cougar, Cougar XR-7								
	8-302	4	—	—	①	5.0	21.0⑨	14.3⑩	14.6
	8-351W	4	—	—	①	5.0	21.0⑨	15.5	16.0
	8-351M	4	—	—	①	5.0	21.0⑨	17.1⑪	17.5⑪
	8-400	4	—	—	①	5.0	21.0⑨	17.1⑪	17.5⑪
'78–'82	Fairmont, Futura, Zephyr								
	4-140	4	—	2.8④	16⑫	⑬	16⑭⑮⑯	8.6⑰	10.2
	6-200	4	3.5	2.8④	19⑫	⑬	16⑭⑯	9.0⑱⑲	9.0⑱⑲
	8-255	4	—	—	16⑫	⑬	16⑭⑯	13.4	13.5
	8-302	4	—	—	20.5⑫	⑬	16⑭	13.9	14.0
'79–'82	Mustang, Capri					⑬			
	4-140	4	—	2.8	⑳⑫	⑬	11.5㉔	8.6⑰	10㉗
	4-140T	4.5	—	3.5	⑳⑫	⑬	11.5㉔	8.6㉖	10.2㉖
	6-170	4.5	—	4.5	⑳⑫	⑬	12.5	9.2	9.2
	6-200	4	—	4.5	12⑳㉓	⑬	16㉕㉔	9⑱	9⑱
	8-255	4	—	4.5	19㉓	⑬	12.5㉔	13.4㉘	13.7㉙
	8-302	4	—	4.5	19	⑬	12.5㉔	13.9	14.2
'80–'81	Cougar XR-7, Thunderbird								
	6-200	4	—	—	16㉓	3.5	17.5	13.0	13.2
	8-255	4	—	—	20㉚	3.5	17.5	13.2	13.3
	8-302	4	—	—	20㉚	3.5	17.5	12.7	12.8
'81	Cougar, Granada								
	4-140	4	—	2.8	16	3.5	14.7	8.6	8.6
	6-200	4	—	—	16	3.5	16.0	8.1	8.1
	8-255	4	—	—	19	3.5	16.0	13.4	13.5
'82	Cougar XR-7, Thunderbird, Lincoln Continental								
	6-200	4	—	—	22	3.25	21	8.4	8.4
	6-232	4	—	—	24	3.25	21㉛	8.3	8.6
	8-255	4	—	—	24	3.25	21	14.9	15
	8-302	4	—	—	24	3.25	22.6	13.3	13.4

CAPACITIES—MID SIZE MODELS

Year	Engine No. Cyl. Displacement (Cu. In.)	Engine Crankcase Add 1 Qt For New Filter	Transmission Pts to Refill After Draining Manual 3-Speed	⅘-Speed	Automatic (Total Capacity)	Drive Axle (pts)	Gasoline Tank (gals)	Cooling System (qts) With Heater	With A/C
'82	Cougar, Granada 4-140	4	—	—	16	⑬	16.0㉜	10.2	10.2
	6-200	4	—	—	22	3.25	16.0㉜	8.4	8.4
	6-232	4	—	—	22	3.25	16.0㉜	8.3	8.3
'83–'85	LTD/Marquis 4-140	4	—	2.8	16	3.25㉝	16	8.6	9.4
	4-140P	4	—	—	16	3.25㉝	24	8.6	9.4
	6-200	4	—	—	22	3.25㉝	16	8.4	8.5
	6-232	4	—	—	22㉞	3.25㉝	16	10.7	10.8
'83–'85	Mustang/Capri 4-140	4㊱	—	2.8㉟	16	3.25㉝	15.4	8.6	9.4㉞
	6-232	4	—	—	22	3.25㉝	15.4	8.4	8.4
	8-302	4	—	4.5	—	3.55	15.4	13.1	13.4
'83	Fairmont Futura 4-140	4	—	2.8	16	3.25㉝	16	10.2	10.2
	6-200	4	—	—	22	3.25㉝	16	8.4	8.4
'83–'85	Thunderbird, Cougar Continental 4-140 Turbo	4.5㊱	—	4.75	—	3.25㉝	18	8.4	8.7
	6-232	4	—	—	22㉞	3.25㉝	21	10.4	10.7
	8-302	4	—	—	22㉞	3.25㉝	20.7㊲	13.3	13.4

T—Turbocharged
P—Propane
N/A—Specs not available at time of printing
①C4-20 pts; C6-25 pts; FMX-22 pts
②Station wagon; 21.2 gal
③'79 and later; 20 pts
④4 speed overdrive; 4.5 pts
⑤8 in.-4.5 pts
  8.7 in.-4.0 pts
  9 in.-5.0 pts
⑥1 gal less on certain '76 models; '78–'80; 18 gals
⑦16.5 pts with C4
⑧17 pts for '76
⑨'79 optional tank-27.5 gals

⑩'77-13.5 qts
⑪'78–'79; 16.5 qts
⑫'81-13.25 pts with C4; 14.5 pts w/6 cyl; 19 pts w/V8
⑬6.75 in. axle-2.5 pts; 7.5 in. axle-3.5 pts
⑭'80–'81 Station wagon; 14 gals
⑮'81; 14.7 gals
⑯'82; 20 gal optional
⑰'82; 10.2 qts
⑱'80–'82; 8.1 qts
⑲'82; 8.4 qts
⑳C3-16 pts; C4-14 pts
㉑add ½ qt with filter change
㉒'79; 14 pts
㉓'82; C5-22 pts

㉔'82; 15.4 gal
㉕'80–'81; 12.5 gal
㉖'80–'81; 9.2 qts
㉗'80–'81; 9.0 qts-'82; 10.2 qts
㉘'82; 14.7 qts
㉙'82; 15 qts
㉚AOD transmission; 24 pts
㉛Continental; 20 gals std; 22.6 optional
㉜20 gals optional
㉝Traction-Lok; 3.55 pts
㉞AOD transmission; 24 pts
㉟5 speed transmission; 4.75 pts
㊱4.5 Turbo add .5 with filter
㊲22.3 Continental
㊳10.5—Turbo models

CAPACITIES—FULL SIZE MODELS

Year	Engine No. Cyl. Displacement (Cu. In.)	Engine Crankcase Add 1 Qt For New Filter	Automatic Transmission (Total capacity)	Drive Axle (pts)	Gasoline Tank (gals) ■	Cooling System With Heater	With A/C
'78	8-302	4	①	4④	24.2	15.1	15.1
	8-351W	4	①	4④	24.2	16.2	16.2
	8-351M	4	①	4④	24.2	16.9	16.9⑤

CAPACITIES—FULL SIZE MODELS

Year	Engine No. Cyl. Displacement (Cu. In.)	Engine Crankcase Add 1 Qt For New Filter	Automatic Transmission (Total capacity)	Drive Axle (pts)	Gasoline Tank (gals) ■	Cooling System With Heater	With A/C
'78	8-400	4	①	4④	24.2	16.9	16.9⑤
	8-460	4	①	5	24.2	18.6	19.0
	8-460PI	6②	①	5	24.2	19.7	19.7
'79	8-302	4	①	⑥	19	13.3	13.8
	8-351W	4	①	⑥	19	14.6	15.2
'80	8-302	4	①	⑥	19	13.3	13.4
	8-351W	4	①	⑥	19	14.4	14.5
'81	8-255	4	24	⑥	20	14.8	15.2
	8-302	4	24	⑥	20	13.0	13.3
	8-351	4	24	⑥	20	13.9	14.0
'82–'85	8-225⑦	4	24	⑥	20	14.8	15.2
	8-302	4	24	⑥	20⑧	13.3	13.4
	8-351	4	24	⑥	20	13.8	13.8

■ Station wagons:
'79–'80—20 gals
through '78—21 gals
M Modified Cleveland
PI Police Interceptor
— Not applicable
① See Automatic Trans. Capacities Chart
② 7.5 w/oil cooler

③ With auxiliary fuel tank; sedan—32.3 gals; wagon—29.0 gals.
④ 5 with locker or 3.0:1 ratio
⑤ Trailer Towing: 17.4
⑥ 7.5 inch axle—3.5 8.5 inch axle—4.0
⑦ Discontinued for 1983
⑧ Lincoln: 18

① AUTOMATIC TRANSMISSION CAPACITIES
(Pts)

Year	Code	Capacities
'78–'80	X	22
'78–'80	W	20.5
'78–'80	U, Z	25
'80–'84	T	24

VALVE SPECIFICATIONS

Year	Engine No. Cyl. Displacement (cu in.)	Seat Angle (deg)	Face Angle (deg)	Spring Test Pressure (lbs @ in.)	Spring Installed Height (in.)	Stem To Guide Clearance (in.) Intake	Exhaust	Stem Diameter (in.) Intake	Exhaust
'78–'84	6-200	45	44	150 @ 122⑧	1¹⁹⁄₃₂	.0008–.0025	.0010–.0027	.3104	.3102
'78–'80	6-250	45	44	150 @ 122⑧	1¹⁹⁄₃₂	.0008–.0025	.0010–.0027	.3104	.3102
'78–'79	8-302	45	44	①	③	.0010–.0027	.0015–.0032	.3420	.3415
'78–'79	8-351W	45	44	②	⑤	.0010–.0027	.0015–.0032	.3420	.3415
'78	8-351⑥	45	44	228 @ 1.39	1¹³⁄₁₆	.0010–.0027	.0015–.0032	.3420	.3415
'78–'79	8-400	45	44	226 @ 1.39	1¹³⁄₁₆	.0010–.0027	.0015–.0032	.3420	.3415
'78–'85	4-140	45	44	⑨	1⁹⁄₁₆	.0010–.0027	.0015–.0032	.3420	.3415
'78–'79	V6-170	45	44	138–149 @ 1.22	1¹⁹⁄₃₂	.0008–.0025	.0018–.0035	.3163	.3152
'80–'81	8-255	45	44	⑩	⑪	.0010–.0027	.0015–.0032	.3420	.3415
'80–'85	8-302	45	44⑮	⑩	⑪	.0010–.0027	.0015–.0032	.3420	.3415
'80–'81	8-351W	45	44	⑩	⑫	.0010–.0027	.0015–.0032	.3420	.3415
'82–'85	8-351	45	45	204 @ 1.33⑱	1⁴⁹⁄₆₄⑲	.0010–.0027	.0015–.0027	.3416–.3423	.3411–.3418
	8-460	44½–45	45½–45¾	⑳	1¹³⁄₁₆	.0010–.0027	.0010–.0027	.3420	.3420
	8-460 PI	44½–45	45½–45¾	㉑	1¹³⁄₁₆	.0010–.0027	.0010–.0027	.3420	.3420

VALVE SPECIFICATIONS

Year	Engine No. Cyl. Displacement (cu in.)	Seat Angle (deg)	Face Angle (deg)	Spring Test Pressure (lbs @ in.)	Spring Installed Height (in.)	Stem To Guide Clearance (in.) Intake	Stem To Guide Clearance (in.) Exhaust	Stem Diameter (in.) Intake	Stem Diameter (in.) Exhaust
'82–'85	V6-232	⑬	⑭	215 @ 1.79	⑰	.0010–.0027	.0015–.0032	.3420	.3415
'82	8-255	⑬	⑭	⑯	—	.0010–.0027	.0015–.0032	.3420	.3415

① Intake: 200 @ 1.31
　Exhaust: 200 @ 1.20
② Intake: 200 @ 1.34
　Exhaust: 200 @ 1.20
③ Intake: 1¹¹⁄₁₆
　Exhaust: 1⅝
⑤ Intake: 1²⁵⁄₃₂
　Exhaust: 1⅝
⑥ Cleveland or modified Cleveland 2 bbl
⑦ Cleveland or modified Cleveland 4 bbl
⑧ 1980–81 Intake: 51–57 @ 1.59

⑨ 1978: 180–198 @ 1.16
　1979–81: Intake 71–79 @ 1.56
　　　　　 Exhaust: 159–175 @ 1.16
　1982: 167 @ 1.16
　1983: 149 @ 1.12
　1984: 154 @ 1.12
⑩ Intake: 196–212 @ 1.36
　Exhaust: 190–210 @ 1.20
⑪ Intake: 1¹¹⁄₁₆
　Exhaust: 1¹⁹⁄₃₂
⑫ Intake: 1²⁵⁄₃₂

Exhaust: 1¹⁹⁄₃₂
⑬ 44° 30'–45°
⑭ 45° 30'–45° 45'
⑮ 1982—45
⑯ Intake: 192 @ 1.40
　Exhaust: 191 @ 1.23
⑰ 1¾
⑱ Exhaust: 205 @ 1.15
⑲ Exhaust: 1³⁷⁄₆₄
⑳ Intake: 240 @ 1.33; Exhaust: 253 @ 1.33
㉑ Intake: 3.5 @ 1.32; Exhaust: 315 @ 1.33

CRANKSHAFT AND CONNECTING ROD SPECIFICATIONS

All measurements are given in inches

Year	Engine No. Cyl. Displacement (cu in.)	Crankshaft Main Brg. Journal Dia	Crankshaft Main Brg. Oil Clearance	Crankshaft Shaft End-Play	Crankshaft Thrust on No.	Connecting Rod Journal Diameter	Connecting Rod Oil Clearance	Connecting Rod Side Clearance
'78–'84	6-200	2.2482–2.2490	.0005–.0022①	.004–.008	5	2.1232–2.1240	.0008–.0015	.0035–.0105
	6-250	2.3982–2.3990	.0005–.0022①	.004–.008	5	2.1232–2.1240	.0008–.0015	.0035–.0105
	8-255, 302	2.2482–2.2490	.0005–.0015②	.004–.008	3	2.1228–2.1236	.0008–.0026③	.010–.020
	8-351W	2.9994–3.0002	.0008–.0015②	.004–.008	3	2.3103–2.3111	.0008–.0026③	.010–.020
	8-351M	2.9994–3.0002	.0008–.0015④	.004–.008	3	2.3103–2.3111	.0008–.0015④	.010–.020
	8-400	2.9994–3.0002	.0008–.0015	.004–.008	3	2.3103–2.3111	.0008–.0015	.010–.020
'78	8-460	2.9994–3.0002	.0008–.0015	.004–.008	3	2.4992–2.5000	.0008–.0015	.010–.020
'78–'85	4-140	2.3990–2.3982	.0008–.0015	.004–.008	3	2.0464–2.0472	.0008–.0015	.0035–.0105
'78–'79	V6-170	2.2433–2.2441	.0008–.0015	.004–.008	3	2.1252–2.1260	.0006–.0015	.004–.011
'82–'85	V6-232	2.5190	.0001–.001	.004–.008	3	2.3103–2.3111	.0008–.0026	.0047–.0114

① .0008–.0015 in. in 1977–81
② .0001–.0015 No. 1 bearing only
③ .0008–.0015 in. in 1977–81
④ 351M 4-bbl—.0011–.0015

PISTON AND RING SPECIFICATIONS

(All measurements in inches)

Engine Displacement (cu. in.)	Piston Clearance	Ring Gap Top Compression	Ring Gap Bottom Compression	Ring Gap Oil① Control	Ring Side Clearance Top Compression	Ring Side Clearance Bottom Compression	Ring Side Clearance Oil Control	Wear Limit
4-140(2.3L)	0.0014–0.0022	.010–.020	.010–.020	.015–.055	.002–.004	.002–.004	Snug	.006
4-140(2.3L) ('79–'82 Turbo)	0.0034–0.0042	.010–.020	.010–.020	.015–.055	.002–.004	.002–.004	Snug	.006
4-140(2.3L) ('83–'85 Turbo)	0.0030–0.0038	.010–.020	.010–.020	.015–.055	.002–.004	.002–.004	Snug	.006
6-170(2.8L)	0.0011–0.0019	.015–.023	.015–.023	.015–.055	.002–.0033	.002–.0033	Snug	.006

PISTON AND RING SPECIFICATIONS

(All measurements in inches)

Engine Displacement (cu. in.)	Piston Clearance	Ring Gap			Ring Side Clearance			Wear Limit
		Top Compression	Bottom Compression	Oil① Control	Top Compression	Bottom Compression	Oil Control	
6-200(3.3L) 250(4.1L)	0.0013–0.0021	.008–.016	.008–.016	.015–.055	.002–.004	.002–.004	Snug	.006
6-232(3.8L)	0.0014–0.0028	.010–.020	.010–.020	0.15–.055	.002–.004	.002–.004	Snug	.006
8-255(4.2L) 302(5.0L) 351W(5.8L)	0.0018–0.0026	.010–.020	.010–.020	.015–.055	.002–.004	.002–.004	Snug	.006
8-351M(5.8L) 8-400(6.6L)	0.0014–0.0022	.010–.020	.010–.020	.015–.055	.002–.004	.002–.004	Snug	.006

①Steel rails

CAMSHAFT SPECIFICATIONS

(All measurements in inches)

Engine	Journal Diameter					Bearing Clearance	Lobe Lift		Endplay
	1	2	3	4	5		Intake	Exhaust	
4-140 (2.3L)	1.7713–1.7720	1.7713–1.7720	1.7713–1.7720	1.7713–1.7720	—	.001–.003	.2437①	.2437①	.001–.007
6-200 (3.3L)	1.8095–1.8105	1.8095–1.8105	1.8095–1.8105	1.8095–1.8105	—	.001–.003	.245	.245	.001–.007
6-232 (3.8L)	2.0505–2.0515	2.0505–2.0515	2.0505–2.0515	2.0505–2.0515	—	.001–.003	.240	.241	②
6-250 (4.1L)	1.8095–1.8105	1.8095–1.8105	1.8095–1.8105	1.8095–1.8105	—	.001–.003	.245	.245	.001–.007
8-255 (4.2L)	2.0805–2.0815	2.0655–2.0665	2.0505–2.0515	2.0355–2.0365	2.0205–2.0215	.001–.003	.2375	.2375	.001–.007
8-302 (5.0L)	2.0805–2.0815	2.0655–2.0665	2.0505–2.0515	2.0355–2.0365	2.0205–2.0215	.001–.003	.2375③	.2474③	.001–.003
8-351W (5.8L)	2.0805–2.0815	2.0655–2.0665	2.0505–2.0515	2.0355–2.0365	2.0205–2.0215	.001–.003	.260④	.260④	.001–.007
8-351M (5.8L) 8-400 (6.6L)	2.1238–2.1248	2.0655–2.0665	2.0505–2.0515	2.0355–2.0365	2.0205–2.0215	.001–.003	.235 .247	.235 .250	.001–.003
8-460 (7.5L)	2.1238–2.1248	2.1238–2.1248	2.1238–2.1248	2.1238–2.1248	2.1238–2.1248	.001–.003	.253④	.278④	.001–.006

①'84 and later: .2381
②Endplay controlled by button and spring on camshaft end.
③HO engine: Intake—.2600; Exhaust—.2780
④HO engine: Intake—.2780; Exhaust—.2830

WHEEL ALIGNMENT SPECIFICATIONS—PINTO/BOBCAT/MUSTANG II

Year	Model	Caster		Camber		Toe-in (in.)	Steering Axis Inclin.	Wheel Pivot Ratio (deg)	
		Range (deg)	Pref Setting (deg)	Range (deg)	Pref Setting (deg)			Inner Wheel	Outer Wheel
'78–'80	Pinto, Bobcat	¼P to 1¾P	1P	¼N to 1¼P	½P	0 to ¼	10.018	20	18.84
'78–'80	Sta. Wag.	½N to 1P	¼P	¼N to 1¼P	½P	0 to ¼	10.018	20	18.84
'78	Mustang II	⅛P to 1⅝P	⅞P	¼N to 1¼P	½P	0 to ¼	9.763	20	18.84

N Negative   P Positive

WHEEL ALIGNMENT SPECIFICATIONS—MID SIZE MODELS

Year	Model	Caster Range (deg)	Caster Pref Setting (deg)	Camber Range (deg)	Camber Pref Setting (deg)	Toe-in (in.)	Steering Axis Inclin. (deg)	Wheel Pivot Ratio (deg) Inner Wheel	Wheel Pivot Ratio (deg) Outer Wheel
'78–'79	Cougar, LTD II, '78–'79 Thunderbird	3¼P to 4¾P	4P	①	②	0 to ¼	9③	20	18.06
'78–'80	Monarch, Granada, Versailles	1¼N to ¼P	½N	½N to 1P	¼P	0 to ¼	6¾	20	④
'78–'79	Fairmont, Zephyr, Mustang, Capri	⑤	⅞P	⑤	⅜P	3/16 to 7/16	15¼	20	19.74
'80–'81	Fairmont and Zephyr (exc. Station Wagon)	⅛P to 1⅞P⑤	1P	5/16N to 1 3/16P⑤	7/16P	1/16 to 5/16	15¼	20	19.84
'80–'81	Fairmont and Zephyr (Station Wagon)	⅛N to 1⅝P⑤	¾P	¼N to 1¼P⑤	½P	1/16 to 5/16	15¼	20	19.84
'80–'82	Thunderbird, Cougar XR-7	⅛ to 1⅞P⑤	1P	½N to 1¼P⑤	⅜P	1/16 to 5/16	15⅓	20	24.9⑥
'80–'82	Mustang, Capri	¼P to 1¾P⑤	1P	½N to 1P⑤	¼P	1/16 to 5/16	15¼	20	19.84
'81–'82	Cougar, Granada	⅛P to 1⅞P	1P	5/16N to 1 3/16P⑤	7/16P	1/16 to 5/16	15¼	20	19.84
'82–'83	Fairmont, Futura, Zephyr	⅛P to 1⅞P	1P	5/16N to 1 3/16P⑤	7/16P	1/16 to 5/16	15¼	20	19.84
'83–'85	Thunderbird Cougar XR-7	½P to 2P	1¼P	½N to 1P	¼P	1/16 to 5/16	—	20	19.73
'83–'85	LTD, Marquis (Sedan)	1⅛P to 2⅛P	1⅛P	5/16N to 1 3/16P	7/16P	1/16 to 5/16	—	20	19.84
'83–'85	LTD, Marquis (Station Wagon)	⅛N to 1⅞P	⅞P	¼N to 1¼P	½P	1/16 to 5/16	—	20	19.84
'83–'85	Mustang, Capri	½P to 2P	1¼P	¾N to ¾P	0	1/16 to 5/16	—	20	19.84
'82–'83	Lincoln Continental	⅜P to 2⅛P	1¼P	½N to 1¼P	⅜P	0 to ¼	—	20	19.13

①Left—¼N to 1¼P
Right—½N to 1P
②Left—½P
Right—¼P
③Thunderbird—9½
④Granada/Monarch, Versailles w/PS—18.20; w/o PS—18.43
⑤Caster and camber are preset and nonadjustable
⑥1981–82—19.77; 83–85 N.A.
N Negative P Positive
N.A.—Not Available

WHEEL AIGNMENT SPECIFICATIONS—FULL SIZE MODELS

Year	Model	Caster Range (deg)	Caster Pref Setting (deg)	Camber Range (deg)	Camber Pref Setting (deg)	Toe-in (in.)	Steering Axis Inclin. (deg)	Wheel Pivot Ratio (deg) Inner Wheel	Wheel Pivot Ratio (deg) Outer Wheel
'78	Ford, Mercury	1¼P to 2¾P	2P	①	②	1 1/16 to 5/16	9.44	20	18.72
'79	Ford, Mercury	2¼P to 3¾P	3P	¼N to 1¼P	½P	1/16 to 5/16	11.20	20	18
'78–'79	Mark V	3¼P–4¾P	4P	①	②	1/16–5/16	9½	20	18.09
'77–'79	Continental	1P–2P	2P	①	②	0–¼	9	20	18.16
'80–'85	Lincoln	2¼P to 3¾P	3P	¼N to 1¼P	½P	1/16–3/16	10.87	—	18.50
'80–'85	Ford, Mercury	2¼P to 3¾P	3P	¼N to 1¼P	½P	1/16 to 3/16	10 31/32	—	18.50

N: Negative P: Positive
①Left ¼N to 1¼P
Right ½N to 1P
②Left ½P
Right ¼P

DIESEL 2.4L SPECIFICATIONS

ENGINE
Type ....6-cylinder, in-line, 4-cycle, overhead valve, water-cooled
Bore .... 3.150 in. (80mm)
Stroke .... 3.189 in. (81mm)
Displacement .... 149 cu. in. (2442.9cc)
Compression ratio 23:1
Horsepower ....114 at 4800 rpm
Minimum Torque ....150 lb. ft. at 2400 rpm
Compression pressure .... 348 psi (2400 kPa)
Valve clearance (cold engine) .... Intake: 0.010 in. (0.3mm)
                                             Exhaust: 0.010 in. (0.3mm)

Cam Timing
   Intake valve opens ....6° BTDC
   Intake valve closes .... 34° ABDC
   Exhaust valve opens .... 46° BBDC
   Exhaust valve closes ....6° ATDC
   Intake valve lift ....0.374 in. (9.5mm)
   Exhaust valve lift .... 0.376 in. (9.55mm)
Weight .... 433 lbs. (196.4 kg) dry
FUEL SYSTEM
Injection firing order 1 5 3 6 2 4
Idle speed ....750 + 50 − 0 rpm
Fast idle (cold-start) speed .... 900–1050 rpm
Injection pump timing .... 2.5° BTDC at 750–800 rpm
LUBRICATION SYSTEM
Complete System w/o oil cooler ....7.1 qts. (6.7L)
Complete System ....7.9 qts. (7.5L)
Engine oil pressure ....57–85 psi at 4000 rpm

NOTE: Do to the late introduction of this engine, normal specifications were unavailable at the time of publication.

DIESEL 2.4L TORQUE SPECIFICATIONS

Description	Ft. lbs.	Description	Ft. lbs.
Main bearing caps	43–48	Oil line from turbocharger to crankcase 22mm width across flats hollow bolt	29–36
Engine support straps	28–34		
Valve cover	6–7	Water pump to crankcase	14–17
Oil trap to valve cover	11–14	Fan coupling to water pump nut with left-hand threads	36
Cylinder head bolts			
Step 1	36–43	Fan to fan coupling	6–7
Step 2	65–69	Pulley to water pump	6–7
Step 3 (torque angle)	90 ± 5°	Thermostat housing	6–7
Oil spray bar to cylinder head	14–17	Bleeder screw	4–7
Oil drain plug	24–26	Temperature sensor/temperature switch	12–14
Oil pan to crankcase	6.5–7		
Front/rear end covers to crankcase	6–7 / 14–17	Intake manifold to cylinder head	14–17
Flywheel to crankshaft (installed with Loctite No. 270)	71–81	Exhaust manifold to cylinder head (upper row of staybolts installed with Loctite 270)	14–17
		Turbocharger to exhaust manifold	17–20
Vibration damper hub to crankshaft	282–311	Exhaust to turbocharger	31–35

DIESEL 2.4L TORQUE SPECIFICATIONS

Description	Ft. lbs.	Description	Ft. lbs.
Pulley/vibration damper to vibration damper hub	16–17	Vacuum pump	6–7
Connecting rod bolts		Pulse sensor to engine (holder)	6–7
Step 1	14	Glow plugs	14–22
Step 2 (torque angle)	70°	Temperature switch to fuel filter housing	22
Sprocket to camshaft	40–47	Wire to glow plug	3–4
Bearing cap of camshaft	6–7 14–17	Fuel filter housing to holder	31–35
Tensioning roller holder to crankcase	14–17	Injection pump to holder, rear (nuts and bolts)	14–17
Clamping bolt in rocker arm	5–6.5	Injection pump to holder, front	14–17
Sprocket to auxiliary shaft	40–47	Electric shut-off to injection pump	11–18
Oil pressure switch	22–29	Electric valve for cold start accelerator to injection pump	11–14
Oil pump to crankcase	16–17	Injection pump gear to injection pump	33–36
Oil pump cover	6–7		
Oil filter housing to crankcase	14–17	Tensioning torque for tensioning roller holder	33–36
Oil filter cover	15–18	Tensioning roller holder to engine (M8 nut and bolt)	18
Oil filter drain plug	7–9		
Oil spray jet to crankcase	6–7	Combination fuel injector in cylinder head	29–33
Oil cooler oil lines to oil filter housing	22–29	Injection line (coupling nut)	14–18
Oil lines to turbocharger	14–17	Nozzle holder to injection pump	33
		Spill valve to injection pump (hollow bolt)	14–22

CHARGING SYSTEM

NOTE: Charging system testing procedures can be found in the Unit Repair section under "Charging and Starting Systems".

Alternator

NOTE: There are two different-style alternators used on these vehicles; side terminal and rear terminal alternators. Removal and installation procedures are the same for both.

REMOVAL & INSTALLATION

1. Disconnect the negative battery ground cable.
2. Loosen the alternator mounting bolts and remove the adjustment arm to alternator attaching bolt. Remove the drive belt. Models equipped with a single drive belt (serpentine): lever the tensioner away from

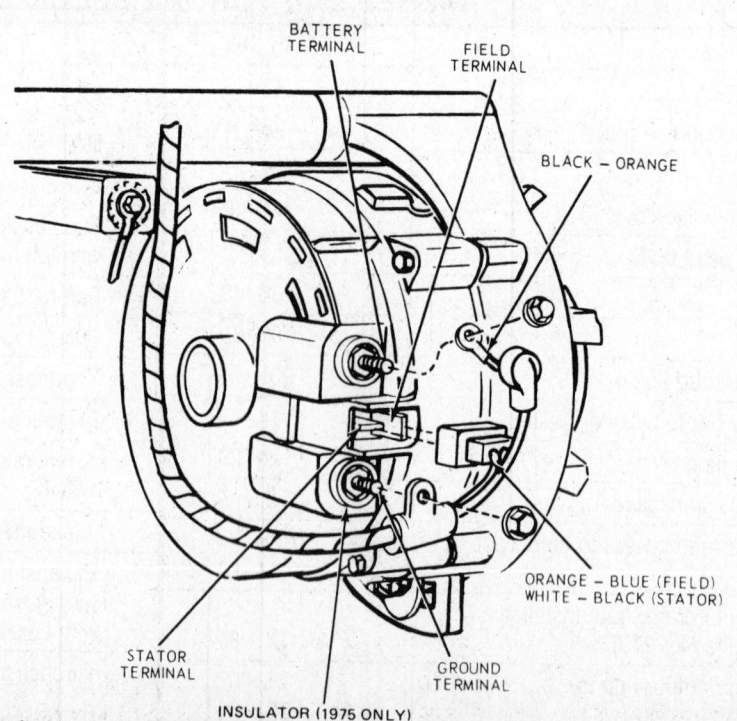

Typical connector details for the side terminal alternator (© Ford Motor Co.)

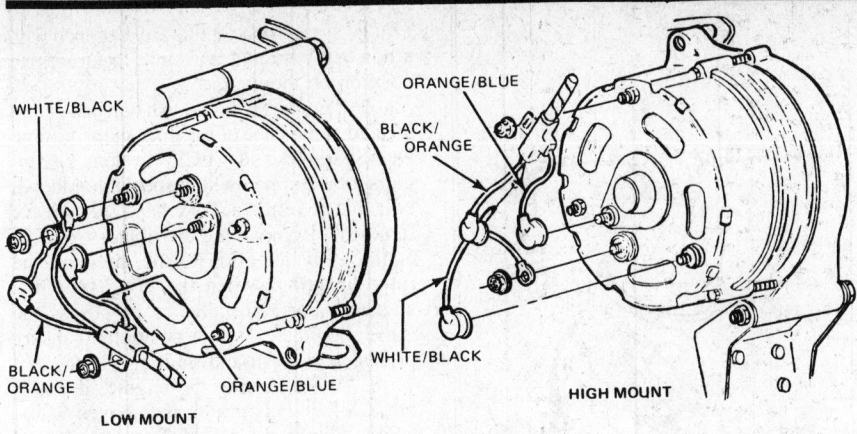

Typical connector details for the rear terminal alternator (© Ford Motor Co.)

the belt and remove belt from alternator pulley. See Note below.

NOTE: Various models are equipped with a 5-rib or 6-rib K-section (V-ribbed) belt and an automatic absorber tensioner. A special tool must be fabricated to remove the tension from the absorber assembly arm so that the belt can be removed and installed. Loosen the idler pulley pivot and adjustment bolts before using tool to remove belt.

3. Remove the electrical connectors from the alternator and remove the alternator. On some models it is necessary to remove the alternator mounting bolts and the alternator wiring ground bolt from engine to gain access to the electrical connectors.

4. Install the alternator to the bracket and connect the electrical connectors. Adjust the drive belt tension so that there is approximately 1/4–1/2 in. of deflection on the longest span of belt between pulleys. Apply pressure to the front of the alternator housing when adjusting belt tension.

5. On models equipped with a single drive belt, install the alternator to the bracket, attach the electrical connectors, slide the serpentine belt over the alternator pulley, and release the automatic tensioner. If the vehicle is equipped with AOD transmission and air conditioning, install the pulleys, then place the absorber arm deflection tool on the arm and push the absorber pulley downward to the bottom of the slot (never push on the ribs of the pulley). Fit the belt over the rest of the pulleys. While holding the absorber pulley down, adjust the idler pulley by hand until it is snug and tighten the adjustment bolt and pivot bolt on the idler pulley assembly. Release the deflection tool. The proper tension will be set automatically.

Voltage Regulator

NOTE: This procedure applies to models equipped with an external mounted regulator.

REMOVAL & INSTALLATION

NOTE: 1979 and later models have electronic voltage regulators. Always disconnect the connector plug from the regulator before removing the mounting screws on these models. Some regulator wiring connectors have a snap-lock that can be disengaged by inserting and twisting an appropriate tool.

1. Disconnect the negative battery cable.
2. Disconnect the wire harness connector. Remove the mounting screws and the regulator.
3. Mount the regulator in position and tighten the attaching screws. If equipped with a radio suppression capacitor, mount the capacitor in position.
4. Connect the wiring harness. Connect the negative battery cable.

STARTING SYSTEM

NOTE: Starting system servicing procedures can be found in the "Charging and Starting" Systems Unit Repair Section.

Starter

REMOVAL & INSTALLATION

Gas Engines

1. Disconnect the negative battery cable.
2. Raise the vehicle and support it safely.
3. Disconnect the starter cable from the starter.

NOTE: If clearance is a problem, it may be necessary to remove a brace, raise the engine, etc. Refer to Step 4.

4.a. On Granada, Monarch and Versailles with 302 CID engine, remove the right engine mount and raise the engine.

b. On Fairmont and Zephyr with 200 CID engine, remove the wish-bone brace.

c. Pinto, Bobcat and Mustang, remove the crossmember from under the bell housing and remove the steering gear assembly from the side rail.

d. On 1980 and later Thunderbirds and Cougars, XR-7s, LTDs Marquis and Continentals remove the cross brace.

5. Remove the starter housing bolts and crossmember from under the engine. Remove the heat shield, if equipped.

6. Manipulate the starter so that it can be lowered through the steering linkage. On some engine/chassis combinations, this can be accomplished by turning the front wheels either right or left, or by removing the idler arm bracket attaching bolts and lowering the steering linkage away from the engine.

7. The installation of the starter assembly is the reverse of the removal procedure. Tighten the mounting bolts to 15–20 ft. lbs.

2.4L Diesel Engine

1. Disconnect the battery ground (negative) cable.
2. Remove the bolt holding the dipstick tube to the intake manifold.
3. Remove the wires from the starter solenoid. Remove the front starter support bracket.
4. Remove the two starter to torque converter housing mounting bolts.
5. Pull the dipstick tube outward slightly allowing clearance for starter motor removal. Remove the starter motor.
6. Position the starter to torque converter housing and install the two bolts. Tighten to 30–40 ft. lbs.
7. Install the starter support bracket and tighten the attaching bolts to 14–20 ft. lbs.
8. Connect the cables to the starter solenoid. Tighten the red wire to 80–120 inch lbs. Tighten the black wire to 25 inch lbs.
9. Reposition the dipstick to the intake manifold, install the bolt and tighten to 6–7 ft. lbs.
10. Install the battery ground cable.

IGNITION SYSTEM

NOTE: Complete service and troubleshooting information on "Dura Spark" systems can be found in the "Electronic Ignition" section of Unit Repair.

Distributor

REMOVAL & INSTALLATION

1. Remove the air cleaner on V6 and V8 engines. On 4 and 6 cylinder in-line engines, removal of a thermactor (air) pump mounting bolt and drive belt will allow the

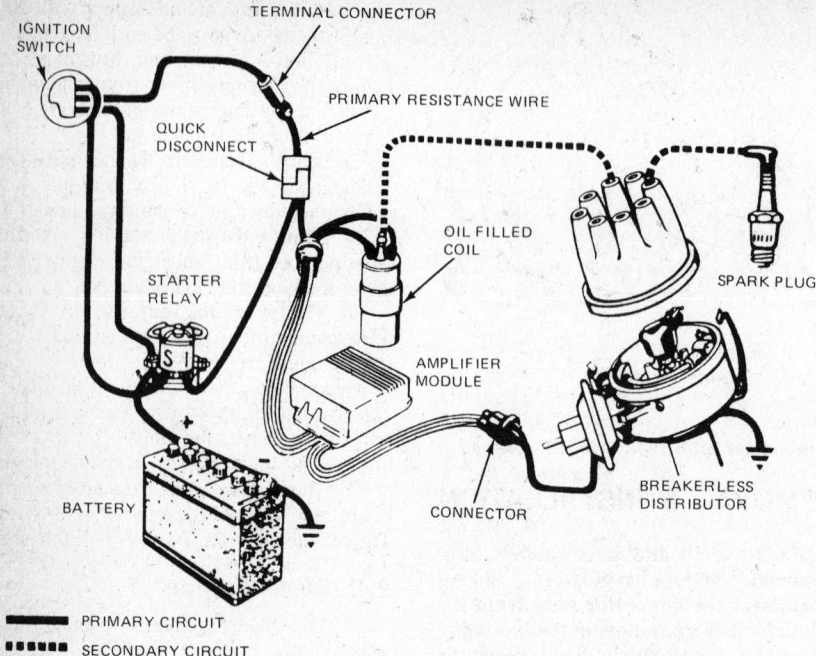

Typical electronic ignition system schematic (© Ford Motor Co.)

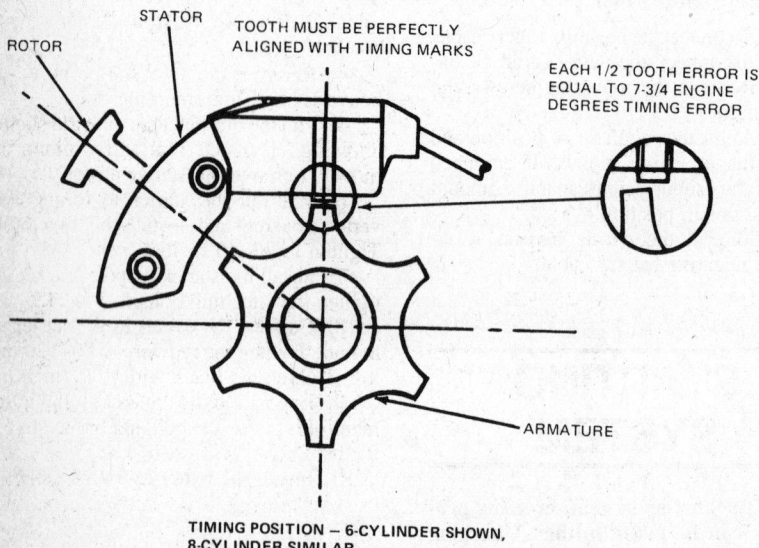

Distributor firing position with electronic ignition (© Ford Motor Co.)

EECIV system distributors are equipped with a notched base and will only locate at one position on the engine.

7. Remove the holddown bolt and clamp located at the base of the distributor. (Some DuraSpark III and EECIV system distributors are equipped with a special holddown bolt that requires a Torx head wrench for removal). Remove the distributor from the engine. Pay attention to the direction the rotor tip points when the drive gear disengages. For reinstallation purposes, the rotor should be at this position to insure proper gear mesh and timing.

8. Avoid turning the engine, if possible, while the distributor is removed. If the engine is turned from TDC position, TDC timing marks will have to be reset before the distributor is installed; Steps 4 and 5.

9. Position the distributor in the engine with the rotor aligned to the marks made on the distributor, or to the place the rotor pointed when the distributor was removed. The stator and armature or "polarizing square" and shaft plate should also be aligned. Engage the oil pump intermediate shaft and insert the distributor until fully seated on the engine, if the distributor does not fully seat, turn the engine slightly to fully engage the intermediate shaft.

10. Follow the above procedures on models equipped with an indexed distributor base. Make sure when positioning the distributor that the slot in the distributor base will engage the block tab and the sleeve/adaptor slots are aligned.

11. After the distributor has been fully seated on the block install the hold down bracket and bolt. On models equipped with an indexed base, tighten the mounting bolt. On other models, snug the mounting bolt so the distributor can be turned for ignition timing purposes.

12. The rest of the installation is in the reverse order of removal. Check and reset the ignition timing on applicable models.

NOTE: A silicone compound is used on rotor tips, distributor cap contacts and on the inside of the connectors on the spark plugs cable and module couplers. Always apply Silicone Dielectric Compound after servicing any component of the ignition system. Various

pump to be moved to the side and permit access to the distributor. If necessary, disconnect the thermactor air filter and lines as well.

2. Remove the distributor cap and position the cap and ignition wires to the side.

3. Disconnect the wire harness plug from the distributor connector. Disconnect and plug the vacuum hoses from the vacuum diaphragm assembly. (DuraSpark III systems are not equipped with a vacuum diaphragm).

4. Rotate the engine (in normal direction of rotation) until No. 1 piston is on TDC (Top Dead Center) of the compression stroke. The TDC mark on the crankshaft pulley and the pointer should align. Rotor tip pointing at No. 1 position on distributor cap.

5. On DuraSpark I or II, turn the engine a slight bit more (if required) to align the stator (pick-up coil) assembly pole with an (the closest) armature pole. On DuraSpark III, the distributor sleeve groove (when looking down from the top) and the cap adaptor alignment slot should align. On models equipped with EECIV (1984 and later), remove the rotor (2 screws) and note the position of the "polarizing square" and shaft plate for reinstallation reference.

6. Scribe a mark on the distributor body and engine block to indicate the position of the rotor tip and position of the distributor in the engine. DuraSpark III and some

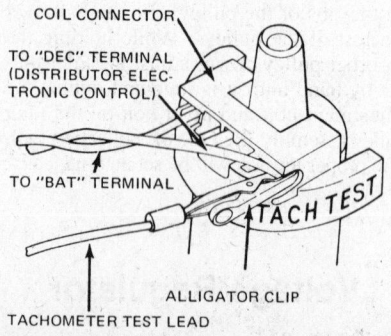

Electronic ignition test tachometer hookup (© Ford Motor Co.)

models use a multi-point rotor which do not require the application of dielectric compound.

Ignition Timing

NOTE: Some engines have monolithic timing set at the factory. The monolithic system uses a timing receptacle on the front of the engine which can be connected to digital read-out equipment, which electronically determines timing. Timing can also be adjusted in the conventional way. Many 1980 and later models are equipped with EEC engine controls. All ignition timing is controlled by the EEC module. Initial ignition timing is not adjustable and no attempt at adjustment should be made on EECIII models, or models equipped with an indexed distributor base. For a description of EEC systems, refer to the Unit Repair sections on "Electronic Ignition Systems" and on "Engine Controls."

NOTE: Requirements vary from model to model. Always refer to the "Emissions Specification Sticker" for exact timing procedures.

1. Locate the timing marks and pointer on the lower engine pulley and engine's front cover.

2. Clean the marks and apply chalk or bright-colored paint to the pointer.

3. On 1981 and later models, if the ignition module has (-12A244-) as a basic part number, disconnect the two wire connector (yellow and black wires). On engines equipped with the EECIV system, disconnect the single white (black on some models) wire connector near the distributor.

4. Attach a timing light and tachometer according to manufacturer's specifications.

5. Disconnect and plug all vacuum lines leading to the distributor.

6. Start the engine, allow it to warm to normal operating temperature, then set the idle to the specifications given on the underhood sticker (for timing).

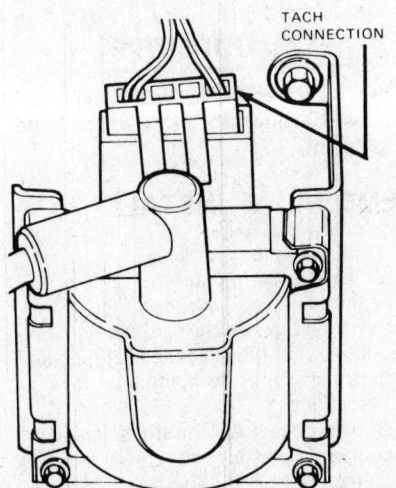

Tach connection, "E" coil

7. On 1981 and later models equipped with the module mentioned in Step 3, jumper the pins in the module connector for the yellow and black wires.

8. Aim the timing light at the timing mark and pointer on the front of the engine. If the marks align when the timing light flashes, remove the timing light, set the idle to its proper specification, and connect the vacuum lines at the distributor. If the marks do not align when the light flashes, turn the engine off and loosen the distributor hold-down clamp slightly.

9. Start the engine again, and observe the alignment of the timing marks. To advance the timing, turn the distributor counterclockwise, on six cylinder engines except the 232 (3.8L) V6, or clockwise, for the 232 (3.8L) V6 and V8 engines. When altering the timing, it is wise to tap the distributor lightly with a wooden hammer handle to move it in the desired direction. Grasping the distributor with your hand may result in a painful electric shock. When the timing marks are aligned, turn the engine off and tighten the distributor hold-down clamp. Remove the test equipment, reconnect the vacuum hoses and white (black) single wire connector (EECIV).

10. On 1981 and later models equipped with the module mentioned in Step 3, remove the jumper connected in Step 7 and reconnect the two wire connector. Test the module operation as follows:

a. Disconnect and plug the vacuum source hose to the ignition timing vacuum switch.

b. Using an external vacuum source, apply vacuum greater than 12 in. Hg to the switch, and compare the ignition timing with the requirements below:

4 cylinder—per specifications less $32°$–$40°$

6 cylinder—per specifications less $21°$–$27°$

8 cylinder—per specifications less $16°$–$20°$

Tachometer Connection

The coil connector used with DuraSpark is provided with a cavity for connection of a tachometer, so that the connector doesn't have to be removed to check engine rpm.

Install a tach lead with an alligator clip on its end into the cavity marked TACH TEST and connect the other lead to a good ground.

If the coil connector must be removed, pull it out horizontally until it is disengaged from the coil terminal.

GASOLINE FUEL .SYSTEM

NOTE: See the "Emission Controls" section in this Car Section for a descrip-

tion of models equipped with Electronic Fuel Injection (EFI). Additional information is given in the "Fuel Injection" Unit Repair section.

Mechanical Fuel Pump

REMOVAL & INSTALLATION

NOTE: Before removing the pump, rotate the engine so that the low point of the cam lobe is against the pump arm. This can be determined by rotating the engine with the fuel pump mounting bolts loosened slightly; when tension (resistance) is removed from the arm, proceed.

1. Remove the inlet outlet and return vapor (if equipped) lines from the pump.

2. Remove the fuel pump retaining screws and remove the pump and gasket. Remove the fuel pump pushrod on 2800 V6 engines.

3. Clean all gasket material from the pump mounting surface on the engine, and apply a coat of oil-resistant sealer to the new gasket.

4. Reinstall the pushrod on models equipped. Position pump on engine and install retaining screws.

5. Reinstall lines, start engine and check for leaks.

NOTE: If resistance is felt while positioning the fuel pump on the block, the camshaft eccentric is in the high position. To ease installation, connect a remote engine starter switch to the engine and tap the remote switch until resistance fades.

Electric Fuel Pump

REMOVAL & INSTALLATION

NOTE: A single internally gas tank mounted pump is used on fuel injected models through 1983 and on 1984 and later Lincoln Town Car, Ford Crown Victoria and Mercury Grand Marquis models (with EFI). Other 1984 and later models equipped with a high output injected or turbocharged injected engine are equipped with two electric pumps. A low-pressure pump is mounted in the tank and a high pressure pump is externally mounted.

——— CAUTION ———

Before servicing any part of the fuel injection it is necessary to depressurize the system. A special tool is available for testing and bleeding the system.

———————————

In-Tank Pump

1. Disconnect the negative battery cable.

2. Depressurize the system and drain as much gas from the tank by pumping out through the filler neck.

3. Raise the back of the car and safely support on jackstands.

4. Disconnect the fuel supply, return and vent lines at the right and left side of the frame.

5. Disconnect the wiring to the fuel pump.

6. Support the gas tank, loosen and remove the mounting straps. Remove the gas tank.

7. Disconnect the lines and harness at the pump flange.

8. Clean the outside of the mounting flange and retaining ring. Turn the fuel pump lock ring counterclockwise and remove.

9. Remove the fuel pump.

10. Clean the mounting surfaces. Put a light coat of grease on the mounting surfaces and on the new sealing ring. Install the new fuel pump.

11. Installation is in the reverse order of removal. If single high pressure pump system, fill the tank with at least 10 gals. of gas. Turn the ignition key ON for three seconds. Repeat 6 or 7 times until the fuel system is pressurized. Check for any fitting leaks. Start the engine and check for leaks.

External Pump

1. Disconnect the negative battery cable.
2. Depressurize the fuel system.
3. Raise and support the rear of the vehicle on jackstands.
4. Disconnect the inlet and outlet fuel lines.
6. Bend down the retaining tab and remove the pump from the mounting bracket ring.
7. Install in reverse order, make sure the pump is indexed correctly in the mounting bracket insulator.

"Quick-Connect" Fuel Line Fittings

REMOVAL & INSTALLATION

NOTE: "Quick-Connect" (push) type fuel fittings are used on most models equipped with a pressurized fuel system. The fittings must be disconnected using proper procedures or the fitting may be damaged. Two types of retainers are used on the push connect fittings. Line sizes of 3/8 in. and 5/16 in. use a "hairpin" clip retainer. 1/4 in. line connectors use a "duck bill" clip retainer.

Hairpin Clip

1. Clean all dirt and/or grease from the fitting. Spread the two clip legs about an 1/8 inch each to disengage from the fitting and pull the clip outward from the fitting and pull the clip outward from the fitting. Use finger pressure only, do not use any tools.

2. Grasp the fitting and hose assembly and pull away from the steel line. Twist the fitting and hose assembly slightly while

pulling, if necessary, when a sticking condition exists.

3. Inspect the hairpin clip for damage, replace the clip if necessary. Reinstall the clip in position on the fitting.

4. Inspect the fitting and inside of the connector to insure freedom of dirt or obstruction. Install fitting into the connector and push together. A click will be heard when the hairpin clip snaps into proper connection. Pull on the line to insure full engagement.

Duck Bill Clip

1. A special tool is available from Ford for removing the retaining clips (Ford Tool No. T82L-9500-AH). If the tool is not on hand see Step 2. Align the slot on the push connector disconnect tool with either tab on the retaining clip. Insert the tool to disengage the clip. Pull the line from the connector.

2. If the special clip tool is not available, use a pair of narrow 6 in. channel lock pliers with a jaw width of 0.2 in. or less. Align the jaws of the pliers with the openings of the fitting case and compress the part of the retaining clip that engages the case. Compressing the retaining clip will release the fitting which may be pulled from the connector. Both sides of the clip must be compressed at the same time to disengage.

3. Inspect the retaining clip, fitting end and connector. Replace clip if any damage is apparent.

4. Push the line into the steel connector until a click is heard, indicating clip is in place. Pull on line to check engagement.

Fuel Filter

REMOVAL & INSTALLATION

Carbureted Engines

A separate in-line fuel filter is used, except on some models with a Variable Venturi (VV) carburetor.

IN-LINE HOSE CONNECTED FILTERS

1. Remove the air cleaner.
2. Loosen the hose clamps.
3. Unscrew the filter from the carburetor.
4. Disconnect the filter from the hose and discard the filter, hose and clamps. Replacement filters usually come with a length of hose and new clamps, always use the new parts when filter replacement is necessary.

5. Reverse the procedure to install the fuel filter. After installation, start the engine and check for fuel leakage.

INVERTED NUT (STEEL LINE) CONNECTED FILTERS

1. Remove the air cleaner assembly.
2. Position an 11/16 open end wrench on the filter hex nut, to hold the filler in po-

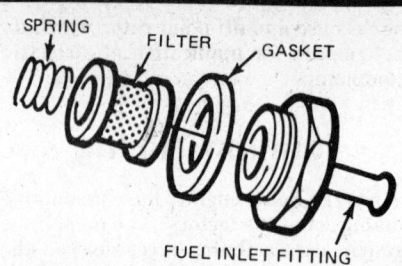

SPRING   FILTER   GASKET

FUEL INLET FITTING

Model 2700 VV fuel filter (© Ford Motor Co.)

sition and remove the steel fuel line from the filter using a suitable wrench.

3. Unscrew the filter from the carburetor.
4. Install the new filter in reverse order of removal.

IN CARBURETOR FILTERS (VV CARBS)

1. Remove the air cleaner.
2. Disconnect the fuel line from the carburetor inlet fitting, while holding the inlet fitting with a suitable wrench.
3. Remove inlet fitting and fuel filter.
4. Install the spring, filter, gasket and fitting.
5. Connect the fuel line, start engine and check for leaks.

Fuel Injected Engines

Models equipped with EFI actually have four fuel filters; a nylon mesh "sock" at the fuel pump inlet in the fuel tank; a large paper element filter mounted in the fuel line under the car; a small canister filter mounted in the engine compartment; and individual mesh filters at each injector fuel inlet. Of these, only the undercar paper element filter is scheduled for regular replacement (at 50,000 mile intervals). Filter replacement requires discharging of the fuel injection system pressure prior to filter change. Discharge pressure, disconnect the fuel lines and remove filter retainer. Note the direction of the fuel flow arrow on filter. Install new filter in reverse order.

Carburetors

NOTE: Refer to the Unit Repair section on Carburetors for overhaul and adjustment.

REMOVAL & INSTALLATION

1. Remove the air cleaner.
2. Disconnect the throttle cable or rod at the throttle lever. Disconnect the distributor vacuum line, exhaust gas recirculation line, inline fuel filter, choke heat tube and the positive crankcase ventilation hose at the carburetor.
3. Disconnect the throttle solenoid (if so equipped) and electric choke assist at their connectors.
4. Remove the carburetor retaining nuts. Lift off the carburetor carefully, taking care

not to spill any fuel. Remove the carburetor mounting gasket and discard it. Remove the carburetor mounting spacer, if so equipped, from the intake manifold.

5. Prior to installation, clean the gasket mounting surfaces of the intake manifold, spacer (if so equipped), and carburetor. When using a spacer, use two new gaskets, sandwiching the spacer between the gaskets. If a spacer is not used, only one new carburetor mounting gasket is required.

6. Place the new gasket(s) and spacer (if so equipped) on the carburetor mounting studs. Position the carburetor on top of the gasket and hand tighten the retaining nuts. Then tighten the nuts in a crisscross pattern to 10–15 ft. lbs.

7. Connect the throttle linkage, the distributor vacuum line, exhaust gas recirculation line, inline fuel filter, choke heat tube, positive crankcase ventilation hose, throttle solenoid (if so equipped) and electric-choke assist. Adjust to correct idle speed.

Fuel Injection

NOTE: For service and troubleshooting procedures refer to "Fuel Injection" in the Unit Repair Section.

Idle Speed

ADJUSTMENTS

1978–80 2.3L (140) OHC ENGINE

1. Set the parking brake and block the wheels. Turn off all accessories, bring the engine to normal operating temperature, connect a tachometer and check the ignition timing.

2. Remove or relocate the air cleaner. On 1978 models, leave all air cleaner vacuum hoses attached. On 1980 models, remove and plug the molded rubber fitting from the EGR cold weather modulator in the air cleaner (if equipped). On 1979 models, disconnect and plug all air cleaner hoses.

3. On engines with Thermactor systems: On 1978 models with vacuum hoses at the side of the dump valve, disconnect and plug the hose(s). On 1978 models with one vacuum hose at the top of the dump valve, remove the hose at the dump valve and plug, then connect a slave hose from the dump valve to manifold vacuum. On 1979–80 models, apply vacuum to 1-port dump valves and plug all hoses to 2-port dump valves. Disconnect and plug the charcoal canister purge valve vacuum hose, being careful not to damage the purge valve.

4. Check the throttle linkage for freedom of movement.

5. Run the engine at 2500 rpm for 15 seconds before each speed check.

6. There are several different idle speed control devices used. Some models have no speed control devices other than the curb idle screw. Others are equipped with a

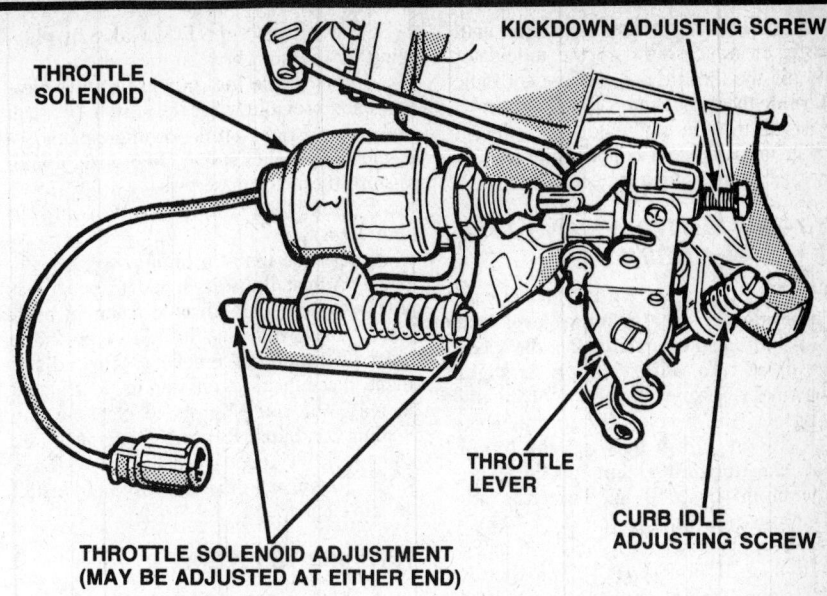

Typical idle speed solenoid adjusting locations

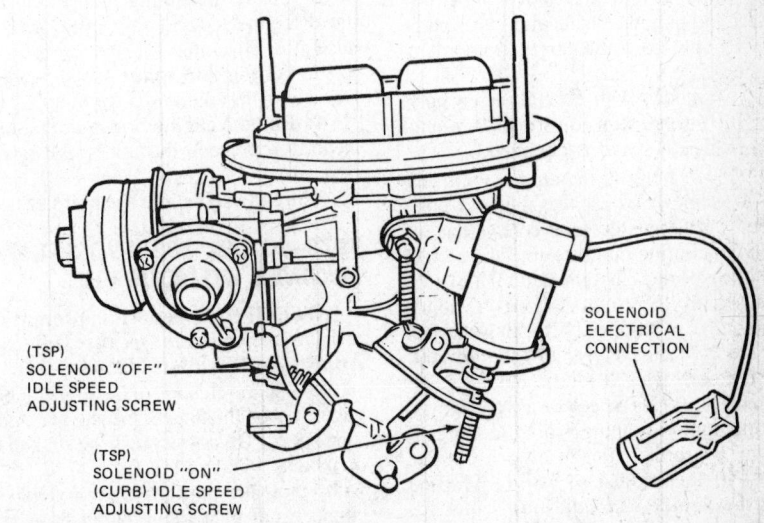

Model 6500 carburetor idle adjustments—with TSP (Throttle Stop Positioner) (© Ford Motor Co.)

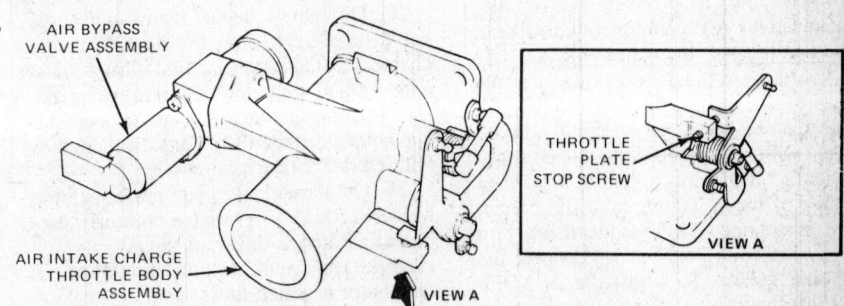

Multi-point injection adjustment

Throttle Stop Positioner (TSP) solenoid which can be accompanied by a throttle modulator (A/C only), or a dashpot. Air conditioned models without the TSP are equipped with the throttle modulator alone.

7. On models with curb idle screw only, adjust the idle speed using the screw. On models with TSP or TSP and A/C, adjust the idle at the TSP-ON adjusting screw, then collapse the TSP plunger with the throttle lever and adjust the TSP-OFF idle speed to specifications. On models with the throttle modulator alone (A/C equipped), loosen the locknut securing the throttle

modulator and rotate the modulator until there is clearance between the modulator stem and the throttle pad. Adjust curb idle by turning the throttle stop adjusting screw. Adjust the throttle modulator by turning it back in until its stem contacts the throttle lever pad, then tighten the locknut.

1978–79 2.8L (170) V6 AND 1978 302 CU. IN. ENGINES

NOTE: On engines with 2700 VV carburetor, the accelerator pump lever lash must be adjusted every time the idle speed is adjusted. To adjust, apply a slight downward pressure on the top of the nylon nut on the accelerator pump, then check the lever lash between the top of the accelerator pump stem and the lever. Lash should be .010 in. Turn the adjusting nut to adjust.

1. Complete steps 1–2 and 4–6 under "1978–80 2.3L (140) OHC". Skip Step 3. Under step 2, follow procedures for 1978 models.

2. In addition to the above steps, disconnect and plug the charcoal canister purge valve vacuum hose. Be careful not to damage the purge valve.

3. On models with curb idle screw only, adjust the throttle stop adjusting screw until the correct idle speed is obtained.

4. On 302 engines equipped with TSP (non-A/C only), adjust the solenoid positioner by rotating the long screw (part of the TSP mounting bracket) until the correct curb idle speed is obtained. On 2.8L V6 engines with TSP (non-A/C only), adjust the solenoid positioner by turning the hex head, located on the rear of the solenoid, until the correct curb idle is obtained. To adjust the TSP-OFF speed on V8 and 4 cyl., with the engine running, collapse the TSP plunger by forcing the throttle lever pad against it, then adjust to TSP-OFF speed using the throttle stop adjusting screw.

5. On models with A/C TSP (A/C only), move the climate control to the A/C ON position, open the throttle to allow the TSP to fully extend, then release the throttle. Disconnect the A/C compressor clutch wire at the compressor, then check the A/C-ON idle speed and adjust as follows. For the 302, turn the long screw (part of the TSP mounting bracket) until speed is correct. For the 2.8L V6, adjust the solenoid positioner by turning the hex head, located on the rear of the solenoid, until the correct speed is obtained. After adjustment, turn the climate control off and reconnect the A/C clutch wire. To adjust the A/C-OFF idle, turn the throttle stop adjusting screw.

1978 351M AND 400 V8 ENGINES

1. Set the parking brake and put the transmission in Drive. Turn the air conditioner OFF.

2. Remove the air cleaner and plug the vacuum hoses from the intake manifold to the air cleaner.

3. Disconnect the EGR valve by plugging the vacuum hose at the valve.

4. If the idle fuel mixture screws have not been previously set, be sure they are at maximum rich (full counterclockwise) against the limiter stops. Otherwise, do not disturb the mixture screws.

5. Start the engine and warm it thoroughly.

6. Set the ignition timing.

7. Adjust the idle speed to specifications with the TSP (throttle solenoid positioner) energized. Use the TSP screw in the solenoid mounting bracket. After adjustment, place the transmission in Neutral and increase the rpm slightly to clear up any loading condition. Return the engine to idle and check the speed in Drive.

8. Reconnect the EGR valve and install the air cleaner.

1978 460 V8 ENGINE

1. Warm the engine to operating temperature.

2. Check the timing with the advance line disconnected and plugged. Connect the hose after checking.

3. Set the idle rpm to specification in Drive with the solenoid positioner engaged.

4. Run the engine briefly at fast idle in Neutral and check the idle speed again in Drive.

5. Readjust the idle speed if necessary.

1978–80 255, 302 AND 351 W ENGINES WITHOUT EEC

NOTE: If equipped with automatic overdrive transmission, see the "Idle Speed Adjustment" section following.

1. The air cleaner must be installed. If engine speed fluctuates, use the average engine speed. Do not depress the brake pedal on models with hydro-boost brakes. On cars with automatic parking brake release, disconnect and plug the vacuum hose at the parking brake pedal. Set the parking brake, turn off all accessories, warm the engine to operating temperature, and shut off.

2. Disconnect the fuel evaporation purge valve hose by tracing the hose from the charcoal canister to the first fitting. Disconnect and plug the hose; also cap the fitting. Connect a tachometer. A special tachometer is needed on California engines with Dura-Spark I ignitions.

3. On all models except those with the Model 2700 VV (variable venturi) carburetor: Remove the spark delay valve (if equipped) and route the hose directly to the distributor advance fitting.

On engines with the VV carburetor: disconnect and plug the distributor vacuum advance hose.

4. Trace the EGR hose to the carburetor. If an EGR/PVS valve is located in the hose, disconnect and plug the hose at the EGR valve.

5. Start the engine (choke fully open, transmission in Park). Place the fast idle lever on the specified step of the cam (see

the emission control sticker on the engine for specification). Adjust if not within 100 rpm of specifications. Run the engine to 2500 rpm for 15 seconds and recheck the adjustment.

6. On engines with the VV carburetor only, turn off the engine and disconnect and plug the hose from the throttle modulator. Attach a spare length of vacuum hose from an engine vacuum source to the modulator. Start the engine, open the throttle until the modulator plunger is fully extended. Release the throttle. Check the auxiliary fast idle rpm (engine sticker). Adjustment is made by loosening the modulator locknut and turning the modulator or, on some models, by turning the adjuster bolt on which the modulator rides. Reconnect the hose after adjustment.

7. After fast idle rpm is set, reconnect the vacuum lines (and spark delay valve, if equipped) removed earlier.

8. Before each idle speed check following, run the engine at 2500 rpm for 15 seconds (transmission in Neutral), then allow the engine to return to curb idle.

9. The air conditioning must be off, engine warm, choke fully open, parking brake set, and transmission in gear specified on the engine sticker (usually in Drive). If engine rpm in each case is not within 50 rpm of specifications, adjustment is required.

10. If no solenoid is present: turn the throttle stop adjusting screw until specified rpm (engine sticker) is obtained. If equipped with a dashpot, shut off the engine, collapse the dashpot plunger, and measure the clearance between the plunger and the throttle lever pad. Adjust to specifications (sticker) if necessary.

11. On non-air conditioned cars with an anti-diesel TSP (throttle solenoid position): adjust the TSP by rotating the long screw (part of the mounting bracket) until the specified curb idle rpm (engine sticker) is obtained. Then, collapse the TSP plunger by forcing the throttle lever pad against the plunger. Adjust the throttle stop screw until the specified TSP-OFF rpm (sticker) is obtained.

12. On air conditioned cars with an A/C TSP:

a. Turn the A/C on;

b. Open the throttle to allow the TSP plunger to extend, then release the throttle;

c. Disconnect the A/C compressor clutch wire at the compressor;

d. Check A/C-ON rpm and adjust, if necessary, by turning the long screw on the TSP BRACKET UNTIL THE SPECIFIED A/C-ON rpm is obtained. Then turn the A/C off, connect the compressor clutch wire, and adjust the throttle stop screw until the specified A/C-OFF rpm is obtained.

1979 AND LATER ENGINES WITH EEC

NOTE: If equipped with automatic overdrive transmission, see the Idle Speed Adjustment Section following.

1. The air cleaner must be installed. If the engine speed fluctuates, use the average engine speed. Do not depress the brake pedal on models equipped with hydroboost brakes. On cars with automatic parking brake release, disconnect and plug the vacuum hose at the parking brake pedal. Set the parking brake, turn off all the accessories, warm the engine up to operating temperature and shut it off.

2. Connect a tachometer.

3. Disconnect and plug the EGR line at the EGR valve.

4. Disconnect the evaporative emission purge hose at the intake manifold. Plug the hose connection.

5. Start the engine and allow it to run for at least one minute. Run the engine at 2500 rpm for 15 seconds and place the fast idle lever on the proper step of the fast idle cam (see the underhood sticker). Allow the engine speed to stabilize for about 15 seconds and measure the fast idle speed. Check the sticker for the proper setting. If it is not within 100 rpm of the specification, reset it and repeat this step to check it.

6. Turn the throttle stop adjusting screw to adjust the idle speed.

1981 AND LATER 225, 302 AND 351 ENGINES

NOTE: If equipped with automatic overdrive transmission, see Idle Speed Adjustment section following.

1. Place the transmission in Park. Apply the emergency brake and block the wheels.

2. Bring the engine to normal operating temperature. Turn off all accessories and connect a tachometer.

3. On carbureted models, disconnect and plug the vacuum hose at the throttle kicker, place the transmission in the gear specified on the underhood sticker and check and adjust the curb idle rpm. Adjust at the curb idle screw at the throttle valve lever or at the saddle bracket adjusting screw.

4. On EFI engines, shut the engine off, restart it and run at 2,000 rpm for 60 seconds in neutral then let the engine stabilize for 15 seconds. Place the transmission in drive and check/adjust the curb idle rpm. Adjust at the saddle bracket adjusting screw. If rpm is low, turn the screw clockwise one full turn then repeat step 4 until correct rpm is reached. If the rpm is high, turn the screw counterclockwise to specific rpm and recheck.

5. On carbureted models, place transmission in Neutral or Park, rev the engine once, place the transmission in the specified gear (sticker) and recheck the curb idle rpm.

6. On EFI engines, make sure the scribe mark on the throttle position sensor is aligned with the mark on the throttle body. Adjust as necessary.

7. Reconnect the throttle kicker vacuum hose on the 7200 VV carburetor and apply pressure to the nylon nut on the accelerator pump to take up linkage clearance, then adjust the clearance between the top of the accelerator pump and the pump lever to .010 in., using the nylon nut on the pump rod. Turn the pump rod one turn counterclockwise to set the lever lash preload.

8. Reconnect all hoses.

9. To set the throttle kicker speed, set the transmission in Neutral or Park, bring the engine to normal operating temperature and turn off all accessories. Disconnect the vacuum hose at the Vacuum Operated Throttle Modulator (kicker) and connect an external vacuum source (10 in. Hg. minimum) to the kicker.

10. Place the transmission in the gear specified on the underhood sticker (apply parking brake, block wheels).

11. Disconnect the A/C compressor clutch wire, place the A/C selector to max. blower cooling and check/adjust the VOTM kicker speed. If adjustment is required, turn the saddle bracket adjusting screw.

12. Reconnect all components.

351W WITH 7200 VV CARBURETOR

1. Follow Steps 1–3 of the "302 EFI" procedure. Additionally, disconnect and plug the EGR vacuum hose from the EGR valve. Disconnect the evaporative emission (charcoal canister) purge hose from the intake manifold; cap the manifold connection.

2. Curb idle with Cold Start VOTM: Warm the engine to normal operating temperature. If the rpm is higher than specified, adjust the throttle stop-screw counterclockwise. If the rpm is low, shut off the engine, turn the throttle stop adjusting screw one turn clockwise, start the engine, and recheck the adjustment. Open and close the throttle and check the speed. See Step 7 of the "302 EFI" procedure.

3. Curb idle with Dashpot: If the car has air conditioning, shut it off. Start the engine and turn the throttle stop adjusting screw until the specified idle speed is reached. Turn the engine off and check the clearance between the dashpot plunger and the throttle lever pad. Adjust if not correct (see the emission control sticker on the car for proper clearance measurement). Start the engine, open and close the throttle and recheck the idle speed; shut off the engine and recheck the dashpot clearance. See Step 7 of the "302 EFI" procedure.

4. Curb Idle without Dashpot: If the car has neither a dashpot nor a VOTM, simply start the engine (A/C off, if equipped) and turn the throttle stop adjusting screw until the specified speed is reached. Open and close the throttle and recheck the adjustment. See Step 7 of the "302 EFI" procedure.

1980 AND LATER, 302 EFI, V6 (232) EFI

1. Leave all hoses and wires connected to the air cleaner case. The air cleaner assembly can be removed for adjustments, but must be installed when measuring idle speed. If the car has speed control and correct idle speed cannot be achieved, disconnect the accelerator cable at the throttle lever.

2. Apply the parking brake and block the front wheels. If the car has a vacuum-operated parking brake pull-off, disconnect and plug the vacuum hose from the parking brake.

3. Turn off all accessories. Start the engine and allow it to reach normal operating temperature. Check the throttle linkage for freedom of movement and correct as necessary. Connect a tachometer to the engine.

4. The throttle stop screw is not to be adjusted.

5. If the throttle speed is high, adjust the Vacuum Operated Throttle Modulator (VOTM) bracket adjusting screw counterclockwise. When the idle speed is as specified, open and close the throttle and recheck.

6. If the rpm is low, shut off the engine. Turn the VOTM bracket adjusting screw one turn clockwise. Start the engine and run at 2000 rpm for ten seconds. Let the idle stabilize for one minute (time not

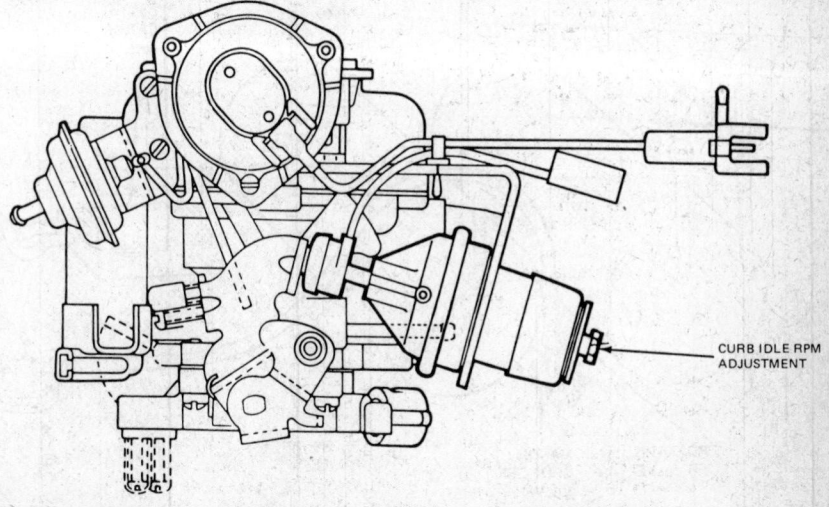

Typical VOTM curb idle adjustment

CURB IDLE RPM ADJUSTMENT

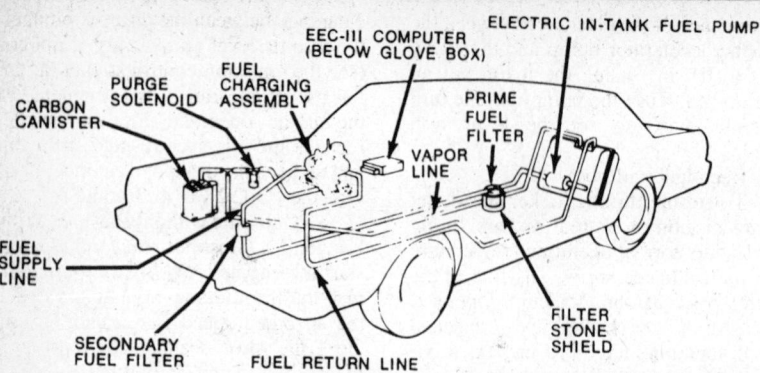

EFI system components (@ Ford Motor Co.)

to exceed two minutes) and recheck the idle speed. Repeat as necessary.

7. If the idle speed has been altered more than 50 rpm, the Automatic Overdrive Transmission throttle valve control linkage must be adjusted. See the Automatic Transmissions Unit Repair section.

AUTOMATIC OVERDRIVE (AOD) Idle Speed Adjustment

If the car is equipped with Ford's automatic overdrive transmission, and the idle speed is adjusted by more than 50 rpm, the adjustment screw on the linkage lever at the carburetor must also be adjusted:

Idle Speed Change	Turns on Linkage Lever Screw
Less than 50 rpm	No change
500–100 rpm increase	1½ turns out
50–100 rpm increase	1½ turns in
100–150 rpm increase	2½ turns out
100–150 rpm decrease	2½ turns in

FUEL MIXTURE ADJUSTMENT

NOTE: The factory recommended procedure for adjusting the idle mixture requires the addition of an artificial mixture enrichment substance (propane) to the air intake. This method requires special tools not generally available to the public. Mixture is not adjustable on engines equipped with EEC or MCU.

Propane Fuel System

The propane fuel system is a completely closed system which contains a supply of pressurized liquid propane fuel. The liquid propane is delivered by specially approved fuel lines to a fuel lock and a converter/regulator. The converter/regulator changes the pressurized liquid to a low pressure vapor and meters fuel vapor de-

livery to a simple carburetor. The carburetor, responding to the engine vacuum, mixes fuel vapor with air and regulates delivery to the engine.

CAUTION

Close the fuel tank manual shut-off valve securely before performing any service, except idle adjustment, on a propane-fueled vehicle. If the fuel system is to be serviced, run the engine out of fuel after shutting the tank valve. If the engine continues to run more than 2–3 minutes, reseat the tank valve. Failure to close the shut-off valve and run the engine out of fuel could result in fuel leakage creating a fire hazard.

NOTE: Open the fuel valve slowly after completing service. Listen for the sound of fuel filling the lines. When the filling sound stops, open the valve fully. If the valve is opened too quickly, the sudden flow will cause the excess flow valve in the tank to block fuel delivery. Should the excess fuel valve close, close the manual shut-off valve for 10 seconds. You will hear a faint click from inside the tank when the excess flow valve resets. Slowly reopen the shut-off valve.

DIESEL FUEL SYSTEM
Injection Pump
REMOVAL & INSTALLATION

1. Disconnect the battery ground cable. Drain the cooling system.
2. Remove the accessory drive belts.
3. Remove the fan and clutch assembly or electric motor and fan assembly.

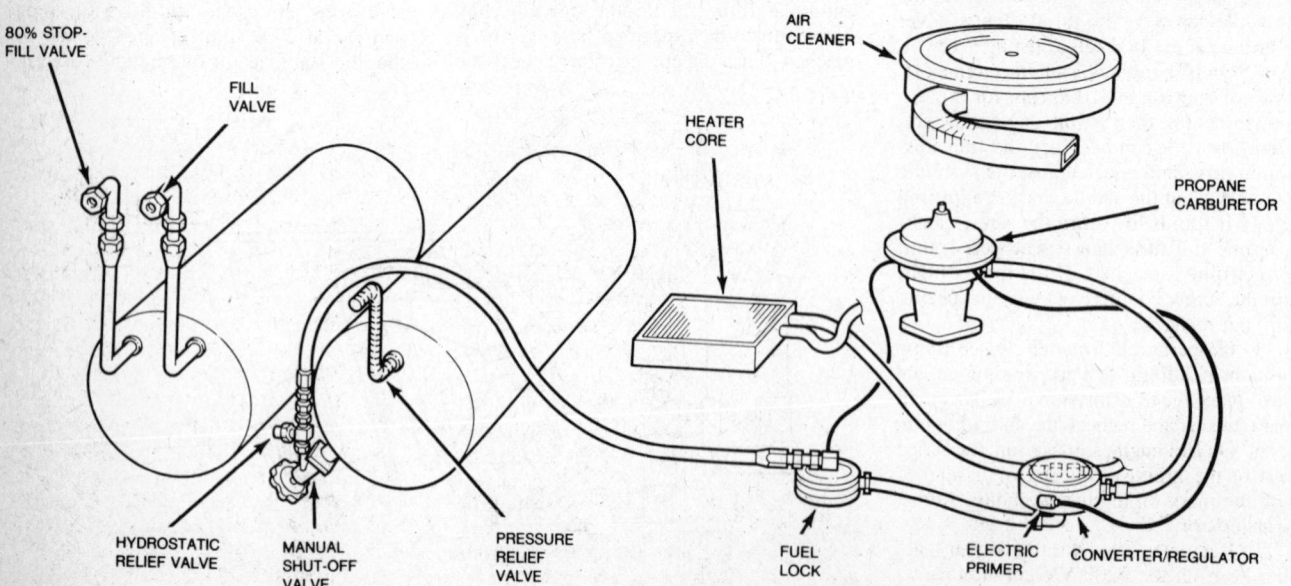

Propane fuel system

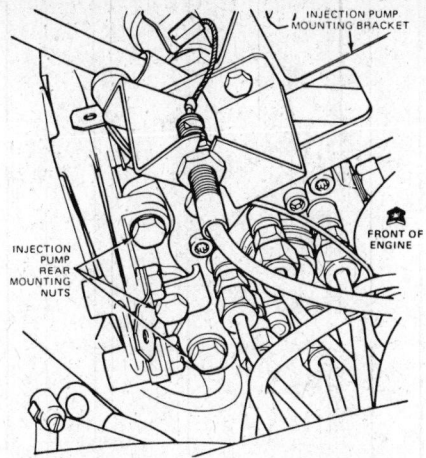

Injection pump rear mounting bolts—2.4L diesel engine

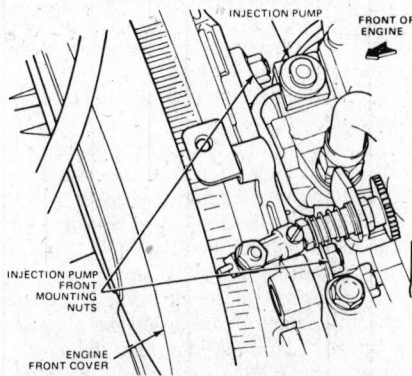

Injection pump front mounting bolts—2.4L diesel engine

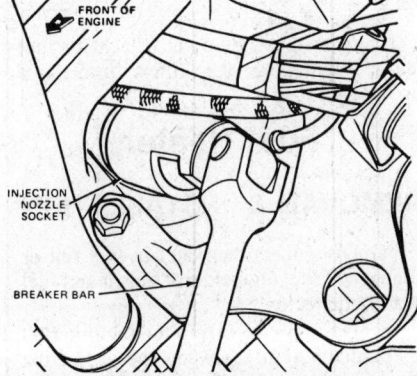

Injector nozzle removal and installation

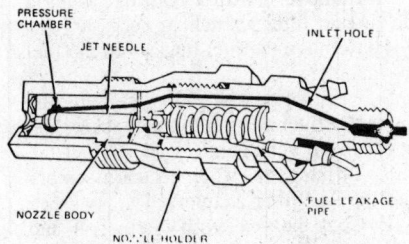

Injector nozzle

4. Remove the camshaft drive belt.
5. Install Injection Pump Sprocket

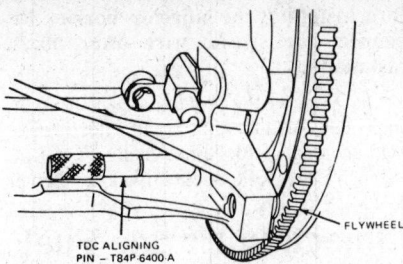

TDC aligning tool installation—2.4L diesel engine

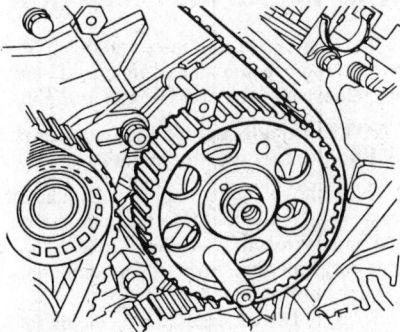

Injector pump aligning tool—2.4L diesel engine

Aligning Pin T84P-9000-A or equivalent and remove nut and washer attaching sprocket to the injection pump.

6. Install puller T67L-3600-A or equivalent and remove the sprocket. Remove the woodruff key from pump shaft.

7. Disconnect the clamp attaching the oil dipstick tube to the intake manifold, and position out of the way.

8. Disconnect the turbo pressure indicator switch connector. Remove the diagnostic plug bracket and position out of the way.

9. Loosen the clamp attaching the turbo crossover pipe boot to the intake manifold.

10. Remove the nuts attaching the intake manifold to cylinder head, and remove the intake manifold.

NOTE: To prevent fuel system contamination, cap all fuel lines and fittings.

11. Disconnect and cap the nozzle fuel lines at nozzles.

12. Remove the injection nozzle lines from injection pump using Fuel Line Nut Wrench T84P-9396-A or equivalent. Install caps on each end of each fuel line and pump fitting as it is removed and identify each fuel line accordingly.

13. Disconnect the coolant hoses from the idle speed boost housing.

14. Disconnect the electrical connectors to the fuel shut-off and cold start accelerator valves, micro-switch and fuel pressure switch.

15. Disconnect the nozzle return line at the injection pump.

16. Disconnect the fuel return hose from the fuel return line on the left fender apron.

17. Disconnect the fuel inlet hose from the fuel inlet line on the left fender apron.

18. Disconnect the vacuum hoses at the altitude compensation valve. Note position of hoses, so they may be returned to the original position.

19. Disconnect the throttle cable and speed control cable, if equipped, from the injection pump.

20. Remove the three nuts attaching the injection pump to mounting bracket.

21. Remove the two nuts attaching the injection pump to the engine front cover, and remove the injection pump.

22. Install the injection pump in position. Line up the mark on the front cover with the mark on the injection pump mounting boss. Install attaching nuts and bolts. Tighten to 14–17 ft. lbs.

23. Connect the throttle cable, and speed control cable, if so equipped.

24. Remove the protective caps and install the fuel inlet hose to the fuel inlet line on left fender apron. Connect the fuel return hose to the fuel return line on the left fender apron.

25. Connect the vacuum hoses to the altitude compensation valve. Refer to the VECI decal.

26. Connect the nozzle return line to the injection pump.

27. Connect the electrical connectors to the fuel pressure sensor, micro-switch, cold start accelerator valve and fuel shut-off valve.

28. Connect the coolant hoses to the idle speed boost housing.

29. Install the fuel lines on injection pump, using Tool T84P-9396-A or equivalent, and tighten to 14–17 ft. lbs.

30. Connect the fuel lines to the nozzles and tighten to 14–17 ft. lbs.

31. Clean the intake manifold and cylinder head gasket mating surfaces. Position a new intake manifold gasket on the cylinder head, and install the intake manifold. Be sure the intake manifold inlet port is inserted into the turbo crossover pipe boot. Tighten attaching bolts to 14–17 ft. lbs. Tighten the clamp at the crossover pipe boot.

32. Install the diagnostic plug bracket on the cylinder head, and tighten to 14–17 ft. lbs.

33. Connect the turbo pressure indicator switch connector.

34. Position the oil dipstick tube to the intake manifold and install clamp.

35. Install the woodruff key in injection pump shaft.

36. Install the sprocket on injection pump. Install injection Pump Aligning Pin T84P-9000-A or equivalent, in sprocket. Install the sprocket attaching washer and nut and tighten to 33–36 ft. lbs.

37. Install and adjust camshaft drive belt.

38. Install the camshaft drive belt cover and tighten to 6–7 ft. lbs.

39. Install fan and clutch assembly or electric motor and fan assembly.

40. Install and adjust the accessory drive belts.

41. Fill and bleed the cooling system.

42. Air bleed the fuel system.

43. Adjust the injection pump timing.

44. Connect the battery ground cable.
45. Start the engine and check for fuel, coolant and oil leaks.
46. Adjust the curb idle, fast idle and injection pump timing.

Fuel Shut-Off Valve

REMOVAL & INSTALLATION

1. Disconnect the battery ground cable.
2. Remove the nut attaching the electrical connector to the shut-off valve and remove the connector.
3. Remove the shut-off valve.

—————— CAUTION ——————
Piston and spring may fall out when removing valve.

4. Replace the O-ring and valve, and install the valve on the injection pump. Tighten to 11–18 ft. lbs.

—————— CAUTION ——————
Piston and spring may fall out when installing valve.

5. Install the connector on the shut-off valve. Tighten nut to 3–3.5 ft. lbs.
6. Connect the battery ground cable. Run the engine and check for fuel leaks.

Injection Nozzles

REMOVAL & INSTALLATION

1. Pull off the leak oil lines from the injector nozzles.

NOTE: Make sure area around injector is clean.

2. Remove the fuel lines at the injectors and at the fuel injection pump with Fuel Line Wrench T84P-9395-A or equivalent. Cap all fuel lines and openings as the fuel lines are removed.
3. Unscrew the fuel injectors with Injector Nozzle Socket T84P-9527-A or equivalent. Note injector order for installation.

NOTE: On injectors with sensors, disconnect the sensor plug wires and guide sensor wires through Injector Nozzle Socket T84P-9527-A or equivalent, while installing tool on the injector.

4. Plug the cylinder block injector nozzle opening.
5. Clean the injector nozzle opening in the cylinder block.
6. Install new heat shields into the injection nozzle openings.
7. Apply a copper based, anti-sieze compound to the injector nozzle threads. Remove the protective plug in the cylinder block and install injector nozzles in original positions with Injector Nozzle Socket T84P-9527-A or equivalent. Tighten to 30–33 ft. lbs.

NOTE: On injectors with sensors, guide the sensor plug wire through socket be-

fore installing the injector nozzle. Reconnect the sensor wire after nozzle installation.

8. Remove the protective caps from the fuel lines, injector pump and injector nozzles and install fuel lines using Fuel Line Wrench T84P-9396-A or equivalent. Tighten to 15–18 ft. lbs.

Injection Nozzle Fuel Lines

REMOVAL & INSTALLATION

1. If all the fuel lines are being removed, remove the intake manifold, and then remove all the fuel lines as an assembly.

NOTE: Do not remove the two clamps holding the fuel lines together.

2. Remove fuel line(s) at the injector nozzles and at the fuel injection pump with Fuel Line Wrench T84P-9395-A or equivalent. Cap all fuel lines and openings as fuel lines are removed.
3. If only one fuel line is being removed, remove the clamps holding fuel lines together and remove the fuel line.
4. If the fuel lines are being installed as an assembly, remove the protective caps and install fuel lines (with clamps installed) to the injector nozzles and injection pump using Fuel Line Wrench T84P-9395-A or equivalent.
5. If only one fuel line is being installed, remove protective caps and position fuel line to the injector nozzle, and injection line using Fuel Line Wrench T84P-9395-A or equivalent. Install clamps holding the fuel lines together.
6. Install the intake manifold if it was previously removed.

Glow Plugs

REMOVAL & INSTALLATION

1. Disconnect the battery ground cable.
2. Unscrew the glow plug electrical connection and remove the wire.
3. Remove the glow plug using a 12mm deepwell socket.
4. Coat the glow plug threads with a copper based, anti-sieze compound.
5. Install the glow plug into the engine block using a 12mm deepwell socket.
6. Tighten the glow plug to 15–22 ft. lbs.
7. Connect the electrical wire to the glow plug with the nut and tighten to 3–4 ft. lbs.
8. Connect the battery ground cable.

Fuel Filter

REMOVAL & INSTALLATION

1. Drain the fuel from the fuel filter by opening the vent screw on the top of the

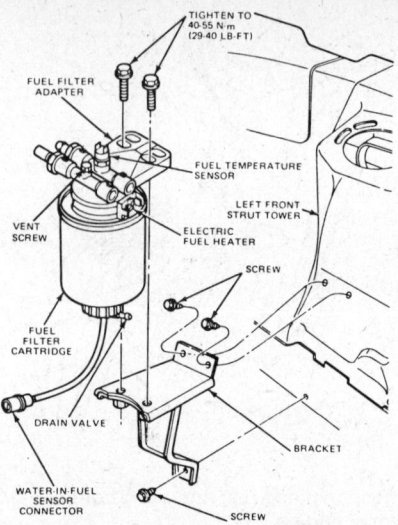

Diesel fuel filter assembly

filter and then depressing the drain valve on the bottom of the filter.
2. Disconnect the Water-in-Fuel sensor connector.
3. Remove the filter cartridge using a standard oil filter wrench, if necessary.
4. Remove the protective cover.
5. Remove the drain valve from the old filter and install on the new filter.
6. Install the protective cover.
7. Coat the surface of the sealing gasket with engine oil and install the filter on the adapter. Turn the filter until the gasket contacts the sealing surface of the filter adapter.
8. Turn the filter an additional one-half turn.
9. Close the vent screw.
10. Start the engine and check for fuel leaks, tightening the filter further, if necessary.

Fuel Heater

REMOVAL & INSTALLATION

1. Disconnect the water-in-fuel sensor connector, fuel temperature sensor and fuel heater connector.
2. Drain the fuel from the fuel filter by opening the vent screw on the top of the filter and depressing the drain valve on the bottom of the filter.
3. Remove the filter cartridge using a standard oil filter wrench, if necessary.
4. Remove the fuel lines from the fuel filter adapter.
5. Remove the two bolts retaining the fuel heater/filter adapter to the bracket, and remove from vehicle.
6. Unscrew the fuel heater assembly from the fuel filter adapter.
7. Coat the seal with engine oil and install the fuel heater on the fuel filter adapter.
8. Position the fuel filter adapter (with fuel heater attached) to the bracket and install with two bolts. Tighten to 29–40 ft. lbs.

9. Coat the surface of the sealing gasket with engine oil and install the filter on the adapter. Turn the filter until the gasket contacts the sealing surface of the filter adapter. Turn the filter an additional half turn.

10. Connect the Fuel-in-Water sensor, temperature sensor and fuel heater connectors.

11. Reconnect the fuel lines to the fuel filter and tighten the vent screw.

12. Start the engine and check for fuel leaks, tightening the filter further, if necessary.

Electric Fuel Pump

REMOVAL & INSTALLATION

1. Disconnect the electric fuel pump electrical connector.

2. Remove the hose clamp on the inlet and outlet lines and remove the hoses from the fuel pump.

3. Remove the two fuel pump retaining screws and remove the fuel pump.

4. To install, reverse the removal steps. Tighten attaching screws to 9–11 ft. lbs.

COOLING SYSTEM

Radiator

REMOVAL & INSTALLATION

1. Drain cooling system.

2. Disconnect upper, lower and overflow hoses at the radiator.

3. On automatic transmission-equipped cars, disconnect the fluid cooler lines at radiator.

4. Depending on model, remove the two top mounting bolts and remove radiator and shroud assembly, or remove the shroud mounting bolts and position the shroud out of the way. If the air conditioner condenser is attached to the radiator, remove the retaining bolts and position the condenser out of the way. DO NOT disconnect the refrigerant lines.

5. Remove radiator attaching bolts or top brackets and lift out the radiator.

6. If a new radiator is to be installed, transfer the petcock from the old radiator to the new one. On cars equipped with automatic transmissions, transfer the fluid cooler line fittings from the old radiator.

7. Position the radiator and install, but do not tighten, the radiator support bolts. On cars equipped with automatic transmissions, connect the fluid cooler lines. Then tighten the radiator support bolts or shroud and mounting bolts.

8. Connect the radiator hoses. Close the radiator petcock. Fill and bleed the cooling system.

9. Start the engine and bring to operating temperature. Check for leaks.

10. On cars equipped with automatic transmissions, check the cooler lines for leaks and interference. Check transmission fluid level.

Water Pump

REMOVAL & INSTALLATION

Gasoline Engines

1. Drain cooling system.

2. Disconnect the negative battery cable.

3. On cars with power steering, remove the drive belt.

4. If the vehicle is equipped with air conditioning, remove the idler pulley bracket and air conditioner drive belt.

5. On engines with Thermactor, remove the belt.

6. Disconnect the lower radiator hose and heater hose from the water pump.

7. On cars equipped with a fan shroud, remove the retaining screws and position the shroud rearward.

8. Remove the fan, fan clutch and spacer from the engine, and if the car is equipped with an electric motor driven fan, remove the fan as an assembly for working clearance.

9. On 4-cylinders, remove the cam belt outer cover.

10. On cars equipped with water pump mounted alternators, loosen alternator mounting bolts, remove the alternator belt and remove the alternator adjusting arm bracket from the water pump. If interference is encountered, remove the air pump pulley and pivot bolt. Remove the air pump adjusting bracket. Swing the upper bracket aside. Detach the air conditioner compressor and lay it aside. Do not disconnect any of the A/C lines. Remove any accessory mounting brackets from the water pump.

11. Loosen bypass hose at water pump, if equipped.

12. Remove water pump retaining screws and remove pump from engine. On V6-170 engines, the two bolts through the thermostat housing must also be removed; they retain the lower portion of the pump housing.

13. Clean any gasket material from the pump mounting surface. On engines equipped with a water pump backing plate; remove the plate, clean gasket surfaces, install a new gasket and plate on the water pump.

NOTE: The 250 6 cylinder engine originally uses a one-piece gasket for the cylinder front cover and water pump. Trim away the old gasket at the edge of the cylinder cover and replace with service gasket.

14. Remove the heater hose fitting from the old pump and install it on the new pump.

15. Coat both sides of the new gasket with a water-resistant sealer, then install the pump reversing the procedure.

Diesel Engine

1. Drain the cooling system.

2. Loosen and remove the accessory drive belts.

3. Remove the fan and motor assembly.

4. Remove the water pump pulley.

5. Disconnect the heater hose from the thermostat housing.

6. Remove the camshaft drive belt cover.

7. Remove the three bolts attaching the water pump to the crankcase and remove the water pump.

NOTE: Do not loosen cam belt.

8. Clean the gasket mating surfaces of the water pump and crankcase.

9. Install the water pump with a new gasket, on the crankcase and tighten bolts to 14–17 ft. lbs.

10. Install the camshaft drive belt cover and tighten bolts to 6–7 ft. lbs.

11. Connect the heater hose to the thermostat housing.

12. Install the water pump pulley and tighten bolts to 6–7 ft. lbs.

13. Install the fan and motor assembly.

14. Install and adjust the accessory drive belts.

Thermostat

REMOVAL & INSTALLATION

1. Open the drain cock and drain the radiator so the coolant level is below the coolant outlet elbow which houses the thermostat.

NOTE: On some models it will be necessary to remove the distributor cap, rotor and vacuum diaphragm in order to gain access to the thermostat housing mounting bolts.

2. Remove the outlet elbow retaining bolts and position the elbow sufficiently clear of the intake manifold or cylinder head to provide access to the thermostat. The 170 cu in. V6 thermostat is located on the lower water pump housing, under the lower radiator hose inlet.

3. Remove the thermostat and the gasket.

4. Clean the mating surfaces of the outlet elbow and the engine to remove all old gasket material and sealer. Coat the new gasket with water-resistant sealer. Install the thermostat in the block on 351W and 400 V8s (or in the intake manifold on 460 V8s), then install the gasket. On all other engines, position the gasket on the engine, and install the thermostat in the coolant elbow. The thermostat must be rotated clockwise to lock it in position on all 255, 302 and 351W V8s. On 4-cylinders, be sure the full width of the heater outlet tube is visible within the thermostat port. On 170 cu in. V6s, the thermostat must be installed into the pump housing first, then the O-ring, and finally the gasket and inlet elbow.

5. Install the outlet elbow and retaining bolts on the engine. Torque the bolts to 12–15 ft. lbs.

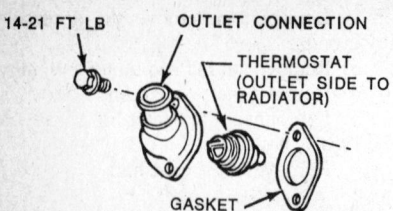

14-21 FT LB — OUTLET CONNECTION — THERMOSTAT (OUTLET SIDE TO RADIATOR) — GASKET

2300 cc engine thermostat installation
(© Ford Motor Co.)

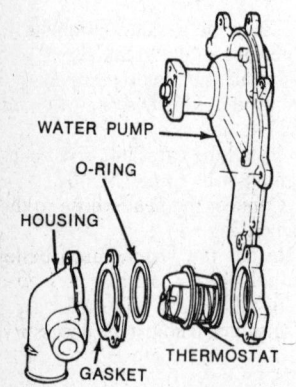

WATER PUMP — O-RING — HOUSING — THERMOSTAT — GASKET

Thermostat installation—V6 2800 engine

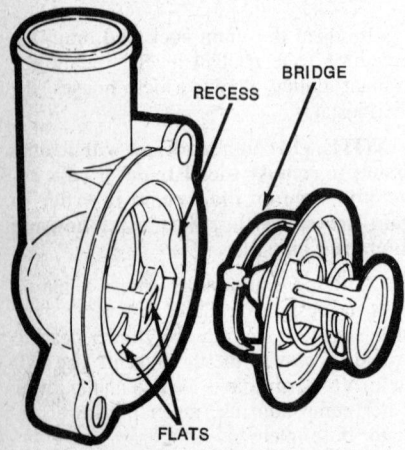

RECESS — BRIDGE — FLATS

V8 engine thermostat installation
(© Ford Motor Co.)

6. Refill the radiator. Run the engine at operating temperature and check for leaks. Recheck the coolant level.

ELECTRO-DRIVE COOLING FAN

Gasoline Engines

Various models, are equipped with a bracket-mounted electric cooling fan that replaces the conventional water pump mounted fan.

Operation of the fan motor is dependent on engine coolant temperature and air conditioner compressor clutch engagement. The fan will run only when the coolant temperature is approximately 108°F. or higher

or when the compressor clutch is engaged. The fan, motor and mount can be removed as an assembly after disconnecting the wiring harnesses and mounting bolts.

—— CAUTION ——

The cooling fan is automatic and may come on at any time without warning even if the ignition is switched OFF. To avoid possible injury, always disconnect the negative battery cable when working near the electric cooling fan.

Diesel Engine

1. Disconnect the battery ground cable.
2. Raise the vehicle and support on jackstands.
3. Remove the bolts and nuts attaching the mounting brackets to the radiator support.
4. Disconnect the electrical connector to fan.
5. Remove the bolts securing the hood-latch to the radiator support and position the latch out of the way.
6. Remove the bolts and nuts attaching the mounting brackets to fan and motor assembly.
7. Remove the fan and motor assembly from the vehicle.
8. Position the fan and motor assembly in the vehicle.
9. Position the mounting brackets on the fan and motor assembly. Tighten the nuts to 4–5 ft. lbs.
10. Install the hood latch.
11. Connect the electrical connector to the fan and motor assembly.
12. Position the mounting brackets in the vehicle. Tighten the mounting bolts to 6–8 ft. lbs. Tighten mounting nuts to 4–5 ft. lbs.
13. Lower the vehicle.
14. Connect the battery ground cable.

EMISSION CONTROLS

NOTE: See the "Emission Control Systems" and "Electronic Ignition" Unit Repair sections for details on all systems described here.

Some emission controls used on earlier models are carried over: air injection, PCV, EGR, evaporative controls, and catalytic converters. However some revisions have been made.

Physically larger catalytic converters are used. Improved breakerless electronic ignition called Dura-Spark which generates up to 42,000 volts is standard on all engines. Engine modifications include larger intake valves and revised combustion chambers for the 200 and 250 cu in. six-cylinder engines. The 302 and 351W V8 engines have modified combustion chambers and pistons. Cylinder heads also have larger coolant passages for improved spark plug and exhaust valve cooling. There are reduced size passages in the intake manifolds to increase velocity of the air/fuel mixture which aids combustion and improves performance at low rpm.

A variable venturi two-barrel carburetor was introduced in 1977 and is used on various models in conjunction with the EEC system. This carburetor changes the size of the venturis as a function of speed and load. Tapered metering rods, attached to the venturi valves, slide in the main jets to control fuel flow. Venturi valve position is controlled by a spring (closed), and by control vacuum operating through a rubber diaphragm (open). The venturi valves are not directly linked to the throttle shaft. Throttle

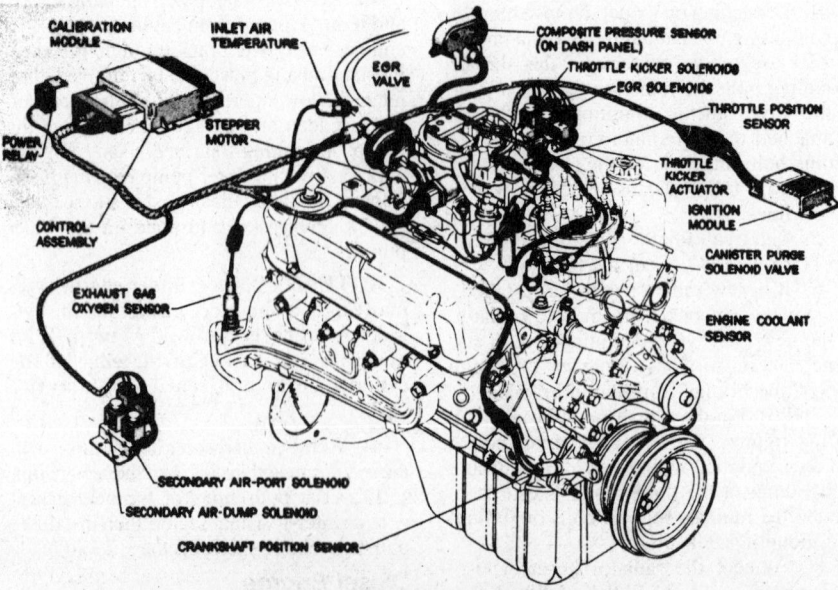

Typical EEC system components (EEC II shown)

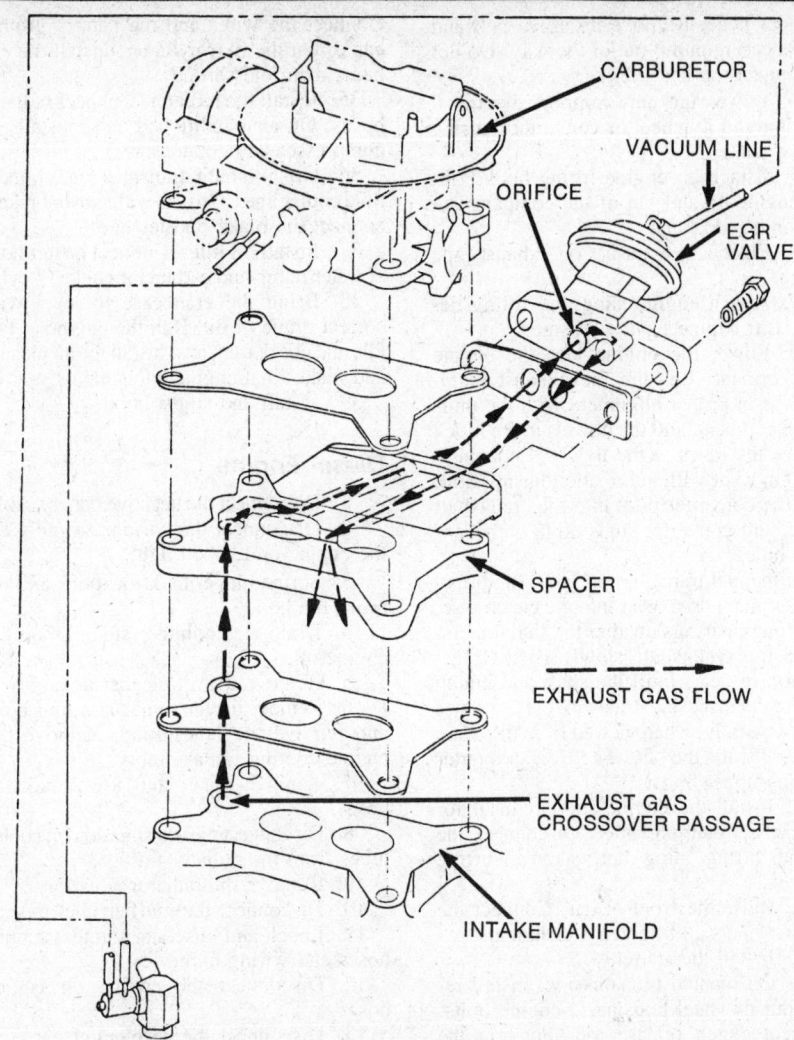

Exhaust Gas Recirculation (EGR) System (© Ford Motor Co)

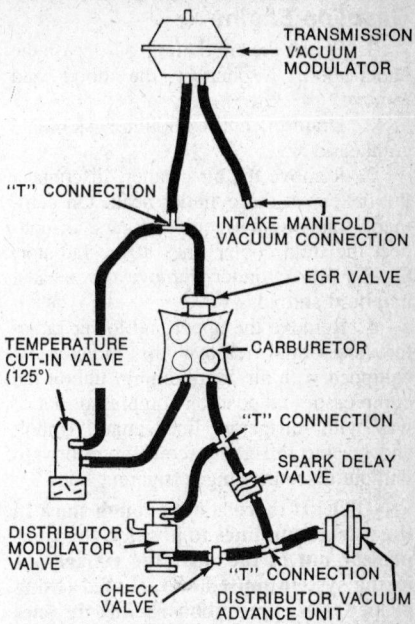

Typical vacuum hose schematic with EGR
(© Ford Motor Co)

plate opening results in a stronger control vacuum signal which causes the venturi valves to open, increasing venturi size. The control vacuum and opposing spring select the precise air/fuel ratio for all speed and load conditions except wide open throttle.

The Electronic Engine Control (EEC) was introduced on the Versailles model. The system was updated in 1979 (EEC II) in 1980 (EEC III) and again in 1983 (EEC IV). EEC is an integrated electronic system designed to continuously monitor engine and ambient conditions, and continuously compute and alter ignition timing, EGR flow rate, air/fuel mixture, idle speed, charcoal canister vapor purge, and Thermactor air flow accordingly. EEC control of the functions mentioned means that ignition timing, idle speed, and idle mixture are not adjustable in the conventional way. More details on the EEC system can be found in the Emission Controls Unit Repair Section.

A Microprocessor Control Unit (MCU) system which controls the air/fuel mixture and Thermactor (air pump) injection was introduced on some 1981 models. The MCU system, if used, is identified on the under-

hood sticker. Major components include the MCU electronic unit, a feedback carburetor, a three-way catalyst, an oxygen sensor, and the Thermactor system. MCU is a conventional feedback carburetor system; more details can be found in the Emission Control Systems Unit Repair Section, under "Computer Controlled Carburetors".

Some V6 and V8 models are equipped with Central Fuel Injection (CFI). CFI includes two fuel injectors vertically mounted in a throttle body installed on the intake manifold. The throttle body resembles a conventional carburetor, but in fact retains only the fuel supply and throttle plate functions of a carburetor. Fuel is supplied to the injectors by a high pressure pump mounted inside the fuel tank. A primary fuel filter is located in the fuel supply line beneath the passenger compartment, and a smaller filter is installed in the supply line in the engine compartment. A fuel pressure regulator is mounted to the throttle body just ahead of the injectors, maintaining fuel pressure at 39 psi. Excess fuel supplied by the pump is returned to the tank via a return line.

Fuel discharge from the injectors is controlled by the EEC module, which computes engine temperature, speed, timing and fuel requirements to determine how long to electrically energize the injectors for optimum engine performance and economy and minimal exhaust emissions. Frequency of injection is constant at four pulses per engine revolution (two for each injector); the length of time the injectors fire is controlled so closely by the EEC computer that it is measured in milliseconds.

Other models are equipped with a multipoint, pulse-time Electronic Fuel Injection (EFI) system in conjunction with a blow-through turbocharger. The system meters fuel into the air intake system in accordance with engine demand through four injectors mounted on a turned intake manifold. An on board computor accepts information from various sensors to compute the required fuel flow rate necessary to maintain necessary air/fuel ratio throughout the entire engine operational range.

ENGINE

REMOVAL & INSTALLATION

NOTE: Disconnect the negative battery cable before beginning any work. Always label all disconnected hoses, vacuum lines and wires, to prevent incorrect reassembly. Do not disconnect any air conditioning lines unless you are thoroughly familiar with A/C systems and the hazards involved; escaping refrigerant (freon) will freeze any surface it contacts, including skin and eyes. Have the system discharged professionally before required repairs are started.

Gasoline Engine

1. Scribe the hood hinge outline on the under-hood, disconnect the hood and remove.

2. Drain the entire cooling system and crankcase.

3. Remove the air cleaner, disconnect the battery at the cylinder head. On automatic transmission equipped cars, disconnect the fluid cooler lines at the radiator. On the four cylinder, remove the exhaust manifold shroud.

4. Remove the upper and lower radiator hoses and remove the radiator. If equipped with air conditioning, unbolt the compressor and position compressor out of way with refrigerant lines intact. Unbolt and lay the refrigerant condenser forward without disconnecting refrigerant lines.

NOTE: If there is not enough slack in the refrigerant lines to position the compressor out of the way, the refrigerant in the system must be evacuated (using proper safety precautions) before the lines can be disconnected from the compressor.

5. Remove the fan, fan belt and upper pulley. On models equipped with an electric cooling fan, disconnect the power lead and remove the fan and shroud as an assembly.

6. Disconnect the heater hoses from the engine. On four cylinder engines, disconnect the heater hose from the water pump and choke fittings.

7. Disconnect the alternator wires at the alternator, the starter cable at the starter, the accelerator rod at the carburetor.

8. Disconnect and plug the fuel tank line at the fuel pump on models equipped with fuel injection, de-pressurize the fuel system.

9. Disconnect the coil primary wire at the coil. Disconnect wires at the oil pressure and water temperature sending units. Disconnect the brake booster vacuum line, if so equipped.

10. Remove the starter and dust seal.

11. With manual transmission, remove the clutch retracting spring. Disconnect the clutch equalizer shaft and arm bracket at the underbody rail and remove the arm bracket and equalizer shaft.

12. Raise the car and safely support on jackstands. Remove the flywheel or converter housing upper retaining bolts.

13. Disconnect the exhaust pipe or pipes at the exhaust manifold. Disconnect the right and left motor mount at the underbody bracket. Remove the flywheel or converter housing cover. On models equipped, disconnect the engine roll dampner on the left front of the engine to frame.

14. On manual shift, remove the lower wheel housing bolts.

15. On automatic transmission, disconnect throttle valve vacuum line at the intake manifold and disconnect the converter from the flywheel. Remove the converter housing lower retaining bolts. On power steering, disconnect power steering pump from

cylinder head. Remove the drive belt and wire steering pump out of the way. Do not disconnect the hoses.

16. Lower the car. Support the transmission and flywheel or converter housing with a jack.

17. Attach an engine lifting hook. Lift the engine up and out of the compartment and onto workstand.

18. Place a new gasket on exhaust pipe flange.

19. Attach engine sling and lifting device. Lift engine from workstand.

20. Lower the engine into the engine compartment. Be sure the exhaust manifold/s is in proper alignment with the muffler inlet pipe/s, and the dowels in the block engage the holes in the flywheel housing.

On a car with automatic transmission, start the converter pilot into the crankshaft make sure converter studs align with flexplate holes.

On manual transmission, start the transmission main drive gear into the clutch disc. If the engine hangs up after the shaft enters, rotate the crankshaft slowly (with transmission in gear) until the shaft and clutch disc splines mesh. Rotate 4 cyl. engines clockwise only, when viewed from the front.

21. Install the flywheel or converter housing upper bolts.

22. Install the engine support insulator to bracket retaining nuts. Disconnect the engine lifting sling and remove lifting brackets.

23. Raise the front of car. Connect the exhaust line/s and tighten attachments.

24. Install the starter.

25. On manual transmission, install remaining flywheel housing-to-engine bolts. Connect clutch release rod. Position the clutch equalizer bar and bracket, and install retaining bolts. Install clutch pedal retracting spring.

26. On automatic transmission, remove the retainer holding the converter in the housing. Attach the converter to the flywheel. Install the converter housing inspection cover and the remaining converter housing retaining bolts.

27. Remove the support from the transmission and lower the car.

28. Connect the engine ground strap and coil primary wire.

29. Connect the water temperature gauge wire and the heater hose at coolant outlet housing. Connect the accelerator rod at the bellcrank.

30. On automatic transmission, connect the transmission filler tube bracket. Connect the throttle valve vacuum line.

31. On power steering, install the drive belt and power steering pump bracket. Install the bracket retaining bolts. Adjust the drive belt to proper tension.

32. Remove the plug from the fuel tank line. Connect the flexible fuel line and the oil pressure sending unit wire.

33. Install the pulley, belt, spacer, and fan. Adjust belt tension.

34. Tighten the alternator adjusting bolts.

Connect the wires and the battery ground cable. On the four cylinder, install the exhaust manifold shroud.

35. Install the radiator. Connect radiator hoses. On air conditioned cars, install the compressor and condensor.

36. On automatic transmission, connect fluid cooler lines. On cars with power brakes, connect the brake booster line.

37. Install oil filter. Connect heater hose at water pump and carburetor choke (4 cyl.).

38. Bring the crankcase to level with correct grade of oil. Run the engine at fast idle and check for leaks. Install the air cleaner and make final engine adjustments.

39. Install and adjust hood.

Diesel Engine

1. Disconnect the negative battery cable.

2. Disconnect the wiring assembly for the engine underhood light.

3. Scribe hinge mark locations and remove the hood.

4. Drain the cooling system. Drain the engine oil.

5. Remove the air cleaner assembly.

6. Remove the fan shroud attaching bolts and remove the fan shroud. Remove the engine cooling fan assembly.

7. Remove upper and lower radiator hoses.

8. Disconnect the transmission oil cooler tubes from the radiator fittings.

9. Remove the radiator assembly.

10. Disconnect the muffler inlet pipe.

11. Label and disconnect the vacuum hoses and wiring harnesses.

12. Disconnect the engine oil cooler hoses.

13. Disconnect the accelerator cable at the fuel injection pump.

14. Disconnect the fuel line from the tank to fuel injection pump.

15. Disconnect the transmission gear shift linkage.

16. Disconnect the battery ground cable at engine.

17. Remove the coolant expansion bottle and position it out of the way.

18. Disconnect the heater hoses at the dash panel (firewall).

19. Disconnect the wire to A/C compressor clutch.

20. Disconnect the power steering pump hose(s).

21. Disconnect the fuel line to the injectors.

22. Disconnect the wiring harness to instrument panel. Disconnect engine ground leads.

23. Install an engine support Tool D79F-6000-A or equivalent (bar and "J" hook or chain).

24. Raise the vehicle and safely support on jackstands.

25. Remove the muffler inlet pipe.

26. Remove the lower engine oil cooler bracket and brace.

27. Remove the stabilizer bar, bracket retaining bolts and position forward.

28. Remove the left hand front fender splash shield.

29. Disconnect the steering gear input shaft to steering column shaft coupling.

30. Remove the retainer nuts to the engine insulator supports.

31. Position a jack under the engine. Raise the engine assembly. Position the steering gear out of the way.

32. Lower the engine assembly.

33. Remove the converter housing access cover.

34. Remove the converter assembly retainer nuts.

35. Insert a pair of locking pliers in the converter housing to hold the converter in place during engine removal.

NOTE: Make sure that the upper jaw of the locking pliers contacts the converter while clamped to the converter housing. This will apply adequate pressure on the converter to prevent separation during engine movements and removal.

36. Remove No. 3 crossmember retainer nuts.

37. Remove the transmission gear shift lever bellcrank.

38. Raise the transmission.

39. Remove No. 3 crossmember retainer bolts. Lower the transmission.

40. Remove engine to transmission converter housing retainer bolts.

41. Install crossmember (No. 3) retainer bolts.

42. Lower the vehicle.

43. Install engine lifting equipment.

44. Remove the engine support Tool D79T-6000-A or equivalent.

45. Remove the engine assembly.

46. Position engine and install on engine work stand and service as necessary.

47. Install engine lifting equipment. Raise the engine and install in vehicle.

48. Install engine support Tool D79T-6000-A or equivalent.

49. Remove the engine lifting equipment. Raise vehicle and safely support on jackstands.

50. The remainder of the installation procedure is in reverse order of removal.

Intake Manifold

REMOVAL & INSTALLATION
2.3L (140) OHC-4 Cylinder Engine

CARBURETOR EQUIPPED

1. Drain the cooling system and remove the air cleaner.

2. Disconnect the accelerator cable.

3. Disconnect and label the vacuum hoses at the carburetor.

4. Remove the engine oil dipstick.

5. Disconnect the heat tube at the EGR valve.

6. Disconnect and plug the fuel line at the carburetor.

7. Remove the bolt attaching the dipstick to the manifold.

8. Remove the PCV valve from the manifold.

9. Remove the two distributor cap screws and the distributor cap.

10. Remove the intake manifold attaching bolts and remove the manifold.

11. Clean all dirt and gasket material from the surfaces on the cylinder head and intake manifold.

12. Position a new gasket and the manifold on the studs. Torque the bolts and nuts to the specified torque in two stages.

13. Connect the crankcase ventilation hose to the manifold. Connect the heater hoses to the choke cover and manifold, if equipped.

14. Replace the heat tube, accelerator cable and dipstick assembly.

15. Connect the distributor vacuum lines to the manifold.

16. Connect the fuel line to the carburetor.

17. Install the air cleaner assembly. Fill the cooling system, if drained, and check for leaks.

Fuel Injected Models

NOTE: Refer to the Unit Repair "Fuel Injection" section for procedures.

6 Cylinder Inline Engine

Sixes have intake manifolds that are integral with the cylinder head and cannot be removed.

2.8L (170) V6 Engine

1. Remove the air cleaner assembly and disconnect the battery.

2. Disconnect the throttle cables.

3. Drain the cooling system. Disconnect and remove the hose from the water outlet to the radiator and the hoses and line from the water outlet to the water pump.

4. Remove the distributor cap and spark plug wires as an assembly. Disconnect the distributor wire and the vacuum line.

5. Mark the position of the distributor and remove it.

6. Remove the fuel line and filter between the fuel pump and the carburetor and then remove the rocker arm covers.

7. Remove the intake manifold bolts and nuts. Tap the manifold lightly with a plastic hammer to break the gasket seal, and then lift off the manifold.

8. Remove all the gasket material and dirt from the manifold and cylinder heads.

9. Apply sealing compound to the joining surfaces. Place the manifold gasket in place (make sure that the tap on the right bank of the cylinder head gasket fits into the cutout of the manifold gasket).

10. Install the intake manifold. Tighten the attaching bolts until they are hand tight, and then tighten them, in sequence, to the proper torque.

NOTE: Tightening bolt No. 7 with a torque wrench will require an attachment called a "crow's foot."

11. Install the distributor so the rotor is pointing to the mark made previously.

12. Connect the distributor wire and vacuum line.

13. Install the carburetor, fuel line, fuel filter, and the rocker arm covers.

14. Install the distributor cap and wires.

15. Install and adjust the carburetor linkage. Install the coolant hoses and refill the cooling system.

16. Install the air cleaner assembly and air cleaner tube to the carburetor. Connect the battery.

17. Adjust the ignition timing.

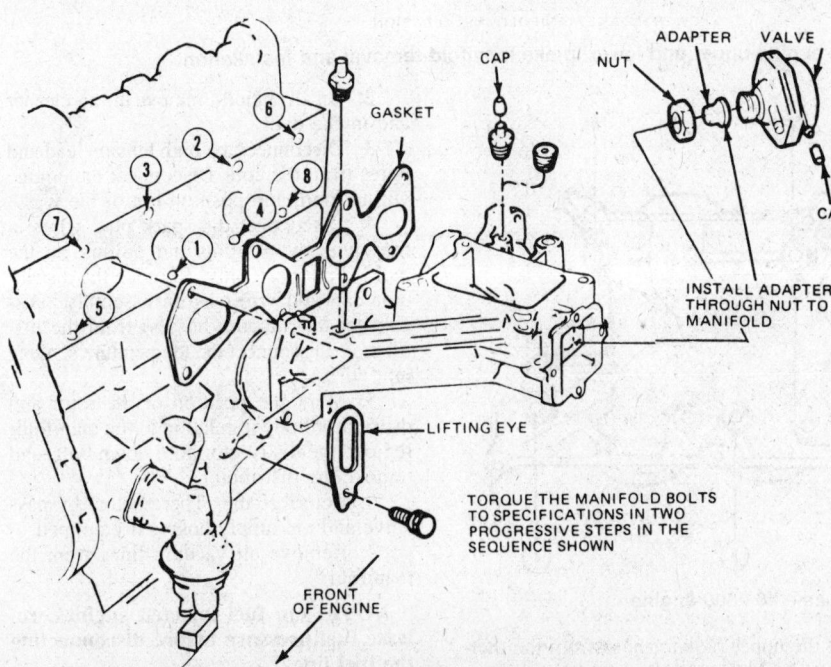

2300 cc engine intake manifold tightening sequence (© Ford Motor Co.)

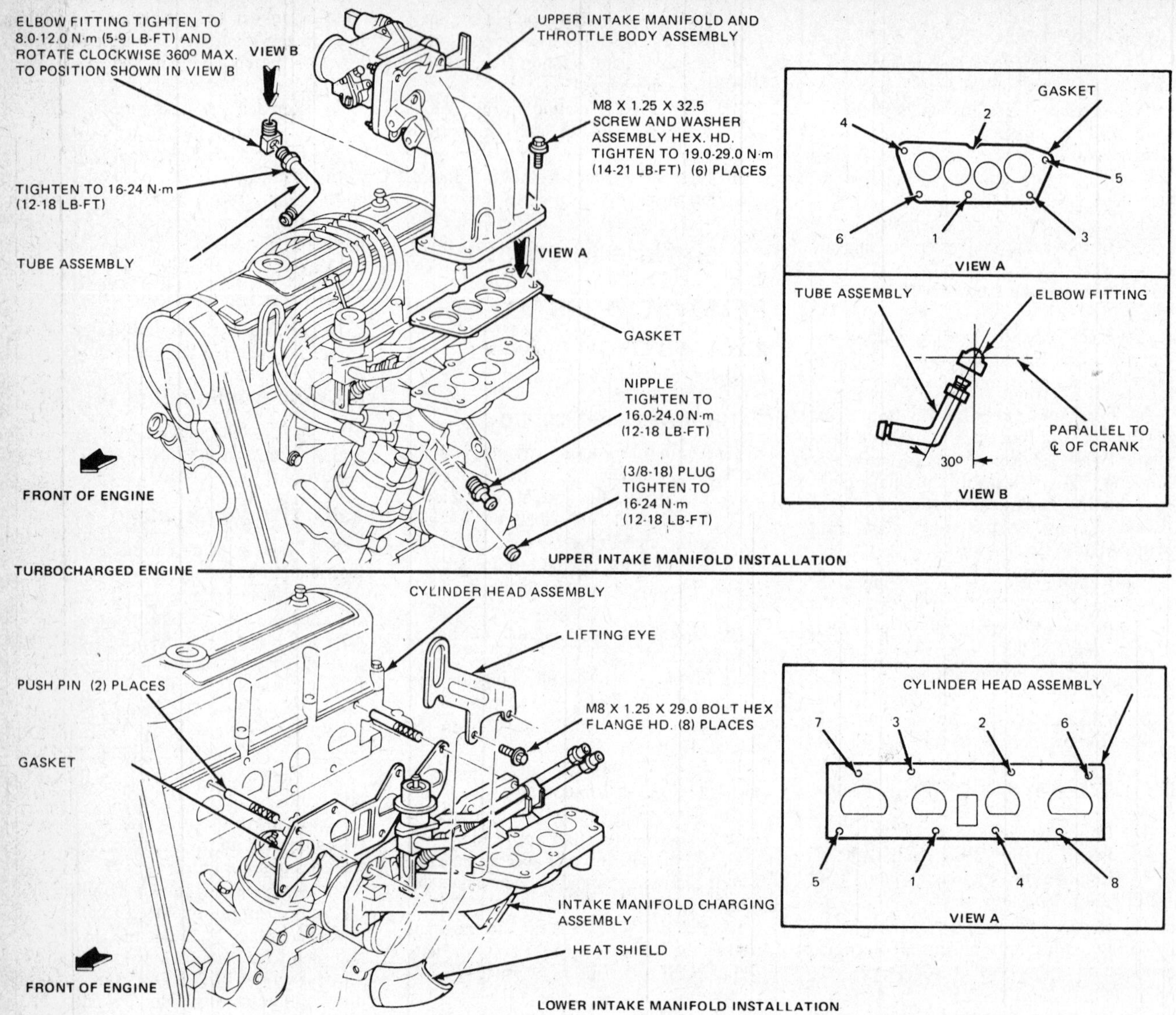

ELBOW FITTING TIGHTEN TO 8.0-12.0 N·m (5-9 LB-FT) AND ROTATE CLOCKWISE 360° MAX. TO POSITION SHOWN IN VIEW B

VIEW B

UPPER INTAKE MANIFOLD AND THROTTLE BODY ASSEMBLY

M8 X 1.25 X 32.5 SCREW AND WASHER ASSEMBLY HEX. HD. TIGHTEN TO 19.0-29.0 N·m (14-21 LB-FT) (6) PLACES

TIGHTEN TO 16-24 N·m (12-18 LB-FT)

TUBE ASSEMBLY

VIEW A

GASKET

NIPPLE TIGHTEN TO 16.0-24.0 N·m (12-18 LB-FT)

(3/8-18) PLUG TIGHTEN TO 16-24 N·m (12-18 LB-FT)

FRONT OF ENGINE

TURBOCHARGED ENGINE

UPPER INTAKE MANIFOLD INSTALLATION

GASKET

4 — 2 — GASKET — 5

6 — 1 — 3

VIEW A

TUBE ASSEMBLY — ELBOW FITTING

PARALLEL TO ₵ OF CRANK

30°

VIEW B

CYLINDER HEAD ASSEMBLY

LIFTING EYE

PUSH PIN (2) PLACES

GASKET

M8 X 1.25 X 29.0 BOLT HEX FLANGE HD. (8) PLACES

INTAKE MANIFOLD CHARGING ASSEMBLY

HEAT SHIELD

FRONT OF ENGINE

LOWER INTAKE MANIFOLD INSTALLATION

CYLINDER HEAD ASSEMBLY

7 — 3 — 2 — 6

5 — 1 — 4 — 8

VIEW A

Multi-point injection, 2.3L (140) engine-upper and lower intake manifold removal and installation

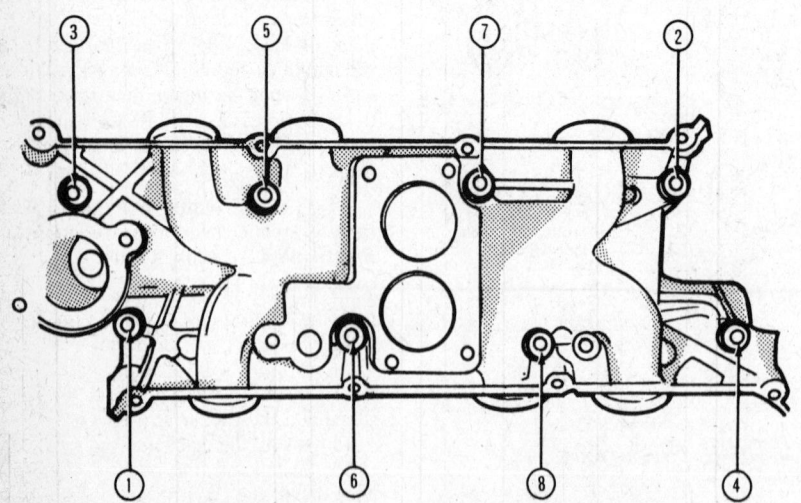

Intake manifold torque sequence—V6 2800 engine

V6 (232) and V8 Engines

1. Drain the cooling system, disconnect the upper radiator hose from the thermostat housing, and the bypass hose from the manifold.

2. On all engines, remove the air cleaner and intake duct.

3. Disconnect the high tension lead and wires from the coil. Disconnect the engine wiring loom and position out of the way.

4. Disconnect the spark plug wires at the plugs by twisting and pulling on the molded plug cap only. Remove the distributor cap and wires as an assembly. Disconnect the vacuum hose(s) from the distributor. Disconnect the temperature sending unit wire.

5. Mark the position of the rotor and distributor body in relation to the manifold, remove the distributor hold down bolt, and remove the distributor.

6. Remove the Thermactor by-pass valve and air supply hoses, if equipped.

7. Remove all vacuum lines from the manifold.

NOTE: On fuel injected engines, release fuel pressure before disconnecting the fuel line.

8. Disconnect the fuel line and vacuum

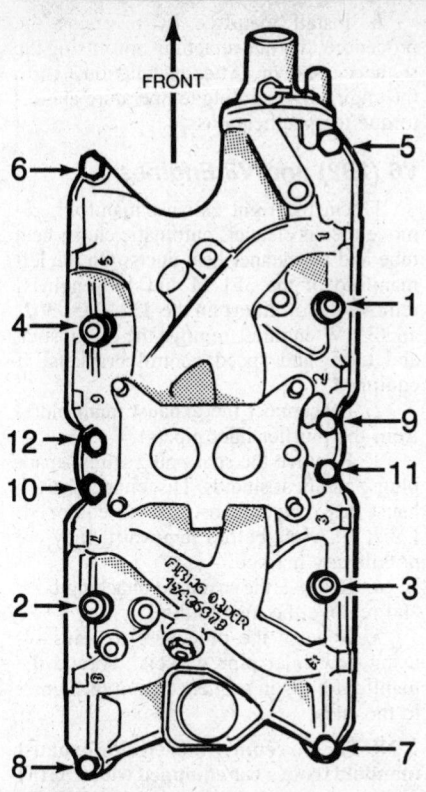

Intake manifold torque sequence—255, 302, 351W; V6 similar

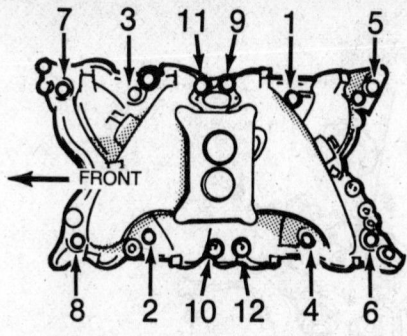

Intake manifold torque sequence—351C, 351M, 400 V8

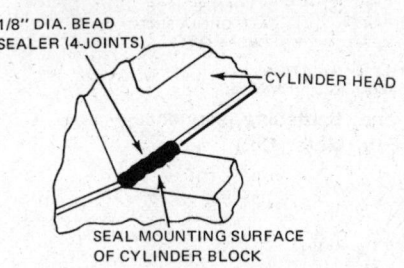

1/8" DIA. BEAD SEALER (4-JOINTS)

CYLINDER HEAD

SEAL MOUNTING SURFACE OF CYLINDER BLOCK

INTAKE MANIFOLD GASKET

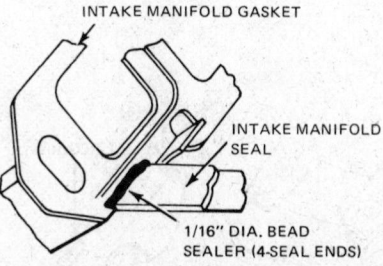

INTAKE MANIFOLD SEAL

1/16" DIA. BEAD SEALER (4-SEAL ENDS)

Intake manifold sealer application (© Ford Motor Co.)

hoses at the carburetor. Disconnect the accelerator linkage and downshift linkage, if so equipped, and position out of the way.

9. Disconnect the crankcase vent hose at the rocker cover.

10. On 351M and 400 V8s, remove the heater hoses from the retaining strap, and position out of the way. If the car is air conditioned, remove the compressor mounting brackets from the manifold and position the compressor out of the way. Do not disconnect any A/C hoses. Also, on these models, remove the coil.

11. Remove the intake manifold and carburetor as an assembly. Be careful not to damage any gasket sealing surfaces.

12. Clean the mating surfaces of the manifold, block, and heads. Apply a ⅛ in. bead of silicone seal to the four engine block-to-cylinder head mating surfaces. Do not apply any sealer to the waffle section of the end seals on 351M and 400 V8s.

13. Position the new end seals into place on the block, pressing the locating tabs into place. Position new manifold gaskets into place on the heads, and apply a ⅛ in. bead of silicone seal to the four end seal-to-manifold gasket joints. Do not allow the sealer to fall into the engine valley.

NOTE: The V6 232 cu. in. engine uses RTV sealant instead of end seals. Be sure to apply an even bead of sealant when installing the manifold.

14. Carefully lower the manifold into place. After it is positioned, run your finger around the seal area to be sure the seals are

properly positioned. If they are not, remove the manifold and reposition the seals.

15. Torque the manifold to specification in three stages, according to the pattern given. The rest of installation is the reverse of removal. After installation, run the engine to operating temperature and retorque the manifold bolts.

Diesel Engine

1. Disconnect the battery ground cable.
2. Remove the diagnostic plug bracket and position out of the way.
3. Disconnect the turbo boost pressure indicator connector.
4. Disconnect the oil dipstick tube clamp from intake manifold and position out of the way.
5. Loosen the clamp at the turbo crossover pipe boot.
6. Remove the bolts attaching the intake manifold to the cylinder head and remove the intake manifold.
7. Clean the intake manifold and cylinder head gasket mating surfaces.
8. Install the intake manifold on the cylinder head, with a new gasket, making sure the inlet port is installed in the turbo crossover pipe boot.

9. Tighten the intake manifold bolts to 14–17 ft. lbs., and tighten the crossover pipe boot clamp.

10. Connect the turbo boost pressure indicator switch connector.

11. Install the diagnostic plug bracket and tighten the bolts to 14–17 ft. lbs.

12. Connect the battery ground cable. Start the engine and check for intake leaks.

Exhaust Manifold

REMOVAL & INSTALLATION

2.3L (140) OHC—4 Cylinder Engine

NOTE: Refer to the Turbocharger section and Unit Repair Section on Fuel Injection for reference when servicing high performance models.

1. Remove the air cleaner. Remove the heat shroud from the exhaust manifold. Disconnect the hose from the thermactor check valves, if equipped. Disconnect the oxygen sensor wiring, on models equipped.

2. Place a block of wood under the exhaust pipe, and then disconnect it from the manifold.

3. Remove the attaching nuts and remove the manifold from the head. Clean the mating surfaces.

4. Install a light coat of graphite grease on the exhaust manifold mating surface and position the manifold on the cylinder head.

5. Install the attaching nuts and tighten them to the proper torque.

6. Connect the exhaust pipe to the manifold and remove the wood support from under the pipe.

7. Install the air cleaner, and check valve hose and oxygen sensor wiring if present.

2.8L (170) V6 Engine

1. Remove the air cleaner.
2. Remove the four attaching nuts from the exhaust manifold shroud (right side only).
3. Disconnect the attaching nuts from the muffler inlet pipe. Remove air pump hoses and components as necessary. Disconnect the choke heat tube at the carburetor, if so equipped.
4. Remove the exhaust manifold attaching nuts and remove the manifold.
5. These manifolds do not use gaskets. When installing the manifold, smear a light coat of graphite grease on the mating surfaces.
6. Position the manifold on the studs and install the bolts handtight then torque them evenly to the proper torque.
7. Install a new inlet pipe gasket and the attaching nuts.
8. Position the exhaust manifold shroud on the manifold and install the attaching nuts (right side).
9. Install the air cleaner. Install any air pump components removed and the choke heat tube.

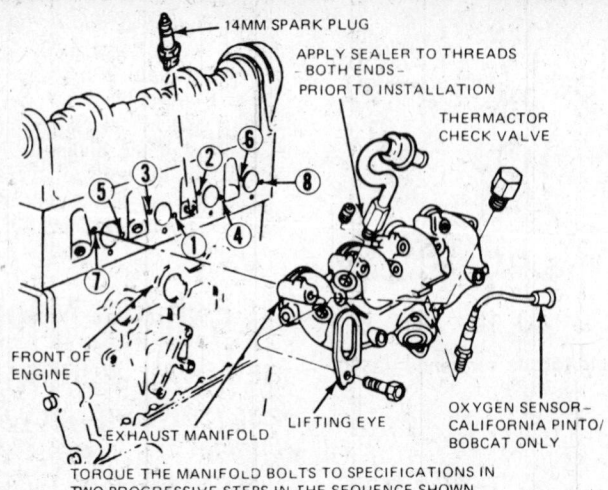

Exhaust manifold installation and tightening sequence—2300 cc engine (© Ford Motor Co.)

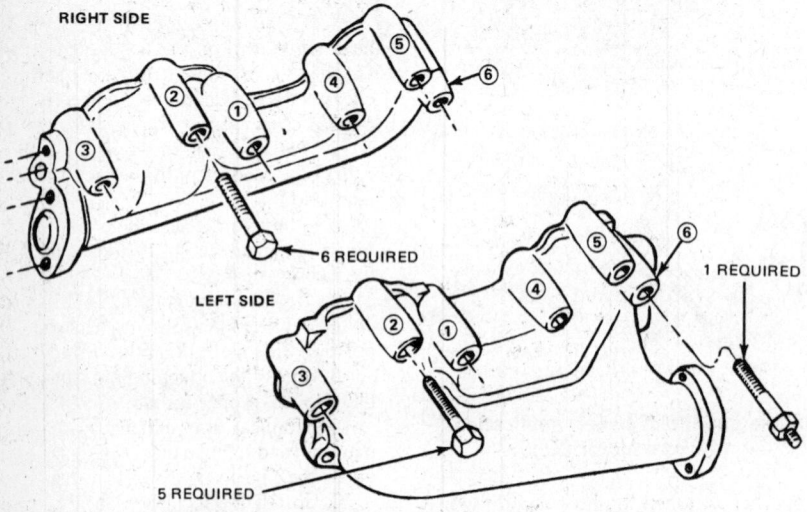

Exhaust manifold torque sequence—V6 2800 engine

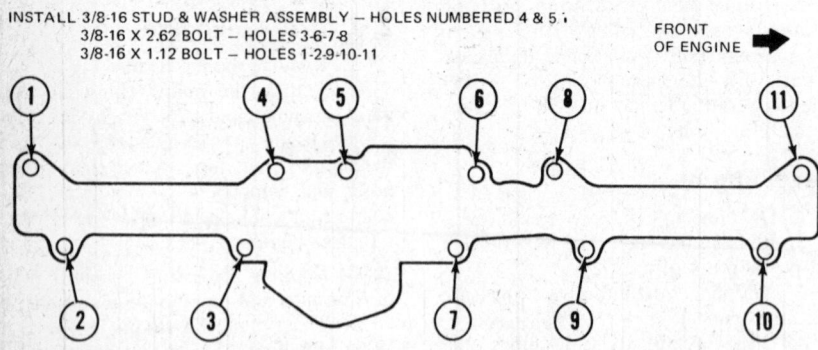

Six cylinder exhaust manifold torque sequence (© Ford Motor Co.)

6 Cylinder Inline Engine

1. Remove the air cleaner and heat duct body.

2. Disconnect the muffler inlet pipe and remove the choke hot air tube from the manifold.

3. Remove the EG tube and any other emission components which will interfere with manifold removal.

NOTE: Some models have a catalytic converter bolted to the manifold; the converter mounts on four manifold flange studs.

4. Bend the exhaust manifold attaching bolt lock tabs back, remove the bolts and the manifold.

5. Clean all manifold mating surfaces and place a new gasket on the muffler inlet pipe.

6. Install manifold by reversing the procedure. Torque attaching bolts using the sequence shown. After installation, warm the engine to operating temperature and re-torque to specifications.

V6 (232) and V8 Engines

1. On the right exhaust manifold, remove the air cleaner, automatic choke heat tube and air cleaner heat ducts. On the left manifold of the 351 M and 400 engines, remove the oil filter; on the 232, 255, 302, and 351W engines, remove the oil dipstick and tube, and speed control brackets, if equipped.

2. Disconnect the exhaust manifold(s) from the muffler inlet pipe(s).

3. Remove the spark plug wires, spark plugs, and heat shields. Disconnect the exhaust gas oxygen sensor, if so equipped. Label all wires before removal if they are not already marked.

4. Remove the manifold attaching bolts and remove the manifold(s).

5. Reverse the procedure to reinstall, using new inlet pipe gaskets. Torque the manifold bolts in sequence from the center to the ends.

NOTE: To remove the left side exhaust manifold from a car equipped with a 351M or 400 engine, it is necessary to remove the transmission selector cross shaft or clutch linkage and equalizer shaft bracket, depending on transmission type.

Diesel Engine

1. Disconnect the battery ground cable.

2. Disconnect the muffler inlet pipe at the turbo outlet and cap turbo outlet.

3. Disconnect the EGR valve vacuum line.

4. Disconnect the inlet duct at turbo and cap turbo inlet.

5. Loosen the clamp at the turbo crossover pipe boot.

6. Remove the clamp attaching the turbo oil feed tube to the oil return tube.

7. Remove the bolts attaching the oil feed tube to the turbo.

— CAUTION —
Cap the oil feed tube and oil feed inlet port on the turbo, to prevent contamination of the turbo oiling system.

8. Disconnect the oil return line from the turbo oil drain port.

— CAUTION —
Cap the oil return line and the oil return port on the turbo, to prevent contamination of the turbo oiling system.

9. Remove the bolts attaching the exhaust manifold to the cylinder head and remove the exhaust manifold and turbo as an assembly. Cap turbo outlet to crossover pipe.

10. Clean the exhaust manifold and cylinder head gasket mating surfaces.

11. Install the exhaust manifold, with a

new gasket, making sure the turbo outlet is installed in crossover pipe boot. Tighten bolts to 14–17 ft. lbs., and tighten the crossover pipe boot clamp.

12. Remove the caps and install the oil feed line, with a new gasket, on the turbo oil inlet port. Tighten bolts to 14–17 ft. lbs.

13. Remove the caps and connect the oil return line to the turbo oil return port. Tighten fitting to 29–36 ft. lbs.

14. Install the oil feed tube to the exhaust manifold clamp and tighten to 6.5–7 ft. lbs.

15. Remove the cap and connect the inlet duct to the turbo inlet.

16. Remove the cap and connect the muffler inlet pipe to the turbo exhaust outlet. Tighten bolts to 31–35 ft. lbs.

17. Connect the EGR valve vacuum line.

18. Connect the battery ground cable.

19. Run the engine and check for intake, exhaust and oil leaks.

Turbocharger

REMOVAL & INSTALLATION

Gasoline Engine

1. Allow engine to cool. Disconnect intake hose between turbocharger and injector unit.

2. Disconnect oil supply lines.

3. Unbolt exhaust pipe. Disconnect sensors.

4. Loosen and remove mounting bolts. Remove turbocharger.

5. Install in the reverse order.

NOTE: When installing the turbocharger, or after an oil and filter change, disconnect the distributor feed harness and crank the engine with the starter motor until the oil pressure light on the dash goes out. Oil pressure must be up before starting the engine.

Diesel Engine

— **CAUTION** —

Do not accelerate the engine before engine oil pressure has been built up. Also do not switch off the engine while it is running at high speed (the turbocharger will continue to spin for a long time without oil pressure). These conditions can damage the engine and/or turbocharger.

1. Remove the two bolts attaching the exhaust pipe to the turbocharger.

2. Remove the EGR tube and clamps.

3. Loosen the four hose clamps on the crossover tube and then remove tube.

4. Remove the air cleaner assembly and bellows. Cap turbocharger openings.

5. Remove the two oil supply line bolts on top of the turbocharger center housing.

6. Remove the clamp from oil lines.

7. Remove the oil return line.

8. Remove the bolt and sealing washers attaching the oil supply line to oil filter housing.

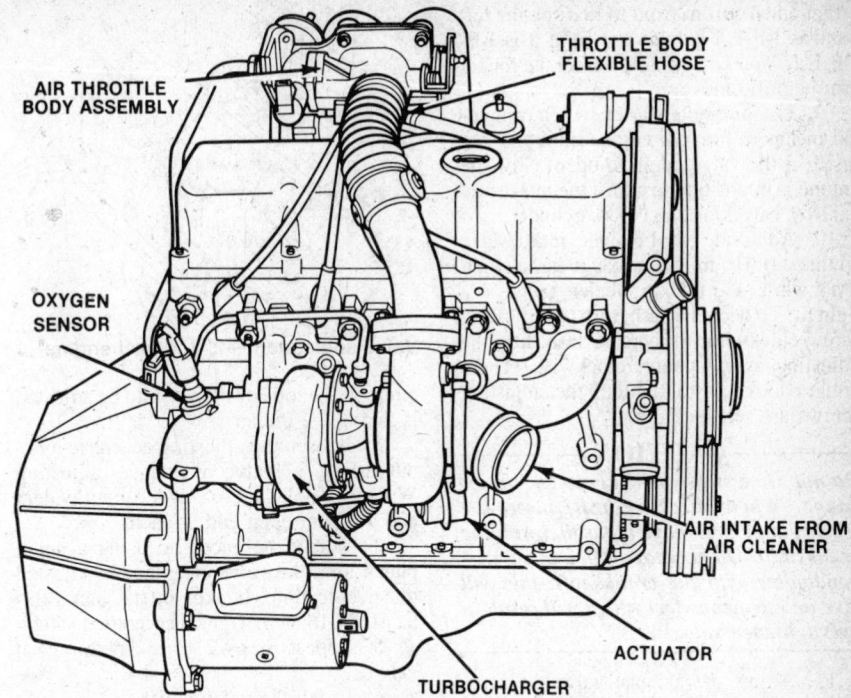

Turbo–charger mounting

9. Disconnect and remove the EGR valve.

10. Remove the four bolts attaching the turbocharger to the exhaust manifold and remove the turbocharger.

11. Clean the mating surfaces of the turbocharger and exhaust manifold.

12. Position the turbocharger on the exhaust manifold and install the four mounting bolts. Tighten to 17–20 ft. lbs.

13. Install the EGR valve. Tighten to 18 ft. lbs.

14. Install the oil supply line using new seals. Tighten the bolt to 26–33 ft. lbs.

— **CAUTION** —

Do not overtighten bolt. Oil leaks may occur if overtightened.

15. Install the clamp retaining the oil lines.

16. Install the oil supply line bolts to the turbocharger housing and tighten to 15–18 ft. lbs.

17. Remove the protective caps from the turbocharger and install the air cleaner assembly and bellows.

18. Install the crossover tube. Tighten the hose clamps snug.

19. Install the EGR tube clamp.

20. Install the two bolts attaching the exhaust pipe to the turbocharger and tighten to 17–20 ft. lbs.

21. Run the engine and check for oil and air leaks.

Torque Specs	Ft. Lbs. (in. lbs.)
EGR Valve	18
Hose Clamps	(15–22)
Oil Supply Line	15–18

To Turbo	
To Engine Block	26–33
Oil Return Line—To Turbo	15–18
Turbocharger-to-Exhaust Manifold	17–20
Turbocharger-to-Exhaust Pipe	17–20

Valve Clearance

ADJUSTMENT

2.8L (170) V6 Engine

If the valves are being adjusted for tuneup, the engine must be at normal operating temperature. If the valves are being adjusted after engine assembly, the engine must not be started until a preliminary adjustment has been made. Final adjustment can then be made after the engine is warmed up.

1. Remove the air cleaner assembly and disconnect the negative battery cable.

2. Remove the Thermactor air bypass valve and its mounting bracket.

3. Remove the two engine lifting eyes; remove the alternator drive belt, loosen the alternator mounting bolts and swing the alternator outward toward the fender.

4. Remove the plug wires and remove the rocker covers.

5. When removing the rocker covers, remove or reposition any wires or hoses which block the removal of the rocker covers.

6. Torque the rocker arm support bolts to 46 ft. lbs.

7. Reconnect the battery cable, place the transmission in Neutral (manual) or Park (automatic), and apply the parking brake.

8. Place a finger on the adjusting screw of the intake valve rocker arm for cylinder No. 5. Cylinder numbering is shown under Firing Order at the start of the section. Valve

arrangement, from front to rear, on the left bank is I-E-E-I-E-I; on the right it is I-E-I-E-E-I. You will be able to feel the rocker arm begin to move.

9. Use a remote starter switch or manual means to turn the engine until you can just feel the valve begin to open. Now the engine is in position to adjust the intake and exhaust valves on the No. 1 cylinder.

10. Adjust the No. 1 cylinder intake valve so that a 0.016 in. feeler gauge has a slight drag while a 0.017 in. feeler gauge is a tight fit. To decrease lash, turn the adjusting screw clockwise; to increase lash, turn the adjusting screw counterclockwise. There are no locknuts to tighten; the adjusting screws are self-locking.

CAUTION

Do not use a step-type, "go-no go" feeler gauge. When checking lash, insert the feeler gauge and move it parallel with the crankshaft. Do not move it in and out perpendicular with the crankshaft: this will give an erroneous feel which will result in overtightened valves.

11. Adjust the exhaust valve the same way so that an 0.018 in. feeler gauge has a slight drag, while a 0.019 in. gauge is a tight fit.

12. The rest of the valves are adjusted in the same way, in their firing order (1-4-2-5-3-6), by positioning the engine according to the following chart:

V6 CLEARANCE ADJUSTMENT

Intake valve just opening in cylinder No.:	Adjust both valves in this cylinder: (Intake 0.016; Exhaust—0.018 in)
5	1
3	4
6	2
1	5
4	3
2	6

13. Remove all the old gasket material from the cylinder heads and rocker cover gasket surfaces, and disconnect the negative cable from the battery.

14. Remove the spark plug wires and reinstall the rocker arm covers.

15. Reinstall any hoses and wires which were removed.

16. Reinstall the spark plug wires, the alternator drive belt, and the Thermactor air bypass valve and its mounting bracket.

17. Reconnect the battery cable, replace the air cleaner assembly, start the engine, and check for leaks.

Diesel Engine

NOTE: Adjustment procedure is for cold engine only.

1. Remove the valve cover.
2. Position the camshaft so that base

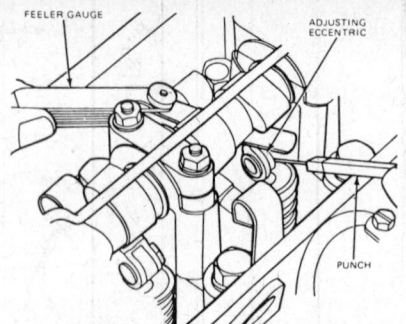

Valve adjustment—2.4L diesel engine

circle of the lobe of the valve to be adjusted is facing the rocker arm.

3. Loosen the adjusting eccentric locknut using a valve clearance adjusting Wrench, Tool T84P-6575-A, or equivalent and a 12mm open end wrench.

4. Rotate the eccentric using a small punch until the valve clearance is adjusted to specification: Intake: 0.012 inch; Exhaust: 0.016 inch. Tighten eccentric locknut.

5. Repeat Steps 2, 3 and 4 for each valve.

6. Install the valve cover.

7. Start the engine and check for oil leaks.

Rocker Arm Assembly

REMOVAL & INSTALLATION

2.3L (140) OHC—4 Cylinder Engine

1. Remove the valve cover and associated parts as required.

2. Rotate the camshaft so that the base circle of the cam is against the cam follower you intend to remove.

3. Remove the retaining spring from the cam follower, if so equipped.

4. Using a valve spring compressor tool for a 2300cc engine, collapse the lash adjuster and/or depress the valve spring, as necessary, and slide the cam follower over the lash adjuster and out from under the camshaft.

5. Install the cam follower in the reverse order of removal. Make sure that the lash adjuster is collapsed and released before rotating the cam shaft.

6 Cylinder Inline Engine

1. Remove the air cleaner and PCV line, and the accelerator control cable bracket.

2. Remove the rocker arm cover and gasket.

3. Remove the rocker shaft bolts, two turns at a time each, working from the ends toward the center.

4. Lift off the rocker shaft assembly. Keep the pushrods in order, if removed, for installation in their original positions.

5. Installation is the reverse of removal. Torque the rocker shaft bolts, two turns at a time, working from the center toward the ends, to 30–35 ft. lbs.

2.8L (170) V6 Engine

1. Remove any emission control equipment as necessary to remove the rocker cover(s), remove the spark plug wires, remove the throttle linkage to the carburetor as necessary, and remove the valve rocker cover(s).

2. Remove the rocker arm shaft stand retaining bolts; loosen them each 2 turns at a time in sequence. Lift the rocker arm and shaft assembly and the oil baffle.

3. Before installing the rocker shaft assemblies, back off the adjusting screws on the rockers a few turns. Install the rocker shafts in the reverse order of removal; tighten the rocker shaft stand retaining bolts 2 turns at a time in sequence until they are tightened to 46 ft. lbs. Adjust the valve clearance as previously described.

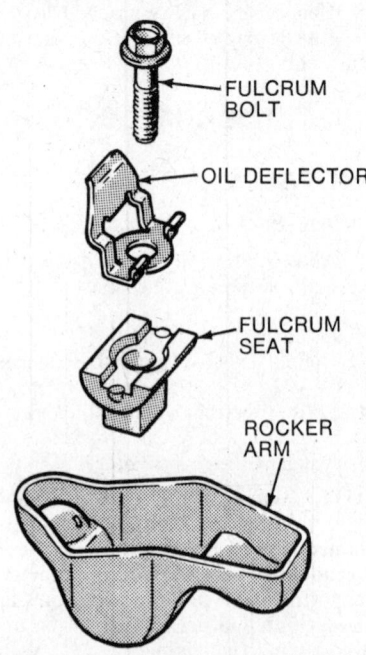

Late model V8 rocker arm mounting—V6 similar (© Ford Motor Co.)

232, 255, 302 and 351W

1. Right side
   a. disconnect the automatic choke heat chamber air inlet hose.
   b. remove the air cleaner and duct.
   c. remove the automatic choke heat tube (232, 302).
   d. remove the PCV fresh air tube from the rocker cover, and disconnect the EGR vacuum amplifier hoses.

2. Remove the Thermactor by-pass valve and air supply hoses.

3. Disconnect the spark plug wires.

4. On the left side:
   a. remove the wiring harness from the clips.
   b. remove the rocker arm cover.

5. Remove the rocker arm stud nut or bolt, fulcrum seat and rocker arm.

6. Lubricate all parts with heavy SE oil before installation. When installing, rotate the crankshaft until the lifter is on the base

Chilton's TIME SAVER

The following is a method for replacing valve springs, oil seals or spring retainers without removing the cylinder head.

1. **Purchase an air chuck with a spark plug hole adapter.**
2. **Remove the valve rocker cover. Remove the rocker arm from the valve to be worked on.**
3. **Remove the spark plug from the cylinder to be worked on.**
4. **Turn the crankshaft to bring the piston of this cylinder down, away from possible contact with the valve head. Sharply tap the valve retainer to loosen the valve lock.**
5. **Then turn the crankshaft to bring the piston in this cylinder to the Exact Top of its Compression Stroke.**
6. **Screw the air chuck fitting into the spark plug hole.**
7. **Hook up an air hose to the chuck and turn on the pressure (about 200 psi).**
8. **With a strong and constant supply of air holding the valve closed, compress the valve spring and remove the lock and retainer.**

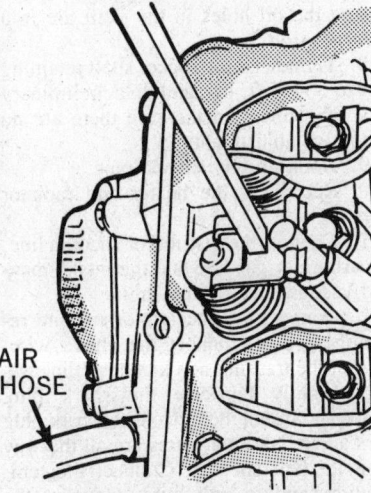

Compressing valve spring

9. **Make the necessary replacements and reassemble.**
NOTE: It is important that the operation be performed exactly as stated, in this order. The piston in the cylinder must be on exact top-center to prevent air pressure from turning the crankshaft.

of the cam circle (all the way down) and assemble the rocker arm. Torque the nut or bolt to 17–23 ft. lb.

NOTE: Later engines are using RTV sealant instead of valve cover gaskets.

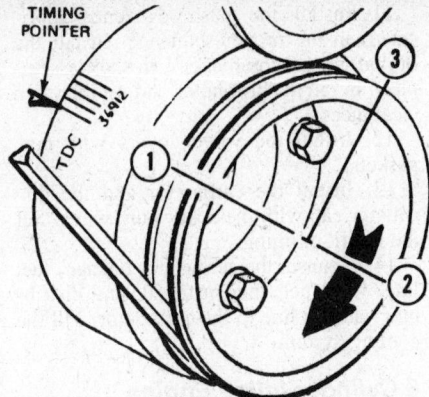

POSITION 1 — No. 1 at TDC at end of compression stroke.
POSITION 2 — Rotate the crankshaft 180 degrees (one half revolution) clockwise from POSITION 1.
POSITION 3 — Rotate the crankshaft 270 degrees (three quarter revolution) clockwise from POSITION 2.

Crankshaft positions for rocker arm installation (© Ford Motor Co)

Chilton's TIME SAVER

Frequently valves become bent or warped or their seats become blocked with carbon or other material. Left unattended, this can cause burnt valves, damaged cylinder heads and other expensive troubles. To detect leaking valves early, perform this test whenever the cylinder head is removed.

1. **After removing head, replace spark plugs. Removing spark plugs before removing heads eliminates breakage.**
2. **Place head on bench with valves, springs, retainers and keys installed and combustion chambers up.**
3. **Pour enough gasoline in each combustion chamber to completely cover both valves. Watch combustion chambers for two minutes for any leakage.**

Always apply an even ⅛ in. bead of sealant along the channel of the valve cover after cleaning.

351M and 400

1. Remove the air cleaner and duct.
2. Remove the hoses from the cover.
3. Disconnect the spark plug wires.
4. Remove the cover(s).
5. Remove the rocker arm bolt, oil deflector, fulcrum seat and the rocker arm.
6. Before installation, lubricate all parts with heavy SF/SE engine oil. When installing, position No. 1 piston on TDC of the compression stroke and assemble the rocker arms on the following valves:

No. 1 intake and exhaust

No. 4 intake
No. 3 exhaust
No. 8 intake
No. 7 exhaust
Turn the crankshaft 180° clockwise and assemble the rocker arms for:
No. 3 intake
No. 2 exhaust
No. 7 intake
No. 6 exhaust
Turn the crankshaft 270° clockwise and assemble the rocker arms for:
No. 2 intake
No. 4 exhaust
No. 5 intake and exhaust
No. 6 intake
No. 8 exhaust
Torque the bolts to 18–25 ft. lb. Be sure the fulcrum seat base is seated before tightening the bolts.

7. Assemble the remaining parts.

Cylinder Head

REMOVAL & INSTALLATION

NOTE: The engine should be "overnight" cold before removing the cylinder head(s), to prevent warpage or distortion. Always label all disconnected hoses and wires to assure proper assembly.

2.3L (140) OHC—4 Cylinder Engine

1. Drain the cooling system.
2. Remove the air cleaner and the valve rocker cover.
3. Remove the intake and exhaust manifolds. The intake manifold, decel valve (if equipped) and carburetor can be removed as an assembly.
4. Remove the camshaft drive belt cover.
5. Loosen the drive belt tensioner and remove the drive belt.
6. Remove the water outlet from the cylinder head.
7. Remove the cylinder head bolts evenly, and remove the cylinder head.
8. Position a new cylinder head gasket on the block. Rotate the camshaft so that the locating pin is at the five o'clock position, to avoid valve damage.
9. Position the cylinder head and camshaft assembly on the block. Install the bolts finger tight, then torque to specifications in two stages.

NOTE: If difficulty in positioning the head on the block is encountered, guide

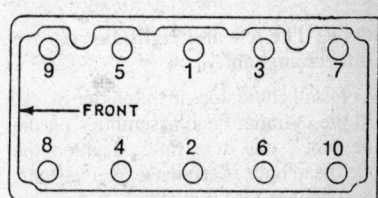

2300 cc head bolt tightening sequence (© Ford Motor Co.)

pins may be fabricated by cutting the heads off two extra cylinder head bolts.

10. Set the crankshaft at TDC and be sure that the camshaft drive gear and distributor are positioned correctly as explained under Timing Belt Replacement.

11. Install the camshaft drive belt and release the tensioner. Rotate the crankshaft two full turns clockwise (facing the engine) to remove all slack from the belt. The timing marks should again be aligned. Tighten the tensioner lockbolt and pivot bolt.

12. Install the camshaft drive belt cover.

13. Apply sealer to the water outlet and new gasket, and install.

14. Install the intake and exhaust manifolds.

15. Adjust the valve clearance.

16. Install a new valve cover gasket and install the valve cover.

17. Install the air cleaner and crankcase ventilation hose.

18. Refill the cooling system.

2.8L (170) V6 Engine

1. Remove the air cleaner assembly and disconnect the battery and accelerator linkage. Drain the cooling system.

2. Remove the distributor cap with the spark plug wires attached. Remove the distributor vacuum line and distributor. Remove the hose from the water pump to the water outlet which is on the carburetor.

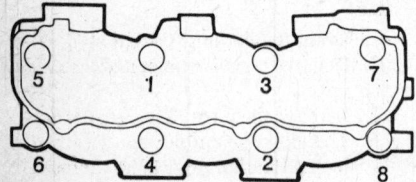

V6 cylinder head bolt torque sequence
(© Ford Motor Co.)

3. Remove the valve covers, fuel line and filter, carburetor, and the intake manifold.

4. Remove the rocker arm shaft and oil baffles. Remove the pushrods, keeping them in the proper sequence for installation.

5. Remove the exhaust manifold, referring to the appropriate procedures.

6. Remove the cylinder head retaining bolts and remove the cylinder heads and gaskets.

7. Remove all gasket material and carbon from the engine block and cylinder heads.

8. Place the head gaskets on the engine block.

NOTE: The left and right gaskets are not interchangeable.

9. Install guide studs in the engine block. Install the cylinder head assemblies on the engine block one at a time. Tighten the cylinder head bolts in sequence, and in steps, to the specified torque.

10. Install the intake and exhaust manifolds.

11. Install the pushrods (ends lubricated) in the proper sequence. Install the oil baffles and the rocker arm shaft assemblies. Install the distributor. Adjust the valve clearances.

12. Install the valve covers with new gaskets.

13. Install the carburetor and the distributor cap with the spark plug wires. Set the ignition timing.

14. Connect the accelerator linkage, fuel line, with fuel filter installed, and distributor vacuum line to the carburetor. Fill the cooling system.

6 Cylinder Inline Engine

1. Drain cooling system, remove the air cleaner and disconnect the battery cable at the cylinder head.

2. Disconnect exhaust pipe at the manifold end, swing the exhaust pipe down and remove the flange gasket.

3. Disconnect the fuel and vacuum lines from the carburetor. Disconnect the intake manifold line at the intake manifold.

4. Disconnect the accelerator and retracting spring at the carburetor. Disconnect the transmission kick-down linkage, if equipped.

5. Disconnect the carburetor spacer outlet line at the spacer. Disconnect the radiator upper hose and the heater hose at the water outlet elbow. Disconnect the radiator lower hose and the heater hose at the water pump.

6. Disconnect the distributor vacuum control line(s) at the distributor. Disconnect the gas filter line on the inlet side of the filter.

7. Disconnect and label the spark plug wires and remove the plugs. Disconnect the temperature sending unit wire.

8. Remove the rocker arm cover.

9. Loosen the rocker arm shaft attaching bolts and remove the rocker arm and shaft assembly. Remove the valve pushrods, in order, for installation in their original positions.

10. Remove one cylinder head bolt from each end of the head (at opposite corners) and install cylinder head guide studs for lifting the head. Remove the remaining cylinder head bolts and lift off the cylinder head. Do not pry under the cylinder head as damage to the mating surfaces can easily occur.

To help in removal and installation of cylinder head, two 6 in. × 7/16—14 bolts with heads cut off and the head end slightly tapered and slotted, for installation and removal with a screwdriver, will reduce the possibility of damage during head replace-

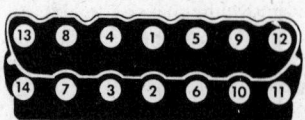

**Cylinder head bolt tightening sequence
—200, 250 6 cyl. (© Ford Motor Co.)**

ment. These guide studs make a handy tool during head removal and gasket and head replacement.

11. Clean the cylinder head and block surfaces. Check for warpage and surface damage; correct as necessary.

12. Apply cylinder head gasket sealer to both sides of the new gasket and slide the gasket down over the two guide studs in the cylinder block.

NOTE: Apply gasket sealer only to steel shim head gaskets. Steel/asbestos composite head gaskets are to be installed without any sealer.

13. Carefully lower the cylinder head over the guide studs. Place the exhaust pipe flange on the manifold studs (new gasket).

14. Coat the threads of the end bolts for the right side of the cylinder head with a small amount of water-resistant sealer. Install, but do not tighten, two head bolts at opposite ends to hold the head gasket in place. Remove the guide studs and install the remaining bolts.

15. Cylinder head torquing should proceed in three steps and in prescribed order. Tighten to 55 ft. lbs., then give them a second tightening to 65 ft. lbs. The final step is to 75 ft. lbs., at which they should remain undisturbed.

16. Lubricate both ends of the pushrods and install them in their original locations.

17. Apply lubricant to the rocker arm pads and the valve stem tips and position the rocker arm shaft assembly on the head. Be sure the oil holes in the shaft are in a down position.

18. Tighten all the rocker shaft retaining bolts to 30–35 ft. lbs. and do a preliminary valve adjustment (make sure there are no tight valve adjustments).

19. Hook up the exhaust pipe.

20. Reconnect the heater and radiator hoses.

21. Connect the distributor vacuum line, the carburetor gas line and the intake manifold vacuum line on the engine.

22. Connect the accelerator rod and retracting spring. Connect the choke wire. Connect the transmission kickdown linkage.

23. Lightly lubricate the spark plug threads and install them. Connect spark plug wires and be sure the wires are all the way down in their sockets. Connect the temperature sending unit wire. Connect the negative battery cable.

24. Coat one side of a new rocker cover gasket with oil-resistant sealer. Lay the treated side of the gasket on the cover and install the cover. Be sure the gasket seals evenly all around the cylinder head.

25. Fill the cooling system. Install the PCV system and air cleaner. Start the engine and check for leaks.

V6 (232) and V8 Engines

1. Remove the valve covers and disconnect the negative battery cable.

2. Remove the intake manifold and carburetor assembly.

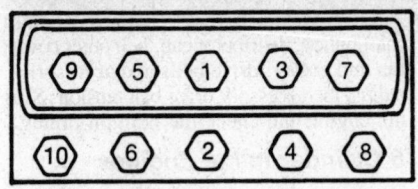

Cylinder head bolt tightening sequence all V8s (© Ford Motor Co.)

3. On cars equipped with air conditioning, remove the compressor from the engine and position it to one side, *without disconnecting the refrigerant lines.*

4. If removing the left cylinder head, on cars equipped with power steering, remove the pump, bracket, and drive belt and position to one side *without disconnecting the lines.* On cars with Thermactor emission control system, disconnect the hose from the air manifold on the left cylinder head.

5. If removing the right cylinder head, remove the alternator mounting bracket bolt and spacer, ignition coil, and air cleaner inlet duct. On cars equipped with Thermactor emission control, remove the air pump and bracket. Disconnect the hose from the right cylinder head.

6. Disconnect the exhaust manifold/s from the exhaust pipe/s.

7. Loosen the rocker arm stud nuts or bridge bolts so that the arms can rotate to the side to clear the pushrods. Remove the pushrods. Keep them in order for installation in their original positions.

8. Remove the cylinder head bolts and lift off the cylinder head. On some 351 engines, it may be necessary to remove the exhaust manifold to gain access to the lower cylinder head bolts.

9. Reverse the procedure for installation taking care to follow the specified torque sequence. Perform a preliminary valve adjustment before starting the engine.

Diesel Engine

1. Disconnect the battery ground cable.
2. Drain the cooling system. Disconnect the heater hose(s).
3. Loosen and remove accessory drive belts.
4. Remove the valve cover.
5. Disconnect the diagnostic connectors.
6. Disconnect the coolant temperature switch and glow plug connector.
7. Disconnect the breather hose and bracket.
8. Remove the clamp attaching the oil dipstick tube to the intake manifold and position out of the way.
9. Disconnect the boost pressure switch connector.
10. Disconnect the radiator hose from the cylinder head.
11. Disconnect the temperature controlled idle boost coolant hose.
12. Remove the vacuum pump from cylinder head.
13. Disconnect No. 1 nozzle to the in-

jection pump leak hose.

14. Disconnect the injection lines from the nozzles and injection pump.

— **CAUTION** —

Cap nozzles and lines.

15. Disconnect the turbocharger oil lines.
16. Rotate the crankshaft until No. 1 cylinder is at TDC of compression stroke (intake and exhaust valves on base circle). Install TDC Aligning Pin, T84P-6400-A or equivalent.
17. Loosen the camshaft drive sprocket retaining bolt.
18. Loosen the camshaft drive belt tensioning roller nut and bolt, and remove drive belt.
19. Loosen the cylinder head bolts in sequence, and remove cylinder head.
20. Clean gasket sealing surfaces on the cylinder head and crankcase. Check for warpage.

— **CAUTION** —

Use care when cleaning gasket surfaces. Slight scoring of these surfaces can cause leakage due to high compression pressures.

21. Clean the top of each piston.
22. Using a dial indicator D82L-4201-A and Piston Height Gauge D84P-6100-A or equivalent, measure the amount the piston top extends above crankcase gasket surface as follows:
    a. Mount the dial indicator and bracket with dial indicator tip on piston.
    b. Rotate the crankshaft to position piston at TDC, using dial indicator.
    c. Zero the dial indicator with tip on crankcase.

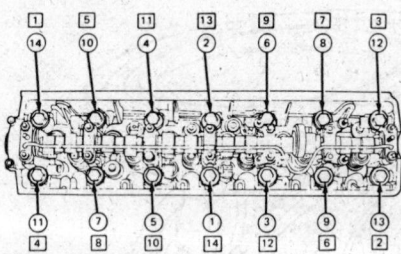

2.4L diesel engine cylinder head torque sequence

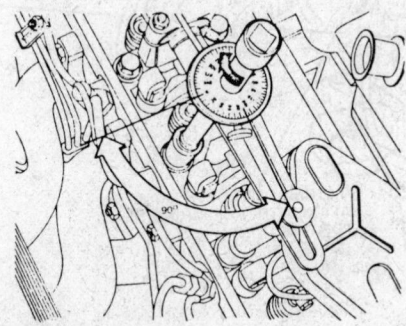

Cylinder head bolt tightening—2.4L diesel engine

d. Move the tip to the front of the piston. Record measurement.
    e. Move the tip to the rear of the piston. Record measurement.
    f. Repeat this procedure for each cylinder.
    g. Average the two readings for each cylinder.
    h. Using the measurement of highest piston, refer to the chart provided and select correct cylinder head gasket.

23. Clean carbon and oil deposits from the cylinder head bolts.

— **CAUTION** —

Keep oil and/or antifreeze from entering cylinder head bolt holes. If either enters bolt holes, carefully blow out with compressed air. The presence of oil and/or antifreeze in bolt holes could result in insufficient cylinder head bolt tightening, or a cracked crankcase.

24. Position the correct cylinder head gasket on the crankcase.
25. Carefully lower the cylinder head onto the crankcase, using care not to damage gasket.
26. Install and tighten the cylinder head bolts, in sequence to 36–43 ft. lbs. Wait 15 minutes and tighten the bolts, in sequence to 65–69 ft. lbs.
27. Install and adjust the drive belt.
28. Connect the turbocharger oil lines and tighten to 14–17 ft. lbs.
29. Connect the nozzle high pressure lines to the nozzles and injection pump. Tighten to 14–18 ft. lbs., using fuel line wrench.
30. Connect No. 1 nozzle to the injection pump leak hose.
31. Install the vacuum pump on the cylinder head and tighten to 6–7 ft. lbs.
32. Connect the temperature controlled, idle boost coolant hose.
33. Connect the radiator hoses to the cylinder head.
34. Connect the oil pressure switch connector.
35. Install the oil dipstick tube.
36. Install the breather hose and bracket.
37. Connect the coolant temperature switch and glow plug connectors.
38. Connect the diagnostic connectors.
39. Install the valve cover.
40. Install and adjust accessory drive belts.

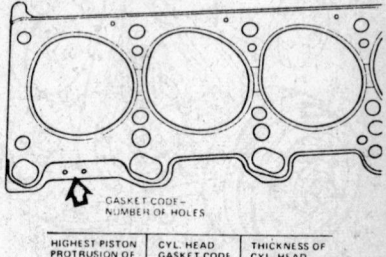

HIGHEST PISTON PROTRUSION OF ALL 6 PISTONS mm	CYL. HEAD GASKET CODE NO. OF HOLES	THICKNESS OF CYL. HEAD GASKET mm
0.60 – 0.70	1	1.4
0.70 – 0.85	2	1.5
0.85 – 1.00	3	1.6

Cylinder head gasket identification—2.4L diesel engine

41. Connect the heater hose(s).

42. Fill and bleed coolant system. Connect the battery ground cable.

Timing Cover, Belt/Chain

REMOVAL & INSTALLATION

2.3L (140) OHC—4 Cylinder Engine

Should the camshaft drive belt jump timing by a tooth or two, the engine could still run; but very poorly. To visually check for correct timing of the crankshaft, auxiliary shaft, and the camshaft on the 2300 cc engines, follow this procedure:

On 2300 cc engines, there is an access plug provided in the cam drive belt cover so that the camshaft timing can be checked without removing the drive belt cover. Remove the access plug, turn the crankshaft until the timing mark on the crankshaft damper indicates TDC, and observe that the timing mark on the camshaft drive sprocket is aligned with the pointer on the inner belt cover. Also, the rotor of the distributor must align with the No. 1 cylinder firing position.

NOTE: Never turn the crankshaft of any of the overhead cam engines in the opposite direction of normal rotation. Backward rotation of the crankshaft may cause the timing belt to slip and alter the timing.

— CAUTION —

After any procedure requiring removal of the rocker arms on the 2300, each lash adjuster must be fully collapsed after assembly, then released. This must be done before the camshaft is turned.

TIMING BELT

1. Set the engine to TDC as described for checking valve timing. The crankshaft and camshaft timing marks should align with their respective pointers and the distributor rotor should point to the No. 1 plug tower.

2. Loosen the adjustment bolts on the alternator and accessories and remove the drive belts. To provide clearance for removing the camshaft belt, remove the fan and pulley.

3. Remove the belt outer cover.

4. Remove the distributor cap from the distributor and position it out of the way.

5. Loosen the belt tensioner adjustment and pivot bolts. Lever the tensioner away from the belt and retighten the adjustment bolt to hold it away.

6. Remove the crankshaft bolt and pulley. Remove the belt guide behind the pulley.

7. Remove the camshaft drive belt.

8. Install the new belt over the crankshaft pulley first, then counterclockwise over the auxiliary shaft sprocket and the camshaft sprocket. Adjust the belt fore and aft so that it is centered on the sprockets.

9. Loosen the tensioner adjustment bolt, allowing it to spring back against the belt.

10. Rotate the crankshaft two complete turns in the normal rotation direction to remove any belt slack. Turn the crankshaft until the timing check marks are lined up. If the timing has slipped, remove the belt and repeat the procedure.

11. Tighten the tensioner adjustment bolt to 14–21 ft. lbs., and the pivot bolt to 28–40 ft. lbs.

12. Replace the belt guide and crankshaft pulley, distributor cap, belt outer cover, fan and pulley, drive belts and accessories. Adjust the accessory drive belt tension. Start the engine and check the ignition timing.

6 Cylinder Inline Engines

1. Drain the cooling system and crankcase.

2. Disconnect the upper radiator hose from the intake manifold and the lower hose from the water pump. On cars with automatic transmission, disconnect the cooler lines from the radiator.

3. Remove the radiator, fan and pulley, and engine drive belts. On models with air conditioning, remove the condenser retaining bolts and position the condenser forward. *Do not disconnect the refrigerant lines.*

4. Remove the crankshaft pulley bolt and use a puller to remove the vibration damper.

5. On 200 cu. in. engines remove the cylinder front cover retaining bolts and front oil pan bolts and gently pry the cover away from the block. On 250 engines, it is necessary to remove the oil pan before remoing the front cover.

6. With a socket wrench of the proper size on the crankshaft pulley bolt, gently rotate the crankshaft in a clockwise direction until all slack is removed from the left side of the timing chain. Scribe a mark on the engine block parallel to the present position of the left side of the chain. Next, turn the crankshaft in a counterclockwise direction to remove all the slack from the right side of the chain. Force the left side of the chain outward with the fingers and measure the distance between the reference point and the present position of the chain. If the distance exceeds ½ inch, replace the chain and sprockets.

7. Crank the engine until the timing marks are aligned as shown in the illustration. Remove the bolt, slide sprocket and chain forward and remove as an assembly.

8. Position the sprockets and chain on the engine, making sure that the timing marks are aligned, dot to dot.

9. On 250 engines, install the chain snubber in the front cover.

10. Reinstall the front cover, applying oil resistant sealer to the new gasket.

NOTE: On 200 engines, reinstall the oil pan.

11. On 250 engines, reinstall the oil pan.

12. Install the fan, pulley and belts. Adjust belt tension.

13. Install the radiator, connect the radiator hoses and transmission cooling lines. If equipped with air conditioning, install the condenser.

14. Fill the crankcase and cooling system. Start the engine and check for leaks.

Diesel Engine

BELT

1. Disconnect the battery ground cable.

ACCESS PLUG

TIMING POINTER MUST INDEX WITH TIMING MARK ON SPROCKET

DISTRIBUTOR ROTOR MUST ALIGN WITH NO. 1 FIRING POSITION

TIMING POINTER MUST ALIGN WITH TDC MARK ON DAMPER

Crankshaft, camshaft, and distributor timing marks—2300 cc engine
(© Ford Motor Co.)

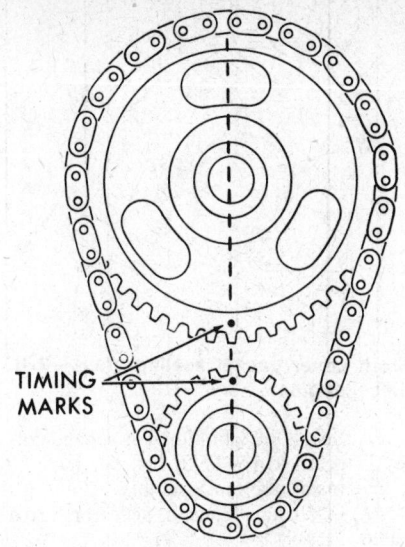

Timing mark alignment

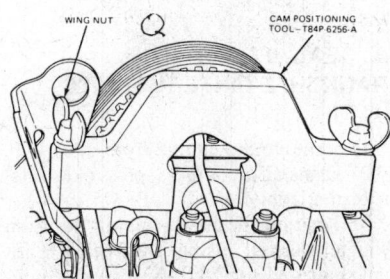

Cam positioning tool—2.4L diesel engine

2. Drain the cooling system.
3. Remove the accessory drive belts.
4. Remove fan assembly and water pump pulley assembly.
5. Remove the vibration damper and pulley.
6. Disconnect the heater hose from the thermostat housing.
7. Remove the four bolts attaching the camshaft drive belt cover to crankcase, and remove the cover.
8. Remove the rocker cover.
9. Rotate the engine until No. 1 cylinder is at TDC on compression stroke (intake and exhaust valves on base circle), and install TDC Aligning Pin T84P-6400-A or equivalent.
10. Install Cam Positioning Tool T84P-6256-A or equivalent.

NOTE: Flat side of nut or cam position tool should be facing down.

11. Loosen the camshaft sprocket bolt.
12. Using a piece of chalk, or similar marker, mark the direction of engine rotation on drive belt, unless a new belt is to be installed.
13. Loosen the two bolts on the belt tensioner.
14. Remove the camshaft drive belt.
15. Insert a 0.098 in. (2.5mm) thick feeler gauge blade between Cam Positioning Tool T84P-6256-A or equivalent, at the right front corner of the gasket mating surface of the

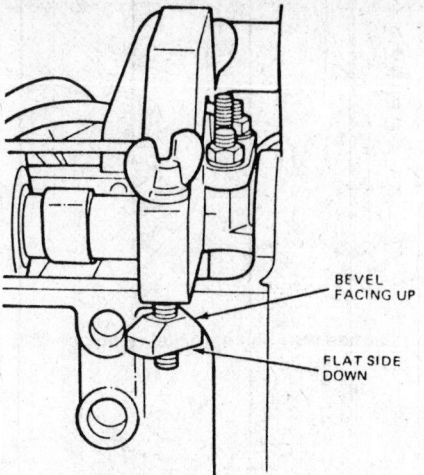

Cam positioning tool nut—2.4L diesel engine

cylinder head if using a new drive belt or a drive belt used with less than 10,000 miles.

16. Install Injection Pump Aligning Pin T84P-9000-A or equivalent, through injection pump sprocket.
17. Rotate the cam sprocket clockwise against pin.
18. Install the camshaft drive belt. Starting at the crankshaft, route the belt around the intermediate shaft sprocket, injection pump sprocket, camshaft sprocket and then tension roller, keeping slack to a minimum.

——— CAUTION ———
Used drive belts must be installed in same direction of engine rotation as removed.

——— CAUTION ———
Make sure V side of belt is correctly positioned in V's of the pulley.

19. Hand tighten belt with the belt tensioner until all slack is gone.
20. Remove Injection Pump Aligning Pin, T84P-9000-A or equivalent, from the injection pump sprocket.
21. Adjust the belt tension by tightening the belt tensioner. Tighten belt tensioner to 34–36 ft. lbs. on belts with less than 10,000 miles and 23–25 ft. lbs. for belts with more than 10,000 miles.

NOTE: Use only a dial type torque wrench.

22. Tighten the two belt tensioner holding bolts to 15–18 ft. lbs.
23. Tighten the camshaft sprocket to 41–47 ft. lbs.
24. Remove the Cam Positioning Tool, T84P-6265-A, and TDC Aligning Pin, T84P-6400-A or equivalent.
25. Install the camshaft drive belt cover and tighten bolts to 6–7 ft. lbs.
26. Connect the heater hose to the thermostat housing.
27. Install the vibration damper.
28. Install fan and water pump pulley assembly.
29. Install and adjust accessory drive belts. Refer to Section 27-02.

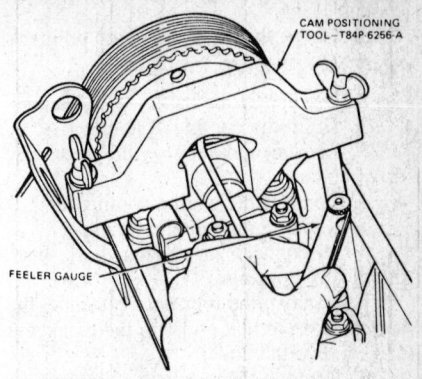

Cam positioning tool with feeler gauge—2.4L diesel engine

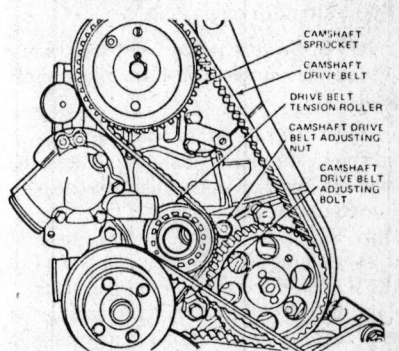

Camshaft drive belt installation—2.4L diesel engine

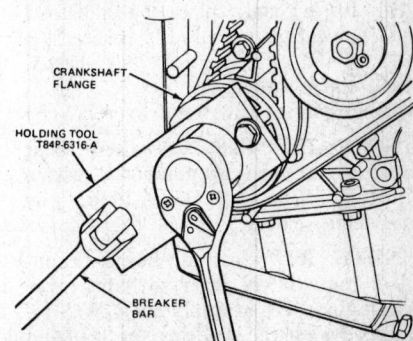

Crankshaft flange removal—2.4L diesel engine

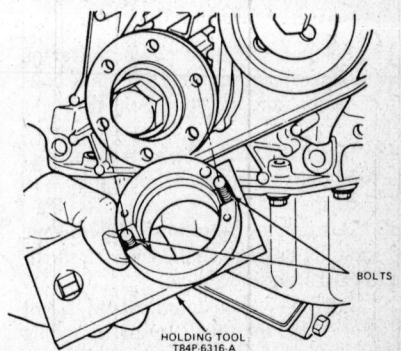

Alignment of bolts in the vibration damper—2.4L diesel engine

30. Fill and bleed the cooling system.
31. Connect the battery ground cable.
32. Run the engine and check for oil and

C235

coolant leaks.

33. Check the injection pump timing.

ENGINE FRONT COVER

1. Disconnect the battery ground cable.
2. Drain the cooling system.
3. Loosen and remove the accessory drive belts.
4. Remove the engine cooling fan.
5. Remove the vibration damper.
6. Disconnect the heater hose from thermostat housing.
7. Remove the four bolts attaching the camshaft drive belt cover to the crankcase and remove the cover.
8. Remove the camshaft drive belt.
9. Remove the bolts attaching the intermediate shaft sprocket using Holding Tool T84P-6316-A or equivalent.

NOTE: Be sure Allen head screws are aligned with holes in intermediate shaft sprocket.

10. Remove the vibration damper flange and sprocket retaining bolt and remove the flange and sprocket using puller, T67L-3600-A or equivalent.
11. Remove the three oil pan-to-front cover attaching bolts. Loosen, but **DO NOT REMOVE,** the remaining oil pan bolts.
12. Remove the six bolts attaching the front cover to the crankcase, and remove cover.
13. Clean the front cover and crankcase gasket mating surfaces.
14. Inspect and replace the crankshaft and intermediate shaft oil seals, if necessary.
15. If the oil pan gasket is damaged, install a new pan gasket.
16. Install the new front cover gasket.

NOTE: Coat the areas where front cover gasket meets oil pan gasket with a ¼ inch RTV Sealant, D6AZ-19562-A or equivalent sealer.

NOTE: RTV Sealant should be applied immediately prior to front cover installation. When applying RTV Sealant always use the bead size specified and join the components within 15 minutes of application. After this amount of time the sealant begins to ''set-up'' and its sealing effectiveness may be reduced.

17. Position the front engine cover on the crankcase, and tighten the 6mm bolts to 6–7 ft. lbs. and the 8mm bolts to 14–17 ft. lbs.
18. Install the three oil pan-to-front cover attaching bolts. Tighten the oil pan bolts to 6.5–7 ft. lbs.
19. Position the vibration damper flange and sprocket on crankshaft, with the shoulder toward front of vehicle.
20. Position the intermediate shaft sprocket on the intermediate shaft, guiding the locating pin into the bore.
21. Install Holding Tool T84P-6316-A or equivalent.

NOTE: Align Allen head screws in tool with holes in intermediate shaft.

22. Install and tighten the vibration

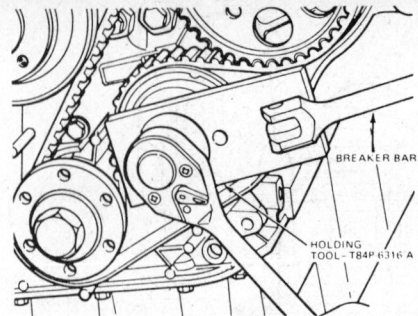

Intermediate shaft sprocket removal—2.4L diesel engine

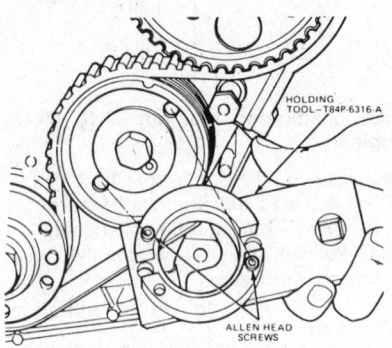

Intermediate shaft allen head screws—2.4L diesel engine

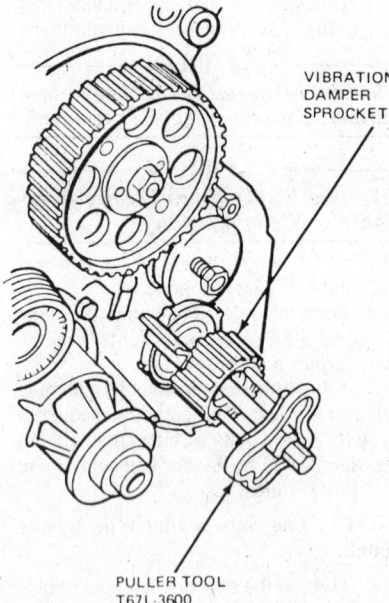

Vibration damper sprocket removal—2.4L diesel engine

damper flange and sprocket bolt to 282–311 ft. lbs.

23. Install and tighten the intermediate shaft sprocket bolt to 40–47 ft. lbs. Remove Tool T84P-6316-A or equivalent.
24. Install and adjust the camshaft drive belt.
25. Install the camshaft drive belt cover and tighten bolts to 6–7 ft. lbs.
26. Connect the heater hose to thermostat housing.

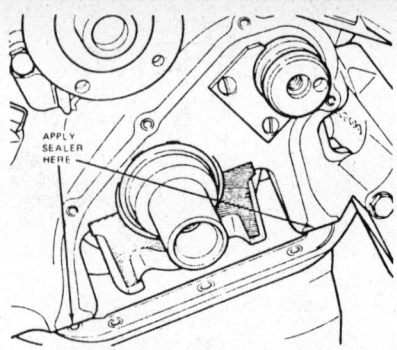

Front cover gasket sealing areas—2.4L diesel engine

27. Install the vibration damper and pulley. Tighten to 16–17 ft. lbs.
28. Install the fan assembly.
29. Install and adjust the accessory drive belts.
30. Connect the battery ground cable.
31. Start and idle engine. Check for oil leaks.

OIL SEAL, FRONT—CRANKSHAFT/INTERMEDIATE SHAFT

1. Remove the engine front cover.
2. Using an arbor press, press old seal(s) out of the front cover.
3. Position the new seals on the front cover and install, using T84P-6019-B for crankshaft seal, or T84P-6020-A or equivalent for intermediate shaft seal.
4. Lubricate the sealing lips with engine oil.
5. Install engine front cover.

2.8L (170) V6 Engine
FRONT COVER

1. Remove the oil pan as described in the following section.
2. Remove the radiator and any other necessary parts such as the water pump, to allow clearance.
3. Remove the alternator and drive belts. Remove the water pump and water lines.
4. Remove the fan.
5. Remove the crankshaft pulley with a puller.
6. Remove the front cover retaining bolts and remove the front cover. If the front cover plate gasket needs replacement, remove the two screws and the plate to replace the gasket. If necessary, remove the guide sleeves from the cylinder block.
7. To install, reverse the procedures, cleaning all surfaces of gasket material and installing new gaskets and sealing compound.

NOTE: If the guide sleeves were removed, install them with new seat rings but do not use sealing compound.

OIL SEAL

1. Remove the timing cover.
2. Drive out the old seal with a punch and make sure that the inside rim is clean.

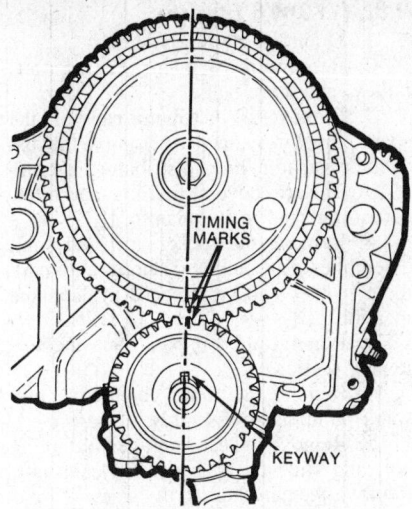

Timing gear alignment—V6 2800 engine

3. Coat a new seal with grease and place it into position on the case.

4. Drive the seal in until fully seated; check to make sure that the spring is properly positioned in the seal.

5. Reinstall the timing cover.

GEARS

1. Remove the front cover.

2. Align cam and crankshaft gear timing marks.

3. Remove the crankshaft gear using a suitable puller.

4. Remove the cam gear from the camshaft using a suitable puller.

5. Install the new gears in reverse order. Confirm timing mark alignment.

V6 (232) and V8 Engines

1. Drain cooling system, remove air cleaner and disconnect the battery.

2. Disconnect radiator hoses and remove the radiator.

3. Disconnect heater hose at water pump. Slide water pump by-pass hose clamp toward the pump.

4. Loosen alternator mounting bolts at the alternator. Remove the alternator support bolt at the water pump. Remove Thermactor pump on all engines so equipped. If equipped with power steering or air conditioning, unbolt the component, remove the belt, and lay the pump aside with the lines attached.

5. Remove the fan, spacer, pulley, and drive belt.

6. Drain the crankcase.

7. Remove pulley from crankshaft pulley adapter. Remove cap screw and washer from front end of crankshaft. Remove crankshaft pulley adapter with a puller.

8. Disconnect fuel pump outlet line at the pump. Remove fuel pump retaining bolts and lay the pump to the side. Remove the engin oil dipstick. Remove the distributor on V6 232 engines.

NOTE: On the 232 V6 and 351M, 400 V8 engines, it is necessary to drop the

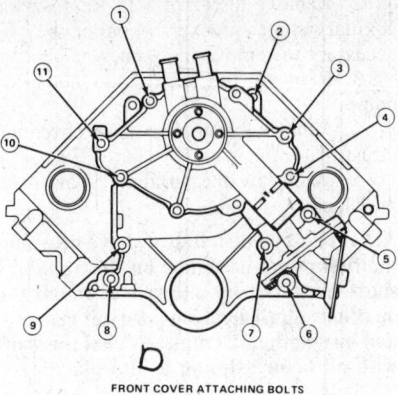

Front cover attaching bolts—V6 (232) engine

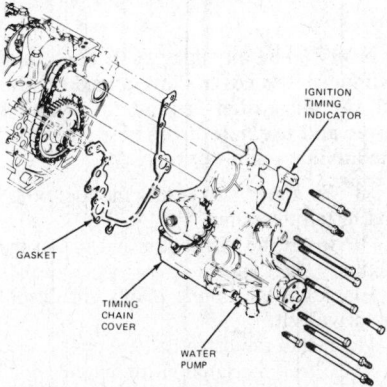

Front cover removal and installation—V6 (232) engine

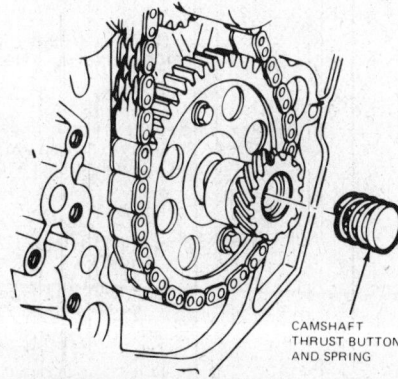

Camshaft thrust button and spring—V6 (232) engine

oil pan before the front cover can be removed.

9. Remove the front cover attaching bolts. On the 232 V6 engine, remove the water pump and front cover as an assembly.

10. Remove the crankshaft oil slinger if so equipped. On the 232 V6 engine, remove the camshaft thrust button and spring.

11. Check timing chain deflection, using the procedure outlined in Step 6 of the six cylinder cover and chain removal.

12. Crank engine until sprocket timing marks are aligned as shown in the valve timing illustration.

13. Remove crankshaft sprocket cap screw, washers, and fuel pump eccentric. Slide both sprockets and chain forward and off as an assembly.

14. Position sprockets and chain on the camshaft and crankshaft with both timing marks dot to dot on a centerline. Install fuel pump eccentric, washers and sprocket attaching bolt. Torque the sprocket attaching bolt to 40–45 ft. lbs.

15. Install the crankshaft front oil slinger.

NOTE: When replacing the front cover on the 232 V6 engine, RTV sealer is used. Apply an even ⅛ in. bead on the cover "gasket" surface.

16. Clean front cover and mating surfaces of old gasket material. Install a new oil seal in the cover. Use a seal driver tool, if available. Oil the lips of the seal to prevent damage.

17. Coat a new cover gasket with sealer and position it on the block.

NOTE: On all except 351M and 400 engines, trim away the exposed portion of the oil pan gasket flush with the cylinder block. Cut and position the required portion of a new gasket to the oil pan, applying sealer to both sides of it. On 232 V6, 351M and 400 engines, after installing the cylinder front cover, install the oil pan using a new gasket.

18. Install front cover, using a crankshaft-to-cover alignment tool. Coat the threads of the attaching bolts with sealer. Torque attaching bolts to 12–15 ft. lbs.

19. Install fuel pump, connect fuel pump outlet tube.

20. Install crankshaft pulley adapter and torque attaching bolt. Install crankshaft pulley.

21. Install water pump pulley, drive belt, spacer and fan.

22. Install alternator support bolt at the water pump. Tighten alternator mounting bolts. Adjust drive belt tension. Install Thermactor pump if so equipped.

23. Install radiator and connect all coolant and heater hoses. Connect battery cables.

24. Refill cooling system and the crankcase. Install the dipstick.

25. Start engine and operate at fast idle.

26. Check for leaks, install air cleaner. Adjust ignition timing and make all final adjustments.

Cover Seal

REMOVAL & INSTALLATION

It is recommended to replace the cover seal any time the front cover is removed.

1. With the cover removed from the car, drive the old seal from the rear of cover with a pinpunch. Clean out the recess in the cover.

2. Coat the new seal with grease and drive it into the cover until it is fully seated. Check the seal after installation to be sure the spring is properly positioned in the seal.

Camshaft
REMOVAL & INSTALLATION

2.3L (140) OHC—4 Cylinder Engine

CAMSHAFT

1. Remove the cylinder head as previously described.
2. Remove the rocker arms.
3. Remove the camshaft drive gear attaching bolt and washer, and remove the gear and belt guide plate.
4. The camshaft is removed through the front of the cylinder head after removing the front cam bearing seal. Use a new seal during assembly.
5. Reverse the removal procedure to install the camshaft and cylinder head.

NOTE: Coat the camshaft with oil before sliding it into the cylinder head. Apply a coat of sealer or teflon tape to the cam drive gear bolt before installation.

——————— **CAUTION** ———————
After any procedure requiring removal of the rocker arms on the 2300, each lash adjuster must be fully collapsed after assembly, then released. This must be done before the camshaft is turned.

AUXILIARY SHAFT

1. Remove the camshaft drive belt cover.
2. Remove the drive belt. Remove the auxiliary shaft sprocket. A puller may be necessary to remove the sprocket.
3. Remove the distributor and fuel pump.
4. Remove the auxiliary shaft cover and thrust plate.
5. Withdraw the auxiliary shaft from the block.

NOTE: The distributor drive gear and the fuel pump eccentric on the auxiliary shaft must not be allowed to touch the auxiliary shaft bearings during removal and installation. Completely coat the shaft with oil before sliding it into place.

6. Slide the auxiliary shaft into the housing and insert the thrust plate to hold the shaft.
7. Install a new gasket and auxiliary shaft cover.

NOTE: The auxiliary shaft cover and cylinder front cover share a gasket. Cut off the old gasket around the cylinder cover and use half of the new gasket on the auxiliary shaft cover.

8. Fit a new gasket into the fuel pump and install the pump.
9. Insert the distributor and install the auxiliary shaft sprocket.
10. Align the timing marks and install the drive belt.
11. Install the drive belt cover.
12. Check the ignition timing.

2.8L (170) V6 Engine

1. Drain the cooling system.
2. Remove the radiator, fan, spacer, pulley, and drive belts.
3. Remove the distributor cap with the spark plug wires attached. Remove the distributor vacuum line, distributor, alternator, rocker arm covers, fuel line and filter, carburetor, and intake manifold.
4. Remove the rocker arm and shaft assemblies. Lift out the pushrods and mark them so they can be replaced in the same location.
5. Remove the oil pan. (See the following sections.)
6. Remove the timing chain cover and water pump as an assembly.
7. Remove the camshaft gear retaining bolt and slide the gear off the camshaft. Remove the camshaft thrust plate.
8. Remove the valve lifters from the engine block with a magnet. Lifters should be identified to permit installation in the same location.
9. Carefully pull the camshaft from the engine block, avoiding damage to the camshaft bearings. Remove the key and spacer ring.
10. Coat the camshaft with a cam lubricant or heavy engine oil.
11. Install the camshaft, carefully avoiding damage to the bearings.

NOTE: When installing the camshaft, do not push it hard into the engine. There

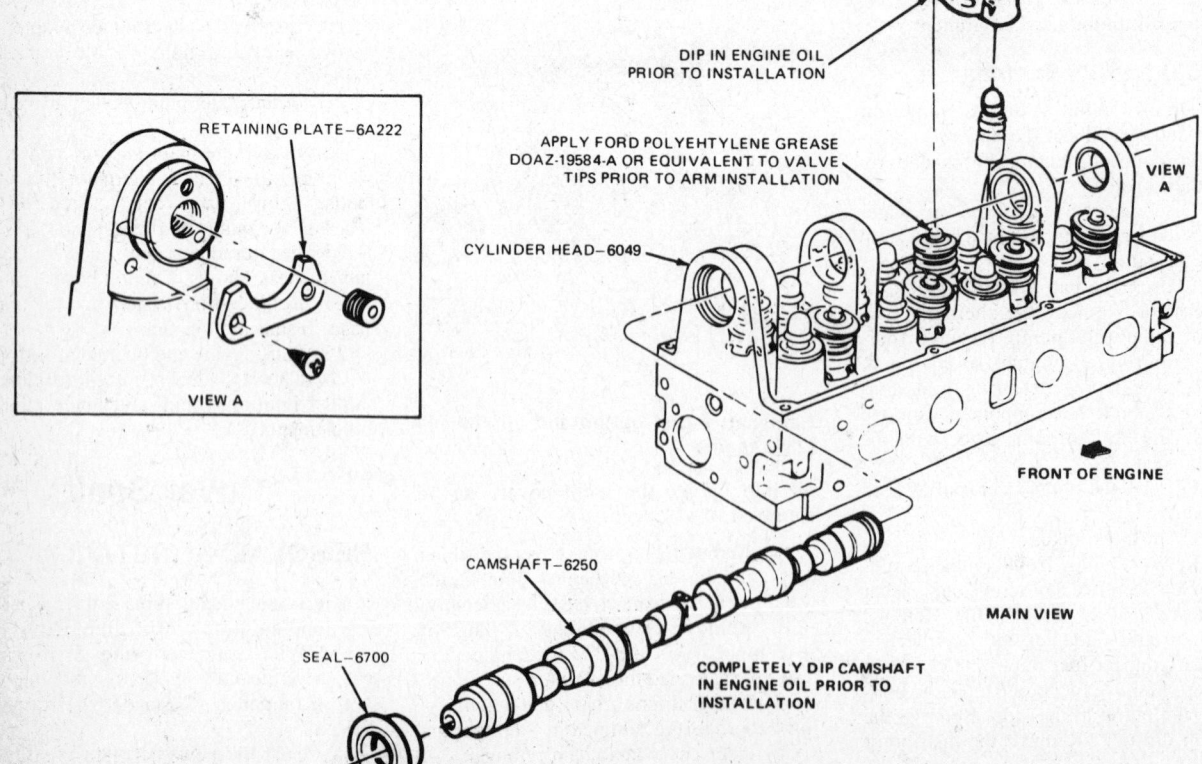

Camshaft installation—2.3L (140) engine

is an oil plug at the rear of the engine block called the "bore plug." If the camshaft is forced into the engine, it could push this plug out, resulting in oil leakage onto the clutch and pressure plate.

12. Install the spacer ring with the chamfered side toward the engine. Insert the camshaft key. Install the thrust plate. Camshaft end-play should be 0.001–0.004 in. The spacer ring and thrust plate are available in two sizes for adjustment.

13. Install the camshaft timing gear and align the timing marks. Install the retaining washer and bolt.

14. Install the valve lifters.

15. Install the timing cover.

16. Install the belt drive pulley and secure it with the washer and retaining bolt.

17. Install the oil pan.

18. Install the pushrods in the same locations from which they were removed. Install the intake manifold.

19. Install the oil baffles and rocker arm shaft assemblies. Adjust the valves.

20. Install the carburetor, fuel line and filter, alternator, distributor cap, and wires.

21. Fill the cooling system.

22. Install the rocker arm covers but not permanently. Run the engine, check for leaks, and set the ignition timing.

23. Set the valves at their hot setting. Install the valve covers with sealer.

Diesel Engine

1. Disconnect the battery ground cable.

2. Remove the valve cover.

3. Remove the vacuum pump.

4. Remove the fan assembly.

5. Remove the camshaft drive belt cover.

6. Remove the rocker arms.

7. Rotate engine until No. 1 cylinder is at TDC of compression stroke. Install TDC Aligning Pin, T84P-6400-A, or equivalent.

8. Loosen the camshaft sprocket bolt.

9. Loosen the drive belt tension roller nut and bolt.

10. Remove the camshaft sprocket.

11. Remove the camshaft bearing caps and mark the caps so that they can be installed in their original position, and remove camshaft.

12. Install the camshaft in position on the cylinder head.

13. Install the camshaft bearing caps, making sure they are installed in the correct position. Tighten 6mm nuts to 6–7 ft. lbs. and 8mm nuts to 14–17 ft. lbs.

14. Install the camshaft sprocket but do not tighten at this time.

15. Install and adjust the camshaft drive belt.

16. Adjust the cam and pump timing.

17. Remove the TDC Aligning Pin Tool T84P-6400-A or equivalent.

18. Install the rocker arms.

19. Install the camshaft drive belt cover and tighten the bolts to 6–7 ft. lbs.

20. Install the fan assembly.

21. Install the vacuum pump.

22. Install the rocker arm cover.

23. Connect the battery ground cable.

24. Run the engine and check for oil, intake air, and coolant leaks.

6 Cylinder Inline Engines

1. Remove the cylinder head.

2. Remove the timing case cover (and oil pan on 250 engines), timing chain and sprockets as outlined in the preceding section.

3. Disconnect and remove the grille. Remove the radiator. If equipped with air conditioning, unbolt the condenser and move it aside *without disconnecting any lines*.

4. Using a magnet, remove the valve lifters and keep them in order so that they can be installed in their original positions.

5. Remove the camshaft thrust plate and remove the camshaft by pulling it from the front of the engine. Use care not to damage the camshaft or bearings while removing the cam from the engine.

6. Before installing the camshaft, coat the lobes with engine assembly lubricant and the journals and all valve parts with heavy oil. Clean the oil passage at the rear of the cylinder block with compressed air.

7. Reverse the procedure to install, following recommended torque settings and tightening sequences.

V6 (232) and V8 Engines

1. Remove the intake manifold as outlined previously.

2. Remove the cylinder front cover, timing chain and sprockets as directed previously.

3. Remove the grille and radiator. On models with air conditioning, remove the condenser retaining bolts and position it out of the way. *Do not disconnect refrigerant lines.* On the Versailles, the hood latch assembly, ambient temperature switch wiring, and the support bracket must be removed.

4. Remove the rocker arm covers.

5. Remove the pushrods and lifters and keep them in order so that they can be installed in their original positions.

6. Remove the camshaft thrust plate and washer if so equipped. Remove the camshaft from the front of the engine. Use care not to damage camshaft lobes or journals while removing the cam from the engine.

7. Before installing the camshaft, coat the lobes with engine assembly lubricant and the journals and valve parts with heavy oil.

8. Reverse the procedure to install.

Oil Pan

REMOVAL & INSTALLATION

NOTE: On certain engine-chassis combinations, interference will be encountered between the oil pan and oil pump while attempting to remove the oil pan. If interference occurs, lower the oil pan as far as possible, reach inside and remove the bolts mounting the oil pump or pickup tube. Lower the pump and/or pickup tube into the oil pan. Remove the oil pan. Interference may also occur between the pan and the rear counter balance weight of the crankshaft. Turn the

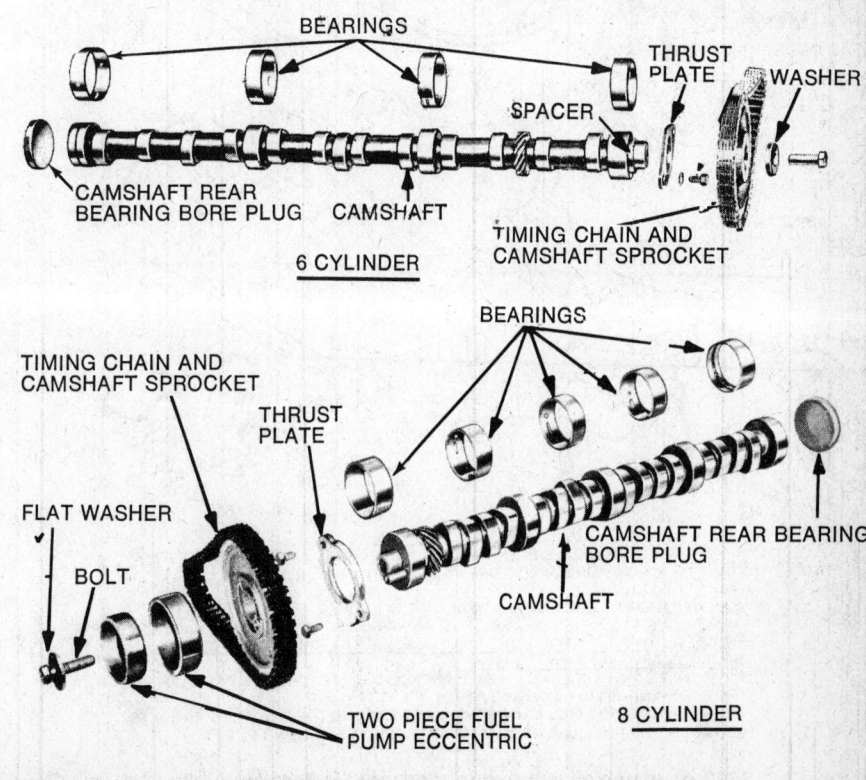

Camshaft and related parts (© Ford Motor Co)

crank to position the weight in an upward position if necessary.

NOTE: Certain late models use "Quick-Connect" transmission oil cooler line fittings. Refer to the "Fuel" section for removal and installation procedures.

2.3L (140) OHC—4 Cylinder Engine

BOBCAT/MUSTANG II/PINTO

1. Drain the crankcase.
2. Remove the oil dipstick.
3. Disconnect the steering shaft connection from the rack and pinion.
4. Disconnect the rack and pinion from the crossmember and move it forward to provide clearance.
5. Remove the flywheel housing inspection cover.
6. Remove the oil pan attaching bolts and remove the pan.
7. Clean the gasket mounting surface of the block and the pan.

8. Coat the block surface and the oil pan gasket with oil resistant sealer and position the gasket on the block.
9. Coat the oil pan front oil seal and the front cover with oil resistant sealer and position the seal on the front cover, making sure the ends of the seal contact the oil pan gasket.
10. Coat the rear oil pan seal with oil resistant sealer and install it in the rear main bearing cap.
11. Position the pan on the block and tighten the bolts to specification. Tighten all bolts to 7–9 ft. lbs., except 8 mm bolts on the 2300. Tighten these to 11–13 ft. lbs.
12. Reverse Steps 1–5 to complete installation.

MUSTANG/CAPRI

1. Disconnect the negative battery cable.
2. Remove the fan shroud or fan shroud and electric fan assembly.
3. Drain the crankcase.
4. Remove the right and left engine support bolts and nuts.

5. Using a jack with a piece of wood between the raising point and jack contact points, raise the engine as high as it will go. Place blocks of wood between the mounts and chassis brackets. Remove the jack. Remove shake brace.
6. Remove the sway bar retaining bolts and lower the sway bar.
7. Remove the starter motor.
8. Remove steering gear retaining bolts and lower the gear.
9. Remove the oil pan retaining bolts. Allow the oil pan to drop to the crossmember and remove.
10. Install new oil pan gasket and end seals.
11. Position oil pan to the cylinder block and install retaining bolts.
12. Reposition the steering gear and install bolts and nuts.
13. Install starter.
14. Raise the engine enough to remove the wood blocks, lower the engine and remove jack. Install shake brace.
15. Install the right and left engine support bolts and nuts.
16. Install the sway bar.
17. Install the fan shroud.
18. Fill the crankshaft with oil.
19. Connect battery cable, run engine and check for leaks.

FAIRMONT/ZEPHYR/GRANADA/ COUGAR/THUNDERBIRD

1. Disconnect negative battery cable.
2. Drain the crankcase.
3. Remove the right and left engine support bolts and nuts.
4. Using a jack, raise the engine as far as it will go. Place blocks of wood between the mounts and the chassis brackets. Remove the jack.
5. Remove the steering gear retaining nuts and bolts. Remove the bolt retaining the steering flex coupling to the steering gear. Position the steering gear forward and down.
6. Remove the shake brace and starter.
7. Remove the engine rear support to crossmember nuts.
8. Position a jack under the transmission and raise.
9. Remove oil pan retaining bolts. Remove the oil pan.
10. Position the new oil pan gasket and end seals to the cylinder block with cement.
11. Position the oil pan to the cylinder block and install its retaining bolts.
12. Lower the jack under the transmission and install the crossmember nuts.
13. Replace the oil filter.
14. Position the flex coupling to the steering gear and install the retaining bolt.
15. Install the steering gear.
16. Install the shake brace. Install the starter.
17. Raise the engine enough to remove the wood blocks. Lower the engine and remove the jack. Install engine support bolts and nuts.

DRAIN PLUG

OIL PAN

M6X 16.0MM LONG
SCREWS AND WASHERS—
18 PLACES

M8X 20.0 LONG
SCREWS AND WASHERS—
FOUR PLACES

PAN GASKET (L)

PAN GASKET (R)

(SEE BONDING NOTE BELOW)

SEAL

SEAL

GUIDE PINS

HOLE "A"

OIL RESISTANT SEALER—
APPROXIMATELY .125" WIDE
BEAD TO JOINT OF BLOCK
AND FRONT COVER

OIL PAN GASKET

BLOCK

FRONT COVER
OR REAR CAP

SEAL TAB

FRONT

1. APPLY GASKET ADHESIVE EVENLY TO OIL PAN FLANGE AND TO PAN SIDE GASKETS. ALLOW ADHESIVE TO DRY PAST WET STAGE, THEN INSTALL GASKETS TO OIL PAN.
2. APPLY SEALER TO JOINT OF BLOCK AND FRONT COVER. INSTALL SEALS TO FRONT COVER AND REAR BEARING CAP AND PRESS SEAL TABS FIRMLY INTO BLOCK. BE SURE TO INSTALL THE REAR SEAL BEFORE THE REAR MAIN BEARING CAP SEALER HAS CURED.
3. POSITION 2 GUIDE PINS AND INSTALL THE OIL PAN. SECURE THE PAN WITH THE FOUR M8 BOLTS SHOWN ABOVE.
4. REMOVE THE GUIDE PINS AND INSTALL AND TORQUE THE EIGHTEEN M6 BOLTS, BEGINNING AT HOLE "A" AND WORKING CLOCKWISE AROUND THE PAN.

2300 cc engine oil pan torque sequence (© Ford Motor Co.)

18. Lower the vehicle and fill the crankcase with oil.

19. Connect the battery.

20. Start the engine and check for leaks.

2.8L (170) V6 Engine

BOBCAT/MUSTANG II/PINTO

1. Remove the dipstick. Remove the bolt attaching the fan shroud to the radiator. Position the shroud over the fan. Disconnect the battery ground cable at the battery. Loosen the alternator bracket and adjusting bolts. Drain the coolant and remove the radiator hoses and automatic transmission cooler lines.

2. Raise the vehicle on a hoist. Disconnect the steering gear and set it out of the way. Disconnect the sway bar ends.

3. Drain the crankcase.

4. Remove the splash shield. Remove the starter.

5. Remove the engine front support nuts.

6. Raise the engine and place wood blocks between the engine front supports and the chassis brackets. Remove the clutch or converter housing cover.

7. Remove the oil pan attaching bolts and remove the oil pan.

8. Clean the gasket surfaces of the block and the oil pan. The oil pan has a two-piece gasket.

9. Coat the block surface and the oil pan gasket with sealer. Position the oil pan gaskets on the cylinder block.

10. Position the oil pan front seal on the cylinder front cover. Be sure that the tabs on the seal are over the oil pan gasket.

11. Place the end seals in position flush with the cylinder block oil pan rail, if previously removed. Position the oil pan rear seal on the rear main bearing cap. Be sure that the tabs on the seal are over the oil pan gasket.

12. Position the oil pan centered on the cylinder block. Install two bolts at both ends (front and rear) of the oil pan, then install the remaining bolts and tighten them to 5–7 ft. lbs., starting with the bolt at the left front corner on the leading edge of the oil pan and working clockwise around the circumference of the pan.

13. Replace the converter housing or clutch cover.

14. Raise the engine and remove the wood blocks from between the engine supports and chassis brackets. Lower the engine and install the engine support nuts.

15. Replace the starter and splash shield, steering gear, and sway bar.

16. Lower the vehicle.

17. Install the alternator.

18. Connect the battery ground wire.

19. Install the fan shroud.

20. Install the dipstick. Fill the crankcase with oil. Start engine and check for leaks.

MUSTANG/CAPRI

1. Remove the oil level dipstick. Remove the bolts attaching the fan shroud to the radiator. Position the shroud over the fan.

2. Loosen the alternator bracket and adjusting bolt.

3. Drain the crankcase.

4. Remove the splash shield. Remove the starter.

5. Remove the engine front support nuts.

6. Raise the engine and place wood blocks between the engine front supports and chassis brackets.

7. Remove the clutch or converter housing cover.

8. Remove the oil pan.

9. Coat the block surface and the oil pan gasket with sealer. Position the oil pan gaskets on the cylinder block.

10. Position the oil pan front seal on the cylinder front cover. Be sure the tabs on the seal are over the oil pan gasket.

11. Place end seals in position flush with cylinder block oil pan rail.

12. Position the oil pan rear seal on the rear main bearing cap. Be sure the tabs on the seal are over the oil pan gasket.

13. Position the oil pan centered on the cylinder block. Install four bolts to secure the front and rear ends of the oil pan. Install the remaining bolts.

14. Replace the converter housing or clutch cover.

15. Raise the engine and remove the wood blocks from between the engine supports and chassis brackets. Lower the engine and install the engine support nuts.

16. Replace the starter and splash shield.

17. Position the alternator. Tighten the bolts. Adjust belt tension.

18. Install the fan shroud.

19. Install the oil level dipstick. Fill the crankcase with engine oil. Start the engine and check for oil leaks.

6 Cylinder Inline Engines

1. Disconnect two oil cooler lines at radiator.

2. Remove radiator top support two bolts. Remove or position fan shroud back over fan.

3. Remove oil level dipstick, drain crankcase.

4. Remove four bolts and nuts attaching sway bar to chassis and allow sway bar to hang down.

5. Remove K brace.

6. Lower front steering rack and pinion, or center link and linkage, if necessary for clearance.

7. Remove stater.

8. Remove two nuts attaching engine mounts to support brackets.

9. Loosen two rear insulator-to-crossmember attaching bolts.

10. Raise engine and place 1¼ in. spacer between engine support insulator and chassis brackets.

11. Position jack under transmission and raise slightly.

12. Remove oil pan attaching bolts and lower pan to crossmember. Position transmission cooler lines out of the way and remove oil pan (rotating crankshaft if required).

13. The oil pan has a two piece gasket. Coat the block surface and the oil pan gasket surfaces with oil resistant sealer, and position gaskets to cylinder block.

14. Position the oil pan seals in the cylinder front cover and rear bearing cap.

15. Insert gasket tabs under front and rear seals.

16. Position oil pan to cylinder block and install attaching bolts.

17. Position transmission cooler lines.

18. Lower jack under transmission.

19. Raise engine to remove spacers and lower engine to chassis.

20. Tighten two nuts attaching rear support insulator to crossmember.

21. Install two engine support to chassis through bolts and nuts.

22. Install starter motor and sway bar.

23. Install "K" brace, fill crankcase with oil.

24. Connect oil cooler lines to radiator and install upper radiator support.

25. Lower vehicle, start engine and check for leaks.

V6 (232) Engine

1. Remove the air cleaner assembly including the air intake duct.

2. Remove the fan shroud attaching bolts and position the shroud back over the fan.

3. Remove the oil level dipstick.

4. Remove the screws attaching the vacuum solenoids to the dash panel. Lay the solenoids on the engine without disconnecting the vacuum hoses or electrical connectors.

5. Remove the exhaust manifold to exhaust pipe attaching nuts.

6. Drain the crankcase.

7. Remove the oil filter.

8. Remove the bolts attaching the shift linkage bracket to the transmission bell housing. Remove the starter motor for more clearance if necessary.

9. Disconnect the transmission cooler lines at the radiator. Remove power steering hose retaining clamp from frame.

10. Remove the converter cover.

11. On models equipped with rack and pinion steering vehicles proceed with the following steps.

    a. Remove the engine damper to No. 2 crossmember bracket attaching bolt. The damper must be disconnected from the crossmember.

    b. Disconnect steering flex coupling. Remove two bolts attaching steering gear to main crossmember and let steering gear rest on the frame away from oil pan.

12. Remove the nut and washer assembly attaching the front engine insulator to the chassis.

13. Raise the engine 2–3 in. and insert wood blocks between the engine mounts and the vehicle frame.

NOTE: On some models equipped with rack and pinion steering such as Granada/Cougar, Thunderbird/XR-7,

LTD/Marquis, it may be necessary to raise the engine as much as 5 inches to provide adequate pan-to-crossmember clearance.

CAUTION

Watch the clearance between the transmission dipstick tube and the thermactor downstream air tube. If the tubes contact before adequate pan-to-crossmember clearance is provided, lower the engine and remove the transmission dipstick tube and the downstream air tube.

---

14. Remove the oil pan attaching bolts. Work the oil pan loose and remove.

15. On models with limited clearance, lower the oil pan onto the crossmember. Remove the oil pickup tube attaching nut. Lower the pick-up tube/screen assembly into the pan and remove the oil pan through the front of the vehicle.

16. Remove the oil pan seal from the main bearing cap.

17. Clean the gasket surfaces on the cylinder block, oil pan and oil pick-up tube.

18. Apply ⅛ in. bead of RTV sealer to all matching surfaces of oil pan and engine front cover.

19. Install the oil pan.

NOTE: On models with limited clearance place the oil pick-up tube/screen assembly in the oil pan.

20. Install all other components removed.

21. Fill the crankcase to the correct level with the oil.

22. Start the engine and check the fluid levels in the transmission.

23. Check for engine oil, and transmission fluid leaks.

V8 Engines

NOTE: On vehicles equipped with a dual sump oil pan, both drain plugs must be removed to thoroughly drain the crankcase.

NOTE: When raising the engine for oil pan removal clearance; drain cooling system, disconnect hoses, check fan to radiator clearance when jacking. Remove radiator if clearance is inadequate.

1. Remove the fan shroud attaching bolts, positioning the fan shroud back over the fan. Remove the dipstick and tube assembly. Disconnect negative battery cable.

2. Drain the crankcase.

3. Remove the stabilizer bar from the chassis (Versailles only). Disconnect the engine stabilizer on models equipped.

4. On rack and pinion models disconnect steering flex coupling. Remove two bolts attaching steering gear to main crossmember and let steering gear rest on frame away from oil pan. Disconnect power steering hose retaining clamp from frame. Remove the starter motor.

6. Remove the idler arm bracket retaining bolts (models equipped) and pull the linkage down and out of the way.

7. Disconnect and plug the fuel line

from the gas tank at the fuel pump. Disconnect and lower the exhaust pipe/converter assemblies if they will interfere with pan removal/installation. Raise the engine and place two wood blocks between the engine mounts and the vehicle frame. Remove converter inspection cover.

NOTE: On fuel injected model, depressurize system prior to line disconnection.

8. Remove rear K braces (four bolts).

9. Remove the oil pan attaching bolts and lower oil pan to the frame.

10. Remove oil pump attaching bolts and the inset tube attaching nut from the No. 3 main bearing cap stud and lower the oil pump into the oil pan.

11. Remove the oil pan, rotating the crankshaft as necessary to clear the counterweights.

12. Clean the gasket mounting surfaces thoroughly. Coat the surfaces on the block and pan with sealer. Position the pan side gaskets on the engine block. Install the front cover oil seal on the cover, with the tabs over the pan side gaskets. Install the rear main cap seal with the tabs over the pan side gaskets.

13. Position oil pump and inlet tube into oil pan. Slide oil pan into position under the engine. With the oil pump intermediate shaft in position in the oil pump, position the oil pump to the cylinder block, and the inlet tube to the stud on No. 3 main bearing cap attaching bolt. Install the attaching bolts and nut and tighten to specification.

Position the oil pan on the engine and install the attaching bolts. Tighten the bolts (working from the center toward the ends) 9–11 ft. lbs. for 5⁄16 in. bolts and 7–9 ft. lbs. for ¼ in. bolts.

14. Position the steering gear to the main crossmember. Install the two attaching bolts and tighten to specification. Connect steering flex coupling.

15. Position rear K braces and install the four attaching bolts.

16. Raise engine and remove wood blocks.

17. Install stabilizer bar (Versailles only).

18. Lower the engine and install engine mount attaching bolts. Tighten to specification. Install converter inspection cover.

19. Install oil dipstick and tube assembly, and fill crankcase with the specified engine oil. Install idler arm.

20. Connect transmission oil cooler lines. Connect battery cable.

21. Position the shroud to the radiator and install the two attaching bolts. Start engine and check for leaks.

Piston and Connecting Rod

POSITIONING

Four and six cylinder in-line and "V"-type engines should have their piston and rod assemblies installed with the notch on the

piston crown toward the front and the oil squirt hole in the rod toward the right side. V8 pistons are assembled with the notch or arrow on the piston crown toward the front and the numbered side of the rod toward the outside.

Oil Pan and Pump

REMOVAL & INSTALLATION
Diesel Engine

1. With the engine removed from vehicle and placed on an engine stand, remove the bolts attaching the oil pan to the crankcase.

2. Remove the two bolts attaching the oil pump pickup to the crankcase.

3. Remove the three bolts attaching the oil pump to the crankcase, and remove the oil pump.

4. Remove the oil pump driveshaft, if necessary.

5. Install the oil pump driveshaft, if removed, making sure it is fully engaged with intermediate shaft.

6. Install the oil pump on the crankcase, making sure driveshaft is fully engaged in the oil pump. Tighten the oil pump and oil pick-up bolts to 16–17 ft. lbs.

Oil Pump

REMOVAL & INSTALLATION
Except V6 (232) Engines

1. Remove oil pan.

2. Remove oil pump inlet tube and screen assembly.

3. Remove oil pump attaching bolts and remove oil pump gasket and intermediate shaft.

4. Prime oil pump by filling inlet and outlet port with engine oil and rotating shaft of pump to distribute it.

5. Position intermediate drive shaft into distributor socket.

6. Position new gasket on pump body and insert intermediate drive shaft into pump body.

7. Install pump and intermediate shaft as an assembly.

NOTE: Do not force pump if it does not seat readily. The drive shaft may be misaligned with the distributor shaft. To align, rotate intermediate drive shaft into a new position.

8. Install and torque oil pump attaching screws to 12–15 ft. lbs. on in line six cylinder, 20–25 ft. lbs. on V8s.

9. Install oil pan.

V6 (232) Engines

NOTE: The oil pump is mounted in the front cover assembly.

NOTE: Oil pan removal is necessary for pick-up tube/screen replacement or service.

1. Raise and safely support the vehicle on jackstands.

2. Remove the oil filter.

3. Remove the cover/filter mount assembly.

4. Lift the two pump gears from their mounting pocket in the front cover.

5. Clean all gasket mounting surfaces.

6. Inspect the mounting pocket for wear. If excessive wear is present, complete timing cover assembly replacement is necessary.

7. Inspect the cover/filter mount gasket to timing cover surface for flatness. Place a straight edge across the flat and check clearance with a feeler gauge. If the measured clearance exceeds .004 inch, replace the cover/filter mount.

8. Replace the pump gears if wear is excessive.

9. Remove the plug from the end of the pressure relief valve passage using a small drill and slide hammer. Use caution when drilling.

10. Remove the spring and valve from the bore. Clean all dirt, gum and metal chips from the bore and valve. Inspect all parts for wear. Replace as necessary.

11. Install the valve and spring after lubricating them with engine oil. Install a new plug flush with machined surface.

12. Install the pump gears and fill the pocket with petroleum jelly. Install cover/filter mount using a new mounting gasket. Tighten the mounting bolts to 18–22 ft. lbs. Install the oil filter, add necessary oil for correct level.

Rear Main Oil Seal

REMOVAL & INSTALLATION

NOTE: Refer to the "build" dates listed below to determine if the engine is equipped with a split-type or one piece rear main oil seal. Engines after the date indicated have a one-piece oil seal. 2.3 (140) OHC: after 9/28/81; 232 V6: after 4/1/83; 302 V8: after 12/1/82; 351W-V8: after 7/11/83. The 2.8L (170) V6 engine is equipped with a one piece seal. Engine prior to the date indicated are equipped with a split type seal.

Split-Type Seal—Gas Engines

NOTE: The rear oil seal installed in these engines is a rubber type (split-Lip) seal.

1. Remove the oil pan, and, if required, the oil pump.

2. Loosen all main bearing caps allowing the crankshaft to lower slightly.

NOTE: The crankshaft should not be allowed to drop more than $\frac{1}{32}$ in.

3. Remove the rear main bearing cap and remove the seal from the cap and block. Be very careful not to scratch the sealing surface. Remove the old seal retaining pin from the cap, if equipped. It is not used with the replacement seal.

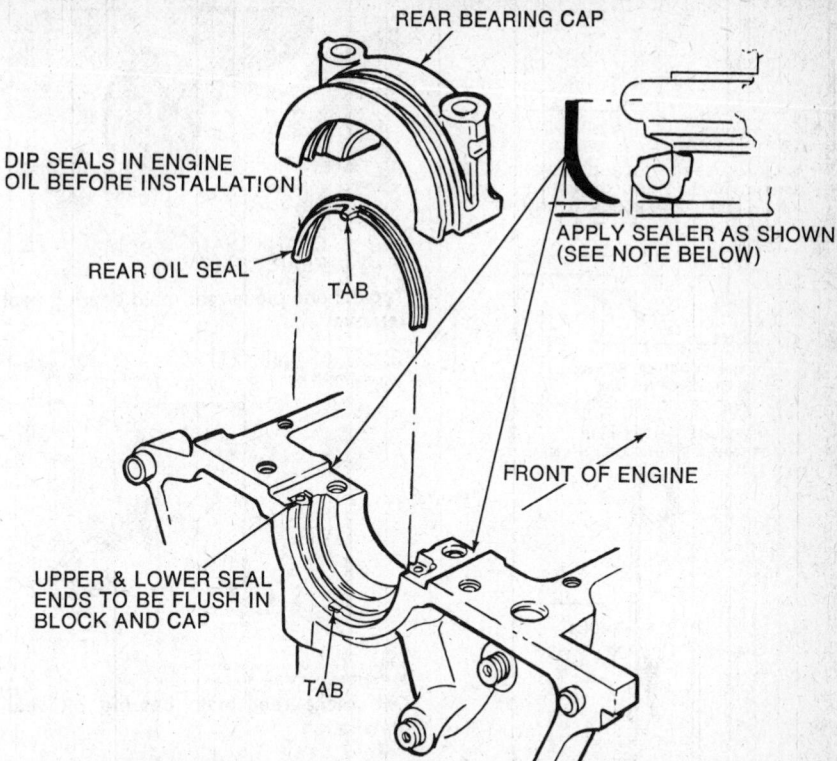

NOTE: CLEAN THE AREA WHERE SEALER IS TO BE APPLIED BEFORE INSTALLING THE SEALS. AFTER THE SEALS ARE IN PLACE, APPLY A 1/16 INCH BEAD OF SEALER AS SHOWN. *SEALER MUST NOT TOUCH SEALS*

Replacement of the rear main bearing oil seal—2.3L (140) engine with split seal

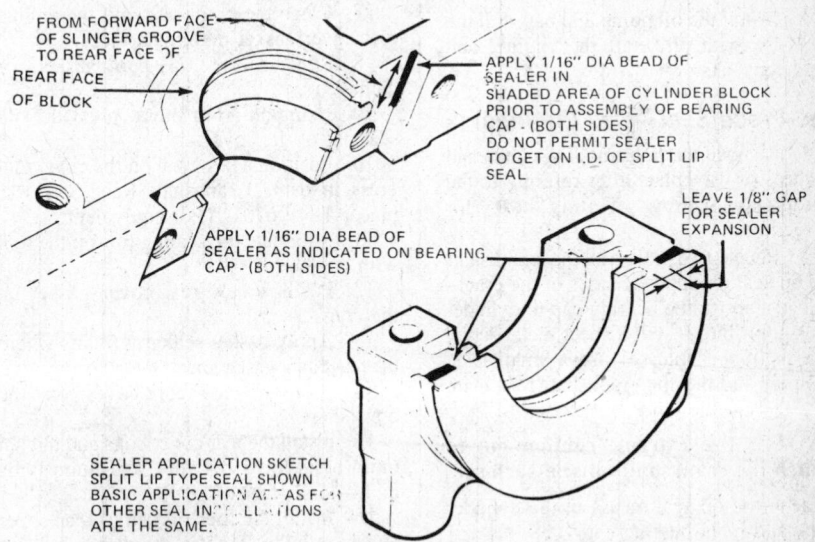

Rear main bearing cap sealer application—with split seal

4. Carefully clean the seal grooves in the cap and block with solvent.

5. Soak the new seal halves in clean engine oil.

6. Install the upper half of the seal in the block with the undercut side of the seal toward the front of the engine. Slide the seal around the crankshaft journal until $\frac{3}{8}$ in. protrudes beyond the base of the block.

7. Tighten all the main bearing caps (except the rear main bearing) to specifications.

8. Install the lower seal into the rear cap, with the undercut side facing the front of the engine. Allow $\frac{3}{8}$ in. of the seal to protrude above the surface, at the opposite end from the block seal.

9. Squeeze a $\frac{1}{16}$ in. bead of silicone sealant onto the areas shown.

10. Install the rear cap and torque to specifications.

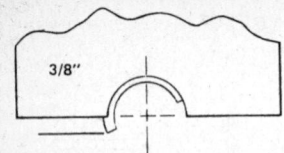

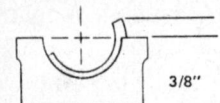

SEAL HALVES TO PROTRUDE BEYOND PARTING FACES THIS DISTANCE TO ALLOW FOR CAP TO BLOCK ALIGNMENT

3/8"

REAR FACE OF REAR MAIN BEARING CAP AND CYLINDER BLOCK

INSTALL SEAL WITH LIP TOWARDS FRONT OF ENGINE

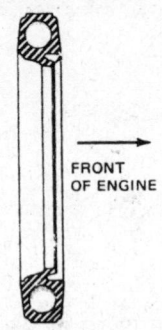

FRONT OF ENGINE

VIEW LOOKING AT PARTING FACE OF SPLIT, LIP-TYPE CRANKSHAFT SEAL

Rear main bearing seal installation—with split seal

11. Install the oil pump and pan. Fill the crankcase with oil, start the engine, and check for leaks.

One-Piece Seal—Gas Engines

1. Remove the transmission, clutch and flywheel or driveplate after refering to the appropriate section of this text for instructions.

2. Punch two holes in the crankshaft rear oil seal on opposite sides of the crankshaft just above the bearing cap to cylinder block split line. Install a sheet metal screw in each of the holes or use a small slide hammer, and pry the crankshaft rear main oil seal from the block.

NOTE: Use extreme caution not to scratch the crankshaft oil seal surface.

Clean the oil seal recess in the cylinder block and main bearing cap.

4. Coat the seal and all of the seal mounting surfaces with oil and install the seal in the recess, driving it in place with an oil seat installation tool or a large socket.

5. Install the driveplate or flywheel and clutch and transmission in the reverse order of removal.

Diesel Engine

1. Raise the vehicle and safely support on jackstands.
2. Remove the transmission.
3. Remove the flywheel.

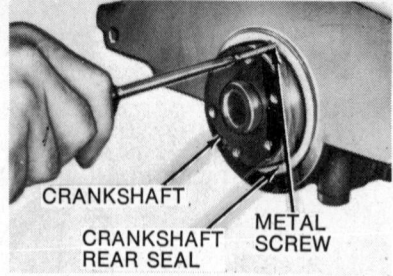

CRANKSHAFT

CRANKSHAFT REAR SEAL

METAL SCREW

Typical one piece rear main bearing seal removal

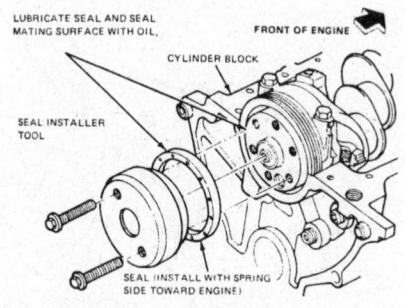

LUBRICATE SEAL AND SEAL MATING SURFACE WITH OIL.

FRONT OF ENGINE

CYLINDER BLOCK

SEAL INSTALLER TOOL

SEAL (INSTALL WITH SPRING SIDE TOWARD ENGINE.)

NOTE: REAR FACE OF SEAL MUST BE WITHIN 0.127mm (0.005 INCH) OF THE REAR FACE OF THE BLOCK

One piece rear main bearing oil seal installation

4. Remove the four oil pan to rear engine cover attaching bolts.

5. Loosen, but **DO NOT REMOVE** the remaining oil pan bolts.

6. Remove the six engine rear cover bolts and remove the cover.

7. Clean the crankcase and the engine rear cover gasket mating surfaces.

8. Replace the oil pan gasket, if damaged.

9. Using an arbor press, press the old seal out of the cover.

10. Position a new seal on the cover and press in using Crankshaft Rear Seal Replacer T84P-6701-A, or equivalent.

11. Lubricate the sealing lips on the seal with engine oil.

12. Position new rear cover gasket on the crankcase.

13. Apply gasket sealer at points where the rear cover gasket meets the oil pan gasket.

14. Position the rear cover on the crankshaft.

15. Install the rear cover bolts and tighten 6mm bolts to 6–7 ft. lbs. and 8mm bolts to 14–17 ft. lbs.

16. Install the four oil pan to rear cover attaching bolts. Tighten all oil pan bolts to 6.5–7 ft. lbs.

17. Install the flywheel.
18. Install the transmission.
19. Lower the vehicle.
20. Run the engine and check for oil leaks.

CLUTCH

NOTE: All 1981 and later models have self-adjusting clutches. No adjustments are necessary.

SELF-ADJUSTING CLUTCH

The free play in the clutch is adjusted by a built in mechanism that allows the clutch controls to be self-adjusted during normal operation.

The self-adjusting feature should be checked every 5000 miles. This is accomplished by insuring that the clutch pedal travels to the top of its upward position. Grasp the clutch pedal with your hand or put your foot under the clutch pedal, pull up on the pedal until it stops. Very little effort is required (about 10 lbs.) During the application of upward pressure, a click may be heard which means an adjustment was necessary and has been accomplished.

ADJUSTMENT

Pinto and Bobcat

1. Loosen the cable locknut on the transmission side of the flywheel housing.

2. Pull the cable toward the front of the car until the tabs on the adjuster nut are clear of the housing. Rotate the nut toward the front of the car about ¼ in.

3. Release the cable. Then pull the cable forward again until there is no release lever free movement. Rotate the adjusting nut toward the housing until the tabs touch the housing, then drop the tabs into the nearest groove.

4. Tighten the locknut.

Mustang II

1. Remove the cable retaining clip at the firewall.

2. Remove the screw holding the cable attaching bracket on the fender apron.

3. Pull the cable toward the front of the vehicle until the adjusting nut can be turned. Rotate the nut away from the adjustment sleeve about ¼ in.

4. Release the cable, and then pull the cable again until free movement of the release lever is eliminated.

5. Rotate the adjusting nut toward the adjustment sleeve until contact is made, then index it into the next notch.

6. Reinstall the cable retaining clip and cable attaching bracket, and the screw on the fender apron.

All Except Fairmont, Zephyr, Mustang and Capri

1. Disconnect clutch return spring from release lever.

2. Loosen release lever rod locknut and adjusting nut. On models through 1980, remove the release lever rod locking pin and loosen the adjusting nut.

3. Move clutch release lever rearward until release bearing lightly contacts clutch pressure plate release fingers.

4. Adjust rod length until rod seats in release lever pocket.

5. Insert specified feeler gauge between adjusting nut and swivel sleeve. Tighten adjusting nut against gauge.

Clutch/Transmission

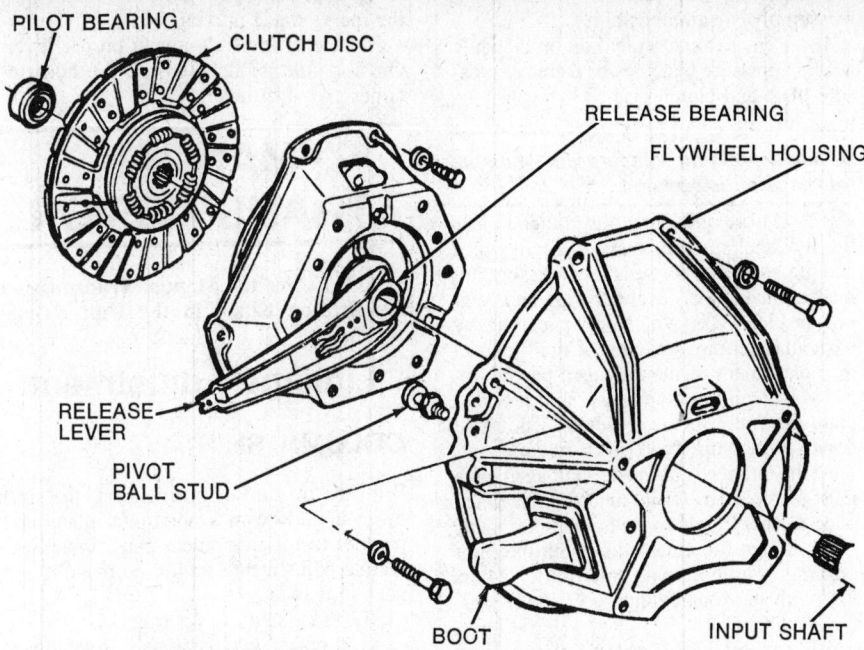

Exploded view of clutch and related parts (© Ford Motor Co)

6. Tighten locknut against adjusting nut, taking care not to disturb adjustment. On models through 1980, rotate the rod to align the flat with the pin hole in the adjusting nut and install the pin. Remove feeler gauge.

7. Install clutch return spring.

8. Check free travel at pedal. Readjust if necessary to obtain specified travel. Moving adjusting nut away from swivel sleeve increases travel. Moving adjusting nut toward swivel sleeve decreases travel.

9. As final check, measure pedal free travel with transmission in neutral and engine running at 3,000 rpm. If pedal travel is not minimum of ½ in., readjust free travel.

1978 Fairmont and Zephyr
FOUR CYLINDER ENGINE

1. Working under the car, remove the release lever spring and the dust boot.

2. Loosen the cable locknut and adjusting nut at the release lever.

3. Move the lever forward until free movement is eliminated. Hold forward during adjustment.

4. Insert a 0.30 in. spacer against the release lever cable spacer. Tighten the adjusting nut against the spacer finger tight.

5. Tighten the locknut against the adjusting nut. Remove the spacer. Apply and release the clutch five times. Check for about 1½ ins. of free play. Install the dust boot and return spring.

SIX CYLINDER ENGINES

1. Pull the clutch cable forward until the adjusting nut can be rotated. Unscrew the adjusting nut approximately 0.30 in. from the rubber insulator. The nylon nut will not rotate until it is free of the insulator. It may be necessary to remove the clutch pedal bumper to provide enough slack. Replace the rubber bumper before continuing.

2. Release the cable. Pull the cable slightly forward again to remove slack. Free movement of the lever should be eliminated.

3. Tighten the adjusting nut until it contacts the insulator, then index the tabs into the next notch. Apply and release the clutch five times and check the free play. It should measure approximately 1½ in.

1979–80 Fairmont, Zephyr, Mustang and Capri

These models no longer have free-play adjustments. Pedal height is adjusted instead.

FOUR CYLINDER 255 AND 302 V8

1. Working under the car, remove the dust shield.

2. Loosen the clutch cable locknut. To raise the pedal, turn the adjusting nut clockwise; to lower the pedal, turn it counterclockwise.

3. On the four cylinder engine, adjust the pedal height to 5.3 in.; on the 255 and 302 V8 adjust the height to 6.5 in.

4. Tighten the locknut. When the pedal is adjusted properly, the pedal can be raised about 2¾ in. on the four cylinder model and about 1½ in. on the V8 to reach the pedal stop.

5. Install the dust shield.

IN-LINE SIX CYLINDER

1. Pull the clutch cable toward the front of the car until the adjusting nut can be rotated. In order to free the nut from the rubber insulator, it may be necessary to block the clutch release forward so the clutch is partially disengaged.

2. Rotate the adjusting nut to obtain a 5.3 in. pedal height. Depress the pedal a few times and recheck the adjustment. When the pedal is properly adjusted, it can be raised about 2¾ in. to reach the pedal stop.

REMOVAL & INSTALLATION
Pinto and Bobcat

1. Place the gearshift lever in the Neutral position. Raise the car and remove the back-up light switch from the transmission extension housing.

2. Loosen the shift lever locknut. Remove the knob and the locknut from the shift lever. Remove the four rubber boot attaching screws and remove the boot.

3. Compress the corrugated rubber spring, then remove the retaining snap-ring and slide the spring upward on the lever.

4. Bend the shift lever locktabs up, then thread the plastic dome nut from the extension housing.

5. Lift the shift lever from the extension housing.

6. Working from under the hood, remove the upper flywheel housing-to-engine attaching bolts.

7. Raise the vehicle and match-mark the driveshaft and the rear axle pinion flange.

8. Disconnect and remove the driveshaft. Place rags in the extension housing to prevent loss of lubricant.

9. Remove the clutch release lever dust cover.

10. Disconnect the clutch cable from the clutch release lever.

11. Remove the starter motor attaching bolts and position the motor out of the way.

12. Remove the speedometer cable-to-transmission attaching screw and remove the cable and gear from the transmission. Plug the opening in the transmission to prevent lubricant spillage.

13. Support the rear of the engine with a jack and remove the crossmember-to-body attaching bolts.

14. Remove the bolts that attach the crossmember to the transmission extension housing and remove the crossmember from the car.

15. Lower the engine to gain working room, and remove the remaining flywheel housing-to-engine attaching bolts.

16. Slide the transmission rearward and remove it from the car.

17. If the clutch is to be removed loosen the six pressure plate attaching bolts evenly to release spring pressure gradually. If the same pressure plate and cover are to be reused, mark the position of the pressure plate and flywheel so they can be returned to their original location.

18. Remove the pressure plate attaching bolts and remove the pressure plate and clutch from the car.

19. Installation is in reverse order.

Mustang II

1. Place the shift lever in Neutral. Remove the carpet and boot. Remove the three metric lever base bolts and remove the shift lever.

2. Raise the car safely. Remove the

driveshaft, after matchmarking its location, and plug the end of the transmission.

3. Disconnect the seat belt sensing switch, if any, and the backup light wires.

4. Remove the attaching screw and pull out the speedometer cable. Plug the hole.

5. The remainder of the procedure is the same as for Pinto and Bobcat, starting with Step 13. The major difference is that the transmission is removed separately, leaving the clutch housing in place.

Except Pinto/Bobcat/Mustang II

1. Disconnect and remove starter and dust ring, if the clutch is to be removed. On floorshift models, remove the boot retainer and shifter lever.

2. On models with the ET four speed transmission: working under the hood, remove the upper clutch housing-to-engine bolts.

3. Raise the car.

4. Matchmark the driveshaft and axle flange for reassembly. Disconnect the driveshaft at the rear universal joint and remove the driveshaft. Plug the extension housing.

5. Disconnect the speedometer cable at the transmission extension. Disconnect the seat belt sensor wires and the back-up lamp switch wires. Remove the clutch lever boot and cable on models so equipped.

6. Disconnect the gear shift rods from the transmission shift levers. If car is equipped with four speed, except SROD models, remove bolts that secure shift control bracket to extension housing. Support the engine with a jack.

7. Remove the bolt holding the extension housing to the rear support, and remove the muffler inlet pipe bracket to housing bolt.

8. Remove the two rear support bracket insulator nuts from the underside of the crossmember. Remove crossmember.

9. Place a jack (equipped with a protective piece of wood) under the rear of the engine oil pan. Raise or lower the engine slightly as necessary to provide access to the bolts.

10. Remove transmission-to-flywheel housing bolts.

11. Slide the transmission back and out of the car. It may be necessary to slide the catalytic converter bracket forward to provide clearance on some models.

12. To remove the clutch, remove release lever retracting spring. Disconnect pedal at the equalizer bar, or the clutch cable from the housing, as applicable.

13. Remove bolts that secure engine rear plate to front lower part of bellhousing.

14. Remove bolts that attach bell housing to cylinder block and remove housing and release lever as a unit. Remove the clutch release lever by pulling it through the window in the housing until the retainer spring disengages from the pivot.

15. Loosen six pressure plate cover attaching bolts evenly to release spring pressure. Mark cover and flywheel to facilitate

reassembly in same position.

16. Remove six attaching bolts while holding pressure plate cover. Remove pressure plate and clutch disc.

—— CAUTION ——

Do not depress the clutch pedal while the transmission is removed.

17. Before installing the clutch, clean the flywheel surface. Inspect the flywheel and pressure plate for wear, scoring, or burn marks (blue color). Light scoring and wear may be cleaned up with emery paper; heavy wear may require refacing of the flywheel or replacement of the damaged parts.

18. Attach the clutch disc and pressure plate assembly to the flywheel. The three dowel pins on the flywheel, if so equipped, must be properly aligned. Damaged pins must be replaced. Avoid touching the clutch plate surface. Tighten the bolts finger tight.

19. Align the clutch disc with the pilot bushing. Torque cover bolts to 12–24 ft. lbs. with the four cylinder, 12–20 ft. lbs. for all others.

20. Lightly lubricate the release lever fulcrum ends. Install the release lever in the flywheel housing and install the dust shield.

21. Apply very little lubricant on the release bearing retainer journal. Fill the groove in the release bearing hub with grease. Clean all excess grease from the inside bore of the hub to prevent clutch disc contamination. Attach the release bearing and hub on the release lever.

22. Make sure the flywheel housing and engine block are clean. Any missing or damaged mounting dowels must be replaced. Install the flywheel housing and torque the attaching bolts to 38–61 ft. lbs. on all V8s and 250 sixes, 38–55 ft. lbs. on 200 sixes, and 28–38 ft. lbs. on fours and 170-V6s. Install the dust cover and torque the bolts to 17–20 ft. lbs.

23. Connect the release rod or cable and the retracting spring. Connect the pedal-to-equalizer-rod at the equalizer bar.

24. Install starter and dust ring.

25. After moving the transmission back just far enough for the pilot shaft to clear the clutch housing, move it upward and into position on the flywheel housing. It may be necessary to put the transmission in gear and rotate the output shaft to align the input shaft and clutch splines.

26. Move the transmission forward and into place against the flywheel housing, and install the transmission attaching bolts finger-tight.

27. Tighten the transmission bolts to 37–42 ft. lbs. on all cars.

28. Install the crossmember and torque the mounting bolts to 20–30 ft. lbs. Slowly lower the engine onto the crossmember.

29. Torque the rear mount to 30–50 ft. lbs.

30. Connect gear shift rods and the speedometer cable.

31. Remove the plug from the extension housing and install the driveshaft, aligning

the marks made previously.

32. Refill transmission to proper level. On floorshift models, install the boot retainer and shift lever.

MANUAL TRANSMISSION

NOTE: See the Manual Transmission Application Chart in the Unit Repair section.

Linkage Adjustment

COLUMN SHIFT

With the transmission in neutral, the shift lever should be in a horizontal plane and parallel to the instrument panel line. Corrective adjustments should be made at the gear shift rods.

1. Place lever in neutral.

2. Loosen two gear shift rod adjustment nuts.

3. Insert 3/16 in. diameter alignment pin through first and reverse gear shift lever and second and third gear shift lever. Align levers to insert pin.

4. Tighten gear shift rod adjustment nuts, and remove pin.

5. Check gear lever for smooth crossover.

THREE-SPEED FLOOR AND CONSOLE SHIFT

1. Loosen three shift linkage adjustment nuts.

2. Install a 1/4 in. diameter alignment pin through control bracket and levers.

3. Tighten three shift linkage adjustment nuts and remove alignment pin.

4. Check gear lever for smooth crossover.

FOUR-SPEED

NOTE: This procedure is for 1978 Granada and Monarch four speed overdrive transmissions. 1978 and later Fairmont and Zephyr, and all 1979 and later four speeds have internal shift rails with no provision for adjustment.

1. Place shifter lever in neutral position, then raise car on a hoist.

2. Insert a 1/4 in. rod into the alignment holes of the shift levers.

3. If the holes are not in exact alignment, check for bent connecting rods or loose lever locknuts at the rod ends. Make replacements or repairs, then adjust as follows.

4. Loosen the three rod-to-lever retaining lock nuts and move the levers until the 1/4 in. gauge rod will enter the alignment holes. Be sure that the transmission shift levers are in neutral and the reverse shifter lever is in the neutral detent.

5. Install the shift rods and tighten the locknuts.

6. Remove the ¼ in. gauge rod.

7. Operate the shift levers to assure correct shifting.

8. Lower the car and road test.

AUTOMATIC TRANSMISSION

NOTE: Refer to the "Automatic Transmission" Unit Repair section for linkage and band adjustments and fluid and filter changes.

Transmissions may be identified by the code on the vehicle certification label.

TRANSMISSION CODES

C.	C5 automatic
S.	JATCO automatic
T.	AOD (automatic overdrive)
U.	C6 automatic
V.	C3 automatic
W.	C4 automatic
X.	FMX automatic
Z.	C6 police automatic

C3

Removal

1. Raise the vehicle on a hoist.

2. Place a drain pan under the transmission fluid pan. Starting at the rear of the pan and working toward the front, loosen the attaching bolts and allow the fluid to drain. Then remove all of the pan attaching bolts except two at the front, to allow the fluid to further drain. After all the fluid has drained, install two bolts on the rear side of the pan to temporarily hold it in place.

3. Remove the converter drain plug access cover and adapter plate bolts from the lower end of the converter housing.

4. Remove the four flywheel to converter attaching nuts. Crank the engine to turn the converter to gain access to the nuts, using a wrench on the crankshaft pulley attaching bolt. On belt driven overhead camshaft engines, never turn the engine backwards.

5. Crank the engine until the converter drain plug is accessible and remove the plug. Place a drain pan under the converter to catch the fluid. After all the fluid has been drained from the converter, reinstall the plug and tighten to specification.

6. Remove the driveshaft and install the extension housing seal replacer tool in the extension housing.

7. Remove the speedometer cable from the extension housing.

8. Disconnect the shift rod at the transmission manual lever. Disconnect the downshift rod at the transmission downshift lever.

9. Remove the starter-to-converter housing attaching bolts and position the starter out of the way.

10. Disconnect the neutral start switch wires from the switch.

11. Remove the vacuum line from the transmission vacuum unit.

12. Position a transmission jack under the transmission and raise it slightly.

13. Remove the engine rear support-to-crossmember nut.

14. Remove the crossmember-to-frame side support attaching bolts and remove the crossmember.

15. Remove the inlet pipe steady rest from the inlet pipe and rear engine support; then disconnect the muffler inlet pipe at the exhaust manifold and secure it.

16. Lower the jack under the transmission and allow the transmission to hang.

17. Position a jack to the front of the engine and raise the engine to gain access to the two upper converter housing-to-engine attaching bolts.

18. Disconnect the oil cooler lines at the transmission. Plug all openings to keep out dirt.

19. Remove the lower converter housing-to-engine attaching bolts.

20. Remove the transmission filler tube.

21. Secure the transmission to the jack with a safety chain.

22. Remove the two upper converter housing-to-engine attaching bolts. Move the transmission to the rear and down to remove it from under the vehicle.

Installation

1. Tighten the converter drain plug to 20–30 ft. lb. if not previously done.

2. Position the converter to the transmission making sure the converter hub is fully engaged in the pump gear.

3. With the converter properly installed, place the transmission on the jack and secure with safety chain.

4. Rotate the converter so the drive studs and drain plug are in alignment with their holes in the flywheel.

5. With the transmission mounted on a transmission jack, move the converter and transmission assembly forward into position being careful not to damage the flywheel and the converter pilot.

During this move, to avoid damage, do not allow the transmission to get into a nosed down position as this will cause the converter to move forward and disengage from the pump gear. The converter must rest squarely against the flywheel. This indicates that the converter pilot is not binding in the engine crankshaft.

6. Install the two upper converter housing-to-engine attaching bolts and tighten to 28–38 ft. lbs.

7. Remove the safety chain from the transmission.

8. Insert the filler tube in the stub tube and secure it to the cylinder block with the attaching bolt. Tighten the bolt to 28–38 ft. lb. If the stub tube is loosened or dislodged, it should be replaced.

9. Install the oil cooler lines in the retaining clip at the cylinder block. Connect the lines to the transmission case.

10. Remove the jack supporting the front of the engine.

11. Position the muffler inlet pipe support bracket to the converter housing and install the four lower converter housing-to-engine attaching bolts. Tighten the bolts to 28–38 ft. lb.

12. Raise the transmission. Position the crossmember to the frame side supports and install the attaching bolts. Tighten the bolts to 30–40 ft. lb.

13. Lower the transmission and install the rear engine support-to-crossmember nut. Tighten the nut to 30–40 ft. lb.

14. Remove the transmission jack.

15. Install the vacuum hose on the transmission vacuum unit. Install the vacuum line into the retaining clip.

16. Connect the neutral start switch plug to the switch.

17. Install the starter and tighten the attaching bolts.

18. Install the four flywheel-to-converter attaching nuts.

When assembling the flywheel to the converter, first install the attaching nuts and tighten to 20–34 ft. lb.

19. Install the converter drain plug access cover and adaptor plate bolts. Tighten the bolts to 15–20 ft. lb.

20. Connect the muffler inlet pipe to the exhaust manifold.

21. Connect the transmission shift rod to the manual lever.

22. Connect the downshift rod to the downshift lever.

23. Connect the speedometer cable to the extension housing.

24. Install the driveshaft. Tighten the companion flange U-bolt attaching nuts to 30 ft. lb.

25. Adjust the manual and downshift linkage as required.

26. Lower the vehicle. Fill the transmission to the proper level with Dexron® II.

Pour in five quarts of fluid; then run the engine and add fluid as required.

27. Check the transmission, converter assembly and oil cooler lines for leaks.

C4 AND JATCO

Removal

1. Raise the vehicle on a hoist.

2. Place the drain pan under the transmission fluid pan. Remove the fluid filler tube from the pan and drain the transmission fluid. On some models it may be necessary to loosen the pan attaching bolts and allow the fluid to drain. Start loosening the bolts at the rear of the pan and work toward the front. Finally remove all of the pan attaching bolts except two at the front, to allow the fluid to further drain. After the fluid has drained, install two bolts on the rear side of the pan to temporarily hold in place.

3. Remove the converter drain plug access cover from the lower end of the converter housing.

4. Remove the converter-to-flywheel attaching nuts. Place a wrench on the crankshaft pulley attaching bolt to turn the converter to gain access to the nuts.

5. With the wrench on the crankshaft pulley attaching bolt, turn the converter to gain access to the converter drain plug. Then, remove the plug. Place a drain pan under the converter to catch the fluid. After the fluid has been drained from the converter, reinstall the plug.

6. Remove the drive shaft and install the extension housing seal replacer tool in the extension housing.

7. Remove the vacuum line hose from the transmission vacuum unit. Disconnect the vacuum line from the retaining clip. Disconnect the transmission regulated spark (T.R.S.) switch wire at the transmission, if so equipped.

8. Remove the engine support to crossmember bolts or nuts.

9. Remove the speedometer cable from the extension housing.

10. Disconnect the oil cooler lines from the transmission case.

11. Disconnect the selector rod or cable at the transmission manual lever. Disconnect the downshift rod at the transmission downshift lever.

12. On console and floor shift vehicles, disconnect the column lock rod at the transmission, if so equipped.

13. Disconnect the starter cable. Remove the starter attaching bolts and remove the starter from the converter housing.

14. Remove the bolt that secures the transmission fluid filler tube to the cylinder head and lift the fluid filler tube from the case.

15. Position the transmission jack to support the transmission and secure the transmission to the jack with a safety chain.

16. Remove the crossmember attaching bolts and lower the crossmember.

17. Remove the five converter housing-to-engine attaching bolts. Lower the transmission and remove it from under the vehicle.

Installation

1. Torque the converter drain plug to 20–30 ft. lb.

2. Position the converter to the transmission making sure the converter drive flats are fully engaged in the pump gear.

3. With the converter properly installed, place the transmission on the jack. Secure the transmission to the jack with the safety chain.

4. Rotate the converter so that the studs and drain plugs are in alignment with their holes in the flywheel.

5. With the transmission mounted on a transmission jack, move the converter and transmission assembly forward into position, using care not to damage the flywheel and the converter pilot. The converter must rest squarely against the flywheel. This indicates that the converter pilot is not binding in the engine crankshaft.

6. Install the five converter housing-to-engine attaching bolts. Torque the bolts to 23–28 ft. lb. on 4 and 6 cylinder cars; 40–50 ft. lbs. on V8. Remove the safety chain from the transmission.

7. Position the crossmember and install the attaching bolts. Torque the bolts to 40–50 ft. lb.

8. Lower the transmission and install the engine support to crossmember bolts or nuts. Torque the bolts or nuts to 30–40 ft. lb.

9. Install the flywheel to converter attaching nuts. Torque the nuts to 23–28 ft. lb. on C4; 29–36 ft. lb. on JATCO.

10. Remove the transmission jack. Install the fluid filler tube in the transmission case or pan. Secure the tube to the cylinder head with the attaching bolt. Install the vacuum hose on the transmission vacuum unit. Install the vacuum line retaining clip. Connect the transmission regulated spark (T.R.S.) switch wire to the switch, if so equipped.

11. Connect the fluid cooling lines to the transmission case.

12. Connect the downshift rod to the downshift lever.

13. Connect the selector rod or cable to the transmission manual lever. Connect the column lock rod on console and floor shift vehicles, if so equipped.

14. Connect the speedometer cable to the extension housing.

15. Install the converter housing cover and torque the attaching bolts to 12–16 ft. lb.

16. Install the starter and torque the attaching bolts to 25–30 ft. lb. Connect the starter cable.

17. Install the drive shaft. Torque the companion flange U-bolts attaching nuts to 25–30 ft. lb.

18. Lower the vehicle. Fill the transmission to the proper level with Type F fluid on models through 1979; Dexron II, 1980 and later and all JATCO transmissions. Adjust the manual and downshift linkage as required.

C5

Removal

1. Open the hood and install protective covers on the fenders.

2. Disconnect the battery negative cable.

3. On Granada/Cougar models equipped with a 3.8L engine, remove the air cleaner assembly.

4. Remove the fan shroud attaching bolts and position the shroud back over the fan.

5. On Granada/Cougar models equipped with a 3.8L engine, and on Mustang/Capri models equipped with a 4.2L, loosen the clamp and disconnect the thermactor air injection hose at the catalytic converter check valve. The check valve is located on the right side of the engine compartment near the dash panel.

6. On Granada/Cougar models equipped with a 3.8L engine, remove the two transmission-to-engine attaching bolts located at the top of the transmission bell housing. These bolts are accessible from the engine compartment.

7. Raise the vehicle.

8. Remove the driveshaft.

9. Disconnect the muffler inlet pipe from the catalytic converter outlet pipe. Support the muffler/pipe assembly by wiring it to a convenient underbody bracket.

10. Remove the nuts attaching the exhaust pipe(s) to the exhaust manifold(s).

11. Pull back on the catalytic converters to release the converter hangers from the mounting bracket.

12. Remove the speedometer clamps bolt and pull the speedometer out of the extension housing.

13. Separate the neutral start switch harness connector.

14. Disconnect the kick down rod at the transmission lever.

15. Disconnect the shift linkage at the linkage bellcrank. On vehicles equipped with floor mounted shift, remove the shift cable routing bracket attaching bolts and disconnect the cable at the transmission lever.

16. Remove the converter dust shield.

17. Remove the torque converter to drive plate attaching nuts. To gain access to the converter nuts, turn the crankshaft and drive plate using a ratchet handle and socket on the crankshaft pulley attaching bolt.

18. Remove the starter attaching bolts.

19. Loosen the nuts attaching the rear support to the No. 3 crossmember.

20. Position a transmission jack under the transmission oil pan. Secure the transmission to the jack with a safety chain.

21. Remove the through bolts attaching the No. 3 crossmember to the body brackets.

22. Lower the transmission enough to allow access to the cooler line fittings. Disconnect the cooler lines.

23. On Granada/Cougar models, remove the (4) remaining transmission-to-engine attaching bolts (2 each side). On all other models, remove the (6) transmission-to-engine attaching bolts.

24. Pull the transmission back to disengage the converter studs from the drive plate. Lower the transmission out of the vehicle.

Installation

1. Raise the transmission into the vehicle. As the transmission is being slowly raised into position, rotate the torque converter until the studs and drain plug are aligned with the holes in the drive plate.

2. Move the converter/transmission assembly forward against the back of the engine. Make sure the converter studs engage the drive plate and that the transmission dowels on the back of the engine engage the bolt holes in the bell-housing.

3. On Granada/Cougar models equipped with a 3.8L engine, install four transmission-to-engine attaching bolts (2 each side). On all other models, install the (6) transmission-to-engine attaching bolts. Tighten the attaching bolts to 40–50 ft. lb.

4. Connect the cooler lines.

5. Raise the transmission and install the No. 3 crossmember through bolts. Tighten the attaching nuts to 20–30 ft. lb.

6. Remove the safety chain and transmission jack.

7. Tighten the rear support attaching nuts to 30–50 ft. lb.

8. Position the starter and install the attaching bolts.

9. Install the torque converter to drive plate attaching nuts. Tighten the attaching nuts to 20–30 ft. lb.

10. Position the dust shield and on vehicles with column mounted shift, position the linkage bellcrank bracket. Install the attaching bolts and tighten to 12–16 ft. lb.

11. Connect the shift linkage to the linkage bellcrank. On vehicles equipped with floor mounted shift, connect the cable to the shift lever and install the routing bracket attaching bolt.

12. Connect the kick down rod to the transmission lever.

13. Connect the neutral start switch harness.

14. Install the speedometer and the clamp bolt. Tighten the clamp bolt to 36–54 in. lb.

15. Install the catalytic converters using new seal(s) at the pipe(s) to exhaust manifold connection(s).

16. Install the pipe(s) to exhaust manifold attaching nuts. Do not tighten the attaching nut.

17. Remove the wire supporting the muffler/pipe assembly and connect the pipe to the converter outlet. Do not tighten the attaching nuts.

18. Align the exhaust system and tighten the manifold and converter outlet attaching nuts.

19. Install the driveshaft.

20. Check and if necessary, adjust the shift linkage.

21. Lower the vehicle.

22. On Granada/Cougar models equipped with a 3.8L engine, install the two transmission-to-engine attaching bolts located at the top of the transmission bell housing.

23. On Granada/Cougar models equipped with a 3.8L engine, connect the thermactor air injection hose to the converter check valve.

24. Position the fan shroud and install the attaching bolts.

25. On Granada/Cougar models equipped with a 3.8L engine, install the air cleaner assembly.

26. Connect the battery negative cable.

27. Start the engine. Make sure the engine cranks only when the selector lever is positioned in the neutral (N) or Park (P) detent.

28. Fill the transmission with type H fluid.

29. Raise the vehicle and inspect for fluid leaks.

C6
Removal

1. Working from the engine compartment, remove the two bolts retaining the fan shroud to the radiator.

2. Connect a remote control starter button on vehicles equipped with a 400 CID engine.

3. Raise the vehicle on a hoist or stands.

4. Place the drain pan under the transmission fluid pan. Starting at the rear of the pan and working toward the front, loosen the attaching bolts and allow the fluid to drain. Finally remove all of the pan attaching bolts except two at the front, to allow the fluid to further drain. After the fluid has drained, install two bolts on the rear side of the pan to temporarily hold it in place.

5. Remove the converter drain plug access cover and adapter plate bolts from the lower end of the converter housing.

6. Remove the converter-to-flywheel attaching nuts. On vehicles equipped with a 400 CID engine, crank the engine until the nuts are accessible.

7. Crank the engine on vehicles with a 400 CID engine to turn the converter to gain access to the converter drain plug. Then, remove the plug. Place a drain pan under the converter to catch the fluid. After the fluid has been drained from the converter, reinstall the plug.

8. Disconnect the drive shaft from the rear axle and slide the shaft rearward from the transmission. Install a seal installation tool in the extension housing to prevent fluid leakage.

9. Disconnect the speedometer cable from the extension housing.

10. Disconnect the downshift rod from the transmission downshift lever.

11. Disconnect the shift cable from the manual lever at the transmission.

12. Remove the two bolts that secure the shift cable bracket to the converter housing and position the cable and bracket out of the way.

13. Remove the starter motor attaching bolts and position the starter out of the way.

14. Disconnect the rubber hose from the vacuum diaphragm at the rear of the transmission. Remove the vacuum tube from the retaining clip at the transmission. Disconnect the transmission regulated spark (T.R.S.) switch wire at the transmission, if so equipped.

15. Disconnect the muffler inlet pipe at the exhaust manifolds and allow the pipe to hang.

16. Remove the crossmember to frame side support bolts and nuts. Remove the nuts securing the rear engine supports to the crossmember. Position a jack under the transmission and raise it slightly. Remove the bolts securing the rear engine supports to the extension housing and remove the crossmember and rear supports from the vehicle.

17. Loosen the parking brake adjusting nut at the equalizer and remove the cable from the idler hook attached to the floor pan.

18. Lower the transmission, then disconnect the oil cooler lines from the transmission case.

19. Secure the transmission to the jack with a chain.

20. Remove the six bolts that attach the converter housing to the cylinder block.

21. Remove the bolt that secures the transmission filler tube to the cylinder block. Lift the filler tube and dipstick from the transmission.

22. Move the transmission away from the cylinder block.

23. Carefully lower the transmission and remove it from under the vehicle.

24. Remove the converter and mount the transmission in a holding fixture.

Installation

1. Torque the converter drain plug to 14–28 ft. lb.

2. Position the converter to the transmission making sure the converter drive flats are fully engaged in the pump gear.

3. With the converter properly installed, place the transmission on the jack. Secure the transmission to the jack with the safety chain.

4. Rotate the converter so that the studs and drain plug are in alignment with their holes in the flywheel.

5. With the transmission mounted on a transmission jack, move the converter and transmission assembly forward into position using care not to damage the flywheel and converter pilot. The converter must rest squarely against the flywheel. This indicates that the converter pilot is not binding in the engine crankshaft.

6. Install a new O-ring on the lower end of the transmission filler tube. Insert the tube in the transmission case and secure the tube to the engine with the attaching bolt.

7. Install the converter housing-to-engine attaching bolts. Torque the bolts to 40–50 ft. lb. Remove the safety chain from the transmission.

8. Connect the oil cooler lines to the transmission case.

9. Raise the transmission.

10. Position the parking brake cable in the idler hook and tighten the adjusting nut at the equalizer.

11. Place the rear engine supports on the crossmember and position the crossmember on the frame side supports.

12. Secure the engine rear supports to the extension housing with the attaching bolts. Torque the bolts to 35–40 ft. lb.

13. Remove the transmission jack from under the vehicle and install the crossmember-to-frame side support bolts and nuts. Torque the bolts and nuts to 35–40 ft. lb.

14. Install and torque the engine rear support-to-crossmember attaching nuts.

15. Connect the muffler inlet pipe to the exhaust manifolds.

16. Connect the vacuum line to the vacuum diaphragm making sure that the metal tube is secured in the retaining clip. Connect the transmission regulated spark (T.R.S.) switch wire to the switch, if so equipped.

17. Position the starter motor to the converter housing and secure it with the attaching bolt.

18. Install the torque converter-to-flywheel attaching nuts and torque them to 20–30 ft. lb.

19. Position the shift cable bracket to the converter housing and install the two attaching bolts.

20. Connect the shift cable to the manual lever at the transmission.

21. Connect the downshift rod to the lever on the transmission.

22. Connect the speedometer cable to the extension housing.

23. Install the drive shaft.

24. Install the converter drain plug access cover and adapter plate bolts. Torque the bolts to 12–16 ft. lb.

25. Adjust the manual and downshift linkage as required.

26. Lower the vehicle.

27. Working from the engine compartment, position the fan shroud to the radiator and secure with the two attaching bolts.

28. Remove the remote starter button on vehicles equipped with the 400 CID engine.

29. Fill the transmission to the proper level with Dexron® II.

30. Check the transmission, converter assembly and oil cooler lines for leaks.

FMX

Removal

1. Drive the vehicle on a hoist, but do not raise at this time.

2. Remove the two upper bolts and lockwashers which attach the converter housing to the engine.

3. Raise the vehicle.

4. Place the drain pan under the transmission fluid pan. Starting at the rear of the pan and working toward the front, loosen the attaching bolts and allow the fluid to drain. Finally remove all of the pan attaching bolts except two at the front to allow the fluid to further drain. With fluid drained, install two bolts on the rear side of the pan to temporarily hold it in place.

5. Remove the converter drain plug access cover from the lower end of the converter housing.

6. Remove the converter-to-flywheel attaching nuts. Place a wrench on the crankshaft pulley attaching bolt to turn the converter to gain access to the nuts.

7. With the wrench on the crankshaft pulley attaching bolt, turn the converter to gain access to the converter drain plug, and remove the plug. Place a drain pan under the converter to catch the fluid. After the fluid has been drained, reinstall the plug.

8. Disconnect the driveshaft from the rear companion flange (marking it to assure correct assembly). Slide the shaft rearward from the transmission. Position a seal installation tool in the extension housing to prevent fluid leakage.

9. Disconnect the vacuum hoses from the vacuum diaphragm unit and the tube from the extension housing clip.

10. Install the converter housing front plate to hold the converter in place when the transmission is removed. Under no conditions should the converter be left attached to the engine when the transmission is removed. This could damage the input shaft, converter and pump.

11. Disconnect the starter cables from the starter and remove the starter.

12. Disconnect the oil cooler lines from the transmission.

13. Disconnect the downshift linkage from the transmission.

14. Disconnect the selector rod or cable from the transmission manual lever.

15. Disconnect the speedometer cable from the extension housing. Disconnect the exhaust inlet pipes at the exhaust manifolds (LTD II, Thunderbird and Cougar).

16. Support the transmission on a transmission jack. Secure the transmission to the jack with safety chain. Remove the two engine rear support to transmission bolts. Remove the two crossmember to frame side rail attaching bolts and nuts. Raise the transmission slightly to take the weight off the crossmember. Remove the rear support to crossmember bolt and nut and remove the crossmember.

17. Lower the transmission slightly and disconnect the fluid filler tube.

18. Remove the remaining converter housing to engine attaching bolts. Move the transmission and converter assembly to the rear and down to remove it.

Installation

1. Torque the converter drain plug to 15–28 ft. lb.

2. If the converter has been removed from the converter housing, carefully position the converter to the transmission making sure the converter drive flats are fully engaged in the pump gear.

3. With the converter properly installed, place the transmission on the jack. Secure the transmission to the jack with safety chain.

4. Rotate the converter until the studs and drain plug are in alignment with their holes in the flywheel.

5. With the transmission mounted on a transmission jack, move the converter and transmission assembly forward into position, using care not to damage the flywheel and converter pilot. The converter must rest squarely against the flywheel. This indicates that the converter pilot is not binding in the engine crankshaft.

6. Install the lower converter housing-to-engine bolts. Torque bolts to 40–50 ft. lb. Remove the safety chain from the transmission.

7. Connect the fluid filler tube.

8. Install the crossmember.

9. Lower the transmission until the extension housing rests on the crossmember, and then install the rear support-to-crossmember bolts. Connect the exhaust inlet pipes at the exhaust manifolds (LTD II,

Thunderbird and Cougar).

10. Install the converter attaching nuts. Install the access plates.

11. Connect the oil cooler inlet and outlet lines to the transmission case.

12. Coat the front universal joint yoke seal and spline with whitelube, and install the drive shaft. Be sure that the drive shaft markings match those of the companion flange for correct balance.

13. Connect the speedometer cable at the transmission.

14. Connect the manual selector rod or cable to the transmission manual lever.

15. Connect the downshift linkage at the transmission downshift lever.

16. Install the starter motor and connect the starter cables.

17. Connect the vacuum hoses to the vacuum diaphragm unit and the tube to its clip.

18. Lower the transmission and install the upper two converter housing-to-engine bolts. Torque bolts to 40–50 ft. lb.

19. Lower the vehicle and fill the transmission with type F fluid.

20. Check the transmission, converter assembly, and fluid cooler lines for fluid leaks. Adjust the manual and downshift linkages.

AUTOMATIC OVERDRIVE (AOD)

Removal

1. Raise the vehicle on a hoist or stands.

2. Place the drain pan under the transmission fluid pan. Starting at the rear of the pan and working toward the front, loosen the attaching bolts and allow the fluid to drain. Finally remove all of the pan attaching bolts except two at the front, to allow the fluid to further drain. With fluid drained, install two bolts on the rear side of the pan to temporarily hold it in place.

3. Remove the converter drain plug access cover from the lower end of the converter housing.

4. Remove the converter-to-flywheel attaching nuts. Place a wrench on the crankshaft pulley attaching bolt to turn the converter to gain access to the nuts.

5. Place a drain pan under the converter to catch the fluid. With the wrench on the crankshaft pulley attaching bolt, turn the converter to gain access to the converter drain plug and remove the plug. After the fluid has been drained, reinstall the plug.

6. Disconnect the driveshaft from the rear axle and slide shaft rearward from the transmission. Install a seal installation tool in the extension housing to prevent fluid leakage.

7. Disconnect the cable from the terminal on the starter motor. Remove the three attaching bolts and remove the starter motor. Disconnect the neutral start switch wires at the plug connector.

8. Remove the rear mount-to-crossmember attaching bolts and the two crossmember-to-frame attaching bolts.

9. Remove the two engine rear support-to-extension housing attaching bolts.

10. Disconnect the TV linkage rod from the transmission TV lever. Disconnect the manual rod from the transmission manual lever at the transmission.

11. Remove the two bolts securing the bellcrank bracket to the converter housing.

12. Raise the transmission with a transmission jack to provide clearance to remove the crossmember. Remove the rear mount from the crossmember and remove the crossmember from the side supports.

13. Lower the transmission to gain access to the oil cooler lines.

14. Disconnect each oil line from the fittings on the transmission.

15. Disconnect the speedometer cable from the extension housing.

16. Remove the bolt that secures the transmission fluid filler tube to the cylinder block. Lift the filler tube and the dipstick from the transmission.

17. Secure the transmission to the jack with the chain.

18. Remove the converter housing-to-cylinder block attaching bolts.

19. Carefully move the transmission and converter assembly away from the engine and, at the same time, lower the jack to clear the underside of the vehicle.

20. Remove the converter and mount the transmission in a holding fixture.

Installation

1. Tighten the converter drain plug to 20–28 ft. lb.

2. Position the converter on the transmission, making sure the converter drive flats are fully engaged in the pump gear by rotating the converter.

3. With the converter properly installed, place the transmission on the jack. Secure the transmission to the jack with a chain.

4. Rotate the converter until the studs and drain plug are in alignment with the holes in the flywheel. IMPORTANT: Lube pilot.

5. Align the yellow balancing marks on converter and flywheel for Continental.

6. Move the converter and transmission assembly forward into position, using care not to damage the flywheel and the converter pilot. The converter must rest squarely against the flywheel. This indicates that the converter pilot is not binding in the engine crankshaft.

7. Install and tighten the converter housing-to-engine attaching bolts to 40–50 ft. lb. Make sure that the vacuum tube retaining clips are properly positioned.

8. Remove the safety chain from around the transmission.

9. Install a new O-ring on the lower end of the transmission filler tube. Insert the tube in the transmission case and secure the tube to the engine with the attaching bolt.

10. Connect the speedometer cable to the extension housing.

11. Connect the oil cooler lines to the right side of transmission case.

12. Position the crossmember on the side supports. Position the rear mount on the crossmember and install the attaching bolt and nut.

13. Secure the engine rear support to the extension housing and tighten the bolts to 35–40 ft. lb.

14. Lower the transmission and remove the jack.

15. Secure the crossmember to the side supports with the attaching bolts and tighten them to 35–40 ft. lb.

16. Position the bellcrank to the converter housing and install the two attaching bolts.

17. Connect the TV linkage rod to the transmission TV lever. Connect the manual linkage rod to the manual lever at the transmission.

18. Secure the converter-to-flywheel attaching nuts and tighten them to 20–30 ft. lb.

19. Install the converter housing access cover and secure it with the attaching bolts.

20. Secure the starter motor in place with the attaching bolts. Connect the cable to the terminal on the starter. Connect the neutral start switch wires at the plug connector.

21. Connect the driveshaft to the rear axle.

22. Adjust the shift linkage as required.

23. Adjust throttle linkage.

24. Lower the vehicle.

25. Fill the transmission to the correct level with Dexron® II. Start the engine and shift the transmission to all ranges, then recheck the fluid level.

ZF Transmission
REMOVAL & INSTALLATION

1. Remove the kickdown (TV) cable and insert from the injection pump side lever and cable bracket in the engine compartment.

2. Place the transmission selector lever in N (Neutral). Raise the vehicle on a hoist.

3. Remove the outer manual lever and nut from the transmission selector shaft.

4. Remove position sensor from converter housing.

5. Remove the engine brace from the lower end of the converter housing.

6. Place a transmission jack under the transmission.

7. Place a wrench on the crankshaft pulley attaching bolt and turn the converter to gain access to the converter-to-flywheel attaching nuts. Remove the converter-to-flywheel attaching nuts.

NOTE: The converter studs are installed in the converter with Loc-Tite®. During disassembly the nuts may override the Loc-Tite® and the nut and stud come out as a "bolt". This poses no concern. The stud and converter threads should be cleaned, Loc-Tite® applied, and the "bolt" reinstalled and tightened to specification.

8. Disconnect the driveshaft from the rear axle and slide shaft rearward from the transmission.

NOTE: To maintain driveshaft balance, mark the rear driveshaft yoke and axle companion flange so the driveshaft can be installed in its original position. Install a seal installation tool in the extension housing to prevent fluid leakage.

9. Disconnect the neutral start switch electrical connector.

10. Remove the extension housing damper.

11. Remove the rear support-to-crossmember attaching nuts and the two crossmember-to-side support attaching bolts.

12. Remove the two engine rear support-to-extension housing attaching bolts and remove the rear mount from the exhaust system.

NOTE: On some models, exhaust system hardware may have to be removed to facilitate removal of crossmember and transmission.

13. On Continental with column shift, remove the two bolts securing the bellcrank bracket to the engine-to-transmission brace.

14. Disconnect each oil line from the fittings on the transmission using push connect service Tool T82L-9500-AH or equivalent.

15. Disconnect the speedometer wiring harness from the extension housing.

16. Remove the two converter housing to starter motor bolts.

17. Secure the transmission to the jack with a safety chain and lower the jack slightly.

18. Remove the four converter housing-to-cylinder block attaching bolts.

19. Remove the filler tube and dipstick.

20. Carefully move the transmission and converter assembly away from the engine and, at the same time, lower the jack to clear the underside of the vehicle.

21. Mount the transmission in a holding fixture.

22. Place the transmission on the jack. Secure the transmission to the jack with a safety chain.

23. Rotate the converter until the studs are in alignment with the holes in the flywheel and flexplate.

24. Move the converter and transmission assembly forward into position, using care not to damage the flywheel, flexplate and the converter pilot. The converter face must seat squarely against the flexplate (This indicates that the converter pilot is not binding in the engine crankshaft).

25. Install the filler tube and dipstick, position bracket over the upper right housing to engine bolt holes.

26. Install and tighten the four converter housing-to-engine attaching bolts to 38–48 ft. lbs.

27. Remove the safety chain from around the transmission.

28. Connect the oil cooler lines by pushing them into the fittings on the transmis-

sion (located on the intermediate plate).

29. Connect the speedometer wiring harness to the extension housing.

30. Install the extension housing damper with three bolts. Tighten bolts to 18–25 ft. lbs.

31. Install the rear support on the exhaust system.

32. Install the crossmember on the side supports and install the attaching bolts and nuts. Position the rear support on the crossmember and tighten the nuts to specification.

33. Secure the engine rear support to the extension housing and tighten the bolts to specification.

34. If removed, install exhaust system hardware.

35. Lower the transmission and remove the jack.

36. On the Continental equipped with column shift, position the bellcrank to the engine-to-transmission brace and install the two attaching bolts. Tighten the bolts to 10–20 ft. lbs.

37. Guide the kickdown (TV) cable up into the engine compartment.

38. Install the outer manual lever on the transmission selector shaft. Tighten the attaching nut to 10–20 ft. lbs.

39. Install the converter to flywheel attaching nuts (or bolts) and tighten to 20–34 ft. lbs.

40. Install the engine brace on the lower end of the converter housing and engine block. Tighten the bolts to 15–18 ft. lbs.

41. Connect the neutral start switch harness at the transmission.

42. Install position sensor to converter housing.

43. Connect the driveshaft to the rear axle. Install the driveshaft so the index marks, made during removal, are correctly aligned.

NOTE: Lubricate the yoke splines with C1AZ-19590-B or equivalent.

44. Lower the vehicle and adjust the kickdown (TV) cable.

45. Fill the transmission to the correct level with the specified fluid. Start the engine and shift the transmission to all positions, then recheck the fluid level.

TV CABLE ADJUSTMENT

1. Set the injection pump lever at the full throttle position.

2. Tighten the rear adjusting nut on the threaded barrel until a gap of (1.54–1.57 in.) exists between the edge of the crimped bead on the cable closest to the barrel and the end of the threaded barrel.

3. Tighten the forward adjusting nut to lock the cable assembly to the bracket to 80–106 inch lbs.

4. Recheck the gap and readjust as necessary.

NOTE: Kickdown on this transmission is controlled by the injection pump linkage adjustments.

DRIVESHAFT AND U-JOINTS

Driveshaft

REMOVAL & INSTALLATION

NOTE: Universal joints are retained at the rear by either U-bolts or a coupling flange that is bolted to the pinion (differential) flange. Various models are equipped with a double Cardan-type universal joint at the rear. Service for the front U-joint on these models is the same as for other models.

1. Matchmark the rear driveshaft yoke and the companion flange so that the parts may be reassembled in the same way to maintain balance.

2. Remove the U-bolts and straps or coupling flange nuts and bolts at the rear of the driveshaft, and tape the loose bearing caps to the spider.

3. Allow the rear of the driveshaft to drop down slightly. Pull the driveshaft and slip yoke out of the transmission extension housing.

4. Plug the transmission to prevent fluid leakage.

5. To install, lubricate the yoke splines and install the yoke into the transmission extension housing, aligning the splines. Be careful not to bottom the slip yoke hard against the transmission seal.

6. Rotate the pinion flange as necessary to align the matchmarks made earlier. Install the matchmarks made earlier. Install the U-bolts and tighten to 8–15 ft. lbs. On the Versailles, tighten the coupling-to-pinion flange bolts to 70–90 ft. lbs.

Various models use special wax-dipped coupling-to-pinion flange bolts which may not be reused. They must be replaced with special new bolts, torqued to 71–96 ft. lbs.

Universal Joint

OVERHAUL

Universal joint and Double-Cardan joint overhaul procedures are given in the "U-Joints and CV-Joints" Unit Repair section.

REAR AXLE

Both integral and removable carrier type axles are used. Traction-Lok (limited slip) axles are available only as removable carrier types.

The axle type and ratio are stamped on a plate attached to a rear housing cover bolt. Axle types also indicate whether the axle

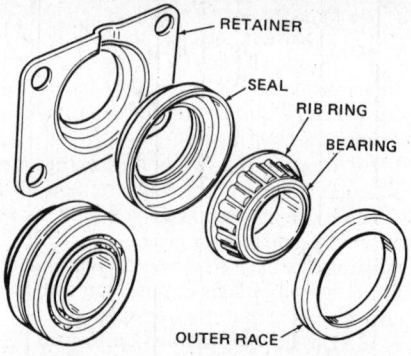

Tapered bearing and retainer–removable carrier axle (© Ford Motor Co)

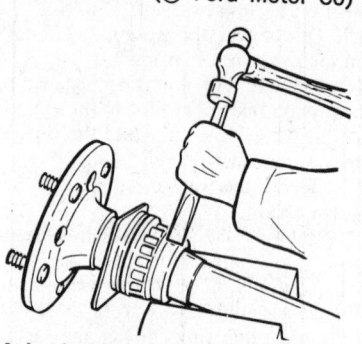

Axle shaft bearing retainer removal —removable carrier axle (© Ford Motor Co.)

shafts are retained by C-locks. To properly identify a C-lock axle, drain the lubricant, remove the rear cover and look for the C-lock on the end of the axle shaft in the differential side gear bore. If the second letter of the axle model code is F, it is a Traction-Lok axle. Always refer to the axle tag code and ratio when ordering parts.

Axle, Bearing and Seal

REMOVAL & INSTALLATION
Except C-Lock Type

NOTE: Bearings must be pressed on and off the shaft with an arbor press. Unless you have access to one, it is inadvisable to attempt any repair work on the axle shaft bearing assemblies.

1. Remove the wheel, tire, and brake drum. With disc brakes, remove the caliper, retainer nuts, and rotor. New anchor plate bolts will be needed for reassembly.

2. Remove the nuts holding the retainer plate to the backing plate, or axle shaft retainer bolts from the housing. Disconnect the brake line with drum brakes.

3. Remove the retainer and install nuts, finger-tight, to prevent the brake backing plate from being dislodged.

4. Pull out the axle shaft and bearing assembly, using a slide hammer.

On models with a tapered roller bearing, the tapered cup will normally remain in the axle housing when the shaft is removed.

The cup must be removed from the housing to prevent seal damage when the shaft is reinstalled. The cup can be removed with a slide hammer and an expanding puller.

NOTE: If end-play is found to be excessive, the bearing should be replaced. Shimming the bearing is not recommended as this ignores end-play of the bearing itself and could result in improper bearing seating.

5. Using a chisel, nick the bearing retainer in 3 or 4 places. The retainer does not have to be cut, but merely collapsed sufficiently to allow the bearing retainer to be slid from the shaft. On Fords and Mercurys, first drill a ¼ in. hole not more than ⁵⁄₁₆ in. deep in the ring surface.

6. Press off the bearing and install the new one by pressing it into position. With tapered bearings, place the lubricated seal and bearing on the axle shaft (cup rib ring facing the flange). Make sure that the seal is the correct length. Disc brake seal rims are black, drum brake seal rims are grey. Press the bearing and seal onto the shaft.

7. Press on the new retainer.

NOTE: Do not attempt to press the bearing and the retainer on at the same time.

8. On ball bearing models, to replace the seal: remove the seal from the housing with an expanding cone type puller and a slide hammer. The seal must be replaced whenever the shaft is removed. Wipe a small amount of sealer onto the outer edge of the new seal before installation; do not put sealer on the sealing lip. Press the seal into the housing with a seal installation tool.

9. Assemble the shaft and bearing in the housing, being sure that the bearing is seated properly in the housing. On ball bearing models, be careful not to damage the seal with the shaft. With tapered bearings, first install the tapered cup on the bearing, and lubricate the outer diameter of the cup and the seal with axle lube. Then install the shaft and bearing assembly into the housing.

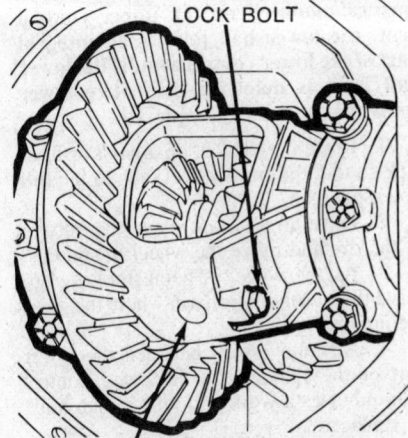

LOCK BOLT

DIFFERENTIAL PINION SHAFT
Removing the differential pinion shaft lockbolt

10. Install the retainer, drum or rotor and caliper, wheel and tire. Bleed the brakes.

C-Lock Type

1. Jack up and support the rear of the car.

2. Remove the wheels and tires from the brake drums.

3. Place a drain pan under the housing and drain the lubricant by loosening the housing cover.

4. Remove the locks securing the brake drums to the axle shaft flanges and remove the drums.

5. Remove the housing cover and gasket, if used.

6. Position jackstands under the rear frame member and lower the axle housing. This is done to give easy access to the inside of the differential.

7. Working through the opening in the differential case, remove the side gear pinion shaft lockbolt and the side gear pinion shaft.

8. Push the axle shafts inward and remove the C-locks from the inner end of the axle shafts. Temporarily replace the shaft and lockbolt to retain the differential gears in position.

9. Remove the axle shafts with a slide hammer. Be sure the seal is not damaged by the splines on the axle shaft.

10. Remove the bearing and oil seal from the housing. Both the seal and bearing can be removed with a slide hammer. Two types of bearings are used on some axles, one requiring a press fit and the other a loose fit. A loose fitting bearing does not necessarily indicate excessive wear.

11. Inspect the axle shaft housing and axle shafts for burrs or other irregularities. Replace any work or damaged parts. A light yellow color on the bearing journal of the axle shaft is normal, and does not require replacement of the axle shaft. Slight pitting and wear is also normal.

12. Lightly coat the wheel bearing rollers with axle lubricant. Install the bearings in the axle housing until the bearing seats firmly against the shoulder.

13. Wipe all lubricant from the oil seal bore, before installing the seal.

14. Inspect the original seals for wear. If necessary, these may be replaced with new seals, which are prepacked with lubricant and do not require soaking.

15. Install the oil seal.

— **CAUTION** —
Installation of the seal without the proper tool can cause distortion and seal leakage. Seals may be colored coded for side identification. Do not interchange seals from side to side, if they are coded.

16. Remove the lockbolt and pinion shaft. Carefully slide the axle shafts into place. Be careful that you do not damage the seal with the splined end of the axle shaft. Engage the splined end of the shaft with the differential side gears.

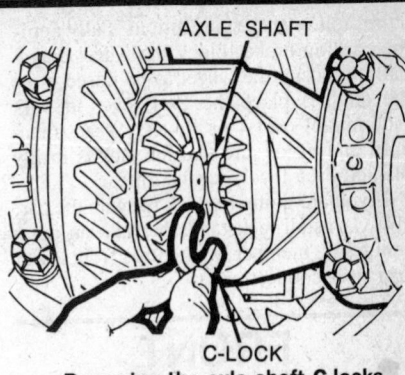

AXLE SHAFT

C-LOCK
Removing the axle shaft C-locks

17. Install the axle shaft C-locks on the inner end of the axle shafts and seat the C-locks in the counterbore of the differential side gears.

18. Rotate the differential pinion gears until the differential pinion shaft can be installed. Install the differential pinion shaft lockbolt. Tighten to 15–22 ft. lbs.

19. Install the brake drum on the axle shaft flange.

20. Install the wheel and tire on the brake drum and tighten the attaching nuts.

21. Clean the gasket surface of the rear housing and install a new cover gasket and the housing cover. Some models do not use a ''paper'' gasket. On these models, apply a bead of silicone sealer on the gasket surface. The bead should run inside of the bolt holes.

22. Raise the rear axle so that it is in the running position. Add the amount of specified lubricant to bring the lubricant level to ½ in. below the filler hole.

JACKING

— **CAUTION** —
The electrical power supply to the air suspension system on vehicles equipped, must be shut off prior to hoisting, jacking or towing an air suspension vehicle. This can be accomplished by disconnecting the battery or turning off the power switch located in the trunk on the LH side. Failure to do so may result in unexpected inflation or deflation of the air springs, which may result in shifting of the vehicle during these operations. Before lowering a vehicle on to its tires after lifting, hoisting and/or towing, it is necessary to check the air springs to insure that they are not creased or deflated but properly folded and in place.

When it becomes necessary to raise the car for service, proper safety precautions must be taken. Depending on year and model a bumper jack or screw-type jack is provided. Bumper slots or frame rail notches are provided for jack placement. Never crawl under the car when it is supported only by the jack. If the jack should slip or tip over, as jacks sometimes do, you would be pinned under 2 tons of automobile.

When raising the car with a jack to change

a tire, follow these precautions: Fully apply the parking brake, block the wheel diagonally opposite the wheel to be raised, stop the engine, place the gear lever in Park (automatic) or 1st or Reverse gear (manual), and make sure that the jack is firmly planted on a level, solid surface.

If you are going to work beneath the car, always install jackstands beneath an adjacent frame member, or at either front lower arm strut connection.

FRONT SUSPENSION

NOTE: For models equipped with air suspension refer to section following "Front and Rear Suspension".

NOTE: Different front suspension designs are used depending on year and model. They are

 Type 1: Coil Spring on Upper Control Arm

 Type 2: Coil Spring on Lower Control Arm

 Type 3: Strut Type Suspension

Type 1: Coil Spring on Upper Arm
REMOVAL & INSTALLATION
Shock Absorber

NOTE: Purge a new shock of air by repeatedly extending it in its normal position and compressing it while inverted.

1. Raise the hood and remove the three shock absorber-to-spring tower attaching bolts.

2. Raise the front of the vehicle and place jackstands under the lower control arms.

3. Remove the shock absorber lower attaching nuts, washers, and insulators.

4. Lift the shock absorber and upper bracket from the spring tower and remove the bracket from the shock absorber. Remove the insulators from the lower attaching studs.

5. Install the upper mounting bracket on the shock absorber. Torque to 22–25 ft. lbs. Install the insulators on the lower attaching studs.

6. Place the shock absorber and upper bracket assembly in the spring tower, making sure that the shock absorber lower studs are in the pivot plate holes.

7. Install the two washers and attaching nuts on the lower studs of the shock absorbers. Torque to 8–12 ft. lbs.

8. Install the shock absorbers upper mounting bracket attaching nuts. Torque to 32–48 ft. lbs.

9. Remove the jackstands and lower the vehicle.

Coil Spring

— CAUTION —

Do not attempt to remove or install coil springs without a spring compressor. If a coil spring is removed without the use of a spring compressor, severe injury may result.

1. Remove the shock absorber and mounting bracket.

2. Jack up the car and install a jackstand beneath the inboard end of the lower control arm. Remove the wheel. Place a wooden block between the control arm and frame.

3. Remove the grease cap, cotter pin, lock nut and outer bearing from the hub.

4. Remove the disc brake caliper and rotor.

5. Install a spring compressor(s) on the coil spring and compress the spring until tension is released from the control arm.

6. Remove the two nuts retaining the upper control arm to the spring tower and swing the arms outboard from the tower.

7. Slowly release the spring compressor from the spring, remove the tool and remove the spring from the vehicle.

8. To install, tape the spring upper insulator on the top of the spring. Place the spring in the tower. Install the spring compressor and compress the spring.

9. Swing the upper control arm inboard and insert the retaining bolts through the bolt holes in the spring tower. Install the retaining nuts and torque them to 110–130 ft. lbs.

10. Slowly release the spring compressor, while guiding the lower end of the spring into the upper control arm spring seat. The end of the spring must be no more than ½ inch from the tab on the spring seat.

11. Remove the spring compressor.

12. Reinstall the rotor and the caliper. Install the outer bearing, washer and adjusting nut on the spindle. Adjust the wheel bearing. Install the locknut, cotter pin and grease cap.

13. Install the wheel, remove the jackstand and lower the vehicle. Install the shock absorber and upper mounting bracket.

Lower Ball Joint

NOTE: On cars which have the coil springs mounted on the upper control arm, the lower ball joint is an integral part of the lower control arm. If the lower ball joint is defective the entire lower control arm must be replaced.

1. Raise the vehicle on a hoist or floor jack so that the front wheel falls to the full down position.

2. Have an assistant grasp the bottom of the tire and move the wheel in and out.

3. As the wheel is being moved, observe the lower control arm where the spindle attaches to it.

4. Any movement between the lower part of the spindle and the lower control arm indicates a worn ball joint which must be replaced.

NOTE: During this check, the upper ball joint will be unloaded and may move; this is normal and not an indication of a

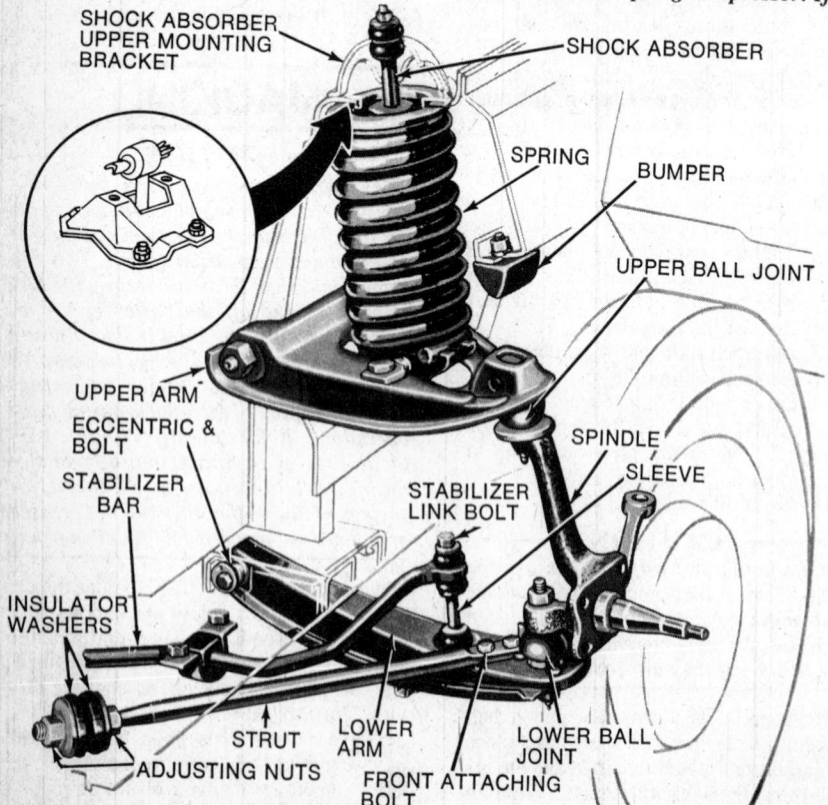

SHOCK ABSORBER UPPER MOUNTING BRACKET

SHOCK ABSORBER

SPRING

BUMPER

UPPER BALL JOINT

UPPER ARM

ECCENTRIC & BOLT

STABILIZER BAR

STABILIZER LINK BOLT

SPINDLE

SLEEVE

INSULATOR WASHERS

STRUT

ADJUSTING NUTS

LOWER ARM

FRONT ATTACHING BOLT

LOWER BALL JOINT

Front suspension—spring on upper arm (© Ford Motor Co)

bad ball joint. Also, do not mistake a loose wheel bearing for a worn ball joint.

5. Position a support between the upper arm and side rail.

6. Raise the vehicle, position jack stands and remove the wheel and tire.

7. Remove the stabilizer bar to link attaching nut and disconnect the bar from the link.

8. Remove the link bolt from the lower arm.

9. Remove the strut bar to lower control arm attaching nuts and bolts.

10. Remove the lower ball joint cotter pin and back off the nut. Using a ball joint removal tool, loosen the ball joint stud in the spindle.

11. Remove the nut from the lower ball joint stud and lower the arm.

12. Remove the lower arm to underbody cam attaching parts and remove the arm.

13. To install, position the lower arm in the underbody and install the ball joint and cam attaching parts loosely.

14. Raise the lower arm, install the ball joint stud into place and loosely install the stud nut.

15. Install the stabilizer and strut and tighten the stabilizer nuts to 6–12 ft. lbs. Tighten the strut-to-arm nuts to 90–115 ft. lbs.

16. Tighten the ball joint stud to 75 ft. lbs., then continue to tighten until the cotter pin holes align. Install a new cotter pin. Tighten the lower arm bolts to 85–100 ft. lbs.

17. Lower the car and remove the upper arm support.

18. Front end alignment must be rechecked.

Upper Ball Joint

1. Raise the vehicle on a hoist or floor jack so that the front wheels hang in full down position.

2. Have an assistant grasp the wheel top and bottom and apply alternate in and out pressure to the top and bottom of the wheel.

3. Radial play of ¼ in. is acceptable measured at the inside of the wheel adjacent to the upper arm on all models except the Granada, Monarch, and Versailles; on those models only, any detectable play indicates worn ball joints.

NOTE: This radial play measurement is multiplied at the outer circumference of the tire and should not be measured here. Measure only at the inside of the wheel.

NOTE: The factory procedure for ball joint replacement is to install a new upper control arm. The factory does not recommend installation of a new ball joint. However, ball joint replacements are available from auto parts dealers, and may be installed using the following procedure.

4. Position a support between the upper arm and frame rail.

5. Raise the vehicle and remove the tire and wheel.

6. Remove the upper ball joint cotter pin and loosen the nut.

7. Using a ball joint removal tool, loosen the ball joint in the spindle.

8. Remove the three ball joint retaining rivets using a large chisel.

9. Remove the nut from the ball joint stud and remove the ball joint.

10. Clean and remove all burrs from the ball joint mounting area of the control arm before installing new ball joint.

11. Install the ball joint in the upper arm using the service part nuts and bolts. Do not attempt to rivet a new ball joint to the arm.

12. Install and tighten the ball joint stud nut and install the cotter pin.

13. Lubricate the new joint with a hand type grease gun only; using an air pressure gun may loosen the ball joint seal.

14. Install wheel, lower vehicle and remove upper arm support.

15. Check front end alignment.

Upper Control Arm

NOTE: The upper arm shaft and bushings may not be replaced separately from the upper arm.

1. Remove the shock absorber and upper mounting bracket from the car as an assembly. Install a wood block as a support between the upper arm and the body.

2. Raise the vehicle and remove the wheel and tire as an assembly.

3. Install spring compressor tool.

4. Place a safety stand under the lower arm.

5. Remove the cotter pin from the upper ball joint and loosen the nut.

6. Using a ball joint removal tool, loosen the ball joint in the spindle, then remove the nut and lift the stud from the spindle.

7. Remove the upper arm attaching nuts from the engine compartment and remove the upper arm.

8. To install the arm, position it on the

mounting bracket and install the attaching nuts on the inner shaft attaching nuts on the inner shaft attaching bolts. Torque to 110–130 ft. lbs.

9. Install the upper ball joint stud in the spindle and tighten the nut according to the procedure in Step 12 of the lower ball joint procedure. Install a new cotter pin.

10. Remove spring compressor and position spring on upper arm. Install wheel and check front end alignment.

Type 2: Coil Spring on Lower Arm

REMOVAL & INSTALLATION

Shock Absorber

NOTE: Purge a new shock of air by repeatedly extending it in its normal position and compressing it while inverted.

1. Remove the nut, washer, and bushing from the upper end of the shock absorber.

2. Raise the vehicle and install jackstands under the frame rails.

3. Remove the two bolts securing the shock absorber to the lower control arm and remove the shock absorber.

4. Install a new bushing and washer on the top of the shock absorber and position the unit inside the front spring. Install the two lower attaching bolts and torque them to 8–15 ft. lbs.

5. Remove the jackstands and lower the vehicle.

6. Place a new bushing and washer on the shock absorber top stud and install a new attaching nut. Torque to 22–30 ft. lbs.

Coil Spring and Lower Control Arm

1978

1. Raise car and support it with stands placed in back of lower arms.

2. Remove the wheel from the hub. Remove the bolts and washers that hold the caliper and brake hose bracket to the spindle. Remove the caliper from the rotor and wire it back out of the way. Then, remove the hub and rotor from the spindle.

3. Disconnect lower end of the shock absorber and push it up to the retracted position.

4. Disconnect stabilizer bar link from the lower arm.

5. Remove cotter pins from the upper and lower ball joint stud nuts.

6. Remove the two bolts and nuts holding the strut to the lower arm. Remove the jounce bumper, if equipped.

7. Loosen the lower ball joint stud nut two turns. Do not remove this nut.

8. Install a spreader tool between the upper and lower ball joint studs.

9. Expand the tool until the tool exerts considerable pressure on the studs. Tap the spindle near the lower stud with a hammer

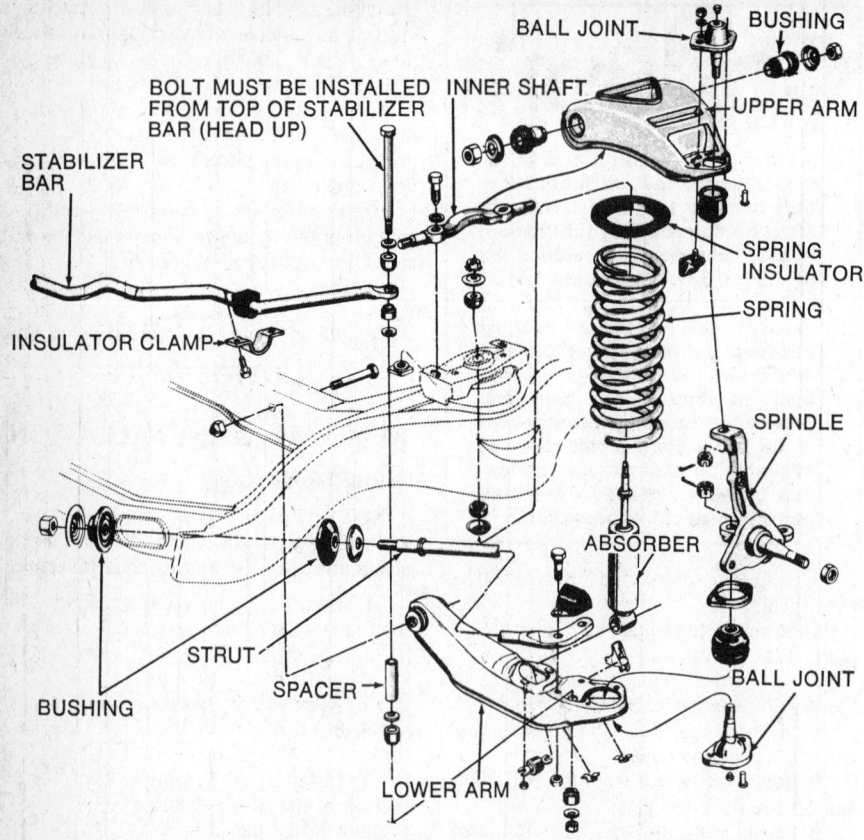

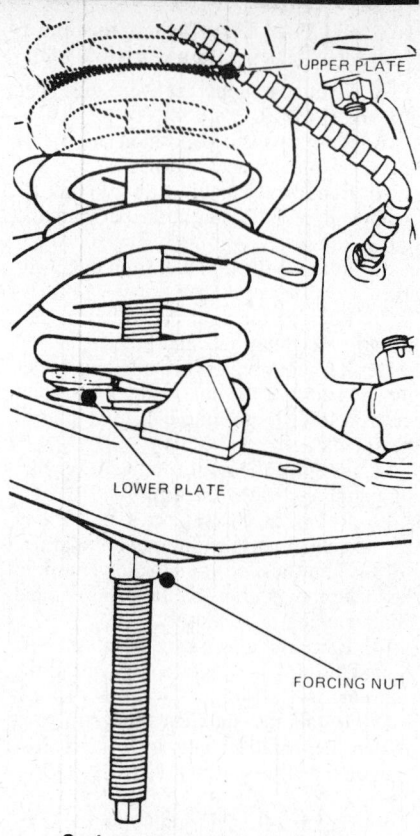

Front suspension—spring on lower arm (© Ford Motor Co)

Spring compressor installed
(© Ford Motor Co.)

to loosen the stud. Do not loosen the stud with tool pressure only.

10. Position floor jack under the lower arm and remove the lower ball joint stud nut.

11. Lower floor jack and remove the spring and insulator.

12. Remove the A-arm to crossmember attaching parts, and remove the arm from the car.

13. To install, loosely attach the lower arm to the crossmember using a new pivot bolt and nut. Do not tighten.

14. Position the spring and insulator within the control arms; the lower end of the spring must be no more than ½ in. from the end of the lower arm depression. Raise the arm with the floor jack, aligning the ball joint stud with the spindle.

15. Install the stud nut and torque to 105 ft. lbs., then continue to tighten until the holes align. Install new cotter pins in the upper and lower studs.

16. Reattach the shock absorber (8–15 ft. lbs.) and the jounce bumper. Using new bolts and nuts, install the stabilizer bar and torque to 6–12 ft. lbs. Reinstall the brake parts and wheel; lower the car. Torque the lower arm pivot bolt to 95–110 ft. lbs. Check the alignment.

1979 AND LATER

NOTE: All 1979 Lincoln models use the "1978" procedure.

1. Raise the car and support it with jackstands. Remove the tire and wheel.

2. Disconnect the stabilizer bar link from the lower arm.

3. Remove the lower shock absorber attaching bolts.

4. Remove the shock absorber upper nut and remove the shock.

5. Remove the steering center link from the pitman arm.

6. Install a spring compressor tool. Insert the securing pin through the upper ball nut and the compression rod. This pin can only be inserted one way. With the upper ball nut secured, turn the upper plate so it walks up the coil and contacts the upper spring seat. Back the nut off ½ turn.

7. Install the lower ball nut and the thrust washer on the compression rod and tighten the forcing nut until the spring is free in the seat.

8. Remove the two lower control arm pivot bolts.

9. Disengage the arm from the frame and remove the spring assembly.

10. If a new spring is being installed, mark the position of the upper and lower plates on the old spring. Also, measure the length of the spring and the amount of curvature in order to simplify the compressing and installation of the new spring.

11. Loosen the forcing nut and remove the spring from the tool.

12. Assemble the spring compressor tool on the new spring in the same position as the old spring was removed.

13. Position the spring in the lower arm.

14. Reverse the removal procedure to reinstall.

Lower Ball Joint

1. Raise the vehicle by placing a floor jack under the lower arm; or, raise the vehicle on a hoist and place a jack stand under the lower arm and lower the vehicle onto it to remove the preload from the lower ball joint.

2. Have an assistant grasp the wheel top and bottom and apply alternate in and out pressure to the top and bottom of the wheel.

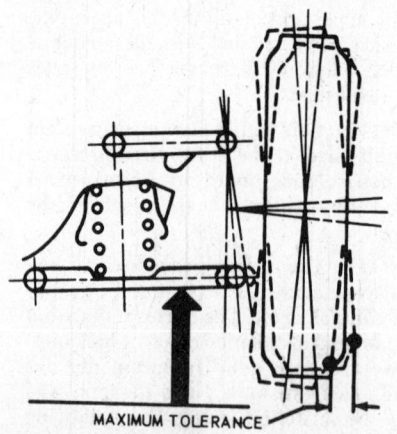

Measuring lower ball joint radial play
–spring on lower arm (© Ford Motor Co)

3. Radial play of ¼ in. is acceptable measured at the inside of the wheel adjacent to the lower arm.

4. For replacement procedures see Steps 4–11 of "Upper Ball Joint".

NOTE: This radial play is multiplied at the outer circumference of the tire and should be measured only at the inside of the wheel.

Upper Ball Joint

1. Raise the vehicle by placing a floor jack under the lower arm. Do not allow the lower arm to hang freely with the vehicle on a hoist or bumper jack.

2. Have an assistant grasp the bottom of the tire and move the wheel in and out.

3. As the wheel is being moved, observe the upper control arm where the spindle attaches to it. Any movement between the upper part of the spindle and the upper ball joint indicates a bad ball joint which must be replaced.

NOTE: During this check the lower ball joint will be unloaded and may move; this is normal and not an indication of a bad ball joint. Also, do not mistake a loose wheel bearing for a defective ball joint.

NOTE: Ford Motor Company recommends replacement of the control arm and ball joint as an assembly. However, aftermarket replacement parts are available, which can be installed using the following procedure. This procedure may be used on both upper and lower ball joints.

4. Raise the vehicle on a hoist and allow the front wheels to fall to their full down position.

5. Drill a ⅛ in. hole completely through each ball joint attaching rivet.

6. Using a large chisel, cut off the head of each rivet and drive them from the arm.

7. Place a jack under the lower arm and lower the vehicle about 6 in.

8. Remove the cotter pin and attaching nut from the ball joint stud.

9. Using a ball joint removal tool, loosen the ball joint stud from the spindle and remove the ball joint from the arm.

10. Clean all metal burrs from the arm and install the new ball joint, using the service part nuts and bolts to attach the ball joint. Do not attempt to rerivet the ball joint once it has been removed.

11. Check front end alignment.

Upper Control Arm

1. Raise the car and support the frame with jackstands placed just behind the lower arm pivot (rear pivot on 1979 and later models). Remove the wheel.

2. Remove the cotter pin from the upper ball joint stud nut. Loosen the nut a few turns but do not remove.

3. Install a ball joint removal tool between the upper and lower ball joint studs. Expand the tool until it places the upper stud under compression. Tap the spindle near the stud with a hammer to loosen the stud.

4. Remove the tool. Raise the lower arm with a jack until pressure is relieved from the upper stud. Remove the upper stud nut.

5. Remove the upper shaft attaching bolts and the upper arm.

6. To install, position the arm to the frame, install the attaching nuts, and torque to 120–140 ft. lbs. Connect the upper stud to the spindle. Install the attaching nut, and tighten to 75 ft. lbs., then continue to tighten until the cotter pin holes align. Install a new cotter pin. Install the wheel, adjust the wheel bearings, and lower the car. Caster, camber, and toe must be adjusted after installation.

Type 3: Strut Suspension

REMOVAL & INSTALLATION

Except Merkur

STRUT AND UPPER MOUNT

1. Raise the front of the car and place stands under the jacking pads just aft of the lower arms.

2. Remove the wheel and tire. Raise the lower arm with a floor jack to compress the spring.

3. On models through 1978, remove the two lower shock strut nuts and bolts. Leave the strut in position.

4. Remove the three upper strut mounting nuts from within the engine compartment.

5. On 1979 and later models, remove the two lower shock strut nuts. Leave the bolts in place.

6. Compress the strut to clear the upper mount. On 1979 and later models, remove the lower shock strut through bolts. Remove the strut.

7. To install, place the lower end into the spindle, then extend the upper portion until the bolts are positioned. Install the upper nuts and torque to 60–75 ft. lbs.

8. Install the two lower retaining bolts and tighten to 150–180 ft. lbs.

9. Lower the jack and install the wheel and tire.

BALL JOINT

Only one ball joint is used on each side, located in the lower arm. It is provided with a grease fitting, which projects beyond the ball joint cover. When the checking surface (the round boss into which the grease fitting is threaded) is flush with the cover, the ball joint is due for replacement.

The ball joint and lower arm must be replaced as an assembly. Follow the instructions for arm replacement.

COIL SPRING

1978

1. Raise and support the car with stands placed under the pads just behind the lower arms.

2. Remove the wheel and tire. Disconnect the stabilizer bar from the arm.

3. Remove the brake caliper, rotor, and dust shield.

4. Support the arm with a jack placed under both bushings.

5. Remove the steering gear bolts and move the gear out of the way.

6. Remove the two lower arm to crossmember bolts and nuts. Slowly lower the jack to relieve spring tension, and remove the spring.

7. To install, secure the upper spring insulation to the spring with tape. Install the spring damper within the spring, and

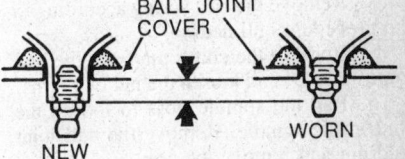

Ball joint wear indicator (© Ford Motor Co.)

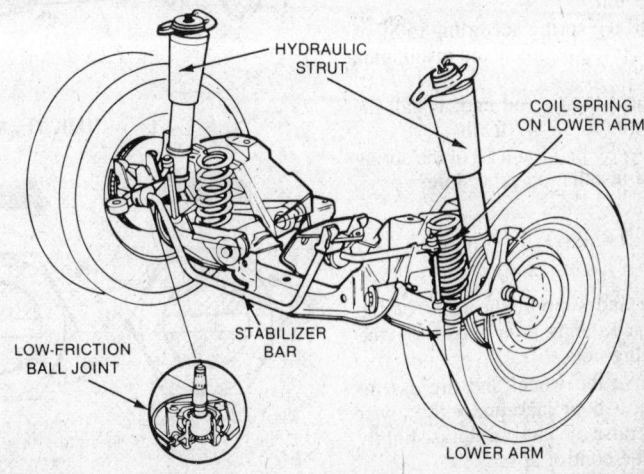

Single arm front suspension components (© Ford Motor Co.)

C257

the rubber hose over the last coil.

8. Place the spring in the upper pocket. Position the lower end between the two holes in the arm.

9. Raise the arm with the floor jack. Install the two bolts and nuts, and tighten to a snug fit.

10. Install the steering gear bolts; torque to 80–100 ft. lbs.

11. Install the rotor shield. Install the stabilizer bar link, and tighten to 9–12 ft. lbs.

12. Install the wheel and tire, remove the stands, and lower the car. With the weight of the car on the suspension, tighten the arm nuts to 200–220 ft. lbs.

1979 AND LATER

1. Refer to Steps 1, 2 and 5 of the above procedure.

2. Disconnect the tie rod from the steering spindle using a puller.

3. Install a spring compressor. Turn the tightening nut on the tool so the spring is free in the seat.

4. Remove the two lower control arm pivot bolts and disengage the arm from the frame.

5. Remove the spring.

6. Reverse to install. Be sure the lower end of the spring is properly positioned between the two holes in the lower arm spring pocket.

LOWER ARM

1. Perform Steps 1–3 of the "1978" spring removal and installation procedure.

2. Remove the steering gear bolts and position the gear out of the way.

3. Remove the tie rod end from the spindle with a tie rod end puller.

4. Remove the coil spring according to the procedure outlined.

5. Remove the cotter pin from the ball joint stud nut, and loosen the nut two turns.

6. Rap the spindle boss to loosen the stud in the spindle. Remove the ball joint stud nut and remove the arm.

7. To install, position the arm to the spindle, installing the stud in place. Tighten the stud nut to 80 ft. lbs., then continue to tighten to align the cotter pin holes. Install a new cotter pin.

8. Install the spring according to Steps 7–10 of the spring removal and installation procedure.

9. Connect the tie rod end, install the nut, and torque to 35–47 ft. lbs.

10. Follow Steps 11 and 12 of the spring removal and installation procedure.

Merkur

STRUT

1. Raise and support the front of the vehicle on jackstands after loosening the front wheel lug nuts.

2. Remove the wheel and tire assembly. Position a floor jack under the lower control arm, raise the jack until it is slightly lower than the control arm.

3. Remove the pinch bolt that secures the strut to the lower control arm. Use a small pry bar to spread the mounting flange ears and push down on the lower control arm to separate the arm and strut. Lower the jack if necessary, but do not allow the brake hose to stretch. When separated, rest the control arm on the jack.

4. Hold the top of the strut by inserting a 6 mm hex wrench in the slot provided and remove the locknut.

5. Remove the strut assembly from the vehicle.

6. Install replacement strut in the reverse order of removal.

LOWER CONTROL ARM

1. Raise and support the front of the vehicle on jackstands, after loosening the front wheel lug nuts.

2. Remove the wheel and tire assembly.

3. Remove the control arm to cross-member mounting bolt.

4. Remove the lower control arm ball joint from the spindle assembly.

5. Remove the stabilizer from the lower control arm and remove the control arm.

6. Install in the reverse order.

STABILIZER

1. Raise and support the front of the vehicle on jackstands.

2. Bend back the locking tabs and remove the bolts that secure the bushing brackets to the body.

3. Remove the stabilizer to lower control arm mounting nuts.

4. Remove one lower control arm inner mounting bolt and pull the control arm from the mounting bracket.

5. Remove the stabilizer bar from the control arms.

6. Install in the reverse order.

Front Wheel Bearing

ADJUSTMENT

1. Raise and support the front of the vehicle on jackstands.

2. Remove the wheel cover and grease cap.

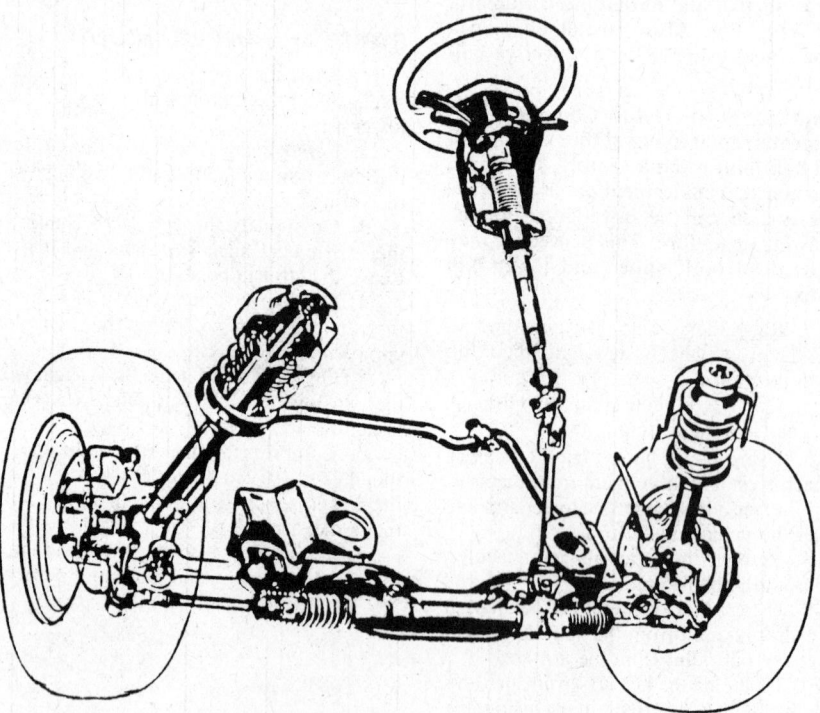

[MK 1] = Merkur XR4Ti–front suspension

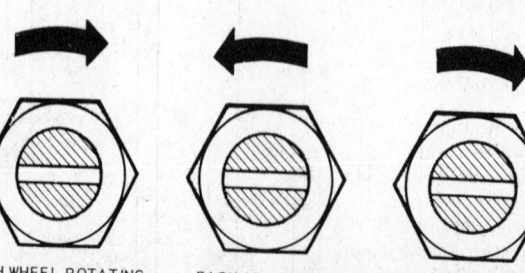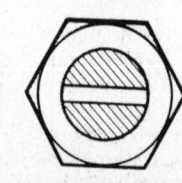

WITH WHEEL ROTATING, TORQUE ADJUSTING NUT, TO 17-25 FT. LBS. | BACK ADJUSTING NUT OFF 1/2 TURN | TIGHTEN ADJUSTING NUT TO 10-15 IN.-LBS. | INSTALL THE LOCK AND A NEW COTTER PIN

Front wheel bearing adjustment (© Ford Motor Co)

3. Remove the cotter pin and nut lock.

4. Loosen the adjusting nut three turns and rock the wheel back and forth a few times to release the brake pads from the rotor.

5. While rotating the wheel and hub assembly, tighten the adjusting nut to 17–25 ft. lbs.

6. Back off the adjusting nut ½ turn, then retighten to 10–15 in. lbs.

7. Install the locknut and a new cotter pin. Check the wheel rotation. If it is noisy or rough, the bearings either need to be cleaned and repacked, or readjusted. After adjustments are complete, replace the grease cap.

REAR SUSPENSION

NOTE: For models equipped with air suspension refer to the section following "Rear Suspension".

NOTE: Rear suspension differs de-pending on year and model. The basic designs are leaf spring, coil spring (either between the axle housing and frame, or control arm and frame) and independent strut controlled suspension.

Leaf Spring Suspension

REMOVAL & INSTALLATION

Leaf Spring

1. Raise the vehicle and place supports beneath the underbody and axle.

2. Disconnect the lower end of the shock absorber and position it out of the way. Remove the supports from under the axle.

3. Remove the spring plate nuts from the U-bolt and remove the spring plate. With a jack, raise the rear axle just enough to remove the weight of the housing from the spring.

4. Remove the two rear shackle attaching nuts, the shackle bar, and the two inner bushings.

5. Remove the rear shackle assembly and the two outer bushings.

6. Remove the nut from the spring mounting bolt and tap the bolt out of the bushing at the front hanger. Lift out the spring assembly.

NOTE: All used attaching components (nuts, bolts, etc.) must be discarded and replaced with new ones prior to assembly. Bushings may be lubricated with soap and water to ease bolt installation; do not use grease or oil.

7. Position the leaf spring under the axle housing and insert the shackle assembly into the rear hanger bracket and the rear eye of the spring.

8. Install the shackle inner bushings, the shackle plate, and the locknuts. Hand-tighten the locknuts.

9. Position the spring eye in the front hanger, slip the washer on the front hanger bolt, and, from the inboard side, insert the bolt through the hanger and eye. Install the locknut on the hanger bolt finger-tight.

10. Lower the rear axle housing so that it rests on the spring. Place the spring plate on the U-bolt and tighten the nuts.

11. Attach the lower end of the shock absorber to the spring plate using a new nut.

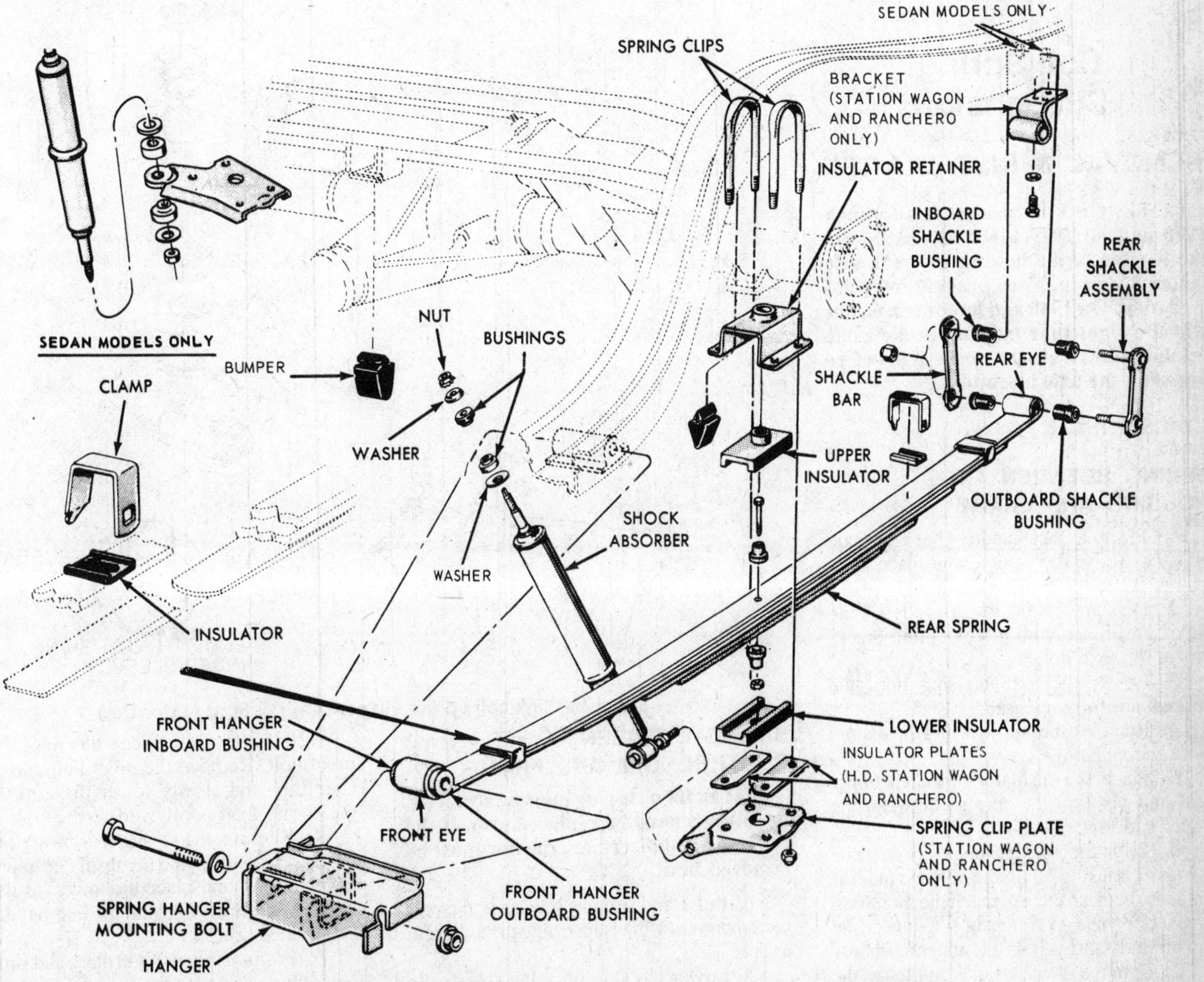

Exploded view of leaf spring rear suspension (© Ford Motor Co)

12. Place jackstands under the rear axle. Lower the vehicle until the spring is in the approximate curb load position, and tighten the front hanger locknut.

13. Tighten the rear shackle locknuts.

14. Remove the jackstands and lower the vehicle.

Shock Absorber

NOTE: **Purge a new shock of air by repeatedly extending it in its normal position and compressing it while inverted.**

1. Remove the lower end of the shock absorber from the spring plate.

2. Remove the nut retaining the upper end of the shock absorber to the mounting bracket underneath the car.

3. Compress and remove the shock absorber. Discard the nuts.

4. Transfer the washers and bushings to the new shock absorber. Insert the upper stud through the mounting bracket, and install a new attaching nut finger-tight.

5. Compress and install the shock absorber to the spring plate. Install the washers, bushings, and attaching nuts.

6. Tighten the upper and lower attaching nuts.

Coil Spring Suspension

REMOVAL & INSTALLATION

NOTE: **On Full Size models through 1978 and all 1979 Lincolns, disconnect the flexible brake hose at the rear axle before lowering, bleed brakes after reinstallation. On 1980 and later models, unclip the right rear parking brake cable retaining clip from the upper arm before lowering the axle assembly.**

Coil Spring

SPRING BETWEEN AXLE HOUSING AND FRAME

1. Place a jack under the rear axle housing. Raise the vehicle and place jackstands under the frame side rails.

2. Disconnect the lower studs of the shock absorbers from the mounting brackets on the axle housing.

3. Lower the axle housing until the springs are fully released.

4. Remove the springs and insulators from the vehicle.

5. Place the insulators in each upper seat and position the springs between the upper and lower seats.

6. With the springs in position, raise the axle housing until the lower studs of the rear shock absorbers reach the mounting brackets on the axle housing. Connect the lower studs and install the attaching nuts.

7. Remove the jackstands and lower the vehicle.

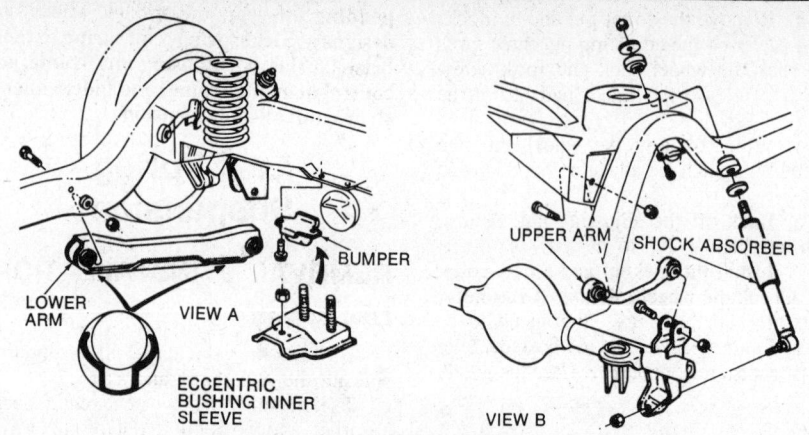

Coil spring rear suspension (© Ford Motor Co)

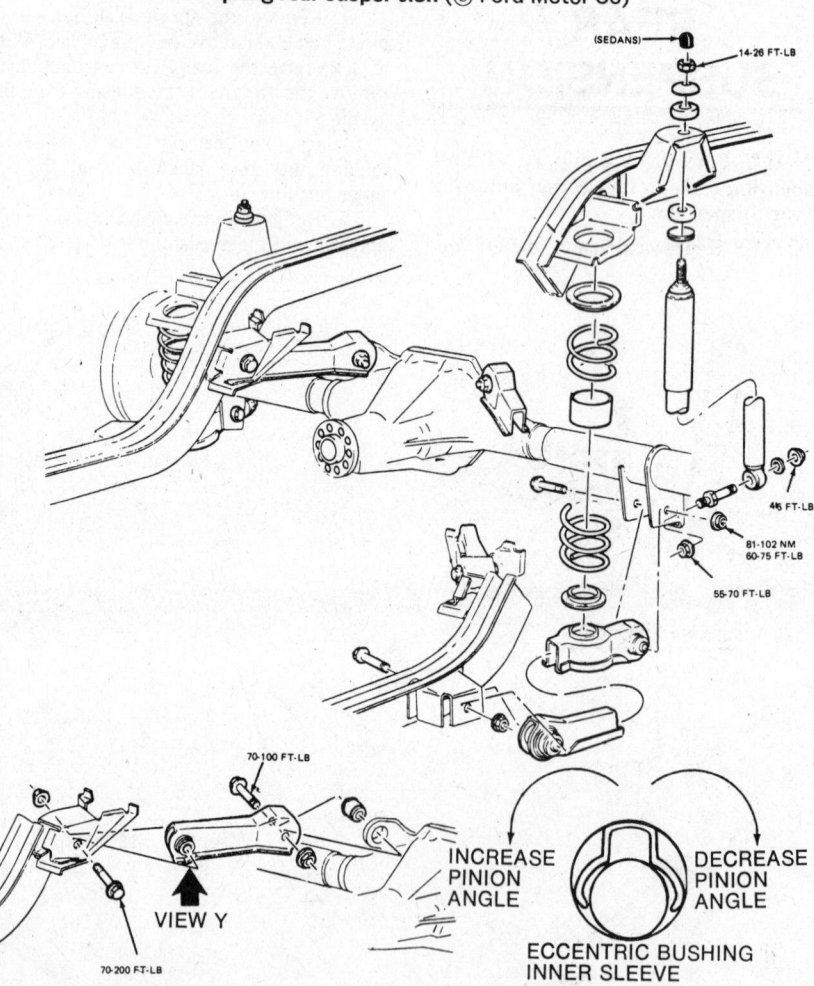

Four-bar link coil spring suspension (© Ford Motor Co.)

SPRING BETWEEN LOWER CONTROL ARM AND FRAME

NOTE: **If one spring must be replaced, the other should be replaced also. If the car has a stabilizer bar, the bar must be removed first.**

1. Raise and support the car at the rear crossmember, while supporting the axle with a jack.

2. Lower the axle until the shocks are fully extended.

3. Place a jack under the lower arm pivot bolt. Remove the pivot bolt and nut. Carefully and slowly lower the arm until the spring load is relieved.

4. Remove the spring and insulators.

5. To install, tape the insulator in place in the frame, and place the lower insulator in place on the arm. Install the internal damper in the spring.

6. Position the spring in place and slowly raise the jack under the lower arm. Install the pivot bolt and nut, with the nut facing

outwards. Do not tighten the nut.

7. Raise the axle to curb height, and tighten the lower pivot bolt to 70–100 ft. lbs.

8. Install the stabilizer bar, if removed. The proper torque is 20–27 ft. lbs. Remove the crossmember stands and lower the car.

Shock Absorber

NOTE: Purge a new shock of air by repeatedly extending it in its normal position and compressing it while inverted.

SPRING BETWEEN AXLE HOUSING AND FRAME

1. Raise the vehicle and install jackstands.

2. Remove the shock absorber outer attaching nut, washer and insulator from the stud at the top side of the spring upper seat. Compress the shock sufficiently to clear the spring seat hole, and remove the inner insulator and washer from the upper attaching stud.

3. Remove the locknut and disconnect the shock absorber lower stud at the mounting bracket on the axle housing. Remove the shock absorber.

4. Position a new inner washer and insulator on the upper attaching stud. Place the upper stud in the hole in the upper spring seat. While maintaining the shock in this position, install a new outer insulator, washer, and nut on the stud from the top side of the spring upper seat.

5. Extend the shock absorber. Locate the lower stud in the mounting bracket hole on the axle housing and install the locknut.

SPRING BETWEEN LOWER CONTROL ARM AND FRAME

1. Remove the upper attaching nut, washer, and insulator. Access is through the trunk on sedans or side panel trim covers on station wagons and hatchbacks. Sedan studs have rubber caps.

2. Raise the car. Compress the shock to clear the upper tower. Remove the lower nut and washer; remove the shock.

3. Purge the shock of air and compress. Place the lower mounting eye over the lower stud and install the washer and a new locking nut. Do not tighten the nut yet.

4. Place the insulator and washer on the upper stud. Extend the shock, installing the stud through the upper mounting hole.

5. Torque the lower mounting nut to 40–55 ft. lbs.

6. Lower the car. Install the outer insulator and washer on the upper stud, and install a new nut. Tighten to 14–26 ft. lbs. Install the trim panel on station wagons and hatchbacks or the rubber cap on sedans.

Independent Rear Suspension

REMOVAL & INSTALLATION

Coil Spring

1. Loosen the rear wheel lug nuts. Raise and support the rear of the vehicle. Remove the tire and wheel assembly and brake drum.

2. Position a floor jack under the rear control arm and take a slight amount of weight off of the spring.

3. Disconnect the rear brake hose at the body bracket (rubber line from steel line).

4. Remove the bolts that attach the rear axle flange and brake backing plate to the control arm. Remove the axle shaft from the vehicle. Secure the backing plate back in position with two bolts to prevent damage to the steel brake line.

5. Remove the bolt that secures the lower mounting eye of the shock absorber to the control arm.

— CAUTION —

Make sure that the lower arm and spring tension is supported by a floor jack.

6. Remove the bolts and pin that mount the axle beam to the floor pan/crossmember mount.

7. Carefully lower the suspension arm on the jack and remove the coil spring and rubber spring seat.

8. Insert the rear spring with the rubber spring seat onto the lower arm. Raise the jack slowly and make sure the spring and seat are correctly located. Install in the reverse order of removal.

Shock Absorber

1. Raise and support the rear of the vehicle on jackstands. Position a floor jack under the lower control arm of the side requiring shock replacement. Raise the jack until it contacts the control arm.

2. Remove the luggage compartment cover. Remove the upper shock mount trim cover.

3. Remove the upper shock mount through bolt and nut.

4. Remove the lower shock mount bolt and nut. Remove the shock absorber.

5. Install the replacement shock in the reverse order.

Stabilizer Bar

1. Loosen the wheel lug nuts on one side of the vehicle.

2. Raise and support the rear of the vehicle.

3. Remove one wheel and tire assembly.

4. Use a small pry bar and unclip the connector from the end of the bar to lower control arm. Repeat on the other side of the vehicle.

5. Remove the bushing bracket retaining bolts from the floor pan and remove the stabilizer bar assembly.

6. Install in the reverse order.

AIR SUSPENSION

Components

REMOVAL & INSTALLATION

WARNING: DO NOT REMOVE AN AIR SPRING UNDER ANY CIRCUMSTANCES WHEN THERE IS PRESSURE IN THE AIR SPRING. DO NOT

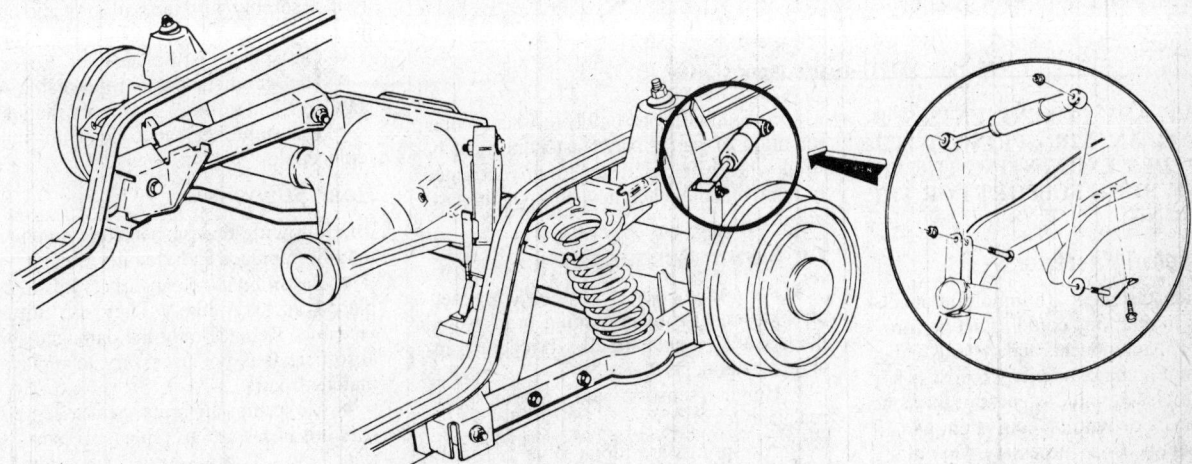

Hydra-trac rear suspension showing dampers

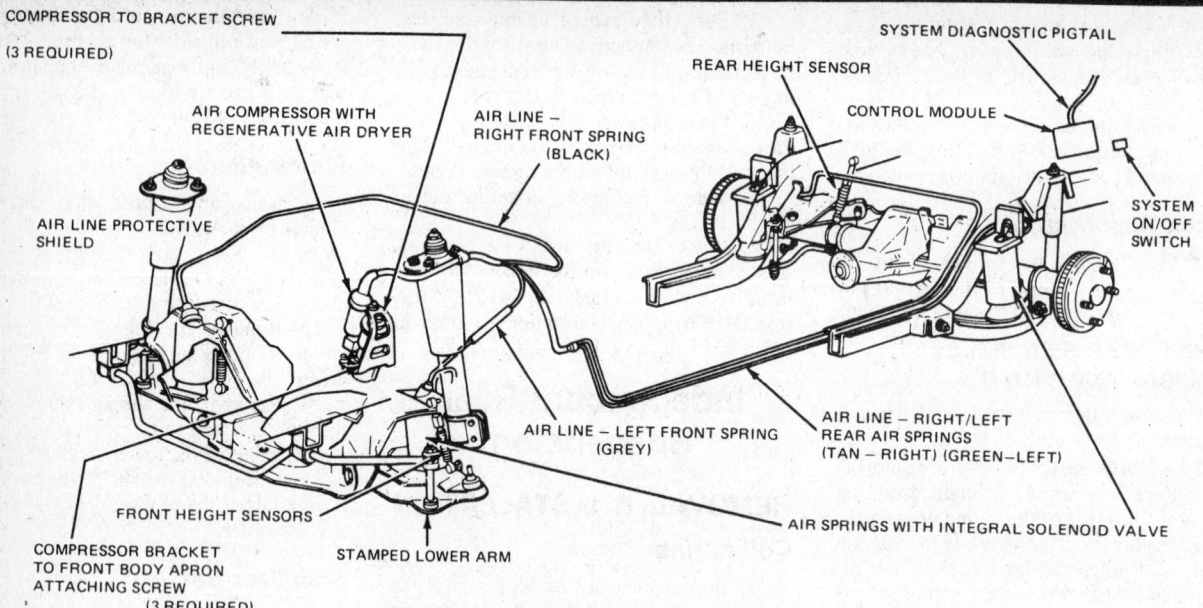

THE SYSTEM CONSISTS OF AN ELECTRIC AIR COMPRESSOR WITH REGENERATIVE AIR DRYER, THREE ELECTRONIC HEIGHT SENSORS, EIGHT QUICK CONNECT AIR FITTINGS, FOUR AIR SPRINGS WITH INTEGRAL SOLENOIDS, FOUR ONE-PIECE AIR LINES CONNECTING EACH SPRING TO THE COMPRESSOR AND A CONTROL MODULE WITH A SINGLE CHIP MICROCOMPUTER.

Air suspension

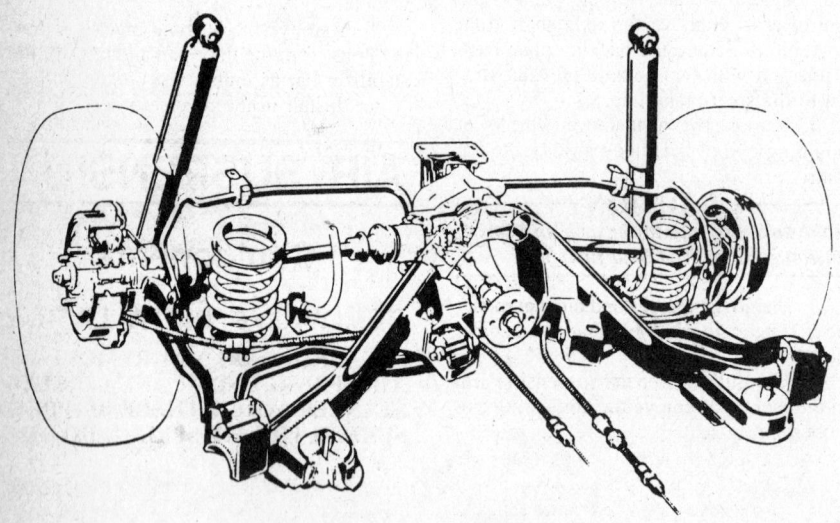

Merkur XR4Ti—rear suspension

REMOVE ANY COMPONENTS SUPPORTING AN AIR SPRING WITHOUT EITHER EXHAUSTING THE AIR OR PROVIDING SUPPORT FOR THE AIR SPRING.

Suspension Fasteners

Suspension fasteners are important attaching parts in that they could affect performance of vital components and systems and/or could result in major service expense. They must be replaced with fasteners of the same part number, or with an equivalent part, if replacement becomes necessary. **Do not** use a replacement part of lesser quality or substitute design. Torque values must be used,

as specified, during assembly to assure proper retention of parts. New fasteners must be used whenever old fasteners are loosened or removed and when new component parts are installed.

Air Spring Suspension

- Air compressor (less dryer), regenerative dryer, O-ring, mounting bracket and the isolator mounts are all serviced as separate components.
- Height sensors and modules are replaceable.
- Air springs are replaceable as assemblies (including the solenoid valve).
- Air spring solenoid valves and exter-

nal O-rings are replaceable.
- Air lines are replaceable, however quick connect unions and bulk tubing are available to mend a damaged air line.
- Collet and O-rings of the quick connect type fittings are replaceable.

Front Suspension

- Gas filled shock absorber struts must be replaced as assemblies. They are not serviceable. Replace only the damaged shock absorber strut. It is not necessary to replace in matched pairs.
- Strut upper mounts may be replaced individually.
- Air springs are replaced as assemblies. It is not necessary to replace in pairs.
- The lower control arm is replaceable as an assembly with the ball joint and bushings included.
- The spindle is replaceable.
- The stabilizer bar is replaceable with stabilizer bar-to-body insulators included.
- The stabilizer bar-to-body bushing is replaceable.

Rear Suspension

The following rear suspension components may be replaced individually:
- Gas filled shock absorbers must be replaced as assemblies. They are not serviceable. Replace only the damaged shock absorber. It is not necessary to replace in matched pairs.
- Air springs are replaced as assemblies. It is not necessary to replace in pairs.
- Lower control arms, including both end bushings, are replaceable as assemblies. (Must be replaced in pairs).

• Upper control arms, including body end bushing, are replaceable as assemblies. (Must be replaced in pairs.)

• Upper control arm axle and bushings are replaceable individually. (Must be replaced in pairs).

• Stabilizer bar is replaceable with stabilizer bar-to-axle insulator included.

• Stabilizer bar-to-body bushings are replaceable.

JACKING AND SUPPORTING

--------- CAUTION ---------

The electrical power supply to the air suspension system must be shut off prior to hoisting, jacking or towing an air suspension vehicle. This can be accomplished by disconnecting the battery or turning off the power switch located in the trunk on the LH side. Failure to do so may result in unexpected inflation or deflation of the air springs which may result in shifting of the vehicle during these operations.

Raise the front of the vehicle at the No. 2 crossmember until the tires are above the floor. Support the vehicle body with jackstands at each front corner and then lower the floor jack so that the front suspension is in full rebound. Repeat this procedure for the rear suspension, except raise the body at the rear jacking location.

AIR SPRING SYSTEM COMPONENTS

--------- CAUTION ---------

Power to the air system must be shut-off by turning the air suspension switch (in luggage compartment) Off or by disconnecting the battery when servicing any air suspension components.

• *Do not attempt to install or inflate any air spring that has become unfolded .*

• *Any spring which has unfolded must be refolded, prior to being installed in a vehicle.*

• *Do not attempt to inflate any air spring which has been collapsed while uninflated from the rebound hanging position to the jounce stop.*

• *After inflating an air spring in hanging position, it must be inspected for proper shape.*

• *Failure to follow the above procedures may result in a sudden failure of the air spring or suspension system.*

Air Spring Solenoid

The air spring solenoid valve has a two stage solenoid pressure relief fitting similar to a radiator cap. A clip is first removed, and rotation of the solenoid out of the spring will release air from the assembly before the solenoid can be removed.

1. Turn the air suspension switch Off.
2. Raise the vehicle. Remove wheel and tire assembly.

3. Disconnect the electrical connector and then disconnect the air line.

4. Remove the solenoid clip. Rotate the solenoid counterclockwise to the first stop.

5. Pull the solenoid straight out slowly to the second stop to bleed air from the system.

--------- CAUTION ---------

Do not fully release solenoid until air is completely bled from the air spring.

6. After the air is fully bled from the system, rotate the solenoid counterclockwise to the third stop, and remove the solenoid from the air spring assembly.

7. Check the solenoid O-ring for abrasion or cuts. Replace O-ring as required. Lightly grease the O-ring area of solenoid with silicone dielectric compound WA-10, D7AZ-19A331-A or equivalent.

8. Insert the solenoid into the air spring end cap and rotate clockwise to the third stop, push into the second stop, then rotate clockwise to the first stop.

9. Install solenoid clip. Connect the air line and the electrical connector.

10. Refill the air spring(s). Install the wheel and tire assembly.

Air Spring Fill

1. Turn On the air suspension switch. Diagnostic pigtail is to be ungrounded.

2. Connect a battery charger to reduce battery drain.

3. Cycle the ignition from the Off to Run position, hold in the Run position for a minimum of five seconds, then return to the Off position. Driver's door is open with all other doors shut.

4. Change the diagnostic pigtail from an ungrounded state to a grounded state by attaching a lead from the diagnostic pigtail to vehicle ground. The pigtail must remain grounded during the spring fill sequence.

5. While applying the brakes, turn the ignition switch to the Run position. (The door must be open. Do not start the vehicle). The warning lamp will blink continuously once very two seconds to indicate the spring pump sequence has been entered.

6. To fill a rear spring(s), close and open the door once. After a 6 second delay, the rear spring will be filled for 60 seconds.

7. To fill a front spring(s), close and open the door twice. After a 6 second delay, the front spring will be filled for 60 seconds.

8. To fill rear and front springs, fill the rear springs first (Step 6). When the rear fill has finished, close and open the door once to initiate the front spring fill.

9. Terminate the air spring fill by turning the ignition switch to Off, actuating the brake, or ungrounding the diagnostic pigtail. The diagnostic pigtail must be ungrounded at the end of spring fill.

10. Lower vehicle and start engine. Allow the vehicle to level with doors closed.

Air Spring—Front or Rear

1. Turn the air suspension switch Off.

2. Raise and support the vehicle. Suspension must be at full rebound.

3. Remove tire and wheel assembly.

4. Remove the air spring solenoid.

5. Remove the spring to lower arm fasteners. Remove the clip for front spring and/or remove bolts for rear spring.

6. Push down on the spring clip on the collar of the air spring and rotate collar counterclockwise to release the spring from the body spring seat. Remove the air spring.

7. Install the air spring solenoid. Correctly position the solenoid. For LH installation (front or rear spring), the notch on the collar is to be in line with the centerline of the solenoid. For RH installation (front or rear), the flat on the collar is to be in line with the centerline of the solenoid.

8. Install the air spring into the body spring seat, taking care to keep the solenoid air and electrical connections clean and free of damage. Rotate the air spring collar until the spring clip snaps into place. Be sure that the air spring collar is retained by the three rolled tabs on the body spring seat.

9. Attach the air line and electrical connector to the solenoid assembly.

10. Align and secure the lower arm to spring attachment with suspension at full rebound and supported by the shock absorbers.

--------- CAUTION ---------

The air springs may be damaged if suspension is allowed to compress before spring is inflated.

11. Replace the tire and wheel assembly.

12. Lower the vehicle until the tire and wheel assembly are 1–3 inches above floor. Refill the air spring(s).

Air Compressor and Dryer Assembly

1. Turn the air suspension switch Off.
2. Disconnect the electrical connector located on the compressor.
3. Remove the air line protector cap from the dryer by releasing the two latching pins located on the bottom of the cap 180 degrees apart.
4. Disconnect the four air lines from dryer.
5. Remove the three screws retaining the air compressor to mounting bracket.
6. Position the air compressor and dryer assembly to the mounting bracket and install the three mounting screws.
7. Connect the four air lines into the dryer.
8. Connect the electrical connection. Install the air line protector cap onto the dryer.
9. Turn the air suspension switch On.

Dryer, Air Compressor

1. Turn the air suspension switch Off.
2. Remove the air line protector cap from the dryer by releasing the two latching pins located on the bottom of the cap 180 degrees apart.

3. Disconnect the four air lines from the dryer.

4. Remove the dryer retainer clip and screw.

5. Remove from the head assembly.

6. Check to ensure the old O-ring is not in the head assembly.

7. Check the dryer end to ensure new O-ring is in proper position.

8. Insert the dryer into the head assembly and install the retainer clip and screw.

9. Connect the four air lines into the dryer.

10. Install the air line protector cap onto the dryer.

11. Turn the air suspension switch On.

Mounting Bracket, Air Compressor

1. Turn the air suspension switch Off.

2. Remove the air compressor and dryer assembly.

3. Raise and support the vehicle on jackstands.

4. Remove the left front tire and wheel assembly.

5. Remove the left front inner fender liner.

6. Remove the three bolts attaching the mounting bracket to body side apron.

7. Position the mounting bracket to the body side apron with the two locating tabs.

8. Secure the three bolts attaching the bracket to the body side apron.

9. Install the left front inner fender liner.

10. Install the tire and wheel assembly.

11. Lower the vehicle.

12. Install compressor and dryer assembly. Turn the air suspension switch On.

Height Sensors—Front

1. Turn the air suspension switch Off.

2. Disconnect the sensor electrical connector. The front sensor connectors are located in the engine compartment behind the shock towers.

3. Push the front sensor connector through the access hole in the rear of the shock tower.

4. Raise and support the vehicle on jackstands. Suspension must be at full rebound.

5. Disconnect the bottom and then the top end of the sensor from the attaching studs.

6. Disconnect the sensor wire harness from the plastic clips on the shock tower and remove sensor.

7. Connect the top and then the bottom end of the sensor to the attaching studs. Route the sensor electrical connector as required to connect to the vehicle wire harness.

8. Lower the vehicle. Connect the sensor connector. Turn the air suspension switch On.

Height Sensor—Rear

1. Turn the air suspension switch Off.

2. Disconnect the sensor electrical con-

nector located in the luggage compartment in front of the forward trim panel. Also pull the luggage compartment carpet back for access to the sensor sealing grommet located on the floor pan.

3. Raise and support the vehicle on jackstands. Suspension must be at full rebound.

4. Disconnect the bottom and then the top end of the sensor from the attaching studs.

5. Push upwards on the sealing grommet to unseat and then push sensor through the floor pan hole into the luggage compartment.

6. Lower the vehicle.

7. Connect the sensor connector and then push sensor through the floor pan hole being sure to seat the sealing grommet. Replace the luggage compartment carpet.

8. Raise and support the vehicle on jackstands.

9. Connect the top and then the bottom end of the sensor. Lower the vehicle.

10. Turn the air suspension switch On.

Control Module

1. Turn the air suspension switch Off. Ignition switch is also to be Off.

2. Remove the LH luggage compartment trim panel.

3. Disconnect the wire harness from the module.

4. Remove the three attaching nuts.

5. Remove the module.

6. Position the module and secure it with the three attaching nuts.

7. Connect the wire harness to the module.

8. Attach the LH luggage compartment trim panel. Turn the air suspension switch On.

Nylon Air Line

If a leak is detected in an air line, it can be serviced by carefully cutting the line with a sharp knife to ensure a good, clean, straight cut. Then, install a service fitting. If more tube is required, it can be obtained in bulk. The four air lines are color coded to show which spring they are connecting, but do not require orientation at the air compressor dryer. A protective plastic cap and convoluted tube protect the air lines from the dryer rearward over the left shock tower in the engine compartment. Routing of the lines after exiting the protective tube follows:

● **Left Front/Grey:** Down and through the rear wall of the left shock tower to the air spring solenoid.

● **Right Front/Back:** To cowl and along cowl on the right side of the vehicle, forward and down through the rear wall of the right shock tower to the air spring solenoid.

● **Left Rear/Green, Right Rear/Tan:** Through the left side apron into the fender well, through the left upper dash panel (sealing grommet) into the passenger compartment, down the dash panel to the left rocker, along the rocker to the left rear fender well, over the fender well into the luggage

compartment. The left air line goes down through the floor pan (sealing grommet) in front of the left rear shock tower. The right air line goes across the rear seat support and then down through the floor pan (sealing grommet) in front of the right rear shock tower.

Quick Connect Fittings

If a leak is detected in any of the eight quick connect fittings, it can be serviced using a repair kit containing a new O-ring, collet, release ring, and O-ring removal tool. The outer housing of the fitting cannot be serviced.

To remove the collet and O-ring, insert a scrap piece of air line, grasp the air line firmly (do not use pliers) and pull straight out (DO NOT use the release button). A force of 30–50 lbs. is required to remove the collet. After the retainer is removed, use the repair tool to remove the old O-ring.

To service, insert the new O-ring and seat it in the bottom of the fitting housing. Then, insert the new collet, being sure the end with four prongs is inserted. Press the collet into position with finger pressure. Install the new release button.

O-ring Seals

The areas that have O-ring seals that can be serviced are:

● Air compressor head to dryer: One O-ring.

● Air spring solenoid to end cap: Two O-rings each solenoid.

● Quick connect fitting: Four O-rings at dryer, one O-ring at each spring.

If air leaks are detected in these areas, the components can be removed, following the procedures outlined in this Section, and new O-rings can be installed.

Air Suspension Switch

1. Disconnect the electrical connector.

2. Depress the retaining clips that retain the switch to the brace, and remove switch.

3. Push the switch into position in the brace, making sure retaining clips are fully seated.

4. Connect electrical connector.

Compressor Relay

1. Disconnect the electrical connector.

2. Remove the screw retaining the relay to the left front shock tower and remove the relay.

3. Position the relay on the shock tower and install the retaining screw.

4. Connect the electrical connector.

FRONT SUSPENSION COMPONENTS

——— CAUTION ———
Power to the air system must be shut-off by turning the air suspension switch (in

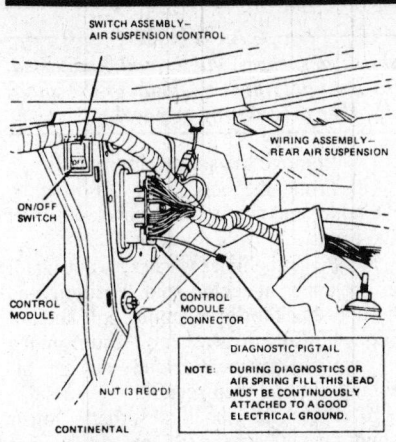

Air suspension cut-off switch— Continental

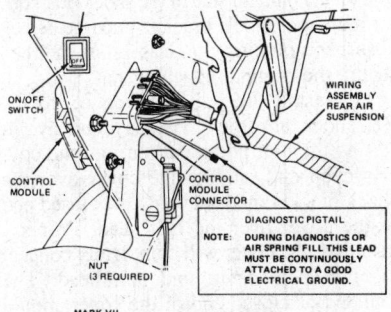

Air suspension cut-off switch—Mark VII

luggage compartment) Off or by disconnecting the battery when servicing any suspension components.

Stabilizer Bar Link Insulators

To replace the link insulators on each stabilizer link, use the following procedure:
1. Turn the air suspension switch Off.
2. Raise the vehicle and support on jackstands.
3. Remove the nut, washer, and insulator from the end of the stabilizer bar link attaching bolt.
4. Remove the bolt and the remaining washers, insulators and spacer.
5. Install the stabilizer bar link insulators by reversing the removal procedure.
6. Tighten the attaching nut.
7. Lower the vehicle. Turn air suspension system On.

Stabilizer Bar and/or Bushing

1. Turn the air suspension switch Off.
2. Raise the vehicle and support on jackstands.
3. Disconnect the stabilizer bar from each link and bushing U-clamps. Remove the stabilizer bar assembly.
4. Remove the adapter brackets and U-clamps.
5. Cut the worn bushings from the stabilizer bar.
6. Coat the necessary parts of the stabilizer bar with Ford Rubber Suspension Insulator Lubricant, E25Y-19553-A or

equivalent, and slide bushings onto the stabilizer bar. Reinstall the U-clamps.
7. Reinstall the adapter brackets on the U-clamps.
8. Using a new nut and bolt, secure each end of the stabilizer bar to the lower suspension arm.
9. Using new bolts, clamp the stabilizer bar to the attaching brackets on the side rail.
10. Lower the vehicle. Turn air suspension switch On.

Shock Strut Replacement

1. Turn the air suspension switch Off.
2. Turn the ignition key to the unlocked position to allow free movement of the front wheels.
3. From the engine compartment, loosen but do not remove the one 16mm strut-to-upper mount attaching nut. A suitable tapered tool inserted in the slot will hold the rod stationary while loosening the nut. The vehicle should be in place to be raised and must not be driven with the nut loosened or removed.
4. Raise and support the vehicle. Position safety stands under the lower control arms as far outboard as possible being sure that the lower sensor mounting bracket is clear. Lower until vehicle weight is supported by the lower arms.
5. Remove tire and wheel assembly.
6. Remove the brake caliper and wire out of the way.
7. Remove the strut-to-upper mount attaching nut and then the two lower nuts and bolts attaching the strut to the spindle.

NOTE: The strut should be held firmly during the removal of the last bolt since the gas pressure will cause the strut to fully extend when removed.

8. Lift the strut up from the spindle to compress the rod and then remove the strut.
9. Prime the new strut by extending and compressing the strut rod five times.
10. Place the strut rod through the upper mount, hand start and secure a new 16mm nut.
11. Compress the strut, and position onto the spindle.
12. Install two new lower mounting bolts, and hand start the nuts.
13. Raise the vehicle to remove load from the lower control arms, and tighten the lower mounting nuts.
14. Install the brake caliper. Install the tire and wheel assembly.
15. Remove safety stands and lower the vehicle to the ground.
16. Turn air suspension switch On.

NOTE: Front wheel alignment should be checked and adjusted, if out of specification.

Upper Mount Assembly

NOTE: Upper mounts are one piece units and cannot be disassembled.

1. Turn the air suspension system Off.

2. Turn the ignition key to the unlocked position to allow free movement of the front wheels.
3. From the engine compartment, loosen but do not remove the three 12mm upper mount retaining nuts. Vehicle should be in place over a hoist and must not be driven with these nuts removed. Do not remove the pop rivet holding the camber plate in position.
4. Loosen 16mm strut rod nut at this time.
5. Raise the vehicle and position safety stands under the lower control arms as far outboard as possible being sure that the lower sensor mounting bracket is clear. Lower until the vehicle weight is supported by the lower arms.
6. Remove the tire and wheel assembly.
7. Remove brake caliper and rotate out of position and wire securely out of the way.
8. Remove the upper mount retaining nuts and the two lower nuts and bolts that attach the strut to the spindle.

NOTE: The strut should be held firmly during the removal of the last bolt since the gas pressure will cause the strut to fully extend when removed.

9. Lift the strut up from the spindle to compress the rod, and then remove the strut.
10. Remove the upper mount from the strut.
11. Install a new upper mount on the strut and hand start a new 16mm nut.
12. Position the upper mount studs into the body and start and secure three new nuts. Secure the strut rod 16mm nut.
13. Compress the strut and position onto the spindle.
14. Install two new lower mounting bolts, and hand start nuts.
15. Raise the vehicle to remove load from the lower control arms and tighten the lower mounting nuts to 126–179 ft. lbs.
16. Install the brake caliper. Install the tire and wheel assembly.
17. Remove safety stands and lower vehicle to the ground.
18. Turn air suspension switch On.
19. Front wheel alignment should be checked and adjusted if out of specification.

Spindle Assembly

1. Turn the air suspension switch Off.
2. Raise and support the vehicle on jackstands.
3. Remove the wheel and tire assembly.
4. Remove the brake caliper, rotor and dust shield.
5. Remove the stabilizer link from the lower arm assembly.
6. Remove the tie rod end from the spindle.
7. Remove the cotter pin from the ball joint stud nut, and loosen the nut one or two turns.

—— **CAUTION** ——
DO NOT remove the nut from the ball joint stud at this time.

8. Tap the spindle boss smartly to relieve stud pressure.

9. Place a floor jack under the lower arm, compress the air spring and remove the stud nut.

10. Remove the two bolts and nuts attaching the spindle to the shock strut. Compress the shock strut until working clearance is obtained.

11. Remove the spindle assembly.

12. Place the spindle on the ball joint stud, and install the new stud nut. DO NOT tighten at this time.

13. Lower the shock strut until the attaching holes are in line with the holes in the spindle. Install two new bolts and nuts.

14. Tighten ball joint stud nut and install cotter pin.

15. Lower the floor jack from under the suspension arm, and remove jack.

16. Tighten the shock strut to spindle attaching nuts.

17. Install stabilizer bar link and tighten attaching nut.

18. Attach the tie rod end, and tighten the retaining nut.

19. Install the disc brake dust shield, rotor, and caliper.

20. Install the wheel and tire assembly.

21. Remove the safety stands, and lower the vehicle.

22. Turn air suspension switch On.

23. Front wheel alignment should be checked and adjusted if out of specification.

Suspension Control Arm

1. Turn the air suspension switch Off.

2. Raise the vehicle and support on jackstands, so the control arms hang free (full rebound).

3. Remove the wheel and tire assembly.

4. Disconnect the tie rod assembly from the steering spindle.

5. Remove the steering gear bolts, if necessary, and position the gear so that the suspension arm bolt may be removed.

6. Disconnect the stabilizer bar link from the lower arm.

7. Disconnect the lower end of the height sensor from the lower control arm sensor mounting stud. Remove the sensor mounting stud and unscrew from lower arm, noting the position of stud on the lower arm bracket.

8. Remove the cotter pin from the ball joint stud nut, and loosen the ball joint nut one or two turns. DO NOT remove the nut at this time. Tap spindle boss smartly to relieve stud pressure.

9. Vent the air spring(s) to atmospheric pressure. Then, reinstall the solenoid.

10. Remove the air spring to lower arm fastener clip.

11. Remove the ball joint nut, and raise the entire strut and spindle assembly (strut, rotor, caliper and spindle). Wire it out of the way to obtain working room.

12. Remove the suspension arm to crossmember nuts and bolts, and remove the arm from the spindle.

13. Position the arm into the crossmember and install new arm to crossmember bolts and nuts. DO NOT tighten at this time.

14. Remove the wire from the strut and spindle assembly and attach to the ball joint stud. Install a new ball joint stud nut. DO NOT tighten at this time.

15. Position the air spring in the arm and install a new fastener.

16. Attach the sensor mounting stud and screw to lower arm in the same position as original arm location. Connect the lower end of sensor to the lower arm mounting stud.

17. With a suitable jack, raise the suspension arm to curbheight.

18. With the jack still in place, tighten the lower arm to crossmember attaching nut to 150–180 ft. lbs.

19. Tighten ball joint stud nut to 100–120 ft. lbs., and install a new cotter pin. Remove jack.

20. Install the steering gear to crossmember bolts and nuts (if removed). Hold the bolts, and tighten nuts to 90–100 ft. lbs.

21. Position the tie rod assembly into the steering spindle, and install the retaining nut. Tighten the nut to 35 ft. lbs., and continue tightening the nut to align the next castellation with cotter pin hole in the stud. Install a new cotter pin.

22. Connect the stabilizer bar link to the lower suspension arm, and tighten the attaching nut to 9–12 ft. lbs.

23. Install the wheel and tire assembly, and lower the vehicle but DO NOT allow tires to touch the ground.

24. Turn the air suspension switch On.

25. Refill the air spring(s).

26. Front wheel alignment should be checked and adjusted if out of specification.

REAR SUSPENSION COMPONENTS

Shock Absorber

--- CAUTION ---

Power to the air system must be shut-off by turning the air suspension switch (in luggage compartment) Off or by disconnecting the battery when servicing any suspension components.

1. Turn the air suspension switch Off.

2. Open the luggage compartment and remove inside trim panels to gain access to the upper shock stud.

3. Loosen but do not remove the shock rod attaching nut.

4. Raise the vehicle and position two safety stands under the rear axle. Lower the vehicle until weight is supported by the rear axle.

5. Remove the upper attaching nut, washer and insulator and then remove the lower shock protective cover (right shock only) and lower shock absorber cross bolt and nut from the lower shock brackets.

6. From under the vehicle, compress the shock absorber to clear it from the hold in the upper shock tower.

--- CAUTION ---

Shock absorbers will extend unassisted. Do not apply heat or flame to the shock absorber tube during removal.

7. Remove the shock absorber.

8. Prime the new shock absorber by extending and compressing shock absorber five times.

9. Place the inner washer and insulator on the upper attaching stud. Position stud through shock tower mounting hole and position an insulator, washer on stud from the luggage compartment. Hand start the attaching nut and then secure.

10. Place the shock absorber's lower mounting eye between the ears of the lower shock mounting bracket, compressing shock as required. Insert the bolt, (bolt head must seat on the inboard side of the shock bracket), through the shock bracket and the shock absorber mounting eye. Hand start and then secure the original attaching nut.

11. Install the protective cover, to the RH shock absorber. This is done by inserting the bolt point and nut into the cover's open end, sliding the cover over the shock bracket, and snapping the closed end of the cover over the bolt head. Properly installed, the cover will completely conceal the bolt point, nut, and bolt head. The rounded or closed end of the cover should be pointing inboard.

12. Raise the vehicle and remove safety stands from under axle, then lower the vehicle.

13. Reinstall the inside trim panels.

14. Turn air suspension switch On.

Lower Control Arm

NOTE: If one arm requires replacement, replace the other arm also.

1. Turn the air suspension switch Off.

2. Raise and support the vehicle so that the suspension will be at full rebound.

3. Remove tire and wheel assembly.

4. Vent air spring(s) to atmospheric pressure. Then, reinstall the solenoid.

5. Remove the two air spring-to-lower arm bolts and remove the air spring from the lower arm.

6. Remove the frame-to-arm and the axle-to-arm bolts and remove the arm from the vehicle.

7. Position the lower arm assembly into the front arm brackets, and insert a new, arm-to-frame pivot bolt and nut with nut facing outwards. DO NOT tighten at this time.

8. Position the rear bushing in the axle bracket and install a new arm-to-axle pivot bolt and nut with nut facing outwards. DO NOT tighten at this time.

9. Install two new air spring-to-arm bolts. DO NOT tighten at this time.

10. Using a suitable jack, raise the axle to curb height. Tighten the lower arm front bolt, the rear pivot bolt, and the air spring to arm bolt being sure that the air spring piston is flat on the lower arm. Remove the jack.

11. Replace tire and wheel assembly.
12. Lower the vehicle.
13. Turn the air suspension switch On.
14. Refill the air spring(s).

Upper Control Arm and Axle Bushing

NOTE: If one arm requires replacement, replace the other arm also.

1. Turn the air suspension switch Off.
2. Raise and support the vehicle so that the suspension will be at full rebound.
3. On the RH side detach rear height sensor from side arm. Note position of the sensor adjustment bracket on the upper arm.
4. Remove the upper arm-to-axle pivot bolt and nut.
5. Remove the upper arm-to-frame pivot bolt and nut. Remove upper arm from vehicle.

If upper arm axle bushing is to be replaced, use Tool T78P-5638-A or equivalent and the following procedure:

6. Place the upper arm axle bushing remover tool in position and remove the bushing assembly.
7. Using the installer tool, install the bushing assembly into the bushing ear of the rear axle.
8. Place the upper arm into the bracket of body side rail. Insert a new upper arm-to-frame pivot bolt and nut (nut facing outboard). DO NOT tighten at this time.
9. Align the upper arm-to-axle pivot hole with the hole in the axle bushing. If required, raise the axle using a suitable jack to align. Install a new pivot bolt and nut (nut inboard). DO NOT tighten at this time.
10. On the RH side, reattach rear height sensor to the arm. Set the adjustment bracket to the same position as on the replaced arm and tighten nut.
11. Using a suitable jack, raise the axle to curb height, and tighten the front upper arm bolt, and the rear upper arm bolt.
12. Remove the jackstands supporting the axle.
13. Lower the vehicle.
14. Turn the air suspension switch On.

Stabilizer Bar Link Insulators

1. Turn the air suspension switch Off.
2. Raise and support the vehicle on jackstands.
3. Remove the nut, washer and insulator from the end of the stabilizer bar link attaching bolt.
4. Remove the bolt and the remaining spacer, washer and insulators.
5. Install the stabilizer bar link insulators by reversing the removal procedure. A new bolt and nut must be used.
6. Tighten the attaching nut.
7. Lower the vehicle.
8. Turn the air suspension switch On.

Stabilizer Bar Bushings

1. Turn the air suspension switch Off.
2. Raise and support the vehicle on jackstands.

3. Disconnect the stabilizer bar from each link and bushing U-clamp. Remove the stabilizer bar assembly.
4. Remove the U-clamps.
5. Cut the worn bushings from the stabilizer bar.
6. Coat the necessary parts of the stabilizer bar with Ford Rubber Suspension Insulator Lubricant E25Y-19553-A or equivalent and slide new bushings onto the stabilizer bar. Reinstall U-clamps.
7. Using new bolts and nuts, attach stabilizer bar to the axle. Do not tighten bolts at this time.
8. Using new bolts and nuts, attach the link end of the stabilizer bar to the body. Tighten the link attaching nut and then the axle attaching bolts.
9. Lower the vehicle.
10. Turn the air suspension switch On.

BRAKES

An independent parking brake operates the rear wheel brake shoes or pads through a mechanical cable linkage. Front disc brakes are used. Rear disc brakes are standard on Versailles and available on various models when equipped with the hydraulically assisted Hydro-Boost System. Complete service procedures are in the Unit Repair Section.

Master Cylinder

REMOVAL & INSTALLATION

A tandem-type (dual) master cylinder is used on all models. This design divides the brake hydraulic system into two independent and hydraulically separated halves. In the event of a single hydraulic failure, 50% braking efficiency is maintained.

Standard Brakes

1. Working under the dash, disconnect the master cylinder pushrod from the brake pedal. The pushrod cannot be removed from the master cylinder.
2. Disconnect the stoplight switch wires and remove the switch from the brake pedal, using care not to damage the switch.
3. Disconnect the brake lines from the master cylinder.
4. Remove the attaching screws from the firewall and remove the master cylinder from the car.
5. Reinstall in reverse order, leaving the brake line fittings loose at the master cylinder.
6. Fill the master cylinder, and with the brake lines loose, slowly bleed the air from the master cylinder using the foot pedal.

Power Brakes

1. Disconnect the brake lines from the master cylinder.

2. Remove the two nuts and lockwashers that attach the master cylinder to the brake booster.
3. Remove the master cylinder from the booster.
4. Reverse the procedure to reinstall.
5. Fill master cylinder and bleed entire brake system.
6. Refill master cylinder.

Power Brake Vacuum Unit

REMOVAL & INSTALLATION

1. Working inside the car below the instrument panel, disconnect booster valve operating rod from the brake pedal assembly.

To do this, disconnect the stop light switch wires at the connector. Remove the hairpin retainer and nylon washer from the pedal pin. Slide the switch off just enough for the outer arm to clear the pin. Remove the switch. Slide the booster push rod, bushing and inner nylon washer off the pedal pin.

2. Remove the air cleaner for working clearance if necessary. On four cylinder models, disconnect the accelerator cable at the carburetor. Remove the securing screw from the accelerator shaft bracket and remove the cable from the bracket. Remove the two screws attaching the bracket to the manifold; rotate the bracket toward the engine.
3. Disconnect the brake lines at the master cylinder outlet fittings.
4. Disconnect manifold vacuum hose from the booster unit. On cars equipped with speed control, remove the left cowl screen in the engine compartment. Remove three nuts retaining the speed control servo to the firewall and move the servo out of the way.
5. Remove the four bracket-to-firewall attaching bolts.
6. Remove the booster and bracket assembly from the firewall, sliding the valve operating rod out from the engine side.
7. Installation is the reverse of removal. Bleed the brakes after installation is complete.

Hydro-Boost Power Unit

REMOVAL & INSTALLATION

1. Open the hood and remove the two nuts attaching the master cylinder to the brake booster.
2. Remove the master cylinder from the Hydro-Boost accumulator.
3. Set the master cylinder aside without disturbing the hydraulic lines.
4. Disconnect the pressure, steering and return lines from the accumulator.
5. Plug the lines and ports.

6. Working below the instrument panel, disconnect the Hydro-Boost pushrod from the brake pedal. To do this, disconnect the stoplight switch at the connector. Remove the hairpin retainer. Slide the stoplight switch from the brake pedal pin far enough to clear the switch outer pin hole. Remove the switch from the pin.

7. Loosen the Hydro-Boost attaching nuts and remove the pushrod, washers and bushing from the brake pedal pin.

8. Remove the accumulator.

9. Installation is the reverse of removal. Leave the Hydro-Boost mounting nuts loose until the pushrod and stoplight switch are connected to the brake pedal. After installation, remove the coil wire from the distributor. Fill the power steering reservoir, and while cranking the engine, pump the brake pedal. Do not move the steering wheel until all the air has been pumped out of the system. Check the power steering fluid level, install the coil wire, start the engine and pump the brakes while steering from lock to lock. Check for leaks.

Parking Brake

ADJUSTMENT

NOTE: If a new cable is installed, prestretch it by applying and releasing five times before making any adjustments.

Rear Drum Brakes

In most cases, a rear brake shoe adjustment will provide satisfactory parking brake action. However, if parking brake cables are excessively loose after releasing the handbrake, proceed as follows:

Hand Operated Lever

1. Fully release the parking brake.
2. Place the transmission in Neutral and raise the rear axle until the rear wheels clear the floor.
3. Pry the handle cover up inside the car. The rear of the cover is held by two screws. Tighten the adjusting nut until the rear brakes drag when the rear wheels are turned.
4. Loosen the adjusting nut until the rear wheels can be turned without the rear brakes dragging. Apply the parking brake, release it, and repeat Steps 3 and 4 one time.
5. Lower the rear of the vehicle and check the operation of the parking brake.

Foot Operated Lever

1. Fully release the parking brake.
2. Loosen locknut on equalizer rod under the car. Then loosen the nut in front of the equalizer, several turns.
3. Turn the locknut forward against the equalizer until the cables are tight enough so that the rear wheels cannot be turned by hand. Then, back off the adjustment until the rear wheels turn freely.

4. When cables are properly adjusted, tighten both nuts against the equalizer.
5. Apply and release the brake and feel for freeness of rear wheels.

Disc Brakes

1. Fully release the parking brake.
2. Place the transmission in Neutral. If it is necessary to raise the car to reach the adjusting nut and observe the parking brake levers, use an axle hoist or a floor jack positioned beneath the differential. This is necessary so that the rear axle remains at the curb attitude, not stretching the parking brake cables.

─── CAUTION ───
If you are raising the rear of the car only, block the front wheels.

3. Locate the adjusting nut beneath the car on the driver's side. While observing the parking brake actuating levers on the rear calipers, tighten the adjusting nut until the levers just begin to move. Then, loosen the nut sufficiently for the levers to fully return to the stop position. The levers are in the stop position when a ¼ in. pin can be inserted past the side of the lever into the holes in the cast iron housing.
4. Check the operation of the parking brake. Make sure the actuating levers return to the stop position by attempting to pull them rearward. If the lever moves rearward, the cable adjustment is too tight, which will cause a dragging rear brake and consequent brake overheating and fade.

STEERING

Tie-Rod End

REMOVAL & INSTALLATION
Except Rack and Pinion

1. Raise and support the front end.
2. Remove the cotter pin and nut from the rod end ball stud.
3. Loosen the sleeve clamp bolts and remove the rod end from the spindle arm center link using a ball joint separator.
4. Remove the rod end from the sleeve, counting the exact number of turns required.
5. Install the new end using the exact number of turns it took to remove the old one.
6. Install all parts. Torque the stud to 40–43 ft. lbs., and the clamp to 20–22 ft lbs.
7. Check the toe-in.

Rack and Pinion Models

1. Remove the cotter pin and nut at the spindle. Separate the tie-rod end stud from the spindle with a puller.
2. Matchmark the position of the lock-

nut with paint on the tie-rod. Unscrew the locknut. Unscrew the tie-rod end, counting the number of turns required to remove.
3. Install the new end the same number of turns. Attach the tie-rod end stud to the spindle. Install the nut and torque to 35 ft. lbs., then continue to tighten until the cotter pin holes align. Install a new cotter pin. Check the toe and adjust if necessary, then torque the tie-rod end locknut to 35 ft. lbs.

Manual Steering Gear

REMOVAL & INSTALLATION
Worm and Recirculating Ball

1. Position the steering wheel in the straight ahead position.
2. Remove the bolt(s) retaining the flex coupling to the steering shaft. Match mark the coupling and steering shaft and separate.

NOTE: Separation can be accomplished when the steering gear box is lowered, if necessary.

3. Remove the retaining nut and washer from the pitman arm to sector shaft. Using a puller, separate the pitman arm from the sector shaft.

NOTE: It may be necessary to match mark the two components before separation.

4. It may be necessary to disconnect the clutch linkage on vehicles equipped with manual transmissions. V8 models may have to have the exhaust system lowered to provide clearance for the removal of the steering gear.
5. Remove the steering gear to side rail retaining bolts and remove the steering gear from the vehicle.
6. The installation is the reverse of the removal procedure. Be sure to align the reference marks when reinstalling.

Rack and Pinion

1. Disconnect the battery negative cable.
2. Remove the retaining bolt from the flexible coupling to the steering shaft.
3. Place the ignition switch in the "ON" position and raise the vehicle and support safely.
4. Remove the right and left tie-rod end retaining nuts and separate the studs from the spindle arms, using a separator tool.
5. Support the steering rack and pinion assembly and remove the retaining nuts, bolts and washers insulators.

NOTE: On certain models such as the Mustang, it is necessary to remove the crossmember to allow clearance for the removal of the rack and pinion.

6. Remove the rack and pinion from the vehicle.
7. The installation is the reverse of the removal procedure.

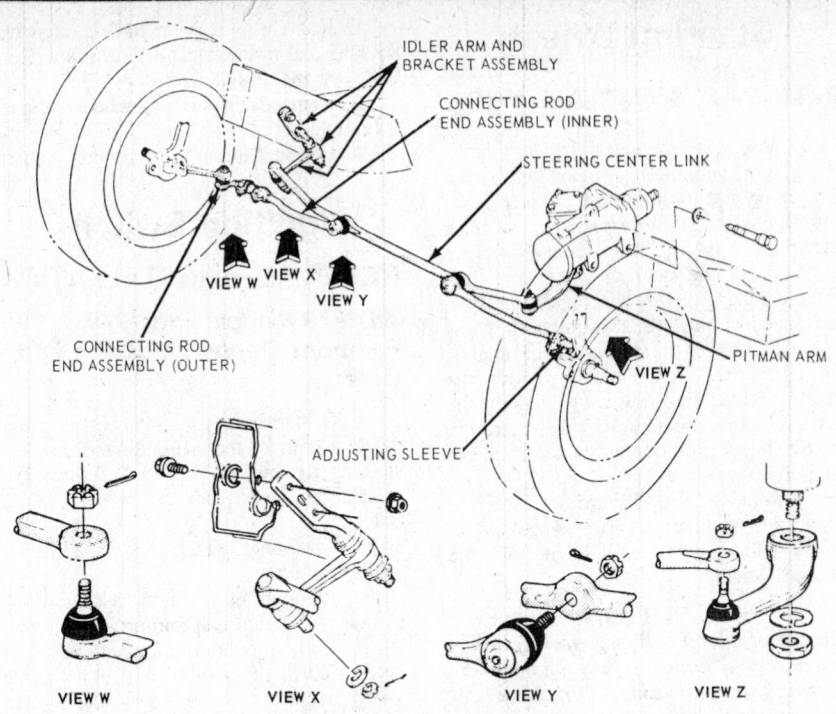

Typical steering linkage

Power Steering Gear

REMOVAL & INSTALLATION

Non-Integral—Control Valve Assembly

1. Raise the vehicle and support safely.
2. Remove the clamp retaining the fluid lines to the outside of the control valve.
3. Disconnect the fluid lines after marking each for reassembly. Allow the fluid to drain.
4. Turn the wheels to the left and right several times to force the fluid from the system.
5. Loosen the clamping bolt at the end of the control valve sleeve.
6. Remove the roll-pin from the steering arm to center link through the slot in the control valve sleeve.
7. Remove the cotter pin and the control valve ball stud nut. Remove the ball stud from the sector shaft arm (pitman arm).

NOTE: A special control valve ball stud removing tool should be used to prevent damage to the control valve assembly during removal.

8. Remove the valve assembly from the centerlink by turning the control valve counterclockwise until the valve assembly separates from the centerlink.
9. The installation should follow the outlined procedure:

    a. Thread the control valve on the centerlink until approximately four threads are visible on the centerlink.

    b. Position the ball stud in the sector shaft arm and measure the distance between the center of the left spindle connecting rod hole in the centerlink to the end of the control valve. This distance must be 2.55–2.65 in.

    c. If the distance is not correct, disengage the ball stud from the sector shaft arm and turn the control valve on the centerlink to increase or decrease the distance.

    d. When the ball stud is correctly positioned, align the hole in the steering arm to centerlink with the slot near the end of the valve sleeve and install the roll pin.

    e. Complete the assembly in the reverse of the removal procedure, fill with fluid and bleed the system.

Power Cylinder

1. Raise the vehicle and support safely.
2. Disconnect the fluid lines from the power cylinder and allow to drain.
3. Remove the PAL crimp nut, washer and the insulator from the end of the power cylinder rod.
4. Remove the cotterpin and nut that retains the power cylinder to the center link.
5. Disconnect the power cylinder stud from the center link by using a steering arm remover tool.
6. Remove the insulator sleeve and washer from the end of the power cylinder rod. Remove the cylinder rod boot and discard the clamp.
7. The installation of the power cylinder is the reverse of the removal procedure. Fill with fluid and bleed the system.

Integral Gear Assembly

1. Remove the stone shield, if equipped.
2. Tag the fluid lines and remove from the steering gear. Allow to drain.

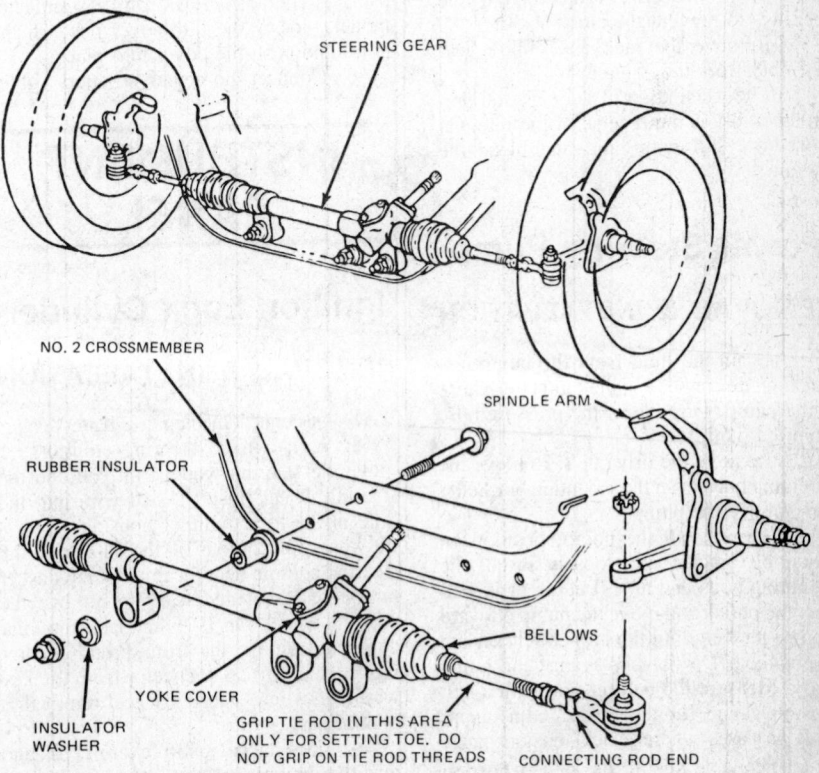

Rack and pinion steering linkage (© Ford Motor Co.)

C269

3. Plug the lines and ports to avoid entry of dirt.

4. Remove the bolts that retain the flexible coupling to the steering column and gear.

5. Raise the vehicle and support safely. Remove the sector shaft nut and washer.

6. Remove the pitman arm with a special pulling tool to avoid damage to the shaft.

7. Support the steering gear assembly and remove the gear box retaining bolts from the side rail or bracket.

8. Remove the clamping bolt from the flexible coupling and work the steering gear from the flex coupling and remove from the vehicle.

9. The installation of the steering gear is the reverse of the removal procedure. Fill with fluid and bleed the system.

Rack and Pinion Power Steering

1. Disconnect the negative battery cable.

2. Remove the bolt retaining the flexible coupling to the steering input shaft.

3. Place the ignition key in the ''ON'' position and raise the vehicle and support safely.

4. Remove the two tie rod end retaining nuts and cotter pins. Separate the tie rod stud from the spindle arms with the use of a separator tool.

5. Support the rack and pinion and remove the retaining nuts, washers and bolts from the rack and pinion to the crossmember.

6. Lower the gear assembly slightly to gain access to the pressure and return line fittings. Disconnect the fittings and plug the openings to prevent the entry of dirt.

7. Remove the rack and pinion gear assembly from the vehicle.

8. The installation of the rack and pinion assembly is the reverse of the removal procedure. Fill with fluid and bleed the system.

Power Steering Pump

REMOVAL & INSTALLATION

1. Drain the fluid from the pump reservoir by disconnecting the fluid return hose at the pump. Disconnect the pressure hose from the pump.

2. Remove the drive belt. Remove the mounting bolts from the mounting bracket(s) and remove the pump.

3. To reinstall the pump, position on mounting bracket and loosely install the mounting bolts and nuts. Put the drive belt over the pulley and move the pump outward against the belt until the proper belt tension is obtained. Do not pry against the pump body. Measure the belt tension with a belt tension gauge for the proper adjustment. Only in cases where a belt tension gauge is not available should the belt deflection method be used.

4. Tighten the mounting bolts and nuts.

Steering Wheel

REMOVAL & INSTALLATION

1. Disconnect the negative battery cable.

2. If the vehicle is equipped with a horn ring, remove it by rotating it counterclockwise. If equipped with a steering wheel crash pad, remove the retaining screws from the underside of the steering wheel and then remove the crash pad. Disconnect the horn and speed control (if so equipped) wires from the inside of the steering wheel center. On 1980 and later models, remove the steering wheel hub cover by pushing the cover retaining posts out with a rod through the two holes provided on the back side of the hub.

3. Remove and discard the steering wheel nut, install a steering wheel puller on the end of the shaft, and remove the steering wheel.

CAUTION

The use of a knockoff type steering wheel puller and a hammer may damage the steering column bearing or (in the case of the collapsible-type steering wheel) the column itself.

---

4. With the front wheels positioned straight ahead, line up the marks on the steering wheel and column and install the steering wheel and a new locknut. Tighten the nut to 30–40 ft. lbs.

5. Connect the horn and speed control wires and install the horn ring and the crash pad and retaining screws. On 1980 and later models, locate the hub cover posts in the holes and push the cover into place.

6. Connect the negative battery cable.

INSTRUMENT PANEL

Ignition Lock Cylinder

REMOVAL & INSTALLATION

1. Disconnect the negative battery cable.

2. With a fixed steering column, remove the steering wheel trim pad and the steering wheel. Insert a stiff wire into the hole in the lock cylinder housing. With a tilt wheel, this hole is on the outside of the steering column near the emergency flasher button; it is not necessary to remove the steering wheel. On 1979 and later modular columns, remove the trim shroud and remove the electrical connector from the key warning switch; steering wheel removal is unnecessary.

3. Place the gear shift lever in Park and turn the ignition key to the ON position.

4. Depress the wire and remove the lock cylinder and wire.

5. Insert the new cylinder into the housing and turn to the OFF position. This will lock the cylinder into position.

6. Reinstall the steering wheel and pad if removed.

7. Connect the negative battery cable.

Ignition Switch

REMOVAL & INSTALLATION

All 1978 Models and 1979 Fairmont, Zephyr, Mustang and Capri

1. Disconnect the negative battery cable.

2. Remove the shrouding from the steering column, and detach and lower the steering column from the brake support bracket.

3. Disconnect the switch wiring at the multiple plug.

4. Remove the two nuts that retain the switch to the steering column.

5. With a column mounted gearshift lever, detach the switch plunger from the switch actuator rod and remove the switch. With console mounted gearshift lever, remove the pin connecting the plunger to the actuator and remove the switch.

6. To re-install the switch, place both the lock mechanism at the top of the column and the switch itself in lock position for correct adjustment. To hold the column in the lock position, place the shift lever in PARK and turn to LOCK and remove the key. New switches are held in the LOCK position by plastic shipping pins. To pin used switches, pull the switch plunger out as far as it will go and push it back into the first detent. Insert wire in the locking hole in the top of the switch.

NOTE: A 5/64 in. lock pin hole is located on the right side of the blade type switch, next to the steering column. A 3/32 in. lock pin hole is located on the uppermost part of the switch at the metal junction on the pigtail type switch.

7. Connect the switch plunger to the switch actuator rod.

8. Position the switch on the column and install the attaching nuts. Do not tighten them.

9. Move the switch up and down to locate mid-position of rod lash, and then tighten the nuts.

10. Remove the locking pin or wire.

11. Attach the steering column to the brake support bracket and install the shrouding.

All Models 1979 and Later Except 1979 Fairmont, Zephyr, Mustang and Capri

1. Disconnect the negative battery cable.

2. Remove the upper shroud below the steering wheel by unsnapping the retaining clips. On the tilt column it will be necessary to remove the five attaching screws.

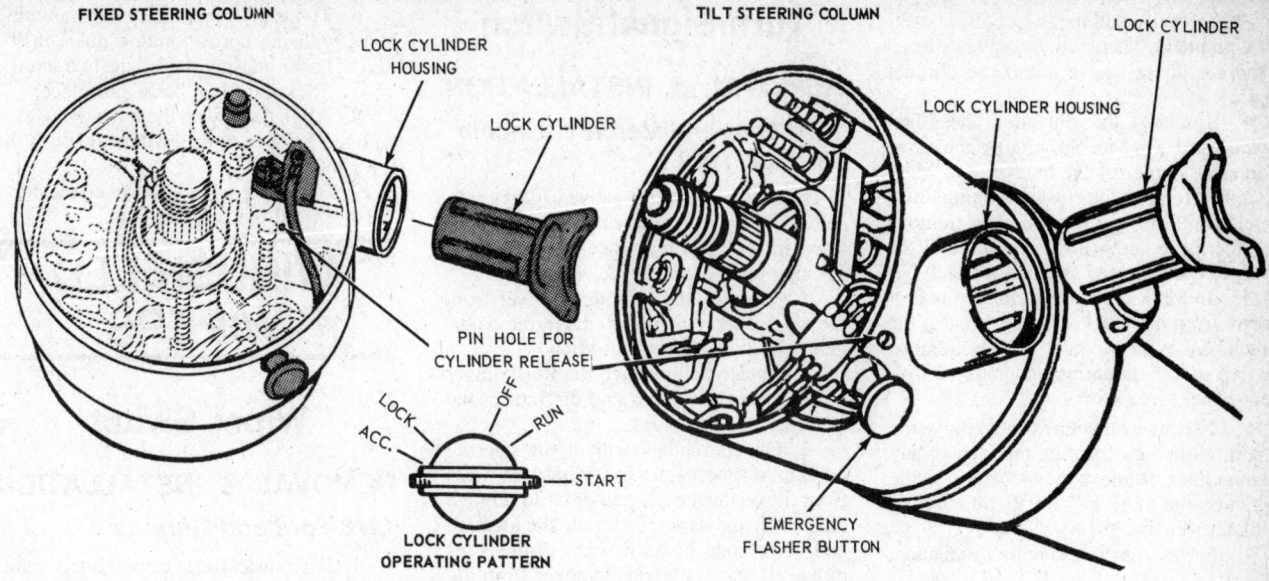

FIXED STEERING COLUMN

LOCK CYLINDER HOUSING

LOCK CYLINDER

PIN HOLE FOR CYLINDER RELEASE

LOCK CYLINDER OPERATING PATTERN

LOCK
ACC.
OFF
RUN
START

TILT STEERING COLUMN

LOCK CYLINDER HOUSING

LOCK CYLINDER

EMERGENCY FLASHER BUTTON

Lock cylinder replacement with locking column (© Ford Motor Co)

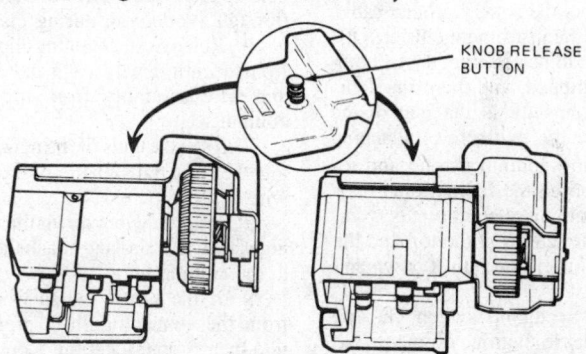

KNOB RELEASE BUTTON

Headlight switch and release button location (© Ford Motor Co.)

3. Disconnect the electrical connector from the ignition switch.

4. Drill out the bolts holding the switch to the lock cylinder using a ⅛ in. drill bit.

5. Remove the bolts using an Easy-Out® bolt extractor.

6. Disengage the switch from the actuator pin.

7. Adjust the new ignition switch by sliding the carrier to the Lock position. Insert a small drill bit through the switch housing and into the carrier to restrict movement of the carrier with respect to the switch housing. A new replacement comes with an adjusting pin already installed.

8. Turn the ignition key to the Lock position.

9. Install the ignition switch on the actuator pin.

10. Install new "break-off head" bolts and tighten them until the heads break off. Tighten bolts evenly.

11. Remove the drill bit or adjusting pin.

12. Connect all electrical connections and the negative battery cable.

13. Start the car and check for proper operation of the switch.

14. Install the steering column shroud.

Headlight Switch

REMOVAL & INSTALLATION

1978 Ford and Mercury

1. Disconnect the negative battery cable. Remove the knob from the washer switch.

2. Remove the instrument panel pad, and instrument cluster.

3. Pull the headlight switch control knob to the full ON position and press the release knob on the switch. With the knob depressed, pull the knob and shaft from the switch.

4. Remove the wire connector from the back of the switch and, if equipped with headlight doors, remove the vacuum hoses.

5. Remove the bezel retaining nut and remove the switch from the dash.

6. Reverse the above procedure to reinstall. When installing the headlight switch control knob and shaft, turn the shaft in the switch until a distinct click is heard, locking the shaft in place.

1979 and Later Ford and Mercury

1. Disconnect the negative battery cable.

2. Underneath the instrument panel, depress the shaft retaining knob and pull the knob straight out.

3. Unscrew the trim bezel and remove the locknut.

4. Underneath the instrument panel, move the switch toward the front of the car while tilting it downward.

5. Disconnect the wiring from the switch and remove the switch from the car.

6. Installation is the reverse of removal.

Lincoln Through 1979 Without Headlamp Delay System

1. Disconnect the negative battery terminal.

2. Remove the knob and shaft by pressing release knob button on the switch housing behind the instrument panel with the knob in full on position.

3. Remove the moulding nut from switch.

4. Remove the wiring connector from switch.

5. Reverse the procedure for installation.

Mark IV and V Without Headlamp Delay System

1. Disconnect the negative battery terminal.

2. Remove the instrument cluster trim panel.

3. Remove the lighting switch mounting plate.

4. Remove the bezel nut and disconnect the multiple connector.

5. Remove the vacuum lines and the switch.

6. Reverse the procedure to install.

Lincoln, Mark IV, Mark V with Headlamp Delay System, and All 1980 and Later Models

1. Disconnect the battery ground cable.

2. Remove the switch knob and shaft.

3. Carefully pull the two control bezels out with pliers. There will be only one bezel if the car doesn't have automatic dimmer control.

4. Unscrew the threaded headlight switch bezel. On Lincoln, remove the screw at the rear corner of the bracket. On Mark IV and V, remove the cluster opening finish panel. On 1980 and later models, remove the steering column lower shroud and the lower left instrument panel trim bezel.

5. On Mark IV and V, remove the four screws from the bracket on the front of the switch. On 1980 and later models, remove the five switch mounting bracket-to-instrument panel screws.

6. Disconnect the wires and remove the switch. Note their location and detach any vacuum lines. Remove the bracket from the switch on the Mark IV and V and all 1980 and later models.

7. Reverse the procedure for installation.

Pinto and Bobcat Through 1979

1. Disconnect the battery ground cable.

2. Remove the instrument cluster. Disconnect the speedometer cable, the tachometer cable if equipped, and the printed circuit multiple connector at the rear of the cluster. Remove the two screws attaching the lower steering column shroud and remove it; then loosen the forward and rearward steering column attaching nuts ½ in. Remove the four screws at the top and the bottom of the cluster and pull it down and away.

3. Pull the headlamp switch On and depress the release button. Remove the headlight switch control knob, shaft and retaining nut.

4. Disconnect the multiple connector from the switch and remove the switch from instrument cluster opening.

5. Reverse above procedure to install.

1980 Pinto and Bobcat

1. Disconnect the negative battery cable.

2. Pull the headlight switch out to the On position.

3. Reach under the dashboard and depress the knob and shaft retainer button on the headlight switch.

4. Disconnect the wiring and remove the switch.

5. Reverse to install.

Mustang II

1. Disconnect the battery ground cable.

2. Through the hole in the underside of the instrument panel, press the release button with a screwdriver, and remove the knob and shaft assembly.

3. Remove the bezel nut, lower switch and disconnect the multiple connector.

4. Remove the switch.

5. Install the headlight switch in the reverse order of removal.

Turn Signal Switch

REMOVAL & INSTALLATION

1978 Ford and Mercury, Lincoln Through 1979

1. Disconnect the negative battery cable.

2. Remove the steering wheel as outlined in the Steering Wheel Removal and Installation section.

3. Unscrew the turn signal lever from the side of the column. Remove the emergency flasher retainer and knob.

4. Locate and remove the finish cover on the steering column and disconnect the wiring connector plugs.

5. On all models with a tilt steering column, it is necessary to separate the wires from the connector plug in order to remove the switch and wires. First note the location and color code of each wire, prior to removal. Remove the plastic cover from the wiring harness. Attach a piece of heavy cord to the switch wires to pull them down through the column during installation.

6. Remove the retaining clips and screws from the turn signal switch and lift the switch and wire assembly from the top of the column.

7. Tape the ends of the new switch wires together and transfer the pull cord to these wires.

8. Pull the wires down through the columns with the cord and attach the new switch to the column hub.

9. If the switch wires were separated from the connector plug, press the wires into their proper location. Connect the wiring connector plugs and install the finish cover on the column.

10. Install the turn signal lever. Install the emergency flasher retainer and knob, if so equipped.

11. Install the steering wheel as outlined in the Steering Wheel Removal and Installation section.

12. Connect the negative battery cable and test the operation of the turn signals, horn, emergency flashers, and speed control, if so equipped.

1979 and Later Ford, Mercury 1980 and Later Lincoln

1. On standard steering columns, remove the upper extension shroud (below the steering wheel) by snapping the shroud from the retaining clip. On tilt columns, remove the trim shroud by removing the five self-tapping screws.

2. Use a pulling and twisting motion, while pulling straight out, to remove the turn signal switch lever.

3. Peel back the piece of foam rubber from around the switch.

4. Disconnect the two switch electrical connectors.

5. Remove the two self-tapping screws which secure the switch to the lock cylinder housing, and disengage the switch from the housing.

6. To install, align the switch mounting holes with the corresponding holes in the lock cylinder housing. Install the two screws.

7. Stick the foam back into place.

8. Align the key on the turn signal lever with the keyway in the switch and push the lever into place.

9. Install the two electrical connectors.

10. Install the trim shrouds.

WINDSHIELD WIPERS

Wiper Switch

REMOVAL & INSTALLATION

1978 Ford and Mercury

1. Disconnect the negative battery cable.

2. Remove the control knobs for the wiper/washer and headlamp switches.

3. Remove the headlamp switch bezel and the trim panel.

4. Remove the wiper washer switch retaining screws and move the switch rearward.

5. Disconnect the multiple wire connector at the rear of the switch and remove the switch.

6. Reverse the removal procedure to install the switch assembly.

1978–79 Mark IV, V

1. Disconnect the battery ground cable.

2. Remove the instrument cluster finish panel.

3. Remove the wiper switch mounting plate and disconnect the wiper switch and cigar lighter wiring. Remove the retaining nut and remove the wiper switch.

4. The installation of the switch is the reverse of the removal procedure.

1978 Lincoln Continental

1. Disconnect the battery ground cable.

2. Remove the wiper switch knob.

3. Remove the bezel nut and pull the wiper switch from the mounting hole.

4. Disconnect the wiring connector and remove the switch.

5. Reverse the removal procedure to install the switch.

1978 Mustang, Granada, Monarch, 1978–80 Versailles

1. Disconnect the negative battery cable.

2. Separate the wiring connector after releasing the locking tabs.

3. Remove the two lower instrument panel screws and remove the lower instrument panel shield.

4. Remove the two steering column cover screws and separate the steering column cover halves.

5. Remove the wiring shield.

6. Using a number T-20 internal driver bit or its equivalent, remove the retaining

screw and remove the windshield wiper/washer-turnsignal arm assembly.

NOTE: The wiper/washer switch is an integral part of the turnsignal switch arm and cannot be repaired separately.

1979 and Later Ford, Mercury, Fairmont, Zephyr, 1980 and Later Lincoln, Mark VI, Thunderbird, XR-7, Cougar, 1979–81 Mustang, Capri

1. Disconnect the negative battery cable.
2. Remove the split steering column cover retaining screws.
3. Separate the two halves and remove the wiper switch retaining screws.
4. Disconnect the wire connector and remove the wiper switch.
5. The installation of the wiper switch is the reverse of the removal procedure.

1978–79 Thunderbird, Cougar, LTD II

1. Disconnect the battery ground cable.
2. Remove the wiper switch knob.
3. Remove the bezel nut and pull the switch assembly out of the mounting hole.
4. Remove the wire connector and withdraw the switch.
5. Reverse the removal procedure to install the switch.

1978–80 Pinto, Bobcat

1. Disconnect the battery ground cable.
2. Remove the instrument cluster.
3. Remove the wiper switch knob and the bezel nut.
4. Disconnect the wiring connector on the switch and remove the switch from the dash.

5. Reverse the removal procedure to install.

Wiper Motor

REMOVAL & INSTALLATION

1978–79 Lincoln Continental, Thunderbird, Cougar, Mark V, 1978–79 LTD II

1. Disconnect the battery ground cable.
2. Remove the wiper arms and blades from the pivot shafts.
3. Remove the left cowl screen for access through the cowl opening.
4. Disconnect the linkage drive arm from the motor output arm crankpin by removing the retaining clip.
5. From the engine side of the dash, disconnect the two push-on wire connectors from the motor.
6. Remove the three bolts that retain the motor to the dash and remove the motor.

NOTE: If the output arm catches on the dash during the removal, hand turn the arm clockwise so that it will clear the opening in the dash.

7. To install, be sure the output arm is in the park position and reverse the removal procedure.

1979 and Later Ford, Mercury, 1980–81 Lincoln Continental, 1982 and Later Lincoln Town Car, 1980 and Later Mark VI

1. Disconnect the battery ground cable.
2. 1982 and later models, remove the hood seal.
3. Disconnect the right washer nozzle

hose and remove the right wiper arm and blade assembly from the pivot shaft.
4. Remove the windshield wiper motor and linkage cover by removing the two attaching screws.
5. Disconnect the linkage drive arm from the motor output arm crankpin by removing the retaining clip.
6. Disconnect the two push-on wire connectors from the motor.
7. Remove the three bolts that retain the motor to the dash panel extension and remove the motor.
8. To install, be sure the output arm is in the park position and reverse the removal procedure.

1978–79 Fairmont, Zephyr

1. Disconnect the battery ground cable.
2. Remove left hand wiper arm from pivot shaft and lay on cowl top grille.
3. Remove cowl top grille screws.
4. Raise forward left hand corner of cowl top grille for access to linkage drive arm.
5. Disconnect the linkage drive arm from motor output crank arm pin by removing retaining clip.
6. Disconnect wiper motor wire connector.
7. Remove bolts that retain motor to cowl panel and remove motor.
8. To install, reverse above procedure.

1980 and Later Fairmont, Zephyr, Thunderbird, Cougar, XR-7, 1981 and Later Mustang, Capri, Granada

1. Disconnect the battery ground cable.
2. Remove the right wiper and blade assembly.

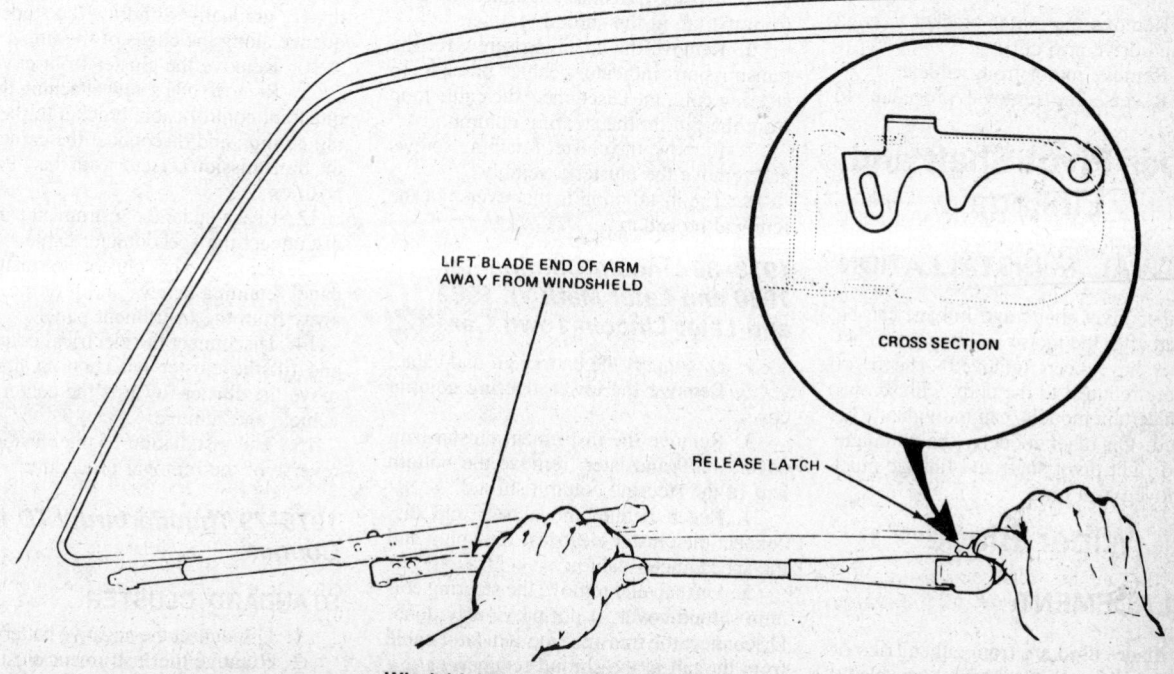

Windshield wiper arm removal typical

NOTE: On Fairmont, Zephyr, Granada and Cougar models, also remove the left wiper arm and blade.

3. Remove the grille on the top of the cowl.

4. Disconnect the linkage drive arm from the motor crankpin after removing the clip.

5. Disconnect the wiper motor electrical connector and remove the three attaching screws from the motor. Pull the motor from the opening.

6. Be sure the motor crank arm is in the park position and reverse the removal procedure to install.

1978–80 Pinto, Bobcat, Mustang, 1979–80 Capri

1. Loosen the two nuts and disconnect the pivot shaft and link assembly from the motor drive arm ball on the Pinto and Bobcat models. Remove the link retaining clip on the Mustang and Capri models.

2. Remove the three motor attaching screws and lower the motor away from under the left side of the instrument panel.

3. Disconnect the wiper motor electrical wires and remove the motor.

4. Be sure the motor is in the park position and reverse the removal procedure to install.

1978–80 Granada, Monarch, Versailles

1. Disconnect the battery ground cable.

2. Remove the instrument panel pad.

3. Remove the radio speaker mounting bracket and remove the speaker.

4. Remove the defroster nozzle and the air distribution duct.

5. Remove the interlock module from the bracket and disconnect the multiple connector.

6. Remove the motor bracket to cowl bolts and drive arm clip.

7. Remove motor from vehicle.

8. Reverse the removal procedure to install.

Wiper Pivot Shaft and Linkage

REMOVAL & INSTALLATION

The wiper pivot shafts and linkage can be removed after the motor and wiper arm assemblies have been removed. The pivot shafts are retained to the body with screws and, on certain models, can individually be removed. On other models, the complete left and right pivot shaft and linkage must be removed as a unit.

Wiper Blade

REPLACEMENT

Wiper blades used are from either Trico or Anco companies. With a bayonet type blade, the blade saddle slides over the end of the arm and is engaged by a locking stud. With a side saddle pin type, a pin on the arm enters the side of the blade saddle and engages a loaded spring (Trico) or a loaded clip (Anco) in the saddle.

Instrument Cluster

REMOVAL & INSTALLATION

―――― CAUTION ――――

Extreme care must be exercised during the removal and installation of the instrument cluster and dash components to avoid damage or breakage. Wooden paddles should be used to separate dash components, if required. Tape or cover dash areas that may be damaged by the removal and installation of the dash components.

NOTE: During the removal and installation procedures, slight variations may be required from the general outline, to facilitate the removal and installation of the instrument panel and cluster components, due to slight changes from model year to model year.

All Full-Size Models—Except Below

1. Disconnect the battery ground cable.

2. Remove the lower steering column cover.

3. Remove the instrument cluster trim cover, 1979 and later, remove the bottom half of the steering column shroud.

4. Reach behind the cluster and disconnect the cluster electrical feed plug and the speedometer cable.

5. Unsnap and remove the steering column shroud cover, if not previously done. Disconnect the transmission indicator cable from the tab in the shroud retainer.

6. Remove the attaching screw for the transmission indicator cable bracket to steering column. Disconnect the cable loop from the pin on the steering column.

7. Remove the cluster retaining screws and remove the cluster assembly.

8. The installation is the reverse of the removal procedure.

1978–80 Lincoln Continental, 1980 and Later Mark VI, 1982 and Later Lincoln Town Car

1. Disconnect the battery ground cable.

2. Remove the lower steering column cover.

3. Remove the instrument cluster trim cover. 1979 and later, remove the bottom half of the steering column shroud.

4. Reach behind the cluster and disconnect the cluster electrical feed plug and the speedometer cable.

5. Unsnap and remove the steering column shroud cover, if not previously done. Disconnect the transmission indicator cable from the tab in the shroud retainer.

6. Remove the attaching screw for the transmission indicator cable bracket to steering column. Disconnect the cable loop from the pin on the steering column.

7. Remove the cluster retaining screws and remove the cluster assembly.

8. The installation is the reverse of the removal procedure.

AUXILIARY INSTRUMENT CLUSTER

1. Remove the main instrument cluster as previously outlined.

2. Remove the auxiliary cluster housing trim from the instrument panel.

3. Disconnect the electrical connection from the rear of the cluster.

4. Remove the auxiliary instrument cluster from the rear, though the opening of the removed main instrument cluster.

5. The installation is the reverse of the removal procedure.

1978–79 Mark V

1. Disconnect the negative battery cable.

2. Remove the three screws retaining the upper access cover to the instrument panel pad.

3. Remove one screw retaining the lower cluster applique cover below the instrument panel.

4. Remove the steering column shroud.

5. Remove the heated rear window control knob.

6. From under the instrument panel, depress the headlamp switch knob and shaft release button and pull the knob and shaft from the light switch.

7. Remove the headlamp switch bezel, the wiper/washer control knob and bezel.

8. Remove the cigar lighter from its socket and remove the four screws retaining the cluster front cover.

9. Using a standard right angle screwdriver, gradually withdraw the studs in sequence along the edges of the finish panel.

10. Remove the cluster front cover.

11. Remove one screw attaching the shift quadrant control cable bracket to the steering column and disconnect the cable while the transmission selector is in the ''PARK'' position.

12. Reach under the instrument panel and disconnect the speedometer cable.

13. Remove the cluster to instrument panel retaining screws and pull the cluster away from the instrument panel.

14. Disconnect the electrical connectors and tilt the cluster out, bottom first, and move the cluster towards the center of the vehicle and remove.

15. The installation of the cluster is the reverse of the removal procedure.

1978–79 Thunderbird, LTD II and Cougar

STANDARD CLUSTER

1. Disconnect the negative battery cable.

2. Remove the instrument cluster trim cover and attaching screws.

3. Remove the clock or cover attaching screws. Remove the clock or cover.

4. Remove the retaining screws from the instrument cluster to instrument panel.

5. Pull the cluster away from the instrument panel and disconnect the speedometer cable and the cluster electrical connector.

6. Remove the cluster from the instrument panel.

7. The installation is the reverse of the removal procedure.

PERFORMANCE CLUSTER

1. Disconnect the negative battery cable.

2. Remove the instrument cluster trim cover and attaching screws.

3. Remove the instrument cluster retaining screws, pull the cluster away from the panel and disconnect both the speedometer cable and the cluster electrical connector.

4. Disconnect the overlay harness connector and remove the cluster from the dash.

5. The installation is the reverse of the removal procedure.

1980 and Later Thunderbird, Cougar XR-7 and Continental

1. Disconnect the negative battery cable.

2. Disconnect the speedometer cable (Standard cluster).

3. Remove the instrument panel trim cover and steering column lower shroud.

4. Remove the cluster retaining screws (Electronic cluster).

5. Remove the attaching screw from the transmission indicator quadrant cable bracket to the steering column. Disconnect the cable loop from the pin on the steering column.

6. Remove the cluster retaining screws (Standard cluster).

7. Pull the cluster away from the instrument panel and disconnect the speedometer cable (Electronic cluster).

8. Disconnect the electrical connections from the cluster. Disconnect the ground wire (Electronic cluster).

9. Remove the cluster from the instrument panel.

10. Reverse the removal procedure to install.

1978 and Later Fairmont, Zephyr 1981 and Later Granada, Cougar

NOTE: Certain special ordered cluster assemblies have two printed circuits.

1. Disconnect the battery negative cable.

2. Remove the steering column shroud and the cluster trim cover.

3. Remove one screw from the shift quadrant control cable bracket to steering column and disconnect the cable loop from the pin on the shift cane lever. Remove the plastic clamp from around the steering column.

4. Remove the retaining screws holding the cluster to the instrument panel.

5. Pull the cluster away from the instrument panel and disconnect the speedometer cable. Disconnect the electrical connectors and remove the cluster from the dash.

6. To install the cluster, reverse the removal procedure.

1978–80 Granada, Monarch, Versailles

1. Disconnect the negative battery cable.

2. Remove the retaining screws from the lower cluster applique cover, below the steering column.

3. Remove the steering column shroud.

4. From under the instrument panel, release the headlamp switch control knob and shaft assembly.

5. Remove the threaded headlight switch bezel.

6. Remove the retaining screws from the cluster front cover.

7. Insert a right angle standard tip screwdriver along the edges of the finish panel, withdrawing the studs in sequence gradually around the outer edge of the panel.

8. Remove the cluster front cover.

9. If the vehicle is equipped with automatic transmission, remove one screw attaching the shift quadrant control cable bracket to the steering column. Disconnect the cable loop from the pin on the steering column.

10. From under the instrument panel, disconnect the speedometer cable.

11. Remove the retaining screws and pull the cluster away from the instrument panel.

12. Disconnect the electrical connectors from the rear of the cluster.

13. Remove the cluster from the instrument panel.

14. To install the cluster, reverse the removal procedure.

1978 Mustang 1979 and Later Mustang, Capri

1. Disconnect the battery ground cable.

2. On 1978 models, remove the light switch knob and dash bezel.

3. Remove the instrument trim cover.

4. From under the dash, reach up and disconnect the speedometer cable.

5. Remove the cluster retaining screws and pull the cluster away from the dash. Disconnect the tachometer and wiring connectors. Remove the cluster assembly.

NOTE: 1979 and later Mustang and Capri models have two printed circuit boards.

6. The installation is the reverse of the removal procedure.

1983 and Later LTD, Marquis
STANDARD CLUSTER

1. Disconnect the negative battery cable.

2. Disconnect the speedometer cable. Remove the screws retaining the cluster trim panel and remove the panel.

3. Remove the steering wheel shroud. Remove the screw retaining the shift in-

dicator control cable to the steering column. Disconnect the indicator cable loop from the shift lever pin. Remove the plastic clamp from the steering column.

4. Remove the cluster retaining screws. Disconnect the cluster feed plug from the printed circuit. Disconnect the engine warning lamp.

5. Remove the instrument cluster.

6. Install the cluster in the reverse order of removal.

ELECTRONIC CLUSTER

1. Disconnect the negative battery cable.

2. Remove the screws retaining the lower instrument cluster trim panel. Remove the steering column cover.

3. Remove the screws retaining the instrument cluster to the instrument panel.

4. Remove the screw attaching the transmission indicator cable bracket to the steering column. Disconnect the cable loop from the pin on the steering column.

5. Carefully pull the instrument cluster away from the panel and disconnect the speedometer cable. Disconnect the cluster feed plug and ground receptacle from the cluster back plate.

6. Remove the cluster assembly.

7. Install the cluster in the reverse order of removal.

Instrument Panel

REMOVAL & INSTALLATION
1983 and Later—Mustang and Capri (Manual A/C)

1. Disconnect the ground cable from the battery.

2. Remove the instrument panel pad.

3. Remove the two screws attaching the steering column lower cover to the instrument panel and remove the cover.

4. Remove the steering column trim shrouds by removing the screws on the underside of the shroud.

5. Remove the four nuts attaching the steering column to the brake pedal support and carefully lower the steering column only enough for access to the transmission gear shift selector lever and cable assembly (automatic transmission vehicles only).

NOTE: Care must be used to assure that the column is not lowered too far to prevent damage to the selector lever and/or cable.

6. Reach between the steering column and the instrument panel and gently lift the selector lever cable off the shift selector lever. Then, remove the cable clamp from the steering column tube.

7. Lay the steering column to rest on the front seat.

8. Remove the one screw attaching the instrument panel to the brake pedal support at the steering column opening.

9. Remove the one screw attaching the lower brace to the lower edge of the instrument panel below the radio.

10. Remove the one screw attaching the brace to the lower edge of the instrument panel below the glovebox.

11. Disconnect the temperature control cable from the temperature blend door and the evaporator case bracket.

12. Disconnect the 7-port vacuum hose connector at the evaporator case.

13. Disconnect the blower resistor wire connector from the resistor on the evaporator housing, and the blower motor feed wire at the in-line connector near the blower resistor wire connector.

14. Support the instrument panel and, with an angle phillips screwdriver, remove three screws attaching the top of the instrument panel to the cowl.

15. Remove the screws attaching each end of the instrument panel to the cowl side panels.

16. Move the instrument panel rearward and disconnect the speedometer cable from the speedometer and any wires that will not allow the instrument panel to lay on the front seat. Use care not to scratch the instrument panel or the steering column.

17. Place the instrument panel near the installed position and connect any wires or connectors that were disconnected during removal.

18. Connect the speedometer cable to the speedometer.

19. Place the instrument panel in position and install one screw at each end of the instrument panel.

20. Install the three screws along the top front edge of the instrument panel with an angle phillips screwdriver.

21. Connect the two support braces to the lower edge of the instrument panel with one screw each.

22. Connect the temperature control cable to the temperature blend door crank arm and the bracket.

23. Connect the vacuum hoses at the 7-port connector and the blower motor wires at the resistor and in-line connector near the resistor.

24. Install the screw attaching the instrument panel to the brake pedal support.

25. Position the steering column near the brake panel support.

26. Connect the transmission gear shift selector lever cable to the shift selector lever. Then, connect the cable clamp to the steering column tube.

27. Position the steering column against the brake pedal support and install the four attaching nuts.

28. Adjust the transmission selector indicator.

29. Install the steering column shroud.

30. Position the steering column opening cover to the instrument panel and install the two attaching screws.

31. Install the instrument panel pad and connect the ground cable to the battery.

32. Connect the temperature control cable to the temperature blend door crank arm and adjust as necessary.

1983 and Later—Thunderbird/Cougar (Manual A/C)

1. Disconnect the ground cable from battery.

2. Remove the three screws attaching steering column opening cover to instrument panel. Then, pull the panel rearward to disengage the clips and remove the cover.

3. Remove the three screws attaching the reinforcement to the instrument panel below the steering column opening and remove the reinforcement.

4. Remove the two nuts retaining the hood latch release handle mounting bracket to the brake pedal support below the steering column.

5. Remove the sound insulator from under left side of the instrument panel.

6. Remove the two nuts retaining the steering column clamp to the brake pedal support and allow the steering column to rest on the seat.

7. Remove the instrument panel pad.

8. Disconnect the speedometer cable from the speedometer head.

9. Remove the two screws attaching the console tray (automatic transmission) or console cover around the gear shift lever (manual transmission) to the console. Then, remove the tray or cover from the console.

10. Remove the four console switch panel cover attaching screws. Disconnect the switch wires and remove the switch panel.

11. Open the console box cover and remove the two screws from the bottom of the console box and the two screws from the top front of the box.

12. Remove the two screws attaching front end of the console to the lower edge of the instrument panel.

13. Remove the two screws attaching the bracket at the front end of console and lower the edge of the instrument panel to the floor pan. Then, lift the rear end of the console and pull the console rearward to disengage it from the instrument panel. Position the console out of the way.

14. Remove the two plastic push pins attaching the glove box door straps to the glove box. Allow the glove box and door to hang by the hinge.

15. Remove the one bolt attaching instrument panel brace to the instrument panel at the glove box opening.

16. Remove the one nut attaching the lower edge of the instrument panel to the brake pedal support.

17. Remove the one bolt attaching a second instrument panel brace to the lower edge of instrument panel just to the left of the console extension.

18. Remove the one bolt attaching each end of the instrument panel to the cowl side panel.

19. Support the instrument panel and remove the three screws attaching top edge of instrument panel to cowl top panel.

20. Cover the steering column and seats. Then, carefully position the instrument panel

toward seat disconnecting wires and vacuum harness as necessary. Allow instrument panel to rest on front seat.

21. Place the instrument panel in position and connect any wires and vacuum harness that were disconnected during instrument panel removal. Then, install the three screws to attach top edge of instrument panel to cowl top panel.

22. Install one bolt to attach each end of instrument panel to cowl side panel.

23. Install one bolt each to attach the instrument panel left and right braces to the lower edge of instrument panel near the console extension.

24. Install a nut to attach lower edge of instrument panel to the brake pedal support.

25. Position the console to vehicle and install two screws to attach the front bracket to the floor.

26. Install two screws to attach the console box to the floor and two screws to attach the top front of box to the support bracket.

27. Position the console switch panel to the console and connect wires. Then, install four panel cover attaching screws.

28. Position the console tray or cover around gear shift lever to console and install the two attaching screws.

29. Connect the speedometer cable to the speedometer.

30. Install the instrument panel pad.

31. Position the steering column to brake pedal support and install retaining clamp (two nuts).

32. Position the reinforcement across the steering column opening of instrument panel and install the three attaching screws.

33. Position the steering column opening cover to the instrument panel and install three attaching screws.

34. Install the sound insulator under left side of instrument panel.

35. Connect the support straps to the glove box.

36. Connect the ground cable to the battery.

37. Check for proper operation of all instruments and controls.

1983 and Later—LTD/Marquis (Manual A/C)

1. Remove the instrument panel upper finish panel and pad assemblies.

2. Loosen the steering column and carefully lower only enough for access to transmission gear shaft selector lever and cable assembly.

NOTE: Care must be used to assure that the column is not lowered too far to prevent damage to the selector lever and/or cable.

3. Reach between the steering column and the instrument panel and gently lift the selector lever cable off the shift selector lever. Then, remove the cable clamp from the steering column tube.

4. Lay the steering column to rest on the front seat.

5. Remove one screw attaching the instrument panel to the brake pedal support at the steering column opening.

6. Disconnect the temperature control cable from the temperature blend door and the evaporator case bracket.

7. Disconnect the vacuum hose connectors at the evaporator case.

8. Disconnect the blower resistor wire connector from the resistor on the evaporator housing, and the blower motor feed wire at the in-line connector near the blower resistor wire connector.

9. Support the instrument panel and remove three screws attaching the top of the instrument panel to the cowl.

10. Remove one screw attaching each end of the instrument panel to the cowl side panels.

11. Remove two screws holding instrument panel to floor.

12. Move the instrument panel rearward and disconnect the speedometer cable from the speedometer and any wires that will not allow the instrument panel to lay on the front seat. Use care not to scratch the instrument panel or the steering column.

13. Place the instrument panel near the installed position and connect any wires or connectors that were disconnected during removal.

14. Connect the speedometer cable to the speedometer.

15. Place the instrument panel in position and install one screw at each end of the instrument panel.

16. Install three screws along the top front edge of the instrument panel.

17. Install two screws retaining instrument panel to floor.

18. Connect the temperature control cable to the temperature blend door crank arm and the bracket.

1983 and Later—Thunderbird/Cougar (Automatic A/C)

1. Disconnect the ground cable from the battery.

2. Remove three screws attaching the steering column opening cover to the instrument panel. Then, pull the panel rearward to disengage the clips and remove the cover.

3. Remove three screws attaching the reinforcement to the instrument panel below the steering column opening and remove the reinforcement.

4. Remove two nuts retaining the hood latch release handle mounting bracket to the brake pedal support below the steering column.

5. Remove the sound insulator from under the left side of the instrument panel.

6. Remove two nuts retaining the steering column clamp to the brake pedal support and allow the steering column to rest on the seat.

7. Remove the instrument panel pad.

8. Disconnect the speedometer cable from the speedometer head.

9. Remove two screws attaching the console tray (automatic transmission) or the console cover around the gear shift lever (standard transmission) to the console. Then, remove the tray or cover from the console.

10. Remove four console switch panel cover attaching screws. Disconnect the switch wires and remove the switch panel.

11. Open the console box cover and remove two screws from the bottom of the console box and two screws from the top front of the box.

12. Remove two screws attaching the front end of the console to the lower edge of the instrument panel.

13. Remove two screws attaching the bracket at the front end of the console and lower edge of the instrument panel to the floor pan. Then, lift the rear end of the console and pull the console rearward to disengage it from the instrument panel. Position the console out of the way.

14. Remove two plastic push pins attaching the glove box door straps to the glove box. Allow the glove box and door to hang by the hinge.

15. Remove one bolt attaching the instrument panel brace to the instrument panel at the glove box opening.

16. Remove one nut attaching the lower edge of the instrument panel to the brake pedal support.

17. Remove one bolt attaching a second instrument panel brace to the lower edge of the instrument panel just to the left of the console extension.

18. Remove one bolt attaching each end of the instrument panel to the cowl side panel.

19. Support the instrument panel and remove three screws attaching the top edge of the instrument panel to the cowl top panel.

20. Cover the steering column and seats. Then, carefully position the instrument panel toward the seat disconnecting wires and vacuum harness as necessary. Allow the instrument panel to rest on the front seat.

21. Place the instrument panel in position and connect any wires and vacuum harness that were disconnected during instrument panel removal. Then, install the three screws to attach the top edge of the instrument panel to the cowl top panel.

22. Install one bolt to attach each end of the instrument panel to the cowl side panel.

23. Install one bolt each to attach the instrument panel left and right braces to the lower edge of the instrument panel near the console extension.

24. Install the nut to attach the lower edge of the instrument panel to the brake pedal support.

25. Position the console to the vehicle and install two screws to attach the front bracket to the floor.

26. Install two screws to attach the console box to the floor and two screws to attach the top front of the box to the support bracket.

27. Position the console switch panel to the console and connect the wires. Then, install the four panel cover attaching screws.

28. Position the console tray or the cover around the gear shift lever to the console and install the two attaching screws.

29. Connect the speedometer cable to the speedometer.

30. Install the instrument panel pad.

31. Position the steering column to the brake pedal support and install the retaining clamp (two nuts).

32. Position the reinforcement across the steering column opening of the instrument panel and install the three attaching screws.

33. Position the steering column opening cover to the instrument panel and install the three attaching screws.

34. Install the sound insulator under the left side of the instrument panel.

35. Connect the support straps to the glove box.

36. Connect the ground cable to the battery.

37. Check for proper operation of all instruments and controls.

1983 and Later—LTD/Marquis (Automatic A/C)

1. Remove the instrument panel upper finish panel and pad assemblies.

2. Loosen the steering column and carefully lower only enough for access to transmission gear shift selector lever and cable assembly.

NOTE: Care must be used to assure that the column is not lowered too far to prevent damage to the selector lever and/or cable.

3. Reach between the steering column and the instrument panel and gently lift the selector lever cable off the shift selector lever. Then, remove the cable clamp from the steering column tube.

4. Lay the steering column to rest on the front seat.

5. Remove one screw attaching the instrument panel to the brake pedal support at the steering column opening.

6. Disconnect the servo motor from the temperature blend door.

7. Disconnect the vacuum hose connectors at the evaporator case.

8. Disconnect the blower resistor wire connector from the resistor on the evaporator housing, and the blower motor feed wire at the in-line connector near the blower resistor wire connector.

9. Support the instrument panel and remove three screws attaching the top of the instrument panel to the cowl.

10. Remove one screw attaching each end of the instrument panel to the cowl side panels.

11. Remove two screws holding instrument panel to floor.

12. Move the instrument panel rearward and disconnect the speedometer cable from the speedometer and any wires that will not allow the instrument panel to lay on the front seat. Use care not to scratch the instrument panel or the steering column.

13. Place the instrument panel near the installed position and connect any wires or connectors that were disconnected during removal.

14. Connect the servo motor to the temperature blend door crank arm and the bracket.

15. Connect the vacuum hoses at the 7-port connectors and the blower motor wires at the resistor and in-line connector near the resistor.

16. Connect the speedometer cable to the speedometer.

17. Place the instrument panel in position and install one screw at each end of the instrument panel.

18. Install three screws along the top front edge of the instrument panel.

19. Install two screws retaining instrument panel to floor.

20. Install the screw attaching the instrument panel to the brake pedal support.

21. Position the steering column near the brake pedal support.

22. Connect the transmission gear shift selector lever cable to the shift selector lever. Then, connect the cable clamp to the steering column tube.

23. Position the steering column against the brake pedal support and install the four attaching nuts.

24. Adjust the transmission selector indicator as necessary.

25. Install the steering column shroud.

26. Position the steering column opening cover to the instrument panel and install the two attaching screws.

27. Install the instrument panel pad and connect the ground cable to the battery.

Speedometer Cable

REMOVAL & INSTALLATION

1. Reach up behind the speedometer and depress the flat, quick-disconnect tab, while pulling back on the cable.

2. If the inner cable is broken, raise and support the car and remove the cable-to-transmission clamp and pull the cable from the transmission.

3. Pull the core from the cable.

4. Installation is the reverse of removal. Lubricate the core with speedometer cable lubricant prior to installation.

RADIO

For the best FM reception, adjust the antenna, if adjustable, to 31 in. height. Fading or weak AM reception may be corrected by adjusting the trimmer control. The trimmer control is located either on the right rear or front side of the radio. See the owner's manual for position if you are in doubt. To adjust the trimmer:

1. Extend the antenna to maximum height.

2. Tune the radio to a weak station around 1600 KC. Adjust the volume so that the sound is barely audible.

3. Adjust the trimmer to obtain maximum volume.

REMOVAL & INSTALLATION
1978–79 Lincoln

1. Disconnect the battery ground cable.

2. Remove the knobs. Remove the screws holding the radio bezel plate to the instrument panel. Remove the screws holding the radio mounting plate.

3. Detach the radio from the lower rear support bracket.

4. Disconnect the power, antenna, and speaker leads.

5. Remove the mounting plate and rear upper support from the radio.

6. Reverse the procedure for installation.

Mark IV and V

1. Disconnect the negative battery cable.

2. Pull the radio control knobs off the radio shafts. Disconnect and lower the Twilight Sentinal amplifier, if equipped.

3. Remove the nuts from both radio control shafts. Disconnect the air conditioning duct under the radio.

4. Remove the radio rear support to panel attaching screw. On some 1977 and later models, this screw was replaced with a rivet. In order to remove the rivet you must drill it out with a ¼ in. drill bit. When you replace the radio, replace the rivet with a ¼ in. nut and bolt.

5. Disconnect the radio power wires. Disconnect the speaker wires at the connectors.

6. Disconnect the antenna lead and remove the radio.

7. Reverse the procedure to install.

Lincoln—1980 and Later

1. Disconnect the negative battery cable.

2. Remove the four radio plate-to-panel screws. Pull the radio with the front plate attached rearward until the rear bracket is clear.

3. Disconnect the wires from the chassis. If equipped with premium sound, remove the control assembly attaching nut and washer, remove the switch, and remove the illumination lamp socket from the front bracket.

4. Remove the radio with the front plate attached. Remove the four screws and remove the plate. Installation is the reverse of removal.

Ford and Mercury—Full Size

1. Disconnect the battery ground cable.

2. On all-electronic radios, remove the radio-to-mounting plate screws and remove the mounting plate.

3. Remove the radio knobs, the screws that attach the bezel to the instrument panel, and remove the bezel.

4. Remove the radio mounting plate attaching screws (standard radios), and disengage the radio by pulling it from the lower rear support bracket.

5. Disconnect all the leads from the radio.

6. Remove the radio mounting plate and the rear upper support; remove the radio from the instrument panel.

7. Reverse the procedure to install.

LTD II, Cougar and Thunderbird Through 1979

1. Disconnect the battery.

2. Pull radio control knobs off shafts.

3. Remove radio support to instrument panel attaching screw.

4. Remove two bezel nuts from radio control shafts. Remove the rear support bracket, if so equipped.

5. Lower radio and disconnect antenna, speaker, and power leads. Remove radio.

6. To install, connect antenna, speaker and power leads to radio.

7. Position radio in instrument panel and install two bezel nuts.

8. Install radio support bracket to instrument panel attaching screw.

9. Reconnect the battery.

Granada, Monarch, Versailles Through 1980

1. Disconnect the negative battery cable.

2. Remove the headlight switch from the instrument panel. Remove the heater, air conditioner, windshield wiper/washer knobs, and radio knobs and discs.

3. Remove the six screws which attach the applique to the instrument panel and remove the applique. Disconnect the antenna lead-in cable from the radio.

4. Remove the four screws which attach the radio bezel to the instrument panel. Slide the radio and bezel out of the lower rear support bracket and instrument panel opening toward the interior far enough to disconnect the electrical connections, and remove the radio.

5. Remove the nut attaching the rear support bracket to the radio and remove the bracket. Remove the nuts and washer from the radio control shafts and remove the bezel.

6. To install, attach the rear support bracket to the radio. Install the bezel, washers and nuts.

7. Insert the radio with rear support bracket and bezel through the instrument panel opening far enough to connect the electrical leads and antenna lead-in cable. Install the radio upper rear support bracket into the lower rear support bracket.

8. Center the radio and bezel in the opening and install the four bezel attaching screws.

9. Install the instrument panel applique with its six attaching screws. Install all knobs removed from the instrument panel and radio. Install the headlight switch.

10. Connect the negative battery cable.

Fairmont, Zephyr, Mustang, Capri, 1981 and Later Granada and Cougar, Futura

1. Disconnect the negative battery cable. On models through 1978, remove the seat belt interlock module underneath the radio.
2. Disconnect the electrical, speaker, and antenna leads from the radio.
3. Remove the knobs, discs, and control shaft nuts and washers from the radio shafts.
4. On 1979 and later models, remove the ash tray receptacle and bracket.
5. Remove the rear support nut from the radio.
6. On 1979 and later models, remove the instrument panel lower reinforcement and the heater or air conditioning floor ducts.
7. Remove the radio from the rear support, and drop the radio down and out from behind the instrument panel.
8. To install, reverse the removal procedure.

1980 and Later Thunderbird and Cougar XR-7, 1982 and Later Continental, 1983 and Later LTD, Marquis

1. Disconnect the negative battery cable.
2. Remove the radio knobs (pull off). Remove the center trim panel.
3. Remove the radio mounting plate screws. Pull the radio towards the front seat to disengage it from the lower bracket.
4. Disconnect the radio and antenna connections.
5. Remove the radio. Remove the nuts and washers (conventional radios) or mounting plate screws (electronic radios) as necessary.
6. On electronic radios, install the mounting plates before installing the retaining nuts and washers or screws. The rest of installation is the reverse of removal.

HEATER

Heater Assembly

REMOVAL & INSTALLATION

Pinto, Bobcat, Mustang II— Without A/C

NOTE: Improved heater performance is available, through the installation of revised components, for 1978 Bobcats, Pintos, and Mustangs equipped with the 2300 engine. The parts include a new water outlet connection, hose tee, thermostat, and the necessary hoses and clamps, to revise the coolant circulation pattern. In the revised system, coolant first flows to the core, then to the intake manifold, rather than vice versa. The parts are available from your dealer. De-tails are given in Technical Service Bulletin 155, dated April 1978.

1. Drain the cooling system and disconnect the negative battery cable.
2. Disconnect the blower motor ground wire (black) at the engine side of the firewall.
3. Disconnect the heater hoses at the engine block.
4. Remove the four nuts that attach the heater assembly to the firewall, from the engine side.
5. Working inside the car, remove the glove box.
6. Disconnect the control cables from the heater. Disconnect the motor lead. Remove the radio.
7. Remove the snap-rivet that attaches the forward side of the defroster air duct to the heater assembly. Move the air duct back into the defroster nozzle and disengage it from the tabs on the heater box. Tilt the forward edge of the duct up and forward to disengage it from the nozzle, and remove it from the left side of the heater assembly.
8. Remove the heater assembly to instrument panel support bracket mounting screw and remove the heater assembly. At the same time, pull the heater hoses through the firewall. Then, disconnect the hoses from the heater core in the case.
9. Install in the reverse order of removal.

Pinto and Bobcat—With A/C
———— CAUTION ————
This procedure requires the evacuation of the air conditioning system. This operation should not be attempted by anyone lacking the skill and experience to do so safely, as the freon gas can cause serious injury on contact. Have the system evacuated by a professional if in doubt.

1. Drain the engine coolant, discharge the air conditioning system and disconnect the battery.
2. Remove the two hex screws attaching the evaporator manifold plate to the expansion valve body and the STV housing manifold from the evaporator manifold plate. Use new O-rings between the valve body and manifold plate on reassembly.
3. Disconnect the two heater hoses from the core tubes in the engine compartment.
4. Remove the A/C condensation drain hose in the engine compartment.
5. Remove the glove box.
6. Disconnect the vacuum hoses from the evaporator case.
7. Disconnect the temperature control cable from the blend door crank arm.
8. Remove the heat distribution duct. On the Mustang II, remove the mode door vacuum motor which is retained to the evaporator case assembly by two nuts and a spring nut.
9. On the Pinto or Bobcat, to remove the A/C defrost plenum:
  a. Cut and remove the two staples which retain the fold down door in the closed position on the plenum.
  b. Bend the fold down door away from the locating tabs on each side of the plenum to allow removal of the adaptor duct.
  c. Remove the adapter duct.
10. Remove the blower motor and wheel from the blower scroll.
11. Install one ¼-20 hex-washer head screw to the mounting tab on the inlet duct to upper cowl bracket to hold the duct in place. Leave this screw in place when installing the case assembly.
12. Remove the three inlet duct-to-evaporator case attaching screws through the blower scroll opening.
13. Remove the one upper case-to-inlet duct attaching screw located under the outside-recirculating motor mounting bracket.
14. Remove the two evaporator-to-upper cowl bracket attaching screws.
15. Remove the four evaporator-to-dash panel attaching nuts in the engine compartment.
16. Rotate the evaporator assembly down and away from the dash panel and out from under the instrument panel.
17. Install the heater/evaporator case in the reverse order of removal. During installation, position the fold down door of the defrost plenum between the locating tabs on each side of the plenum and tape it in position with two pieces of black tape 1 in. wide by 4 in. long.

Mustang II—With A/C

NOTE: This procedure requires evacuation of the air conditioning system. This should not be attempted by untrained persons; personal injury may result. See the preceeding "CAUTION." This is also a major disassembly operation.

1. Remove the battery, drain the coolant, and discharge the air conditioner.
2. Remove the instrument panel pad, the radio speaker, both A-pillar moldings, both side kick panel assemblies, and the lower steering column cover.
3. Remove the steering column to cowl panel brace.
4. Remove the accelerator pedal. Disconnect the lower control cables.
5. Remove the bottom bolt holding the center brace to the instrument panel.
6. Disconnect the radio antenna lead. Detach the five connectors at the left cowl panel. Unplug the dimmer switch. Disconnect the blower motor resistor.
7. Disconnect the temperature control cable. Remove the two upper cowl bracket screws.
8. Detach the main wiring harness in the engine compartment. Push the harness into the passenger compartment. Do the same with the last three connectors.
9. Disconnect the turn signal switch. Remove the four steering column nuts, unplug the ignition switch, unplug the stoplight switch, and remove the column center support bracket.
10. Remove the four retaining bolts and the instrument panel.

11. Detach the heater hoses from the core tubes. Disconnect the two lines at the evaporator manifold assembly. Remove the manifold from the bracket. Remove the outer manifold.

12. Remove the nuts and remove the assembly from the firewall.

13. Installation is carried out in the reverse order of removal. Fill the cooling system and charge the air conditioner.

Blower

REMOVAL & INSTALLATION

Lincoln Through 1979

1. Remove hood.
2. Remove right hood hinge and right fender inner support brace as an assembly.
3. Disconnect the blower motor air cooling tube from the motor.
4. Disconnect motor lead wire from harness and ground wire from firewall.
5. Disconnect rear section of right front fender panel apron from fender around wheel opening and remove two lower fender to cowl mounting screws.
6. Separate fender apron from fender wheel opening so that apron can be pushed downward away from blower motor.
7. Remove four blower motor plate screws. Move motor and wheel forward out of blower scroll and remove assembly through opening while applying pressure to fender apron to enlarge opening at hinge area. Reverse procedure to install.

Mark IV

1. Remove the glove box.
2. Remove the recirculation air register and duct assembly from the blower assembly.
3. Remove the two screws that attach the blower lower housing to the dash panel.
4. Disconnect the white hose from the outside-recirc air door vacuum motor and remove the vacuum motor from the blower lower housing. It is held in place by two screws. Leave the motor actuator connected to the door crank arm.
5. Disconnect the orange blower motor lead wire from the harness connector, and disconnect the black motor ground wire.
6. Remove the six upper-to-lower blower housing flange screws.
7. Separate the blower lower housing and motor assembly from the upper housing and remove it from beneath the instrument panel.
8. Remove the blower motor and wheel assembly from the lower housing. It is held by four screws.
9. The upper flange of the recirculation duct is retained to the blower upper housing with two S-clips that remained on the housing during removal. Be certain that the duct is properly installed in the two clips during reinstallation. Reverse procedure to install.

Mark V

1. Remove the instrument panel pad and the glovebox.

2. Remove the side cowl trim panel. Remove the instrument panel attachment on the right side.
3. Remove the blower housing to firewall nut in the engine compartment. Remove the blower housing to firewall nut in the passenger compartment.
4. Remove the blower housing mounting bracket and cowl top inner screw.
5. Disconnect the white air door vacuum motor hose.
6. Disconnect the blower motor wire plug and the ground wire screw.
7. Remove the blower assembly.
8. Reverse the procedure for installation.

Lincoln—1980 and Later

See the procedures for ''1979 and later Ford/Mercury''.

1978 Ford and Mercury

1. Disconnect the blower motor lead wire. This is an orange wire located at the rear of the right hood hinge.
2. Remove the mounting screw from the black ground wire located at the upper cowl. Remove both wires from the clip.
3. Remove the right front tire and wheel.
4. In order to get to the blower motor, an access hole must be cut out in the right front fender apron. The pattern for this hole has been outlined on the apron by the factory. It appears as a beaded line.
5. A small indentation or drill dimple is present ½ in. from the center line of the bead. Drill a 1 in. diameter hole at this drill dimple. Be careful not to damage the heater case by over drilling.
6. Using sheet metal snips, cut along the bead to create the opening. Do not use a saber saw.
7. Remove the blower motor mounting plate screws and disconnect the cooler tube from the motor.
8. Remove the motor and wheel assembly from the heater case and through the access hole.
9. To install, reverse the removal procedure. Apply rope sealer to the motor mounting plate. Obtain a cover plate, drill 8, ⅛ in. holes in the fender apron and install the cover plate.

1979 and Later Ford and Mercury—Full Size

1. Disconnect the negative battery cable.
2. Disconnect the blower motor wiring.
3. Remove the blower motor cooling tube from the motor.
4. Remove the four blower motor attaching screws and remove the motor.
5. Reverse to install.

1978–79 Cougar, LTD II, Thunderbird—Without A/C

1. Drain radiator coolant.
2. Disconnect heater hoses at core connections.
3. Remove heater assembly to dash retaining nuts.

4. Disconnect control cables at door crank arms.
5. Disconnect resistor and blower motor wires. Remove defroster nozzle retaining clip.
6. Remove glove box.
7. Remove bolt and nut retaining right air duct control to the instrument panel. Remove nuts retaining right air duct and remove duct assembly.
8. Remove heater assembly.
9. Remove four blower motor mounting screws and remove blower motor assembly.
10. Reverse procedure for installation.

1978–80 Granada, Monarch— Without A/C

1. Drain radiator coolant.
2. Disconnect heater hoses at core connections.
3. Disconnect battery ground cable.
4. Remove glove box.
5. Remove right register air duct.
6. Remove floor discharge duct assembly and defroster nozzle retaining clip.
7. Disconnect the two air door control cables from heater case and doors. Remove right vent cable bracket from instrument panel.
8. Disconnect resistor electrical connector.
9. Remove vent duct to upper cowl mounting bolt.
10. Remove three heater case to dash panel mounting stud nuts and remove heater case and vent duct as an assembly.
11. Remove four mounting screws and slide blower motor assembly from blower scroll in case.
12. Reverse procedure for installation.

Fairmont 1978 and Later, Zephyr 1978 and Later, Mustang 1979 and Later, Capri 1980 and Later, Granada 1981 and Later, Cougar 1981 and Later—Without A/C

1. Remove right ventilator assembly.
2. Disconnect blower motor lead wire from resistor assembly, push wire back thru hole in case.
3. Remove right side cowl trim panel for access to blower motor ground wire connector and remove retaining screw.
4. Remove blower motor flange retaining screws from inside of housing.

NOTE: Blower wheel may be removed to improve access.

5. Remove blower motor from housing.
6. Reverse procedure for installation.

Continental—With A/C

1. Disconnect the ground cable from the battery.
2. Disconnect the blower motor lead connector from the wiring harness connector.
3. Remove the four (4) retaining screws.
4. Turn the motor and wheel assembly

slightly to the right so that the bottom edge of the mounting plate follows the contour of the wheel well splash panel. Lift up on the blower and remove it from the blower housing.

5. Installation is the reverse of removal.

1978–79 Thunderbird, Cougar, LTD II, Mark V—With A/C

1. Remove the instrument panel pad.
2. Remove the glove box.
3. Remove the side cowl trim panel.
4. Remove the instrument panel attachment on the right side.
5. Remove the one nut attaching the blower housing to the dash in the engine compartment and the one nut in the passenger compartment.
6. Remove the blower housing mounting bracket and cowl top inner screw.
7. Disconnect the outside air door vacuum hose. (white)
8. Disconnect the blower motor lead wire from the connector and the motor ground wire.
9. Remove the blower assembly.
10. Installation is in the reverse order of removal.

1978–80 Granada, Monarch— With A/C

1. Disconnect the negative battery cable.
2. Loosen the passenger side door sill scuff plate and the right ''A'' pillar trim cover. Remove the right cowl trim panel.
3. Remove the bolt retaining the lower side of the instrument panel to the cowl. Remove the right cowl side brace bolts.
4. Disconnect the wiring harness connectors at the blower motor.
5. If so equipped, remove the cooling tube from the blower motor.
6. Remove the 4 screws retaining the blower motor and wheel assembly to the scroll. To remove the motor, pull rearward on the lower edge of the instrument panel to provide clearance.
7. Installation is the reverse of removal. If necessary, cement the cooling tube to the blower motor.

Fairmont 1978 and Later, Zephyr 1978 and Later, Mustang 1979 and Later, Capri 1980 and Later, Thunderbird 1980 and Later, XR7 1980 and Later, Granada 1981 and Later, Cougar 1981 and Later, LTD and Marquis 1983 and Later—Models With A/C

1. Remove glove box, disconnect outside-recirc door vacuum motor hose.
2. Remove instrument panel lower right-to-side cowl attaching bolt.
3. Remove support brace to top of air inlet duct retaining screw.
4. Disconnect blower motor lead wire at connector.

5. Remove blower housing lower support bracket to evaporator case retaining nut.
6. Remove side cowl trim panel and remove blower motor ground wire screw.
7. Remove screw securing top of air inlet duct to evaporator case.
8. Remove the air inlet duct and blower housing down and away from evaporator case.
9. Remove four blower motor mounting plate screws and remove blower motor assembly from blower housing.

NOTE: DO NOT remove the mounting plate from blower motor.

10. Reverse procedure for installation.

Versailles 1978–80—With A/C

1. Disconnect battery ground cable.
2. Remove instrument panel lower finish plate.
3. Remove glove box.
4. Loosen right door sill plate and remove right side cowl trim panel.
5. Remove instrument panel to-side cowl lower right attaching bolt.
6. Remove bolt securing the brace to the lower edge of the instrument panel below glove box.
7. Disconnect blower motor wires.
8. Remove four blower motor attaching screws and remove blower motor assembly.

NOTE: DO NOT remove the mounting plate from the blower motor.

Pinto, Bobcat and Mustang II

WITHOUT A/C

1. Remove the heater assembly.
2. Disconnect the blower motor lead wire from the resistor.
3. Remove the four blower motor mounting plate attaching nuts and remove the motor and wheel.
4. Install in the reverse order.

WITH A/C

The blower motor and wheel is integrally located within the scroll portion of the evaporator assembly on the right-side of the evaporator case. To remove the blower motor and wheel, remove the glove box and remove the four screws retaining the blower motor and wheel in the blower scroll. It may be necessary to remove the instrument panel to right side cowl bolt, to allow the panel to be pulled rearward for clearance. Install the blower motor and wheel in the reverse order of removal.

Heater Core Without A/C

REMOVAL & INSTALLATION

1978 Ford and Mercury

1. Partially drain cooling system.

2. Remove heater hoses at core.
3. Remove retaining screws, core cover and seal from case.
4. Remove core from case.
5. Install in reverse of above, applying a thin coat of silicone to the pads.

1979 and Later Ford and Mercury

1. Drain the coolant and save for reuse.
2. Disconnect the negative cable from the battery.
3. Remove the heater hoses from the heater core.
4. Plug the heater core tubes to prevent coolant from spilling under the dash during plenum removal.
5. Remove the plenum to dash bolt, located under the windshield wiper motor at the left end of the plenum.
6. Remove the one nut from the heater case (engine side).
7. Disconnect the vacuum supply hose from the vacuum fitting and push the grommet and hose into the passenger compartment.
8. Remove the glove box assembly.
9. Loosen the right door sill plate and remove the right side cowl trim panel.
10. Remove the lower right instrument panel to side cowl bolt.
11. Remove the instrument panel pad.
12. Remove the temperature control cable from the top of the plenum. Then, disconnect the temperature control cable from the blend door crank arm.
13. Remove the push clip attaching the center register duct bracket to the plenum and rotate the bracket up to the right.
14. Disconnect the vacuum jumper harness at the multiple vacuum connector near the floor air distribution duct.
15. Disconnect the white vacuum hose from the outside air door vacuum motor.
16. Remove the two (2) screws attaching the seat side of the floor air distribution duct to the plenum.

NOTE: It may be necessary to remove the two (2) screws attaching the lower panel door vacuum motor to the mounting bracket to gain access to the floor air distribution duct screw.

17. Remove the plastic push-pin fastener from the floor air distribution duct and remove the duct.
18. Remove the remaining two (2) plenum retaining nuts from the lower flange of the plenum.
19. Move the plenum toward the seat to allow the heater core tubes to clear the holes in the dash panel.
20. Rotate the top of the plenum down and out from under the instrument panel.
21. Remove the four (4) heater core cover retaining screws and lift off the cover.
22. Remove the heater core tube bracket retaining screw.
23. Pull the heater core and seal from the plenum assembly.

24. Installation is the reverse of removal. Connect the negative battery cable and refill the cooling system. Check heater operation.

1978–79 Cougar, LTD II and Thunderbird

1. Drain coolant.
2. Disconnect both heater hoses at dash.
3. Remove nuts retaining heater assembly to dash.
4. Disconnect temperature and defroster cables at heater.
5. Disconnect wires from resistor, and disconnect blower motor wires and clip retaining heater assembly to defroster nozzle.
6. Remove glove box.
7. Remove bolt and nut from right air duct control to instrument panel. Remove nuts retaining right air duct and remove duct assembly.
8. Remove heater assembly to bench.
9. Remove heater core cover and pad.
10. Slide core out of case.
11. Reverse procedure for installation.

1978–80 Granada and Monarch

1. Drain radiator coolant.
2. Disconnect heater hoses at core connections.
3. Remove glove box.
4. Remove right register air duct.
5. Remove floor discharge duct assembly and clip holding defroster nozzle to the heater.
6. Disconnect air door control cables from heater case and doors. Remove right vent cable bracket from instrument panel.
7. Disconnect resistor assembly electrical connector.
8. Remove vent duct-to-upper-cowl mounting bolt.
9. Remove three heater case to dash panel mounting stud nuts and remove heater case and vent duct as an assembly.
10. Remove heater core cover and pad and slide core out of the case.
11. Reverse procedure for installation.

Fairmont 1978–79, Zephyr 1978–79, Capri 1980 and Later, Mustang 1979 and Later, Granada 1981 and Later, Cougar 1981 and Later

1. Drain radiator coolant.
2. Disconnect heater hoses at core connections.
3. Remove glove box.
4. Remove instrument panel-to-cowl brace retaining screws and brace.
5. Move temperature control lever to warm position.
6. Remove four heater core cover retaining screws.
7. Remove heater core cover through glove box opening.
8. In engine compartment, loosen heater case assembly mounting stud nuts.
9. Push heater core tubes and seal toward passenger compartment to loosen heater

core assembly from heater case assembly.
10. Remove heater core from heater case assembly through the glove box opening.
11. Reverse procedure for installation.

Pinto, Bobcat and Mustang II

1. Remove the heater assembly.
2. Remove the compression gasket from the cowl air inlet and remove the eleven clips from the case. Separate the case and remove the heater core.

Heater Core With A/C Including Automatic Temperature Control

—————— CAUTION ——————

Removal of the heater-air conditioner housing requires evacuation of the air conditioner refrigerant. This operation requires special tools and training. Failure to follow proper safety precautions may cause personal injury. It is recommended that discharging and charging of the A/C system be performed by an experienced professional mechanic.

REMOVAL & INSTALLATION

1978 Ford and Mercury (Full Size), 1978–79 Lincoln

1. Drain the cooling system.
2. Disconnect the heater hoses at the heater core tubes.
3. Remove the seven screws which retain the core cover plate to the plate.
4. Pull the heater core and mounting gasket up out of the case. Remove the core mounting gasket.
5. Reverse the above procedure to install, taking care to ensure that the core and gasket seat firmly forward of the core retention spring in the case. Fill the cooling system with the recommended mixture of water and anti-freeze (coolant).

NOTE: ON AUTOMATIC TEMPERATURE CONTROL SYSTEMS: Removal and installation of the heater core for 1978 Ford, Mercury and Lincoln models is the same procedure as for manual air conditioning systems.

Ford and Mercury (Full Size) 1979 and Later, Lincoln Continental 1980 and Later

1. Disconnect the negative battery cable.
2. Remove the heater hoses from the core tubes and plug the ends to prevent coolant loss.
3. Plug the heater core tubes to prevent coolant loss during plenum and core removal.
4. In the engine compartment, remove the bolt located under the windshield wiper motor. Remove the nut at the upper left corner (engine side) of the evaporator case.
5. Disconnect the control system vacuum supply hose from the vacuum source

and push the grommet and vacuum supply hose into the passenger compartment.
6. Remove the glove box assembly.
7. Loosen the right door sill plate and remove the right side cowl trim panel.
8. Remove the lower right instrument panel to side cowl bolt.
9. Remove the instrument panel pad.
10. Remove the bracket from the temperature control cable housing at the top of the plenum assembly. Disconnect the temperature control cable from the blend door crank arm.
11. Remove the push clip attaching the center register duct bracket to the plenum and rotate the bracket up to the right.
12. Disconnect the vacuum jumper vacuum harness at the multiple vacuum connector near the floor air distribution duct.
13. Disconnect the white vacuum hose from the outside recirculating door vacuum motor.

NOTE: FOR AUTOMATIC TEMPERATURE CONTROL SYSTEMS THE FOLLOWING STEPS ARE CHANGED:

10. Disconnect the temperature control cable from the ATC sensor.
11. Disconnect the vacuum harness connector from the ATC sensor.
12. Disconnect the ATC sensor tube from the sensor and evaporator case connector. Also, disconnect the wire connector from the top end of the electric-vacuum relay, located on the right side of the plenum case.
14. Remove the two (2) attaching screws from the floor air distribution duct, at the seat side of the air distribution duct.
15. Remove the plastic push fastener, holding the air distribution duct to the left of the plenum and remove the air distribution duct.
16. Remove the final two (2) retaining nuts from the lower flange of the plenum assembly.
17. Move the plenum assembly toward the seat to allow the heater core tubes to clear the holes in the dash panel. Rotate the plenum assembly down and out from under the dash panel.
18. Installation is the reverse of removal. Refill the cooling system and check the heater operation.

1978–80 Granada and Monarch

NOTE: The refrigerant system components and charge do not have to be disturbed when removing and installing the heater core.

1. Drain the coolant and disconnect the battery.
2. Disconnect 2 heater hose clamps at the dash panel in the engine compartment. Plug the core tubes to prevent coolant leakage during removal.
3. Remove the heat distribution duct from the instrument panel.
4. Remove the seat belt interlock module and bracket, on 1978 models.
5. Remove the glovebox liner.

6. Loosen the right door sill scuff plate, right "A" pillar trim cover and remove the right cowl side trim panel.

7. Loosen instrument panel-to-right cowl side bolt and remove the instrument panel brace bolt at the lower rail, below the glove box. Remove the tunnel to cowl brace at the left end of the plenum assembly, if equipped on 1979–80 models.

8. Remove the instrument panel crash pad.

9. Remove the radio speaker or panel cowl brace.

10. Remove the 4 defroster nozzle-to-cowl bracket mounting screws.

11. Lift the defroster nozzle upward through the crash pad opening.

NOTE: ON MODELS WITH AUTOMATIC TEMPERATURE CONTROL: Remove the retaining nut and remove the vacuum harness from electro-vacuum relay.

12. Disconnect the vacuum hoses from the A/C-Defrost and Heat/Defrost door motors. Remove the screw from the clip holding the vacuum harness to the plenum.

13. Remove 2 Heat/Defrost door mounting nuts and swing the motor rearward on the door crankarm.

14. Remove 2 screws attaching the plenum to the left mounting bracket. Then remove the 2 screws and 3 clips securing the plenum to the evaporator case.

15. Swing the bottom of the plenum away from the evaporator case to disengage the S-clip on the forward flange of the plenum. Raise the plenum to clear the tabs on the top of the evaporator case.

16. Move the plenum to the left as far as possible, (about 4 inches) pulling rearward on the instrument panel to gain clearance. Take care when pulling back on the instrument panel to avoid cracking the plastic panel.

NOTE: There is very little clearance between the plenum and the wiper motor assembly.

17. Pull the heater core to the left using the tab molded into the rear heater core seal. As the rear surface of the heater core clears the evaporator case, pull the core rearward and downward to clear the instrument panel.

18. Reverse the above procedure to install.

NOTE: Before installing the core, make sure that the heater core tube to dash panel seal is in place between the evaporator case and the dash panel.

1978–79 Thunderbird, Cougar, LTD II and Mark V

1. Drain the engine coolant and disconnect the heater hoses from the heater core.

2. Remove the heater core cover plate.

3. To release the heater core seal from the housing press down on the heater core and tip it towards the front of the vehicle.

4. To remove the heater core lift upward.

NOTE: AUTOMATIC TEMPERATURE CONTROL: Removal and installation of the heater core is the same as for manual control. The heater core is removed from the engine compartment and not affected by ATC, which is basically under the dash.

5. To install press down on the heater core and tip it rearward so that the notch on the seal is aligned with the flange on the evaporator housing.

6. Install the cover plate, connect the hoses and fill the cooling system.

Thunderbird 1980 and Later, Cougar 1980, XR7 1980, LTD and Marquis 1983 and Later

1. Remove the instrument panel and lay it on the front seat.

2. Drain the coolant from the cooling system. Disconnect the heater hoses from the core tubes and plug the tubes to prevent spillage.

3. From the engine compartment side remove the two (2) nuts attaching the evaporator case to the dash panel.

4. Under the dash area remove the screws attaching the evaporator case support bracket and the air inlet duct support bracket to the cowl top panel.

5. Remove the retaining nut from the bracket at the left side of the evaporator case and the nut attaching the heater core access cover to the evaporator case.

6. Carefully pull the evaporator case assembly away from the dash panel to gain access to the screws retaining the heater core access cover to the evaporator case.

7. Remove the heater core cover attaching screws and remove the cover.

8. Lift the heater core and seals from the evaporator case. Remove the two (2) seals from the core tubes.

9. Installation is the reverse of removal. Refill the cooling system and check heater operation.

NOTE: AUTOMATIC TEMPERATURE CONTROL: Removal and installation of the heater core are the same for manual and automatic temperature control systems, on the 1980–81 Thunderbird, Cougar and XR7.

Fairmont 1978 and Later, Zephyr 1978 and Later, Mustang 1979 and Later, Capri 1980 and Later, Granada 1981 and Later, Cougar 1981 and Later

1. Remove instrument panel.

2. Drain radiator coolant.

3. Disconnect heater hoses at core connections.

4. In engine compartment, remove two evaporator case to dash panel retaining nuts.

5. Under dash, remove screws securing evaporator case support bracket and air inlet duct support bracket to the cowl top panel.

6. Remove one nut retaining the bracket at the left end of evaporator case to the dash panel, and one nut securing the bracket below the case to the dash panel.

7. Remove five heater core access cover screws and the cover from the evaporator case.

8. Remove heater core and seals from evaporator case.

9. Reverse procedure for installation.

Versailles 1978–80

1. Drain radiator coolant.

2. Disconnect heater hoses at core connections.

3. Disconnect battery ground cable.

4. Remove instrument panel lower finish panel and support brace bolt under glove box.

5. Remove instrument panel pad.

6. Loosen right door sill plate retaining screws, remove side cowl trim panel attaching screws and remove trim panel.

7. At right end of instrument panel, remove the instrument panel lower attaching screw.

8. Remove two screws and the floor air distribution duct from the plenum assembly.

9. Remove radio speaker or instrument panel to cowl brace.

10. Remove four screws securing defroster nozzle to the cowl mounting tabs. Lift defroster nozzle up and out from behind instrument panel.

11. Remove cowl to floor brace at left side of plenum assembly.

12. Disconnect vacuum from A/C defrost and heat-defrost door vacuum motors.

13. Remove retaining nut and vacuum harness connector from the electro-vacuum relay, located on the right side of the plenum case.

14. Remove screw securing vacuum harness clamp to plenum assembly.

15. Remove two heat-defrost door motor retaining nuts and swing motor to rear.

16. Remove two screws attaching front corner of plenum assembly to the plenum-to-cowl mounting bracket.

17. Remove two screws attaching the lower edge of the plenum to the evaporator case.

18. Remove two clips securing the rear edge of the plenum assembly to the evaporator case.

19. Raise plenum assembly until top edge of plenum is disengaged from evaporator case. Then move plenum to the left as far as possible.

20. Pull rearward on lower edge of instrument panel carefully and remove plenum assembly from behind instrument panel.

21. Pull the heater core from the evaporator housing carefully, using the tab molded into heater core seal.

22. Disengage heater core tubes from dash panel seal as core is removed. As heater core clears evaporator case, pull heater core rearward and down to clear instrument panel.

23. Reverse procedure for installation.

Pinto, Bobcat and Mustang II

1. Remove the evaporator case assembly from the vehicle.

2. Remove the upper-to-lower case attaching screws. Remove the blower motor and wheel.

3. Remove the rubber seal from the heater core tubes.

4. Remove the upper half of the evaporator case.

5. Move the rubber seal on the evaporator core forward to clear the case mounting stud and pull the core out of the lower case.

6. Install in the reverse order of removal. Be sure to install new rope sealer around the flange of the lower case before installing the upper half of the case. Install new O-rings on the manifold plate. Dip the new O-rings in refrigerant oil before installing them.

CIRCUIT PROTECTION

Fuses, Fusible Links and Circuit Breakers

Fusible links are used to protect the main wiring harness and selected branches from complete burn-out, should a short circuit or electrical overload occur.

Circuit breakers are used on certain electrical components requiring high amperage, such as the headlamp circuit, electrical seats and/or windows to name a few. The advantage of the circuit breaker is its ability to open and close the electrical circuit as the load demands, rather than the necessity of a part replacement, should the circuit be opened with another protective device in line.

A fuse panel is used to house the numerous fuses protecting the various branches of the electrical system and is normally the most accessible. The mounting of the fuse panel is usually on the left side of the passenger compartment, under the dash, either on the side kick panel or on the firewall to the left of the steering column. Certain models will have the fuse panel exposed while other models will have it covered with a removable trim cover.

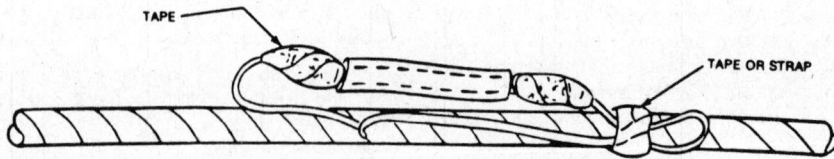

REMOVE EXISTING VINYL TUBE SHIELDING
REINSTALL OVER FUSE LINK BEFORE CRIMPING
FUSE LINK TO WIRE ENDS

TYPICAL REPAIR USING THE SPECIAL #17 GA. (9.00" LONG-YELLOW) FUSE LINK REQUIRED FOR THE AIR/COND. CIRCUITS

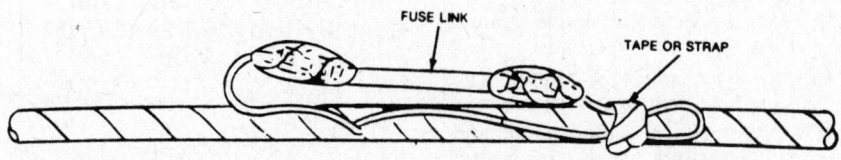

TYPICAL REPAIR FOR ANY IN-LINE FUSE LINK USING THE SPECIFIED GAUGE FUSE LINK FOR THE SPECIFIC CIRCUIT

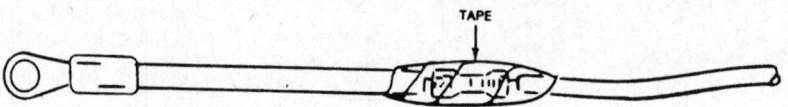

TYPICAL REPAIR USING THE EYELET TERMINAL FUSE LINK OF THE SPECIFIED GAUGE FOR ATTACHMENT TO A CIRCUIT WIRE END

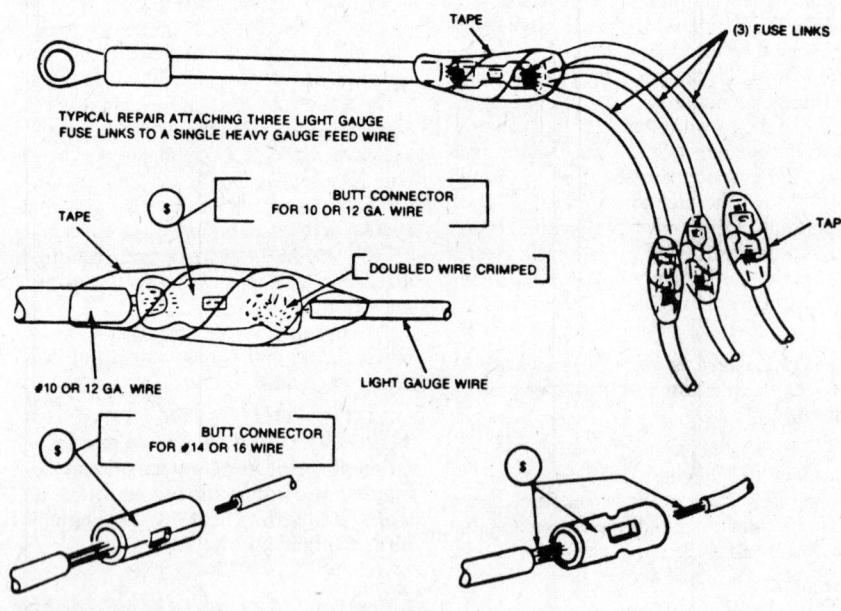

TYPICAL REPAIR ATTACHING THREE LIGHT GAUGE FUSE LINKS TO A SINGLE HEAVY GAUGE FEED WIRE

FUSIBLE LINK REPAIR PROCEDURE

General fuse link repair procedures

Buick
Rear Wheel Drive
Rear Wheel Drive
Electra, Century, Regal,
Riviera, Skylark, LeSabre

YEAR IDENTIFICATION

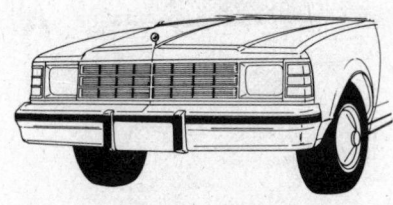

1978 Buick Century

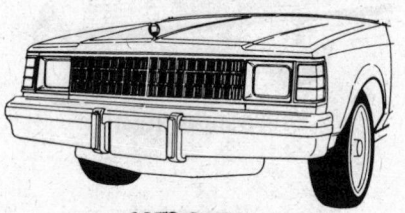

1979 Century

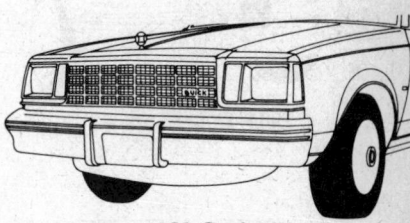

1980 Century

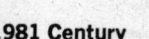

1981 Century

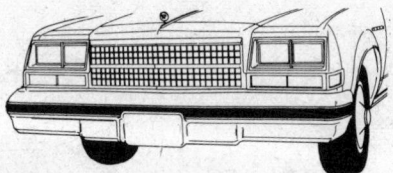

1978 Electra

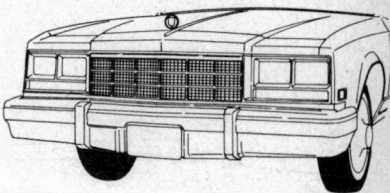

1979 Electra

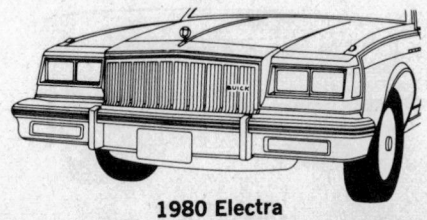

1980 Electra

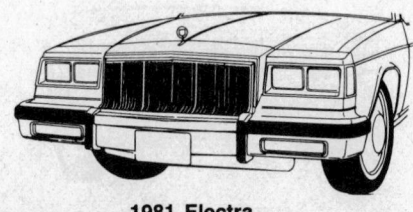

1981 Electra

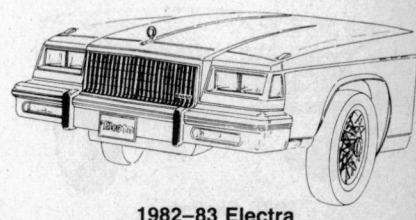

1982–83 Electra

C285

YEAR IDENTIFICATION

1984 Electra

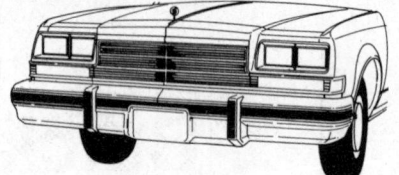

1978 Le Sabre

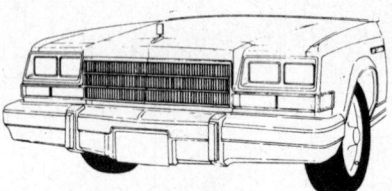

1979 LeSabre

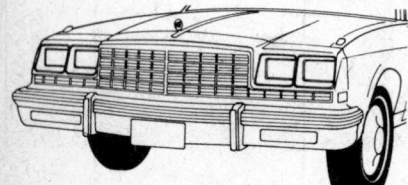

1980 LeSabre

1981 LeSabre

1982–83 LeSabre

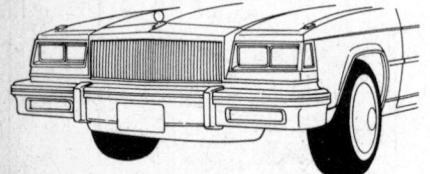

1984–85 LeSabre

1978 Buick Regal

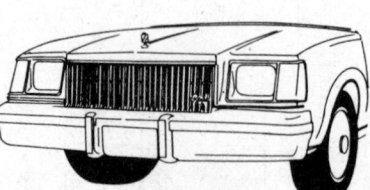

1979 Regal

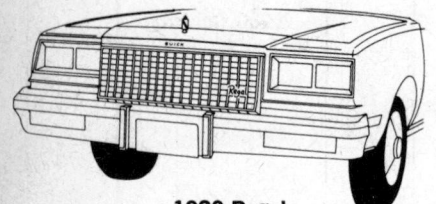

1980 Regal

1981 Regal

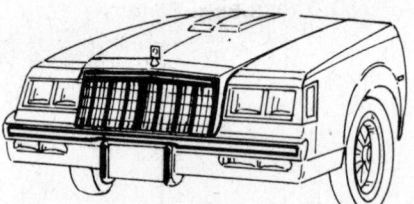

1982–83 Regal

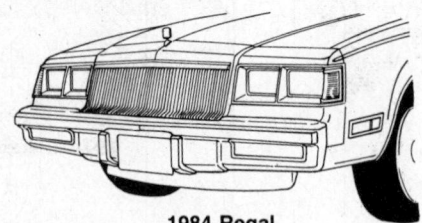

1984 Regal

1985 Regal

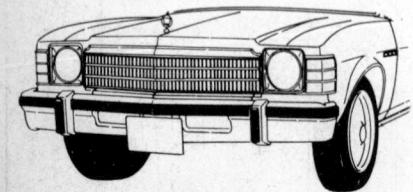

1978 Skylark

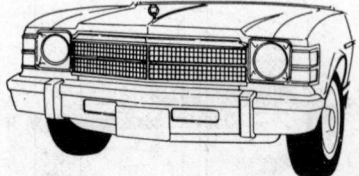

1979 Skylark

1978 Riviera

VEHICLE IDENTIFICATION NUMBER (VIN)

It is important for servicing and ordering parts to be certain of the vehicle and engine identification. The VIN (vehicle identification number) is a 13 or 17 digit number visible through the windshield on the driver's side of the dash and contains the vehicle and engine identification codes. It can be interpreted as follows:

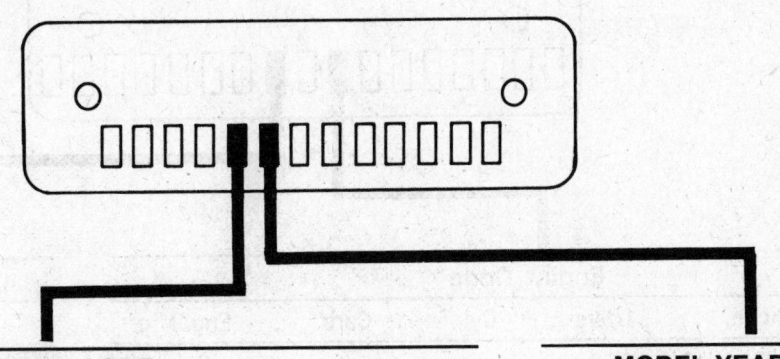

ENGINE CODE

Code	Cu. In.	Liters	Cyl.	Carb.	Eng. Mfg.
C (78–79)	196	3.2	6	2	Buick
A	231	3.8	6	2	Buick
G	231①	3.8	6	2	Buick
2	231	3.8	6	2	Buick
3	231①	3.8	6	4	Buick
4	252	4.1	6	4	Buick
S	265	4.3	8	2	Pont.
Y	301	4.9	8	2	Pont.
W	301	4.9	8	4	Pont.
U	305	5.0	8	2	Chev.
H	305	5.0	8	2	Chev.
G	305	5.0	8	2	Chev.
L	350	5.7	8	4	Chev.
R	350	5.7	8	4	Olds.
X	350	5.7	8	4	Buick
N	350	5.7	8	Diesel	Olds.
Z	400	6.5	8	4	Pont.
K	403	6.6	8	4	Olds.

MODEL YEAR CODE

Code	Year
8	78
9	79
A	80

The thirteen digit Vehicle Identification Number can be used to determine engine application and model year. The 6th digit indicates the model year, and the 5th digit identifies the factory-installed engine.

① Turbocharged

VEHICLE IDENTIFICATION NUMBER (VIN)

It is important for servicing and ordering parts to be certain of the vehicle and engine identification. The VIN (vehicle identification number) is a 13 or 17 digit number visible through the windshield on the driver's side of the dash and contains the vehicle and engine identification codes. It can be interpreted as follows:

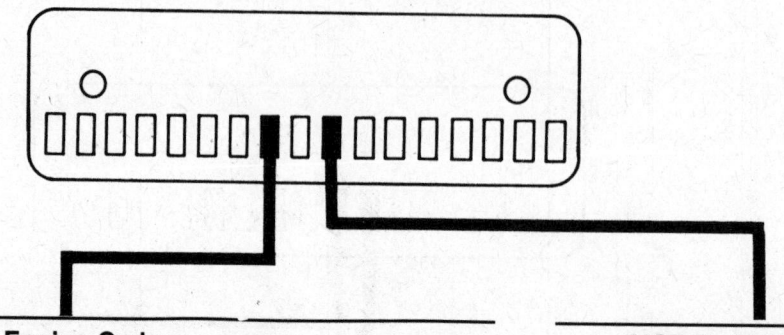

Engine Code

Code	Cu. In.	Liters	Cyl.	Carb.	Eng. Mfg.
A	231	3.8	6	2	Buick
3	231 ①	3.8	6	4	Buick
8	231 ①	3.8	6	4	Buick
9	231	3.8	6	M.F.I.	Buick
4	252	4.1	6	4	Buick
V	263	4.3	6	Diesel	Olds.
S	265	4.3	8	2	Pont.
J	267	4.4	8	2	Chev.
W	301	4.9	8	4	Pont.
H	305	5.0	8	4	Chev.
Y	307	5.0	8	4	Olds.
X	350	5.7	8	4	Buick
N	350	5.7	8	Diesel	Olds.

MODEL YEAR CODE

Code	Year
B	81
C	82
D	83
E	84
F	85

The seventeen digit Vehicle Identification Number can be used to determine engine application and model year. The 10th digit indicates the model year, and the 8th digit identifies the factory-installed engine.
① Turbocharged

GENERAL ENGINE SPECIFICATIONS

Year	Engine V.I.N. Code	Engine Type	Engine Manufacturer	Fuel Delivery	Horsepower @ rpm①	Torque @ rpm (ft lbs)①	Bore × Stroke (in.)	Compression Ratio	Oil Pressure (psi @ rpm)
'78	C	6-196	Buick	2 bbl	90 @ 3600	165 @ 2000	3.500 × 3.400	8.0:1	37 @ 2600
	A	6-231	Buick	2 bbl	105 @ 3400	185 @ 2000	3.800 × 3.400	8.0:1	37 @ 2600
	G	6-231 ②	Buick	2 bbl	150 @ 3800	245 @ 2400	3.800 × 3.400	8.0:1	37 @ 2600
	3	6-231 ②	Buick	4 bbl	165 @ 4000	285 @ 2800	3.800 × 3.400	8.0:1	37 @ 2600
	Y	8-301	Pont.	2 bbl	140 @ 3600	235 @ 2000	4.000 × 3.000	8.2:1	37 @ 2600
	H	8-305	Chev.	2 bbl	145 @ 3800	245 @ 2400	3.736 × 3.480	8.5:1	35-40 @ 2400
	U	8-305	Chev.	4 bbl	160 @ 4000	285 @ 2400	3.736 × 3.480	8.5:1	35-40 @ 2400
	L	8-350	Chev.	4 bbl	170 @ 3800	275 @ 2000	4.000 × 3.480	8.5:1	35-40 @ 2400
	R	8-350	Olds.	4 bbl	170 @ 3600	265 @ 2000	4.057 × 3.385	8.0:1	40 @ 1500
	X	8-350	Buick	4 bbl	155 @ 3400	280 @ 1800	3.800 × 3.850	8.0:1	37 @ 2600
	Z	8-400	Pont.	4 bbl	180 @ 3600	325 @ 1600	4.121 × 3.750	7.7:1	55-60 @ 2600
	K	8-403	Olds.	4 bbl	185 @ 3600	320 @ 2000	4.351 × 3.385	8.0:1	40 @ 1500

GENERAL ENGINE SPECIFICATIONS

Year	Engine V.I.N. Code	Engine Type	Engine Manufacturer	Fuel Delivery	Horsepower @ rpm①	Torque @ rpm (ft lbs)①	Bore × Stroke (in.)	Compression Ratio	Oil Pressure (psi @ rpm)
'79	C	6-196	Buick	2 bbl	105 @ 3800	160 @ 2000	3.500 × 3.400	8.0:1	37 @ 2600
	A	6-231	Buick	2 bbl	115 @ 3800	190 @ 2000	3.800 × 3.400	8.0:1	37 @ 2600
	2	6-231	Buick	2 bbl	115 @ 3800	190 @ 2000	3.800 × 3.400	8.0:1	37 @ 2600
	3	6-231②	Buick	4 bbl	165 @ 4000	285 @ 2800	3.800 × 3.400	8.0:1	37 @ 2600
	Y	8-301	Pont.	2 bbl	140 @ 3600	235 @ 2000	4.000 × 3.000	8.2:1	40 @ 2000
	W	8-301	Pont.	4 bbl	150 @ 3800	255 @ 2400	4.000 × 3.000	8.2:1	40 @ 2600
	G	8-305	Chev.	2 bbl	140 @ 3800	270 @ 2400	3.736 × 3.480	8.5:1	35-40 @ 2400
	H	8-305	Chev.	4 bbl	160 @ 4000	235 @ 2400	3.736 × 3.480	8.5:1	35-40 @ 2400
	L	8-350	Chev.	4 bbl	160 @ 3800	260 @ 2400	4.000 × 3.480	8.5:1	35-40 @ 2400
	R	8-350	Olds.	4 bbl	170 @ 3800	275 @ 2000	4.057 × 3.385	8.0:1	40 @ 1500
	X	8-350	Buick	4 bbl	155 @ 3400	280 @ 1800	3.800 × 3.850	8.0:1	37 @ 2400
	K	8-403	Pont.	4 bbl	185 @ 3600	320 @ 2000	4.351 × 3.385	8.0:1	40 @ 1500
'80	A	6-231	Buick	2 bbl	115 @ 3800	190 @ 2000	3.800 × 3.400	8.0:1	37 @ 2400
	3	6-231②	Buick	4 bbl	165 @ 4000	265 @ 2800	3.800 × 3.400	8.0:1	37 @ 2400
	4	6-252	Buick	4 bbl	125 @ 4000	205 @ 2000	3.965 × 3.400	8.0:1	37 @ 2400
	S	8-265	Pont.	2 bbl	120 @ 3600	210 @ 1600	3.750 × 3.000	8.0:1	40 @ 2600
	W	8-301	Pont.	4 bbl	150 @ 4000	240 @ 2000	4.000 × 3.000	8.2:1	40 @ 2600
	H	8-305	Chev.	4 bbl	155 @ 4000	235 @ 2400	3.736 × 3.480	8.5:1	35-40 @ 2400
	N	8-350	Olds.	Diesel	120 @ 3600	220 @ 2200	4.057 × 3.385	22.5:1	37 @ 1500
	R	8-350	Olds.	4 bbl	170 @ 3800	275 @ 2000	4.057 × 3.385	8.5:1	37 @ 1500
	X	8-350	Buick	4 bbl	155 @ 3400	280 @ 1800	3.800 × 3.850	8.0:1	37 @ 2400
'81	A	6-231	Buick	2 bbl	110 @ 3800	190 @ 1600	3.800 × 3.400	8.0:1	37 @ 2400
	3	6-231②	Buick	4 bbl	170 @ 4000	275 @ 2400	3.800 × 3.400	8.0:1	37 @ 2400
	4	6-252	Buick	4 bbl	125 @ 4000	205 @ 2000	3.965 × 3.400	8.0:1	37 @ 2400
	S	8-265	Pont.	2 bbl	119 @ 4000	204 @ 2000	3.750 × 3.000	8.0:1	35-40 @ 2600
	J	8-267	Chev.	2 bbl	115 @ 4000	200 @ 2400	3.500 × 3.480	8.3:1	45 @ 2000
	W	8-301	Pont.	4 bbl	155 @ 4000	240 @ 2000	4.000 × 3.000	8.2:1	40 @ 2600
	H	8-305	Chev.	4 bbl	155 @ 3800	230 @ 2400	3.736 × 3.480	8.6:1	35-40 @ 2400
	Y	8-307	Olds.	4 bbl	148 @ 3800	250 @ 2400	3.800 × 3.385	8.0:1	40 @ 1500
	X	8-350	Buick	4 bbl	NA	NA	3.800 × 3.850	8.0:1	37 @ 2400
	N	8-350	Olds.	Diesel	125 @ 3600	225 @ 1600	4.057 × 3.385	22.5:1	40 @ 1500
'82	A	6-231	Buick	2 bbl	110 @ 3800	190 @ 1600	3.800 × 3.400	8.0:1	37 @ 2400
	3	6-231②	Buick	4 bbl	170 @ 3800	275 @ 2600	3.800 × 3.400	8.0:1	37 @ 2400
	4	6-252	Buick	4 bbl	125 @ 4000	205 @ 2000	3.965 × 3.400	8.0:1	37 @ 2400
	V	6-263	Olds.	Diesel	85 @ 3600	165 @ 1600	4.057 × 3.385	21.6:1	30-45 @ 1500
	J	8-267	Chev.	2 bbl	115 @ NA	205 @ NA	3.500 × 3.480	8.3:1	35-40 @ 2600
	H	8-305	Chev.	4 bbl	140 @ 3600	240 @ 1600	3.736 × 3.480	8.0:1	35-40 @ 2600
	Y	8-307	Olds.	4 bbl	150 @ 3800	260 @ 2400	3.800 × 3.385	8.5:1	30-45 @ 1500
	N	8-350	Olds.	Diesel	105 @ 3200	200 @ 1600	4.057 × 3.385	22.5:1	30-45 @ 1500

GENERAL ENGINE SPECIFICATIONS

Year	Engine V.I.N. Code	Engine Type	Engine Manufac-turer	Fuel Delivery	Horsepower @ rpm①	Torque @ rpm (ft lbs)①	Bore × Stroke (in.)	Compression Ratio	Oil Pressure (psi @ rpm)
'83–'84	A	6-231	Buick	2 bbl	110 @ 3800	190 @ 1600	3.800 × 3.400	8.0:1	37 @ 2400
	8	6-231②	Buick	4 bbl	170 @ 3800	275 @ 2600	3.800 × 3.400	8.0:1	37 @ 2400
	9	6-231②④	Buick	MFI	100 @ 4000	300 @ 2480	3.800 × 3.400	8.0:1	37 @ 2400
	4	6-252	Buick	4 bbl	125 @ 4000	205 @ 2000	3.965 × 3.400	8.0:1	37 @ 2400
	V	6-263	Olds.	Diesel	85 @ 3600	165 @ 1600	4.057 × 3.385	21.6:1③	30-45 @ 1500
	Y	8-307	Olds.	4 bbl	150 @ 3800	260 @ 2400	3.800 × 3.385	8.5:1	30-45 @ 1500
	N	8-350	Olds.	Diesel	105 @ 3200	200 @ 1600	4.057 × 3.385	22.5:1	30-45 @ 1500
'85	A	6-231	Buick	2 bbl	110 @ 3800	190 @ 1600	3.800 × 3.400	8.0:1	37 @ 2400
	8	6-231②	Buick	4 bbl	170 @ 3800	275 @ 2600	3.800 × 3.400	8.0:1	37 @ 2400
	9	6-231②④	Buick	MFI	100 @ 4000	300 @ 2480	3.800 × 3.400	8.0:1	37 @ 2400
	4	6-252	Buick	4 bbl	125 @ 4000	205 @ 2000	3.965 × 3.400	8.0:1	37 @ 2400
	V	6-263	Olds.	Diesel	85 @ 3600	165 @ 1600	4.057 × 3.385	22.5:1	30-45 @ 1500
	Y	8-307	Olds.	4 bbl	150 @ 3800	260 @ 2400	3.800 × 3.385	8.5:1	30-45 @ 1500
	N	8-350	Olds.	Diesel	105 @ 3200	200 @ 1600	4.057 × 3.385	22.5:1	30-45 @ 1500

NA—Not available at time of publication.
MFI—Multi-point fuel injection
① Horsepower and torque are SAE net figures. They are measured at the rear of the transmission with all accessories installed and operating. Since the figures vary when a given engine is installed in different models, some are representative rather than exact.
② Turbocharged engine
③ 1984—22.5:1
④ Engine Code 9: 1984 and later

TUNE-UP SPECIFICATIONS

When analyzing compression test results, look for uniformity among cylinders rather than specific pressures

Year	Engine V.I.N. Code	Engine Type	Engine Manufac-turer	Spark Plugs Type①	Gap (in.)	Ignition Timing (deg. B.T.D.C.)② Manual Transmission③	Ignition Timing (deg. B.T.D.C.)② Automatic Transmission③	Intake Valve Opens (°B.T.D.C.)	Fuel Pump Pressure (psi)	Idle Speed (rpm)④ Manual Transmission③	Idle Speed (rpm)④ Automatic Transmission③
'78	C	6-196	Buick	R46TSX	.060	15 @ 800	15	18	4½–5½	800/600	600
	A	6-231	Buick	R46TSX	.060	15 @ 800	15	17	4½–5½	800/600	670/600
	G	6-231	Buick	R44TSX	.060	—	15 @ 600	17	4½–5½	—	650
	3	6-231	Buick	R44TSX	.060	—	15 @ 600	17	4½–5½	—	650
	Y	8-301	Pont.	R46TSX	.060	—	12 @ 550	27	7–8.5	—	650/550
	H,U	8–305	Chev.	R45TS	.045	—	4 @ 500 (6 @ 500) [8 @ 600]	28	7½–9	—	600/500 (650/500) [700/600]
	L	8-350	Chev.	R45TS	.045	—	8 @ 500 [8 @ 600]	28	7½–9	—	600/500 [650/600]
	R	8-350	Olds.	R46SZ	.060	—	20 @ 1100	16	5½–6½	—	650/550 [700/600]
	X	8-350	Buick	R46TSX	.060	—	15 @ 600	16	7½–9	—	550
	Z	8-400	Pont.	R45TSX	.060	—	16	29	7–8½	—	650
	K	8-403	Olds.	R46SZ	.060	—	20 @ 1100	16*	5½–6½	—	650/550 [700/600]

TUNE-UP SPECIFICATIONS

When analyzing compression test results, look for uniformity among cylinders rather than specific pressures

Year	Engine V.I.N. Code	Engine Type	Engine Manufacturer	Spark Plugs Type [1]	Gap (in.)	Ignition Timing (deg. B.T.D.C.) [2] Manual Transmission [3]	Automatic Transmission [3]	Intake Valve Opens (°B.T.D.C.)	Fuel Pump Pressure (psi)	Idle Speed (rpm) [4] Manual Transmission [3]	Automatic Transmission [3]
'79	C	6-196	Buick	R45TSX or R46TSX	.060 .060	15 @ 800	15 @ 600	16	4¼–5¾	800/600	670/550
	A	6-231	Buick	R45TSX or R46TSX	.060 .060	15 @ 800	15 @ 600	16	4¼–5¾	800/600	670/550 (600) [600]
	2	6-231	Buick	R45TSX or R46TSX	.060 .060	—	15 @ 580	16	4¼–5¾	—	670/580
	3	6-231	Buick	R44TSX	.060	—	15	16	4¼–5¾	—	650
	Y	8-301	Pont.	R46TSX	.060	—	12 @ 650	27	7–8½	—	650/500
	W	8-301	Pont.	R45TSX	.060	—	12 @ 650	27	7–8½	—	650/500
	G	8-305	Chev.	R45TS	.045	—	4 @ 600	28	7½–9	—	[5]
	H	8-305	Chev.	R45TS	.045	—	4 @ 500 [8 @ 600]	28	7½–9	—	600/500 [650/600]
	L	8-350	Chev.	R45TS	.045	—	8 @ 600 [8 @ 500]	28	7½–9	—	600/500 [650/600]
	R	8-350	Olds.	R46SZ	.060	—	20 @ 1100	16	6–7½	—	650/550 (600/500) [700/600]
	X	8-350	Buick	R45TSX or R46TSX	.060 .060	—	15	13½	6–7½	—	550
	K	8-403	Olds.	R46SZ	.060	—	20 @ 1100	16	6–7½	—	650/550 (600/500) [700/600]
'80	A	6-231	Buick	R45TSX	.060	15 @ 550	15 @ 550	16	5½–6½	800/600	670/550 [6] (620/550) [7] 550 [8]
	3	6-231	Buick	R45TS	.040	—	15 @ 650	16	5½–6½	—	650
	4	6-252	Buick	R45TSX	.060	—	15 @ 550	—	5½–6½	—	680/550 [9] 550 [8]
	S	8-265	Pont.	R45TSX	.060	—	10 @ 700	27	7–8½	—	650/550 [9] 550 [8]
	W	8-301	Pont.	R45TSX	.060	—	12 @ 500	27	7–8½	—	650/500 [9] 550 [8]
	H	8-305	Chev.	R45TS	.035	—	4 @ 550	28	7½–9	—	650/550 [9] 550 [8]
	R	8-350	Olds.	R46SX or R47SX	.080 .080	—	18 @ 1100	16	5½–6½	—	650/550
	X	8-350	Buick	R45TSX	.060	—	15 @ 550	13½	6–7½	—	550
'81	A	6-231	Buick	R45TS8	.080	—[10]—		16	5½–6½	—[10]—	
	3	6-231	Buick	R45TS	.040	—[10]—		16	5½–6½	—[10]—	
	4	6-252	Buick	R45TS8	.080	—[10]—		16	5½–6½	—[10]—	
	S	8-265	Pont.	R45TSX	.060	—[10]—		27	5½–6½	—[10]—	
	J	8-267	Chev.	R45TS	.045	—[10]—		28	5½–6½	—[10]—	
	W	8-301	Pont.	R45TSX	.060	—[10]—		27	5½–6½	—[10]—	
	H	8-305	Chev.	R45TS	.045	—[10]—		28	5½–6½	—[10]—	
	Y	8-307	Olds.	R45TS4	.060	—[10]—		20	5½–6½	—[10]—	
	X	8-350	Buick	R45TSX	.060	—[10]—		13½	5½–6½	—[10]—	
'82	A	6-231	Buick	R45TS8	.080	—[10]—		16	5½–6½	—[10]—	
	3	6-231	Buick	R45TSX	.060	—[10]—		16	5½–6½	—[10]—	
	4	6-252	Buick	R45TS8	.080	—[10]—		16	5½–6½	—[10]—	

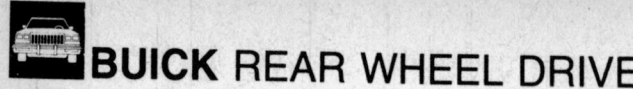

TUNE-UP SPECIFICATIONS

When analyzing compression test results, look for uniformity among cylinders rather than specific pressures

Year	Engine V.I.N. Code	Engine Type	Engine Manufacturer	Spark Plugs Type①	Spark Plugs Gap (in.)	Ignition Timing (deg. B.T.D.C.)② Manual Transmission③	Ignition Timing (deg. B.T.D.C.)② Automatic Transmission③	Intake Valve Opens (°B.T.D.C.)	Fuel Pump Pressure (psi)	Idle Speed (rpm)④ Manual Transmission③	Idle Speed (rpm)④ Automatic Transmission③
'82	J	8-267	Chev.	R45TS	.045	—⑩—		28	5½–6½	—⑩—	
	H	8-305	Chev.	R45TS	.045	—⑩—		28	5½–6½	—⑩—	
	Y	8-307	Olds.	R46SX	.080	—⑩—		20	5½–6½	—⑩—	
'83	A	6-231	Buick	R45TS8	.080	—⑩—		16	5½–6½	—⑩—	
	8	6-231	Buick	R45TSX	.060	—⑩—		16	5½–6½	—⑩—	
	4	6-252	Buick	R45TS8	.080	—⑩—		16	5½–6½	—⑩—	
	Y	8-307	Olds.	R46SX	.080	—⑩—		20	5½–6½	—⑩—	
'84	A	6-231	Buick	R45TSX	.060	—⑩—		16	5½–6½	—⑩—	
	9	6-231	Buick	R44TS	.045	—⑩—		16	26–51	—⑩—	
	4	6-252	Buick	R45TSX	.060	—⑩—		16	5½–6½	—⑩—	
	Y	8-307	Olds	R46SX	.080	—⑩—		20	5½–6½	—⑩—	
'85	A	6-231	Buick	R45TSX	.060	—⑩—		16	5½–6½	—⑩—	
	9	6-231	Buick	R44TS	.045	—⑩—		16	26–51	—⑩—	
	4	6-252	Buick	R45TSX	.060	—⑩—		16	5½–6½	—⑩—	
	Y	8-307	Olds	R46SX	.080	—⑩—		20	5½–6½	—⑩—	

NOTE: The underhood specifications sticker often reflects tune-up specification changes made in production. Sticker figures must be used if they disagree with those in this chart.

① All models use electronic ignition systems.
B.T.D.C.—Before top dead center (No. 1 cylinder)
C.I.D.—Cubic inch displacement
Min.—Minimum
　Part numbers in this chart are not recommendations by Chilton for any product by brand name.
② On some models, the engine must be held at a specific rpm to accurately check and adjust the ignition timing. See the text for specific procedures.
③ Figure in parenthesis ( ) indicates a special figure for California models; figure in brackets [ ] indicates a special figure for high-altitude models.
④ Most 1979 and later carburetors have idle mixture screws concealed with hardened steel plugs. Normal idle mixture adjustments are not required on these carburetors. Plug removal should be performed only by professional technicians.
⑤ With the solenoid energized, set the solenoid screw to 600 rpm; with the solenoid de-energized, set the carburetor screw to 550 rpm for models with air conditioning, 500 for models without air conditioning.
⑥ With air conditioning, 49 states models only
⑦ With air conditioning, California models only
⑧ All models without air conditioning
⑨ All models with air conditioning
⑩ On vehicles equipped with computerized emissions systems (which have no distributor vacuum advance unit), the idle speed and ignition timing are controlled by the emissions computer. These adjustments should be performed professionally on models so equipped.

DIESEL TUNE-UP SPECIFICATIONS

Year	Engine No. of cyl.-Displacement-Manufacturer	Fuel Pump Pressure (psi)	Compression Pressure (psi)②	Intake Valve Opens (°B.T.D.C.)	Idle Speed (rpm)
'81–'84	8-350-Olds	5.5–6.5	275 minimum	16	①
'82–'84	6-263 Olds	5.8–8.7	275 minimum	16	①

NOTE: The underhood specifications sticker often reflects tune-up specification changes made in production. Sticker figures must be used if they disagree with those in this chart.
B.T.D.C.—Before top dead center (No. 1 cylinder)
① See the underhood specifications sticker.
② The lowest cylinder reading must not be less than 70% of the highest cylinder reading.

FIRING ORDERS

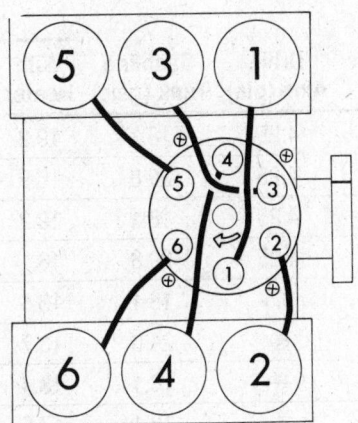

GM (Buick) 231, 252 V6
Engine firing order: 1-6-5-4-3-2
Distributor rotation: clockwise

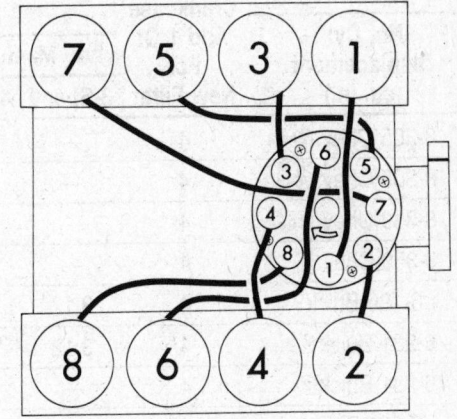

Buick-manufactured V8 engines
Engine firing order: 1-8-4-3-6-5-7-2
Distributor rotation: clockwise

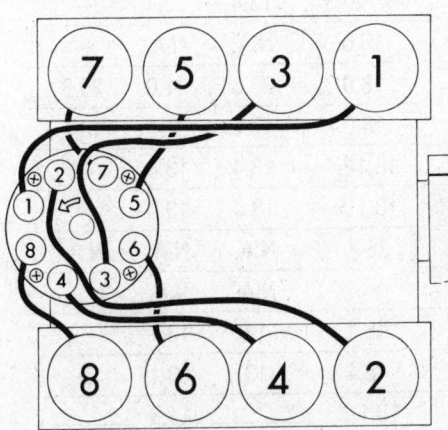

Oldsmobile-manufactured V8 engines
Engine firing order: 1-8-4-3-6-5-7-2
Distributor rotation: counterclockwise

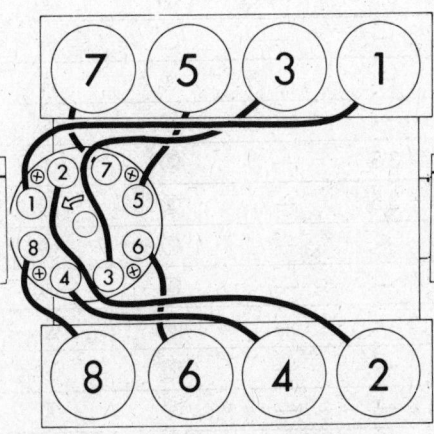

Pontiac-manufactured V8 engines
Engine firing order: 1-8-4-3-6-5-7-2
Distributor rotation: counterclockwise

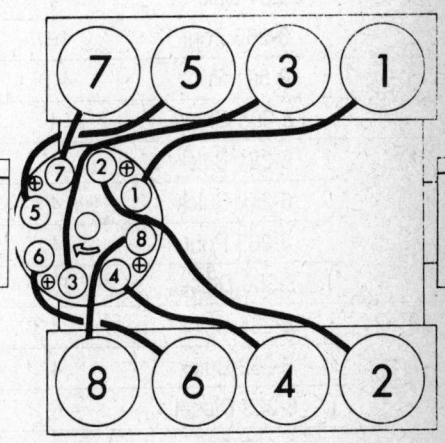

Chevrolet-manufactured V8 engines
Engine firing order: 1-8-4-3-6-5-7-2
Distributor rotation: clockwise

CAPACITIES
Century, Regal and Skylark

Year	Engine No. Cyl. Displacement (cu. in.)	Engine Crankcase Add 1 Qt For New Filter	Transmission Pts to Refill After Draining Manual 3-Speed	4-Speed	Automatic ●	Drive Axle (pts)	Gasoline Tank (gals)	Cooling System (qts) With Heater	With A/C	Heavy Duty
'78	6-196 Buick	4	3.5	—	3.0	4.25	18.1	13.1	13.2	13.1
	6-231 Buick②	4	3.5	3.5	⑤	4.25	18.1	13.1	13.2	13.1
	6-231 Buick⑥	4	3.5	—	3.0	4.25	20.8	13.6	13.7	13.5
	6-231 Buick⑦	4	—	3.5	3.0	3.75	18.5	11.7	12.1	12.6

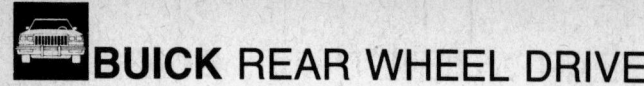
CAPACITIES
Century, Regal and Skylark

Year	Engine No. Cyl. Displacement (cu. in.)	Engine Crankcase Add 1 Qt For New Filter	Transmission Pts to Refill After Draining Manual 3-Speed	Transmission Pts to Refill After Draining Manual 4-Speed	Automatic ●	Drive Axle (pts)	Gasoline Tank (gals)	Cooling System (qts) With Heater	Cooling System (qts) With A/C	Cooling System (qts) Heavy Duty
'78	8-305 Chev.②	4	—	—	⑤	4.25	18.1	19.2	18.9	19.6
	8-305 Chev.④	4	—	—	⑤	4.25	20.8	15.9	16.3	16.9
	8-350 Chev.②	4	—	—	3.0	4.25	18.1	19.2	18.9	19.6
	8-350 Chev.④	4	—	—	3.0	4.25	20.8	16.1	16.9	16.9
'79	6-196 Buick	4	3.12	—	③	3.5	18.1	13.5	13.5	13.4
	6-231 Buick④	4	3.12	—	6.0	⑥	21.0	13.7	13.8	—
	6-231 Buick②	4	—	3.5	③	—	18.1	13.4	13.4	—
	8-301 Pont.	4	—	—	③	⑥	18.1	17.6	17.9	17.9
	8-305 Chev.④	4	—	—	③	⑥	21.0	15.9	16.3	16.9
	8-305 Chev.④	4	—	—	③	⑥	18.1	17.6	18.1	18.1
	8-350 Chev.④	4	—	—	③	⑥	18.1	17.6	18.1	18.1
	8-350 Chev.④	4	—	—	③	⑥	21.0	16.1	16.9	16.9
'80	6-231 Buick②	4	3.5	—	③	⑥	18.1①①	13.4	13.4	—
	8-265 Pont.	4①	—	—	③	⑥	18.0	N.A.	N.A.	—
	8-301 Pont.	4①	—	—	③	⑥	18.0	20.3	21.0	20.8
	8-305 Chev.	4	—	—	③	⑥	18.0	17.6	—	18.1
'81	6-231 Buick	4	3.5	—	③	⑥	18.1⑤	13.4	13.4	—
	6-252 Buick	4	3.5	—	③	⑥	18.1⑤	13.0	13.0	—
	8-265 Pont.	4	—	—	③	⑥	25⑧	N.A.	N.A.	N.A.
	8-350 Diesel	7⑨	—	—	③	⑥	—	N.A.	N.A.	N.A.
'82	6-231 Buick	4	—	—	⑨	⑥	18.1	13	13.1	—
	6-252 Buick	4	—	—	⑨	⑥	18.1	13	13.1	—
	6-263 Diesel	6	—	—	⑨	⑥	18.1⑦		14.8	
	8-267 Chev.	4	—	—	⑨	⑥	18.1⑦		21	
	8-305 Chev.	4	—	—	⑨	⑥	18.1⑦		19	
	8-350 Diesel	6	—	—	⑨	⑥	18.1⑦		17.3	
'83–'84	6-231 Buick	4	—	—	⑨	⑥	19	13	13.1	—
	6-252 Buick	4	—	—	⑨	⑥	19	13	13.1	—
	6-263 Diesel	6	—	—	⑨	⑥	19		14.8	
	8-350 Diesel	6	—	—	⑨	⑥	19		17.3	

CAPACITIES
Century, Regal and Skylark

Year	Engine No. Cyl. Displacement (cu. in.)	Engine Crankcase Add 1 Qt For New Filter	Transmission Pts to Refill After Draining			Drive Axle (pts)	Gasoline Tank (gals)	Cooling System (qts)		
			Manual		Automatic ●			With Heater	With A/C	Heavy Duty
			3-Speed	4-Speed						
'85	6-231 Buick	4	—	—	⑨	⑥	19	13	13.1	—
	6-252 Buick	4	—	—	⑨	⑥	19	13	13.1	—
	6-263 Diesel	6	—	—	⑨	⑥	19	—	14.8	—
	8-350 Diesel	6	—	—	⑨	⑥	19	—	17.3	—

• Specifications do not include torque
  convertor
N.A.—Not available
—: Not applicable
① 4 quarts total
② Century and Regal
③ THM 200—6; THM 350—3
④ Skylark
⑤ Wagon—18.2

⑥ 7.5 in. ring gear—3.5; 8.5 in. ring
  gear—4.25; 8.75 in. ring gear—5.4
⑦ Station wagon—18.2 gal.
⑧ Station wagon—22 gal.
⑨ THM 200 & 200R-4—7 pts.; THM
  250C—8 pts.; THM 350C—6.3 pts.

CAPACITIES
Electra, LeSabre, Riviera

Year	Engine No. Cyl. Displacement (cu. in.)	Engine Crankcase Add 1 Qt For New Filter	Transmission Pts to Refill After Draining			Drive Axle (pts)	Gasoline Tank (gals)	Cooling System (qts)		
			Manual		Automatic ●			With Heater	With A/C	Heavy Duty
			3-Speed	4-Speed						
'78	6-231 Buick	4	—	—	⑦	①	21.0	12.9	12.9	12.9
	8-301 Pont.	5	—	—	⑦	①	21.0④	20.9	20.9	21.6
	8-305 Chev.	4	—	—	⑦	①	21.0④	16.6	16.7	16.7
	8-350 Buick	5	—	—	⑦	①	25.3②⑤	14.1	14.1	14.9
	8-350 Chev.	4	—	—	⑦	①	21.0④	16.6	16.7	18.0
	8-350 Olds.	4	—	—	⑦	①	21.0⑤⑥	14.6	14.5	15.4
	8-403 Olds.	4	—	—	⑦	①	25.3⑤⑥	15.7	16.6	16.6
'79	6-231 Buick④	4	—	—	⑦	①	25.3	12.9	12.9	12.9
	8-301 Pont.④	4	—	—	⑦	①	21.0	20.9	20.9	21.6
	8-305 Chev.④	4	—	—	⑦	①	21.0	20.9	20.9	21.6
	8-350 Buick④	4	—	—	⑦	①	21.0	14.1	14.1	14.9
	8-350 Buick⑧	4	—	—	⑦	①	25.3	14.1	14.1	14.9
	8-350 Olds④	4	—	—	⑦	①	21.0	14.6	14.5	15.4
	8-350 Olds⑧	4	—	—	⑦	①	25.3	14.6	14.5	15.4
	8-403 Olds④	4	—	—	⑦	①	21.0	15.7	16.6	16.6
	8-403 Olds⑧	4	—	—	⑦	①	25.3	15.7	16.6	16.6

CAPACITIES
Electra, LeSabre, Riviera

Year	Engine No. Cyl. Displacement (cu. in.)	Engine Crankcase Add 1 Qt For New Filter	Manual 3-Speed	Manual 4-Speed	Automatic ●	Drive Axle (pts)	Gasoline Tank (gals)	With Heater	With A/C	Heavy Duty
'80–'81	6-231 Buick④	4	—	—	⑦	①	25.0④	13.0	13.0	13.0
	6-252 Buick	4	—	—	⑦	①	25.0	13.0	13.0	13.0
	8-301 Pont.④	4	—	—	⑦	①	25.0④	18.9	18.9	18.9
	8-307 Olds.	4	—	—	⑦	①	25.0④	15.6⑩	16.3⑩	16.0⑩
	8-350 Buick④ ⑧	4	—	—	⑦	①	25.0④	14.3	14.2	14.7
	8-350 Olds.④ ⑧	4	—	—	⑦	①	25.0④	—	14.5	15.2
	8-350 Diesel	6	—	—	⑦	①	23.0⑨	18.3	18.0	18.0
'82	6-231, 6-252	4	—	—	⑦	①	③	13	13.1	—
	8-307	4	—	—	⑦	①	③	15.4	16.2	16.1
	8-350 Diesel	6	—	—	⑦	①	③	—	17.9	—
'83–'85	6-231, 6-252	4	—	—	⑦	①	25	13	13.1	—
	8-307	4	—	—	⑦	①	25	15.4	16.2	16.1
	8-350 Diesel	6	—	—	⑦	①	25	—	17.9	—

• Specifications do not include torque converter
—: Not applicable
① 7.5 in. ring gear—3.5; 8.5 in. ring gear—4.25; 8.75 in. ring gear—5.4
② Station wagon—18.2 gal.
③ Not available at time of publication
④ LeSabre
⑤ Estate wagon—22 gal.
⑥ Electra—25.3

⑦ THM 200 & 200R-4, 350, 400— Add 6 pts, start engine and allow to warm up, fill as required
⑧ Electra
⑨ Wagon—27 gal.
⑩ Riviera 16.4 (Heater), 16.4 (A.C.), 16.2 (H.D.)

TORQUE SPECIFICATIONS
Century, Regal, and Skylark
(All readings in ft lbs)

Year	Engine No. Cyl. Displacement (cu in.)	Cylinder Head Bolts	Rod Bearing Bolts	Main Bearing Bolts	Crankshaft Bolt	Flywheel to Crankshaft Bolts	Intake	Exhaust
'78–'79	6-196, 231 Buick	80	40	100	225	60	45	25
	8-301 Pont.	90	35	60①	160	95	40	35
	8-305, 350 Chev.	65	45	70	60	60	30	20
'80–'81	6-231 Buick	80	40	100	225	60	45	25
	8-350 Diesel	130②	42	120	200–310	60	40②	25
	265 Pont.	95	35	70①	160	95	40	35
	8-305 Chev.	65	45	70	60	60	30	20
	6-252 Buick	80	40	100	225	60	45	25

TORQUE SPECIFICATIONS
Century, Regal, and Skylark
(All readings in ft lbs)

Year	Engine No. Cyl. Displacement (cu in.)	Cylinder Head Bolts	Rod Bearing Bolts	Main Bearing Bolts	Crankshaft Bolt	Flywheel to Crankshaft Bolts	Manifold	
							Intake	Exhaust
'82	6-231 Buick	80	40	100	225	60	45	25
	6-263 Diesel	142③	42	107	160–350	48	41	29
	8-267 Chev.	65	45	70	60	60	30	20
	8-305 Chev.	65	45	70	60	60	30	20
	8-305 Chev.	65	45	70	60	60	30	20
	8-350 Diesel	130②	42	120	200–310	60	40②	25
'83–'85	6-231 Buick	80	40	100	225	60	45	25
	6-252 Buick	80	40	100	225	60	45	25
	6-263 Diesel	142③	42	105	160–350	57	41	29
	8-350 Diesel	130②	42	120	200–310	60	40	25

① 100—rear main
② Dip bolt in oil before tightening
③ No. 5, 6, 11, 12, 13 and 14 (59 ft. lbs.)

TORQUE SPECIFICATIONS
Electra, LeSabre, and Riviera
(All readings in ft lbs)

Year	Engine Displacement (cu in.)	Cylinder Head Bolts	Rod Bearing Bolts	Main Bearing Bolts	Crankshaft Pulley or Balancer Bolt	Flywheel to Crankshaft Bolts	Manifold	
							Intake	Exhaust
'78–'82	6-231 Buick	80	40	100	225②	60	45	25
	6-252 Buick	80	40	100	225②	60	45	25
	8-301 Pont.	90	35	60①	160	95	40	35
	8-305 Chev.	65	45	70	60	60	30	20
	8-350 Buick	80	40	100	225②	60	45	25
	8-350 Chev.	65	45	70	60	60	30	20
	8307, 350, 403 Olds.	130	42	80③	255②	60④	40	25
	8-350 Diesel	130	42	120	200–310②	60	40	25
'83–'85	6-231 Buick	80	40	100	225	60	45	25
	6-252 Buick	80	40	100	225	60	45	25
	8-307 Olds	125	42	80③	200–310	60	45	25
	8-350 Diesel	130	42	120	200–310	60	40	25

① Rear main—100 ft. lbs.
② Fan pulley to balancer —20 ft. lbs.
③ Rear main—120 ft. lbs.
④ Manual transmission—90 ft. lbs.

VALVE SPECIFICATIONS
Century, Regal, Skylark

Year	Engine No. Cyl. Displacement (cu in.)	Seat Angle (deg)	Face Angle (deg)	Spring Test Pressure (lbs @ in.)	Spring Installed Height (in.)	Stem to Guide Clearance (in.)		Stem Diameter (in.)	
						Intake	Exhaust	Intake	Exhaust
'78	6-196 Buick	45	45	168 @ 1.327	$1^{47}/_{64}$	.0015–.0032	.0015–.0032	.3405–.3412	.3405–.3412
	6-231 Buick	45	45	168 @ 1.327	$1^{47}/_{64}$	.0015–.0032	.0015–.0032	.3405–.3412	.3405–.3412
	8-305 Chev.	46	45	200 @ 1.160	$1^{23}/_{32}$ ②	.0010–.0037	.0010–.0037	.3410	.3410
	8-350 Chev.	46	45	200 @ 1.160	$1^{23}/_{32}$ ②	.0010–.0037	.0010–.0037	.3410	.3410
'79–'80	6-196 Buick	45	45	164 @ 1.340	$1^{47}/_{64}$	.0015–.0032	.0015–.0032	.3405–.3412	.3405–.3412
	6-231 Buick	45	45	164 @ 1.340①	$1^{47}/_{64}$	.0015–.0032	.0015–.0032	.3401–.3412	.3405–.3412
	8-265 Pont.	46	45	170 @ 1.260	$1^{47}/_{64}$	.0017–.0020	.0017–.0020	.3400	.3400
	8-301 Pont.	46	45	170 @ 1.260	$1^{47}/_{64}$	.0017–.0020	.0017–.0020	.3400	.3400
	8-305 Chev.	46	45	200 @ 1.250	$1^{23}/_{32}$	.0010–.0037	.0010–.0047	.3410	.3410
	8-350 Chev.	46	45	200 @ 1.250	$1^{23}/_{32}$	.0010–.0037	.0010–.0037	.3410	.3410
'81	6-231 Buick	45	45	182 @ 1.340	$1^{23}/_{32}$	.0015–.0035	.0015–.0032	.3402–.3412	.3405–.3412
	6-252 Buick	45	45	182 @ 1.340	$1^{47}/_{64}$	.0015–.0035	.0015–.0032	.3407	.3409
	8-265 Pont.	46	45	187 @ 1.296	$1^{21}/_{32}$	.0010–.0027	.0010–.0027	.3418–.3425	.3418–.3425
	8-350 Olds (Diesel)	③	④	151 @ 1.300	$1^{43}/_{64}$	.0010–.0027	.0015–.0032	.3429	.3424
'82	6-231 Buick	45	45	182 @ 1.340	$1^{47}/_{64}$	.0015–.0035	.0015–.0032	.3407	.3409
	6-263 Olds Diesel	⑦	⑦	⑧	⑥	.0010–.0027	.0015–.0032	⑩	⑨
	8-267 Chev.	46	45	180 @ 1.25	$1^{23}/_{32}$	.0010–.0027	.0010–.0027	.3414	.3414
	8-305 Chev.	46	45	180 @ 1.25	$1^{23}/_{32}$ ⑤	.0010–.0027	.0010–.0027	.3414	.3414
	8-350 Olds Diesel	③	④	151 @ 1.300	$1^{43}/_{64}$	.0010–.0027	.0015–.0032	.3429	.3424
'83–'85	6-231 Buick	45	45	182 @ 1.34	$1^{47}/_{64}$	.0015–.0035	.0015–.0032	.3401–.3412	.3405–.3412
	6-252 Buick	45	45	182 @ 1.34	$1^{47}/_{64}$	.0015–.0035	.0015–.0032	.3401–.3412	.3405–.3412
	6-263 Diesel	⑦	⑦	209 @ 1.22	—	.0010–.0027	.0015–.0032	.3425–.3432	.3420–.3427
	8-350 Diesel	⑦	⑦	209 @ 1.22	$1^{47}/_{64}$	.0010–.0027	.0015–.0032	.3425–.3432	.3420–.3427

① Exhaust—182 @ 1.34
② Exhaust—$1^{19}/_{32}$
③ Intake—45°, exhaust 31°
④ Intake—46°, exhaust—30°
⑤ Exhaust—$1^{19}/_{32}$
⑥ Not available at time of publication
⑦ Intake—44° face; 45° seat: Exhaust—30° face; 31° seat
⑧ 203–217 @ 1.220 in.
⑨ .3420–.3427
⑩ .3425–.3432

RING GAP
Electra, LeSabre, and Riviera
(All measurements are given in inches)

Year	Engine No. Cyl. Displacement (cu in.)	Top Compression	Bottom Compression	Oil Control
'79–'80	6-231, 252 Buick	.013–.023	.013–.023	.015–.035
	8-301 Pont.	.010–.020	.010–.020	.035 max
	8-305 Chev.	.010–.030	.010–.035	.015–.065
	8-307 Olds.	.010–.020	.010–.020	.015–.055
	8-350 Buick	.010–.020③	.010–.020③	.015–.035
	8-350 Olds.	.010–.023①	.010–.023①	.015–.055
	8-350 Diesel	.015–.025	.015–.025	.015–.055
	8-403 Olds.	.010–.023②	.010–.023②	.015–.055
'81–'82	6-231, 252 Buick	.013–.023	.013–.023	.015–.035
	8-307 Olds.	.009–.019④	.009–.019④	.015–.055⑤
	8-350 Diesel	.015–.025	.015–.025	.015–.055
'83–'85	6-231, 252 Buick	.010–.020	.010–.020	.015–.055
	8-307 Olds	.009–.019④	.009–.019④	.015–.055⑤
	8-350 Diesel	.015–.025	.015–.025	.015–.055

① w/Sealed Power Rings—.010–.020
② w/Sealed Power Rings—.009–.019
③ 1980—.013–.023
④ w/TRW Rings .010–.020
⑤ w/TRW Rings .010–.025

RING SIDE CLEARANCE
Century, Regal, and Skylark
(All measurements are given in inches)

Year	Engine No. Cyl. Displacement (cu in.)	Top Compression	Bottom Compression	Oil Control
'78–'85	6-231, 252 Buick	.0030–.0050	.0030–.0050	.0035 Max.
'78–'80	8-301 Pont.	.0015–.0035	.0015–.0035	.0015–.0035
'78	8-305, 350 Chev.	.0012–.0042	.0012–.0042	.0020–.0080
'79–'82	8-267, 305, 350 Chev.	.0012–.0032	.0012–.0032	.0020–.0080
'78–'79	6-196 Buick	.0030–.0050	.0030–.0050	.0035 Max
'81–'85	8-350 Olds Diesel	.005–.007	.0018–.0038	.001–.005
'83–'85	6-263 Olds Diesel	.005–.007	.003–.005	.001–.005

RING SIDE CLEARANCE
Electra, LeSabre, and Riviera
(All measurements are given in inches)

Year	Engine	Top Compression	Bottom Compression	Oil Control
'78	6-231 Buick	.0030–.0050	.0030–.0050	.0035
	8-301 Pont.	.0015–.0035	.0015–.0035	.0015–.0035
	8-305 Chev.	.0012–.0042	.0012–.0042	.0020–.0080
	8-350 Buick	.0030–.0050	.0030–.0050	.0035
	8-350 Chev.	.0012–.0042	.0012–.0042	.0020–.0080
	8-350 Olds.	.0020–.0040	.0020–.0040	.0015–.0035
	8-403 Olds.	.0020–.0040	.0020–.0040	.0015–.0035
'79–'82	6-231, 252 Buick	.0030–.0050	.0030–.0050	.0035
	8-301 Pont.	.0015–.0035	.0015–.0035	.0015–.0035
	8-305 Chev.	.0012–.0032	.0012–.0032	.0020–.0080
	8-307 Olds.	.0020–.0040	.0020–.0040	.0010–.0050
	8-350 Buick	.0030–.0050	.0030–.0050	.0035
	8-350 Diesel	.004–.006	.0018–.0038	.001–.005
	8-350 Olds.	.0020–.0040	.0020–.0040	.001–.005
	8-403 Olds.	.0020–.0040	.0020–.0040	.001–.005
'83–'85	6-231, 252 Buick	.0030–.0050	.0030–.0050	.0035
	8-307 Olds.	.0020–.0040	.0020–.0040	.001–.005
	8-350 Diesel	.005–.007	.003–.005	.001–.005

CRANKSHAFT AND CONNECTING ROD SPECIFICATIONS
Century, Regal, and Skylark
(All measurements are given in inches)

Year	Engine No. Cyl. Displacement (cu in.)	Crankshaft Main Brg. Journal Dia	Crankshaft Main Brg. Oil Clearance	Crankshaft Shaft End-Play	Thrust on No.	Connecting Rod Journal Diameter	Connecting Rod Oil Clearance	Connecting Rod Side Clearance
'78–'81	6-196, 231 Buick	2.4995	.0003–.0018	.003–.009 ⑤	2	2.2487–2.2495	.0005–.0026	.006–.023 ④
	8-350 Diesel	3.0000	.0005–.0021 ①	.0035–.0135	3	2.1238–2.1248	.005–.0026	.006–.020
	265 Pont.	3.000	.0004–.0020 ⑥	.006–.022 ⑦	4	2.250 ⑧	.0005–.0025	.006–.022 ④
	8-305, 350 Chev.	③	.0035 max. ②	.002–.006	5	2.099–2.100	.0035 max.	.006–.014
	6-252 Buick	2.4955	.0003–.0018	.011–.003	2	2.2487–2.2495	.0005–.0026	.006–.023
'82	6-231 Buick	2.4995	.0003–.0018	.003–.011	2	2.2487–2.2495	.0005–.0026	.006–.023 ④
	6-263 Diesel	2.9993–3.0003	.0005–.0021	.0035–.0135	3	2.1238–2.2148	.0005–.0026	.006–.020
	8-267 Chev.	③	.0008–.0020 ⑨	.002–.006	5	2.0986–2.0998	.0013–.0035	.006–.14
	8-305 Chev.	③	.0008–.0020	.002–.006	5	2.0986–2.0998	.0013–.0035	.006–.014
	8-350 Diesel	3.0000	.0005–.0021 ①	.0035–.0135	3	2.1238–2.1248	.0005–.0026	.006–.020

CRANKSHAFT AND CONNECTING ROD SPECIFICATIONS
Century, Regal, and Skylark
(All measurements are given in inches)

Year	Engine No. Cyl. Displacement (cu in.)	Crankshaft				Connecting Rod		
		Main Brg. Journal Dia	Main Brg. Oil Clearance	Shaft End-Play	Thrust on No.	Journal Diameter	Oil Clearance	Side Clearance
'83	6-231 Buick	2.4995	.0003–.0018	.003–.011	2	2.2487–2.2495	.0005–.0026	.006–.023 ④
	6-252 Buick	2.4995	.0003–.0018	.003–.011	2	2.2487–2.2495	.0005–.0026	.006–.023
	6-263 Diesel	2.9993–3.0003	.0005–.0021	.0035–.0135	3	2.1238–2.2148	.0005–.0026	.006–.020
	8-350 Diesel	2.9993–3.0003	.0005–.0021 ⑩	.0035–.0135	3	2.2495–2.2500	.0005–.0026	.006–.020
'84–'85	6-231 Buick	2.4995	.0003–.0018	.003–.011	2	2.2487–2.2495	.0005–.0026	.006–.023 ④
	6-252 Buick	2.4995	.0003–.0018	.003–.011	2	2.2487–2.2495	.0005–.0026	.006–.023
	6-263 Diesel	2.9993–3.0003	.0005–.0021	.0035–.0135	3	2.1238–2.2148	.0005–.0026	.006–.020
	8-350 Diesel	2.9993–3.0003	.0005–.0021 ⑩	.0035–.0135	3	2.2495–2.2500	.0005–.0026	.006–.020

① No. 5—.0015–.0031
② No. 1—.002 max.
③ #1: 2.4484–2.4493 #2,3,4: 2.4481–2.4490 #5: 2.4479–2.4488
④ Total for both rods per journal
⑤ 1981—.003–.011

⑥ 1981—.0002–.0018
⑦ 1981—.0035–.0085
⑧ 1981—2.000
⑨ Intermediate—.0011–.0023 Rear—.0017–.0033
⑩ .0020–.0034 No 5

CRANKSHAFT AND CONNECTING ROD SPECIFICATIONS
Electra, LeSabre, and Riviera
(All measurements are given in in.)

Year	Engine Displacement (cu in.)	Crankshaft				Connecting Rod		
		Main Brg. Journal Dia	Main Brg. Oil Clearance	Shaft End-Play	Thrust on No.	Journal Diameter	Oil Clearance	Side Clearance
'78	6-231 Buick	2.4995	.0003–.0017	.004–.008	2	2.2487–2.2495	.0005–.0026	.006–.027
	8-301 Pont.	3.0000	.0004–.0020	.006–.022	4	2.2500	.0005–.0025	.006–.022
	8-305 Chev.	③	.0010–.0035 ⑤	.002–.006	5	2.0990–2.1000	.0010–.0035	.008–.014
	8-350 Buick	3.0000	.0004–.0015	.003–.009	3	1.9910–2.0000	.0005–.0026	.006–.027
	8-350 Chevl.	③	.0010–.0035 ⑤	.002–.006	5	2.0990–2.1000	.0010–.0035	.008–.014
	8-350 Olds.	2.4985–2.4995 ②	.0005–.0021 ①	.0035–.0135	3	2.1238–2.1248	.0004–.0033	.006–.020
	8-403 Olds.	2.4985–2.4995 ②	.0005–.0021 ①	.0035–.0135	3	2.1238–2.1248	.0004–.0033	.006–.020
'79–'81	6-231 Buick	2.4995	.0003–.0018	.003–.009	2	2.2487–2.2498	.0005–.0026	.006–.023
	6-252 Buick	2.4995	.0003–.0018	.003–.009	2	2.2487–2.2495	.0005–.0026	.006–.023
	8-301 Pont.	3.000	.0004–.0020	.006–.022	4	2.250	.0005–.0025	.006–.022
	8-305 Chev.	③	④	.002–.006	5	2.099–2.100	.0035 max	.006–.014
	8-307 Olds.	2.49793–2.4998 ⑥	.0005–.0021 ①	.0035–.0135	3	2.1238–2.1248	.0004–.0033	.006–020
	8-350 Buick	3.000	.0004–.0015	.003–.009	3	1.991–2.000	.0005–.0026	.006–.023
	8-350 Olds	2.4985–2.4995 ②	.0005–.0021 ①	.0035–.0135	3	2.1238–2.1248	.0004–.0033	.006–.020
	8-350 Diesel	2.9993–3.0003	.0005–.0021 ①	.0035–.0135	3	2.2495–2.2500	.0005–.0026	.006–.020
	8-403 Olds.	2.4985–2.4995	.0005–.0021 ①	.0035–.0135	3	2.1238–2.1248	.0005–.0033	.006–.020

CRANKSHAFT AND CONNECTING ROD SPECIFICATIONS
Electra, LeSabre, and Riviera
(All measurements are given in in.)

Year	Engine Displacement (cu in.)	Crankshaft				Connecting Rod		
		Main Brg. Journal Dia	Main Brg. Oil Clearance	Shaft End-Play	Thrust on No.	Journal Diameter	Oil Clearance	Side Clearance
'82	6-231 Buick	2.4995	.0003–.0018	.003–.009	2	2.2487–2.2495	.0005–.0026	.006–.023
	6-252 Buick	2.4995	.0003–.0018	.003–.009	2	2.2487–2.2495	.0005–.0026	.006–.023
	8-307 Olds	2.4973–2.4998 ⑥	.0005–.0021 ①	.0035–.0135	3	2.1238–2.1248	.0004–.0033	.006–.020
	8-350 Diesel	2.9993–3.0003	.0005–.0021	.0035–.0135	3	2.2495–2.2500	.0005–.0026	.006–.020
'83	6-231 Buick	2.4995	.0003–.0018	.003–.011	2	2.2487–2.2495	.0005–.0026	.006–.023
	6-252 Buick	2.4995	.0003–.0018	.003–.011	2	2.2487–2.2495	.0005–.0026	.006–.023
	8-307 Olds	2.4973–2.4998 ⑥	.0005–.0021 ①	.0035–.0135	3	2.1238–2.1248	.0004–.0033	.006–.020
	8-350 Diesel	2.9993–3.0003	.0005–.0021	.0035–.0135	3	2.2495–2.2500	.0005–.0026	.006–.020
'84–'85	6-231 Buick	2.4995	.0003–.0018	.003–.011	2	2.2487–2.2495	.0005–.0026	.006–.023
	6-252 Buick	2.4995	.003–.0018	.0003–.011	2	2.2487–2.2495	.0005–.0026	.006–.023
	8-307 Olds	2.4973–2.4998 ⑥	.0005–.0021 ①	.0035–.0135	3	2.1238–2.1248	.0004–.0033	.006–.020
	8-350 Diesel	2.9993–3.0003	.0005–.0021	.0035–.0135	3	2.2495–2.2500	.0005–.0026	.006–.020

① Number five main bearing clearance—.0015–.0031
② – 1: 2.4988–2.4998
③ #1: 2.4484–2.4493 2,3,4: 2.4481–2.4490 #5: 2.4479–2.4488
④ 1979 #1: .0020, all others .0035. 1980: #1: .0015, #2,3,4: .0025, #5: .0035

⑤ #1: .0020 max.
⑥ 2.4990–2.4995 (#2,3,4,5)

WHEEL ALIGNMENT SPECIFICATIONS
Electra, LeSabre, and Riviera

Year	Model	Caster		Camber		Toe-in (in.)
		Range (deg)	Pref Setting (deg)	Range (deg)	Pref Setting (deg)	
'78–'82	All except '79–'82 Riviera	2P to 4P	3P	0 to 1⅝P	13/16P	1/16 to 1/4
'83–'85	All	2P–4P	3P	0–1.6P	—	1/16–1/4

P Positive

WHEEL ALIGNMENT SPECIFICATIONS
Century, Regal, and Skylark

Year	Model	Caster		Camber		Toe-in (in.)
		Range (deg)	Pref Setting (deg)	Range (deg)	Pref Setting (deg)	
'78–'81	Century, Regal manual steer.	½P to 1½P	1P	0 to 1P	½P	1/16 to 3/16
	Century, Regal power steer.	2½P to 3½P	3P	0 to 1P	½P	1/16 to 3/16
	Skylark—1978–79 manual steer.	½N to 1½N	1N	⅓P to 1⅓P	⅘P	1/16 to 3/16
	Skylark—1978–79 power steer.	½P to 1½P	1P	⅓P to 1⅓P	⅘P	1/16 to 3/16
'82	Regal	3P ± ½	3P	½P ± ½	½P	1/8 ± 1/16

Year	Model	Caster		Camber		Toe-in (in.)
		Range (deg)	Pref Setting (deg)	Range (deg)	Pref Setting (deg)	
'83–'85	All	2P–4P	3P	.3N–1.3P	①	1/16–1/4

① Not available   N Negative   P Positive

CHARGING SYSTEM

The Delco SI alternator system is standard on all models.

For further information on the charging system, please refer to "Charging and Starting" in the Unit Repair section.

NOTE: See the "Oldsmobile Rear Wheel Drive" section for a description of the diesel charging system.

Alternator

REMOVAL & INSTALLATION

Disconnect the negative battery cable at the battery. Disconnect and label the electrical connections. Remove the bolt holding the slotted adjusting bracket to the unit. Release the drive belt. Remove the through-bolt to release the alternator from the engine. When reinstalling, adjust the drive belt to allow 1/2 in. play on the longest run between pulleys.

NOTE: On some models, it may be necessary to loosen and rotate the fan shroud. On models with air conditioning, it may be necessary to remove the compressor bracket. Do not discharge the A/C.

Voltage Regulator

REMOVAL & INSTALLATION

The voltage regulator is in the alternator, and requires no adjustment. The alternator must be disassembled to remove the regulator.

STARTING SYSTEM

For further information on the starting system, please refer to "Charging and Starting" in the Unit Repair section.

NOTE: See the Oldsmobile Rear Wheel Drive section for a description of the diesel starting system.

Starter

REMOVAL & INSTALLATION

1. Disconnect the negative battery cable.
2. Jack up the car and remove the starter brace and any shields which are in the way. On some automatic transmission models, it may be necessary to remove the exhaust crossover pipe. On 1978 and later manual transmission models, loosen the engine crossmember by removing the six cross-member bolts and the two stabilizer shaft bolts from the passenger's side and loosening the four crossmember bolts on the driver's side.
3. Label and disconnect the wires from the solenoid.
4. Remove the starter bolts, taking note of any shims and their placement.
5. Remove the starter.
6. Installation is the reverse of removal.

IGNITION SYSTEM

A solid-state, High Energy Ignition system (HEI) is standard equipment. Most 1981 and later models use an (EST) Electronic Spark Timing distributor. The EST distributor uses no mechanical or vacuum advance and is easily identified by the absence of a vacuum advance and the presence of a four terminal connector. On both distributors there are no contact points or condenser to replace, nor any cam or rubbing block to wear out, thus eliminating distributor maintenance.

For further information on the ignition system, please refer to "Electronic Ignition Systems" in the Unit Repair section.

NOTE: See the Oldsmobile Rear Wheel Drive section for a description of the diesel engine compression-ignition process.

Distributor
REMOVAL

1. Remove the distributor cap, primary wire and vacuum line at the distributor. Unplug the V6 and V8 distributor cap HEI connectors.
2. Scribe a mark on the distributor body, to locate the position of the rotor. Then scribe another mark on the engine block to show the position of the distributor body in the block.
3. Remove the hold-down clamp. Mark the position of the rotor, then lift the distributor out of the block until the rotor stops turning. Mark the position of the rotor again and remove the distributor.

INSTALLATION

For firing order and cylinder numbering, see the specifications at the beginning of this section.

1. If the engine has not been disturbed, insert the distributor into the engine, making sure the tip of the rotor is aligned with the marks that were scribed on the distributor housing and the engine block.
2. If the engine has been cranked with the distributor out, remove the No. 1 spark plug and place a finger over the hole. Slowly turn the engine until compression is felt. Align the timing marks so No. 1 cylinder is in firing position. Position the distributor in the block with the rotor at No. 1 firing position. Make sure the oil pump intermediate drive shaft is properly seated in the oil pump.
3. Install the distributor lock but do not tighten.
4. Rotate the distributor body clockwise. Tighten the retaining screw.
5. Connect the primary wire and the vacuum line to the distributor, then install distributor cap.
6. Start the engine and check the timing with a timing light.

Ignition Timing

NOTE: On all models with computer-controlled ignition systems (no vacuum advance unit), refer to the specific timing adjustment procedure shown on the underhood emissions sticker.

Timing marks are located on the front engine cover and on the harmonic balancer or pulley.

1. Disconnect the distributor vacuum advance hose from the distributor and plug the hose.

2. On most 1981 and later models with the EST distributor disconnect the four-terminal connector from the wiring harness.

3. Make sure the timing marks are clean and readable. The engine must be at normal operating temperature.

NOTE: It may be necessary to put a small amount of white paint or chalk on the timing marks to make them more visible.

4. Connect a timing light to No. 1 cylinder.

5. Loosen the distributor clamp.

6. Start the engine and run it at the rpm specified in the Tune-up Specifications chart. Rotate the distributor until the correct marks line up. Tighten the distributor clamp and recheck the timing.

7. Reconnect the vacuum hose or the four-terminal connector.

TIMING LIGHT AND TACHOMETER HOOK-UP

1. Use an adapter between the No. 1 spark plug and No. 1 spark plug lead when connecting a timing light. Connect the timing light to the adapter; DO NOT pierce the spark plug lead. Because of the higher voltage used in the HEI system, any break in the insulation will cause electricity to jump to the nearest ground, making the No. 1 plug misfire.

2. The tachometer terminal is next to the ignition switch connector on the cap of V6 and V8 distributors.

3. Most new tachometers can be used. Tachometers without a relay can't be used. Check the tach's instructions if you aren't sure. If you don't have the instructions, hook up the tach and check the readings on both the high and low rpm scales. If they agree, the tach is OK; if they don't, use another tach.

4. There is no way of adjusting dwell, since this is controlled by the electronic module.

5. If you want to crank the engine without starting it, disconnect the ignition switch wire at the distributor cap.

FUEL SYSTEM

For diesel engine fuel injection adjustments, timing, and removal and installation procedures, see Oldsmobile Rear Wheel Drive section.

For additional information on the fuel system, please refer to "Carburetors" or "Diesel Maintenance" in the Unit Repair section.

Carburetor Adjustments

IDLE SPEED

1978 2GC, 2GE Carburetor

1. Run the engine to normal operating temperature. Make sure that the choke is fully opened, set the parking brake, block the drive wheels, turn the air conditioning off and connect a tachometer to the engine according to the manufacturer's instructions.

2. Disconnect and plug the vacuum hoses at the vapor canister and EGR valve.

3. Place the transmission in Park (AT) or Neutral (MT).

4. Disconnect and plug the vacuum advance hose at the distributor. Set the ignition timing.

5. Reconnect the vacuum advance hose and turn the idle speed screw to obtain the specified rpm.

6. Connect all hoses and remove the tachometer.

1978-80 M2ME/M2MC/E2ME-210 Carburetor

1. Run the engine to normal operating temperature.

2. Make sure that the choke is fully opened, set the parking brake, block the wheels, connect a tachometer to the engine according to the manufacturer's instructions, disconnect the compressor clutch wire, turn the A/C off, place the transmission in Drive, and disconnect and plug the vacuum advance hose at the distributor.

NOTE: If instructions on car's underhood sticker differ from these, follow underhood sticker.

3. Set the ignition timing, if necessary.

4. Reconnect the vacuum advance hose.

5. Disconnect the purge hose at the vapor canister.

6. On cars without A/C: set the idle speed by turning the idle screw to obtain the specified rpm. On cars with A/C: set the idle speed screw to the specified rpm. Turn the A/C on. Open the throttle mo-

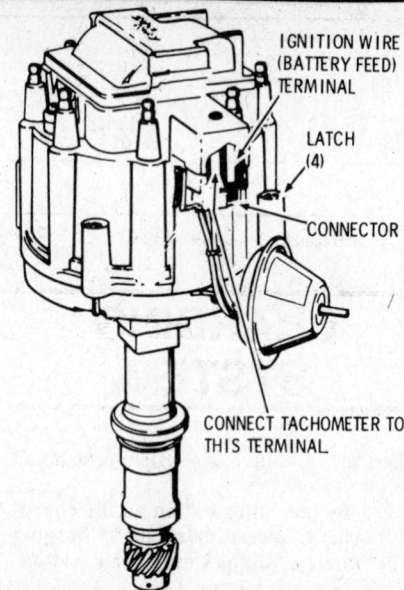

Tachometer connection for the HEI system

mentarily to extend the solenoid plunger, then adjust the solenoid screw to obtain the solenoid idle speed shown on the underhood sticker. Turn the A/C off.

7. Connect all hoses, and remove the tachometer.

1978 and Later M4MC-M4ME Carburetor with Idle Speed Solenoid

1. Run the engine to normal operating temperature.

2. Make sure that the choke is fully opened, turn the A/C off, set the parking brake and block the wheels.

3. Connect a tachometer to the engine according to the manufacturer's instructions.

4. Disconnect the purge hose from the vapor canister. On the 350, plug the purge hose.

5. Disconnect and plug the EGR vacuum hose at the valve. Disconnect and plug the vacuum advance hose.

6. Place the transmission in Park.

7. Check and adjust the timing.

8. Reconnect the vacuum advance hose.

9. Place the transmission in Drive.

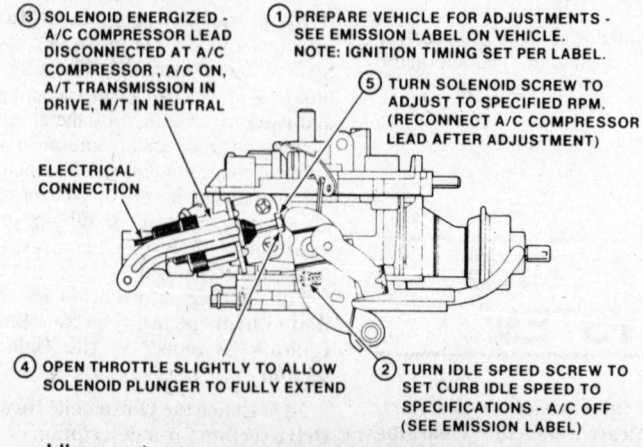

③ SOLENOID ENERGIZED - A/C COMPRESSOR LEAD DISCONNECTED AT A/C COMPRESSOR, A/C ON, A/T TRANSMISSION IN DRIVE, M/T IN NEUTRAL

① PREPARE VEHICLE FOR ADJUSTMENTS - SEE EMISSION LABEL ON VEHICLE. NOTE: IGNITION TIMING SET PER LABEL.

⑤ TURN SOLENOID SCREW TO ADJUST TO SPECIFIED RPM. (RECONNECT A/C COMPRESSOR LEAD AFTER ADJUSTMENT)

ELECTRICAL CONNECTION

④ OPEN THROTTLE SLIGHTLY TO ALLOW SOLENOID PLUNGER TO FULLY EXTEND

② TURN IDLE SPEED SCREW TO SET CURB IDLE SPEED TO SPECIFICATIONS - A/C OFF (SEE EMISSION LABEL)

Idle speed solenoid adjustment (© Buick Div., GM Corp.)

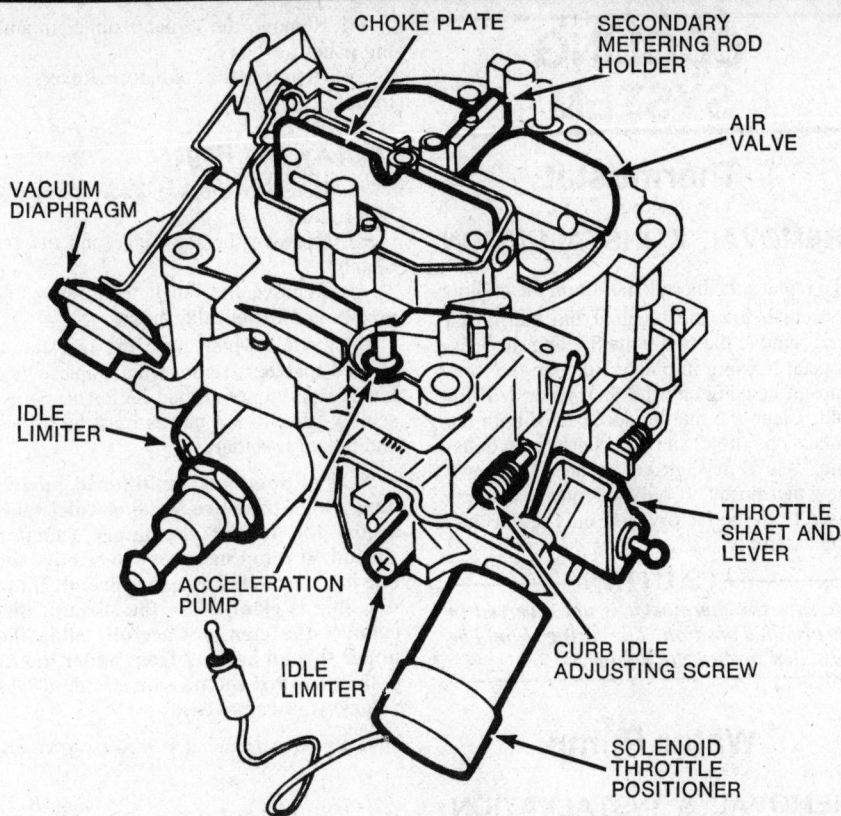

CHOKE PLATE

SECONDARY METERING ROD HOLDER

AIR VALVE

VACUUM DIAPHRAGM

IDLE LIMITER

ACCELERATION PUMP

IDLE LIMITER

THROTTLE SHAFT AND LEVER

CURB IDLE ADJUSTING SCREW

SOLENOID THROTTLE POSITIONER

4 bbl carburetor

IDLE MIXTURE ADJUSTMENT

1978-80

Adjustments of idle mixture in 1978-80 car carburetors are impossible without using a propane enrichment system. Such systems are not available to the general public. Backing out the mixture screw alone will have little or no effect on the mixture. Most 1979 and later carburetors have mixture screws concealed by staked-in plugs. Mixture adjustments are possible only during carburetor overhaul.

1981 and Later

On these models the air/fuel mixture is controlled by the electronic control module of the computer command control system. No adjustment should be attempted.

Fuel Pump

All air conditioned cars with V8 engines have a special fuel pump. This pump has a vapor return line which returns hot fuel and fuel vapor to the fuel tank. The possibility of vapor lock is thus greatly reduced by keeping cool fuel circulating through the pump.

REMOVAL & INSTALLATION

1. Disconnect the fuel inlet hose from the pump. Disconnect the vapor return hose, if so equipped. Disconnect the inlet hose.
2. Remove the two bolts.
3. Remove the fuel pump.
4. Install a new gasket.
5. Install a new pump and bolts.

NOTE: If instructions on the underhood sticker differ from these, follow underhood sticker.

10. On cars without A/C: Turn the idle speed screw to obtain the specified rpm.

On cars with A/C: Turn the idle speed screw to set the specified curb idle speed. Turn the A/C ON and disconnect the compressor clutch wire. Open the throttle momentarily to extend the solenoid plunger. Adjust the solenoid screw to obtain the solenoid idle speed shown on the underhood sticker. Reconnect the compressor clutch and turn the A/C off.

11. Reconnect all hoses and remove the tachometer.

1981-85 M4MC/M4ME Carburetor without Idle Speed Solenoid

Most 1981 and later models are equipped with an Idle Speed Control (ISC) mounted on the float bowl. Idle speeds are computer controlled and the ICS should not be adjusted.

On some V8 models an Idle Load Compensator (ILC) is mounted on the float bowl to control the curb idle speed. The ILC is adjusted at the factory and capped to prevent readjustment. If an idle problem is suspected on either of the above systems it is recommended that it be corrected by a qualified technician.

On cars that do not include either an ISC or ILC, but are equipped with air conditioning, an idle speed solenoid is used to maintain idle speed. For adjustment of these models refer to the previous 1978-85 adjustment procedures.

NOTE: The underhood sticker specifies which idle system your car is equipped with.

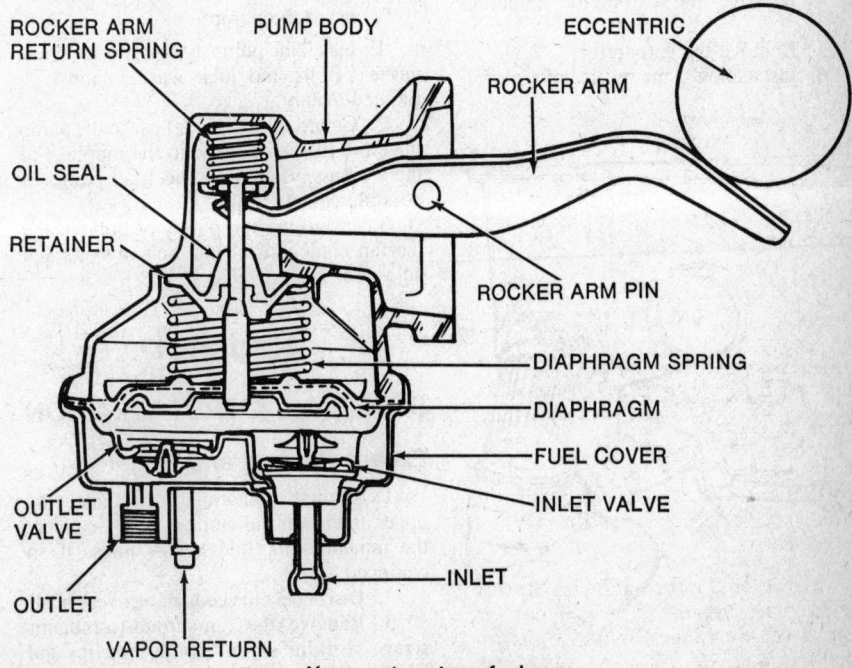

ROCKER ARM RETURN SPRING

PUMP BODY

ECCENTRIC

ROCKER ARM

OIL SEAL

RETAINER

ROCKER ARM PIN

DIAPHRAGM SPRING

DIAPHRAGM

FUEL COVER

INLET VALVE

OUTLET VALVE

OUTLET

INLET

VAPOR RETURN

Vapor return type fuel pump

6. Tighten the bolts alternately and evenly.

7. Reconnect the hoses, start the engine, and check for leaks.

Fuel Filter

REMOVAL & INSTALLATION

NOTE: **When purchasing a new filter, be sure that it matches the old one EXACTLY.**

1. Disconnect the fuel line connection at the inlet of the carburetor.

2. Remove the inlet fuel filter nut from the carburetor with a box wrench.

3. Remove the filter element and spring.

4. If it is a bronze element, blow through the cone end—the element should allow air to pass freely.

5. Install the element spring and a new element into the carburetor. Bronze elements are installed with the small section of the cone facing outward.

6. Install a new gasket on the fitting nut and install the nut.

7. Install the fuel line and tighten it securely. Start the engine and check for leaks.

Carburetors

REMOVAL & INSTALLATION

1. Remove the air cleaner.

2. Disconnect the fuel line.

3. Disconnect and label all vacuum lines to the carburetor.

4. Remove the carburetor mounting bolts.

5. Remove the carburetor.

6. Installation is the reverse of removal.

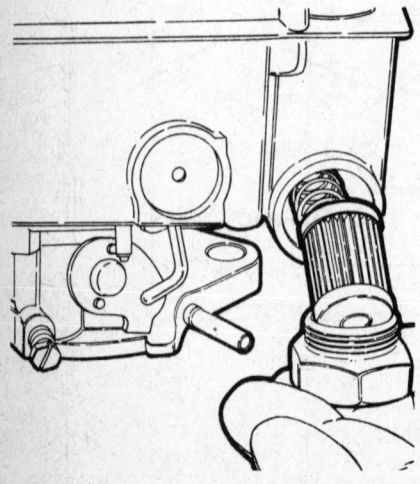

Typical fuel filter

COOLING SYSTEM

Thermostat

REMOVAL & INSTALLATION

To replace the thermostat, drain the cooling system below the level of the thermostat and remove the two bolts holding the thermostat housing in place. Remove the thermostat housing and the thermostat will lift out. Clean the mating surfaces of both the intake manifold and the thermostat housing. Use a new gasket when installing a new thermostat. If only silicone sealer was used from the factory, use only sealer during assembly.

———— CAUTION ————
Be sure the thermostat is not reversed in its installed position. The spring should be installed toward the engine.

Water Pump

REMOVAL & INSTALLATION

1. Drain the cooling system. Remove the fan shroud, if necessary for clearance.

2. Loosen the belt or belts, then remove the fan blades and pulley or pulleys from the hub on the water pump shaft. Remove the belt or belts.

3. Disconnect the hose from the water pump inlet and the heater hose from the nipple. Remove the bolts, then remove the pump and gasket from the timing case cover or engine block.

To install the pump:

1. Install the pump assembly with a new gasket. Bolts and lock washers must be torqued evenly.

2. Connect the radiator hose to the pump inlet and the heater hose to the nipple. Fill the cooling system and check all points of possible coolant leaks.

3. Install the fan pulley or pulleys and the fan blade. Install the belt or belts and adjust for correct tension.

Radiator

REMOVAL & INSTALLATION

Except Century and Regal

1. Drain the radiator and disconnect the upper and lower radiator hoses. Disconnect the transmission fluid cooler lines, if so equipped.

2. Disconnect the coolant recovery hose.

3. Remove the fan-shroud-to-radiator screws. Lift the shroud out of the clips and hang the shroud over the fan.

4. Remove the radiator upper mounting panel.

5. Remove the radiator. Reverse to install.

Century and Regal

1. Refer to Steps 1-2 of the above procedure.

2. Remove the fan blade and the fan clutch.

3. Remove the fan housing attaching screws and lift out the shroud.

On models which have the fan shroud stapled together, remove the staples, then remove the upper shroud half. During assembly, the shroud halves must be drilled and bolted together.

NOTE: **Some air conditioned models have a high-pressure A/C line which runs across the top of the upper radiator shroud. It is not necessary to remove the line in order to remove the shroud. If the A/C line is clamped to the shroud, disconnect the clamp. Carefully slide the upper shroud half out from under the A/C line, toward the passenger side of the vehicle (fan removed).**

4. Remove the radiator. Reverse to install.

EMISSION CONTROLS

There are three types of emissions to be controlled: crankcase emission, carburetor and gas tank gas vapor emissions, and exhaust emissions.

For additional information on emission controls, please refer to "Emission Controls" in the Unit Repair section.

ENGINE

NOTE: **Refer to the charts in the beginning of this section to determine the type and manufacturer of the engine used in your vehicle. Specific repair information for engines other than those manufactured by Buick may be found in the car section of the engine manufacturer (e.g.—Chevrolet 267 and 305 engines will be found in the Chevrolet Rear Wheel Drive section of this book).**

REMOVAL & INSTALLATION

1. Scribe marks at the hood hinges and the hinge brackets. Remove the hood.

2. Disconnect the battery and drain the coolant.

3. Remove the air cleaner.

4. On cars with air conditioning (A/C),

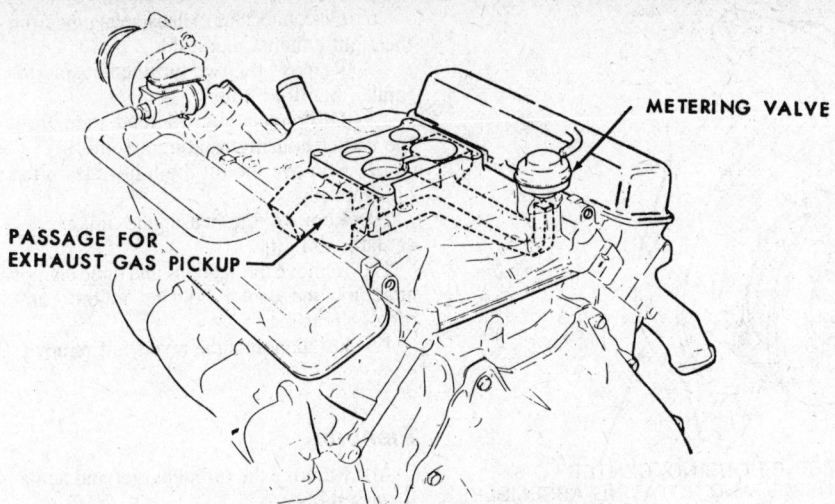

Exhaust Gas Recirculation system
(© Buick Div., G.M. Corp)

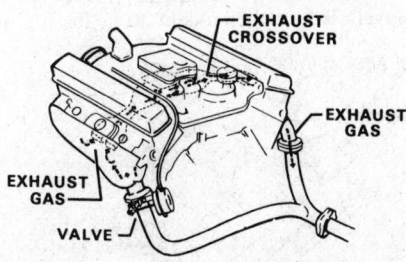

Early fuel evaporation system overview
(© Buick Div., GM Corp.)

disconnect the compressor ground wire from the bracket. Remove the electrical connector from the compressor. Remove the compressor and position the compressor out of the way. Do not disconnect any hoses.

CAUTION

If the compressor refrigerant lines do not have enough slack to position the compressor out of the way without disconnecting the refrigerant lines, the air conditioning system will have to be discharged by a trained air conditioning specialist. Under no conditions should an untrained person attempt to disconnect the air conditioning refrigerant lines. These lines contain pressurized freon, which can be extremely dangerous.

5. Remove the fan blade, pulley, and belts.

6. Disconnect the radiator and heater hoses. Remove the radiator and shroud assembly.

7. Remove the power steering pump and move it out of the way. Do not disconnect any hoses.

8. Remove the fuel pump hoses and plug them.

9. Disconnect the vapor emission lines, from the carburetor, the vacuum supply hose from the carburetor to the vacuum manifold, and the power brake vacuum hoses, if so equipped.

10. Disconnect the throttle linkage at the carburetor.

11. Disconnect the oil and coolant switchs.

12. Disconnect the engine-to-body ground strap.

13. Raise the car and disconnect the starter wires.

14. Disconnect the pipes from the exhaust manifold and support the exhaust system.

15. On Pontiac-built engines:
    a. On models with automatic transmission, remove the converter cover, the converter retaining bolts and slide the converter to the rear.
    b. On models with manual transmission, disconnect the clutch linkage and remove the clutch cross-shaft, starter motor and the lower flywheel cover.
    c. Remove two bellhousing bolts from each side.
    d. On automatic transmission models, disconnect the transmission filler tube.
    e. Remove the two front motor mount nuts.
    f. Lower the car and support the transmission.
    g. Remove the remaining bellhousing bolts and raise the transmission slightly.
    h. Remove the engine.

16. On Oldsmobile-built engines:
    a. Remove the torque converter cover and the converter-to-flywheel retaining bolts.
    b. Remove the engine mounting bolts.
    c. Remove the three engine-to-transmission bolts from the right side.
    d. Remove the starter motor.
    e. Lower the car and support the transmission with a floor jack.
    f. Remove the three engine-to-transmission bolts from the left side and remove the engine.

17. On Chevrolet and Buick-built engines:
    a. Remove the flywheel and converter cover.

    b. On cars with automatic transmission, remove the flywheel-to-converter attaching bolts. Matchmark the converter to the flywheel. On all automatic transmission models, remove the engine-to-transmission attaching bolts. On manual transmission models, disconnect the driveshaft, the shaft linkage, the clutch equalizer shaft and the transmission mount.
    c. Remove the motor mount fasteners and the cruise control bracket, if so equipped.
    d. Lower the car and support the transmission, except for models with manual transmissions.
    e. Raise the engine *slightly* so the engine mount through bolts can be removed. On models with manual transmissions, remove the engine and transmission as a unit.

18. Install the engine in the reverse order of removal. Note that there are dowel pins in the block that have matching holes in the bellhousing. These dowel pins must be in almost perfect alignment before the engine will go together with the transmission. See ''Manual Transmission, Removal and Installation'' for clutch alignment procedures.

Turbocharger Precautions

There are certain steps to be taken when performing maintenance on a turbocharged engine.

a. When changing the oil and filter, or performing any other operation which results in oil loss or drainage, before restarting the engine, disconnect the pink wire from the distributor, crank the engine several times for short intervals, until the oil light goes out.

b. Any time a main bearing, connecting rod bearing or camshaft bearing needs replacing, the oil and filter should be changed as part of the procedure. If the change is the result of sudden damage to the bearing, the turbocharger should be flushed with clean engine oil to reduce the chance of contamination.

c. Any time the center housing or part of the turbocharger which includes the center housing, is replaced, the oil and filter should be changed as part of the procedure.

Component

REMOVAL & INSTALLATION

NOTE: In the course of servicing the engine, component parts of the turbocharger assembly, including the unit itself, piping, hoses and lines, and electrical connections may have to be removed or disconnected. If removal and installation of turbocharger components be-

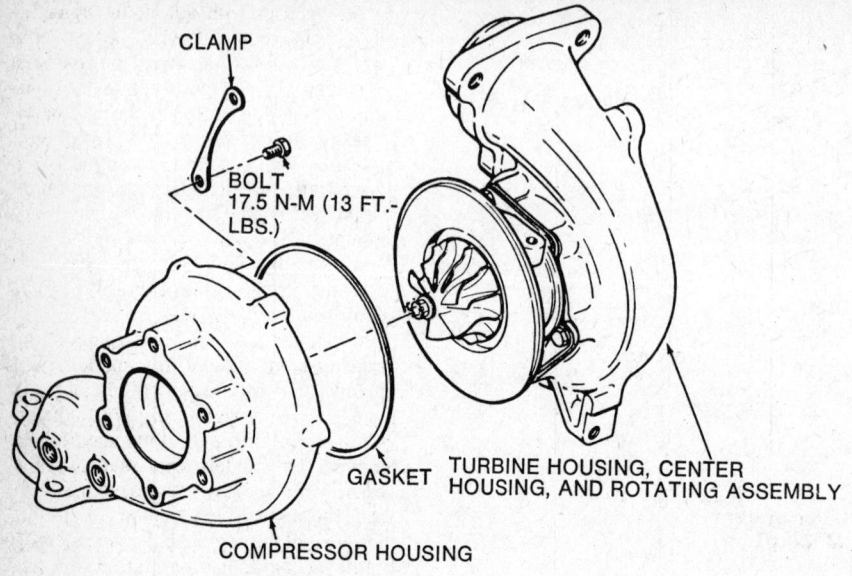

Compressor Housing (© Buick Div., G.M. Corp.)

comes necessary, refer to the proper service procedure below.

————— CAUTION —————

If the turbocharger unit has to be removed, first clean around the unit thoroughly with a non-caustic solution. When removing the turbocharger, take great care to avoid bending, nicking or in ANY WAY damaging the compressor or turbine blades. Any damage to the blades will result in imbalance, failure of the center housing bearing, damage to the unit and possible personal injury or damage to other engine parts.

ESC Detonation Sensor

1. Squeeze the side of the connector and carefully pull it straight up.
2. Using a deep socket, unscrew the sensor.
3. To install, reverse the removal procedure. Torque the sensor to 14 ft. lbs. Do not over-torque the sensor or apply a side-load when installing.

Wastegate Actuator Assembly

1. Disconnect the two hoses from the actuator.
2. Remove the wastegate linkage-to-actuator rod clip.
3. Remove the two bolts attaching the actuator to the compressor housing.
4. Installation is the reverse of removal.

Center Housing

1. Disconnect the exhaust outlet pipe from the elbow assembly.
2. Raise and support the car.
3. Disconnect the exhaust outlet pipe from the catalytic converter.
4. Lower the car.
5. Disconnect the exhaust inlet pipe from the turbine housing.

6. Disconnect the exhaust inlet pipe from the right exhaust manifold.
7. Remove the two turbine housing-to-intake manifold bolts.
8. Disconnect the oil feed pipe from the center housing rotating assembly.
9. Remove the oil drain hose from the oil drain pipe.
10. Remove the wastegate linkage-to-actuator rod clip.
11. Remove the six bolts and three clamps attaching the center housing to the compressor housing.
12. Installation is the reverse of removal.

Plenum

1. Remove the turbocharger and actuator assembly.
2. Remove the four bolts attaching the carburetor to the plenum.
3. Installation is the reverse of removal. Torque the bolts to 20 ft. lbs.

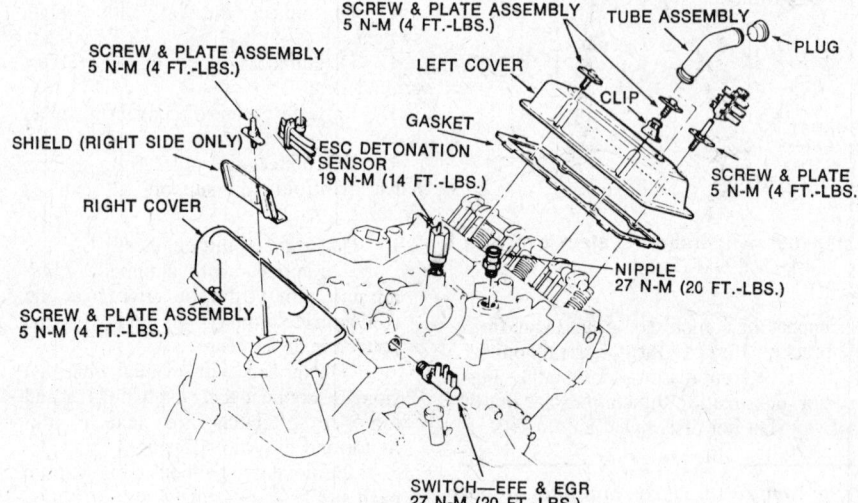

ECS Detonation Sensor (© Buick Div., G.M. Corp.)

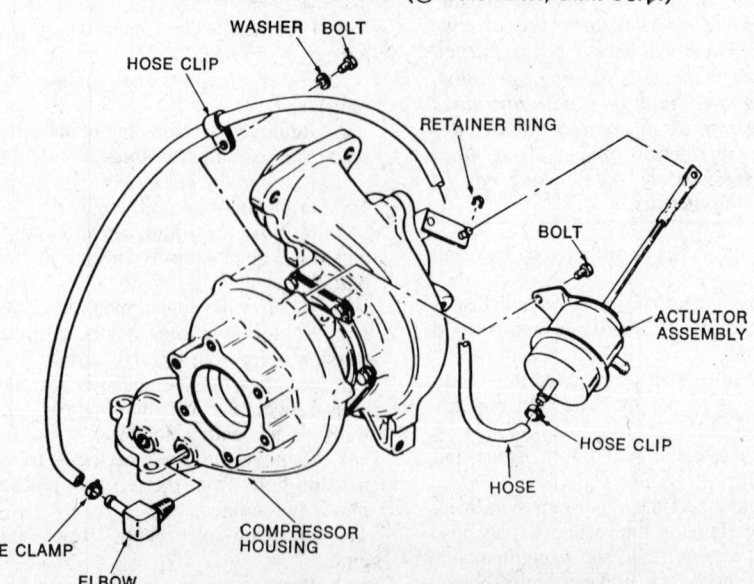

Wastegate Actuator (© Buick Div., G.M. Corp.)

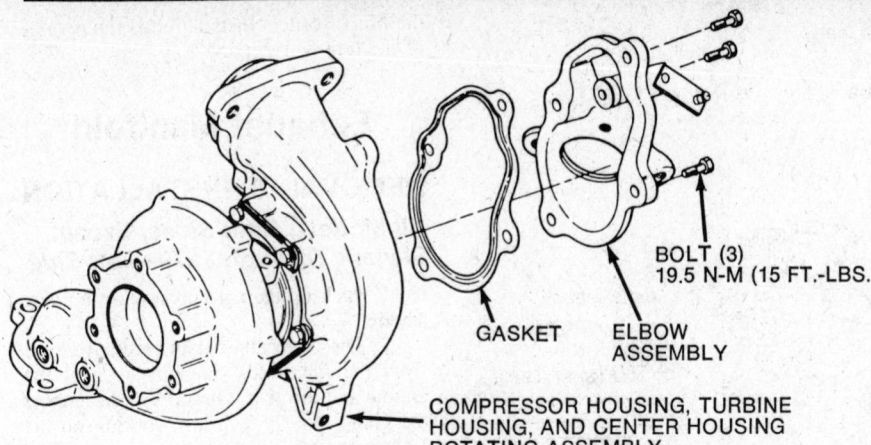

Elbow Assembly (© Buick Div., G.M. Corp.)

BOLT (3)
19.5 N-M (15 FT.-LBS.)

GASKET   ELBOW
          ASSEMBLY

COMPRESSOR HOUSING, TURBINE
HOUSING, AND CENTER HOUSING
ROTATING ASSEMBLY

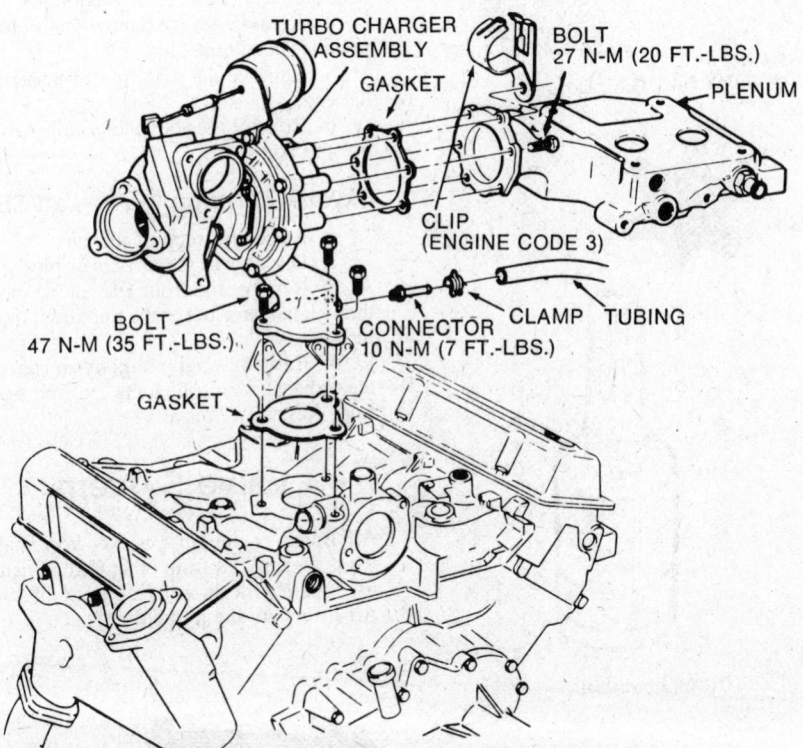

TURBO CHARGER
ASSEMBLY
GASKET
BOLT
27 N-M (20 FT.-LBS.)
PLENUM
CLIP
(ENGINE CODE 3)
BOLT
47 N-M (35 FT.-LBS.)
CONNECTOR
10 N-M (7 FT.-LBS.)
CLAMP   TUBING
GASKET

Turbocharger and Plenum Assembly (© Buick Div., G.M. Corp.)

Turbocharger

REMOVAL & INSTALLATION

1. Disconnect the exhaust inlet and outlet pipes from the turbocharger.

2. Disconnect the oil feed pipe from the center housing.

3. Remove the nut attaching the air intake elbow to the carburetor and remove the elbow and flex tube from the carburetor.

4. Disconnect the accelerator, cruise and detent linkages from the carburetor. Disconnect the plenum linkage bracket.

5. Remove the two bolts attaching the plenum to the side bracket.

6. Disconnect the fuel line and all vacuum lines from the carburetor.

7. Drain the cooling system.

8. Disconnect the coolant lines from the front and rear of the plenum.

9. Disconnect the power brake vacuum line from the plenum.

10. Remove the two bolts attaching the turbine housing to the intake manifold bracket.

11. Remove the two bolts attaching the EGR valve manifold to the plenum. Loosen the two bolts attaching the EGR valve to the intake manifold.

12. Remove the AIR bypass hose from the check valve.

13. Remove the three bolts attaching the compressor housing to the intake manifold.

14. Remove the turbocharger, actuator, carburetor and plenum from the engine.

15. Remove the six bolts attaching the carburetor and plenum to the turbocharger and actuator.

16. Remove the oil drain from the center housing.

To install:

1. Install the oil drain on the center housing. Torque to 15 ft. lbs.

2. Install the six turbocharger/actuator-to-carburetor/plenum bolts.

3. Place the assembly on the engine and connect all vacuum hoses.

4. Install the three bolts attaching the compressor housing to the intake manifold. Torque to 35 ft. lbs.

5. Install the AIR bypass hose.

6. Loosely install the two bolts attaching the EGR valve manifold to the plenum. Tighten the two bolts attaching the EGR valve to 15 ft. lbs. Tighten the EGR manifold-to-plenum bolts to 15 ft. lbs.

7. Install the two bolts attaching the turbine housing to the intake manifold bracket. Torque to 20 ft. lbs.

8. Connect the power brake vacuum line at the plenum. Torque to 10 ft. lbs.

9. Connect the plenum front bracket and install one bolt attaching the bracket to the manifold. Torque to 20 ft. lbs.

10. Connect the coolant hoses to the plenum.

11. Refill the cooling system.

12. Connect the carburetor fuel line and remaining vacuum hoses.

13. Install the two bolts attaching the plenum to the side bracket. Torque to 20 ft. lbs.

14. Connect the linkage bracket to the plenum. Torque to 20 ft. lbs.

15. Connect the accelerator, detent and cruise linkages to the carburetor.

16. Install the nut attaching the air intake elbow to the carburetor. Torque to 15 ft. lbs.

17. Connect the oil feed pipe to the center housing. Torque to 7 ft. lbs.

18. Connect the inlet and outlet pipes to the turbocharger. Torque to 14 ft. lbs.

Intake Manifold

REMOVAL & INSTALLATION
V6 and V8

1. Disconnect the negative battery cable and drain the radiator.

2. Remove the air cleaner.

3. Disconnect the upper radiator hose and the heater hose at the manifold.

4. Disconnect the accelerator linkage at the carburetor and the linkage bracket at the manifold. Remove the cruise control chain, if so equipped.

5. Remove the fuel line from the carburetor and the booster vacuum pipe from the manifold. Remove turbocharger, if so equipped.

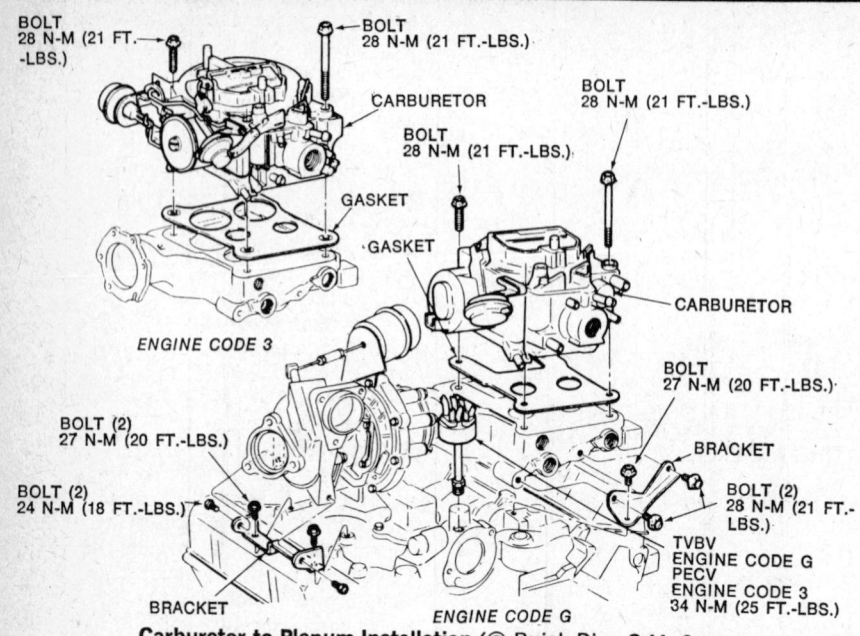

Carburetor to Plenum Installation (© Buick Div., G.M. Corp.)

6. Disconnect and label the transmission vacuum modulator line, idle stop solenoid wire (if so equipped), distributor wires and the temperature sending unit wire.

7. Disconnect and mark the vacuum hoses at the distributor and the carburetor.

8. Disconnect the coolant bypass hose at the manifold.

9. On six cylinder models, remove the distributor cap and wires to gain access to the Torx® head bolt. Remove the bolt.

10. Remove the throttle linkage springs.

11. Remove the A/C compressor top bracket, if so equipped.

12. Remove the manifold.

13. Use a new gasket to install. Use sealer on the ends of the rubber gasket seals. Carefully guide the manifold onto the engine block dowel pin. Observe ''Turbocharger Precautions'' given with the previous Turbocharger information. Tighten the bolts in

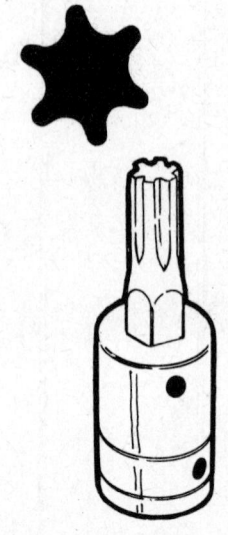

TORX® head bolt

the proper order. Installation is the reverse of the removal steps.

Exhaust Manifold

REMOVAL & INSTALLATION

All Models, Both Sides, Except Skylark Through 1979—Left Side

1. Jack up the car and support on jack stands.

2. Disconnect the exhaust crossover pipe from the manifolds on both sides of the engine and lower it. On the V6, disconnect the choke pipe if you are working on the right side, the EFE line if you are working on the left side.

3. If equipped with manual transmission, remove the equalizer shaft. Disconnect the turbocharger, if so equipped.

4. Remove the exhaust manifold-to-cylinder head bolts.

5. Remove the manifold from beneath the car.

6. Reverse the above to install. Always use the bolt locks.

Skylark Through 1979—Left Side

1. Raise and support the car.

2. Disconnect the crossover pipe.

3. Remove the front left engine mount through bolt and loosen the right front mount through bolt.

4. Raise the engine slightly and remove the exhaust manifold bolts and the manifold. Reverse to install.

Valve System

All Buick engines use rocker arm shafts, while the engines from other GM Divisions use separate rocker arms mounted on studs. All lifters are the hydraulic type.

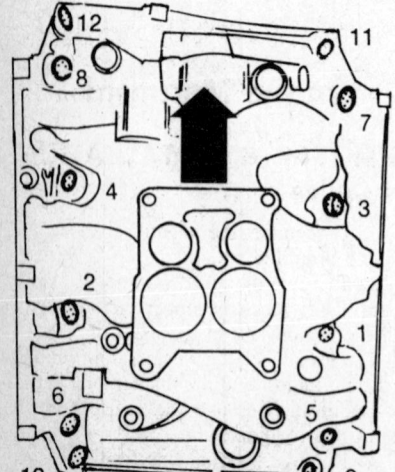

Intake manifold torque sequence for the Buick-manufactured V8 engine

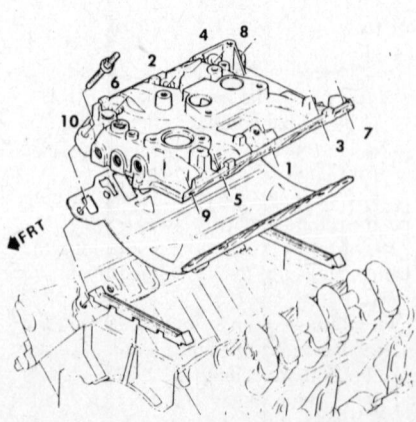

Intake manifold bolt tightening sequence

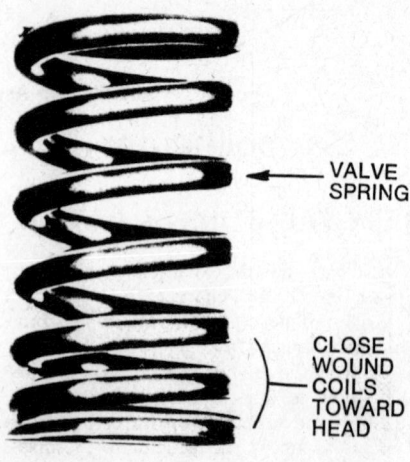

Progressively wound valve spring
(© Buick Div., G.M. Corp)

NOTE: Some of the engines use progressively wound valve springs. The coils are closer together at one end than the other. The close wound end must go against the cylinder head.

See the NOTE at the beginning of the Engine Section.

Valve Adjustment

The valves on Buick engines cannot be adjusted. If there is excessive clearance in the valve train, look for worn push rods, rocker arms, valve springs or collapsed or stuck lifters. Chevrolet engines require initial lash adjustment whenever rocker arms are removed. See the "Chevrolet" section for details.

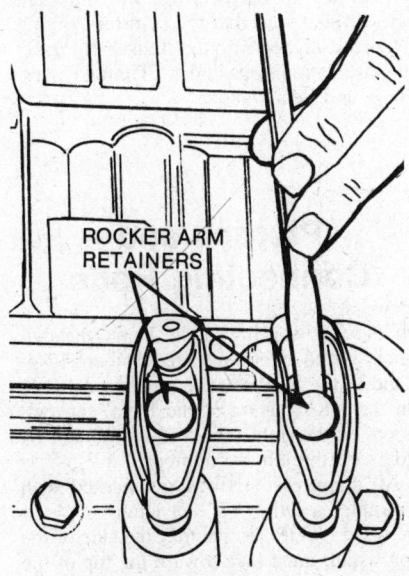

Removing nylon rocker arm retainer
(© Buick Div., G.M. Corp)

Rocker Arm

REMOVAL & INSTALLATION

1. Remove the rocker arm cover.
2. Remove the rocker arm shaft assembly bolts and the assembly.
3. Remove the nylon arm retainers by prying them out.
4. Remove the rocker arms.
5. Install the rocker arms on the shaft and lubricate them with oil.
6. Center each arm on the 1/4 in. hole in the shaft. Install new nylon rocker arm retainers in the holes using a 1/2 in. drift.
7. Locate the push rods in the rocker arms and insert the shaft-to-cylinder head bolts. Tighten the bolts a little at a time until they are tightened to 30 ft. lbs.
8. Install the rocker cover and use a new gasket.

Cylinder Head

REMOVAL & INSTALLATION

See the NOTE at the beginning of the Engine Section.

1. Disconnect the battery.
2. Drain the coolant.
3. Remove the air cleaner.
4. Remove the air conditioning compressor, *but do not disconnect any lines.* Disconnect the AIR hose at the check valve. Remove the turbocharger assembly, if so equipped.
5. Remove the intake manifold.
6. When removing the right cylinder head, loosen the alternator belt, disconnect the wiring and remove the alternator. If equipped with A/C, remove the compressor from the mounting bracket and position it out of the way. Do not disconnect any of the hoses.
7. When removing the left cylinder head, except Skylark, remove the dipstick, power steering pump and air pump if so equipped.
8. Disconnect and label the plug wires.
9. Disconnect exhaust manifold from the head being removed.
10. Remove the rocker arm cover and rocker shaft assembly. Lift out the push rods. Be extremely careful to avoid getting dirt into the valve lifters. Keep the pushrods in order; they must be returned to their original positions.
11. When removing the left head on Skylark:
    a. Disconnect the power brake hose at the rear of the head.

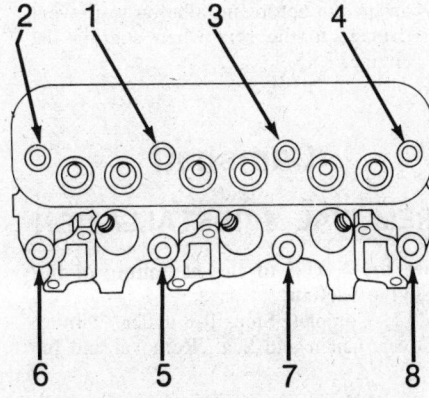

V6 231,252 cylinder head torque sequence

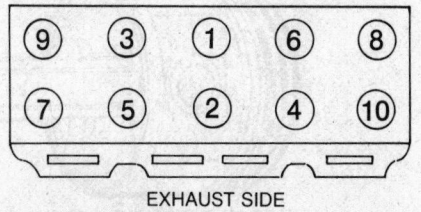

EXHAUST SIDE

Cylinder head bolt torque sequence for the Buick-manufactured V8 engine

b. Disconnect the exhaust crossover pipes.
c. Remove the left engine mount through-bolt, and loosen the right front mount through-bolt.
d. Raise the engine with a jack or hoist.
12. Remove the cylinder head bolts.
13. Remove the cylinder head and gasket.
14. Reverse the above steps to install. Torque the head bolts to specifications in three steps.

Timing Cover, Chain and Seal

REMOVAL & INSTALLATION

1. Drain the cooling system.
2. Remove the radiator, fan, pulley and belt.
3. Remove the fuel pump and alternator, if necessary to remove cover.
4. Remove the distributor. If the timing chain and sprockets will not be disturbed, note the position of the distributor for installation in the same position.
5. Remove the thermostat bypass hose.
6. Remove the harmonic balancer.
7. Remove the timing chain-to-crankcase bolts.
8. Remove the oil pan-to-timing chain cover bolts and remove the timing chain cover.
9. Using a punch, drive out the old seal and the shedder toward the rear of the seal.
10. Coil the new packing around the opening so the ends are at the top. Drive in the shedder using a punch. Properly size the packing by rotating a hammer handle around the packing until the balancer hub can be inserted through the opening.
11. Align the timing marks on the sprockets.
12. Remove the camshaft sprocket bolt without changing the position of the sprocket. On the V6, remove the oil pan.
13. Remove the front crankshaft oil slinger.
14. On the 350, remove the crankshaft distributor drive gear retaining bolt and washer. Remove the drive gear and the fuel pump eccentric. On the V6, remove the camshaft sprocket bolts.
15. Using two large screwdrivers, carefully pry the camshaft sprocket and the crankshaft sprocket forward until they are free. Remove the sprockets and the chain.
To install:
1. Make sure, with sprockets temporarily installed, that No. 1 piston is at top dead center and the camshaft sprocket O-mark is straight down and on the centerline of both shafts.
2. Remove the camshaft sprocket and assemble the timing chain on both sprockets. Then slide the sprockets-and-chain assembly on the shafts with the O-marks in their closest together position and on a centerline with the sprocket hubs.

REMOVE BOLTS MARKED *
FOR COMPLETE REMOVAL,
REVERSE PROCEDURE
FOR INSTALLATION

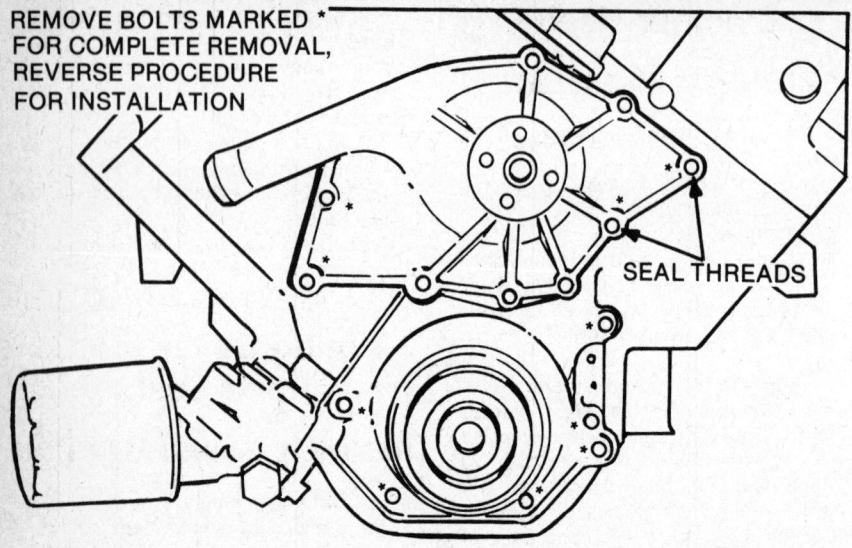

SEAL THREADS

Timing chain cover removal and installation—Buick-manufactured V8 engine

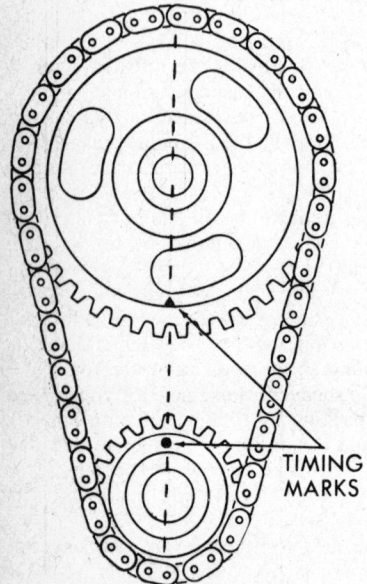

TIMING
MARKS

Valve timing marks

3. Assemble the slinger on the crankshaft with I.D. against the sprocket, (concave side toward the front of engine). Install the oil pan, if removed.

4. On the 350, slide the fuel pump eccentric on the camshaft and the Woodruff key with the oil groove forward. On the V6 install the chamshaft sprocket bolts.

5. Install the distributor drive gear.

6. Install the drive gear and eccentric bolt and retaining washer. Torque to 40-55 ft. lbs.

7. Install the timing case cover. Install a new seal by lightly tapping it in place. The lip of the seal faces inward. Pay particular attention to the following points.

a. Remove the oil pump cover and pack the space around the oil pump gears completely full of petroleum jelly. There

must be no air space left inside the pump. Reinstall the pump cover using a new gasket.

b. The gasket surface of the block and timing chain cover must be clean and smooth. Use a new gasket correctly positioned.

c. Install the chain cover being certain the dowel pins engage the dowel pin holes before starting the attaching bolts.

d. Lube the bolt threads before installation and install them.

e. If the car has power steering the front pump bracket should be installed at this time.

f. Lube the O.D. of the harmonic balancer hub before installation to prevent damage to the seal when starting the engine.

Camshaft

REMOVAL & INSTALLATION

See the NOTE at the beginning of the Engine Section.

1. Complete Steps 1–8 under "Timing Cover, Chain and Seal, Removal and In-

stallation" above. Skip Steps 9 and 10, complete Steps 11–15.

NOTE: If equipped with air conditioning, unbolt the condenser and position it out of the way. If this is not possible, have a mechanic discharge the system. Never attempt to discharge the system yourself.

2. Remove the hydraulic lifters, keeping them in order for installation.

3. Slide the camshaft forward, out of the bearing bores. Do this carefully, to avoid damage to the bearing surfaces and bearings.

4. Reverse to install. Clean all gasket surfaces thoroughly and use new gaskets. Lubricate the camshaft lobes with heavy oil before installation, and be careful not to contact any of the bearings with the cam lobes. Make sure that the camshaft timing marks are aligned with the crankshaft marks. See installation steps under "Timing Cover, Chain and Seal" above.

Pistons and Connecting Rods

On the V6, starting at the front, the cylinders in the right bank are numbered 2-4-6 and the left bank are numbered 1-3-5. On the V8, starting at the front, the cylinders on the right are 2-4-6-8 and the cylinders on the left are numbered 1-3-5-7.

All compression rings are marked with a dimple, a letter "T", a letter "O", or the word "TOP" to identify the side of the ring which must face toward the top of the piston.

When the piston and connecting rod assembly is properly installed, the oil spurt hole in the connecting rod will face the camshaft. The notch on the piston will face the front of the engine. On all engines, the chamfered corners of the bearing caps should face toward the front of the left bank and toward the rear of the right bank. The boss on the connecting rod should face toward the front of the engine for the right bank and to the rear of the engine on the left bank.

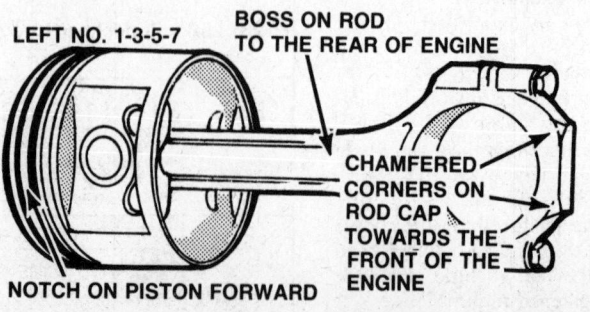

LEFT NO. 1-3-5-7

BOSS ON ROD
TO THE REAR OF ENGINE

CHAMFERED
CORNERS ON
ROD CAP
TOWARDS THE
FRONT OF THE
ENGINE

NOTCH ON PISTON FORWARD

350 Buick V8 piston and connecting rod assembly—left bank

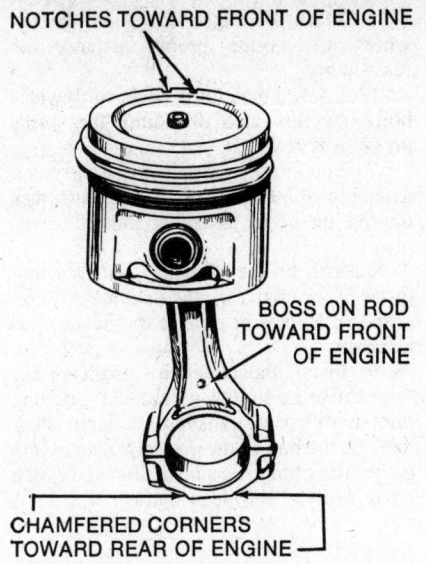

NOTCHES TOWARD FRONT OF ENGINE

BOSS ON ROD TOWARD FRONT OF ENGINE

CHAMFERED CORNERS TOWARD REAR OF ENGINE

RIGHT NO. 2-4-6

Right bank piston and rod positioning—231 and 252

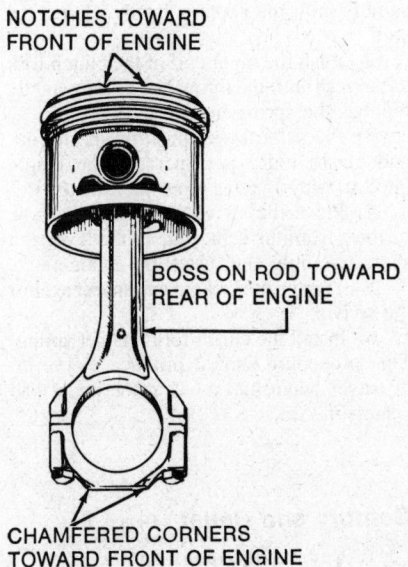

NOTCHES TOWARD FRONT OF ENGINE

BOSS ON ROD TOWARD REAR OF ENGINE

CHAMFERED CORNERS TOWARD FRONT OF ENGINE

LEFT NO. 1-3-5

Left bank piston and rod positioning—231 and 252

Oil Pump

REMOVAL & INSTALLATION

See the NOTE at the beginning of the Engine Section.

On the V6 and V8, the oil pump is located on the left side of the timing chain cover, where it is connect by a drilled passage in the cylinder crankcase to an oil screen housing and standpipe assembly.

1. Remove the oil filter.
2. Unbolt the pump cover assembly from the timing chain cover.

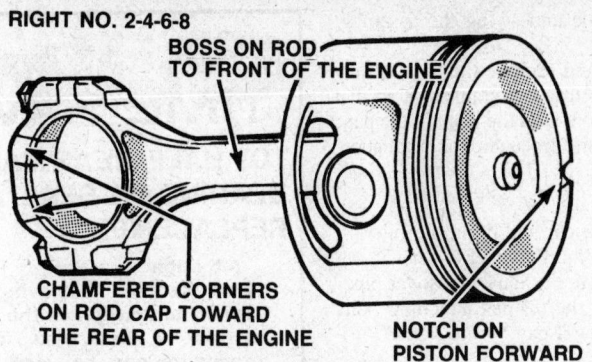

RIGHT NO. 2-4-6-8

BOSS ON ROD TO FRONT OF THE ENGINE

CHAMFERED CORNERS ON ROD CAP TOWARD THE REAR OF THE ENGINE

NOTCH ON PISTON FORWARD

350 Buick V8 piston and connecting rod assembly—right bank

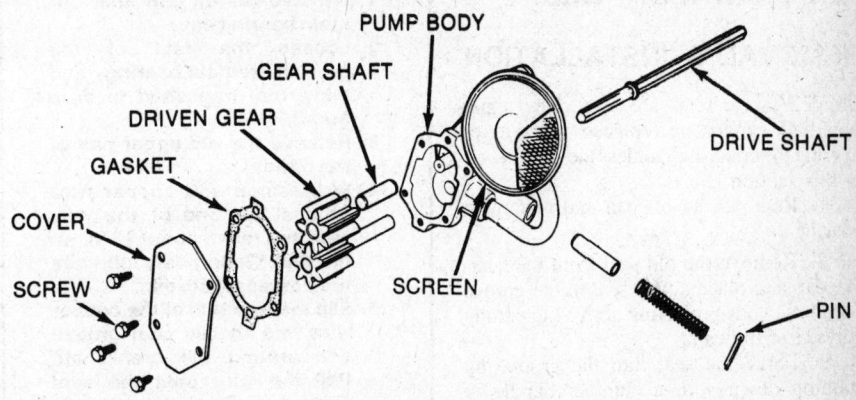

PUMP BODY

GEAR SHAFT

DRIVEN GEAR

GASKET

COVER

SCREW

SCREEN

DRIVE SHAFT

PIN

Typical oil pump assembly
(© Buick Div., G.M. Corp)

3. Remove the cover assembly and slide out the pump gears.
4. Remove the oil pressure relief valve cap, spring, and valve. Do not remove the oil filter by-pass valve and spring.
5. Check that the relief valve spring isn't worn on its side or collapsed. Check that the relief valve is no more than an easy slip fit in its bore in the cover. If there is any perceptible sideplay, replace the valve. If there is still sideplay, replace the cover.
6. Check the filter by-pass valve for good condition.

To assemble the pump:

7. Lubricate and install the pressure relief valve and spring in the cover bore. Install the gasket and cap, torquing the cap to 35 ft. lbs.
8. Install the gears and check that gear-to-cover end clearance is between 0.002-0.006 in. If the clearance is less, check the timing cover gear pocket for wear.
9. Remove the gears and pack the gear pocket full of petroleum jelly. Don't use grease.

—— **CAUTION** ——
Unless the pump is primed this way, it won't produce any oil pressure when the engine is started.

10. Install the gears. Install a new gasket and the cover. Torque the bolts evenly to 10 ft. lbs. Replace the filter.

Oil Pan

REMOVAL & INSTALLATION

V8 Engines

1. Disconnect the battery ground cable.
2. Remove the fan shroud-to-radiator screws.
3. Remove the air cleaner and disconnect the throttle linkage.
4. Raise the front end and support it on jackstands.
5. Drain the oil.
6. Disconnect the exhaust crossover pipe at the engine.
7. Remove the lower flywheel housing cover.
8. Remove the shift linkage bolt and swing it out of the way.
9. Remove the front engine mount bolts.
10. Raise the front of the engine, either by placing a block of wood and a jack under the crankshaft pulley mounting or by lifting it with a hoist.

—— **CAUTION** ——
On air conditioned cars, place a support under the right-side of the transmission before raising the engine. If you don't do this, the weight of the air conditioner will flip the engine and transmission to the right.

11. On the Skylark, disconnect the idler

arm at the frame and swing the assembly down.

12. Unbolt and remove the pan. It may be necessary to turn the crankshaft so that it doesn't interfere with the front of the pan.

13. Reverse the procedure for installation.

V6 Engines

1. Raise the car and drain the oil.
2. Remove the flywheel cover.
3. Remove the exhaust crossover pipe.
4. Remove the oil pan attaching bolts and remove the oil pan.

Rear Main Seal

REMOVAL & INSTALLATION

Braided fabric seals are used. The upper seal half cannot be replaced without removing the crankshaft, unless the Time Saver in this section is used.

1. Remove the oil pan and rear main bearing cap.

2. Remove the old seal from the bearing cap and place a new seal in the groove with both ends projecting above the parting surface of the cap.

3. Force the seal into the groove by rubbing down with a hammer handle or smooth tool, until the seal projects above the groove not more than 1/16 in. Cut the ends off flush with the surface of the cap. Use a razor blade.

4. On the 231, 252, and 350, place new neoprene seals in the grooves in the sides of the bearing cap after soaking the seals in kerosene for a minute or two.

NOTE: The neoprene composition seals will swell up once exposed to the oil and heat. It is normal for the seals to leak for a short time, until they become properly seated. The seals must not be cut to fit.

5. To install, reverse the above. Use a small amount of sealer on the bearing cap mating surface. The engine must be operated at low rpm when first started, after a new seal is installed.

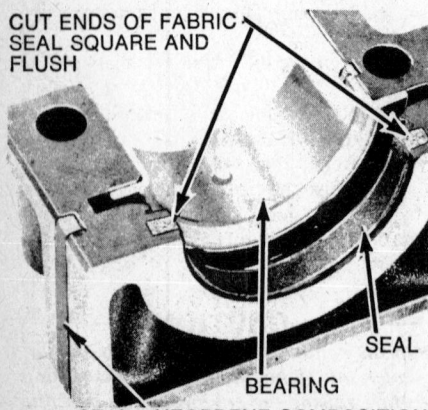

CUT ENDS OF FABRIC SEAL SQUARE AND FLUSH

SEAL

BEARING

SEAL—NEOPRENE COMPOSITION

Rear main bearing cap (© Buick Div., G.M. Corp.)

Chilton's TIME SAVER

TOP HALF, REAR MAIN BEARING OIL SEAL REPLACEMENT

Although the factory recommends removing the crankshaft to replace the top half of the oil seal, the following procedure can be used without removing the crankshaft.

1. **Remove the oil pan and rear main bearing cap.**
2. **Loosen the rest of the crankshaft main bearings and allow the crankshaft to drop about 1/16 in.**
3. **Remove the old upper half of the oil seal.**
4. **Wrap some soft copper wire around the end of the new seal and leave about 12 in. on the end. Generously lubricate the new seal with oil.**
5. **Slip the free end of the copper wire into the oil seal groove and around the crankshaft. Pull the wire until the seal protrudes an equal amount on each side. Rotate the crankshaft as the seal is pulled into place.**
6. **Remove the wire. Push any excess seal that may be protruding back into the groove.**
7. **Before tightening the crankshaft bearing caps, visually check the bearings to make sure they are in place. Torque the bearing cap bolts to specifications. Make sure there is no oil on the parting surfaces.**
8. **Replace the oil pan. Run the engine slowly for the first few minutes of operation.**

CLUTCH

The only service adjustment necessary on the clutch is to maintain the correct pedal free-play (see Linkage Adjustment, below).

REMOVAL & INSTALLATION

1. Remove the pedal return spring from the clutch fork. Remove the transmission as outlined under Manual Transmission.
2. Remove the flywheel housing.
3. Remove the throw-out bearing from the clutch fork.
4. Disconnect the clutch fork from the ball stud.

---

5. Mark the clutch cover and the flywheel to assure proper balance on reassembly.

6. Loosen the clutch cover to flywheel bolts one turn at a time until the spring pressure is released.

7. Support the pressure plate and cover assembly while removing the last bolts, then remove the cover assembly and the driven plate.

8. Inspect the flywheel for scoring, grooves, or signs of overheating (discoloration). Reface or replace the flywheel as necessary.

9. Install the clutch by reversing the removal procedure. Use a clutch aligning pilot or a spare transmission input shaft through the hub of the driven plate and into the pilot bushing. Be sure to align the clutch cover-to-flywheel index marks.

LINKAGE ADJUSTMENT

1978—79 Skylark

1. Turn the clutch lever and shaft assembly until the pedal is firmly against the stop.

2. Push the outer end of the clutch fork to the rear until the throw-out bearing lightly touches the spring fingers.

3. Place the lower pushrod in the fork and gauge hole, and increase the length until all play is gone from the linkage.

4. Place the swivel or rod in the hole furthest from the centerline of the lever and shaft assembly and install the retainer.

5. Tighten the locknut and spacer against the swivel.

6. Install the clutch fork retainer spring. This procedure should produce 1–1½ in. of travel when measured at the pedal pad center-line.

Century and Regal

1. Remove the return spring.
2. Turn the clutch lever and shaft assembly until the pedal is firmly against the stop.
3. Push the outer end of the clutch fork to the rear until the throwout bearing touches the spring fingers.
4. Install the lower pushrod in the fork and the swivel in the gauge hole. Turn the rod clockwise as viewed from the front to remove all play from the linkage.
5. Remove the swivel from the gauge hole and install it in the hole furthest from the centerline of the lever and shaft assembly. Install the washers and retainer.
6. Tighten the locknut against the swivel, being careful not to change the rod length.
7. Install the clutch retainer spring. The above procedure should produce ⅔ to 1⅓ in. of free play when measured at the pedal pad center.

MANUAL TRANSMISSION

A fully-synchronized Saginaw three-speed transmission has been available in these cars. It can be identified by the single bolt at the top of the side cover. The production code and transmission serial number are on the right side of the transmission case.

The only 4 speed used is a Saginaw unit. The production code and transmission serial number are stamped on the right side of the transmission case.

For overhaul procedures, please refer to "Manual Transmission Overhaul" in the Unit Repair section.

REMOVAL & INSTALLATION

1. Raise the vehicle on a hoist and drain the transmission fluid.

2. Mark the universal joint and transmission shaft companion flange to aid proper alignment at the time of installation. Remove the two U-bolts and disconnect the driveshaft at the rear joint. Slide the driveshaft rearward as far as possible and remove it.

3. Disconnect the shift linkage from the transmission.

4. Disconnect the speedometer cable and the back-up light switch at the transmission.

5. Remove the crossmember-to-transmission mounting bolts, the catalytic converter-to-transmission bracket (if so equipped) and remove the cross-member-to-frame bolts. Raise the transmission slightly and remove the crossmember.

6. Remove the two upper transmission-to-flywheel housing bolts and insert guide pins.

7. Remove the lower transmission-to-flywheel housing bolts.

NOTE: If guide pins are not used, damage to the clutch driven plate can result.

8. Slide the transmission back until the drive gear shaft disengages the clutch disc and clears the flywheel housing. Lower the transmission.

9. On installation, install the guide pins in the upper and lower rightside bolt holes for alignment. If the guide pins aren't used, the clutch plate might be damaged.

LINKAGE ADJUSTMENT

Column Shift

1. Place the column shift lever in Reverse. Turn the ignition lock to the LOCK position.

2. Loosen first-reverse clamp bolt.

3. Place the transmission first-reverse lever (the rear one) into the reverse (forward) position. Pull down on the shift rod and tighten the clamp bolt.

4. Unlock the ignition lock and shift the transmission levers into their neutral (center) positions.

5. Loosen second-third clamp bolt.

6. Install a 3/16 in. diameter rod through the second-third lever, selector plate, first-reverse lever, and alignment plate at the bottom of the column.

7. Tighten second-third clamp bolt.

8. With the shift lever in Reverse, the key must move freely to the LOCK position. You should not be able to get into the LOCK position in any gear position other than Reverse.

Three Speed Floorshift

1. Place the transmission levers into neutral.

2. Loosen the shift rod adjusting clamp bolts.

3. Place a rod (¼ in. diameter 1978) in the notch in the rear portion of the shift bracket assembly.

4. Move both shift levers back against the rod.

5. Tighten the shift rod adjusting bolts.

Four-Speed Floorshift

1. Place the transmission levers in neutral positions.

2. Place a 5/16 in. diameter rod in the rear lower portion of the shift bracket assembly.

3. Adjust all three shift levers back against the rod.

4. Tighten the adjusting clamp bolts.

AUTOMATIC TRANSMISSION

Many different automatic transmissions have been used in rear wheel drive Buick models. Basically, all of the transmissions used fall into 3 basic groups, as follows:

THM-200 GROUP	
THM-200	3S-standard duty
THM-200-C	3S-LTC
THM-200-4R	4S-LTC

THM-350 GROUP	
THM-250	3S-light duty
THM-350	3S-standard duty
THM-350-C	3S-LTC
THM-375-B	3S-heavy duty

THM-400 GROUP	
THM-400	3S-heavy duty

3S-3 speed, 4S-4 speed
LTC-Locking torque convertor

For further information on automatic transmissions, please refer to "Automatic Transmissions" in the Unit Repair section.

REMOVAL & INSTALLATION

1. Disconnect the negative battery cable at the battery.

2. If so equipped, disconnect the detent/downshift cable at its upper end (accelerator pedal or carburetor).

3. Raise the vehicle and support it safely with jackstands. Preferably, the front AND rear of the vehicle should be raised to provide adequate clearance for transmission removal.

4. Disconnect the exhaust crossover pipe at the manifolds, if exhaust system-to-transmission interference is obvious. It may be necessary to remove the catalytic converter, exhaust pipe, or just the brackets in order to clear the transmission.

— CAUTION —
Exhaust system services must be performed while all components are COLD.

5. Remove the transmission inspection cover.

6. Remove the torque converter-to-flywheel bolts. The relationship between the flywheel and converter must be marked so

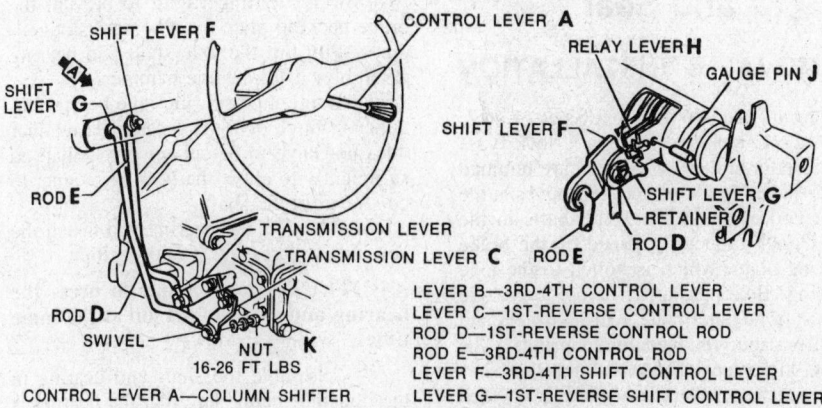

SHIFT LEVER **F**
SHIFT LEVER **G**
CONTROL LEVER **A**
RELAY LEVER **H**
GAUGE PIN **J**
SHIFT LEVER **F**
ROD **E**
TRANSMISSION LEVER
TRANSMISSION LEVER **C**
ROD **E**
SHIFT LEVER **G**
RETAINER
ROD **D**
ROD **D**
SWIVEL
NUT **K**
16-26 FT LBS
CONTROL LEVER A—COLUMN SHIFTER

LEVER B—3RD-4TH CONTROL LEVER
LEVER C—1ST-REVERSE CONTROL LEVER
ROD D—1ST-REVERSE CONTROL ROD
ROD E—3RD-4TH CONTROL ROD
LEVER F—3RD-4TH SHIFT CONTROL LEVER
LEVER G—1ST-REVERSE SHIFT CONTROL LEVER

Skylark column shift transmission linkage—through 1979
(© Buick Div., G.M. Corp.)

that proper balance is maintained after installation.

7. Matchmark the drive shaft and the rear yoke (for reinstallation purposes). With a drain pan positioned under the front yoke, unbolt and remove the drive shaft.

8. Mark and disconnect the vacuum lines, wiring, and speedometer cable from the transmission, as required.

9. Place a transmission jack (carefully) up against the transmission oil pan, then secure the transmission to the jack.

10. Remove the transmission mounting pad bolt(s), then carefully raise the transmission just enough to take the weight of the transmission off of the supporting crossmember.

— CAUTION —

Exercise extreme care to avoid damage to underhood components while raising or lowering the transmission.

11. Unbolt and remove the transmission crossmember, complete with the mount. It may be necessary to raise or lower the transmission *a small amount* to remove the crossmember.

12. Remove the transmission dipstick, then unbolt and remove the filler tube.

13. Disconnect the shift linkage (or cable on floor shift-equipped models) and oil cooler lines from the transmission.

14. Support the engine using a jackstand placed beneath the engine oil pan. Be sure to put a block of wood between the jackstand and the oil pan, to prevent damage to the pan.

15. Securely wire the torque converter to the transmission case.

16. Remove the transmission-to-engine mounting bolts, then carefully move the transmission rearward, downward, and out from beneath the vehicle.

— CAUTION —

If interference is encountered with the cable(s), cooler lines, etc., remove the component(s) before finally lowering the transmission.

Refer to the Automatic Transmission segment of the Unit Repair section for further information.

Installation is the reverse of the previous steps. Note the following points during and after installation:

1. Torque the transmission-to-engine mounting bolts to 30-40 ft. lbs.

2. Align the matchmarks of the drive shaft with the marks of the rear yoke before installing the joint straps and bolts.

3. Align the converter and flywheel markings before installing the converter bolts.

4. Add the proper type and quantity of transmission fluid. If the converter was replaced, an additional 4 pints (approx.) should be added. NEVER overfill the transmission.

5. Adjust the shift linkage (or cable) and the detent/downshift cable.

6. Make sure that all vacuum lines,

electrical connections, and oil cooler line connections are secure before driving the vehicle.

7. Check for fluid leakage, then after the transmission is hot, recheck the fluid level.

DRIVESHAFT AND U-JOINTS

Driveshaft

REMOVAL & INSTALLATION

1. Mark the driveshaft rear yoke and the differential flange to assure correct alignment upon reassembly.

2. Remove the bolts and straps from the differential flange.

3. Remove the driveshaft assembly by first sliding the driveshaft sufficiently forward to disengage the differential flange and then slide the shaft downward and rearward to disengage the front splined yoke from the transmission output shaft.

4. Installation is the reverse of removal. Be sure to align the match marks made before disassembly.

U-Joint

REMOVAL & INSTALLATION

For all U-joint repair procedures, please refer to "U-Joints/CV-Joints" in the Unit Repair section.

REAR AXLE

Axle Shaft, Bearing and Seal

REMOVAL & INSTALLATION

These cars use two different types of drive axle, the C-lock and the non C-lock type. Axle shafts in the C-lock type are retained by C-shaped locks, which fit grooves at the inner end of the shaft. Axle shafts in the non C-lock type are retained by the brake backing plate, which is bolted to the axle housing. Bearings in the C-lock type axle consist of an outer race, bearing rollers and a roller cage, retained by snaprings. The non C-lock type axle uses a unit roller bearing (inner race, rollers and outer race), which is pressed onto the shaft up to a shoulder. It is imperative to determine the axle type before attempting any service.

The axle identification number is stamped on the front of the passenger side axle tube next to the differential carrier on all models except those with an 8 1/2 in. ring gear. These models have the I.D. on a tag under one of the differential rear cover bolts.

Non C–Lock Type

— CAUTION —

Before attempting any service to the drive axle or axle shafts, remove the differential carrier cover and visually determine if the axle shafts are retained by C-shaped locks at the inner end, or by the brake backing plate at the outer end. If the shafts are not retained by C-locks, proceed as follows

Design allows for maximum axle shaft endplay of 0.022 in., which can be measured with a dial indicator. If end-play is found to be excessive, the bearing should be replaced. Shimming the bearing is not recommended as this ignores end-play of the bearing itself and could result in improper seating of the bearing.

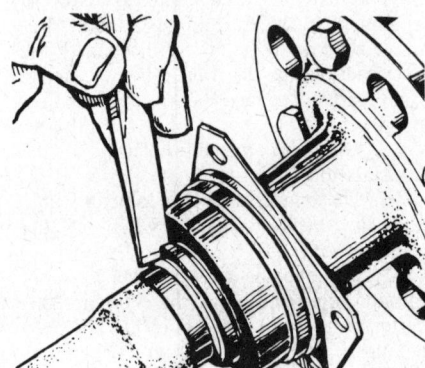

Breaking the bearing retainer with a chisel

1. Remove the wheel, tire and brake drum.

2. Remove the nuts holding the retainer plate to the backing plate. Disconnect the brake line.

3. Remove the retainer and install the two lower nuts fingertight, to prevent the brake backing plate from being dislodged.

4. Pull out the axle shaft and bearing assembly, using a slide hammer.

5. Using a chisel, nick the bearing retainer in three or four places. The retainer does not have to be cut, merely collapsed sufficiently to allow the bearing retainer to be slid from the shaft.

6. Press off the bearing and install the new one by pressing it into position.

NOTE: Do not attempt to press the bearing and the retainer on at the same time.

7. Assemble the shaft and bearing in the housing, being sure that the bearing is seated properly in the housing.

8. Install the retainer, drum, wheel and tire. Bleed the brakes.

C—Lock Type

— CAUTION —

Before attempting any service to the drive axle or axle shafts, remove the carrier cover and visually determine if the axle shaft(s) are retained by C-shaped locks at the inner ends or by a brake backing plate at the outer end. If they are **retained by C-shaped locks, proceed as follows**

1. Raise the vehicle and remove the wheels.

2. The differential cover has already been removed (see Caution note above). Remove the differential pinion shaft lockscrew and the differential pinion shaft.

3. Push the flanged end of the axle shaft toward the center of the vehicle and remove the C-lock from the end of the shaft.

4. Remove the axle shaft from the housing, being careful not to damage the oil seal.

5. Remove the oil seal by inserting the button end of the axle shaft behind the steel case of the oil seal. Pry the seal loose from the bore.

6. Seat the legs of a bearing puller behind the bearing. Seat a washer against the bearing and hold it in place with a nut. Use a slide hammer to pull the bearing.

7. Pack the cavity between the seal lips with wheel bearing lubricant and lubricate a new wheel bearing with same.

8. Use a suitable driver and install the bearing until it bottoms against a tube. Install the oil seal.

9. Slide the axle shaft into place. Be sure that the splines on the shaft do not damage the oil seal. Make sure that the splines engage the differential side gear.

10. Install the axle shaft C-lock on the inner end of the axle shaft and push the shaft outward so that the C-lock seats in the differential side gear counterbore.

11. Position the differential pinion shaft through the case and pinions, aligning the hole in the case with the hole for the lockscrew.

12. Install the pinion shaft lockscrew.

13. Use a new gasket and install the carrier cover. Be sure that the gasket surfaces are clean before installing the gasket and cover.

14. Fill the axle with lubricant to the bottom of the filler hole.

15. Install the brake drum and wheels and lower the car. Check for leaks and road test the car.

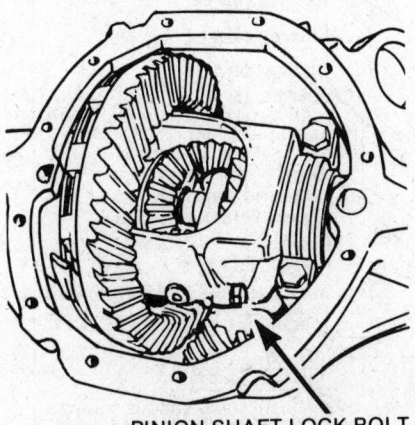

PINION SHAFT LOCK BOLT

Removing pinion shaft lock bolt from differential

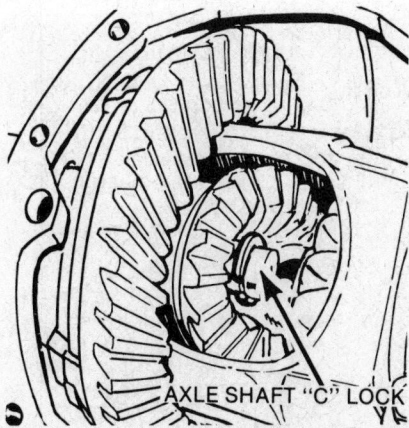

AXLE SHAFT "C" LOCK

Removing the axle shaft C lock

JACKING, HOISTING

Jack the car at the front spring seat of the lower control arm or center of the cross member.

Jack the car at the center of the rear axle housing.

To lift at the frame, use the side rails in front of the body floor pan and at the rear side rail at the lower control arm front pivot. Never lift the car by the rear lower control arms. Skylark models use a bolted-in front subframe and a unit-type rear subframe; DO NOT raise the car with the jack positioned on the body, between the frame sections.

FRONT SUSPENSION

Ball Joint

INSPECTION

Lower Ball Joint

All cars have visual wear indicators on the lower ball joints. The lower ball joint grease plug screws into the wear indicator which protrudes from the bottom of the ball joint housing. As long as the wear indicator extends out of the ball joint housing, the ball joint is not worn. If the tip of the wear indicator is parallel with, or recessed into the ball joint housing, the ball joint is, defective.

Upper Ball Joint

1. Place a jack under each lower control arm between the suspension spring pocket and the ball joint and raise the car.

2. Grasp the wheel at the 6 and 12 o'clock position and shake the top of the wheel in and out. Observe the steering knuckle for any movement relative to the control arm. If the ball joint is loose, it must be replaced.

Upper Control Arm and/or Ball Joint

REMOVAL & INSTALLATION

1. Raise the car and place a jack under the frame. Remove the wheel and tire.

2. With another jack, support the car weight under the outer edge of the lower control arm. Raise the jack enough to free the upper control arm from the upper ball stud.

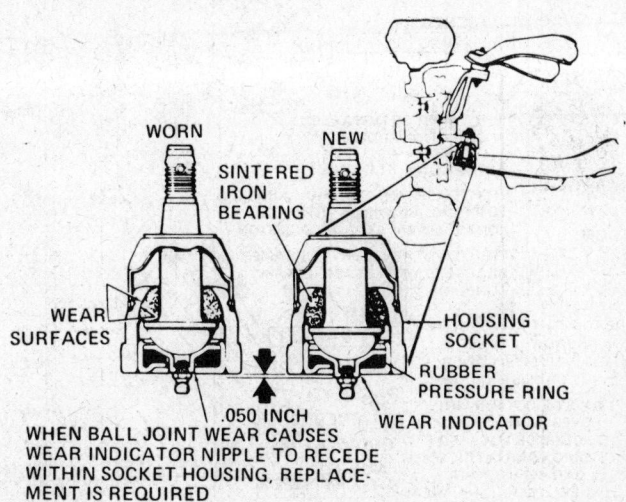

Lower ball joint wear indicator (© Buick Div., G.M. Corp.)

3. Remove the cotter pin from the upper ball joint stud.

4. Loosen, but do not remove, the nut.

CAUTION

If the nut is removed, the full force of the coil spring could be released.

Use a ball joint removal tool to free the stud from the knuckle.

5. Wire the brake and knuckle in place to prevent brake hose damage, then lift the upper arm from the knuckle.

NOTE: If only the ball joints are to be replaced, stop at this point. Center punch and drill out the four rivets, then chisel off their heads. Remove the old ball joint. The new joint comes with four specially hardened bolts which must be torqued to 8 ft. lbs. The nut goes on top.

6. Remove the upper control arm shaft-to-bracket nuts and lock washers. Carefully note the number, thickness, and location of the adjusting shims. Remove the control arm assembly.

7. Reverse the above steps to install. Observe the following torque figures: Upper control arm-to-frame nuts; 75 ft. lbs. for Skylark; 46 ft. lbs. for all others. Ball joint stud nut 60-65 ft. lbs. Upper control arm bushing nuts, 55 rear, 90 front through 1978, 45 front, 55 rear for 1979 and 85 front and rear for 1980 and later. The upper control arm bushing nuts must be torqued with the weight of the car on the wheels.

CAUTION

When installing the cotter pin, never loosen the nut to align the cotter pin holes. Always tighten the nut to the next slot that lines up with the hole.

Lower Control Arm Or Spring

REMOVAL & INSTALLATION

1. Raise the front of the car and remove the wheel.

2. Disconnect and remove the shock absorber.

3. Remove the front stabilizer rod link from the lower control arm.

4. Disconnect the brake reaction rod from the lower control arm.

5. As a safety precaution and to gain maximum leverage, place a jack about 1/2 in. below the lower ball joint stud. Now, remove the ball stud cotter pin and loosen the nut about 1/8 in. Do not remove the nut.

CAUTION

If the nut is removed, the full force of the coil spring could be released

---

6. Rap the steering knuckle in the area of the stud or use a ball joint removal tool to separate the stud from the knuckle.

7. After the stud has broken loose from the knuckle, raise the jack against the control arm. Remove the nut and separate the steering knuckle from the tapered stud.

8. Carefully lower the jack under the control arm and release the spring. With the jack entirely lowered, it may be necessary to pry the spring off its seat on the lower control arm with a pry bar.

9. After the spring is removed, the lower control arm may be removed by removing

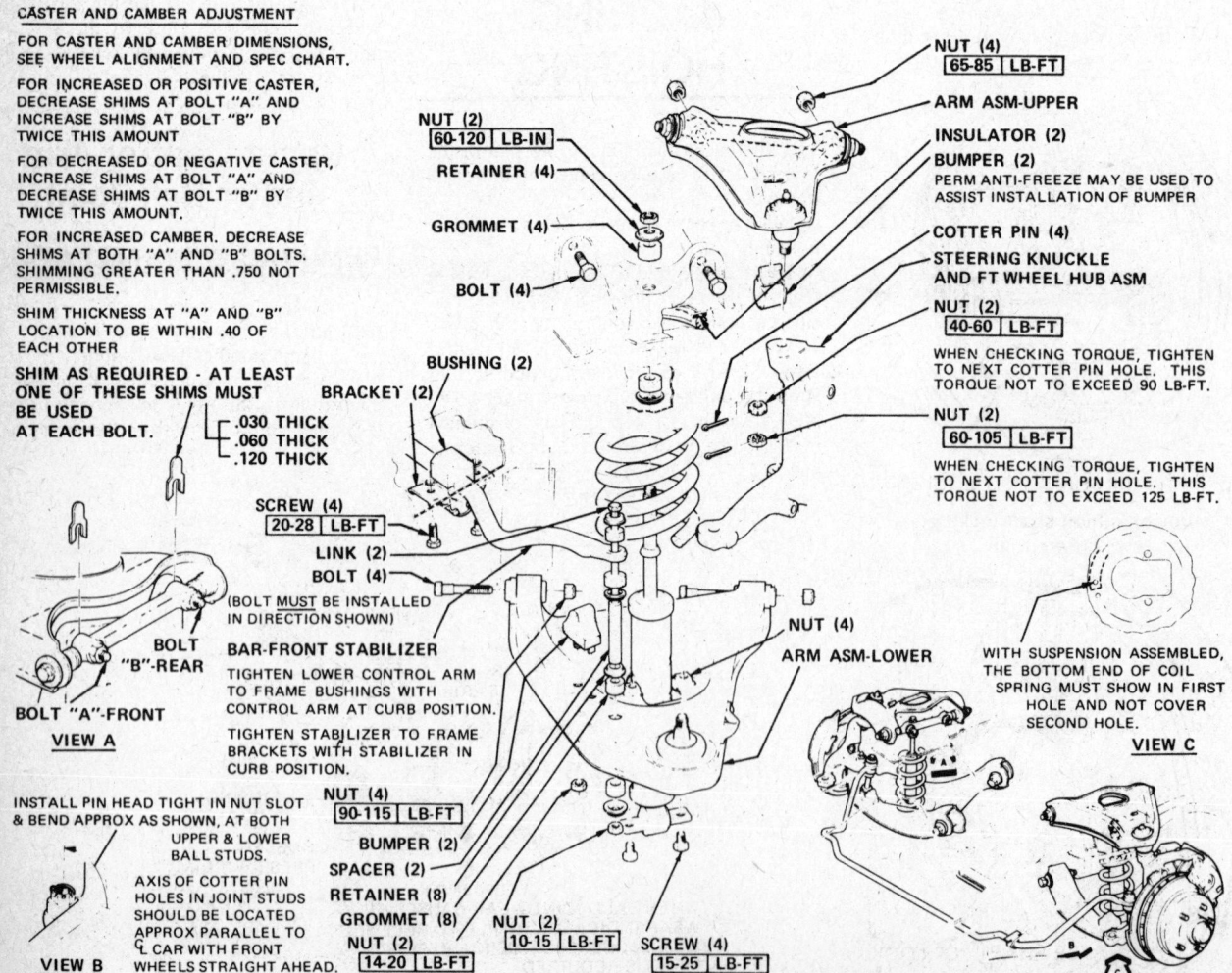

Typical front suspension (© Buick Div., G.M. Corp)

the lock nut which attaches the control arm to the frame.

10. Reverse to install. Torque the control arm to frame bolts, with the car on the ground, to the following settings:

Year/Model	Ft. Lbs.
1978-'85 exc. Skylark frt. and rr	85
1978-'79 Skylark frt. and rr	95

Lower Ball Joint

REMOVAL & INSTALLATION

1. Refer to Steps 1-7 of the "Lower Control Arm" procedure.
2. Install a ball joint remover and tighten the tool to force the ball joint out of the lower control arm.
3. Reverse the above to install. Tighten the castellated nut to 85-90 ft. lbs. Always tighten the castellated nut to the next slot if necessary to align the cotter pin.

Wheel Bearing

ADJUSTMENT

1. Lift the wheel off the ground by jacking under the lower control arm.
2. Remove the dust cap from the hub.
3. Remove the cotter pin and discard it.
4. Tighten the spindle nut to 12 ft. lbs. while turning the wheel. Then back off the nut 1/4-1/2 turn.
5. Retighten the nut by hand until it is finger-tight.
6. Loosen the nut no more than 1/6 of a turn until the nearest hole in the spindle lines up with the slot in the spindle nut, and insert a new cotter pin.
7. Feel the looseness in the hub assembly. There should be 0.001-0.005 in. endplay.
8. Replace the dust cover and lower the car.

Shock Absorber

REMOVAL & INSTALLATION

1. Remove the upper shock absorber attaching nut, grommet retainer, and grommet.
2. Remove the lower retaining screws. Lower the shock through the hole in the lower control arm.

NOTE: Purge new shocks of air by repeatedly extending them in their nor-mal position and compressing them while inverted.

3. Reverse the above steps to install. Tighten the upper nut to 8 ft. lbs.; the lower bolts to 20 ft. lbs.

REAR SUSPENSION

Shock Absorber

REMOVAL & INSTALLATION

NOTE: Purge new shocks of air by repeatedly extending them in their normal position and compressing them while inverted.

1. Raise the car at the axle housing.
2. Remove the nut, retainer, and grommet, or nut and lockwasher, as equipped, which attaches the lower end of the shock absorber to its mounting.
3. Remove the two shock absorber upper attaching screws and remove the shock absorber.
4. Reverse the removal procedures to install. Tighten the upper bolts to 18-20 ft. lbs. for all models. The nuts that lock the upper bolts on some models are torqued to 12 ft. lbs. Tighten the lower nut to 45 ft. lbs. on the Skylark and 65 ft lbs. for all others.

Leaf Spring

REPLACEMENT

1. Raise the rear of the car on stands.

2. Support the rear axle to take its weight off the springs.
3. Disconnect the bottom of the shock absorber.
4. Loosen the front spring eye bolt.
5. Unbolt the spring front bracket from the underbody.
6. Lower the axle slightly and remove the front bracket from the spring.
7. Pry the parking brake cable out of its retainer bracket on the axle spring mounting plate.
8. Unbolt the spring from the axle.
9. Remove the spring plate and cushion from the bottom of the spring. There should also be a cushion between the axle and the spring.
10. Remove the upper bolt from the rear spring shackle. Lower the spring and remove the bottom bolt.
11. On installation, attach the front bracket to the spring eye. The head of the bolt should be toward the center of the car.
12. Assemble the shackle loosely to the rear spring eye.
13. Raise the rear end of spring and install the upper shackle bolt loosely, making sure that the parking brake cable goes under the spring.
14. Raise the front end of the spring and loosely attach the front bracket to the underbody. Make sure that the bracket tab goes into its slot.
15. Make sure that the upper and lower spring cushions are aligned properly. The upper one has locating ribs and the lower one, a locating dowel.
16. Install the spring lower mounting plate over the locating dowel and loosely install the nuts. Don't forget the parking brake cable bracket.
17. Attach the bottom of the shock absorber.

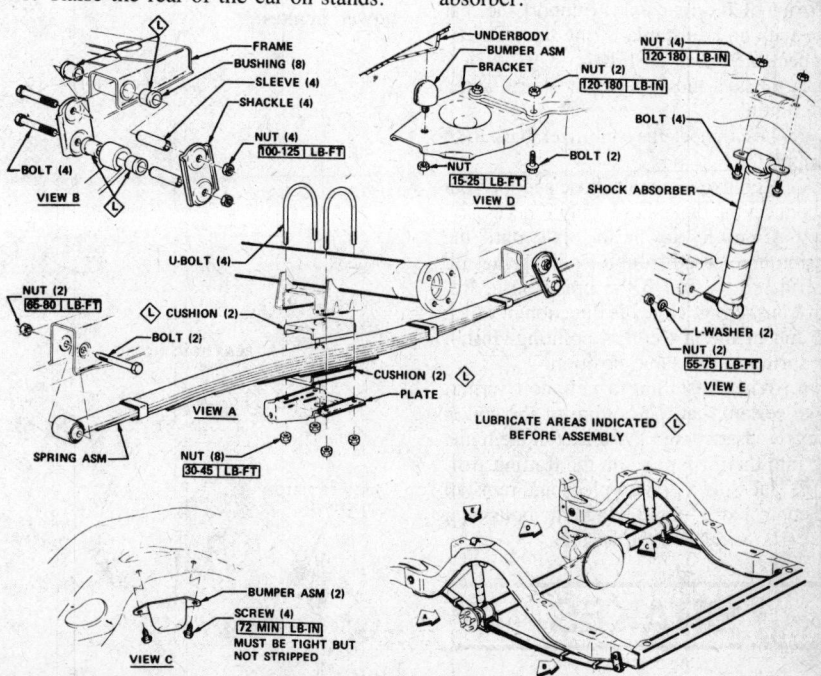

Rear leaf spring suspension details

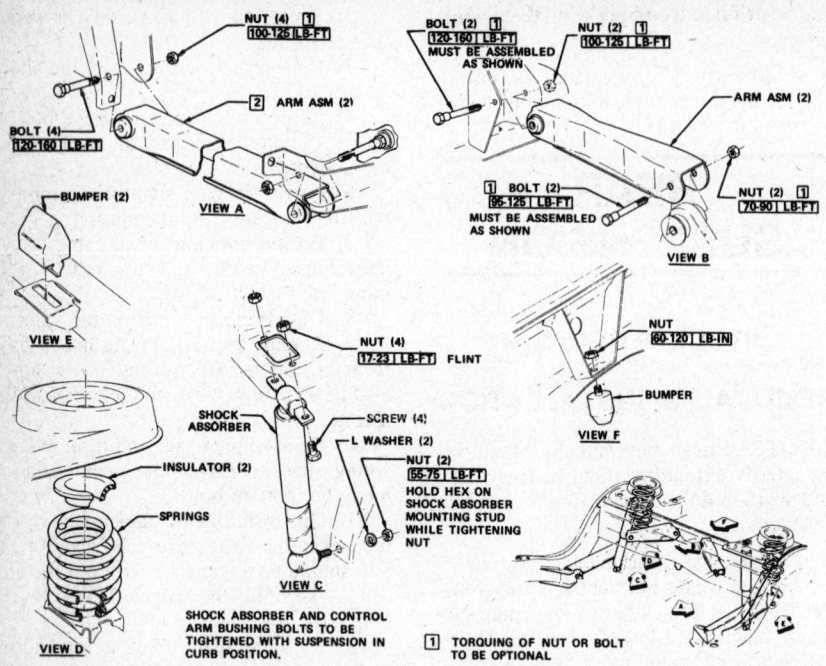

Rear suspension details—typical with coil springs (© Buick Div., G.M. Corp)

18. Attach the parking brake cable to the bracket on the lower spring plate.

19. Let the vehicle weight down on the springs. Tighten all the bolts. Torques are: rear shackle bolts—40-60 ft. lbs., front eye bolt—65-80 ft. lbs., and axle bolts—35-50 ft. lbs.

Coil Spring

REPLACEMENT

1. Jack up the back of the car and support both sides on jack stands on the frame, in front of the rear axle. Support the rear axle with an adjustable lifting device. Disconnect the shock absorber.

2. Detach the upper control arm at the differential.

3. Disconnect the stabilizer bar, if so equipped.

4. Remove any brake hose supports but disconnect the brake hose, only if necessary.

5. Carefully lower the axle until the tension is released from the coil spring. Be careful not to stretch the brake hose. Remove the spring. Note the direction in which the end of the last coil is pointing. Install the spring in the same position.

6. When installing a new coil spring, make certain that the bottom of the coil is properly inserted into the socket in the frame and into the form plate on the trailing arm.

7. Jack the axle into place and reinstall the control arm bolt. Tighten the bolts with the car's weight on the springs.

BRAKES

For information of the brake system not detailed below, please refer to "Brakes" in the Unit Repair section.

Master Cylinder

REMOVAL & INSTALLATION

1. Disconnect the brake lines from the master cylinder and tape the end of the lines to keep dirt out.

2. Disconnect the brake pedal from the master cylinder at the pushrod.

NOTE: This step isn't required with power brakes.

3. Remove the master cylinder-to-dash retaining bolts. Remove the master cylinder. Be careful not to spill brake fluid on the paint. Reverse the above steps to install. Bleed the master cylinder after it is reinstalled.

Power Brake Booster

REMOVAL & INSTALLATION

1. Unbolt the master cylinder from the power unit. Being careful not to kink or bend the brake lines, pull the master cylinder away from the power unit without disconnecting the brake lines.

2. Disconnect and plug the vacuum hose.

3. Disconnect the power brake pushrod from the brake pedal.

4. Unbolt the power brake unit from the firewall.

5. Remove the unit.
To install:

6. Mount the unit to the firewall.

7. Install the master cylinder to the power unit and torque the nuts to 15 ft. lbs. on the Century (through 1981) and Regal, and 25 ft. lbs. on all others.

8. Connect the vacuum hose.

9. Connect the power brake pushrod to the brake pedal.

Parking Brake

ADJUSTMENT

NOTE: Be sure that the parking brake does not drag. An overtightened, dragging parking brake on a car with auto-

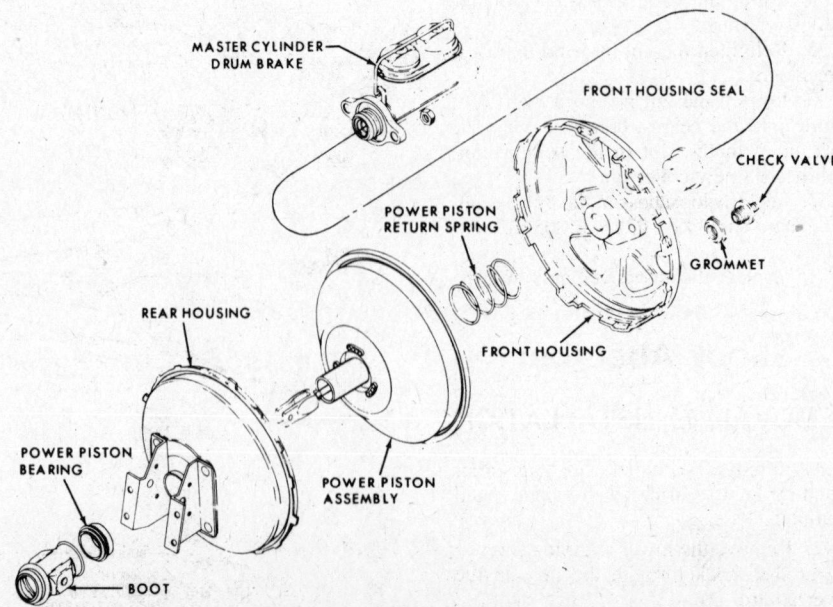

Power brake unit and master cylinder (© Buick Div., G.M. Corp.)

matic brake adjusters will result in an extremely short life for rear brake linings.

Adjustment of the parking brake is necessary whenever the rear brake cables have been disconnected or the parking brake pedal can be depressed more than eight rachet clicks under heavy foot pressure. The car should first be raised on a lift.

1. Make sure that the service brakes are properly adjusted.

2. Depress the parking brake pedal two rachet clicks.

3. Loosen the jam nut on the equalizer adjusting nut. Tighten the adjusting nut until the left rear wheel can just be turned rearward by hand, but not forward.

4. Release the rachet one click; the rear wheel should rotate rearward freely and forward with a slight drag.

5. Release the rachet fully; the rear wheel should turn freely in either direction.

STEERING

Power Steering Pump

REMOVAL & INSTALLATION

1. Remove the hoses at the pump and tape the openings shut to prevent contamination. Position the disconnected lines in a raised position to prevent leakage.

2. Remove the pump belt.

3. Loosen the retaining bolts and any braces, and remove the pump.

4. Install the pump on the engine with the retaining bolts hand-tight.

5. Connect and tighten the hose fittings.

6. Refill the pump with fluid and bleed by turning the pulley counterclockwise (viewed from the front). Stop the bleeding when air bubbles no longer appear.

7. Install the pump belt on the pulley and adjust the tension.

Steering Wheel

REMOVAL & INSTALLATION

Except Tilt and Telescope Column

1. Disconnect the battery ground and unplug the horn wire connector from the steering column.

2. On cars with a standard wheel or optional wood-rim wheel, pull off the cap, remove the three screws and the contact, insulator, and spring. On cars with the bar-type horn actuator, remove the screws securing the actuator from the underside of the steering wheel, unhook the lead connector plug, and remove the actuator assembly.

3. Loosen the steering wheel nut.

4. Apply the steering wheel puller and pull the wheel up to the nut. Now remove the puller, nut and steering wheel.

--- **CAUTION** ---
Don't pound on the steering wheel in either direction or the collapsible steering column will collapse, requiring replacement.

On installation:

NOTE: Location marks are provided on the steering wheel and shaft to simplify proper indexing at the time of installation.

1. Install wheel with the location mark aligned with that of the shaft.

2. Install the wheel nut and torque to 30 ft. lbs.

3. Reinstall horn button or actuator assembly.

Tilt and Telescope Column

1. Disconnect the battery ground.

2. Remove the attaching screws and lift the pad from the column.

3. Disconnect the horn wire by pushing in the connector and turning it counterclockwise.

4. Push the locking lever counterclockwise until full release is obtained.

5. Mark the lock plate-to-locking lever position and remove the plate and lever.

6. Remove the steering wheel retaining nut and remove the wheel with a puller.

7. Install a 5/16 in. × 18 set screw into the upper shaft at the fully extended position and lock it.

8. Install the steering wheel, observing the aligning mark on the hub and the slash mark on the end of the shaft. Make certain that the unattached end of the horn upper contact assembly is seated flush against the top of the horn contact carrier button.

9. Install the nut on the upper steering shaft and torque to 30 ft. lbs.

10. Remove the set screw installed in Step 7.

11. Install the plate assembly finger tight.

12. Position the locking lever in the vertical position and move it counterclockwise until the holes in the plate align with the holes in the lever. Install the attaching screws.

13. Align the pad assembly with the holes in the steering wheel and install the retaining screws.

14. Connect the battery.

15. Make certain that the locking lever securely locks the wheel travel and that the wheel travel is free in the unlocked position.

Steering Gear

REMOVAL & INSTALLATION

1. Remove flexible coupling shield.

--- **CAUTION** ---
Failure to disconnect the flexible coupling

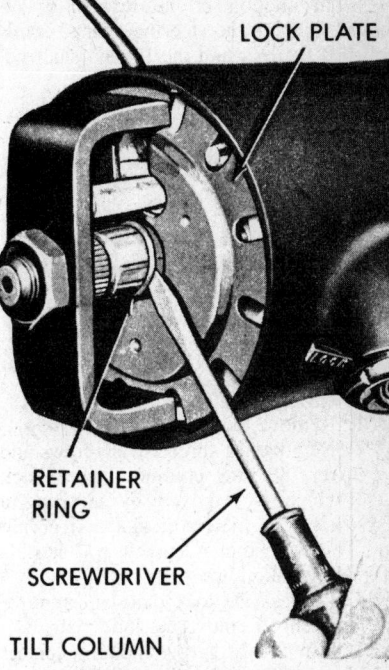

RETAINER RING

SCREWDRIVER

TILT COLUMN

Removing lock plate
(© Buick Div., G.M. Corp)

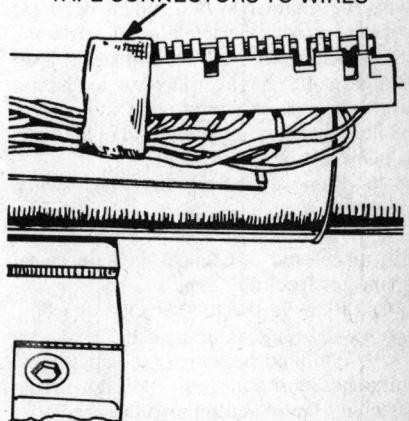

TAPE CONNECTORS TO WIRES

Tape the connector to the wires so that it will slip easily up the steering column

from the steering gear stub shaft can result in damage to the steering gear and/or intermediate shaft. This damage can cause loss of steering control which could result in a vehicle crash and bodily injury.

2. Disconnect the hoses from the gear and cap the hose fittings.

3. Hoist the car.

4. Remove the Pitman shaft nut, then disconnect the Pitman arm from the pitman shaft using Puller J-29107 or a similar puller.

5. Remove the three bolts attaching the gear to the frame side rail and remove the gear with the hoses attached.

NOTE: If mounting threads are stripped, do not repair. Replace housing.

6. Installation is the reverse of removal. Tighten the steering gear to frame bolts 80 ft. lbs., and the Pitman shaft nut 180 ft. lbs.

Turn Signal Switch

REMOVAL & INSTALLATION

Except Tilt and Telescope Column

NOTE: The steering wheel must always be supported. Use extreme care not to bend the steering column.

1. Remove the steering wheel.
2. Remove the three cover screws and the cover. Steering columns have a lock plate which is removed by inserting a screwdriver in the cover slot and prying out. This is done in at least two of the slots to avoid breaking the plate.
3. Depress the lock plate and remove the snap-ring. Remove the lock plate.
4. Remove the spring and horn contact signal cancelling cam. Remove the thrust washer.
5. Place the turn signal lever in the right turn position, remove the attaching screw and remove the turn signal lever. On models with the dimmer switch mounted on the column, remove the actuator arm screw and the actuator arm. Pull the turn signal lever straight out to remove. Depress the hazard warning knob, and remove the knob. Some models have a screw in the end of the knob which must be removed.
6. Remove the three turn signal switch mounting screws.
7. Remove the instrument panel lower trim panel and disconnect the turn signal connector from the harness.
8. Remove the four bracket attaching screws and remove the bracket.
9. On models with automatic transmissions, loosen the shift indicator needle attaching screw and remove the needle.
10. Remove the two steering column supporting bolts while supporting the column. Do not allow the column to drop suddenly.
11. Remove the bracket and wiring from the column. Loosely reinstall the column supporting bolts, if removed.
12. Pull the switch straight up with the wire protector and wire harness.
13. Reverse the above steps to install.

Tilt and Telescope Column

1. Disconnect the battery ground.
2. Remove the steering wheel and lock plate as previously described.
3. Remove the upper bearing preload spring.
4. Position the turn signal lever in the right turn position and remove the lever and screw.
5. With column mounted dimmer switches, remove the actuator arm and screw,

then remove the turn signal arm by pulling it straight out.
6. Push in on the warning hazard knob, then remove the retaining screw and knob.
7. Position the column in the center position and remove the three turn signal switch attaching screws.
8. Remove the instrument panel lower trim pad and disconnect the turn signal harness connector. Lift the connector from the mounting bracket on the right side of the jacket.
9. Remove the toe pan bolts.
10. Remove the four bolts attaching the bracket assembly to the jacket.
11. Remove the shift indicator retaining clip.
12. Support the column and remove the bracket assembly. Remove the wire protector from the turn signal wiring. Pull the turn signal switch and wiring from the column.
13. Prior to installation, coat all moving parts with lithium-base grease.
14. Insert switch wiring into the column.
15. Place the switch in the right turn position and push it straight down until seated.

--- CAUTION ---
Angling or cocking of the switch can cause damage to the buzzer terminal or tangs

16. Install the switch attaching screws and torque them to 25 inch lbs.
17. Position the turn signal in the center.
18. Connect the wiring to the harness.
19. Install the hazard warning knob and turn signal lever.
20. Install the lock plate and carrier and the steering wheel.
21. Install the wiring protector and bracket. Torque the bracket bolts to 18 ft. lbs. and the nuts to 24 ft. lbs.
22. Install the shift indicator needle or clip.
23. Position the harness connector in the bracket on the right side of the jacket.
24. Install the instrument panel lower trim pad and connect the battery ground.

Ignition Switch and Lock Cylinder

REMOVAL & INSTALLATION

Standard Column

1. Refer to the "Turn Signal Switch Replacement" procedure, Steps 1-6.
2. Disconnect the turn signal connector from the harness and pull out the turn signal switch. Allow it to hang.
3. With the lock cylinder in the RUN position, insert a small screwdriver into the slot next to the turn signal switch mounting screw boss (right-hand slot), depress the spring latch and remove the key lock.
4. Pull the buzzer switch straight out, depressing the switch clip with pliers.

5. Place the ignition switch in the OFF-UNLOCKED position by pulling up on the connecting rod until there is a definite stop or detent felt.
6. Remove the two attaching screws and the ignition switch.
7. Assembly is the reverse of the above. However, note the following steps before proceeding with the reassembly.
8. To install the steering lock, hold the lock cylinder sleeve and rotate the knob clockwise against the stop. Insert the cylinder into the cover bore with the key on the cylinder sleeve aligned with the keyway in the housing. Then push the cylinder in until it bottoms. Maintaining a light inward pressure, rotate the knob counterclockwise until the drive section of the cylinder mates with the drive shaft. Push in until the snapring pops into the groove and the lock cylinder is secured in the cover. Check for free rotation.
9. Move the switch slider to the extreme left position (ACC), then two detents to the right, to the OFF-UNLOCKED position. Fit the actuator rod into the hole and attach the switch to the column.
10. The neutral start switch is adjusted with the shift lever in the Drive position.

Tilt Column

1. Refer to the "Turn Signal Switch Replacement" procedure for tilt and telescopic columns, Steps 1-6.
2. Position the tilt column in the center position and remove the three turn signal switch screws. Tape the wires to the wire connector at the upper end and place the shift bowl in Low. Pull the switch straight up and out, allowing it to hang.
3. Insert a small screwdriver into the slot next to the turn signal switch mounting screw boss (right-hand slot), depress the spring latch and remove the key lock. On 1979 and later models, remove the retaining screw and the lock cylinder.
4. Remove the buzzer switch straight out, depressing the switch clip with pliers.
5. Remove the three housing cover screws and cover.
6. Install the tilt release lever and place column in full UP position.
7. Place a screwdriver in the slot of the tilt spring retainer, press in about 3/16 in. and turn counterclockwise. Remove the spring and guide.

NOTE: The spring is very strong—be careful.

8. Place the column in neutral position, push in on the upper steering shaft, remove the inner race seat and race.
9. Remove the upper flange pinch bolt, place the ignition switch in the accessory position, remove the two switch mounting screws and switch.

NOTE: The neutral start switch can be removed at this time, if necessary.

10. Assembly is the reverse of the above. However, note the following steps before

proceeding with the reassembly.

11. To install the steering lock, hold the lock cylinder sleeve and rotate the knob clockwise against the stop. Insert the cylinder into the cover bore with the key on the cylinder sleeve aligned with the keyway in the housing. Push the cylinder in until it bottoms. Maintaining a light inward pressure, rotate the knob counterclockwise until the drive section of the cylinder mates with the drive shaft. Push in until the snap-ring pops into the groove and the lock cylinder is secured in the cover. Check for free rotation.

12. When installing the ignition switch, be sure the lock cylinder is in the LOCK position. Put the shift bowl or shroud in the PARK position. Make sure the ignition switch is in the LOCK position. Insert the actuator rod into the switch and assemble the switch to the column.

13. The neutral-start switch is adjusted with the shift lever in the DRIVE position.

Tie-Rod End

REMOVAL & INSTALLATION

1. Raise and support the car. Loosen the tie-rod adjuster sleeve clamp nuts.

2. Remove the tie-rod stud nut cotter pin and nut.

3. Remove the tie-rod stud from the steering arm or intermediate rod. This is a taper fit. Removal is accomplished using a ball joint removal tool or by hitting the steering arm sharply with a hammer, while using a heavy hammer as a backup.

4. Unthread the tie rod from the adjusted sleeve. Outer tie rods have right-hand threads and inner tie rods have left-hand threads. Count the number of turns the tie rod must be rotated to remove it from the adjusting sleeve. This will allow a reasonably accurate realignment upon reassembly.

NOTE: If a turning force of more than 7 ft. lbs. is needed for end removal, after breakaway, the nuts and bolts should be replaced

5. Reverse the removal procedures to install. Clean rust and dirt from the threads. Observe the following torque specifications: steering arm-to-tie-rod end nut, 35 ft. lbs.; tie rod clamp nuts, 11-14 ft. lbs.; tie rod-to-intermediate nut, 40 ft. lbs. Check the alignment and adjust as necessary.

INSTRUMENT PANEL

Light Switch

REPLACEMENT

1. Disconnect the battery.
2. Disconnect the multiple connector from the switch.

3. Pull the switch knob to the last notch and depress the spring loaded latch button on top of the switch while pulling the knob and rod out of the switch. Depress the retainer tab behind the knob and remove the knob.

NOTE: On cars with air conditioning, remove the left duct.

4. Remove the escutcheon and the switch.
5. Install in the reverse of the above.

Speedometer Cable

REMOVAL & INSTALLATION

1. Reach up underneath the instrument panel and disconnect the cable housing from the cluster housing. On some models you might first have to remove the left air conditioning duct.

2. Carefully pull the cable housing down and pull out the cable.

3. Hold the cable vertically and turn it slowly between your fingers. If it is kinked, you will notice it flopping around. Replace any kinked cable.

4. If the cable is broken, raise and support the car. Disconnect the cable housing from the transmission, remove the gear and pull the cable from the cable housing.

5. Install the new cable in the cable housing after thoroughly lubricating it.

Instrument Cluster

REMOVAL & INSTALLATION

1. Pull steering column collar filler out.
2. Remove headlamp switch knob and bezel:
   - To remove knob use an awl and push forward in slot on knob to release clip while pulling knob out.
   - Bezel unscrews unless vehicle is equipped with twilight sentinel. Then it simply comes off by pulling straight out.
3. Grasp trim plate on both sides and gently pull out.

NOTE: The gauges can be removed after removing the instrument panel cover.

4. Installation is the reverse of removal.

WINDSHIELD WIPERS

Wiper Motor

REMOVAL & INSTALLATION

1. Disconnect the battery.
2. Remove the cowl screen on Skylark models.
3. Loosen the two nuts on the adjustable motor drive link at the crank arm and slip the drive link off.
4. Remove the electrical connectors from the washer motor and pump.
5. Disconnect the washer pump hoses.
6. Remove the three bolts securing the motor to the cowl and carefully lift the motor away from the cowl.
7. Reverse the above steps for installation.

Wiper Blade

REMOVAL & INSTALLATION

Any one of three methods of blade attachment may be used on these models. If there is a small tab on top of the blade, depress it and slide off the blade. If there is a small spring visible in the top of the blade, insert a screwdriver in the opening, press down and slide the blade off. If there is a clip on the under side of the arm, press down on the clip and slide the blade off.

Wiper blade element replacement is covered in the Maintenance Unit Repair Section.

RADIO

The antenna trim must be adjusted on AM radios, when major repair has been done to the unit or the antenna changed. The trimmer screw is located behind the right side knob. Raise the antenna to its full height. Tune to a weak station around 1400 and turn the volume down until barely audible. Turn the trimmer screw until the maximum volume is achieved.

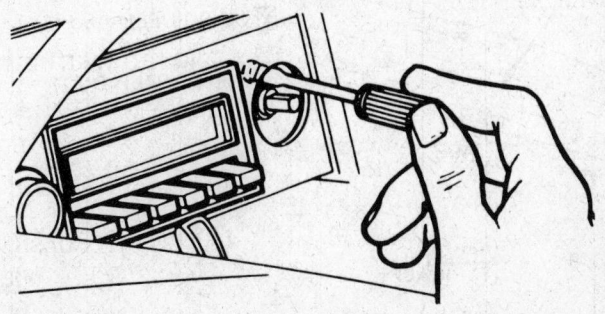

Antenna trim screw (© Buick Div., G.M. Corp.)

REMOVAL & INSTALLATION

CAUTION

Don't turn on the radio without first connecting the speaker. The output transistors may be damaged.

Skylark

1. Disconnect the negative battery cable.
2. Remove the radio knobs, bezels, nuts and the side brace screw.
3. Disconnect the radio wiring and the antenna lead.
4. Remove the radio from under the dash. Reverse to install.

Century and Regal

1. Disconnect the negative battery cable and remove the radio knobs.
2. Remove the center trim plate.
3. Remove the glove box to gain access to the radio.
4. Disconnect the radio mounting bracket.
5. Disconnect the radio wiring.
6. Remove the radio with the bracket attached. Reverse to install.

Electra, LeSabre and Riviera

1. Disconnect the battery ground cable.
2. Remove the ashtray and bracket.
3. Pull off the radio knobs and trim washers.

4. Remove the lower left air duct.
5. Remove the two retaining nuts from the control shafts.
6. Unplug the power lead, speaker wire, and antenna lead.
7. Remove the rear radio mounting nut.
8. Reverse the procedure for installation.

NOTE: On 1981 and later models, remove the headlight switch and place the gear shift lever in the LOW position to remove the left hand instrument panel.

HEATER

NOTE: Vacuum hose routing clips, electrical wires and relays, weather seals, and other items, may be attached to the heater housing, and will have to be relocated during removal and replacement of the heater core and/or the blower motor. Always tag any disconnected hoses or wires for installation.

Blower Motor

REMOVAL & INSTALLATION

Century and Regal

1. Disconnect the blower motor wire.
2. Remove the blower motor attaching screws and the motor.

Skylark

1. Disconnect the battery ground cable.
2. Raise the car. Remove all the fender skirt bolts except those holding the skirt to the radiator support.
3. Pull out and down on the fender skirt. Put a wood block between the skirt and fender to allow clearance for removing the motor.
4. Disconnect the motor wiring.
5. Remove the screws and the motor.
6. Reverse the procedure on installation.

Electra, LeSabre and Riviera

1. Disconnect the blower motor wires.
2. On A/C equipped cars, disconnect the cooling tube from the case.
3. Remove the motor attaching screws and lift the motor from the case.
4. Installation is the reverse of removal. Replace any damaged sealer.

Heater Core

REMOVAL & INSTALLATION

Without A/C

SKYLARK

1. Disconnect the battery ground cable.
2. Drain the radiator.
3. Disconnect the heater hoses and plug the tubes to prevent spillage, when you remove the assembly from inside the car.

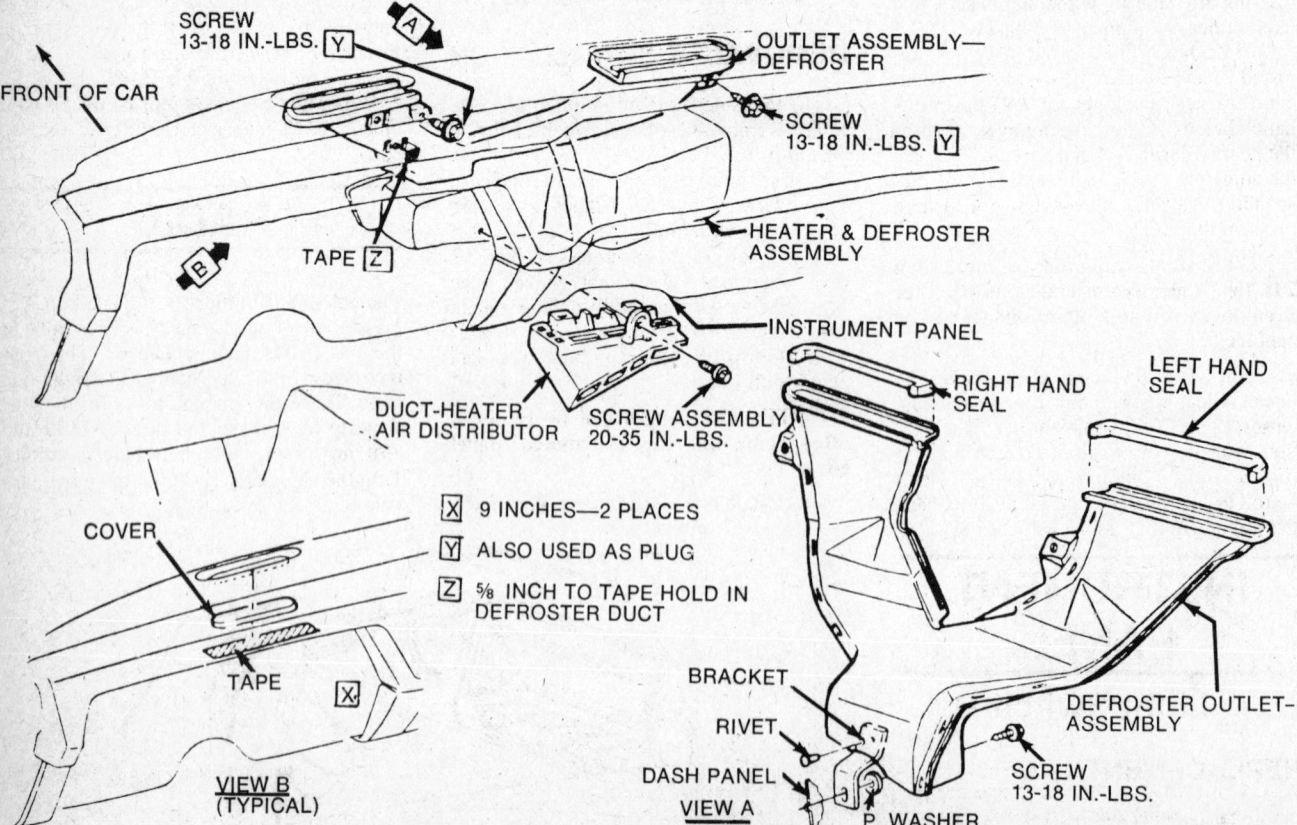

Heater-defroster outlets and defroster opening cover, Skylark through 1979 (Buick Div., G.M. Corp.)

4. Remove the retaining nuts from the studs on the engine side of the firewall.

5. Remove the glove compartment and door.

6. Drill out the lower right heater case stud from inside the car.

7. Pull the core and case assembly from below the instrument panel.

8. Detach the cables and wiring from the case and remove the case from the car.

9. Remove the core from the case.

10. Reverse the procedure on installation, replacing the drilled out stud with a new screw and stamped nut.

CENTURY AND REGAL

1. Disconnect the heater hoses at the core tubes. Place the hoses in an up position to prevent excess coolant loss.

2. Disconnect all electrical connectors at the module case.

3. Remove the front case from the module on 1978-79 models and the top module cover on 1980-85 models.

4. Remove the core. On later models, remove core bracket and ground screws to gain access.

5. Reverse the above for installation. Replace any damaged sealer.

ELECTRA, LESABRE AND RIVIERA

1. Drain the radiator.

2. Disconnect the heater core inlet and outlet hoses at the firewall.

3. Detach the electrical connections.

4. Remove the screws holding the front case to the heater module assembly.

5. Remove the front case, then the heater core.

6. On installation, reseal the case.

Heater Core

REMOVAL & INSTALLATION

With A/C

CENTURY/REGAL—THROUGH 1979

NOTE: Includes removal of Heater assembly

1. Drain the radiator and disconnect the heater hoses.

2. Disconnect the temperature control cable and the vacuum hoses.

3. Remove the resistor assembly. Reach through the opening and remove the attaching nut. Remove the attaching nut directly over the transmission and the two attaching nuts to the upper and lower inboard evaporator case half.

4. From inside the car, remove the screw in the lower right corner of the passenger side.

5. Remove the lower attaching outlets. Work the assembly to the rear until the studs clear. Remove the heater assembly.

6. On installation, adjust the control cable to get about 1/8 in. springback in the hot position.

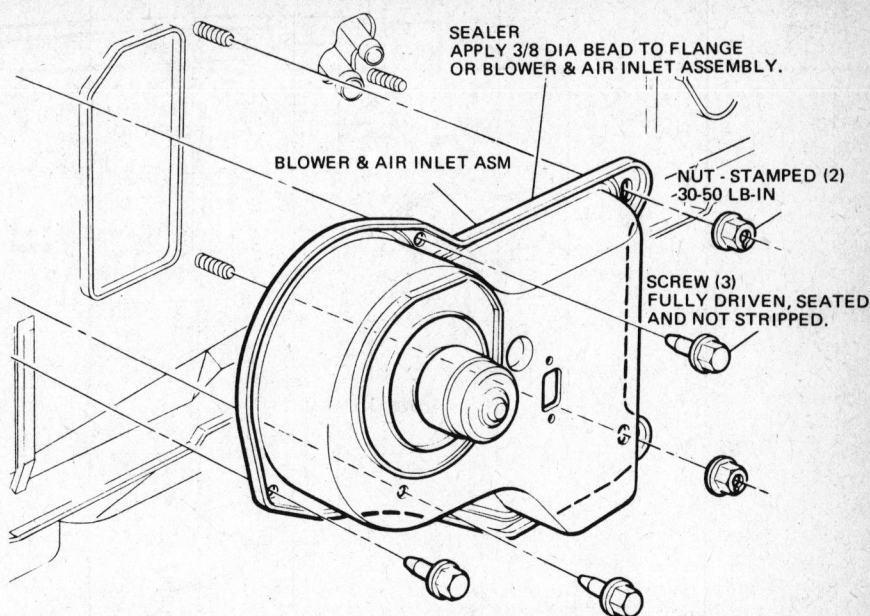

SEALER
APPLY 3/8 DIA BEAD TO FLANGE OR BLOWER & AIR INLET ASSEMBLY.

BLOWER & AIR INLET ASM

NUT - STAMPED (2) -30-50 LB-IN

SCREW (3) FULLY DRIVEN, SEATED AND NOT STRIPPED.

Blower motor and air inlet assembly—Century, Regal (© Buick Div., G.M. Corp.)

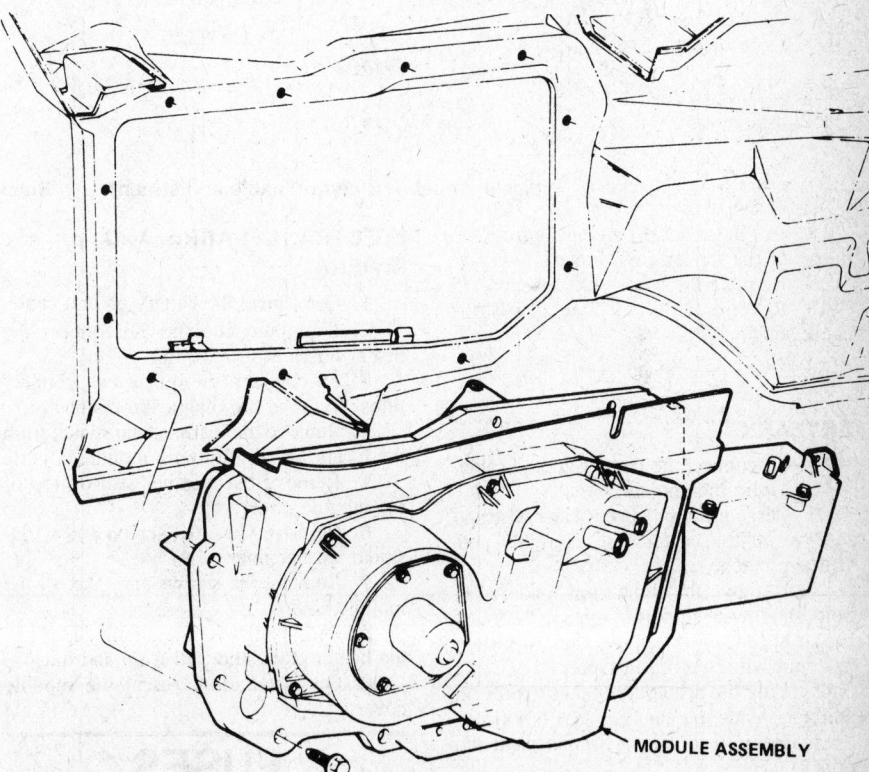

MODULE ASSEMBLY

Blower motor and housing—Electra, LeSabre and 1978 Riviera (© Buick Div., GM Corp.)

1980-81 CENTURY AND 1980-85 REGAL

1. Engage the right-hand wiper arm so it is in the UP position.

2. Drain the radiator enough so you can disconnect the heater core hoses, then disconnect the hoses and plug them. Disconnect the battery ground cable.

3. Pull off the trim seal and remove the screens from the assembly. Mark and remove any electrical connections in the way.

4. Loosen and move up the lower windshield trim. Remove the windshield molding cowl brackets.

5. Tape a strip of wood below the lower edge of the windshield glass near the module for protection. Remove all module cover screws.

6. Cut through the sealing material along the cowl with a knife.

7. Pry the module cover off from the side, not down from the top, to insure you don't damage the windshield.

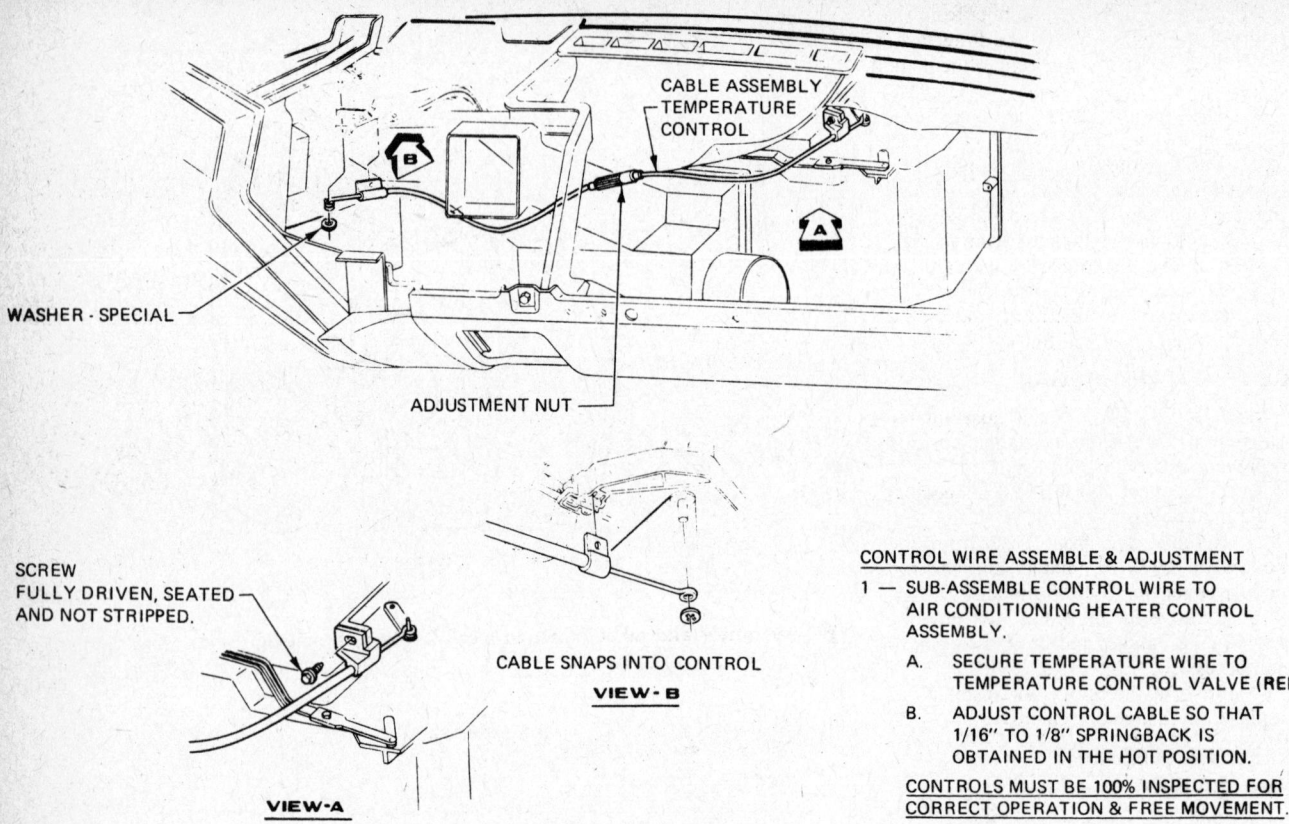

CABLE ASSEMBLY
TEMPERATURE
CONTROL

WASHER - SPECIAL

ADJUSTMENT NUT

SCREW
FULLY DRIVEN, SEATED
AND NOT STRIPPED.

CABLE SNAPS INTO CONTROL
VIEW - B

VIEW-A

CONTROL WIRE ASSEMBLE & ADJUSTMENT

1 — SUB-ASSEMBLE CONTROL WIRE TO
AIR CONDITIONING HEATER CONTROL
ASSEMBLY.

A. SECURE TEMPERATURE WIRE TO
TEMPERATURE CONTROL VALVE (**RED**)

B. ADJUST CONTROL CABLE SO THAT
1/16" TO 1/8" SPRINGBACK IS
OBTAINED IN THE HOT POSITION.

CONTROLS MUST BE **100%** INSPECTED FOR
CORRECT OPERATION & FREE MOVEMENT.

Typical manual A/C control cable adjustment (© Buick Div., G.M. Corp)

8. Lift the cover off and away from the flange of the fender-cowl brace.

9. Remove the core.

10. Reverse to install. Use new strip-caulk sealer.

SKYLARK

1. Disconnect the battery ground cable.

2. Drain the coolant.

3. Disconnect the upper heater hose and remove all the heater case assembly nuts you can reach.

4. Remove the right front fender skirt bolts and lower the skirt to remove the lower heater hose clamp. Remove the lower right case nut while you're in there.

5. Plug the heater core tubes to prevent spillage inside the car.

6. Remove the glove compartment and door.

7. Remove the diaphragm at the right kick panel.

8. Remove the heater outlet at the bottom of the heater case.

9. Remove the cold air duct from the heater case.

10. Remove the heater case extension screws and separate the extension from the case.

11. Disconnect the heater cables and wiring.

12. Remove the core and case assembly.

13. Reverse the whole procedure on installation.

ELECTRA, LESABRE AND RIVIERA

1. Disconnect the battery ground cable.

2. Drain the coolant. Disconnect the heater hoses at the firewall.

3. Disconnect the electrical connections. Remove the diagnostic connector.

4. Remove the thermostatic switch from the heater/air conditioning module cover.

5. Remove the weather seal on top of the module cover.

6. Remove the cowl screen and windshield washer nozzle.

7. Remove the screws and take off the module cover.

8. Remove the core retaining clip, twist the heater core, and pull it up and out.

9. On installation, reseal the module cover.

FUSES

The fuse block is located beneath the instrument panel above the headlight dimmer floor switch. Fuse holders are labeled as to their service and the correct amperage. Always replace blown fuses with new ones of the correct amperage. Otherwise electrical overloads and possible wiring damage will result.

FUSIBLE LINKS

Fusible links are sections of wire, with special insulation, designed to melt under electrical overload. Replacements are simply spliced into the wire. There may be as many as five of these in the engine compartment wiring harnesses. These are:

1. Horn relay-to-fuse panel circuit—one link.

2. Charging circuit, from the starter solenoid to the horn relay—two links.

3. Starter solenoid-to-ammeter circuit—one link.

4. Horn relay-to-rear window defroster circuit—one link.

The fusible links are all two wire gauge sizes smaller than the wires they protect.

NOTE: Most models have fusible links at these locations.

REPLACEMENT

1. Disconnect the battery ground cable.

2. Disconnect the fusible link from the junction block or starter solenoid.

3. Cut the harness directly behind the connector to remove the damaged fusible link.

4. Strip the harness wire approximately ½ in.

5. Connect the new fusible link to the harness wire using a crimp-on connector. Soder the connection using rosin-core solder.

6. Tape all exposed wires with plastic electrical tape.

7. Connect the fusible link to the junction block or starter solenoid and reconnect the battery ground cable.

Cadillac
Rear Wheel Drive
Rear Wheel Drive
Deville, Fleetwood, Seville

YEAR IDENTIFICATION

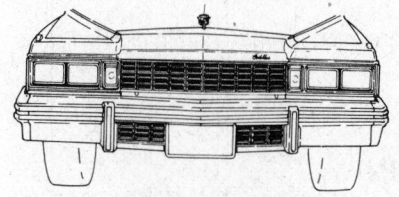

1977 Cadillac

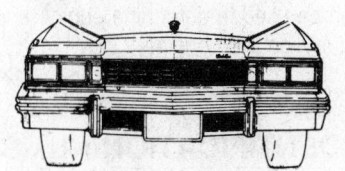

1978 Cadillac

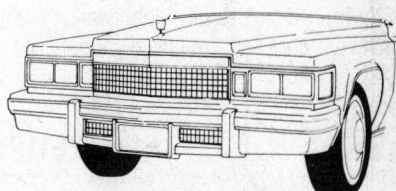

1979 Cadillac

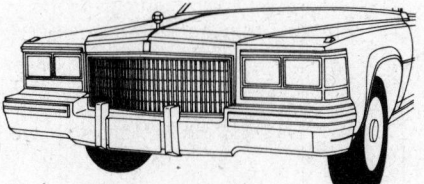

1980 Cadillac

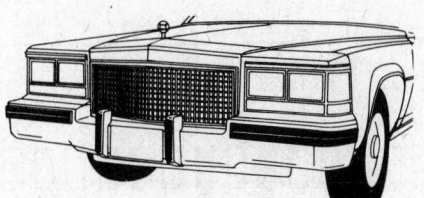

1981 Cadillac

1982–85 Cadillac

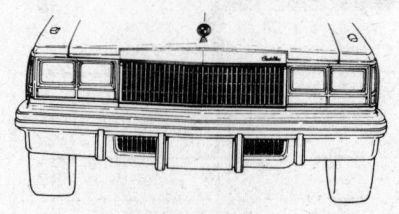

1977 Seville

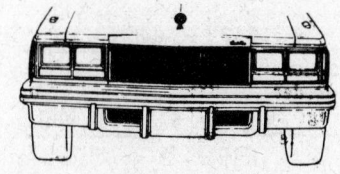

1978 Seville

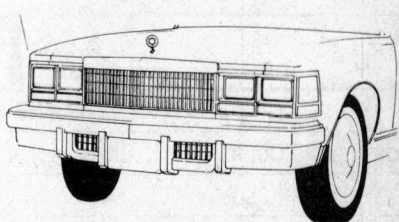

1979 Seville

VEHICLE IDENTIFICATION NUMBER (VIN)

It is important for servicing and ordering parts to be certain of the vehicle and engine identification. The VIN (vehicle identification number) is a 13 or 17 digit number visible through the windshield on the driver's side of the dash and contains the vehicle and engine identification codes. It can be interpreted as follows:

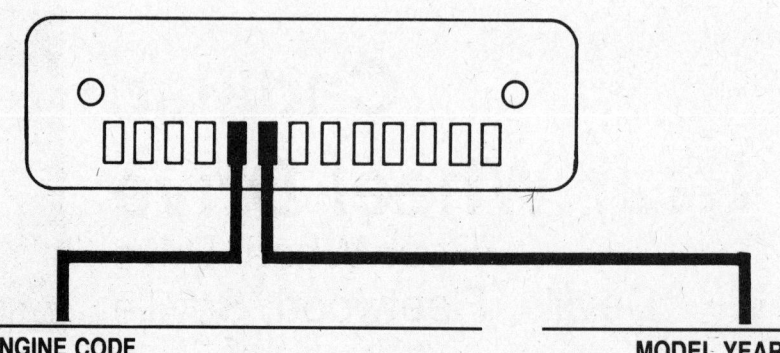

ENGINE CODE							MODEL YEAR CODE	
Code	Cu. In.	Liters	Cyl.	Carb.	Eng. Mfg.		Code	Year
R	350	5.7	8	EFI	Olds.		8	78
B	350	5.7	8	EFI	Olds.		9	79
N	350	5.7	8	Diesel	Olds.		A	80
6	368	6.0	8	4bbl	Cad.			
T	425	7.0	8	EFI	Cad.			
S	425	7.0	8	4bbl	Cad.			

The thirteen digit Vehicle Identification Number can be used to determine engine application and model year. The 6th digit indicates the model year, and the fifth digit identifies the factory installed engine.

VEHICLE IDENTIFICATION NUMBER (VIN)

It is important for servicing and ordering parts to be certain of the vehicle and engine identification. The VIN (vehicle identification number) is a 13 or 17 digit number visible through the windshield on the driver's side of the dash and contains the vehicle and engine identification codes. It can be interpreted as follows:

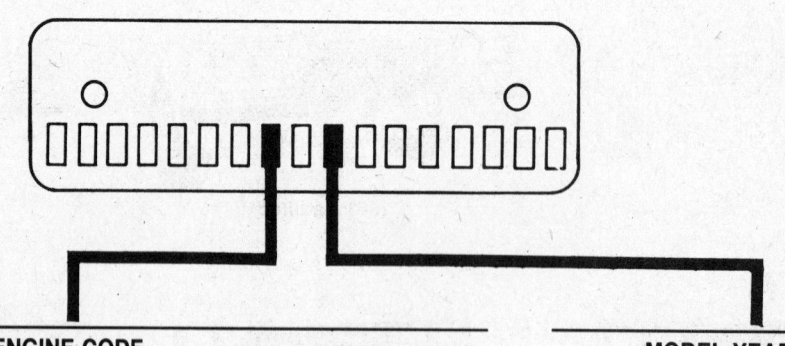

ENGINE CODE							MODEL YEAR CODE	
Code	Cu. In.	Liters	Cyl.	Carb.	Eng. Mfg.		Code	Year
8	250	4.1	8	DFI	Cad.		B	81
4	252	4.1	6	4bbl	Buick		C	82
N	350	5.7	8	Diesel	Olds.		D	83
9	368	6.0	8	EFI	Cad.		E	84
							F	85

The seventeen digit Vehicle Identification Number can be used to determine engine application and model year. The 10th digit indicates the model year, and the 8th digit identifies the factory installed engine.

GENERAL ENGINE SPECIFICATIONS

Year	Eng. V.I.N. Code	Engine Displacement Cu. In.	Eng. Mfg.	Fuel Delivery	Horsepower @ rpm ∎	Torque @ rpm (ft lbs) ∎	Bore x Stroke (in.)	Compression Ratio	Oil Pressure @ 2000 rpm
'78	S	425	Cad.	4 bbl	180 @ 3600	260 @ 2000	4.082 × 4.060	8.5:1	35
	T	425	Cad.	EFI	215 @ 3600	260 @ 2000	4.082 × 4.060	8.5:1	35
	B	350	Olds.	EFI	180 @ 4400	275 @ 2000	4.057 × 3.385	8.0:1	35
	N	350	Olds.	Diesel	120 @ 3600	220 @ 1800	4.057 × 3.385	22.0:1	40
'79	B	350	Olds.	EFI	170 @ 4200	270 @ 2000	4.057 × 3.385	8.5:1	35
	N	350	Olds.	Diesel	120 @ 3600	220 @ 2200	4.057 × 3.385	22.5:1	40
	S	425	Cad.	4 bbl	180 @ 4000	320 @ 2000	4.082 × 4.060	8.2:1	35
	T	425	Cad.	EFI	195 @ 3800	320 @ 2400	4.082 × 4.060	8.2:1	35
'80	N	350	Olds.	Diesel	105 @ 3200	205 @ 1600	4.057 × 3.385	22.5:1	40
	6	368	Cad.	4 bbl	150 @ 3800	265 @ 1600	3.800 × 4.060	8.2:1	35
'81-'82	N	350	Olds.	Diesel	105 @ 3200	205 @ 1600	4.057 × 3.385	22.5:1	40
	9	368	Cad.	DFI, DFI-MD	140 @ 3800	265 @ 1400	3.800 × 4.060	8.2:1	35
	8	250	Cad.	DFI	125 @ 4200	190 @ 2000	3.465 × 3.307	8.5:1	30
	4	252	Buick	4 bbl	125 @ 3800	210 @ 2000	3.965 × 3.400	8.0:1	35
'83	8	250	Cad.	DFI	135 @ 4200	190 @ 2000	3.465 × 3.307	8.5:1	30
	N	350	Olds.	Diesel	105 @ 3200	205 @ 1600	4.057 × 3.385	22.5:1	40
'84-'85	8	250	Cad.	DFI	135 @ 4400	200 @ 1600	3.465 × 3.307	8.5:1	30
	N	350	Olds.	Diesel	105 @ 3200	205 @ 1600	4.057 × 3.385	22.5:1	40

∎ Horsepower and torque are SAE net figures. They are measured at the rear of the transmission with all accessories installed and operating. Since the figures vary when a given engine is installed in different models, some are representative rather than exact.

EFI Electronic fuel injection

DFI-MD Digital Fuel Injection-Modulated Displacement

TUNE-UP SPECIFICATIONS

(When analyzing compression test results, look for uniformity among cylinders rather than specific pressures.)

Year	V.I.N. Code	Displacement (cu in.)	Mfg.	Fuel Delivery	Orig. Type	Gap (in.)	Point Dwell (deg)	Point Gap (in.)	Ignition Timing (deg) ▲ Auto. Trans.	Valves Intake Opens ■ (deg)	Fuel Pump Pressure (psi)	Idle Speed (rpm) ▲ Auto. Trans.
'78	S,T	425	Cad.	⑦	R-45NSX	.060	Electronic	—	18B @ 1400	21	5¼-6½	650
	B	350	Olds.	EFI	R-47SX	.060	Electronic	—	10B(8B)	22	5¼-6½	600
	N	350	Olds.	Diesel	—	—	—	—	5B①	16	8-12③	575
'79	B	350	Olds.	EFI	R-47SX	.060	Electronic	—	10B	22	5.5-6.5	600
	N	350	Olds.	Diesel	—	—	—	—	5B①	16	5.5-6.5③	600
	S,T	425	Cad.	⑦	R-45NSX	.060	Electronic	—	23B②	21	5.5-6.5	650
'80	N	350	Olds.	Diesel	—	—	—	—	5B①	16	5.5-6.5③	650/575
	6	368	Cad.	4 bbl	R-45NSX	.060	Electronic	—	18B	11	5.5-6.5	575
	4	252	Buick	4 bbl	R-45TSX	.060	Electronic	—	15B	16	4¼-5¾	550④
'81	9	368	Cad.	DFI-MD	R-45NSX	.060	Electronic	—	10B	11	12-14	450⑤
	N	350	Olds.	Diesel	—	—	—	—	—	16	5½-6½③	⑥
	4	252	Buick	4 bbl	R-45TSX	.060	Electronic	—	15B	16	4¼-5¾	550④
'82	9	368	Cad.	DFI	R-45NAX	.060	Electronic	—	⑧	11	12-14	450⑤
	N	350	Olds.	Diesel	—	—	—	—	⑧	16	5½-6½	⑥
	8	250	Cad.	DFI	R-43NTS6	.060	Electronic	—	⑧	37	12-14	450
	4	252	Buick	4 bbl	R-45TSX	.060	Electronic	—	⑧	16	4¼-5¾	550④
'83	8	250	Cad.	DFI	R-43NTS6	.060	Electronic	—	⑧	37	12-14	⑧
	N	350	Olds.	Diesel	—	—	—	—	⑧	16	5½-6½	⑧
'84-'85	8	250	Cad.	DFI	R-43NTS6	.060	Electronic	—	⑧	37	12-14	⑧
	N	350	Olds.	Diesel	—	—	—	—	⑧	16	5½-6½	⑧

NOTE: The underhood specifications sticker often reflects tune-up specification changes made in production. Sticker figures must be used if they disagree with those in this chart. Part numbers in this chart are not recommendations by Chilton for any product by brand name.

▲ See text for procedure
■ All figures Before Top Dead Center

B Before Top Dead Center
EFI Electronic fuel injection
DFI-MD Digital Fuel Injection-Modulated Displacement
— Not applicable
① Static
② EFI: 18B
③ Injector opening pressure: 1800 psi
④ In drive
⑤ Drive or neutral
⑥ 600 RPM in drive, warm engine; 750 RPM in drive, cold engine
⑦ Eng. Code "S"-4bbl., "T"-E.F.I.
⑧ See underhood decal

FIRING ORDERS

NOTE: To avoid confusion, always replace spark plugs and wires one at a time.

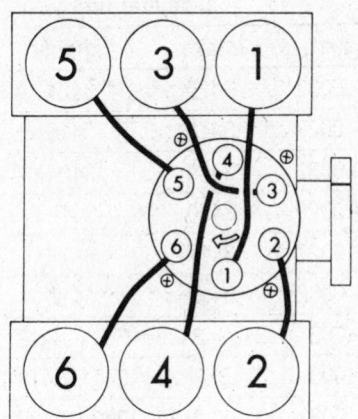

GM (Buick) 252 (4.1 L) V6
Engine firing order: 1-6-5-4-3-2
Distributor rotation: clockwise

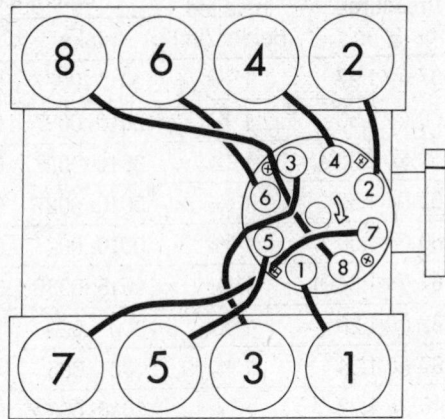

GM (Cadillac) 368,425,
V8 Engine firing order: 1-5-6-3-4-2-7-8
Distributor rotation: clockwise

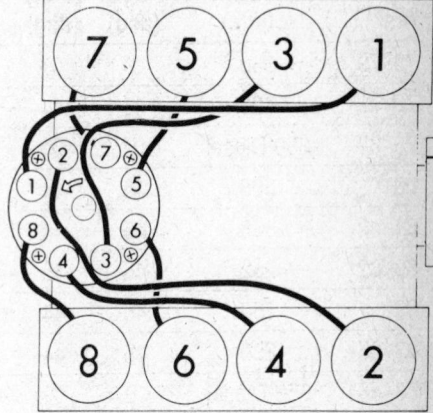

GM(Cadillac) 250 (4.1 L) V8,
GM(Oldsmobile) 350 V8 w/EFI
Engine firing order: 1-8-4-3-6-5-7-2
Distributor rotation: counterclockwise

CAPACITIES

Year	Engine Displacement (Cu. In.)	Engine Crankcase Add 1 Qt For New Filter	Transmission Automatic Pts To Refill After Draining ●	Drive Axle (pts)	Gasoline Tank (gals)	Cooling System (qts)	
						With Heater	With A/C
'78	350	4	8	4.25	21	18.9	18.9
'78	350 Diesel	6	6	4.25	21	18.9	18.9
'78	425	4	8	4.25	24	19.8	19.8
'79	425	4	9	4.25	①	20.8	20.8
'79	350	4	9	4.25	①	17.2	17.2
'79	350 Diesel	6	7	4.25	①	20.0	20.0
'80-'82	350 Diesel	6	6	4.25	27	23.7	23.7
'80	368	4	8	4.25	25	21.4	21.4
'81-'82	368	4	8	4.25	25	21.4	21.4
'81-'82	252	4	8	4.25	25	18.2	18.2
'82	250	4	8	4.25	25	10.8	10.8
'83-'85	250	4	10	4.25	24	11	11
'83-'85	350 Diesel	6	10	4.25	26	23	23

● Specifications do not include torque converter

① Seville—21; All others—25

VALVE SPECIFICATIONS

Year	Engine Displacement (cu in.)	Seat Angle (deg)	Face Angle (deg)	Spring Test Pressure (lbs @ in.)	Spring Installed Height (in.)	Stem-to-Guide Clearance (in.)		Stem Diameter (in.)	
						Intake	Exhaust	Intake	Exhaust
'78-'79	350	①	②	187 @ 1.27	1⁴³⁄₆₄	.0010-.0027	.0015-.0032	.3429	.3424
'78-'79	425	45	44	160 @ 1.50	1¹⁵⁄₁₆	.0010-.0027	.0010-.0027	.3416	.3416
'78-'82	350 Diesel	①	②	151 @ 1.30④	1⁴⁷⁄₆₄	.0010-.0027	.0015-.0032	.3429	.3424
'80	368	45	44	160 @ 1.50	1¹⁵⁄₃₂	.0010-.0027	.0012-.0029	.3420	.3418
'81-'82	368	45	44	160 @ 1.50	1¹⁵⁄₃₂	.0010-.0027	.0010-.0027	.3417	.3417
'80-'82	252	45	45	164 @ 1.34③	1¹¹⁄₃₂	.0015-.0035	.0015-.0032	.3412	.3412
'82	250	45	44	182 @ 1.28	1⁴³⁄₆₄	.001-.003	.001-.003	.3413-.3420	.3411-.3418
'83-'85	250	45	44	167 @ 1.34	1⁴³⁄₆₄	.001-.003	.001-.003	.3413-.3420	.3411-.3418
'83-'85	350 Diesel	①	②	210 @ 1.22	1⁴⁷⁄₆₄	.0010-.0027	.0015-.0032	.3425-.3432	.3420-.3427

① Intake 45°; exhaust 31°
② Intake 44°; exhaust 30°
③ Exhaust 182 @ 1.34
④ 210 @ 1.30—1981-82

CRANKSHAFT AND CONNECTING ROD SPECIFICATIONS

(All measurements are given in inches)

Year	Engine Displacement (cu in.)	Crankshaft				Connecting Rod		
		Main Brg. Journal Dia	Main Brg. Oil Clearance	Shaft End-Play	Thrust on No.	Journal Diameter	Oil Clearance	Side Clearance
'79	350	2.4985-2.4995①	.0005-.0021②	.004-.014	3	2.1238-2.1248	.0004-.0033	.006-.020
'78-'79	425	3.250	.0001-.0026	.002-.012	3	2.6243-2.6250	.0005-.0028	.008-.020
'78-'82	350 Diesel	2.9993-3.0003	.0005-.0021②	.004-.014	3	2.1238-2.1248	.0005-.0026	.006-.020
'80-'82	368	3.250	.0001-.0026	.002-.012	3	2.5000	.0005-.0028	.008-.020
'81-'82	252	2.4995	.0003-.0018	.003-.009	2	2.2487-2.2495	.0005-.0026	.006-.023
'81-'82	250	2.640	.0004-.003	.001-.007	3	1.9300	.0005-.0028	.008-.020
'83-'85	250	2.64	.0004-.0027	.001-.007	3	2.052-2.054	.0005-.0028	.008-.020
'83-'85	350 Diesel	2.9993-3.0003	.0005-.0021②	.004-.014	3	2.1238-2.1248	.0005-.0026	.006-.020

① No. 1—2.4988-2.4998 in.
② No. 5—.0015-.0031 in.

TORQUE SPECIFICATIONS

(All readings in ft lbs)

Year	Engine Displacement (cu in.)	Cylinder Head Bolts	Rod Bearing Bolts	Main Bearing Bolts	Crankshaft Bolt	Flywheel-to-Crankshaft Bolts	Manifold Intake	Manifold Exhaust
'78-'80	350	130	42	80②	310	60	40	25
'78-'79	425	95	40	90	Press fit	75	30	①
'78-'82	350 Diesel	130③	42	120	200-310	60	40③	25
'80-'82	368	95③	40	90	Press fit	75	30	①
'81-'82	252	80	40	100	225	60	45	25
'82-'85	250	④	20	85	Press fit	20	⑤	20
'83-'85	8-350 Diesel	130③	42	120	200-310	60	40④	25

N.A. Not Available
① Long bolt—35, Short bolt—12
② 120 ft lbs. on No. 5
③ Dip bolt in oil before tightening
④ Tighten all bolts in sequence to 45 ft. lbs., then in sequence to 90 ft. lbs.
⑤ Tighten bolts 1, 2, 3, 4 in sequence to 11-15 ft. lbs.; tighten bolts 5 thru 16 to 18-22 ft. lbs., Retighten all bolts in sequence to 18-22 ft. lbs.

PISTON AND RING SPECIFICATIONS

Year	Engine Displ. Cu. In.	Piston-Bore Clearance	Ring Side Clearance Top Compression	Ring Side Clearance Bottom Compression	Ring Side Clearance Oil Control	Ring Gap Top Compression	Ring Gap Bottom Compression	Ring Gap Oil Control
'78-'79	350	.0010–.0020	.0020–.0040	.0020–.0040	.0006–.0096	.010–.023	.010–.023	.015–.055
	350 Diesel	.0005–.0006	.005–.007	.0018–.0038	.0078 max.	.015–.025	.015–.025	.015–.055
	425	.0006–.0014	.0017–.0040	.0017–.0040	None①	.013–.023	.013–.023	.015–.055
	500	.0006–.0010	.0017–.0040	.0017–.0040	None①	.013–.025	.013–.025	.015–.055
'80-'82	252	.0013–.0035	.0030–.0050	.0030–.0050	.0035 max.	.013–.023	.013–.023	.015–.035
	250	.0010–.0018	.0016–.0037	.0016–.0037	None①	.009–.020	.009–.020	.010–.050
	350	.0010–.0020	.0020–.0040	.0020–.0040	.0006–.0096	.010–.023	.010–.023	.015–.055
	350 Diesel	.0005–.0006	.005–.007	.0018–.0038	.0078 max.	.015–.025	.015–.025	.015–.055
	368	.0006–.0014	.0017–.0040	.0017–.0040	None①	.013–.023	.013–.023	.015–.055
'83-'85	8-250	.0008	.0016–.0037	.0016–.0037	None①	.015–.025	.015–.025	.010–.050
	8-350 Diesel	.0035–.0045	.005–.007	.003–.005	.001–.005	.019–.027	.013–.021	.015–.055

① Side sealing

CADILLAC REAR WHEEL DRIVE

RIDE HEIGHT ADJUSTMENT SPECIFICATIONS

Model and Year	Front Suspension		Rear Suspension	
	Inches	MM	Inches	MM
Brougham				
'78-'79	1⁷⁄₈-2⁵⁄₈	48-67	5³⁄₈-6¹⁄₈	137-161
'80-'85 W/ALC (Gas)	1¹¹⁄₁₆-2½	43-63	4³⁄₄-5¹⁷⁄₃₂	120-140
'80-'85 W/O ALC (Diesel)	1⁷⁄₈-2⁵⁄₈	47-67	5⁵⁄₁₆-6⁵⁄₆₄	134-154
'80-'85 W/O ALC (Gas)	1¹³⁄₁₆-2¹²⁄₃₂	45-65	5⁹⁄₃₂-6¹⁄₁₆	134-154
DeVille, Calais				
'77-'79 W/O ALC	2¹⁄₈-2⁷⁄₈	54-73	5³⁄₄-6½	146-170
'77-'79 W/ALC	2¹⁄₈-2⁷⁄₈	54-73	5³⁄₄-6½	146-170
'80-'85 W/ALC (Diesel)	1³⁄₄-2⁹⁄₁₆	45-65	4²⁵⁄₃₂-5⁹⁄₁₆	121-141
'80-'85 W/ALC (Gas)	1¹¹⁄₁₆-2½	43-63	4³⁄₄-5¹⁷⁄₃₂	120-140
'80-'85 W/O ALC (Diesel)	1⁷⁄₈-2⁵⁄₈	46-66	5¹⁄₈-5¹⁵⁄₁₆	130-150
'80-'85 W/O ALC (Gas)	1¹³⁄₁₆-2¹²⁄₃₂	45-65	5⁷⁄₆₄-5²⁹⁄₃₂	129-140
Seville				
'77-'79 W/ALC Disconnected	2½	63	3½	89
'77-'79 W/ALC Connected	2½	63	3⁷⁄₈	98

ALC—Automatic Load Control

WHEEL ALIGNMENT SPECIFICATIONS

Year	Model	Caster		Camber		Toe-in (in.)	Steering Axis Inclin. (deg)
		Range (deg)	Pref Setting (deg)	Range (deg)	Pref Setting (deg)		
'78	Cadillac	2½P to 3½P	3P	⅛P to ⅞P	½P	¹⁄₁₆N to ¹⁄₁₆P	5
'78	Seville	1½P to 2½P	2P	⅜N to ⅜P	0	0 to ⅛	5
'79	Seville	1½P to 2½P	2P	⅜N to ⅜P	0	0 to ⅛	10.35
'79	Cadillac	2½P to 3½P	3P	⅛P to ⅞P	½P	¹⁄₁₆N to ¹⁄₁₆P	10.59
'80-'85	Cadillac	2P to 3P	2½P	½N to ½P	0	½N to ½P	10¹⁹⁄₃₂

N Negative   P Positive

CHARGING SYSTEM

For further information on the charging system, please refer to "Charging and Starting" in the Unit Repair section.

Alternator

REMOVAL & INSTALLATION

1. Disconnect the negative battery cable.
2. Disconnect the electrical leads from the alternator.
3. Remove the screw from the alternator adjusting bracket.
4. Remove the screw from the rear of the alternator, retaining the shims for reinstallation.
5. Loosen the alternator pivot bolt and remove the drive belt.
6. Remove the air pump pulley for access to the pump bolt behind the pulley.
7. Loosen the two screws securing the front bracket to the engine.
8. Remove the alternator, spacer and lower through bolt by twisting the alternator toward the fender for clearance.
9. Install the alternator in the reverse order of removal.

NOTE: On Heavy Duty Alternator ONLY (100/145 amp. with external voltage adjuster): after connecting the negative cable, momentarily connect a jumper wire between "Bat" and "R" alternator terminals to polarize the charging system. Start the engine and run it at fast idle for ten seconds; the charge light should go out.

STARTING SYSTEM

Cadillac V8 starter motors are located on the right hand side of the engine; on the 350 V8, both gasoline and diesel, it is on the left side.

The diesel engine starter is of conventional design, but somewhat larger and with a greater power output to turn the engine at least 100 rpm for starting.

For further information on the starting system, please refer to "Charging and Starting" in the Unit Repair section.

Starter

REMOVAL & INSTALLATION

1. Disconnect the negative battery terminal, jack up the car and support it with jack stands.

2. Disconnect the battery lead and the wires from the solenoid.
3. Remove the bolt that holds the support bracket to the starter.
4. Remove the two starter-to-engine bolts.
5. Remove the starter by pulling it forward and down.
6. To install, reverse the removal procedure.

NOTE: On some models it may be necessary to remove the crossover pipe to complete this procedure.

IGNITION SYSTEM

The High Energy Ignition system is standard equipment on all models. The HEI system consists of an ignition coil, electronic module and a magnetic pick-up assembly all within the distributor.

A terminal in the top of the distributor cap is provided for the connection of a tachometer. The terminal is marked TACH.

Starting 1978, an electronic spark selection system was introduced on the 350 V8. It was used through mid-1980. The system continuously and automatically controls ignition system spark advance (or retard) to improve fuel economy, reduce emissions, and aid hot starting.

Unlike the gasoline engine, which is a spark-ignition design, the diesel engine is a compression-ignition type. When air is highly compressed, high temperatures are produced. At the moment of peak compression a small quantity of fuel is sprayed, under high pressure, into the combustion chambers. The temperature of compression ignites the tiny fuel droplets. A temperature of about 1750°F is required for ignition. Glow plugs are required, as an aid to cold starting.

For more details on the ignition system, please refer to "Electronic Ignition Systems" in the Unit Repair section.

Distributor

REMOVAL

Unplug (HEI) and remove the distributor cap. On EFI cars, disconnect the speed sensor connector at the distributor trigger. Disconnect the vacuum line. Disconnect the primary lead at the distributor.

Using a scribe mark, index the distributor body to the cylinder block, and the tip of the rotor to the distributor housing so that the distributor body will be correctly replaced at reassembly. Remove the clamp bolt or nut and distributor.

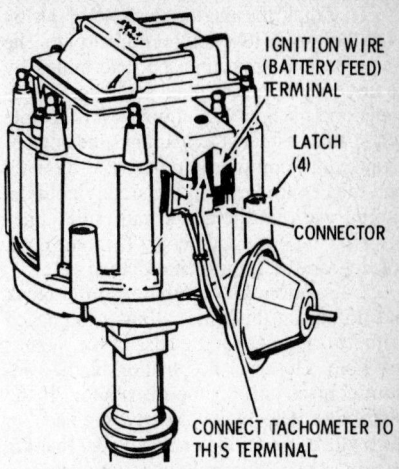

HEI tachometer hookup

NOTE: On the 4.1–250 cu. in. V-8 engine a special tool No. J-29791 is used to loosen the hold down nut.

NOTE: On the 4.1–250 cu. in. V8 engine, a thrust washer is used between the distributor drive gear and the crankcase. This washer may stick to the bottom of the distributor as it is removed. Make sure this washer is at the bottom of the distributor bore before installation.

NOTE: On DFI systems (Digital Fuel Injection), the malfunction trouble codes must be cleared after removal or adjustment of the distributor. This is accomplished by removing battery voltage to terminal "R" for 10 seconds. See the CCC system in the "Emission Controls" of the Unit Repair section for an explanation.

INSTALLATION

Install the distributor so that the vacuum advance unit aligns with the match-mark made at removal. Turn the rotor slightly left of center so that as the gear engages the camshaft it will revolve into the proper position, pointing to the No. 1 contact in the cap.

Install the hold-down clamp. Connect the primary lead and install the cap. Rotate the lubricator. Plug the distributor vacuum line to the carburetor. Connect a timing light to the No. 1 spark plug wire. Clean the crankshaft pulley markings and the pointer. Set the timing to specifications. Tighten the clamp bolt or nut. Remove the plug and adapter pin and reconnect the vacuum line to the advance unit.

INSTALLATION (ENGINE DISTURBED)

If the engine has been disturbed (cranked) after removing the distributor, perform the following procedure for installation:

1. Crank the engine until no. 1 piston is at the top of its compression stroke. The compression stroke can be determined by removing the spark plug from no. 1 cylinder and placing your thumb over the hole while an assistant slowly cranks the engine. Crank until compression is felt at the hole and then continue cranking slowly until the timing mark on the crankshaft pulley lines up with the zero degrees (0°) timing mark located on the timing chain cover.

2. Position the distributor in the block but do not, at this time, allow it to engage with its drive gear at the base of the mounting hole. Observe the position of the vacuum control unit on the distributor. If the distributor is located correctly, the vacuum unit will be positioned normally so that the vacuum hose can easily connect to it.

3. Rotate the distributor shaft so that the rotor points between No. 1 and No. 8 spark plug towers and push the distributor down to engage the camshaft. It may be necessary to turn the rotor a small amount in either direction in order to achieve this engagement. The rotor will rotate slightly as the distributor gear engages. If installed correctly, the rotor should point toward the No. 1 spark plug terminal in the distributor cap.

4. Press down firmly on the distributor housing. This will ensure that the distributor shaft engages the oil pump shaft, thereby allowing the distributor to fully contact the engine block.

5. Install the hold-down clamp and tighten the bolt until it is snug.

6. Install the distributor cap, making sure that the rotor points to No. 1 terminal in the cap.

7. Attach all wires and the vacuum advance hose.

8. Start the engine. If it fails to start, or runs roughly, the distributor may be 180° out of time. Lift up on the distributor, turn the rotor one-half revolution, and install the distributor. Repeat steps 1–8 if the engine continues to run poorly.

9. Check the timing and change it as necessary.

IGNITION TIMING

1. Loosen the distributor hold-down bolt so that the distributor can be turned without being too loose.

NOTE: On the 4.1-250 cu. in. V-8 engine a special tool No. J-29791 is used to loosen the hold down nut.

2. Follow the instructions on the tune up label located in the engine compartment.

3. Connect the timing light. With HEI, connect it at the No. 1 distributor terminal. Make certain that the timing marks are visible.

4. Connect a tachometer to the engine following the manufacturer's hook-up directions. Secure the parking brake and block the wheels. Start the engine and place the selector in Drive.

NOTE: Do not stand in front of the vehicle while performing the next step.

5. Adjust the idle speed to the specified rpm, then place the transmission in Park or Neutral.

6. Point the timing light at the pulley and observe the notch in the pulley in relation to the notches on the front cover. Check the specification chart for the correct timing setting.

7. If the setting is not correct, rotate the distributor until the correct timing is obtained. Tighten the distributor clamp nut and recheck the timing.

8. Reconnect all vacuum hoses.

FUEL SYSTEM

CARBURETED GASOLINE ENGINES

The standard Cadillac fuel system (except Seville) includes the fuel pump, fuel filter, lines, carburetor and intake manifold.

DIESEL ENGINE

The diesel engine is produced by General Motor's Oldsmobile division. Details on the diesel fuel system can be found in the "Oldsmobile" car section.

FUEL INJECTED GASOLINE ENGINES

Electronic Fuel Injection is standard on Cadillac Sevilles through 1979 and optional on 1978 and later full size models.

For more information on fuel injection, please refer to "Fuel Injection" in the Unit Repair section.

A microprocessor Digital Fuel Injection (DFI) system was introduced in 1980 on Cadillac Sevilles. The DFI system is now standard on all 1981 and later 6.0 liter 368 cu. in. and 1982 and later 4.1 liter 250 cu. in. engines. Not only is the air/fuel mixture monitored and controlled by the DFI, but also the electronic spark timing, idle speed and EGR control. The system also incorporates a diagnostic readout of problems or system malfunctions.

The EFI system consists of four basic subsystems: the fuel delivery system, air induction system, the network of sensors, and the electronic control unit (ECU). The DFI system includes the same subsystems as the EFI, uses a more detailed digital electronic control module (ECM) and adds four more subsystems. The additional subsystems are; the electronic spark timing system (EST), idle speed control system (ISC), EGR control system, and the failure operation circuit and diagnostics readout system.

Fuel Pump and Filter

The fuel pump on carbureted engines is mounted on the left-hand side of the engine. The pump is operated by an eccentric on the camshaft. The fuel filter is mounted in the carburetor behind the fuel inlet nut. A check valve is included in the fuel filter. On air conditioned cars, the fuel filter has a passage and a connecting line to the fuel tank to return fuel vapors to the tank under high temperature conditions.

Vehicles with EFI have two electric fuel pumps; one is mounted in the fuel tank and is integral with the fuel level sending unit and the other, a chassis-mounted pump, is located in front of the rear axle either on the right or left side. A fuel filter is mounted on a bracket at the lower left front of the engine. On Seville models the fuel filter is mounted on the left side of the frame near the fuel pump.

Vehicles with DFI have one, in-tank, fuel pump. The fuel filter is located on the left side of the chassis just ahead of the rear axle.

Fuel Pump

REMOVAL & INSTALLATION

Carbureted Engines

1. Raise and support the car on jackstands.

2. Disconnect the fuel line and the vapor return hose from the fuel pump. Have a towel handy to catch any fuel that leaks out. Plug the hoses.

3. Disconnect the fuel pump-to-carburetor line and position it out of the way.

4. Remove the pump mounting screws and, tipping the pump upward, remove it from the car.

5. Installation is the reverse of removal. Remember to use a new gasket.

Fuel Injected Engines

CHASSIS-MOUNTED PUMP: EFI SYSTEM

— CAUTION —
Fuel is under high pressure; if the steps below are not followed, the fuel could spray out and result in a fire hazard and possible injury.

1. Disconnect the negative battery terminal.

2. Locate the pressure fitting in the fuel line and remove the protective cap.

3. Loosely install a special valve depressor (G.M. tool no. J-5420) on the fitting.

4. Wrap a towel around the fitting to block any spray and slowly tighten the tool until the pressure has been relieved.

5. Remove the tool and reinstall the protective cap.

6. Remove the fuel hoses from the pump.

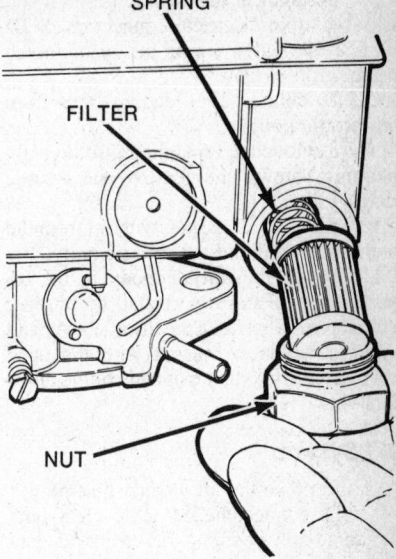
7. Peel back the rubber boot and remove the two nuts, one from each electrical terminal. Remove the electrical leads.

NOTE: These nuts have metric threads.

8. Remove the two screws and flat washers holding the fuel pump to the bracket and remove the pump assembly.

9. Install the fuel pump in the reverse order of removal. Connect the green wire to the positive terminal on the pump and the black wire to the negative terminal. Check to make sure the fuel pump is resting evenly on its two mounts and not grounding against the bracket or frame.

IN-TANK PUMP: DFI AND EFI SYSTEMS

1. Disconnect the negative battery terminal, open the fuel tank filler door and disconnect the sending unit feed wire.

2. Siphon the fuel from the fuel tank. If the rear of the car is raised one foot higher than the front, more fuel can be taken out.

3. Raise the rear of the car and remove the screw securing the ground wire to the cross member.

4. Disconnect the fuel line, evaporative emission lines and the fuel return lines at the front of the tank.

5. Support the tank with a jack and wooden block and remove one screw on each side securing the fuel tank support straps to the body at the front of the tank.

6. Lower the jack and tank enough so that the fuel pump electrical lead can be disconnected. Disconnect the wire.

7. Remove the fuel tank from the car.

8. Remove the locknuts securing the fuel gauge tank unit and fuel pump feed wires to the tank unit.

9. Turn the cam locking ring counterclockwise with a soft non-ferrous punch and hammer. When the lock ring is disengaged, remove it and lift the gauge/pump unit from the tank.

10. Install in the reverse order of removal. Tighten the fuel tank retaining strap screws to 25 ft. lbs.

Filter

REMOVAL & INSTALLATION

Carbureted Engines

1. Disconnect the fuel line at the carburetor inlet.

2. Remove the fuel inlet nut from the carburetor using a box wrench.

3. Remove the fuel filter element and spring.

4. Install the filter spring and new fuel filter element into the carburetor.

5. Install a new gasket on the fuel inlet nut and install the nut.

6. Connect the fuel line to the fuel inlet nut and tighten securely. Start the engine and check for leaks.

Fuel Injected Engines

NOTE: The fuel filter element can be replaced by unscrewing the bottom cover and removing it.

1. Bleed the pressure from the fuel delivery system as outlined in Steps 1–4 of the ''Chassis-Mounted Fuel Pump'' removal procedure and remove the fuel inlet and outlet hoses from the fuel filter.

2. Remove the two screws retaining the fuel filter to the bracket and remove the filter from the engine or frame.

3. Remove the inlet and outlet fittings from the filter assembly if they are needed for the new filter.

4. Install the fittings to the new filter, using a sealer on the threads.

5. Attach the filter to the bracket and tighten the retaining screws to 12 ft lbs.

6. Connect the inlet and outlet line, using new clamps.

NOTE: It may require considerable cranking before the engine starts due to the drained fuel lines.

Throttle Body

REMOVAL & INSTALLATION

EFI System

1. Remove the air cleaner.

2. Disconnect the two throttle return springs from the throttle lever.

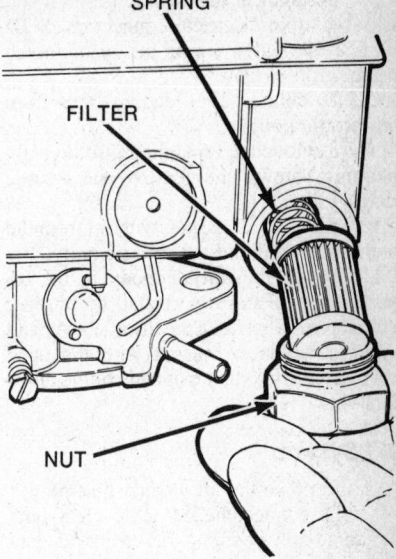

Fuel filter—typical of all carbureted models

3. Remove the cruise control chain retainer and chain, if so equipped.

4. Remove the clip and disconnect the throttle cable from the throttle lever.

5. Remove the left rear throttle body mounting screw and remove the one screw holding the throttle bracket to the intake manifold.

6. Remove the downshift switch from the throttle lever and position bracket. Move the switch and linkage aside.

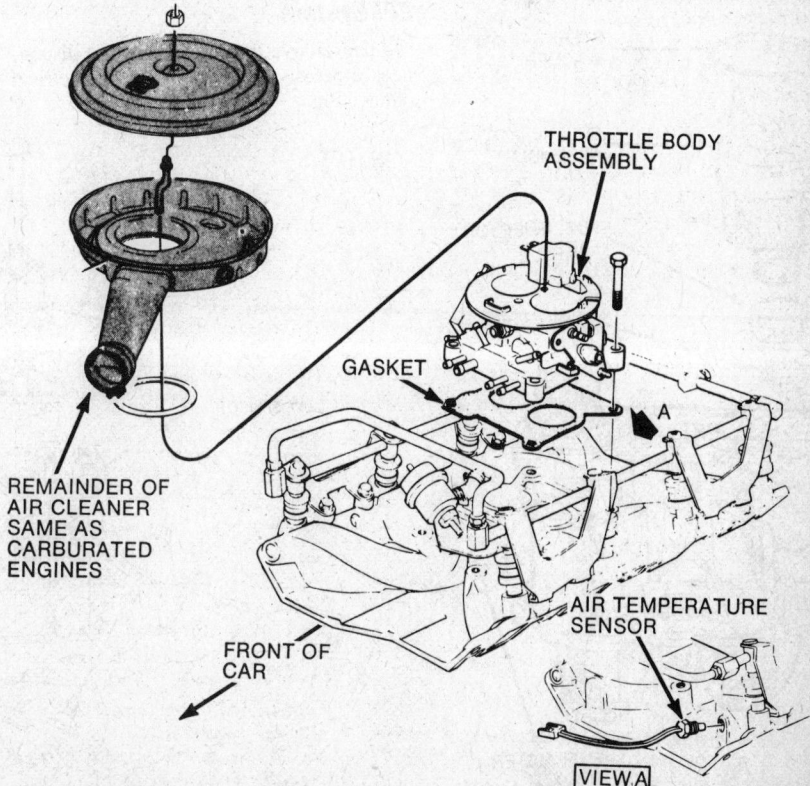

Mounting of the throttle body assembly and air temperature sensor—EFI
(© Cadillac Div., G.M. Corp.)

7. Disconnect the throttle position and fast idle valve electrical connectors. Slide the fast idle valve wiring out of the notch in the throttle body.

8. Disconnect the vacuum lines from the throttle body.

9. Remove the remaining throttle body retaining screws and remove the throttle body.

10. Remove all gasket material from the intake manifold and the throttle body.

11. Install the throttle body in the reverse order of removal. Install the throttle return springs between the throttle lever and pressure regulator bracket with the open end of the spring on the outside of the throttle lever.

DFI System

1. Remove the air cleaner assembly.

2. Disconnect the ISC motor, IPS, both injectors, and position the electrical connections out of the way.

3. Remove both throttle return springs, cruise control, throttle linkage, and downshift cable.

4. Disconnect the fuel inlet and return line, brake booster line, MAP hose and AIR hose from the rear of the throttle body.

5. Remove the PCV, EVAP, and EGR hoses from the front of the throttle body.

6. Remove the three throttle body mounting bolts and remove the throttle body and gasket.

7. Installation is the reverse of removal. After installation, check and adjust the throttle position sensor (TPS) and the idle speed control (ISC) motor as necessary.

Throttle Position Switch

REMOVAL & INSTALLATION

EFI System

NOTE: The throttle position switch is an electrical unit—do not immerse in any cleaner. Use care to avoid damage to the switch or wiring.

1. Remove the throttle body from the engine.

2. Remove the two mounting screws and remove the switch from the throttle body.

3. Install the switch on the right side of the throttle body so that the tab on the switch engages the flat on the throttle shaft.

4. Install the two mounting screws and tighten the screws so that the switch will move but is still firmly attached.

5. Adjust the throttle position switch as outlined under "Adjustments".

6. Reinstall the throttle body.

Fast Idle Valve

REMOVAL & INSTALLATION

EFI System

1. Remove the air cleaner and disconnect the fast idle valve heater electrical connection.

2. Remove the air cleaner mounting stud.

3. Push down and twist the fast idle valve heater counterclockwise 90° to remove it.

4. Remove the fast idle valve, spring and seat from the throttle body.

5. Install the fast idle valve seat, spring and valve in the throttle body.

6. Position the heater on top of the fast idle valve and push it down to compress the spring. Be careful to avoid damaging the micro-switch contact arm on the bottom of the heater housing.

7. Align the tabs on the fast idle valve heater with the cut-out portion of the throttle body and compress the spring further.

8. Rotate the heater clockwise 90° to secure it in position.

9. Connect the electrical lead and install the air cleaner stud and air cleaner.

Fuel Injector

REMOVAL & INSTALLATION

Except Seville: EFI Systems

———— CAUTION ————
Use a back-up wrench when removing the fuel lines to avoid kinking the lines.

1. Relieve the pressure from the fuel system as outlined in Steps 1–4 of the "Chassis-Mounted Fuel Pump" removal procedure.

2. Remove the pressure regulator-to-front fuel line securing clamp.

3. Remove the flare nut from each end of the fuel line.

4. Disconnect the front line from the pressure regulator and remove it from the car.

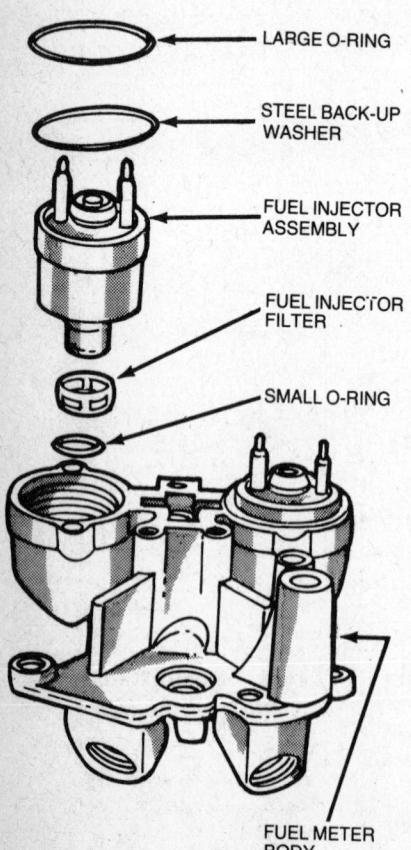

— LARGE O-RING

— STEEL BACK-UP WASHER

— FUEL INJECTOR ASSEMBLY

— FUEL INJECTOR FILTER

— SMALL O-RING

FUEL METER BODY

Fuel injector removal-DFI System

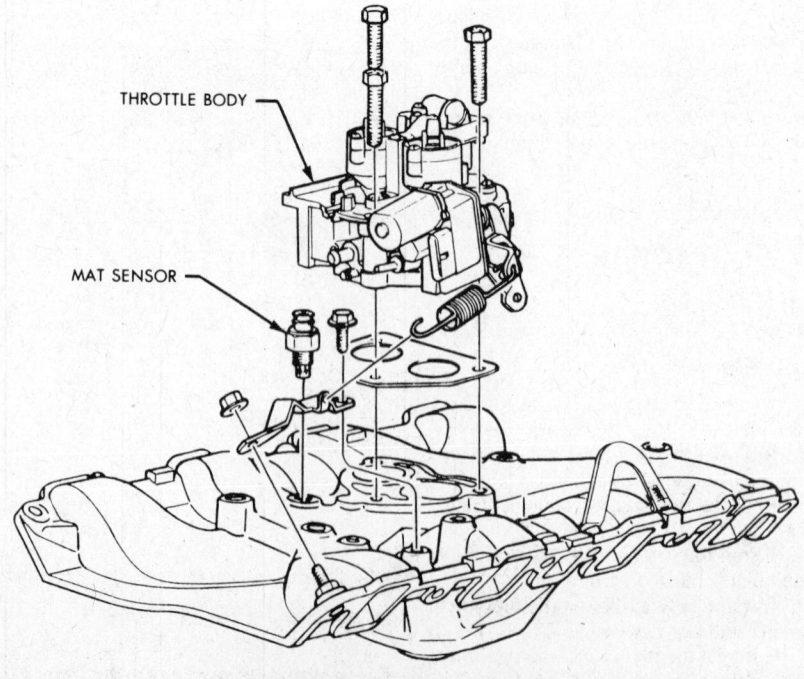

THROTTLE BODY

MAT SENSOR

Throttle body installation-DFI System (© Cadillac Div., G.M. Corp.)

5. Remove the fuel inlet line from the rear fuel line.

6. Remove the flare nut at each side line and remove the rear fuel line.

7. Remove the electrical wiring from the injector brackets.

8. Remove the two screws holding each injector bracket to the intake manifold and remove the brackets and grommets.

9. Disconnect the electrical lead from all of the injectors on the fuel rail being removed.

10. Remove the fuel rail and injectors from the engine as an assembly. Some injectors may stick to the intake manifold and others will come off with the fuel rail. Remove the injectors from the fuel rail and manifold as required.

11. Remove and discard all of the used O-rings used to seal the injectors at the fuel rail and intake manifold.

12. Before installing the new O-ring seals, lubricate them with a suitable lubricant and install the O-rings on the fuel rail end of each injector.

13. Install the injectors into the fuel rail with the electrical connector facing inward.

14. Install new O-rings into each injector port in the intake manifold.

15. Install the fuel rail/injector assembly to the intake manifold. Make certain that each injector is properly positioned in the manifold O-ring.

16. Install the rubber grommets, flanges down, on the fuel rail and install the injector brackets in position.

17. Install and tighten the bracket retaining screws to 5 ft. lbs.

18. Route and secure the electrical harness along the bracket. Connect all eight injectors as follows: the two front and two rear cylinders' injectors are connected to the red/black wires; the four center cylinders' injectors are connected to the black/white wires.

19. Install the front and rear fuel rails.

20. Turn the ignition on and off a few times to build up fuel pressure in the system and check for leaks.

21. Start the engine and check for leaks. It may require considerable cranking to start the engine due to the drained condition of the fuel lines.

Seville: EFI System

─────── CAUTION ───────
Use a back-up wrench when disconnecting the fuel lines to avoid kinking the lines.

1. Disconnect the electrical lead from all injectors on the fuel line which are being removed. Position the wiring out of the way.

2. Relieve the fuel system pressure as outlined in Steps 1–4 of the "Chassis-Mounted Fuel Pump" removal procedure.

3. Remove the fuel inlet line at the fuel rail.

4. Disconnect the return hose and the vacuum hose at the pressure regulator.

5. Disconnect the fuel line from the pressure regulator.

6. Remove the injector brackets attaching screws and remove the brackets.

7. Remove the fuel line and the injectors as a unit.

8. Reverse to install, using new O-rings.

DFI Systems

1. Disconnect the negative battery terminal.

2. Remove the air cleaner assembly.

3. Disconnect the Idle Speed Control (ISC) motor and the Throttle Position Sensor (TPS).

4. Remove the screws securing the pressure regulator assembly and remove the regulator.

5. Use a small pair of pliers to gently grasp the center collar of the injector (between the electrical terminals) and carefully remove the injectors with a lifting-twisting motion.

6. Discard the upper and lower O-rings. Note the presence of the backup washer under the upper O-ring.

7. Installation is the reverse of removal. Lubricate the new O-rings with oil prior to installing them on the injector.

NOTE: Do not attempt to make any adjustments to the pressure regulator during this procedure as all adjustments are preset at the factory.

Fuel Pressure Regulator

REMOVAL & INSTALLATION
EFI System

─────── CAUTION ───────
When disconnecting the fuel lines, use a back-up wrench to avoid kinking the lines.

1. Remove the vacuum hose from the top of the pressure regulator.

2. Bleed off the pressure in the fuel delivery system as outlined in Steps 1–4 of the "Chassis-Mounted Fuel Pump" removal procedure and disconnect the flexible fuel hose between the fuel rail and the regulator. Disconnect the fuel return line.

3. Remove the one nut securing the pressure regulator to the bracket. This nut has metric threads.

4. Remove the regulator.

5. Install the regulator in the reverse order of removal.

Carbureted Engine

IDLE SPEED AND MIXTURE ADJUSTMENTS

Changes have been made in the carburetors for these model years that make idle speed and mixture adjustments impossible without the use of a propane enrichment system which is not readily available to the general public.

Most 1979 and later carburetors have mixture needles concealed under staked-in screws. Mixture adjustments are possible only during carburetor overhaul.

NOTE: Vehicles equipped with the Computer Command Control System can't use the propane enrichment or lean drop methods of idle mixture adjustment.

Fuel Injected Engine

IDLE SPEED ADJUSTMENT

NOTE: No idle speed adjustments are possible on the DFI system.

EFI

1. Adjust the ignition timing to the correct specifications.

2. Disconnect and plug the distributor vacuum line at the distributor, the parking brake release cylinder vacuum line at the release cylinder, and the air leveling compressor hose at the air cleaner. Set the parking brake and block the wheels.

3. Connect a tachometer to the engine, start it, allow the engine to reach normal operating temperature.

4. Place the transmission selector in Drive, and turn the air conditioning Off.

5. Loosen the lock nut on the idle by-pass adjusting screw on the front of the throttle body. On Seville, a conventional spring-loaded adjusting screw is used.

6. Using an allen wrench, adjust the idle by-pass adjusting screw to obtain an idle speed of 600 rpm for the 1978 Seville, 650 rpm for the full size Cadillac, and 600 rpm for the 1979 and later Eldorado and Seville.

7. Tighten the lock nut on the adjusting screw, stop the engine, remove the tachometer, and install the air cleaner and vacuum hoses.

Throttle Position Switch

ADJUSTMENT
EFI

1. Loosen the two throttle position switch mounting screws.

2. While holding the throttle valves in the idle position, turn the throttle position switch counterclockwise carefully until the end-stop is reached.

3. Tighten the mounting screws.

4. Check and make sure that the throttle valves close to the throttle stop. Readjust, if necessary.

5. Rotate the throttle lever until the first click is heard. Insert a feeler gauge between the throttle lever and the idle stop screw.

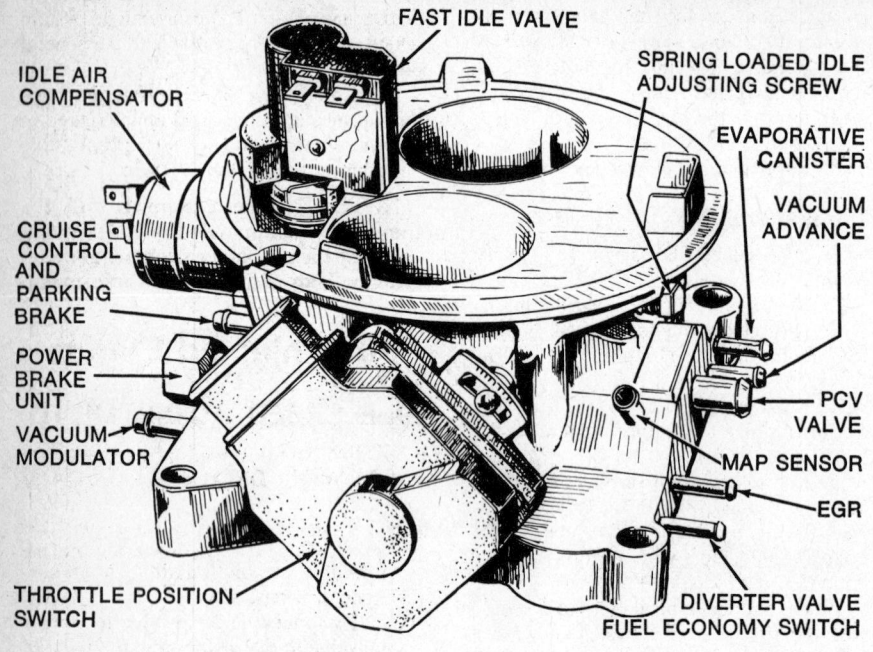

IDLE AIR COMPENSATOR

FAST IDLE VALVE

SPRING LOADED IDLE ADJUSTING SCREW

EVAPORATIVE CANISTER

VACUUM ADVANCE

CRUISE CONTROL AND PARKING BRAKE

POWER BRAKE UNIT

VACUUM MODULATOR

PCV VALVE

MAP SENSOR

EGR

THROTTLE POSITION SWITCH

DIVERTER VALVE FUEL ECONOMY SWITCH

1978 Seville throttle body has a standard type idle adjusting screw

If the clearance is over 0.020 in., adjust the switch slightly clockwise and recheck the adjustment to obtain less than 0.020 in. clearance. If the switch cannot be adjusted, it must be replaced.

Throttle Position Sensor

ADJUSTMENT

DFI

1. Remove the air cleaner and run the engine to normal operating temperature.

2. Connect a tachometer and a high impedance voltmeter as follows:

A. Plus (+) lead to the TPS harness test point which connects to pin A (0.8 dark blue wire).

B. Negative (−) lead to the TPS harness test point which connects to pin B (0.8 black/white wire).

C. Select the 2V DC scale.

3. Open the set timing connector.

4. Retract the ISC motor by pressing the plunger (switch activated) in while the throttle is opened to approximately 1500 rpm. When the ISC motor fully retracts, disconnect the ISC connector before releasing the throttle.

5. Jump the ISC harness connector pins A and B together.

6. The ISC plunger should not be touching the throttle lever. If contact is noted, adjust the plunger (turn in) with pliers.

7. The idle speed should now be approximately 375–400 rpm. Adjust the throttle stop screw to the proper rpm if necessary.

8. The digital voltmeter should indicate .50 volts. If necessary adjust the TPS

as outlined in Steps 9–11. If the voltmeter is correct, proceed to step twelve.

9. Remove the throttle body assembly from the intake manifold. Invert the throttle body assembly to gain access to the spot welds that hold the TPS screws in place. Use a 5/16 drill bit to drill through the spot welds to gain access to the screws. Loosen the screws enough to permit rotation of the sensor.

10. With the engine idling 375–400 rpm loosen the TPS mounting screws and position the TPS lever so the voltmeter reads .50 volts.

11. Tighten the TPS mounting screws with the sensor in this position. Recheck the voltmeter to make sure the adjustment hasn't changed.

12. Remove all test equipment and reconnect all connections including the set timing connector.

13. Turn off the ignition for ten seconds. The ISC motor should move to the extended position.

14. The above procedure may have turned on the (Check Engine) light, and may have set a trouble code. Refer to the procedure at the end of "Idle Speed Control (ISC) Motor Adjustment—DFI," to clear the trouble code from the system.

Idle Speed Control

ADJUSTMENT

DFI

Adjustment of the ISC motor is necessary to establish the initial position of the motor after it has been replaced. It may be necessary if the throttle pedal ratchets when the ignition is turned off or on.

1. Remove the air cleaner, and run the engine to normal operating temperature.

2. Connect a tachometer to the engine.

3. Check the TPS adjustment as previously outlined.

4. Open the set timing connector.

5. Disconnect the TPS connector.

6. Turn the ignition off for ten seconds and observe the plunger movement. It should extend fully.

7. When the ISC plunger is fully extended, disconnect the ISC connector. Jump the ISC harness pins A and B together.

8. Reconnect the TPS and start the engine.

9. The engine idle speed should be 1500 rpm. If not turn the ISC plunger till the engine reaches 1500 rpm.

10. Reconnect the ISC motor and repeat Steps 5–8.

11. Remove all test equipment and connect all connections including the set timing connector.

12. Turn the ignition off for ten seconds. Start the engine and check the ISC for proper operation.

13. Turn the ignition off for ten seconds. The ISC motor should move to the full extended position.

14. This procedure may have turned on the check engine light, and may have set a trouble code. To clear the code from the system, turn the key on, and simultaneously press and hold the OFF and WARMER buttons in the climate control panel until "88" appears in the readout. To clear the codes, depress the OFF and HI buttons simultaneously.

Carburetor

REMOVAL & INSTALLATION

1. Remove the air cleaner.

2. Disconnect the fuel line.

3. Disconnect the throttle linkage.

4. Disconnect and label all vacuum hoses.

5. Remove the retaining bolts.

6. Remove the carburetor.

7. Installation is the reverse of removal.

COOLING SYSTEM

Cadillac uses a cooling system designed to remain sealed at all times. A coolant reservoir allows fresh coolant to be added. There is no need to open the radiator cap.

NOTE: On the 4.1 Liter 250 cu. in. V8 engine use only a coolant solution specifically designed for use in aluminum engines.

Radiator

REMOVAL & INSTALLATION

1. Disconnect the battery ground cable.
2. Drain the cooling system.
3. Disconnect the air conditioning compressor, if so equipped, and position it out of the way without disconnecting the hoses.
4. Remove the clamp that holds the A/C high pressure vapor line to the cradle.
5. Loosen the hose clamps and disconnect the upper and lower radiator hoses.
6. Disconnect the two transmission cooler lines and plug them.

NOTE: Disconnect the heater return hose, if so equipped.

7. Remove the two top radiator cradle clamps, straps or sheet metal cover and the fan shroud. Disconnect the reservoir hose from the filler neck.
8. Remove the vacuum hoses, if so equipped. Mark them for proper installation.
9. Pull the radiator straight up and out of the car.
10. Reverse to install.

Water Pump

REMOVAL & INSTALLATION

1978 and Later Except Seville

1. Disconnect the negative battery cable and drain the radiator.
2. Remove two screws from the radiator support rods on each side. Loosen one screw on each side and move the support rod out of the way.
3. Remove the two screws from the upper fan shroud and remove the radiator hose brace-to-shroud screw.
4. Drill out the upper fan shroud attaching rivets and remove the upper shroud.

5. Loosen the alternator bracket and remove the pulley so the fan can be rotated. Remove the four screws attaching the fan hub to the water pump.
6. Loosen the power steering pump bracket and remove the belt.
7. Disconnect the hose at the water pump.
8. Disconnect the fuel line at the carburetor and the fuel pump and remove the line.
9. Loosen the four crankshaft pulley-to-hub screws.
10. Remove the water pump attaching screws and remove the pump.
11. Reverse to install, using a new gasket.

Seville

1. Drain the radiator into a clean container. The coolant may be re-used if it is clean.
2. Remove the hose at the water pump.
3. Remove the upper radiator hose-to-fan shroud attaching screw and the shroud-to-radiator cover attaching screws. Lift up the shroud and position it over the fan.
4. Remove the four fan attaching nuts and remove the fan.

5. Loosen the front A/C compressor, alternator and power steering pump brackets and remove all the belts.

NOTE: Do not remove the high and low pressure lines from the compressor rear head.

6. Remove the front A/C compressor bracket, the power steering pump bracket and the front A.I.R. pump bracket and the supporting rod.
7. Remove the water pump mounting bolts and remove the pump.
8. Reverse to install, using a new gasket.

Thermostat

REMOVAL & INSTALLATION

1. Drain the cooling system until the coolant level is below the level of the thermostat.
2. Remove the upper radiator hose at the thermostat housing.
3. On the Seville, loosen the A.I.R. pump support rod at the pump and pivot the rod out of the way.

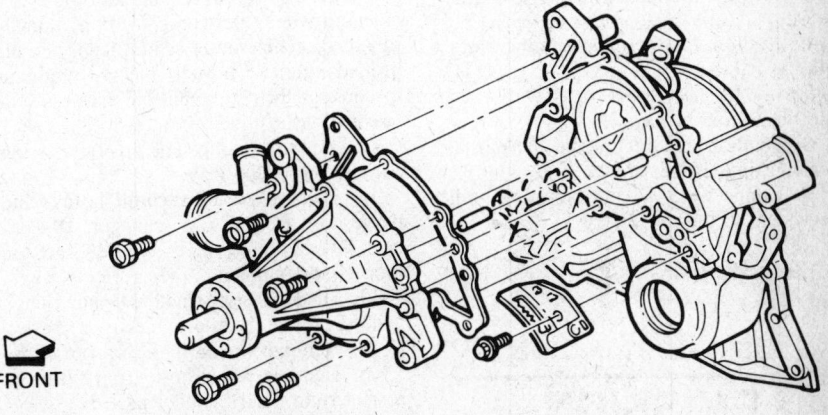

FRONT

Water pump to front cover installation—V6 engine

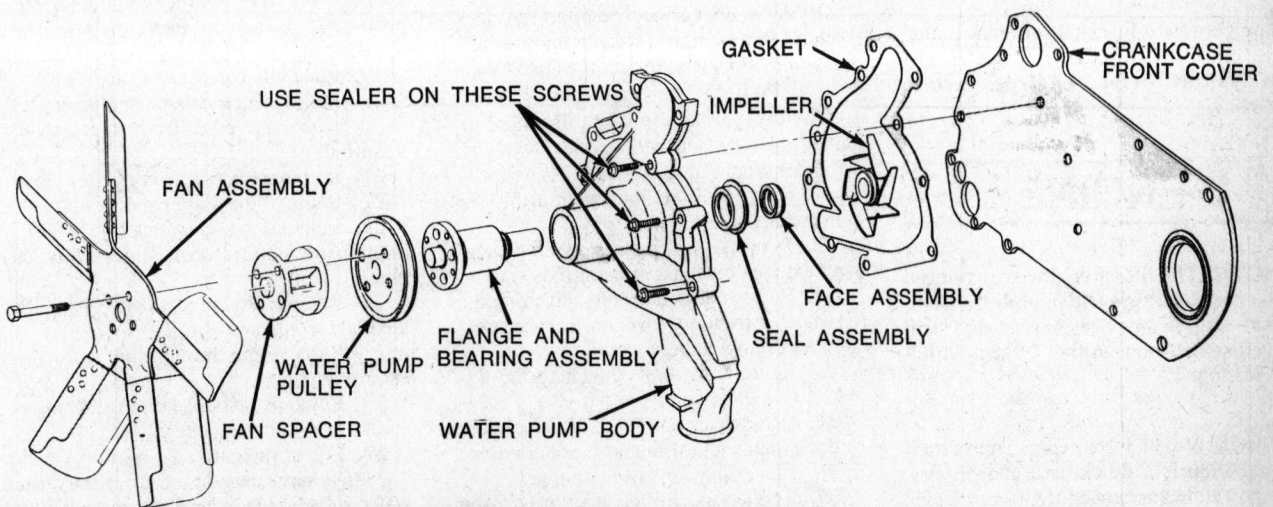

Water pump—368 and 425 cu. in. engines

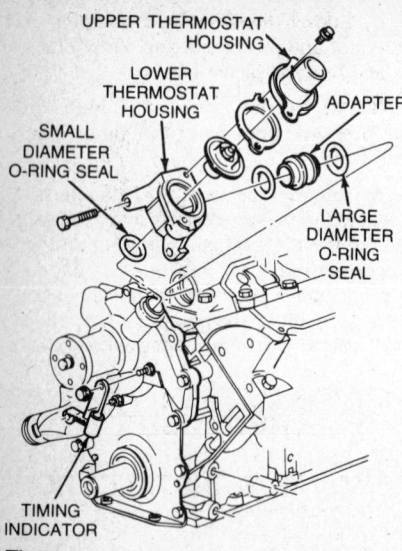

UPPER THERMOSTAT HOUSING

LOWER THERMOSTAT HOUSING

ADAPTER

SMALL DIAMETER O-RING SEAL

LARGE DIAMETER O-RING SEAL

TIMING INDICATOR

Thermostat and housing installation—250 V8 engine

4. Remove the two thermostat housing attaching bolts. Remove the housing. On the Seville remove the housing from the bypass hose and discard the gasket.

5. Pull the thermostat from the engine block.

6. Position the thermostat in the block with the valve up.

7. Install a new gasket coated with sealer onto the engine block.

8. Position and secure the thermostat housing; tighten the screws.

9. Connect the radiator hose and refill the system to the proper level.

EMISSION CONTROLS

For complete information concerning emission controls, please refer to "Emission Controls" in the Unit Repair section.

ENGINE

NOTE: The diesel engine is produced by General Motor's Oldsmobile division. Diesel engine service procedures will therefore be found in the "Oldsmobile" car section.

The 252 V-6 (4.1 liter) engine introduced in mid-1980 is a Buick-built engine. Service procedures are contained in the "Buick Rear Wheel Drive" car section.

REMOVAL & INSTALLATION

Full Size Cadillac

1. Disconnect the negative battery cable.

2. Remove hood, after scribing hood hinge outline for proper alignment.

3. Remove air cleaner and heat shroud.

4. Drain cooling system. Unfasten the fender struts from the radiator shroud.

5. Remove radiator hose bracket, radiator cover and fan.

6. Remove upper radiator hose.

7. Disconnect throttle and Cruise Control linkage at carburetor.

8. Disconnect the brake vacuum hose from the vacuum pipe. Remove Cruise Control power unit on cars so equipped.

9. Disconnect power steering pump bracket and swing pump out of way with hoses still connected. Position power steering fluid cooler out of the way.

10. Remove A/C compressor bracket bolts and swing compressor out of way with hoses still connected. Do not discharge system.

11. Disconnect temperature sender wire, idle speed-up wire (if so equipped), ignition primary wire, downshift switch wire, S.C.S. solenoid (if so equipped) and anti-dieseling solenoid wires, electronic ignition connector, block temperature sender lead, and all ground straps. On fuel injected engines, disconnect the EFI manifold harness and move it out of the way.

12. Bend back clips and position wiring harness out of the way.

13. Disconnect all vacuum hoses, and purge hose from E.L.C. canister. Disconnect the automatic level control line, on models so equipped.

14. Disconnect alternator, heater switch and oil pressure sender wires.

15. Remove wiring harness from clips.

16. Remove water hose from fitting at rear of right-hand cylinder head.

17. Loosen and remove alternator and A.I.R. pumps and remove belts.

18. Disconnect tie struts and swing out of the way.

19. Jack up car and support on jack stands. Remove the six engine-to-transmission bolts and remove each engine mount through bolt.

20. Relieve fuel pressure on fuel injected cars as outlined in the "Chassis-Mounted Fuel Pump Removal" section.

21. Support the engine and transmission with separate jacks.

22. Remove starter motor, then disconnect exhaust pipes from manifolds.

23. Remove the four bolts attaching the flywheel inspection cover to the transmission and remove the cover.

24. Remove the bolts attaching the flywheel to the converter.

25. Disconnect and plug the fuel line and the vapor return line at the fuel pump.

26. Lower the car to the ground.

27. Connect a lifting bracket to the engine.

28. Support transmission with a wood-padded floor jack.

29. Raise engine slightly and pull forward to disengage from transmission, then pull engine up and out.

30. Installation is the reverse of removal.

Seville Through 1979

1. Disconnect the negative battery cable. On the diesel, remove the rear battery and the engine vacuum pump.

2. Drain the cooling system.

3. Remove the hood. Scribe marks on the hinges and their mounting points for installation.

4. Remove the air cleaner assembly.

5. Remove the struts from both right and left wheelhousings.

6. Remove the radiator cover.

7. Disconnect the power brake hose at the point where it joins the steel tube to the rear of the left cylinder head.

8. Disconnect the left and right side sections of the wiring harness and position them out of the way.

9. Disconnect the heater hose from the rear of the intake manifold.

10. Disconnect the upper and lower radiator hoses from the engine and remove the fan assembly from the water pump.

11. Remove the distributor cap and spark plug wires.

12. Disconnect the two ground wires from the compressor bracket and position the harness out of the way.

13. Disconnect the accelerator linkage and vapor canister hose from the throttle body.

14. Relieve fuel pressure as EFI cars as outlined in the "Chassis-Mounted Fuel Pump Removal" section.

15. Disconnect the fuel inlet line from the fuel rail and plug the line.

16. Remove the power steering hoses at the steering gear and plug the hoses and gear. Secure hoses to engine.

17. Disconnect the fuel return line from the pressure regulator outlet fitting.

18. Remove the air conditioner compressor from the engine without disconnecting the refrigerant lines and move it out of the way.

19. Raise the car on a hoist.

20. Disconnect the exhaust pipe and exhaust crossover pipe from the exhaust manifolds.

21. Remove the torque converter cover.

22. Remove the starter motor.

23. Remove the screw and clip securing the transmission oil cooler lines to the engine oil pan.

24. Remove the three bolts securing the flexplate to the converter.

25. Remove the through-bolt from each engine mount.

26. Remove the bolts holding the engine and transmission together.

27. Lower the car.

28. Remove the bolts securing the heater water valve to the evaporator and move the valve out of the way.

NOTE: Some 350 V8 Seville engines have both standard and 0.010 in. oversize valve lifters. The oversize lifters have O etched on the side of the lifter and the same marking on the lifter housing boss on the cylinder block.

Modulated Displacement

Modulated Displacement (MD) is an electromechanical system which deactivates certain engine cylinders in order to save fuel. Because of the complexity of this system, all adjustments or repairs should be done by an authorized Cadillac dealer.

Rocker Arm

REMOVAL & INSTALLATION

1981 and Later 368 V8 Engines

These engines feature a modulated displacement design that can operate eight, six or four cylinders depending on driving requirements. The selective operation of the number of cylinders is controlled by a microprocessor that operates four engine valve selector units. The selector units are electromechanical devices which can deactivate both the intake and exhaust valves of a cylinder.

It is suggested that any service of the rocker arms on this engine be done by an authorized Cadillac dealer.

All Except the 250 V8 and 1981 and Later 368 V8 Engines

The rocker arms are mounted in pairs (four pairs to each cylinder head). They are of the modified pedestal-mounted type.

Rocker arms may be removed in pairs and do not require cylinder head removal.

Torque rocker arm mounting screws to 70 ft. lbs. on 1978 and later Cadillac models and 25 ft. lbs. on all 350 engines.

Rocker Arm or Rocker Arm Pivot

REMOVAL

250 V8 Engines

1. With the valve cover removed, remove the five nuts from the stud headed head bolts and remove the valve train support with the rocker arms and pivots attached as an assembly.

NOTE: This method is preferred as the pivot assemblies may be damaged if pivot bolt torque is not removed evenly against valve spring pressure.

2. Place the support in a vise and individually rocker arms and pivot.

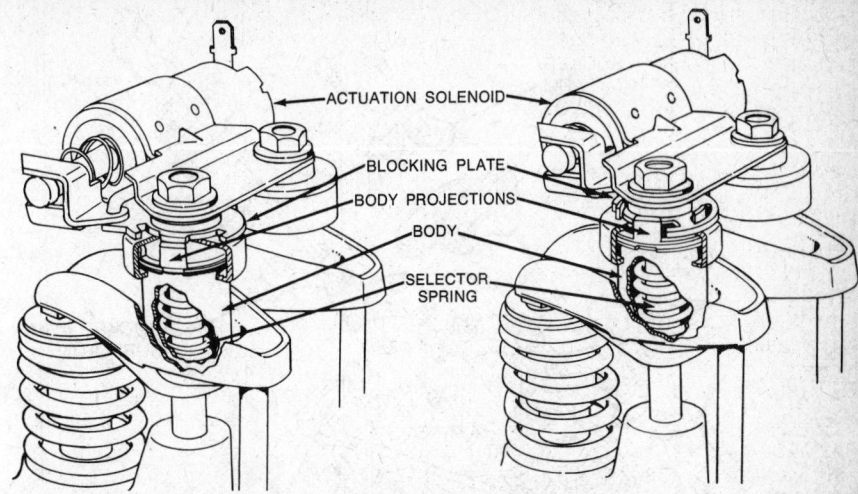

Modulated displacement valve train details: on the left, the selector body is prevented from moving upward by contact between the projections on the body and the blocking plate above it, allowing normal valve operation. On the right, the solenoid has rotated the blocking plate, aligning the windows with the body projections. As the rocker arm rises, the fulcrum rides up the stud and lifts the body. The rocker pivots about the tip of the valve, and the valve stays closed.

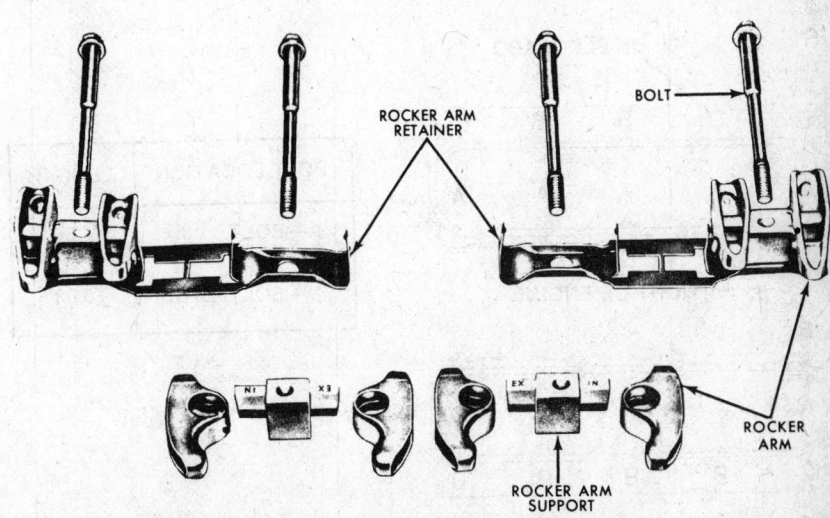

Rocker arm assemblies—368 and 425 cu. in. engines

INSTALLATION

1. With the valve train support secured in a vise, position the rocker arms and pivots to the valve train support and loosely install the pivot bolts. Torque the pivot bolts to 20 ft. lbs.

NOTE: When installing new parts, thoroughly lubricate all parts with an EP lubricant such as an axle lube.

2. Position the valve train support with the rocker arms and pivots installed over the five stud headed head bolts.

3. Position the pushrod into the seat of each rocker arm and loosely install the five retaining nuts. Tighten the five nuts alternately and evenly while checking the positioning of the push rods from time to time. When the nuts are all the way down, tighten to 35 ft. lbs.

4. Install the rocker cover.

Cylinder Head

REMOVAL & INSTALLATION

All Except the 250 V8 and 1981 and Later 368 V8 Engines

NOTE: Care must be used when replacing Cadillac engine cylinder head bolts. They are different lengths. Mark them during removal so they may be installed in their original positions.

NOTE: Due to the complexity of the 1981 and later modulated displacement engine (6.0 liter, 368 cu. in.) it is recommended that any cylinder head service be performed by an authorized Cadillac dealer.

1. Disconnect the negative battery cable. Drain the engine coolant.

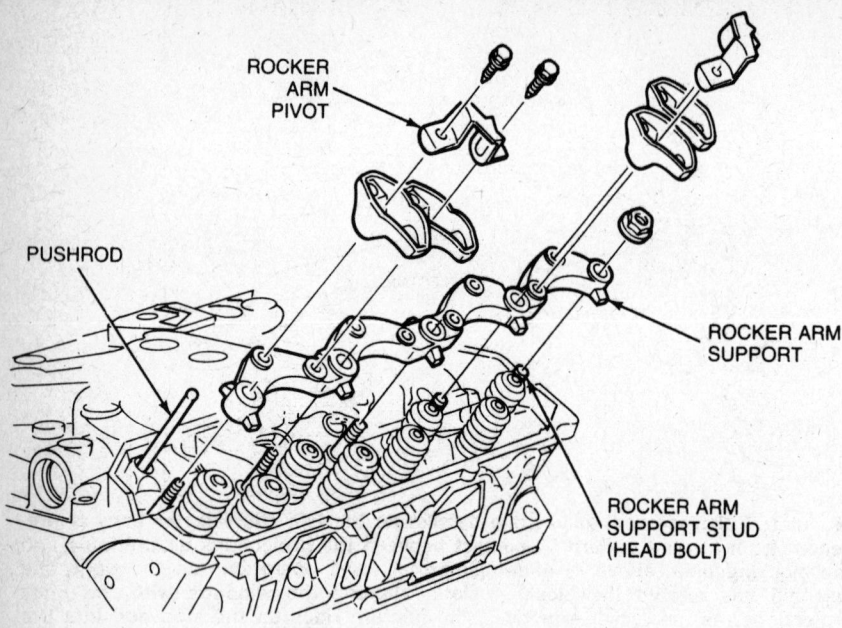

Rocker arm assembly—250 V8 engine

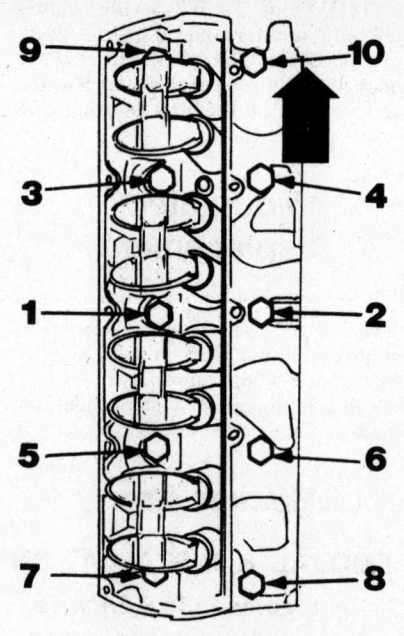

Cylinder head bolt tightening sequence
—Seville 350 V8

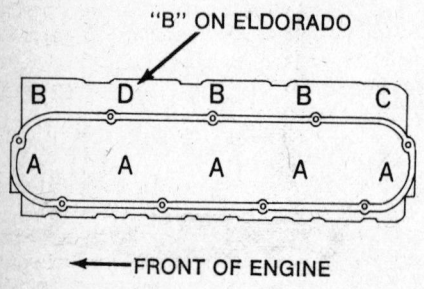

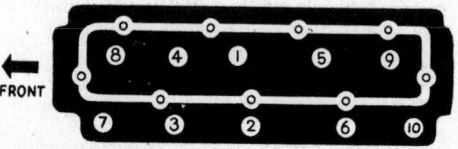

Cylinder head bolt tightening sequence—
368 and 425 cu. in. engines

BOLT LOCATION	LENGTH
A—BOLT	4.36"
B—BOLT	4.77"
C—BOLT	3.02"
D—BOLT/STUD	3.02"

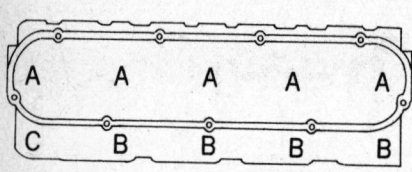

Cylinder head bolt location and length—368 and 425 cu. in. engines

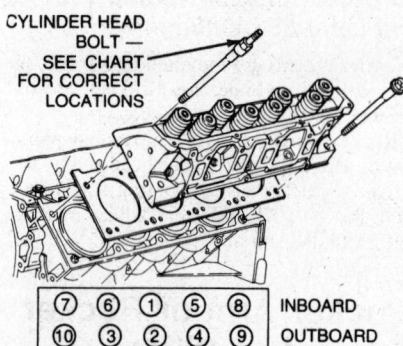

Cylinder head removal and installation—
250 V8 engine

2. Remove the intake and exhaust manifolds.

3. Disconnect all electrical and ground connections from the cylinder head.

4. When removing the left cylinder head, partially remove the power steering pump.

5. When removing the right cylinder head, remove the alternator and the heater hose from the rear of the head. Also remove the A.I.R. pump, if so equipped.

6. Remove bolts holding the rocker arm cover to the heads and remove the cover.

7. On the diesel engine, remove the fuel return lines from the nozzles. Remove the tee fittings one at a time to avoid bending the lines.

8. Remove bolts holding each rocker arm support to cylinder head, then remove

rocker arm assemblies. Store these assemblies so that they may be reinstalled in their correct locations.

9. Remove pushrods and store them with their respective rocker arm assemblies.

10. Install two 7/16 × 6 in. screws to be used as lifting handles in two of the rocker arm support screw holes.

11. Remove ten cylinder head bolts.

12. Lift cylinder head off the block.

13. Remove all gasket material from the cylinder head and block mating surfaces.

14. Install by reversing removal procedures.

15. When torquing the head bolts, use the three-step method. Torque the bolts to 1/3 of the total torque listed in the sequence shown. Once this is done, repeat the same procedure, this time torquing all the bolts

to 2/3 of the total listed torque. Finally torque the bolts to the recommended torque.

250 V8 Engines
RIGHT SIDE

1. Remove both rocker arm covers.

2. Remove the intake manifold.

3. Remove the generator and AIR pump.

4. Remove the ground strap from the right front of the cylinder head.

5. Remove the exhaust manifold from the cylinder head.

6. Remove the screw retaining the AIR pipe to the cylinder head.

7. Remove the head bolts and remove the cylinder head.

8. Installation is the reverse of removal with the exception of the following precautions:

    a. Apply graphite lubricant to the exhaust faces of the cylinder head.

    b. Install the cylinder head bolts finger tight with the studheaded bolts in the upper row and the conventional bolts in the lower row, then tighten all bolts in sequence to 45 ft. lbs. and again in sequence to 90 ft. lbs. as shown in illustration.

LEFT SIDE

1. Remove both rocker arm covers.

2. Remove the intake manifold.

3. Remove the vacuum pump and mounting bracket.

4. Remove the upper bolt and loosen the lower bolt securing the power steering pump to the engine.

5. Remove the exhaust manifold and heat stove from the cylinder head.

6. Remove the AIR pipe from the rear of the cylinder head.

7. Remove the head bolts and remove the cylinder head and gasket.

8. Installation is the reverse of removal. Perform Steps 8a. and 8b. of the "Right Side" procedure.

Timing Case Cover, Chain, and Camshaft

350 EFI and Diesel Engine

For removal and installation procedures, refer to the "Oldsmobile Rear Wheel Drive" section. The procedures for the EFI engine are identical to that of the diesel engine.

Timing Chain Cover, Chain, and Sprocket

REMOVAL

Except 350 (EFI and Diesel) Engines and 250 V8

NOTE: On 368 cu in. Engines with nylon oil pans, the pan must be removed from the engine, not just loosened.

1. Disconnect negative battery cable and drain cooling system.

2. Detach upper radiator hose retainer from cradle and position hose out of the way.

3. Remove the fan, alternator and power steering belts.

4. Remove four capscrews that secure crank pulley to harmonic balancer, then remove the pulley.

5. Remove the plug from the end of the crankshaft. Install the puller and remove the harmonic balancer.

6. Drain the engine oil. Loosen the oil pan bolts enough to allow the front of the oil pan to drop slightly.

NOTE: It may be necessary to remove the starter to gain access to the bolts that are directly behind it.

7. Disconnect lower radiator hose from water pump, then remove the screws that hold front cover to engine. Remove cover with water pump attached.

8. Remove distributor and fuel pump.

9. Remove oil slinger and fuel pump eccentric.

10. Remove capscrews that secure camshaft sprocket.

11. Remove camshaft sprocket along with timing chain.

12. To install, reverse removal procedure. Mount the timing chain over the camshaft and the crankshaft sprocket and start the camshaft sprocket over the shaft, being certain the aligning dowel is in a position where it will enter the hole in the camshaft freely. Make certain that the timing marks on the sprockets are in line between shaft centers.

Camshaft sprockets are a tight fit. However, a comparatively easy way to install a tight-fitting sprocket is to draw it on carefully with two bolts somewhat longer then the regular mounting bolts. By drawing alternately against each bolt, and tapping gently with a plastic hammer, even a very tight camshaft gear sprocket can be installed.

13. When the camshaft is secured, turn the engine two full revolutions until the timing marks again assume the original position. Check to make certain that the punch marks, which are stamped into the front face of the sprockets, are in line between the shaft centers.

250 V8 Engine

1. Disconnect the negative battery cable and drain the radiator.

2. On the Fleetwood and Deville models, remove the two screws on each side of the radiator securing the support rod. Move the support rods out of the way.

3. Remove the wiring harness from the upper fan shroud clamps.

4. Remove the power steering pump reservoir from the upper radiator shroud.

5. Remove the upper fan shroud from the lower fan shroud by removing the staples.

6. Remove the clutch fan assembly.

7. Remove the generator, A.I.R. Pump, vacuum pump, and A/C pump drive belts.

8. Partially remove the A/C compressor from the engine mounting brackets without discharging the system.

9. Remove the alternator and support bracket from the engine.

10. Loosen the clamp and disconnect the coolant reservoir to water pump hose at the pump.

11. Disconnect the inlet and outlet hoses at the water pump.

12. Drain the crankcase by either removing the crankcase plugs (one on each side) or by elevating the rear wheels. This will prevent coolant from draining into the oil pan as the front cover is removed.

13. Remove the water pump and crankcase pulleys.

14. Remove the A/C bracket at the water pump.

15. Remove the timing mark tab from the front cover.

16. Remove the crankcase pulley to hub bolts and separate the pulley from the hub.

17. Remove the plug from the end of the crankshaft. Install a puller and remove the hub or balancer.

18. Remove the remaining front cover attaching screws and remove the cover with the water pump and lower thermostat housing as an assembly.

19. The timing chain and sprocket may now be removed as follows:

20. Remove the oil slinger from the crankshaft.

21. Rotate the engine and line up the timing marks as shown in the illustration.

22. Remove the screw securing the camshaft sprocket to the camshaft, then remove the camshaft and crankshaft sprocket with the chain attached.

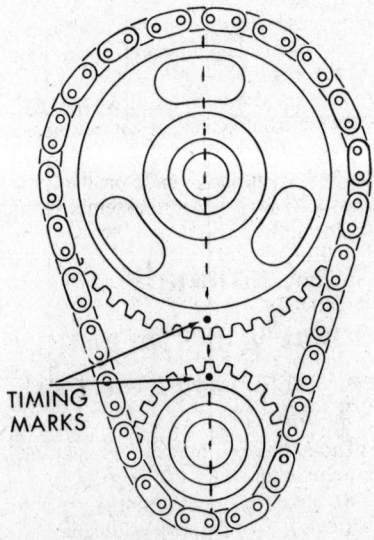

TIMING MARKS

Timing mark alignment—typical

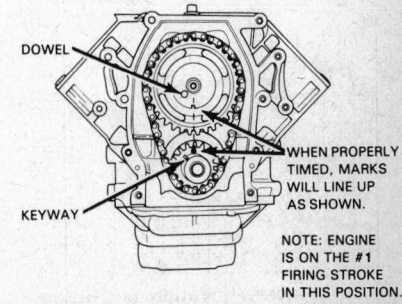

DOWEL

KEYWAY

WHEN PROPERLY TIMED, MARKS WILL LINE UP AS SHOWN.

NOTE: ENGINE IS ON THE #1 FIRING STROKE IN THIS POSITION.

Camshaft timing marks—250 V8 engine

23. Installation is the reverse of removal. After installing the timing chain over the camshaft sprocket rotate the crankshaft until the timing mark on the crank sprocket is positioned straight up.

24. Install the cam sprocket and timing chain over the crankshaft so that the timing marks are aligned as the illustration.

25. Hold the camshaft sprocket in position against the end of the camshaft and press the sprocket on the camshaft by hand. Make sure the index pin in the camshaft is lined up with the index hole in the sprocket.

26. If necessary, keep the engine from rotating while torquing the camshaft sprocket screw to 37 ft. lbs.

NOTE: Engine timing has been set so that the No. 1 cylinder is in the T.D.C. firing position. If for some reason the distributor was removed make sure the rotor is set so that cylinder No. 1 is in the firing position.

27. Install the oil slinger on the crankshaft with the smaller end of the slinger against the crankshaft sprocket.

28. Install the engine front cover by reversing the above removal procedure.

Timing Cover Oil Seal

REMOVAL & INSTALLATION

Except 350 (EFI and Diesel) Engines

All models are equipped with a molded-type front cover crankshaft oil seal. The seal may be replaced without removing the engine front cover.

1. Disconnect the battery and remove the air cleaner.

2. Remove the power steering pump drive belt.

3. Remove the alternator drive belt.

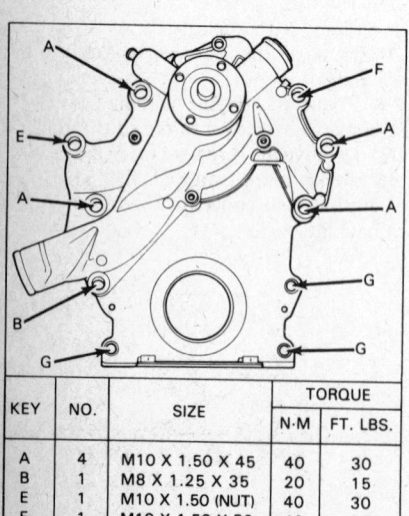

KEY	NO.	SIZE	TORQUE	
			N·M	FT. LBS.
A	4	M10 X 1.50 X 45	40	30
B	1	M8 X 1.25 X 35	20	15
E	1	M10 X 1.50 (NUT)	40	30
F	1	M10 X 1.50 X 50	40	30
G	3	M8 X 1.25 X 20	20	15

Front cover screw location and torque specifications—250 V8 engine

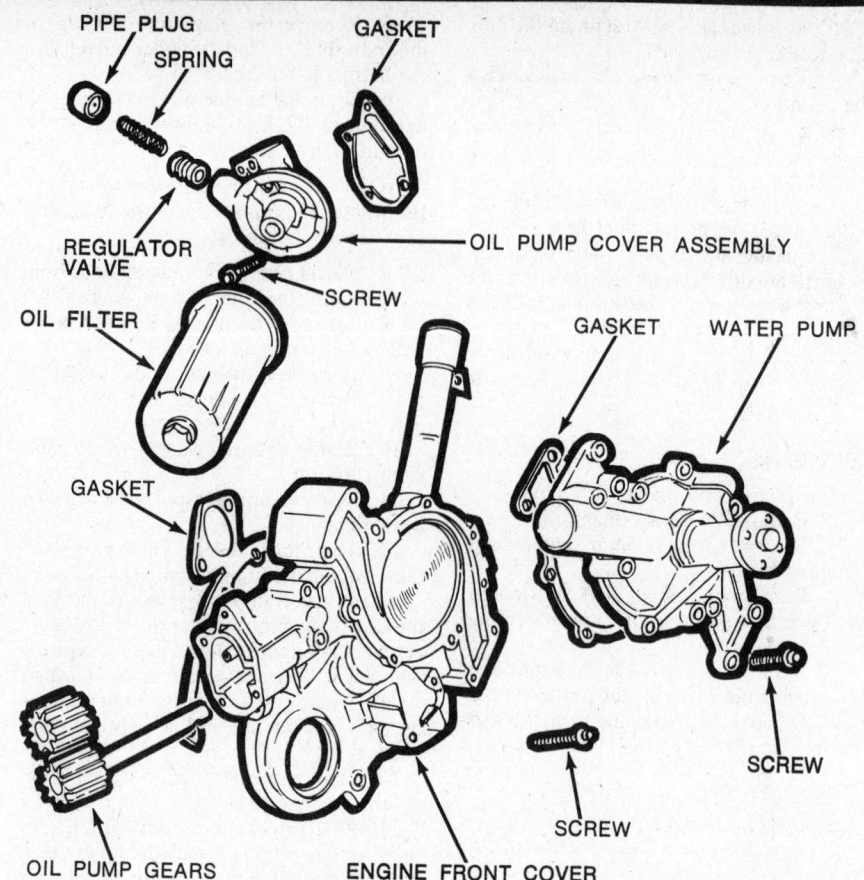

Engine front cover disassembled—252 V6 engine

4. On air conditioned cars, and cars equipped with the A.I.R. system, remove the pump drive belts.

5. Raise and support the front of the car on jack stands. Remove the fan.

6. Remove pulley and harmonic balancer, as outlined in Timing Chain and Sprocket Removal.

7. With a suitable tool, pry out front cover oil seal.

8. Lubricate new oil seal with wheel bearing grease. Position the seal on the end of the crankshaft with the garter spring side toward the engine.

9. Using a seal installer, drive the front seal into the front cover until it bottoms.

10. Assemble and install the remaining parts in reverse order of disassembly.

Camshaft

REMOVAL & INSTALLATION

Except 350 (EFI and Diesel) and 250 V8 Engines

1. Drain the cooling system and remove the radiator.

2. Remove the engine front cover and the distributor as previously outlined.

3. Remove the oil pump and the oil slinger from the crankshaft.

4. Remove the fuel pump and the fuel pump eccentric from the camshaft.

5. Remove the camshaft sprocket and the timing chain.

NOTE: Make certain that the marks on the two sprockets are correctly aligned before removing the timing chain.

6. Remove the lifters and slide the camshaft carefully out of the engine block.

NOTE: Do not allow the camshaft lobes to scratch the camshaft bearings.

7. To install the camshaft, reverse the procedure. Before installation, the camshaft should be lubricated with a thin coat of engine oil and then carefully inserted to avoid bearing damage.

8. The camshaft sprocket screws should be torqued to 18 ft lbs while the fuel pump eccentric screw is tightened to 35 ft lbs.

250 V8 Engines

1. Remove the radiator, timing chain and valve lifters as described in this section.

2. Temporarily reinstall the cam sprocket or a long bolt to use as a handle and slide the camshaft forward until it is out of the engine.

NOTE: Do not allow the camshaft lobes to scratch the camshaft bearings.

3. Installation is the reverse of removal.

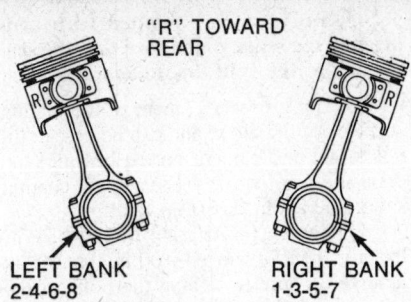

"R" TOWARD REAR

LEFT BANK 2-4-6-8

RIGHT BANK 1-3-5-7

Piston-to-connecting rod relationship—368 and 425 cu. in. engines

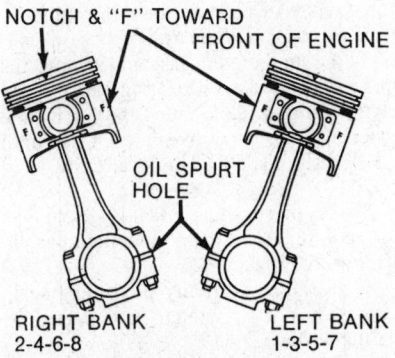

NOTCH & "F" TOWARD FRONT OF ENGINE

OIL SPURT HOLE

RIGHT BANK 2-4-6-8

LEFT BANK 1-3-5-7

Piston and connecting rod positioning—Seville 350 V8

Apply a thin coat of rear axle lubricant or equivalent to the camshaft lobes, distributor gear teeth and bearing journals.

PISTON AND ROD INSTALLATION

The numbers on the connecting rods face away from the camshaft; that is, the numbers on the left bank (even) face to the left; the numbers on the right bank (odd) face to the right. As a double check, the word *rear*, (or R), stamped on the piston, faces the rear of the engine on both banks and an arrow on the piston top points to the front of the engine.

On the 350 Seville V8 and the 250 V8 the piston is placed in the cylinder with the notch in the top of the piston or the F on the side of the piston facing toward the front of the engine. The oil spurt hole in the connecting rod faces toward the camshaft.

LUBRICATION

Oil Pump

REMOVAL & INSTALLATION

250 V8 Engine

1. Jack up the car and support it with jack stands.

2. Remove the oil pan.

3. Remove the two screws and one nut securing the oil pump to the engine.

4. To diassemble, remove the four screws holding the oil pump cover to the housing, then slide the drive shaft, drive gear and driven gear out of the pump housing.

5. Remove the oil pressure regulator valve and spring from the bore in the housing assembly.

6. Inspect the oil pressure regulator valve for nicks and burrs.

7. Measure the free length of the regulator valve spring. It should be 2.57–2.69 in.

8. Inspect the drive gear and driven gear for nicks and burrs.

9. Assemble the pump drive gear over the drive shaft so that the retaining ring is inside the gear. Position the drive gear over the pump housing shaft closest to the pressure regulator bore.

10. Slide the driven gear over the remaining shaft in the pump housing, meshing the driven gear with the drive gear.

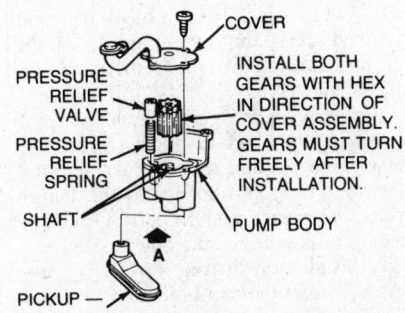

PRESSURE RELIEF VALVE

PRESSURE RELIEF SPRING

SHAFT

PICKUP

COVER

INSTALL BOTH GEARS WITH HEX IN DIRECTION OF COVER ASSEMBLY. GEARS MUST TURN FREELY AFTER INSTALLATION.

PUMP BODY

A

Oil pump disassembled—250 V8 engine

11. Install the oil pressure regulator spring and valve in the bore of the pump housing assembly.

12. Install the pump cover and four retaining screws.

13. Install the oil pump assembly to the block, engaging the drive shaft to the distributor gear. Tighten the nut to 22 ft. lbs. and the two screws to 15 ft. lbs.

14. Install the oil pan and lower the car.

368 and 425 V8 Engines

1. Jack up the car, support it with jack stands, and remove the oil filter.

2. Remove five capscrews that secure oil pump to engine.

NOTE: Remove screw nearest pressure regulator last.

3. Slide drive shaft, drive gear and driven gear out of housing.

4. Remove plug from housing cover, using 5/16 in. wrench. Remove pressure regulator valve and spring.

5. Check free length of regulator spring—it should be 2.57–2.69 in.

6. Inspect gears and housing for burrs or scoring.

7. Check pump clearance limits.

8. On installation, pack the pump with petroleum jelly. Use a new gasket, engage the pump driveshaft with the distributor drive, and install screw nearest pressure regulator first. Install remaining screws and tighten all five screws to 15 ft. lbs. Install oil filter, add one quart oil to engine, run engine and check for leaks.

350 V8 Engine

1. Remove the oil pan.

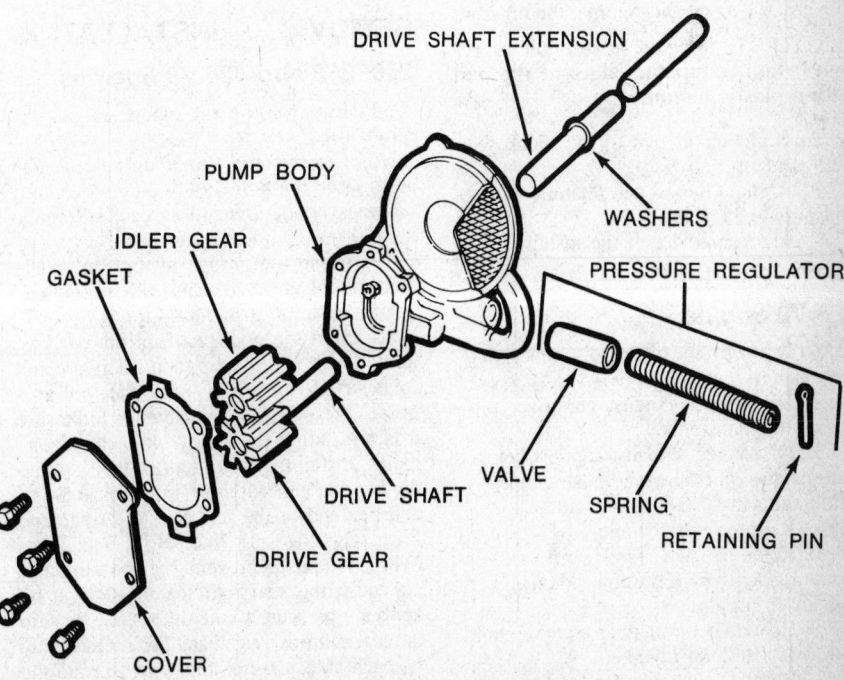

DRIVE SHAFT EXTENSION

PUMP BODY

IDLER GEAR

GASKET

WASHERS

PRESSURE REGULATOR

DRIVE SHAFT

DRIVE GEAR

COVER

VALVE

SPRING

RETAINING PIN

Exploded view of Seville 350 V8 oil pump
(© Cadillac Div., G.M. Corp.)

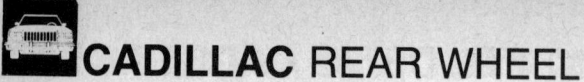

2. Remove the oil pump-to-rear main bearing cap attaching bolts and remove the oil pump and drive shaft extension.

3. Remove the drive shaft extension. Do not attempt to remove the washers from the shaft. The shaft extension and washers must be replaced as an assembly if the washers are not $1\frac{11}{32}$ in. from the end of the shaft.

4. Remove the cotter pin, spring and the pressure regulator valve. Place your thumb over the pressure regulator bore before removing the cotter pin to contain the spring.

5. Remove the oil pump cover attaching screws and remove the cover and gasket.

6. Remove the idler gear and drive gear from the pump body.

7. Check the gears for scoring and any other damage. Install new gears, if necessary.

8. Assemble and install the oil pump in reverse order of removal. The end of the drive shaft extension nearest the washers is inserted into the drive shaft.

Oil Pan

REMOVAL & INSTALLATION

250 V8 Engine

1. Disconnect the negative battery cable.
2. Jack the car up and support it with jack stands.
3. Drain the engine oil and remove the oil filter.
4. Remove the flywheel inspection cover and support struts.
5. Disconnect the exhaust ''Y'' pipe at the exhaust manifolds and remove the one bolt at the catalytic converter bracket.
6. Remove the oil pan screws, lower the exhaust pipe, and remove the oil pan.

NOTE: If the pan is difficult to remove, lightly tap the edges of the pan with a plastic hammer.

7. Seal the oil pan to the block with RTV sealant.
8. Tighten the oil pan retaining screws and nuts to 11 ft.lbs.
9. The remainder of the installation is the reverse of removal.

425 V8 Engine

1. Drain engine oil and disconnect negative battery cable.
2. Disconnect exhaust crossover pipe at exhaust manifolds.
3. Disconnect exhaust support bracket at transmission extension housing, and position exhaust system to one side.
4. Remove starter motor.
5. Remove two idler arm support mounting screws from frame side member, and lower support.
6. Disconnect pitman arm at drag link, and lower steering linkage.
7. Remove transmission lower cover.
8. Remove engine oil pan.

9. When reinstalling, reverse above procedure and torque oil pan screws and nuts to 10 ft. lbs. The transmission cover screws should be torqued to 20 ft. lbs.

350 and 368 V8 Engines

1. Remove the wheel housing struts from the fenders. Disconnect the negative battery terminal.
2. Remove the 3 screws from the upper radiator shroud, two securing the shroud, and one securing the top radiator hose. Drill out the rivets securing the upper shroud to the lower one and remove the shroud. Use bolts and nuts to replace the rivets when reinstalling the shroud.
3. Loosen the drive belts and remove the crankshaft pulley.
4. Jack up your car and support it with jack stands.
5. Remove the through-bolt from each motor mount.
6. Remove the crossover pipe and the converter as an assembly.
7. Remove the starter.
8. Remove the torque converter cover.
9. Drain the oil pan.
10. Using a jack, with a block of wood on top, place it under the crankshaft hub. Jack up the engine, remove the pan bolts and the pan.
11. Clean all the gasket material from the pan and the block mating surfaces. Use a new gasket kit and sealer. Make sure the seals are firmly positioned on the flange surfaces with each seal properly located in the cut-out notches of the pan gasket.
12. Installation is the reverse of removal. Torque the pan bolts to 10 ft. lbs.

Rear Main Seal

REMOVAL & INSTALLATION

250, 368 and 425 V8 Engines

1. Remove the oil pan (See oil pan removal).
2. Remove the rear main bearing cap and loosen the bolts holding the other four bearings about three turns each. Remove the old rear main bearing seals.
3. Clean the groove in the cap and in the block. Lubricate seals with engine oil.
4. Make an installation tool.
5. Start the upper half into the groove in the block with the lip facing forward and rotate it into position, using the tool as a guide. Press firmly on both ends to be sure it is protruding uniformly on each side.
6. Install the lower half of the seal into the bearing cap with the lip facing forward and one end of the seal over the ridge and flush with the split line. Hold one finger over this end to prevent it from slipping, and push the seal into seated position by applying pressure to the other end. Be sure the seal is firmly seated and protrudes evenly on each side. Do not apply pressure to the lip. This may damage the effectiveness of the seal.

NOTE: Vehicles equipped with neopreme type seals, make sure that the seal is flush at the split line to avoid leaks.

7. Apply rubber cement to the mating surfaces of the block and cap being careful not to get any cement on the bearing, the crankshaft or the seal. The cement coating should be about 0.010 in. thick.
8. Tighten the bearing bolts to 89 ft. lbs. for the 250 and 90–100 ft. lbs. for all others. Be sure to tighten the bolts of the other four bearings also. Rotate the crankshaft one full turn to check for binding.
9. Reinstall the oil pan.

350 V8 Engine

The crankshaft need not be removed to replace the rear main bearing upper oil seal.

1. Drain the crankcase and remove the oil pan and rear main bearing cap.
2. Using a blunt-ended tool, drive the upper seal into its groove on each side until it is tightly packed. This is usually $\frac{1}{4}$-$\frac{3}{4}$ in.
3. Cut pieces of new seal $\frac{1}{16}$ in. longer than required to fill the grooves and install, packing into place.
4. Carefully trim any protruding seal, being sure not to scratch or damage the bearing surface.
5. Install a new seal in the bearing cap and install cap, tightening bolts to 120 ft. lbs. Install the oil pan.

AUTOMATIC TRANSMISSION

All Cadillac cars use a Turbo Hydra-Matic transmission. **For all automatic transmission service procedures, please refer to "Automatic Transmissions" in the Unit Repair section.**

REMOVAL

1. Disconnect the neative battery cable.
2. Raise the car and make sure it is supported securely.
3. Disconnect the transmission linkage by removing the one nut from the shaft on the left side of the transmission.
4. Remove the speedometer drive cable.
5. Disconnect and cap the oil cooler pipes at the transmission. Plug the connector holes in the transmission.
6. Disconnect the vacuum modulator hose.
7. Remove the propeller shaft.
8. Remove the lower flex plate housing cover.
9. Remove the three converter to flex plate attaching bolts. Rotate the converter and flexplate until the bolts can be reached for removal. A bolt in the end of the crankshaft balencer can be used to rotate the flexplate.

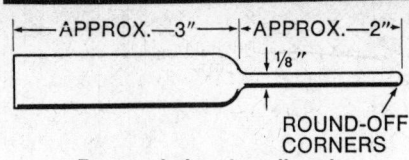

Rear main bearing oil seal installation tool

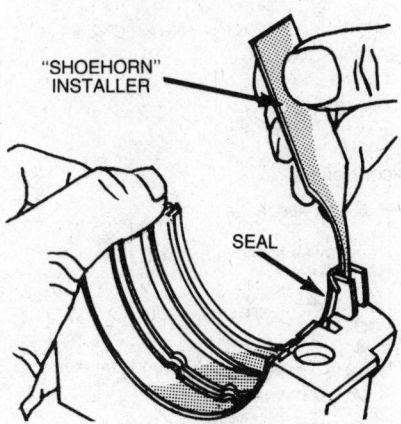

Installing rear main bearing oil seal

NOTE: Do not pry on the flexplate ring gear or transmission case to rotate converter, as flexplate or case may be damaged.

10. Place a jack or other suitable device under the rear of the engine.

11. Remove the two nuts from the tunnel strap and remove the strap.

12. Remove the two rear engine mount to extension housing bolts.

13. Position a transmission jack under the transmission and raise it just enough to take the load off the rear engine support and remove the shim.

14. Remove the four bolts from the rear engine support and swivel the support out of the way. Allow the support to hang by the parking brake cable.

15. Disconnect the exhaust pipe from the exhaust manifold and remove the rear engine support cross member.

16. Remove the six transmission case to engine attaching bolts. If necessary lower the engine and transmission slightly to gain access to the upper attaching bolts.

17. Move the transmission towards the rear of the car, disengaging the transmission from the engine.

18. The converter weighs about 50 pounds. To prevent it from falling out and getting damaged, install a converter holding clamp Tool No. J-21366 on the front of the transmission case, and lower the transmission from the car.

INSTALLATION

1. Install the converter on the turbine shaft making certain that the converter drive hub is fully engaged with the pump gear tangs, and install the converter holding clamp on the front of the transmission case.

2. Align the front of the transmission case dowel holes with the dowels on the engine. Install the six transmission case to engine attaching bolts and tighten the bolts to 35 ft. lbs.

3. Rotate the converter until two of the three weld nuts on the converter line up with the bolt holes in the flexplate.

NOTE: Make certain the converter rotates freely in this position and is not cocked and that the pilot in the center of the converter is properly seated in the crankshaft.

4. Install the two flexplate to converter attaching bolts through the accessible holes in the flexplate and tighten finger tight

NOTE: The bolts must not be tightened at this time to assure proper alignment of the converter.

5. Rotate the converter and install the third attaching bolt. Tighten all bolts to 35 ft. lbs.

6. Lower the transmission carefully and install the two rear engine mount to extension housing bolts. Tighten the bolts to 55 ft. lbs.

7. Install the exhaust pipe, rear engine support cross member and the tunnel strap.

8. The remainder of the installation is the reverse of removal. Add transmission fluid as required.

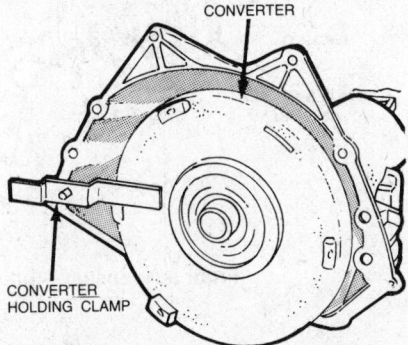

Installation of the converter holding clamp

DRIVESHAFT AND U-JOINTS

Universal joints and driveshafts can be divided into two groups: single-piece shaft models and two-piece shaft models.

For all U-joint removal and repair procedures, please refer to "U-Joints & CV-Joint Overhaul" in the Unit Repair Section.

Single-Piece Shaft

REMOVAL & INSTALLATION

1. Put the transmission in Neutral, then jack up your car and support it with jack stands.

2. Remove the two accessible rear U-joint flange capscrews.

3. Rotate the driveshaft and remove the other two capscrews, while supporting the shaft. Never let the full weight of the driveshaft be supported only by the front universal joint.

4. Push shaft forward to clear pinion flange, then pull rearward to disengage slip yoke from transmission. Plug transmission to prevent oil leakage or entry of dirt.

5. Lubricate slip yoke inside diameter with gear lube, outside of splines with A.T.F.

6. To install, reverse removal procedure, tightening rear U-joint fasteners to 70 ft. lbs. Place transmission in Park to hold shaft while tightening capscrews.

Two-Piece Shaft

REMOVAL & INSTALLATION

1. Follow Steps 1–6 of "Single-Piece Shaft Removal and Installation," with the addition of the following step:

2. Remove center bearing support after matchmarking it and crossmember. When installing, tighten the bolts to 16 ft lbs.

REAR AXLE

Axle Shaft, Bearing, and Seal

REMOVAL & INSTALLATION

Seville and All 1978 and Later Models

1. Raise the car on a hoist and remove the wheel and brake drum.

2. Clean any dirt from the differential cover and loosen the cover attaching bolts, allowing the lubricant to drain out into a suitable container.

3. Remove the pinion cross shaft lockscrew and remove the cross shaft.

4. Push in on the flanged end of the axle shaft and remove the C-lock from the splined end of the axle shaft.

5. Remove the axle shaft from the housing, being cautious not to damage the oil seal.

6. Use a suitable tool to pry the oil seal out of the bore. Use an axle shaft bearing puller on a slide hammer to remove the axle bearing from the bearing bore.

7. Install the new bearing in the bearing bore until it is 0.550 in. from the end of the axle tube. Use a block of wood and a hammer to tap the bearing in place. Install the axle shaft bearing seal until it is flush with the end of the axle tube.

8. Slide the axle shaft into the housing until the splines on the end of the shaft engage the splines of the differential side gear. Handle the shaft gently when trying to engage the splines.

9. Install the axle shaft C-lock on the splined end of the axle shaft in the differential. Push the shaft outward so that the shaft lock seats in the counterbore of the differential side gear.

10. Install the pinion cross shaft through the differential case and pinion gears. Align the lock screw hole and install the lock screw, tightening it to 25 ft. lbs.

11. Clean the differential housing and cover mating surfaces and install the cover with a new gasket.

12. Fill the differential with lubricant, install the brake drum and wheel, and lower the car.

JACKING, HOISTING

Full Size Cadillac

When jacking under the front suspension arms, make sure to lift from the flattened portion on the flange of the lower arms.

When lifting on the frame area, make sure of solid contact at the corners of the frame with the lift points close to the bend at front and rear of the frame.

Seville

To raise the car on a twin-post suspension hoist, place the lift adapters under the lower control arms at the front and under the axle tube near the spring mounting pads at the rear.

When using a frame hoist, place the lift adapters under the front subframe members just in front of the rear cross member and under the rear sub-frame members opposite the front rear spring shackles.

FRONT SUSPENSION

All rear-drive Cadillacs and Sevilles use the same front suspension system. The system is a coil spring suspension which consists of two upper and two lower control arm assemblies, shock absorbers, a stabilizer bar, and two steering knuckles, and a pair of coil springs.

Shock Absorber

REMOVAL & INSTALLATION

NOTE: Purge a new shock of air by repeatedly extending it in its normal position and compressing it while inverted.

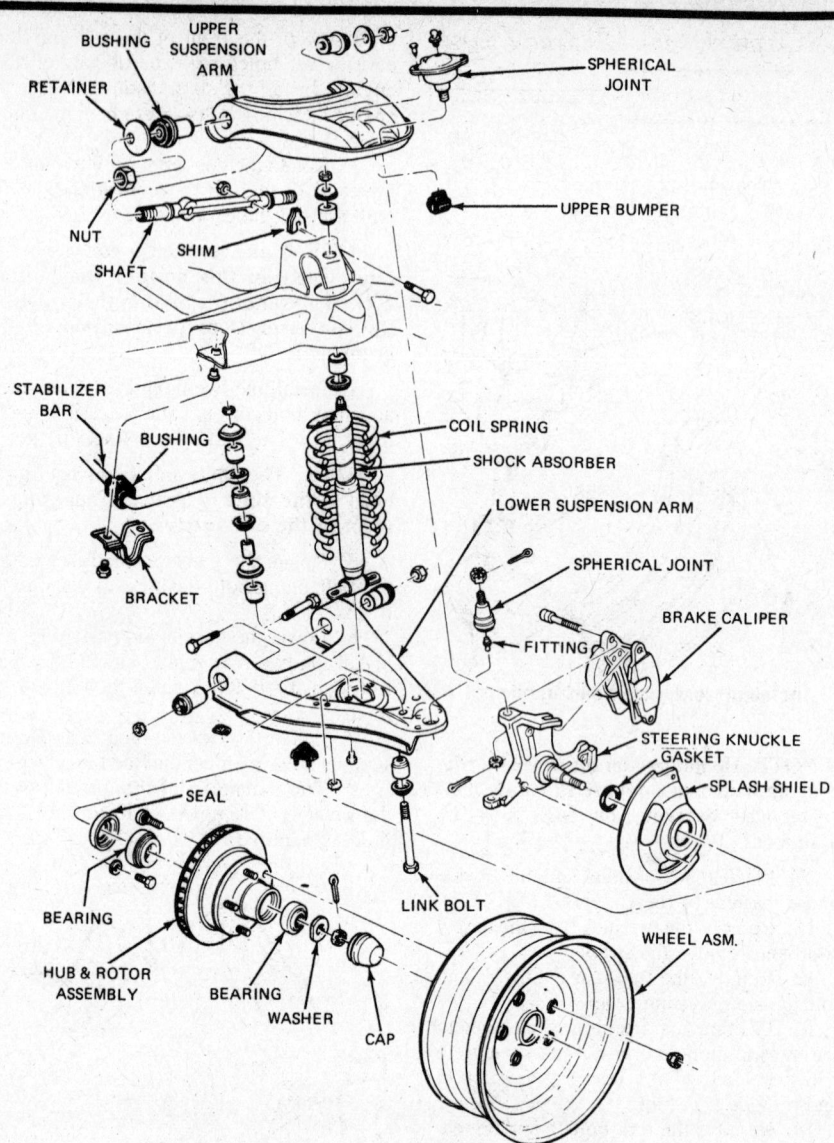

Front suspension—full-size Cadillac models

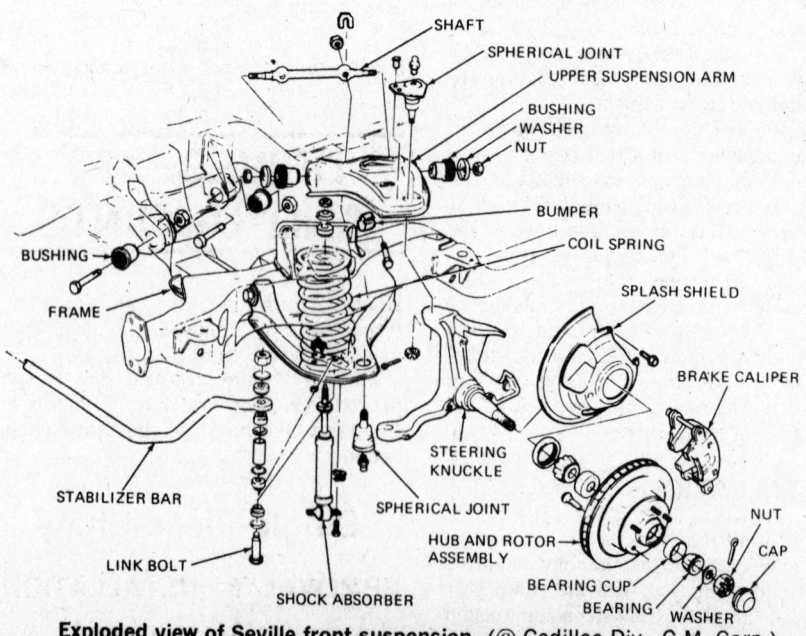

Exploded view of Seville front suspension (© Cadillac Div., G.M. Corp.)

1. Open the hood. Remove the retaining nut from the frame spring tower. Use a pair of locking type pliers, to prevent the shock stem from turning while the nut is being unfastened.

2. Remove the bottom shock absorber bolts.

3. Remove the shock through the bottom of the lower arm.

4. Install the retainer and the lower grommet.

5. Extend the shock rod as far as it will go.

6. Install the shock up through the coil spring and install the top grommet, retainer and nut.

7. Position the lower end of the shock on the lower control arm. Install the bolt, lockwasher, and nut. Tighten the bolt to 22 ft. lbs. on full size models, and 19 ft. lbs. on the Seville.

8. Tighten the retaining nut on the upper stem to 15 ft. lbs., while holding the stem with a pair of locking type pliers keep it from turning. On Seville, tighten the nut to the end of the threads (about 1⅛ in. of stud is above the nut).

NOTE: Hold the shock absorber on the square tip with locking pliers to prevent damaging the threads when removing or installing the top nut.

Lower Control Arm and Coil Spring

REMOVAL & INSTALLATION

Seville and All 1978 and Later Models

1. Raise the car and support it by the frame so the control arms hang freely.

2. Remove the lower shock absorber mounting bolts.

3. Attach a special supporting tool (G.M. tool no. J-23028-01) to a floor jack. Position the tool and the jack so as to cradle the inner bushings.

4. Remove the stabilizer-to-lower control arm attaching bolt.

5. Raise the jack to relieve the tension on the lower control arm pivot bolts. As a safety measure, install a chain around the spring and through the lower control arm.

6. Lower the jack slowly.

7. When all the spring pressure is relieved, remove the safety chain and the spring.

8. Remove the lower ball joint stud cotter pin.

9. Loosen, but do not remove, the ball joint nut.

10. Install a ball stud remover between the studs and screw the threaded end of the tool until the stud is freed.

11. Remove the lower stud nut.

12. Pull outward on the bottom of the tire while at the same time pushing the tire upward to free the steering knuckle from the ball joint stud.

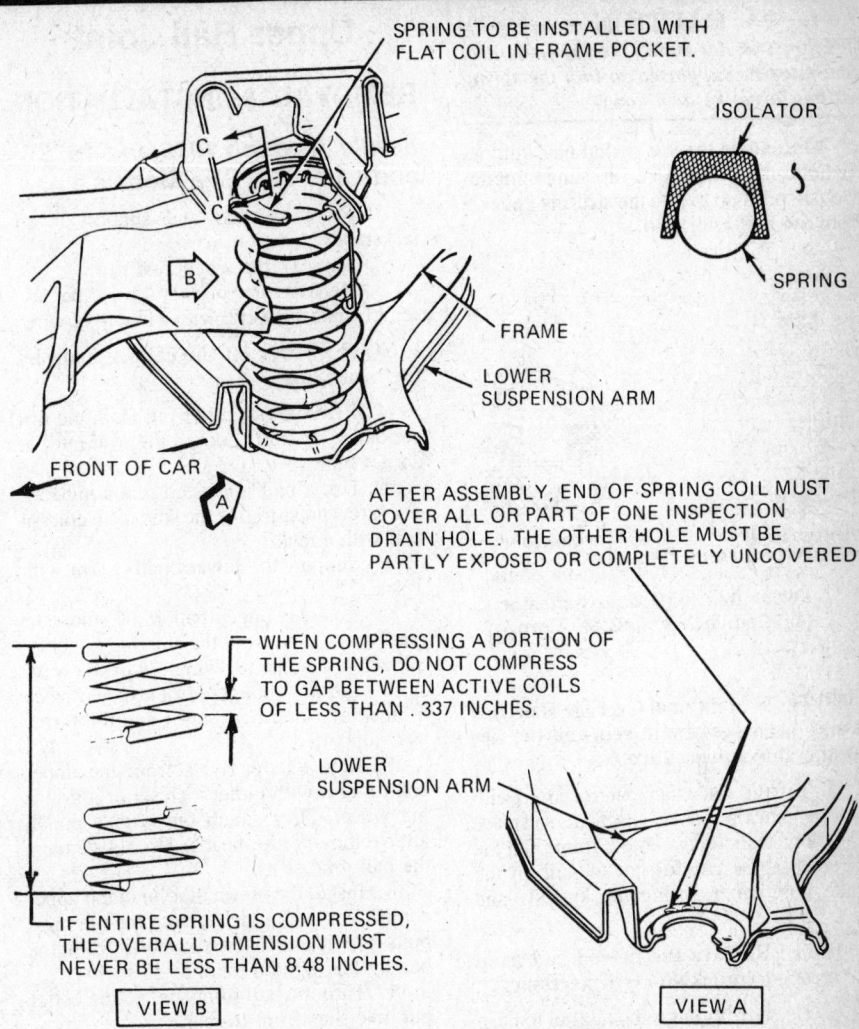

SPRING TO BE INSTALLED WITH FLAT COIL IN FRAME POCKET.

ISOLATOR

SPRING

FRAME

LOWER SUSPENSION ARM

FRONT OF CAR

AFTER ASSEMBLY, END OF SPRING COIL MUST COVER ALL OR PART OF ONE INSPECTION DRAIN HOLE. THE OTHER HOLE MUST BE PARTLY EXPOSED OR COMPLETELY UNCOVERED

WHEN COMPRESSING A PORTION OF THE SPRING, DO NOT COMPRESS TO GAP BETWEEN ACTIVE COILS OF LESS THAN .337 INCHES.

LOWER SUSPENSION ARM

IF ENTIRE SPRING IS COMPRESSED, THE OVERALL DIMENSION MUST NEVER BE LESS THAN 8.48 INCHES.

VIEW B

VIEW A

Installation of Seville front coil spring (© Cadillac Div., G.M. Corp.)

13. Remove the lower control arm from the car.

14. Reverse to install. Tighten the attaching bolts to the following values: lower control arm ball joint stud-to-steering knuckle boss—80 ft. lbs. (tighten to align the cotter pin hole); control arm pivot bolts, except Seville—90 ft. lbs.; control arm pivot bolts, Seville-95 ft. lbs.

BALL JOINT INSPECTION

NOTE: Before performing this inspection, make sure the wheel bearings are adjusted correctly and that the control arm bushings are in good condition.

1. Jack the car up under the front lower control arm at the spring seat.

2. Raise the car until there is 1–2 in. of clearance under the wheel.

3. Insert a bar under the wheel and pry upward. If the wheel raises more than ⅛ in. the ball joints are worn. Determine if the upper or lower ball joint is worn by visual inspection while prying on the wheel.

NOTE: Due to the distribution of forces in the suspension, the lower ball joint is usually the defective joint. Cadillacs and Sevilles are equipped with wear indicators on the lower ball joint. As long as the wear indicator neck extends below the ball stud seat, replacement is unnecessary.

Lower Ball Joint

REMOVAL & INSTALLATION

Seville Through 1979 and 1978 and Later Full Size Models

1. Jack up the car and support it with jack stands. Remove the wheel and tire.

2. Remove the lower ball joint stud cotter pin. Loosen (not more than one turn), but do not remove, the stud nut.

3. Install a ball joint removal tool between the studs and turn the threaded end of the tool until the stud is free of the steering knuckle.

CAUTION

If a hoist is not used, the lower control arm must be supported so that the spring cannot force the arm down.

---

4. Remove the lower stud nut. Pull out on bottom of the brake disc and simultaneously push up to free the steering knuckle from the ball joint stud.

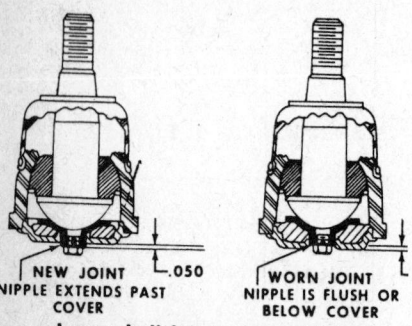

Lower ball joint wear indicator
(© Cadillac Div., G.M. Corp.)

NOTE: If additional leverage is needed it may be necessary to reinstall the tire for the above procedure.

5. Lift up on upper control arm (with steering knuckle and hub attached), and place a block of wood between the frame and the upper arm. Be careful not to pull on the brake hose when lifting the knuckle and hub.

NOTE: Remove the tie-rod end from the steering knuckle only if necessary.

6. Use a ball joint removal tool to push the ball joint from the lower control arm.

7. To install, place the lower ball joint in the lower control arm and seat it. Position the bleed vent in the rubber boot of the new ball joint facing inward.

8. Turn the ball joint stud cotter pin hole fore and aft. Remove the wood block holding the upper control arm.

NOTE: Examine the tapered hole in the steering knuckle. Clean the area. The knuckle MUST be replaced if any out-of-roundness, deformation, or damage is found.

9. Attach the ball joint stud to the steering knuckle and install the stud nut. Torque the nut to 80 ft. lbs. and install a new cotter pin.

NOTE: 125 ft lbs. or ⅙ turn maximum is allowed to align the cotter pin slot. Do not back off the nut to install the cotter pin.

10. Lubricate the ball joint. If removed, install the tie-rod end and torque the nut to 35 ft. lbs. Install the cotter pin.

11. Install the wheel and tire and lower the car. Have the front wheel alignment checked and adjusted as necessary.

Upper Ball Joint

REMOVAL & INSTALLATION

Seville Through 1979 and 1978 and Later Full Size Models

1. Raise the car and support it on jackstands.
2. Remove the wheel and tire.
3. Remove the disc brake caliper assembly and support it with a length of wire.

NOTE: Never let the caliper hang by the brake hose.

4. Remove the cotter pin from the upper ball joint stud. Loosen the stud nut but do not remove it.

5. Use a ball joint stud removing fork or a screw press to free the stud from control arm with a jack.

6. Support the lower control arm with a jack.

7. Remove upper ball joint stud nut; remove the joint from the steering knuckle; allow the knuckle to swing out of the way.

8. Lift the upper control arm and place a block of wood between it and the frame as a support.

9. Remove the rivets from the upper control arm with either a chisel or a grinding wheel. Drive them out with a punch after removing the heads. Do not damage the ball joint seat.

10. Install the new ball joint in the upper control arm and attach it with the nuts and bolts provided. Insert the bolts from the bottom and tighten them to 25 ft. lbs.

11. Turn the ball joint stud so the cotter pin hole runs front-to-rear.

12. Remove the block of wood from between the frame and the upper control arm.

13. Before installing the ball joint stud in the steering knuckle, check the tapered hole and remove any dirt or debris. If the hole is distorted or damaged, the steering knuckle must be replaced.

14. Install the ball joint stud in the hole in the top of the steering knuckle. Install the castellated nut and tighten it to 60 ft. lbs. Tighten the nut to a maximum of 100 ft. lbs. to install the cotter pin. Do not back the nut off in order to install the cotter pin.

15. Install the brake caliper assembly.
16. Grease the ball joint.
17. Install the wheel and tire and lower the car.

Upper Control Arm

REMOVAL & INSTALLATION

1. Raise and support the car.
2. Place a jack stand under the lower control arm.
3. Remove the wheel.
4. Remove the upper ball joint stud from the steering knuckle.
5. Remove the two nuts securing the

upper arm shaft to the frame bracket and remove the arm.

6. Note the number and position of shims for reassembly.

NOTE: In some cases, on Seville, it is necessary to remove the upper arm attaching bolts to allow clearance to remove the arm assembly. The bolts are splined into the frame and are removed as follows:

   a. Gently tap the bolt down with a brass drift.
   b. Using a box wrench, gently pry the bolt up.
   c. Remove the nut, and, using a pry bar and block of wood, pry the bolts from the frame.
   d. Remove the arm from the car.
To install:
7. Position the new upper arm attaching bolts in frame.

NOTE: For Seville only, install the prealignment shim with the thick area toward the rear of the car. The plate should be against the shaft.

8. Install the suspension arm cross shaft on the attaching bolts.
9. Using a freerunning nut instead of a locknut, tighten both nuts until the serrated bolts are reseated.
10. Remove the free running nuts and install the locknuts.
11. Install the shims as removed.
12. Torque the mounting nuts to 75 ft. lbs.

NOTE: Tighten the nut on the thinner shim pack first.

13. Install the ball joint stud through the knuckle and tighten the nut to 60 ft. lb. Install the cotter pin.
14. Install the wheel and torque the lug nuts to 100 ft. lb.

Wheel Bearing

ADJUSTMENT

1. Raise the front of the car. Remove the dust cap from the wheel bearing and remove the cotter pin.
2. While spinning the wheel, tighten the adjusting nut to 12 ft. lbs. Stop spinning the wheel.
3. Back off the nut until it is free and then tighten it finger tight.

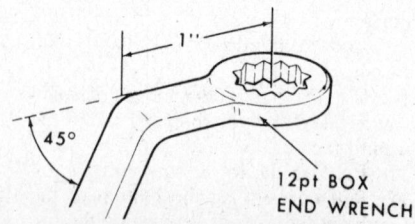

Rear shock absorber wrench
(© Cadillac Div., G.M. Corp)

4. Insert the cotter pin. If the pin cannot be installed in this position, back off the nut until the holes align. Make certain that the pin fits tightly.

REAR SUSPENSION

Full Size Cadillac

A four-link rear suspension system, consisting of upper and lower control arms, coil springs and shock absorbers is used. The coil springs are placed on brackets on the rear axle housing at their lower ends, the upper ends being seated in the frame crossmember. Some vehicles are equipped with Electronic Level Control.

Commercial Chassis and Seville

The Commercial Chassis and Seville use semi-elliptic leaf springs. Electronic Level Control is standard on Seville models and optional on Commercial Chassis.

Shock Absorber

REMOVAL & INSTALLATION

NOTE: Purge a new shock of air by repeatedly extending it in its normal position and compressing it while inverted.

Full Size Cadillac

1. Raise the rear of the vehicle and support both the frame and the axle with separate jack stands.
2. If the vehicle is equipped with Electronic Level Control, remove the air lines at the shocks.

— CAUTION —

The shocks act as rebound stops for the rear suspension and under no circumstances should the rear end be raised excessively high while disconnecting the shocks, unless both the rear axle and the frame are supported.

3. Remove the upper retaining bolts and nuts. To do this, bend a ½ in. box end wrench, as illustrated, to form a 45° angle at a point one inch from the center of the box diameter. This is used to hold the upper mounting nut.
4. Remove the lower retaining nut while holding the stem by the grommet to keep the stem from turning. Pull the shock off.
5. Installation is the reverse of removal.

Seville

1. Raise the car and support both the frame and rear axle.
2. Remove the air lines at the shock absorbers.

— CAUTION —

The shocks act as rebound stops for the rear suspension and under no circumstances should the rear end be raised excessively high while disconnecting the shocks, unless both the rear axle and the frame are supported.

3. Remove the shock absorber upper and lower retaining bolts and remove the shock absorber.

NOTE: The left-hand shock absorber has two air line connections; the right has only one.

4. To install, position the crossbar of the upper mount to the underbody so that the shock angles toward the lower mount. The line connections are to the front on the left-side; to the rear on the right-side.
5. Install and tighten the upper retaining bolts to 18 ft. lbs.
6. Place the shock absorber lower mount into the mounting bracket. Install and tighten the retaining bolt and nut to 45 ft. lbs.
7. Install the air line fittings at the shocks. (The line with the black and white stripe goes to the lower port on the left-hand shock). Tighten the fittings to 35 inch lbs.
8. Inflate the reservoir through the service valve to 140 psi.
9. Disconnect the overtravel lever at the underbody bracket and push the arm up to inflate the shock absorbers. Do not put the car weight on the shocks until they are inflated or they may be damaged.
10. Return the overtravel lever to the normal position and reconnect it to the axle bracket.
11. Lower the car and check system for proper operation.

Coil Spring

REMOVAL & INSTALLATION

1. Raise and support the car.
2. Place a jack under the differential housing.
3. Remove the wheels.
4. If the car has level control, disconnect the link at the overtravel lever and position it in its center location.
5. Remove the shock absorber lower retaining nuts and washers.

— CAUTION —

The shock absorbers act as stops for the suspension. Make certain that both the axle and the frame are supported before continuing.

6. Disconnect the brake line retaining clip from the axle and frame, but do not disconnect the brake line. This should allow enough slack as the axle is lowered to eliminate the need for disconnecting and reconnecting the brake line. If enough slack cannot be obtained, disconnect the brake line

from the hose and plug both openings. Be sure to bleed the brakes after installation.
7. Disconnect rear U-joint and wire the driveshaft out of the way. Do not allow the driveshaft to hang unsupported.
8. Remove nuts and bolts that secure both upper control arms to the axle brackets.
9. Lower rear axle assembly slowly until the springs are free and remove the springs.

— CAUTION —

Do not allow the differential to wind up as it is lowered as the spring may fly out.

10. To install, reverse removal procedure. Tighten upper and lower control arm bolts to 75 ft. lbs.

Leaf Spring

REMOVAL & INSTALLATION

Seville

1. Raise the rear of the car and support it so the axle can be raised or lowered. Raise the axle so that all tension is relieved from the spring.
2. Disconnect the rear automatic leveling valve over-travel lever from its link and hold the lever in the exhaust position (down) to deflate the shock absorbers.
3. Disconnect the lower half of the shock absorbers and move them out of the way.
4. Loosen the parking brake adjustment at the equalizer and remove the parking brake cable clip from the front retaining bracket on the spring. Remove the cable clamps from the under side of the springs.
5. Loosen the spring front eye bushing-to-retaining bracket bolt.
6. Remove the bolts retaining the front spring bracket to the underbody.
7. Lower the axle enough to permit access to the front eye bolt and remove the bracket from the spring.

NOTE: The front eye bushing can be replaced at this time.

8. Remove the U-bolt and T-bolt nuts retaining the lower spring plate to the axle and stabilizer bar brackets.
9. Remove the upper and lower spring pads and spring plate.
10. Support the spring with a jack stand and remove the two nuts from the rearshackle.
11. Separate the shackle and remove the spring from the vehicle.
12. If the spring is being replaced, remove the spring damper for installation on the new spring by removing the clamp bolt and bending the bottom half of the clamp down about 2 in. Slide the clamp rearward over the damper and remove the damper from the spring.
13. Position the spring damper on the new spring and position it ⅛ in. from the front spring eye. Slide the clamp forward over the damper and position the clamp at the second leaf of the spring.

NOTE: The clamp must face upward and the nut must be on the outside of the spring.

Install the clamp bolt pointing up and tighten to 20 ft. lbs.

NOTE: Do not tighten any of the attaching hardware to specifications until Step 25. Allow the retaining nuts and bolts to remain only finger tight.

14. Position the front eye of the spring to the front mounting bracket and install the attaching bolt and washer with the bolt head on the inside. Bolt torque is 105 ft. lbs.

15. Install the upper shackle bushings in the frame. Position the shackles to the bushings and install the bolt and nut. Torque is 50 ft. lbs.

16. Install the bushing halves in the rear spring eye and install the spring to the shackle. Lower shackle bolt and nut torque is 50 ft. lbs.

17. Raise the front end of the spring and position the bracket to the underbody. Make sure the tab on the bracket is aligned in the slot in the underbody.

18. Install the screws retaining the front spring bracket to the underbody. Torque is 30 ft. lbs.

19. Position the spring upper cushion between the spring and the axle bracket so the cushion ribs align with the bracket locating ribs.

20. Position the lower mounting plate over the locating dowel on the lower spring pad and install the retaining nuts. Torque is 45 ft. lbs.

21. Position the stabilizer brackets to the lower spring plate. Retaining bolts and nut torque is 30 ft. lbs.

22. Connect the lower shock absorber mount to the lower spring bracket. Torque is 45 ft. lbs.

23. Install the parking brake cable under the leaf spring and secure it at the front of the spring with the wire clip and clamp. Adjust the parking brake cable.

24. Connect the rear leveling over-travel lever to its link.

25. Tighten all of the attaching hardware to the specified torques.

26. Lower the vehicle.

BRAKES

Hydro-boost is installed on all diesel-engined cars. Hydro-boost is a hydraulically-assisted power brake booster. The power steering pump provides the hydraulic fluid pressure to operate both the power brake booster and the power steering gear.

For all brake system removal, installation and adjustment procedures not detailed below, please refer to "Brakes" in the Unit Repair section.

Vacuum Power Brake Unit

REMOVAL & INSTALLATION
Full Size Cadillac

1. Disconnect and cap hydraulic lines from master cylinder.

2. Disconnect vacuum line from vacuum check valve on unit.

3. Remove steering column lower cover.

4. Remove cotter pin, washer and spring spacer that secure power unit pushrod to brake pedal arm.

5. Remove the four nuts that secure power unit to firewall, then remove power unit.

6. To install, reverse removal procedure. Bleed the hydraulic system.

Seville

1. Remove any vacuum from the booster by depressing the brake pedal several times with the engine turned off.

2. Disconnect the front and rear brake outlet lines and electrical connector from the combination valve. Plug the lines and outlets to prevent entry of dirt.

3. Remove the two attaching nuts securing the master cylinder to the booster. Remove the master cylinder and combination valve assembly from the car.

4. Disconnect the booster vacuum hose from the check valve.

5. From under the instrument panel, remove the clip and washer from the brake pedal push rod pin. Do not remove the push rod from the brake pedal assembly yet.

6. Remove the two screws retaining the twilight sentinel amplifier, if so equipped, to the brake pedal bracket. Lower the amplifier and discard the connectors.

7. Remove the four booster-to-cowl retaining nuts and discard the nuts. Slide the studs through the cowl. Move the booster toward the engine and keep the mounting surface parallel to the cowl. Slide the push rod from the brake pedal pin and remove the booster from the car. Do not pry the push rod from the pedal as damage to the booster could result.

8. Install the booster in the reverse order of removal, using new attaching nuts. Tighten the booster-to-cowl nuts to 15 ft. lbs., and the master cylinder-to-booster nuts to 20 ft. lbs.

9. Bleed the brake hydraulic system. Start the engine and check the brake vacuum system for leaks and operation.

Hydro-Boost Power Brake Unit

REMOVAL & INSTALLATION

——— CAUTION ———
Power steering fluid and brake fluid are incompatible. If brake seals contact steering fluid or steering seals contact brake fluid, the seals will be ruined.

1. With the engine off, pump the brake pedal four or five times to empty the accumulator of pressurized fluid.

2. On 1979 and later models, disconnect the brake lines from the master cylinder and cap the lines. On 1978 models, remove the two master cylinder-to-booster attaching nuts and move the master cylinder away from the booster with the brake lines attached.

3. Remove and plug the three hydraulic lines from the booster. Remove the washer and retainer that secures the booster pedal rod to the brake pedal arm.

NOTE: To avoid booster damage, do not pry the pedal rod off the pedal arm.

4. Remove the four nuts holding the booster to the firewall.

5. Loosen the booster from the firewall and move the booster pedal rod inboard until it disconnects from the brake pedal arm. Remove the spring washer from the brake pedal arm and remove the booster.

6. To install, reverse the removal procedure. Tighten the booster mounting nuts to 15 ft. lbs. through 1978, 30 ft. lbs. for 1979 and later, and the master cylinder to booster mounting nuts to 20 ft. lbs. Bleed the Hydro-boost system as explained in the "Brakes" Unit Repair section.

Parking Brake

ADJUSTMENT
Rear Drum Brakes

NOTE: Make certain that the rear brakes are properly adjusted before adjusting the parking brake.

1. Make a check of the parking brake linkage for the free movement of all the cables. Lubricate, if necessary.

2. Depress the parking brake pedal 1½ in.

3. Raise the rear wheels off the ground.

4. While holding the cable stud to keep it from turning, tighten the equalizer nut until a light drag is felt on either wheel when they are spun in the forward direction.

5. When the parking brake is released there should be no brake shoe drag.

Rear Disc Brakes

1. Lubricate the parking brake cables at the underbody rub points, and at the equalizer hooks on Seville.

2. Make sure the parking brake pedal is in the fully released position.

3. Raise the rear wheels.

4. Hold the brake cable stud from turning and tighten the equalizer nut until the cable slack is removed.

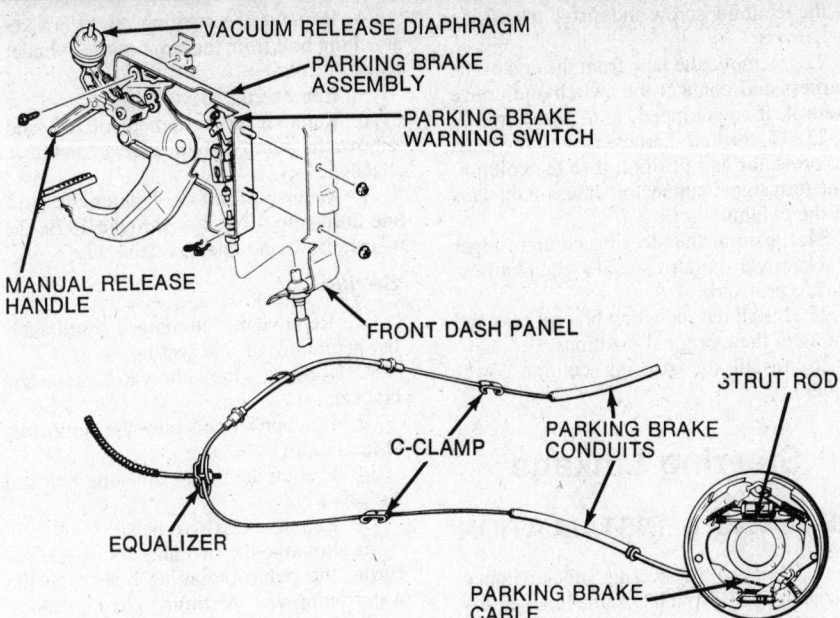

Parking brake system details for full-size models (© Cadillac Div., G.M. Corp.)

5. Make sure the caliper levers are against the stops on the caliper housing after tightening the equalizer nut.

6. If the levers are off the stops, loosen the cable until the levers return to stops.

7. Operate the parking brake several times to check the adjustment.

8. Lower the car.

NOTE: The levers must be on the caliper stops after adjustment. Back off the adjuster if necessary.

Master Cylinder

REMOVAL & INSTALLATION

NOTE: It is possible to remove the master cylinder unit without removing the power booster from the vehicle.

1. Disconnect and plug the front and rear brake lines at the master cylinder.

2. Remove the two securing nuts which hold the master cylinder to the power booster.

3. Remove the master cylinder.

4. To install, reverse the removal procedure. Bleed the hydraulic system.

STEERING

Steering Wheel

REMOVAL & INSTALLATION

——— CAUTION ———

Do not strike the end of the steering column in an effort to remove the steering wheel. Delicate parts of the column may be damaged.

1. Disconnect the negative battery cable.

2. Remove the screws on the underside of the steering wheel spokes near the center and remove the pad assembly.

3. Remove the horn contact wire from the plastic tower by pushing it on the wire and turning it counterclockwise. Turning the ignition on will facilitate the removal.

4. Remove the nut holding the steering wheel to the steering shaft.

5. On tilt wheels, remove locking lever and flange and screw assembly.

6. Matchmark the shaft and wheel for installation in the original position and use a puller to remove the steering wheel.

7. On installation, tighten the steering shaft nut to 30 ft. lbs. (through 1981) 35 ft. lbs. (1982 and later)

Turn Signal Switch

REMOVAL & INSTALLATION

Standard Column

1. Disconnect the negative battery cable.

2. Remove the steering wheel.

3. Insert a thin screwdriver into the lockplate and remove the lockplate cover assembly.

4. Install a spring compressor onto the steering shaft. Tighten the tool to compress the lockplate and the spring. Remove the snap-ring from the groove in the shaft.

——— CAUTION ———

When the snap-ring is removed do not allow the shaft to slide out the bottom of the column.

5. Remove the lockplate and slide the turn signal cam and the upper bearing preload spring and the thrust washer off the upper steering shaft.

6. Remove the steering column lower cover.

7. Unscrew the turn signal lever and remove it from the column.

8. On cars with cruise control:

a. Disconnect the cruise control wire from the harness near the bottom of the column.

b. Remove the harness protector from the cruise control wire.

c. Remove the turn signal lever. Do not remove the wire from the column.

9. Remove the two vertical bolts at the steering column upper support. Remove the shim packs. Keep the shims in order for reinstallation.

10. Remove the four screws securing the column upper mounting bracket to the column and remove the bracket.

11. Disconnect the turn signal wiring and remove the wires from the plastic protector.

12. Remove the turn signal switch mounting screws.

13. Slide the switch connector out of the bracket on the steering column.

14. If the switch is known to be bad, cut the wires and discard the switch. Tape the connector of the new switch to the old wires, and pull the new harness down through the steering column while removing the old wires.

15. If the original switch is to be reused, wrap tape around the wire and connector and pull the harness up through the column. It may be helpful to attach a length of wire or string to the harness connector before pulling it up through the column to facilitate installation.

16. After freeing the switch wiring protector from its mounting, pull the turn signal switch straight up and remove the switch, switch harness, and the connector from the column.

17. To reassemble reverse the removal procedure.

Tilt and Telescopic Columns

1. Disconnect the battery and remove the steering wheel.

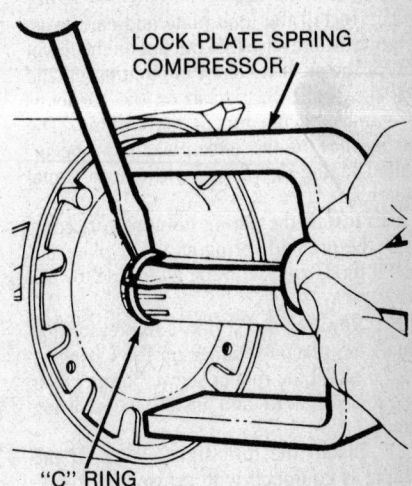

Removing the C-ring

2. Remove the rubber sleeve bumper from the steering shaft.

3. Remove the plastic retainer with a screwdriver, disengaging the tabs on the retainer from the C-ring.

4. Compress the upper steering shaft preload spring with a spring compressor and remove the C-ring. When installing the spring compressor, pull the upper shaft up about 1 in. and turn the ignition to the LOCK position to hold the shaft in place.

5. Remove the spring compressor and remove the upper steering shaft lock plate, horn contact carrier and the preload spring.

6. Remove the steering column lower cover.

7. Unscrew and remove the turn signal lever. If equipped with cruise control:

a. Disconnect the cruise control wire from the harness near the bottom of the steering column.

b. Remove the lever attaching screw and carefully pull the lever out enough to allow the removal of the turn signal switch.

8. Remove the two nuts and shim packs from the upper column support. Keep the shims together as a unit for reinstallation.

9. Remove the bracket from the steering column by removing the two attaching screws from each side.

10. Disconnect the turn signal wiring harness from the car harness and remove the wires from the plastic protector.

11. Remove the turn signal switch retaining screws and pull the switch up out of the steering column.

12. If the switch is to be replaced, cut the wires from the switch and tape the new switch connector to the old wires. Carefully pull the new harness down through the column as the old wires are removed.

13. If the old switch is to be reused, tape the connector to the wires and carefully pull the harness up out of the column.

14. Feed the wiring harness down through the steering column to replace the old switch.

15. Secure the switch in the steering column.

16. Install the upper shaft preload spring.

17. Install the lock plate and carrier assembly. Make sure that the flat on the lower end of the steering shaft is pointing up and that the small plastic tab on the carrier is up or nearest the top of the column. The flat surface of the lock plate must be installed facing down against the turn signal switch.

18. Install the spring compressor, compress the preload spring and lock plate and install the C-ring with the wide side toward the keyway.

19. Remove the spring compressor and install the plastic retainer on the C-ring.

20. Install the rubber sleeve bumper over the steering shaft and install the steering wheel.

21. Install the turn signal lever. If the vehicle is equipped with cruise control:

a. Secure the lever to the switch with

the retaining screw and install the wiring harness.

22. Remove the tape from the end of the harness and connect the switch and cruise control, if so equipped, to the car harness.

23. Cover both harnesses with the plastic protector and position it to the column. The turn signal connector slides on the tabs of the column.

24. Position the steering column upper bracket over the turn signal switch harness plastic protector.

25. Install the mounting bracket nuts and shims in their original positions.

26. Install the steering column lower cover.

Steering Linkage

REMOVAL & INSTALLATION

1. Remove the steering shock damper, if so equipped, from the frame bracket. Remove cotter pins and nuts from outer tie-rod pivots.

2. Remove outer tie-rod pivots from steering knuckles using a tie-rod end puller.

3. Remove idler arm screws and lockwashers from side member.

4. Remove pitman arm cotter pin, nut and washer at steering linkage.

5. Remove steering linkage from pitman arm.

6. Remove intermediate rod with tie-rods and idler arm attached.

7. Remove cotter pins and nuts from idler arm pivot and inner tie-rod pivots.

8. Remove tie-rod.

9. Remove idler arm from intermediate rod.

10. Remove dust seals from pitman arm and idler arm pivot studs.

11. Remove outer tie-rod pivots by loosening nuts on outer clamp bolts and unscrewing the pivot from adjuster tubes.

12. To install, reverse removal procedure. Tighten the idler arm nuts to 35 ft. lbs. on the full size cars and to 40 ft. lbs. on the Seville models. Install the cotter pin. Do not tighten more than 10 ft. lbs. over specification to align the cotter pin.

Power Steering Pump

REMOVAL & INSTALLATION
Except Seville

1. On models equipped with the 350 V8 diesel engine, partially remove the cruise control servo, if so equipped, and also the generator. Leave the through bolt in and tilt the alternator up and out of the way.

2. Disconnect and plug the fluid lines at the pump. On some models it may be necessary to remove the vacuum pump if so equipped.

3. Remove the nut securing the pump mounting bracket to the cylinder head stud.

4. Remove the steering pump bracket attaching bolt from the front of the cylinder block.

5. Remove the drive belts.

6. Remove the bottom pivot bolt and remove the pump with the bracket and filter attached.

7. Reverse to install. Tighten the fluid line fittings to 40 ft. lbs. through 1979, 20 ft. lbs. 1980 and later models.

Seville

1. Remove the alternator as outlined in the beginning of this section.

2. Remove the alternator adjusting bracket.

3. Disconnect and plug the fluid lines at the pump.

4. Loosen the pump adjusting bolt and the pivot bolt.

5. Remove the drive belt.

6. Remove the two nuts and spacer securing the pump mounting bracket to the water pump and the timing chain cover.

7. Remove the bracket bolt and remove the pump with the bracket attached.

8. Reverse to install. Tighten the fluid line fittings to 40 ft. lbs.

NOTE: To adjust the power steering pump belt, loosen the pump to mounting bracket screws, and move the pump upward until the belt is tight. Tighten the mounting bracket screws. Run the engine faster than idle speed, and turn the steering wheel full right or left. If the belt squeals, it is too loose and should be tightened more.

Steering Gear

REMOVAL & INSTALLATION

1. Position container under gear to catch dripping fluid.

2. Disconnect pressure and return lines at steering gear. Plug all openings to prevent loss of fluid and entrance of dirt into system.

3. Disconnect stone shield from return pipe.

4. Remove pinch bolt and disconnect flex coupling from gear:

—————— CAUTION ——————
Failure to disconnect the flexible coupling from the steering gear stub shaft can result in damage to the steering gear and/or intermediate shaft. This damage can cause loss of steering control which could result in a vehicle crash and bodily injury.

5. Raise car and support it with jack stands.

6. Remove one nut and lockwasher from pitman shaft. Using pitman arm puller, remove pitman arm from steering gear.

7. Remove three screws and flat washers that hold gear to frame side rail, and lower gear assembly down and out of car.

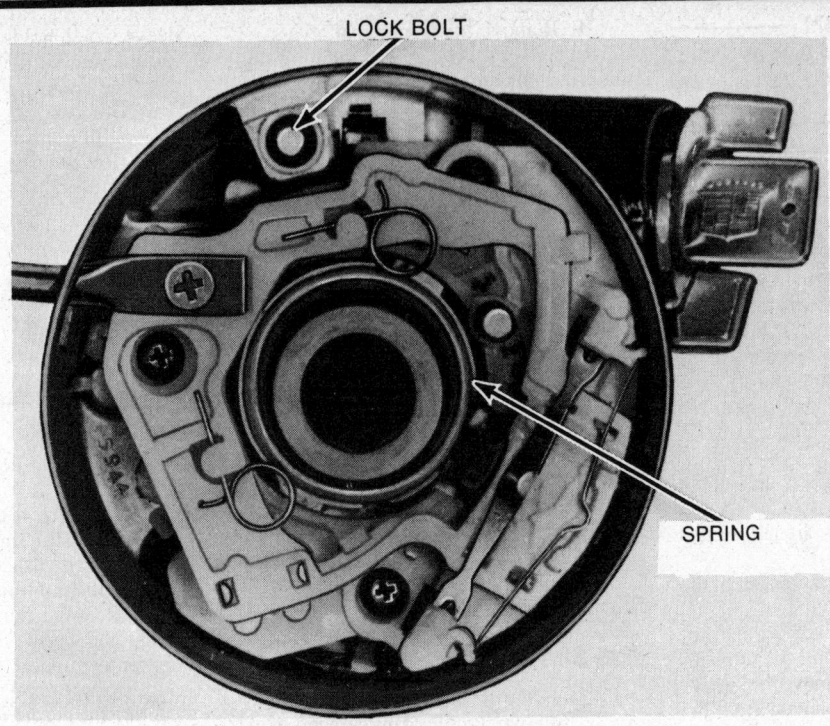

Turn signal switch (© Cadillac Div., G.M. Corp.)

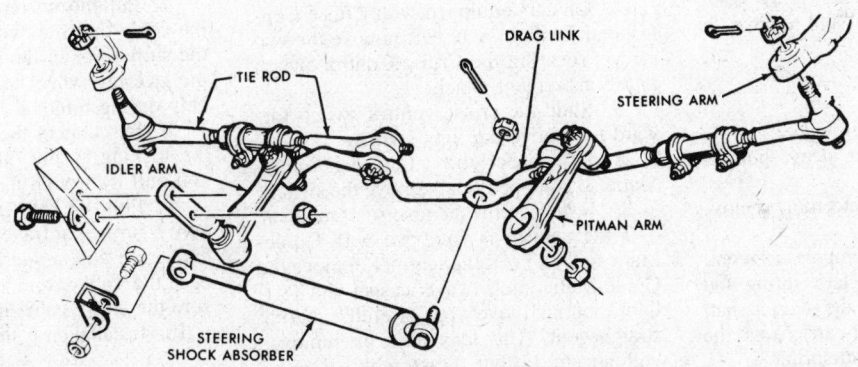

Cadillac steering linkage (© Cadillac Div., G.M. Corp.)

8. Installation is the reverse of removal. The following torques are necessary; pinch bolt 30 ft. lbs., steering gear bolts 70 ft. lbs, pitman arm 185 ft. lbs.

Ignition Switch

REPLACEMENT

1. Disconnect the negative battery terminal.
2. Position lock cylinder in lock position.
3. Remove steering column lower cover.
4. Loosen two nuts on upper steering column, allowing column to drop.

─────── **CAUTION** ───────

Do not remove the nuts, as the column may bend under its own weight.

5. Disconnect ignition switch connector at switch.
6. Remove two screws securing ignition switch to steering column. Remove switch.
7. To install, first assemble ignition switch on actuator rod and adjust to lock position, as follows:

a. Standard Column—Hold switch actuating rod stationary with one hand while moving switch toward bottom of column until switch reaches end of travel (Acc. position). Back off one detent, then, with key also in lock position, tighten two switch mounting screws to 35 inch lbs.

b. Tilt column—Hold switch actuating rod stationary with one hand while moving switch toward upper end of column until switch reaches end of travel (Acc. position). Back off one detent, then,

with key also in lock position, tighten two switch mounting screws to 35 inch lbs.

8. Connect wires, tighten two steering column nuts, install lower cover and reconnect battery.

Lock Cylinder

REPLACEMENT

Standard Steering Column

1. Remove the steering wheel.
2. Remove the lockplate cover assembly.
3. After compressing the lockplate spring, remove the snap-ring from the groove in the shaft.

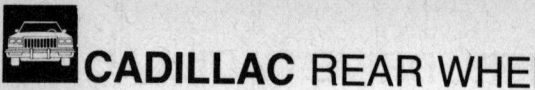

— CAUTION —

When the snap-ring is removed do not allow the shaft to slide out the bottom of the column.

4. Remove the lockplate and slide the turn signal cam and the upper bearing preload spring off the upper steering shaft.

5. Remove the thrust washer from the shaft.

6. Remove the hazard warning switch from the column along with the turn signal lever.

7. Use the following procedure if the car is equipped with Cruise Control.

　a. Attach a piece of stiff wire to the connector on the Cruise Control switch harness.

　b. Gently pull the harness up and out of the column.

8. Remove the turn signal switch mounting screws.

9. Slide the switch connector out of the bracket on the steering column.

10. After freeing the switch wiring protector from its mounting, pull the turn signal switch straight up and remove the switch, switch harness and the connector from the column.

11. Turn the ignition switch to on or run and then insert a small drift pin into the slot next to the switch mounting screw boss. Push the lock cylinder tab and remove the lock cylinder.

Tilt Column

1. Remove the steering wheel.

2. Remove the rubber sleeve bumper from the steering shaft.

3. Using an appropriate tool, remove the plastic retainer.

4. Using a spring compressor, compress the upper steering shaft spring and remove the C-ring. Release the steering shaft lockplate, the horn contact carrier, and the upper steering shaft preload spring.

5. Remove the four screws which hold the upper mounting bracket and then remove the bracket.

6. Slide the harness connector out of the bracket on the steering column. Tape the upper part of the harness and connector.

7. Disconnect the hazard button and position the shift bowl in Park. Remove the turn signal lever from the column.

8. Use the following procedure for cars with Cruise Control.

　a. Remove the harness protector from the harness.

　b. Attach a piece of piano wire to the switch harness connector.

　c. Before removing the turn signal lever, loop a piece of piano wire and insert it into the turn signal lever opening. Using the wire, pull the Cruise Control harness out through the opening.

　d. Pull the rest of the harness up through and out of the column.

　e. Remove the guide wire from the connector and secure the wire to the column.

f. Remove the turn signal lever.

9. Pull the turn signal switch up until the end connector is within the shift bowl. Remove the hazard flasher lever. Allow the switch to hang.

10. Place the ignition key in the run position.

11. Depress the center of the lock cylinder retaining tab with a screwdriver and then remove the lock cylinder.

12. To install reverse the procedure.

INSTRUMENT PANEL

Headlight Switch

REMOVAL & INSTALLATION
Full Size Models

1. Disconnect the battery ground.

2. Remove the left instrument panel insert.

3. Remove the three screws securing the switch to the instrument panel.

4. On cars equipped with Cruise Control and Twilight Sentinel, remove the two screws securing the Cruise Control switch to the instrument panel.

5. Slide the cruise control switch forward to remove the light switch.

6. Disconnect the wires and Guide-Matic, if equipped, and remove the switch.

7. Installation is the reverse of removal.

If the vehicle is equipped with Guide-Matic and/or Twilight Sentinel, remove the Guide-Matic knob, wave washer and Twilight Sentinel lever by carefully pulling straight out. The lens may be removed without any further disassembly. Remove the spanner nut to remove the potentiometer(s) from the backplate.

Seville

1. Disconnect the negative battery cable.

2. Remove the lower steering column cover.

3. Remove all the attaching screws from the left side lower instrument panel.

4. Pull the panel down to gain access to the electrical connectors. Disconnect the wiring and mark the wires for proper installation.

5. Pull the headlight switch to the ON position. Depress the spring loaded button on the bottom of the switch and remove the shaft and knob.

6. Remove the four headlight switch case attaching screws and separate the switch from the instrument panel.

7. Remove the sleeve holding the headlight switch to the case.

8. On models without the Guide-Matic or Twilight Sentinel option, remove the

sleeve which holds the escutcheon, washer and the lens to the back plate. On models with the option, remove the Guide-Matic knob, washer and sentinel lever by carefully pulling them out.

9. Reverse the above to install.

Speedometer Cable

REMOVAL & INSTALLATION
Full Size Models

1. Remove the left instrument panel insert.

2. Disconnect the battery ground.

3. Place the shift lever in Park and remove the screw securing the shift indicator cable to the column.

4. Remove the two upper screws securing the cluster assembly to the panel horizontal support.

5. Remove the two lower inside screws securing the cluster to the horizontal support.

6. Remove the screw located directly above the steering column securing the cluster to the speedometer mounting plate.

7. Pull the cluster outward to disengage the cable and remove the cluster. Placing the shift lever in the low range and tilting the steering wheel all the way down will help during removal.

8. Disconnect the cable housing from the locking spring on the mounting plate and pull it through the firewall.

9. Pull the core from the cable. If the core is broken or frayed on the transmission end, raise and support the car and disconnect the cable from the transmission. Be sure the entire cable has been removed.

10. Installation is the reverse of removal.

Seville

1. Disconnect the battery ground.

2. Remove the lower steering column cover.

3. Remove the 4 screws securing the cluster bezel to the instrument panel and cluster.

4. Press the bezel downward slightly, rotate the top outward and remove the bezel.

5. Place the shift lever in Park and remove the screw holding the indicator cable to the column.

6. Remove the two upper cluster screws and the two lower inboard screws.

7. Pull the cluster outward to disengage the cable.

8. Disconnect the cable housing from the locking spring and pull it through the firewall.

9. Remove the core from the cable. If the core is broken, raise the car and remove the cable from the transmission.

10. Installation is the reverse of removal.

Instrument Cluster

REMOVAL & INSTALLATION

1. Loosen the set screw in the left climate control outlet door knob and remove knob.

2. Remove left climate control air outlet grille using tool J24612-01 or its equal.

3. Remove screws securing bezel to instrument panel. One is located inside of left A/C outlet grille opening.

4. Remove screws in lower steering column cover.

5. Disconnect steering column seal on lower surface and remove trim plate.

6. Disconnect negative battery cable.

7. With shift lever in park, remove shift indicator clip from steering column.

8. Remove upper screws securing cluster assembly to instrument panel horizontal support.

9. Pull cluster outward and release the speedometer cable.

NOTE: Disconnect the speed control sensor electrical connector if so equipped.

10. Disconnect the printed circuit connector from cluster.

11. Remove the cluster.

NOTE: Removal or installation can be done by placing shift lever in low range and tilting the wheel to the lowest position if so equipped.

12. Installation is the reverse of removal.

WINDSHIELD WIPERS

Wiper Motor

REMOVAL & INSTALLATION

1. Disconnect the negative battery cable.

2. Remove the cowl screen.

3. Reach through the opening and disengage the transmission drive link from the wiper crank arm by loosening two nuts.

4. Disconnect the wiring and washer hoses.

5. Remove the bolts that secure the wiper/washer unit to firewall.

6. Remove the entire assembly.

7. To install, reverse the removal procedure, making sure the wiper crank arm is in the Park position.

Wiper Blade

REPLACEMENT

Two methods are used to retain the blades to the arms. One method uses a press type tab. When the tab is depressed, the blade assembly can be slid off the arm. The other method uses a spring retainer. A suitable tool must be inserted on top of the spring and the spring pushed downward. The blade assembly can then be slid off the pin.

The rubber element can be replaced separately from the blade. Replacement procedures are given in the Maintenance Section at the rear of this book.

RADIO

REMOVAL & INSTALLATION

All Except Seville

1. Remove the radio knobs and anti-rattle springs. Disconnect the negative battery terminal.

2. Remove the two hex nuts securing the bezel to the radio.

3. Remove the two center air conditioning outlet grilles. Remove the one screw in each outlet.

4. Remove the maplights and remove the center panel insert.

5. Unbolt and remove the radio from the panel.

6. Disconnect the wiring.

7. Installation is the reverse of removal.

Seville

1. Disconnect the negative battery ground.

2. Loosen the right forward screw which secures the fuel injection electronic control unit cover to the unit.

3. Remove the remaining three screws from the cover.

4. Remove the three screws which secure the unit to the panel supports.

5. Carefully lower the control unit enough to disconnect the three electrical connectors from the left hand side and the hose from the front of the unit. Remove the unit.

6. Remove the screw securing the climate control outlet extension to the heater case.

7. Disconnect the antenna.

8. Remove the radio support rod.

9. Remove the control knobs, anti-rattle springs, control rings and both hex nuts.

NOTE: The control knobs on radios with 8-track are retained with 5/64 in. allen screws.

10. Remove the radio. Installation is the reverse of removal.

FUSES

The fuse block is located beneath the instrument panel above the headlight dimmer floor switch. Fuse holders are labeled as to their service and the correct amperage. Always replace blown fuses with new ones of the correct amperage. Otherwise electrical overloads and possible wiring damage will result.

FUSIBLE LINKS

Fusible links are sections of wire, with special insulation, designed to melt under electrical overload. Replacements are simply

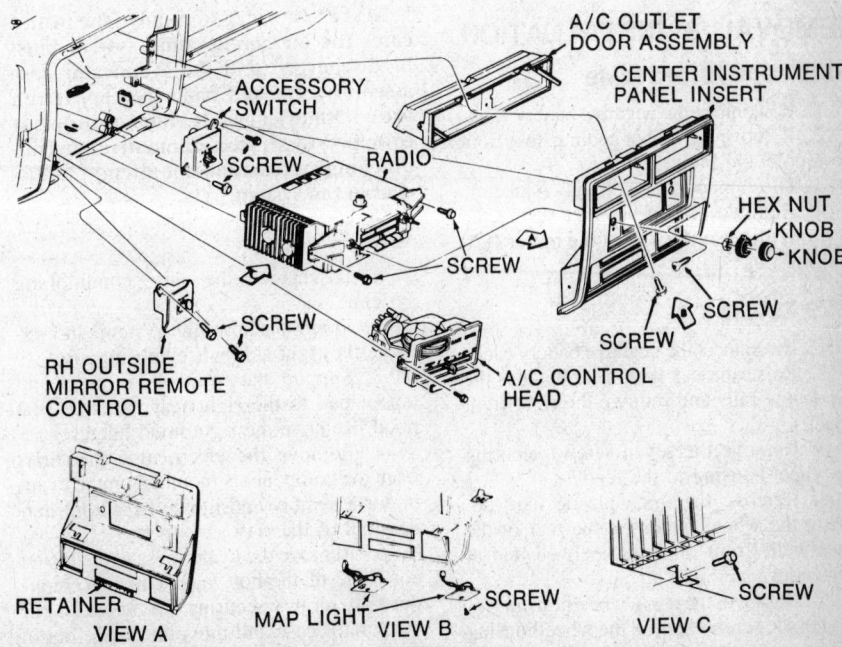

RETAINER VIEW A — MAP LIGHT VIEW B — SCREW — SCREW VIEW C

1977 and later full-size car radio details (© Cadillac Div., G.M. Corp.)

spliced into the wire. There may be as many as five of these in the engine compartment wiring harnesses. These are:

1. Horn relay to fuse panel circuit—one link.
2. Charging circuit, from the starter solenoid to the horn relay—two links.
3. Starter solenoid to ammeter circiut—one link.
4. Horn relay to rear window defroster circuit—one link.

The fusible links are all two wire gauge sizes smaller than the wires they protect.

NOTE: Most models have fusible links at these locations.

REPLACEMENT

1. Disconnect the battery ground cable.
2. Disconnect the fusible link from the junction block or starter solenoid.
3. Cut the harness directly behind the connector to remove the damaged fusible link.
4. Strip the harness wire approximately ½ in.
5. Connect the new fusible link to the harness wire using a crimp on connector. Soder the connection using rosin core solder.
6. Tape all exposed wires with plastic electrical tape.
7. Connect the fusible link to the junction block or starter solenoid and reconnect the battery ground cable.

HEATER

Heater Blower

REMOVAL & INSTALLATION

All Except 1979 Seville

1. Disconnect the negative battery cable.
2. Remove the rubber cooling hose from the nipple and blower motor.
3. Disconnect the electrical connector.
4. Remove the screws that secure the motor to the case, then twist the motor 180° and pull out.

1979 Seville

1. Disconnect the negative battery cable.
2. Raise the car with a jack under the side frame rails and remove the right front wheel.
3. Remove the seven screws securing the wheel housing to the fender.
4. Remove the three plastic nails securing the wheelhousing at the rear of the wheelwell, front of the wheelwell and at the fender.
5. Remove the two wheelhousing-to-cowl brace screws behind the wheelhousing seal at the rear of the wheelwell.

6. Remove the battery, or batteries, and the supporting tray or trays.
7. Remove the wheelhousing-to-radiator support attaching screws and retainer from under the horns.
8. Carefully remove the wheelhousing from the vehicle. Some prying and bending may be necessary.
9. Refer to Steps 2–4 of the above procedure.
10. Reverse to install.

Heater Core

REMOVAL & INSTALLATION

Full Size Models

1. Disconnect wiring from the blower, resistors, and thermostatic cycling switch.
2. Remove the right windshield washer nozzle.
3. Remove the right air inlet screen from the plenum.
4. Remove the two screws securing the thermostatic cycling switch to the module and carefully reposition the switch off the module cover.
5. Remove the 16 fasteners securing the module cover and remove the cover.
6. Remove the hoses from the core nipples.
7. Remove one screw and retainer holding the core to the frame at the top.
8. Place the temperature door in the max. hot position and reach through the temperature housing and push the lower forward corner of the heater core away from the housing. This causes the core to snap out of the lower clamp. The core may not be removed in a vertical direction.
9. Installation is the reverse of removal.

Seville

NOTE: In order to remove the heater core, the air conditioning system must be discharged and the evaporator case assembly removed from the car. If you are not knowledgeable about or properly equipped to service automotive air conditioning systems, do not attempt to discharge the system.

1978

1. Discharge the air conditioning system.
2. Drain the cooling system and remove the right side wheelhousing strut.
3. Support the front of the hood and tape a pad to the right rear corner of the hood. Remove the right hood hinge.
4. Remove the electrical connections from the components mounted on the evaporator assembly and move the wiring harness out of the way.
5. Remove the heater hose at the heater core side of the hot water valve. Remove the two screws securing the valve to the evaporator case and move the valve out of the way.

6. Jack up the front of the car and support it with jackstands. Remove the right front wheel.
7. Remove the five screws securing the wheelhousing to the fender at the wheel opening.
8. Remove the two screws attaching the wheelhousing at the front.
9. Remove the three plastic retainers securing the wheel housing seal at the rear of the wheelwell, front of the wheelwell, and at the fender, forward of the wheel opening.
10. Remove the two screws behind the wheelwell securing the wheelhousing to the cowl brace.
11. Remove the battery and battery tray.
12. Remove the three screws and retainer securing the wheelhousing to the radiator support under the horns.
13. Remove the wheelhousing damper upper mounting bolt and move the damper out of the way.
14. Remove the wheelhousing from the car. Some prying and bending may be necessary.
15. Remove the heater hoses from the heater core nipples.
16. Disconnect and plug the refrigeration lines at the receiver.
17. Remove the screws and nuts retaining the evaporator case and remove the case from the vehicle.
18. Separate the case and remove the heater core.
19. Install in the reverse order. Use new O-rings at the connection of the refrigeration lines to the receiver. Fill the cooling system and evacuate and recharge the air conditioning system.

1979

1. Drain the cooling system.
2. Remove the right side wheelhousing as outlined in Blower Motor Removal and Installation for the 1979 Seville.
3. Remove the hoses from the heater core pipes and plug the pipes to prevent spillage. Handle the core pipes carefully.
4. Remove the radio knobs, anti-rattle spring, control rings and both hex nuts.
5. Remove the ash tray receptacle.
6. Through the ash tray opening, remove the screw from behind the right side of the right hand instrument panel insert.
7. Close the ash tray door and remove the three instrument panel insert attaching screws.
8. Pull the insert out enough to disconnect the electrical connectors from the cigarette lighter and any other accessory switches.
9. Remove the mirror control cable clip from the back and remove the insert.
10. Remove the radio as outlined under Radio Removal and Installation.
11. Remove the door and the inner liner of the glove compartment.
12. Remove the litter receptacle.

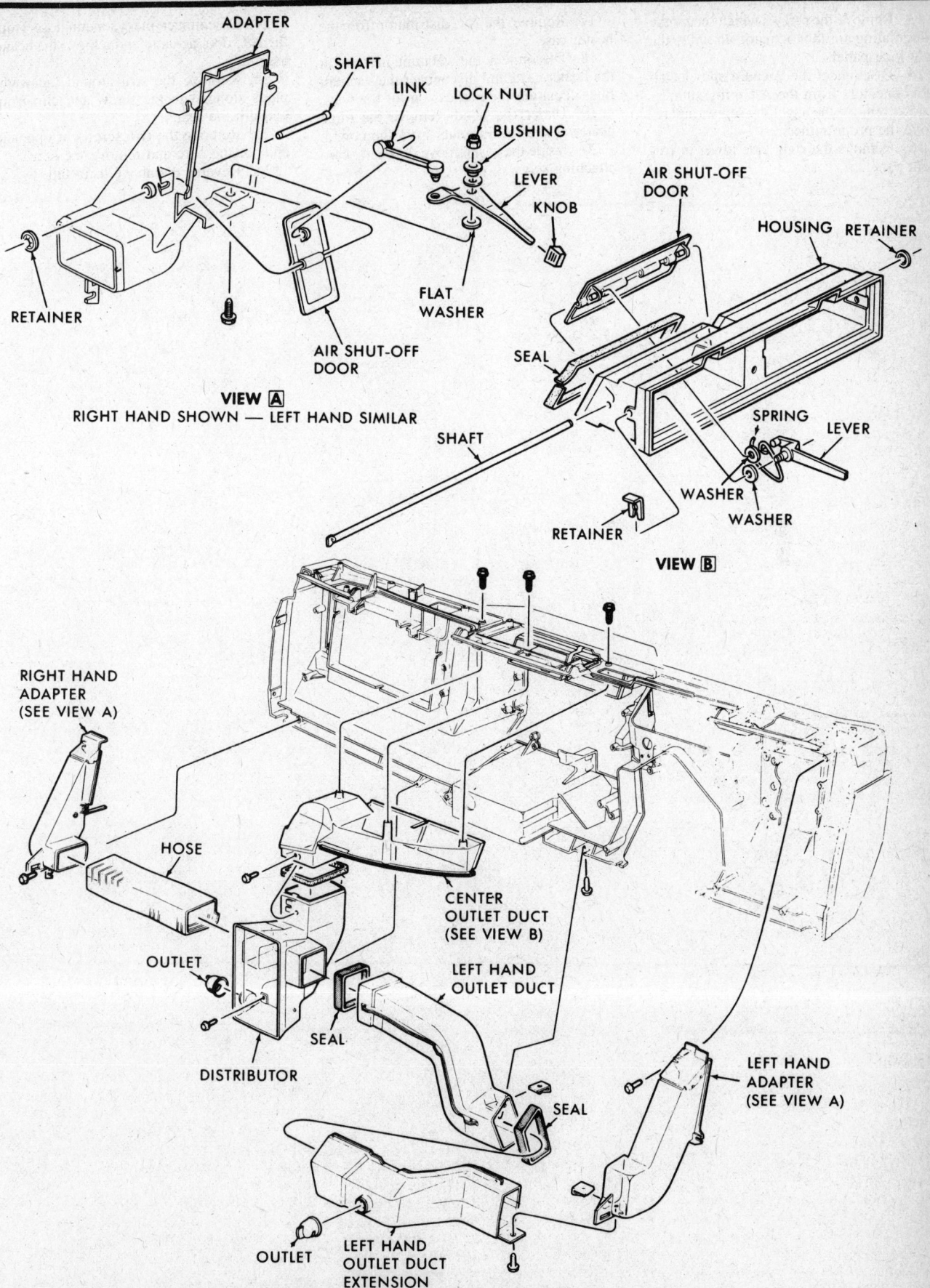

ADAPTER

SHAFT

LINK

LOCK NUT

BUSHING

AIR SHUT-OFF DOOR

HOUSING   RETAINER

LEVER

KNOB

RETAINER

FLAT WASHER

AIR SHUT-OFF DOOR

SEAL

VIEW A
RIGHT HAND SHOWN — LEFT HAND SIMILAR

SHAFT

SPRING   LEVER

WASHER

WASHER

RETAINER

VIEW B

RIGHT HAND ADAPTER (SEE VIEW A)

HOSE

OUTLET

DISTRIBUTOR

SEAL

CENTER OUTLET DUCT (SEE VIEW B)

LEFT HAND OUTLET DUCT

LEFT HAND ADAPTER (SEE VIEW A)

SEAL

OUTLET

LEFT HAND OUTLET DUCT EXTENSION

Air conditioning ducts---DeVille and Brougham

13. Remove the screws which secure the recirculating air door actuator shroud to the right kick panel.

14. Disconnect the vacuum and electrical connectors from the A/C programmer.

15. Remove the attaching screws and remove the programmer.

16. Remove the right side lower instrument panel.

17. Remove the A/C distributor from the heater case.

18. Disconnect the vacuum harness at the heater case and disconnect the vacuum lines. Position the harness out of the way.

19. Under the hood, remove the three heater case attaching nuts from the cowl.

20. Inside the car, remove the heater case attaching screws.

21. Disconnect the vacuum hose from the A/C door actuator and remove the heater assembly.

22. Remove the seal around the water pipes along with the screw and clip from beneath the seal.

23. Remove the two screws at opposite ends of the core and remove the core.

24. Reverse the above to install.

Chevrolet
Corvette

YEAR IDENTIFICATION

1978 Corvette

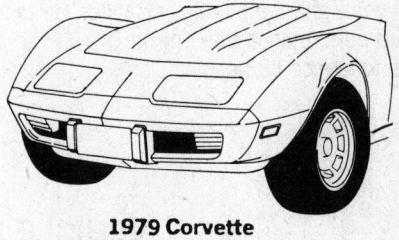

1979 Corvette

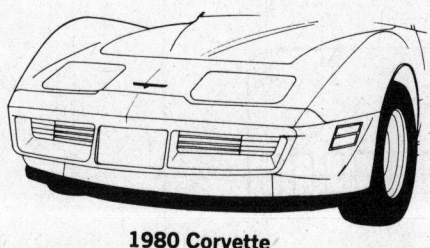

1980 Corvette

1981-82 Corvette

1984—85 Corvette

VEHICLE IDENTIFICATION NUMBER (VIN)

It is important for servicing and ordering parts to be certain of the vehicle and engine identification. The (VIN) (vehicle identification number) is a 13 or 17 digit number visible through the windshield on the driver's side of the dash and contains the vehicle and engine identification codes. It can be interpreted as follows:

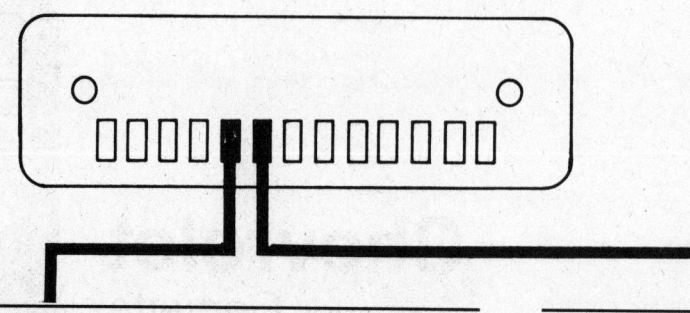

Engine Code						Model Year Code	
Code	Cu. In.	Liters	Cyl.	Carb.	Eng. Mfg.	Code	Year
L①	350	5.7	8	4 bbl.	Chev.	8	78
4②	350	5.7	8	4 bbl.	Chev.	9	79
8①	350	5.7	8	4 bbl.	Chev.	A	80
H	305	5.7	8	4 bbl.	Chev.		
6②	350	5.7	8	4 bbl.	Chev.		

The thirteen digit Vehicle Identification Number can be used to determine engine application and model year. The 6th digit indicates the model year, and the 5th digit identifies the factory installed engine.
① Standard performance L48 engine
② High performance L82 engine

VEHICLE IDENTIFICATION NUMBER (VIN)

It is important for servicing and ordering parts to be certain of the vehicle and engine identification. The VIN (vehicle identification number) is a 13 or 17 digit number visible through the windshield on the driver's side of the dash and contains the vehicle and engine identification codes. It can be interpreted as follows:

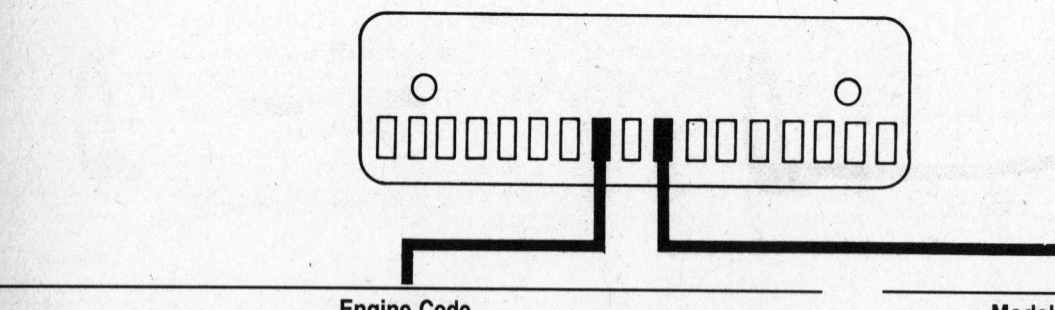

Engine Code						Model Year Code	
Code	Cu. In.	Liters	Cyl.	Carb.	Eng. Mfg.	Code	Year
6	350	5.7	8	4 bbl.	Chev.	B	81
8	350	5.7	8	TBI	Chev.	C	82
						E	84
						F	85

The seventeen digit Vehicle Identification Number can be used to determine engine application and model year. The 10th digit indicates the model year, and the 8th digit identifies the factory installed engine. There is no 1983 Corvette model.
T.B.I.—Throttle body (fuel) injection

GENERAL ENGINE SPECIFICATIONS

Year	Engine No. of Cyl.- Displacement (Cu. In.)	Engine V.I.N. Code	Fuel Delivery	Horsepower @ rpm①	Torque @ rpm (ft. lbs.)①	Bore × Stroke (in.)	Compression Ratio	Oil Pressure @ 2000 rpm
'78	8-350	L	4 bbl.	185 @ 4000	280 @ 2400	4.000 × 3.480	8.4:1	40
	8-350	4	4 bbl.	220 @ 5200	260 @ 3600	4.000 × 3.480	8.9:1	40
'79	8-350	8	4 bbl.	195 @ 4000	285 @ 3200	4.000 × 3.480	8.2:1	45
	8-350	4	4 bbl.	225 @ 5200	270 @ 3600	4.000 × 3.480	8.9:1	45
'80	8-305	H	4 bbl.	180 @ 4200	255 @ 2000	3.736 × 3.480	8.6:1	45
	8-350	8	4 bbl.	190 @ 4400	280 @ 2400	4.000 × 3.480	8.2:1	45
	8-350	6	4 bbl.	230 @ 5200	275 @ 3600	4.000 × 3.480	9.0:1	45
'81	8-350	6	4 bbl.	190 @ 4200	280 @ 1600	4.000 × 3.480	8.2:1	45
'82	8-350	8	TBI	200 @ 4200	285 @ 2800	4.000 × 3.480	9.0:1	45
'84	8-350	8	TBI	205 @ 4300	290 @ 2800	4.000 × 3.480	9.0:1	50–65
'85	8-350	NA	MFI	240 @ 4300	330 @ 2900	4.000 × 3.480	9.0:1	50–65

NOTE: All engines used in the Corvette are manufactured by Chevrolet Motor Division, G.M. Corp.
NA-Not available at time of publication
TBI-Throttle body fuel injection system
MFI-Multiport fuel injection system
①Horsepower and torque are SAE net figures. They are measured at the rear of the transmission with all accessories installed and operating. Since the figures vary when a given engine is installed in different models, some are representative rather than exact.

TUNE UP SPECIFICATIONS

(When analyzing compression test results, look for uniformity among cylinders rather than specific pressures.)

Year	Engine No. of Cyl.- Displacement (Cu. In.)	V.I.N. Code	Option Code	Horse-power	Spark Plugs Type (A.C.)	Gap (in.)	Ignition Timing (deg)⑤⑥ Man. Trans.	Auto. Trans.	Valves Intake Opens ⑦(deg)	Fuel Pump Pressure (psi)	Idle Speed (rpm)⑤ Man. Trans.	Auto. Trans.
'78	8-350	L	L48	185	R45TS	.045	6B	6B(8B)	28	7½–9	700	500②
	8-350	4	L82	220	R45TS	.045	12B	12B	52	7½–9	900	700
'79	8-350	8	L48	195	R45TS	.045	6B	③	28	7½–9	④	④
	8-350	4	L82	225	R45TS	.045	12B	12B	25	7½–9	④	④
'80	8-305	H	LG4	180	R45TS	.045	4B	4B	28	7½–9	④	④
	8-350	8	L48	190	R45TS	.045	6B③	6B	28	7½–9	④	④
	8-350	6	L82	230	R45TS	.045	12B	12B	52	7½–9	④	④
'81	8-350	6	L81	190	R45TS	.045	6B	6B	38	7½–9	④	④
'82	8-350	8	L83	200	R45TS	.045	①	④	32	9–13	①	④
'84	8-350	8	L83	205	R45TS	.045	④	④	32	9–13	④	④

TUNE UP SPECIFICATIONS

(When analyzing compression test results, look for uniformity among cylinders rather than specific pressures.)

Year	Engine No. of Cyl.-Displacement (Cu. In.)	V.I.N. Code	Option Code	Horse-power	Spark Plugs Type (A.C.)	Gap (in.)	Ignition Timing (deg)⑤⑥ Man. Trans.	Auto. Trans.	Valves Intake Opens ⑦(deg)	Fuel Pump Pressure (psi)	Idle Speed (rpm)⑤ Man. Trans.	Auto. Trans.
'85	8-350	NA	NA	240	R45TS	.045	④	④	NA	NA	④	④

NOTE: All models use electronic ignition systems. No adjustments are necessary. The underhood specifications sticker often reflects tuneup specification changes made in production. Sticker figures must be used if they disagree with those in this chart. Part numbers in this chart are not recommendations by Chilton for any product by brand name.

B–Before Top Dead Center
① Manual transmission not available
② High Altitude: 600
③ Except Calif. and High Altitude: 6B Calif. and High Altitude: 8B
④ See Underhood Sticker
⑤ See text for procedure
⑥ Figure in parentheses indicates California engine
⑦ All figures Before Top Dead Center

FIRING ORDER

NOTE: To avoid confusion, always replace spark plug wires one at a time.

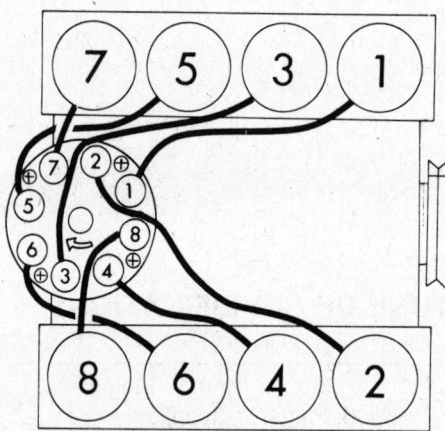

GM (Chevrolet) V8
Engine firing order: 1-8-4-3-6-5-7-2
Distributor rotation: clockwise

CAPACITIES

Year	Engine No. of Cyl.-Displacement (Cu. In.)	Engine Crankcase (Add 1 Qt For New Filter)	Transmission (Pts To Refill After Draining) Manual 4-Speed	Automatic ②	Drive Axle (pts)	Gasoline Tank (gals)	Cooling System (qts) With Heater	With A/C
'78	8-350	4	3	8	3.75	24	21	21
'79	8-350	4	3①	8	4	24	21	21

CAPACITIES

Year	Engine No. of Cyl.- Displacement (Cu. In.)	Engine Crankcase (Add 1 Qt For New Filter)	Transmission (Pts To Refill After Draining)			Gasoline Tank (gals)	Cooling System (qts)	
			Manual 4-Speed	Automatic ②	Drive Axle (pts)		With Heater	With A/C
'80–'81	8-305, 350	4	3	8	4	24	21	22
'82	8-350	4	—	10	4	24	21	22
'84–'85	8-350	4	3.5③	8	3.75	20	15	15

① Optional close-ratio 4-speed—2.75
② For pan removal and filter change only —Not applicable
③ Four speed overdrive uses Dexron® II in the overdrive section

VALVE SPECIFICATIONS

Year	Engine No. of Cyl.- Displacement (cu. in.)	Seat Angle (deg)	Face Angle (deg)	Spring Test Pressure (lbs. @ in.)	Spring Installed Height (in.)	Stem-To-Guide Clearance (in.)		Stem Diameter (in.)	
						Intake	Exhaust	Intake	Exhaust
'78–'80	8-305, 350 (std. perf.)	46	45	180–188 @ 1.25	1²³⁄₃₂	.0010– .0027	.0010– .0027	.3410– .3417	.3410– .3417
'78–'80	8-350 (high perf.)	46	45	196–204 @ 1.25	1²³⁄₃₂①	.0010– .0027	.0010– .0027	.3410– .3417	.3410– .3417
'81–'82	All	46	45	196–204 @ 1.25	1²³⁄₃₂①	.0010– .0027	.0010– .0027	.3410– .3417	.3410– .3417
'84–'85	8-350	46	45	194–206 @ 1.25②	1²³⁄₃₂①	.0010– .0027	.0010– .0027	.3410– .3417	.3410– .3417

① 1¹⁹⁄₃₂ for the exhaust valve spring
② 1.16 exhaust valve

CRANKSHAFT AND CONNECTING ROD SPECIFICATIONS

(All measurements are given in inches)

Year	Engine No. of Cyl.- Displacement (Cu. In.)	Crankshaft				Connecting Rod		
		Main Brg. Journal Dia.	Main Brg. Oil Clearance	Shaft End-Play	Thrust on No.	Journal Diameter	Oil Clearance	Side Clearance
'78–'85	8-305, 350	2.4484– 2.4493①	.0008– .0020②	.002– .006	5	2.0988– 2.0998	.0013– .0035	.008– .014

① Nos. 2, 3, 4—2.4481–2.4490; No. 5— 2.4479–2.4488
② Nos. 2, 3, 4—.0011–.0023; No. 5— .0017–.0033

C371

TORQUE SPECIFICATIONS

(All readings in ft. lbs.)

Year	Engine No. of Cyl.- Displacement (Cu. In.)	Cylinder Head Bolts	Rod Bearing Bolts	Main Bearing Bolts	Crankshaft Balancer Bolt	Flywheel-to- Crankshaft Bolts	Manifold	
							Intake	Exhaust
'78–'85	8-305, 350	65	45	75①④	60	60	30③	②

① Engines with 4-bolt mains—Outer bolts: 70 ft. lbs.
② Center bolts—30, end bolts 20
③ Also torque the throttle body plate bolts to 20–34 ft. lbs. on 1982 and 84 models.
④ 1984—80 ft. lbs.

PISTON AND RING SPECIFICATIONS

(All measurements are given in inches)

Year	Engine No. of Cyl.- Displacement (Cu. In.)	Ring Gap			Ring Side Clearance			Piston-to-Bore Clearance (in.)
		Top Compression	Bottom Compression	Oil Control	Top Compression	Bottom Compression	Oil Control	
'78–'80	8-305, 350 (exc. L82)	.010–.020	.010–.023①	.015–.065	.0012–.0032	.0012–.0032	.0020–.0080	.0007–.0027
'78–'80	8-350 (L82)	.010–.020	.010–.023	.015–.065	.0012–.0032	.0012–.0032	.0020–.0080	.0036–.0061
'81	8-350	.010–.020	.010–.023	.015–.065	.0012–.0032	.0012–.0032	.0020–.0080	.0046–.0061
'82	8-350	.010–.020	.010–.023	.015–.065	.0012–.0032	.0012–.0032	.0020–.0080	.0025–.0045
'84–'85	8-350	.010–.020	.010–.025	.015–.055	.0012–.0032	.0012–.0032	.002–.007	.00025–.00035

① 185 and 195 horsepower engines—.010–.025

WHEEL ALIGNMENT SPECIFICATIONS

(All measurements stated in degrees, unless noted)

Year	Front Wheel Caster		Front Wheel Camber		Rear Wheel Camber		Toe-In (in.)	
	Range	Preferred	Range	Preferred	Range	Preferred	Front Wheel	Rear Wheel
'77–'78	2P–2½P	2¼P	¼P–1¼P	¾P	⅞N ± ¼	—	3/16–5/16	1/16 ± 1/32
'79–'80	2P–2½P	2¼P	¼P–1P	¾P	½N ± ½	—	3/32–5/32	3/32 ± 1/32
'81–'82	1¾P–2¾P	2¼P	¼P–1¼P	¾P	0 ± ½	—	¼ ± 1/16	1/16 ± 1/16
'84–'85	2½P–3½P	3P	½N–½P		11/32 ± ¼	—	¼ ± 1/16	0 ± 1/32

N—Negative
P—Positive

CHARGING SYSTEM

For further information on the charging system, please refer to "Charging and Starting" in the Unit Repair Section.

Alternator

REMOVAL & INSTALLATION

1. Disconnect the negative battery terminal.
2. Disconnect and identify the wire leads from the alternator.
3. Remove the alternator brace bolt, then remove the drive belt.
4. Remove the alternator pivot attaching bolt and remove alternator from vehicle.
5. To install, reverse the above procedure and adjust the belt tension.

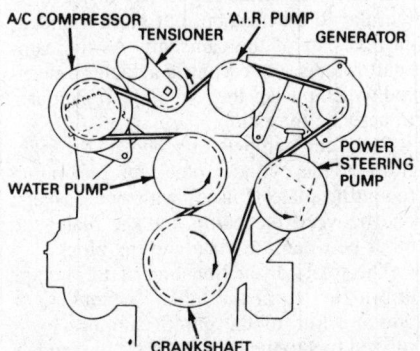

Serpentine drive belt tensioner—1984 and later

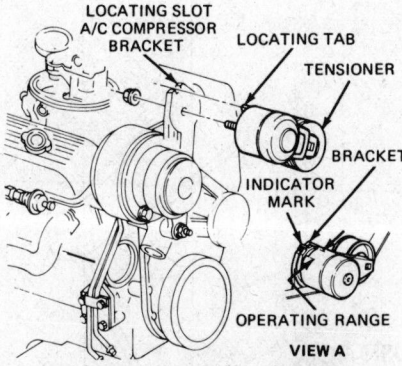

Serpentine drive belt installation

NOTE: On all 1984 and later engines, a single serpentine belt is used to drive all accessories formerly driven with V-belts. Belt tension is maintained by a spring loaded tensioner which has the ability to maintain belt tension over a broad range of belt lengths. There is an indicator to make sure the tensioner is adjusted to within its operating range. The belt tension is adjusted with a ½ inch breaker bar inserted into the square hole

in the tensioner arm and a belt tension gauge (BT 7825 or equivalent) to 120–140 lbs, as read on the tension gauge installed between the alternator and the A.I.R. pump.

STARTING SYSTEM

For further information on the starting system, please refer to "Charging and Starting" in the Unit Repair section.

Starter

REMOVAL & INSTALLATION

1. Disconnect the battery cables at the battery.
2. Raise the front of the vehicle to a convenient working height and support with jackstands.
3. Disconnect the wiring from the starter solenoid. Replace each connector nut as the terminals are removed as the thread sizes differ between connectors. Note or tag the wiring positions to avoid improper connections during installation.
4. Remove the front starter support bracket and the heat shield (if so equipped).
5. Loosen the two main starter mounting bolts, support the starter and remove the bolts. Lower the starter front end first and remove the starter.
6. Reverse the previous steps to install the starter. Torque the two main starter mounting bolts to 25–35 ft. lbs.

Solenoid Replacement

1. Remove the screw and washer from the motor connector strap terminal.
2. Remove the two solenoid retaining screws.
3. Twist the solenoid clockwise to remove the solenoid flange key from the keyway in the housing. Remove the solenoid.
4. To reinstall the unit, place the return spring on the plunger and place the solenoid body on the drive housing. Push the solenoid inward and turn counterclockwise to engage the flange key. Install and tighten the solenoid retaining screws and the screw and washer which secure the strap terminal.

IGNITION SYSTEM

For further information on the ignition system, please refer to "Electronic

Ignition Systems" in the Unit Repair Section.

Distributor

REMOVAL

1. Rotate the engine until the timing mark on the balancer is aligned with the top dead center mark (TDC or "O") on the timing tab scale.
2. Remove the air cleaner assembly and the ignition shielding.
3. With the ignition switch off, disconnect the feed, module, and tachometer wiring from the drivers side of the distributor cap. Do so by releasing the connector retaining tabs and pulling downward on the connectors. On 1981 and later models, also disconnect the four-wire connector installed in the wiring from the opposite side of the distributor.

—— CAUTION ——
Never allow the "Tach" terminal to touch ground.

4. Locate the locking tabs of the spark plug wire retaining ring (on the distributor cap). Move each of the two locking tabs outward to release the retaining ring. With the plug wires still attached to the ring, carefully remove the retaining ring from the distributor cap. Pull the plug wires out of the locating looms (if so equipped) and move the ring (with the wires still attached) out of the way.
5. Release the distributor cap hold-down screws (push downward and turn counterclockwise) and lift the cap assembly off of the distributor. Check that the firing tip of the rotor is pointed at the No. 1 terminal of the distributor cap; if it is not, rotate the engine one full revolution and again align the timing marks. Recheck the position of the rotor.
6. Disconnect the vacuum line from the distributor vacuum advance unit, if so equipped.
7. Disconnect the battery cables at the battery.
8. Mark the relationships between the following items:
   a. Rotor firing tip and distributor body
   b. distributor body and either the firewall or the intake manifold
The combination of these marks will assure that the distributor gear is properly meshed with the camshaft and the ignition timing will be close enough to start the engine after the distributor is reinstalled.
9. Remove the distributor hold-down bolt and plate.
10. Carefully pull the distributor from the engine. Note the rotation of the rotor as the distributor is pulled upward, caused by the angled distributor drive teeth.

—— CAUTION ——
Do not rotate the engine while the distributor is removed.

11. Installation is the reverse of removal.

INSTALLATION—ENGINE DISTURBED

1. Turn the crankshaft until the No. 1 cylinder is at the top of its compression stroke. Remove the No. 1 spark plug to feel the compression.

2. Align the timing mark on the vibration damper with the TDC indicator or 0 mark on the timing scale.

3. With distributor body oriented in its normal position hold the rotor pointing toward the No. 1 plug wire location, then turn the rotor approximately ⅛ turn counterclockwise and push the distributor down until it engages the camshaft, rotating the shaft slightly if necessary.

4. Press down on the distributor and crank the engine to make sure the oil pump shaft is engaged.

5. Return the crankshaft to No. 1 cylinder compression stroke with the timing marks aligned, then tighten the distributor clamp bolt.

6. Install the distributor cap, checking that the rotor points to the No. 1 terminal. Make sure that the spark plug wires are in their supports and are securely connected.

7. Connect distributor vacuum line (if so equipped) and primary wire.

8. Start engine and set the timing.

9. Install the ignition shielding.

HEI SYSTEM TACHOMETER HOOKUP

Connect one dwell/tach lead to the TACH terminal on the side of the distributor and the other to ground. Some tachometers must be connected to the TACH terminal and the battery positive terminal. Not all tachometers will operate correctly with the HEI

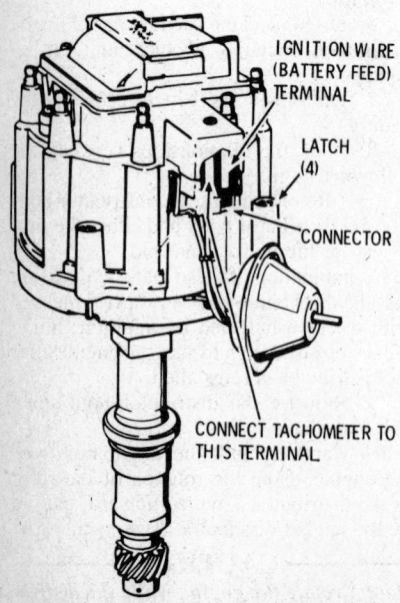

IGNITION WIRE (BATTERY FEED) TERMINAL

LATCH (4)

CONNECTOR

CONNECT TACHOMETER TO THIS TERMINAL

HEI system tachometer hookup

system. Check with the manufacturer if there is any doubt.

CAUTION

The TACH terminal should never be connected to ground.

When hooking up a remote starter switch, disconnect the BATT terminal.

Ignition Timing

NOTE: Before using the timing light, wipe the dirt and grease from the scale and mark the notch on the harmonic balancer with white paint or chalk. Refer to the underhood emissions label for the proper timing adjustment procedure.

The use of an inductive-pickup timing light is recommended for H.E.I. systems. Follow the timing light manufacturers instructions to attach the timing light. Due to the battery location of Corvettes, 12VDC timing lights may be connected as follows: positive lead-alternator BAT terminal; negative lead-ground on engine.

CAUTION

DO NOT use an older style timing light which requires piercing of the spark plug lead.

Disconnect the distributor spark advance hose and plug the vacuum opening. Start the engine and run it at idle speed. Aim the timing light at the degree scale just over the harmonic balancer. Adjust the timing by loosening the securing clamp and rotating the distributor until the desired ignition advance is achieved, then tighten the clamp. To advance the timing, rotate the distributor opposite to the normal direction of rotor rotation. Retard the timing by rotating the distributor in the normal direction of rotor rotation. On 1980 and later models with computer controlled emissions systems, follow the information on the underhood decal to set the timing which clamps around the plug wire.

The ignition timing of 1982–84 models is adjusted in basically the same manner as previously described. The exception to this is that the EST BYPASS wire from the distributor must be disconnected prior to the timing adjustment. Trace the four wires from the distributor housing which join at a common multi-connector, close to the distributor. Follow the tan wire with a black stripe (EST BYPASS wire) from the multiconnector. Past the multiconnector, the EST BYPASS wire has its own, single connector. Separate this connector before adjusting the timing. While the EST BYPASS wire is disconnected, the CHECK ENGINE light on the instrument panel will illuminate. After adjusting the timing, reconnect the EST BYPASS connector; the CHECK ENGINE light will go out.

NOTE: It is not necessary to adjust the idle speed on 1982 and later models

prior to the timing adjustment, though the engine must be at normal operating temperature.

1984 models incorporate an Electronic Spark Control (ESC) into the distributor which retards the spark advance when engine detonation occurs. If the controller fails, the result could be no ignition, no retard or full retard. Some engines will also have a magnetic timing probe hole for use with electronic timing equipment. Consult the manufacturer's instructions for the use of this equipment.

FUEL SYSTEM

Mechanical Fuel Pump

The 1978–81 Corvette fuel pump is a mechanically operated diaphragm-type pump. The camshaft of the engine has an eccentric (similar to a cam lobe, but more rounded) cast as part of the camshaft. As the camshaft rotates, the eccentric actuates a pushrod which pushes the fuel pump rocker arm to activate the pump.

The fuel pump is attached to the right front of the cylinder block. A fuel pump mounting plate is used, with two gaskets; one between the pump and the plate; the other between the plate and the block.

The inlet, or suction line of the pump, draws fuel from the tank. The outlet, or pressure line of the pump, supplies pressurized fuel to the carburetor. Some models use a third line, which is a vapor return. The purpose of the vapor return is to route the hot fuel and fuel vapor from the pump

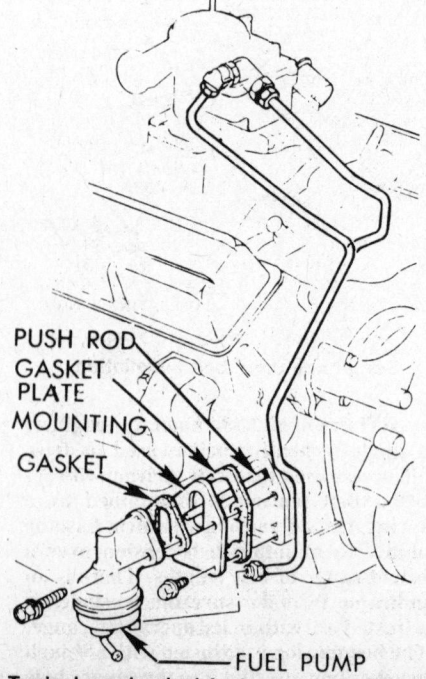

PUSH ROD
GASKET
PLATE
MOUNTING
GASKET

FUEL PUMP

Typical mechanical fuel pump mounting

back to the fuel tank, which considerably reduces the chance of vapor lock.

NOTE: The fuel pump is not rebuildable—if defective, it must be replaced.

REMOVAL & INSTALLATION

1. Disconnect the fuel inlet, outlet, and vapor return (if equipped) lines from the pump.

2. Remove the bolt from the front right face of the engine block which is almost opposite the forward pump mounting bolt. Insert a longer bolt (⅜ × 16 × 2 in.) in this hole and snug down the bolt. This will hold the fuel pump pushrod in place.

3. Remove the fuel pump mounting bolts and remove the fuel pump.

4. Installation of the pump is the reverse of the previous steps. Replace the fuel pump gasket(s) during installation. Start the engine and check the pump for proper operation, and check for leaks.

TESTING

If the engine exhibits a tendency to "starve-out", never assume that the fuel pump is defective until you test the pump. In most cases, a "starve-out" condition is caused by a weak ignition system, plugged fuel filter, or restricted fuel line.

1. Disconnect the fuel line from the carburetor. While this line is disconnected, check the fuel filter.

2. Run a piece of fuel-resistant rubber hose from the line to a graduated container.

3. Disconnect the BAT connector from the coil terminal.

4. Crank the engine. Fuel should be pumped into the container at a rate of 1 pint in 30 seconds.

5. Remove the added hose and container and connect a fuel pressure gauge to the fuel line. Crank the engine and read the highest pressure obtained on the gauge. See the Tune-Up Specifications chart.

If the pump failed the tests of either step 4 or 5, replace the pump as previously outlined. If the pump checked okay, remove the pressure gauge and reconnect the fuel line to the carburetor. Reconnect the ignition wiring as originally connected.

Electric Fuel Pump

An electric, impeller-type fuel pump is used on all 1982 and later Corvettes. The pump is designed to deliver a constant flow of fuel to the throttle body fuel injection units. The fuel pressure is regulated at the pressure regulator and compensator units, both of which are integrated with the throttle body injection units.

The pump is mounted inside the fuel tank as part of the fuel gauge sending unit. The pump can be replaced independently of the sending unit.

FUEL SYSTEM BLEEDING

— CAUTION —
This procedure must be performed before ANY work is done to the fuel system which requires that a fuel line be disconnected.

With the engine Off, remove the fuse from the fuse block designated "F.P." (fuel pump). Start the engine and allow it to run until it dies due to fuel starvation. Turn the ignition Off, replace the fuel pump fuse, and service the fuel system as required.

REMOVAL & INSTALLATION
1982 and later

1. Disconnect the battery cables at the battery.

2. Remove the fuel filler door and bezel.

3. Remove the fuel filler neck seal and drain hose.

4. Disconnect the lines and electrical connectors from the sending unit/pump assembly, and remove the screws which retain the assembly.

5. Remove the sending unit/pump as-

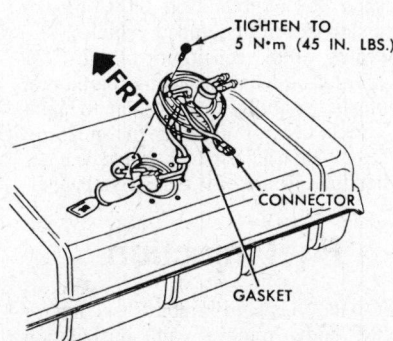

TIGHTEN TO 5 N·m (45 IN. LBS.)
FRT
CONNECTOR
GASKET

Electric fuel pump and gauge sender assembly, used with T.B.I.-equipped models

sembly and the gasket.

6. Separate the pump from the sending unit.

7. Installation is the reverse of the previous steps. DO NOT connect the battery until all other steps have been completed.

TESTING

NOTE: A special fuel pressure gauge (Kent-Moore J-29658) is required to safely perform this test.

1. Remove the air cleaner assembly and plug the vacuum connection(s) at the TBI unit.

2. Remove the fuel tube which connects between both TBI units.

NOTE: Use two line wrenches of the appropriate sizes to disconnect each fitting, one wrench to hold the large fitting, the other to loosen the smaller fitting.

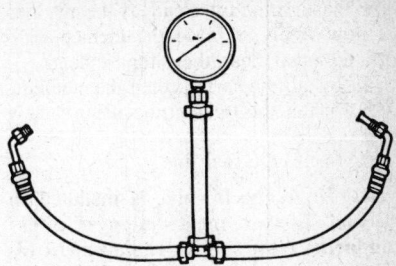

Fuel pressure gauge used to test the fuel pressure on T.B.I.-equipped models

— CAUTION —
A small amount of fuel will be released from the connections.

3. Install the fuel pressure guage between the two TBI units.

4. Turn the ignition switch On and check for fuel leakage at the gauge arrangement. If leakage is noted, turn the ignition switch Off and correct the leak.

5. Start the engine and read the fuel pressure on the gauge. Fuel pressure should be 9-13 psi. Turn the engine Off. Replace the fuel pump if the pressure is not within this range.

6. Remove the fuel pressure gauge, install the fuel tube assembly, and check for leaks.

7. Reinstall the air cleaner and connect the vacuum lines as originally connected.

Fuel Filter

REMOVAL & INSTALLATION
1978–81

Fuel filters are integral with the carburetor body. The filter element can be replaced as follows:

1. Disconnect the fuel line.

2. Remove the fuel filter nut from the carburetor.

3. Remove the filter element and spring.

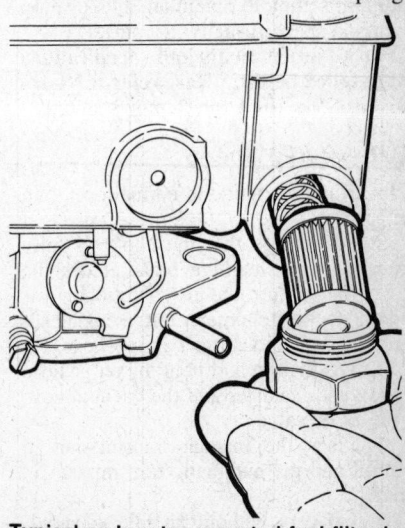

Typical carburetor-mounted fuel filter installation

Blow through the filter end. If the air does not flow freely, replace the element. Do not attempt to clean the filter element.

4. Install the spring, then the element.
5. Install the inlet fitting using a new gasket.
6. Install the fuel line.

NOTE: A check valve is installed in the fuel filter to meet roll over safety standards. New service replacement filters (paper) include the check valve. Install the check valve end of the filter toward the fuel line.

1982 and later

On these models, an inline fuel filter is used. The filter is mounted on the passenger-side frame rail, beneath the vehicle. Replacement is a simple matter of bleeding the system (as previously outlined), disconnecting the hoses, and dismounting the filter. Check for leaks after installing the new filter.

Carburetor

REMOVAL & INSTALLATION

1. Remove the air cleaner.
2. Disconnect the fuel line.
3. Disconnect the throttle linkage.
4. Disconnect and label all vacuum hoses.
5. Remove the retaining bolts.
6. Remove the carburetor.
7. Installation is the reverse of removal.

IDLE SPEED AND MIXTURE ADJUSTMENTS

When adjusting a carburetor with two idle mixture screws, adjust them alternately and evenly, unless otherwise stated.

In the following adjustment procedures the term "lean roll" means turning the mixture adjusting screws in (clockwise) from optimum setting to obtain an obvious drop in engine speed (usually 20 rpm).

For all adjustments and specifications not detailed below, please refer to "Carbureturs" in the Unit Repair section.

1978–79 Idle Speed

1. Run the engine to normal operating temperature.
2. Make sure that the choke is fully opened, set the parking brake, block the drive wheels, turn the air conditioning off and connect a tachometer to the engine according to manufacturer's instructions.
3. Disconnect and plug the purge hose at the vapor canister and the vacuum hose at the EGR valve.
4. Place the manual transmission in Neutral and the automatic transmission in Drive.
5. On cars without an idle solenoid, turn the idle speed screw to obtain the spec-

ified rpm. On cars with an idle solenoid, turn the idle screw to obtain the rpm specified on the underhood sticker. Disconnect the compressor clutch lead and turn the A/C on. Momentarily open the throttle to extend the solenoid plunger. Turn the solenoid screw to obtain the specified rpm.

1980 and Later Idle Speed

Refer to the underhood tune-up decal for specific procedures concerning your vehicle.

1978–80 Idle Mixture

Changes in the idle systems of these models make it impossible to adjust the mixture without the aid of a propane enrichment system, not available to the general public. Backing out the mixture screw, of itself, will have little or no effect. Most 1979 and later carburetors have mixture screws concealed under staked-in plugs. Mixture adjustments are possible only during carburetor overhaul.

1981 and Later Idle Mixture

The previously used propane enrichment or lean drop methods should not be used when adjusting carburetors used on Computer Command Control equipped vehicles.

Because of the sensitivity of the CCC system any adjustments to the carburetor can impair the ability of the system to maintain correct control of the air/fuel mixture.

The only time adjustments should be made is when the carburetor is being overhauled.

Fuel Injection

Refer to the "Camaro/Firebird" section for throttle body removal and installation procedures.

For further information on fuel injection, please refer to "Fuel Injection" in the Unit Repair section.

COOLING SYSTEM

Most 1979–82 Corvettes equipped with the heavy duty cooling system option use an auxiliary electric cooling fan. The auxiliary fan is used to supplement the engine-mounted fan during conditions of very high engine temperatures. The auxiliary fan circuit is energized anytime the ignition switch is in the RUN position, though the fan itself will not operate until the engine coolant temperature reaches 238°F., as sensed by the cylinder head-mounted coolant temperature sensor. When the coolant temperature decreases to approximately 201°F., the fan will turn off.

— **CAUTION** —
Keep hands, tools, clothing, etc. clear of the auxiliary fan. The fan can come on automatically even when the engine is not running.

1984 and later models use an electric, single-speed cooling fan mounted directly to the radiator shroud. Fan operation is determined by coolant temperature, operating only enough to maintain engine coolant at or below a preset maximum temperature. The cooling fan is energized through a relay controlled by a sending unit located in the right cylinder bank. The fan only operates when road speed is below 35 mph.

Radiator

REMOVAL & INSTALLATION

1978–82

1. Disconnect the negative battery cable at the battery.
2. Drain the cooling system.
3. Remove the air cleaner snorkel.
4. Raise the front of the vehicle and support it with jack stands.
5. Disconnect the fan shroud from the radiator support bracket.
6. If so equipped disconnect the automatic transmission cooler lines from the radiator.
7. Remove the radiator support brackets.
8. Disconnect the radiator upper and lower hoses and the overflow tube from the radiator.
9. Remove the radiator.
10. Installation is the reverse of removal. When installing the radiator make sure it is seated in the mounting pads. When replacing the radiator cap make sure the arrows line up with the overflow tube.

NOTE: It may be necessary to remove the fan shroud when removing the radiator.

1984 and later

1. Disconnect the negative battery cable.
2. Drain the cooling system.
3. Remove the upper and lower radiator hoses.
4. Remove overflow hose at radiator.
5. Remove A/C accumulator and move aside.
6. Remove transmission cooler line.
7. Remove fan wires from fan and shroud.
8. Remove fan to gain access to lower cooler line.
9. Remove transmission cooler line at fitting.
10. Remove upper shroud bolts.
11. Remove upper shroud.
12. Remove radiator.
13. Installation is the reverse of removal.

Water Pump

REMOVAL & INSTALLATION

1978–82

1. Drain the radiator and loosen the fan pulley bolts.
2. Disconnect the heater hose, lower radiator hose and, if applicable, the bypass hose at the water pump.
3. Remove the alternator upper brace. Loosen the swivel bolt and remove the fan belt.
4. Remove the fan blade and pulley. Replace a bent or damaged fan.

NOTE: Thermostatic fan clutches must be kept in an "in-car" position. When removed from the car the assembly should be supported so that the clutch disc remains in a vertical plane to prevent silicone fluid leakage.

5. Remove the water pump attaching bolts and, if applicable, the power steering-to-pump bolts and remove the pump and gasket.
6. Install the pump assembly using a new gasket. Coat the gasket on both sides with sealer. Tighten the ⅜ in. bolts to 30 ft. lbs.
7. Install the pulley and fan.
8. Connect the hoses and fill the cooling system.
9. Install the alternator upper brace and fan belt. Install the power steering pump bolt.
10. Adjust the belts, then start the engine and check for leaks.

1984 and later

NOTE: If the compressor lines do not have enough slack to move the compressor out of the way without disconnecting the refrigerant lines, the air conditioning system must be evacuated, using the required tools, before the refrigerant lines can be disconnected.

——————— CAUTION ———————
Do not disconnect any refrigerant lines unless you have experience with air conditioning systems. Escaping refrigerant will freeze any surface it contacts, including your skin and eyes.

1. Disconnect the negative battery cable.
2. Drain cooling system.
3. Remove serpentine drive belt.
4. Remove water pump pulley.
5. Remove AIR pump pulley.
6. Remove air management valve adapter.
7. Remove AIR pump.
8. Disconnect fuel inlet and return lines.
9. Remove rear A/C compressor braces.
10. Remove lower A/C compressor mounting bolt.
11. Remove A/C compressor and idler pulley bracket nuts.
12. Disconnect A/C compressor wires.

13. Slide mounting bracket forward and rear A/C compressor bolt.
14. Remove A/C compressor.
15. Remove right and left AIR hoses at check valve.
16. Remove AIR pipe at intake and power steering reservoir bracket.
17. Remove power steering reservoir bracket including top alternator bolt.
18. Remove lower AIR bracket on water pump.
19. Remove lower radiator and heater hose at water pump.
20. Remove water pump.
21. Installation is the reverse of removal. Tighten the water pump bolts 100-125 inch lbs.

Thermostat

REMOVAL & INSTALLATION

The thermostat is located on the front of the intake manifold directly in the center. It is not necessary to remove the top radiator hose to remove the thermostat.

1. Drain the cooling system about halfway.
2. Remove the two retaining bolts from the thermostat housing and lift up the housing with the hose attached. Remove the thermostat.
3. Insert the new thermostat, spring end down, and install the housing with a new gasket.

EMISSION CONTROLS

For all information on emission controls, please refer to "Emission Controls" in the Unit Repair section.

ENGINE

NOTE: Engine application and specification tables may be found at the beginning of this section. Refer to the "Chevrolet Rear Wheel Drive" section for the following removal and installation procedures: Intake and exhaust manifolds, cylinder head and valve system, timing case cover and pulley, camshaft, pistons and connecting rods.

REMOVAL

This procedure is basically the same for all models regardless of which engine is used. Certain pieces of optional equipment require minor specific changes, but overall, the operation remains the same.

1. Mark the relationship between each hood hinge, and the hood. Remove the hood.
2. Disconnect the battery cables at the battery.
3. Remove the air cleaner assembly and cover the carburetor. Mark any disconnected hoses so that they may be reinstalled properly.
4. Raise the front of the vehicle and support it with jackstands.
5. Locate and remove the engine coolant drain plugs. There is a drain plug on each side of the engine block, just above the top of the oil pan.
6. Loosen the radiator drain petcock and allow the coolant to drain from the radiator.
7. Remove the radiator hoses and the heater hoses.
8. Remove the radiator fan shroud, radiator, engine cooling fan(s) and fan clutch (if so equipped).
9. Drain the engine oil.
10. Remove the ignition shielding and release the distributor cap hold-down screws. Move the distributor cap (with wires still intact) out of the way (away from the firewall).
11. During this step, mark the location and/or connection point of each item so that these items may be properly reinstalled/reconnected.
   a. Disconnect the wiring from the starter and distributor.
   b. Disconnect the wiring from the alternator.
   c. Disconnect the wires from both the water temperature sender and oil pressure sender.
   d. Disconnect the engine ground wires.
   e. Disconnect the wiring from the idle solenoid, if so equipped.
   f. Disconnect the wiring from the various emission control items, as applicable (e.g.- oxygen sensor, barometric sensor, air control valve, etc.)
   g. Disconnect the accelerator and transmission linkage (or cables, on late models) at the carburetor or throttle body injection (T.B.I.) unit. If equipped with cables, unbolt the cable brackets from the engine.
   h. Disconnect the fuel supply and evaporative emission lines at the fuel pump. On TBI equipped models, disconnect the flexible hoses which connect the frame-mounted lines to the engine-mounted lines. In either case, plug the fuel supply line to prevent fuel siphoning from the tank.
   i. Disconnect any vacuum lines which run from a body-mounted item to an engine-mounted item (e.g.-power brake unit, cruise control, etc.)
12. Remove the drive belt(s) from both the power steering pump and the air conditioning compressor, if equipped with these items. Unbolt the pump and compressor from their respective mounting brackets and tie these units out of the way (with lines

still attached—DO NOT disconnect the refrigerant lines from the A/C compressor).

13. Disconnect the cruise control chain or cable from the engine, if so equipped.

14. Disconnect the exhaust pipes from the exhaust manifold flanges.

15. Remove the starter and solenoid as an assembly.

16. Remove the flywheel splash shield or convertor underpan, as applicable.

17. On automatic transmission equipped vehicles, remove the torque convertor-to-flywheel attaching bolts. Also, on these models, remove the transmission dipstick and tube.

18. On manual transmission equipped models, disconnect the linkage from each of the two levers of the clutch cross shaft. Loosen the outer ball stud nut and slide the stud out of the bracket slot. Move the cross shaft as required to clear the inboard ball stud. Remove the cross shaft from the vehicle.

19. Unless you have a suitable plug to prevent the transmission from draining after the driveshaft is removed, drain the transmission. On automatics without drain plugs it will be necessary to carefully remove the transmission pan, drain the fluid, and reinstall the pan. Using chain or heavy wire, secure the torque convertor to the transmission so that the convertor will not fall out as the engine is removed (auto. trans. only).

20. Matchmark the driveshaft to the rear axle flange. Unbolt the universal joint straps from the flange and remove the driveshaft assembly.

21. Support the transmission using a floor jack and remove the transmission-to-engine mounting bolts (auto, trans.) or the bellhousing-to-engine mounting bolts (man. trans.).

22. Remove the engine mount "through" bolts (one per side, positioned front-to-back).

23. Attach the engine lifting devices to the engine lifting brackets. Most engines are equipped with these brackets bolted to the intake manifold. If your engine does not have these brackets, remove the valve covers and the center head bolt from each cylinder head. Attach the lifting apparatus to the cylinder heads and secure with the cylinder head bolts.

———— CAUTION ————

Be absolutely sure that the chain which you are using has a weight rating greater than the weight of the engine. If possible, use chain rated at least at 1000 lbs. Avoid using chains with a lesser rating; serious injury could result if you use an inferior chain.

24. Move the engine forward, enough to disengage the engine from the transmission. Raise the engine enough to clear the front of the car and carefully move the engine over and away from the nose of the vehicle.

25. Service the existing engine as necessary, or install a replacement.

———— CAUTION ————

Do not allow the engine to hang from the engine hoist for an extended period of time. Never work on the engine when it is attached to the hoist. Support the engine safely on the floor or on an engine stand.

INSTALLATION

Installation of the engine is the reverse of the removal procedure. Make note of the following points before installing the engine:

1. Be sure that all wires, lines, etc., are connected as they originally were.

2. Be absolutely sure that the fuel lines are tightened properly and the throttle return springs are installed properly before attempting to start a new or rebuilt engine.

3. Follow all available bolt torque specifications.

4. Be sure to fill the engine, transmission, and cooling system with the correct quantities and qualities of fluids.

5. If a new camshaft was installed in the engine, the engine should be run for at least one hour after started at a minimum of 1500 rpm to properly "break-in" a new cam. If the cam manufacturers instructions differ, follow their recommendations.

6. Even though most head gasket manufacturers state that their gaskets require no "hot retorque", it is good practice to retorque the head bolts after the engine has been run for a couple of hours.

7. During engine installation, it is wise to replace "disposable" items such as radiator hoses, heater hoses, belts, and flexible fuel lines to prevent annoying (and possibly dangerous) post-installation problems associated with these items (e.g.-coolant leaks, fuel leaks, overheating, etc.).

8. Adjust all belt(s) to the proper tension. If the belts are new, recheck their tension after about a ½ hour of running time (with a new cam, do this after the cam "break-in" period). Note that a belt is considered "used" after just 5 minutes of running time, and additional belt stretch will usually occur.

9. ALWAYS check for coolant, fuel, and oil leaks after the engine is started. If there is leakage, turn off the engine, determine the source of leakage and fix the problem before restarting the engine.

10. Adjust the ignition timing after the engine is started.

Valve Clearance Adjustment

Engines equipped with hydraulic lifters VERY RARELY need adjustment of the valve lash. If the vehicle runs well and there is no audible "clicking" in the valvetrain, leave it alone. This is because removal of the valve covers on vehicles equipped with air conditioning, various emission controls, cruise control, etc., can be a major project in itself.

On air conditioned models, the A/C compressor must be moved out of the way to gain access to one of the valve covers. Do not disconnect the refrigerant lines to move the compressor.

LUBRICATION

Oil Pan

REMOVAL & INSTALLATION

NOTE: Before attempting this procedure, it may be necessary to remove the exhaust crossover pipe from the exhaust manifolds.

1. Disconnect the negative battery terminal.

2. Jack up your car and support it with jack stands.

3. Drain the oil and remove the filter.

4. Remove the starter and flywheel splash shield.

5. Disconnect the idler arm and lower steering linkage.

6. Remove the oil pan bolts and the pan.

7. Discard the old seals and gaskets.

8. On high performance engines the oil baffle must be removed before additional operations can be performed.

9. Installation is the reverse of removal. Remember to always install new gaskets.

Oil Pump

REPLACEMENT

The oil pump is located in the oil pan, and it is driven by a tang from the distributor shaft.

The oil pump is bolted to the rear, main bearing cap. Oil is fed from the pump up through the rear main bearing cap. The pump may be removed after removing the oil pan as previously outlined.

Rear Main Bearing Oil Seal

NOTE: Removal and installation procedures for Corvette engines are given in the "Camaro/Firebird" section.

CLUTCH

CAUTION

When servicing clutch parts, do not create dust by grinding or sanding clutch disc or by cleaning parts with a dry brush or with compressed air. (A water dampened cloth—NOT SOAKED—should be used) The clutch disc contains asbestos fibers which can become airborne if dust is created during servicing. Breathing dust containing asbestos fibers may cause serious bodily harm.

Clutches on 1978–82 models are of the diaphragm spring type. The throwout bearing is a ball bearing with no provision for lubrication. The throwout fork pivots on a ball stud which is mounted in the rear face of the bellhousing.

1984 and later models use a hydraulic clutch system. The hydraulic system consists of a master cylinder and a slave cylinder. When pressure is applied to the clutch pedal (pedal depressed), the push rod contacts the plunger and pushes it up the bore of the master cylinder. In the first 1/32 in. of movement, the center valve seal closes the port to the fluid reservoir tank and as the plunger continues to move up the bore of the cylinder, the fluid is forced through the outlet line to the slave cylinder mounted on the clutch housing. As fluid is pushed down the pipe from the master cylinder, this in turn forces the piston in the slave

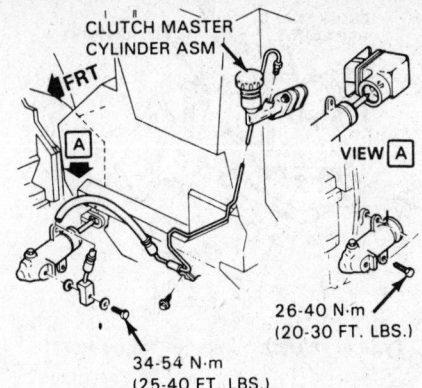

Exploded view of hydraulic clutch components

CLUTCH MASTER CYLINDER ASM

FRT

VIEW A

A

26-40 N·m
(20-30 FT. LBS.)

34-54 N·m
(25-40 FT. LBS.)

cylinder outward. A push rod is connected to the slave cylinder and rides in the pocket of the clutch fork. As the slave cylinder piston moves rearward the push rod forces the clutch fork and release bearing to disengage the pressure plate from the clutch disc. On the return stroke (pedal released), the plunger moves back as a result of the return pressure of the clutch. Fluid returns to the master cylinder and the final movement of the plunger lifts the valve seal off the seat, allowing an unrestricted flow of fluid between system and reservoir. A piston return spring in the slave cylinder preloads the clutch linkage and assures contact of the release bearing with the clutch release fingers at all times. As the driven disc wears, the diaphragm spring fingers move rearward forcing the release bearing, fork and push rod to move. This movement forces the slave cylinder piston forward in its bore, displacing hydraulic fluid up into the master cylinder reservoir, thereby providing the "self-adjusting" feature of the hydraulic clutch linkage system.

REMOVAL & INSTALLATION

1. Support the engine and remove the transmission as described in the Manual Transmission section.
2. Disconnect the clutch fork pushrod and spring. On 1984 and later models, remove the slave cylinder attaching bolts.
3. Remove the flywheel housing.
4. Slide the clutch fork from the ball stud and remove the fork from the dust boot. The ball stud is threaded into the clutch housing and is easily replaced, if necessary.
5. Install a clutch pilot tool.

NOTE: Look for the assembly markings "X" on the flywheel and the clutch cover (pressure plate assembly). If there are none, scribe marks to identify the position of the clutch cover relative to the flywheel.

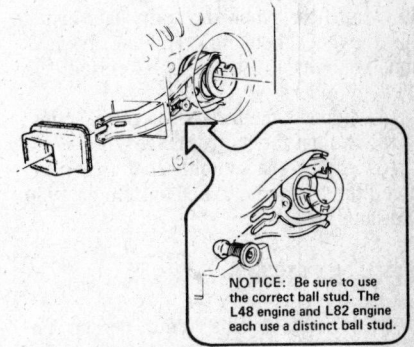

NOTICE: Be sure to use the correct ball stud. The L48 engine and L82 engine each use a distinct ball stud.

Ball stud attachment

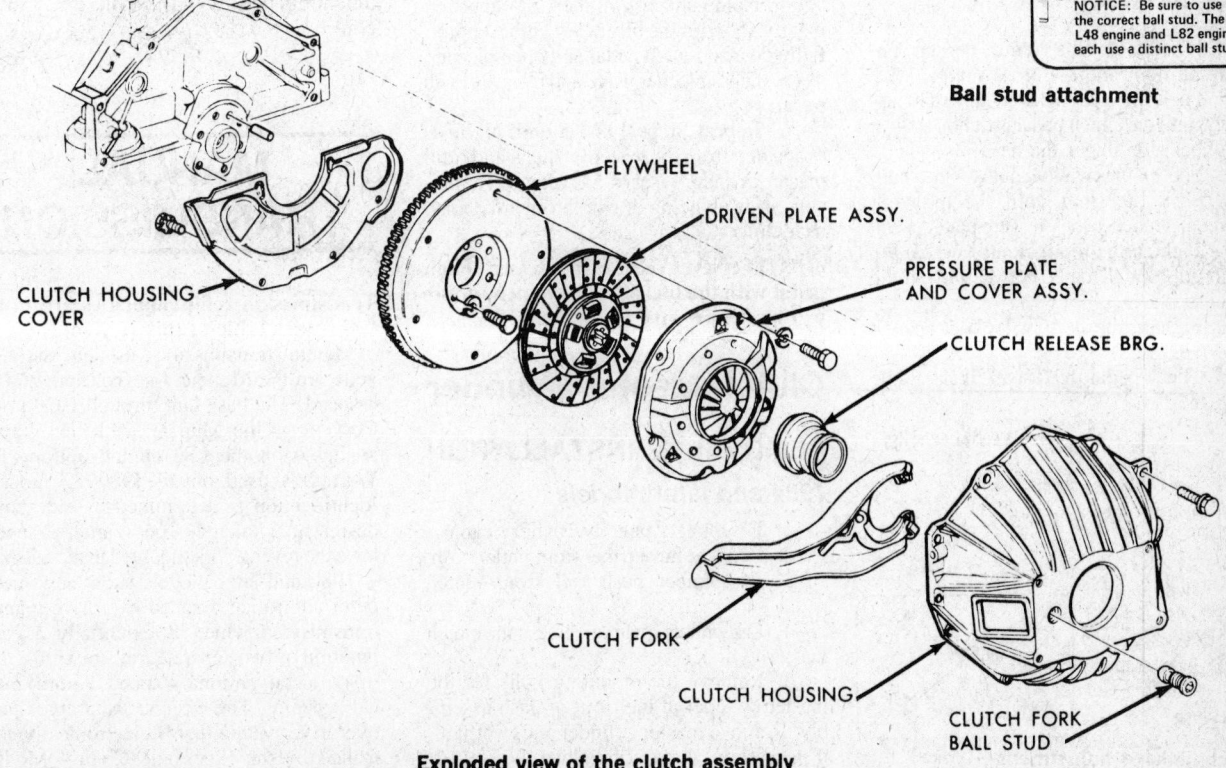

CLUTCH HOUSING COVER

FLYWHEEL

DRIVEN PLATE ASSY.

PRESSURE PLATE AND COVER ASSY.

CLUTCH RELEASE BRG.

CLUTCH FORK

CLUTCH HOUSING

CLUTCH FORK BALL STUD

Exploded view of the clutch assembly

6. Loosen the clutch cover bolts evenly until the spring pressure is relieved, then remove the bolts and clutch assembly.

7. Before installing, clean the pressure plate and the flywheel face.

8. Position the disc and pressure plate assembly on the flywheel and install a pilot tool.

NOTE: On single-disc models, the clutch disc is installed with the damper springs and slinger toward the transmission. On dual disc models, the discs are installed with the springs away from the flywheel.

9. Install the pressure plate assembly bolts. Make sure the mark on the cover is aligned with the mark on the flywheel. Tighten the bolts alternately and evenly to 35 ft. lbs.

10. Remove the pilot tool.

11. Remove the release fork and lubricate the ball socket and the fork fingers at the throwout bearing with graphite or Moly Grease. Reinstall the release fork.

12. Lubricate the inside recess and the fork groove of the throwout bearing with a light coat of graphite or Moly Grease.

13. Install the clutch release fork and dust boot in the clutch housing and the throwout bearing on the fork, then install the flywheel housing. Tighten flywheel housing bolts to 30 ft. lbs. Reinstall the slave cylinder.

14. Connect the fork pushrod and spring.

15. Adjust the shift linkage.

16. Adjust the clutch pedal free play. Bleed the hydraulic clutch system on 1984 and later models.

ADJUSTMENT

1. Disconnect the return spring between the floor and the cross shaft.

2. Push the clutch lever and shaft assembly until the clutch pedal is tightly against the rubber stop under the dash.

3. Loosen the two locknuts on the shaft.

4. Push the shaft until the throwout bearing just touches the pressure plate spring.

5. Tighten the top locknut towards the swivel until the distance between it and the swivel is 0.4 in.

6. Tighten the bottom locknut against the swivel.

7. Check pedal free travel. It should be 1–1½ in.

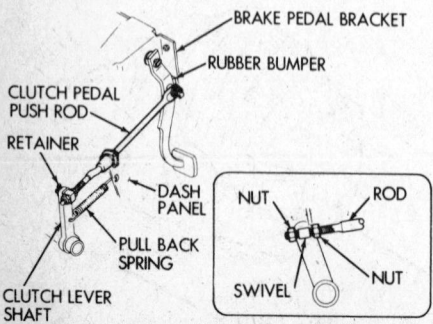

Clutch linkage adjustment—typical

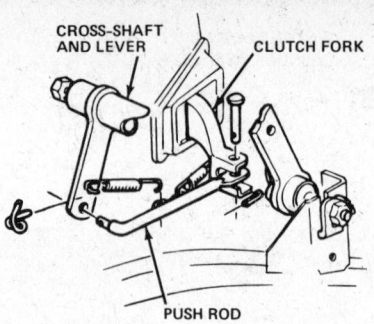

Typical clutch linkage adjustment

BLEEDING HYDRAULIC CLUTCH

1984 and later models

Bleeding air from the hydraulic clutch system is necessary whenever any part of the system has been disconnected, or level of fluid in the reservoir has been allowed to fall so low that air has been drawn into the master cylinder.

1. Fill master cylinder reservoir with new brake fluid conforming to Dot 3 or Dot 4 specifications.

————— **CAUTION** —————

Never, under any circumstances, use fluid which has been bled from a system to fill the reservoir as it may be aerated, have too much moisture content and possibly be contaminated.

2. Raise the vehicle and support it safely.

3. Remove the slave cylinder attaching bolts.

4. Hold slave cylinder at approximately 45° with the bleeder at highest point. Fully depress clutch pedal and open bleeder.

5. Close bleeder valve and release clutch pedal.

6. Repeat Steps 4 and 5 until all air is evacuated from the system. Check and refill master cylinder reservoir as required to prevent air from being drawn through the master cylinder.

NOTE: Never release a depressed clutch pedal with the bleeder screw open, or air will be drawn into the system.

Clutch Master Cylinder

REMOVAL & INSTALLATION

1984 and later models

1. Disconnect negative battery cable.

2. Remove hush panel from under dash.

3. Disconnect push rod from clutch pedal.

4. Disconnect hydraulic line at the clutch master cylinder.

5. Remove the mounting bolts for the master cylinder at the front of dash assembly. Remove master cylinder and overhaul, if necessary, as described later.

6. Install mounting bolts for, master cylinder at front of dash. Torque bolts to 15–22 ft. lbs. (20–30 Nm).

7. Connect hydraulic line at master cylinder.

8. Connect push rod at clutch pedal. Lubricate pivot point.

9. Install hush panel.

10. Fill master cylinder with new hydraulic fluid conforming to Dot 3 or Dot 4 specifications.

11. Raise vehicle and bleed hydraulic clutch system as previously described. Check all hydraulic lines and fittings for damage or leaks.

Clutch Slave Cylinder

REMOVAL & INSTALLATION

1. Disconnect negative battery cable.

2. Raise the vehicle and support it safely.

3. Disconnect hydraulic line at slave cylinder.

4. Remove mounting bolts for the slave cylinder at clutch housing.

5. Remove the push rod and slave cylinder from the vehicle. Overhaul, if necessary, as described later.

6. Install the hydraulic line to the slave cylinder.

7. Fill master cylinder with new brake fluid conforming to Dot 3 or Dot 4 specifications.

8. Bleed the hydraulic system as previously outlined.

9. Install slave cylinder to clutch housing. Lubricate leading end of cylinder with Girling Rubber Lube or equivalent. Torque mounting bolts to 20–30 ft. lbs. (26–40 Nm).

MANUAL TRANSMISSION

Transmission refill capacities are in the Capacities table of this section.

Manual transmissions used in the Corvette are the Muncie 4-speed, and Warner 4-speed. The base unit through 1979 in the Corvette is the Muncie, with the Warner available on the L82 engine option. The Warner is used on all 1980–82 models. Identification is determined by side cover design and linkage. The Warner 4-speeds have the reverse fork mounted in the tailshaft.

1984 and later models use a new, computer controlled 4 speed overdrive manual transmission which is essentially a combination of two separate transmissions. The first is a conventional 4 speed (83mm) manual system. The second is a two-speed overdrive system that is electronically controlled by the Electronic Control Module

(ECM). By combining these two transmissions, the complete unit is actually capable of operating with seven separate gear ratios. The two-speed (overdrive) unit performs its function using a planetary gear system in combination with two sets of clutch packs controlled by hydraulic pressure just like the automatic transmission. The ECM is programmed to control the entire overdrive unit by monitoring both road speed and throttle position. Overdrive is locked out when the transmission is in first gear and automatically engages at road speeds above 110 mph. The overdrive can be locked out by a switch on the console.

Shift Linkage

ADJUSTMENT

1978–81

1. Place the shift lever in the Neutral position.
2. Raise the vehicle and support it safely with jackstands.
3. Disconnect the shift rods from the transmission levers.
4. Preform this step for each of the transmission levers individually: Rotate the transmission lever counterclockwise (forward detent position) then turn it back until the first detent is felt (Neutral position). This is done to verify that each transmission lever is in its Neutral position.
5. Fabricate a locating gauge according to the accompanying illustration. Insert the locating gauge into the notch of the shifter housing and through the shift levers to properly align the levers. It may be necessary to move the shift lever(s) to install the locating gauge completely.
6. Loosen the locknuts of the 3–4 shift rod swivel (front of transmission side cover) and turn the swivel as necessary to allow the swivel to easily enter the hole of the 3–4 transmission lever. Apply a slight rearward pressure to the transmission lever and tighten the swivel locknuts. Attach the shift rod to the transmission lever with the retaining clip (and washer, if used).
7. Repeat step 6 for the 1–2 and reverse shift rods.
8. Remove the locating gauge and lower the vehicle.

NOTE: After the adjustments have been made, the centerlines of the shifter levers must be aligned to prevent rubbing.

1984 and later

1. Disconnect the negative battery cable.
2. Remove the left seat from the vehicle. If equipped with power seats, disconnect the electrical leads.
3. Remove the shift knob.
4. Remove the console cover.
5. Remove the glove box lock.
6. Remove the left side panel from the console.

7. Remove the shifter cover.
8. Loosen the adjusting nuts on the shifter rods.
9. With the transmission and shifter in neutral, install the alignment pin in shifter as illustrated.
10. Equalize the swivels on all three shift levers. Hand tighten the forward and rear adjusting nuts at the same time with equal force. Do this for all three shifter rods and then torque the forward and rear adjusting nuts at the same time to specifications.
11. Reinstall the components removed by reversing Steps 1 through 7. Lubricate all linkage pivot points.

If, after adjusting the linkage, it is found that high shift effort still exists, an anti-chatter lubricant (positraction additive) may be used. The lubricant is available in a small plastic bottle and can be squirted into the transmission through the filler plug.

REMOVAL & INSTALLATION

1978–82

1. Disconnect the battery ground cable.
2. Remove the shifter ball and "T" handle.
3. Remove the console trim plate.
4. Raise the vehicle on a hoist.
5. Remove the right and left exhaust pipes. It may be necessary to remove the catalytic converter and its mounting bracket to gain sufficient clearance to remove the transmission.
6. Disconnect the driveshaft at the transmission, lower the driveshaft and remove the slip yoke from the transmission.
7. Remove the rear mount to bracket bolts, then jack the engine enough to raise the transmission from the mount.
8. Remove the transmission linkage mounting bracket to frame bolts.
9. Disconnect the shift levers at the transmission.
10. Remove the bolts attaching the gearshift assembly to mounting bracket and remove the mounting bracket. Remove the shifter mechanism with the rods and levers attached.
11. Disconnect the speedometer cable.
12. Remove the transmission mount bracket.
13. Remove the transmission to clutch housing retaining bolts and the lower left extension bolt.
14. Pull the transmission rearward until it is clear of the clutch housing, then rotate it clockwise while pulling to the rear.
15. To allow room for the transmission removal slowly lower the rear of the engine until the distributor gently touches the fire wall.

NOTE: Do not allow the engine to rest against the distributor as damage may result. Place two blocks of wood directly behind the heads to keep the engine weight off the distributor.

16. Installation is the reverse of removal. Adjust the shift linkage. Torque the transmission-to-clutch housing bolts to 52 ft. lb. Torque the crossmember bolts to 25 ft. lb.

1984 and later

1. Disconnect the negative battery cable.
2. Remove the air cleaner assembly.
3. Disconnect the throttle valve (T.V.) cable at the left TBI unit.
4. Remove the distributor cap and lay aside.
5. Raise the vehicle and support it safely.
6. Remove the complete exhaust system assembly as follows:
    a. Disconnect A.I.R. pipe at the catalytic converter.
    b. Disconnect A.I.R. pipe clamps at exhaust manifold.
    c. Disconnect oxygen sensor electrical lead.
    d. Remove the bolts attaching the mufflers to the hangers.
    e. Remove hanger bracket at the converter.
    f. Disconnect the exhaust pipes from the exhaust manifolds and remove the exhaust system.
7. Remove the exhaust hanger at the transmission.
8. Support the transmission with a jack.
9. Remove the bolts attaching the driveline beam at the axle and transmission. Remove the driveline beam from the vehicle.
10. Mark the relationship of the propeller shaft to the axle companion flange. Remove the trunnion bearing straps and disengage the rear universal joint from the axle. Slide the propeller shaft slip yoke out from the overdrive unit and remove shaft from the vehicle.
11. Disconnect the cooler lines at the overdrive unit.
12. Disconnect the T.V. cable at the overdrive unit.
13. Disconnect the shift linkage at the side cover.
14. Disconnect the electrical connectors at the side cover switches, backup light switch, overdrive unit and speedometer sensor.
15. Lower the transmission and support the engine.
16. Remove the bolts attaching the

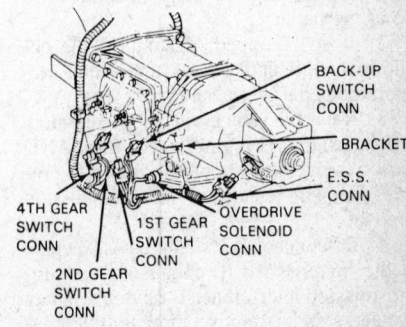

Electrical connectors on 4–speed overdrive transmission

transmission to the bellhousing. Slide the transmission rearward to disengage the input shaft from the clutch. Remove the transmission from the vehicle.

17. Inspect the clutch components for signs of wear or heat damage. See the Clutch Section, if necessary.

18. Installation is the reverse of removal. Clean and repack the clutch release bearing.

19. Refer to the Rear Suspension Section for installation and specifications for the driveline beam.

20. Torque all fasteners to specifications. Do not overtighten.

21. Adjust the throttle valve (T.V.) cable.

22. Refill the transmission with fluid (4 Speed) SAE-80W or SAE-80W-90 GL-5 gear lube (Overdrive Unit) Dexron® II Automatic Transmission Fluid.

— CAUTION —

Do not over-torque the bolts attaching the driveline beam to the transmission. Over-torquing can damage the bushing and seal in the overdrive unit and result in fluid leakage. Inadequate fluid level will damage the transmission.

OVERHAUL

For all overhaul information, please refer to "Manual Transmission Overhaul" in the Unit Repair section.

AUTOMATIC TRANSMISSION

Two Turbo HydraMatics have been available. The 700R-4 is the only automatic available in 1982 and later models. Identification can be made by the shape of the pan.

For all automatic transmission adjustment and identification details, please refer to "Automatic Transmissions" in the Unit Repair section.

REMOVAL & INSTALLATION

1. Disconnect the negative battery cable at the battery.

2. If so equipped, disconnect the detent/downshift cable at its upper end (accelerator pedal or carburetor).

3. Raise the vehicle and support it safely with jackstands. Preferably, the front AND rear of the vehicle should be raised to provide adequate clearance for transmission removal.

4. Disconnect the exhaust crossover pipe at the manifolds, if exhaust system-to-transmission interference is obvious. It may be necessary to remove the catalytic convertor, exhaust pipe, or just the brackets in order to clear the transmission.

— CAUTION —

Exhaust system services must be performed while all components are COLD.

5. Remove the transmission inspection cover.

6. Remove the torque convertor-to-flywheel bolts. The relationship between the flywheel and convertor must be marked so that proper balance is maintained after installation.

7. Matchmark the drive shaft and the rear yoke (for reinstallation purposes). With a drain pan positioned under the front yoke, unbolt and remove the drive shaft.

8. Mark and disconnect vacuum lines, wiring, and the speedometer cable from the transmission, as required.

9. Place a transmission jack (carefully) up against the transmission oil pan, then secure the transmission to the jack.

10. Remove the transmission mounting pad bolt(s), then carefully raise the transmission just enough to take the weight of the transmission off of the supporting crossmember. Remove the transmission mounting pad.

— CAUTION —

Exercise extreme care to avoid damage to underhood components while raising or lowering the transmission.

11. Remove the transmission dipstick, then unbolt and remove the filler tube.

12. Disconnect the shift linkage (or cable on floor shift-equipped models) and oil cooler lines from the transmission.

13. Support the engine using a jack placed beneath the engine oil pan. Be sure to put a block of wood between the jack and the oil pan, to prevent damage to the pan.

14. Securely wire the torque convertor to the transmission case.

15. Remove the transmission-to-engine mounting bolts, then carefully move the transmission rearward, downward, and out from beneath the vehicle.

— CAUTION —

If interference is encountered with the cable(s), cooler lines, etc., remove the component(s) before finally lowering the transmission.

Installation is basically the reverse of previous steps. Note the following points during and after installation:

a. Torque the transmission-to-engine mounting bolts to 30–40 ft. lbs.

b. Align the matchmarks of the drive shaft with the marks of the rear yoke before installing the joint straps and bolts.

c. Align the converter and flywheel markings before installing the converter bolts.

d. Add the proper type and quantity of transmission fluid. If the converter was replaced, an additional 4 pints (approx.) should be added. NEVER overfill the transmission.

e. Adjust the shift linkage (or cable) and the detent/downshift cable.

f. Make sure that all vacuum lines, electrical connections, and oil cooler line connections are secure before driving the vehicle.

g. Check for fluid leakage, then after the transmission is hot, recheck the fluid level.

DRIVESHAFT AND U-JOINTS

NOTE: For driveshaft removal, refer to the procedure listed in the Chevrolet Rear Wheel Drive car section. For all universal joint information refer to "U-Joints/CV-Joints" in the Unit Repair section. The 1984 Corvette uses two types of driveshafts, one made from aluminum and the other from steel.

REAR AXLE

Differential

REMOVAL & INSTALLATION

1978–79

Corvette is equipped with an independent rear suspension. The differential is solidly attached to the car frame, the rear wheels being driven through tubular rear axles, each fitted with two universal joints. A transverse, multiple leaf rear spring provides rear suspension. Brake torque and driving forces are transmitted through radius arms to the frame. The spring supports vertical loads, while lateral forces, on turns etc., are taken by the axles and control rods to the fixed differential and to the frame.

1. Raise the vehicle on a hoist.

2. Disconnect the spring and link bolts.

3. Disconnect the axle shafts at the carrier by removing the U-bolts on the universal joint trunnions.

4. Disconnect the carrier front support bracket at the frame crossmember.

5. Disconnect the driveshaft at the companion flange.

6. Scribe marks indicating the cam and bolt relative location on the strut rod bracket and loosen the cam bolts.

7. Remove the four bolts which secure the bracket to the carrier lower surface and drop the bracket. Remove the camber cam bolts and swing the strut rods up and out of the way.

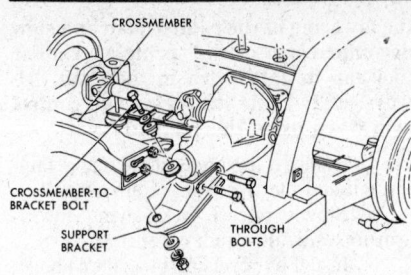

Differential carrier front support bracket —through 1979

8. Remove the eight carrier to cover bolts, loosening the bolts gradually to permit the lubricant to drain out.

9. Pull the carrier partially out of the cover, drop the nose to clear the crossmember, then gradually work the carrier down and out.

10. To install, clean the carrier cover and grease the gasket surface.

11. Using a new gasket and two ½ in.-13 × 1¼ in. studs as aligning studs, raise the carrier into position. Cut the head off of a 9/16 in.-18 × 1¼ in. bolt and slot the unthreaded end. Install this bolt into the carrier underside to aid in installing the strut rod bracket.

12. Install the carrier to cover bolts, tightening securely.

13. Install the driveshaft to the companion flange, tightening the clamp bolts securely.

14. Install the rubber cushion on the bracket and position to the frame crossmember. Install the nut, tightening to 50 ft. lbs.

15. Install the axle trunnions to the yokes with the U-bolts.

16. Assemble the strut rods to the bracket and raise the bracket into position under the carrier. Install the four bolts, tightening to 35 ft. lbs.

17. Move the camber cams to the marked locations and tighten the cam nuts.

18. Connect the spring end link bolts.

19. Fill the housing with lubricant to the level of the filler hole.

Differential Carrier and Cover

REMOVAL & INSTALLATION

1980–82

1. Raise the vehicle on a hoist.
2. Remove the spare tire.
3. Remove the support hooks attached to the carrier cover and remove the spare tire cover.
4. Remove the exhaust system.
5. Place jackstands under the front control arms to support the vehicle.
6. Remove the heat shield.
7. Using an adjustable floor jack and a C-clamp raise the spring to relieve load and disconnect the spring.

8. Remove the transverse spring at the cover plate.
9. Mark the cam bolt and remove from the bracket.
10. Remove the two bolts attaching the strut bracket to the carrier and lower the strut rods by pushing away on the tire and wheel assembly.
11. Mark the driveshaft and disconnect it at the companion flange in order to gain access to the insulator attaching bolt.

NOTE: It may be necessary to support the driveshaft to gain access to the insulator attaching bolt.

12. Place a jackstand under the carrier, and remove the carrier-to-body attaching bolts.
13. Lower the differential in order to gain access to all cover bolts.
14. Drain the differential and remove the cover.
15. To remove the carrier disconnect the driveshaft at the spindle companion flange.
16. Lower and remove the differential assembly and remove the driveshafts from the side yokes.
17. Installation is the reverse of removal.

1984 and later

1. Remove air cleaner.
2. Disconnect distributor cap from distributor.
3. Raise vehicle and support it with jackstands.
4. Remove spare tire.
5. Remove spare tire cover by removing support hooks.
6. Remove the complete exhaust system as an assembly by:
   a. Disconnect A.I.R. pipe at the converter.
   b. Disconnect A.I.R. pipe clamps at exhaust manifold.
   c. Disconnect oxygen sensor electrical lead.

d. Remove the bolts attaching the mufflers to the hangers.
   e. Remove hanger bracket at converter.
   f. Disconnect the exhaust from the exhaust manifold and remove the exhaust system.
7. Disconnect leaf spring at the knuckles and remove attaching bolts at the cover. Remove leaf spring from vehicle.
8. Scribe mark on cam bolts and mounting bracket so they can be realigned in the same position. Remove cam bolts and then mounting bracket from carrier.
9. Disconnect both tie rod ends from the knuckles.
10. Remove the axle shaft union straps from the side gear yokes. Push wheel and tire assemblies outboard to disengage the trunnions from the side gear yokes.
11. Remove prop shaft trunnion straps at pinion flange. Push prop shaft forward into transmission and tie shaft to the support beam.
12. Support transmission.
13. Remove differential cover/beam attaching bolts at frame brackets.

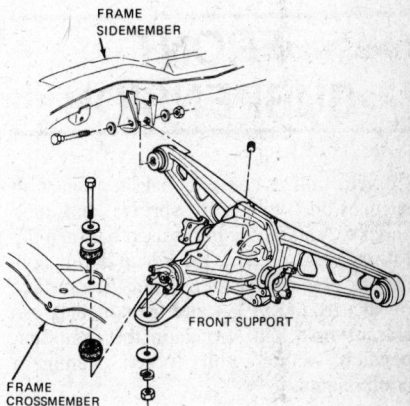

Differential carrier installation—1980 and later

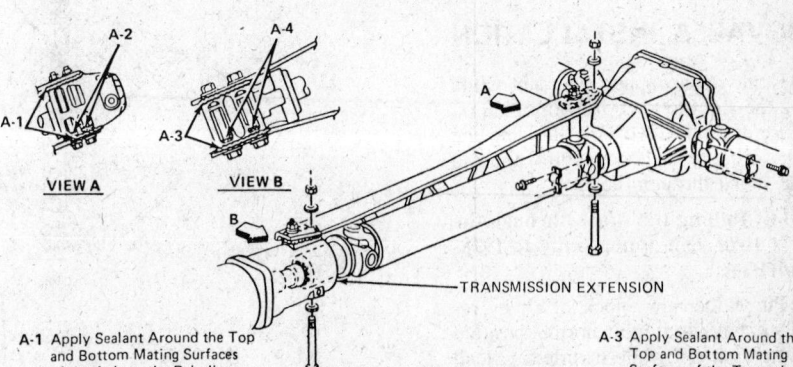

Sealing Drive Line Support

A-1 Apply Sealant Around the Top and Bottom Mating Surfaces of the Axle to the Driveline Support

A-2 Apply Sealant Around the Driveline Support and Axle Attaching Bolts at the Bottom Cavity 360° Around the Bolts

NOTE: ABOVE SEALING OPERATIONS TO BE PERFORMED ONLY AFTER FINAL ASSEMBLY OF DRIVELINE SUPPORT TO THE TRANSMISSION EXTENSION AND AXLE (DIFFERENTIAL CARRIER ASM.)

A-3 Apply Sealant Around the Top and Bottom Mating Surfaces of the Transmission Extension to the Driveline Support

A-4 Apply Sealant Around the Driveline and Transmission Extension Attaching Bolts at the Bottom Cavity 360° Around the Bolts

14. Remove support beam attaching bolts at the front of the differential carrier. Remove differential carrier assembly from the vehicle.

15. Installation is the reverse of removal.

JACKING, HOISTING

When jacking the car, place the jack at the spring seat of the lower control arm in the front and at the axle housing in the rear.

—— **CAUTION** ——
Never crawl under a vehicle unless it is properly supported with jackstands.

To hoist the car, position the hoist arms at the frame side rails immediately in front of the rear wheels and immediately behind the front wheels.

FRONT SUSPENSION

Corvette utilizes conventional short-long arm suspension, with coil springs and tube shocks. A stabilizer bar is used between the lower arms to reduce body lean during cornering, thereby keeping more tire surface on the ground. 1984 and later models use a transverse leaf spring on the front suspension, along with forged aluminum components.

Shock Absorber

REMOVAL & INSTALLATION

1. Remove the upper stem nut while holding the stem to keep it from turning.

2. Remove the two bolts holding the shock absorber to the lower control arm and pull the shock through the arm.

NOTE: Pulling the shock through the lower control arm applies only to 1978-82 models.

3. Purge the new shock of air by repeatedly extending it in its normal position and compressing it while inverted. Extend the shock absorber and insert it up through the lower control arm. Make sure that the upper stem goes through the hole in the upper control arm frame bracket.

4. Install the grommet, retainer cup, and nut to the shock absorber upper stem.

5. Hold the shock absorber stem and tighten the upper nut to 8 ft. lbs. 1978–82, 18 ft. lb. 1984 and later models.

6. Install the lower control arm retaining bolts and tighten to 13 ft. lbs. 1978–82, 22 ft. lbs. 1984 and later models.

DISPOSAL OF PRESSURIZED SHOCK ABSORBERS

1984 and later models

Due to the high pressure of gas it is advised that, upon scrapping or disposal of these shock absorbers, the pressure be released. This is carried out as follows:

1. Clamp shock in vise with piston rod pointing down.

2. Measure approx. 0.5 in. (10–15mm) from bottom of shock and drill an appox. 5mm hole so the gas can escape.

3. Measure approx. 5.5–6.0 in. (140–150mm) from first hole and drill an approx. 5 mm hole to facilitate drainage of oil. Drain all oil from shock absorber.

Spring

REMOVAL & INSTALLATION

1978-82

1. Raise the car on hoist and remove nut, retainer and grommet from the top of the shock absorber. Support car so that the control arms swing free.

2. Disconnect stabilizer bar from lower control arm and remove shock absorber.

3. Bolt a spring remover tool to a suitable jack and place it under the lower control arm bushings so that the bushings seat in the grooves of the tool.

NOTE: This tool is a cradle which, when fastened to a hydraulic jack, allows the lowering of the control arm and slow decompression of the spring. A similar tool can be fabricated in the shop. Always safety-chain the spring and control arm when using this method.

4. Remove the cross shaft rear retaining nut and the two front retaining bolts.

5. Slowly release jack, swing control arm forward, then remove spring.

6. Install by reversing procedure above. Torque the retaining nut to 92 ft. lb. Torque the retaining bolts 59-75 ft. lb.

NOTE: Chevrolet recommends this cradle spring removal tool for all models. Other methods may be used, depending on the availability of tools.

NOTE Spring to be installed with tape at lowest position. Bottom of spring is coiled helical, and the top is coiled flat with a gripper notch near end of wire.

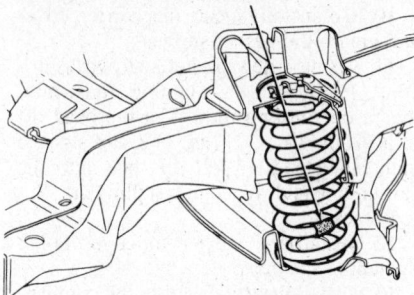

NOTE After assembly, end of spring coil must cover all or part of one inspection drain hole. The other hole must be partly exposed or completely uncovered.

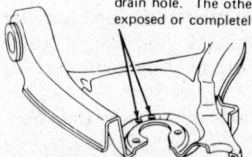

Front spring positioning

NOTE Hold stud at this point to obtain torque.

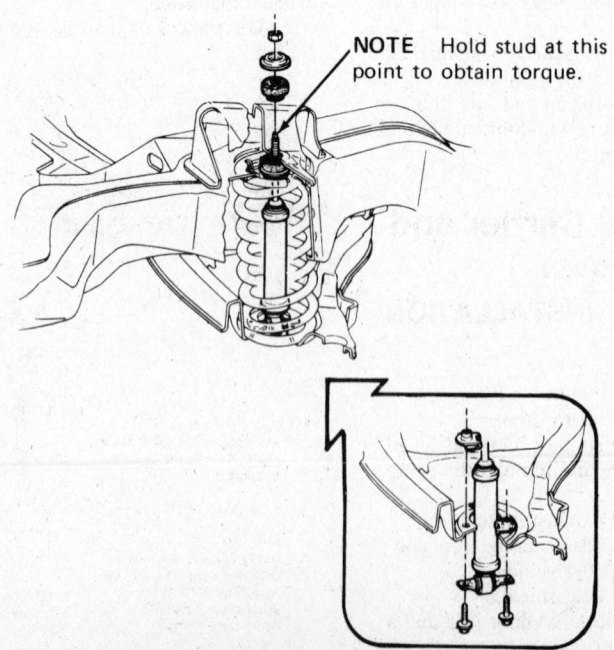

Front shock absorber installation

1984 and later

1. Raise the vehicle on a hoist.

2. Remove the wheels and tires, left side.

3. Remove the left front caliper bracket and rotor.

4. Remove spring protectors both sides.

5. Install spring compressor J-33432-4 or its equivalent.

6. Disconnect outer tie rod left side.

7. Remove the stabilizer link, left side.

8. Remove the lower shock mount, left side.

9. Compress special tool J-33432-4.

10. Remove the lower ball joint, left side.

11. Remove the spring hold down brackets.

12. Remove the transverse spring from the left side.

13. Installation is the reverse of removal. The following torques are needed during reinstallation: Spring protector to crossmember 18 ft. lbs., Stabilizer link 35 ft. lbs.

BALL JOINT INSPECTION

NOTE: Before performing this inspection, make sure the wheel bearings are adjusted correctly and that the control arm bushings are in good condition.

1. Jack the car up under the front lower control arm at the spring seat.

2. Raise the car until there is 1–2 in. of clearance under the wheel.

3. Insert a bar under the wheel and pry upward. If the wheel raises more than 1/8 in. the ball joints are worn. Determine if the upper or lower ball joint is worn by visual inspection while prying on the wheel.

NOTE: Due to the distribution of forces in the suspension, the lower ball joint is usually the defective joint.

Upper & Lower Ball Joint

REMOVAL & INSTALLATION

1. Raise the car on a hoist.
2. Remove the tire and wheel assembly.

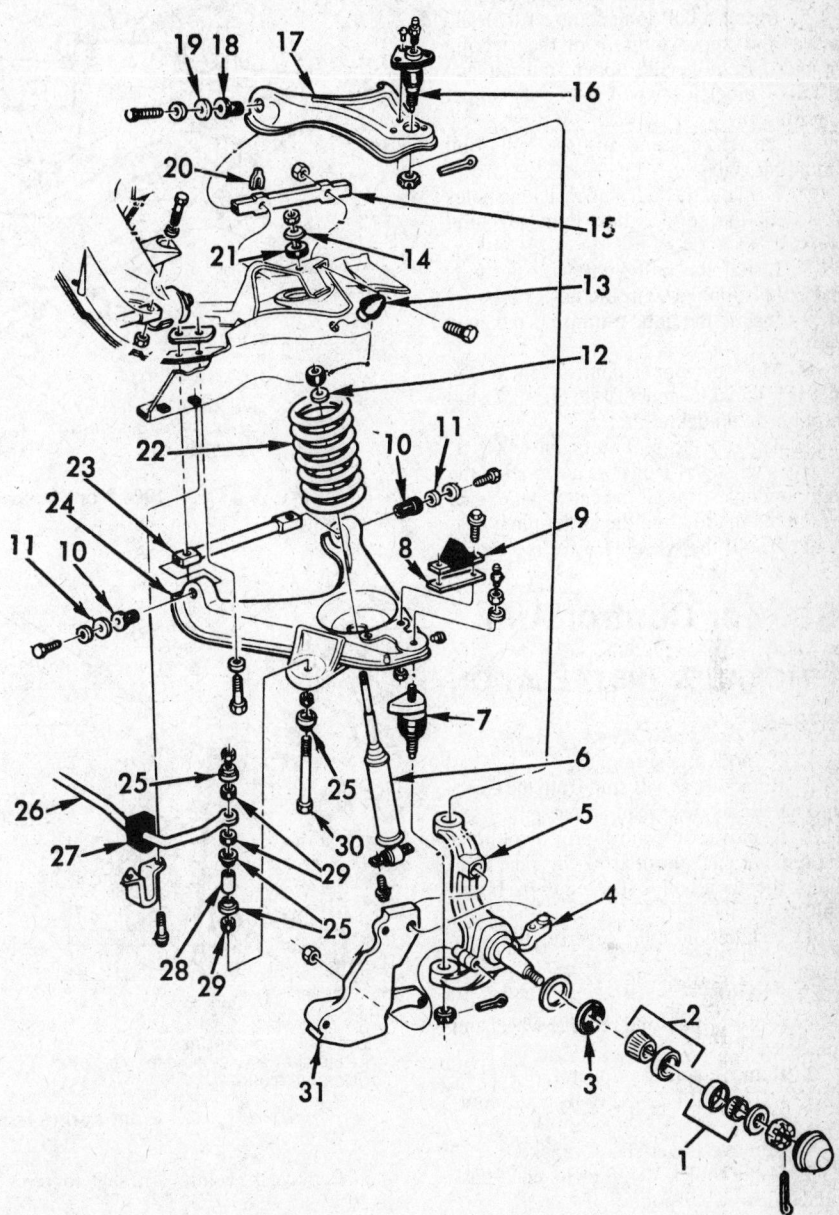

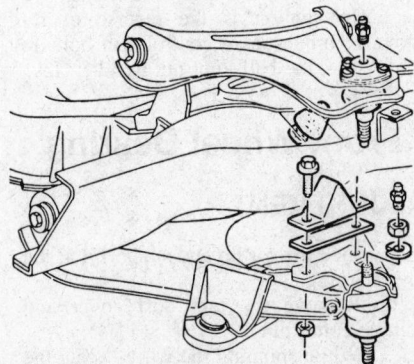

Upper and lower ball joints

1	Front wheel bearing (outer)	10	Bushing	21	Grommet
2	Front wheel bearing (inner)	11	Retainer	22	Coil spring
3	Seal assy. (inner)	12	Stabilizer link retainer	23	Lower arm shaft
4	Steering knuckle arm	13	Upper bumper	24	Lower control arm
5	Steering knuckle assy.	14	Washer	25	Retainer
6	Shock absorber	15	Upper arm shaft	26	Stabilizer shaft
7	Lower ball joint	16	Upper ball joint	27	Stabilizer bushing
8	Lower bumper spacer	17	Upper control arm	28	Spacer
9	Lower bumper	18	Bushing	29	Grommet
		19	Retainer	30.	Stabilizer link unit
		20	Shim	31	Caliper adapter bracket

Exploded view of front suspension

3. Support the lower control arm with a jack.

4. Loosen the upper ball stud nut.

5. Install a ball joint remover tool and unseat the upper joint from the steering knuckle. Remove the upper stud nut and install a block of wood under the upper control arm.

6. Chisel or grind off the ball joint mounting rivets.

7. Drill out the ball stud attaching holes to accept the service ball joint attaching bolts.

8. Install the ball joint with the nuts and bolts supplied with the new joint.

9. Install the lube fitting in the new joint.

10. Mate the upper control arm to the steering knuckle and install the ball stud through the knuckle boss.

11. Tighten the ball stud nut to 50 ft. lbs. plus whatever is necessary to align the cotter pin holes. Install the cotter pin. Never loosen the nut to align the cotter pin holes.

12. Install the wheel. Lower the car.

Lower Control Arm

REMOVAL & INSTALLATION

1978–82

1. Remove the spring.

2. Remove the ball stud from the steering knuckle as described above.

3. Remove the control arm pivot bolts and remove the control arm. On some Corvettes, the pivot bolt is secured to the frame with two bolts.

4. Installation is the reverse.

1984 and later

1. Raise vehicle and remove wheel and tire.

2. Remove spring protector.

3. Using tool J-33432 or its equal compress spring.

4. Remove lower shock bracket.

5. Using tool J-33436 or its equal disconnect lower ball joint.

6. Remove lower control arm.

7. Installation is the reverse of removal. Torque the ball joint nut to 48 ft. lbs.

Upper Control Arm

REMOVAL & INSTALLATION

1978–82

1. Raise the vehicle on a hoist.

2. Support the outer end of the lower control arm, with a jack.

3. Remove the wheel.

4. Separate the upper ball joint from the steering knuckle as described above under "Upper Ball Joint Removal and Installation".

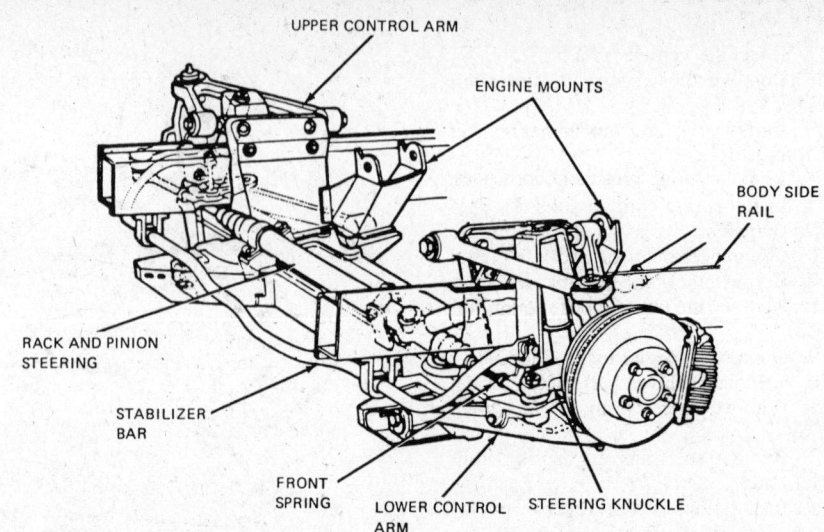

1984 front suspension components

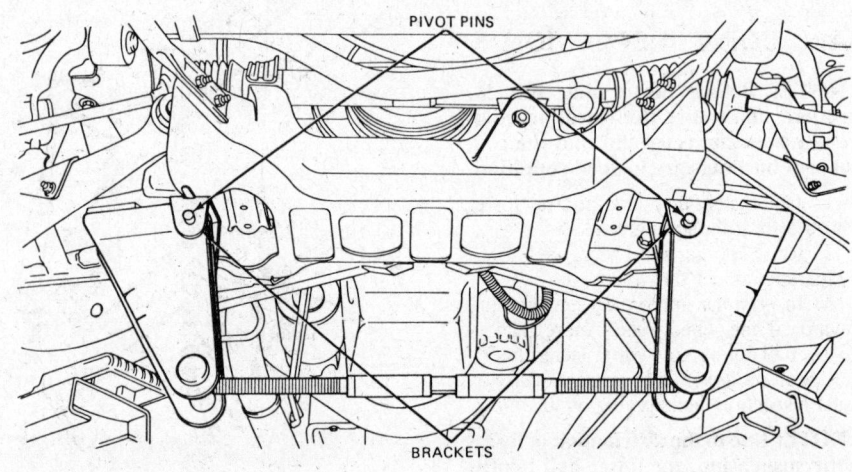

NOTE: PIVOT PINS ARE REMOVED SO THAT THE BRACKET MAY BE PLACED OVER THE TOP OF THE SPRING.

Front spring removal/installation

5. Remove the control arm shaft to frame nuts.

NOTE: Tape the shims together and identify them so that they can be installed in the positions from which they were removed.

6. Remove the bolts which attach the control arm shaft to the frame and remove the control arm. Note the positions of the bolts.

7. Install in the reverse order of removal. Make sure the shaft to frame bolts are installed in the same position they were in before removal and that the shims are in their original positions. Tighten the shaft to frame bolts to 55 ft. lbs. The control arm shaft nuts are torqued to 60 ft. lbs.

1984 and later

1. Raise vehicle and remove wheel and tire.

2. Remove spring protector.

3. Using spring compressor J-33432 or its equal, compress and loosen the spring.

4. Use tool J-33436 or its equal to disconnect the upper ball joint from the knuckle.

5. Remove the upper control arm.

6. Installation is the reverse of removal. Torque upper control arm bolts to 63 ft. lbs., the ball joint nut to 32 ft. lbs.

Front Wheel Bearing

ADJUSTMENT

1. Jack the car up and support it at the lower arm.

2. Remove the hub dust cover and spindle cotter pin.

3. While spinning the wheel, snug the nut down to seat the bearings. Do not exert over 12 ft. lbs. of force on the nut.

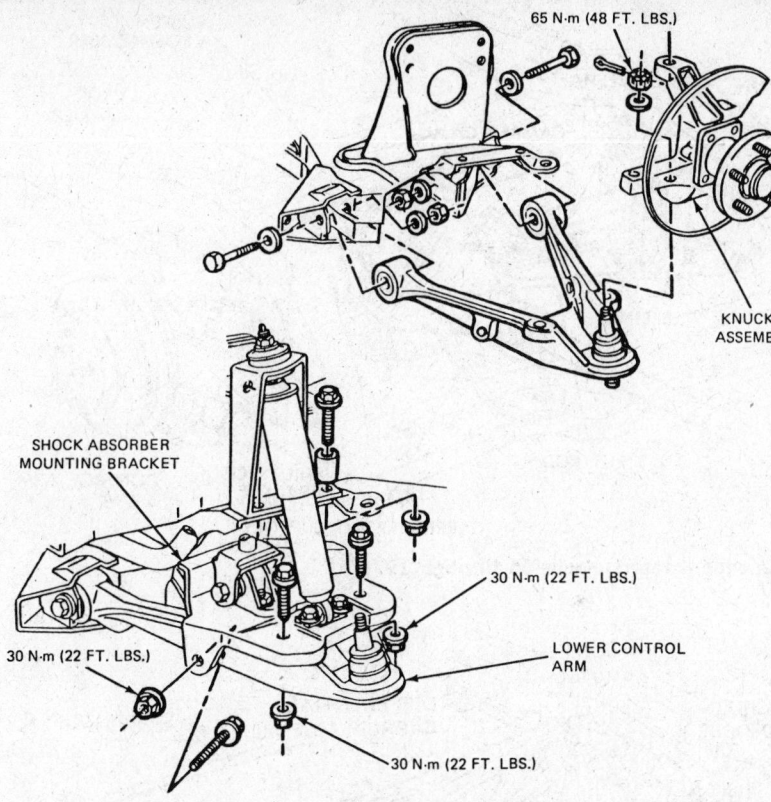

65 N·m (48 FT. LBS.)

KNUCKLE
ASSEMBLY

SHOCK ABSORBER
MOUNTING BRACKET

30 N·m (22 FT. LBS.)

30 N·m (22 FT. LBS.)

LOWER CONTROL
ARM

30 N·m (22 FT. LBS.)

Lower control arm removal/installation

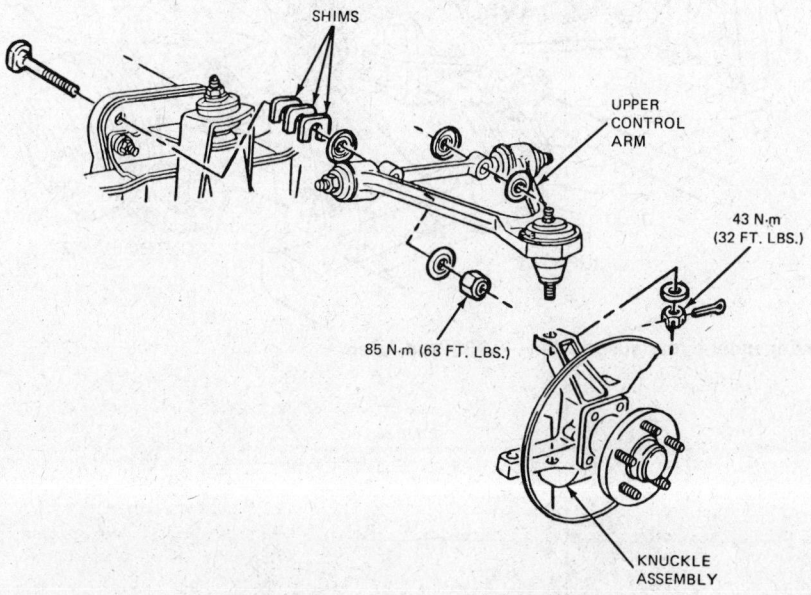

SHIMS

UPPER
CONTROL
ARM

43 N·m
(32 FT. LBS.)

85 N·m (63 FT. LBS.)

KNUCKLE
ASSEMBLY

Upper control arm removal/installation

4. Back the nut off ¼–½ a turn. Tighten the nut *finger-tight* (if the roller bearings are preloaded with the wheel off the ground, the inner edges of the bearings will be forced against the bearing cage), then *loosen* the nut as required to line up the cotter pin hole in the spindle with the hole in the nut.

5. Insert the cotter pin. End-play should be 0.001–0.005 in. If play exceeds this tolerance, the wheel bearings should be replaced.

REAR SUSPENSION

On 1978–82 models, the Corvette uses a three-link, independent suspension with a transverse spring. On 1984 and later, the rear suspension features a light weight fi-

berglass transverse spring mounted to the fixed differential carrier cover beam. Light weight aluminum components such as the knuckles, upper and lower control arms, camber control support rods, differential carrier cover beam and the drive line support beam are used throughout the rear suspension. Each wheel is mounted by a five link independent suspension. The five links are identified as the wheel drive shaft, camber control support rod, upper and lower control arms and tie rod.

Shock Absorber

REMOVAL & INSTALLATION

NOTE: Purge new shocks of air by repeatedly extending them in their normal position and compressing them while inverted.

1. Jack the car to a convenient working height.
2. Remove the upper bolt and nut.
3. Remove the lower mounting nut and washers.
4. Pivot the top of the shock absorber out of the frame bracket and pull the bottom off the strut shaft.
5. Slide the upper shock absorber eye into the frame bracket and install the bolt, lockwasher, and nut.
6. Install the rubber grommets on the lower shock eye and place the shock over the strut shaft. Install the washers and nut.
7. Torque the upper bolt to 50 ft. lbs. and the lower nut to 35 ft. lbs. Lower the car.

NOTE: It may be easier to remove the rear wheels before attempting to remove the shocks. See the note on gas-filled shocks under "Front Suspension."

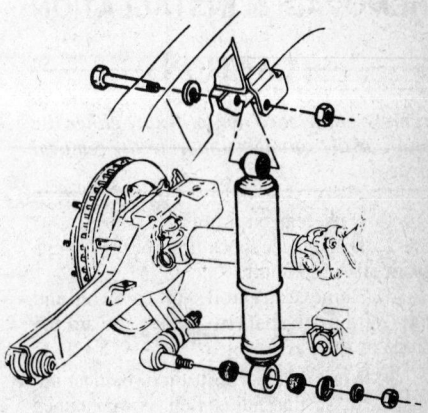

Rear shock absorber mounting

Transverse Leaf Spring

REMOVAL & INSTALLATION

NOTE: Some 1981 and most 1982 Corvettes have a single leaf fiberglass rear spring. All 1984 and later models use a single leaf rear spring.

1. Raise car and support it by the frame, slightly forward of torque control pivot points. Remove wheel assemblies.

2. Place a floor jack under the spring near the link bolt, and raise the spring until it is nearly flat.

3. Tie the end of the spring to the suspension crossmember to hold this flat attitude, with a ¼ in. or 5⁄16 in. chain and grab hook wrapped around the spring and crossmember. To prevent chain slipping, use a C-clamp on the spring adjacent to the chain.

4. Remove link bolt and rubber bushings.

5. Support and raise the spring end, as before, and remove chain.

6. Carefully lower jack to completely relax spring.

7. Repeat the procedure on the other side of the car.

8. Remove bolts and washers attaching the springs at the center.

9. Remove the spring by sliding it over the exhaust pipes and out one side of the car.

10. Install by reversing removal procedure. Always use new link bolts and cushions. Torque the rear spring to carrier bolts to 33 ft. lbs. through 1979 and 50 ft. lbs. 1981 and later. Install the nut on the link bolt just far enough to expose the cotter pin hole, then insert the pin.

Strut Rod & Bracket

REMOVAL & INSTALLATION

——— CAUTION ———
The strut rod shaft is often very hard to remove; take care not to distort either the shaft or the spindle support in the removal process.

1. Raise car on a hoist.

2. Disconnect shock absorber lower eye from strut rod shaft.

3. Remove strut rod shaft cotter pin and nut. Withdraw shaft by pulling toward the front of the car.

4. Mark related position of camber adjustment, so that adjustment is maintained upon reassembly.

5. Loosen camber bolt and nut. Remove four bolts holding strut rod bracket to carrier and lower the bracket.

6. Remove cam bolt and cam bolt as-

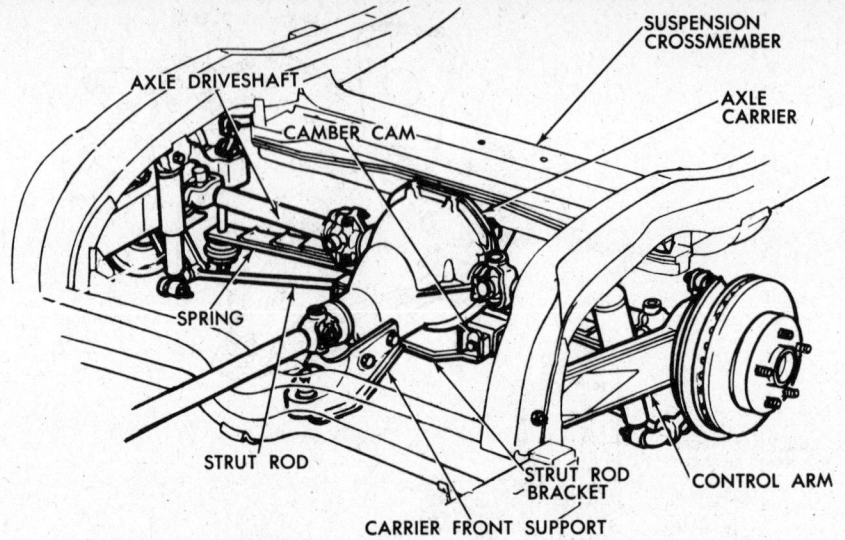

Independent rear suspension through 1979

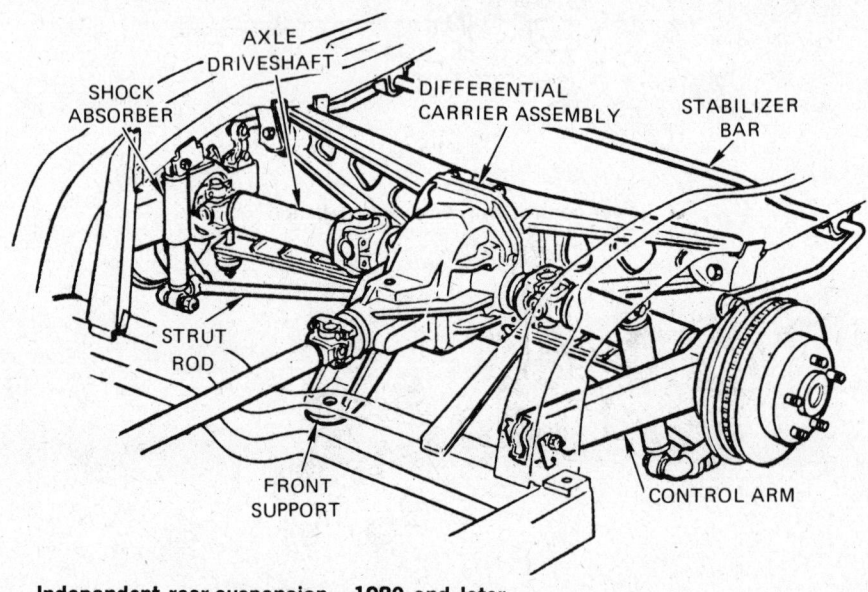

Independent rear suspension—1980 and later

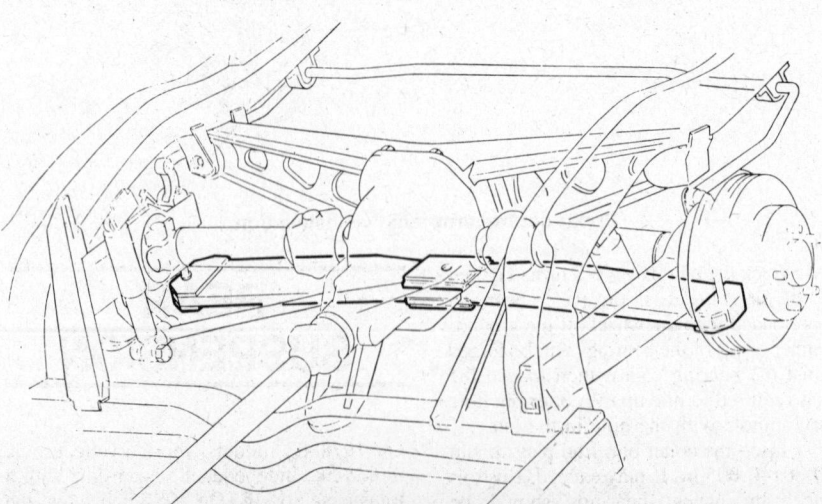

Fiberglass-reinforced plastic (F.R.P.) single leaf rear spring—most 1981 and later models

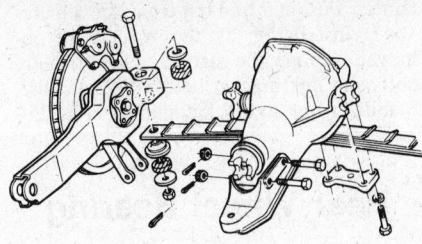

Transverse spring mounting

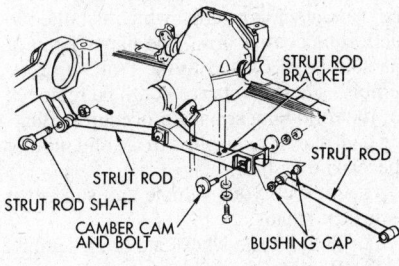

Strut rod mounting

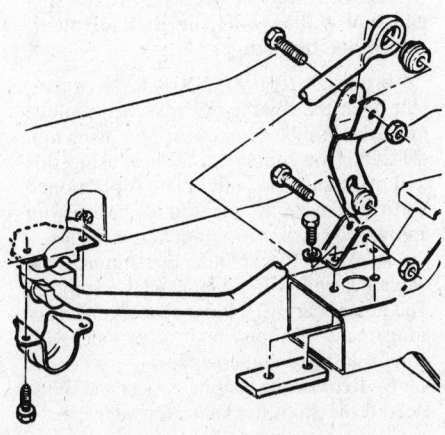

Stabilizer shaft installation, Corvette

sembly. Pull strut down out of bracket and remove bushing caps.

7. Inspect strut rod bushings for wear and replace where necessary. Replace strut rod if it is bent or damaged in any way.

NOTE: The strut rod shaft has a flat side which should line up with the matching flat in the spindle support.

8. Install by reversing removal procedure. Torque the strut rod-to-spindle support to 75 ft. lb. plus as needed to align cotter pin hole. Torque the bracket-to-carrier to 35 ft. lb., 20 ft. lb. on 1981 and later.

9. Check rear wheel camber and adjust to specifications.

Spindle Support Rod

REMOVAL & INSTALLATION

1984 and later

1. Raise and support vehicle.
2. Scribe mark on cam bolt and mounting bracket so they can be realigned in the same position.
3. Remove cam bolt and separate spindle support rod from the mounting bracket.
4. Remove the spindle support rod bolt at the knuckle and remove rod.
5. Installation is the reverse of removal. Torque the spindle end of support rod 95–188 ft. lbs.; differential end 47–62 ft. lbs.

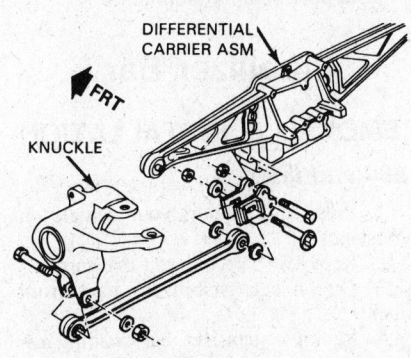

Spindle support rod

Torque Control Arm

REMOVAL & INSTALLATION

1. Disconnect spring on the side from which the torque arm is to be removed. Follow procedure for "Spring Removal and Installation".

NOTE: If so equipped, disconnect stabilizer rod from torque arm.

2. Remove shock absorber lower eye from strut rod shaft.
3. Disconnect and remove strut rod shaft and swing strut rod down.
4. Remove four bolts holding the axle driveshaft to spindle flange and disconnect drive shaft.
5. Disconnect the brake line at the caliper and from the torque arm. Disconnect parking brake cable.
6. Remove the torque arm pivot bolt and toe-in shims. Pull the torque arm out of the frame. Tape the shims together to assure proper reassembly.
7. To install, place torque arm in frame opening.
8. Position toe-in shims in original location on both sides of torque arm. Install pivot bolt and lightly tighten at this time.
9. Raise axle driveshaft into position and install to drive flange. Torque bolts to 75 ft. lbs.

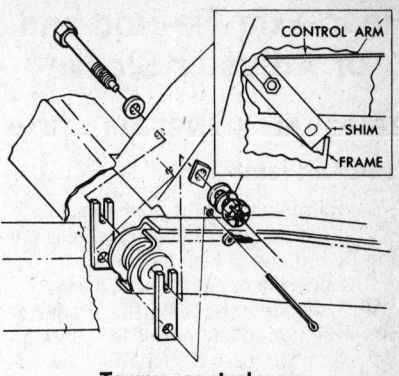

Torque control arm

10. Raise the strut into position and insert the strut rod shaft so that the flat portion of the shaft lines up with the flat portion on the spindle fork. Install the nut and torque it to 80 ft. lbs.
11. Install shock absorber lower eye and tighten nut to 35 ft. lbs.
12. Connect spring end as outlined under Leaf Spring Removal and Installation.

NOTE: If car is so equipped, connect stabilizer shaft.

13. Install brake disc and caliper, and wheel. Then lower the car. Tighten torque pivot bolt to 50 ft. lbs.
14. Bleed brakes and check camber and toe-in. Adjust if necessary.

Upper/Lower Control Arms

REMOVAL & INSTALLATION

1984 and later

1. Raise and support the vehicle.
2. Remove shock absorber.
3. Remove control arm bolt at the knuckle.
4. Remove control arm bolt at the body bracket and remove the arm.
5. Installation is the reverse of removal. Torque the control arm to body bolts 55–70 ft. lbs.; control arm to knuckle 125–154 ft. lbs.

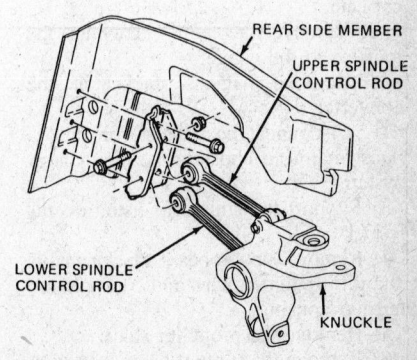

Control arms.

Rear Axle Tie-Rod and/ or Adjuster Sleeve

REMOVAL & INSTALLATION

1984 and later

1. Raise and support your vehicle.
2. Remove cotter pin and retaining nut from tie-rod end at knuckle.
3. Loosen jam nut on tie-rod end.
4. Using tool J-24319-01, or equivalent, press tie-rod end out of the knuckle.
5. Remove tie-rod end from the adjusting sleeve. Count the number of turns.
6. Remove adjuster sleeve.
7. Installation is the reverse of removal. Install the same number of turns as removal. Torque tie-rod end-to-knuckle: 29–36 ft. lbs.; tie-rod housing to cover beam: 35–44 ft. lbs. Realign suspension if necessary.

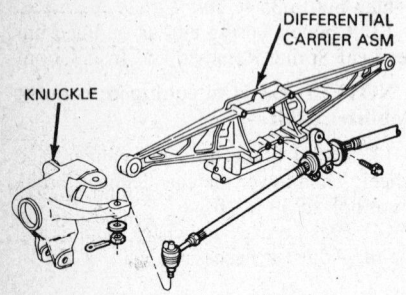

Tie rod assembly

Support Beam

REMOVAL & INSTALLATION

1984 and later

1. Raise vehicle and support with jackstands. Allow exhaust system to cool.
2. Remove the complete exhaust system as an assembly by:
   a. Disconnect A.I.R. pipe at the converter.
   b. Disconnect A.I.R. pipe clamps at exhaust pipe.
   c. Disconnect oxygen sensor electrical lead.
   d. Remove the bolts attaching the mufflers to the hangers.
   e. Remove hanger bracket at the converter.
   f. Disconnect the exhaust from the exhaust manifold and remove the exhaust system.
3. Support transmission, using a suitable jack.
4. Remove support beam attaching bolts at the differential carrier and transmission extension housing.
5. Remove the propeller shaft.
6. Remove the support beam by prying transmission to the driver side of vehicle. Remove support beam from the vehicle.

7. Installation is the reverse of removal. Torque the rear support beam bolts: 51–66 ft. lbs.; front beam bolts: 47–55 ft. lbs. Apply sealant as illustrated during installation.

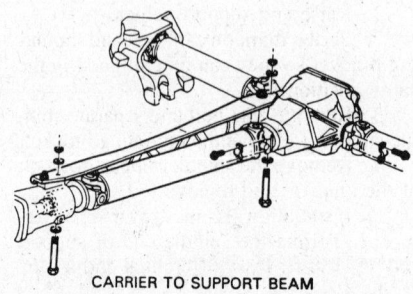

Support beam attachments

Stabilizer Bar

REMOVAL & INSTALLATION

1984 and later

1. Raise and support your vehicle on jack stands.
2. Remove spare tire and tire carrier.
3. Disconnect stabilizer bar from knuckles.
4. Remove stabilizer bar bushing re-

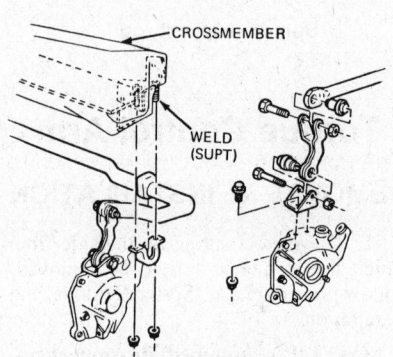

Rear stabilizer bar

tainers, bushings and bar from the vehicle.
5. Installation is the reverse of removal. Torque the stabilizer bar to body bolts and link bracket bolts 14–22 ft. lbs.; Stabilizer link to bracket and bar bolts 25–35 ft. lbs.

Rear Wheel Bearing

REMOVAL & INSTALLATION

1978–82

The Corvette rear wheel spindle is mounted on two tapered roller bearings contained in the spindle support arm, which is bolted to the torque control arm. The flanged end of the spindle is riveted to the brake disc assembly. These rivets are not to be removed for the following service procedures. Bearing end-play is controlled by a solid tubular spacer and a shim.

1. Jack up your vehicle and support it with jack stands.
2. Remove the wheel and tire assembly.
3. Remove the axle drive shaft.
4. Apply the parking brake to prevent the rotors from turning.
5. Remove the cotter pin, nut and flange.

NOTE: It may be necessary to use special tool #J08614-01, or its equivalent, to remove the flange.

6. Install tool #J-21859-1, or equivalent, over the spindle threads, then remove the drive spindle from its support using tool #J-22602 or equivalent. When using this tool make sure the puller plate is positioned vertically in the torque control arm before applying pressure to the puller screw.
7. When the spindle is removed, the outer bearing will remain on the spindle. The inner bearing, tubular spacer, end-play adjustment shim and both outer races will remain in the spindle support.
8. Remove the bearing, spacer and shim. Record the shim thickness for later use.

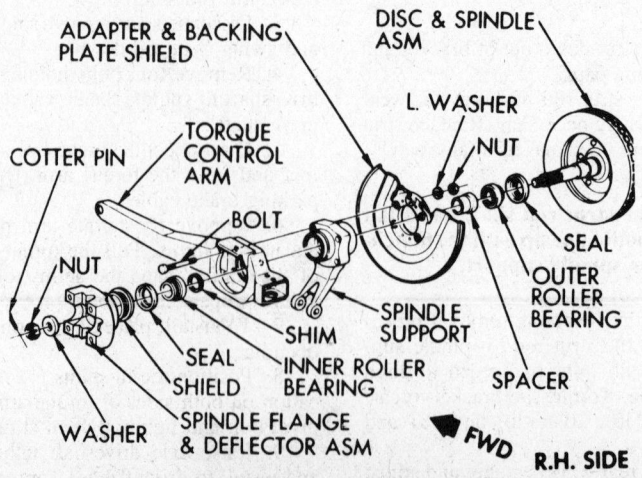

Exploded view of spindle

9. With the spindle assembly on the bench, position tool #J24489-1, or equivalent, between the outer bearing and the seal.

10. Using puller #J-8433-1, or equivalent, draw the bearing off the spindle.

11. Remove the outer seal from the spindle shaft and inspect it for damage. Replace if necessary.

12. Remove the outer races from the spindle shaft and install new ones, using tool #J-7817, or equivalent.

13. Pack the new wheel bearing with grease.

14. Installation is the reverse of removal.

Rear Hub & Bearing

REMOVAL & INSTALLATION

1984 and later

1. Remove center cap from wheel.

2. Remove cotter pin, spindle nut and washer.

3. Raise vehicle and support with jack stands.

4. Remove wheel and tire.

5. Remove brake caliper and support.

6. Remove brake rotor.

7. Disconnect tie rod end from the knuckle.

8. Disconnect transverse spring from the knuckle.

9. Scribe mark on cam bolt and mounting bracket so they can be realigned in the same position.

10. Remove cam bolt and separate spindle support rod from the mounting bracket.

11. Remove the trunnion straps at the side yoke shaft. Push out on theknuckle and separate axle shaft from the side gear yoke shaft. Remove the axle shaft from the vehicle.

12. Using J-34161 (Torx #45) or its equivalent, remove the hub and bearing mounting bolts.

13. Remove hub and bearing from the vehicle and support the parking brake backing plate.

14. Installation is the reverse of removal. Check suspension alignment and adjust as needed.

WHEEL BEARING END PLAY CHECK

The rear wheel bearings should have end play of 0.001–0.008 inches. When necessary, adjust them using the following procedure.

1. Jack up your vehicle and support it with jack stands.

2. Remove the tire and wheel assembly.

3. Remove the axle drive shaft.

4. Mark the camber cam in relation to the bracket. Loosen and turn the camber bolt until the strut rod forces the torque control arm outward.

5. Mount a dial indicator on the torque control surface and rest the pointer on the flange end.

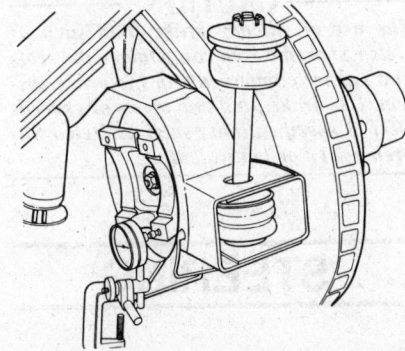

Checking spindle bearing end play

6. Grasp the rotor and move it in and out. If the bearing movement is with specifications no adjustment is necessary. If the adjustment is not within these limits you must add or subtract shims accordingly.

BRAKES

— **CAUTION** —
When servicing wheel brake parts, do not create dust by grinding or sanding brake linings or by cleaning wheel brake parts with a dry brush or with compressed air (a water dampened cloth should be used). Many wheel brake parts contain asbestos fibers which can become airborne if dust is created during servicing. Breathing dust containing asbestos fibers may cause serious bodily harm.

Brake adjustments, lining replacement, bleeding procedure, master and wheel cylinder and caliper overhaul can be found in the Unit Repair Section.

A dual hydraulic brake system is employed. The front and rear brakes are each separate systems with a common tandem master cylinder. In the event of a failure in either of the systems, the other will remain operable.

NOTE: Caliper bore corrosion is a relatively common problem with Corvettes. If the corrosion is too severe to be removed with a hone, it may be best to replace the calipers with stainless steel-sleeved units available from the aftermarket. If new original calipers are used, the corrosion problem will return over a period of time.

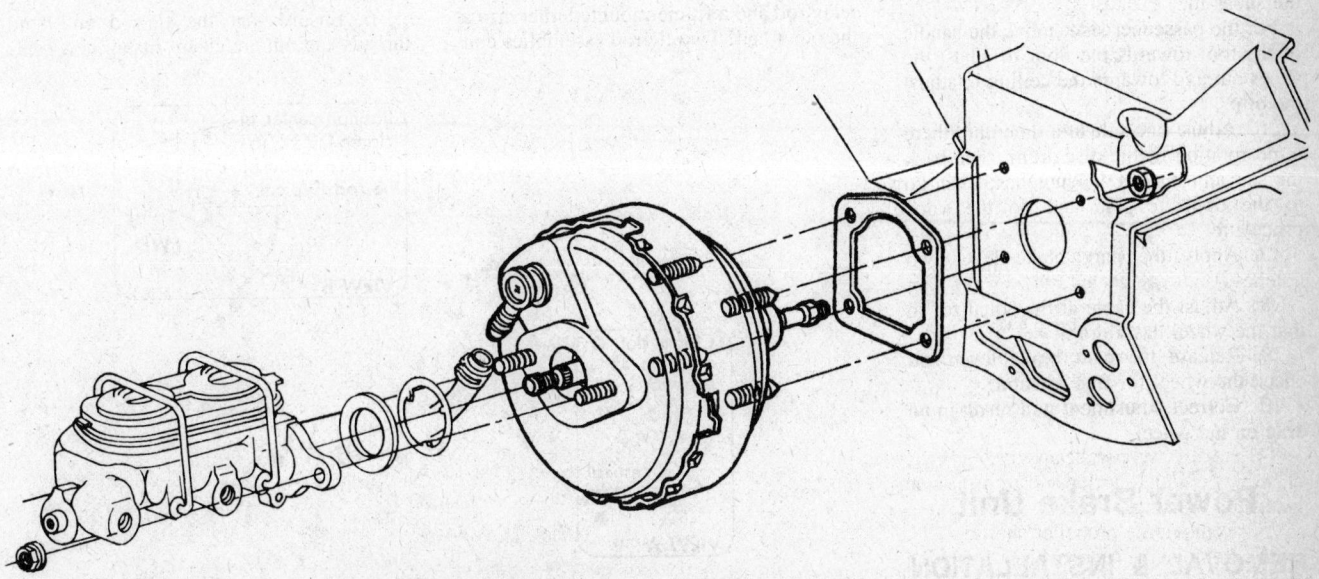

Power brake booster installation

Parking Brake

ADJUSTMENT

1978–82

1. Jack up your vehicle and support it with jack stands. Remove the rear wheels. Loosen the brake cables at the equalizer nuts, until the parking brake levers move freely to the Off position with slack in the cables.
2. Rotate the disc until the adjusting screw can be seen through the hole in the disc.
3. Insert an appropriate tool in this hole and adjust with an up-and-down motion.
4. Tighten the adjuster until the disc cannot move, then back off 6–8 notches.
5. Install the rear wheels.
6. Apply the parking brake to the 13th notch.
7. Tighten the check nuts until an 80 lb. pull is obtained while pulling into the 14th notch.
8. Torque the check nuts to 70 inch lbs.
9. Release the parking brake and check for a no drag condition.

1984 and later

1. Raise the vehicle and remove the rear wheels, place two wheel lug nuts opposite of each other to insure correct disc/drum position.
2. Back the caliper piston into its bore.
3. Loosen the park brake cable so that there is no tension on the park brake shoes.
4. Rotate the disc so that the hole in the disc/drum face will align with the star adjuster.
5. To make the adjustment, insert a brake adjusting spoon through the hole in the disc face.
For the driver's side, move the handle of the tool towards the ceiling to adjust the shoes out and towards the floor to adjust the shoes in.
For the passenger side, move the handle of the tool towards the floor to adjust the shoes out and towards the ceiling to adjust them in.
6. Adjust one side at a time until there is no rotation of the disc/drum, then back the star adjuster off 5–7 notches. Then go to the opposite side and do the same procedure.
7. Apply the park brake lever two notches.
8. Adjust the cable at the equalizer so that the wheel has a drag.
9. Release the park brake lever and check the wheel for free rotation.
10. Correct adjustment will result in no drag on the wheel.

Power Brake Unit

REMOVAL & INSTALLATION

1. Remove the vacuum hose from the brake booster.
2. Disconnect the hydraulic brake lines from the master cylinder.

NOTE: Do not spill brake fluid on painted surfaces.

3. Remove the master cylinder from the brake booster.
4. Disconnect the push rod at the brake pedal.
5. Remove the nuts and lockwashers that secure the unit to the firewall.
6. Installation is the reverse of removal. Torque the mounting bolts to 24 ft. lbs. Remember to bleed the brake system.

Master Cylinder

REMOVAL & INSTALLATION

1. Disconnect the brake lines at the master cylinder.
2. Remove the two mounting nuts and lift off the cylinder.
3. Installation is the reverse of removal. Torque the nuts to 24 ft. lbs. and bleed the system.

— CAUTION —
The use of silicone brake fluid such as Delco Supreme #24 can damage the seals and rubber components in the brake system. Use brake fluid that meets or exceeds DOT 3 specifications, such as Delco Supreme #11 or equivalent.

STEERING

The manual steering gear on the Corvette is of the recirculating ball type. Relay-type steering linkage is used on all models, with a pitman arm connected to one end of a relay rod and a frame-mounted idler arm at the other end. Two tie-rod assemblies connect the relay rod to the steering arms. The tie-rod ends are threaded into sleeves to provide adjustment.

The Corvette uses a linkage assist power steering system. A valve attached to the linkage modulates pressure according to power requirements. A power cylinder supplies the actual assist. 1984 and later models use a power rack and pinion system. This system has a rotary control valve which directs hydraulic fluid, coming from the hydraulic pump, to either side of the rack piston. The integral rack piston is attached to the rack and converts hydraulic pressure to a linear force which moves the rack left or right. The force is then transmitted through the inner and outer tie rods to the steering knuckles which turn the wheels.

NOTE: Procedures for removal and installation of the ignition switch, key warning buzzer switch, and ignition lock cylinder can be found in the "Chevrolet" car section.

Tie-Rod

REMOVAL & INSTALLATION

NOTE: Before attempting this procedure mark the tie-rod threads with paint or chalk for easy reinstallation.

1. Remove the cotter pins and nuts from the tie-rod end studs.
2. Tap on the steering arm near the tie-rod end (use another hammer as backing) and pull down on the tie-rod, if necessary, to free it.
3. Remove the inner stud in the same manner as the outer.
4. Loosen the clamp bolts and unscrew the ends if they are being replaced.
5. Lubricate the tie-rod end threads with chassis grease if they were removed. Install each end assembly an equal distance from the sleeve.
6. Ensure that the tie-rod end stud threads and nut are clean. Install new seals

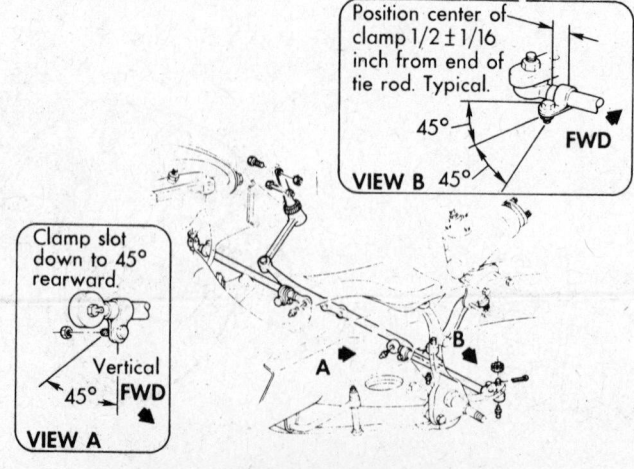

Steering linkage

and install the studs into the steering arms and relay rod.

7. Install the stud nuts. Tighten the nuts to 35 ft. lbs. plus as needed to align the cotter pin hole.

8. Adjust the toe-in as described in the "Front End Alignment" section.

NOTE: Before tightening the sleeve clamps, ensure that the clamps are positioned so that the adjusting sleeve slot is covered by the clamp.

Steering Gear

REMOVAL & INSTALLATION

1978-84

1. Disconnect battery ground cable.
2. Remove retaining nuts, lock washers, and bolts at steering coupling to steering shaft flange.
3. Remove pitman arm nut and washer from pitman shaft and mark relation of arm position to shaft.
4. Remove pitman arm with Tool J-6632, or its equivalent.
5. Remove screws securing steering gear to frame and remove gear from vehicle.
6. Installation is the reverse of removal. Torque the gear-to-frame nuts: 30

Steering gear attachment

ft. lbs; flange-to-flex-coupling bolt: 30 ft. lbs.

1984 and later

1. Raise the vehicle on a hoist.
2. Remove the drivers side wheel and tire.
3. Disconnect the power steering hoses and cap them off.
4. Disconnect power steering tie rod ends both sides.
5. Remove the upper and lower mounting bolts, passenger side.
6. Remove the mounting bolt, drivers side.
7. Remove the intermediate shaft lower flexible joint at the rack and pinion assembly.
8. Remove the stabilizer bar.
9. Remove the electric fan.
10. Remove the rack and pinion assembly from the vehicle.
11. Installation is the reverse of removal.

Power Steering Pump

REMOVAL & INSTALLATION

1. Remove the hoses at the pump. Tape the openings shut to prevent contamination. Position the disconnected lines in a raised position to prevent leakage.
2. Remove the pump belt.
3. Loosen the retaining bolts and any braces, and remove the pump.
4. Install the pump on the engine with the retaining bolts hand-tight.
5. Connect and tighten the hose fittings.
6. Refill the pump and bleed by turning the pulley counterclockwise (viewed from the front). Stop the bleeding when air bubbles no longer appear.
7. Install the pump belt on the pulley and adjust the tension.

BLEEDING POWER STEERING SYSTEM

1. Run engine until power steering fluid

reaches normal operating temperature, approximately 170°F (80°C), then shut engine off. Remove reservoir filler cap and check oil level.

2. If oil level is low, add power steering fluid to proper level and replace filler cap. When adding or making a complete fluid change, always use GM #1050017, or equivalent, power steering fluid. Do not use transmission fluid.

3. When checking fluid level after the steering system has been serviced, air must be bled from the system. With wheels turned all the way to the left, add power steering fluid to level indicated on reservoir.

4. Start engine, and running at fast idle, recheck fluid level. Add fluid if necessary.

5. Bleed system by turning wheels from side to side without hitting stops. Maintain fluid level just above internal pump casting. Fluid with air in it will have a light tan or milky appearance. This air must be eliminated from fluid before normal steering action can be obtained.

6. Return wheels to center position and continue to run engine for two or three minutes, then shut engine off.

7. Road-test vehicle to make sure steering functions normally and is free from noise.

8. Recheck fluid level as described in Steps 1 and 2.

Steering Wheel

REMOVAL & INSTALLATION

1978—Standard Wheel

1. Disconnect the battery ground cable.
2. Pry off the horn button cap.
3. Remove the snap ring then the steering wheel nut.
4. Install a wheel puller in the threaded holes provided. Butt the center bolt of the tool against the steering shaft and turn clockwise to remove the hub assembly.
5. When installing make sure the turn signal is in the neutral position, then install the hub on the steering shaft and secure it with the nut. Torque the nut to 30 ft. lbs.
6. Install the snap ring.
7. Attach the steering wheel to the hub assembly with the attaching screws.
8. Install the horn contact and attach with the three screws.
9. Snap the horn button in place.
10. Connect the battery ground cable.

1978 and Later—Tilt Telescoping Wheel

1. Disconnect the battery ground cable.
2. Pry off the horn button cap.
3. Remove the three screws and remove the upper horn contact assembly.
4. If used, remove the shim then remove the screw securing the center star screw. Remove the star screw and lever.
5. Remove the snap ring and nut from the shaft and remove the steering wheel assembly with a wheel puller.

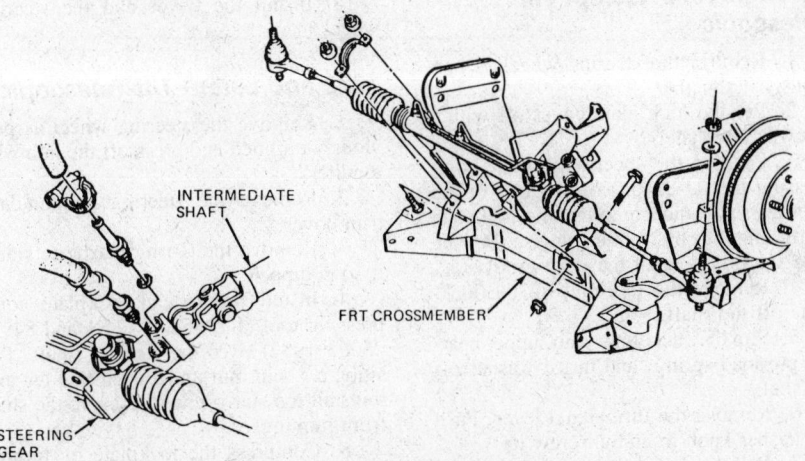

Power rack and pinion assembly

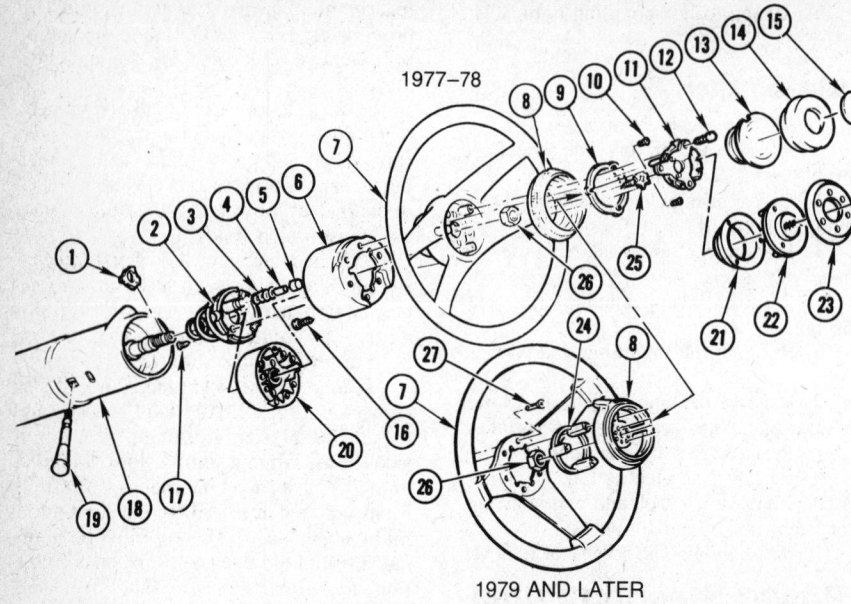

1977-78

1979 AND LATER

1978 and later tilt and telescoping steering wheel assembly

1. Steering wheel retainer
2. Horn button and blowing ring lower contact
3. Horn contact spring
4. Contact (with eyelet)
5. Contact insulator
6. Steering wheel extension
7. Steering wheel assembly
8. Steering column lock lever
9. Horn shim
10. Screw (#8–10 × ¼")
11. Horn button and blowing ring upper contact
12. Screw (#8–82 × 13/32")
13. Horn button cap retainer
14. Horn blowing cap.
15. Emblem
16. Screw (#8–18 × ½")
17. Screw (#10–32 × ⅜")
18. Steering column assembly
19. Steering wheel release lever
20. Hub assembly
21. Horn button cap retainer
22. Emblem
23. Horn button cap
24. Steering column spacer
25. Lock knob screw
26. Nut (M14 × 1.5)
27. Screw (#10–24 × .75)

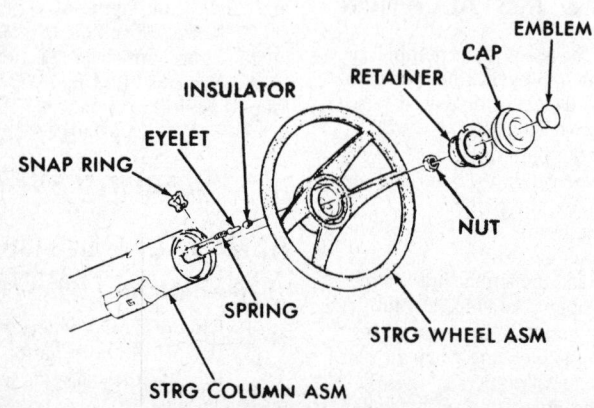

Standard steering wheel—1978 and later

6. If it is necessary to disassemble the steering wheel, remove the three screws securing the steering wheel and separate; then remove the four screws securing the extension to the steering wheel then separate.

7. To assemble the steering wheel, position the extension to the steering wheel and install the attaching screws. Torque the screws to 20 inch lbs.

8. Position the spring, eyelet and insulator to the lower contact assembly. Position the assembly to the steering wheel and install the three screws.

9. Position the steering wheel assembly to the steering column and torque the nut to 30 ft. lbs.

10. Install the snap ring.

11. Position the lever to the steering column and install the star screw. Install the screws. Remove the switch by pulling it.

12. Position the upper contact assembly and shim if used and install the three retaining screws.

13. Install the retainer and horn button cap.

14. Connect the battery ground cable.

Turn Signal Switch

REMOVAL & INSTALLATION
Through 1979—Except Tilt-Telescopic

1. Remove the steering wheel as previously outlined.

2. Pry the lock plate cover off with a screwdriver blade.

3. Position the special lockplate compressing tool (J-23653) on the end of the steering shaft and compress the lockplate by turning the shaft nut clockwise. Pry the wire snap-ring out of the shaft groove.

4. Remove the tool and lift the lockplate off the shaft.

5. Slip the cancelling cam, upper bearing pre-load spring, and thrust washer off the shaft.

6. Remove the turn signal lever. Push the flasher knob in and unscrew it.

7. Pull the switch connector out of the mast jacket and tape the upper part to facilitate switch removal. On tilt wheels, place

the turn signal and shifter housing in Low position and remove the harness cover.

8. Remove the three switch mounting screws. Remove the switch by pulling it straight up while guiding the wiring harness cover through the column.

9. Install the replacement switch by working the connector and cover down through the housing and under the bracket. On tilt models, the connector is worked down through the housing, under the bracket, and then the cover is installed on the harness.

10. Install the switch mounting screws and the connector on the mast jacket bracket. Install the column-to-dash trim plate.

11. Install the flasher knob and the turn signal lever.

12. With the turn signal lever in neutral and the flasher knob out, slide the thrust washer, upper bearing pre-load spring, and cancelling cam onto the shaft.

13. Position the lockplate on the shaft and press it down until a new snap-ring can be inserted in the shaft groove.

14. Install the cover and the steering wheel.

1978 and Later—Tilt-Telescopic

1. Remove the steering wheel as previously outlined and press off the hub with a puller.

2. Remove the steering column/dash trim cover.

3. Remove the C-ring plastic retainer, if so equipped.

4. Install the special lockplate compressing tool (J-23653 1977-81 and 84; J-23063 1982) over the steering shaft. Position a ⁵/₁₆ in. nut under each tool leg and reinstall the star screw to prevent the shaft from moving.

5. Compress the lockplate by turning the shaft nut clockwise until the C-ring can be removed.

6. Remove the tool and lift out the

lockplate, horn contact carrier, and the upper bearing preload spring.

7. Pull the switch connector out of the mast jacket and tape the upper part to facilitate switch removal.

8. Remove the turn signal lever. Push the flasher in and unscrew it.

9. Position the turn signal and shifter housing in Low position. Remove the switch by pulling it straight up while guiding the wiring harness out of the housing.

10. Install the replacement switch by working the harness connector down through the housing and under the mounting bracket.

11. Install the harness cover and clip the connector to the mast jacket.

12. Install the switch mounting screws, signal lever, and the flasher knob.

13. With the turn signal lever in neutral and the flasher knob out, install the upper bearing pre-load spring, horn contact carrier, and lockplate onto the shaft.

14. Postion the tool as in Step 4 and compress the plate far enough to allow the C-ring to be installed.

15. Remove the tool. Install the plastic C-ring retainer.

16. Install the column/dash trim cover. Install the steering wheel.

INSTRUMENT PANEL

Headlight Switch

REMOVAL & INSTALLATION

1. Disconnect the negative battery terminal.

2. Remove the left air distribution duct.

3. Remove the instrument cluster attaching screws and pull the cluster rearward.

4. Disconnect the speedometer cable, electrical connectors and remove the cluster.

5. Remove the instrument panel to left door pillar attaching screws and pull the left side of the instrument panel slightly forward for access.

6. Depress the shaft retainer, pull the knob and shaft assembly out and remove the switch bezel.

7. Disconnect the vacuum hoses from the switch, tagging them for installation.

8. Pry the connector from the switch and remove the switch from the panel.

9. Installation is the reverse of removal.

Instrument Cluster

REMOVAL & INSTALLATION
1978–82

1. Disconnect negative battery cable.

2. Remove left air distribution duct.

3. Remove lens to bezel attaching screws and remove lens.

4. Remove cluster to instument panel attaching screws.

5. Pull cluster assembly slightly forward to obtain clearance for removal of speedometer cable housing, headlamp switch connectors and panel illuminating lamps.

6. Install by reversing removal procedure, being careful not to kink the speedometer cable casing.

1984 and Later

NOTE: Repairs to the instument panel must only be completed by your local Chevrolet dealer.

1. Disconnect battery ground cable.

2. Remove light switch knob (spring loaded), and light switch nut.

3. Remove steering column trim cover.

4. Remove 2 steering column attaching bolts and lower steering column for access.

5. Remove cluster bezel front and left side attaching screws.

6. Remove cluster bezel from instument panel.

7. Remove 4 cluster to instument panel attaching screws.

8. Pull cluster rearward for access to disconnect cluster electrical connectors. Metal retaining clips are located at back side of connectors.

9. Remove cluster from instrument panel. Odometer may be removed for service or replacement.

10. Reverse above procedure to install.

Speedometer Cable

REMOVAL & INSTALLATION

Reach behind the speedometer and depress the retaining clip. Pull the cable from the casing. If the cable is broken, raise the car and disconnect the cable at the transmission. Lubricate only the bottom ¾ of the cable with speedometer cable lubricant. Reconnect all parts.

NOTE: This procedure is easier to complete if the instrument panel cluster has previously been removed.

WINDSHIELD WIPERS

Motor

REMOVAL & INSTALLATION
1978–82

1. With wiper motor in park position and hood open, disconnect the washer hoses and all wiring from the motor assembly.

2. Remove the plenum chamber grill.

3. Remove the nut which retains the crank arm to the motor assembly.

4. Remove the ignition shield, if used, and distributor cap. Remove and identify the left bank spark plug leads.

5. Remove the motor mounting screws or nuts and remove the motor.

6. To install, reverse the above procedure.

1984 and Later

1. Open hood and install fender covers.

2. Remove wiper arms.

3. Remove air inlet leaf screen.

4. Turn ignition on, and activate motor with wiper switch. Allow motor crank arm to rotate to point to a position between 4 and 5 o'clock as viewed from passenger compartment. Stop crank arm in this position by turning off ignition switch.

5. Disconnect battery ground cable.

6. Disconnect upper motor electrical connectors.

7. Remove motor mounting bolts.

8. With crank arm in position described in Step 4 above, motor may now be removed from vehicle. Lower electrical connector may be disconnected as motor is partially removed.

9. To install, reverse the above procedure.

Wiper Transmission

REMOVAL & INSTALLATION

1. Make sure the wiper is in the park position.

2. Disconnect the battery ground cable.

3. Open the hood and remove the plenum chamber screen.

4. Loosen the nuts retaining the ball sockets to the crank arm and detach the drive rod from the crank arm.

5. Remove the transmission nuts, then lift the rod assemblies from the plenum chamber.

6. Remove the transmission linkage from the plenum chamber.

7. To install, reverse the removal procedure. Make sure the wipers are in the park position.

RADIO

REMOVAL & INSTALLATION
1978 and Later

1. Disconnect the battery ground cable.

2. Remove the console tunnel side panels.

3. Pull the radio control knobs from the shaft.

4. Remove the two screws that secure the console trim plate to the instrument cluster.

5. Remove the rear defogger switch if so equipped.

6. Remove the five screws from around the upper perimeter of the instrument cluster.

7. Pull the instrument cluster enough to disconnect the electrical connector from the rear of the cluster.

NOTE: The center instrument cluster trim panel is designed to collapse under impact. Do not deflect the panel to gain access to the radio.

8. Remove the screw holding the radio bracket reinforcement to the floor pan.

9. Pull the radio outward and disconnect the wiring from the back.

10. Installation is the reverse of removal. If a new radio is being installed, save the mounting bracket from the rear of the old one.

NOTE: The radio heat sink must be removed when radio service is required. It is located behind the passenger side dash panel.

FUSES

The fuse block is located beneath the instrument panel above the headlight dimmer floor switch. Fuse holders are labeled as to their service and the correct amperage. Always replace blown fuses with new ones of the correct amperage. Otherwise electrical overloads and possible wiring damage will result.

The fuse block on some models is a swing-down unit located in the underside of the instrument panel adjacent to the steering column. Access to the fuse block on some models is gained through the glove box opening. The Convenience Center on some models is a swing-down unit located on the underside of the instrument panel. The swing-down feature provides center location and easy access to buzzers, relays and flasher units. All units are serviced by plug-in replacement. Location of Convenience Center on specific models may vary.

Circuit Breaker

A circuit breaker is an electrical switch which breaks the circuit during an electrical overload. The circuit breaker will remain open until the short or overload condition in the circuit is corrected.

Fusible Links

Fusible links are sections of wire, with special insulation, designed to melt under elec-

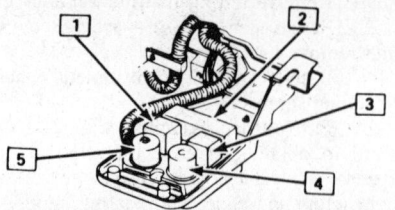

HORN RELAY   **HAZARD FLASHER**
CHOKE RELAY   **TURN SIGNAL**
WARNING BUZZER   **FLASHER**

Swing–down convenience center—typical

trical overload. Replacements are simply spliced into the wire. There may be as many as five of these in the engine compartment wiring harnesses. These are:

1. Horn relay to fuse panel circuit—one link.

2. Charging circuit, from the starter solenoid to the horn relay—two links.

3. Starter solenoid to ammeter circuit—one link.

4. Horn relay to rear window defroster circuit—one link.

The fusible links are all two wire gauge sizes smaller than the wires they protect.

NOTE: Most models have fusible links at these locations.

REPLACEMENT

1. Disconnect the battery ground cable.
2. Disconnect the fusible link from the junction block or starter solenoid.
3. Cut the harness directly behind the connector to remove the damaged fusible link.
4. Strip the harness wire approximately ½ in.
5. Connect the new fusible link to the harness wire using a crimp on connector. Solder the connection using rosin core solder.
6. Tape all exposed wires with plastic eletrical tape.
7. Connect the fusible link to the junction block or starter solenoid and reconnect the battery ground cable.

HEATER

Blower

REMOVAL & INSTALLATION
1978—82

1. Disconnect the negative battery cable at the battery.

2. On 1981–82 models, unbolt the A/C compressor and move the compressor out of the way. DO NOT disconnect the refrigerant lines from the compressor.

3. Remove the coolant recovery jar, if so equipped.

4. Disconnect the wiring from the motor and the cooling tube from the motor case, if so equipped.

5. Remove the mounting screws from the blower motor and remove the motor. If the motor sticks to the case due to the sealer, pry the motor GENTLY away from the case.

6. Installation is the reverse of the previous steps.

1984 and Later

1. Open the hood and disconnect the battery ground cable.

2. Remove the front wheel house rear panel and move wheel house seal aside.

3. Remove the motor cooling tube.

4. Remove the relay.

5. Remove the blower motor assembly to case attaching screws.

6. Remove the motor and impeller.

To install, reverse the replacement procedure and check the operation.

Heater Core

REMOVAL & INSTALLATION
1978–79 Without A/C

1. Disconnect the battery ground cable.

2. Drain the cooling system and remove and plug the water hoses from the heater connections.

3. Remove the air-distributor duct stud nuts on the firewall.

4. Remove the right instrument panel pad, right-hand dashboard braces, center dash console duct, and the floor outlet duct.

5. Remove the radio and center dashboard console.

6. Pull the distributor duct from the firewall and remove the resistor wires when clearance is sufficient.

7. Remove the heater core retaining springs and remove the core.

8. Installation is the reverse of removal. If core-to-case sealer was damaged during removal, replace with new sealer.

1978–80 With A/C

1. Disconnect the battery ground cable.

2. Drain the cooling system. It is not necessary to evacuate the A.C. refrigerant.

3. Disconnect the heater hoses at the firewall and plug the pipes.

4. Remove the nuts from the distributor studs protruding through the firewall.

5. Remove the right side dash pad and center dash cluster.

6. Disconnect the right dash outlet from the center duct.

7. Remove the center duct from the selector duct.

8. Remove the selector duct to the dash panel and pull it to the right and to the rear.

9. Remove the cables and wiring con-

nectors from the selector and remove it from the car.

10. Remove the temperature door cam plate from the selector duct.

11. Remove the heater core and housing from the selector.

12. Reverse the removal procedure to install.

1981–82 All Models

1. Disconnect the negative cable at the battery.

2. Drain the coolant from the radiator.

3. Raise the right front of the vehicle and support it safely.

4. Disconnect the heater hoses at the heater core connections.

5. Remove the heater case retaining nut which is located on the top of the blower case.

6. Remove the glove box.

7. Remove the console side panels.

8. Remove the knobs and nuts from the radio shafts.

9. Remove the two screws which secure the console trim plate to the instrument cluster.

10. Remove the instrument cluster attaching screws.

11. Pull the cluster out slightly and disconnect the electrical connector from the rear of the cluster.

12. Remove the radio as previously outlined.

13. Remove the right side windshield pillar trim panel.

14. Remove the right side dash panel retaining screws and pull the panel rearward to release the upper retaining clip.

15. Remove the following ducts:
   a. Right side vent
   b. Main vent distribution
   c. Lower heater deflector
   d. Heater-defroster distribution duct assembly (Disconnect the vacuum line).

16. Disconnect both the temperature cable and the vacuum line at the heater housing.

17. Remove the heater core from the housing.

18. Installation is the reverse of the previous steps.

1984 and Later

1. Disconnect the negative battery cable. Drain the cooling system.

2. Remove the instrument cluster bezel including the tilt wheel lever and instrument panel pad.

3. Remove the A/C distributor duct and disconnect the flex hose.

4. Remove the right side hush panel.

5. Remove the side window defroster flex hose.

6. Remove the side window defroster to heater cover screws and disconnect the extension.

7. Remove the temperature contol cable and bracket assembly at heater cover including disconnecting heater door control shaft.

8. Remove the ECM (Electric Contol Module) and disconnect the electrical connectors.

─────── **CAUTION** ───────
Make sure the ignition switch is OFF when disconnecting ECM
──────────────────────────

9. Remove the tubular support brace from the door pillar to aluminum, instrument panel reinforcement brace.

10. Remove heater core cover attaching screws.

11. Remove heater pipe and heater water control bracket attaching screws.

12. Remove heater hose at heater core pipes.

13. Remove the heater core.

14. Installation is the reverse of removal.

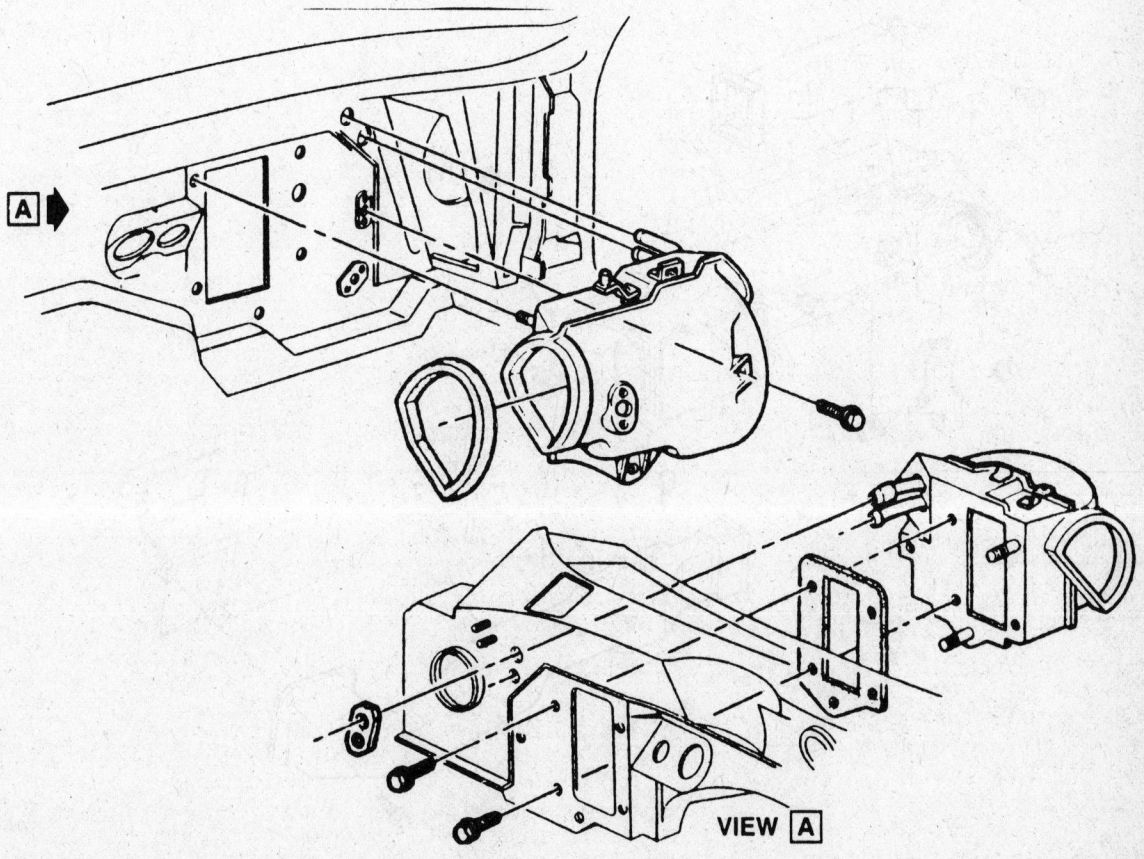

Heater core case—1984 and later

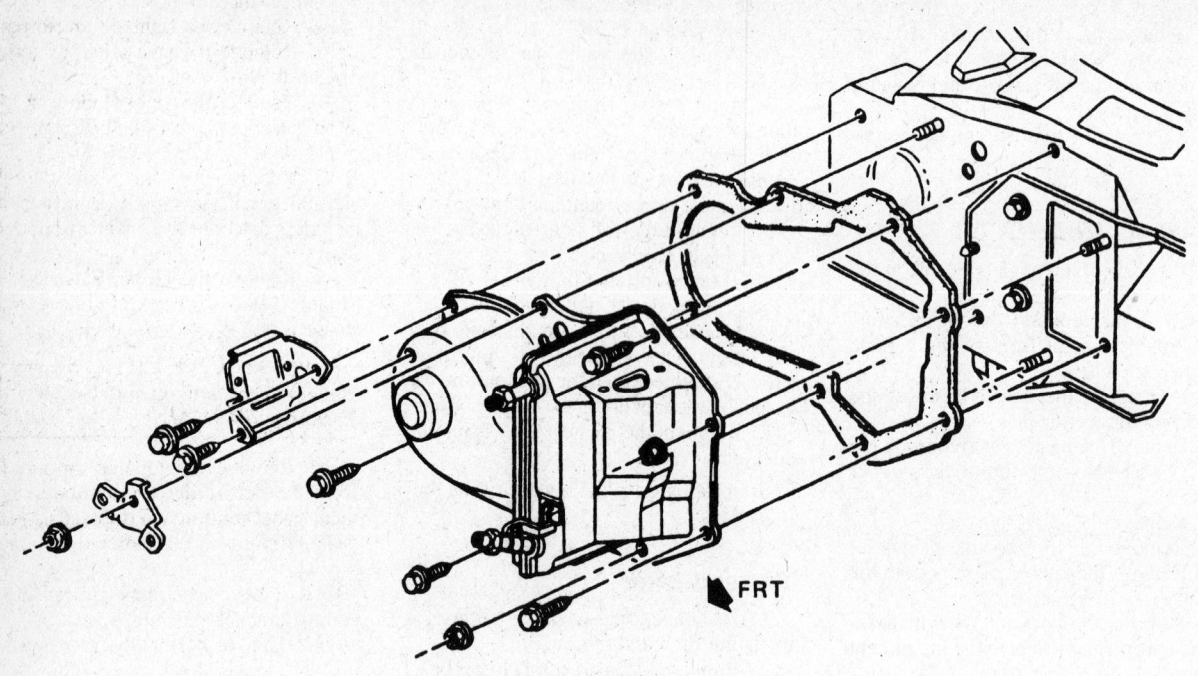

Blower motor and evaporator module—1984 and later

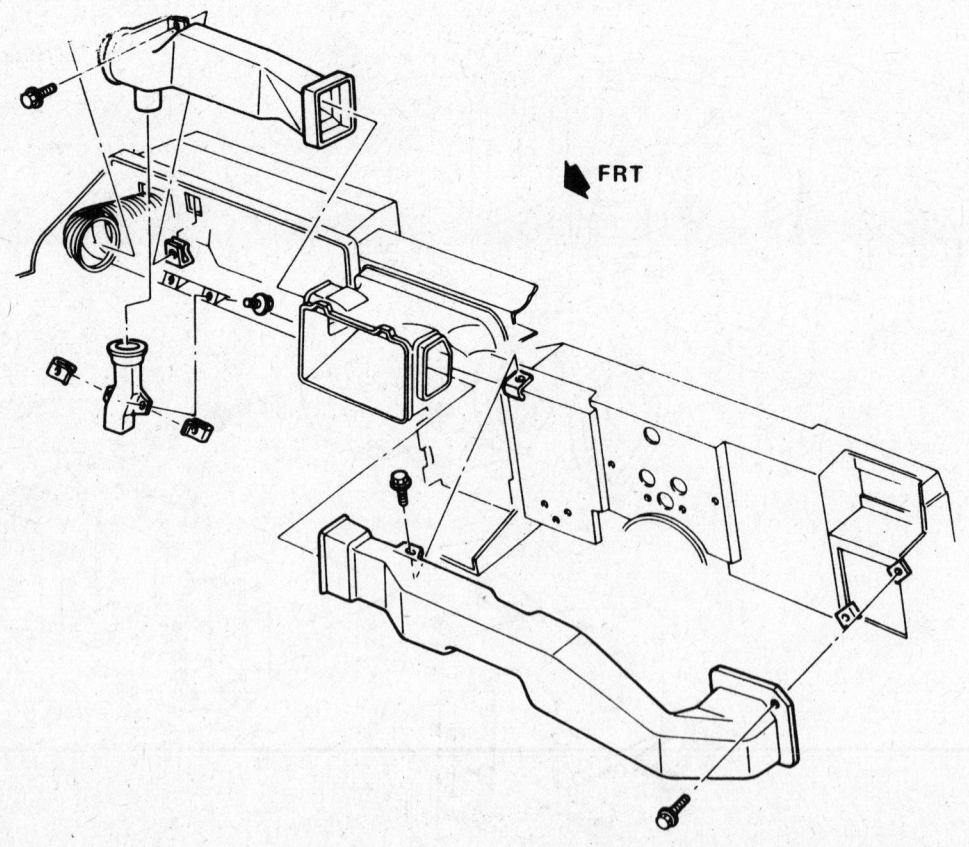

Duct assembly—1984 and later

Chevrolet
Rear Wheel Drive
Caprice, Impala, Nova, Malibu, Monte Carlo

YEAR IDENTIFICATION

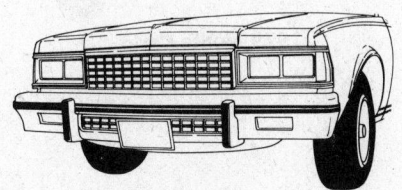

1978 Caprice

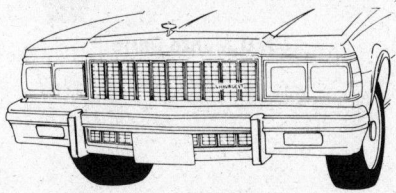

1979 Caprice

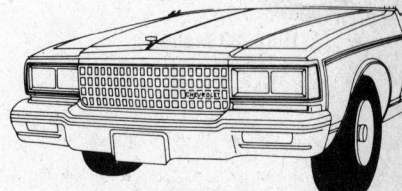

1980 Caprice

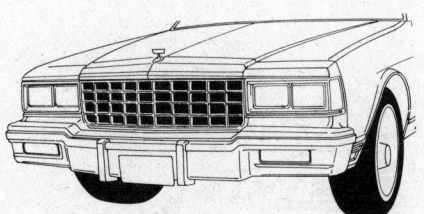

1981–85 Caprice

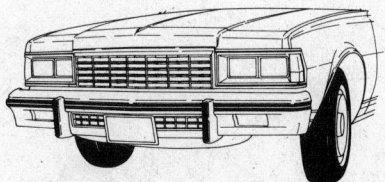

1978 Impala

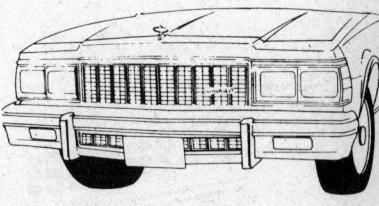

1979 Impala

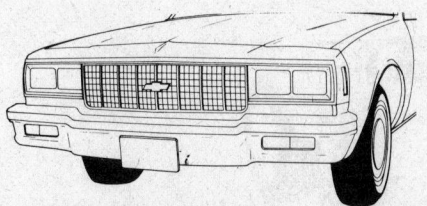

1980 Impala

1981–85 Impala

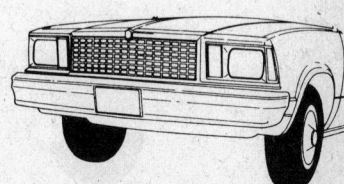

1978 Malibu Classic

YEAR IDENTIFICATION

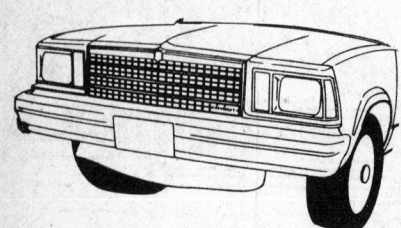

1979 Malibu Classic

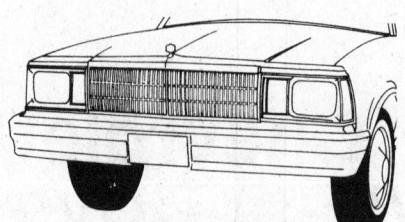

1980 Malibu

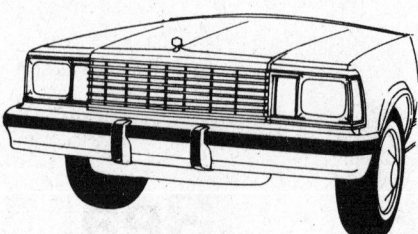

1981 Malibu

1982–83 Malibu

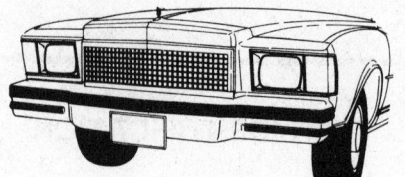

1978 Monte Carlo

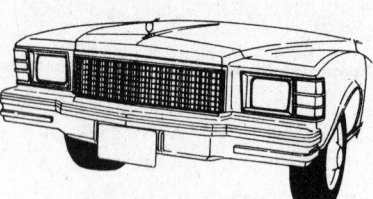

1979 Monte Carlo

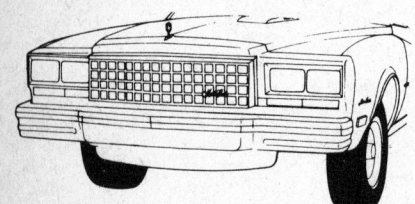

1980 Monte Carlo

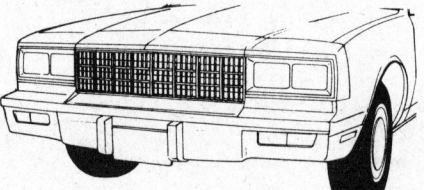

1981 Monte Carlo

1982 Monte Carlo

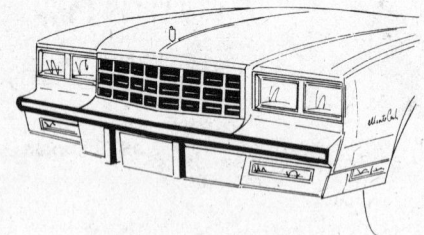

1983–85 Monte Carlo

1984–85 Monte Carlo SS

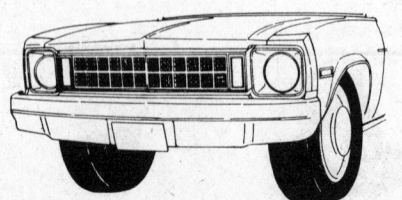

1978 Nova

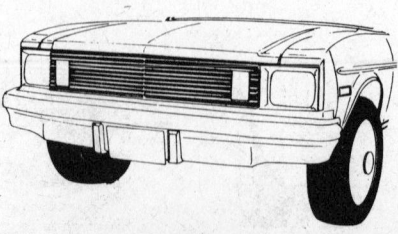

1979 Nova

VEHICLE IDENTIFICATION NUMBER (VIN)

It is important for servicing and ordering parts to be certain of the vehicle and engine identification. The VIN (vehicle identification number) is a 13 or 17 digit number visible through the windshield on the driver's side of the dash and contains the vehicle and engine identification codes. It can be interpreted as follows:

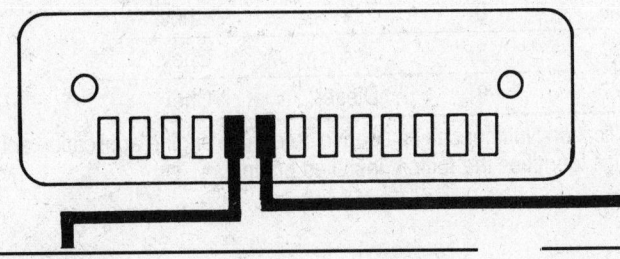

Engine Code							Model Year Code	
Code	Cu. In.	Liters	Cyl.	Carb.	Eng. Mfg.		Code	Year
M	200	3.3	6	2	Chev.		8	1978
D	250	4.1	6	1	Chev.		9	1979
K	229	3.8	6	2	Chev.		A	1980
A	231	3.8	6	2	Buick			
3	231	3.8	6	Turbo	Buick			
J	267	4.4	8	2	Chev.			
U	305	5.0	8	2	Chev.			
G	305	5.0	8	2	Chev.			
H	305	5.0	8	4	Chev.			
L	350	5.7	8	4	Chev.			
N	350	5.7	8	Diesel	Olds.			

The thirteen digit Vehicle Identification Number can be used to determine engine application and model year. The sixth digit indicates the model year, and the fifth digit identifies the factory installed engine.

VEHICLE IDENTIFICATION NUMBER (VIN)

It is important for servicing and ordering parts to be certain of the vehicle and engine identification. The VIN (vehicle identification number) is a 13 or 17 digit number visible through the windshield on the driver's side of the dash and contains the vehicle and engine identification codes. It can be interpreted as follows:

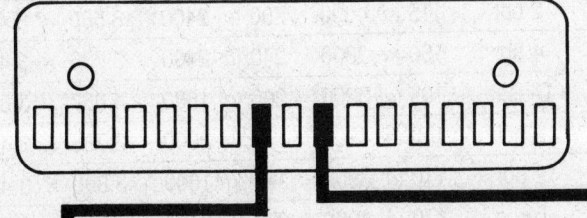

ENGINE CODE							MODEL YEAR CODE	
Code	Cu. In.	Liters	Cyl.	Carb.	Eng. Mfg.		Code	Year
K	229	3.8	6	2	Chev.		B	'81
9	229	3.8	6	2	Chev.		C	'82
A	231	3.8	6	2	Buick		D	'83
3	231	3.8	6	Turbo	Buick		E	'84
V	263	4.3	6	Diesel	Olds.		F	'85
J	267	4.4	8	2	Chev.			

Engine Code

Code	Cu. In.	Liters	Cyl.	Carb.	Eng. Mfg.
G	305	5.0	8	4	Chev.
H	305	5.0	8	4	Chev.
6	305	5.7	8	4	Chev.
N	350	5.7	8	Diesel	Chev.

The seventeen digit Vehicle Identification Number can be used to determine engine application and model year. The tenth digit indicates the model year, and the eighth digit identifies the factory installed engine.

GENERAL ENGINE SPECIFICATIONS

Year	Eng. V.I.N. Code	Engine No. Cyl. Displacement Cu. In.	Eng. Mfg.	Carburetor Type	Horsepower @ rpm ∎	Torque @ rpm (ft. lbs.) ∎	Bore × Stroke (in.)	Compression Ratio	Oil Pressure @ 2000 rpm
'78	M	6-200	Chev.	2 bbl	94 @ 4000	154 @ 2000	3.500 × 3.480	8.2:1	40
	A	6-231	Buick	2 bbl	105 @ 3400	185 @ 2000	3.800 × 3.400	8.0:1	37
	D	6-250	Chev.	1 bbl	110 @ 3800	190 @ 1600	3.875 × 3.530	8.1:1	40
	U	8-305	Chev.	2 bbl	145 @ 3800	245 @ 2400	3.736 × 3.480	8.4:1	40
	L	8-350	Chev.	4 bbl	170 @ 3800	270 @ 2400	4.000 × 3.480	8.4:1	40
'79	M	6-200	Chev.	2 bbl	94 @ 4000	154 @ 2000	3.500 × 3.480	8.2:1	40
	A	6-231	Buick	2 bbl	105 @ 3400	185 @ 2000	3.800 × 3.400	8.0:1	37
	D	4-250	Chev.	1 bbl	110 @ 3800	190 @ 1600	3.875 × 3.530	8.1:1	40
	J	8-267	Chev.	2 bbl	125 @ 3800	215 @ 2400	3.500 × 3.480	8.2:1	40
	G	8-305	Chev.	2 bbl	130 @ 3200	245 @ 2000	3.736 × 3.480	8.4:1	40
	H	8-305	Chev.	4 bbl	155 @ 3800	260 @ 2800	3.736 × 3.480	8.4:1	45
	L	8-350	Chev.	4 bbl	170 @ 3800	270 @ 2400	4.000 × 3.480	8.2:1	40
'80	K	6-229	Chev.	2 bbl	110 @ 4200	170 @ 2000	3.736 × 3.480	8.6:1	37.5
	A	6-231	Buick	2 bbl	110 @ 3800	190 @ 1600	3.800 × 3.400	8.0:1	45
	3	6-231	Buick	Turbo	170 @ 4000	275 @ 2400	3.800 × 3.400	8.0:1	37
	J	8-267	Chev.	2 bbl	115 @ 4000	200 @ 2400	3.500 × 3.480	8.3:1	45
	H	8-305	Chev.	4 bbl	150 @ 2800	240 @ 2400	3.736 × 3.480	8.6:1	45
	N	8-350	Olds.	Diesel	105 @ 3200	205 @ 1600	4.057 × 3.385	22.5:1	30–45①
'81	K	6-229	Chev.	2 bbl	110 @ 4200	170 @ 2000	3.736 × 3.480	8.6:1	45
	A	6-231	Buick	2 bbl	110 @ 3800	190 @ 1600	3.800 × 3.400	8.0:1	45
	3	6-231	Buick	Turbo	170 @ 4000	275 @ 2400	3.800 × 3.400	8.0:1	37
	J	8-267	Chev.	2 bbl	115 @ 4000	200 @ 2400	3.500 × 3.480	8.3:1	45
	H	8-305	Chev.	4 bbl	150 @ 3800	240 @ 2400	3.736 × 3.480	8.6:1	45
	N	8-350	Olds.	Diesel	105 @ 3200	205 @ 1600	4.057 × 3.385	22.5:1	30–45①
'82	K	6-229	Chev.	2 bbl	115 @ 4000	170 @ 2000	3.736 × 3.480	8.6:1	45
	A	6-231	Buick	2 bbl	110 @ 3800	190 @ 1600	3.800 × 3.400	8.0:1	45
	J	8-267	Chev.	2 bbl	115 @ 2000	200 @ 2400	3.500 × 3.480	8.3:1	45
	H	8-305	Chev.	4 bbl	150 @ 3800	240 @ 2400	3.736 × 3.480	8.6:1	45
	N	8-350	Olds.	Diesel	105 @ 3200	205 @ 1600	4.057 × 3.385	22.5:1	30–45①

GENERAL ENGINE SPECIFICATIONS

Year	Eng. V.I.N. Code	Engine No. Cyl. Displacement Cu. In.	Eng. Mfg.	Carburetor Type	Horsepower @ rpm ■	Torque @ rpm (ft. lbs.) ■	Bore × Stroke (in.)	Compression Ratio	Oil Pressure @ 2000 rpm
'83	9	6-229	Chev.	2 bbl	115 @ 4000	170 @ 2000	3.736 × 3.480	8.6:1	45
	A	6-231	Buick	2 bbl	110 @ 3800	190 @ 1600	3.800 × 3.400	8.0:1	45
	V	6-263	Olds.	Diesel	85 @ 3200	111 @ 1600	4.057 × 3.385	21.6:1	45①
	H	8-305	Chev.	4 bbl	150 @ 3800	240 @ 2400	3.736 × 3.480	8.6:1	45
	N	8-350	Olds.	Diesel	105 @ 3200	205 @ 1600	4.057 × 3.385	22.5:1	30–45①
'84–'85	9	6-229	Chev.	2 bbl	115 @ 4000	170 @ 2000	3.736 × 3.480	8.6:1	45
	A	6-231	Buick	2 bbl	110 @ 3800	190 @ 1600	3.800 × 3.400	8.0:1	45
	G	8-305HO	Chev.	4 bbl	180 @4800	235 @ 3200	3.736 × 3.480	9.5:1	45
	H	8-305	Chev.	4 bbl	150 @ 3800③	240 @ 2400④	3.736 × 3.480	8.6:1②	45
	N	8-350	Olds.	Diesel	105 @ 3200	205 @ 1600	4.057 × 4.485	22.5:1	30–45①
	6	8-350	Chev.	4 bbl	NA	NA	4.000 × 3.480	NA	45

The seventeen digit Vehicle Identification Number can be used to determine engine application and model year. The tenth digit indicates the model year, and the eighth digit identifies the factory installed engine.

■Horsepower and torque are SAE net figures. They are measured at the rear of the transmission with all accessories installed and operating. Since the figures vary when a given engine is installed in different models, some are representative rather than exact.

NA Not Available
① @ 1500
② 1985: 9.5:1
③ 1985: 165 @ 4200
④ 1985: 245 @ 2400

TUNE-UP SPECIFICATIONS
Nova

(When analyzing compression test results, look for uniformity among cylinders rather than specific pressures.)

		Engine			Spark Plugs		Distributor		Ignition Timing (deg) ▲ ●		Valves Intake Opens	Fuel Pump Pressure (psi)	Idle Speed (rpm) ▲ *	
Year	Eng. V.I.N. Code	No. Cyl. Displacement (cu. in.)	Eng. Mfg.	hp	Orig. Type ◆	Gap (in.)	Point Dwell (deg)	Point Gap (in.)	Man Trans	Auto Trans	■ (deg) ●		Trans Man ●	Trans Auto
'78	D	6-250	Chev.	All	R-46TS	.035	Electronic		6B	①	16	4–5	800/425	500(600)/425(400)
	U	8-305	Chev.	All	R-45TS	.045	Electronic		4B	4B(6B)	28	7.5–9	600	500
	L	8-350	Chev.	All	R-45TS	.045	Electronic		—	8B	28	7.5–9	—	500
'79	D	6-250	Chev.	All	R-46TS	.035	Electronic		8B	10B(6B)	16	4.5–6.0	800	500
	G	8-305	Chev.	All	R-45TS	.045	Electronic		4B	4B	28	7.5–9.0	600	500
	L	8-350	Chev.	All	R-45TS	.045	Electronic		—	8B	28	7.5–9.0	—	500

NOTE: The underhood specifications sticker often reflects tuneup specification changes made in production. Sticker figures must be used if they disagree with those in this chart.

▲See text for procedure
●Figure in parentheses indicates California engine
■All figures before top dead center
◆ See the Spark Plug Replacement Chart

*When two idle speed figures are separated by a slash, the lower figure is with the idle speed solenoid disconnected.
① 49 states without A/C: 10B
   49 states with A/C: 8B
   Calif.: 6B

—Not applicable
Part numbers in this chart are not recommendations by Chilton for any product by brand name.

TUNE-UP SPECIFICATIONS
Chevelle, Monte Carlo and Malibu

(When analyzing compression test results, look for uniformity among cylinders rather than specific pressures.)

Year	Eng. V.I.N. Code	Engine No. Cyl. Displacement (cu. in.)	Eng. Mfg.	hp	Spark Plugs Orig. Type	Spark Plugs Gap (in.)	Distributor Point Dwell (deg)	Distributor Point Gap (in.)	Ignition Timing (deg) ▲ ● Man Trans	Ignition Timing (deg) ▲ ● Auto Trans	Valves Intake Opens ■ (deg) ●	Fuel Pump Pressure (psi)	Idle Speed (rpm) ▲ * Trans Man ●	Idle Speed (rpm) ▲ * Trans Auto
'78	M	6-200	Chev.	95	R-45TS	.045	Electronic		8B	8B	28	7.5–9	700	600
	A	6-231	Buick	105	R-46TSX	.060	Electronic		15B	15B	17	6–7	600	500
	U	8-305	Chev.	145	R-45TS	.045	Electronic		4B	①	28	7.5–9	600	500②
	L	8-350	Chev.	170	R-45TS	.045	Electronic		—	8B	28	7.5–9	—	500
'79	M	6-200	Chev.	All	R-45TS	.045	Electronic		8B	12B	34	4.5–6.0	700	600
	A	6-231	Buick	All	R-46TSX	.060	Electronic		15B	15B	16	4.25–5.75	600	600
	J	8-267	Chev.	All	R-45TS	.045	Electronic		4B	10B	28	7.5–9.0	600	500
	G	8-305	Chev.	All	R-43TS	.045	Electronic		4B	4B	28	7.5–9.0	600	500
	L	8-350	Chev.	All	R-43TS	.045	Electronic		—	8B	28	7.5–9.0	—	500
'80	K	6-229	Chev.	All	R-45TS	.045	Electronic		8B	12B	42	4.5–6.0	700	600
	A	6-231	Buick	All	R-45TSX	.060	Electronic		—	15B	16	4.25–5.75	—	560(600)
	3	6-231	Buick	Turbo	R-45TSX	.060	Electronic		—	15B	16	4.25–5.75	—	550(600)
	J	8-267	Chev.	All	R-45TS	.045	Electronic		—	4B	28	7.5–9.0		500
	H	8-305	Chev.	All	R-45TS	.045	Electronic		4B	4B	28	7.5–9.0	700	500(550)
'81	K	6-229	Chev.	All	R-45TS	.045	Electronic		6B	6B	42	4.5–6.0	700	600
	A	6-231	Buick	All	R-45TS	.045	Electronic		—	15B	16	4.25–5.75	—	500
	J	8-267	Chev.	All	R-45TS	.045	Electronic		—	6B	44	7.5–9.0	—	500
	H	8-305	Chev.	All	R-45TS	.045	Electronic		6B	6B	44	7.5–9.0	700	500
'82	K	6-229	Chev.	All	R-45TS	.045	Electronic		6B③	6B③	42	4.5–6.0	700	600
	A	6-231	Buick	All	R-45TS	.045	Electronic		—	15B③	16	4.25–5.75	—	500
	V	6-263	Olds.	Diesel	—	—	—		—	③	16	5.5–6.5	—	③
	J	8-267	Chev.	All	R-45TS	.045	Electronic		—	6B③	44	5.5–7.0		500
	H	8-305	Chev.	All	R-45TS	.045	Electronic		—	6B③	44	5.5–7.0		500
	N	8-350	Olds.	Diesel	—	—	—		—	③	16	5.5–6.5		③
'83	9	6-229	Chev.	All	R-45TS	.045	Electronic		—	6B③	42	4.5–6.0	700③	600③
	A	6-231	Buick	All	R-45TS	.045	Electronic		—	15B③	16	4.25–5.75	—	500③
	V	6-263	Olds.	Diesel	—	—	—		—	③	16	5.5–6.5	—	③
	H	8-305	Chev.	All	R-45TS	.045	Electronic		—	6B③	44	5.5–7.0		500③
	N	8-350	Olds.	Diesel	—	—	—		—	③	16	5.5–6.5	—	③

TUNE-UP SPECIFICATIONS
Chevelle, Monte Carlo and Malibu

(When analyzing compression test results, look for uniformity among cylinders rather than specific pressures.)

| | | Engine | | | Spark Plugs | | Distributor | | Ignition Timing (deg) ▲ ● | | Valves Intake Opens | Fuel Pump | Idle Speed (rpm) ▲ * | |
| | | | | | | | Point Dwell | Point Gap | | | | | | |
Year	Eng. V.I.N. Code	No. Cyl. Displacement (cu. in.)	Eng. Mfg.	hp	Orig. Type	Gap (in.)	(deg)	(in.)	Man Trans	Auto Trans	■ (deg) ●	Pressure (psi)	Trans Man ●	Trans Auto
'84-85	9	6-229	Chev.	All	R-45TS	.045	Electronic		—	③	42	4.5–6.0	③	③
	A	6-231	Buick	All	R-45TS	.060	Electronic		—	③	16	4.25–5.75	③	③
	H	8-305	Chev.	All	R-45TS	.045	Electronic		—	③	44	5.5–7.0	③	③
	G	8-305	Chev.	All	R-45TS	.045	Electronic		③	③	NA	7.5–9.0	③	③
	N	8-350	Olds.	Diesel	—	—	—		—	③	16	5.5–6.5	③	③

NOTE: The underhood specifications sticker often reflects tune-up specification changes made in production. Sticker figures must be used if they disagree with those in this chart.

▲See text for procedure
●Figure in parentheses indicates California engine
■All figures Before Top Dead Center
*When two idle speed figures are separated by a slash, the lower figure is with the idle speed solenoid disconnected

B Before Top Dead Center
TDC Top Dead Center
—Not applicable
NA—Not available
Part numbers in this chart are not recommendations by Chilton for any product by brand name.

① 49 states: 4B
  Calif.: 6B
  High Altitude: 8B
② High Altitude: 600
③ Refer to underhood specifications sticker

TUNE-UP SPECIFICATIONS
Chevrolet

(When analyzing compression test results, look for uniformity among cylinders rather than specific pressures.)

| | | Engine | | | Spark Plugs | | Distributor | | Ignition Timing (deg) ▲ | | Valves Intake Opens | Fuel Pump | Idle Speed (rpm) ▲ ● | |
| | | | | | | | Point Dwell | Point Gap | | | | | | |
Year	Eng. V.I.N. Code	No. Cyl. Displacement	Eng. Mfg.	Hp (cu. in.)	Orig. Type	Gap (in.)	(deg)	(in.)	Man Trans	● Auto Trans	■ (deg) ●	Pressure (psi)	Man Trans	Auto Trans
'78	D	6-250	Chev.	110	R-46TS	.035	Electronic		—	①	16	4–5	—	550(600)
	U	8-305	Chev.	145	R-45TS	.045	Electronic		—	4B(6B)	28	7–9	—	500
	L	8-350	Chev.	170	R-45TS	.045	Electronic		—	6B(8B)	28	7–9	—	500
'79	D	6-250	Chev.	110	R-46TS	.035	Electronic		—	10B(6B)	16	4.5–6.0	②	②
	H	8-305	Chev.	145	R-45TS	.045	Electronic		—	4B	28	7.5–9.0	②	②
	L	8-350	Chev.	170	R-45TS	.045	Electronic		—	6B(8B)	28	7.5–9.0	②	②
'80	K	6-229	Chev.	All	R-45TS	.045	Electronic		—	②	42	4.5–6.0	②	②
	A	6-231	Buick	110	R-45TS	.045	Electronic		—	②	16	4.5–6.0	②	②
	J	8-267	Chev.	All	R-45TS	.045	Electronic		—	②	28	7.5–9.0	②	②
	H	8-305	Chev.	All	R-43TS	.045	Electronic		—	②	28	7.5–9.0	②	②
	N	8-350	Olds.	Diesel	—	—	—		—	—	16	5.5–6.5	②	②
'81	K	6-229	Chev.	110	R-45TS	.045	Electronic		—	6B	42	4.5–6.0	—	②
	A	6-231	Buick	110	R-45TS	.045	Electronic		—	15B	16	4.25–5.75	—	②
	J	8-267	Chev.	115	R-45TS	.045	Electronic		—	6B	44	7.5–9.0	—	②
	H	8-305	Chev.	150	R-45TS	.045	Electronic		—	6B	44	7.5–9.0	—	②
	N	8-350	Olds.	Diesel	—	—	—		—	—	16	5.5–6.5	—	②

TUNE-UP SPECIFICATIONS
Chevrolet

(When analyzing compression test results, look for uniformity among cylinders rather than specific pressures.)

Year	Eng. V.I.N. Code	No. Cyl. Displacement	Eng. Mfg.	Hp (cu. in.)	Spark Plugs Orig. Type	Spark Plugs Gap (in.)	Distributor Point Dwell (deg)	Distributor Point Gap (in.)	Ignition Timing (deg) ▲ Man Trans	Ignition Timing (deg) ▲ ● Auto Trans	Valves Intake Opens ■ (deg) ●	Fuel Pump Pressure (psi)	Idle Speed (rpm) ▲ ● Man Trans	Idle Speed (rpm) ▲ ● Auto Trans
'82	K	6-229	Chev.	115	R-45TS	.045	Electronic	—	—	6B②	42	4.5–6.0	—	②
	A	6-231	Buick	110	R-45TS	.045	Electronic	—	—	15B②	16	4.25–5.75	—	②
	J	6-267	Chev.	115	R-45TS	.045	Electronic	—	—	6B②	44	5.5–7.0	—	②
	H	8-305	Chev.	150	R-45TS	.045	Electronic	—	—	6B②	44	5.5–7.0	—	②
	N	8-350 Diesel	Olds.	105	—	—	—	—	—	②	16	5.5–6.5	—	②
'83	9	6-229	Chev.	115	R-45TS	.045	Electronic	—	—	②	42	4.5–6.0	—	②
	A	6-231	Buick	110	R-45TS	.045	Electronic	—	—	②	16	4.25–5.75	—	②
	H	8-305	Chev.	150	R-45TS	.045	Electronic	—	—	②	44	5.5–7.0	—	②
	N	8-350	Olds. Diesel	—	—	—	—	—	—	②	16	5.5–6.5	—	②
'84-85	9	6-229	Chev.	All	R-45TS	.045	Electronic	—	—	②	42	4.5–6.0	—	②
	A	6-231	Buick	All	R-45TS8	.060	Electronic	—	—	②	16	4.25–5.75	—	②
	H	8-305	Chev.	All	R-45TS	.045	Electronic	—	—	②	44	5.5–7.0	—	②
	N	8-350	Olds. Diesel	—	—	—	—	—	—	②	16	5.5–6.5	—	②

NOTE: The underhood specifications sticker often reflects tune-up specification changes made in production. Sticker figures must be used if they disagree with those in this chart.

▲ See text for procedure
● Figure in parentheses indicates California engine
■ All figures Before Top Dead Center
B   Before Top Dead Center
TDC Top Dead Center
— Not applicable

Part numbers in this chart are not recommendations by Chilton for any product by brand name.
① Non-California, non-air conditioning: 10B
   Non-California, with air conditioning: 8B
   California: 6B
② See underhood specifications sticker

FIRING ORDERS

NOTE: To avoid confusion, always replace spark plug wires one at a time.

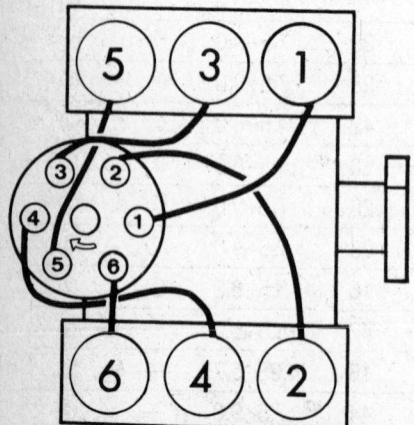

Chevrolet-built V6 engine
Engine firing order: 1-6-5-4-3-2
Distributor rotation: clockwise

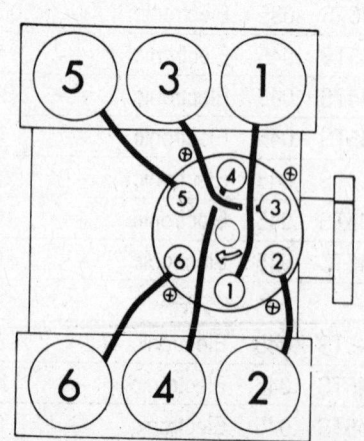

GM (Buick) 231 V6
Engine firing order: 1-6-5-4-3-2
Distributor rotation: clockwise

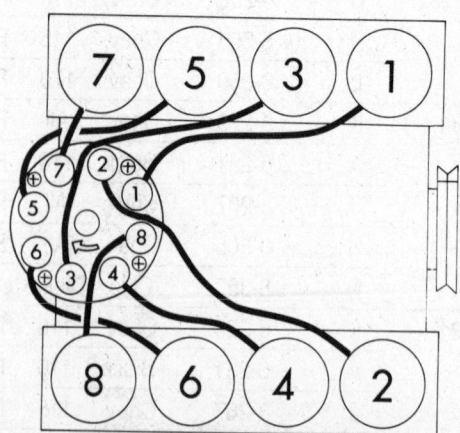

GM (Chevrolet) V8
Engine firing order: 1-8-4-3-6-5-7-2
Distributor rotation: clockwise

FIRING ORDER

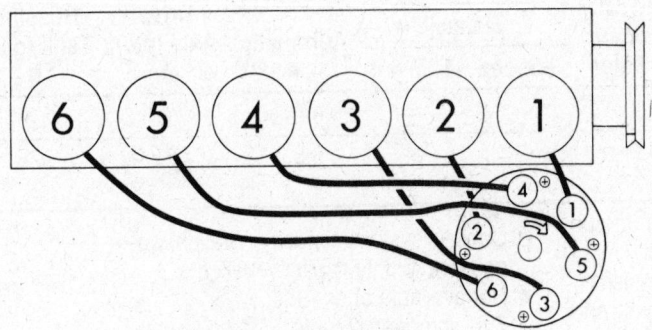

GM (Chevrolet) 250 6-cyl.
Engine firing order: 1-5-3-6-2-4
Distributor rotation: clockwise

CAPACITIES
Chevrolet

Year	Engine No. Cyl. (Cu. In.) Displacement	Engine Crankcase Add 1 Qt For New Filter	Transmission Pts To Refill After Draining Manual 3-Speed	4-Speed	Automatic ●	Drive Axle (pts) ▲	Gasoline Tank (gals) ■	Cooling System (qts) With Heater	With A/C
'78	6-250	4	—	—	6.0	3.25	21	14.2	14.2
	8-305	4	—	—	6.0	3.25	21	16.6	16.6
	8-350	4	—	—	6.0	3.25	21	16.6	16.6
'79	6-250	4	—	—	7.0	4.0	21	14.2	14.2
	8-305	4	—	—	8.0	4.0①	21	16.6	16.6
	8-350	4	—	—	8.0	4.0①	21	16.6	16.6
'80–'82	6-229	4③	—	—	7.0	4.0	18.5	—	14¼④
	6-231	4③	—	—	7.0	4.0①	18.5	—	11¾④
	8-267	4	—	—	6.0②	4.0①	18.5	—	16¾
	8-305	4	—	—	6.0	4.0①	18.5	—	15½
	8-350⑤	4	—	—	6.0	4.0①	18.5	—	16¼
	8-350 Diesel	7	—	—	6.0	4.0①	18.5	—	16¼
'83	6-229	4	—	—	6.0	⑥	⑦	—	14¼④
	6-231	4	—	—	6.0	⑥	⑦	—	11¾④
	8-305	4	—	—	6.0⑧	⑥	⑦	—	15½
	8-350 Diesel	6	—	—	6.0	⑥	⑦	—	18.3
'84–'85	6-229	4	—	—	6.0	⑥	⑦	—	14¼
	6-231	4	—	—	6.0	⑥	⑦	—	11¾

CAPACITIES
Chevrolet

Year	Engine No. Cyl. (Cu. In.) Displacement	Engine Crankcase Add 1 Qt For New Filter	Transmission Pts To Refill After Draining		Automatic ●	Drive Axle (pts) ▲	Gasoline Tank (gals) ■	Cooling System (qts)	
			Manual					With Heater	With A/C
			3-Speed	4-Speed					
	8-305	4	—	—	6.0⑧	⑥	⑦	—	15½
	8-350 Diesel	6	—	—	6.0	⑥	⑦	—	18.3

● Specifications do not include torque converter

Add just enough fluid to fill the transmission to the proper level. It takes only one pint to raise the level from "ADD" to "FULL" with a hot transmission. Do not overfill.

■ Station wagons: 22 gals

▲ '78 and later 8.5 and 8.75: 4.0 pts

— Not applicable

① with 7.5 inch ring gear: 3.25

② 7.5 pt. w/200 T.H. Trans.

③ 4 qt. with filter change

④ Cooling system capacity, Station wagon heavy duty capacity 16¾ qts.

⑤ Not available after 1980.

⑥ 7.5" ring gear: 3.5 pts
8.75" ring gear: 5.0 pts

⑦ Gasoline coupe and sedan—25 gal; diesel—27 gal.
All station wagons—22 gal.

⑧ Automatic Overdrive; 10 pts

CAPACITIES
Chevelle, Monte Carlo, Malibu and Nova

Year	Engine No. Cyl. Displacement (Cu. In.)	Engine Crankcase Add 1 Qt For New Filter ■	Transmission (Pts To Refill After Draining)		Automatic ●	Drive Axle (pts)	Gasoline Tank (gals)	Cooling System (qts)	
			Manual					With Heater	With A/C
			3-Speed	4-Speed					
'78	6-200 Chev.	4	3	—	6.0	3.5	18.1⑪	16.8	16.8
	6-231 Buick	4	3	3	6.0	3.5	18.1⑪	14.79	14.79
	6-250 Chev.	4	3	—	6.0	⑧	18.1⑪	14.6	14.6
	8-305 Chev.	4	—	3	6.0	⑧	18.1⑪	①	①
	8-350 Chev.	4	—	3	6.0	⑧	18.1⑪	②	②
'79	6-200 Chev.	4	3.0	—	8.0	3.25	18.1⑪	18.8	18.8
	6-231 Buick	4	3.0	—	8.0	3.25	18.1⑪	15.4	15.4
	6-250 Chev.	4	3.0	—	8.0	⑧	18.1⑪	⑨	⑨
	8-267 Chev.	4	—	3.4	8.0	3.25	18.1⑪	20.6	20.6
	8-305 Chev.	4	—	3.4	8.0	⑧	18.1⑪	①	①
	8-350 Chev.	4	3.0	3.4	8.0	⑧	18.1⑪	②	②
'80–'81	6-229 Chev.	4	3.0	3.4	8.0③	3.25	18.1	18.8⑩	18.8⑩
	6-231 Buick	4	3.0	3.4	8.0③	3.25	18.1	15.4⑤	15.4⑤
	8-267 Chev.	4	3.0	3.4	8.0③	3.25	18.1	20.6⑪	20.6⑯
	8-305 Chev.	4	3.0	3.4	8.0③	⑧	18.1	①	①
	8-350 Chev.	4	3.0	3.4	8.0	4.25	18.1	16.4⑫	16.4
'82	6-229 Chev.	4	—	—	6.0	3.5	18.1	15.0	15.0
	6-231 Buick	4	—	—	6.0	3.5	18.1	12.5	12.2
	6-263 Diesel	6④	—	—	6.0	3.5	18.1	15.0	15.0

CAPACITIES
Chevelle, Monte Carlo, Malibu and Nova

Year	Engine No. Cyl. Displacement (Cu. In.)	Engine Crankcase Add 1 Qt For New Filter ■	Transmission (Pts To Refill After Draining) Manual 3-Speed	4-Speed	Automatic ●	Drive Axle (pts)	Gasoline Tank (gals)	Cooling System (qts) With Heater	With A/C
'82	8-267 Chev.	4	—	—	6.0	3.5	18.1	18.9	18.0
	8-305 Chev.	4	—	—	6.0	3.5	18.1	16.5	16.5
	8-350 Diesel	7④	—	—	6.0	3.5	18.1	18.0	18.0
'83	6-229 Chev.	4	—	—	6.0	3.5	18.1	15.0	15.0
	6-231 Buick	4	—	—	6.0	3.5	18.1	15.0	15.0
	6-263 Diesel	6④	—	—	6.0	3.5	18.1	15.0	15.0
	8-305 Chev.	4	—	—	6.0	3.5	18.1	15.0	15.0
	8-350 Diesel	7④	—	—	6.0	3.5	18.1	18.0	18.0
'84	6-229 Chev.	4	—	—	6.0	3.5	18.1	15.0	15.0
	6-231 Buick	4	—	—	6.0	3.5	18.1	15.0	15.0
	8-305 Chev.⑫	4	—	—	6.0	3.5	18.1	16.6	16.6
	8-305 Chev.	4	—	—	6.0	3.5	18.1	16.3	16.3
	8-350 Diesel	7④	—	—	6.0	3.5	19.8	17.3	17.3

● Specifications do not include torque converter

Add just enough fluid to fill the transmission to the proper level. It takes only one pint to raise the level from "ADD" to "FULL" with a hot transmission. Do not overfill.

■ On models with micro oil filters, capacity is the same with or without new filter

① Malibu, Monte Carlo 19.2 (thru 1980), 16.5 (1981)
Nova: 16.0

② Malibu: 19.2
Nova: 16.1

③ 1981–82: 7.0 pts. w/200, 200C, 200-4R; 8.0 pts w/250, 250C; 6.3 pts w/350, 350C

④ Includes mandatory filter change

⑤ 1981: 12.5 w/heater, 12.2 w/A/C

⑥ With 7.5 inch ring gear: 3.5 with 8.5 inch ring gear: 4.25

⑦ Nova: 13.6

⑧ 1981: 15.2 w/heater, 15 w/A/C

⑨ 1981: 18.9 w/heater, 18 w/A/C

⑩ 1981: 16.61 w/heater, 16.63 w/A/C

— Not applicable

⑪ '78–'79—Nova: 21 gal

⑫ Eng. Code G

VALVE SPECIFICATIONS

Year	Engine No. Cyl. Displacement (cu. in.)	Seat Angle (deg)	Face Angle (deg)	Spring Test Pressure (lbs. @ in.)	Spring Installed Height (in.)	Stem To Guide Clearance (in.) Intake	Exhaust	Stem Diameter (in.) Intake	Exhaust
'78–'79	6-200 Chev.	46	45	180 @ 1.27②	1²³⁄₃₂①	.0010–.0027	.0010–.0027	.3414	.3414
	6-231 Buick	45	45	168 @ 1.33	1⁴⁷⁄₆₄	.0015–.0032	.0015–.0032	.3407	.3409
	6-250 Chev.	46	45	175 @ 1.26	1.67	.0010–.0027	.0015–.0032	.3414	.3414
	8-267 Chev.	46	45	180 @ 1.25②	1.70	.0010–.0027	.0010–.0027	.3414	.3414
	8-305 Chev.	46	45	200 @ 1.25	1.70①	.0010–.0027	.0010–.0027	.3414	.3414
	8-350 Chev.	46	45	200 @ 1.25	1.70①	.0010–.0027	.0010–.0027	.3414	.3414

VALVE SPECIFICATIONS

Year	Engine No. Cyl. Displacement (cu. in.)	Seat Angle (deg)	Face Angle (deg)	Spring Test Pressure (lbs. @ in.)	Spring Installed Height (in.)	Stem To Guide Clearance (in.)		Stem Diameter (in.)	
						Intake	Exhaust	Intake	Exhaust
'80–'85	6-229 Chev.	46	45	200 @ 1.25	1.70	.0010–.0027	.0010–.0027	.3414	.3414
	6-231 Buick	45	45	168 @ 1.32	1.72	.0015–.0032	.0015–.0032	.3407	.3409
	6-263 Olds. Diesel	45⑤	44⑤	210 @ 1.22	1.67	.0010–.0027	.0015–.0032	.3429	.3424
	8-267 Chev.	46	45	200 @ 1.25	1.70	.0010–.0027	.0010–.0027	.3414	.3414
	8-305 Chev.	46	45	200 @ 1.25	1.70	.0010–.0027	.0010–.0027	.3414	.3414
	8-350 Chev.	46	45	200 @ 1.25	1.70	.0010–.0027	.0010–.0027	.3414	.3414
	8-350 Olds. Diesel	45③	44④	205 @ 1.300	1.67	.0010–.0027	.0015–.0032	.3429	.3424

① Exhaust valve—1¹⁹⁄₃₂
② Exhaust: 190 @ 1.16
③ Exhaust: 31°
④ Exhaust: 30°
⑤ Exhaust: Face 30°; Seat 31°

CRANKSHAFT AND CONNECTING ROD SPECIFICATIONS

(All measurements are given in inches)

Year	Engine No. Cyl. Displacement (cu. in.)	Crankshaft				Connecting Rod		
		Main Brg. Journal Dia.	Main Brg. Oil Clearance	Shaft End-Play	Thrust on No.	Diameter Journal	Clearance Oil	Clearance Side
'77	6-250 Chev.	2.2988	.0003–.0029	.002–.006	7	1.9928–2.000	.0007–.0027	.007–.016
	8-305 Chev.	2.4489⑦	③	.002–.006	5	2.099–2.100	.0013–.0035	.008–.014
	8-350 Chev.	2.4489⑦	③	.002–.006	5	2.099–2.100	.0035–.0035	.008–.014
'78	6-200 Chev.	2.4489⑦	.0020–.0035⑬	.002–.007	4	2.0988–2.0998	.0013–.0035	.008–.014
	6-231 Buick	2.4995	.0004–.0015	.004–.008	2	2.2487–2.2495	.0005–.0026	.006–.027
	6-250 Chev.	2.2988	.0010–.0024⑫	.002–.006	7	1.9980–2.0000	.0010–.0026	.006–.017
	8-267 Chev.	2.4489⑦	.0020–.0035⑬	.002–.007	5	2.0978–2.0988	.0013–.0035	.006–.016
	8-305 Chev.	2.4489⑦	.0011–.0023⑪	.002–.006	5	2.0988–2.0998	.0013–.0035	.008–.014
	8-350 Chev.	2.4489⑦	.0011–.0023⑪	.002–.006	5	2.0988–2.0998	.0013–.0035	.008–.014
'79–'85	6-200 Chev.	2.4484–2.4493⑤	.0008–.0020⑥	.002–.006	4	2.0986–2.0998	.0013–.0035	.006–.014
	6-229 Chev.	2.4484–2.4493⑤	.0008–.0020⑥	.002–.006	4	2.0986–2.0998	.0013–.0035	.006–.014
	6-231 Buick	2.4995	.0004–.0015	.004–.008	2	2.2495–2.2487	.0005–.0026	.006–.027
	6-250 Chev.	2.2979–2.2994	.0010–.0024⑫	.002–.006	7	1.998–2.000	.0010–.0026	.006–.017
	6-263 Olds. Diesel	2.9993–3.0003	.0005–.0021①	.0035–.0135	3	2.2490–2.2510	.0005–.0026	.006–.020
	8-267 Chev., 8-305 Chev., 8-350 Chev.	2.4484–2.4493⑤	.0008–.0020⑥	.002–.006	5	2.0986–2.0998	.0013–.0035	.006–.014
	8-350 Olds. Diesel	2.9993–3.0003	.0005–.0021②	.0035–.0135	3	2.1238–2.1248	.0005–.0026	.006–.020

① No. 4: .0020–.0034
② No. 5: .0015–.0031
③ w/Man. trans.—No. 5—.0023–.0033
  w/Auto. trans.—No. 1—.0019–.0031
  Nos. 2–4—.0013–.0025
  No. 5—.0023–.0033
⑤ Intermediate—2.4481–2.4490
  Rear—2.4479–2.4488
⑥ Intermediate—.0011–.0020
  Rear—.0017–.0032
⑦ No. 2–4: 2.4486
  No. 5: 2.4484
⑧ No. 5: 2.6485
⑨ No. 2–4: .001–.0023
  No. 5: .0017–.0033
⑩ No. 5: .0024–.0070
⑪ #1: .0008–.0020
⑫ #7: .0016–.0035
⑬ #4: .0005–.0015

TORQUE SPECIFICATIONS
(All readings in ft. lbs.)

Year	Engine No. Cyl. Displacement (cu. in.)	Cylinder Head Bolts	Rod Bearing Bolts	Main Bearing Bolts	Crankshaft Bolt	Flywheel to Crankshaft Bolts	Manifold	
							Intake	Exhaust
'78–'79	6-250	95	35	65	60	60	35③	30②⑤
'78–'85	6-200, 6-229, 8-267, 8-305, 8-350	65	45	70	60	60	30	20①
'78–'85	6-231	80	40	100	175⑥	60	45	25
'82–'85	8-350 Diesel	130④	42	120	310	60	40⑧	25
'82–'83	6-263 Diesel⑫	142⑦	42	107	160–350	48	41	29

① Inside bolts on 350—30
② Exhaust-to-intake
③ Manifold-to-head
④ Dip bolt in oil before tightening
⑤ With intake manifold integral with head—
   30 center, 20 on four end bolts
⑥ '83–'85: 225 ft. lbs.
⑦ Bolts No. 5, 6, 11, 12, 13, 14: 59 ft. lbs.

RING GAP
(All measurements are given in inches)

Year	Engine	Top Compression	Bottom Compression	Year	Engine	Oil Control
'78–'85	All V-8 (Gas)	.010–.020	.010–.025	'78–'85	All V-8	.015–.055
'78–'82	6-231	.010–.020	.010–.020	'78–'84	6-231 Buick	.015–.035
'83–'85	6-231	.013–.023	.013–.023	'79–'80	6-200, 6-229	.015–.055
'79–'85	6-200, 6-229	.010–.020	.010–.025	'81–'82	6-229	.010–.035
'82–'84	8-350 (Diesel)	.015–.025	.015–.025	'83–'84	6-229	.015–.055
'82–'83	6-263 (Diesel)	.015–.025	.015–.025	'82–'83	6-263 Diesel	.015–.035

RING SIDE CLEARANCE
(All measurements are given in inches)

Year	Engine	Top Compression	Bottom Compression	Year	Engine	Oil Control
'78–'79	6-250	.0012–.0027	.0012–.0032	'79	6-250	.0000–.0050
'78–'85	6-200, 229	.0012–.0032	.0012–.0032	'78–'85	6-200, 229, 8-267, 305, 350	.002–.007
'78–'85	8-267, 305, 350	.0012–.0032	.0012–.0032	'78–'85	6-231	.0035 Max.
'78–'85	6-231	.0030–.0050	.0030–.0050	'82–'83	6-263 Diesel	.001–.005
'82–'83	6-263 Diesel	.005–.007	.003–.005	'82–'85	8-350 Diesel	.001–.005
'82–'85	8-350 Diesel	.005–.007	.003–.005			

PISTON CLEARANCE

Year	Engine	Piston to Bore Clearance (in.)
'78–'79	6-250	.0015
'78–'85	All V8 exc. Diesel	.0012
'78–'85	6-231	.0008–.0020
'78–'85	6-200, 229	.0012
'82–'85	8-350 Diesel	.005–.006
'82–'83	6-263 Diesel	.003–.004

WHEEL ALIGNMENT SPECIFICATIONS
Chevrolet

Year	Model	Caster Range (deg)	Caster Pref Setting (deg)	Camber Range (deg)	Camber Pref Setting (deg)	Toe-in (in.)	Steering Axis Inclin. (deg)
'78	Chevrolet	2½P–3½P	3P	⅓P–1⅓P	⅘P	1/16–3/16	—
'79–'82	Chevrolet	2½P–3½P	3P	⅓P–1⅓P	⅘P	1/16–3/16	—
'83–'85	Chevrolet	2P–4P	3P	0–1.6	—	1/16–¼	—

N Negative
P Positive
— Not specified
① Left wheel given, right wheel is ¼N to 1¼P, preferred ½P
② Left wheel given, right wheel is ½P
③ ½P–1½P w/bias belted tires

WHEEL ALIGNMENT SPECIFICATIONS
Chevelle, Malibu, Monte Carlo and Nova

Year	Model	Caster Range (deg)	Caster Pref Setting (deg)	Camber Range (deg)	Camber Pref Setting (deg)	Toe-In (in.)	Steering Axis (deg) Inclination
'78	Nova Man. Steer.	½N to 1½N	1N	⅓P to 1⅓P	⅘P	1/16 to 3/16	—
	Nova Pow. Steer.	½P to 1½P	1P	⅓P to 1⅓P	⅘P	1/16 to 3/16	—
	Malibu/Monte Carlo	½P to 1½P	1P	2½P to 3½P	3P	1/16 to 3/16	—
'79–'85	Malibu, Monte Carlo, Pow. Steer.	0 to 2P	1P	5/16N to 15/16P	½P	1/16 to ¼	7⅞
	Malibu, Monte Carlo, Pow. Steer.	2P to 4P	3P	5/16N to 15/16P	½P	1/16 to ¼	7⅞
	Nova, Man. Steer.	2N to 0	1N	0 to 1⅝P	13/16P	1/16 to ¼	10
	Nova, Pow. Steer.	0 to 2P	1P	0 to 1⅝P	13/16P	1/16 to ¼	10

N Negative   P Positive

CHARGING SYSTEM

The voltage regulator is a solid-state, non-adjustable unit integral with the alternator. The alternator must be disassembled to remove the regulator.

For further information on the charging system, please refer to "Charging and Starting" in the Unit Repair section.

Alternator

REMOVAL & INSTALLATION

1. Disconnect battery ground cable to prevent diode damage.
2. Disconnect and label the alternator wiring.
3. Remove brace bolt. If power steering equipped, loosen pump brace and mount nuts. Detach drive belt(s).
4. Support the alternator and remove mount bolt(s). Remove unit from vehicle.
5. Reverse procedure to install. Adjust drive belt to have ¼–½ in. play on longest run of belt.

INTEGRAL VOLTAGE REGULATOR

An alternator with an integral voltage regulator is standard equipment. There are no adjustments possible with this unit; testing procedures will be found in the Charging and Starting Systems Unit Repair Section.

STARTING SYSTEM

Diesel starting system services are covered in the Oldsmobile Rear Wheel Drive Section.

For further information on the starting system, please refer to "Charging and Starting" in the Unit Repair Section.

Starter

REMOVAL & INSTALLATION

1. Disconnect battery ground cable.
2. Raise and support vehicle.
3. Disconnect all wires at solenoid terminals. Note color coding of wires for reinstallation.
4. Remove starter support bracket mount bolts. On engines with solenoid heat shield, remove front bracket upper bolt and detach bracket from starter motor.
5. Loosen the front bracket bolt or nut

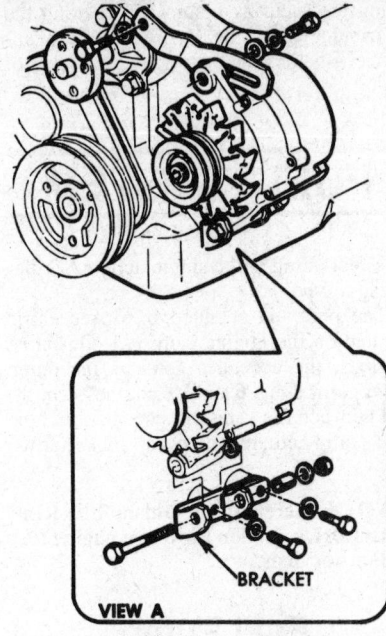

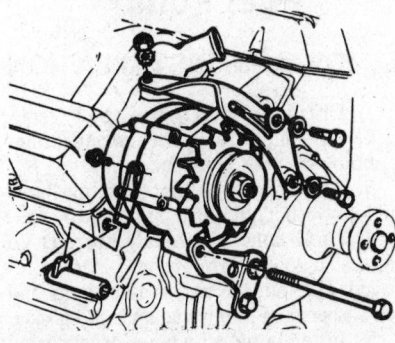

Alternator mounting on the inline six cylinder engine (top) and the Chevrolet V6 and V8 engines (bottom)—typical (© Chevrolet Div., G.M. Corp.)

and rotate bracket clear. Lower and remove starter. Note the location of any shims so that they may be replaced in the same positions upon installation.
6. Reverse procedure to install.

IGNITION SYSTEM

All models with gasoline engines are equipped with the HEI distributor and ignition system. This system uses no points and is, therefore, relatively maintenance free.

When using an auxiliary starter switch on HEI systems, the distributor BATT lead must be disconnected. Failure to do this may cause damage to the grounding circuit in the ignition switch.

For further details on the ignition system, please refer to "Electronic Ignition Systems" in the Unit Repair section.

HEI SYSTEM TACHOMETER HOOKUP

On coil-in-cap type distributors, there is a terminal marked TACH on the side of the HEI distributor. Connect one tachometer lead to this terminal and the other to ground. On some tachometers, the leads must be connected to the TACH terminal and to the battery positive terminal.

On inline six cylinder models with external coils, the TACH terminal is opposite the BATT terminal on the connector plug on the externally mounted coil.

— **CAUTION** —
Never ground the TACH terminal; serious system damage will result. If there is any doubt as to the correct tachometer hookup, check with the tachometer manufacturer.

Distributor

REMOVAL & INSTALLATION

The distributor is driven by the camshaft through a drive gear attached to the distributor shaft. If it becomes necessary to remove the distributor, carefully mark the position of the rotor in relation to the engine block and the distributor housing so that, if the engine is not turned after the distributor is taken out, the rotor can be returned to the position from which it was removed without difficulty.

To remove the distributor, take off the carburetor air cleaner (V6 and V8), disconnect the coil primary wire and the vacuum line, remove the distributor cap, loosen and remove the distributor holddown clamp and take out the distributor body. Mark the position of the body relative to the block, and then work the distributor up out of the block.

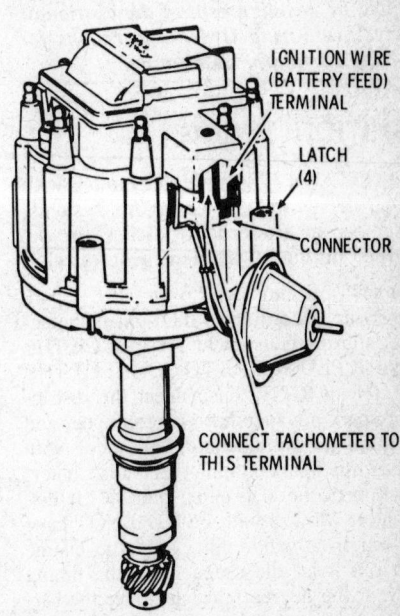

IGNITION WIRE (BATTERY FEED) TERMINAL

LATCH (4)

CONNECTOR

CONNECT TACHOMETER TO THIS TERMINAL

HEI system tachometer hookup

When installing the distributor, turn the rotor about 1/8 turn counterclockwise past the alignment mark before pushing the distributor into place. The marks should align when the distributor seats. Check the timing.

DISTRIBUTOR INSTALLATION (ENGINE DISTURBED)

All Engines

1. Turn the crankshaft until the No. 1 cylinder is at the top of its compression stroke. Remove the No. 1 spark plug to feel the compression.

2. Align the timing mark on the vibration damper with the TDC indicator or 0 mark on the timing scale.

3. With distributor body oriented in its normal position, hold the rotor pointing toward the No. 1 plug wire location, then turn the rotor approximately 1 1/8 turn counterclockwise and push the distributor down until it engages the camshaft, rotating the shaft slightly if necessary.

4. Press down on the distributor and crank the engine to make sure the oil pump shaft is engaged.

5. Return the crankshaft to No. 1 cylinder compression stroke with the timing marks aligned, then tighten the distributor clamp bolt.

6. Install the distributor cap, checking that the rotor points to the No. 1 terminal. Make sure that the spark plug wires are in their supports and are securely connected.

7. Connect distributor vacuum line (if so equipped) and primary wire.

8. Start engine and set the timing.

--- CAUTION ---

On Chevrolet V6 and V8 models the distributor body is involved in the engine lubricating system. The lubricating circuit to the right-bank valve train can be interrupted by misalignment of the distributor body. See Firing Order illustrations for correct distributor positioning.

IGNITION TIMING

NOTE: On 1980 and later models with computer-controlled emissions systems, refer to the underhood sticker for the proper timing adjustment procedure.

Connect a timing light to the No. 1 spark plug wire according to the light manufacturer's instructions. DO NOT PIERCE THE SPARK PLUG WIRE TO CONNECT THE TIMING LIGHT. Disconnect the distributor spark advance hose (if equipped) and plug the vacuum opening. On models with Electronic Spark Timing (EST) distributor, disconnect the 4 terminal plug at the distributor. Models with EST DO NOT have a vacuum advance unit. Start the engine and run it at idle speed. Aim the timing light at the degree scale just over the harmonic balancer. Adjust the timing by loos-

ening the securing clamp and rotating the distributor until the desired ignition advance is achieved, then tighten the clamp.

FUEL SYSTEM

The fuel pump is the single action AC diaphragm type.

The pump is actuated by an eccentric located on the engine camshaft. On inline engines, the eccentric actuates the pump rocker arm. On V6 and V8 engines, a pushrod between the camshaft eccentric and the fuel pump actuates the pump rocker arm.

NOTE: Refer to the Oldsmobile Rear Wheel Drive Section for diesel engine fuel system services.

Fuel Pump

REMOVAL & INSTALLATION

1. Disconnect the negative battery cable.
2. Disconnect fuel inlet and outlet lines at pump and plug pump inlet line.
3. Remove two pump mounting bolts and lockwashers; remove pump and gasket.
4. On all small block and Chevrolet V6 engines, if rocker arm pushrod is to be removed: take out the two adapter bolts and lockwashers and remove adapter and gasket.
5. Install pump with new gasket coated

with sealer. Coat mounting bolt threads with sealer and tighten bolts.

NOTE: On Chevrolet V6 and V8 engines, mechanical fingers or heavy grease can be used to hold pump pushrod in place during installation. Coat pipe plug threads or adapter gasket with sealer if pushrod was removed.

6. Connect inlet and outlet lines, start engine and check for leaks.

--- CAUTION ---

A fuel pump may fail to function at the time of replacement as a result of error in positioning or damage to the fuel pump pushrod of the V8 engine. This pushrod can slip out of place during the process of pump replacement and result in no pump action from the newly replaced unit. Before tightening the fuel pump to the engine, have someone spin the engine with the starter while feeling the fuel pump body for movement. If the pump and pushrod are in correct position, movement will be felt in the pump as the pushrod pressure is applied and released from the pump arm.

Fuel Filter

REMOVAL & INSTALLATION

All fuel filters use a check valve to prevent fuel spillage in an accident. When you replace the filter, make sure the new one has a check valve.

1. Disconnect fuel line connection at inlet of carburetor.

Chilton's TIME SAVER

When replacing a fuel pump on small block V8, V6-200 and V6-229 engines, considerable time can be saved as follows:

1. Before removing the old pump, remove the upper bolt from the engine's right front mounting boss on the front of the block. This bolt hole is in direct alignment with the fuel pump pushrod positioning. The threaded bolt hole continues into the pump pushrod bore. The bolt acts as an oil plug.

2. Temporarily insert a longer bolt, (about 3/8—16 x 2 in.) into the hole. Screw the bolt into the bore until it bottoms against the pump pushrod. (Don't tighten the bolt with a wrench or the rod can be damaged.)

3. The mechanic is now free to remove and install the fuel pump without worrying about

fuel pump pushrod misalignment.

--- CAUTION ---

Don't forget to reinstall the original bolts.

The design of big block V8 engines prevents the use of the bolt method of simplifying fuel pump pushrod positioning while installing a fuel pump. However, to hold the pump pushrod in position while installing the fuel pump, the following works satisfactorily:

1. Clean oil from pushrod.

2. Pack a small quantity of non-fibrous grease in the area around the fuel pump pushrod to hold it in suspension long enough to position the fuel pump.

3. Install and check pump action, then torque attaching bolts.

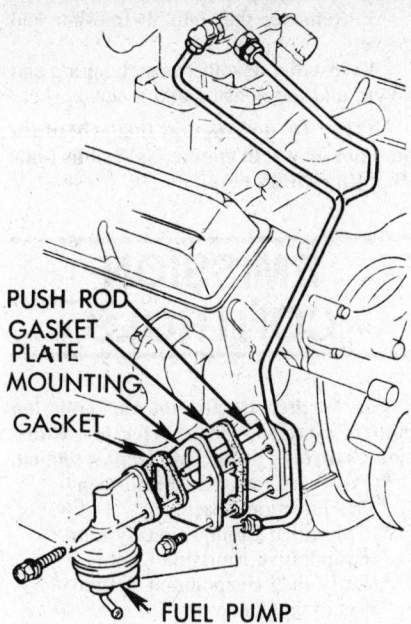

PUSH ROD
GASKET
PLATE
MOUNTING
GASKET

FUEL PUMP

Typical small block V8 fuel pump
(© Chevrolet Div., G.M. Corp)

2. Remove inlet fuel filter nut from carburetor using a box wrench.

3. Remove filter element and spring.

4. If a bronze element, blow through cone end—element should allow air to pass freely.

5. Install element spring and new element into carburetor. Bronze elements are installed with small section of cone facing outward.

6. Install new gasket on fitting nut and install nut.

7. Install fuel line and tighten securely. Start engine and check for leaks.

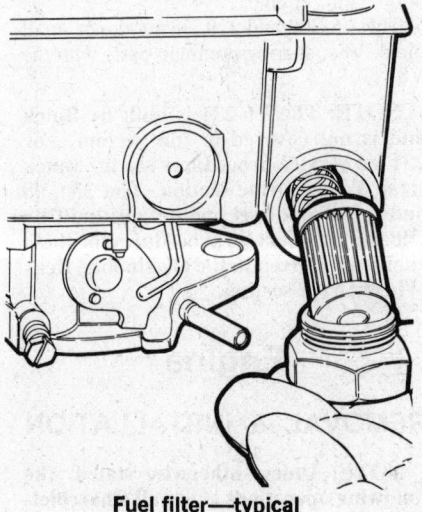

Fuel filter—typical

Carburetor

For further information on carburetors, please refer to "Carburetors" in the Unit Repair section.

ADJUSTMENTS

When adjusting a carburetor with two idle mixture screws, adjust them alternately and evenly, unless otherwise stated.

In the following adjustment procedures the term "lean roll" means turning the mixture adjusting screws in (clockwise) from optimum setting to obtain an obvious drop in engine speed (usually 20 rpm).

1978–80 Idle Speed Adjustment

NOTE: An idle speed control system is used on some engines to control the idle speed. No adjustments are necessary with this system.

6-250

1. Run the engine to normal operating temperature.

2. Make sure that the choke is fully opened.

3. Turn the A/C Off and disconnect the vacuum line at the vapor canister. Plug the line.

4. Set the parking brake, block the drive wheels and place the transmission in Drive (AT) or Neutral (MT). Connect a tachometer to the engine according to the manufacturer's instructions.

5. Turn the solenoid hex nut to obtain the specified solenoid-on speed.

6. Disconnect the solenoid wire and turn the ⅛ inch hex screw in the solenoid end, to achieve the solenoid-off speed.

7. Remove the tachometer, connect the canister vacuum line and shut off the engine.

6-200, 6-229, 6-231, 8-267, 8-305

1. Run the engine to normal operating temperature.

2. Make sure that the choke is fully opened, turn the A/C Off, set the parking brake, block the drive wheels and connect a tachometer to the engine according to the manufacturer's instructions.

3. Disconnect and plug the vacuum hoses at the EGR valve and the vapor canister.

4. Place the transmission in Park (AT) or Neutral (MT).

5. Disconnect and plug the vacuum advance hose at the distributor. Check and adjust the timing.

6. Connect the distributor vacuum line.

7. Manual transmission cars without A/C and without solenoid: place the idle speed screw on the low step of the fast idle cam and turn the screw to achieve the specified idle speed.

Cars with A/C: set the idle speed screw to the specified rpm. Disconnect the compressor clutch wire and turn the A/C On. Open the throttle momentarily to extend the solenoid plunger. Turn the solenoid screw to obtain the specified rpm.

Automatic transmission cars without A/C; manual transmission cars without A/C, solenoid-equipped carburetor: momentarily open the throttle to extend the solenoid plunger. Turn the solenoid screw to obtain

the specified rpm. Disconnect the solenoid wire and turn the idle speed screw to obtain the slow engine idle speed.

8-350

1. Run the engine to normal operating temperature.

2. Set the parking brake and block the drive wheels.

3. Connect a tachometer to the engine according to the manufacturer's instructions.

4. Disconnect and plug the purge hose at the vapor canister. Disconnect and plug the EGR vacuum hose at the EGR valve.

5. Turn the A/C Off.

6. Place the transmission in Park (AT) or Neutral (MT).

7. Disconnect and plug the vacuum advance line at the distributor. Check and adjust the timing.

8. Connect the vacuum advance line. Place the automatic transmission in Drive.

9. Manual transmission cars without A/C: adjust the idle stop screw to obtain the specified rpm. Cars with A/C: with the A/C off, adjust the idle stop screw to obtain the specified rpm. Disconnect the compressor clutch wire and turn the A/C on. Open the throttle slightly to allow the solenoid plunger to extend. Turn the solenoid screw to obtain the solenoid rpm listed on the underhood emission sticker.

10. Connect all hoses and remove the tachometer.

1978–80 Idle Mixture Adjustment

Changes in the carburetors have made the adjustment of the idle mixture impossible without a propane enrichment system not available to the general public. Backing out the mixture screw will have little or no effect on the mixture. Most 1979 and later carburetors have mixture screws concealed under staked-in plugs. Mixture adjustments are possible only during carburetor overhaul.

NOTE: The propane enrichment system cannot be used on 1979 and later models equipped with computer-controlled emissions systems. See the Emission Control Unit Repair Section for more information on these systems.

1981 and Later Idle Speed and Mixture Adjustments

The idle speed on 1981 and later models equipped with an Idle Speed Control (ISC) motor is automatically adjusted by the Computer Command Control System, making manual adjustment unnecessary. The underhood specifications sticker will indicate ISC motor use.

On non-A/C models not equipped with ISC, the idle speed is adjusted at the idle speed screw on the carburetor. Before adjusting, check the underhood sticker for any preparations required.

On A/C equipped models which do not have an ISC motor, an idle speed solenoid similar to the ones on earlier models is used. This solenoid is adjusted at the solenoid screw, using the same procedures as on earlier models. Consult the underhood specifications sticker for special instructions.

Idle mixture adjustments are not possible on any 1981 and later cars. Mixture adjustments are a function of the Computer Command Control (CCC) system. See the Emission Control Unit Repair section for more information.

REMOVAL & INSTALLATION

1. Remove the air cleaner.
2. Disconnect the fuel lines.
3. Disconnect the throttle linkage.
4. Disconnect and label all vacuum hoses.
5. Remove the retaining bolts.
6. Remove the carburetor.
7. Installation is the reverse of removal.

COOLING SYSTEM

A standard pressure cooling system is used on all models. The radiator cap is designed to maintain a cooling system pressure of about 13 or 15 psi. The water pump requires no attention except to make certain the air vent at the top of the housing and the drain holes in the bottom do not become clogged.

NOTE: When servicing models with diesel engines, refer to the Oldsmobile Rear Wheel Drive section.

Radiator

REMOVAL & INSTALLATION

NOTE: Due to the awkward position of the bottom hose clamp it may be necessary to secure a long screwdriver (about 24 in. long) before attempting this procedure.

1. Drain radiator.
2. Disconnect hoses and transmission fluid cooler lines.
3. Remove radiator upper panel and shroud (if so equipped).

On air conditioned (A/C) models which have the shroud halves stapled together, remove the staples in order to remove the upper shroud half. The halves must be drilled and bolted together to assemble.

If an A/C line is attached to the upper shroud, disconnect the line clamp from the shroud and the overflow hose from the radiator. The shroud may be maneuvered out from underneath the A/C line, towards the passenger side of the vehicle.

4. Remove radiator attaching bolts and lift radiator out of car.
5. Slide radiator into position.
6. Install attaching bolts, shroud, and upper panel.

7. Install hoses and close drain.
8. Fill cooling system, run engine with radiator cap off until operating temperature has been reached. Again fill cooling system and check for leaks.

Water Pump

REMOVAL & INSTALLATION

1. Drain the radiator and loosen the fan pulley bolts. Remove accessory drive belts as necessary.
2. Disconnect the heater hose, lower radiator hose and, if applicable, the bypass hose at the water pump.
3. On V6 and V8 engines, remove the alternator upper and/or lower brackets, and, if necessary, the power steering pump lower bracket from the water pump and swing aside.
4. Remove the fan blade and pulley.

NOTE: Thermostatis fan clutches must be kept in an "in-car" position. When removed from the car the assembly should be supported so that the clutch disc remains in a vertical plane to prevent silicone fluid leakage.

5. Remove the water pump attaching bolts and, if applicable, the power steering-to-pump bolts and remove the pump and gasket.

NOTE: On inline six-cylinder engines, pull the pump straight out of the block first to avoid damage to the impeller.

6. Install the pump assembly using a new gasket. Coat the gasket on both sides with sealer. Tighten the 5/16 in. bolts to 15 ft. lbs (inline six-cylinder) and the 3/8 in. bolts (V6 and V8) to 30 ft. lbs.
7. Install the pulley and fan.
8. Remaining installation is the reverse of removal. Fill the cooling system, adjust the belts, start the engine and check for leaks.
9. Adjust the belts, then start the engine and check for leaks.

Thermostat

REMOVAL & INSTALLATION

The thermostat is located inside a housing on the front of the cylinder head on inline six cylinder engines, and directly on the top front center of the manifold on V6 and V8 engines.

NOTE: It is not necessary to remove the radiator hose from the thermostat housing to complete this procedure.

1. Drain the cooling system approximately halfway.
2. Remove the two retaining bolts from the thermostat housing and remove the housing.

3. Remove the old thermostat and gasket.
4. Install a new thermostat, spring end down, and the housing and a new gasket.

NOTE: Do not attempt this procedure on a hot or warm engine, as serious bodily injury could result.

EMISSION CONTROLS

For further details on the emission control systems, please refer to "Emission Controls" in the Unit Repair section.

- Positive Crankcase Ventilation
- Air Injection Reactor
- Controlled Combustion System
- Evaporative Emission Control
- Early Fuel Evaporation System
- Catalytic Convertor
- Exhaust Gas Recirculation
- Computer Controlled Catalytic Converter System (C-4)
- Computer Command Control (ccc)
- Deceleration Valve

ENGINE

The 250 six cylinder engines are of the inline type, with seven main bearings. V8 engines are of two basic types. All engines of each type are generally similar in design and have some interchangeability of parts. The first type is the small block V8 series. This includes the 262, 267, 305, 350, and 400 cu. in. engines.

The V6-200 and 229 are cut down small block V8s, sharing common parts with the V8.

NOTE: The V6-231 is built by Buick and is not covered in this section. For 231 V6 service procedures see the Buick Rear Wheel Drive section. The 350 V8 and 4.3L V6 diesel engines are built by Oldsmobile. Service procedures for these engines are given in the Oldsmobile Rear Wheel Drive section.

Engine

REMOVAL & INSTALLATION

NOTE: Unless otherwise stated, the following operations cover all Chevrolet-built engines. Always label all disconnected hoses and wires to assure correct assembly.

——— **CAUTION** ———
Do not discharge the compressor or disconnect the A/C lines. Damage to the A/C system or personal injury could result.

1. Raise car and support on jackstands.

2. Drain cooling system, transmission, and crankcase.

3. Scribe alignment marks on underside of hood and around hood hinges, and remove hood from hinges.

4. Disconnect coolant and heater hoses at engine attachment. Disconnect and plug the automatic transmission cooler lines at the radiator, if so equipped.

5. Disconnect battery cables at battery, negative cable first.

6. Remove radiator and shroud assembly. Remove fan and pulley.

7. Remove air cleaner.

8. Disconnect and label the distributor, starter and alternator wires, engine-to-body ground strap, oil pressure and engine temperature sender wires, and any other wires.

9. Disconnect and plug engine fuel lines.

10. Disconnect accelerator control cable at the carburetor and unbolt the cable bracket. Tie the cable out of the way.

11. Disconnect power brake vacuum line at the intake manifold or carburetor.

12. Disconnect exhaust pipe from manifold on inline-six models. Disconnect the crossover pipe on V6 and V8 models, if so equipped.

13. Disconnect clutch shaft bracket at frame and disconnect clutch linkage. On automatic transmission models, remove transmission oil filler tube and plug the opening.

14. Attach engine lifting apparatus. Attach to hoist and secure the engine.

15. Remove driveshaft.

16. Remove and set aside power steering pump and air conditioning compressor. Do not disconnect hoses.

17. Remove engine rear mounting bolts.

18. Disconnect speedometer cable, transmission control rod linkage lower ends, T.C.S. switch torque converter clutch wiring, downshift switch wiring (THM400's), and transmission oil cooler lines.

19. Loosen front engine mounting bolts.

20. Raise engine slightly and remove bolts.

21. Remove transmission crossmember and free the transmission rear mounting.

22. Remove engine and transmission as a unit from the car.

On installation:

1. Bolt engine lifting equipment to engine and lower engine and transmission into chassis as a unit. Guide engine to align front engine mounts with mounts on frame.

2. Install one rear transmission crossmember side bolt, swing crossmember up

under transmission mount and install bolt in opposite side rail.

3. Align and install rear mount bolts.

4. Install engine front mount bolts and remove lifting equipment from engine.

5. Install and connect all items in reverse order of engine removal procedure.

Intake and Exhaust Manifold

REMOVAL & INSTALLATION

Inline Six

1. Remove the air cleaner.

2. Remove the power steering and air pump brackets.

3. Remove the EFE valve bracket.

4. Disconnect the throttle linkage and return spring.

1	Cap nipple	21	Pulley
2	Rotor	22	Fan
3	Spring clip	23	Spacer
4	Distributor	24	Pulley
5	Distributor gear	25	Water pump
6	Gasket	26	Thermostat
7	Intake manifold	27	Water neck
8	Gasket	28	Carburetor stud
12	Oil pump shaft	29	Gasket
13	Oil pump	30	Shaft
14	Sleeve	31	Vacuum unit
15	Drain plug	32	Distributor cap
16	Cylinder block		
17	Gasket		
18	Gasket		
19	Timing cover		
20	Damper		

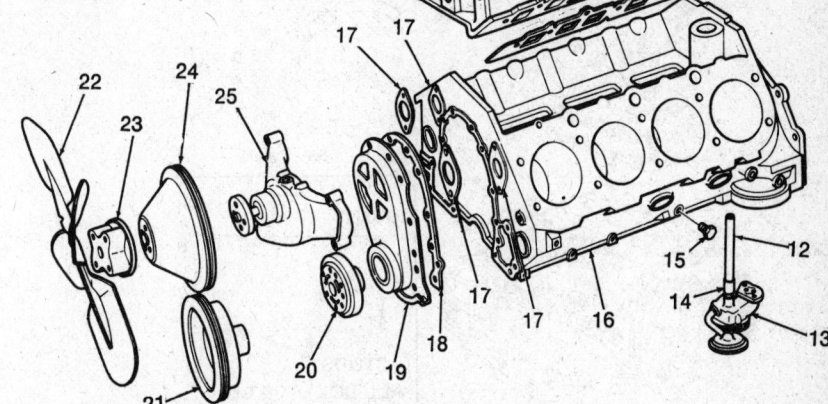

Mark IV (big block) exploded view (© Chevrolet Div., G.M. Corp)

5. Unbolt the exhaust pipe from the flange.

6. Unbolt and remove the manifold.

7. Reverse the procedure for installation. Torque the manifold bolts according to the accompanying illustration.

Intake Manifold

REMOVAL & INSTALLATION

V6 and V8

NOTE: Some engines will require the use of RTV silicone sealant during installation of the manifold.

1. Remove the air cleaner.

2. Drain the radiator.

3. Disconnect:

a. Battery cables at the battery.

b. Upper radiator and heater hoses at the manifold.

c. Crankcase ventilation hoses as required.

d. Fuel line at the carburetor.

e. Accelerator linkage at the pedal lever.

f. Vacuum hose at the distributor.

g. Power brake hose at the carburetor base or manifold, if applicable.

h. Ignition coil and temperature sending switch wires.

i. Any interfering wires.

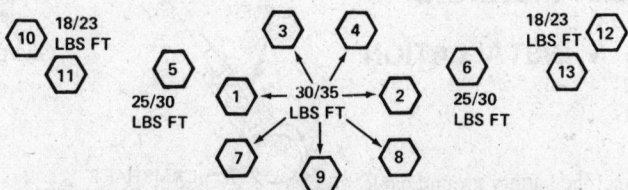

Exhaust manifold torque sequence—inline six cylinder with integral intake manifold (© Chevrolet Div., G.M. Corp.)

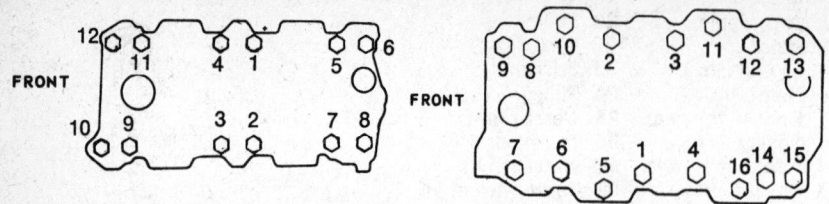

Intake manifold torque sequence: small block V8 (left); Mark IV (big block) V8 (right) (© Chevrolet Div., G.M. Corp.)

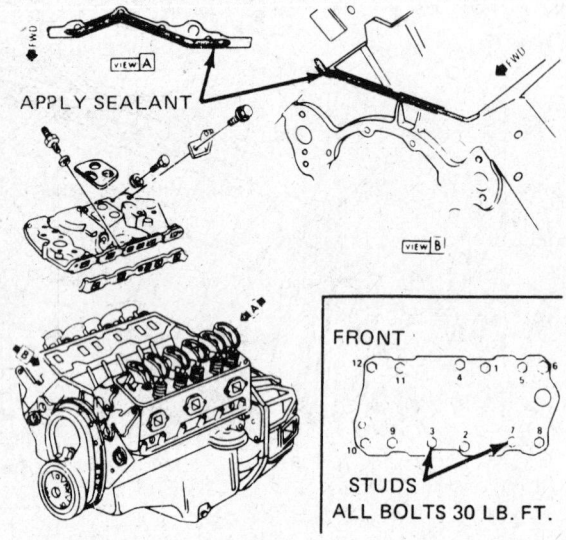

Intake manifold seal installation and tightening sequence for the Chevrolet-built 200 and 229 V6 engine (© Chevrolet Div., G.M. Corp.)

4. Remove the distributor cap and scribe the rotor position relative to distributor body.

5. Remove the distributor.

6. If applicable, remove the alternator upper bracket.

7. Remove the manifold to head attaching bolts, then remove the manifold and carburetor as an assembly.

NOTE: On 1981 and later 4 bbl carbureted engines, remove the carburetor from the manifold, then remove the attaching bolts and remove the manifold.

8. If the manifold is to be replaced, transfer the carburetor (and mounting studs), water outlet and thermostat (use a new gasket), heater hose adapter and, if applicable, the choke coil and EGR valve with its vacuum line.

9. Before installing the manifold, thoroughly clean the gasket and seal surfaces of the cylinder head and manifold.

10. Install the manifold end seals, folding the tabs, if applicable, and the manifold/head gaskets, using a sealing compound around the water passages. Make sure the gaskets are firmly cemented in place before installing the manifold.

NOTE: On those engines not having front and rear manifold seals, place a ³⁄₁₆ inch bead of RTV silicone sealant on the front and rear ridges of the cylinder case. Extend the bead ½ inch up each cylinder

head to seal and retain the manifold side gaskets. Use sealer at water passages.

11. When installing the manifold, care should be taken not to dislocate the end seals. It is helpful to use a pilot in the distributor opening. Tighten the manifold bolts in the sequence illustrated.

12. Install the ignition coil.

13. Install the distributor with the rotor in its original location as indicated by the scribe line. If the engine has been disturbed, refer to Distributor Removal and Installation.

14. If applicable, install the alternator upper bracket, and adjust the belt tension.

15. Connect all components disconnected in Step above.

16. Fill the cooling system, start the engine, check for leaks and adjust the ignition timing and carburetor idle speed and mixture.

Exhaust Manifold

REMOVAL & INSTALLATION
V6 and V8

LEFT SIDE

1. Disconnect the battery ground cable and raise the car. Disconnect the exhaust pipe at the manifold.

2. Remove the front manifold to exhaust pipe flange stud, and then remove the rear spark plug shield; lower the car.

3. Remove the air conditioning compressor and set it aside. DO NOT disconnect any air conditioning lines.

4. Disconnect and label the spark plug wires and their holder, the temperature sending unit lead and the dipstick.

5. Remove the attaching bolts and remove the manifold.

6. To install, reverse the removal procedure.

RIGHT SIDE

1. Disconnect the ground cable, and remove the fan shroud upper bolts and loosen the fan shroud. Remove the air cleaner intake pipe. If equipped with an air pump, remove the air injector manifold assembly.

2. Raise the car and disconnect the exhaust pipe at the manifold.

3. On some models, there will not be enough clearance to remove the manifold. If so, perform the following: Remove the right side engine mounting bracket through bolt, and loosen the left side mounting bracket through bolt. Jack up the right side of the engine, reinstall the right side through bolt, and lower the engine until the through bolt is resting on the mounting bracket.

4. Remove the rear spark plug shield bolt.

5. Lower the car and remove the spark plug wires (label them first), air cleaner heat stove pipe, and the air cleaner intake pipe. Remove the rear spark plug shield.

6. Remove the manifold to engine bolts, and remove the manifold, the EFE valve and the vacuum can.

7. To install, reverse the removal procedure.

Valve System

Chevrolet uses a hydraulic tappet system with adjustable rocker mounting nuts to obtain zero lash. No periodic adjustment is necessary. However, if the rocker arms or

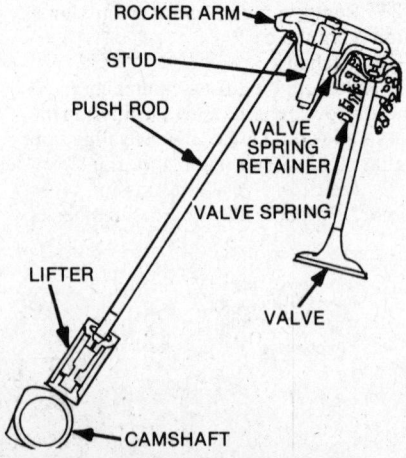

V8 engine valve system

cylinder heads are removed and replaced, the rocker arms must be adjusted for zero lash.

Valve guides are integral with the cylinder head. Valve guide bores may be reamed to accommodate oversize valve stems or the guides may be knurled (if wear permits) to allow the retention of standard size valves.

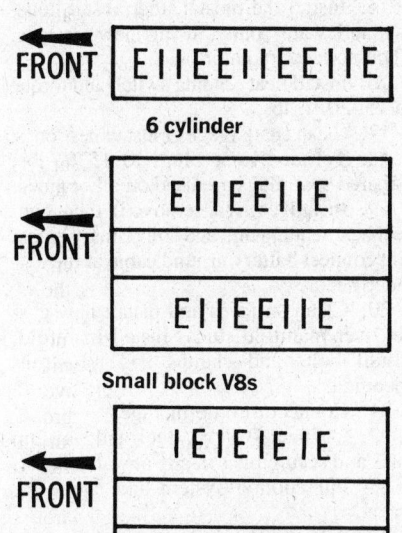

6 cylinder

Small block V8s

Big block V8s

Chevrolet intake(I) and exhaust(E) valve arrangements (except the V6 engine)

Rocker

REMOVAL & INSTALLATION

NOTE: Some engines are assembled using RTV (Room Temperature Vulcanizing) silicone sealant in place of rocker arm cover gasket. If the engine was assembled using RTV, never use a gasket when reassembling. Conversely, if the engine was assembled using a rocker arm cover gasket, never replace it with RTV. When using RTV, an 1/8 inch bead is sufficient. Always run the bead on the inside of the bolt holes.

Rocker arms are removed by removing the adjusting nut. Be sure to adjust valve lash after replacing rocker arms.

NOTE: When replacing an exhaust rocker, move an old intake rocker to the exhaust rocker arm stud and install the new rocker arm on the intake stud.

Rocker arm studs that have damaged threads or are loose in the cylinder heads may be replaced with new studs available in 0.003 in. and 0.013 in. oversize, or the bores may be tapped and screw-in replacement studs used. Do not attempt to install an oversize stud without reaming the stud bore. Studs are press-fit.

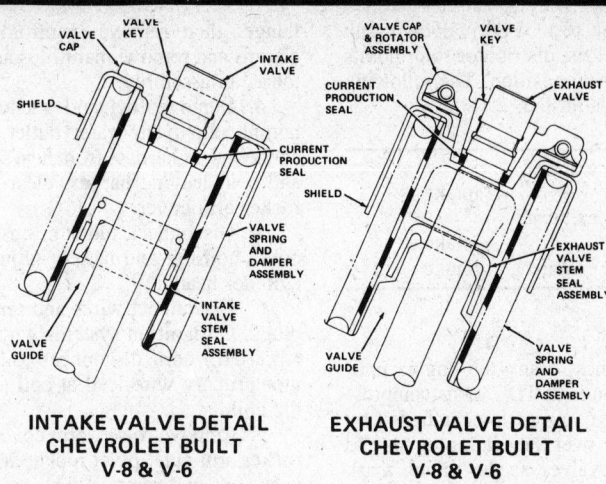

INTAKE VALVE DETAIL CHEVROLET BUILT V-8 & V-6

EXHAUST VALVE DETAIL CHEVROLET BUILT V-8 & V-6

Valve seal and retainer details for the Chevrolet V6 and V8 engines (© Chevrolet Div., G.M. Corp.)

NOTE: If engine is equipped with the A.I.R. exhaust emission control system, the interfering components of the system must be removed. Disconnect the lines at the air injection nozzles in the exhaust manifolds.

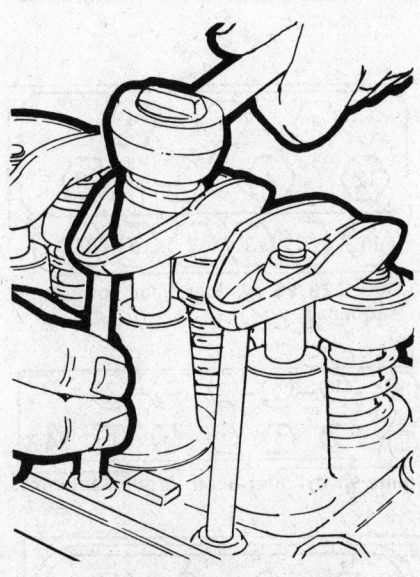

Valve adjustment—typical

⇐ FRONT

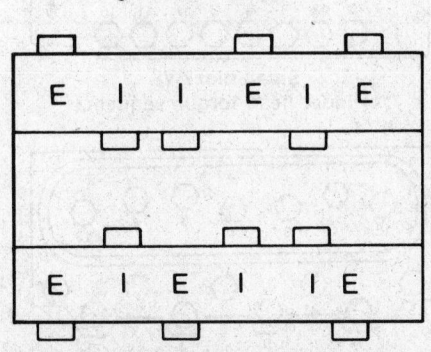

Valve arrangement of the Chevrolet-built V6 engines (E-exhaust; I-intake)

Valve Clearance

ADJUSTMENT

On inline six-cylinder (250 cu. in.) engines, crank the engine until the distributor rotor points to the No. 1 firing position. The following valves may be adjusted:

No. 1	exhaust	intake
No. 2		intake
No. 3	exhaust	
No. 4		intake
No. 5	exhaust	

- LOCK RING
- PUSH ROD CUP
- METERING DISC
- PLUNGER
- BALL
- SPRING
- BALL RETAINER
- SPRING
- BODY

Hydraulic lifter plunger and body are fitted pairs and must not be mismated (© Chevrolet Div., G.M. Corp)

To adjust the rest of the valves, crank the engine until the distributor rotor points to the No. 6 firing position. The following valves may be adjusted:

No. 2	exhaust	
No. 3		intake
No. 4	exhaust	
No. 5		intake
No. 6	exhaust	intake

On V8 engines, crank the engine until the No. 1 piston is at TDC of its compression stroke (the compression can be felt by placing a finger over the spark plug hole or by feeling the valves as the timing mark passes ''0''—if the valves don't move, the No. 1 piston is at the top of its compression stroke). With the crankshaft in this position the following valves may be adjusted:
Exhaust—1,3,4,8
Intake—1,2,5,7
Rotate the crankshaft one full revolution until the timing pointer is again aligned with the ''0''. With the crankshaft thus in No. 6 cylinder firing position, the following valves may be adjusted:
Exhaust—2,5,6,7
Intake—3,4,6,8
On the 200 and 229 V6, crank the engine until the timing mark aligns with the ''0'' mark on the timing scale, and both valves in No. 1 cylinder are closed. If the valves are moving as the timing marks align, the engine is in the No. 4 firing position. Turn the crankshaft one more revolution. With the engine in the No. 1 firing position, adjust the following valves:
Exhaust—1,5,6
Intake—1,2,3
Rotate the crankshaft one full revolution, until it is in the No. 4 firing position. Adjust the following valves:
Exhaust—2,3,4
Intake—4,5,6

Cylinder Head

REMOVAL & INSTALLATION

NOTE: The engine should be "overnight" cold before the cylinder head is removed to prevent warpage.

————— CAUTION —————
Do not discharge the compressor or disconnect the A/C lines. Personal injury could result.

Inline Six Cylinder

1. Drain cooling system and remove air cleaner. Disconnect P.C.V. hose.
2. Disconnect accelerator pedal rod at the bellcrank on the manifold, and fuel and vacuum lines at carburetor.
3. Disconnect exhaust pipe at manifold

flange, then remove manifold bolts and clamps and remove manifolds and carburetor as an assembly.
4. Remove fuel and vacuum line retaining clip from water outlet. Then disconnect wire harness from heat sending unit and coil, leaving harness clear of clips on rocker arm cover.
5. Disconnect radiator hose at water outlet housing and battery ground strap at cylinder head.
6. Disconnect wires and remove spark plugs. On ignition systems without the integral HEI coil, disconnect coil to distributor primary wire lead at coil and remove the coil.
7. Remove rocker arm cover. Back off rocker arm nuts, pivot rocker arms to clear push rods and remove push rods.
8. Remove cylinder head bolts, cylinder head and gasket.
9. Place a new cylinder head gasket over dowel pins in cylinder block.
10. Guide and lower cylinder head into place over dowels and gasket.
11. Oil cylinder head bolts, install and run them down snug.
12. Tighten the cylinder head bolts a little at a time with a torque wrench in the

correct sequence. Final torque should be as specified in the Torque Specifications chart at the beginning of this section.
13. Install valve pushrods down through the cylinder head openings and seat them in their lifter sockets.
14. Install rocker arms, balls and nuts and tighten rocker arm nuts until all pushrod play is taken up.
15. Install thermostat, thermostat housing and water outlet using new gaskets. Then connect radiator hose.
16. Install heat sending switch and torque to 15–20 ft. lbs.
17. Clean spark plugs or install new ones.
18. Torque ⅝ in. plugs to 15 ft. lbs. Tapered seat plugs are used on all engines.
19. Install coil (if removed) then connect heat sending unit and coil primary wires, and connect battery ground cable at the cylinder head.
20. Clean surfaces and install new gasket over manifold studs. Install manifold. Install bolts and clamps and torque as specified.
21. Connect throttle linkage.
22. Connect P.C.V., fuel and vacuum lines and secure lines in clip at water outlet.
23. Fill cooling system and check for leaks.
24. Adjust valve lash.
25. Install rocker arm cover and position wiring harness in clips.
26. Clean and install air cleaner.

V6 and V8

1. Drain coolant. Remove air cleaner.
2. Disconnect:
   a. battery
   b. radiator and heater hose from manifold
   c. throttle linkage
   d. fuel line
   e. coil wires
   f. temperature sending unit
   g. power brake hose, distributor vacuum hose, and crankcase vent hoses.
3. Remove:
   a. distributor, marking position
   b. alternator upper bracket
   c. coil and bracket
   d. manifold attaching bolts
   e. intake manifold and carburetor.
4. Remove:
   a. rocker arm covers
   b. rocker arm nuts, balls, rocker arms, and pushrods. These items must be replaced in their original locations.
5. Remove cylinder head bolts, cylinder head, and gasket.
6. Reverse procedure to install. Tighten head bolts evenly to the specified torque. On engines having steel gasket, use sealer on both sides. No sealer should be used on steel-asbestos gaskets. Adjust the valve lash.

OVERHAUL

For all cylinder head overhaul procedures, please refer to "Engine Rebuilding" in the Unit Repair section.

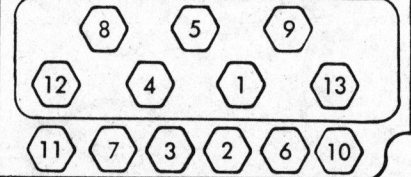

200, 229 V6 cylinder head torque sequence

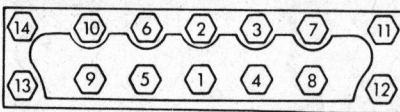

Inline six cylinder head torque sequence

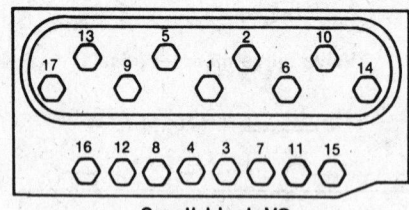

Small block V8 cylinder head torque sequence

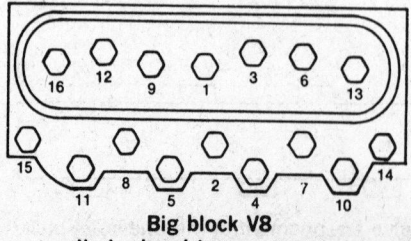

Big block V8 cylinder head torque sequence

Timing Cover, Chain, and Camshaft

All inline 6 cylinder engines have gear driven camshafts, while the V6 and V8 camshafts are driven by a timing chain. Inline 6 cylinder timing gear replacement requires camshaft removal.

Cover

REMOVAL & INSTALLATION

NOTE: If the timing chain is to be replaced, position the engine to align the timing marks at TDC ("0" on the scale) with the No. 1 cylinder on its compression stroke (valves closed). DO NOT rotate the cam or crankshaft while the chain is removed.

1. Drain and remove radiator.
2. Remove the fan belt and accessory drive belts. Remove the crankshaft pulley.
3. Remove harmonic balancer, using a puller.

NOTE: The outer ring (weight) of the harmonic balancer is bonded to the hub with rubber. The balancer must be removed with a puller which acts on the inner hub only. Pulling on the outer portion of the balancer will break the rubber bond or destroy the tuning of the torsional damper.

4. Remove the V6 and V8 water pump. If the oil pan isn't to be removed, cut the pan seal off flush with the block.
5. Remove timing gear cover attaching screws, and cover and bracket.
6. Clean all the gasket mounting surfaces on the front cover, block, and exposed portion of the oil pan (inline six). On the inline six temporarily position a new oil pan front seal on the front of the oil pan and trim off the edges of the new seal so that it will fit flush with the block.
7. Apply a bead of silicone sealer to the oil pan-to-cylinder block joint.
8. Install a centering tool in the crank-

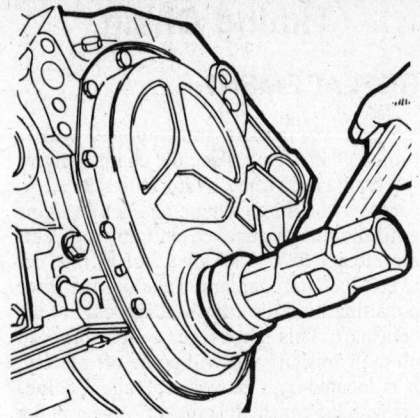

The front cover seal may be installed without removing the cover from the engine

shaft snout hole in the front cover and install the cover.

9. Install the front cover bolts finger tight, remove the centering tool and tighten the cover bolts. Install the harmonic balancer, pulley, water pump, belts, radiator, and all other parts.

— CAUTION —
The engines use a harmonic balancer. Breakage may occur if the balancer is hammered back onto the crankshaft. A special installation tool is necessary.

Oil Seal

REMOVAL & INSTALLATION

1. After removing the timing cover, pry oil seal out of front of cover with large screwdriver.
2. Install new lip seal with lip (open side of seal) inside and drive or press seal carefully into place.

NOTE: The timing cover oil seal can be replaced without removing the cover.

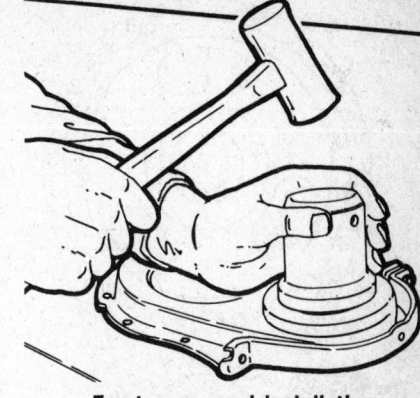

Front cover seal installation

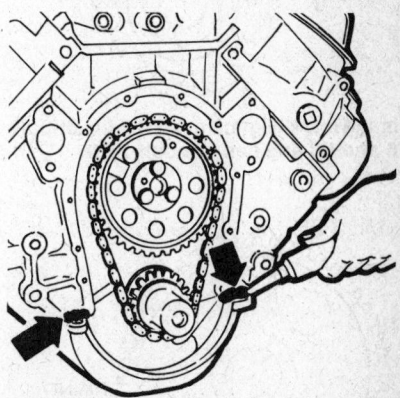

Sealer application to the oil pan-to-front cover joint

Remove the fan belts, crankshaft pulley and harmonic balancer. Pry the oil seal out of the cover with a small pry bar working carefully to prevent damage to the seal mating surface. Lubricate the new seal and drive it into place with the open side toward the engine. Use a seal installer to avoid damaging or cocking the seal.

When replacing the crankshaft damper, it has been found that lightly polishing the crankshaft damper with crocus cloth will greatly ease replacement. This procedure will also assist in any future removals, as it is sometimes difficult to pull a damper even with a puller. Be sure that the polishing is not overdone, or the damper will wobble on the crankshaft.

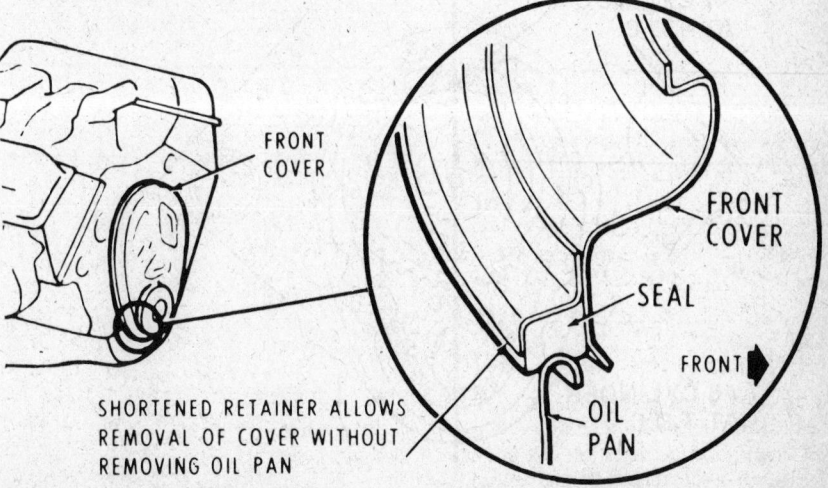

On Chevrolet V6 and V8 engines, it is not necessary to lower or remove the oil pan in order to remove the timing cover. The seal retainer is short enough to clear the pan

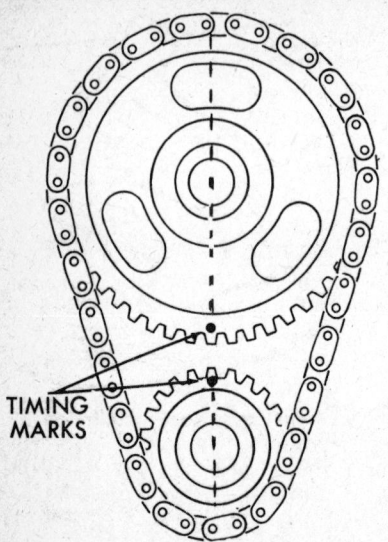

Timing mark alignment on Chevrolet-built V6 and V8 engines through 1979

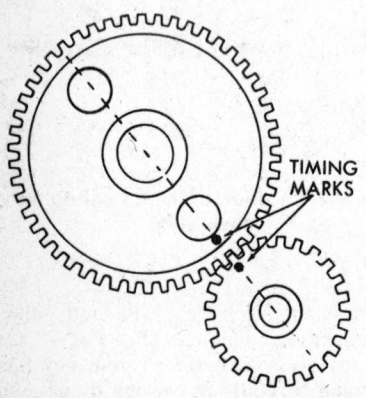

Timing mark alignment on the inline six cylinder engine

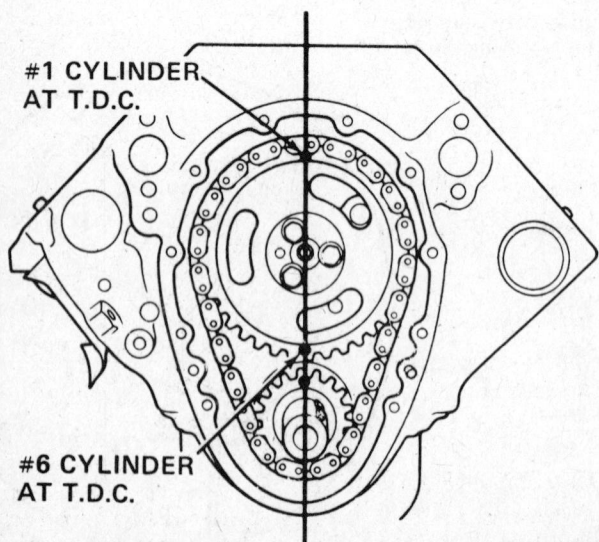

#1 CYLINDER AT T.D.C.

#6 CYLINDER AT T.D.C.

Timing mark alignment on Chevrolet-built V6 and V8 engines— 1980 and later models
(© Chevrolet Div., G.M. Corp.)

Timing Chain

REPLACEMENT

V6 and V8 models are equipped with a timing chain. To replace the chain, remove the crankcase front cover. This will allow access to the timing chain. Crank the engine until the marks punched on both sprockets are closest to one another and in line between the shaft centers. Take out the three bolts that hold the camshaft sprocket to the camshaft. This sprocket is a light press fit on the camshaft and will come off readily. It is located by a dowel. The chain comes off with the camshaft sprocket. A gear puller will be required to remove the crankshaft sprocket.

Without disturbing the position of the engine, mount the new crank sprocket on the shaft, then mount the chain over the camshaft sprocket. Arrange the camshaft sprocket in such a way that the timing marks will line up between the shaft centers and the camshaft locating dowel will enter the dowel hole in the cam sprocket.

Place the cam sprocket, with its chain mounted over it, in position on the front of the camshaft and pull up with the three bolts that hold it to the camshaft.

After the sprockets are in place, turn the engine two full revolutions to make certain that the timing marks are in correct alignment between the shaft centers.

Camshaft

REMOVAL & INSTALLATION

NOTE: Cam lobes must be lubricated with engine assembly lubricant or heavy oil before installation. Be careful that the cam bearings are not damaged during removal or installation of the camshaft.

Inline 6 Cylinder

The manufacturer recommends that the engine be removed from the car to remove the camshaft. However, in most cases the following procedure can be used. You may also have to raise the front of the engine for clearance.

1. In addition to removing the timing gear cover, remove the grille assembly. Remove the radiator. If equipped with air conditioning, unbolt the condenser and move it aside *without disconnecting any lines*.

2. Remove valve cover and gasket, loosen all the valve rocker arm nuts and pivot the arms clear of the pushrods.

3. Remove distributor and fuel pump.

4. Remove coil, side cover and gasket. Remove pushrods and valve lifters.

5. Remove the two camshaft thrust plate retaining screws by working through holes in the camshaft gear.

6. Remove camshaft and gear assembly by pulling it out through the front of the block.

NOTE: If renewing either camshaft or camshaft gear, the gear must be pressed off the camshaft. The replacement parts must be assembled in the same manner (under pressure). In placing the gear on the camshaft, press the gear onto the shaft until it bottoms against the gear spacer ring. The end clearance of the thrust plate should be 0.001–0.005 in.

7. Install camshaft assembly in the engine.

8. Turn crankshaft and camshaft to align and bring the timing marks together. Push the camshaft into this aligned position. Install camshaft thrust plate-to-block screws and torque them to 6–7½ ft. lbs.

9. Runout on either crankshaft or camshaft gear should not exceed .003 in.

10. Backlash between the two gears should be between 0.004 and 0.006 in.

11. Install timing gear cover and gasket.

12. Install harmonic balancer. Line up keyway in balancer with key on crankshaft and drive balancer onto shaft until it bottoms against crankshaft gear.

13. Install valve lifters and pushrods into their original locations. Install side cover with new gasket. Attach coil wires; install fuel pump.

14. Install distributor and set timing as described under distributor at the beginning of the section.

15. Pivot rocker arms over pushrods and adjust the valves.

16. Add oil to the engine. Install and adjust fan belt.

17. Install radiator or shroud.

18. Install grille assembly.

19. Fill cooling system, start engine and check for leaks.

20. Check and adjust timing.

V6 and V8

The camshaft can be removed with the engine in the car on all models.

1. Remove intake manifold, valve lifters and timing chain cover as described in this section. Remove the radiator. If the car is equipped with air conditioning, unbolt the condenser and move it aside *without disconnecting any lines*.

2. Remove grille, except on Nova. On this model, remove both front motor mount bolts and right motor mount, then lower engine until it rests on frame.

3. On Nova, remove the two center bolts and the one lower bolt that secure the hood latch support. This will give adequate clearance for the cam.

4. Remove fuel pump and pump pushrod.

5. Remove camshaft sprocket bolts, sprocket and timing chain. A light blow to the lower edge of a tight sprocket should free it (use a plastic mallet).

6. Install two bolts in cam bolt holes and pull cam from block.

7. To install, reverse removal procedure aligning the sprocket timing marks.

LUBRICATION

Oil Pan

REMOVAL & INSTALLATION

Inline 6 Cylinder (250)
EXCEPT CAPRICE AND IMPALA

1. Disconnect battery ground cable.

2. Remove front engine mount bolts. Remove upper radiator panel or side mount bolts.

3. Drain coolant. Remove radiator hoses.

4. Remove fan.

5. Drain engine oil.

6. On models with manual transmission, disconnect and remove the starter.

7. Disconnect oil cooler lines and remove converter on flywheel housing underpan.

8. Rotate crankshaft until timing mark on torsional damper is at 6:00 o'clock position.

9. Unbolt oil pan. On some models it may be necessary to remove the oil pump and intake pipe for clearance. On Nova, remove the left engine mount and frame bracket. Lower the pan slightly and roll it into the area where the mount was. Then tilt the front of the pan up and pull it down and to the rear. Lower pan.

10. Installation is the reverse of removal.

CAPRICE AND IMPALA

The oil pan can be removed, either after removing the engine, or as follows:

1. Drain radiator and oil pan.

2. Disconnect gas tank line at fuel pump and upper and lower radiator hoses.

3. Remove clutch housing-to-engine block bolt above dowel on right side.

PISTON AND CONNECTING ROD POSITIONING

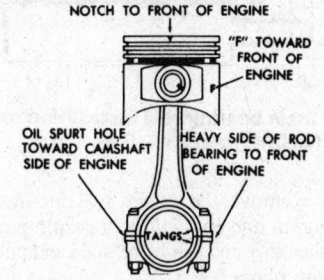

Proper piston-to-connecting rod relationship of the inline six cylinder engine (© Chevrolet Div., G.M. Corp.)

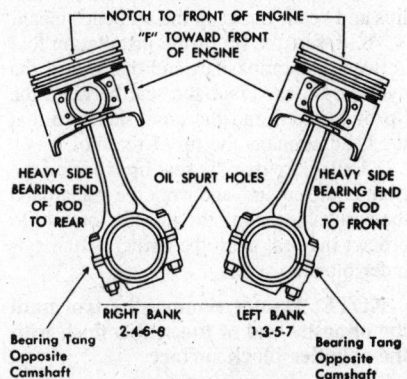

Piston-to-rod relationship—small block V8 and all V6

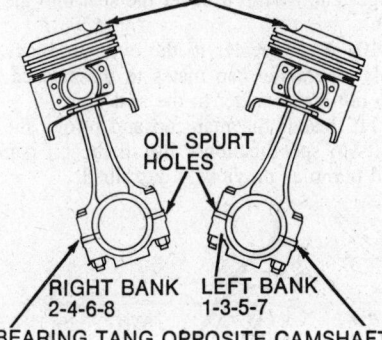

Piston-to-rod relationship—Mk. IV (big block) V8

4. Raise vehicle on hoist or place on jack stands.

5. Rotate engine to align distributor rotor between No. 3 and No. 5 plug wire. (This locates No. 6 crank throw part way up.)

6. Remove starter and flywheel front cover plate (or converter housing shield).

7. Remove front mount through bolts.

8. Jack up front of engine. Raise as far as possible always using care by checking various dash and body tunnel clearances.

9. Remove front engine mount frame bracket on right side and remove oil filter where necessary.

10. Remove oil pan screws and lower pan to frame.

11. Remove oil pump to gain clearance, then remove oil pan by sliding and rotating front to right and then to rear, and down at an angle.

12. Install in reverse of above.

V6 ENGINES

1. Drain the oil. On models on which the engine must be raised (see Step 7), remove the upper fan shroud.

2. Remove the oil dipstick and tube.

3. Raise and support the car.

4. Remove the exhaust crossover pipe.

5. On cars with automatic transmission, remove the converter housing underpan.

6. Remove the starter brace and inboard bolt. Swing the starter aside.

7. On 1980 and later models, remove the left-hand engine mount through bolt; loosen the right-hand through bolt. Raise the engine and install the left-hand through bolt.

8. Remove the oil pan and discard the gaskets and seals. On some engines, RTV sealant is used in place of a gasket. Apply a continuous bead about 1/8 in. wide.

9. Thoroughly clean the gasket surfaces and install the pan in reverse of removal. Always use new gaskets and seals.

V8 Engines
EXCEPT CAPRICE AND IMPALA

1. Disconnect battery ground cable.

2. Remove distributor cap.

3. Remove radiator upper mounting panel or fan shroud.

4. Remove fan.

5. Drain engine oil.

6. Disconnect exhaust or crossover pipes.

7. Remove converter housing underpan and splash shield. On cars with manual transmission, remove the starter, then remove the flywheel cover.

8. Rotate crankshaft until timing mark on torsional damper is at 6:00 o'clock position.

9. Remove front engine mount through bolts.

10. Raise engine and insert blocks under engine mounts. Block thickness should be 2 in. for Nova and 3 in. for Chevelle, Malibu and Monte Carlo.

11. Remove oil pan.

12. Installation is the reverse of removal.

CAPRICE AND IMPALA

1. Disconnect the negative battery terminal.

2. Remove distributor cap from distributor to prevent breakage against firewall.

3. Drain cooling system. Remove radiator hoses, and remove oil dipstick and tube, where necessary.

4. Remove fan blade assembly. On cars with A/C, remove the vacuum reservoir.

5. Raise car, and drain engine oil.

6. Remove bolts from engine front mounts. Disconnect and remove starter.

7. On cars with automatic transmissions, remove converter housing underpan.

8. Disconnect the exhaust Y pipe from the manifolds.

9. Rotate crankshaft until timing mark on the damper is at six o'clock position.

10. Using a block of wood and a suitable jack, raise engine enough to insert 2 × 4 in. wood blocks under engine mounts then lower engine onto blocks.

11. Remove engine oil pan.

12. Install by reversing removal procedures. Torque the pan bolts to 7½ ft. lb. Torque the engine mount bolts to 50 ft. lb.

Oil Pump

REMOVAL & INSTALLATION

1. Remove oil pan.

2. Remove pump and pickup tube and screen assembly on inline six cylinder engine and pump to rear main bearing cap bolt on the V6 and V8. Remove the pump and extension shaft on the V6 and V8.

3. To install, reverse removal procedure.

Rear Main Seal

REMOVAL & INSTALLATION

The rear main bearing seal may be replaced without removing the crankshaft. Seals should only be replaced as a pair. The seal lips should face the front of the engine when properly installed.

1. Remove the oil pan, and pump as previously outlined, and remove the rear main bearing cap.

2. Pry the lower seal out of the bearing cap with a screwdriver, being careful not to gouge the cap surface.

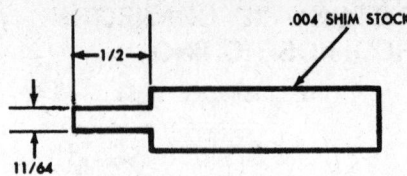

Rear main bearing seal installation tool
(© Chevrolet Div., G.M. Corp)

3. Remove the upper seal by lightly tapping on one end with a brass pin punch until the other end can be grasped and pulled out with pliers.

4. Clean the bearing cap, cylinder block, and crankshaft mating surfaces with solvent. Inspect all these surfaces for gouges, nicks, and burrs.

5. Apply light engine oil on the seal lips and bead, but keep the seal ends clean.

6. Insert the tip of the installation tool between the crankshaft and the seal of the cylinder block. Place the seal between the tip of the tool and the crankshaft, so that the bead contacts the tip of the tool.

7. Be sure that the seal lip is facing the front of the engine, and work the seal around the crankshaft using the installation tool to protect the seal from the corner of the cylinder block.

NOTE: Do not remove the tool until the opposite end of the seal is flush with the cylinder block surface.

8. Remove the installation tool, being careful not to pull the seal out at the same time.

9. Using the same procedure, install the lower seal into the bearing cap. Use your finger and thumb to lever the seal into the cap.

10. Apply sealer to the cylinder block only where the cap mates to the surface. Do not apply sealer to the seal ends.

11. Install the rear cap and torque the bolts to specifications. Install the oil pan and pump as previously described.

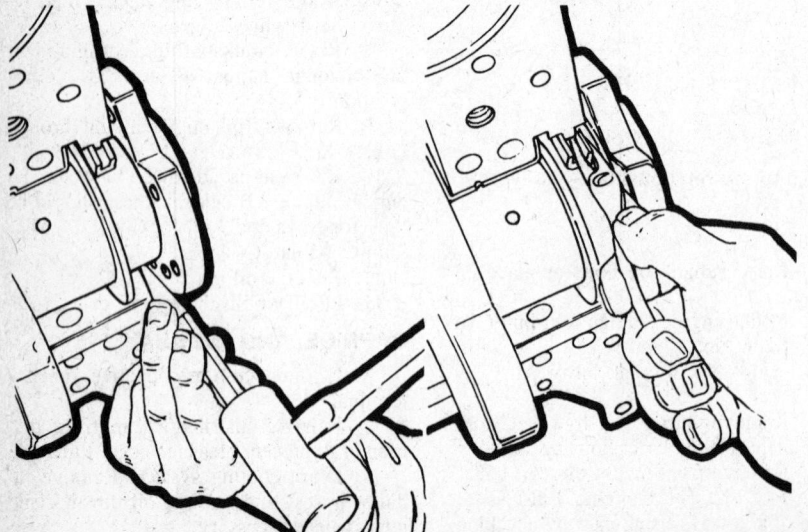

Rear main seal installation (© Chevrolet Div., G.M. Corp)

CLUTCH

The only service adjustment necessary on the clutch is to maintain the correct pedal free play. Clutch pedal free play, or throwout bearing lash, decreases with driven disc wear.

REMOVAL & INSTALLATION

1. Support engine and remove transmission.

2. Disconnect clutch fork push rod and spring.

3. Remove flywheel housing.

4. Slide clutch fork from ball stud and remove fork from dust boot. Ball stud is threaded into clutch housing and may be replaced, if necessary.

5. Install an alignment tool (dummy shaft) to support the clutch assembly during removal. Mark the relationship between the flywheel and clutch cover for reinstallation, if they do not already have X marks.

6. Loosen clutch to flywheel attaching bolts evenly, one turn at a time, until spring pressure is released. Remove bolts and clutch assembly.

On installation:

1. Clean pressure plate and flywheel face. Inspect all parts for wear and replace as necessary. If the flywheel shows any sign of overheating, discoloration, or if it is grooved or scored, it should be refaced or replaced.

2. Support clutch disc and pressure plate with alignment tool. The driven disc is installed with the damper springs on the transmission side. The grease slinger is always on the transmission side.

3. Turn clutch assembly until mark on cover lines up with mark on flywheel, then install bolts. Tighten down evenly and gradually to avoid distortion.

4. Remove alignment tool.

5. Lubricate ball socket and fork fingers at release bearing end with high melting point grease. Lubricate recess on inside of throwout bearing and throwout fork groove with a light coat of graphite or other high melting point grease.

6. Install clutch fork and dust boot into housing. Install throwout bearing to throwout fork. Install flywheel housing. Install transmission.

7. Connect fork push rod and spring. Lubricate spring and pushrod ends.

8. Adjust shift linkage and clutch pedal free-play.

FREE PLAY ADJUSTMENT

This adjustment must be made under the vehicle on the clutch operating linkage. Free play is measured at the clutch pedal.

1. Disconnect the return spring at the clutch operating fork.

2. Use the linkage to push the clutch pedal up against its rubber bumper stop.

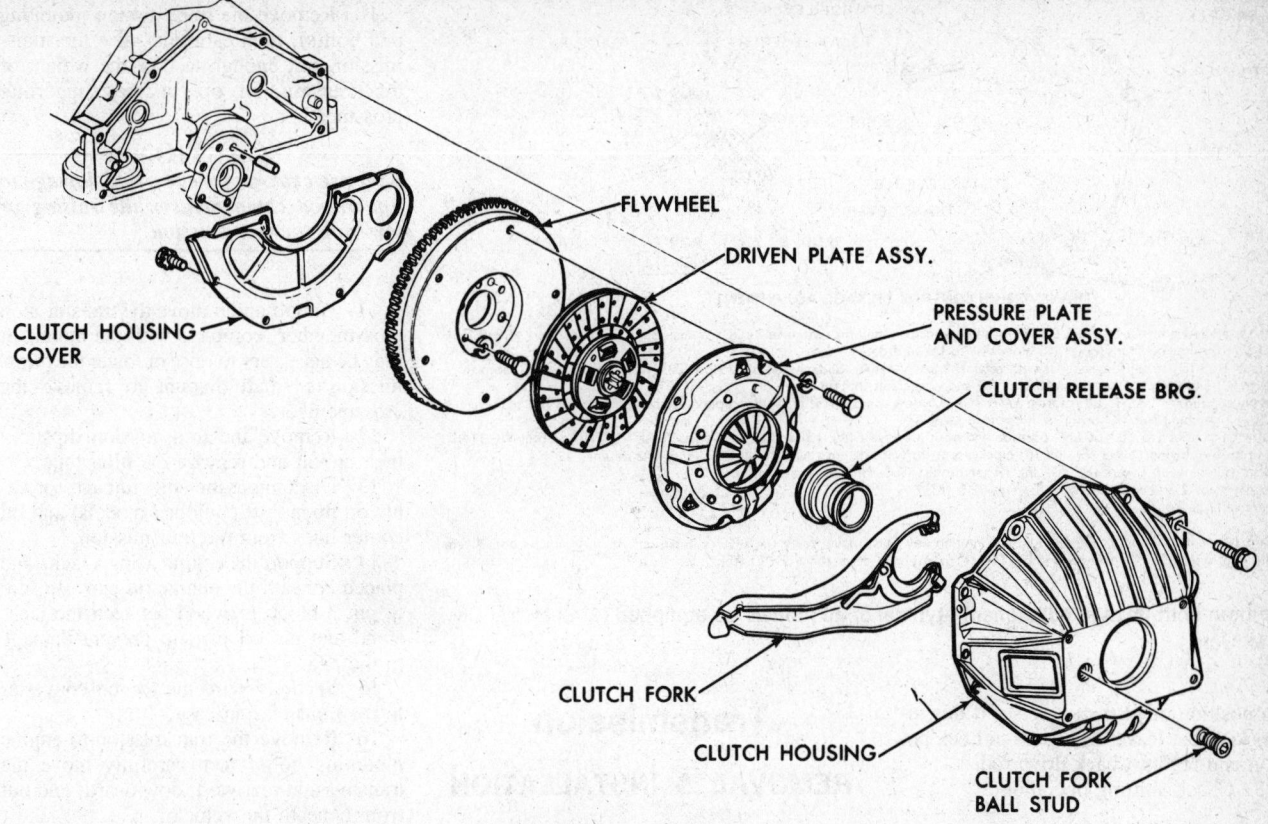

FLYWHEEL

DRIVEN PLATE ASSY.

PRESSURE PLATE
AND COVER ASSY.

CLUTCH RELEASE BRG.

CLUTCH HOUSING
COVER

CLUTCH FORK

CLUTCH HOUSING

CLUTCH FORK
BALL STUD

Exploded view of a typical clutch assembly (© Chevrolet Div., G.M. Corp.)

On 1978 and later models, rotate the clutch level until the pedal is firmly against the bumper.

3. Push the end of the clutch operating fork to the rear until the release bearing can just be felt to contact the pressure plate fingers.

4. Detach the front end of the operating rod from the clutch pivot shaft arm and place it in the gauge hole on the arm.

5. Loosen the locknut and lengthen the rod just enough to take all the play out of the linkage. Tighten the locknut.

6. Replace the operating rod in its original location.

7. Replace the return spring and check the free play at the pedal pad. It should be about 1–1¼ inches.

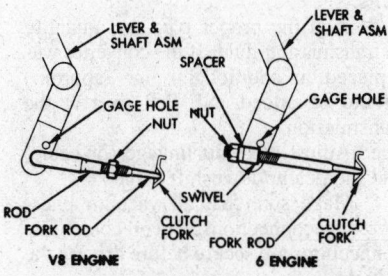

LEVER &
SHAFT ASM

LEVER &
SHAFT ASM

SPACER

GAGE HOLE

GAGE HOLE

NUT

ROD

FORK ROD

CLUTCH
FORK

SWIVEL

FORK ROD

CLUTCH
FORK

V8 ENGINE

6 ENGINE

Clutch pedal free-play adjustment
(© Chevrolet Div., G.M. Corp)

MANUAL TRANSMISSION

The three speed and four speed transmissions are Saginaw units.

For further identification and overhaul information, please refer to "Manual Transmission Overhaul" in the Unit Repair section.

REMOVAL & INSTALLATION

1. On floorshift models, remove the shift knob. Remove the boot.
2. Raise the car.
3. Disconnect the speedometer cable at the transmission.
4. Remove the driveshaft.
5. Support the rear of the engine and remove the crossmember.
6. Detach the shift rods from the transmission levers.
7. On floorshift models, remove the shifter from the transmission.
8. Remove the upper transmission to clutch housing bolts and replace them with headless guide pins. Remove the lower bolts.
9. Slide the transmission back along the guide pins until the input shaft clears the clutch. Remove the transmission.
10. Reverse the procedure for installa-

tion. If the input shaft won't engage the clutch splines, put the transmission in gear and turn the output shaft slightly. Torque the transmission to clutch housing bolts to 75 ft. lbs.

SHIFT LINKAGE ADJUSTMENT

Column Shift

Refer to the accompanying illustration for a detailed linkage adjustment procedures.

Floorshift

1. Turn ignition switch to Off.
2. Loosen locknuts on shift rods and reverse rod.
3. Set transmission levers in neutral positions.
4. Set floorshift lever in neutral. Install locating gauge, ⅛ in. thick, 41/64 in. wide, 3 in. long, into control lever bracket assembly alignment slot. Some later models may take a locating pin.
5. Adjust length of shift rods. Tighten locknut.
6. Remove locating gauge. Shift into reverse and lock the switch.
7. Pull down slightly on back drive (to column) rod to remove any slack and tighten locknut. Ignition switch must move freely to Lock position and it must not be possible to turn key to Lock when in any transmis-

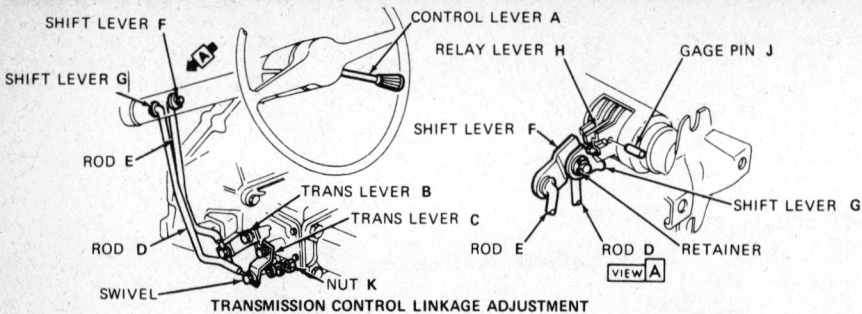

1. Set Levers (A) and (C) in "REVERSE" position and turn ignition switch to "LOCK" position. [NOTE] Obtain REVERSE position by moving Trans Lever (C) clockwise to forward detent.
2. Attach Rod (D) to Shift Lever (G) with retainer. See View A. Slide swivel onto Rod (D). Insert Swivel with Clamp into Lever (C) and loosely assemble with Nut (K) and washers at this time.
3. Remove column "LASH" by rotating Lever (G) in a downward direction and complete attachment of Rod (D) to Lever (C) by tightening Nut (K) using recommended torque.
4. Turn ignition key to "UNLOCK" position and position Levers (A), (B) and (C) in "NEUTRAL". [NOTE] Obtain NEUTRAL position by moving Levers (B) and (C) clockwise to forward detent then counter-clockwise one detent.
5. Align gage holes in Levers (F), (G) and (H) and insert Gage Pin (J). See View A.
6. Repeat steps 2 & 3 for Rod (E) & Levers (B) & (F).
7. Remove Gage Pin (J).

[NOTE] With shift lever in "REVERSE" the ignition key must move freely to "LOCK" position. It must not be possibly to obtain ignition "LOCK" position in "NEUTRAL" or any gear other than "REVERSE".

Column shift linkage adjustment—typical of all models so equipped (© Chevrolet Div., G.M. Corp.)

sion position other than reverse. If this interlock binds, leave the switch in Lock position and readjust back drive rod.

8. Check shifting operation.

— CAUTION —

Any inaccuracies in shift linkage adjustments may result in premature failure of the transmission due to operation without the controls in full detent. Such operation results in reduced fluid pressure and in turn, partial engagement of the affected clutches. Partial engagement of the clutches, with sufficient pressure to permit apparently normal vehicle operaton will result in failure of the clutches and/or other internal parts after only a few miles of operation.

AUTOMATIC TRANSMISSION

Identification can be made by the shape of the pan. See the Unit Repair Section for further visual differences and service procedures.

SHIFT LINKAGE ADJUSTMENT, BAND ADJUSTMENT, FLUID AND FILTER CHANGE

For all automatic transmission service procedures, please refer to "Automatic Transmissions" in the Unit Repair section.

Transmission

REMOVAL & INSTALLATION

1. Disconnect the negative battery cable at the battery.
2. If so equipped, disconnect the detent/downshift cable at its upper end (accelerator pedal or carburetor).
3. Raise the vehicle and support it safely with jackstands. Preferably, the front AND rear of the vehicle should be raised to provide adequate clearance for transmission removal.
4. Disconnect the exhaust crossover pipe at the manifolds, if exhaust system-to-transmission interference is obvious. It may be necessary to remove the catalytic convertor, exhaust pipe, or just the brackets in order to clear the transmission.

— CAUTION —

Exhaust system services must be performed while all components are COLD.

5. Remove the transmission inspection cover.
6. Remove the torque converter-to-flywheel bolts. The relationship between the flywheel and converter must be marked so that proper balance is maintained after installation.
7. Matchmark the propeller shaft and the rear yoke (for reinstallation purposes). With a drain pan positioned under the front yoke, unbolt and remove the propeller shaft.
8. Mark and disconnect vacuum lines, wiring, and the speedometer cable from the transmission, as required.
9. Place a transmission jack (carefully) up against the transmission oil pan, then secure the transmission to the jack.

10. Remove the transmission mounting pad bolt(s), then carefully raise the transmission just enough to take the weight of the transmission off of the supporting crossmember.

— CAUTION —

Exercise extreme care to avoid damage to underhood components while raising or lowering the transmission.

11. Unbolt and remove the transmission crossmember, complete with the mount. It may be necessary to raise or lower the transmission a small amount to remove the crossmember.
12. Remove the transmission dipstick, then unbolt and remove the filler tube.
13. Disconnect the shift linkage (or cable on floor shift-equipped models) and oil cooler lines from the transmission.
14. Support the engine using a jackstand placed beneath the engine oil pan. Be sure to put a block of wood between the jackstand and the oil pan, to prevent damage to the pan.
15. Securely wire the torque converter to the transmission case.
16. Remove the transmission-to-engine mounting bolts, then carefully move the transmission rearward, downward, and out from beneath the vehicle.

— CAUTION —

If interference is encountered with the cable(s), cooler lines, etc., remove the component(s) before finally lowering the transmission.

Refer to the "Automatic Transmissions" in the Unit Repair section for further information.

Installation is basically the reverse of the previous steps. Note the following points during and after installation:

a. Torque the transmission-to-engine mounting bolts to 30–40 ft. lbs.

b. Align the matchmarks of the propeller shaft with the marks of the rear yoke before installing the joint straps and bolts.

c. Align the converter and flywheel markings before installing the converter bolts.

d. Add the proper type and quantity of transmission fluid. If the converter was replaced, an additional 4 pints (approx.) should be added. NEVER overfill the transmission.

e. Adjust the shift linkage (or cable) and the detent/downshift cable.

f. Make sure that all vacuum lines, electrical connections, and oil cooler line connections are secure before driving the vehicle.

g. Check for fluid leakage, then after the transmission is hot, recheck the fluid level.

DRIVESHAFT/ DRIVE AXLE AND U-JOINTS

The universal joints are lubricated and sealed at the factory and require no periodic maintenance. Two basic universal joints are used. The Dana or Cleveland type uses snapring bearing cap retainers. The Saginaw uses injection molded plastic to retain the bearing caps. On the Saginaw type there is a snap-ring groove in the bearing housing inboard of the yoke to facilitate installation of a repair kit.

Driveshaft

REMOVAL & INSTALLATION

The driveshaft may be held to the differential pinion flange by a circular mounting flange, or the bearing cups may be retained to the pinion flange by U-bolts or straps.

1. Raise and support the car. Matchmark the pinion flange and driveshaft for assembly. The parts were balanced at the factory, and should be assembled in the same relationship.

2. Unbolt the flange or remove the U-bolts or straps. If straps or U-bolts are used, tape the bearing cups in place.

3. Drop the driveshaft down at the rear, then pull it backwards out from the transmission extension housing. The transmission housing should be plugged to prevent leakage.

4. Before installation, inspect the transmission yoke seal. Replace if necessary. Apply a light coat of transmission lubricant to the sliding splines.

5. Insert the front yoke of the driveshaft into the transmission. Do not allow the yoke to bang into the transmission seal.

6. Raise the rear of the driveshaft into place and align the matchmarks made during removal. Bolt the driveshaft to the pinion flange.

Universal Joint

For all U-joint repair information, please refer to "U-Joint/CV-Joint Overhaul" in the Unit Repair section.

REAR AXLE

These cars use two different types of drive axle, the C-lock and the non C-lock type. Axle shafts in the C-lock type are retained by C-shaped locks, which fit grooves at the inner end of the shaft. Axle shafts in the

non C-lock type are retained by the brake backing plate, which is bolted to the axle housing. Bearings in the C-lock type axle consist of an outer race, bearing rollers and a roller cage, retained by snap-rings. The non C-lock type axle uses a unit roller bearing (inner race, rollers and outer race), which is pressed onto the shaft, up to a shoulder. It is imperative to determine the axle type before attempting any service.

Non C-Lock Type
──── CAUTION ────

Before attempting any service to the drive axle or axle shafts, remove the axle carrier cover and visually determine if the axle shafts are retained by C-shaped locks at the inner end or by the brake backing plate at the outer end. If the shafts are not retained by C-locks, proceed as follows.

Design allows for maximum axle shaft end-ply of 0.002 in., which can be measured with a dial indicator. If end-play is found to be excessive, the bearing should be replaced. Shimming the bearing is not recommended as this ignores end-play of the bearing itself and could result in improper seating of the bearing.

1. Remove the wheel, tire and brake drum.

2. Remove the nuts holding the retainer plate to the backing plate. Disconnect the brake line.

3. Remove the retainer and install the nuts fingertight to prevent the brake backing plate from being dislodged.

4. Pull out the axle shaft and bearing assembly, using a slide hammer.

5. Using a chisel, nick the bearing retainer in three or four places. The retainer does not have to be cut, merely collapsed sufficiently to allow the bearing retainer to be slid from the shaft.

6. Press off the bearing and install the new one by pressing it into position.

7. Press on the new retainer.

NOTE: Do not attempt to press the bearing and the retainer on at the same time.

8. Assemble the shaft and bearing in the housing, being sure that the bearing is seated properly in the housing.

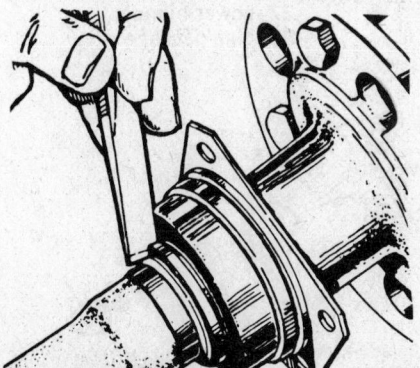

Breaking the bearing retainer with a chisel

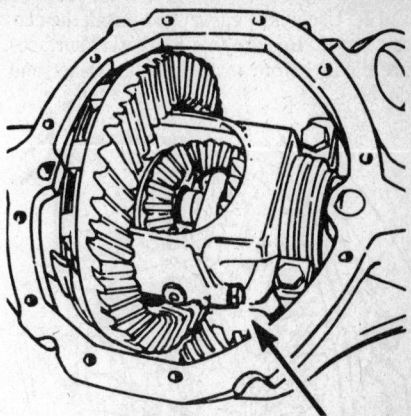

PINION SHAFT LOCK BOLT
Removing pinion shaft lock bolt from differential

9. Install the retainer, drum, wheel and tire. Bleed the brakes.

C-Lock Type
──── CAUTION ────

Before attempting any service to the drive axle or axle shafts, remove the carrier cover and visually determine if the axle shaft(s) are retained by C-shaped locks at the inner ends or by a brake backing plate at the outer end. If they are retained by C-shaped locks, proceed as follows.

1. Raise the vehicle and remove the wheels and brake drums.

2. The differential cover has already been removed (see Caution). Remove the differential pinion shaft lock-screw and the differential pinion shaft.

3. Push the flanged end of the axle shaft toward the center of the vehicle and remove the C-lock from the end of the shaft.

4. Remove the axle shaft from the housing, being careful not to damage the oil seal.

5. Remove the oil seal by inserting the button end of the axle shaft behind the steel case of the oil seal. Pry the seal loose from the bore.

6. Seat the legs of a bearing puller behind the bearing. Seat a washer against the bearing and hold it in place with a nut. Use a slide hammer to pull the bearing.

7. Pack the cavity between the seal lips with wheel bearing lubricant and lubricate a new wheel bearing with same.

8. Use a suitable driver to install the bearing until it bottoms against the tube. Install the oil seal.

9. Slide the axle shaft into place. Be sure that the splines on the shaft do not damage the oil seal. Make sure that the splines engage the differential side gear.

10. Install the C-lock on the inner end of the axle shaft and push the shaft outward so that the C-lock seats in the differential side gear counterbore.

11. Position the differential pinion shaft through the case and pinions, aligning the hole in the case with the hole for the lockscrew.

12. Use a new gasket and install the carrier cover. Be sure that the gasket surfaces are clean before installing the gasket and cover.

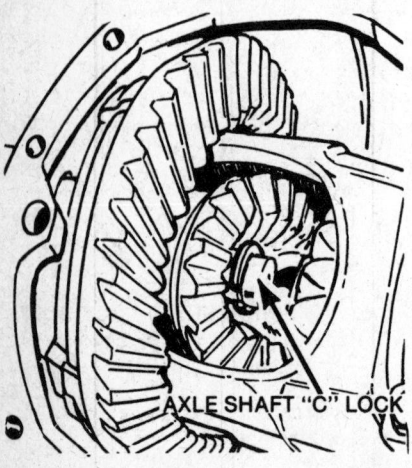

Axle shaft C-clips inside the differential

13. Fill the axle with lubricant to the bottom of the filler hole.

14. Install the brake drum and wheels and lower the car. Check for leaks and road test the car.

JACKING, HOISTING

Except Caprice and Impala

1. Jack car at front spring seat of lower control arm. Jack car at rear axle housing except when equipped with rear stabilizer bar. On these models, jack at frame rails.

2. To lift at frame, use side rails in front of body floor pan and at rear corner at squared off corner of box ahead of rear wheel.

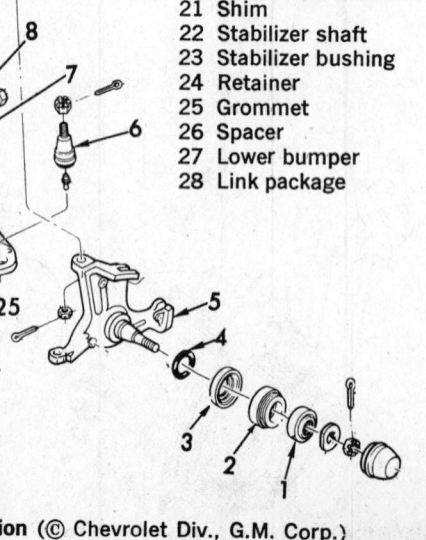

1	Front wheel bearing (outer)
2	Front wheel bearing (inner)
3	Front seal assy.
4	Gasket (splash shield)
5	Steering knuckle (r.h.)
6	Lower ball joint
7	Lower control arm
8	Rear bushing
9	Shock absorber
10	Coil spring
11	Spring insulator
12	Retainer
13	Grommet
14	Upper bumper
15	Retainer
16	Upper ball joint
17	Retainer
18	Front bushing
19	Upper control arm
20	Shaft package
21	Shim
22	Stabilizer shaft
23	Stabilizer bushing
24	Retainer
25	Grommet
26	Spacer
27	Lower bumper
28	Link package

Exploded view of front suspension (© Chevrolet Div., G.M. Corp.)

Caprice and Impala

When jacking the car, place the jack at the spring seat of the lower control arm in the front and at the axle housing in the rear. A bumper jack may be used.

To hoist the car, position the hoist arms at the frame side rails immediately in front of the rear wheels and immediately behind the front wheels.

FRONT SUSPENSION

Coil Spring

REMOVAL & INSTALLATION

1. Remove the shock absorber. Disconnect the stabilizer bar.

2. Support the car at the frame so the control arms hang free.

3. Support the inner end of the control arm with a floor jack. (Dealers have a device that cradles the inner bushings).

4. Raise the jack enough to take the tension off the lower control arm pivot bolts.

5. Chain the spring to the lower control arm, for safety's sake.

6. Remove first the rear, then the front pivot.

7. Cautiously lower the jack until all spring tension is released.

8. Note the way in which the spring is installed to the control arm and remove it.

9. On installation, position the spring to the control arm and raise it into place.

10. Install the pivot bolts and torque the nuts to 100 ft. lbs. for Nova models. Torque to 62 ft. lbs. for the Malibu and Monte Carlo. On Caprice and Impala, torque the retaining nut to 92 ft. lbs. and the bolts to 75 ft. lbs.

11. Replace the shock absorber and stabilizer bar.

Shock Absorber

REMOVAL & INSTALLATION

1. Remove the shaft nut while holding the shaft to keep it from turning.

NOTE: Inexpensive special tools are available to hold the shaft. DON'T use pliers to hold the shaft.

2. Remove the two bolts holding the shock absorber to the lower control arm, and pull the shock through the arm.

3. Extend the new shock absorber and insert it up through the lower control arm. Make sure that the upper shaft goes through the hole in the upper control arm frame bracket.

NOTE: Purge new shocks of air by repeatedly compressing them while inverted and extending them in their normal installed position.

4. Install the grommet, retainer cup and nut to the shock absorber upper shaft.

5. Hold the shock absorber shaft and tighten the upper nut to 8 ft. lbs.

6. Install the lower control arm retaining bolts and tighten to 20 ft. lbs.

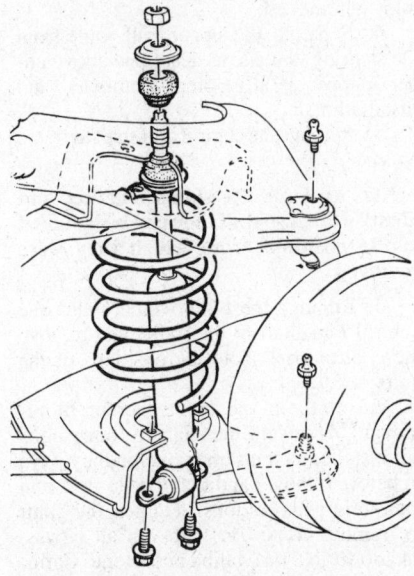

Installing shock absorbers—typical (© Chevrolet Div., G.M. Corp)

Front Wheel Bearing

ADJUSTMENT

1. Jack the car up and support it at the lower arm.

2. Remove the hub dust cover and spindle cotter pin. Loosen the nut.

3. While spinning the wheel, snug the nut down to seat the bearings. Do not exert over 12 ft. lbs. of force on the nut.

4. Back the nut off ¼–½ a turn or until it is just loose. Line up the cotter pin hole in the spindle with the hole in the nut.

5. Insert a new cotter pin. Endplay should be between 0.001 and 0.005 in. If play exceeds this tolerance, the wheel bearings should be replaced.

Ball Joints

INSPECTION

NOTE: Before performing this inspection, make sure the wheel bearings are adjusted correctly and that the control arm bushings are in good condition.

1. Jack the car up under the front lower control arm at the spring seat.

2. Raise the car until there is 1–2 in. of clearance under the wheel.

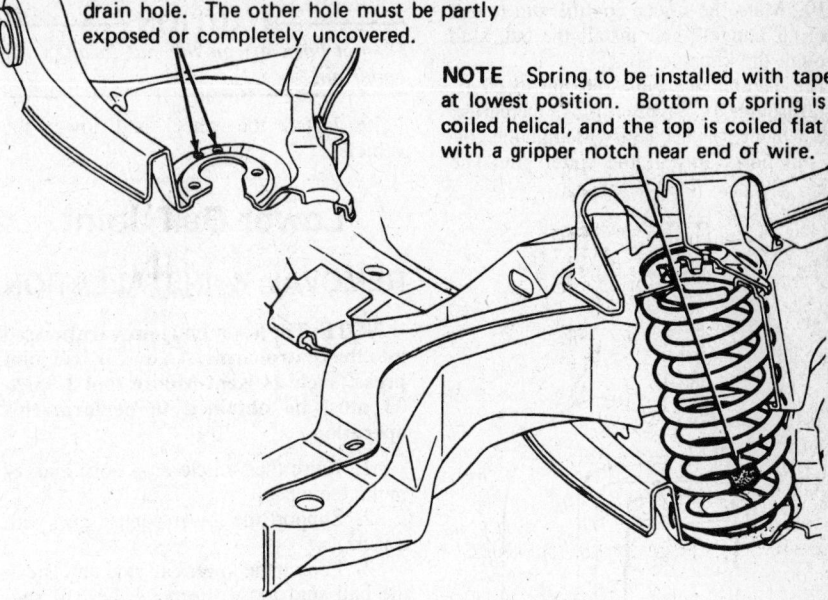

NOTE After assembly, end of spring coil must cover all or part of one inspection drain hole. The other hole must be partly exposed or completely uncovered.

NOTE Spring to be installed with tape at lowest position. Bottom of spring is coiled helical, and the top is coiled flat with a gripper notch near end of wire.

Coil spring positioning (© Chevrolet Div., G.M. Corp.)

3. Insert a bar under the wheel and pry upward. If the wheel raises more than ⅛ in., the ball joints are worn. Determine if the upper or lower ball joint is worn by visual inspection while prying on the wheel.

4. The upper ball joint can be further inspected after partial suspension disassembly. If the stud has any detectable side-to-side movement or if it can be twisted with your fingers it should be replaced.

NOTE: Due to the distribution of forces in the suspension, the lower ball joint is usually the defective joint. Because of this, most models are equipped with wear indicators on the lower ball joint. As long as the indicator extends below the ball stud seat, replacement is unnecessary.

Upper Ball Joint

REMOVAL & INSTALLATION

1. Raise the car on a hoist.

2. Remove the tire and wheel assembly.

3. Support the lower control arm with a jack.

4. Remove the upper ball stud nut.

5. Remove the ball stud from the knuckle.

6. Chisel or grind off the ball joint mounting rivets.

7. Drill out the ball stud attaching holes to accept the service ball joint attaching bolts.

8. Install the ball joint with the nuts and bolts supplied with the new joint, nuts on top.

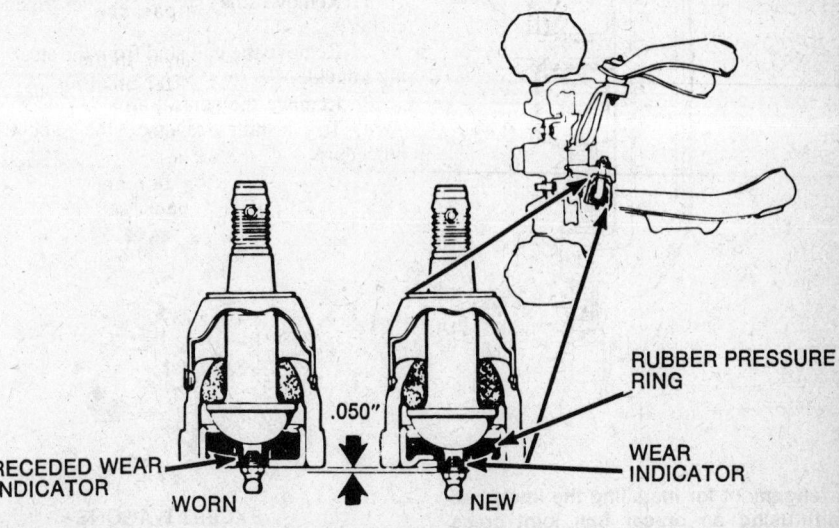

Wear indicator arrangement used on the lower ball joint (© Chevrolet Div., G.M. Corp.)

9. Install the lube fitting in the new joint.

10. Mate the upper control arm to the steering knuckle and install the ball stud through the knuckle boss.

11. Tighten the ball stud nut to 60 ft. lbs. through 1979, 65 ft. lbs. thereafter, plus whatever is necessary to align the cotter pin holes. Install the cotter pin. The

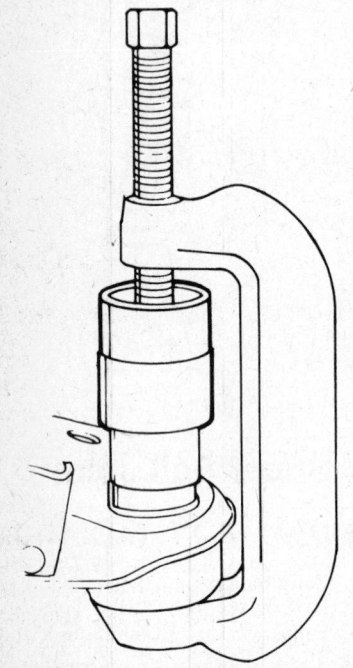

Arrangement for removing the lower ball joint using an on-car ball joint press (© Chevrolet Div., G.M. Corp.)

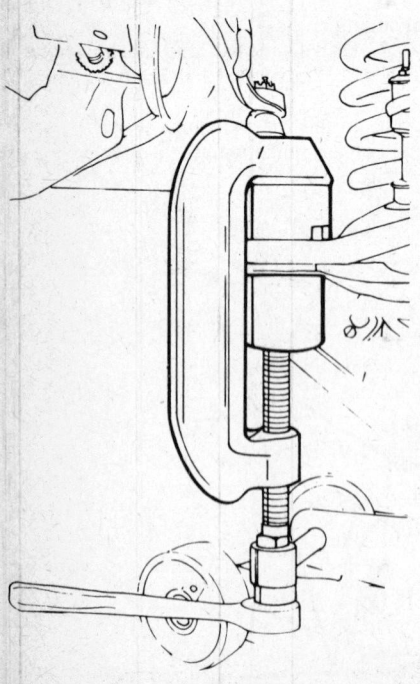

Arrangement for installing the lower ball joint using an on-car ball joint press (© Chevrolet Div., G.M. Corp.)

cotter pin must be installed from the rear to the front on Malibus and Monte Carlos.

— CAUTION —
Do not back off on the nut to align the cotter pin.

12. Install the wheel and lower the vehicle.

Lower Ball Joint

REMOVAL & INSTALLATION

NOTE: The lower ball joints are pressed into the control arms. An on-car ball joint press, such as Kent-Moore tool J-9519-03 must be obtained to perform this operation.

1. Raise the vehicle on a hoist and remove the wheel.

2. Support the lower control arm with a jack.

3. Loosen the lower ball stud nut. Break the ball stud loose. Remove the ball stud nut.

4. Remove the ball stud from the steering knuckle.

5. Press the joint out of the control arm using the tool mentioned earlier. Using the same tool, press the new joint into the control arm until it is fully seated.

6. Install the ball stud in the steering knuckle boss. This may be done by raising the lower control arm with the jack.

7. Install the nut on the ball stud, tightening to 83 ft. lbs on all models. Continue to tighten the nut until the cotter pin holes align and install the pin. Do not back off the nut to align the holes.

8. Install the lube fitting.

Lower Control Arm

REMOVAL & INSTALLATION

1. Remove the spring as described earlier.

2. Remove the ball stud from the steering knuckle.

3. Remove the control arm.

4. To install, reverse the above procedure.

Upper Control Arm

REMOVAL & INSTALLATION

1. Raise the vehicle on a hoist.

2. Support the outer end of the lower control arm with a jack.

3. Remove the wheel. Support the hub assembly to prevent its weight from damaging the brake hose when the upper ball joint is removed.

4. Separate the upper ball joint from the steering knuckle as described above under Upper Ball Joint Removal and Installation.

5. Remove the control arm shaft to frame nuts.

NOTE: Tape the shims together and identify them so that they can be installed in the positions from which they were removed.

6. Remove the bolts which attach the control arm shaft to the frame and remove the control arm. Note the positions of the bolts.

7. Install in the reverse order of removal. Make sure the shaft to frame bolts are installed in the same position they were in before removal and that the shims are in their original positions. Tighten the shaft to frame bolts to 75 ft. lbs on all Novas; and 46 ft. lbs. on Malibu and Monte Carlo. For the Caprice and Impala, torque the shaft-to-frame bolts to 85 ft. lbs. The control arm shaft nuts are torqued to 75 ft. lbs. on all models.

REAR SUSPENSION

The Malibu, and Monte Carlo have a coil spring rear suspension located by two lower control arms and two diagonally mounted upper control arms. Fore and aft axle movement is prevented by the lower control arms. Lateral movement is prevented by the upper control arms.

The Nova has a leaf spring rear suspension.

EXCEPT WAGONS

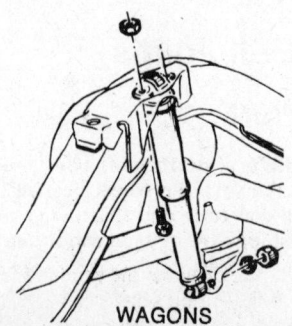

WAGONS

Typical rear shock absorber mounting (© Chevrolet Div., G.M. Corp.)

The Caprice and Impala also use a coil sprung axle located by two trailing arms on each side.

Shock Absorber

REMOVAL & INSTALLATION

1. Jack the car to a convenient working height. Support the rear axle assembly.
2. Remove the retaining bolts from the upper mounting bracket.
3. Remove the lower shock mounting bolt and nut.
4. Remove the shock.
5. Installation is the reverse of removal. Tighten the upper bolts to 12 ft. lbs; the bottom bolt to 65 ft. lbs.

NOTE: Purge new shocks of air by repeatedly compressing them while inverted and extending them in their normal installed position.

Spring

REMOVAL & INSTALLATION

Malibu, And Monte Carlo

If the springs have been in use for any length of time, it will probably be necessary to replace both to maintain an even ride height.

1. Raise the car by frame so that the rear axle can be independently raised and lowered.
2. Support the rear axle with a floor jack.
3. Disconnect the shock absorber from the axle. You don't have to disconnect both shocks unless you are removing both springs.
4. Disconnect the brake line clip at the axle housing junction block. Do not dis-

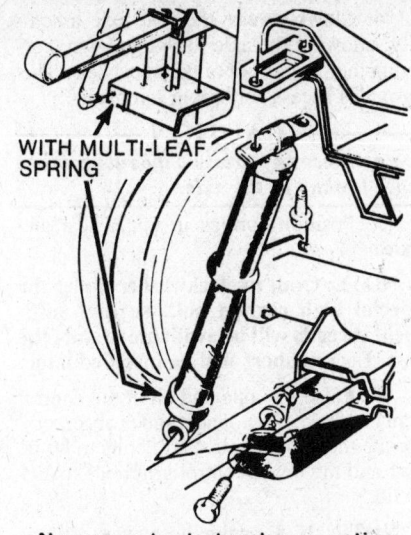

Nova rear shock absorber mounting
(© Chevrolet Div., G.M. Corp)

connect the brake hose. Disconnect the upper control arms at the axle.

5. Lower the axle to the limits of its travel, being careful of the brake lines.
6. Pry the lower end of the spring over the axle bracket vertical retainer. Remove the spring and insulator. Reverse the procedure for installation. Torque the upper control arm to axle mount to 80 ft. lbs.

Nova

1. Raise the car by the frame so that the rear axle can be independently raised and lowered.
2. Support the rear axle with a floor jack.

STATION WAGON

Chevelle rear shock absorber mounting
(© Chevrolet Div., G.M. Corp)

3. Disconnect the shock absorber lower mount.
4. Loosen the retaining bolt through the front spring eye. Unbolt the front bracket from the body.
5. Lower the axle enough to remove the bracket and retaining bolt from the front spring eye.
6. Pry the parking brake cable from the spring mounting plate retainer.
7. Remove the U-bolt nuts, the spring plate, and the upper and lower spring pads.
8. Support the spring. Remove the lower rear shackle bolt. Remove the spring.
9. On installation, install the front bracket to the spring eye, install the rear shackle, bolt the front bracket in place, install the U-bolts, and replace the shock absorber. Tighten the bolts with the weight of the car on the springs. Torque the front bracket mounting bolts to 25–30 ft. lbs.,

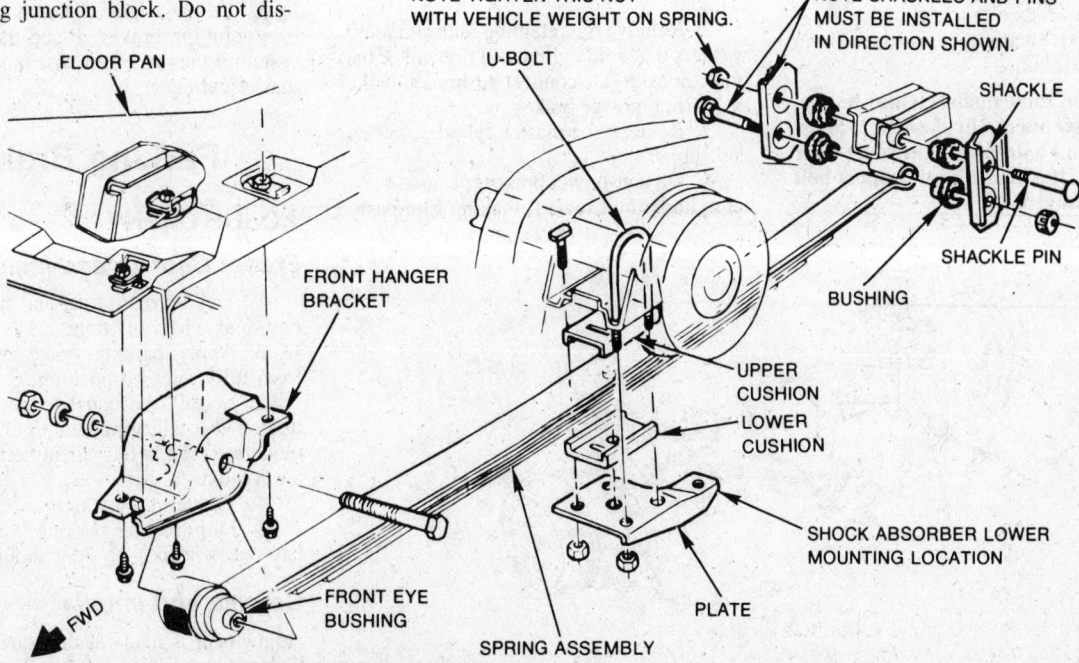

Mounting of the leaf spring—typical (© Chevrolet Div., G.M. Corp.)

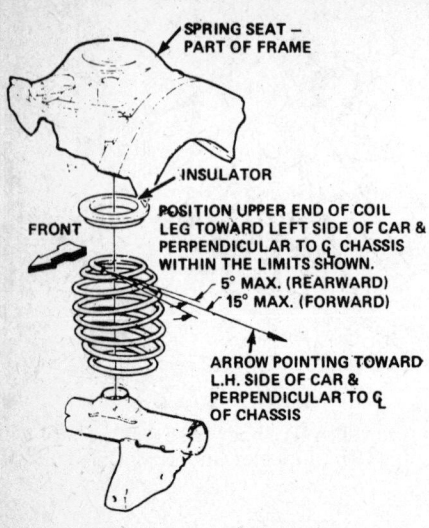

POSITION UPPER END OF COIL LEG TOWARD LEFT SIDE OF CAR & PERPENDICULAR TO ℄ CHASSIS WITHIN THE LIMITS SHOWN.
5° MAX. (REARWARD)
15° MAX. (FORWARD)

SPRING SEAT – PART OF FRAME

INSULATOR

FRONT

ARROW POINTING TOWARD L.H. SIDE OF CAR & PERPENDICULAR TO ℄ OF CHASSIS

Coil spring positioning

the front eye bolt to 75 ft. lbs., the U-bolts to 40 ft. lbs., and the rear shackle bolts to 50 ft. lbs.

Caprice And Impala With Coil Springs

1. Raise rear of vehicle and place jack stands under frame. Support weight of vehicle at rear axle housing separately from the frame position.
2. Remove both rear wheels.
3. With car supported as in Step 1, and springs compressed by weight of vehicle:
   a. Disconnect both rear shocks from the anchor pin lower connection.
   b. Loosen the upper control arm(s) rear pivot bolt (do not remove the nut).
   c. Loosen both left and right lower control arm rear attachment (do not disconnect from axle brackets).
   d. Remove rear suspension tie rod from stud on axle tube.

NOTE: On some models it may be necessary to disconnect a brake hose to allow for additional axle drop. On some later models only the brake hose support bolt need be removed.

4. Slowly lower the rear axle assembly, allowing the axle to swing down, carrying the springs out of the upper seat. This provides access for spring removal.

───── **CAUTION** ─────
Do not place any stress on the rubber brake hose leading to the axle.

5. Position springs in upper seat and axle.

NOTE: Omit the lockwasher under the special high carbon bolt, so that sufficient threads will be available to start the nut. Lockwashers will be installed later.

6. Raise the axle and align the control arm bolt holes. Reconnect shock absorbers, torque the upper control arm bolts to 80 ft. lbs. and the lower control arm bolts to 125 ft. lb.

NOTE: If a brake hose was disconnected during removal the brake system must be bled.

7. Install rear wheels and lower car to floor.

BRAKES

For all information on the brake system not detailed below, please refer to "Brakes" in the Unit Repair section.

Master Cylinder

REMOVAL & INSTALLATION

1. Disconnect hydraulic lines at master cylinder.
2. Remove the retaining nuts and lockwashers that hold cylinder to firewall or the brake booster. Disconnect pushrod at brake pedal (non-power brakes only).
3. Remove the master cylinder, gasket and rubber boot.
4. On non-power brakes, position master cylinder on firewall, making sure push-

rod goes through the rubber boot into the piston. Reconnect pushrod clevis to brake pedal. With power brakes, install the cylinder on the booster.

5. Install nuts and lockwashers.
6. Install hydraulic lines then check brake pedal free play.
7. Bleed brakes, as described in Unit Repair Section.

NOTE: Cars having disc brakes do not have a check valve in the front outlet port of the master cylinder. If one is installed, front discs will quickly wear out due to residual hydraulic pressure holding pads against rotor.

Power Brake Booster

REMOVAL & INSTALLATION

1. Disconnect vacuum hose from vacuum check valve.
2. Unbolt the master cylinder and carefully move it aside without disconnecting the hydraulic lines.

NOTE: If sufficient booster clearance cannot be obtained, it will be necessary to disconnect the hydraulic lines from the master cylinder, then remove the master cylinder.

3. Disconnect pushrod at brake pedal assembly.

NOTE: Some Nova brake boosters may also be held on with a sealant. This can be easily removed with tar remover.

4. Remove nuts and lockwashers that secure booster to firewall and remove booster from engine compartment.
5. Install by reversing removal procedure. Make sure to check operation of stop lights. Allow engine vacuum to build before applying brakes. Bleed the hydraulic system if the lines were disconnected at the master cylinder.

Parking Brake

ADJUSTMENT

Except Caprice and Impala

1. Jack up rear of car and support with both rear wheel off floor.
2. Apply parking brake two notches from fully released position.
3. Loosen the equalizer locknut, then tighten the adjusting nut until a light to moderate drag is felt when the rear wheels are rotated.
4. Tighten the locknut.
5. Fully release parking brake and rotate rear wheels—no drag should be felt.

Caprice and Impala

Adjustment is made at the equalizer while the parking brake pedal is applied one notch from the full release position. Loosen the

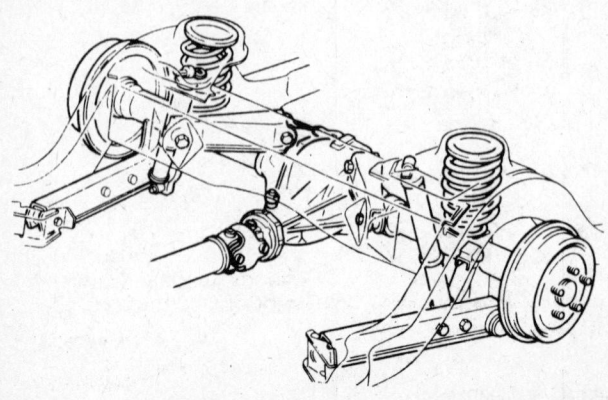

Typical coil spring rear suspension

forward equalizer adjusting nut, tighten the rear nut until the left rear wheel is locked. Then tighten the forward adjusting nut. Check operation after adjustment. With the cable fully released, the wheels should turn freely in either direction.

STEERING

Tie-Rod

REMOVAL & INSTALLATION

1. Remove the cotter pins and nuts from the tie-rod end studs.

2. Tap on the steering arm near the tie-rod end (use another hammer as backing) and pull down on the tie-rod if necessary, to free it.

3. Remove the inner stud in the same manner as the outer.

4. Loosen the clamp bolts and unscrew the ends if they are being replaced.

5. Lubricate the tie-rod end stud threads with chassis grease if they were removed. Install each end assembly an equal distance from the sleeve.

6. Ensure that the tie-rod end stud threads and nut are clean. Install new seals and install the studs into the steering arms and relay rod.

7. Install the stud nuts. Tighten to 35 ft. lbs. If necessary, you can tighten the nuts to as much 50 ft. lbs. to install the cotter pins.

8. Adjust the toe-in.

NOTE: Before tightening the sleeve clamps, ensure that the clamps are positioned so that adjusting sleeve slot is covered by the clamp.

Power Steering Pump

REMOVAL & INSTALLATION

1. Remove the hoses at the pump and tape the openings shut to prevent contamination. Position the disconnected lines in a raised position to prevent leakage.

2. Remove the pump belt.

3. Loosen the retaining bolts and any braces, and remove the pump.

4. Install the pump on the engine with the retaining bolts hand-tight.

5. Connect and tighten the hose fittings.

6. Refill the pump and bleed by turning the pulley counterclockwise (viewed from the front). Stop the bleeding when air bubbles no longer appear.

7. Install the pump belt on the pulley and adjust the tension. Bleed the system.

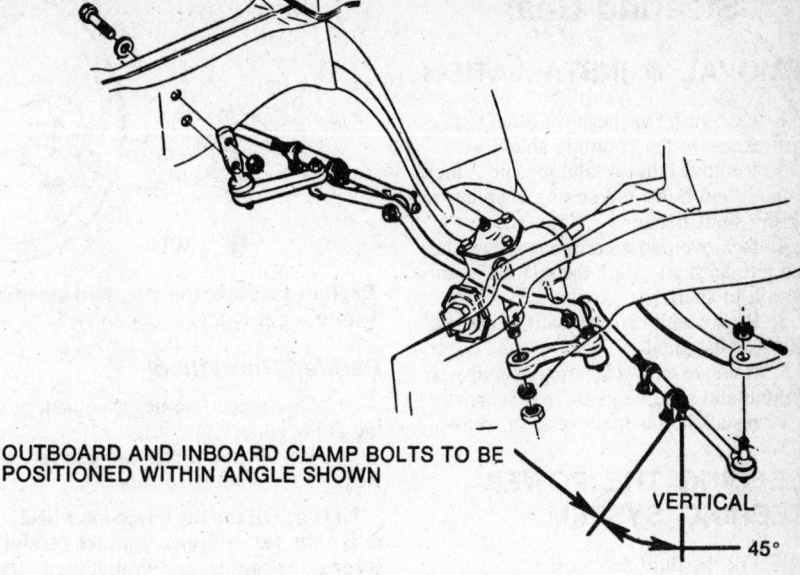

OUTBOARD AND INBOARD CLAMP BOLTS TO BE POSITIONED WITHIN ANGLE SHOWN

VERTICAL

45°

Malibu and Monte Carlo steering linkage

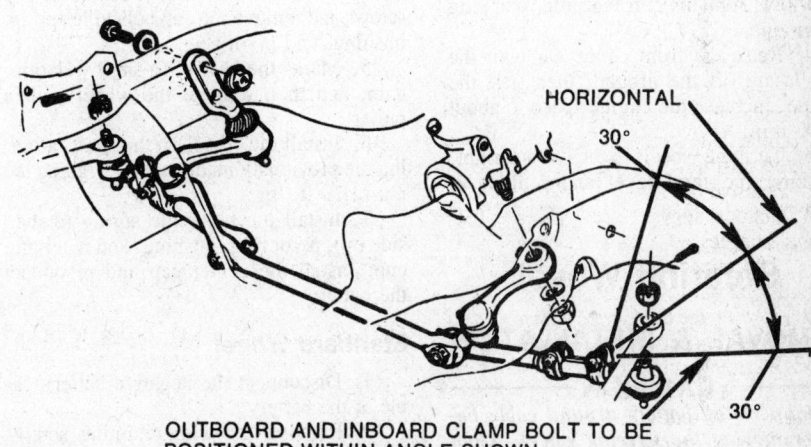

HORIZONTAL

30°

30°

OUTBOARD AND INBOARD CLAMP BOLT TO BE POSITIONED WITHIN ANGLE SHOWN.

Nova steering linkage (© Chevrolet Div., G.M. Corp)

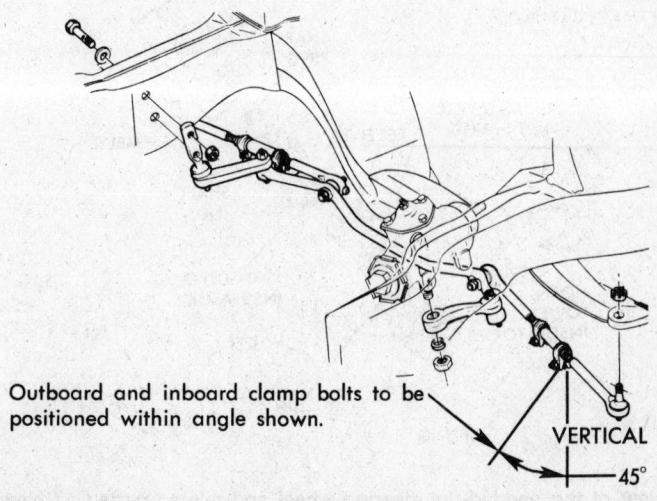

Outboard and inboard clamp bolts to be positioned within angle shown.

VERTICAL

45°

Caprice and Impala steering linkage—typical (© Chevrolet Div., G.M. Corp.)

Steering Gear

REMOVAL & INSTALLATION

1. Disconnect the negative battery cable.
2. Remove the coupling shield.
3. Remove the retaining nuts, lock washers, and bolts and stering coupling to steering shaft flange.
4. Remove pitman arm nut and washer from pitman shaft. Mark the relation of arm position to shaft.
5. Remove pitman arm with special tool J-6632 or its equal.
6. Remove screws securing steering gear to frame and remove gear from vehicle.
7. Installation is the reverse of removal.

BLEEDING THE POWER STEERING SYSTEM

1. Fill the fluid reservoir.
2. Let the fluid stand undisturbed for two minutes, then crank the engine for about two seconds. Refill reservoir if necessary.
3. Repeat Steps 1 and 2 above until the fluid level remains constant after cranking the engine.
4. Raise the front of the car until the wheels are off the ground, then start the engine. Increase the engine speed to about 1,500 rpm.
5. Turn the wheels to the left and right, checking the fluid level and refilling if necessary.

Steering Wheel

REMOVAL & INSTALLATION

— CAUTION —

Disconnect the battery ground cable before removing the steering wheel. When installing a steering wheel, always make sure that the turn signal lever is in the neutral position.

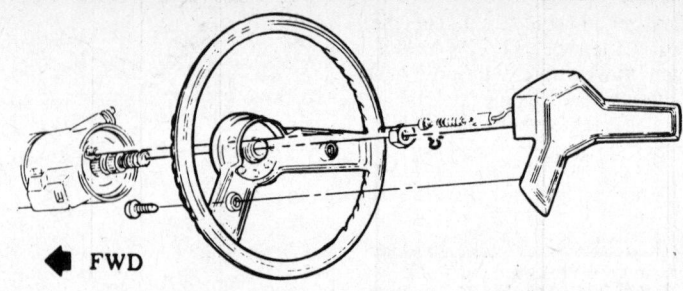

Exploded view of the standard steering wheel and related parts (© Chevrolet Div., G.M. Corp.)

Padded Rim Wheel

1. Disconnect the negative battery cable at the battery.
2. Pry out the center cap and retainer. Remove the shaft snap-ring.

NOTE: On the tilt-telescope wheel, remove the three upper contact retaining screws, the contact and shim if used. Then remove the center star screw and lever.

3. Remove the steering wheel nut and washer.
4. Remove the three receiving cup screws and remove the cup belleville spring, bushing, and pivot ring.
5. Mark the wheel-to-shaft relationship, and then remove the wheel with a puller.
6. Install the wheel on the shaft, aligning the previously made marks. Tighten the nut to 30 ft. lbs.
7. Install the belleville spring (dished side up), pivot ring, bushing, and receiving cup. Install the center cap and reconnect the battery.

Standard Wheel

1. Disconnect the negative battery cable at the battery.
2. Remove the trim retaining screws from behind the wheel. On wheels with a center cap, pull off the cap.
3. Lift the trim off and pull the horn wires from the turn signal cancelling cam.

NOTE: On the tilt-telescope wheel, remove the three upper contact retaining screws, the contact and shim if used. Then remove the center star screw and lever.

4. Remove the shaft snap-ring. Remove the steering wheel nut.
5. Mark the wheel-to-shaft relationship, and then remove the wheel with a puller.
6. Install the wheel on the shaft aligning the previously made marks. Tighten the nut to 30 ft. lbs.
7. Insert the horn wires into the cancelling cam.
8. Install the center trim and reconnect the battery cable.

Turn Signal Switch

REMOVAL & INSTALLATION

Except Caprice and Impala

1. Remove the steering wheel as previously outlined. Remove the trim cover.
2. Pry the cover off with a screwdriver, and lift the cover off the shaft.
3. Position the U-shaped lockplate compressing tool on the end of the steering shaft and compress the lock plate by turning the shaft nut clockwise. Pry the wire snapring out of the shaft groove.
4. Remove the tool and lift the lockplate off the shaft.
5. Slip the cancelling cam, upper bearing preload spring, and thrust washer off the shaft.
6. Remove the turn signal lever. Push the flasher knob in and unscrew it. On later models so equipped, remove the button retaining screw and remove the button, spring and knob.
7. Pull the switch connector out the mast jacket and tape the upper part to facilitate switch removal. Attach a long piece of wire to the turn signal switch connector. When installing the turn signal switch, feed this wire through the column first, and then use this wire to pull the switch connector into position. On tilt wheels, place the turn signal and shifter housing in low position and remove the harness cover.
8. Remove the three switch mounting screws. Remove the switch by pulling it straight up while guiding the wiring harness cover through the column.

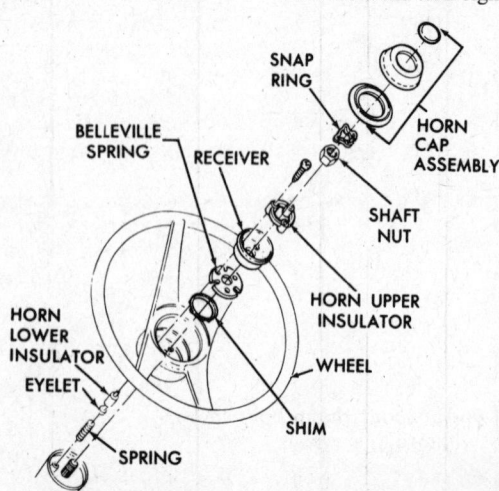

Exploded view of the padded-rim steering wheel and related parts (© Chevrolet Div., G.M. Corp.)

9. Install the replacement switch by working the connector and cover down through the housing and under the bracket. On tilt models, the connector is worked down through the housing, under the bracket, and then the cover is installed on the harness.

10. Install the switch mounting screws and the connector on the mast jacket bracket. Install the column-to-dash trim plate.

11. Install the flasher knob and the turn signal lever.

12. With the turn signal lever in neutral and the flasher knob out, slide the thrust washer, upper bearing preload spring, and cancelling cam onto the shaft.

13. Position the lock plate on the shaft and press it down until a new snap-ring can be inserted in the shaft groove. Always use a new snap-ring when assembling.

14. Install the cover and the steering wheel.

Caprice and Impala

1. Remove the steering wheel as previously outlined.

2. Remove the column to instrument panel trim cover.

3. Position a suitable tool into the cover slot. Pry up and out to remove the cover from the lockplate.

4. Attach the U-shaped lockplate compressing tool onto the steering shaft as far as it will go.

5. Compress the lockplate by turning the center post nut clockwise.

6. Pry the round wire snap-ring out of the groove and discard it.

7. Remove the tool and the lockplate.

8. Slide the directional signal cancelling cam, upper bearing preload spring, and thrust washer off the shaft.

9. Pull the turn signal lever straight out.

10. Unscrew the hazard warning knob and remove it.

11. Remove the switch actuator arm mounting screw and arm. Then remove the three switch mounting screws.

12. Pull the switch connector out of the jacket. Feed the switch connector through the column support bracket and pull the switch straight up guiding the wiring har-

Depressing the lock cylinder spring latch on models through 1978
(© Chevrolet Div., G.M. Corp.)

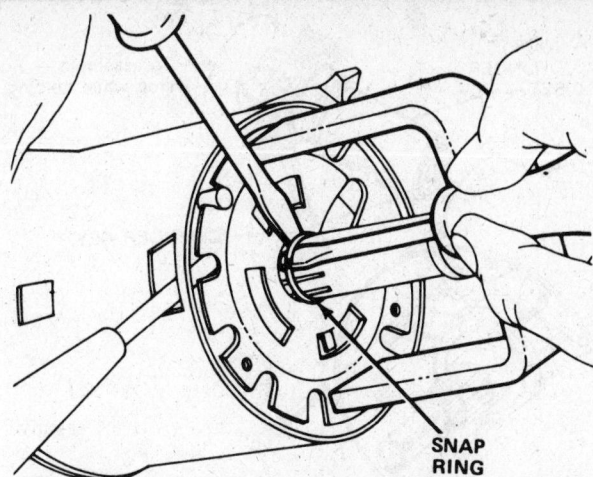

Compressing steering wheel lockplate and removing snap-ring

ness through the column housing and protector.

13. Remove the wire protector by pulling downward out of the column with pliers.

NOTE: On tilt columns position the directional signal and shifter housing in the low position.

14. Pull the switch straight up, guiding the harness and cover through the column housing.

15. Installation is the reverse of removal.

NOTE: It is extremely important that only the screws be used during reassembly. Use of overlength screws could prevent a portion of the assembly from compressing under impact.

Ignition Switch

REPLACEMENT

The switch is located inside the channel section of the brake pedal support and is completely inaccessible without first lowering the steering column. The switch is actuated by a rod and rack assembly. A gear on the end of the lock cylinder engages the toothed upper end of the rod.

1. Lower the steering column; be sure to properly support it.

2. Position the switch in the "Off-Unlocked" position. With the cylinder removed, the rod is in "Off-Unlocked" when it is two detents from the top.

3. Remove the two switch screws and remove the switch assembly.

4. Before installing, place the new switch in the "Off-Unlocked" position and make sure the lock cylinder and actuating rod are in "Off-Unlocked" (third detent from the top) position.

5. Install the activating rod into the switch and assemble the switch on the column. Tighten the mounting screws. Use only the specified screws since overlength screws could impair the collapsibility of the column.

6. Reinstall the steering column.

Ignition Lock Cylinder

REMOVAL & INSTALLATION

All 1978 Models

1. Remove the steering wheel as previously described.

2. Remove the turn signal as previously described.

NOTE: Pull the switch rearward far enough to slip it over the end of the shaft. It is not necessary to pull the harness out of the column.

3. Do not remove the buzzer switch or lock damage will result.

4. Place the cylinder in the Lock position. Insert a small drift pin or similar tool into the turn signal housing slot. Keep the tool to the right of the slot, break the housing slot loose and at the same time, depress the spring latch at the lower end of the cylinder. With the latch depressed, the lock cylinder can be removed from the housing.

5. Hold the lock cylinder sleeve and rotate the knob clockwise against the stop. Insert the cylinder into the housing bore with the key on the cylinder sleeve aligned with the keyway in the housing. Push the cylinder into the abutment of the sector and cylinder.

6. Rotate the cylinder counterclockwise, maintaining a light pressure until the drive section of the cylinder mates with the sector.

7. Push in until the snap ring pops into the grooves and the lock cylinder is secured in the housing. Check for free rotation.

8. Install the turn signal and steering wheel.

All 1979 and Later Models

1. Turn the lock to the run position.

2. Remove the lockplate, turn signal switch and buzzer switch.

NOTE: Pull the turn signal switch rearward far enough to slip it over the end of the shaft. It is not necessary to pull the harness out of the column.

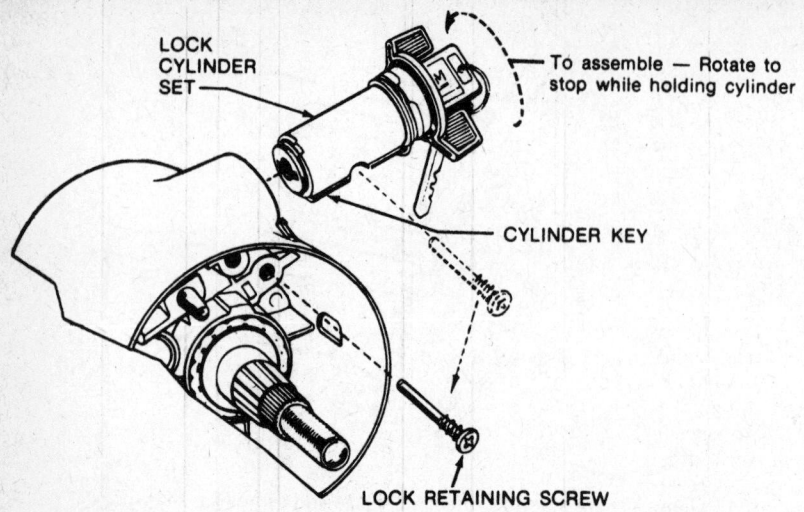

LOCK
CYLINDER
SET

To assemble — Rotate to
stop while holding cylinder

CYLINDER KEY

LOCK RETAINING SCREW

Lock cylinder removal, 1979 and later (© Chevrolet Div., G.M. Corp.)

3. Remove the lock retaining screw and remove the cylinder.

CAUTION

Be careful not to drop the screw into the column.

4. To install, rotate the lock assembly clockwise while holding the cylinder and align the cylinder key with the keyway in the housing.

5. Push the lock all the way in and install the retaining screw. Tighten to 41 in. lbs. regular columns, 23 in. lbs. adjustable columns.

6. Install the turn signal and buzzer switch.

INSTRUMENT PANEL

Headlight Switch

REPLACEMENT

Caprice and Impala

1. Disconnect the negative battery terminal.

2. Pull knob out to On position.

3. Reach under instrument panel and depress the switch shaft retainer. Remove knob and shaft assembly. Remove the windshield wiper switch.

4. Remove the retaining ferrule nut.

5. Remove switch from instrument panel.

6. Disconnect the multi-plug connector from the switch.

7. Replace in reverse of above. (In checking lights before installation, switch must be grounded to test dome light.)

Nova

1. Disconnect battery.

2. Pull the knob out to on position.

3. Reach under instrument panel and depress the switch shaft retainer, and remove knob and shaft assembly.

4. Remove the retaining ferrule nut.

5. Remove switch from instrument panel.

6. Disconnect the multi-plug connector from the switch.

7. Reverse the procedure to install.

Malibu, Monte Carlo

1. Disconnect battery ground cable.

2. Remove six screws and instrument panel pad.

3. Remove the 3 windshield wiper/light switch mounting screws.

4. Pull knob to on position.

5. Reach behind instrument panel and depress switch shaft retainer. Remove knob and shaft assembly.

6. Remove ferrule nut and switch assembly from instrument panel.

7. Reverse procedure to install.

Speedometer Cable

REMOVAL & INSTALLATION

Caprice and Impala

1. Disconnect the negative battery terminal.

2. Remove the four attaching screws and lower the steering column bottom cover.

3. Disconnect the shift lever indicator from the steering column.

4. Unbolt the column from the instrument panel.

5. Remove the six screws and three plastic snap retainers and lift off the lens.

6. Remove the two screws from the upper surface of the grey sheet metal trim plate.

7. Remove the nuts from two studs in the lower corner of the cluster.

8. Reach behind the cluster, depress the cable retaining clip and remove the speedometer cable.

9. Pull the core from the casing. If the core is broken, raise the car and disconnect the cable from the transmission.

10. Lubricate the new cable core with speedometer cable lubricant and install it in the casing.

11. Assemble all parts in reverse order of removal.

Nova

1. Remove the radio.

2. Disconnect the battery ground cable.

3. Reach up behind the speedometer and depress the retaining tab while pushing in, then out on the cable end.

4. Remove the firewall panel sealing plug to allow movement of the cable.

5. Pull the core from the casing. If the core is broken, it will be necessary to raise

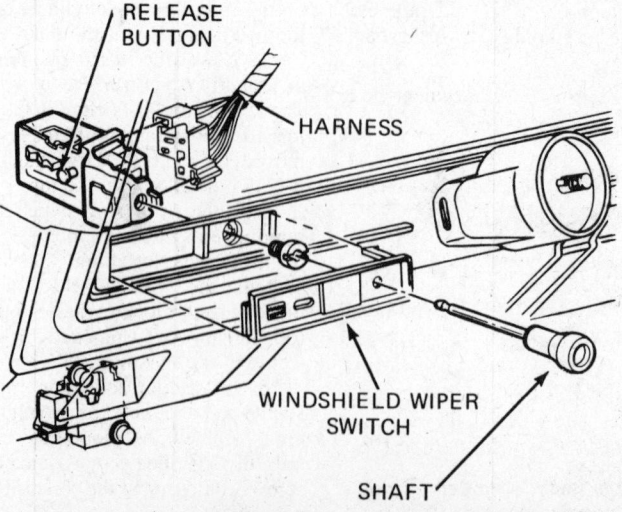

RELEASE
BUTTON

HARNESS

WINDSHIELD WIPER
SWITCH

SHAFT

Headlight switch installation (© Chevrolet Div., G.M. Corp.)

the car and disconnect the cable from the transmission.

6. Lubricate the core with cable lubricant and insert it into the casing. Connect the case to the speedometer and install the dash sealing plug.

Malibu and Monte Carlo

1. Disconnect the battery ground cable.
2. Remove the radio knobs and clock stem.
3. Remove the instrument bezel retaining screws.
4. Disconnect the tailgate release or defogger switch.
5. Remove the instrument cluster bezel.
6. Remove the speedometer head.
7. Disconnect the cable from the head by depressing the clip.
8. Pull the core from the casing. If the core is broken, raise the vehicle and remove the lower cable end from the transmission.
9. Lubricate the core with cable lubricant and install it in the casing.

Instrument Cluster

For further information on the instruments, please refer to "Gauges and Indicators" in the Unit Repair section.

REMOVAL & INSTALLATION

1. Disconnect the negative battery cable.
2. Remove four screws securing steering column lower cover and remove cover.
3. Disconnect shift indicator cable from steering column.
4. Remove two screws securing steering column to instrument panel and lower steering column.
5. Remove six screws and three snap-in-plastic fasteners from perimeter of instrument cluster lens.
6. Remove two screws from upper surface of grey sheet metal trim plate.
7. Remove nuts from two studs in lower corner of cluster.
8. Reach behind instrument cluster and disconnect speedometer cable and remove cluster by pulling outward.
9. Install replacement instrument cluster in reverse order of removal.

WINDSHIELD WIPERS

Motor

REMOVAL & INSTALLATION

All models except Nova with the Rectangular Motor

1. With wiper motor in the park position and hood open, disconnect the washer

hoses and all wiring from the motor assembly.

2. Remove the access cover.
3. Loosen the nuts which retain the drive link to the crank arm ball stud.
4. Remove the motor mounting screws or nuts and remove the motor.
5. To install, reverse the above procedure.

Nova—Rectangular Motor

1. Remove the cowl screen or grille.
2. Disconnect the electrical leads.
3. Loosen but do not remove the transmission drive link attaching nuts to the motor crank arm.
4. Disconnect the drive link from the motor crank arm.
5. Remove the three motor attaching screws, and remove the motor while guiding the crank arm through the hole.
6. On models with air conditioning, remove the screws and while supporting the motor, remove the motor crank arm nut using lockring type pliers and a closed end wrench. The motor attaching screws must be removed first to avoid damage to the nylon gear inside the motor.
7. Reverse the procedure to install.

Wiper Blade

REPLACEMENT

Two methods are used to retain the wiper blades to the arms. One is the press tab type release; the tab is pressed and the blade may be pulled from the arm. The other is the coil spring retainer; a screwdriver must be inserted on top of the spring and the spring pushed downward. The blade may then be pulled off.

For details on rubber element replacement, please refer to "General Maintenance" in the Unit Repair section.

RADIO

REMOVAL & INSTALLATION

Caprice and Impala

1. Disconnect the negative battery terminal.
2. Pull the control knobs off of the radio.
3. Remove the three screws and the trim plate.
4. Remove the two screws and the bottom nut holding the radio to the instrument panel.
5. Detach the wiring and the antenna.
6. Remove the radio and the mounting bracket.
7. Reverse the procedure for installation.

Malibu and Monte Carlo

1. Disconnect the battery ground.
2. Pull the control knobs from the shafts.
3. Remove the trim plate.
4. Remove the wiring and antenna cable from the rear of the radio.
5. Remove the receiver stud nut at the right side bracket.
6. Remove the control knob nuts.
7. Remove the instrument panel bracket.
8. Remove the radio through the panel opening.
9. Installation is the reverse of removal.

Nova

1. Disconnect the battery ground cable.
2. Pull off the knobs and bezels.
3. Remove the control shaft nuts and washers.
4. Remove the mounting bracket screws or nuts.
5. Move the radio back until the shafts clear the instrument panel. Lower it and disconnect the antenna, speaker, and power wires.

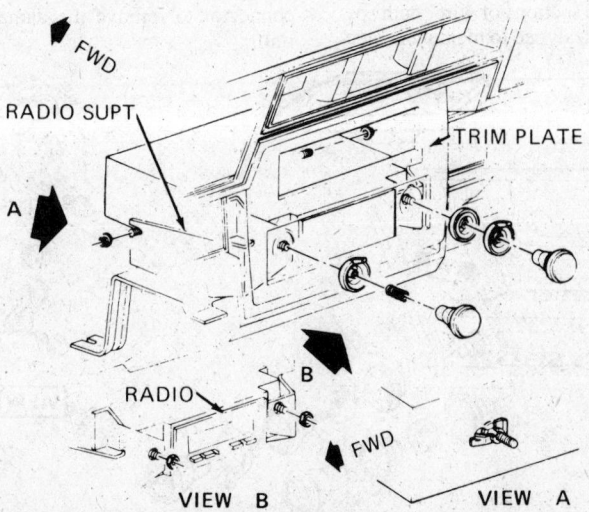

Typical Caprice and Impala radio mounting details

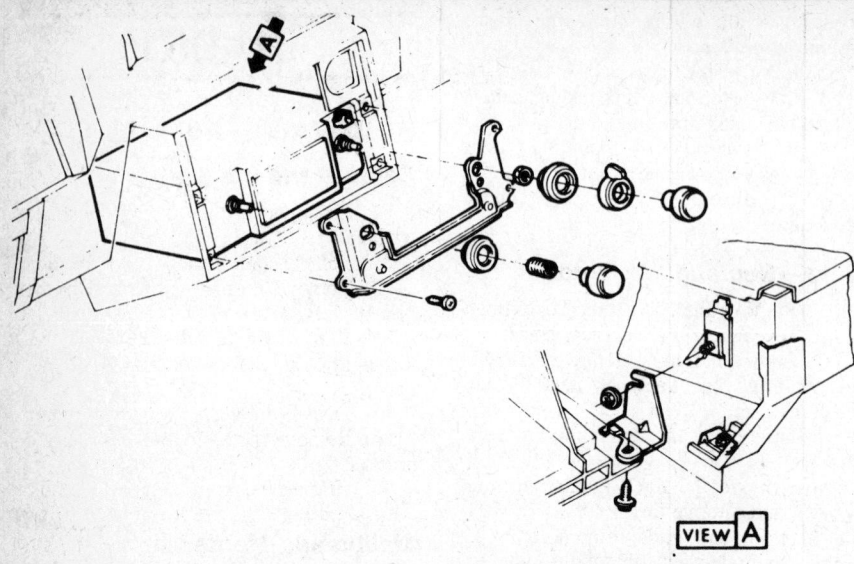

Typical Malibu and Monte Carlo radio mounting details

6. Remove the radio. Reverse the procedure for installation. Make sure to hook up the speaker leads before turning the radio on; operating without a speaker will damage the transistors.

FUSES

The fuse block is located beneath the instrument panel above the headlight dimmer floor switch. Fuse holders are labeled as to their service and the correct amperage. Always replace blown fuses with new ones of the correct amperage. Otherwise electrical overloads and possible wiring damage will result.

Fusible Links

Fusible links are sections of wire, with special insulation, designed to melt under electrical overload. Replacements are simply spliced into the wire. There may be as many as five of these in the engine compartment wiring harnesses. These are:

1. Horn relay to fuse panel circuit—one link.
2. Charging circuit, from the starter solenoid to the horn relay—two links.
3. Starter solenoid to ammeter circuit—one link.
4. Horn relay to rear window defroster circuit—one link.

The fusible links are all two wire gauge sizes smaller than the wires they protect.

NOTE: Most models have fusible links at these locations.

REPLACEMENT

1. Disconnect the battery ground cable.
2. Disconnect the fusible link from the junction block or starter solenoid.
3. Cut the harness directly behind the connector to remove the damaged fusible link.

4. Strip the harness wire approximately ½ in.
5. Connect the new fusible link to the harness wire using a crimp on connector. Solder the connection using rosin core solder.
6. Tape all exposed wires with plastic electrical tape.
7. Connect the fusible link to the junction block or starter solenoid and reconnect the battery ground cable.

HEATER

Blower

REMOVAL & INSTALLATION
Caprice and Impala

1. Disconnect the negative battery terminal.
2. Disconnect the blower lead wire.
3. Remove the attaching screws and gently pry the blower from the case. The sealer may act as an adhesive.
4. To install, reverse the procedure. Replace the sealer if it was damaged.

Nova

1. Disconnect battery ground cable.
2. Disconnect hoses and wiring from right side fender panel.
3. Remove the eight rear fender skirt screws instead.
4. Pull out, then down, on panel. Place a block between panel and fender.
5. Remove blower to case attaching screws. Remove the air-cooling hose from the motor on air-conditioned cars. Separate the blower wheel and motor then remove the blower assembly.
6. Remove blower wheel retaining nut and separate the motor and wheel.
7. Reverse procedure to install. Open end of blower should be away from motor.

Malibu and Monte Carlo

1. Disconnect the battery ground cable.
2. Disconnect the motor lead wire. On cars with A/C, disconnect the cooling tube.
3. Remove the blower to case screws and the blower.
4. Remove the retaining nut to separate the motor and wheel.
5. Reverse the procedure for installation. The open end of the blower wheel should be away from the motor.

Heater Core

REMOVAL & INSTALLATION
Caprice and Impala without A/C

1. Disconnect the negative battery terminal.
2. Drain the radiator.

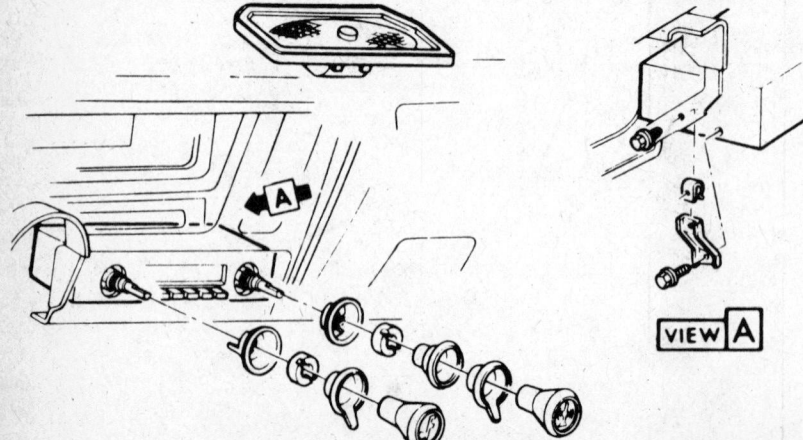

Radio mounting details of the Nova (© Chevrolet Div., G.M. Corp.)

TEMP. DOOR CRANK

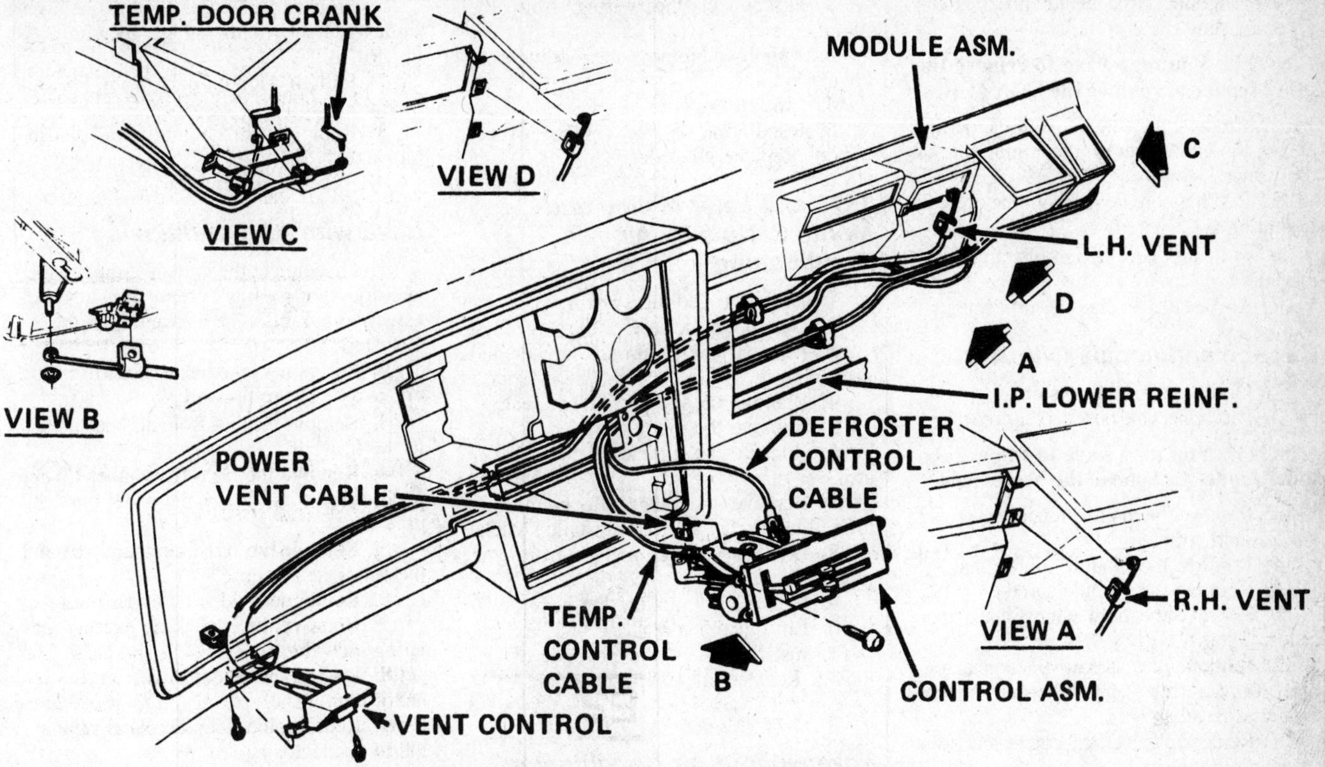

VIEW D

VIEW C

VIEW B

MODULE ASM.

C

L.H. VENT

D

A

I.P. LOWER REINF.

POWER VENT CABLE

DEFROSTER CONTROL CABLE

TEMP. CONTROL CABLE

B

VENT CONTROL

R.H. VENT

VIEW A

CONTROL ASM.

Chevrolet heater control cable adjustments

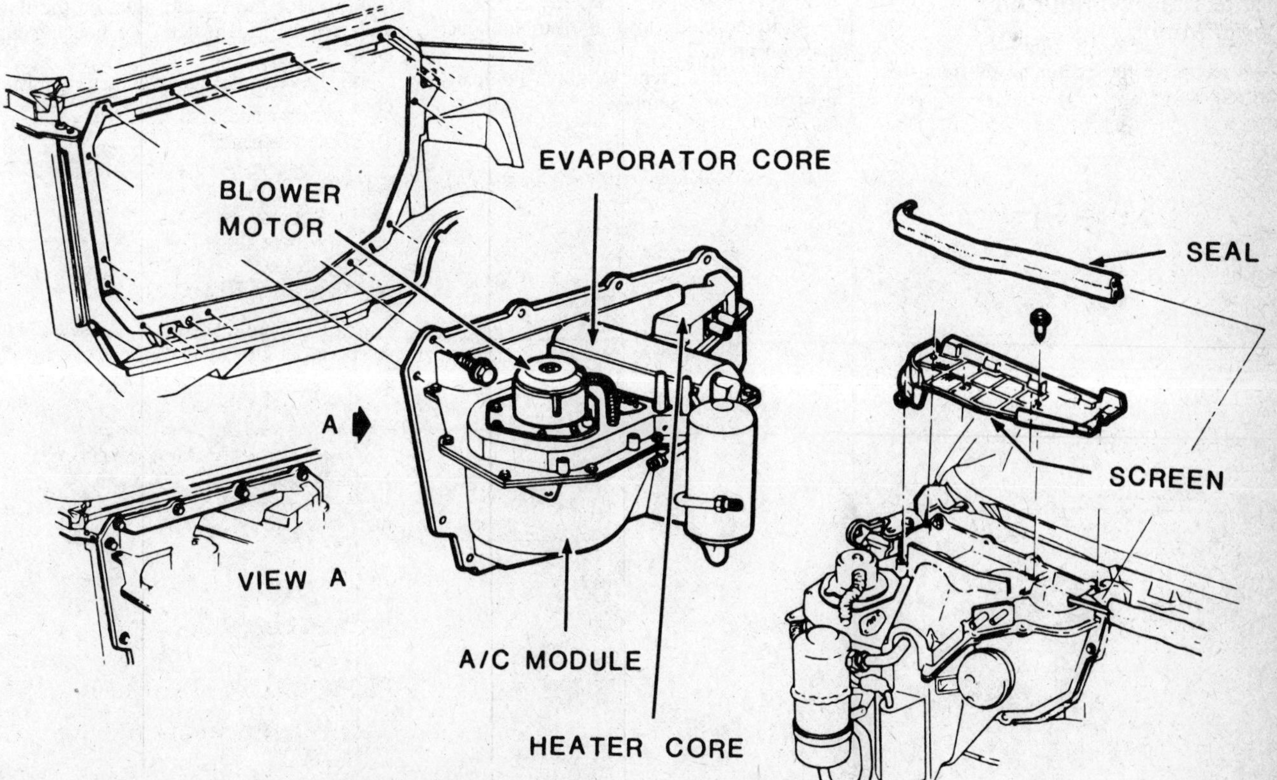

EVAPORATOR CORE

BLOWER MOTOR

SEAL

A

VIEW A

SCREEN

A/C MODULE

HEATER CORE

Air conditioner module mounting

C439

3. Disconnect the heater hoses at the core and plug the core tubes.

NOTE: You may have to remove the inner fender to remove the heater hoses.

4. Remove the screws from the perimeter of the core cover on the engine side of the firewall.

5. Pull the core cover from the firewall mounting.

6. Pull the core assembly from the module.

7. To install, reverse the procedure.

Caprice and Impala with A/C

1. Drain the cooling system.
2. Disconnect the hoses at the core tubes.

NOTE: You may have to remove the inner fender to remove the heater hoses.

3. Remove the module retaining bracket and ground strap.

4. Remove the module rubber seal.

5. Remove the module screen.

6. Remove the right windshield wiper arm.

7. Remove the diagnostic connector, high blower relay and thermal switch mounting screws.

8. Remove all electrical connectors from the module top.

9. Remove the module top cover.

10. Lift out the core.

11. Installation is the reverse of removal. Replace all sealer.

1978 and Later Malibu and Monte Carlo without Air Conditioning

1. Remove the heater hoses from the core tubes.

2. Disconnect the wiring from the module case.

3. Unbolt and remove the module front cover.

4. Lift out the core.

5. Installation is the reverse of removal. Replace all sealer.

1978 and Later Malibu and Monte Carlo with Air Conditioning

1. Drain the cooling system.
2. Disconnect the hoses at the core tubes.
3. Remove the retaining bracket and ground strap.
4. Remove the module rubber seal.
5. Remove the module screen.
6. Remove the right windshield wiper arm.
7. Remove the diagnostic connector, high blower relay and thermostatic switch.
8. Disconnect all wiring from the module.
9. Remove the module top cover.
10. Lift out the core.
11. Installation is the reverse of removal. Replace all sealing material.

Nova without Air Conditioning

1. Disconnect battery ground cable.
2. Drain radiator.
3. Disconnect heater hoses. Plug core inlet and outlet.

NOTE: The larger hose goes to the water pump.

4. Remove nuts from air distributor duct studs on firewall.

5. On Nova, remove glove compartment and door assembly.

6. From under Nova dash, drill out lower right hand distributor duct stud with a ¼ in. drill.

7. Pull distributor duct from firewall mounting. Remove resistor wires.

8. Remove core assembly from distributor duct.

9. Reverse procedure to install.

Nova with Air Conditioning

1. Disconnect the battery ground cable and drain the cooling system. It is not necessary to purge the refrigerant from the A/C system.

2. Disconnect the heater hose from the upper pipe at the firewall.

3. Remove the nuts from the heater studs in the firewall.

4. Remove the right front inner fender panel screws and lower the panel onto the tire.

5. Remove the remaining stud nut and the lower heater hose.

6. Remove the glove compartment.

7. Remove the right kick pad recirculating air valve.

8. Detach the center duct from the selector duct.

9. Remove the floor duct and separate the two selector halves.

10. Remove the selector duct from the firewall.

11. Disconnect the control cables and electrical wires.

12. Scribe the temperature door camming plate-to-selector duct relationship and remove the plate.

13. Place the selector duct on the floor and remove the heater core housing and core.

14. Reverse the removal steps to install core.

Oldsmobile
Rear Wheel Drive
Cutlass, Omega, 88, 98

YEAR IDENTIFICATION

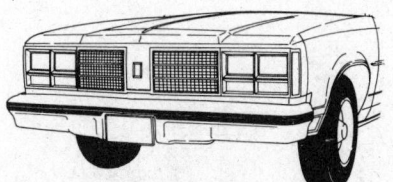

1978 Delta 88

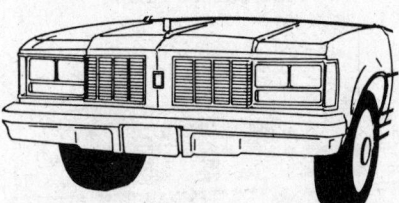

1979 Delta 88

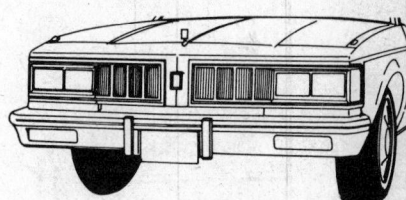

1980 88

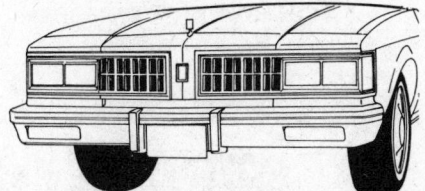

1981 88

1982 Delta 88

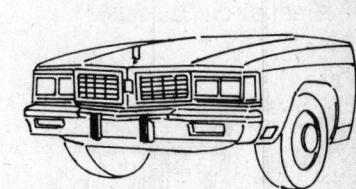

1983–84 Delta 88

1985 Delta 88 Royale Coupe

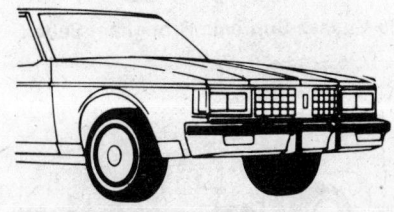

1985 Delta 88 Royale Brougham LS Sedan

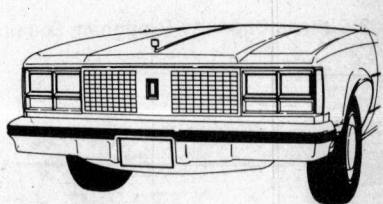

1975 98

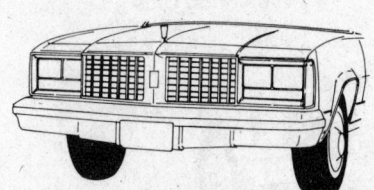

1979 98

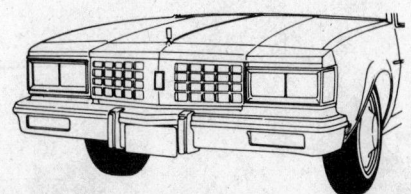

1980 98

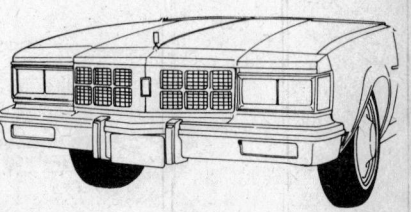

1981-82 98

C441

YEAR IDENTIFICATION

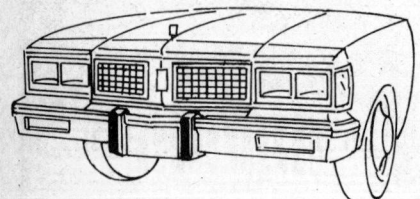

1983–84 98

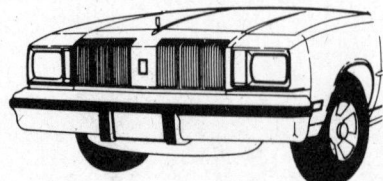

1978 Cutlass

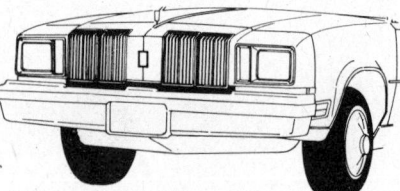

1979 Cutlass

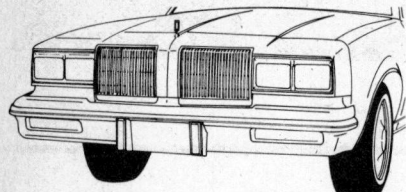

1980 Cutlass Supreme

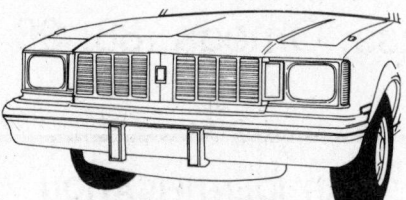

1980 Cutlass Salon

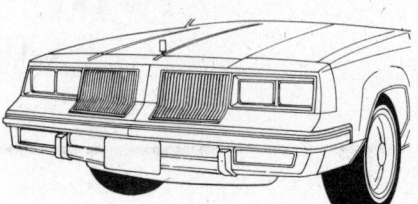

1981-82 Cutlass Supreme

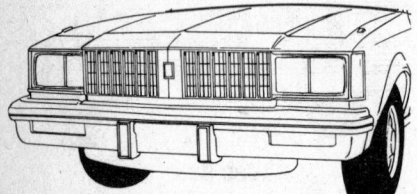

1981-82 Cutlass Salon

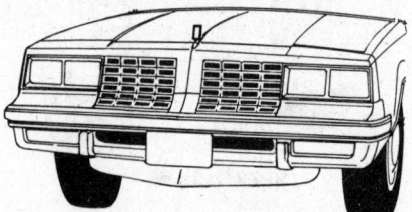

1981 Cutlass Supreme Brougham

1982-83 Cutlass Supreme

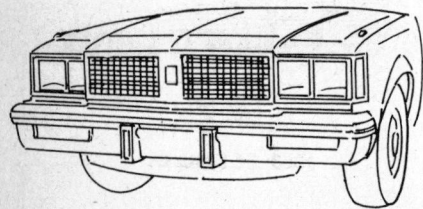

1983 Cutlass Supreme Brougham Sedan

1985 Cutlass Supreme Brougham Sedan

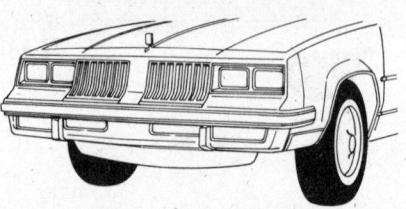

1984 Cutlass Supreme Coupe

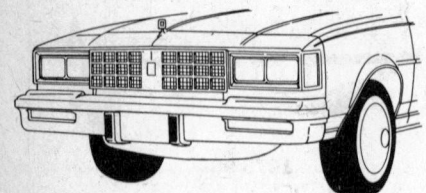

1984 Cutlass Supreme Sedan

1985 Cutlass Supreme Coupe

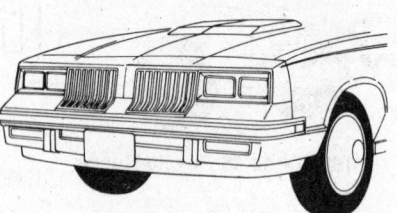

1984 Hurst/Olds

1978 Omega

1979 Omega

VEHICLE IDENTIFICATION NUMBER (VIN)

It is important for servicing and ordering parts to be certain of the vehicle and engine identification. The VIN (vehicle identification number) is a 13 or 17 digit number visible through the windshield on the driver's side of the dash and contains the vehicle and engine identification codes. It can be interpreted as follows:

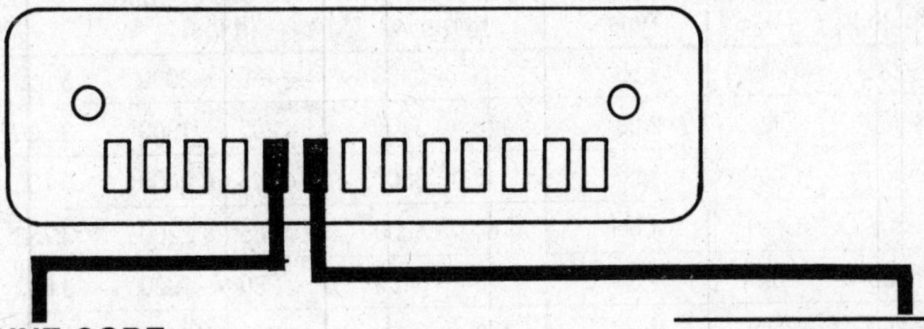

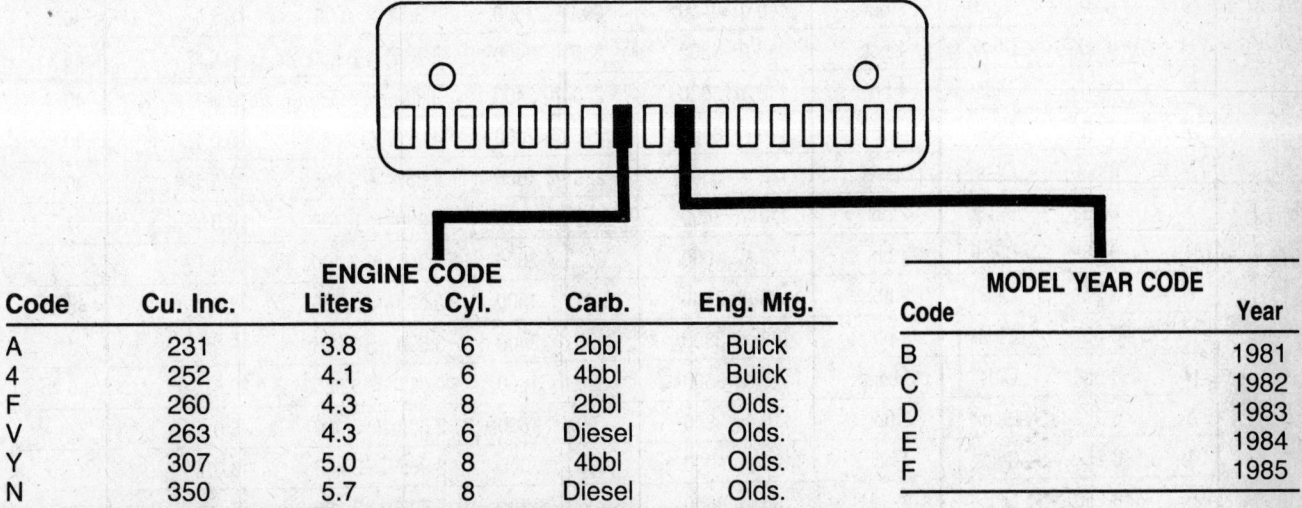

ENGINE CODE

Code	Cu. In.	Liters	Cyl.	Carb.	Eng. Mfg.
C	231	3.8	6	2bbl	Buick
A	231	3.8	6	2bbl	Buick
2	231	3.8	6	2bbl	Buick
F	260	4.3	6	2bbl	Olds.
P	260	4.3	8	Diesel	Olds.
S	265	4.3	8	2bbl	Pont.
Y (79)	301	4.9	8	2bbl	Pont.
U	305	5.0	8	2bbl	Chev.
H	305	5.0	8	4bbl	Chev.
G	305	5.0	8	2bbl	Chev.
Y (80)	307	5.0	8	4bbl	Olds.
R	350	5.7	8	4bbl	Olds.
L	350	5.7	8	4bbl	Chev.
N	350	5.7	8	Diesel	Olds.
X	350	5.7	8	4bbl	Buick
8	350	5.7	8	4bbl	Chev.

MODEL YEAR CODE

Code	Year
8	1978
9	1979
A	1980

The thirteen digit Vehicle Identification Number can be used to determine engine application and model year. The 6th digit indicates the model year, and the 5th digit identifies the factory installed engine.

VEHICLE IDENTIFICATION NUMBER (VIN)

It is important for servicing and ordering parts to be certain of the vehicle and engine identification. The VIN (vehicle identification number) is a 13 or 17 digit number visible through the windshield on the driver's side of the dash and contains the vehicle and engine identification codes. It can be interpreted as follows:

ENGINE CODE

Code	Cu. Inc.	Liters	Cyl.	Carb.	Eng. Mfg.
A	231	3.8	6	2bbl	Buick
4	252	4.1	6	4bbl	Buick
F	260	4.3	8	2bbl	Olds.
V	263	4.3	6	Diesel	Olds.
Y	307	5.0	8	4bbl	Olds.
N	350	5.7	8	Diesel	Olds.

MODEL YEAR CODE

Code	Year
B	1981
C	1982
D	1983
E	1984
F	1985

The seventeen digit Vehicle Identification Number can be used to determine engine application and model year. The 10th digit indicates the model year and the 8th digit identifies the factory installed engine.

GENERAL ENGINE SPECIFICATIONS

Year	Eng. V.I.N. Code	Engine No. Cyl. Displacement (cu. in.)	Eng. Mfg.	Carburetor Type	Horsepower @ rpm ■	Torque @ rpm (ft lbs) ■	Bore X Stroke (in.)	Compression Ratio	Oil Pressure @ 2000 rpm
'78	A	6-231	Buick	2 bbl	105 @ 3400	185 @ 2000	3.800 × 3.400	8.0:1	37
	F	8-260	Olds.	2 bbl	110 @ 3400	205 @ 1800	3.500 × 3.385	7.5:1	40
	U	8-305	Chev.	2 bbl	145 @ 3800	245 @ 2400	3.736 × 3.480	8.5:1	40
	H	8-305	Chev.	4 bbl	160 @ 4000	265 @ 2200	3.736 × 3.480	8.5:1	40
	X	8-350	Buick	4 bbl	170 @ 3400	280 @ 1800	3.800 × 3.850	8.0:1	40
	L	8-350	Chev.	4 bbl	170 @ 3800	270 @ 2400	4.000 × 3.480	8.5:1	40
	R	8-350	Olds.	4 bbl	170 @ 3800	275 @ 2000	4.057 × 3.385	8.0:1	40
	N	8-350	Olds.	Diesel	120 @ 3600	220 @ 1800	4.057 × 3.385	22.0:1	40
	K	8-403	Olds.	4 bbl	185 @ 3600	320 @ 2200	4.351 × 3.385	8.0:1	40
'79	A	6-231	Buick	2 bbl	115 @ 3800	190 @ 2000	3.800 × 3.400	8.0:1	37
	2	6-231	Buick	2 bbl	115 @ 3800	190 @ 2000	3.800 × 3.400	8.0:1	37
	F	8-260	Olds.	2 bbl	105 @ 3600	205 @ 1800	3.500 × 3.385	7.5:1	40
	P	8-260	Olds.	Diesel	90 @ 3600	170 @ 2200	3.500 × 3.385	22.5:1	40
	Y	8-301	Pont.	2 bbl	135 @ 3800	240 @ 1600	4.000 × 3.000	8.2:1	35
	G	8-305	Chev.	2 bbl	130 @ 3200	245 @ 2400	3.736 × 3.480	8.5:1	40
	H	8-305	Chev.	4 bbl	160 @ 4000	235 @ 2400	3.736 × 3.480	8.5:1	40
	L	8-350	Chev.	4 bbl	160 @ 3800	260 @ 2400	4.000 × 3.480	8.5:1	40
	N	8-350	Olds.	Diesel	125 @ 3600	225 @ 1600	4.057 × 3.385	22.5:1	40
	R	8-350	Olds.	4 bbl	170 @ 3800	275 @ 2000	4.057 × 3.385	8.0:1	40
	X	8-350	Buick	4 bbl	155 @ 3400	280 @ 1800	3.800 × 3.850	8.0:1	37
	8	8-350	Chev.	4 bbl	185 @ 4000	280 @ 2400	4.000 × 3.480	8.5:1	40
	K	8-403	Olds.	4 bbl	175 @ 3600	310 @ 2000	4.351 × 3.385	7.8:1	40
'80	A	6-231	Buick	2 bbl	110 @ 3800	190 @ 1600	3.800 × 3.400	8.0:1	37
	F	8-260	Olds.	2 bbl	105 @ 3600	205 @ 1800	3.500 × 3.385	7.5:1	40
	P	8-260	Olds.	Diesel	90 @ 3600	170 @ 2200	3.500 × 3.385	22.5:1	40
	S	8-265	Pont.	2 bbl	100 @ 3400	207 @ 1800	3.74 × 3.00	8.2:1	40
	H	8-305	Chev.	4 bbl	160 @ 4000	235 @ 2400	3.736 × 3.480	8.6:1	45
	Y	8-307	Olds.	4 bbl	148 @ 3800	250 @ 2400	3.800 × 3.385	7.9:1	40
	R	8-350	Olds.	4 bbl	170 @ 3800	275 @ 2000	4.057 × 3.385	8.0:1	40
	N	8-350	Olds.	Diesel	125 @ 3600	225 @ 1600	4.057 × 3.385	22.5:1	40
'81	A	6-231	Buick	2 bbl	110 @ 3800	190 @ 1600	3.800 × 3.400	8.0:1	37
	4	6-252	Buick	4 bbl	125 @ 4000	205 @ 2000	3.965 × 3.400	8.0:1	37①
	F	8-260	Olds.	2 bbl	105 @ 3600	205 @ 1800	3.500 × 3.385	7.5:1	40②
	Y	8-307	Olds.	4 bbl	148 @ 3800	250 @ 2400	3.800 × 3.385	8.0:1	40②
	N	8-350	Olds.	Diesel	125 @ 3600	225 @ 1600	4.057 × 3.385	22.5:1	40②
'82	A	6-231	Buick	2 bbl	110 @ 3800	190 @ 1600	3.800 × 3.400	8.0:1	37
	4	6-252	Buick	4 bbl	125 @ 4000	205 @ 2000	3.965 × 3.400	8.0:1	37①
	F	8-260	Olds.	2 bbl	105 @ 3600	205 @ 1800	3.500 × 3.385	7.5:1	40②
	V	6-263	Olds.	Diesel	85 @ 3600	165 @ 1600	4.057 × 3.385	21.6:1	40

GENERAL ENGINE SPECIFICATIONS

Year	Eng. V.I.N. Code	Engine No. Cyl. Displace-ment (cu. in.)	Eng. Mfg.	Carburetor Type	Horsepower @ rpm ■	Torque @ rpm (ft lbs) ■	Bore X Stroke (in.)	Compression Ratio	Oil Pressure @ 2000 rpm
'82	Y	8-307	Olds.	4 bbl	148 @ 3800	250 @ 2400	3.800 × 3.385	8.0:1	40②
	N	8-350	Olds.	Diesel	125 @ 3600	225 @ 1600	4.057 × 3.385	22.5:1	40②
'83	A	6-231	Buick	2 bbl	110 @ 3800	190 @ 1600	3.800 × 3.400	8.0:1	37
	4	6-252	Buick	4 bbl	125 @ 4000	205 @ 2000	3.965 × 3.400	8.0:1	37①
	F	8-260	Olds.	2 bbl	105 @ 3600	205 @ 1800	3.500 × 3.385	7.5:1	40②
	V	6-263	Olds.	Diesel	85 @ 3600	165 @ 1600	4.057 × 3.385	21.6:1	40
	Y	8-307	Olds.	4 bbl	148 @ 3800	250 @ 2400	3.800 × 3.385	8.0:1	40②
	N	8-350	Olds.	Diesel	125 @ 3600	225 @ 1600	4.057 × 3.385	22.5:1	40②
'84–'85	A	6-231	Buick	2 bbl	110 @ 3800	190 @ 1600	3.800 × 3.400	8.0:1	37
	4	6-252	Buick	4 bbl	125 @ 4000	205 @ 2000	3.965 × 3.400	8.0:1	37①
	V	6-263	Olds.	Diesel	85 @ 3600	165 @ 1600	4.057 × 3.385	21.6:1	40
	Y	8-307	Olds.	4 bbl	148 @ 3800	250 @ 2400	3.800 × 3.385	8.0:1	40②
	N	8-350	Olds.	Diesel	125 @ 3600	225 @ 1600	4.057 × 3.385	22.5:1	40②

■ Horsepower and torque are SAE net figures. They are measured at the rear of the transmission with all accessories installed and operating. Since the figures vary when a given engine is installed in different models, some are representative rather than exact.
① @ 2400 rpm
② @ 1500 rpm

TUNE-UP SPECIFICATIONS
Oldsmobile 88, 98

(When analyzing compression test results, look for uniformity among cylinders rather than specific pressures.)

Year	Eng. V.I.N. Code	No. Cyl. Displacement (cu in.)	Eng. Mfg.	hp	Spark Plugs Orig. Type	Gap (in.)	Point Dwell (deg)	Point Gap (in.)	Ignition Timing (deg) ▲ Man Trans	Auto Trans	Valves Intake Opens ■ (deg)	Fuel Pump Pressure (psi)	Idle Speed (rpm) ▲ Man Trans ●	Auto Trans
'78	A	6-231	Buick	105	R-46TSX	.060	Electronic		—	15B	17	5.5-6.5	—	600
	F	8-260	Olds.	110	R-46SZ	.060	Electronic		—	20B @ 1100	14	5.5-6.5	—	500
	X	8-350	Buick	170	R-46TSX	.060	Electronic		—	15B	19	5.5-6.5	—	550
	R	8-350	Olds.	170	R-46SZ	.060	Electronic		—	20B @ 1100	16	5.5-6.5	—	650①
	K	8-403	Olds.	185	R-46SZ	.060	Electronic		—	18B② @ 1100	16	5.5-6.5	—	550③
'79	A	6-231	Buick	115	R-46TSX	.060	Electronic		—	12B	16	5.5-6.5	—	550
	F	8-260	Olds.	110	R-46SZ	.060	Electronic		—	18B @ 1100	14	5.5-6.5	—	550
	Y	8-301	Pont.	All	R-46TSX	.060	Electronic		—	12B	16	5.5-6.5	—	650(500)
	R	8-350	Olds.	170	R-46SZ	.060	Electronic		—	20B @ 1100	16	5.5-6.5	—	550
	K	8-403	Olds.	185	R-46SZ	.060	Electronic		—	24B(20B) @ 1100	16	5.5-6.5	—	550

TUNE-UP SPECIFICATIONS
Oldsmobile 88, 98

(When analyzing compression test results, look for uniformity among cylinders rather than specific pressures.)

Year	Eng. V.I.N. Code	No. Cyl. Displacement (cu in.)	Eng. Mfg.	hp	Orig. Type	Gap (in.)	Point Dwell (deg)	Point Gap (in.)	Ignition Timing (deg) ▲ Man Trans	Auto Trans	Valves Intake Opens ■ (deg)	Fuel Pump Pressure (psi)	Idle Speed (rpm) ▲ Man Trans ●	Auto Trans
'80	A	6-231	Buick	All	R-45TS④	.040⑤	Electronic		—	15B	16	3-4.5	—	670/550⑥
	Y	8-307	Olds.	All	R-46SX	.080	Electronic		—	20B	20	5.5-6.5	—	600/500
	R	8-350	Olds.	All	R-46SX	.080	Electronic		—	18B	16	5.5-6.5	—	600(650)/ 500(550)
'81	A	6-231	Buick	All	R45TSX	.080	Electronic		—	⑦	16	4.25-5.75	—	⑦
	4	6-252	Buick	All	R45TSX	.080	Electronic		—	⑦	16	4.25-5.75	—	⑦
	F	8-260	Olds.	All	R-46SX	.080	Electronic		—	18B	14	5.5-6.5	—	⑦
	Y	8-307	Olds.	All	R-46SX	.080	Electronic		—	15B	20	6-7.5	—	⑦
'82	A	6-231	Buick	All	R-45TS	.040	Electronic		—	⑦	16	4.25-5.75	—	⑦
	4	6-252	Buick	All	R-45TS8	.080	Electronic		—	⑦	16	4.25-5.75	—	⑦
	F	8-260	Olds.	All	R-465X	.080	Electronic		—	⑦	14	5.5-6.5	—	⑦
	Y	8-307	Olds.	All	R-465X	.080	Electronic		—	⑦	—	6-7.5	—	⑦
'83	A	6-231	Buick	All	R-45TS	.040	Electronic		—	⑦	16	4.25-5.75	—	⑦
	4	6-252	Buick	All	R-45TS8	.080	Electronic		—	⑦	16	4.25-5.75	—	⑦
	Y	8-307	Olds.	All	R-46SX	.080	Electronic		—	⑦	—	6-7.5	—	⑦
'84–'85	A	6-231	Buick	All	R45TS	.040	Electronic		—	⑦	16	4.25-5.75	—	⑦
	Y	8-307	Olds.	All	R46SX	.080	Electronic		—	⑦	—	6-7.5	—	⑦

NOTE: The underhood specifications sticker often reflects tuneup specification changes made in production. Sticker figures must be used if they disagree with those in this chart. Part numbers in this chart are not recommendations by Chilton for any product by brand name.

NOTE: Most 1979 and later carburetors have idle mixture screws concealed by staked-in plugs. These are not meant to be removed, except at carburetor overhaul.

① High Altitude: 700
② 88 sta. wgn.: 20B @ 1100
③ High Altitude: 600
④ With C-4 ignition—R45TSX
⑤ With C-4 ignition—.060
⑥ With C-4 ignition—620/550
⑦ See underhood sticker
▲ See text for procedure
■ All figures are in degrees Before Top Dead Center

● Figures in parentheses apply to California engines. Where two idle speed figures appear separated by a slash, the first is idle speed with solenoid energized, the second is idle speed with solenoid disconnected.
B Before Top Dead Center

DIESEL TUNE-UP SPECIFICATIONS

Year	Eng. V.I.N. Code	Engine No. Cyl. Displacement (Cu. in.)	Eng. Mfg.	Fuel Pump Pressure (psi)	Compression (lbs)	Intake Valve Opens (deg)	Idle Speed ● (rpm)
'78	N	8-350	Olds.	5.5-6.5	275 min.	16	650/575
'79	P	8-260	Olds.	5.5-6.5	275 min.	16	650/590
	N	8-350	Olds.	5.5-6.5	275 min.	16	650/675
'80	N	8-350	Olds.	5.5-6.5	275 min.	16	750/600
'81	N	8-350	Olds.	5.5-6.5	275 min.	16	①
'82	V	6-263	Olds.	5-6	②	②	①
	N	8-350	Olds.	5.5-6.5	275 min.	16	①

DIESEL TUNE-UP SPECIFICATIONS

Year	Eng. V.I.N. Code	Engine No. Cyl. Displacement (Cu. in.)	Eng. Mfg.	Fuel Pump Pressure (psi)	Compression (lbs)	Intake Valve Opens (deg)	Idle Speed ● (rpm)
'83	V	6-263	Olds.	5-6	②	②	①
	N	8-350	Olds.	5.5-6.5	275 min.	16	①
'84–'85	V	6-263	Olds.	5-6	②	—	①
	N	8-350	Olds.	5.5-6.5	275 min.	—	①

NOTE: The underhood specifications sticker often reflects tuneup specification changes made in production. Sticker figures must be used if they disagree with those in this chart.
① See underhood specifications sticker
② Not available
● Where two idle speed figures appear separated by a slash, the first is idle speed with solenoid energized, the second is idle speed with solenoid disconnected.

TUNE-UP SPECIFICATIONS
Cutlass, Omega

(When analyzing compression test results, look for uniformity among cylinders rather than specific pressures.)

Year	Eng. V.I.N. Code	Engine No. Cyl Displacement (cu in.)	Eng. Mfg.	hp	Spark Plugs Orig. Type	Spark Plugs Gap ● (in.)	Distributor Point Dwell (deg)	Distributor Point Gap (in.)	Ignition Timing (deg)▲●* Man Trans	Ignition Timing (deg)▲●* Auto Trans	Valves Intake Opens ■(deg)●	Fuel Pump Pressure (psi)	Idle Speed (rpm)▲ Man Trans ●	Idle Speed (rpm)▲ Auto Trans
'78	A	6-231	Buick	105	R-46TSX	.060	Electronic		15B	15B	17	5-6	①	600
	F	8-260	Olds.	110	R-46SZ	.060	Electronic		18B	20B⑤	14	5-6	800	500④
	U	8-305	Chev.	145	R-45TS	.045	Electronic		4B	②	28	7-9	600	500③
	H	8-305	Chev.	160	R-45TS	.045	Electronic		—	4B	28	7-9	—	500
	L	8-350	Chev.	170	R-45TS	.045	Electronic		—	8B	28	7-9	—	600(500)
'79	A	6-231	Olds.	115	R-46TSX	.060	Electronic		15B	15B	17	4-5	800/600	670/550(600)③
	F	8-260	Olds.	110	R-46SZ	.060	Electronic		18B	20B⑤	14	5.5-6.5	800/650	625/500⑩
	P	8-260	Olds.	Diesel	—	—			—	5B⑦	16	8-12⑥	660/575	650/590
	G	8-305	Chev.	145	R-45TS	.045	Electronic		4B	4B⑧	28	7.5-9	700/600	600(650)/500(600)
	H	8-305	Chev.	160	R-44TS	.045	Electronic		4B	4B⑨	28	7.5-9	700	600/500⑪
	8	8-350	Chev.	160	R-45TS	.045	Electronic		—	8B	2B	7.5-9	—	650(600)/600(500)
'80	A	6-231	Buick	110	R-45TS (R-45TSX)	.040 (.060)	Electronic		15B	15B	16	3-4.5	800/600	670/550 (620/550)
	F	8-260	Olds.	All	R-46SX	.080	Electronic		—	20B⑦	—	5.5-6.5	—	625/500
	H	8-305	Chev.	All	R-45TS	.045	Electronic		—	4B	28	7.5-9	—	600(650)/500(550)
	R	8-350	Olds.	All	R-46SX	.080	Electronic		—	18B	16	5.5-6.5	—	600(650)/500(550)
'81	A	6-231	Buick	All	R-45TSX	.080	Electronic		15B	15B	16	4.25-5.75	⑥	⑥
	F	8-260	Olds.	All	R-46SX	.080	Electronic		—	20B⑫	14	5.5-6.5	—	⑥
	Y	8-307	Olds.	All	R-46SX	.080	Electronic		—	15B	14	5.5-6.5	—	⑥
'82	A	6-231	Buick	All	R45TX	.040	Electronic		—	⑥	16	4.25-5.75	—	⑥
	F	8-260	Olds.	All	R46SX	.080	Electronic		—	⑥	—	5.5-6.5	—	⑥
	Y	8-307	Olds.	All	R46SX	.080	Electronic		—	⑥	—	6-7.5	—	⑥
'83	A	6-231	Buick	All	R45TX	.040	Electronic		—	⑥	16	4.25-5.75	—	⑥
	Y	8-307	Olds	All	R46SX	.080	Electronic		—	⑥	—	6-7.5	—	⑥

TUNE-UP SPECIFICATIONS
Cutlass, Omega

(When analyzing compression test results, look for uniformity among cylinders rather than specific pressures.)

Year	Eng. V.I.N. Code	No. Cyl. Displacement (cu in.)	Eng. Mfg.	hp	Spark Plugs Orig. Type	Spark Plugs Gap (in.)	Distributor Point Dwell (deg)	Distributor Point Gap (in.)	Ignition Timing (deg) ▲ Man Trans ■	Ignition Timing (deg) ▲ Auto Trans	Valves Intake Opens ■ (deg)	Fuel Pump Pressure (psi)	Idle Speed (rpm) ▲ Man Trans ●	Idle Speed (rpm) ▲ Auto Trans
'84–'85	A	6-231	Buick	All	R45TX	.040	Electronic		—	⑥	16	4.25–5.75	—	⑥
	Y	8-307	Olds.	All	R46SX	.080	Electronic			⑥		6–7.5	—	⑥

NOTE: The underhood specifications sticker often reflects tune-up specification changes made in production. Sticker figures must be used if they disagree with those in this chart. Part numbers in this chart are not recommendations by Chilton for any product by brand name.

▲ See text for procedure
■ All figures Before Top Dead Center
● Figure in parentheses indicates California engine. Where two idle speed figures appear separated by a slash, the second is with the idle speed solenoid disconnected.
* See sticker for timing rpm.
① MT: 49 states Cutlass except sta. wgn., 49 states Omega, 800 All others—600
② 49 states: 4B
   Calif.: 6B
   High Altitude: 8B
③ High Altitude: 600
④ High Altitude Cutlass, except Sta. Wgn.: 550
⑤ Calif. Cutlass, except Sta. Wgn.: 18B @ 1100
⑥ See underhood sticker
⑦ Cutlass wagon—18B @ 1100
⑧ Calif: 2B
⑨ High Altitude: 8B
⑩ High Altitude: 650/550
⑪ High Altitude: 650/600
⑫ Station wagon—18B @ 1100
B Before Top Dead Center
— Not applicable

FIRING ORDER

NOTE: To avoid confusion, always replace spark plug wires one at a time.

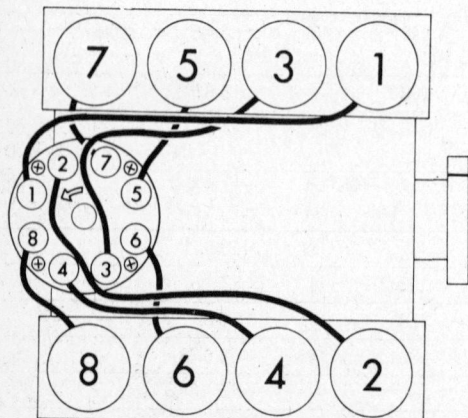

GM (Pontiac) 301 V8
Engine firing order: 1-8-4-3-6-5-7-2
Distributor rotation: counterclockwise

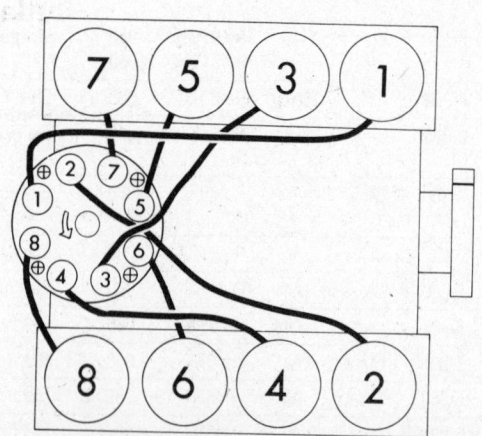

GM (Oldsmobile) 260 V8
Engine firing order: 1-8-4-3-6-5-7-2
Distributor rotation: counterclockwise

FIRING ORDERS

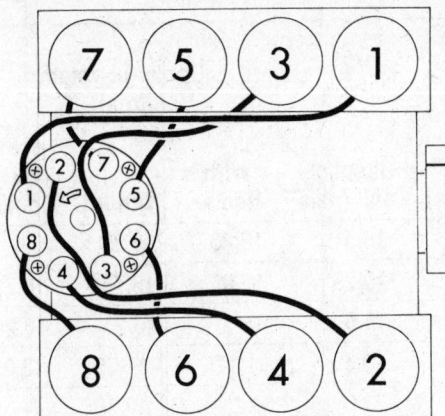

GM (Oldsmobile) 307, 350, 403
Engine firing order: 1-8-4-3-6-5-7-2
Distributor rotation: counterclockwise

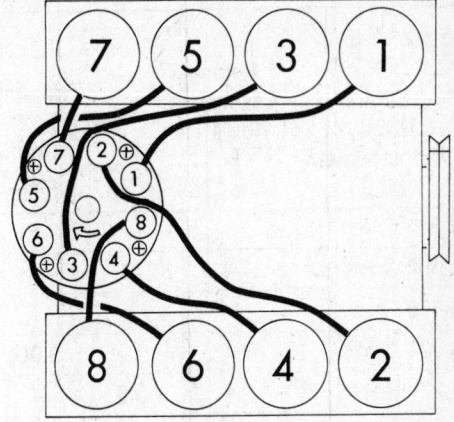

GM (Chevrolet) V8
Engine firing order: 1-8-4-3-6-5-7-2
Distributor rotation: clockwise

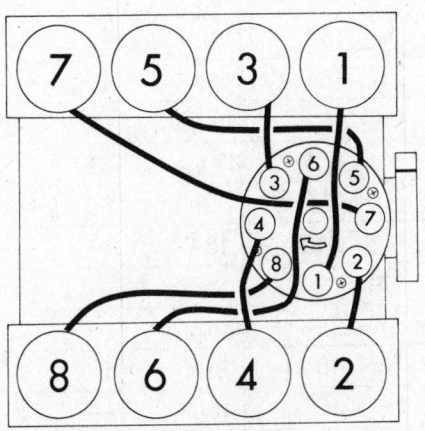

GM (Buick) Omega 350 V8
Engine firing order: 1-8-4-3-6-5-7-2
Distributor rotation: clockwise

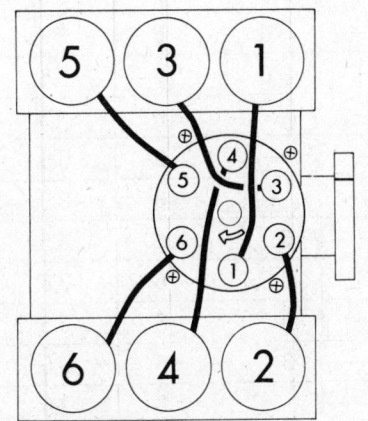

GM (Buick) 231, 252 V6
(3.2 L, 3.8 L, 4.1 L)
Engine firing order: 1-6-5-4-3-2
Distributor rotation: clockwise

V6 harmonic balancers have two timing marks: one is 1/8 in. wide, and one is 1/16 in. wide. Use the 1/16 in. mark for timing with a hand held light. The 1/8 in. mark is used only with a magnetic timing pick-up probe.

CAPACITIES
Cutlass, Omega

Year	Engine No. Cyl. Displacement (Cu. In.)	Engine Crankcase Add 1 Qt For New Filter	Transmission (Pts To Refill After Draining)			Drive Axle (pts)	Gasoline Tank (gals)	Cooling System (qts)		
			3 sp	4sp/5sp	Automatic•			With Heater	With A/C	Heavy Duty Cooling
'78	6-231 Buick④	4	3.5	3.5	6	③	20.75	12.75	12.75	12.75
	6-231 Buick⑤	4	3.5	3.5	6	3.5	18.0⑥	12.0	12.0	12.0
	6-231 Buick	4	—	3.5	6	3.5	18.5	11.75	12.25	—
	8-260 Olds.	4	—	3.5	6	3.5	18.0⑥	16.25	16.25	16.75
	8-305 Chev.④	4	—	3.5	6	③	20/75	15.75	16.0	16.75
	8-305 Chev.⑤	4	—	3.5	6	3.5	18.0⑥	15.5	15.5	16.25

CAPACITIES
Cutlass, Omega

Year	Engine No. Cyl. Displacement (Cu. In.)	Engine Crankcase Add 1 Qt For New Filter	Transmission (Pts To Refill After Draining)			Drive Axle (pts)	Gasoline Tank (gals)	Cooling System (qts)		
			3 sp	4sp/5sp	Automatic•			With Heater	With A/C	Heavy Duty Cooling
'78	8-305 Chev.	4	—	3.5	6	3.5	18.5	16.25	16.25	—
	8-350 Chev.④	4	—	—	6	③	20.75	16.0	16.75	16.75
	8-350 Chev.⑤	4	—	—	6	3.5	18.0⑥	15.5	16.25	16.25
'79	6-231 Buick	4	—	3.0①	6	3.5	18.5	11.75	11.75	12.25
	6-231 Buick	4	3.5	—	6	③	21.0	12.75	12.75	—
	6-231 Buick⑤	4	3.5	3.0	6	3.5	18.2	13.3	13.3	—
	8-260 Olds.⑤	4	—	3.5	6	3.5	18.2	16.25	16.25	16.75
	8-260 Diesel⑤	7②	—	3.5	6	3.5	19.75	19.75	19.75	19.5
	8-305 Chev.	4	—	3.0	6	3.5	18.5	16.2	16.2	—
	8-305 Chev.	4	—	3.0	6	③	21.0	15.8	16	16.75
	8-350 Chev.⑤	4	—	3.0	6	3.5	18.2	15.5	15.5	16.25
	8-350 Chev.④	4	—	—	6	③	21.0	16	16.75	—
	8-350 Olds.⑤	4	—	—	6	3.5	18.2	17.5	17.5	17.5
	8-350 Diesel	7②	—	—	6	3.5	18.2	17.5	17.5	17.5
'80	6-231 Buick	4	—	3	6	3.5	18.5	11.9	12.4	—
	6-231 Buick	4	3	3	6	3.5	18⑥	13	13	—
	8-260 Olds.	4	—	3	6	3.5	18⑥	16	16.5	—
	8-350 Chev.	4	—	3	6	3.5	18	15.25	15.25	16
	8-350 Olds.	4	—	—	6	3.5	18	15	15	—
	8-350 Diesel	7②	—	—	6	3.5	18	17.25	17.25	—
'81	6-231 Buick	4	3	—	6	3.5	18.1	N.A.	N.A.	N.A.
	8-260 Olds.	4	—	—	6	3.5	18.1	15.9	15.6	15.5
	8-307 Olds.	4	—	—	6	3.5	18.1⑥	14.9	15.6	15.5
	8-350 Diesel	7②	—	—	6	3.5	19.8⑥	17.4	17.3	17.3
'82	6-231 Buick	4	3	⑦	6	3.5	18.2	13.3	13.3	—
	6-263 Diesel	6②	—	⑦	6	⑦	19.8	⑦	⑦	—
	8-260 Olds.	4	—	—	6	3.5	18.2	20.0	20.0	—
	8-305 Olds.	4	—	—	6	3.5	18.2	15.5	15.5	—
	8-350 Diesel	7②	—	—	6	3.5	19.8	18	18	—
'83	6-231 Buick	4	—	—	6	3.5	18.2	13.3	13.3	—
	6-263 Diesel	6②	—	—	6	3.5	19.8	12.9	12.9	—
	8-307 Olds	4	—	—	6	3.5	18.2	15.5	15.5	—
	8-350 Diesel	7②	—	—	6	3.5	19.8	18	18	—

CAPACITIES
Cutlass, Omega

Year	Engine No. Cyl. Displacement (Cu. In.)	Engine Crankcase Add 1 Qt For New Filter	Transmission (Pts To Refill After Draining)			Drive Axle (pts)	Gasoline Tank (gals)	Cooling System (qts)		Heavy Duty Cooling
			3 sp	4sp/5sp	Automatic•			With Heater	With A/C	
'84–'85	6-231 Buick	4	—	—	6	3.5	19.8	13.3	13.3	
	6-263 Diesel	6②	—	—	6	3.5	19.8	12.9	12.9	
	8-307 Olds.	4	—	—	6	3.5	18.2	15.5	15.5	
	8-350 Diesel	7②	—	—	6	3.5	19.8	18	18	

• Check dip stick and gradually fill to correct level. See the General Maintenance section of Unit Repair.
① 3 pts. with 70mm 4-speed, 3½ with 5-speed
② Includes mandatory filter change
③ 7.5 inch ring gear: 3.5
8.5 inch ring gear: 4.25 (Omega only)
④ Omega
⑤ Cutlass
⑥ Stawgn.: 18.25
— Not applicable
⑦ Not available at time of publication

CAPACITIES
Oldsmobile 88, 98

Year	Engine No. Cyl. Displacement (Cu. In.)	Engine Crankcase Add 1 Qt For New Filter*	Transmission (Pts To Refill After Draining) Automatic•	Drive Axle (pts)	Gasoline Tank (gals)	Cooling System (qts)		Heavy Duty Cooling
						With Heater	With A/C	
'78	6-231 Buick	4	6	④	25.25	12.25	12.25	12.25
	8-260 Olds.	4	6	④	22.25③	16.25	16.25	16.75
	8-350 Buick	4	6	④	22.25③	14.5	14.5	15.5
	8-350 Olds.	4	6	④	⑤	14.5	14.5	15.5
	8-350 Diesel	7⑥	6	④	22.0	18.0	18.0	18.0
	8-403 Olds.	4	6	④	⑤	15.75	16.5	16.5
'79	6-231 Buick	4	6	4.25	25.0②	13.3	13.3	—
	8-260 Olds.	4	6	4.25	25.0②	16.25	16.25	17.25
	8-350 Olds.	4	6	4.25	25.0②	14.5	14.5	15.5
	8-350 Diesel	7⑥	6	4.25	27	18.0	18	—
	8-403 Olds.	4	6	4.25	25.0②	15.75	16.4	16.25
'80	6-231 Buick	4	6	④	20.75	13.0	13.0	—
	8-307 Olds.	4	6	④	25①	15.5	15.25	16.25
	8-350 Olds.	4	6	④	25	14.5	14.5	15.5
	8-350 Diesel	7⑥	6	④	27③	18.25	18.0	—

CAPACITIES
Oldsmobile 88, 98

Year	Engine No. Cyl. Displacement (Cu. In.)	Engine Crankcase Add 1 Qt For New Filter*	Transmission (Pts To Refill After Draining) Automatic●	Drive Axle (pts)	Gasoline Tank (gals)	Cooling System (qts)		Heavy Duty Cooling
						With Heater	With A/C	
'81	6-231 Buick	4	6	4	N.A.	N.A.	N.A.	N.A.
	6-252 Buick	4	6	4	N.A.	N.A.	N.A.	N.A.
	8-260 Pont.	4	6	4	25③	15.9	15.5	16.6
	8-307 Olds.	4	6	4	25③	14.9	15.6	15.6
	8-350 Diesel	7⑥	6	4	27③	18.0	18.0	18.0
'82	6-231 Buick	4	6	4	25③	13.7	13.7	⑦
	6-252 Buick	4	6	4	25③	13.7	13.7	⑦
	8-260 Olds.	4	6	4	25③	16	16.5	⑦
	8-263 Diesel.	6⑥	6	4	27	⑦	⑦	⑦
	8-307 Olds.	4	6	4	25③	17.5	17.5	⑦
	8-350 Diesel	7⑥	6	4	27③	18.0	18.0	18.0
'83	6-231 Buick	4	6	4	25③	13.7	13.7	⑦
	6-252 Buick	4	6	4	25③	13.7	13.7	⑦
	8-307 Olds.	4	6	4	25③	17.5	17.5	⑦
	8-350 Diesel	7⑥	6	4	27③	18	18	⑦
'84–'85	6-231 Buick	4	6	4	25③	13.7	13.7	⑦
	8-307 Olds.	4	6	4	25③	17.5	17.5	⑦
	8-350 Diesel	7⑥	6	4	27③	18	18	⑦

● Check dipstick and gradually fill to the correct level. See the General Maintenance section of the Unit Repair.
① Royale, Royal Brougham Coupe and Sedan: 20.75
② 20.75 for Calif. 350 or w/power seats
③ 22 gals on station wagon
④ 7.5 inch ring gear: 3.5
  8.5 and 8.75 inch ring gear: 4.25

⑤ 88 Sedan and Calif. Coupe: 21.0
  All others: 25.25
⑥ Includes mandatory filter change
⑦ Not available at time of publication
— Not applicable

VALVE SPECIFICATIONS

Year	Engine No. Cyl. Displacement (cu in.)	Seat Angle (deg)	Face Angle (deg)	Spring Test ■ Pressure (lbs @ in.)	Spring Installed Height (in.)	Stem to Guide Clearance (in.)		Stem Diameter (in.)	
						Intake	Exhaust	Intake	Exhaust
'78	6-231 Buick	45	45	168 @ 1.327	1⁴⁷⁄₆₄	.0015-.0032	.0015-.0032	.3405-.3412	.3405-.3412
	8-260 Olds.	①	④	187 @ 1.270	1⁴⁷⁄₆₄	.0010-.0027	.0015-.0032	.3425-.3432	.3420-.3427
	8-305 Chev.	46	45	200 @ 1.160②	③	.0010-.0037	.0010-.0037	.3414	.3414
	8-350 Buick	45	45	180 @ 1.340	1⁴⁷⁄₆₄	.0015-.0035	.0015-.0032	.3720-.3730	.3723-.3730
	8-350 Chev.	46	45	200 @ 1.160②	③	.0010-.0037	.0010-.0037	.3414	.3414

VALVE SPECIFICATIONS

Year	Engine No. Cyl. Displacement (cu in.)	Seat Angle (deg)	Face Angle (deg)	Spring Test ■ Pressure (lbs @ in.)	Spring Installed Height (in.)	Stem to Guide Clearance (in.) Intake	Exhaust	Stem Diameter (in.) Intake	Exhaust
'78	8-350 Olds.	①	④	187 @ 1.270	1 47/64	.0010-.0027	.0015-.0032	.3425-.3432	.3420-.3427
	8-350 Diesel	①	④	151 @ 1.300	1 47/64	.0010-.0027	.0015-.0032	.3425-.3432	.3420-.3427
	8-403 Olds.	①	④	187 @ 1.270	1 47/64	.0010-.0027	.0015-.0032	.3425-.3432	.3420-.3427
'79-'80	6-231 Buick	45	45	168 @ 1.340	1 47/64	.0015-.0035	.0015-.0032	.3402-.3412	.3405-.3412
	8-260 Olds.	①	④	187 @ 1.270	1 43/64	.0010-.0027	.0015-.0032	.3425-.3432	.3420-.3427
	8-260 Diesel	①	④	151 @ 1.300	1 43/64	.0010-.0027	.0015-.0032	.3425-.3432	.3420-.3427
	8-305 Chev.	46	45	200 @ 1.160	③	.0010-.0037	.0010-.0037	.3414	.3414
	8-307 Olds.	①	④	187 @ 1.270	1 43/64	.0010-.0027	.0015-.0032	.3429	.3424
	8-350 Chev.	46	45	200 @ 1.160	③	.0010-.0037	.0010-.0037	.3414	.3414
	8-350 Olds.	①	④	187 @ 1.270	1 43/64	.0010-.0027	.0015-.0032	.3425-.3432	.3420-.3427
	8-350 Diesel	①	④	151 @ 1.300	1 43/64	.0010-.0027	.0015-.0032	.3425-.3432	.3420-.3427
	8-403 Olds.	①	④	187 @ 1.270	1 43/64	.0010-.0027	.0015-.0032	.3425-.3432	.3420-.3427
'81	6-231 Buick	45	45	182 @ 1.340	1 47/64	.0015-.0035	.0015-.0032	.3407	.3409
	6-252 Buick	45	45	182 @ 1.340	1 47/64	.0015-.0035	.0015-.0032	.3407	.3409
	8-260 Olds.	①	④	187 @ 1.270	1 43/64	.0010-.0027	.0015-.0032	.3429	.3424
	8-307 Olds.	①	④	187 @ 1.270	1 43/64	.0010-.0027	.0015-.0032	.3429	.3424
	8-350 Diesel	①	④	210 @ 1.22	1 43/64	.0010-.0027	.0015-.0032	.3429	.3424
'82	6-231 Buick	45	45	182 @ 1.340	1 47/64	.0015-.0035	.0015-.0032	.3407	.3409
	6-252 Buick	45	45	182 @ 1.340	1 47/64	.0015-.0035	.0015-.0032	.3407	.3409
	6-263 Diesel	①	④	210 @ 1.220		.0010-.0027	.0015-.0032	.3429	.3429
	8-260 Olds.	①	④	187 @ 1.270	1 43/64	.0010-.0027	.0015-.0032	.3429	.3424
	8-307 Olds.	①	④	187 @ 1.270	1 43/64	.0010-.0027	.0010-.0032	.3429	.3429
	8-350 Diesel	①	④	210 @ 1.22	1 43/64	.0010-.0027	.0015-.0032	.3429	.3429
'83	6-231 Buick	45	45	182 @ 1.340	1 47/64	.0015-.0035	.0015-.0032	.3407	.3409
	6-252 Buick	45	45	182 @ 1.340	1 47/64	.0015-.0035	.0015-.0032	.3407	.3409
	6-263 Diesel	①	④	210 @ 1.220	—	.0010-.0027	.0015-.0032	.3429	.3429
	8-307 Olds	①	④	187 @ 1.270	1 43/64	.0010-.0027	.0010-.0032	.3429	.3429
	8-350 Diesel	①	④	210 @ 1.22	1 43/64	.0010-.0027	.0015-.0032	.3429	.3429
'84-'85	6-231 Buick	45	45	182 @ 1.340	1 47/64	.0015-.0035	.0015-.0032	.3407	.3409
	6-263 Diesel	①	④	210 @ 1.220	—	.0010-.0027	.0015-.0032	.3429	.3429
	8-307 Olds	①	④	187 @ 1.270	1 43/64	.0010-.0027	.0010-.0032	.3429	.3429
	8-350 Diesel	①	④	210 @ 1.22	1 43/64	.0010-.0027	.0015-.0032	.3429	.3429

① Intake 45°, exhaust 31°
② Intake 200 @ 1.25
③ Intake: 1 45/64 Exhaust: 1 39/64
④ Intake 44°, exhaust 30°
■ Valve open

TORQUE SPECIFICATIONS

(All readings in ft. lbs.)

Year	Engine	Cylinder Head Bolts	Rod Bearing Bolts	Main Bearing Bolts	Crankshaft Bolt	Flywheel to Crankshaft Bolts	Manifold Intake	Manifold Exhaust
'78-'81	6-231 Buick	80	40	100	225	60	45	25
	6-252 Buick	80	40	100	225	60	45	25
	8-260 Olds.	85③	42	①	200-310	②	40③	25
	8-301 Pont.	95	35	④	160	95	40	25
	8-305 Chev.	65	45	70	60	60	30	20
	8-307 Olds.	130③	42	①	200-310	60	40③	25
	8-350 Buick	80	40	100	225	60	45	25
	8-350 Chev.	65	45	70	60	60	30	③
	8-350 Olds.	130③	42	①	200-310	60	40③	25
	8-260, 350 Diesel	130③	42	120	200-310	60	40③	25
	8-403 Olds.	130③	42	①	200-310	60	40③	25
'82	6-231 Buick	80	40	100	225	60	45	25
	6-252 Buick	80	40	100	225	60	45	25
	6-263 Diesel	142	42	107	160-350	48	41	29
	8-260 Olds.	85③	42	①	200-310	②	40③	25
	8-307 Olds.	130③	42	①	200-310	60	40③	25
	8-350 Diesel	130③	42	120	200-310	60	40③	25
'83-'85	6-231 Buick	80	40	100	225	60	45	25
	6-252 Buick	80	40	100	225	60	45	25
	6-263 Diesel	142	42	107	160-350	57	41	29
	8-307 Olds.	130③	42	①	200-310	60	40③	25
	8-350 Diesel	130③	42	120	200-310	60	40③	25

① 80 on No. 1-4, 120 on No. 5
② A.T. 60 ft lbs.; M.T. 90 ft lbs.
③ Dip bolt in oil before tightening
④ 70 on No. 1-4, 100 on No. 5

CRANKSHAFT AND CONNECTING ROD SPECIFICATIONS

(All measurements are given in inches)

Year	Engine No. Cyl. Displacement (cu in.)	Crankshaft Main Brg. Journal Dia	Crankshaft Main Brg. Oil Clearance	Crankshaft Shaft End-Play	Crankshaft Thrust on No.	Connecting Rod Journal Diameter	Connecting Rod Oil Clearance	Connecting Rod Side Clearance
'78	6-231 Buick	2.4995	.0003-.0017	.004-.008	2	2.2487-2.2495	.0005-.0026	.006-.027
	8-260 Olds.	2.4985-2.4995①	.0005-.0021②	.0035-.0135	3	2.1238-2.1248	.0004-.0033	.006-.020
	8-305 Chev.	③	.0035 max ⑧	.002-.006	3	2.1990-2.2000	.003 max	.008-.014
	8-350 Buick	3.0000	.0004-.0015	.003-.009	3	1.9910-2.0000	.0005-.0026	.006-.027
	8-350 Chev.	③	.0035 max ⑧	.002-.006	3	2.1990-2.2000	.003 max	.008-.014
	8-350 Olds.	2.4985-2.4995①	.0005-.0021②	.0035-.0135	3	2.1238-2.1248	.0004-.0033	.006-.020
	8-260, 350 Diesel	2.9993-3.0003	.0005-.0021②	.0035-.0135	3	2.1238-2.1248	.0005-.0026	.006-.020
	8-403 Olds.	2.4985-2.4995①	.0005-.0021②	.0035-.0135	3	2.1238-2.1248	.0004-.0033	.006-.020

CRANKSHAFT AND CONNECTING ROD SPECIFICATIONS

(All measurements are given in inches)

Year	Engine No. Cyl. Displacement (cu in.)	Crankshaft				Connecting Rod		
		Main Brg. Journal Dia	Main Brg. Oil Clearance	Shaft End-Play	Thrust on No.	Journal Diameter	Oil Clearance	Side Clearance
'79-'80	6-231 Buick	2.4995	.0003-.0018	.004-.008	2	2.2487-2.2495	.0005-.0026	.006-.027
	8-260 Olds.	2.4985-2.4995①	.0005-.0021②	.0035-.0135	3	2.1238-2.1248	.0004-.0033	.006-.020
	8-301 Pont.	3.000	.0002-.0020	.003-.009	4	2.250⑥	.0005-.0025	.006-.022
	8-305 Chev.	③	④	.002-.006	3	2.0986-2.0998	.003 max	.006-.014
	8-307 Olds.	2.4985-2.4995①	.0005-.0021②	.0035-.0135	3	2.1238-2.1248	.0004-.0033	.006-.020
	8-350 Chev.	③	④	.002-.006	3	2.0986-2.0998	.003 max	.006-.014
	8-350 Olds.	2.4985-2.4995①	.0005-.0021②	.0035-.0135	3	2.1238-2.1248	.0004-.0033	.006-.020
	8-260, 350 Diesel	2.9993-3.0003	.0005-.0021②	.0035-.0135	3	2.1238-2.1248	.0005-.0026	.006-.020
	8-403 Olds.	2.4985-2.4995①	.0005-.0021②	.0035-.0135	3	2.1238-2.1248	.0004-.0033	.006-.020
'81	6-231 Buick	2.4995	.0003-.0018	.011-.003	2	2.2487-2.2495	.0005-.0026	.006-.023
	6-252 Buick	2.4955	.0003-.0018	.011-.003	2	2.2487-2.2495	.0005-.0026	.006-.023
	8-260 Olds.	2.5000	.0005-.0021②	.0035-.0135	3	2.1238-2.1248	.0004-.0033	.006-.020
	8-307 Olds.	2.4990-2.4995	.0005-.0021②	.0035-.0135	3	2.1238-2.1248	.0004-.0033	.006-.020
	8-350 Diesel	2.9993-3.0003	.0005-.0021②	.0035-.0135	3	2.24995-2.500	.0005-.0026	.006-.020
'82	6-231 Buick	2.4955	.0003-.0018	.011-.003	2	2.2487-2.2495	.0005-.0026	.006-.023
	6-252 Buick	2.4955	.0003-.0018	.011-.003	2	2.2487-2.2495	.0005-.0026	.006-.023
	6-263 Diesel	2.9993-3.0003	.0005-.0021②	.0035-.0135	3	2.2490-2.2510	.0005-.0026	.006-.020
	8-260 Olds.	2.4990-2.4995⑦	.0005-.0021②	.0035-.0135	3	2.1238-2.1248	.0004-.0033	.006-.020
	8-307 Olds	2.4990-2.4995⑦	.0005-.0021②	.0035-.0135	3	2.1238-2.1248	.0004-.0033	.006-.020
	8-350 Diesel	2.9993-3.0003	.0005-.0021②	.0035-.0135	3	2.2495-2.2500	.0005-.0026	.006-.020
'83	6-231 Buick	2.4995	.0003-.0018	.011-.003	2	2.2487-2.2495	.0005-.0026	.006-.015
	6-252 Buick	2.4995	.0003-.0018	.011-.003	2	2.2487-2.2495	.0005-.0026	.006-.015
	6-263 Diesel	2.9993-3.0003	.0005-.0021②	.0035-.0135	3	2.2490-2.2510	.0005-.0026	.006-.020
	8-307 Olds	2.4990-2.4995⑦	.0005-.0021②	.0035-.0135	3	2.1238-2.1248	.0004-.0033	.006-.020
	8-350 Diesel	2.9993-3.0003	.0005-.0021②	.0035-.0135	3	2.2495-2.2500	.0005-.0026	.006-.020
'84-'85	6-231 Buick	2.4995	.0003-.0018	.011-.003	2	2.2487-2.2495	.0005-.0026	.006-.015
	6-263 Diesel	2.9993-3.003	.0005-.0021②	.0035-.0135	3	2.2490-2.2510	.0005-.0026	.006-.020
	8-307 Olds.	2.4990-2.4995⑦	.0005-.0021②	.0035-.0135	3	2.1238-2.1248	.0004-.0033	.006-.020
	8-350 Diesel	2.9993-3.0003	.0005-.0021②	.0035-.0135	3	2.2495-2.2500	.0005-.0026	.006-.020

① #1: 2.4988-2.4998
② #5: .0015-.0031
③ #1: 2.4484-2.4493
    #2,3,4: 2.4481-2.4490
    #5: 2.4479-2.4488
④ Front—.001-.0015;
    Intermediate—.001-.0025;
    Rear—.0025-.0035
⑤ #1: .0020 max
⑥ Diameter may also be 2.240
⑦ #2,3,4,5—#1 2.4993-2.4998

RING SIDE CLEARANCE

(All measurements are given in inches)

Year	Engine	Top Compression	Bottom Compression	Year	Engine	Oil Control
'78-'85	8-260, 307, 403	.0020-.0040	.0020-.0040	'78-'85	6-231, 252, 8-350 Buick	.000-.0035
'78-'85	6-231, 252, 8-350 Buick	.0030-.0050	.0030-.0050	'78-'82	8-301 Pont.	.0015-.0035
'78-'80	8-305, 350 Chev.	.0012-.0032	.0012-.0032	'78-'82	8-260 Olds.	.005-.011
'79	8-301 Pont.	.0015-.0035	.0015-.0035	'78-'85	8-307, 350 Olds.	.001-.005
'79	8-260 Olds. Diesel	.004-.006	.0018-.0038	'78-'79	8-403 Olds.	.001-.005
'78-'85	8-350 Olds. Diesel	.005-.007	.0018-.0038	'83-'85	6-263 Diesel	.001-.005

RING GAP

(All measurements are given in inches)

Year	Engine	Top Compression	Bottom Compression	Year	Engine	Oil Control
'78	8-260, 350, 403	.010-.023	.010-.023	'78-'82	8-260, 307, 350, 403	.015-.055①
'79-'81	8-260 Olds.	.010-.020①	.010-.020①	'78-'80	6-231, 8-350 Buick	.015-.035
'79-'80	8-350 Olds.	.013-.023②	.013-.023②	'81-'85	6-231, 252 Buick	.015-.055
'79	8-403 Olds.	.010-.020①	.010-.020①	'79	8-301 Pont.	.000-.035
'78-'79	6-231, 8-350 Buick	.010-.020	.010-.020	'78-'80	8-305, 350 Chev.	.015-.065
'80-'85	6-231, 252 Buick	.013-.023	.013-.023	'78-'85	8-260, 350 Olds. Diesel	.015-.055
'79	8-301 Pont.	.010-.020	.010-.020	'82-'85	6-263 Diesel	.015-.055
'78-'80	8-305, 350 Chev.	.010-.030	.010-.035			
'79	8-260 Olds. Diesel	.012-.022	.010-.020			
'78-'85	8-350 Olds. Diesel	.015-.025	.015-.025			
'80-'85	8-307 Olds.	.009-.019	.009-.019			
'82-'85	6-263 Diesel	.015-.025	.015-.025			

① w/Sealed Power rings—.009-.019
② w/Sealed Power rings—.010-.020

PISTON CLEARANCE

Year	Engine	Piston-to-Bore Clearance (in.)	Year	Engine	Piston-to-Bore Clearance (in.)
'78-'80	6-231, 8-350 Buick	.0013-.0035①	'78-'85	8-260, 350 Olds. Diesel	.005-.006①
'78-'78	8-260 Olds	.0010-.0020	'81-'85	6-231, 252 Buick	.0016-.0038①
'80	8-307 Olds.	.0005-.0015	'79-'82	8-260 Olds.	.0008-.0018①
'79	8-403 Olds.	.0005-.0015	'81-'85	8-307 Olds.	.0008-.0018
'79	8-301 Pont.	.0025-.0033	'79-'80	8-350 Olds.	.0008-.0018
'78-'78	8-350, 403 Olds.	.0010-.0020	'82-'85	6-263 Diesel	.003-.004
'78-'80	8-305, 350 Chev.	.0027 max			

① At bottom of skirt

WHEEL ALIGNMENT

Year	Model	Caster Range (deg)	Caster Pref Setting (deg)	Camber Range (deg)	Camber Pref Setting (deg)	Toe-in (in.)	Steering Axis Inclin. (deg)	Wheel Pivot Ratio (deg) Inner Wheel	Wheel Pivot Ratio (deg) Outer Wheel
'78-'79	Omega Pwr. str.	½P to 1½P	1P	⅓P to 1⅓P	⅘P	1/16 to 3/16	—	—	—
	Man. str.	½N to 1½N	1N	⅓P to 1⅓P	⅘P	1/16 to 3/16	—	—	—
'78-'85	Cutlass Pwr. str.	2P to 4P	3P	5/16N to 1 5/16	½P	1/16 to ¼	—	—	—
	Man. str.	0P to 2P	1P	5/16N to 1 5/16	½P	1/16 to ¼	—	—	—
	88-98	2P to 4P	3P	0 to 1⅝P	¾P	0 to ¼	—	—	—

— Not specified
N Negative   P Positive

CHARGING SYSTEM

The Delco SI alternator with integral, non-adjustable regulator is standard on all models. The alternator has integral capacitors to supress radio interference.

In the diesel engine models, a single, standard Delcotron supplies two parallel-connected 12 volt batteries. The two batteries are needed to cope with the load imposed by the eight glow plugs and the larger starter. There are no special switches or relays in the charging system.

See Charging and Starting Systems in the Unit Repair Section for charging system test procedures.

Alternator

REMOVAL & INSTALLATION

NOTE: Before removing the alternator, disconnect the battery ground cable.

1. Disconnect the wiring from the alternator.
2. Remove the mounting bolt, adjusting bolt, and drive belt.
3. Lift out the alternator.
4. To install, reverse the removal procedure, connect the battery ground cable and tighten the alternator belt. Determine belt tension at a point halfway between the pulleys by pressing on the belt with moderate thumb pressure. If the distance between the pulleys (measured at the pulley center) is 13-16 in., the belt should deflect 1/2 in. at the halfway point or 1/4 in. if the distance is 7-10 in.

Regulator

REMOVAL & INSTALLATION

This is a completely sealed unit that cannot be adjusted or disassembled.

STARTING SYSTEM

See Charging and Starting Systems in the Unit Repair Section for starter motor service procedures.

The diesel engine starter is of conventional design, but somewhat larger and with a greater output to turn the engine at 100 rpm for starting. The diesel's high compression ratio makes this necessary.

Starter

REMOVAL & INSTALLATION

1. Disconnect battery and carefully raise the car.
2. Remove upper support attaching bolts and the brace and wire guide tube bolt, if so equipped.
3. Remove the flywheel housing cover.
4. Remove the two starter mounting bolts.
5. Lower starter, disconnect wiring, and remove starter.
6. Install by reversing the procedure. If shims were removed, they must be installed in their original location to assure proper drive pinion-to-flywheel engagement.

IGNITION SYSTEM

A high energy ignition (HEI) system is standard equipment. The HEI distributor replaces the points and condenser with a timing wheel, magnetic pick-up and control module. On V6 and V8 engines, the coil is built into the distributor cap. For further description, as well as service procedures for HEI, see the Electronic Ignition unit repair section.

Unlike the gasoline engine, which is a spark-ignition design, the diesel engine is a compression-ignition type. When air is compressed to an extreme, high temperatures are produced. At the moment of extreme compression a small quantity of fuel is sprayed, under high pressure, into the compression chambers. The temperature of compression ignites the tiny fuel droplets. A temperature of about 1750°F is need for the fuel ignition. Glow plugs are used to start combustion because the combustion chambers are cold prior to an initial start-up, and the first few revolutions of the engine could not produce sufficiently high combustion chamber temperatures for fuel ignition. The glow plugs warm the chambers for a few seconds, bringing them up to the required temperatures to aid in starting combustion. Then glow plugs are automatically shut off.

Distributor

REMOVAL

1. Remove distributor cap, primary (or feed) wire and vacuum line at the distributor.

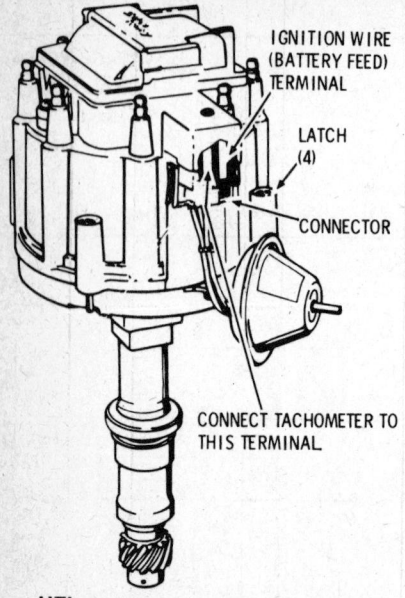

IGNITION WIRE (BATTERY FEED) TERMINAL

LATCH (4)

CONNECTOR

CONNECT TACHOMETER TO THIS TERMINAL

HEI system tachometer hook-up

2. Scribe a mark on the distributor body, locating the position of the rotor, and scribe another mark on the distributor body and engine block, showing the position of the body in the block.

3. Remove the hold-down screw and lift the distributor out of the block.

NOTE: Do not crank the engine with the distributor removed; this will change the timing.

INSTALLATION

If engine has *not* been disturbed (cranked) after removing the distributor, perform the following operations for installation:

1. Turn the rotor until it is about ⅛ turn past the locating mark previously made on the distributor housing.

2. Push the distributor down into the block. It may be necessary to turn the rotor slightly until the shaft engages in the block. The mark on the distributor housing must line up with the mark made on the engine block.

3. Tighten the hold-down bolt until it is snug, then connect the vacuum advance line.

4. Connect the primary wire to the coil or, on HEI, connect the feed wire and install the distributor cap.

5. Check the timing and adjust it as necessary. Tighten the holddown bolt.

If engine has been disturbed (cranked) after removing distributor, perform the following operations for installation:

1. Crank the engine until No. 1 piston is at the top of its compression stroke. The compression stroke can be determined by removing the spark plug from the No. 1 cylinder and placing your thumb over the hole while an assistant slowly cranks the engine. Crank until compression is felt at the hole, then continue cranking slowly until the timing mark on the crankshaft pulley lines up with the 0° timing mark.

2. Position the distributor in the block but do not allow it to engage with its drive gear. Observe the position of the vacuum control unit on the distributor. If the distributor is located correctly, the vacuum unit will be positioned normally so that the vacuum hose can be easily connected to it.

3. Position the distributor rotor so that it is between terminal No. 1 and the last spark plug tower of the firing order on the distributor cap.

4. Install the distributor, making sure the distributor shaft engages the oil pump shaft, thereby allowing the distributor to fully contact the engine block.

5. Install the hold-down clamp and tighten the bolt until it is snug.

6. Install the distributor cap.

7. Attach all wires and the vacuum advance hose.

8. Check the timing and adjust it as necessary.

IGNITION TIMING

NOTE: Always consult the underhood sticker on your car before adjusting timing. If the sticker differs from these procedures, follow the sticker.

1. Disconnect the vacuum advance hose from the distributor and plug it.

NOTE: On 1981 and later models the 4 terminal E.S.T. connector at the distributor must be disconnected before timing the engine.

2. Remove the air cleaner and tape over the vacuum hose fitting.

3. Connect the tachometer and adjust the engine speed to specifications.

4. Connect a timing light, loosen the distributor mounting bolt, and turn the distributor until the specified timing is obtained.

5. Tighten the mounting bolt and recheck timing to see if it changed during tightening.

6. Unplug the vacuum advance hose and connect it to the distributor.

7. Remove the tape from the vacuum hose fitting and install and connect the hose, if so equipped.

8. Install the air cleaner.

NOTE: All 1978 and later V6 engine harmonic balancers have two timing marks, one measuring ⅛ in. wide and one measuring the normal 1/16 in. wide. The smaller mark is used for setting the timing with a hand held timing light. The ⅛ in. wide mark is used in 1978 and later and is required when using magnetic timing equipment. All 1978 and later engines have a mounting bracket on the front cover which will accept a magnetic timing pickup probe.

TIMING LIGHT AND TACHOMETER HOOK-UP FOR HEI

1. Use an adapter between the No. 1 spark plug and No. 1 spark plug lead when connecting a timing light. Connect the timing light to the adapter; DO NOT pierce the spark plug lead. Because of the higher voltage used in the HEI system, any break in the insulation will cause electricity to jump to the nearest ground, making the No. 1 plug misfire.

2. The tachometer terminal is next to the ignition switch connector on the cap of four cylinder, V6 and V8 distributors.

3. Most new tachometers can be used. Tachometers without a relay can't be used. Check the tach's instructions if you aren't sure. If you don't have the instructions, hook up the tach and check the readings on both the high and low rpm scales. If they agree, the tach is OK; if they don't, use another tach.

4. There is no way of adjusting dwell, since this is controlled by the electronic module.

5. If you want to crank the engine without starting it, disconnect the ignition switch wire at the distributor cap.

For further information on High Energy Ignition (HEI) Systems, please refer to "Electronic Ignition Systems" in the Unit Repair section.

Tachometer Hook-Up—Diesel Engine

A magnetic pickup tachometer is necessary because of the lack of an ignition system. The tachometer probe is inserted into the hole in the timing indicator.

Diesel Engine Compression Test

WARNING: *Do not attempt this test without the proper compression gauge (Tool No. J-26999).*

1. Remove the air cleaner and install air crossover cover (Tool No. J-26996-1).

2. Disconnect the wire from the fuel shutoff solenoid terminal of the injection pump.

3. Disconnect the wires from the glow plugs and remove all glow plugs.

4. Screw compression gauge J-26999 into the glow plug hole of the cylinder being checked.

5. Crank the engine, allowing six "puffs" for each cylinder.

The lowest reading cylinder should not be less than 70% of the highest, and no cylinder should be less than 275 pounds.

FUEL SYSTEM

The fuel system is the heart of the diesel engine. The main components are the injection pump, injection lines and fuel injectors. The fuel injection pump is a small, high pressure rotary pump which delivers a small, metered amount of fuel to the injection nozzles at the proper time. The high pressure lines are all of equal length to avoid differences in timing. The nozzles project into the combustion chambers and spray/atomize the fuel entering the chambers. A small, low pressure transfer pump is employed in the inlet line to the injection pump to keep the injection pump supplied. Engine rpm is controlled by a rotary fuel metering valve operated by the accelerator linkage. A fuel filter is located between the transfer pump and the injection pump.

On all engines, the fuel pump is of the mechanical diaphragm type, mounted on the engine.

For further information on the Fuel Injection Systems, please refer to "Fuel Injection" in the Unit Repair Section.

Gasoline Engines Fuel Pump

REMOVAL & INSTALLATION

NOTE: On models equipped with an air pump, this pump must be removed to reach the fuel pump. On A/C equipped models the compressor (with lines attached) must be removed first and put aside.

1. Disconnect the fuel lines at the fuel pump.
2. Remove the two mounting bolts or nuts.
3. Remove the shields and oil filter on V6 engines.
4. Remove the pump and gasket. Installation is in the reverse order of removal.

FUEL FILTER REMOVAL & INSTALLATION

All carburetors have a fuel filter in the carburetor body. To replace the filter element, remove the fuel inlet line, then remove the inlet fitting and pull out the filter element. Be careful when tightening the brass fitting because the threads are easily stripped.

Carburetor

REMOVAL & INSTALLATION

1. Disconnect the negative battery cable.
2. Remove the air cleaner.
3. Disconnect the accelerator linkage.

260 V8 idle speed solenoid

4. Disconnect the transmission detent cable.
5. Disconnect the cruise control, if so equipped.
6. Disconnect the fuel line at the carburetor.
7. Disconnect all necessary vacuum lines. Number them for easy reinstallation.
8. Remove the attaching bolts, then the carburetor.
9. Installation is in the reverse order of removal.

IDLE SPEED AND MIXTURE ADJUSTMENTS

NOTE: When adjusting the idle speed and mixture, always check the underhood specifications sticker. If the sticker gives different instructions from the procedures given here, follow the underhood sticker's instructions.

1978 and Later Idle Speed Adjustment

NOTE: On vehicles equipped with Idle Speed Control (I.S.C.) no adjustments are possible.

2GC AND 2GE 2BBL CARBURETORS

1. Run the engine to normal operating temperature. Make sure that the choke is fully opened, turn the A/C Off and connect a tachometer and timing light to the engine according to the manufacturers' instructions.
2. Set the parking brake and block the drive wheels.
3. Disconnect hoses as instructed on underhood sticker.
4. Place the transmission in Park (AT) and Neutral (MT).
5. Disconnect and plug the vacuum advance hose at the distributor.
6. Check, and if necessary, adjust the timing.
7. Connect the vacuum advance hose.
8. Cars with manual transmission, without A/C: turn the idle speed screw to obtain the specified rpm. Cars with automatic transmission, without A/C: open the throttle momentarily to extend the solenoid plunger. Turn the solenoid screw to adjust the speed to the curb idle rpm listed on the underhood sticker. Turn the idle speed screw to the specified rpm. Cars with A/C: Turn the idle speed screw to obtain the specified rpm. Disconnect the A/C compressor clutch wire. Turn the A/C On. Open the throttle momentarily to extend the solenoid plunger. Turn the solenoid screw to obtain the rpm specified on the underhood sticker. Connect the compressor clutch wire.
9. Connect all hoses. Remove the tachometer and timing light.

M2MC-210 AND M2ME 2BBL CARBURETOR

NOTE: See "NOTE" at beginning of "Idle Speed and Mixture Adjustments."

1. Run the engine to normal operating temperature.
2. Disconnect the A/C compressor clutch wire, turn the A/C Off, make sure the choke is fully opened, place the manual transmission in Neutral, and the automatic transmission in Drive. Set the parking brake and block the drive wheels.
3. Disconnect and plug the vacuum advance hose at the distributor.
4. Check and adjust the timing.
5. Connect the vacuum advance hose.
6. Disconnect the purge hose at the vapor canister.
7. Cars without A/C: turn the idle speed screw to obtain the specified rpm. Cars with A/C: turn the idle speed screw to obtain the specified rpm, turn the A/C On, open throttle momentarily to extend the solenoid plunger and set the solenoid screw to obtain the rpm specified on the underhood sticker. Turn the A/C off.
8. Connect all hoses and remove the tachometer and timing light. Connect the compressor clutch wire.

M4MC 4BBL CARBURETOR

NOTE: See "NOTE" at beginning of "Idle Speed and Mixture Adjustments."

1. Run the engine to normal operating temperature.
2. Make sure the choke is fully opened, turn the A/C Off and connect a tachometer and timing light to the engine according to the manufacturers' instructions. Set the parking brake and block the drive wheels.
3. Disconnect the purge hose at the vapor canister.
4. Disconnect and plug the EGR vacuum hose at the EGR valve. On 350 engines, plug the purge hose at the canister.
5. Place the transmission in Park.
6. Disconnect and plug the vacuum advance line at the distributor.
7. Check and adjust the timing.
8. Connect the vacuum advance line.
9. Place the transmission in Drive.
10. On cars without A/C: adjust the idle speed screw to obtain the specified rpm. On cars with A/C: disconnect the compressor clutch wire. Open the throttle momentarily to extend the solenoid plunger. Turn the A/C ON and adjust the solenoid screw to obtain the rpm specified on the underhood sticker. Connect the compressor clutch wire and turn the A/C off.
11. Connect all hoses and remove the tachometer and timing light.

2SE, E2SE, E2ME 2-BBL, E4ME AND E4MC 4-BBL CARBURETORS

1. Run the engine until it reaches normal operating temperature.
2. Prepare the vehicle for adjustment as indicated on the emission label under the hood.
3. Check the ignition timing and adjust as necessary.
4. Reconnect the vacuum advance line.
5. With the A/C Off, turn the idle speed screw to obtain the curb idle as specified on the emission label.

6. With the automatic transmission in Drive or the manual transmission in Neutral, disconnect the A/C compressor wire at the compressor and turn the A/C On.

7. Open the throttle slightly to extend the solenoid plunger.

8. Turn the solenoid screw to obtain the correct rpm.

9. Turn the engine off and reconnect the A/C compressor line and all hoses.

1978-80 Idle Mixture Adjustment

Changes in the idle system have made adjustment of the fuel mixture impossible without the aid of a propane enrichment system not available to the general public. Backing out the mixture screws will have little or no effect on the mixture. 1979 and later models have their mixture screws concealed by staked-in plugs; mixture is set during manufacture and is not adjustable.

1981 and Later Idle Mixture Adjustment

On 1981 and later models equipped with Computer Control Command no mixture adjustments are possible. Adjustments are controlled by the ECM.

For further information on Carburetors, please refer to "Carburetors" in the Unit Repair Section.

Diesel Engine Fuel Supply Pump

REMOVAL & INSTALLATION

V8

The fuel supply pump on the V8 engine is serviced in the same manner as the fuel pump on the gasoline engine.

V6

NOTE: The fuel pump used on the V6 diesel engine is located at the front of the engine, next to the fuel heater.

1. Disconnect negative battery cable, remove the air cleaner, and unplug all electrical connectors from the pump.

2. Place a rag under the pump inlet and outlet fittings, and carefully unscrew the inlet and the outlet fittings. Cap all fittings to keep dirt out.

3. Remove the pump mounting bracket nut, then the fuel pump.

4. To install fuel pump, reverse above procedure, and tighten the nut of the pump mounting bracket to 18 ft. lbs. Then torque inlet and outlet line fittings to 19 ft. lbs.

NOTE: In some cases you may have to adjust pump position slightly to align pump fittings with the fuel lines.

5. After installing the fuel pump, position a catch basin and disconnect the fuel line at the filter and turn on the ignition switch to prime and bleed the lines. If after torquing the fuel line, the pump runs with

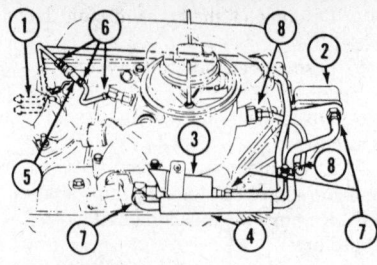

1. RETURN LINE
2. FUEL FILTER
3. FUEL PUMP
4. FUEL LINE HEATER (OPTIONAL)
5. HOUSING PRESSURE ALTITUDE ADVANCE
6. 10 FT. LBS.
7. 19 FT. LBS.
8. 11 FT. LBS.

V6 diesel fuel lines

a click-like sound, or the fuel bubbles, check for leaks in the fuel lines. When the pump quiets down, tighten the fuel line at the filter.

Fuel Filter

REMOVAL & INSTALLATION

The fuel filter is a square assembly located at the back of the engine above the intake manifold. Disconnect the fuel lines and remove the filter. Install the lines to the new filter. Start the engine and check for leaks.

Fuel Injection Pump and Lines

REMOVAL & INSTALLATION

NOTE: This procedure contains throttle rod and transmission cable adjustments.

1. Remove the air cleaner.
2. Remove the filters and pipes from the valve covers and air crossover.
3. Remove the air crossover and cap the intake manifold with screened covers (J-26996-1 on V8's or 29657 V6), or tape.
4. Disconnect the throttle rod and return spring.
5. Remove the bellcrank.

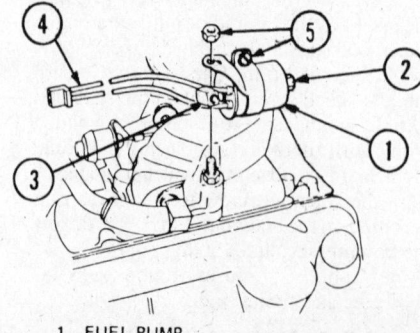

1. FUEL PUMP
2. INLET
3. OUTLET
4. LEAD
5. 18 FT. LBS.

V6 diesel fuel pump

6. Remove the throttle and transmission cables from the intake manifold brackets.

7. Disconnect the fuel lines from the filter and remove the filter.

8. Disconnect the fuel inlet line at the pump.

9. Remove the rear A/C compressor brace and remove the fuel line.

10. Disconnect the fuel return line from the injection pump.

11. Remove the clamps and pull the fuel return lines from each injection nozzle.

12. Using two wrenches, disconnect the high pressure lines at the nozzles.

13. Remove the three injection pump retaining nuts with tool J-26987 or its equivalent.

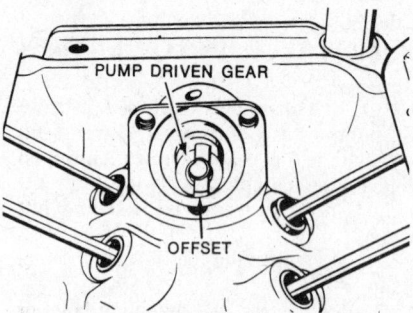

Offset on pump driven gear (© Oldsmobile Div., G.M. Corp.)

14. Remove the pump and cap all lines and nozzles.

To install:

15. Remove the protective caps from all lines and nozzles. Place the engine on TDC for the No. 1 cylinder. The mark on the harmonic balancer on the crankshaft will be aligned with the zero mark on the timing tab, and both valves for No. 1 cylinder will be closed. The index mark on the injection pump driven gear should be offset to the right when No. 1 is at TDC. Check that all of these conditions are met before continuing.

16. Line up the offset tang on the pump driveshaft with the pump driven gear and install the pump.

17. Install, but do not tighten the pump retaining nuts.

18. Connect the high pressure lines at the nozzles.

19. Using two wrenches, torque the high pressure line nuts to 25 ft. lbs.

20. Connect the fuel return lines to the nozzles and pump.

21. Align the timing mark on the injection pump with the line on the timing mark adapter and torque the mounting nuts to 35 ft. lbs. V6—18 ft. lbs. V8.

NOTE: A ¾ in. open end wrench on the boss at the front of the injection pump will aid in rotating the pump to align the marks.

22. Adjust the throttle rod:

a. remove the clip from the cruise control rod and remove the rod from the bellcrank.

b. loosen the locknut on the throttle rod a few turns, then shorten the rod several turns.

c. rotate the bellcrank to the full throttle stop, then lengthen the throttle rod until the injection pump lever contacts the injection pump full throttle stop, then release the bellcrank.

d. tighten the throttle rod locknut.

23. Install the fuel inlet line between the transfer pump and the filter.

24. Install the rear A/C compressor brace.

25. Install the bellcrank and clip.

26. Connect the throttle rod and return spring.

27. Adjust the transmission cable:

a. push the snap-lock to the disengaged position.

b. rotate the injection pump lever to the full throttle stop and hold it there.

c. push in the snap-lock until it is flush.

d. release the injection pump lever.

28. Start the engine and check for fuel leaks.

29. Remove the screened covers or tape and install the air crossover.

30. Install the tubes in the air flow control valve in the air crossover and install the ventilation filters in the valve covers.

31. Install the air cleaner.

32. Start the engine and allow it to run for two minutes. Stop the engine, let it stand for two minutes, then restart. This permits the air to bleed off within the pump.

Slow Idle Speed

ADJUSTMENT

1. Run the engine to normal operating temperature.

2. Insert the probe of a magnetic pickup tachometer into the timing indicator hole.

3. Set the parking brake and block the drive wheels.

4. Place the transmission in Drive and turn the A/C Off.

5. Turn the slow idle screw on the injection pump to obtain the idle specification on the emission control label.

Fast Idle Solenoid

ADJUSTMENT

1978-79

1. Set the parking brake and block the drive wheels.

2. Run the engine to normal operating temperature.

3. Place the transmission in Drive and disconnect the compressor clutch wire. Turn the A/C On. On cars without A/C, disconnect the solenoid wire, and connect jumper wires to the solenoid terminals. Ground one of the wires and connect the other to a 12 volt battery to activate the solenoid.

4. Adjust the fast idle solenoid plunger to obtain 650 rpm.

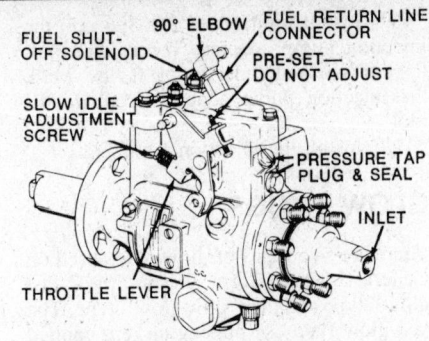

Injection pump slow idle screw (© Oldsmobile Div., G.M. Corp.)

1980 and Later

1. With the ignition off, disconnect the single green wire from the fast idle relay located on the front of the firewall.

2. Set the parking brake and block the drive wheels.

3. Start the engine and adjust the solenoid (energized) to the specifications on the underhood emission control label.

4. Turn off the engine and reconnect the green wire.

Cruise Control Servo Relay Rod

ADJUSTMENT

1. Turn the engine Off.

2. Adjust the rod to minimum slack then put the clip in the first free hole closest to the bellcrank, but within the servo ball.

Injection Timing

ADJUSTMENT

For the engine to be properly timed, the lines on the top of the injection pump adapter and the flange of the injection pump must be aligned.

1. The engine must be off for resetting the timing.

2. Loosen the three pump retaining nuts with J-26987 on V8's or J-25304 on V6's, an injection pump intake manifold wrench, or its equivalent.

3. Align the timing marks and torque the pump retaining nuts to 35 ft. lbs.

NOTE: The use of a ¾ in. open end wrench on the boss at the front of the pump will aid in rotating the pump to align the marks.

4. Adjust the throttle rod. (See "Fuel Injection Pump Removal and Installation," Step 22.)

Injection Nozzle

REMOVAL & INSTALLATION

1978-79

1. Remove the fuel return line from the nozzle.

2. Remove the nozzle hold-down clamp and spacer using tool J-26952.

3. Cap the high pressure line and nozzle tip.

NOTE: The nozzle tip is highly susceptible to damage and must be protected at all times.

4. If an old nozzle is to be reinstalled, a new compression seal and carbon stop seal must be installed after removal of the used seals.

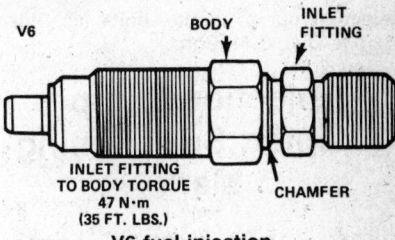

V6 fuel injection

5. Remove the caps and install the nozzle, spacer and clamp. Torque to 25 ft. lbs.

6. Replace return line, start the engine and check for leaks.

1980 and Later

The injection nozzles on these engines are simply unbolted from the cylinder head, after the fuel lines are removed, in similar fashion to a spark plug. Be careful not to damage the nozzle end and make sure you remove the copper nozzle gasket from the cylinder head if it does not come off with the nozzle.

Clean the carbon off the tip of the nozzle with a soft brass wire brush and install the nozzles, with gaskets.

NOTE: 1981 and later models use two types of injectors, CAV Lucas and Diesel Equipment. When installing the inlet fittings, torque the Diesel Equipment injector fitting to 45 ft. lbs. and the CAV Lucas to 25 ft. lbs.

INLET FITTING TO BODY TORQUE
DIESEL EQUIPMENT — 45 FT. LBS.
C.A.V. LUCAS — 25 FT. LBS.

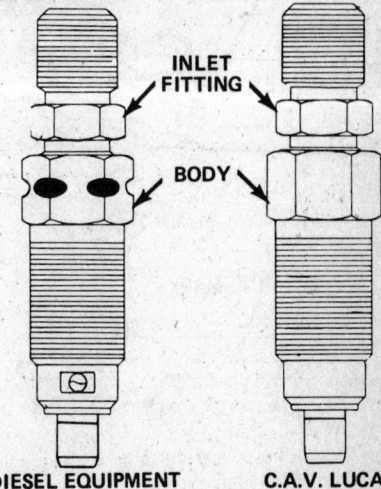

V8 diesel fuel injector identification—1980 and later (© Oldsmobile Div., G.M. Corp.)

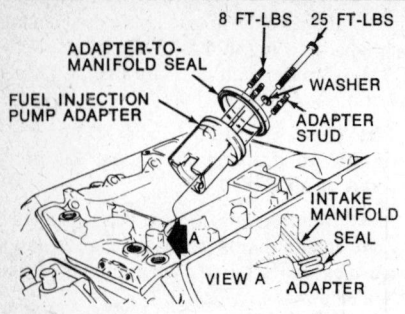

Injection pump adapter bolts (© Oldsmobile Div., G.M. Corp.)

Injection Pump Adapter, Seal, Timing Mark

REMOVAL & INSTALLATION

NOTE: Skip Steps 4 and 9 if a new adapter is not being installed.

1. Remove injection pump and lines as described earlier.
2. Remove the injection pump adapter.
3. Remove the seal from the adapter.
4. File the timing mark from the adapter. Do not file the mark off the pump.
5. Position the engine at TDC of No. 1 cylinder. Align the mark on the balancer with the zero mark on the indicator. The index is offset to the right when No. 1 is at TDC.
6. Apply chassis lube to the seal areas. Install, but do not tighten the injection pump.
7. Install the new seal on the adapter using tool J-28425, or its equivalent.
8. Torque the adapter bolts to 25 ft. lbs.

9. Install timing tool J-26896 into the injection pump adapter. Torque the tool, toward No. 1 cylinder, to 50 ft. lbs. Mark the injection pump adapter. Remove the tool.
10. Install the injection pump.

GLOW PLUGS

There are two types of glow plugs used on General Motors Corp. diesels; the "fast glow" type and the "slow glow" type. The fast glow type use pulsing current applied to 6 volt glow plugs while the slow glow type use continuous current applied to 12 volt glow plugs.

An easy way to tell the plugs apart is that the fast glow (6 volt) plugs have a 5/16 in. wide electrical connector plug while the slow glow (12 volt) connector plug is 1/4 in. wide. Do not attempt to interchange any parts of these two glow plug systems.

COOLING SYSTEM

The diesel engine cooling system is the same as that used on the gasoline engine except that the radiator tank has two oil coolers. One is connected to the transmission, the other to the oil filter base.

Radiator

REMOVAL & INSTALLATION

All Except 1978–79 Omega

1. Drain the cooling system.

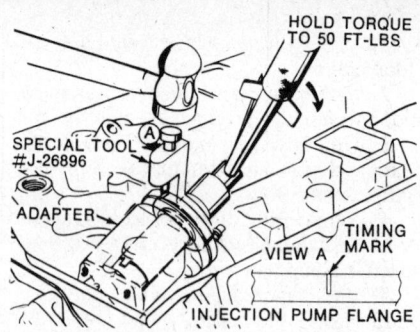

Marking Injection pump adapter (© Oldsmobile Div., G.M. Corp.)

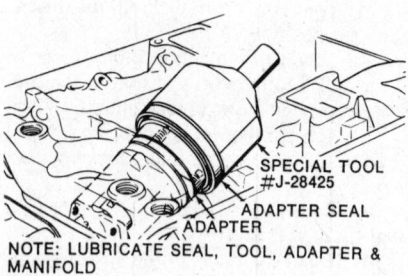

NOTE: LUBRICATE SEAL, TOOL, ADAPTER & MANIFOLD

Installing adapter seal (© Oldsmobile Div., G.M. Corp.)

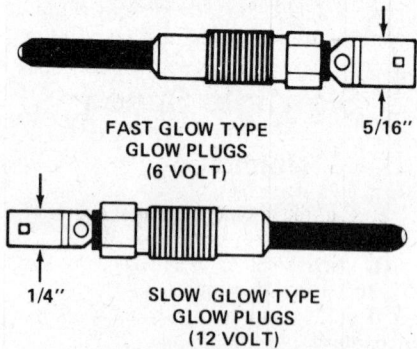

Glow plug identification (© Oldsmobile Div., GM Corp.)

2. Remove the upper radiator baffle and slide the shroud back over the fan.
3. Unfasten the upper and lower hoses from the radiator.
4. Disconnect the overflow hose or the optional coolant recovery system hose.
5. On models equipped with an automatic transmission, disconnect and cap the lines which run to the fluid cooler. On vehicles with diesel engines remove the engine oil cooler lines from the radiator.
6. Unfasten the radiator's securing bolts and move the radiator upward to disengage it from its supports. Remove the radiator from the car.

NOTE: It may be necessary to rotate the fan blades in order to keep them out of the way.

7. Installation is in the reverse order of removal. Refill the cooling system.

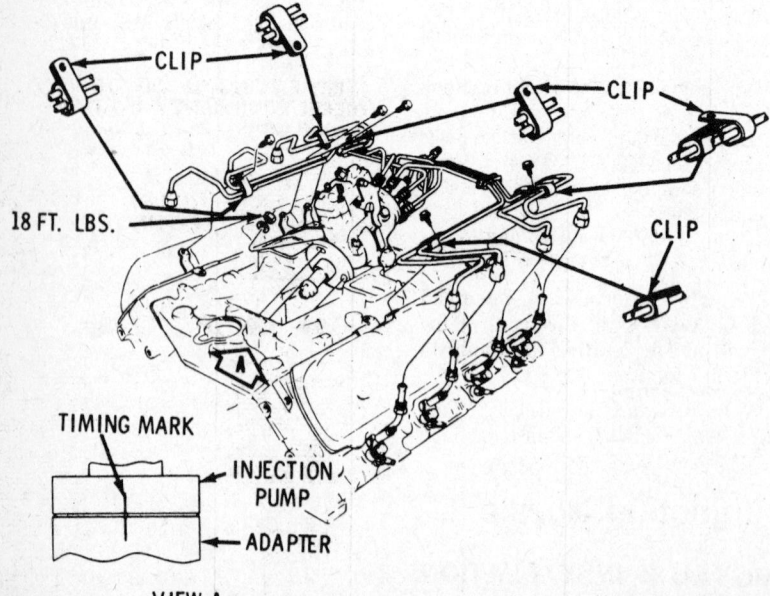

VIEW A

V8 diesel engine injection pump timing marks—V6 similar (© Oldsmobile Div., G.M. Corp.)

1978-79 Omega

1. Disconnect the battery and drain the radiator.

2. Remove the upper radiator baffle and slide the shroud back over the fan.

3. On models with an automatic transmission, disconnect and cap the fluid cooler lines.

4. Remove the upper and lower radiator hoses. Disconnect the coolant recovery system hose.

5. Unfasten its mounting bolts and lift the radiator out of the car.

6. Installation is in the reverse order of removal. Check the coolant and transmission fluid levels.

Water Pump

REMOVAL & INSTALLATION

1. Drain the cooling system.

2. Unfasten the heater, bypass, and lower radiator hoses from the pump.

3. Loosen the drive belts. Remove the fan assembly and the four spacer bolts. On cars with A/C, remove the fan and clutch assembly.

NOTE: Keep the fan in an upright position during removal to prevent the silicone fluid from leaking out of the fan clutch.

4. Remove the alternator, A/C compressor and power steering brackets, if necessary. Do not disconnect any air conditioning hoses.

5. Unfasten the bolts which secure the water pump and remove it.

Installation is as follows:

1. Apply a thin coating of sealer to the pump housing gasket mounting surface.

2. Place a *new* gasket on the housing.

3. Install the pump assembly. Apply a thin coat of sealer to the bolts and tighten them to 13 ft. lbs.

4. Torque the 5/16 in. bolts to 10 ft. lbs.

5. Reverse the removal procedure to install. Properly adjust all belt tensions and refill the cooling system.

Thermostat

REPLACEMENT

1. Drain the coolant level below the thermostat.

2. Remove the hoses from the thermostat housing.

3. Remove the bolts, water outlet, and gasket from the thermostat housing.

4. Install the new thermostat and gasket in the engine. The thermostat may be etched with the word front; if so, front must face the radiator.

5. Connect the hoses and refill the cooling system.

EMISSION CONTROLS

NOTE: For a description and service procedures for the following emission control systems, please refer to the "Emission Control" section of the Unit Repair section. Not all vehicles have all systems.

- Evaporative Control System
- Exhaust Gas Recirculation
- Thermostatic Air Cleaner
- Positive Crankcase Ventilation
- Air Injector Reactor
- Catalytic Converter
- Early Fuel Evaporation
- Electronic Fuel Control
- Electronic Spark Timing
- Electronic Control Module
- Oxygen Sensor
- Diesel EGR Valve

ENGINE

NOTE: The Chevrolet, 8-305, 350 Buick, 231, 252 and 8-350; have been used by Oldsmobile in various models. Service procedures for these engines will be found in car sections dealing with their manufacturer. Service procedures for the Chevrolet built engines can be found in the "Chevrolet Rear Wheel Drive" section, and procedures for the Buick built engines can be found in the "Buick Rear Wheel Drive" section. Only engines manufactured by Oldsmobile—8-260, 6-263 diesel, 307, 350 gas and diesel and the 403—will be covered in this engine section.

Oldsmobile V8 engines are all of the same block design. These are the 307 (introduced in 1980), 350 (discontinued in 1981), the 260 (introduced in 1975), and the 403 (discontinued in 1980). A diesel 350 V8, based on the Oldsmobile 350, was introduced in 1978. The diesel 260 V8, based on the gasoline 260 V8, was introduced in 1979. New for 1982 was the 6-263 diesel which used the same basic design as the 8-350 diesel.

NOTE: For engine identification, see the engine identification code chart at the beginning of this section.

Gasoline Engine

REMOVAL & INSTALLATION

1. Disconnect the negative battery cable. Remove the air cleaner assembly and heat pipe.

2. Scribe the outline of the hood hinges on the hood and remove the hood.

3. Drain the cooling system and disconnect the radiator and heater hoses from the engine.

4. Disconnect the engine ground strap from the cylinder head. Remove the fan shroud.

5. Disconnect and tag all vacuum lines and electrical leads from the engine.

6. Disconnect the throttle linkage. Disconnect the fuel line from the fuel pump. Remove the clutch equalizer on manual transmission cars.

7. If the car is equipped with an automatic transmission, disconnect the cooler lines from the radiator. If equipped with power steering or air conditioning, remove the pump and bracket or compressor and bracket from the engine without disconnecting the lines.

---- **CAUTION** ----
Disconnecting the air conditioner lines could result in personal injury.

8. Remove the radiator. Remove the fan, if necessary to gain working clearance. Raise the car and drain the engine oil.

9. Disconnect the exhaust pipes from the exhaust manifolds. Remove the motor mount throughbolts. Remove the starter.

10. On models equipped with an automatic transmission, remove the torque converter cover. Matchmark the flywheel and converter. Turn the crankshaft pulley to gain access to the three torque converter-to-flywheel attaching bolts and remove the bolts.

11. Remove the transmission or clutch housing-to-engine bolts, place a jack under the transmission, and raise the transmission slightly.

12. Attach a chain hoist to the engine and remove it from the car.

13. Reverse the procedure to install the engine.

Diesel Engine

REMOVAL & INSTALLATION

1. Drain the cooling system.

2. Remove the air cleaner.

3. Mark the hood-to-hinge position and remove the hood.

4. Disconnect the ground cables from the batteries.

5. Disconnect the ground wires at the fender panels and the ground strap at the cowl.

6. Disconnect the radiator hoses, cooler lines, heater hoses, vacuum hoses, power steering pump hoses, air conditioning compressor (hoses attached), fuel inlet hose and all attached wiring.

7. Remove the bellcrank clip.

8. Disconnect the throttle and transmission cables.

9. Remove the upper radiator support and the radiator.

10. Raise and support the car.

11. Disconnect the exhaust pipes at the manifold.

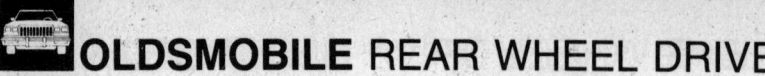

12. Remove the torque converter cover and the three bolts holding the converter to the flywheel.

13. Remove the engine mount bolts or nuts.

14. Remove the three right side transmission-to-engine bolts. Remove the starter.

15. Lower the car and attach a hoist to the engine.

16. Slightly raise the transmission with a jack.

17. Remove the three left side transmission-to-engine bolts and lift out the engine.

18. Installation is in the reverse order of removal. Converter cover bolts are torqued to 40 ft. lbs. on the 350 V8 and 35 ft. lbs. on the 263 V6.

Manifolds

See the NOTE at the beginning of the Engine section.

Intake Manifold

REMOVAL & INSTALLATION

Gasoline Engine

1. Remove the air cleaner, drain the radiator, and disconnect the negative battery terminal.

2. Disconnect the upper radiator hose, by-pass hose, and heater hose from the manifold.

3. Disconnect the throttle linkage, vacuum and gas lines from the carburetor.

4. Remove the alternator and air conditioning compressor brackets if necessary.

— CAUTION —
Do not disconnect the A/C lines. Personal injury could result.

5. Disconnect the temperature gauge wire.

6. Remove the intake manifold bolts and remove the manifold with the carburetor attached.

7. Install in the reverse order of removal, tightening all bolts first to 15 ft. lbs., then to the figure specified in the torque

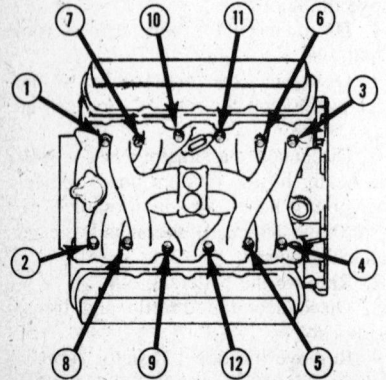

V8 intake manifold bolt tightening sequence—gasoline and diesel engines (© Oldsmobile Div., G.M. Corp.)

chart, in the sequence illustrated. Coat all gasket surfaces with sealer.

Diesel Engine

1. Remove the air cleaner.

2. Drain the radiator. Loosen the upper bypass hose clamp, remove the thermostat housing bolts, and remove the housing and the thermostat from the intake manifold.

3. Remove the breather pipes from the rocker covers and the air crossover. Remove the air crossover.

4. Disconnect the throttle rod and the return spring. If equipped with cruise control, remove the servo.

5. Remove the hairpin clip at the bellcrank and disconnect the cables. Remove the throttle cable from the bracket on the manifold; position the cable away from the engine. Disconnect and label any wiring as necessary.

6. Remove the alternator bracket if necessary. On the 350 cu. in. engine, if equipped with air conditioning, remove the

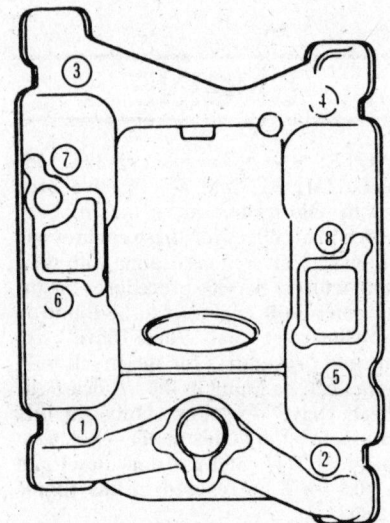

V6 diesel engine intake manifold torque sequence (© Oldsmobile Div., G.M. Corp.)

compressor mounting bolts and move the compressor aside, without disconnecting any of the hoses or wiring. Remove the compressor mounting bracket from the intake manifold.

7. Disconnect the fuel line from the pump and the fuel filter. Remove the fuel filter and bracket.

8. Remove the fuel injection pump and lines. See above for procedures.

9. Disconnect and remove the vacuum pump or oil pump drive assembly from the rear of the engine.

10. Remove the intake manifold drain tube.

11. Remove the intake manifold bolts and remove the manifold. Remove the adapter seal. Remove the injection pump adapter.

12. Clean the mating surfaces of the cylinder heads and the intake manifold using a putty knife.

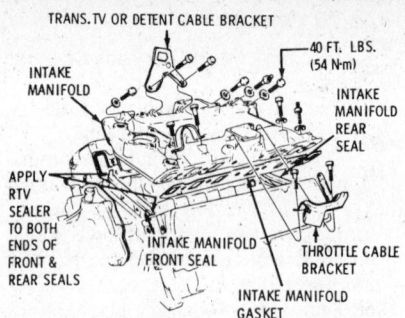

V8 diesel engine intake manifold and gasket

13. Coat both sides of the gasket surface that seal the intake manifold to the cylinder heads with G.M. sealer #1050026 or the equivalent. Position the intake manifold gaskets on the cylinder heads. To install the front and rear end seals, apply 1052915, 22521437, G.E. 1673 RTV sealer or equivalent to the end seals only. Then install the end seals, making sure that the ends are positioned under the cylinder heads.

14. Carefully lower the intake manifold into place on the engine.

15. Clean the intake manifold bolts thoroughly, then dip them in clean engine oil. Install the bolts and on the 350 V8 tighten to 15 ft. lbs. in the sequence shown. Next, tighten all the bolts to 30 ft. lbs., in sequence, and finally tighten to 40 ft. lbs. in sequence. On the 263 V6 eng. tighten to 15 ft. lbs. in the sequence shown, then retorque to 41 ft. lbs.

16. Install the intake manifold drain tube and clamp.

17. Install injection pump adapter. See under "Fuel System," above: "Diesel Engine, Injection Pump Adapter, Adapter Seal and New Adapter Timing Mark Removal and Installation." If a new adapter is not being used, skip Steps 4 and 9.

18. Install the fuel injection pump. See "Diesel Engine," under "Fuel System," above for procedures.

19. Install the vacuum pump or coil pump drive assembly.

— CAUTION —
Do not operate the engine without vacuum pump/oil pump assembly in place as this assembly drives the engine oil pump.

20. Install the remaining components in the reverse sequence of their removal. For throttle rod and transmission cable adjustments, see "Diesel Engine, Fuel Injection Pump" removal and installation, Steps 22 and 27, under "Fuel System," above.

Exhaust Manifold

REMOVAL & INSTALLATION

Right Side Except Diesel

1. Disconnect the negative battery cable.

2. Raise the car and remove the right front wheel, if necessary, the exhaust and crossover pipe, and the manifold bolts.

3. Remove the lower engine mounting bolt and raise the engine slightly, if necessary for clearance.

4. Remove the manifold from below.

Left Side—88 and 98, Omega Through 1979

1. Remove the air cleaner.
2. Remove the hot air shroud.
3. Remove the lower alternator bracket.
4. Raise the car and remove the crossover pipe.
5. Lower the car and remove the manifold.

Left Side—Cutlass 1978 and Later

1. Raise the car and disconnect the left side crossover pipe.
2. Lower the car and disconnect the intermediate steering column shaft.
3. Remove the hot air shroud.
4. Remove the exhaust manifold.

Diesel Engine—Left Side

1. Remove the air cleaner.
2. Remove the alternator lower bracket.
3. Raise and support the car.
4. Remove the crossover pipe.
5. Lower the car.
6. Remove the exhaust manifold.
7. Installation is in the reverse order of removal.

Diesel Engine—Right Side

1. Raise and support the car.
2. Remove the crossover pipe.
3. Disconnect the exhaust pipe.
4. Remove the right front wheel.
5. Remove the exhaust manifold from under the car.
6. Installation is in the reverse order of removal.

Valve System

Hydraulic lifters are used on all engines. Valve guides are not replaceable, but may be reamed oversize. Occasionally a valve guide bore will be oversize as manufactured. These are marked on the inboard side of the cylinder heads on the machined surface just above the intake manifold. Valve lifters and pushrods should be kept in order when removed, so they can be reinstalled in their original locations. Valve lifters used in diesel engines are not the same as those used in gasoline engines.

See the NOTE at the beginning of the Engine section.

Rocker Arm Replacement

Gasoline Engine

Remove the valve covers. Remove the two bolts that attach the rocker arm pivot to the cylinder head. Remove the rocker arms in pairs. Install the rocker arms for each cylinder only when the lifters are off the cam lobe and the valves are closed. Lubricate all pivot and rocker arm wear points with white grease. Torque the hardened flanged retaining bolts to 25 ft. lbs.

V8 Diesel Engine

NOTE: When the diesel engine rocker arms are removed or loosened, the lifters must be bled down to prevent oil pressure buildup inside each lifter, which could cause it to raise up higher than normal and bring the valves within striking distance of the pistons.

1. Remove the valve cover.
2. Remove the rocker arm pivot bolts, the bridged pivot and rocker arms.
3. Remove each rocker set as a unit.
4. To install, lubricate the pivot wear points and position each set of rocker arms in its proper location. Do not tighten the pivot bolts, to prevent bending the valves when the engine is turned.
5. The lifters can be bled down for six cylinders at once with the crankshaft in either of the following two positions:
    a. For cylinders number 3, 5, 7, 2, 4 and 8, turn the crankshaft so the saw slot on the harmonic balancer is at 0° on the timing indicator.
    b. For cylinders 1, 3, 7, 2, 4 and 6, turn the crankshaft so the saw slot on the harmonic balancer is at 4 O'clock.
6. Tighten the rocker arm pivot bolts to 28 ft. lbs. It will take 45 minutes to completely bleed down the lifters in this position. If additional lifters must be bled, rotate the engine to the other position, tighten the rocker arm pivot bolts, and again wait 45 minutes before rotating the crankshaft.
7. Assemble the remaining components in the reverse order of disassembly. The rocker covers do not use gaskets, but instead are sealed with a bead of RTV (room temperature vulcanizing) silicone sealer.

V6 Diesel Engine

NOTE: When the diesel engine rocker arms are removed or loosened, the lifters must be bled down to prevent oil pressure buildup inside each lifter, which could cause it to raise up higher than normal and bring the valves within striking distance of the pistons.

1. Remove the valve cover.
2. Remove the rocker arm pivot bolts, the bridged pivot and rocker arms.
3. Remove each rocker set as a unit.
4. Before installing any removed rocker arms, rotate the engine crankshaft so that No. 1 cylinder is 32° before top dead center. This is 2 in. counterclockwise from the 0° pointer. To verify that No. 1 cylinder TDC is coming up, if only the right valve cover was removed, remove the No. 1 cylinder glow plug, then turn the engine: compression pressure will force air out the glow plug hole. If the left valve cover was removed, rotate the crankshaft until the No. 5 cylinder intake valve pushrod ball is 0.28 in. above the No. 5 cylinder exhaust valve pushrod ball.

NOTE: Use only hand wrenches to torque the rocker arm pivot bolts to avoid engine damage.

5. If removed, install the No. 5 cylinder pivot and rocker arms, then torque the bolts alternately between the intake and exhaust valves until the intake valve begins to open, then stop.
6. Install the remaining rocker arms, except No. 3 exhaust (if this rocker was removed).
7. If removed, install the No. 3 cylinder exhaust valve pivot, but do not torque beyond the point that the valve would be fully open. This is indicated by strong resistance while still turning the pivot retaining bolts. Going beyond this point will bend the pushrod. Torque the bolts SLOWLY, allowing the lifter to bleed down.
8. Finish torquing No. 5 cylinder rocker arm pivot bolt slowly. Do not go beyond the point that the valve would be fully open, as in Step 7.
9. Do not turn the engine for at least 45 minutes.
10. Finish assembling the engine as the lifters are being bled.

VALVE ADJUSTMENT

These valves cannot be adjusted. If there is excessive clearance in the valve train, look for worn pushrods, rocker arms, valve springs, or collapsed or stuck valve lifters.

Cylinder Head

See the NOTE at the beginning of the Engine section.

REMOVAL & INSTALLATION

——— **CAUTION** ———
Do not disconnect the A/C lines. Severe personal injury could result.

Gasoline Engine

1. Drain the cooling system.
2. Remove the intake manifold and carburetor as an assembly.
3. Remove exhaust manifolds.
4. Loosen or remove any accessory brackets which interfere.
5. Remove the valve cover. Loosen any accessory brackets which are in the way.
6. Remove the battery ground strap from the cylinder head.
7. Remove rocker arm bolts, pivots, rocker arms and pushrods. Scribe the pivots and identify the rocker arms and pushrods so that they may be installed in their original locations.
8. Remove cylinder head bolts and cylinder head(s).

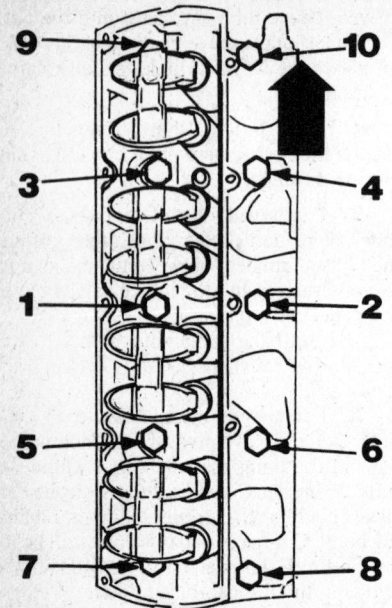

V8 head bolt torque sequence (© Oldsmobile Div., G.M. Corp.)

9. Install in the reverse order of removal. It is recommended that the head gasket be coated on both sides with sealer. Dip head bolts in oil before installing. Tighten all head bolts in the correct sequence to 60-70 ft. lbs., then again in sequence to the specified torque. See Specifications at the beginning of this section for correct head bolt torque. Re-torque the bolts after engine is warmed up.

NOTE: In 1981 and later models the head gaskets must be installed without sealer. The gaskets for the 260 cu. in. V8 are to be installed with the stripe facing up. The 307 cu. in. V8 gaskets do not have a stripe.

Diesel Engine

1. Remove the intake manifold, using the procedure outlined above.
2. Remove the rocker arm cover(s), after removing any accessory brackets which interfere with cover removal.
3. Disconnect and label the glow plug wiring.
4. If the right cylinder head is being removed, remove the ground strap from the head.
5. Remove the rocker arm bolts, the bridged pivots, the rocker arms, and the

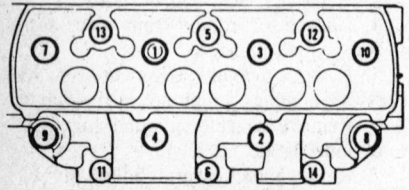

TORQUE ALL BOLTS (EXCEPT 5, 6, 11, 12, 13 & 14) TO 193 N·m (142 FT. LBS.). NUMBERS 5, 6, 11, 12, 13 & 14 TORQUE TO 80 N·m (59 FT. LBS.)

V6 diesel engine cylinder head torque sequence (© Oldsmobile Div., G.M. Corp.)

pushrods, keeping all the parts in order so that they can be returned to their original locations. It is a good practice to number or mark the parts to avoid interchanging them.

6. Remove the fuel return lines from the nozzles.
7. Remove the exhaust manifold(s), using the procedure outlined above.
8. Remove the engine block drain plug on the side of the engine from which the cylinder head is being removed. On V6s, remove the pipe-thread plugs covering the upper cylinder head bolts.
9. Remove the head bolts. Remove the cylinder head.
10. To install, first clean the mating surfaces thoroughly. Install new head gaskets on the engine block. Do NOT coat the gaskets with any sealer. The gaskets have a special coating that eliminates the need for sealer. The use of sealer will interfere with this coating and cause leaks. Install the cylinder head onto the block.
11. Clean the head bolts (and pipe-thread plugs-V6s) thoroughly. On the V8, dip the bolts in clean engine oil and install into the cylinder block until the heads of the bolts lightly contact the cylinder head. On V6s, coat the plug threads, bolt threads and the area under the bolt threads with sealer/lubricant part No. 1052080 or equivalent.

NOTE: The correct sealer must be used or coolant leaks and bolt torque loss will result.

12. On the V8, tighten the bolts, in the sequence illustrated, to 100 ft. lbs. When all bolts have been tightened to this figure, begin the tightening sequence again, and torque all bolts to 130 ft. lbs.
13. On V6s, tighten all head bolts in sequence to the following torques: all except bolts 5, 6, 11, 12, 13 and 14—100 ft. lbs.; bolts 5, 6, 11, 12, 13 and 14—41 ft. lbs. Finally, tighten all bolts except 5, 6, 11, 12, 13 and 14 to 142 ft. lbs., and bolts 5, 6, 11, 12, 13 and 14 to 59 ft. lbs. in the proper sequence. Install the pipe thread plugs.
14. Install the engine block drain plug(s), the exhaust manifold(s), the fuel return lines, the glow plug wiring, and the ground strap for the right cylinder head.
15. Install the valve train assembly. Refer to "Diesel Engine, Rocker Arm Replacement," above, for valve lifter bleeding procedures.
16. Install the intake manifold.
17. Install the rocker cover(s). The valve covers are sealed with RTV (room temperature vulcanizing(silicone sealer instead

Chamfer

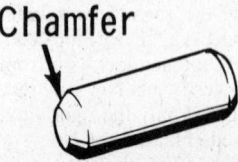

Chamfer the alignment pin (© Oldsmobile Div., GM Corp.)

of a gasket. Use G.M. #1052434 or its equivalent. Install the cover to the head within 10 minutes (while the sealer is still wet).

Timing Case and Camshaft

See the NOTE at the beginning of the Engine section.

REMOVAL & INSTALLATION

Gasoline Engine

1. Drain the coolant. Disconnect the radiator hose and the bypass hose. Remove the fan, belts and pulley.
2. Remove the vibration damper and crankshaft pulley.
3. Drain the oil and remove the oil pan.
4. Remove the front cover attaching bolts and remove the cover, timing indicator and water pump from the front of the engine.
5. On 1978 and later models, grind a chamfer on the end of each dowel pin as illustrated. When installing the dowel pins, they must be inserted chamfered end first. Trim about 1/8 in. from each end of the new front pan seal and trim any excess material from the front edge of the oil pan gasket. Be sure all mating surfaces are clean.
6. Install in the reverse order of removal using a new gasket with sealing compound. Tighten water pump attaching screws to 13 ft. lbs., 5/16 in. front cover attaching bolts to 25 ft. lbs. and the four bottom bolts (cover plate) to 35 ft. lbs. Torque the pulley hub bolt to 310 ft. lbs. Crankshaft pulley bolts should be torqued to 10 ft. lbs. Tighten the fan bolts to 20 ft. lbs.

Diesel Engine

1. Drain the cooling system and disconnect the radiator hoses.

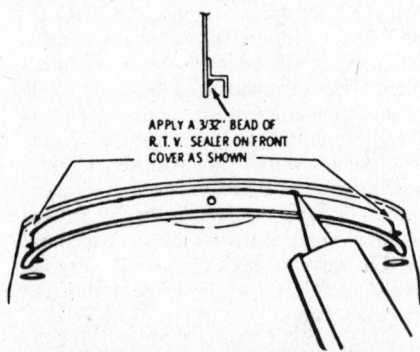

APPLY A 3/32" BEAD OF R.T.V. SEALER ON FRONT COVER AS SHOWN

V6 diesel engine front cover installation—apply R.T.V. sealer on the front cover oil pan seal retainer as shown (© Oldsmobile Div., G.M. Corp.)

2. Remove all belts, fan and pulley, crankshaft pulley and balancer, using a balancer puller.

3. Unbolt and remove the cover, timing indicator and water pump.

4. It may be necessary to grind a flat on the cover for gripping purposes.

5. Grind a chamfer on one end of each dowel pin.

6. Cut the excess material from the front end of the oil pan gasket on each side of the block.

7. Clean the block, oil pan and front cover mating surfaces with solvent.

8. Trim about ⅛ in. off each end of a new front pan seal.

9. Install a new front cover gasket on the block and a new seal in the front cover.

10. Apply sealer to the gasket around the coolant holes.

11. Apply sealer to the block at the junction of the pan and front cover. On V6, apply R.T.V. sealer on the front cover oil pan seal retainer.

12. Place the cover on the block and press down to compress the seal. Rotate the cover left and right and guide the pan seal into the cavity using a small screwdriver. Oil bolt threads and heads, install two to hold the cover in place, then install both dowel pins (chamfered end first). Install remaining front cover bolts.

13. Apply a lubricant, compatible with rubber, on the balancer seal surface.

14. Install the balancer and bolt. Torque the bolt to 200-300 ft. lbs. on V8, 160-350 ft. lbs. on V6.

15. Install all other parts in the reverse order of removal.

V8 Timing Chain

REPLACEMENT & VALVE TIMING

1. Remove the timing case cover turn crankshaft to line uptiming marks, and take off the camshaft sprocket.

NOTE: The fuel pump operating cam is bolted to the front of the camshaft sprocket and the sprocket is mounted on the camshaft by means of a dowel.

2. Remove the oil slinger, timing chain, and the camshaft sprocket. If the crankshaft sprocket is to be replaced, remove it also at this time. Remove the crankshaft key before using the puller. If the key can not be removed, align the puller so it does not

overlap the end of the key, as the keyway is only machined part of the way into the crankshaft gear.

3. Reinstall the crankshaft sprocket being careful to start it with the keyway in perfect alignment since it is rather difficult to correct for misalignment after the gear has been started on the shaft. Turn the timing mark on the crankshaft gear until it points directly toward the center of the camshaft. Mount the timing chain over the camshaft gear and start the camshaft gear onto its shaft with the timing marks as close as possible to each other and in line between the shaft centers. Rotate the camshaft to align the shaft with the new gear.

NOTE: To set crankshaft and camshaft gear marks for timing chain installation; position the engine with the No. 6 piston at top dead center. Slowly rotate the crankshaft one revolution until the camshaft gear mark is at 12 o'clock. No. 1 piston will now be at TDC on the compression stroke.

4. Install the fuel pump eccentric with the flat side toward the rear.

5. Drive the key in with a brass hammer until it bottoms.

6. Install the oil slinger.

NOTE: Whenever the timing chain and gears are replaced on the diesel engine it will be necessary to retime the engine. Refer to the paragraph on "Diesel Engine Injection Timing."

V6 Diesel Timing Chain and Sprocket

REPLACEMENT

1. Remove the front cover. See above for procedure. Remove the valve covers.

2. Loosen all rocker arm pivot bolts evenly so that lash exists between the rocker arms and valves. It is not necessary to completely remove the rocker arms unless related service is being performed.

3. Remove the crankshaft oil slinger and the camshaft sprocket bolt and washer.

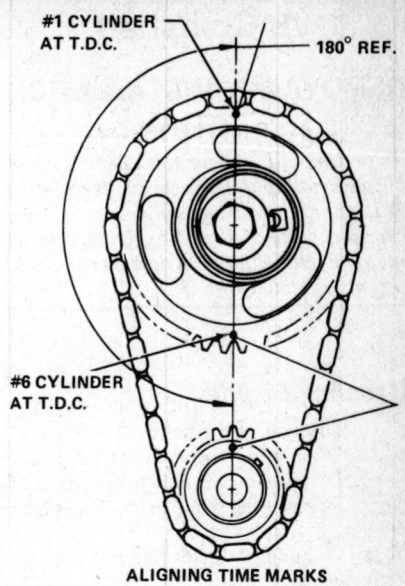

ALIGNING TIME MARKS

V8 engine timing mark alignment

4. Remove the timing chain, camshaft and crankshaft sprockets. If the crankshaft sprocket is a tight fit on the crankshaft use an appropriate puller to remove it.

5. If the camshaft sprocket-to-cam key comes out with the camshaft sprocket, remove the front camshaft bearing retainer and install the key into the injection pump drive gear. Install the bearing retainer.

6. Install the key in the crankshaft, if removed.

7. Install the camshaft sprocket, crankshaft sprocket and the timing chain together, align the timing marks on the camshaft and the crankshaft. Tighten the camshaft sprocket bolt to 70 ft. lbs.

8. Install the oil slinger and the remaining parts of the front cover assembly.

9. After installing the front cover, bleed down the valve lifters as instructed in "Diesel Engine, Rocker Arm Replacement", above.

10. Remaining installation is in the reverse order of removal. Sealant is used in place of valve cover gaskets.

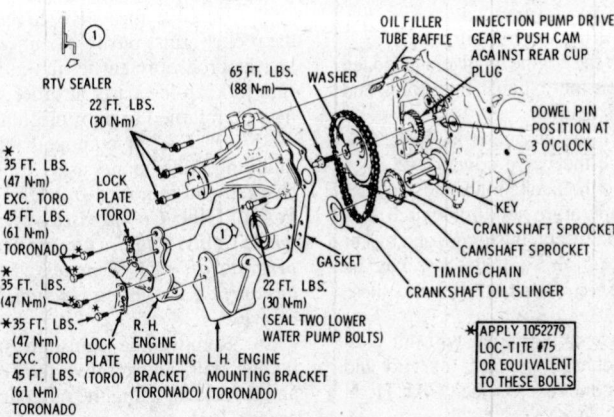

V8 diesel engine front cover and timing chain assembly (© Oldsmobile Div., G.M. Corp.)

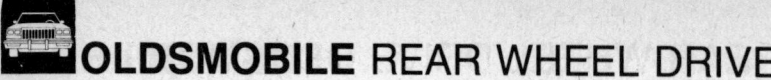
V8 Camshaft

REMOVAL & INSTALLATION

—————— CAUTION ——————

All Oldsmobile V8s require discharging of the air conditioning for camshaft removal. This should not be attempted by anyone who lacks the skill and experience to do so, as contact with the refrigerant can cause serious personal injury.

Gasoline Engine

1. Disconnect the battery.
2. Drain and remove the radiator.
3. Disconnect the fuel line at the fuel pump. Remove the pump on 1978 and later models.
4. Disconnect the throttle cable and the air cleaner.
5. Remove the alternator belt, loosen the alternator bolts, and move the alternator to one side.
6. Remove the power steering pump from its brackets and move it out of the way.
7. Remove the air conditioning compressor from its brackets and move the compressor out of the way without disconnecting the lines.
8. Disconnect the hoses from the water pump.
9. Disconnect the electrical and vacuum connections.
10. Mark the distributor as to location in the block. Remove the distributor. Remove the crankshaft pulley and the hub attaching bolt. Remove the crankshaft hub. Proceed to Step 19.
11. Raise the car and drain the oil pan.
12. Remove the exhaust crossover pipe and starter motor.
13. Disconnect the exhaust pipe at the manifold.
14. Remove the harmonic balancer and pulley.
15. Support the engine and remove the front motor mounts.
16. Remove the flywheel inspection cover.
17. Remove the engine oil pan.
18. Support the engine by placing wooden blocks between the exhaust manifolds and the front crossmember.
19. Remove the engine front cover.
20. Remove the valve covers.
21. Remove the intake manifold, oil filler pipe, and temperature sending switch.
22. Mark the lifters, pushrods, and rocker arms as to location so that they may be installed in the same position. Remove these parts.
23. If the car is equipped with air conditioning, discharge the A/C system and remove the condenser. See CAUTION above.
24. Remove the fuel pump eccentric, camshaft gear, oil slinger, and timing chain.

25. Carefully remove the camshaft from the engine.
26. Inspect the shaft for signs of excessive wear or damage.
27. Liberally coat camshaft and bearings with heavy engine oil or engine assembly lubricant and insert the cam into the engine.
28. Align the timing marks on the camshaft and crankshaft gears. See Timing Chain Replacement and Valve Timing for details.
29. Install the distributor using the locating marks made during removal. If any problems are encountered, see "Distributor Installation."
30. To install, reverse the removal procedure but pay attention to the following points:

   a. Install the timing indicator before installing the power steering pump bracket.

   b. Install the flywheel inspection cover after installing the starter.

   c. Replace the engine oil and radiator coolant.

Diesel Engine

NOTE: If the camshaft is to be removed the air conditioning system must be discharged by a professional and the condenser removed.

Removal of the camshaft also requires removal of the injection pump drive and driven gears, removal of the intake manifold, disassembly of the valve lifters, and re-timing of the injection pump.

1. Disconnect the negative battery cables. Drain the coolant. Remove the radiator.
2. Remove the intake manifold and gasket and the front and rear intake manifold seals. Refer to the intake manifold removal and installation procedure. Remove the oil pump drive assembly on the V6.
3. Remove the balancer pulley and the balancer. See "Caution" under V8 diesel engine front cover removal and installation, above, for V8 engine. Remove the engine front cover using the appropriate procedure. Rotate the engine so that the timing marks align on V6s.
4. Remove the valve covers. Remove the rocker arms, pushrods and valve lifters; see the procedure earlier in this section. Be sure to keep the parts in order so that they may be returned to their original locations.
5. On V8s, if equipped with air conditioning, the condenser must be discharged and removed from the car.

WARNING: *Compressed refrigerant expands (boils) into the atmosphere at a temperature of −21° F or less. It will freeze any surface it contacts, including your skin or eyes.*

6. Remove the camshaft sprocket retaining bolt, and remove the timing chain and sprockets, using the procedure outlined earlier.
7. On V6s, remove the front camshaft bearing retainer bolt and the retainer, then

remove the camshaft sprocket key and the injection pump drive gear.

8. Position the camshaft dowel pin at the 3 o'clock position on the V8.
9. On V8s, push the camshaft rearward and hold it there, being careful not to dislodge the oil plug at the rear of the engine. Remove the fuel injection pump drive gear by sliding it from the camshaft while rocking the pump driven gear.
10. To remove the fuel injection pump driven gear, remove the injection pump intermediate pump adapter (V6s) and the pump adapter (All), remove the snap ring, and remove the selective washer. Remove the driven gear and spring.
11. Remove the camshaft by sliding it out the front of the engine. Be extremely careful not to allow the cam lobes to contact any of the bearings, or the journals to dislodge the bearings during camshaft removal. Do not force the camshaft, or bearing damage will result.
12. If either the injection pump drive or driven gears are to be replaced, replace both gears. Make certain the marks (o) are in alignment on both gears before inserting the cam gear key on the V6.
13. Coat the camshaft and the cam bearings with GM lubricant #1052365 or the equivalent.
14. Carefully slide the camshaft into position in the engine.
15. Fit the crankshaft and camshaft sprockets, aligning the timing marks as shown in the timing chain removal and installation procedure, above. Remove the sprockets without disturbing the timing.
16. Install the injection pump driven gear, spring, shim, and snap ring. Check the gear end play. If the end play is not within 0.002–0.006 in. on V8s through 1979 and V6s, and .002–.015 in. on 1980 and later V8s, replace the shim to obtain the specified clearance. Shims are available in 0.003 in. increments, from 0.080–0.115 in.
17. On V8s, bring the camshaft dowel pin to the 3 o'clock position. Align the zero marks on the pump drive gear and pump driven gear. Hold the camshaft in the rearward position and slide the pump drive gear onto the camshaft. On the V6, align the zero marks on the injection pump drive and driven gears, then install the camshaft sprocket key. Install the camshaft bearing retainer.
18. Install the timing chain and sprockets, making sure the timing marks are aligned.
19. Install the lifters, pushrods and rocker arms. See "Rocker Arm Replacement, Diesel Engine" for lifter bleed down procedures. Failure to bleed down the lifters could bend valves when the engine is turned over.
20. Install the injection pump adapter and injection pump. See the appropriate sections under "Fuel System" above for procedures.
21. Install the remaining components in the reverse order of removal.

Pistons and Connecting Rods Positioning

For the correct positioning of pistons and connecting rods, refer to illustrations.

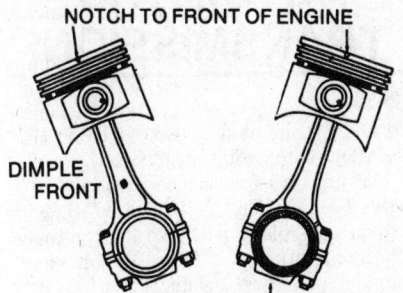

NOTCH TO FRONT OF ENGINE

DIMPLE FRONT

LARGE CHAMFER TOWARD FRONT OF ENGINE

V8 engine piston and rod assembly—260, 307, 350 and 403 engines

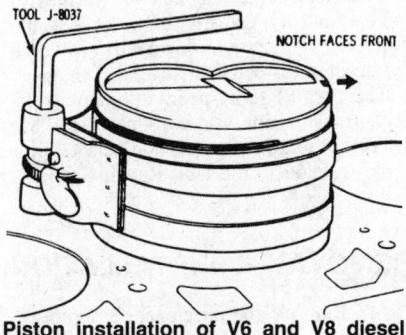

TOOL J-8037

NOTCH FACES FRONT

Piston installation of V6 and V8 diesel engines

Oil Pan

REMOVAL & INSTALLATION

Gasoline Engines

1. Remove the distributor cap and align the rotor to No. 1 firing position. On 1978 and later Cutlass, align the timing marks so No. 1 is at top dead center.
2. Disconnect the battery ground cable and remove the dipstick.
3. Remove the upper radiator support and the fan shroud attaching screws.
4. Raise the car and drain the oil.
5. Remove the flywheel cover.
6. Remove the starter motor assembly.
7. Disconnect the exhaust pipes and the crossover pipe.
8. Disconnect the engine mounts and raise the front of the engine as far as possible.
9. Remove the oil pan attaching bolts and remove the pan.
10. Coat both sides of the new gasket with sealer when installing. Installation is in the reverse order of removal. Torque the attaching bolts to 10 ft. lbs.

Diesel Engines

1. On V8s, remove the vacuum pump

and drive (with A/C) or the oil pump drive (without A/C). On V6s, remove the oil pump drive and vacuum pump.
2. Disconnect the batteries and remove the dipstick.
3. Remove the upper radiator support and fan shroud.
4. Raise and support the car. Drain the oil.
5. Remove the flywheel cover.
6. Disconnect the exhaust and crossover pipes.
7. Remove the oil cooler lines at the filter base.
8. Remove the starter assembly. Support the engine with a jack.
9. Remove the engine mounts from the block.
10. Raise the front of the engine and remove the oil pan.
11. Installation is in the reverse order of removal.

Oil Pump
REMOVAL & INSTALLATION
Gasoline and Diesel

The oil pump is mounted on the bottom of the block and is accessible only by removing the oil pan.

On V8 engines, including diesel, and the V6 diesel, remove the oil pan, then unbolt and remove the oil pump and screen as an assembly.

Rear Main Seal
REPLACEMENT
Gasoline and Diesel

The crankshaft need not be removed to replace the rear main bearing upper oil seal.
1. Drain the crankcase and remove the oil pan and rear main bearing cap.
2. Using a blunt-ended tool, drive the upper seal into its groove on each side until it is tightly packed. This is usually 1/4-3/4 in.
3. Cut pieces of new seal 1/16 in. longer than required to fill the grooves and install, packing into place.
4. Carefully trim any protruding seal, being sure not to scratch or damage the bearing surface.
5. Install a new seal in the bearing cap and install cap, tightening bolts to 120 ft. lbs. (107 ft. lbs. on V6 diesel). Install the oil pan.

CLUTCH

Clutch Pedal
ADJUSTMENT
Cutlass; Omega Through 1979

The clutch pedal free-play should be adjusted to the following specifications, which

are measured from the center of the clutch pedal pad:

1978–82 Cutlass 11/16–5/8 in.
1978–79 Omega—7/8–1-1/2 in.

To adjust free-play, proceed in the following manner:
1. Loosen the locknut on the push rod swivel.
2. Detach the pedal return spring.
3. Turn the clutch lever and shaft assembly until the clutch pedal seats against the rubber bumper on the dash brace.
4. Push the outer end of the clutch fork rearward, so that the throwout bearing just contacts the clutch plate.
5. Remove the retaining clip from the lower push rod swivel and install the swivel in the *upper* gauge hole. Install the retaining clip.
6. Lengthen the push rod until there is no lash.
7. Remove the retaining clip and reinstall the swivel in the *lower* hole on the lever and shaft assembly.
8. Tighten the locknut against the swivel. Be sure the rod length remains unchanged.
9. Install the pedal return spring and check pedal free-play.

REPLACEMENT
Omega Through 1979 and Cutlass

1. Remove the transmission.
2. Detach the clutch return spring and clutch release rod assembly.
3. Remove the throwout bearing.
4. Without removing the starter from the engine, remove the flywheel housing.

NOTE: The release yoke, boot and ball stud will remain in the housing.

5. Scribe a mark opposite the X mark on the flywheel cover. This mark is for proper flywheel balancing.
6. Loosen the pressure plate evenly, one turn at a time.

Clutch installation is performed in the following order:

——— CAUTION ———
Do not lubricate the splines as the lubricant will be forced onto the damper, resulting in clutch rattle.

1. Install the clutch disc/cover assembly and finger-tighten its securing bolts.

NOTE: Align the mark made during removal with the X mark on the flywheel cover.

2. Use a clutch arbor or an old input shaft to align the disc by inserting it through the disc and into the pilot bearing.
3. Tighten every other bolt until the cover assembly is within 1/4 in. of the flywheel.
4. Repeat Step 3 for the three remaining bolts.
5. Tighten the first three bolts to 30 ft. lbs. and then tighten the remaining three bolts to the same torque.

6. Remove the arbor. Lubricate the inside groove of the throwout bearing and the release yoke ball stud with wheel bearing grease.

7. Install the throwout bearing.

8. Install the flywheel housing and the transmission. Adjust clutch freeplay as outlined above.

MANUAL TRANSMISSION

The 3-speed transmission is the Saginaw unit. The standard 4-speed transmission in all models is also a Saginaw unit. On the Saginaw, all three shift rods go to levers on the side cover.

See the Capacities table at the beginning of this section for manual transmission refill capacities. For manual transmission overhaul procedures, see the Unit Repair Section.

Transmission
REMOVAL & INSTALLATION

1. Disconnect throttle linkage and raise car. If applicable, disconnect T.C.S. switch.

2. Remove driveshaft.

3. Support the rear of the engine. Remove the catalytic converter and/or brackets, if they are in the way.

4. On console equipped floorshifts, disconnect shifter assembly at transmission, allowing this unit to remain in car.

5. Disconnect parking brake cables and remove the cross member.

6. Disconnect speedometer cable and back-up light switch.

7. Remove transmission upper and lower bolts.

—— CAUTION ——
During removal, use aligning studs to support the transmission, otherwise distortion of the clutch driven plate will result.

8. Slide transmission rearward and remove. On models equipped with dual exhaust, it may be necessary to disconnect left exhaust pipe at the manifold.

9. Install by reversing the removal procedure. Observe the following torque figures:

Transmission to Clutch	Ft. Lbs.
Housing	53
Crossmember to frame	25
Crossmember to transmission	35
U-joint strap bolt	15

3-Speed Linkage
ADJUSTMENT
1978 and Later
CUTLASS

1. Turn the ignition switch to Off.

2. Raise and support the car.

3. Remove the retainer from the shift rods.

4. Place the transmission levers in Neutral.

5. Align the control levers and place a ¼ in. gauge pin into the levers and brackets, with the shift handle in Neutral.

6. Loosen the nuts on the shift rods and adjust the trunnion and pin assembly on First/Reverse, then tighten the nuts and install the shift rod and retainer.

7. Loosen the shift rod nut and adjust the trunnion and pin assembly on Second/Third, then tighten the nuts and install the shift rod and retainer.

8. Remove the gauge pin from the control lever assembly and check the operation of the control lever. Readjust as required.

9. Lower the car.

1978-79 OMEGA

1. Place the transmission in Reverse and raise and support the car.

2. Loosen the swivel bolts on the shift rods at the transmission. Make certain the rods are free to move in the swivels.

3. While holding the relay rod in position in the First/Reverse lever, push up on the reverse shift rod until the detent in the column is felt and tighten the swivel bolt for the First/Reverse rod.

4. Position the transmission in Neutral and insert a ³⁄₁₆ in. rod through the Second/Third shift lever and into the alignment hole. Tighten the swivel bolt.

5. Lower the car and check the shift operation with the engine off. Start the engine and recheck the operation.

6. Place the transmission in Reverse and the ignition in Lock. Make sure the key can be removed. The transmission should not shift out of Reverse.

7. Turn the ignition to Run and place the transmission in Second. Make sure the key cannot be removed and the steering wheel will turn.

1978-82 4-Speed Linkage

ADJUSTMENT

1. Turn the ignition switch to the Off position.

2. Raise and support the car.

3. Loosen the lock nuts at the swivels on the shift rods.

4. Set the transmission levers in Neutral.

5. Place the shifter in Neutral.

6. Align the control levers and place a ¼ in. gauge pin into the levers and bracket.

7. Tighten the First/Second shift rod nut against the swivel. Torque to 10 ft. lbs.

8. Tighten the Third/Fourth shift rod nut against the swivel. Torque to 10 ft. lbs.

9. Tighten the reverse shift control rod nut to 10 ft. lbs.

10. Remove the gauge pin, check for proper operation of the levers and lower the car.

AUTOMATIC TRANSMISSION

All Oldsmobile models use the Turbo Hydra-Matic automatic transmission.

The transmission can be identified visually: The 200, 250, 350, and 375B have a square or oblong pan with the right rear corner cut off; the 375 and 400 have an irregular pan shape. Some 200s have the word METRIC embossed in the pan. The 200 has ten pan bolts; the 350 and 375B have thirteen. The 250 has an intermediate band adjusting screw on the right side of the case. The 200, 250, 350, and 375B have a downshift cable between the carburetor linkage and the transmission; the 375 and 400 have an electrical downshift switch on the accelerator pedal linkage.

The 200-4R four speed automatic overdrive transmission was introduced in 1981.

For automatic transmission service procedures, refer to the Unit Repair Section.

REMOVAL & INSTALLATION

1. Remove the air cleaner assembly.

2. Disconnect the throttle valve detent cable.

3. Remove the dipstick (and the bolt holding the dipstick tube if accessable).

4. Jack up the car and support it with jack-stands.

5. Remove the driveshaft.

6. Disconnect the speedometer cable and shift linkage.

7. Disconnect any electrical leads.

8. Remove the flywheel cover; match-mark the flywheel and converter to maintain original balance.

9. Remove the torque converter to flywheel bolts and/or nuts.

NOTE: It may be necessary to disconnect the catalytic converter support bracket.

10. Remove the transmission support bracket (rear crossmember).

11. Remove the oil cooler lines.

12. Support the transmission with a transmission jack and remove the bellhousing bolts.

13. Support the engine with a jack and remove the transmission.

NOTE: Carefully remove the transmission to prevent the torque converter from falling off the mainshaft.

14. Installation is in the reverse order of removal.

DRIVESHAFT AND U-JOINTS

Driveshaft

REMOVAL & INSTALLATION

1. Matchmark the relationship of the driveshaft to the differential flange.

2. Unbolt the straps or flange. Tape the bearing caps in place to prevent losing the bearing rollers. Support the driveshaft to prevent excessive strain on the universal joint.

3. Pull the shaft back and remove it. Be careful not to damage the splines at the transmission end.

4. If the transmission splined slip yoke does not have a vent hole at the center, it should be lubricated with engine oil. If it does have a vent hole, it should be lubricated with grease. Slide the slip yoke into place.

5. Align the matchmarks and tighten the bolts. Strap bolts should be tightened to 16 ft. lbs. for 1978 and later. Tighten the U-bolts on 1978-79 Omegas to 16 ft. lbs.

UNIVERSAL JOINT OVERHAUL

See the "U-Joints and CV-Joint" Unit Repair section for overhaul procedures.

JACKING, HOISTING

Lifting Points are illustrated.

REAR AXLE

Axle, Shaft, Bearing and Seal

REMOVAL & INSTALLATION

NOTE: All Omegas (through 1979) and all 1980 and later Oldsmobiles use the C-lock axles. Non C–lock axles were used on some models through 1979.

C-lock Type

These cars use the C-lock type rear axles. The axle shafts are retained by C-shaped locks, which fit grooves at the inner end of the shaft. Bearings in the C-lock type axle

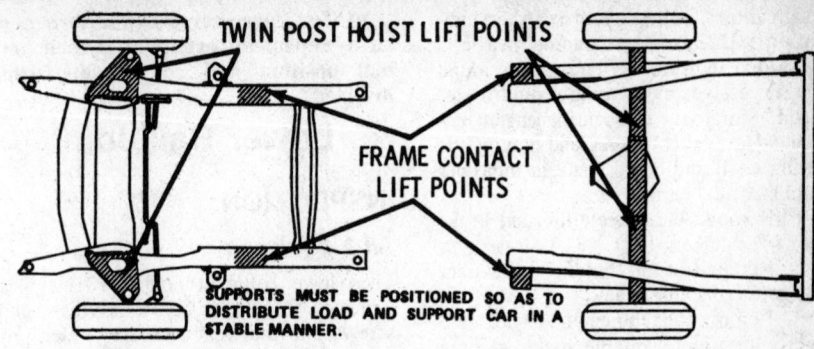

Omega hoisting points through 1979 (© Oldsmobile Div., GM Corp.)

consist of an outer race, bearing rollers and a roller cage, retained by snaprings.

--------- CAUTION ---------

Before attempting any service to the drive axle or axle shafts, remove the carrier cover and visually determine if the axle shaft(s) are retained by C-shaped locks at the inner ends or by a brake backing plate at the outer end. If they are retained by C-shaped locks, proceed as follows.

1. Raise the vehicle and remove the wheels and brake drums.

2. Clean the area of the cover and drain the fluid from the carrier by removing the cover. Remove the differential pinion shaft lockscrew and the differential pinion shaft.

3. Push the flanged end of the axle shaft toward the center of the vehicle and remove the C-lock from the end of the shaft.

4. Remove the axle shaft from the housing, being careful not to damage the oil seal.

5. Remove the oil seal with a pry bar inserted behind the steel case of the oil seal. Pry the seal loose from the bore.

6. Seat the legs of the bearing puller behind the bearing. Seat a washer against the bearing and hold it in place with a nut. Use a slide hammer to pull the bearing.

7. Pack the cavity between the seal lips with wheel bearing lubricant and lubricate a new wheel bearing with same.

8. Use a suitable driver and install the bearing until it bottoms. Lubricate the lips

of the oil seal and tap it into place so it is flush with the axle tube.

9. Slide the axle shaft into place. Be sure that the splines on the shaft do not damage the oil seal. Make sure that the splines engage the differential side gear.

10. Install the axle shaft C-lock on the inner end of the axle shaft and push the shaft outward so that the C-lock seats in the differential side gear counterbore.

11. Position the differential pinion shaft through the case and pinions, aligning the hole in the case with the hole for the lockscrew.

12. Install the pinion shaft lockscrew.

13. Use a new gasket and install the carrier cover. Be sure that the gasket surfaces are clean before installing the gasket and cover.

14. Fill the axle with lubricant to the bottom of the filler hole.

15. Install the brake drum and wheels and lower the car. Check for leaks and road test the car.

Non C-lock Type

--------- CAUTION ---------

Before attempting any service to the drive axle or axle shafts, remove the axle carrier cover and visually determine if the axle shafts are retained by C-shaped locks at the inner end, or by the brake backing plate at the outer end. If the shafts are not retained by C-locks, proceed as follows.

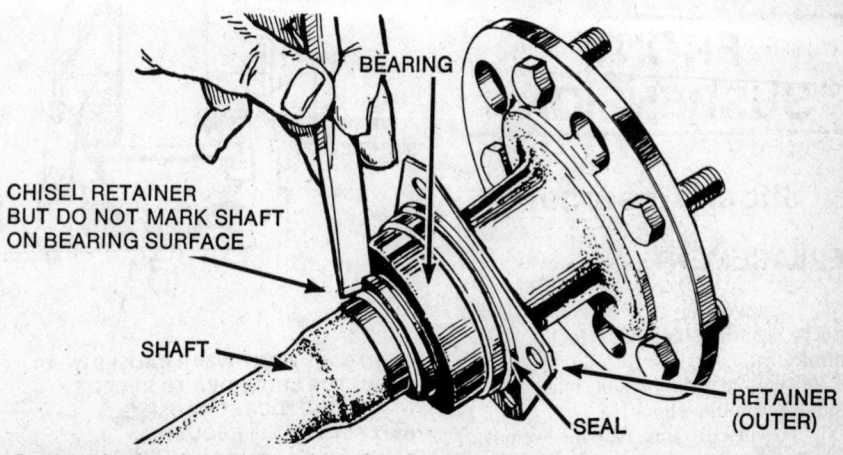

Cutting the bearing retainer (non-C-lock type) (© Oldsmobile Div., G.M. Corp.)

Design allows for maximum axle shaft end-play of 0.022 in., which can be measured with a dial indicator. If end-play is found to be excessive, the bearing should be replaced. Shimming the bearing is not recommended as this ignores end-play of the bearing itself and could result in improper seating of the bearing.

1. Remove the wheel, tire and brake drum.

2. Remove the nuts holding the retainer plate to the backing plate.

3. Remove the retainer and install nuts, fingertight, to prevent the brake backing plate from being dislodged.

4. Pull out the axle shaft and bearing assembly, using a slide hammer.

5. Using a chisel, nick the bearing retainer in three or four places deeply enough to spread the retainer sufficiently, allowing the bearing retainer to be slid from the axle.

6. Press the bearing from the axle and slide the seal and the outer retainer from the shaft.

To install:

7. Place the outer retainer over the axle shaft.

8. Lubricate the inner edge of the seal with EP molybdenum grease after thoroughly cleaning the seal area with a solvent. Place the seal on the sealing surface.

9. Install the bearing over the shaft and press the bearing against the shoulder of the shaft. With a tapered roller bearing, install it so the manufacturer's code can be read.

10. Press on the retainer.

NOTE: Do not attempt to press the bearing and the retainer on at the same time.

11. Apply a thin coat of wheel bearing grease to the bearing recesses of the axle housing and carefully insert the shaft until the splines engage.

12. Remove the nuts holding the backing plate in place and push the shaft into position.

13. Place the retainer over the studs and install the nuts. Install the brake drum, wheel and tire.

FRONT SUSPENSION

Shock Absorber

REPLACEMENT

1. Remove the two bolts and lockwashers securing the shock to the lower control arm.

2. Remove the upper nut, retainer, and grommet from the shock.

3. To install, reverse the removal procedure.

NOTE: Purge new shock absorbers of air by repeatedly extending in their normal position and compressing while inverted.

Lower Ball Joint

INSPECTION

All Models

These lower ball joints contain a visual wear indicator. The lower ball joint grease plug screws into the wear indicator which protrudes from the bottom of the ball joint housing. As long as the wear indicator extends out of the ball joint housing, the ball joint is not worn. If the tip of the wear indicator is parallel with, or recessed into the ball joint housing, the ball joint is defective.

Lower Ball Joint

REMOVAL & INSTALLATION

1. Raise the car and support the frame with jack stands.

2. Remove the tire and wheel.

3. Place a floor jack under the control arm spring seat.

──────── CAUTION ────────
Leave the jack under the spring seat during removal and installation, in order to keep the spring and control arm positioned.

4. Remove the cotter pin from the ball joint stud and, using a ball joint stud removal tool, separate the ball joint from the steering knuckle.

5. When the stud comes loose, remove the stud nut.

6. Guide the lower control arm through the opening in the splash shield using a screwdriver.

7. Block the steering knuckle out of the way by using a block of wood between the frame and the upper control arm.

8. Pry the retainer off the ball joint seal with a driftpin and remove the seal.

9. Using a ball joint remover, remove the lower ball joint from the control arm.

10. Press in a new ball joint until it bottoms on the lower control arm.

NOTE: On disc brake cars, make sure the grease purge on the seal faces away from the brakes.

11. Assemble the suspension and torque the nut to 95 ft. lbs. Install the cotter pin and bend it to the side, not over the top of the nut. The cotter pin on the Cutlass, 1979 and later, must be installed parallel to the center line of the car.

12. Install the ball joint fitting and lube until grease appears at the seal.

13. Install the tire and wheel assembly.

Upper Ball Joint

INSPECTION

1. Jack up the car and place jack stands under the left and right control arms as near as possible to the lower ball joints. Make sure the car sits steadily on the floor stands.

2. Position a dial indicator so that its button contacts the inside lip of the wheel trim.

3. Grasp the wheel at the 6 and 12 o'-clock positions. Push in on the bottom of the wheel while pulling on the top. Read the gauge and reverse the push/pull procedure. If the total deflection on the gauge

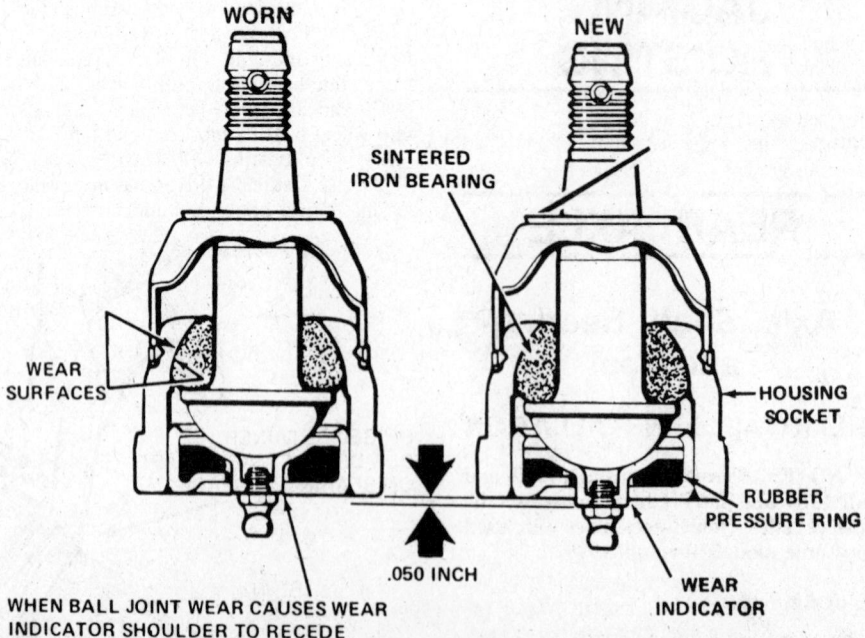

WHEN BALL JOINT WEAR CAUSES WEAR INDICATOR SHOULDER TO RECEDE WITHIN THE SOCKET HOUSING REPLACEMENT IS REQUIRED

Lower ball joint wear indicator (© Oldsmobile Div., GM Corp.)

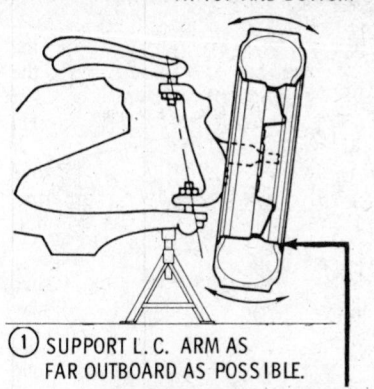

③ ROCK WHEEL IN AND OUT AT TOP AND BOTTOM

① SUPPORT L.C. ARM AS FAR OUTBOARD AS POSSIBLE.

② POSITION DIAL INDICATOR TO CHECK MOVEMENT AT THIS POINT

Checking upper ball joint (© Oldsmobile Div., GM Corp.)

reads more than 0.125 in., the ball joint is worn and must be replaced.

Upper Ball Joint

REMOVAL & INSTALLATION

1. Raise the front of car and place floor stands under the lower control arm between the spring seats and the ball joints.

— CAUTION —

Leave the jack under the spring seat during removal and installation, in order to keep the spring and control arm positioned.

2. Remove the wheel.
3. Remove the cotter pin from the upper ball joint stud and loosen the upper ball joint nut.
4. Using a ball joint remover tool, break the stud loose and remove the nut and pull the stud out of the knuckle. Support the steering knuckle to prevent damage to the brake line.
5. Using a ⅛ in. diameter drill bit, drill into each of the four rivet heads a depth of ¼ in.
6. Drill off the rivet heads with a ½ in. diameter bit.
7. Punch out the rivets and remove the ball joint.
8. To install, place the new ball joint in the upper control arm and secure it with four bolts and nuts in place of rivets. Tighten the nuts to 8 ft. lbs.
9. Connect the ball joint to steering knuckle. Torque the nut to 65 ft. lbs. minimum for 1978 and later models.

NOTE: When replacing ball joints, use only high-quality replacement parts and bolts and nuts specified to be strong enough to endure the stress. Always advance the ball stud nut to align the cotter pin hole.

10. Install the grease fitting and lubricate until grease appears at the seal.
11. Install the wheel.

Upper Control Arm

REMOVAL & INSTALLATION

1. Raise the car and place jack stands between the spring seats and the ball joints of the lower control arms.
2. Remove tire and wheel.
3. Place floor jack under lower control arm spring seat.

— CAUTION —

Leave the jack under the spring seat during removal and installation, in order to keep the spring and control arm positioned.

4. Remove ball joint stud from steering knuckle, by removing cotter pin and nut and pressing joint loose from knuckle with a ball joint remover. Support hub assembly to prevent damage to the brake line.
5. Loosen the pivot shaft-to-frame nuts and remove the alignment shims. Support hub assembly and remove upper arms by sliding shaft off end of bolts.

NOTE: Mark alignment shims for reassembly in their original locations.

6. It is necessary to remove upper control arm attaching bolts to gain clearance to remove arm assembly.
7. Remove control arm from car.
8. To reinstall, position bolts loosely in frame and install pivot shaft on bolts.
9. Install alignment shims placing them in position from which they were removed. Torque the nuts to 73 ft. lbs. for 1978-79 Omega, 88 and 98; 45 ft. lbs. for 1978-82 Cutlass.
10. Connect the ball joint stud to the steering knuckle and torque to 65 ft. lbs. minimum for 1978-79 Omega and 1978 and later Cutlass, 88 and 98. Install the cotter pin.
11. Install the wheel and check the alignment on all models.

Lower Control Arm and/or Spring

REMOVAL & INSTALLATION

1. Place the transmission in Neutral so the steering wheel is unlocked.
2. Raise the car and remove the wheel. Support the car with stands.
3. Remove the shock absorber.
4. Insert a spring removal tool into the shock hole. Rotate the tool so the plate is well seated in the lower control arm spring seat.
5. Rotate the nut on the tool to compress the spring slightly, just enough so it is free in the seat.
6. On all models remove the two lower

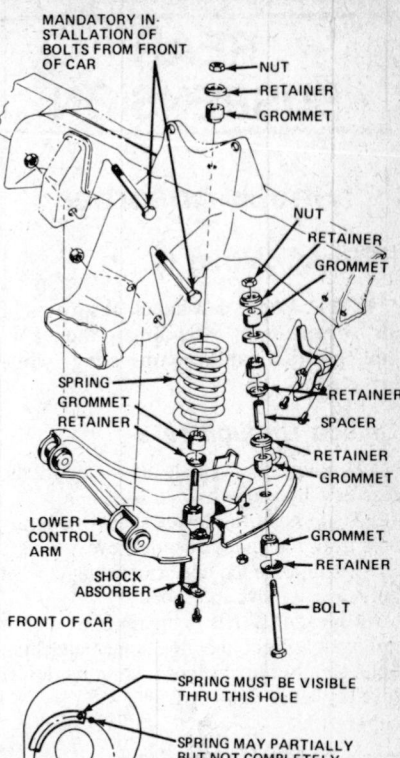

MANDATORY INSTALLATION OF BOLTS FROM FRONT OF CAR

NUT
RETAINER
GROMMET

NUT
RETAINER
GROMMET

SPRING
GROMMET
RETAINER

RETAINER
SPACER

RETAINER
GROMMET

LOWER CONTROL ARM

GROMMET
RETAINER

SHOCK ABSORBER

BOLT

FRONT OF CAR

SPRING MUST BE VISIBLE THRU THIS HOLE

SPRING MAY PARTIALLY BUT NOT COMPLETELY COVER THIS HOLE

Lower front suspension—88 and 98, 1978 and later Cutlass (© Oldsmobile Div., GM Corp.)

control arm pivot bolts and disengage the arm from the frame.

7. Rotate the arm and remove the spring.
8. Loosen the lower ball joint stud nut a few turns. Using a ball joint remover, expand the tool to snap the ball joint loose from the knuckle.
9. Remove the stud nut and the control arm.
10. Installation is in the reverse order of removal. Torque the lower ball joint stud nut to 95 ft. lbs.

Wheel Bearing

ADJUSTMENT

1. Raise the car so the wheel can spin freely. Remove the dust cap.
2. Tighten the adjusting nut to 12 ft. lbs. for 1978 and later, while turning the wheel.
3. Back off on the nut ½ turn.
4. Finger-tighten the nut and install the cotter pin or the retaining ring.

NOTE: If the cotter pin cannot be installed, back off on the nut until the slot aligns with the serrations on the nut. Do not back off on the nut more than ¹⁄₂₄ of a turn.

5. Once adjusted, the front wheel bearings should have 0.001-0.005 in. end-play for 1978 and later.

C473

REAR SUSPENSION

Shock Absorber

REPLACEMENT

NOTE: Purge new shock absorbers of air by repeatedly extending in their normal position and compressing while inverted.

Omega Through 1979

1. Raise the vehicle and support the rear axle housing.
2. Remove the lower shock mounting bolt from the shock absorber eye.
3. Unfasten the upper mounting bracket bolts and remove the shock.
4. Installation is in the reverse order of removal, except that the upper attaching bolts should remain loose while the lower (eye) is being tightened.

Coil Spring

REPLACEMENT

1978 and Later

1. Raise the rear of the car on the axle housing and place jack stands under the frame. Do not lower the jack.
2. Disconnect the brake line at the axle housing and at the differential housing.
3. Disconnect the upper control arms at the differential housing.

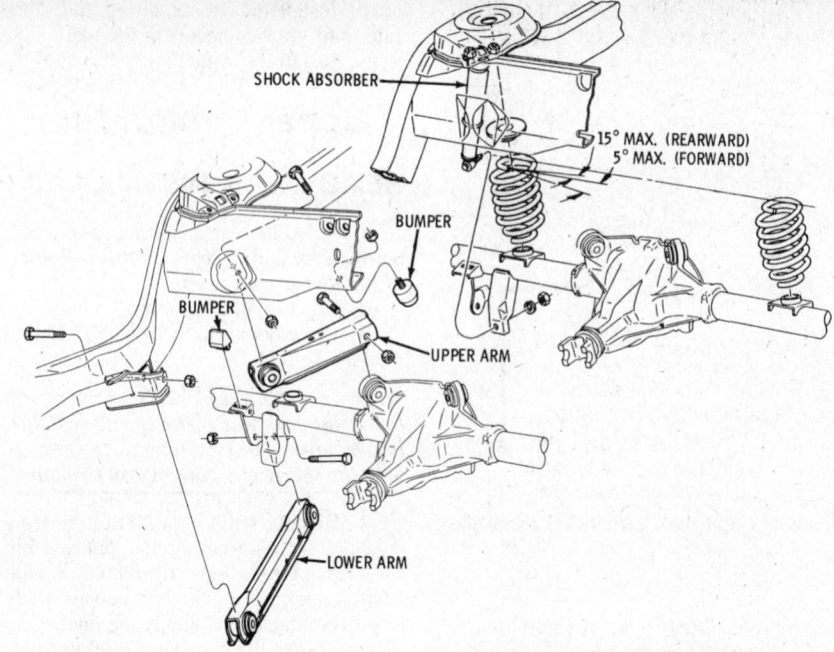

Cutlass, 88 and 98 rear suspension (except wagon) (© Oldsmobile Div., GM Corp.)

4. Remove the shock absorber lower mount and lower the jack. Be careful not to stretch the brake hose.
5. Remove the spring.
Installation is in the reverse order of removal.

Leaf Spring

REPLACEMENT

Omega Through 1979

1. Raise the rear of the car on jack stands.

2. Support the rear axle to take its weight off the springs.
3. Disconnect the bottom of the shock absorber.
4. Loosen the front spring eye bolt.
5. Unbolt the spring front bracket from the underbody.
6. Lower the axle slightly and remove the front bracket from the spring.
7. Pry the parking brake cable out of its retainer bracket on the axle spring mounting plate.
8. Unbolt the spring from the axle.
9. Remove the spring plate and cushion between the axle and the spring.
10. Remove the lower bolt from the rear spring shackle. Remove the spring from the car.
11. On installation, attach the front bracket to the spring eye. The head of the bolt should be toward the center of the car.
12. Assemble the shackle loosely to the rear spring eye.
13. Raise the rear end of spring and install the lower shackle bolt loosely, making sure the parking brake cable goes under the spring.
14. Raise the front end of the spring and loosely attach the front bracket to the underbody. Make sure the bracket tab goes into its slot.
15. Make sure the upper and lower spring cushions are aligned properly. The upper one has locating ribs and the lower one, a locating dowel.
16. Install the spring lower mounting plate over the locating dowel and loosely install the nuts. Don't forget the parking brake cable bracket.
17. Attach the bottom of the shock absorber.
18. Attach the parking brake cable to the bracket on the lower spring plate.

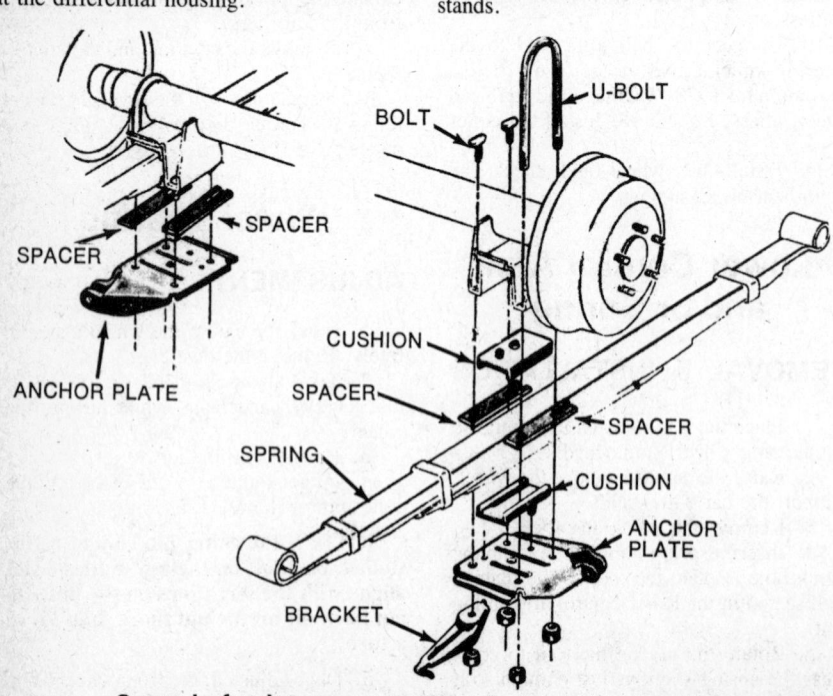

Omega leaf spring rear suspension—Custom Cruiser similar
(© Oldsmobile Div, G.M. Corp)

19. Let the vehicle weight down on the springs. Tighten all the bolts. Torques are: rear shackle bolts—40-60 ft. lbs., front bracket screws—25-35 ft. lbs., front eye bolt—65-80 ft. lbs., and axle bolts—35-50 ft. lbs.

BRAKES

For information on brake adjustments, lining replacement, bleeding procedure, master and wheel cylinder overhaul, please refer to "Brakes" in the Unit Repair section.

Parking Brake

ADJUSTMENT

1. Apply the parking brake exactly two clicks on all 1978 and later models. Raise the rear of the car.
2. Loosen the locknut at the rear of the equalizer adjusting nut. Tighten the adjusting nut until the rear wheels can barely be turned backward (using two hands) but lock up when moved forward. Rear disc brakes will not lock up but will have a drag. Tighten the nut against the adjusting nut.
3. With the parking brake disengaged the rear wheel should turn freely in either direction with no brake drag.

Master Cylinder

REMOVAL & INSTALLATION

NOTE: Be sure the area where the master cylinder is mounted is clean, before beginning removal.

1. Disconnect and cap or plug hydraulic lines. Disconnect the electrical lead, if so equipped.
2. On non-power brakes, disconnect the pushrod at the brake pedal.
3. Remove the attaching bolts and master cylinder.
4. Install in the reverse order of removal. Fill with fluid and bleed.

Power Brake Unit

REMOVAL & INSTALLATION

1. Remove the two nuts holding the master cylinder fastened to the power unit. Carefully position the master cylinder out of the way, being careful not to kink any of the hydraulic lines. It is not necessary to disconnect the brake lines.
2. Disconnect the vacuum hose from the vacuum check valve on the front housing. Plug the hose. On cars with diesel en-

gine, disconnect the three hydraulic lines from the power cylinder. Plug the lines immediately.
3. Loosen the four nuts that hold the power unit mounted on the firewall.
4. Disconnect the pushrod from the brake pedal. Do not force the pushrod to the side when disconnecting.
5. Remove the four mounting nuts and lift the power unit off the studs.
6. Installation is in the reverse order of removal. Torque the master cylinder-to-power brake unit mounting studs to 24 ft. lbs. On Diesel engined cars with, refill the power steering reservoir. See "Power Steering Pump Removal and Installation" for system bleeding.

STEERING

Tie-Rod End

REMOVAL & INSTALLATION

1. Raise and support the car.
2. Remove the cotter pins from the ball studs and remove the castellated nuts.
3. Disconnect the tie-rod end from the steering arm or knuckle with a ball joint separator.
4. Remove the inner ball stud from the intermediate rod with a puller. Mark the tie-rod end position before removal..
5. Loosen the clamp bolts and unscrew the ends from the adjuster tubes. If a force of more than 7 ft. lbs. is required to remove

the ends after breakaway, the fasteners should be replaced.
6. Clean and inspect all parts. When installing, run the tie-rod end to the position marked. Torque the ball stud nuts to 30 ft. lbs.

Steering Gear

REMOVAL & INSTALLATION

1. Remove the flexible coupling shield.

NOTE: Failure to disconnect the flexible coupling from the steering gear stub shaft can result in damage to the steering gear and/or immediate shaft. This damage can cause loss of steering control which could result in a vehicle crash and bodily injury.

2. Disconnect the hoses from the gear and cap the hose fittings.
3. Jack up the car. Support it with jackstands.
4. Remove the pitman shaft nut. Then disconnect the pitman arm from the pitman shaft. Special puller J29107 or its equivalent must be used.
5. Remove the three bolts attaching the gear to the frame side rail. Remove the gear.
6. Installation is in the reverse order of removal.

NOTE: If the threads are stripped, do not repair, replace the housing.
Tighten the gear-to-frame bolts 70 ft. lbs. Pitman shaft 185ft. lbs., coupling flange hub bolts 30 ft. lbs.

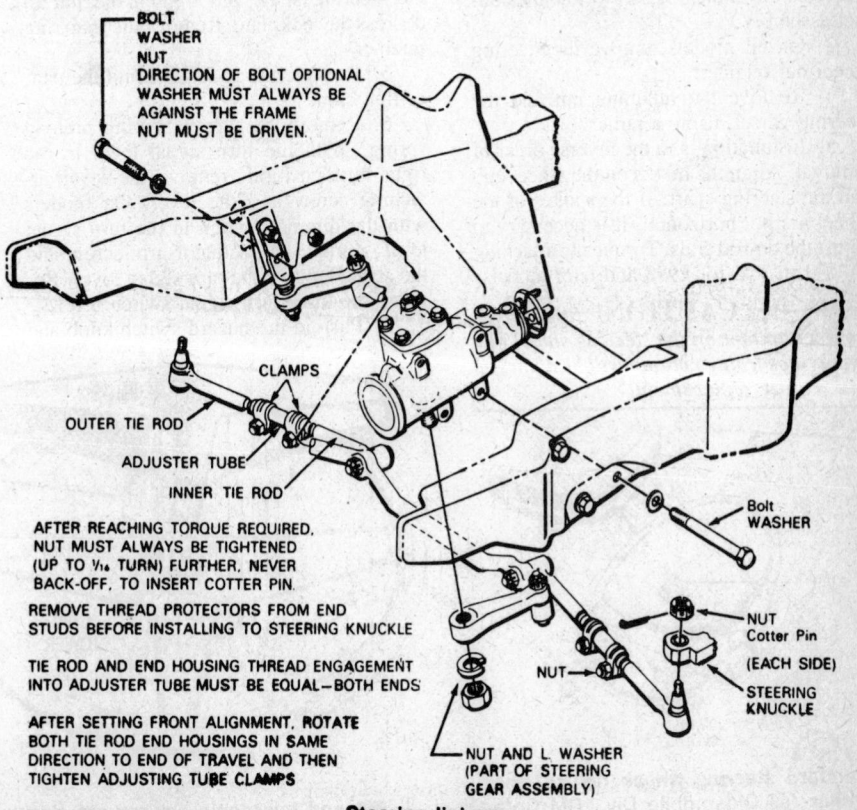

BOLT
WASHER
NUT
DIRECTION OF BOLT OPTIONAL
WASHER MUST ALWAYS BE
AGAINST THE FRAME
NUT MUST BE DRIVEN.

CLAMPS

OUTER TIE ROD

ADJUSTER TUBE

INNER TIE ROD

Bolt
WASHER

AFTER REACHING TORQUE REQUIRED,
NUT MUST ALWAYS BE TIGHTENED
(UP TO 1/14 TURN) FURTHER, NEVER
BACK-OFF, TO INSERT COTTER PIN.

REMOVE THREAD PROTECTORS FROM END
STUDS BEFORE INSTALLING TO STEERING KNUCKLE

TIE ROD AND END HOUSING THREAD ENGAGEMENT
INTO ADJUSTER TUBE MUST BE EQUAL—BOTH ENDS

AFTER SETTING FRONT ALIGNMENT, ROTATE
BOTH TIE ROD END HOUSINGS IN SAME
DIRECTION TO END OF TRAVEL AND THEN
TIGHTEN ADJUSTING TUBE CLAMPS

NUT
Cotter Pin
(EACH SIDE)
STEERING
KNUCKLE

NUT

NUT AND L. WASHER
(PART OF STEERING
GEAR ASSEMBLY)

Steering linkage

Steering Wheel

REMOVAL & INSTALLATION

Except Tilt and Telescope Models

1. Disconnect the battery ground cable.
2. On the stock wheel, remove the two screws attaching the horn pad assembly to the wheel. Disconnect the horn contact from the pad assembly.

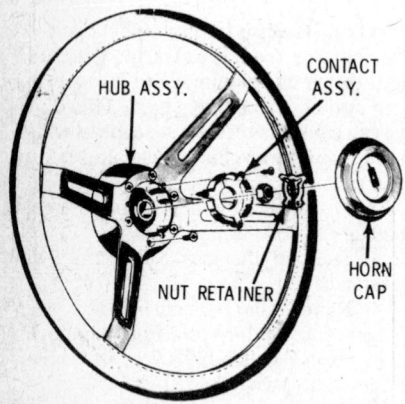

Sport steering wheel
(© Oldsmobile Div., G.M. Corp.)

On the deluxe wheel, remove the pad attaching screws, lift up the pad, and disconnect the horn wire by pushing on the insulator and turning counterclockwise.

On the sport steering wheel, pull up on the emblem to remove it. Remove the contact assembly attaching screws and the contact assembly.

3. On all models remove the steering wheel nut retainer.
4. Remove the retaining nut and the steering wheel, using a puller.
5. Installation is in the reverse order of removal. Align the marks on the wheel hub and the steering shaft. If the spokes of the wheel are not horizontal, it is necessary to adjust the tie-rod ends. Torque the attaching bolt 30 ft. lbs. for 1978 and later models.

— CAUTION —

Do not hammer on the steering shaft. The energy-absorbing column will be damaged and require replacement.

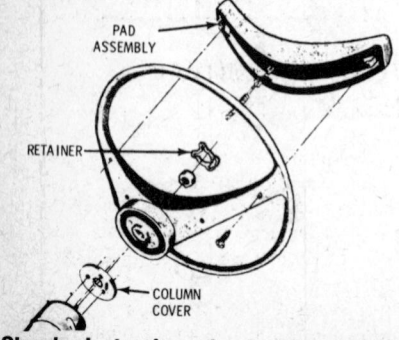

Standard steering wheel; deluxe wheel similar (© Oldsmobile Div., GM Corp.)

Tilt and Telescope Models

1. Disconnect the battery ground.
2. Remove the three pad attaching screws, lift off the pad assembly and disconnect the horn wire.
3. Push the locking lever counterclockwise to full release.
4. Mark the plate assembly where the two attaching screws attach the plate assembly to the locking lever and remove the two screws.
5. Unscrew and remove the plate assembly. Remove the steering wheel nut.
6. Using a puller, remove the steering wheel.
7. Install a 5/16 in. × 18 set screw into the upper shaft at the full extended position and lock.
8. Install the steering wheel, aligning the scribe mark on the hub with the slash mark on the end of the shaft. Make sure that the attached end of the upper horn contact assembly is seated flush against the top of the horn contact assembly.
9. Install the steering wheel nut and torque to 30 ft. lbs. The remainder of the installation is in the reverse order of removal. Remove the set screw after steering wheel installation.

Turn Signal Switch

REPLACEMENT

1. Disconnect the negative battery cable.
2. Remove the steering wheel.
3. Pry the lockplate cover off with a screwdriver.
4. Place a lock plate removal tool over the steering shaft and tighten the nut to depress the lockplate. Remove the snap ring retainer.
5. Remove the lock plate and the cancelling cam.
6. Remove the upper bearing preload spring. With the turn signal lever in the right turn position, remove the lever attaching screw and the lever. On models with the dimmer switch in the turn signal lever, remove the actuator arm screw and the arm. Remove the turn signal lever. Remove the three turn signal switch screws.
7. Push in the hazard switch knob and

remove the retaining screw and the knob. On tilt columns, position the housing in the center position.
8. Remove the lower trim panel from the instrument panel and disconnect the turn signal connector from the wiring harness. Remove the connector.
9. Remove the bolts attaching the surrounding bracket assembly to the jacket. On all column shift automatics remove the shift indicator needle attaching screw and remove or disconnect the needle.
10. Hold the steering column in place and remove the two attaching nuts from below. Remove the bracket assembly and the wire protector. Loosely reinstall the nuts to hold the column in place.

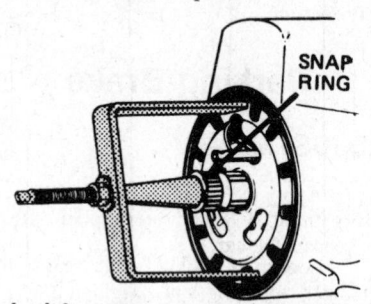

Lock plate removal tool (© Oldsmobile Div., GM Corp.)

11. Carefully remove the turn signal switch and the wiring.
12. To install, place the switch in the right turn position and push the switch in until it is properly seated. Torque the three attaching nuts to 35 inch lbs. Return the switch to the neutral position and reverse the removal procedure.

Power Steering Pump

REMOVAL & INSTALLATION

1. Disconnect negative battery cable, and remove the drive belt.
2. Use a puller to remove the pump pulley.
3. Detach and cap the hoses.
4. Remove the pump and mounting bracket.

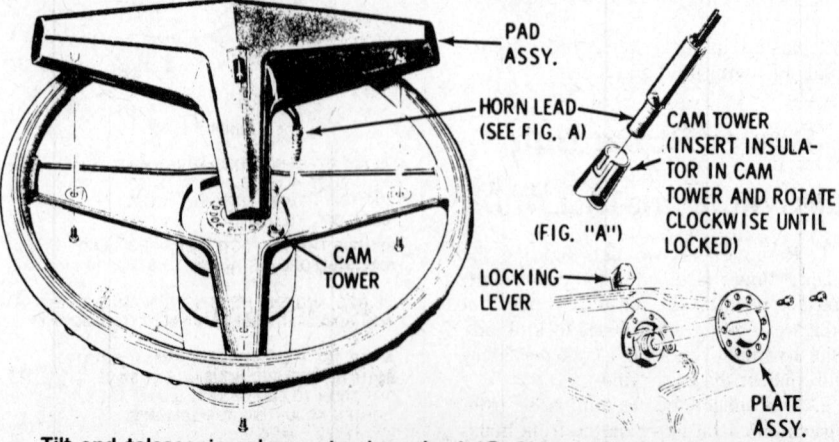

Tilt and telescopic column steering wheel (© Oldsmobile Div., GM Corp.)

5. Reverse the procedure for installation. Bleed the system of air by turning the wheels from side to side without hitting the stops, with the wheels off the floor and the engine running.

Ignition Switch and/or Lock Cylinder

REMOVAL & INSTALLATION

Ignition Switch

1. Disconnect negative battery cable.
2. Place ignition switch in Off-Unlocked, or ACC (tilt wheel).
3. Remove toe pan cover (if applicable) and loosen the toe clamp bolts.
4. Remove lower instrument panel trim and toe pan trim panel.
5. Remove automatic transmission shift indicator needle.
6. Remove steering column instrument panel bracket and let steering wheel rest on the driver's seat.
7. Remove the two dimmer switch retaining screws and remove the switch.
8. Remove two ignition switch attaching screws and lift switch off actuator rod.
9. Disconnect wiring.
10. To install, check that lock cylinder is still in Off-Unlocked or ACC (tilt wheel), and move sliding portion of switch until switch hole is positioned correctly. Hold the switch in this position with a 0.090 in. pin.
11. Connect the wiring to the switch.
12. Position switch over actuator rod, install attaching screws and remove the 0.090 in. pin.
13. Reverse Steps 1–6 to complete installation.

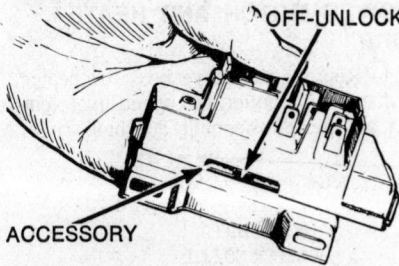

MOVE SWITCH SLIDER TO EXTREME LEFT (ACCESSORY) POSITION THEN MOVE SLIDER TO DETENTS TO THE RIGHT OF "OFF-UNLOCK"

Ignition switch in Off-Unlocked position

Lock Cylinder

1. Refer to the turn signal removal procedure, Steps 1-7.
2. Disconnect the turn signal connector from the harness. Remove the connector from the mounting bracket.
3. Carefully pull the turn signal switch from the column, allowing it to hang.
4. Position the lock assembly in the RUN position. On models through 1978, insert a thin screwdriver into the right hand slot and depress the retainer at the bottom of the slot. Remove the lock. On 1979 and later models, position the lock in the RUN position and remove the retaining screw and the lock.
5. To install the lock cylinder, hold the lock cylinder and rotate the tabs clockwise until they stop. Insert the cylinder into the housing, aligning the keyway groove. Push the cylinder and rotate the tabs counter-clockwise while lightly pushing inward on the cylinder until the drive section of the cylinder mates with drive shaft. Reverse removal procedure.

INSTRUMENT PANEL

Headlight Switch

REMOVAL & INSTALLATION

Cutlass Without A/C, Omega Through 1979

1. Disconnect the negative battery cable.
2. Remove the left hand control panel to gain access to the electrical connector.
3. Remove the connector from the switch.
4. Pull the switch to the ON position, depress the spring-loaded release button on the switch body and pull the knob and stem from the switch.
5. Remove the shaft mounting bushing.
6. Remove the switch. Reverse the above to install.

1978 and Later Cutlass

1. Disconnect the negative battery cable.
2. Remove the instrument cluster pad.
3. Remove the two switch mounting screws and remove the switch.

1978 and Later 88 and 98

1. Disconnect the negative battery cable.
2. Rotate the headlight switch so the notch is on the bottom. Bend a small hook in the end of a paper clip and use it to release the knob retaining clip and remove the knob.
3. Remove the left hand trim cover.
4. Remove the switch mounting plate screws and pull the switch through the opening.
5. Remove the electrical connector and remove the switch.

Speedometer Cable

REMOVAL & INSTALLATION

The speedometer cable is retained at the rear of the speedometer head by quick release clip. To remove the cable, reach up behind the speedometer and depress the clip while pushing in, then pull back on the cable. The cable may then be pulled from the firewall and into the engine compartment. Raise the car and support it on stands. Disconnect the cable from the transmission and remove the core. When replacing the core, coat all but the top ⅓ with speedometer cable lubricant. Cable replacement is in the reverse order of removal.

Instrument Cluster

REMOVAL & INSTALLATION

Cutlass

1. Disconnect the speedometer cable at the cruise control transducer, if so equipped.
2. Remove the instrument cluster pad assembly.
3. Remove the steering column trim cover.
4. Disconnect the shift indicator clip from the steering column shift bowl.
5. Remove the instrument cluster screws.
6. Pull the cluster rearward. Disconnect the speedometer cable.
7. Disconnect the speed sensor, if so equipped.
8. Remove the cluster.
9. Installation is in the reverse order of removal.

88–98

1. Remove the steering column trim cover.
2. Remove the 4 screws attaching the gauge cluster to the left hand trim cover.
3. Pull the gauge cluster rearward. Disconnect gauges wiring, lamp sockets, and speedometer cable.
4. Remove the gauge cluster.
5. Installation is in the reverse order of removal.

WINDSHIELD WIPERS

MOTOR REMOVAL & INSTALLATION

1. Remove the cowl screen or grille.
2. Loosen the linkage drive link-to-crankarm attaching nuts, and remove the link from the arm.
3. Disconnect the wiring and washer hoses.
4. Remove the three motor attaching screws, guide the crankarm through the hole in the dash, and remove the motor.
5. Reverse the above steps to install.

WIPER BLADE REPLACEMENT

Depending on model and availability, one of three methods is used:

    a. A tab on the arm saddle is depressed.

    b. A spring type blade clip is depressed.

    c. A coil spring retainer is depressed with a screwdriver.

Details can be found in the Maintenance Unit Repair Section.

RADIO

REMOVAL & INSTALLATION

1978 and later 88 and 98

1. Disconnect the negative battery cable.
2. Remove the knobs from the radio and pull out the cigarette lighter.
3. Remove the two trim cover attaching screws and remove the cover.
4. Remove the radio bracket attaching screw from the lower tie bar.
5. Remove the four mounting plate screws and pull the radio out to obtain access to the electrical connections. Detach the wiring harness and the antenna lead.
6. Remove the mounting plate nuts and remove the radio. Installation is in the reverse order of removal.

1978 and Later Cutlass

1. Disconnect the negative battery cable.
2. Remove the radio knobs. Pull the lower trim cover outward, off the retaining clips.
3. Remove the four mounting plate screws and the screw from the radio support bracket on the lower tie bar.
4. Pull the radio out and detach the wiring and the antenna lead.

Omega Through 1979

1. Disconnect the battery.
2. Remove the knobs, washers, trim plate and nuts.
3. Disconnect the wiring.
4. Remove the screws or nuts from the rear mounting bracket. Lower the radio to remove.
5. Installation is in the reverse order of removal.

CIRCUIT PROTECTION

Fuses

The fuse block is located beneath the in-strument panel, drivers side of firewall. Fuse holders are labeled as to their service and the correct amperage. Always replace blown fuses with new ones of the correct amperage. Otherwise electrical overloads and possible wiring damage will result.

Fusible Links

Fusible links are sections of wire, with special insulation, designed to melt under electrical overload. Replacements are simply spliced into the wire. There may be as many as five of these in the engine compartment wiring harnesses. These are:

1. Horn relay-to-fuse panel circuit—one link.
2. Charging circuit, from the starter solenoid to the horn relay—two links.
3. Starter solenoid-to-ammeter circuit—one link.
4. Horn relay-to-rear window defroster circuit—one link.

The fusible links are all two wire gauge sizes smaller than the wires they protect.

NOTE: Most models have fusible links at these locations.

Replacement

1. Disconnect the battery ground cable.
2. Disconnect the fusible link from the junction block or starter solenoid.
3. Cut the harness directly behind the connector to remove the damaged fusible link.
4. Strip the harness wire approximately ½ in.
5. Connect the new fusible link to the harness wire using a crimp-on connector. Soder the connection using rosin-core solder.
6. Tape all exposed wires with plastic electrical tape.
7. Connect the fusible link to the junction block or starter solenoid and reconnect the battery ground cable.

HEATER

Blower Motor and Heater Core

REMOVAL & INSTALLATION

Without Air Conditioning

1978 AND LATER 88 AND 98 BLOWER MOTOR

1. Disconnect the negative battery and the blower motor wiring.
2. Remove the retaining screws and remove the motor. Use sealer as needed upon installation for a watertight seal.

1978 AND LATER 88 AND 98 HEATER CORE

1. Disconnect the negative battery cable, the blower motor wiring and the heater core ground strap.
2. Drain the cooling system and disconnect the heat hoses.
3. It may be necessary to move the temperature air valve by disconnecting the cable and tapping the hinge pin down to clear the upper pivot.
4. Remove the screws attaching the blower case to the heater case. Remove the heater core shroud screws and remove the shroud and core.

1978 AND LATER CUTLASS BLOWER MOTOR AND HEATER CORE

1. Remove the glove box, the heater air distribution outlet, the upper level vent duct, and the defroster outlet attaching screw.

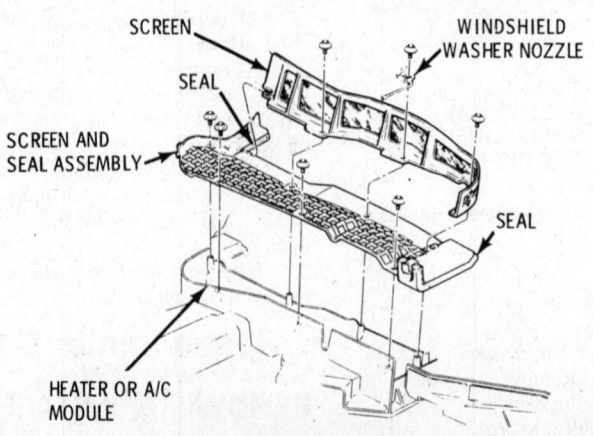

Air inlet screen-88, 98

2. Disconnect the blower motor wiring and the cables at the blower motor.

3. Drain the cooling system.

4. Remove the right hand windshield wiper arm.

5. Remove the leaf screen.

6. Disconnect the heater hoses at the heater assembly. Remove the heater assembly-to-cowl screws and remove the assembly.

7. Remove blower motor mounting screws and remove the motor from the assembly.

8. Remove the front cover screws and remove the heater core. Reverse above procedures to install.

1978–79 OMEGA BLOWER MOTOR

1. Disconnect the negative battery cable and raise the car on a hoist.

2. Remove the right front brake hose retaining clip from the frame spring yoke, if so equipped.

3. Remove all of the fender skirt attaching bolts except those which fasten the skirt to the radiator support.

4. Carefully pull outward and down on the skirt and place a wood block between the fender and the skirt.

5. Disconnect the blower motor wiring at the motor.

6. Remove the hold down screws and remove the motor. To install, reverse the above procedure.

1978–79 OMEGA HEATER CORE

1. Disconnect the negative battery cable and drain the radiator.

2. Disconnect the heater hoses at the core and plug the hoses.

3. On the engine side of the dash, remove the retaining nuts from the core case studs.

4. Remove the glove compartment and door.

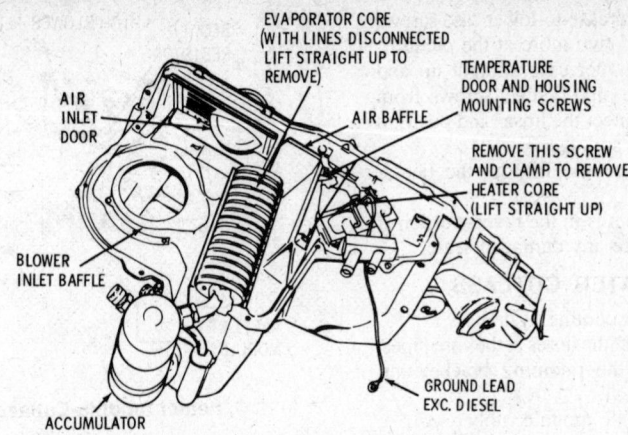

Evaporator and heater core-88, 98

5. Pull the core and case assembly from the dash. Disconnect the heater cables and the resistor connector and remove the assembly.

6. Remove the core tube seal, the retaining straps, and remove the core. Installation is in the reverse order of removal. Use a new sealer if necessary.

Blower Motor

REMOVAL & INSTALLATION
With Air Conditioning

1978 AND LATER 88 & 98

The blower motor is mounted in the upper evaporator and blower case, by 6 screws (7 with noise suppressor). Disconnect the electrical connectors and remove the screws. Lift the blower straight up to remove.

1978–79 OMEGA

The blower motor removal procedure for A/C equipped Omega models is similar to

that of models without A/C, except that the fender fill panel must be unbolted and moved forward and inward.

CUTLASS

1. Disconnect the battery ground.

2. Disconnect the blower wiring.

3. Unbolt and remove the motor.

4. Installation is in the reverse order of removal. Replace any damaged sealer.

Heater Core

REMOVAL & INSTALLATION
With Air Conditioning

1978 AND LATER 88 AND 98

1. Disconnect the battery ground.

2. Disconnect the blower wiring.

3. Remove the thermostatic switch and diagnostic connector.

4. Remove the right end of the hood seal and the air inlet screen screws.

5. Remove the 5 case-to-firewall screws

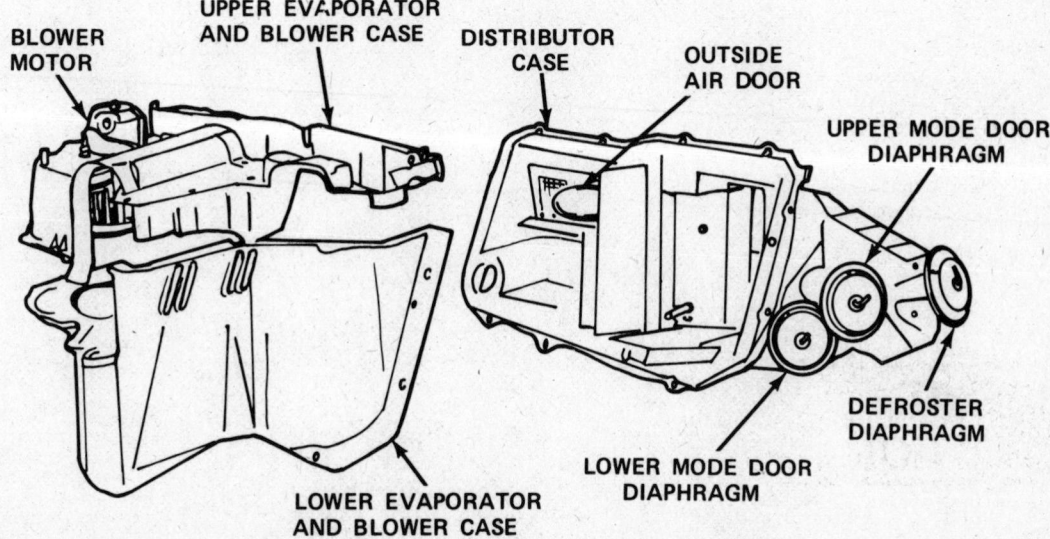

A/C module disassembled view-88, 98

at the top, 9 upper case-to-lower case screws at the flange and two more at the plenum.

6. Lift the upper case straight up and off. Remove the pipe bracket screws from the case. Disconnect the hoses and position them to prevent spillage.

7. Disconnect and lift out the heater core.

8. Installation is in the reverse order of removal. Replace any damaged sealer.

1978 AND LATER CUTLASS

1. Drain the cooling system.
2. Disconnect the hoses at the core pipes.
3. Remove the retaining bracket and ground strap.
4. Remove the module rubber seal.
5. Remove the module screen.
6. Remove the right windshield wiper arm.
7. Remove the diagnostic connector, high blower relay and thermostatic switch mounting screws.
8. Disconnect all electrical connections at the module.
9. Remove the module top cover.
10. Lift out the core.

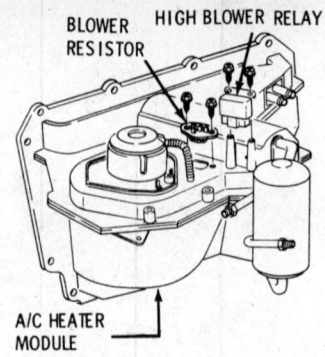

A/C, heater module-Cutlass

11. Installation is in the reverse order of removal. Replace all insulation.

1978-79 OMEGA

1. Disconnect the battery and drain the cooling system.
2. Detach the upper heater hose at the core tube.
3. Remove all accessible heater core and case securing nuts.

4. Unfasten the right-hand front fender filler panel, bolts and lower the panel, in order to gain access to the lower heater hose clamp.

5. Unfasten the hose clamp and detach the hose from the lower heater core tube.

6. Unfasten the lower nut which secures the right-hand heater case/core assembly.

7. Plug both of the core tubes to prevent coolant from leaking.

8. Remove the glovebox and its door.

9. Take the vacuum diaphragm assembly off the right-hand kick-panel.

10. Remove the outlet from the bottom of the heater case.

11. Separate the cold air duct from the heater case.

12. Unfasten the screws which secure the extension to the heater case. Remove the extension from the case.

13. Detach the cables and the wiring from the case. Remove the core and case as an assembly.

14. Remove the core from the case.

15. Installation is in the reverse order of removal.

Pontiac
Rear Wheel Drive
Bonneville, Catalina, Parisienne,
Grand Prix, Lemans, Phoenix, Grand Am

YEAR IDENTIFICATION

1978 LeMans

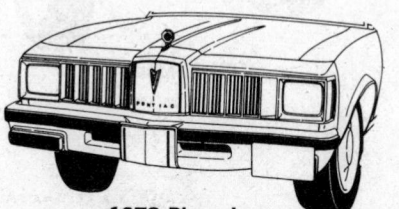

1978 Phoenix

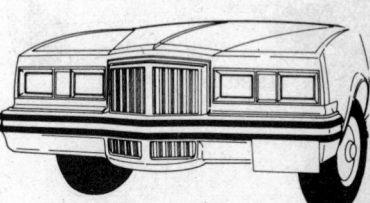

1978 Grand Prix

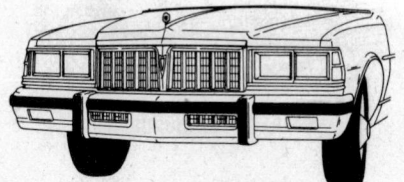

1978 Bonneville

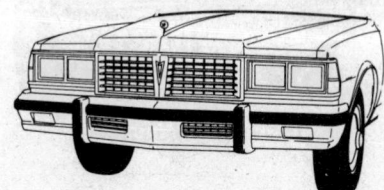

1978 Catalina

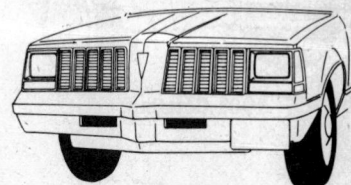

1979 LeMans

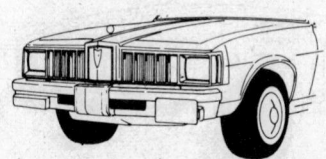

1979 Phoenix

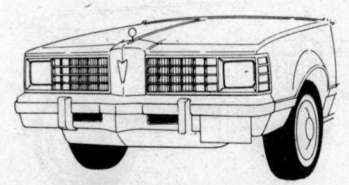

1979 Grand Am

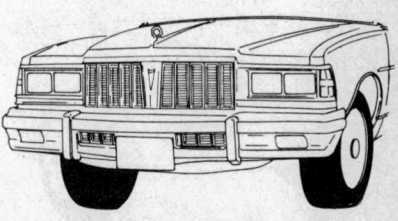

1979 Bonneville

C481

YEAR IDENTIFICATION

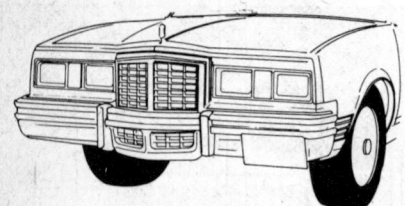

1979 Grand Prix

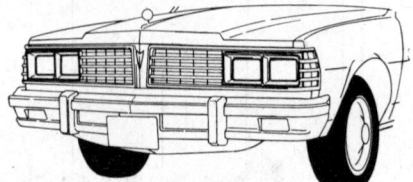

1979 Catalina

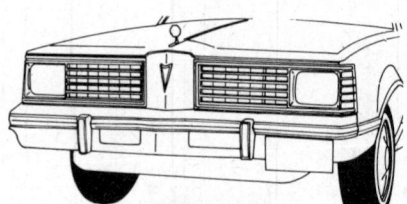

1980 LeMans

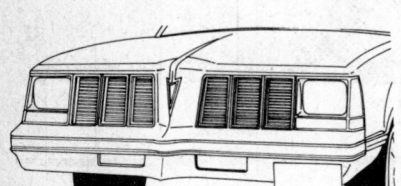

1980 Grand Am

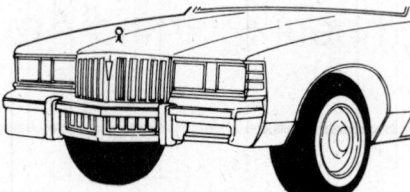

1980 Catalina

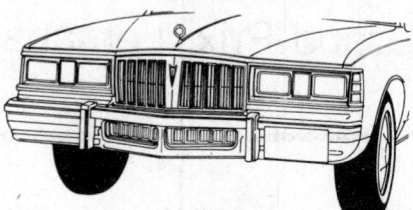

1980 Bonneville

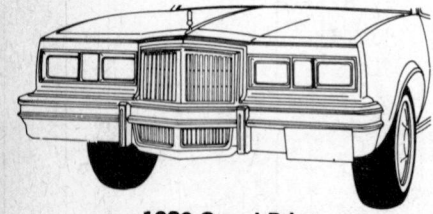

1980 Grand Prix

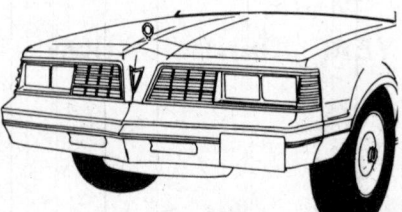

1981 LeMans

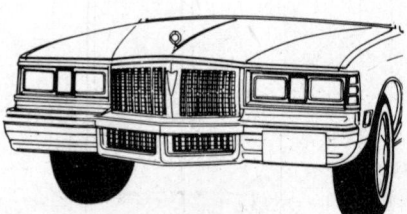

1981 Bonneville

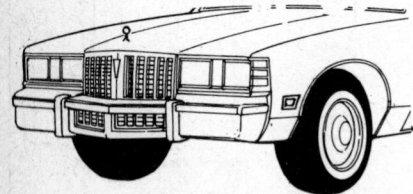

1981 Catalina

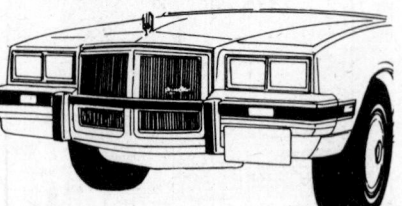

1981–84 Grand Prix

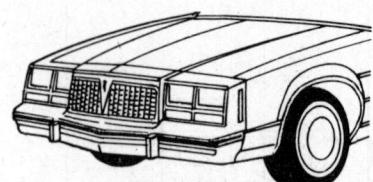

1982–84 Bonneville

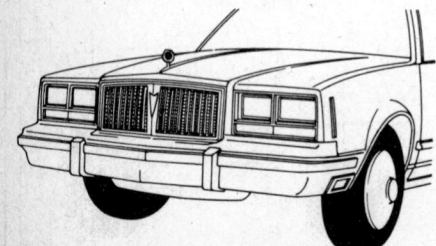

1984–85 Parisienne

1985 Grand Prix

1985 Bonneville

VEHICLE IDENTIFICATION NUMBER (VIN)

It is important for servicing and ordering parts to be certain of the vehicle and engine identification. The VIN (vehicle identification number) is a 13 or 17 digit number visible through the windshield on the driver's side of the dash and contains the vehicle and engine identification codes. It can be interpreted as follows:

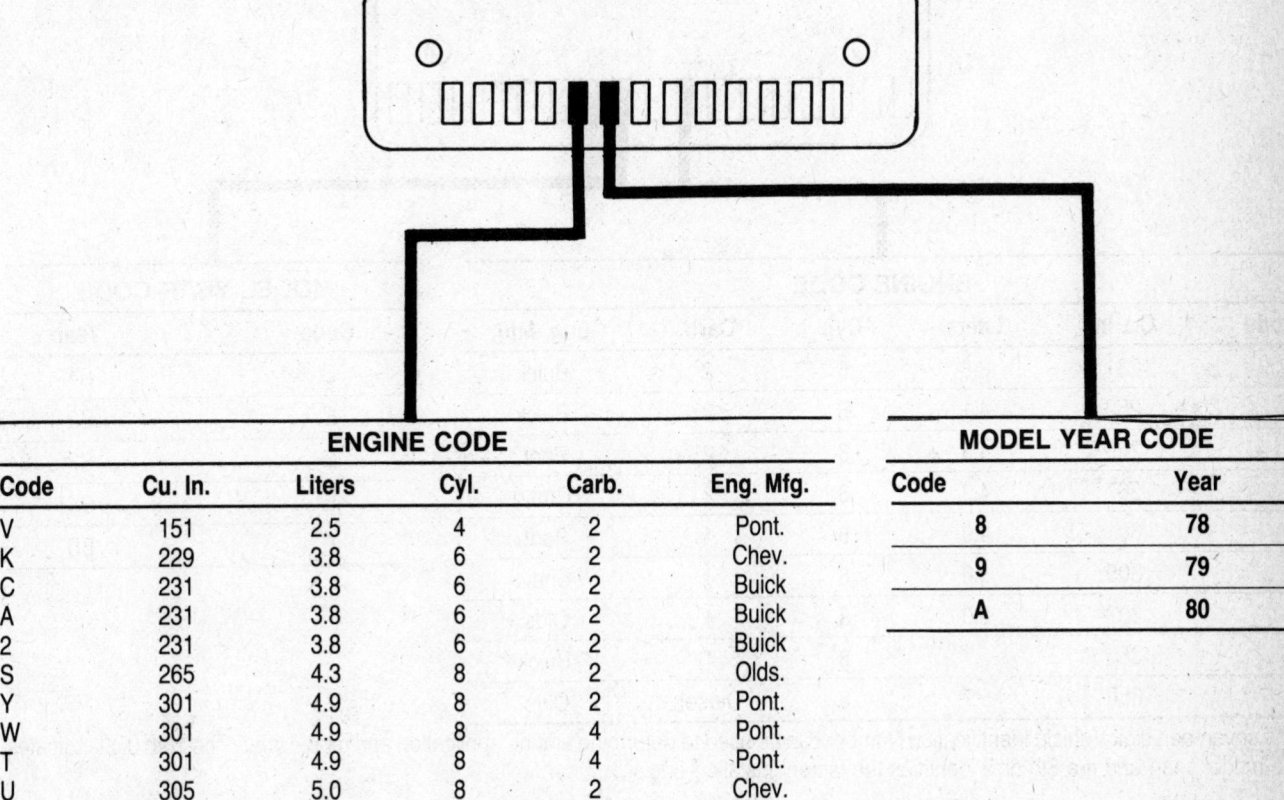

ENGINE CODE

Code	Cu. In.	Liters	Cyl.	Carb.	Eng. Mfg.
V	151	2.5	4	2	Pont.
K	229	3.8	6	2	Chev.
C	231	3.8	6	2	Buick
A	231	3.8	6	2	Buick
2	231	3.8	6	2	Buick
S	265	4.3	8	2	Olds.
Y	301	4.9	8	2	Pont.
W	301	4.9	8	4	Pont.
T	301	4.9	8	4	Pont.
U	305	5.0	8	2	Chev.
H	305	5.0	8	4	Chev.
G	305	5.0	8	2	Chev.
L	350	5.7	8	4	Chev.
P	350	5.7	8	4	Pont.
R	350	5.7	8	4	Olds.
X	350	5.7	8	4	Buick
N	350	5.7	8	Diesel	Olds.
Z	400	6.6	8	4	Pont.
K	403	6.6	8	4	Olds.

MODEL YEAR CODE

Code	Year
8	78
9	79
A	80

The thirteen digit Vehicle Identification Number can be used to determine engine application and model year. The 6th digit indicates the model year, and the 5th digit identifies the factory installed engine.

VEHICLE IDENTIFICATION NUMBER (VIN)

It is important for servicing and ordering parts to be certain of the vehicle and engine identification. The VIN (vehicle identification number) is a 13 or 17 digit number visible through the windshield on the driver's side of the dash and contains the vehicle and engine identification codes. It can be interpreted as follows:

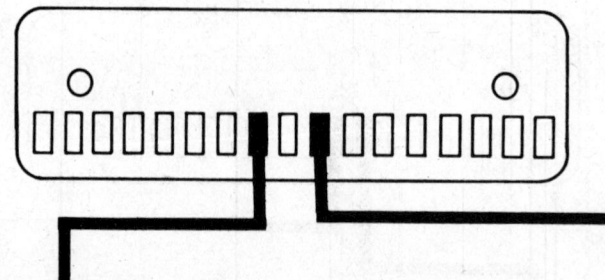

ENGINE CODE

Code	Cu. In.	Liters	Cyl.	Carb.	Eng. Mfg.
A	231	3.8	6	2	Buick
4	252	4.1	6	2	Buick
S	265	4.3	8	2	Pont.
J	267	4.3	8	2	Chev.
W	301	4.9	8	4	Pont.
H	305	5.0	8	4	Chev.
Y	307	5.0	8	4	Olds.
X	350	5.7	8	4	Buick
N	350	5.7	8	Diesel	Olds.

MODEL YEAR CODE

Code	Year
B	81
C	82
D	83
E	84
F	85

The seventeen digit Vehicle Identification Number can be used to determine engine application and model year. The 10th digit indicates the model year, and the 8th digit identifies the factory installed engine.

GENERAL ENGINE SPECIFICATIONS

Year	Eng. V.I.N. Code	Engine No. Cyl. Displacement Cu. In.	Eng. Mfg.	Carburetor Type	Horsepower @ rpm ■	Torque @ rpm (ft lbs) ■	Bore × Stroke (in.)	Compression Ratio	Oil Pressure @ 2000 rpm
'78	V	4-151	Pont.	2 bbl	87 @ 4400	128 @ 2400	4.000 × 3.000	8.3:1	36–41
	A	6-231	Buick	2 bbl	105 @ 3200	185 @ 2000	3.800 × 3.400	8.0:1	37②
	Y	8-301	Pont.	2 bbl	135 @ 4000	250 @ 1600	4.000 × 3.000	8.2:1	35–40②
	W	8-301	Pont.	4 bbl	150 @ 4000	265 @ 1600	4.000 × 3.000	8.2:1	35–40②
	U	8-305	Chev.	2 bbl	145 @ 3800	245 @ 2400	3.736 × 3.480	8.4:1	32–40
	H	8-305	Chev.	4 bbl	155 @ 3800	260 @ 2400	3.736 × 3.480	8.4:1	32–40
	X	8-350	Buick	4 bbl	290 @ 1600	165 @ 4000	3.800 × 3.850	8.0:1	37④
	R	8-350	Olds.	4 bbl	280 @ 1600	160 @ 4000	4.057 × 3.385	7.9:1	30–45③
	L	8-350	Chev.	4 bbl	170 @ 3800	270 @ 2400	4.000 × 3.480	8.2:1	30–45①
	Z	8-400	Pont.	4 bbl	180 @ 3600	325 @ 1600	4.120 × 3.750	7.7:1	35–40②
	Z	8-400	Pont.	4 bbl	188 @ 4000	340 @ 1700	4.120 × 3.750	8.1:1	35–40②
	K	8-403	Olds.	4 bbl	180 @ 3400	315 @ 2200	4.351 × 3.385	7.9:1	30–45③

GENERAL ENGINE SPECIFICATIONS

Year	Eng. V.I.N. Code	Engine No. Cyl. Displacement Cu. In.	Eng. Mfg.	Carburetor Type	Horsepower @ rpm ■	Torque @ rpm (ft lbs) ■	Bore × Stroke (in.)	Compression Ratio	Oil Pressure @ 2000 rpm
'79	V	4-151	Pont.	2 bbl	85 @ 4400	123 @ 2800	4.000 × 3.000	8.3:1	36–41
	2, A	6-231	Buick	2 bbl	115 @ 3800	190 @ 2000	3.800 × 3.400	8.2:1	34
	Y	8-301	Pont.	2 bbl	140 @ 3600	235 @ 2000	4.000 × 3.000	8.1:1	35–40②
	W	8-301	Pont.	4 bbl	150 @ 4000	240 @ 2000	4.000 × 3.000	8.1:1	35–40②
	G	8-305	Chev.	2 bbl	140 @ 3800	270 @ 2400	3.736 × 3.480	8.5:1	40
	H	8-305	Chev.	4 bbl	160 @ 3800	235 @ 2400	3.736 × 3.480	8.5:1	40
	L	8-350	Chev.	4 bbl	160 @ 3800	260 @ 2400	4.000 × 3.480	8.5:1	40
	X	8-350	Buick	4 bbl	155 @ 3400	280 @ 1800	3.800 × 3.850	8.0:1	35
	R	8-350	Olds.	4 bbl	170 @ 3800	275 @ 2000	4.057 × 3.385	8.0:1	35
	K	8-403	Olds.	4 bbl	185 @ 3600	320 @ 2200	4.351 × 3.385	8.0:1	40
'80	K	6-229	Chev.	2 bbl	110 @ 4200	170 @ 2000	3.736 × 3.480	8.6:1	45
	A	6-231	Buick	2 bbl	115 @ 3800	188 @ 2000	3.800 × 3.400	8.0:1	37
	S	8-265	Pont.	2 bbl	120 @ 3600	210 @ 1600	3.750 × 3.000	8.0:1	40②
	W	8-301	Pont.	4 bbl	150 @ 4000	240 @ 2000	4.000 × 3.000	8.2:1	40②
	T	8-301	Pont.	Turbo	185 @ 4000	280 @ 2000	4.000 × 3.000	7.5:1	60②
	H	8-305	Chev.	4 bbl	150 @ 3800	230 @ 2400	3.736 × 3.480	8.5:1	40
	X	8-350	Buick	4 bbl	155 @ 3400	280 @ 1800	3.800 × 3.850	8.0:1	35
	R	8-350	Olds.	4 bbl	160 @ 3800	260 @ 2400	4.000 × 3.480	8.5:1	40
	N	8-350	Olds.	Diesel	125 @ 3600	225 @ 1600	4.057 × 3.385	22.5:1	40③
'81	K	6-229	Chev.	2 bbl	115 @ 4200	170 @ 2000	3.736 × 3.480	8.6:1	45
	A	6-231	Buick	2 bbl	115 @ 3800	188 @ 2000	3.800 × 3.400	8.0:1	37
	S	8-265	Pont.	2 bbl	120 @ 3600	210 @ 1600	3.750 × 3.000	8.0:1	40④
	J	8-267	Chev.	2 bbl	115 @ 4000	200 @ 2400	3.500 × 3.480	8.3:1	45
	W	8-301	Pont.	4 bbl	155 @ 4000	240 @ 2000	4.000 × 3.000	8.2:1	40
	H	8-305	Chev.	4 bbl	210 @ 4000	345 @ 2000	3.736 × 3.480	7.5:1	60
	Y	8-307	Olds.	4 bbl	148 @ 3800	250 @ 2400	3.800 × 3.385	8.0:1	40③
	X	8-350	Buick	4 bbl	155 @ 3400	280 @ 1800	3.800 × 3.850	8.0:1	35
	N	8-350	Olds.	Diesel	105 @ 3200	205 @ 1600	4.057 × 3.385	22.5:1	40③
'82	A	6-231	Buick	2 bbl	110 @ 3800	190 @ 1600	3.800 × 3.400	8.0:1	37
	4	6-252	Buick	4 bbl	125 @ 4000	205 @ 2000	3.965 × 3.400	8.0:1	37
	N	8-350	Olds.	Diesel	105 @ 3200	200 @ 1600	4.057 × 3.385	22.5:1	40
'83–'84	A	6-231	Buick	2 bbl	110 @ 3800	190 @ 1600	3.800 × 3.400	8.0:1	37
	H	8-305	Chev.	4 bbl	150 @ 3800	240 @ 2400	3.736 × 3.480	8.6:1	45
	N	8-350	Olds.	Diesel	105 @ 3200	200 @ 1600	4.057 × 3.385	22.5:1	40③
'85	A	6-231	Buick	2 bbl	110 @ 3800	190 @ 1600	3.800 × 3.400	8.0:1	37
	H	8-305	Chev.	4 bbl	150 @ 3800	240 @ 2400	3.736 × 3.480	8.6:1	45
	N	8-350	Olds.	Diesel	105 @ 3200	200 @ 1600	4.057 × 3.385	22.5:1	40③

① Pressure at 2400 prm ③ Pressure at 1500 rpm
② Pressure at 2600 rpm ④ Above 2600 rpm

TUNE-UP SPECIFICATIONS
LeMans, Grand Am, 1982–'85 Bonneville

(When analyzing compression test results, look for uniformity among cylinders rather than specific pressures.)

Year	Eng. V.I.N. Code	No. Cyl. Displacement (cu in.)	Eng. Mfg.	hp	Spark Plugs Orig. Type	Spark Plugs Gap (in.)	Distributor Point Dwell (deg)	Distributor Point Gap (in.)	Ignition Timing (deg) ▲ Man Trans ●	Ignition Timing (deg) ▲ Auto Trans	Valves Opens ■ (deg)	Fuel Pressure (psi)	Idle Speed ● (rpm) ▲ Man Trans	Idle Speed ● (rpm) ▲ Auto Trans
'78	A	6-231	Buick	105	R-46TSX	.060	Electronic		15B	15B	27	7-8.5	800	670(600)
	Y	8-301	Pont.	135	R-46TSX	.060	Electronic		—	12B	17	4.5-5.5	—	550
	W	8-301	Pont.	150	R-45TSX	.060	Electronic		—	12B	17	4.5-5.5	—	550
	U	8-305	Chev.	145	R-45TS	.045	Electronic		—	④	29	4.5-5	—	⑤
	L	8-350	Chev.	170	R-45TS	.045	Electronic		—	8B	17	4-5	—	650
'79	2,A	6-231	Buick	115	R-46TSX	.060	Electronic		15B	15B	16	4.5-5.5	800	600
	Y	8-301	Pont.	140	R-46TSX③	.060	Electronic		—	12B	16	5.5-6.5	—	650
	W	8-301	Pont.	150	R-45TSX	.060	Electronic		14B	12B	16⑥	5.5-6.5	750	650
	H	8-305	Chev.	160	R-45TS	.045	Electronic		—	4B	28	5.5-6.5	—	500
	L	8-350	Chev.	160	R-45TS	.045	Electronic		—	8B	28	5.5-6.5	—	600
'80	A	6-231	Buick	115	R-45TSX⑦	.060⑦	Electronic		—	15B	16	3-4½	—	620/550①
	K	6-229	Chev.	All	R-45TS	.045	Electronic		—	6B	42	4.5-6.0	②	②
	S	8-265	Pont.	120	R-45TSX	.060	Electronic		—	10B	27	7-8½	—	650/550①
	W	8-301	Pont.	150	R-45TSX	.060	Electronic		—	12B	16	7-8½	—	650/500①
	H	8-305	Chev.	160	R-45TS	.045	Electronic		—	4B	28	7½-9	—	650/550①
'81	A	6-231	Buick	115	R-45TSX	.080	Electronic		15B	15B	16	4.25-5.75	800⑧	500⑧
	K	6-229	Chev.	All	R-45TS	.045	Electronic		—	6B	42	4.5-6.0	②	②
	S	8-265	Pont.	119	R-45TSX	.060	Electronic		—	12B	16	7-8.5	—	450⑧
	W	8-301	Pont.	155	R-45TSX	.060	Electronic		—	12B	16	7-8.5	—	450⑧
'82	A	6-231	Buick	110	R-45TS8	.080	Electronic		—	15B	16	4.25-5.75	—	②
	4	6-252	Buick	125	R-45TS8	.080	Electronic		—	15B	16	4.25-5.75	—	②
	N	8-350	Olds	105	—	—	—		—	②	16	5.5-6.5	—	②
'83–'84	A	6-231	Buick	110	R-45TS8	.080	Electronic		—	15B	16	4.25-5.75	—	②
	H	8-305	Chev.	All	R-45TS	.045	Electronic		—	②	44	5.5-7.0	—	②
	N	8-350	Olds.	105	—	—	—		—	②	16	5.5-6.5	—	②
'85	A	6-231	Buick	All	R-45TS8	.080	Electronic		—	②	16	4.25-5.75	—	②
	H	8-305	Chev.	All	R-45TS	.045	Electronic		—	②	44	5.5-7.0	—	②
	N	8-350	Olds.	All	—	—	—		—	②	16	5.5-6.5	—	②

NOTE: The underhood specifications sticker often reflects tuneup specification changes made in production. Sticker figures must be used if they disagree with those in this chart. Part numbers in this chart are not recommendations by Chilton for any product by brand name.

▲ See text for procedure
● Figure in parentheses indicates California engine
■ All figures are in degrees Before Top Dead Center. Where two figures appear, the first represents timing with manual transmission, the second with automatic transmission.
① Lower figure indicates idle speed with solenoid disconnected
② See underhood sticker
③ High altitude and Calif.: R-45TSX
④ Except California and High Altitude: 4B
   California: 6B
   High Altitude: 8B

⑤ Except California and High Altitude: 600
   California: 650
   High Altitude: 700
⑥ High performance: 27
⑦ Low Altitude w/o C-4, R-45TS, gap .040
⑧ Curb Idle; for base idle see underhood sticker
B Before Top Dead Center
— Not applicable
N.A. Not available

TUNE-UP SPECIFICATIONS
1978-'81 Bonneville, Catalina, Grand Prix, Parisienne

(When analyzing compression test results, look for uniformity among cylinders rather than specific pressures.)

Year	Eng. V.I.N. Code	No. Cyl. Displace-ment	Eng. Mfg.	hp (cu in.)	Orig. Type ●	Gap (in.)	Point Dwell (deg)	Point Gap (in.)	Man Trans ●	Auto Trans	Valves Intake Opens ■ (deg)	Fuel Pump Pressure (psi)	Man Trans	Auto Trans
'78	A	6-231	Buick	105	R-46TSX	.060	Electronic		15B	15B	17	4.5-5.74	800	600
	Y,W	8-301	Pont.	All	R-46TSX④	.060	Electronic		—	12B	27	7-8.5	—	550
	U,H	8-305	Chev.	All	R-45TS	.045	Electronic		—	8B(6B)	28	3-4.5	—	600 (500)
	X	8-350	Buick	170	R-46TSX	.060	Electronic		—	15B	16	4.5-5.5	—	550
	R	8-350	Olds.	170	R-46SZ	.060	Electronic		—	20B @ 1100	17	5.5-6.5	—	550
	Z	8-400	Pont.	180	R-45TSX	.060	Electronic		—	16B	29	7-8.5	—	575
	K	8-403	Pont.	185	R-46SZ	.060	Electronic		—	20B @ 1100	16	6-7.5	—	600 (550)
'79	2,A	6-231	Buick	115	R-46TSX	.060	Electronic		15B	15B	16	4.5-5.5	800	600
	Y	8-301	Pont.	140	R-46TSX	.060	Electronic		—	12B	16	7.0-8.5	—	650
	W	8-301	Pont.	150	R-45TSX	.060	Electronic		14B	12B	16⑤	7.0-8.5	750	500 (650)
	H	8-305	Chev.	160	R-45TS	.045	Electronic		—	4B	28	4.5-5.5	—	①
	X	8-350	Buick	155	R-46TSX	.060	Electronic		—	15B	16	4.5-5.5	—	550
	R	8-350	Olds.	170	R-46SZ	.060	Electronic		—	20B @ 1100	16	5.5-6.5	—	550
	K	8-403	Olds.	185	R-46SZ	.060	Electronic		—	18B(20B) @ 1100	16	5.5-6.5	—	500 (500)
'80	A	6-231	Buick	115	R-45TSX⑥	.060⑥	Electronic		—	15B	16	3-4½	—	620/550
	S	8-265	Pont.	120	R-45TSX	.060	Electronic		—	10B	27	7-8½	—	650/550
	W	8-301	Pont.	150	R-45TSX	.060	Electronic		—	12B	16	7-8½	—	650/500
	H	8-305	Chev.	160	R-45TS	.045	Electronic		—	4B	28	7½-9	—	650/550
	R	8-350	Olds.	160	R-43TS	.045	Electronic		—	6B	28	7½-9	—	650/550
	N	8-350	Olds.	105	—	—			—	5B③	16	5½-6½	—	600
'81	A	6-231	Buick	110	R-45TS8	.080	Electronic		—	②	16	4.25-5.75	—	②
	S	8-265	Pont.	120	R-45TSX	.060	Electronic		—	12B	16	7-8.5	—	②
	Y	8-307	Olds.	148	R-46SX	.080	Electronic		—	15B	14	5.5-6.5	—	②
	N	8-350	Olds.	105	—	—	—		—	②	16	5.5-6.5	—	②
'82	A	6-231	Buick	110	R-45TS8	.080	Electronic		—	15B	16	4.25-5.75	—	②
	4	6-252	Buick	125	R-45TS8	.080	Electronic		—	15B	16	4.25-5.75	—	②
	N	8-350	Olds.	105	—	—	Electronic		—	②	16	5.5-6.5	—	②
'83-'84	A	6-231	Buick	110	R-45TS8	.080	Electronic		—	15B	16	4.25-5.75	—	②
	H	8-305	Chev.	NA	R-45TS	.045	Electronic		—	②		5.5-7.0	—	②
	N	8-350	Olds.	105	—	—	—		—	②	16	5.5-6.5	—	②

TUNE-UP SPECIFICATIONS
1978-'81 Bonneville, Catalina, Grand Prix, Parisienne

(When analyzing compression test results, look for uniformity among cylinders rather than specific pressures.)

Year	Engine				Spark Plugs		Distributor		Ignition Timing (deg) ▲		Valves Intake Opens ■ (deg)	Fuel Pump Pressure (psi)	Idle Speed ● (rpm)▲	
	Eng. V.I.N. Code	No. Cyl. Displace-ment	Eng. Mfg.	hp (cu in.)	Orig. Type ●	Gap (in.)	Point Dwell (deg)	Point Gap (in.)	Man Trans ●	Auto Trans			Man Trans	Auto Trans
'85	A	6-231	Buick	All	R-45TS8	.080	Electronic		—	②	16	4.25-5.75	—	②
	H	8-305	Chev.	All	R-45TS	.045	Electronic		—	②	44	5.5-7.0	—	②
	N	8-350	Olds.	All	—	—	—		—	②	16	5.5-6.5	—	②

NOTE: The underhood specifications sticker often reflects tune-up specification changes made in production. Sticker figures must be used if they disagree with those in this chart.

Part numbers in this chart are not recommendations by Chilton for any product by brand name.

▲ See text for procedure

● Figure in parentheses indicates California engine. Where two idle speeds appear separated by a slash, the second is with the solenoid disconnected.

■ All figures are in degrees Before Top Dead Center. Where two figures appear, the first represents timing with manual transmission, the second with automatic transmission.

① Calif.: 500, High Altitude: 600
② See the underhood sticker
③ Static
④ with 4 bbl: R-45TSX
⑤ High performance: 27
⑥ Low Altitude without C-4: R-45TS; gap: .040
B Before Top Dead Center
— Not applicable

TUNE-UP SPECIFICATIONS
Phoenix

(When analyzing compression test results, look for uniformity among cylinders rather than specific pressures.)

Year	Engine				Spark Plugs		Distributor		Ignition Timing (deg) ▲		Valves Intake Opens ■ (deg)	Fuel Pump Pressure (psi)	Idle Speed ● (rpm) ▲	
	Eng. V.I.N. Code	No. Cyl. Displace-ment	Eng. Mfg.	hp (cu in.)	Orig. Type	Gap (in.)	Point Dwell (deg)	Point Gap (in.)	Man Trans ●	Auto Trans			Man Trans	Auto Trans
'78	V	4-151	Pont.	87	R-43TSX	.060	Electronic		14B	①	33	4-5.5	—	②
	A	6-231	Buick	105	R-46TSX	.060	Electronic		15B	15B	17	3-4.5	800	600
	H	8-305	Chev.	135	R-45TS	.045	Electronic		4B	6B	29	4.5-5	700	③
	L	8-350	Chev.	170	R-45TS	.045	Electronic		—	8B	17	4-5	—	600
'79	V	4-151	Pont.	85	R-43TSX	.060	Electronic		12B(14B)	12B(14B)	33	5.0-6.5	900 (1000)	650
	2,A	6-231	Buick	115	R-46TSX	.060	Electronic		15B	15B	16	4.0-6.5	800	600
	G	8-305	Chev.	145	R-45TS	.045	Electronic		4B	4B	28	5.5-6.5	600	500
	L	8-350	Chev.	160	R-45TS	.045	Electronic		—	8B	28	5.5-6.5	—	600

NOTE: The underhood specifications sticker often reflects tuneup specification changes made in production. Sticker figures must be used if they disagree with those in this chart. Part numbers in this chart are not recommendations by Chilton for any product by brand name.

▲ See text for procedure
■ All figures Before Top Dead Center
B Before Top Dead Center
● Figure in Parentheses for California. When two figures are separated by a slash, the lower figure is idle speed with solenoid disconnected.
① Phoenix: 14B

② Air conditioned models: 650
Without air conditioning: 500
③ Phoenix with air conditioning, except Calif. and high alt.: 600
Phoenix, high altitude: 700
All others: 650

FIRING ORDERS

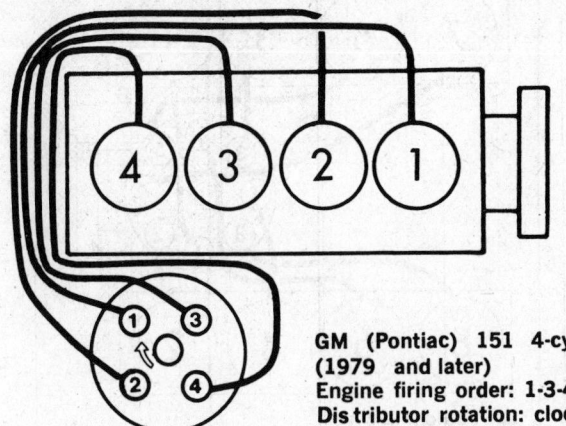

**GM (Pontiac) 151 4-cyl.
(1979 and later)
Engine firing order: 1-3-4-2
Distributor rotation: clockwise**

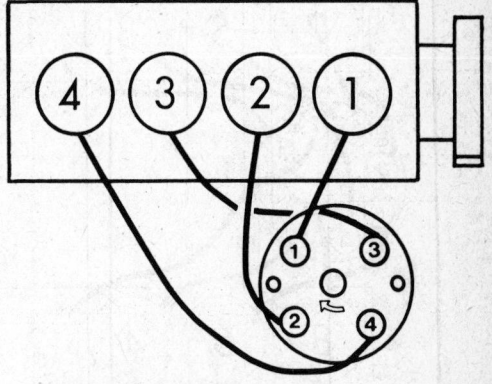

**GM (Pontiac) 151 4-cyl. (through 1978)
Engine firing order: 1-3-4-2
Distributor rotation: clockwise**

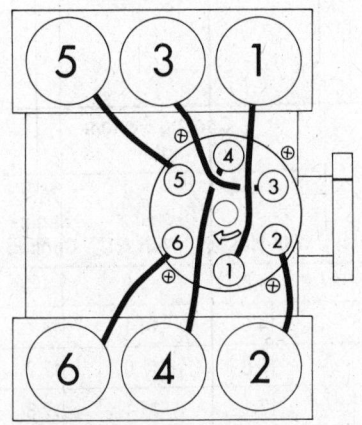

**GM (Buick) 231, 252 V6
Engine firing order: 1-6-5-4-3-2
Distributor rotation: clockwise**

V6 harmonic balancers have two timing marks: one is 1/8 in. wide, and one is 1/16 in. wide. Use the 1/16 in. mark for timing with a hand held light. The 1/8 in. mark is used only with a magnetic timing pick-up probe.

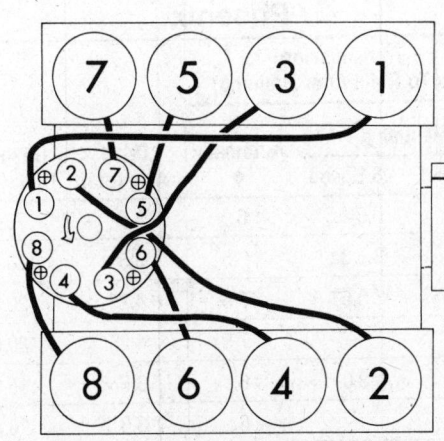

**GM (Oldsmobile) 260 V8
Engine firing order: 1-8-4-3-6-5-7-2
Distributor rotation: counterclockwise**

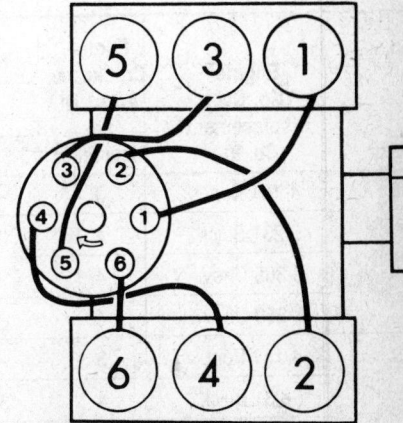

**GM (Chevrolet) 229, V6
Engine firing order: 1-6-5-4-3-2
Distributor rotation: clockwise**

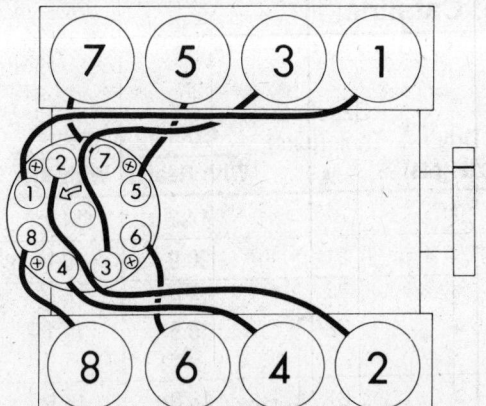

**GM (Oldsmobile) 307, 350, 403 V8
Engine firing order: 1-8-4-3-6-5-7-2
Distributor rotation: counterclockwise**

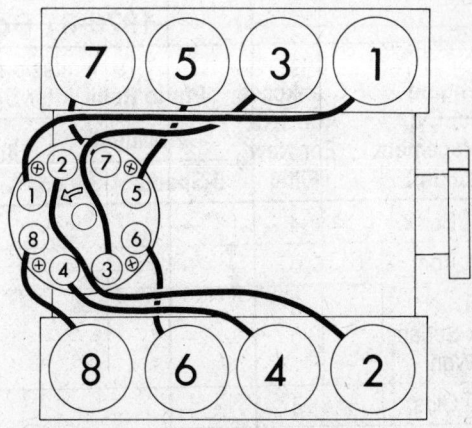

**GM (Pontiac) 265, 301, 350, 400, V8
Engine firing order: 1-8-4-3-6-5-7-2
Distributor rotation: counterclockwise**

FIRING ORDERS

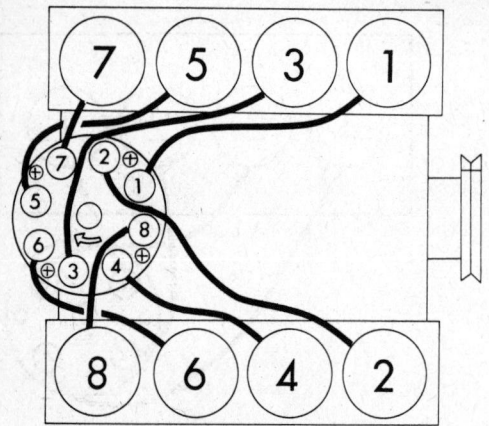

GM (Chevrolet) 305, 350 V8
Engine firing order: 1-8-4-3-6-5-7-2
Distributor rotation: clockwise

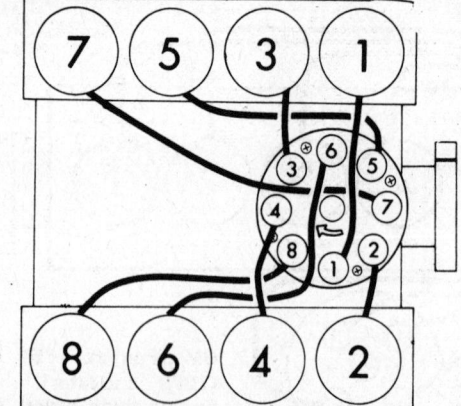

GM (Buick) 350 V8
Engine firing order: 1-8-4-3-6-5-7-2
Distributor rotation: clockwise

CAPACITIES
Phoenix

Year	Engine No. Cyl. Displacement (Cu. In.)	Engine Crankcase Add 1 Qt For New Filter	Transmission (Pts To Refill After Draining) Manual ▲ 3-Speed	4/5 Speed	Automatic ●	Drive Axle (pts)	Gasoline Tank (gals)	Cooling System (qts) With Heater	With A/C	With Super-Cooling
'78	4-151 Pont.	3	—	3.5/3.5	6	3.5	20.8	11.8	11.8	—
	6-231 Buick	4	3.5	3.5/3.5	7.5	3.5	20.8	14.0	14.1	14.1
	8-305 Chev.	4	—	3.5	7.5	4.25	20.8	16.8	17.0	17.2
	8-350 Chev.	4	—	—	7.5	4.25	20.8	17.1	17.1	17.8
'79	4-151 Pont.	3	—	3.0	6	3.5	15.0	13.5	13.5	13.3
	6-231 Buick	4	3.0	—	6	3.5	20.8	14.0	14.1	14.0
	8-305 Chev.	4	—	3.0	6	3.5	20.8	16.8	17.0	17.7
	8-350 Chev.	4	—	—	6	4.25	20.8	17.1	17.8	17.9

▲ 5-speed uses Dexron®
● Specifications do not include torque converter
— Not applicable

CAPACITIES
1978-81 Bonneville, Catalina

Year	Engine No. Cyl. Displacement (cu. in.)	Engine Crankcase Add 1 Qt For New Filter	Transmission Pts to Refill After Draining Manual 3-Speed	4-Speed	Automatic ●	Drive Axle (pts)	Gasoline Tank (gals) ▲	Cooling System With Heater	With A/C	With Super Cooling
'78	6-231 Buick	4	—	—	①	②	21	14.2	14.1	14.1
	8-301 Pont.	5	—	—	①	②	21	20.2	20.1	20.8
	8-350 Buick Sedan	5	—	—	7.5	②	21	16.6	18.5	19.2
	Sta. Wgn.	5	—	—	7.5	5.4	22	18.6	19.1	19.1
	8-350 Olds.	4	—	—	7.5	②	21	16.5	16.5	16.4
	8-400 Pont.	5	—	—	7.5	②	21	26.3	20.3	20.3
	8-403 Olds.	4	—	—	7.5	②	21	17.7	23.0	23.0

CAPACITIES
1978-81 Bonneville, Catalina

Year	Engine No. Cyl. Displacement (cu. in.)	Engine Crankcase Add 1 Qt For New Filter	Transmission Pts to Refill After Draining Manual 3-Speed	4-Speed	Automatic ●	Drive Axle (pts)	Gasoline Tank (gals) ▲	Cooling System With Heater	With A/C	With Super Cooling
'79	6-231 Buick	4	—	—	6	3.5	21	13.9	13.9	13.9
	8-301 Pont.	4	—	—	6	3.5③	21	20.2	20.1	20.8
	8-350 Buick	4	—	—	6	3.5③	21	16.6	18.5	16.6
	8-350 Olds.	4	—	—	6	3.5③	21	16.5	16.4	17.1
	8-403 Olds.	4	—	—	6	3.5③	21	17.7	23.0	18.5
'80	6-231 Buick	4	—	—	8	3.4	20.7	12.6	12.6	—
	8-265 Pont.	4	—	—	8	3.4	20.7	20.0	20.0	20.0
	8-301 Pont.	4	—	—	6	3.4	20.7	20.0	20.0	20.0
	8-350 Chev.	4	—	—	6	3.4	20.7	—	15.5	15.5
	8-350 Olds.	7	—	—	6	3.4	20.7	—	17.0	17.0
'81	6-231 Buick	4	—	—	8	3.4	25.0	13.1	13.3	13.3
	8-265 Pont.	4	—	—	8	3.4	25.0	20.0	20.0	20.0
	8-307 Olds.	4	—	—	8	3.4	25.0	14.9	15.6	15.6
	8-350 Diesel	7	—	—	8	3.4	27.0	—	17.0	17.0

① Turbo Hydra-Matic 200: 6.0
Turbo Hydra-Matic 350: 7.5
② with 8.5 in. ring gear: 4.25
with 8.75 in. ring gear: 5.4

③ Sta. Wgn.: 4.25
● Specifications do not include torque converter

— Not applicable
▲ Station wagon fuel tank (gals) '78-'81, 22

CAPACITIES
Grand Prix and Parisienne

Year	Engine No. Cyl. Displacement (cu. in.)	Engine Crankcase Add 1 Qt For New Filter	Transmission Pts to Refill After Draining Manual 3-Speed	4-Speed	Automatic ●	Drive Axle (pts)	Gasoline Tank (gals)	Cooling System (qts) With Heater	With A/C	With Super Cooling
'78	6-231 Buick	4	—	—	7.5	3.5	18.1	14.3	14.2	14.2
	8-301 Pont.	5	—	—	①	3.5	18.1	20.3	20.2	20.9
	8-305 Chev.	4	—	—	①	3.5	18.1	17.7	17.4	18.1
'79	6-231 Buick	4	3.5	—	6	3.4	18.2	14.2	14.0	14.3
	8-301 Pont.	4	3.5	—	6	3.4	18.2	20.3	20.2	20.8
	8-305 Chev.	4	—	—	6	3.4	18.2	17.7	18.3	18.3
'80	6-231 Buick	4	—	—	6	3.4	18.1	12.6	12.6	—
	8-265 Pont.	4	—	—	6	3.4	18.1	19.2	19.2	19.2
	8-301 Pont.	4	—	—	6	3.4	18.1	19.2	19.2	19.2
	8-305 Chev.	4	—	—	6	3.4	18.1	17.2	17.2	17.2
'81	6-231 Buick	4	—	—	8	3.4	18.1	13.1	13.1	—
	8-265 Pont.	4	—	—	8	3.4	18.1	20.3	20.3	20.3
	8-350 Diesel	7	—	—	8	3.4	19.1	—	17.0	

CAPACITIES
Grand Prix and Parisienne

Year	Engine No. Cyl. Displacement (cu. in.)	Engine Crankcase Add 1 Qt For New Filter	Transmission Pts to Refill After Draining Manual 3-Speed	4-Speed	Automatic ●	Drive Axle (pts)	Gasoline Tank (gals)	Cooling System (qts) With Heater	With A/C	With Super Cooling
'82	6-231 Buick	4②	—	—	8	3.5	18.1	13.0	13.1	13.1
	6-252 Buick	4②	—	—	8	3.5	18.1	13.0	13.1	13.1
	8-350 Diesel	7③	—	—	8	3.5	18.1	17.3	17.3	—
'83–'84	6-231 Buick	4	—	—	6	3.5	17.5	—	12.9	—
	8-305 Chev.	4	—	—	6	3.5	17.5	—	15.3	—
	8-350 Diesel	7③	—	—	6	3.5	19.8	—	17.2	—
'85	6-231 Buick	4	—	—	6	3.5	17.5	—	12.9	—
	8-305 Chev.	4	—	—	6	3.5	17.5	—	15.3	—
	8-350 Diesel	7③	—	—	6	3.5	19.8	—	17.2	—

● Specifications do not include torque converter
① with Turbo Hydra-Matic 200: 6.0

with Turbo Hydra-Matic 350: 7.5
② On micro-filter equipped cars, capacity is the same with or without filter

③ Includes mandatory filter change
— Not applicable or specified

CAPACITIES
LeMans, Grand Am, 1982-85 Bonneville

Year	Engine No. Cyl. Displacement (Cu. In.)	Engine Crankcase Add 1 Qt For New Filter	Transmission (Pts To Refill After Draining) Manual 3-Speed	4/5 Speed	Automatic ●	Drive Axle (pts)	Gasoline Tank (gals)	Cooling System (qts) With Heater	With A/C	With Super-Cooling
'78	6-231 Buick	4	3.5	—	6	3.5	18.1⑤	14.3	14.2	14.2
	8-301 Pont.	5	—	—	6	3.5	18.1⑤	20.3	20.2④	20.9
	8-305 Chev.	4	—	—	6	3.5	18.1⑤	17.7	17.4	18.1
	8-350 Chev.	4	—	—	7.5	3.5	18.1⑤	17.7	17.4	18.1
'79	6-231 Buick	4	3.5	3.5	6	3.5	18.2	14.2	14	14.3
	8-301 Pont.	4	—	3.5	6	3.5	18.2	20.3	20.2	20.8
	8-305 Chev.	4	—	—	6	3.5	18.2	20.3	20.2	20.8
'80	6-231 Buick	4	—	—	8	3.4	18.1⑤	12.6	12.6	—
	8-265 Pont.	4	—	—	8	3.4	18.1⑤	19.2	19.2	19.2
	8-301 Pont.	4	—	—	8	3.4	18.1⑤	19.2	19.2	19.2
	8-301/W72 Pont.	4	—	—	6	3.4	18.1⑤	19.2	19.2	19.2
	8-305 Chev.	4	—	—	8	3.4	18.1⑤	—	17.2	17.2
'81	6-231 Buick	4	3.5	—	8②	3.5	18.1⑤	13.1	13.1	—
	8-265 Pont.	4	—	—	8	3.5	18.1⑤	20.3	20.3	20.3
	8-301 Pont.	4③	—	—	8	3.5	18.1⑤	20.3	21.0	21.0
'82	6-231 Buick	4③	—	—	8	3.5	18.1⑤	13.0	13.1	13.1
	6-252 Buick	4③	—	—	8	3.5	18.1⑤	13.0	13.1	13.1
	8-350 Diesel	7①	—	—	8	3.5	18.1⑤	17.3	17.3	—

CAPACITIES
LeMans, Grand Am, 1982-85 Bonneville

Year	Engine No. Cyl. Displacement (Cu. In.)	Engine Crankcase Add 1 Qt For New Filter	Transmission (Pts To Refill After Draining)		Automatic ●	Drive Axle (pts)	Gasoline Tank (gals)	Cooling System (qts)		With Super-Cooling
			Manual							
			3-Speed	4/5 Speed				With Heater	With A/C	
'83–'84	6-231 Buick	4	—	—	6	3.5	17.5	—	12.9	—
	8-305 Chev.	4	—	—	6	3.5	17.5	—	15.3	—
	8-350 Diesel	7①	—	—	6	3.5	19.8	—	17.2	—
'85	6-231 Buick	4	—	—	6	3.5	17.5	—	12.9	—
	8-305 Chev.	4	—	—	6	3.5	17.5	—	15.3	—
	8-350 Diesel	7①	—	—	6	3.5	19.8	—	17.2	—

● Specifications do not include torque converter
① Includes mandatory filter change
② w/THM 350C—6 pt.
③ On micro-filter equipped cars, capacity is the same with or without filter
④ StaWgn: 20.9
⑤ StaWgn: 18.2

VALVE SPECIFICATIONS
1978-81 Bonneville, Catalina, Grand Prix, Parisienne

Year	Engine No. Cyl. Displacement (cu in.)	Seat Angle (deg) ■	Face Angle (deg) ●	Spring Test Pressure ▲ (lbs @ in.)	Spring Installed Height (in.)	Stem To Guide Clearance (in.)		Stem Diameter (in.)	
						Intake	Exhaust	Intake	Exhaust
'78	6-231 Buick	45	45	182 @ 1.34	1 47/64	.0015-.0032	.0015-.0032	.3402-.3412	.3405-.3412
	8-301 Pont.	46	45	165 @ 1.29	1 2/3	.0010-.0027	.0010-.0027⑤	.3425	.3425
	8-305 Chev.	46	45	190 @ 1.16	1 23/32	.0010-.0037	.0010-.0047	.3410	.3410
	8-350 Buick	45	45	180 @ 1.34	1 47/64	.0015-.0032	.0015-.0035	.3720-.3730	.3723-.3730
	8-350 Olds.	45②	46③	190 @ 1.27	1 47/64	.0010-.0027	.0015-.0032	.3425-.3432	.3420-.3427
	8-400 Pont.	30	29	135 @ 1.18	1 27/50	.0016-.0033	.0021-.0038	.3425	.3425
	8-403 Olds.	45②	46③	190 @ 1.27	1 47/64	.0010-.0027	.0015-.0032	.3425-.3432	.3420-.3427
'79–'80	6-231 Buick	45	45	182 @ 1.340	1 23/32	.0015-.0032	.0015-.0032	.3402-.3412	.3405-.3412
	8-265 Pont.	46	45	170 @ 1.290	1 43/64	.0010-.0027	.0010-.0027	.3425	.3425
	8-301 Pont.	46	45	170 @ 1.290	1 43/64	.0010-.0027	.0010-.0027	.3425	.3425
	6-229, 8-305 Chev.	46	45	200 @ 1.250	1 23/32	.0010-.0027	.0010-.0027	.3414	.3414
	8-350 Chev.	46	45	200 @ 1.250	1 23/32	.0010-.0027	.0010-.0027	.3414	.3414
	8-350 Diesel	①	④	151 @ 1.300	1 43/64	.0010-.0027	.0015-.0032	.3425-.3432	.3420-.3427
'81	6-231 Buick	45	45	182 @ 1.340⑥	1 47/64	.0015-.0035	.0015-.0032	.3401-.3412	.3405-.3412
	8-265 Pont.	46	45	175 @ 1.290	1 43/64	.0010-.0027	.0010-.0027	.3418-.3425	.3418-.3425
	8-307 Olds.	①	④	187 @ 1.270	1 43/64	.0010-.0027	.0015-.0032	.3429	.3424
	8-350 Diesel	①	④	210 @ 1.300	1 43/64	.0010-.0027	.0015-.0032	.3429	.3424
'82	6-231 Buick	45	45	182 @ 1.340	1 23/32	.0015-.0032	.0015-.0032	.3402-.3412	.3405-.3412
	6-252 Buick	45	45	182 @ 1.340	1 47/64	.0015-.0032	.0015-.0032	.3407	.3407
	8-350 Diesel	45⑦	45⑦	152 @ 1.300	1 43/64	.0010-.0027	.0015-.0032	.3432-.3425	.3427-.3420
'83–'84	6-231 Buick	45	45	182 @ 1.340	1.72	.0015-.0032	.0015-.0032	.3402-.3412	.3405-.3412
	8-305 Chev.	46	45	200 @ 1.25	1.70	.0010-.0027	.0010-.0027	.3414	.3414
	8-350 Diesel	46	45	210 @ 1.22	1 43/64	.0010-.0027	.0015-.0032	.3429	.3429

VALVE SPECIFICATIONS
1978-81 Bonneville, Catalina, Grand Prix, Parisienne

Year	Engine No. Cyl. Displacement (cu in.)	Seat Angle (deg) ■	Face Angle (deg) ●	Spring Test Pressure ▲ (lbs @ in.)	Spring Installed Height (in.)	Stem To Guide Clearance (in.)		Stem Diameter (in.)	
						Intake	Exhaust	Intake	Exhaust
'85	6-231 Buick	45	45	182 @ 1.340	1.72	.0015-.0032	.0015-.0032	.3402-.3412	.3405-.3412
	8-305 Chev.	46	45	200 @ 1.25	1²³⁄₃₂	.0010-.0027	.0010-.0027	.3414	.3414
	8-350 Diesel	46	45	210 @ 1.22	1⁴³⁄₆₄	.0010-.0027	.0015-.0032	.3429	.3429

■ Intake valve seat angles are shown. All exhaust valve seat angles are 45° unless otherwise indicated.

● Intake valve face angles are shown. All exhaust valve face angles are 44° unless otherwise indicated.

① Intake 45°; exhaust 31°
② Exhaust 31
③ Exhaust 30
④ Intake 46°; exhaust 60°
⑤ Clearance at bottom: .0020–.0037
⑥ 164 @ 1.34 intake
⑦ Exhaust valve: seat 59° face 60°

▲ INNER SPRING TEST PRESSURE
1978–81 Bonneville

'78-'79	8-400	97 @ 1.14

VALVE SPECIFICATIONS
Phoenix

Year	Engine No. Cyl. Displacement (cu. in.)	Seat Angle (deg) ■	Face Angle (deg) ●	Outer Spring Test Pressure▲ (lbs @ in.)	Spring Installed Height (in.)	Stem To Guide Clearance (In.)		Stem Diameter (In.)	
						Intake	Exhaust	Intake	Exhaust
'78	4-151 Pont.	46	45	82 @ 1.66	1¹¹⁄₁₆	.0010-.0027	.0010-.0027①	.3414	.3400
	6-231 Buick	45	45	182 @ 1.34	1⁴⁷⁄₆₄	.0015-.0032	.0015-.0032	.3402-.3412	.3405-.3412
	8-305 Chev.	46	45	190 @ 1.16	④	.0010-.0037	.0010-.0047	.3414	.3414
	8-350 Chev.	46	45	190 @ 1.16	④	.0010-.0037	.0010-.0047	.3414	.3414
	8-400 Pont.	③	⑤	135 @ 1.18	1³⁵⁄₆₄	.0016-.0033	.0021-.0038	.3425	.3425
	8-403 Olds.	②	②	190 @ 1.27	1⁴³⁄₆₄	.0010-.0027	.0015-.0032	.3425-.3432	.3420-.3427
'79	4-151 Pont.	46	45	82 @ 1.660	1¹¹⁄₁₆	.0010-.0027	.0010-.0027①	.3421	.3421
	6-231 Buick	45	45	182 @ 1.340	1⁴⁷⁄₆₄	.0015-.0032	.0015-.0032	.3402-.3412	.3405-.3412
	8-301 Pont.	46	45	165 @ 1.290	1⁴³⁄₆₄	.0010-.0027	.0010-.0027	.3425	.3425
	8-305 Chev.	46	45	200 @ 1.250	1²³⁄₃₂	.0010-.0027	.0010-.0027	.3414	.3414
	8-350 Chev.	46	45	200 @ 1.250	1²³⁄₃₂	.0010-.0027	.0010-.0027	.3414	.3414
	8-400 Pont.	③	⑤	135 @ 1.180	1³⁵⁄₆₄	.0016-.0033	.0021-.0038	.3425	.3425
	8-403 Olds.	②	②	190 @ 1.270	1⁴³⁄₆₄	.0010-.0027	.0015-.0032	.3425-.3432	.3420-.3427

■ Intake valve seat angles are shown. All exhaust valve seat angles are 45° unless otherwise indicated.

● Intake valve face angles are shown. All exhaust valve face angles are 44° unless otherwise indicated.

① Figure given is at top of guide; .0020-.0037 at bottom
② Intake seat 45°, intake face 44°; exhaust seat 31°, exhaust face 30°
③ Intake: 30

④ Intake: 1²³⁄₃₂
Exhaust: 1¹⁹⁄₃₂
⑤ Intake: 29
Exhaust: 44

Exhaust: 45

VALVE SPECIFICATIONS
Lemans, Grand Am, 1982–85 Bonneville

Year	Engine No. Cyl. Displacement (cu. in.)	Seat Angle (deg) ■	Face Angle (deg) ●	Outer Spring Test Pressure ▲ (lbs @ in.)	Spring Installed Height (in.)	Stem To Guide Clearance (in.) Intake	Exhaust	Stem Diameter (in.) Intake	Exhaust
'78	6-231 Buick	45	45	182 @ 1.340	1²³⁄₃₂	.0015-.0032	.0015-.0032	.3402-.3412	.3412-.3405
	8-301 Pont.	46	45	165 @ 1.290	1⁴³⁄₆₄	.0010-.0027	.0010-.0027	.3425	.3425
	8-305 Chev.	46	45	190 @ 1.160	②	.0010-.0037	.0010-.0047	.3414	.3414
	8-350 Chev.	46	45	190 @ 1.160	②	.0010-.0037	.0010-.0047	.3414	.3414
'79–'80	6-231 Buick	45	45	182 @ 1.340	1²³⁄₃₂	.0015-.0032	.0015-.0032	.3402-.3412	.3405-.3412
	8-265 Pont.	46	45	170 @ 1.290	1⁴³⁄₆₄	.0010-.0027	.0010-.0027	.3425	.3425
	8-301 Pont.	46	45	170 @ 1.290	1⁴³⁄₆₄	.0010-.0027	.0010-.0027	.3425	.3425
	8-305 Chev.	46	45	200 @ 1.250	1²³⁄₃₂	.0010-.0037	.0010-.0047	.3414	.3414
	8-350 Chev.	46	45	200 @ 1.250	1²³⁄₃₂	.0010-.0027	.0010-.0027	.3414	.3414
'81	6-231 Buick	45	45	182 @ 1.340	1²³⁄₃₂	.0015-.0032	.0015-.0032	.3402-.3412	.3405-.3412
	8-265 Pont.	46	45	175 @ 1.290	1⁴³⁄₆₄	.0010-.0027	.0010-.0027	.3418-.3425	.3418-.3425
	8-301 Pont.	46	45	175 @ 1.290	1⁴³⁄₆₄	.0010-.0027	.0010-.0027	.3418-.3425	.3418-.3425
'82	6-231 Buick	45	45	182 @ 1.340	1²³⁄₃₂	.0015-.0032	.0015-.0032	.3402-.3412	.3405-.3412
	6-252 Buick	45	45	182 @ 1.340	1⁴⁷⁄₆₄	.0015-.0032	.0015-.0032	.3407	.3407
	8-350 Diesel	45①	45①	152 @ 1.300	1⁴³⁄₆₄	.0010-.0027	.0015-.0032	.3432-.3425	.3427-.3420
'83–84	6-231 Buick	45	45	182 @ 1.340	1.72	.0015-.0032	.0015-.0032	.3402-.3412	.3405-.3412
	8-305 Chev.	46	45	200 @ 1.25	1.70	.0010-.0027	.0010-.0027	.3414	.3414
	8-350 Diesel	46	45	210 @ 1.22	1⁴³⁄₆₄	.0010.-.0027	.0015-.0032	.3429	.3429
'85	6-231 Buick	45	45	182 @ 1.34	1.72	.0015-.0032	.0015-.0032	.3402-.3412	.3405-.3412
	8-305 Chev.	46	45	200 @ 1.25	1²³⁄₃₂	.0010-.0027	.0010-.0027	.3414	.3414
	8-350 Diesel	46	45	210 @ 1.22	1⁴³⁄₆₄	.0010-.0027	.0015-.0032	.3429	.3429

■ Intake valve seat angles are shown. All exhaust valve seat angles are 45° unless otherwise indicated.
● Intake valve face angles are shown. All exhaust valve face angles are 44° unless otherwise indicated.
① Exhaust valve: seat 59°, face 60°
② Intake: 1²³⁄₃₂ Exhaust: 1¹⁹⁄₃₂

▲ INNER SPRING TEST PRESSURE LeMans

'78-'79	8-400	97 @ 1.14

CRANKSHAFT AND CONNECTING ROD SPECIFICATIONS
1977–'81 Bonneville, Catalina, Grand Prix, Parisienne
(All measurements are given in inches.)

Year	Engine No. Cyl. Displacement (cu. in.)	Crankshaft Main Brg. Journal Dia.	Main Brg. Oil Clearance	Shaft End-Play	Thrust on No.	Connecting Rod Journal Diameter	Oil Clearance	Side Clearance*
'78–'80	6-231 Buick	2.4995–2.5000	.0003–.0017	.003–.009	2	2.2487–2.2495	.0005–.0026	.006–.027①
	8-301 Pont.	3.0000	.0004–.0020	.003–.009	4	2.2500	.0005–.0025	.006–.022
	6-229, 8-305, 350 Chev.	③	④	.002–.007	5	2.0990–2.1000	.0013–.0035	.006–.016
	8-350 Buick	3.0000–3.0005	.0004–.0015	.003–.009	3	1.9910–2.0000	.0005–.0026	.006–.027①
	8-350 Olds.	2.4985–2.4995⑤	.0005–.0021②	.0035–.0135	3	2.1238–2.1248	.0004–.0033	.006–.020
	8-350 Olds. Diesel	2.9993–3.0003	.0005–.0021②	.0035–.0135	3	2.1238–2.1248	.0005–.0026	.006–.020

CRANKSHAFT AND CONNECTING ROD SPECIFICATIONS
1977–'81 Bonneville, Catalina, Grand Prix, Parisienne

(All measurements are given in inches.)

Year	Engine No. Cyl. Displacement (cu. in.)	Crankshaft				Connecting Rod		
		Main Brg. Journal Dia.	Main Brg. Oil Clearance	Shaft End-Play	Thrust on No.	Journal Diameter	Oil Clearance	Side Clearance*
'78–'80	8-400 Pont.	3.0000	.0002–.0020	.003–.009	4	2.2500	.0005–.0025	.006–.022
	8-403 Olds.	2.4985–2.4995 ⑤	.0005–.0021 ②	.0035–.0135	5	2.1238–2.1248	.0005–.0026	.006–.020
'81	6-231 Buick	2.4995–2.5000	.0003–.0018	.003–.009	2	2.2487–2.2495	.0005–.0026	.006–.023
	8-265 Pont.	3.0000	.0002–.0018	.0035–.0085	4	2.0000	.0005–.0026	.006–.022
	8-307 Olds.	2.4985–2.4995 ⑤	.0005–.0021 ②	.0035–.0135	3	2.1238–2.1248	.0004–.0033	.006–.020
	8-350 Diesel	2.9993–3.0003	.0005–.0021 ②	.0035–.0135	3	2.1238–2.1248	.0005–.0026	.006–.020
'82	6-231 Buick	3.4955	.0003–.0018	.003–.011	2	2.2491	.0005–.0026	.006–.023
	6-252 Buick	2.4955	.0003–.0018	.003–.009	2	2.2487–2.2495	.0005–.0026	.006–.023
	8-350 Diesel	3.000	—	.0035–.0135	3	2.1243	.0005–.0026	.006–.020
'83–'84	6-231 Buick	3.4955	.0003–.0018	.003–.011	2	2.2491	.0005–.0026	.006–.020
	8-305 Chev.	③	④	.002–.007	5	2.0995	.0013–.0035	.006–.016
	8-350 Diesel	2.9998	.0005–.0021	.0035–.0135	3	2.1243	.0005–.0026	.006–.020
'85	6-231 Buick	3.4995	.0003–.0018	.003–.011	2	2.1243	.0005–.0026	.006–.020
	8-305 Chev.	③	④	.002–.006	5	2.0995	.0013–.0035	.006–.016
	8-350 Diesel	2.9998	.0005–.0021	.0035–.0135	3	2.1243	.0005–.0026	.006–.020

*Total for two rods
① 1979 and later—.006–.023
② No. 5—.0015–.0031

③ #1: 2.4484–2.4493
　#2, 3, 4: 2.4481–2.4490
　#5: 2.4479–2.4488

④ #1: .0008–.0020
　#2: .0011–.0023
　#3: .0017–.0033
⑤ #1: 2.4988–2.4998

TORQUE SPECIFICATIONS

(All readings in ft. lbs.)

Year	Engine No. Cyl. Displacement (cu. in.)	Cylinder Head Bolts	Rod Bearing Bolts	Main Bearing Bolts	Crankshaft Bolt	Flywheel to Crankshaft Bolts	Manifold	
							Intake	Exhaust
'78–'79	4-151 Pont.	95	30	65	160	55	40	40
	6-231, 8-350 Buick	80	40	100	225	60	45	25
	8-301 Pont.	95	30	70③	160	95	35	40
	8-305 Chev.	65	45	70	60	60	30	20
	8-350 Chev.	65	45	70	60	60	30	20
	8-400 Pont.	95	40	100④	160	95	35	40
	8-403 8-350 Olds.	130	42	80④	220	60	40	25
'80–'81	4-151 Pont.	85	32	70	200	44	29	44
	6-231 Buick	80	40	100	225	60	45	25
	8-265 Pont.	95	30	⑤	160	95	35	40
	8-301 Pont.	95	30	⑤	160	95	35	40
	8-301 Pont. (Turbo)	93	28	100	163	—	37	40

TORQUE SPECIFICATIONS
(All readings in ft. lbs.)

Year	Engine No. Cyl. Displacement (cu. in.)	Cylinder Head Bolts	Rod Bearing Bolts	Main Bearing Bolts	Crankshaft Bolt	Flywheel to Crankshaft Bolts	Manifold	
							Intake	Exhaust
'80–'81	8-305, 350 Chev.	65	45	70	60	60	30	20
	307, 350 Olds.	130①	42	120⑥	200-310	60	40②	25
'82	6-231 Buick	80	40	100	225	60	45	25
	6-252 Buick	80	40	100	225	60	45	25
	8-350 Diesel	130①	42	120	200-310	60	40①	25
'83–84	6-231 Buick	80	40	100	225	60	45	25
	8-305 Chev.	65	45	70	60	60	30	20
	8-350 Diesel	130①	42	120	200-310	60	40①	25
'85	6-231 Buick	80	40	100	225	60	45	25
	8-305 Chev.	65	45	70	60	60	30	20
	8-350 Diesel	130②	42	120	200-310	60	40②	25

①Dip bolts in oil before tightening
②Rear cap—120
③Rear main: 100

④Rear main: 120
⑤7/16" bolt—70 ft. lbs., 1/2" bolt—100 ft.

lbs., rear main bearing—100 ft. lbs.
⑥307:80 on Nos. 1–4, 120 on No. 5

RING GAP
(All measurements are given in inches)

Year	Engine No. Cyl. Displacement (cu. in.)	Top Compression	Bottom Compression	Year	Engine	Oil Control
'78–'81	8-350 Buick	.010–.020	.010–.020	'78–'81	8-350 Buick	.015–.035
'78–'80	8-350 Olds.	.010–.020	.010–.020			
'78	4-151 Pont.	.010–.020	.010–.020	'78	4-151 Pont.	.010–.020
'78	6-231 Buick	.010–.020	.010–.020	'78–'85	6-231 Buick	.015–.035
'79–'85	6-231 Buick	.013–.023	.013–.023	'78–'81	8-301, 400 Pont.	.015–.055
'78–'79	8-301 Pont.	.010–.020	.010–.020	'78–'79	8-403 Olds.	.015–.055
'78–'79	8-403 Olds.	.010–.020	.010–.020	'79	4-151 Pont.	.015–.055
'79	4-151 Pont.	.015–.025	.009–.019	'79	8-400 Pont.	.015–.035
'80–'81	8-301 Pont.	.010–.028	.010–.028	'80–'81	8-265 Pont.	.010–.050
'78	8-400 Pont.	.010–.020	.010–.020	'80–'85	8-350 Diesel	.015–.055
'79	8-400 Pont.	.009–.019	.005–.015	'82	6-252 Buick	.015–.055
'80–'81	8-265 Pont.	.010–.022	.010–.028	'81	8-307 Olds.	.015–.055
'80–'85	8-350 Diesel	.015–.025	.015–.025	'78	8-305 Chev.	.010–.035
'82	6-252 Buick	.010–.020	.010–.020			
'81	8-307 Olds.	.009–.019	.009–.019	'79–'80	8-305 Chev.	.015–.055
'78	8-305 Chev.	.010–.035	.010–.035	'78–'79	8-350 Chev.	.015–.055
				'83–'85	8-305 Chev.	.015–.055
'79–'80	8-305 Chev.	.010–.020	.010–.025	'80	6-229 Chev.	.010–.035

RING GAP
(All measurements are given in inches)

Year	Engine No. Cyl. Displacement (cu. in.)	Top Compression	Bottom Compression	Year	Engine	Oil Control
'78–'79	8-350 Chev.	.010–.020	.010–.025			
'83–'85	8-305 Chev.	.010–.020	.010–.025			
'80	6-229 Chev.	.010–.020	.010–.025			

RING SIDE CLEARANCE
(All measurements are given in inches)

Year	Engine No. Cyl. Displacement (cu. in.)	Top Compression	Bottom Compression
'78	8-350 Chev.	.0012–.0032	.0012–.0027
'79	8-350 Chev.	.0012–.0032	.0010–.0032
'78–'85	6-231 Buick	.0030–.0050	.0030–.0050
'78–'81	8-301 Pont.	.0015–.0035	.0015–.0035
'78	8-305 Chev.	.0012–.0032	.0012–.0027
'79–'81	8-305 Chev.	.0012–.0032	.0012–.0032
'78–'79	4-151 Pont.	.0025–.0033	.0025–.0033
'78–'79	8-403 Olds.	.0020–.0040	.0020–.0040
'80–'81	8-265 Pont.	.0015–.0035	.0015–.0035
'80–'85	8-350 Diesel	.005–.007	.005–.007
'82	6-252 Buick	.0030–.0050	.0030–.0050
'78–'81	8-350 Buick	.0030–.0050	.0030–.0050
'83–'85	8-305 Chev.	.0012–.0032	.0012–.0032
'78–'80	8-350 Olds.	.0020–.0040	.0020–.0040
'81	8-307 Olds.	.0020–.0040	.0020–.0040
'80	6-229 Chev.	.010–.020	.010–.025

Year	Engine	Oil Control
'78	8-350 Chev.	.0000–.0050
'78–'85	6-231 Buick	.0035 max.
'78	8-305 Chev.	.0000–.0050
'78	8-305, 350 Chev.	.010–.035
'79	8-350 Chev.	.0020–.0070
'78–'81	8-301 Pont.	.0015–.0035
'78–'79	8-403 Olds.	.0006–.0096
'79–'81	8-305 Chev.	.002–.008
'80–'81	8-265 Pont.	.0015–.0035
'80–'85	8-350 Diesel	.001–.005
'82	6-252 Buick	.0035
'78–'81	8-350 Buick	.0035 max.
'78–'79	8-151 Pont.	.0025–.0033
'83–'85	8-305 Chev.	.002–.007
'78–'80	8-350 Olds.	.001–.005
'81	8-307 Olds.	.001–.005
'80	6-229 Chev.	.010–.035

PISTON CLEARANCE

Year	Engine No. Cyl. Displacement (cu. in.)	Piston-to-Bore Clearance (in.)	Year	Engine No. Cyl. Displacement (cu. in.)	Piston-to-Bore
'78–80	4-151 Pont.	.0025–.0033④	'81	6-231 Buick	.0016–.0038①
	6-229 Chev.	.0012		8-265 Pont.	.0017–.0041①
	8-265 Pont.	.0017–.0041①		8-267 Chev.	.0012
	6-231 Buick	.0008–.0020⑤		8-301 Pont.	.0017–.0041①
	8-301 Pont.	.0025–.0033④		8-305 Chev.	.0007–.0017
	8-305 Chev.	.0007–.0027②⑥		8-307 Olds.	.0008–.0018
	8-350 Chev.	.0007–.0027②		8-350 Buick	.0013–.0035①
	8-350 Olds.	.0008–.0018		8-350 Diesel	.005–.006

PISTON CLEARANCE

Year	Engine No. Cyl. Displacement (cu. in.)	Piston-to-Bore Clearance (in.)
'78–80	8-350 Buick	.0013–.0035①
	8-400 Pont.	.0025–.0033④
	8-403 Olds.	.0008–.0018③

Year	Engine No. Cyl. Displacement (cu. in.)	Piston-to-Bore
'82	6-231 Buick	.0016–.0038
	6-252 Buick	.0016–.0038
	6-350 Diesel	.005–.006
'83–'84	6-231 Buick	.0016–.0038
	8-305 Chev.	.0008–.0020
	8-350 Diesel	.0008–.0020
'85	6-231 Buick	.0016–.0038
	8-305 Chev.	.0012
	8-350 Diesel	.005–.006

① Bottom of skirt
② 1.15″ from top of piston
③ .75″ below piston pin C/L
④ 1.11″ from top of piston
⑤ Top of skirt
⑥ 1979 and later—.0007–.0017

WHEEL ALIGNMENT SPECIFICATIONS
LeMans, Phoenix, 1982–'85 Bonneville

Year	Model	Caster Range (deg)	Caster Pref Setting (deg)	Camber Range (deg)	Camber Pref Setting (deg)	Toe-in (in.)	Steering Axis Inclin. (deg)
'78	LeMans Man. Str.	1N to 3P	1P	1N to 2P	½P	⅛ to 3/16	10.50
	Pwr. Str.	1P to 5P	3P	1N to 2P	½P	⅛ to 3/16	10.50
	Phoenix Man. Str.	3N to 1P	1N	⅗N to 2⅓P	⅘P	⅛ to 3/16	10.00
	Pwr. Str.	1N to 3P	1P	⅗N to 2⅓P	⅘P	⅛ to 3/16	10.00
'79	LeMans Man. Str.	½P to 1½P	1P	0 to 1P	½P	⅛ to 3/16	8.00
	Pwr. Str.	2½P to 3½P	3P	0 to 1P	½P	⅛ to 3/16	8.00
	Phoenix Man. Str.	½N to 1½N	1N	¼P to 1¼P	¾P	1/16 to 3/16	10.00
	Pwr. Str.	½P to 1½P	1P	¼P to 1¼P	¾P	1/16 to 3/16	10.00
'80–'81	LeMans Man. Str.	½P to 1½P	1P	0 to 1P	½P	1/16 to 3/16	8.00
	Pow. Str.	2½P to 3½P	3P	0 to 1P	½P	1/16 to 3/16	8.00
'82–'83	Bonneville Man. Str.	½P to 1½P	1P	0 to 1P	½P	1/16 to 3/16	—
	Pow. Str.	2½P to 3½P	3P	0 to 1P	½P	1/16 to 3/16	—
'83–'84	Bonneville	2½P–3½P	3P	0 to 1P	½P	1/16 to 3/16	—
'85	Bonneville	2½P–3½P	3P	0 to 1P	½P	1/16 to 3/16	—

N Negative   P Positive

WHEEL ALIGNMENT SPECIFICATIONS
1978–'81 Bonneville, Catalina, Grand Prix, Parisienne

Year	Model	Caster Range (deg)	Caster Pref Setting (deg)	Camber Range (deg)	Camber Pref Setting (deg)	Toe-in (in.)	Steering Axis Inclin. (deg.)
'78–'79	Pontiac	2P to 4P	3P	0 to 1⅔P	⅘P	1/16 to 3/16	10⅓
'78–'79	Grand Prix Man. Str.	0 to 2P	1P	⅓N to 1⅓P	½P	1/16 to 3/16	8
	Pwr. Str.	2P to 4P	3P	⅓N to 1⅓P	½P	1/16 to 3/16	8

WHEEL ALIGNMENT SPECIFICATIONS
1978–'81 Bonneville, Catalina, Grand Prix, Parisienne

| Year | Model | Caster | | Camber | | Toe-in (in.) | Steering Axis Inclin. (deg.) |
		Range (deg)	Pref Setting (deg)	Range (deg)	Pref Setting (deg)		
'80–'81	Pontiac	2P to 4P	3P	0 to 1⅝P	¹³⁄₁₆P	¹⁄₁₆ to ¼	10¹⁹⁄₃₂
'80–'81	Grand Prix Man. Str.	0 to 2P	1P	⁵⁄₁₆P to 1⁵⁄₁₆P	⅛P	¹⁄₁₆ to ¼	8
	Pwr. Str.	2 to 4P	3P	⁵⁄₁₆P to 1⁵⁄₁₆P	⅛P	¹⁄₁₆ to ¼	8
'82	Grand Prix Man. Str.	½P to 1½P	1P	0 to 1P	½P	¹⁄₁₆ to ³⁄₁₆	—
	Pwr. Str.	2½P to 3½P	3P	0 to 1P	½P	¹⁄₁₆ to ³⁄₁₆	—
'83	Grand Prix	2½P-3½P	3	0 to 1P	½P	¹⁄₁₆ to ³⁄₁₆	—
'84–'85	Grand Prix	2½P-3½P	3	0 to 1P	½P	¹⁄₁₆ to ³⁄₁₆	—
'84–'85	Parisienne	2½P-3½P	3P	⅓P–1⅓P	⅘P	¹⁄₁₆ to ³⁄₁₆	—

—Not specified
N Negative
LH lefthand side
P Positive
RH righthand side

CHARGING SYSTEM

For further information on the charging system, please refer to "Charging and Starting" in the Unit Repair section.

Alternator

REMOVAL & INSTALLATION

1. Disconnect the battery cables.
2. Remove the alternator wires or connector.
3. Loosen the adjusting and pivot bolts.
4. Remove the belt.
5. Remove the alternator adjusting and pivot bolts.
6. Remove the alternator.
7. To install, reverse the removal procedure.

Adjust the belt tension so that the longest span of belt between the pulleys can be depressed about ½ in. in the middle by moderate thumb pressure.

— CAUTION —
Pull out on the alternator by hand to avoid damage to the housing and overtightening, which could damage the bearings.

First tighten the adjuster bolt, then the pivot bolt.

STARTING SYSTEM

For information on starting system troubleshooting procedures, please refer to "Charging and Starting" in the Unit Repair section.

Starter

REMOVAL & INSTALLATION

All Except V6

1. Disconnect negative battery cable.
2. If necessary, jack up and support the car.
3. Disconnect solenoid wires.
4. Disconnect starter brace, if any.
5. Remove starter-to-engine bolts and starter.

V6 With Manual Transmission

1. Disconnect the negative battery cable.
2. Raise the car and safely support it.
3. Remove the engine front crossmember-to-body bolts, then remove the right and left crossmember brace bolts.
4. Loosen all the brace bolts to let the crossmember braces hang down enough to allow removal of the crossmember.
5. Remove the crossmember and follow steps for all other engines.

V6 With Automatic Transmission

1. Raise the car and disconnect the negative battery cable.
2. Remove the exhaust crossover pipe and the flywheel cover.
3. Remove the two transmission mount to transmission bolts and place a jack under the extension housing of the transmission.
4. Remove the right transmission support bracket and pivot down.
5. Disconnect and plug the fluid cooler lines and lower the transmission enough to get at the two starter-to-engine block bolts.
6. Remove those two bolts, the terminals on the starter, and the starter.
7. Installation is in the reverse order of removal.

IGNITION SYSTEM

A solid-state, High Energy Ignition system (HEI) is standard equipment. Most 1981 and later models use an (EST) Electronic Spark Timing distributor. The EST distributor uses no mechanical or vacuum advance and is easily identified by the absence of a vacuum advance and the presence of a four terminal connector. Neither type distributor uses contact points or condenser to replace, nor any cam or rubbing block to wear out, thus eliminating distributor maintenance.

For HEI trouble-shooting, please see "Electronic Ignition Systems" in the Unit Repair section.

TACHOMETER HOOKUP

——— **CAUTION** ———

NEVER use a timing light which requires piercing the spark plug lead—only inductive pick-ups should be used with H.E.I.

All models are equipped with the High Energy Ignition System which uses a different tachometer hookup than was used in previous years.

Connect the tachometer to the TACH terminal on the distributor and to a suitable ground.

——— **CAUTION** ———

Never ground the HEI tachometer terminals.

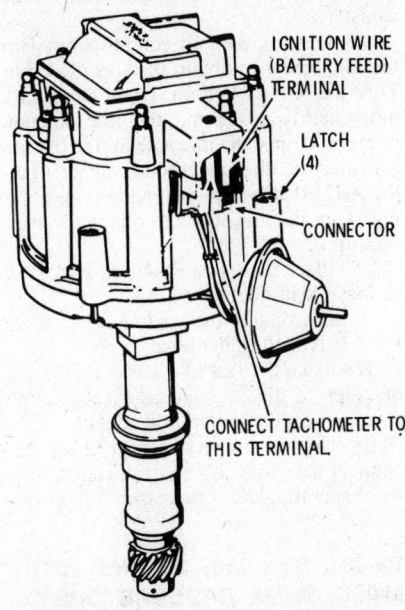

IGNITION WIRE (BATTERY FEED) TERMINAL

LATCH (4)

CONNECTOR

CONNECT TACHOMETER TO THIS TERMINAL

Tachometer hookup; V8 HEI, V6 and 4 cyl. 151 similar

NOTE: Some tachometers must connect to the TACH terminal on the distributors and to the positive terminal on the battery. If there is any doubt, check the tachometer manufacturer's instructions.

Distributor

REMOVAL

1. On V6, 4 cylinder and V8 systems, disconnect the ignition switch battery feed wire from the distributor cap. Don't use a screwdriver or other tool to release the lock tab.
2. Remove the distributor cap. Unlatch the cap by using a screwdriver to disengage the spring–loaded latches or retaining screws.
3. Make reference marks on the block and the distributor housing that align with the tip of the rotor. Do not crank the engine after these marks have been made.
4. Disconnect the vacuum line at the distributor.

5. Remove the distributor clamp screw and hold-down clamp.
6. Lift out the distributor. Notice the slight rotation of the rotor as the distributor is removed from the block.

INSTALLATION

Installation procedure is in the reverse order of the removal procedure. It should be noted, however, that while inserting a gear-driven distributor into the block, the rotor should be moved slightly to one side. This is necessary because of the helical cut of the distributor and camshaft gears. As the distributor seats in its bore, the rotor will turn slightly so the reference marks will once again be in line.

DISTRIBUTOR INSTALLATION IF ENGINE HAS BEEN DISTURBED

1. With No. 1 piston coming up on compression stroke, continue cranking the engine until the pulley timing mark indexes with the zero (0) mark on the engine timing scale. To find No. 1 TDC, remove the No. 1 spark plug and put your finger over the plug hole. Hand crank the engine until air pressure starts building up behind your finger. This means the engine is beginning No. 1 cylinder compression stroke.
2. Replace the distributor.
3. Install the distributor in the block. The rotor should point toward the contact in the cap for No. 1 cylinder. Move the rotor slightly to the side because, as the distributor is pressed into its bore, it will turn a small amount.
4. Reverse the removal procedure to complete installation.

IGNITION TIMING

Timing marks are located on the front engine cover and harmonic balancer or pulley. Follow all instructions on the underhood sticker.

1. Disconnect and plug the distributor vacuum advance hose. On 1981 and later models with the EST Distributor, disconnect the four terminal connector.

NOTE: It may be necessary to put a small amount of white paint or chalk on the timing marks to make them more visible.

2. Connect a timing light to No. 1 spark plug.
3. Loosen the distributor hold-down clamp.
4. Start the engine and rotate the distributor until the correct mark on the cover lines up with the pulley or harmonic balancer mark. Tighten the distributor clamp, and recheck the timing.

FUEL SYSTEM

Gasoline Engines

For information on carburetors, please refer to "Carburetors" in the Unit Repair section.

Chilton's TIME SAVER

When replacing a fuel pump on a Chevrolet 305, 307 or 350 cu. in. engine, considerable time can be saved as follows:
1. Before removing the old pump, remove the upper bolt from the engine's right front mounting boss. This bolt hole is in direct alignment with the fuel pump pushrod. The threaded bolt hole continues into the pump pushrod bore. The bolt acts as an oil plug.
2. Temporarily insert a longer bolt, (about 3/8—16 x 2 in.) into the hole. Screw the bolt into the bore until it bottoms against the pump pushrod. (Don't tighten the bolt with a wrench or the rod can be damaged.)
3. The mechanic is now free to remove and install the fuel pump without worrying about fuel pump pushrod misalignment.

——— **CAUTION** ———

Don't forget to reinstall the original bolt.

Fuel Pump

REMOVAL & INSTALLATION

1. Disconnect fuel inlet, outlet and vapor return lines at pump and plug pump inlet line.
2. Remove two pump mounting bolts and lockwashers; remove pump and gasket.

NOTE: On some models equipped with power steering it is possible, but somewhat difficult, to reach the mounting bolts with the steering pump in place. It may help to loosen the power steering pump, remove its mounting bolts and, with it still connected to its lines, lift it up out of the way.

3. On Chevrolet 305, 307 & 350 V8 engines, if pushrod is to be removed: take out the two adapter bolts and lockwashers and remove adapter and gasket.
4. Install pump with new gasket coated with sealer. Coat mounting bolt threads with sealer and tighten bolts.

NOTE: On Chevrolet 305, 307 & 350 V8 engines, mechanical fingers or heavy grease can be used to hold pump pushrod in place during installation. Coat pipe plug threads or adapter gasket with sealer if pushrod was removed.

5. Install the oil filter, if removed. Connect inlet and outlet lines, start engine and check for leaks.

Fuel Filter

REMOVAL & INSTALLATION

———— CAUTION ————
Bleed the pressure from the fuel system on fuel injected models before servicing system.

1. Disconnect fuel line connection at inlet of carburetor.
2. Remove inlet fuel filter nut from carburetor.
3. Remove filter element and spring.
4. If a bronze element, blow through cone end—element should allow air to pass freely.
5. Install element spring and new element into carburetor. Bronze elements are installed with small section of cone facing outward.
6. Install new gasket on fitting nut and install nut.
7. Install fuel line and tighten securely. Start engine and check for leaks.

Carburetor

REMOVAL & INSTALLATION

1. Remove the air cleaner.
2. Disconnect the fuel line.
3. Disconnect the throttle linkage.
4. Disconnect and label all vacuum hoses.
5. Remove the retaining bolts.
6. Remove the carburetor.
7. Installation is in the reverse order of removal.

IDLE SPEED AND MIXTURE ADJUSTMENTS

1978-80 Idle Speed Adjustment
4-151 WITH 5210-C OR 6510-C CARBURETORS

1. Connect a tachometer to the engine according to the manufacturer's specifications.
2. Run the engine at normal operating temperature, turn the air conditioning off, disconnect and plug the vacuum line between the canister and the PCV valve at the canister, plug the distributor vacuum advance line at the distributor, make sure that the choke is fully opened, set the parking brake, block the wheels and place the transmission in Drive (AT) or neutral (MT).

3. Check, and if necessary, adjust the timing.
4. Unplug and reconnect the distributor vacuum advance hose.
5. Turn the idle screw to obtain the specified idle speed.

NOTE: On cars with manual transmission and air conditioning, or cars with automatic transmission, set the idle as explained earlier, then disconnect the wide open throttle air conditioning override switch located on the accelerator linkage bracket. Turn the air conditioning on, momentarily open the throttle to allow the plunger to fully extend, and adjust the solenoid screw to the rpm specified on the underhood sticker. Reconnect the override switch and turn the A/C off.

6. Unplug and reconnect the PCV-canister hose.

151 WITH 2SE, E2SE CARBURETOR

1. Set the timing and idle speed to the specifications on the underhood sticker following the procedures found there.
2. On cars equipped with A/C:
   a. Turn the idle speed screw on the carburetor to obtain the specified rpm.
   b. Turn the A/C On. Disconnect the A/C compressor wire at the compressor. Block the wheels, set the emergency brake. Put M/T in neutral, A/T in Drive.
   c. Open the throttle slightly to extend the solenoid plunger.
   d. Turn the screw on the solenoid to obtain the specified rpm.
   e. Connect the A/C compressor wire at the compressor.
3. On cars without A/C:
Block the wheels, set the emergency brake. Put M/T in neutral, A/T in Drive.
   a. Turn the screw on the solenoid to obtain the specified rpm.
   b. Disconnect the wire at the solenoid and reset the idle to the specified rpm.
   c. Reconnect the solenoid wire.

V6 WITH 2GE AND V8-305 WITH 2GC CARBURETORS

1. Connect a tachometer to the engine according to the manufacturer's instructions.
2. Run the engine at normal operating temperature. Turn the air conditioning off, make sure that the choke is fully open. Set the parking brake and block the wheels. Disconnect and plug the hoses from the vapor canister at the canister and the EGR valve at the valve.
3. Place the transmission in Park (AT) or neutral (MT).
4. Disconnect and plug the vacuum advance line.
5. Check and if necessary, adjust the timing.
6. Unplug and reconnect the vacuum advance line.
7. Turn the idle screw to the desired rpm.
8. Unplug and reconnect the hoses.

1978-79 V8-301 WITH M2MC, 1980 V6-231, V8-265 WITH M2ME CARBURETORS

1. Connect a tachometer to the engine according to the manufacturer's instructions. Run the engine at normal operating temperature. Disconnect the compressor clutch connector at the clutch. Set the parking brake and block the wheels. Make sure that the choke is fully opened and place the transmission in Drive (AT) or neutral (MT).
2. Disconnect and plug the vacuum advance line at the distributor.
3. Check and, if necessary, adjust the timing.
4. Unplug and reconnect the vacuum advance line.
5. Disconnect the purge hose from the canister.
6. On cars with air conditioning: Turn the idle screw to obtain the specified rpm. Turn the A/C switch on. Open the throttle momentarily to extend the idle solenoid plunger. Adjust the idle solenoid to the rpm specified on the underhood sticker. Turn the A/C off. On cars without air conditioning: Turn the idle screw to obtain the specified rpm.
7. Place the transmission in Park (AT) or leave it in neutral (MT).
8. Disconnect the vacuum hose at the EGR valve. Plug the hose.
9. Place the fast idle screw on the second step of the cam and adjust to the rpm specified on the underhood sticker.
10. Unplug and reconnect the hose. Reconnect the purge hose at the canister and reconnect the A/C compressor clutch wire.

V8-301, 305, 350, 400, 403 WITH M4MC, M4ME CARBURETORS

NOTE: The M4MC carburetor, when used on the 1978-79 V8-301, is equipped with a hot idle compensator valve. For proper idle adjustment, this valve must be closed. To check this, place a finger over the compensator air inlet channel located at the top of the air horn. If no rpm drop is noticed, the valve is closed. If the valve is open, allow the engine to cool to a point where the valve is closed, or plug the hole.

1. Connect a tachometer to the engine following the manufacturer's specifications.
2. Run the engine to normal operating temperature.
3. Make sure that the choke is fully open, turn the air conditioning off, set the parking brake and block the wheels.
4. Disconnect the purge hose from the vapor canister, disconnect and plug the EGR hose at the valve for 1978-79 models, and, on the 350, plug the disconnected purge hose.
5. Place the transmission in Park (AT) for 1978-79, Drive (AT) 1980, or neutral (MT).
6. Disconnect and plug the vacuum advance hose at the distributor.

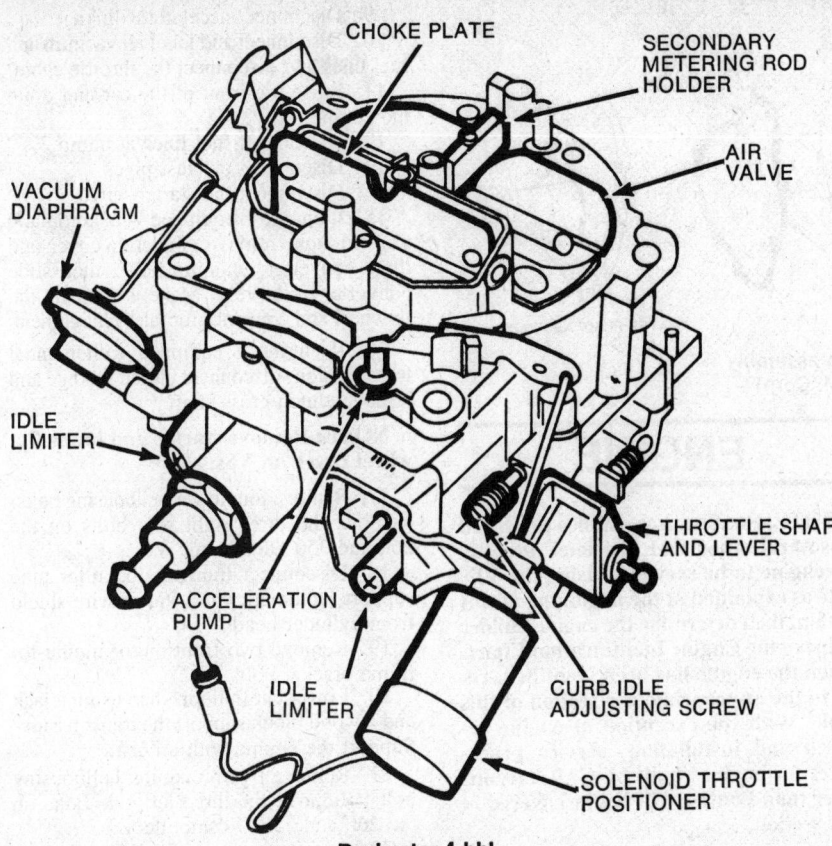

CHOKE PLATE

SECONDARY
METERING ROD
HOLDER

AIR
VALVE

VACUUM
DIAPHRAGM

IDLE
LIMITER

ACCELERATION
PUMP

IDLE
LIMITER

THROTTLE SHAFT
AND LEVER

CURB IDLE
ADJUSTING SCREW

SOLENOID THROTTLE
POSITIONER

Rochester 4 bbl

7. Check and, if necessary, adjust the timing.

8. On all except the 400 with manual transmission, reconnect the vacuum advance line. Disconnect the purge hose at the canister for 1980 models.

9. Place the transmission in Drive (AT) for 1978-79 and turn the idle screw on all models to obtain the specified rpm.

10. On cars with air conditioning: Turn the A/C on and disconnect the compressor clutch wire. Open the throttle momentarily to fully extend the solenoid plunger. Adjust the solenoid screw to the rpm specified on the underhood sticker. Reconnect the compressor clutch and turn the A/C off. On cars without A/C: Turn the idle screw to obtain the specified rpm.

11. Unplug and reconnect the canister and EGR hoses. On the 400 with manual transmission, unplug and reconnect the vacuum advance line.

1981 and Later Idle Adjustment

Most 1981 and later models are equipped with an Idle Speed Control (ISC) mounted on the float bowl. Idle speeds are computer controlled and the ICS should not be adjusted.

On some V8 models an Idle Load Compensator (ILC) is mounted on the float bowl to control the curb idle speed. The ILC is adjusted at the factory and capped to prevent readjustment. If an idle problem is suspected on either of the above systems it is recommended that it be corrected by a qualified technician.

On cars that do not include either an ISC or ILC, but are equipped with air conditioning, an idle speed solenoid is used to maintain idle speed. For adjustment of these models refer to the 1978-80 adjustment procedures.

NOTE: The underhood sticker specifies which idle system your car is equipped with.

1978 and Later Idle Mixture Adjustment

Changes in the carburetors for 1978-80 cars have made the adjustment of idle mixture impossible without the use of a propane enrichment system not available to the general public. Backing out the mixture screw will have little or no effect on the mixture. Most 1979 and later carburetors have mixture screws concealed by staked-in plugs. Mixture adjustments are possible only during carburetor overhaul.

On 1981 and later models the air/fuel mixture is controlled by the electronic control module of the computer command control system. No adjustment should be attempted.

Diesel Engines

See the Oldsmobile Rear Wheel Drive Section for complete diesel engine fuel system service procedures.

COOLING SYSTEM

Radiator

REMOVAL & INSTALLATION

1. Drain coolant.
2. Remove fan shield assembly on the six. Remove the fan.
3. Disconnect upper and lower hoses.
4. Disconnect and plug the fluid cooler lines, if equipped with automatic transmission.
5. Lift radiator and shroud straight up and out of car.

NOTE: On cars equipped with a clutch type fan keep it in an upright position to prevent the fluid from leaking.

6. To install, reverse removal procedure, making sure lower cradles are properly located and automatic transmission is full.

Water Pump

REMOVAL & INSTALLATION

Except 4-151

This is a centrifugal-type waterpump. It is die cast, with sealed bearings and is pressed together. Therefore, it is serviced as a unit.

NOTE: It is sometimes more convenient to remove the radiator than to leave it in place. This depends on the working space available and the options on the car such as air conditioning and power steering.

1. Disconnect the battery and drain the radiator.
2. Loosen the alternator and remove the fan belt.
3. Remove the power steering and air conditioning belts, if so equipped.
4. Remove the fan and water pump pulley.
5. Remove the V8 front alternator bracket.
6. Remove the heater hose and radiator hose at the pump.
7. Remove the water pump retaining bolts and the pump.
8. Install the pump by reversing the above steps. Make sure that all gasket surfaces are clean and smooth. Always use a gasket sealer on both sides of the gasket. Tighten the retaining bolts.

NOTE: If a belt tensioning gauge is available, adjust the belts to 100–130 lb tension on new belts and to 70 lbs. on used belts. If the gauge is not available, adjust the belts so that a ¼–½ inch deflection can be made on the longest span of the belt under moderate thumb pressure.

NOTE: Use an anti-seize compound on the water pump bolt threads.

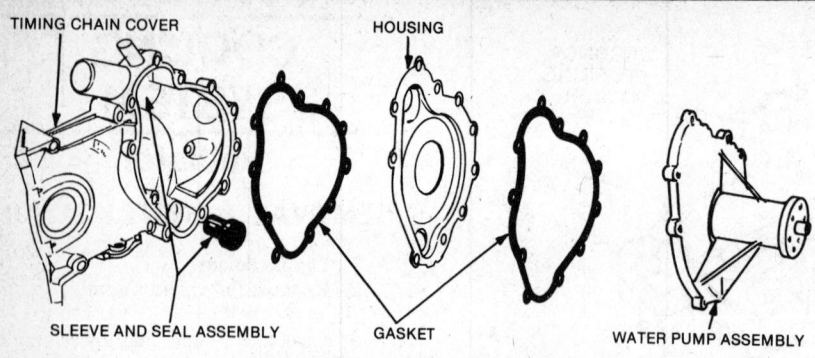

TIMING CHAIN COVER   HOUSING

SLEEVE AND SEAL ASSEMBLY   GASKET   WATER PUMP ASSEMBLY

Pontiac V8 water pump assembly
(© Pontiac Div., G.M. Corp)

4-151

1. Drain the cooling system.
2. Remove all drive belts.
3. Remove the fan and pump pulley.
4. On cars equipped with A/C, remove the compressor system as a whole. Do not disconnect any of the lines. Simply position the compressor out of the way.
5. On 1979 and later cars without A/C, remove the alternator.
6. Remove the heater hose and the lower radiator hose from the pump.
7. Unbolt and remove the pump from the engine.
8. Clean the gasket surfaces, coat the new gasket with non-hardening type sealer and position the gasket on the block.
9. Coat the threaded areas of the bolts with waterproof sealer and install the pump. Torque the bolts to 20 ft. lbs.
10. Reverse above procedure to install water pump. The belts should be adjusted so that a ½ in. deflection is present when they are pressed, mid-point along their longest straight run.

Thermostat

REMOVAL & INSTALLATION

1. Drain coolant to below thermostat level.
2. Disconnect upper hose and remove water outlet assembly. Remove the thermostat.
3. Replace by reversing the above steps. Clean the gasket surfaces and use a gasket sealer and a new gasket.
4. Refill and bleed cooling system.

EMISSION CONTROLS

There are three types of emissions to be controlled: crankcase emissions, carburetor and gas tank gas vapor emissions, and exhaust emission.

For information on emissions, please refer to "Emission Controls" in the Unit Repair section.

ENGINE

NOTE: Pontiac uses engines produced by several other GM divisions. Identify the engine to be serviced, using the VIN code as explained at the beginning of this section, then determine the engine builder by using the Engine Identification Chart. When the engine has been identified, refer to the appropriate car section of this book. With the exception of engine removal and installation, service procedures for engines built by GM divisions other than Pontiac will not be covered in this section.

REMOVAL & INSTALLATION

NOTE: In most cases, engine work may be performed without disconnecting refrigerant lines on air conditioning systems. If, for any reason, the A/C system must be opened, the work is best performed by a professional. An A/C system is under high pressure. Refrigerant contact with the skin is harmful, and contact with the eyes may cause blindness. Failure to observe specific service procedures can also permanently damage the A/C system.

1. Disconnect battery.
2. Drain cooling system.
3. Scribe alignment marks on hood and remove hood from hinges.
4. Disconnect and label the engine wiring harness and ground straps, alternator wires, and the engine-temperature and oil-pressure sending-unit wires.
5. Remove air cleaner and fan shield or shroud.
6. Disconnect radiator and heater hoses.
7. Remove radiator.

NOTE: On some models you can do the job by removing only the radiator or the fan, but it is generally easier to remove them both.

8. Remove fan and fan pulley.

NOTE: If car is equipped with power steering and/or air conditioning, disconnect and swing aside pump/compressor without disconnecting hoses.

9. Disconnect accelerator linkage.
10. Disconnect and label all vacuum and fuel lines and disconnect the throttle cable.
11. Raise the front of the car and drain the engine oil.
12. Disconnect fuel lines at pump.
13. Disconnect exhaust pipes.
14. Disconnect the starter wires.
15. If engine is equipped with automatic transmission, remove converter cover and three converter retaining bolts, then slide converter to the rear. Make a mark on the flywheel and converter for later realignment.
16. If engine is equipped with manual transmission, disconnect clutch linkage and remove clutch cross-shaft.

NOTE: Remove starter and lower flywheel cover on V8s.

17. Remove four lower bellhousing bolts. Remove the three right side bolts on the 260 and 350 Oldsmobile V8.
18. Disconnect transmission filler tube support (automatic) and starter wire shield from cylinder heads.
19. Remove two front motor mount-to-frame bracket bolts.
20. Lower car to floor, then using a jack and a wood block support the transmission. Support the engine with a hoist.
21. Remove two remaining bellhousing bolts. Remove the three left side bolts on the 260 and 350 Oldsmobile V8.
22. Raise transmission slightly, using the jack and wood block, then, using a chain hoist, remove the engine.
23. To install, reverse removal procedure. Install the two upper bellhousing bolts first (with jack still under transmission).

NOTE: Do not lower engine completely until jack and wood block are removed.

Intake Manifold

REMOVAL & INSTALLATION

NOTE: Pontiac doesn't recommend a specific manifold bolt torque sequence for V8 engines.

V8

1. Remove the EGR valves on all engines except the 301. Drain the radiator and block.

NOTE: You can drain most of the coolant through the radiator drain if you raise the rear of the car 15-18 in.

2. Remove the air cleaner and upper radiator hose.
3. Disconnect heater hose.
4. Disconnect temperature gauge wire, then remove two spark plug wire brackets from manifold.
5. Disconnect power brake vacuum and distributor vacuum lines.

NOTE: Vacuum retard line is located at lower rear of vacuum unit on some distributors.

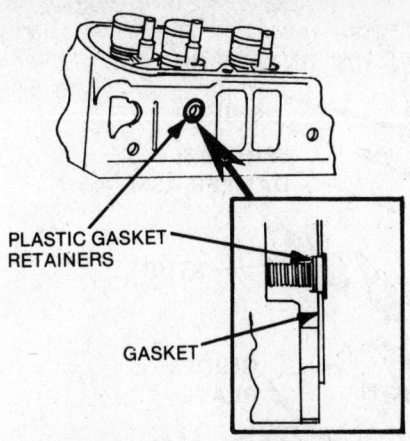

PLASTIC GASKET
RETAINERS

GASKET

Pontiac V8 intake manifold gaskets can be held in place by using plastic retainers, available at Pontiac dealers

6. Disconnect fuel line at carburetor.

7. Disconnect crankcase vent hose and accelerator linkage.

8. Remove bolts that secure accelerator linkage bracket, then remove intake manifold bolts and nuts. If the intake manifold will not clear the distributor, remove the distributor after noting the position of the rotor and the distributor housing.

9. Remove manifold and gasket.

─── **CAUTION** ───

Make sure the O-ring between the intake manifold and timing chain cover is in place, where used.

10. To install, reverse removal procedure, tightening timing chain cover to manifold bolts to 10-20 ft. lbs., manifold hold-down bolts and nuts evenly to the specified torque. Tighten all manifold bolts evenly.

4-151 Intake and Exhaust Manifold

REMOVAL

Through 1978

1. Remove the air cleaner and ducts.
2. Disconnect the fuel and vacuum lines.
3. Disconnect the electrical connectors.
4. Disconnect the carburetor linkage and remove the carburetor and heat shield.
5. Disconnect the exhaust pipe from the manifold.
6. Unbolt and remove the manifold assembly from the head.
7. Disconnect the EGR pipe and re-

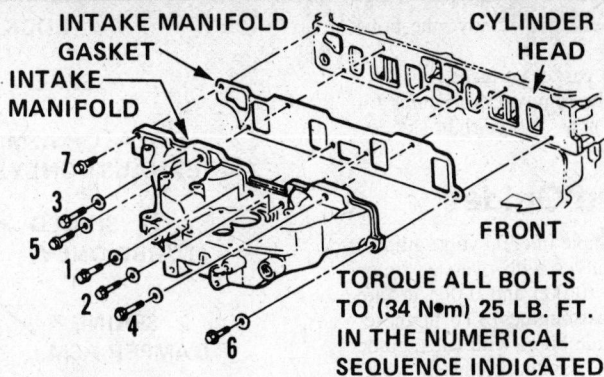

INTAKE MANIFOLD
GASKET
INTAKE
MANIFOLD

CYLINDER
HEAD

FRONT

TORQUE ALL BOLTS TO (34 N•m) 25 LB. FT. IN THE NUMERICAL SEQUENCE INDICATED

1979 and later 4-151 intake manifold bolt torquing sequence

move the four manifold attaching bolts.

8. Installation is in the reverse order of removal. When assembling the manifolds for installation, do the following:

a. Position the two manifolds together and loosely install the four bolts.

b. Place the manifolds on a straight, flat surface.

c. Hold the manifolds securely while tightening the bolts. Failure to follow this procedure could result in stress cracking.

1979 and Later Intake Manifold

1. Remove the air cleaner, Drain the cooling system.

2. Disconnect and label the fuel line, all vacuum lines and electrical connectors from the carburetors, insulator and the intake manifold.

3. Disconnect the throttle linkage.

4. Remove the carburetor and insulator.

5. Remove the alternator rear support bracket from the manifold.

6. Remove the intake manifold bolts and remove the manifold.

7. To install, place a new gasket against the cylinder head, then install the manifold in place by starting all bolts finger-tight.

8. Torque the intake manifold bolts to 25 ft. lbs. in two stages, using the torque sequence shown. The remainder of the installation is in the reverse order of removal.

1979 and Later Exhaust Manifold

1. Remove the air cleaner and the hot air tube.

2. Disconnect the exhaust pipe from the manifold at the flange. Spray the bolts first with penetrating lubricant, if necessary.

3. Remove the engine oil dipstick bracket bolt.

4. Remove the exhaust manifold bolts and remove the manifold from the head.

5. To install, place a new gasket against the cylinder head, then install the exhaust manifold over it. Start all the bolts into the head finger-tight.

6. Torque the exhaust manifold bolts to 37 ft. lbs. in two stages, using the torque sequence illustrated.

7. The remainder of the installation is in the reverse order of removal.

Exhaust Manifold

REMOVAL & INSTALLATION

V8—Right Side

1. Disconnect the exhaust pipes from the manifolds.

2. Straighten the tabs on the manifold bolts, if used, and remove the manifold bolts, manifold, and gasket.

3. Clean the gasket surfaces.

4. Replace the exhaust manifold, using a new gasket; the holes in the end of the gasket are slotted.

NOTE: The installation of the gasket may be simplified by first installing the manifold using only the front and rear bolts to retain the manifold. Allow clearance of about 1/8-3/16 in. between the cylinder head and the exhaust manifold. After inserting the gasket between the head and the manifold, the remaining bolts may be installed.

5. Torque all bolts evenly to specified torque.

6. Bend the tabs against the sides of the bolt heads.

7. Attach the exhaust pipe, using a new gasket.

Exhaust Manifold

REMOVAL & INSTALLATION

V8—Left Side

1. Remove the alternator belt, alternator and mounting bracket as an assembly.

2. Disconnect the exhaust pipes from the manifolds.

3. Straighten the tabs, if used, on the

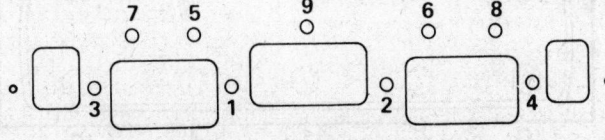

BOLT TORQUE 35 LB.FT.

OHV 4 manifold bolt torque sequence (© Pontiac Div., G.M. Corp.)

manifold bolt locks and remove the bolts and manifold.

4. Clean the gasket surfaces.

5. Reverse the removal procedures for installation. The notes for the right-side apply here.

Valve Guides

Pontiac engines have integral valve guides. Pontiac offers valves with oversize stems for worn guides (0.003 and 0.005 in. are available for most engines). To fit these, enlarge valve guide bores with valve guide reamers to an oversize that cleans up wear. If a large oversize is required, it is best to approach that size in stages. The correct valve stem to guide clearance is given in the Valve Specifications table at the beginning of this section.

As an alternate procedure, some local automotive machine shops fit replacement guides that use standard stem valves.

Rocker Arm

REMOVAL & INSTALLATION

4-151 and V8

1. Remove the valve covers.

2. Remove the rocker arm nut and rocker arm ball.

3. Lift the rocker arm off the rocker arm stud. Always keep the rocker arm assemblies together and assemble them on the same stud.

4. Remove the pushrod from its bore. Make sure the rods are returned to their original bores, with the same end in the block.

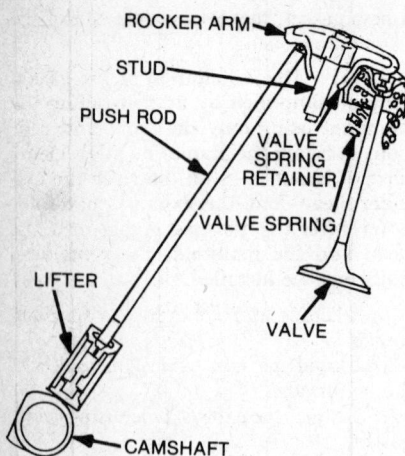

Pontiac V8 valve train assembly

5. Reverse the removal procedure to install the rocker arms. Tighten the rocker arm ball retaining nut to 20 ft. lbs.

Valve Adjustment

All engines are equipped with hydraulic lifters. No routine adjustment is necessary.

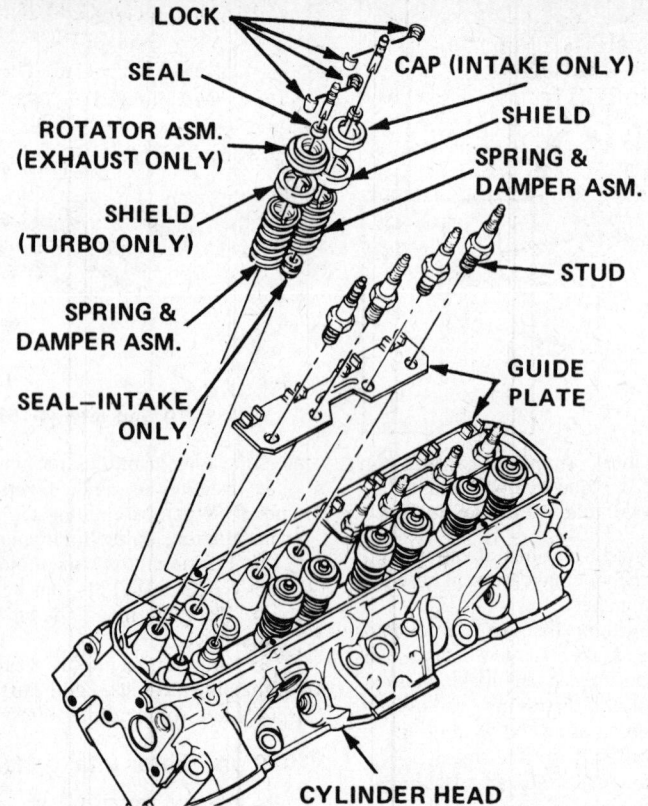

The 1981 and later 265 (4.3L) and 301 (4.9 L) V8s have redesigned valve guides to allow the use of valve stem seals (on the intake only). (© Pontiac Div., G.M. Corp.)

Cylinder Head

REMOVAL & INSTALLATION

4-151

1. Drain the cooling system.

2. Disconnect the accelerator cable at the bellcrank, and the manifold vacuum and fuel lines at the carburetor.

3. Remove the intake and exhaust manifolds.

4. Remove the alternator and power steering pump.

5. Disconnect all electrical connectors at the head.

6. Disconnect the radiator and heater hoses, and the battery ground strap.

7. Remove the spark plugs.

8. Remove the rocker arm cover, rocker arms, and push rods.

9. Unbolt and remove the cylinder head.

10. Clean the gasket surfaces thoroughly.

11. Install a new gasket over the dowels and position the cylinder head.

12. Coat the head bolt threads with sealer and install finger tight.

13. Tighten the bolts in sequence, in three equal steps to the specified torque.

14. Install all parts in the reverse order of removal.

V8

1. Drain the cooling system including the block. Remove the intake manifold, valley cover, and rocker arm cover.

2. Loosen all rocker arm retaining nuts and pivot rockers off the pushrods.

3. Remove the pushrods and place in order. The pushrods must be replaced in the same position with the same end in the block.

4. Remove the exhaust pipe-to-mani-

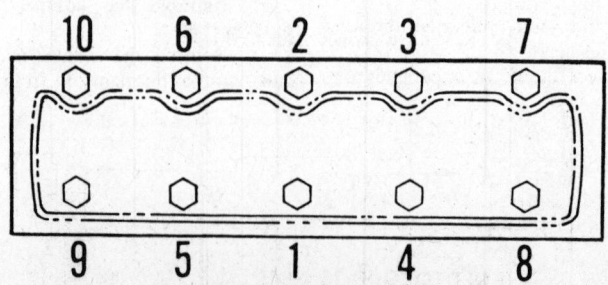

OHV 4 cylinder head bolt torque sequence (© Pontiac Div., G.M. Corp.)

fold attaching bolts. Remove the inner panel of the carburetor heat stove from the two center cylinder head bolts.

5. Remove the battery ground strap and engine ground strap on the left head; engine ground strap and automatic transmission filler tube bracket on the right head.

6. Remove the cylinder head bolts and head, with the exhaust manifold attached.

NOTE: Left head must be maneuvered to clear the power steering and power brake units.

7. Check the head surface for straightness, then place a new head gasket on the block.

NOTE: Bolts are of three different lengths. When they are properly installed, they will project an equal amount from the head, before tightening.

8. Install all the bolts and tighten evenly to the specified torque. Tighten to specifications in three stages.

— CAUTION —
On the 265 and 301 V8 engine, coat all rocker stud lower threads, the cylinder head bolt threads, and the underside of the bolt head with thread sealer.

9. Install the pushrods in their original positions and locations.

10. Position the rocker arms over the pushrods. Tighten the rocker arm ball retaining nut to 20 ft. lbs.

11. Replace the rocker arm cover.

12. Replace the valley cover.

13. Replace the ground straps, oil filler tube bracket, and intake manifold.

NOTE: When installing the intake manifold remember to use new gaskets and O-ring seal, if so equipped.

14. Install the exhaust pipe flange nuts.

Timing Cover and Oil Seal

REMOVAL & INSTALLATION
V8

1. Drain radiator and cylinder block.
2. Loosen alternator adjusting bolts.
3. Remove fan, fan pulley, and accessory drive belts.

4. Disconnect radiator hoses. Remove the water pump.

5. Remove fuel pump.

NOTE: Fuel pump removal is not necessary if only the seal is being replaced.

6. Remove harmonic balancer bolt and washer.

7. Remove harmonic balancer.

NOTE: Do not pry on rubber-mounted balancers. Seal can be removed, using an awl, at this point. Install a new seal with lip inward.

8. Remove front four oil pan-to-timing cover bolts.

9. Remove timing cover bolts and nuts, and cover-to-intake manifold bolt.

10. Pull cover forward and remove.

11. Remove O-ring from recess in intake manifold, then clean all gasket surfaces.

12. To replace seal, pry it out of the cover using an awl. Install the new seal with lip inward.

NOTE: Seal can be replaced with cover installed.

13. To install, reverse removal procedure, making sure all gaskets are replaced.

4-151

1. Remove the crankshaft hub.
2. Remove the oil pan-to-front cover screws.
3. Remove the front cover-to-block screws.
4. Pull the cover slightly forward, just enough to allow cutting of the oil pan front seal flush with the block on both sides.
5. Remove the front cover and attached portion of the pan seal.
6. Clean the gasket surfaces thoroughly.

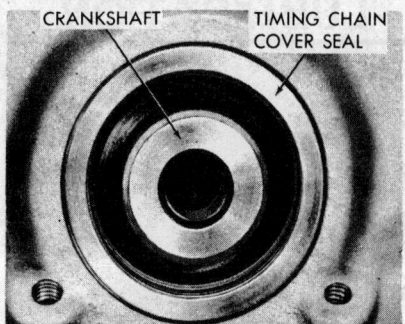

Timing chain cover oil seal
(© Pontiac Div., G.M. Corp)

7. Cut the tabs from the new oil pan front seal.

8. Install the seal on the front cover, pressing the tips into the holes provided.

9. Coat the new gasket with sealer and position it on the front cover.

10. Apply a ⅛ in. bead of silicone sealer to the joint formed at the oil pan and block.

11. Align the front cover seal with a centering tool and install the front cover. Tighten the screws. Install the hub.

Camshaft & Timing Chain

REMOVAL & INSTALLATION

NOTE: If the car is equipped with air conditioning, it may be necessary to unbolt the condenser and move it aside to provide clearance. Do not disconnect any of the air conditioning lines.

V8

1. Drain cooling system and remove air cleaner.

2. Disconnect all water hoses, vacuum lines and spark plug wires. Remove the radiator.

3. Disconnect accelerator linkage, temperature gauge wire, and fuel lines.

4. Remove hood latch brace.

5. Remove PCV hose, then remove rocker covers.

NOTE: On air-conditioned models, remove alternator and bracket.

6. Remove distributor, then remove intake manifold.

7. Remove valley cover.

8. Loosen rocker arm nuts and pivot rockers out of the way.

9. Remove pushrods and lifters (keep them in proper order).

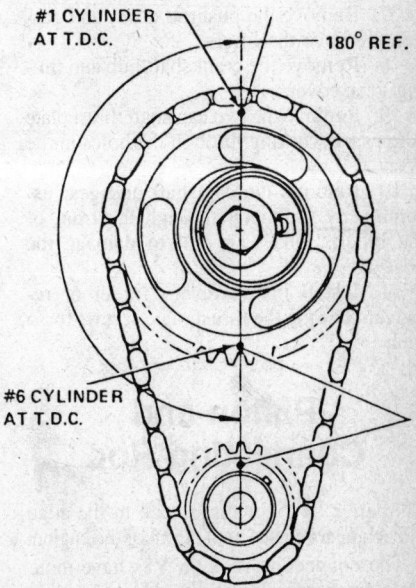

ALIGNING TIME MARKS
V8 engine timing mark alignment

TORQUE SEQUENCES

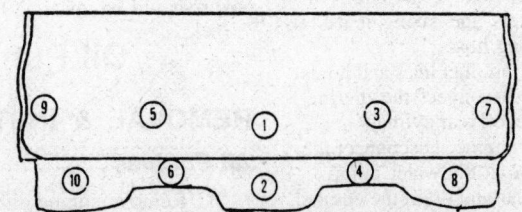

Cylinder head torque sequence—265, 301, and 400 V8's

10. Remove harmonic balancer, fuel pump, and four oil pan-to-timing cover bolts.

11. Remove timing cover and gasket, then remove fuel pump eccentric and bushing.

12. Align timing marks, then remove timing chain and sprockets.

NOTE: To set crankshaft and camshaft gear marks for timing chain installation, position the engine with the No. 6 piston at top dead center. Slowly rotate the crankshaft one revolution until the camshaft gear mark is at 12 o'clock. No. 1 piston will now be at TDC on the compression stroke.

13. Remove camshaft thrust plate.

14. Remove camshaft by pulling straight forward, being careful not to damage cam bearings in the process.

NOTE: It may be necessary to jack up the engine slightly to gain clearance, especially if motor mounts are worn.

15. Install new camshaft, with lobes and journals coated with heavy (SAE 50-60) oil, into the engine, being careful not to damage cam bearings.

16. Install camshaft thrust plate and tighten bolts to 20 ft. lbs.

17. To install timing chain and camshaft, reverse Steps 1-12, tightening camshaft sprocket bolt to 40 ft. lbs., timing cover bolts and nuts to 30 ft. lbs., and oil pan bolts to 12 ft. lbs.

4-151

1. Drain the cooling system.
2. Remove the radiator.
3. Remove the fan and water pump pulley.
4. Remove the grille if necessary.
5. Remove the rocker cover, rocker arms, and pushrods.
6. Remove the distributor, spark plugs, and fuel pump.
7. Remove the pushrod cover and gasket. Remove the lifters.
8. Remove the crankshaft hub and timing gear cover.
9. Remove the two camshaft thrust plate screws by working through the holes in the gear.
10. Remove the camshaft and gear assembly by pulling it through the front of the block. Take care not to damage the bearings.
11. Install in the reverse order of removal. Torque the thrust plate screws to 75 inch lbs.

Piston and Connecting Rod

The letter "F", or the notche in the edge of each piston, goes to the front of the engine.

The connecting rods on V8s have three dimples on one side of the rod and a single dimple on the connecting rod cap. The dim-

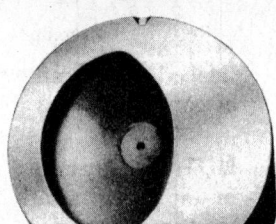
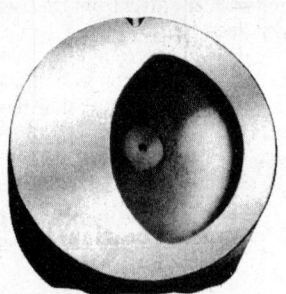

Turbocharged engine piston identification
(© Pontiac Div., G.M. Corp.)

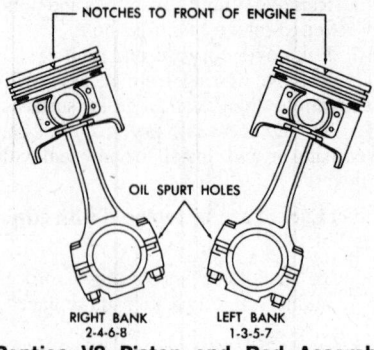

Pontiac V8 Piston and Rod Assembly
(© Pontiac Div., G.M. Corp.)

ples must face forward on the left bank, and to the rear on the right.

Some non-V8 engines have oil squirt holes on the connecting rods; these holes must face the camshaft.

The turbocharged 301 has special low compression pistons. See the illustration for indentification.

LUBRICATION

Oil Pan

REMOVAL & INSTALLATION

V8

1. Disconnect the negative battery terminal.
2. Remove the fan shroud and the power steering belt, then push the pump in toward the block.
3. Remove the fan and pulley.
4. Disconnect the engine ground straps. Drain the radiator.
5. On A/C cars, remove the compressor from the brackets and swing it aside without disconnecting hoses.
6. Check all wiring, fuel lines and hoses for clearance, and disconnect the thermal feed switch from the left rear cylinder head, to allow raising the engine. Disconnect the bottom radiator hose at the water pump.
7. Jack up the car and drain the engine oil.
8. Disconnect the steering idler arm from

the frame and remove the Pitman arm from the steering box on Grand Prix.

9. Remove the exhaust crossover pipe.
10. Remove the flywheel housing cover, starter motor and motor bracket.
11. Attach a hoist to the front of the engine.
12. Support the engine on a hoist and remove the front motor mount bolts and mounts.
13. Loosen the rear motor mount at transmission or, remove it entirely and allow the extension housing to rest on the crossmember.
14. Remove the oil pan bolts, then raise the engine straight up about 4½ in. until the top of the transmission is hitting the floor pan. On some models, it also helps to move the engine forward about 1½ in.
15. Rotate the oil pan forward to clear the oil pump, then remove the oil pan.
16. Place wood blocks between the engine and motor mount brackets for safety.
17. To install, reverse the removal procedure. Clean all gasket surfaces thoroughly. Use gasket cement and a new gasket.

4-151

1. Disconnect the battery ground cable.
2. Remove the fan.
3. Drain the oil.
4. Disconnect the exhaust pipe at the manifold and loosen the hanger bracket.
5. Remove the starter.
6. Remove the flywheel housing inspection cover.
7. Remove the hub bolt and install an engine support. Jack up the engine enough to take the weight off the mounts. Remove the mounts. Remove the pan bolts and raise the engine enough to drop the pan.
8. Thoroughly clean the gasket surfaces and install the pan in the reverse order of removal. The bolts of the timing gear cover should be installed last.

Oil Pump

REMOVAL & INSTALLATION

All Engines

1. Remove engine oil pan.
2. Remove pump attaching screws and carefully lower the pump.

3. Reinstall in the reverse order. To ensure immediate oil pressure on start-up, the oil pump gear cavity should be packed with petroleum jelly.

Rear Main Seal

REPLACEMENT

4-151—1978

1. Remove the oil pan.
2. Remove the rear bearing cap.
3. Remove the oil seal from its groove by prying at the bottom with an awl.
4. Clean and oil the crankshaft surface.
5. Coat a new seal with clean engine oil and insert it in the bearing cap groove. Take care to keep oil off the rear edge, since it is treated with sealant. Gradually push the seal into place with a hammer handle.
6. The upper seal half may be removed by tapping it out of its groove with a hammer and blunt punch.
7. Push the new seal into place with the lip toward the front of the engine.
8. Install the bearing cap with the bolts loose.
9. Move the crankshaft first to the rear and then to the front with a rubber mallet. This will correctly position the thrust bearing.
10. Torque the cap bolts to 65 ft. lbs.
11. Install the oil pan.

4-151—1979 and Later

The rear main oil seal is a one piece unit, and is removed or installed without removal of the oil pan or crankshaft.

1. Remove the transmission, flywheel or torque converter bellhousing, and the flywheel or flex plate.
2. Remove the rear main oil seal with an awl. Be extremely careful not to scratch the crankshaft.
3. Oil the lip of the new seal with clean engine oil. Install a new seal by hand onto the rear crankshaft flange. The helical lip side of the seal should face the engine. Make sure the seal is firmly and evenly installed.

4. Replace the flywheel or flexplate, bellhousing and transmission.

V8

1. Remove the oil pan and baffle.
2. Remove the rear main bearing cap.
3. Make a seal tool as illustrated.
4. Insert the tool against one end of the oil seal in the block and drive the seal gently into the groove until it bottoms. Repeat on the other end of the seal.
5. Form a new seal in the cap. Cut four ⅜ in. long pieces from this seal.
6. Work two of the pieces into each of the gaps which have been made at the end of the seal in the block. Do not cut off any material to make them fit.
7. Form a new seal in the bearing cap.
8. Apply a ⅟₁₆ in. bead of silicone sealer from the center of the seal across to the external gasket groove.
9. Reassemble the cap and torque to specification.

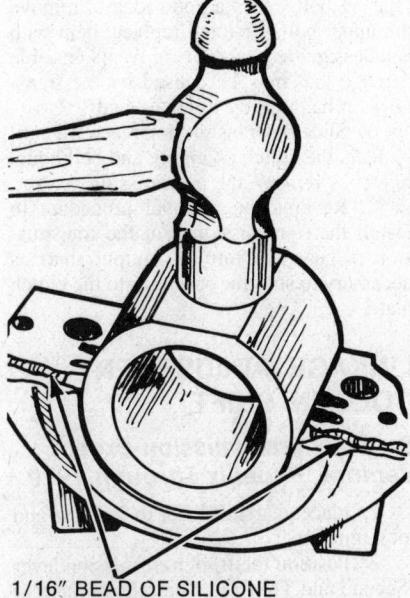

1/16" BEAD OF SILICONE RUBBER SEALER
Forming a new crankshaft seal

CLUTCH

REPLACEMENT

1. Raise car and support on jackstands. Disconnect the battery.
2. Support rear of engine.
3. Remove driveshaft.
4. Remove rear crossmember bolts from frame and transmission mounts, and remove crossmember.
5. Disconnect transmission shift linkage, speedometer cable and clutch return spring. Clutch fork pushrod will now hang free.
6. Remove clutch housing cover plate screws and let plate hang from starter gear housing.
7. Lower engine enough to gain access to clutch housing bolts at engine block, then remove all but uppermost bolt.
8. Hold transmission and clutch housing assembly against block over dowel pins while removing last bolt. Remove transmission and clutch housing as an assembly.
9. Matchmark pressure plate and flywheel with paint to make sure correct balance is maintained.
10. Loosen the cover plate attaching screws, a little at a time, until clutch diaphragm spring tension is released. Remove bolts and clutch assembly.
11. The pilot bearing is an oil-impregnated type bearing pressed into the crankshaft. Inspect and renew, if necessary.

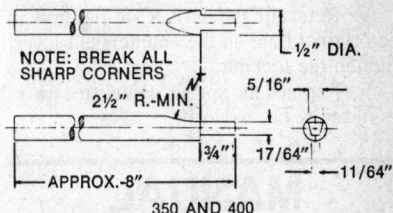

NOTE: BREAK ALL SHARP CORNERS
½" DIA.
5/16"
2½" R.-MIN.
¾" 17/64" 11/64"
APPROX.-8"
350 AND 400

Pontiac V8 rear main bearing upper seal tool

4-151 Upper Main Bearing Seal Removal
(© Pontiac Div., G.M. Corp.)

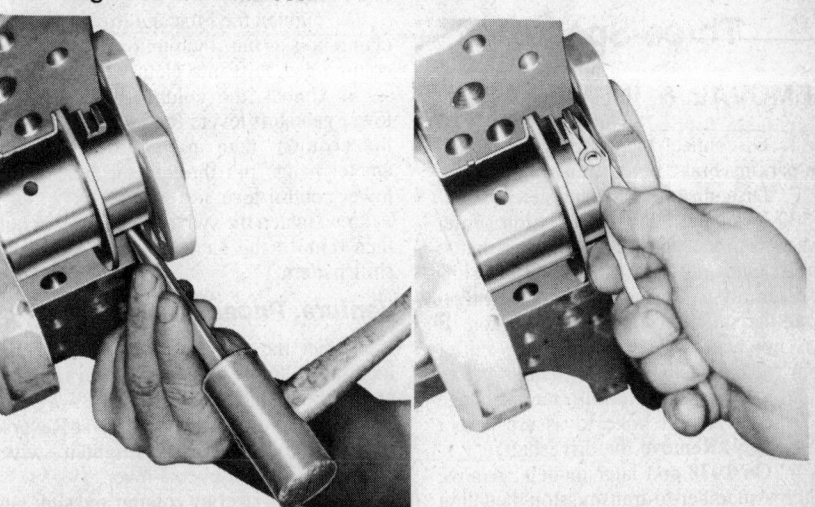

Rear main oil seal removal—upper half (© Pontiac Div., G.M. Corp)

12. Install clutch disc with long hub forward (toward flywheel).

13. Install pressure plate and cover assembly, then align clutch disc by inserting pilot tool, or old transmission input shaft, into splines. Align mark on clutch cover with mark on flywheel, then align nearest bolt holes.

14. Install the bolts in the cover and tighten them alternately.

15. Remove clutch pilot tool and check to see that it can be reinserted and moved freely.

16. Install clutch fork and dust boot into clutch housing. Lubricate throwout bearing with high melting point grease.

17. Complete the reassembly of clutch housing and transmission by reversing removal method. Tighten housing bolts.

18. Adjust shifter and clutch release linkage.

ADJUSTMENT

1. Disconnect the clutch fork return spring.
2. Loosen the pushrod locknut.
3. Detach the swivel or pushrod from the countershaft lever.
4. Install the swivel or pushrod in the gauge hole in the countershaft lever.
5. Push on the countershaft lever so that the clutch pedal is up against the stop.
6. Hold the clutch fork to the rear so that the release bearing lightly contacts the release levers.
7. Adjust the pushrod length to remove all lash from the linkage.
8. Reinstall the swivel or pushrod in the original hole on the countershaft lever. Tighten the locknut.
9. Replace the spring. Pedal free travel should now be ¾-1¼ in.

MANUAL TRANSMISSION

Three-Speed

REMOVAL & INSTALLATION

1. Disconnect the battery and release the parking brake before raising the car.
2. Disconnect the speedometer cable.
3. Disconnect the transmission shifter levers from the transmission shifter shafts. On floorshift models, remove the two shifter assembly-to-shifter support bolts and remove the shifter from the transmission. If it is not necessary to remove the shifter from the car, it may be left hanging from its floor seal. Mark the differential flange and the driveshaft yoke to assure proper reassembly. Remove the driveshaft.
4. On 1978 and later models, remove the crossmember-to-transmission mounting bolts, the catalytic converter-to-transmis-

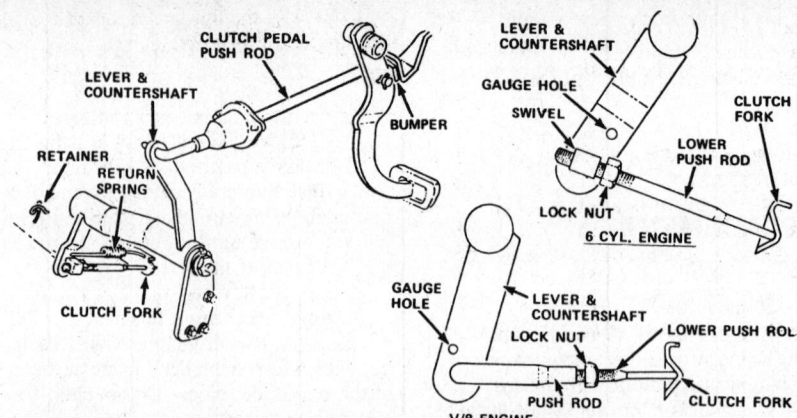

Typical clutch linkage and adjustment points (© Pontiac Div., G.M. Corp.)

sion bracket and the crossmember-to-frame bolts. Using a floor jack, raise the transmission slightly and remove the crossmember.

5. Remove the four transmission-to-bell housing bolts. It is a good idea to remove the upper bolts first and replace them with headless guide pins. This prevents possible damage that may be caused by the transmission hanging by its input shaft.

6. Slide the transmission rearward until it clears the clutch assembly and bell housing, then remove the transmission.

7. Reverse the removal procedure to install the transmission. Put the transmission in gear and turn the output shaft as necessary to start the splines into the clutch plate.

LINKAGE ADJUSTMENT— COLUMN SHIFT

Saginaw Transmission Except Ventura, Phoenix Through 1979

1. Place gearshift lever in Reverse and lock ignition.
2. Position the front transmission lever (Second and Third) in Neutral and the rear transmission shift lever (First and Reverse) in Reverse.
3. Tighten the First and Reverse swivel clamp bolt or nut, then unlock the steering column and shift into Neutral.
4. Unlock the column and align the lower gearshift levers (on column) in Neutral position, then insert a 0.185 in. diameter gauge pin through the hole in the lower control levers.
5. Tighten the swivel clamp bolt or nut, then remove the gauge pin and check the shift pattern.

Ventura, Phoenix Through 1979

1. Set the shift lever in Reverse and lock the column. Loosen the swivel clamp nuts at both shifter levers.
2. Pull down slightly on 1st-Reverse rod to remove slack, then tighten swivel clamp nut at 1st-Reverse lever.
3. Unlock steering column and shift into Neutral. Align column levers and insert a

³⁄₁₆ in. gauge pin through alignment holes.

4. Position 2nd-3rd transmission lever in Neutral, then tighten swivel clamp nut.

5. Remove gauge pin and check shift pattern and ignition lock. With lever in Reverse, key must move to LOCK freely. This should not be possible in any other gear.

LINKAGE ADJUSTMENT— FLOOR SHIFT

1. Place gearshift lever in Neutral.
2. Loosen swivel clamp on gearshift control rod.
3. Loosen trunnion locknuts on 1st Reverse and 2nd-3rd transmission control rods.
4. Insert a ¼ in. drill rod into shifter assembly.
5. If gearshift lever is not properly aligned with floor opening:
   a. *Console*—loosen two shifter-to-support bolts and align shifter. Tighten bolts.
   b. *Without console*—loosen two shifter-to-support bolts and center shifter in boot; tighten bolts.
6. Position both transmission shift levers in Neutral and tighten locknuts.
7. Remove gauge pin and check shift pattern.
8. Place gearshift lever in Reverse, then place steering column lower lever in Lock position and lock ignition.
9. Push up on gearshift control rod to take up lash in column lock mechanism, then tighten adjusting swivel clamp.

Four-Speed

The removal and installation procedures for the four-speed transmissions are the same as for three-speed units.

LINKAGE ADJUSTMENT

1. Place gearshift lever in Neutral and ignition switch in "OFF".
2. Loosen adjusting swivel clamp on gearshift control rod.
3. Loosen locknuts for all others.
4. Insert a ³⁄₁₆ in. drill rod into gauge pin hole in shifter.

5. If the gearshift lever is not properly aligned with floor opening:

a. *Console*—loosen two shifter-to-support bolts and align shifter. Tighten bolts.

b. *Without console*—loosen two shifter-to-support bolts and center shifter in boot; tighten bolts.

6. Place transmission shift levers in Neutral and tighten locknuts.

7. Remove gauge pin and check shift pattern.

8. Place gearshift lever in Reverse, set steering column lower lever in Lock position and lock ignition.

9. Push up on gearshift control rod to take up lash in steering column lock mechanism, then tighten adjusting swivel clamp nut.

5-Speed

REMOVAL & INSTALLATION

1. Remove the boot retainer and slide the boot upward on the shift lever.

2. Remove the foam insulator over the control assembly bolts.

3. Remove the four control lever bolts and remove the control lever.

4. Raise the car, mark the driveshaft-to-yoke position, and remove the driveshaft.

5. Remove the damper assembly, the torque converter bracket, and the torque arm bracket.

6. Disconnect the speedometer cable and the back-up light switch.

7. Remove the nut from the front of the torque arm, the catalytic converter bracket bolts, and the transmission damper, if any. Remove the bolts holding the transmission rubber mount fastened to the support, then place a transmission jack under the transmission and remove the transmission support.

8. Remove the transmission-to-clutch housing bolts and slide the exhaust bracket forward. Install ½″-13 × 2″ guidepins in place of the bolts to support the transmission. This will prevent clutch distortion. After this the transmission can be moved rearward and removed from the car.

9. Installation is in the reverse order of removal, but take note of the following: make sure the drive gear splines are clean and dry; use guidebolts in the bellhousing holes to aid in aligning the transmission to the engine; shift the lever through all the gears to make sure nothing is binding.

AUTOMATIC TRANSMISSION

NOTE: For information on transmission identification and service procedures, please refer to "Automatic Transmissions" in the Unit Repair Section.

NOTE: For automatic transmission removal and installation procedures refer to the "Chevrolet Rear Wheel Drive" section.

DRIVESHAFT AND U-JOINTS

Driveshaft

REMOVAL & INSTALLATION

1. Mark the driveshaft rear yoke and the differential flange to assure correct alignment upon reassembly.

2. Remove the U-bolts and nuts from the differential flange.

3. Remove the driveshaft assembly by first sliding the driveshaft sufficiently forward to disengage the differential flange, then slide the shaft downward and rearward to disengage the front splined yoke from the transmission output shaft.

4. Installation is in the reverse order of removal. Be sure to align the matchmark made before assembly.

U-Joint

REMOVAL & INSTALLATION

For information on universal joint removal, installation and overhaul procedures, please refer to the "U-Joints and CV-Joints" in the Unit Repair section.

REAR AXLE

All Pontiacs use two different types of drive axle, the C-lock and the non C-lock type. Axle shafts in the C-lock type are retained by C-shaped locks, which fit grooves at the inner end of the shaft. Axle shafts in the non C-lock type are retained by the brake backing plate, which is bolted to the axle housing.

Axle Shaft, Bearing and Seal

REMOVAL & INSTALLATION
Non C-Lock Type

——— CAUTION ———
Before attempting any service to the drive axle or axle shafts, remove the axle carrier cover and visually determine if the axle shafts are retained by C-shaped locks at the inner end, or by the brake backing plate at the outer end. If the shafts are not retained by C-locks, proceed as follows.

Design allows for maximum axle shaft end-play of .025 in., which can be measured with a dial indicator. If end-play is found to be excessive, the bearing should be replaced. Shimming the bearing is not recommended as this ignores end-play of the bearing itself and could result in improper seating of the bearing.

1. Remove the wheel, tire and brake drum.

2. Remove the nuts holding the retainer plate to the backing plate. Disconnect the brake line.

3. Remove the retainer and install nuts, fingertight, to prevent the brake backing plate from being dislodged.

4. Pull out the axle shaft and bearing assembly, using a slide hammer.

5. Using a chisel, nick the bearing retainer in three or four places. The retainer does not have to be cut, merely collapsed sufficiently, to allow the bearing retainer to be slid from the shaft.

6. Press off the bearing and install the new one by pressing it into position.

7. Press on the new retainer.

NOTE: Do not attempt to press the bearing and the retainer on at the same time.

8. Assemble the shaft and bearing in the housing, being sure that the bearing is seated properly in the housing.

9. Install the retainer, drum, wheel and tire. Bleed the brakes.

C-Lock Type

——— CAUTION ———
Before attempting any service to the drive axle or axle shafts, remove the carrier cover and visually determine if the axle shafts are retained by C-shaped locks at the inner ends or by a brake backing plate at the outer end. If they are retained by C-shaped locks, proceed as follows.

1. Raise the vehicle and remove the wheels.

2. The differential cover has already been removed (see Caution note above). Remove the differential pinion shaft lockscrew and the differential pinion shaft.

3. Push the flanged end of the axle shaft toward the center of the vehicle and remove the C-lock from the end of the shaft.

4. Remove the axle shaft from the housing, being careful not to damage the oil seal.

5. Remove the oil seal by inserting the button end of the axle shaft behind the steel case of the oil seal. Pry the seal loose from the bore.

6. Seat the legs of the bearing puller behind the bearing. Seat a washer against the bearing and hold it in place with a nut. Use a slide hammer to pull the bearing.

7. Pack the cavity between the seal lips with wheel bearing lubricant and lubricate a new wheel bearing with the same.

8. Use a suitable driver and install

bearing until it bottoms against the tube. Install the oil seal.

9. Slide the axle shaft into place. Be sure that the splines on the shaft do not damage the oil seal. Make sure that the splines engage the differential side gear.

10. Install the axle shaft C-lock on the inner end of the axle shaft and push the shaft outward so that the C-lock seats in the differential side gear counterbore.

11. Position the differential pinion shaft through the case and pinions, aligning the hole for the case with the hole for the lockscrew.

12. Install the pinion shaft lockscrew.

13. Use a new gasket and install the carrier cover. Be sure that the gasket surfaces are clean before installing the gasket and cover.

14. Fill the axle with lubricant to the bottom of the filler hole.

15. Install the brake drum and wheels and lower the car. Check for leaks and road test the car.

JACKING, HOISTING

Jack car at front spring seats of lower control arms. Jack car at rear under axle housing, or under a frame member.

FRONT SUSPENSION

NOTE: Many 1980 and later Pontiacs have been gradually switched over to metric fasteners. Most models use metric prevailing torque nuts to fasten the upper and lower ball joint studs to the steering knuckle. American standard inch calibrated wrenches will not fit metric nuts and bolts.

Shock Absorber

REPLACEMENT

New shock absorbers must be purged of air before installation. This is done by repeatedly extending the shock in its normal mounted position, inverting, and compressing it.

1. Remove the nut, retainer, and grommet, which are attached to the upper end of the shock absorber and seat against the frame bracket.

NOTE: It may be necessary to hold the shock absorber shaft to remove the nut. This may be done with a wrench on the end of the shaft.

2. Raise the car to allow the shock to be dropped from the lower control arm.

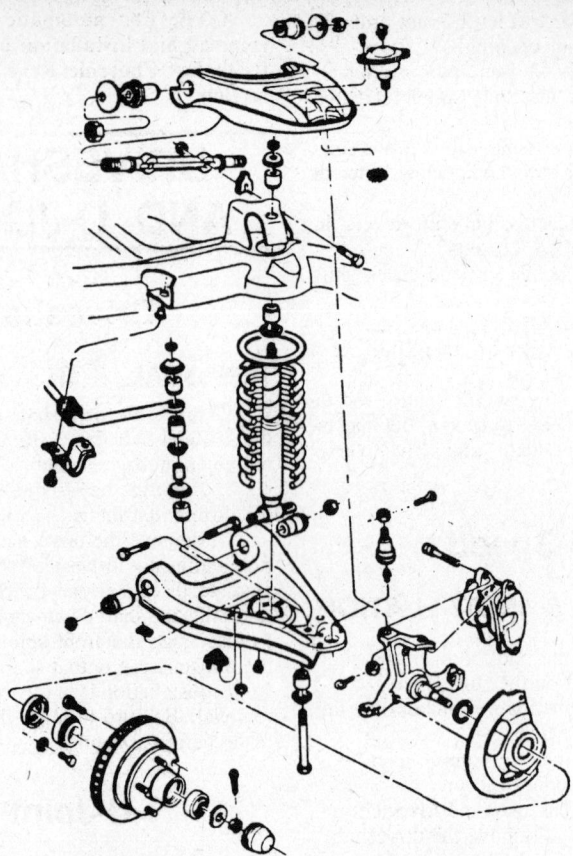

Exploded view of typical front suspension

3. Remove the two shock absorber lower attaching screws and lower the shock from the control arm.

4. Install the shock absorber by reversing the removal steps.

5. Make sure all grommets are in the correct position. Tighten the upper nut.

Coil Spring

REMOVAL & INSTALLATION

1. Jack up car and support on jack stands at frame side rails.

2. Remove shock absorber.

3. Disconnect stabilizer bar at lower control arm.

4. Support lower control arm with a hydraulic floor jack. Install a chain around the spring and through the control arm as a safety measure, then remove the two inner control arm to front crossmember pivot bolts.

5. Carefully lower the control arm, allowing the spring to relax.

—————— **CAUTION** ——————
Allow the spring to completely expand before attempting to remove it.

6. Remove the chain. Reach in and remove spring.

7. To install, reverse the removal procedure. Tighten the lower control arm pivot bolts to 105 ft. lbs. or the nuts to 95 ft. lbs. with the weight of the car on the springs.

Upper Control Arm

REMOVAL & INSTALLATION

1. Support car weight at outer end of lower control arm.

2. Remove wheel and tire.

3. Remove cotter pin and loosen the nut on the upper control arm ball stud.

4. Remove the stud from the knuckle with a pry bar, while tapping with a hammer. The preferred method of doing this is to use a ball joint stud remover tool to push the stud nut.

5. Remove two nuts that hold the upper control arm cross-shaft to front crossmember. Count number of shims at each bolt.

6. Install bolts through holes and install upper control arm to crossmember.

7. Secure two nuts and washers to bolts holding the upper control arm shaft to front crossmember. Install same number of shims as removed at each bolt.

8. Lubricate ball joint with chassis lube.

9. Install ball joint stud through knuckle. Install nut, and torque to 40 ft. lbs. Insert cotter pin.

—————— **CAUTION** ——————
Care should be taken to insure that the steering knuckle hole, ball stud, and nut are free of dirt and grease before tightening the nut. Turn the nut only in the tightening direction to align the slot with the hole to insert the cotter pin. Do not

back off the nut. Maximum torque to align the slot with the hole, should not exceed 100 ft. lbs.

10. Install wheel and tire assembly.
11. Lower car to floor.
12. Be sure to recheck caster and camber.

Ball Joint

INSPECTION

NOTE: Before performing this inspection, make sure the wheel bearings are adjusted correctly and that the control arm bushings are in good condition.

1. Jack the car up under the front lower control arm at the spring seat.
2. Raise the car until there is 1-2 in. of clearance under the wheel.
3. Insert a bar under the wheel and pry upward. If the wheel raises more than ⅛ in., the ball joints are worn. While prying on the wheel, determine by visual inspection whether the upper or lower ball joint is worn.

NOTE: Due to the distribution of forces in the suspension, the lower ball joint is usually the defective joint.

LOWER BALL JOINT WEAR INDICATORS—ALL MODELS

These cars have a visual wear indicator on

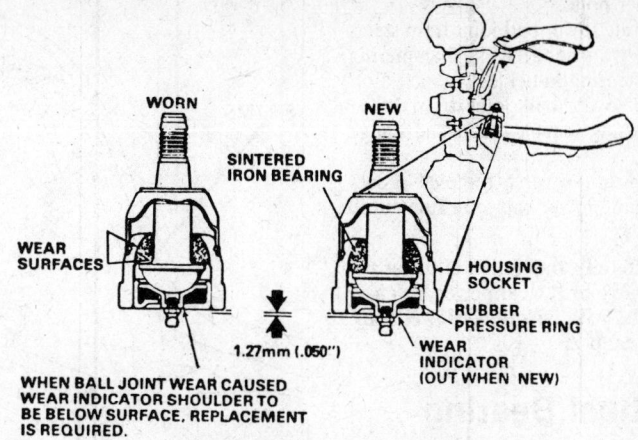

Lower ball joint wear indicator

the lower ball joint. Wear is indicated by the position of the ½ in. nipple into which the grease fitting is screwed. On a new joint, the nipple should project .050 in. beyond the ball joint cover surface. If the nipple is flush or inside the cover surface, replace the ball joint.

Upper Ball Joint

REMOVAL & INSTALLATION

1. Perform Steps 1-4 of Upper Control Arm Removal. Punch the center of the four rivets.
2. Drill through the heads of these rivets.

3. Chisel off rivet heads and tap out rivets with a punch.
4. Install new ball joint against top side of upper control arm. Secure joint to control arm with the four special alloy bolts and nuts furnished with the replacement part.
5. Torque these bolts and nuts to 9 ft. lbs.

Lower Control Arm and Ball Joint

REMOVAL & INSTALLATION

1. Remove coil spring and lower con-

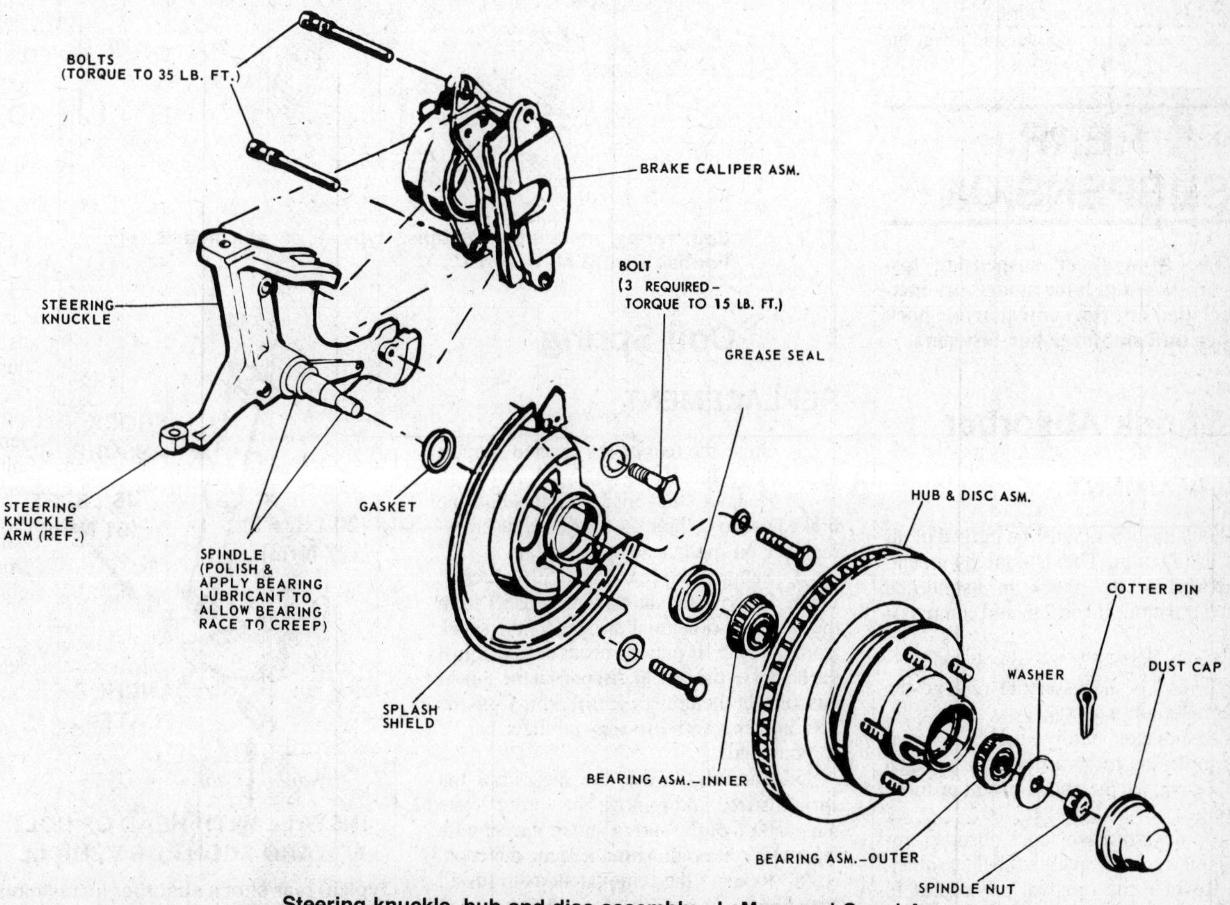

BOLTS
(TORQUE TO 35 LB. FT.)

BRAKE CALIPER ASM.

STEERING KNUCKLE

BOLT
(3 REQUIRED—
TORQUE TO 15 LB. FT.)

GREASE SEAL

STEERING KNUCKLE ARM (REF.)

GASKET

SPINDLE
(POLISH & APPLY BEARING LUBRICANT TO ALLOW BEARING RACE TO CREEP)

SPLASH SHIELD

HUB & DISC ASM.

COTTER PIN

DUST CAP

WASHER

BEARING ASM.—INNER

BEARING ASM.—OUTER

SPINDLE NUT

Steering knuckle, hub and disc assembly—LeMans and Grand Am

trol arm inner bolts.

2. Separate lower ball joint from steering knuckle by prying, while hammering sharply on steering knuckle.

3. Press lower ball joint from lower control arm using suitable arbors and a large bench vise.

4. To install, reverse removal procedure, tightening lower ball joint stud nut to 83 ft. lbs.

NOTE: If only ball joint is to be removed, remove brake caliper or hub and backing plate, with jack under lower arm. Begin with Step 2.

Wheel Bearing

ADJUSTMENT

1. Lift the wheel off the ground by jacking under the lower control arm.

2. Remove the dust cap from the hub.

3. Remove the cotter pin and discard it.

4. Snug up the spindle nut while spinning the wheel to seat the bearings (12 ft. lbs.). Then back off the nut ¼-½ turn.

5. Retighten the nut by hand until it is finger-tight.

6. Loosen the nut until the nearest hole in the spindle lines up with a slot in the spindle nut, then insert a new cotter pin. When the bearing is properly adjusted, there will be 0.001-0.005 in. endplay.

7. Replace the dust cover and lower the car.

REAR SUSPENSION

NOTE: Many rear suspension fasteners on 1979 and later models are metric. Included are the control arm, shock absorber and stabilizer bar fasteners.

Shock Absorber

REPLACEMENT

New shock absorbers must be purged of air before installation. This is done by repeatedly extending the shock in its normal mounted position, inverting, and compressing it.

1. Raise the car at the axle housing.

2. It may be necessary to remove the wheel on station wagons.

3. Remove the nut, retainer, and grommet, or nut, and lockwasher, which attach the lower end of the shock absorber to its mounting.

4. Remove the two shock absorber upper attaching screws and the shock absorber.

5. Reverse the removal procedures to install.

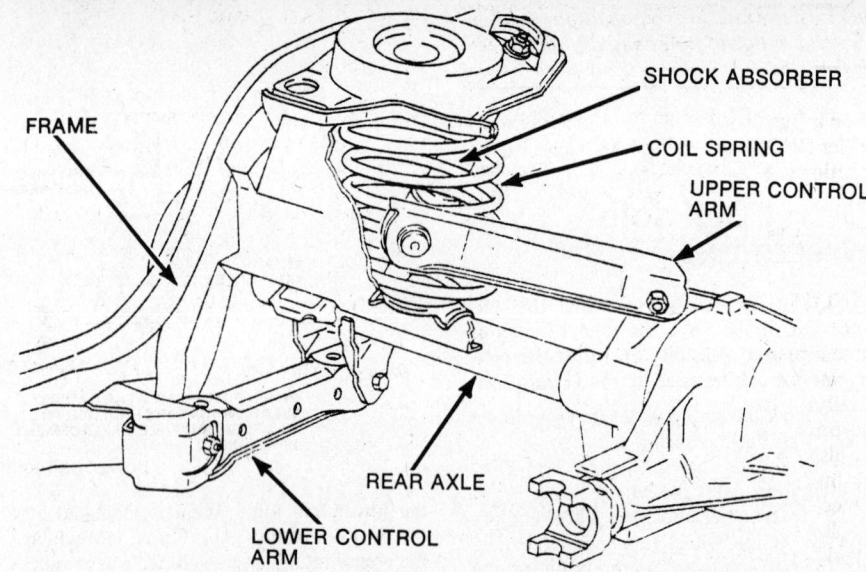

1979 and later Grand Prix rear suspension (© Pontiac Div., G.M. Corp.)

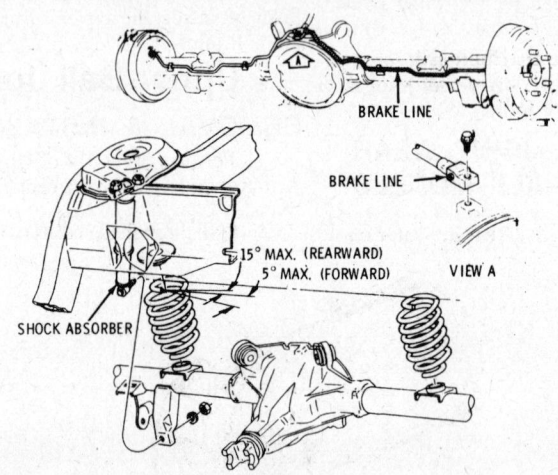

Coil spring installation details, typical of all models (© Pontiac Div., G.M. Corp.)

Coil Spring

REPLACEMENT

1. Raise the rear of the car and support it solidly on the frame rails.

2. Remove the clip that attaches the brake hose to its bracket on the frame crossmember on models so equipped.

3. Support the rear axle with a jack.

4. Remove the nut and lockwasher from the shock absorber and disconnect the shock from the axle. It may be necessary to adjust the height of the jack to disconnect the shock. Disconnect the upper control arms from the axle housing and also the stabilizer bar, if so equipped.

5. Carefully lower the jack until the spring is free and remove the spring. Note the position of the spring and replace it with the lower coil pointing in the same direction.

6. Reverse the removal steps to install the spring.

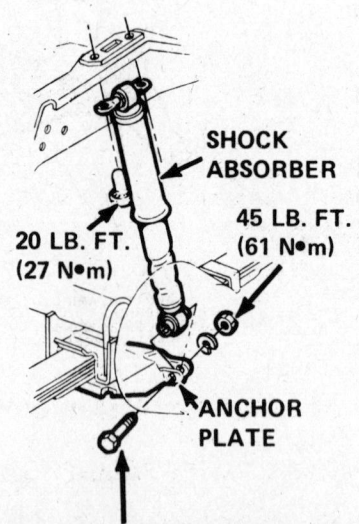

INSTALL WITH HEAD OF BOLT TOWARD FRONT OF VEHICLE.

Typical rear shock absorber installation : 1979 Phoenix shown

BRAKES

For information on brake service, please refer to "Brakes" in the Unit Repair section.

Parking Brake

ADJUSTMENT

The automatic self-adjusting feature incorporated in the rear brake mechanism normally maintains proper parking brake adjustment. For this reason, the rear brake adjustment must be checked before any adjustment of the parking brake cables is made. Check the parking brake mechanism and cables for free movement and lubricate all working surfaces before proceeding.

───── CAUTION ─────

It is very important that the parking brake cables not be too tight. If the cables are too tight, they create a drag and position the secondary shoes so that the self-adjusters continue to operate in compensation for drag wear. The result is rapidly worn rear brake linings.

All except 1978–81 and later Bonneville, Catalina, Grand Prix

1. Jack up both rear wheels.
2. Push parking brake pedal 2 notches for 1978 and later Ventura, 3 notches for 1978 and later LeMans and Grand Am.
3. On 1978 and later models, tighten the adjusting nut until the left rear wheel can be rotated back.
4. Tighten locknut and release parking brake pedal; no drag should be felt.

1978–81 and later Bonneville, Catalina, Grand Prix

1. Jack up both rear wheels. Support the car on jack stands.
2. Set 1978 and later full-size models at 2 clicks; Grand Prix at 6 clicks.
3. Loosen the equalizer locknut. On 1978 and later cars, tighten the adjusting nut until the left wheel can be turned backward with two hands, but is locked in forward rotation.
4. Tighten the locknut.
5. Fully release the parking brake and rotate the rear wheels; no drag should be felt in either direction.

Master Cylinder

REMOVAL & INSTALLATION

1. Disconnect hydraulic lines at master cylinder; disconnect clevis at pedal (except on power brakes).
2. Remove the two retaining nuts and lockwashers that hold the master cylinder

fastened to the firewall or power booster.
3. Remove the master cylinder, gasket and rubber boot.
4. Position master cylinder on firewall; reconnect pushrod clevis to brake pedal.
5. Install nuts and lockwashers.
6. Install hydraulic lines, then check brake pedal free play.
7. Bleed brakes, as described in Unit Repair section.

Power Brake Booster

REMOVAL & INSTALLATION

1. Remove the vacuum hose from the front housing and discard the grommet. Remove the master cylinder and position away from the booster. It is not necessary to disconnect the lines from the master cylinder if it is not to be repaired.
2. Remove the clevis pin retainer from the brake pedal inside the car.
3. Remove the nuts from the vacuum cylinder studs under the dash and remove the vacuum power section. From 1979 on, a 10mm mounting stud is used in place of the ⅜ in. stud and nut of previous years.
4. Reverse the removal procedure to install the booster.

Hydro-Boost Brake Booster

REMOVAL & INSTALLATION

For an explanation, troubleshooting, and bleeding of the Hydro-Boost brake system, please refer to "Brakes" in the Unit Repair section.

1. Turn the engine off and pump the brake pedal 4 or 5 times to deplete the accumulator.
2. Remove the two nuts from the master cylinder, then move the master cylinder away from the booster, with brake lines still attached.
3. Remove the three hydraulic lines from the booster.
4. Remove the retainer and washer at the brake pedal.
5. Remove the four attaching nuts retaining the booster fastened to the firewall, and remove the booster. On installation, bleed the system.

STEERING

Tie-Rod End

REPLACEMENT

1. Loosen the tie-rod adjuster sleeve clamp nut.

2. Remove the tie-rod cotter pin and nut. 1980 and later models use prevailing torque nuts; no cotter pin is used.

NOTE: If the torque required to remove the nuts and bolts exceeds 7 ft. lbs., it's best to discard them and use new fasteners of equal grade quality.

3. Remove the tie-rod stud from the steering arm or intermediate rod. This is a taper fit. Removal is accomplished by using a ball joint removal tool.
4. Unthread the tie-rod from the adjuster sleeve. Outer tie-rods have right-hand threads and inner tie-rods have left-hand threads. Count the number of turns the tie rod must be rotated to remove it from the adjusting sleeve. This will allow a reasonably accurate realignment upon reassembly.
5. Reverse the removal procedures for installation. Clean all rust and dirt from the threads. Check the alignment and adjust if necessary.

Steering Gear

REMOVAL & INSTALLATION

1. Disconnect the pressure and return hoses from the steering gear housing.
2. Disconnect battery ground cable and remove coupling shield.

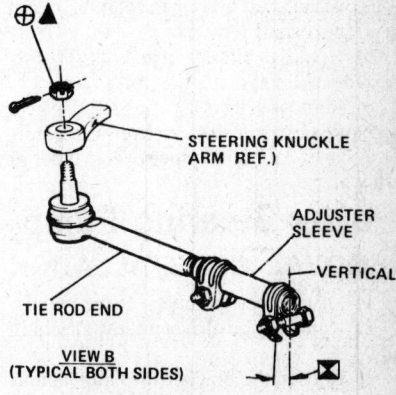

Tie rod assembly—typical
(© Pontiac Div., G.M. Corp)

POSITION OF TIE ROD ADJUSTER
SLEEVE & CLAMP

NOTE: SLOT IN TIE ROD ADJUSTER
SLEEVE MAY BE IN ANY
POSITION EXCEPT AT EDGES
OF CLAMP JAWS.

Tie rod clamp installation
(© Pontiac Div., G.M. Corp)

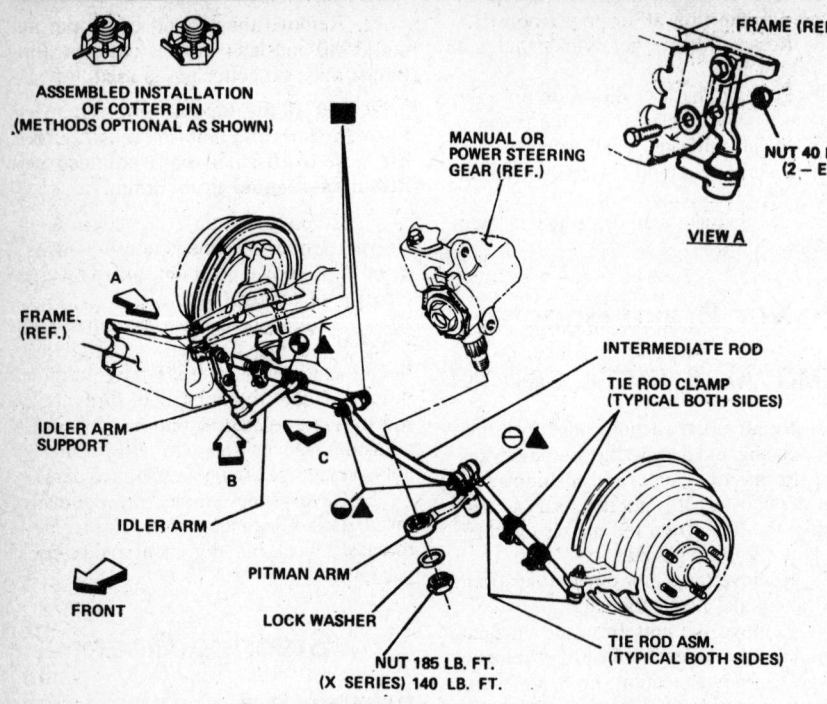

ASSEMBLED INSTALLATION OF COTTER PIN (METHODS OPTIONAL AS SHOWN)

FRAME. (REF.)

IDLER ARM SUPPORT

IDLER ARM

PITMAN ARM

LOCK WASHER

FRONT

A
B
C

NUT 185 LB. FT. (X SERIES) 140 LB. FT.

MANUAL OR POWER STEERING GEAR (REF.)

FRAME (REF.)

NUT 40 LB. FT. (2 – EACH)

VIEW A

INTERMEDIATE ROD

TIE ROD CLAMP (TYPICAL BOTH SIDES)

TIE ROD ASM. (TYPICAL BOTH SIDES)

Steering linkage (© Pontiac Div., G.M. Corp)

3. Remove retaining nuts, lock washers, and bolts at steering coupling to steering shaft flange.

4. Remove pitman arm nut and washer from pitman shaft and mark relation of arm position to shaft.

5. Remove pitman arm with Tool J-6632 or its equivalent.

6. Remove screws securing steering gear to frame and remove gear from vehicle.

7. Installation is in the reverse order of removal.

Power Steering Pump
REMOVAL & INSTALLATION

1. Disconnect the hoses at the pump.

2. Remove the drive pulley attaching nut.

3. Loosen the bracket-to-pump mounting bolts and remove the drive belt.

4. Slide the pulley from the shaft with a gear puller. Do not hammer on the pulley.

5. Remove the bracket-to-pump mounting bolts and remove the pump.

6. Reverse the removal steps for installation. Bleed the pump of air by turning the pulley counterclockwise until no bubbles appear in the reservoir.

7. Bleed the system. See the "Power Steering" Unit Repair section for procedures.

NOTE: On some engines, the power steering pump is located low on the engine. Do not attempt to check the fluid level with the engine running or personal injury can result.

Steering Wheel

REMOVAL & INSTALLATION

1. On deluxe models, remove the screws holding the trim cover on the wheel, or if equipped with a horn button, lift the button off.

2. Remove the snap-ring, if any, and steering wheel nut from the steering shaft.

3. Position the wheels in the straight-ahead position and matchmark the steering shaft and steering wheel.

4. Using a puller, remove the steering wheel.

— CAUTION —

Don't pound on the steering wheel or the steering shaft. The collapsible column could be damaged enough to require replacement.

5. Disconnect the horn wire insulator by rotating the insulator counterclockwise to the unlock position, then pull up.

6. Reverse the removal procedures for installation. Make sure the matchmarks are lined up when installing the wheel.

Turn Signal Switch

REPLACEMENT

1. Remove the steering wheel.

2. Remove the three cover screws and lift the cover off the shaft.

3. Depress the lockplate and remove the snap-ring. All 1978 and later steering columns have a redesigned lock plate which is removed by inserting a prybar in the cover slot and prying out. This is done in at least two of the slots to avoid breaking the plate. Remove the retaining ring and lockplate.

4. Slide the upper bearing spring and turn signal cam off the shaft. Remove the thrust washer.

5. Remove the turn signal lever screw and lever, or on some later models remove a snap ring and lever.

NOTE: On LeMans with tilt steering wheel, the lever is held in place with a snap-ring.

6. Push the hazard warning switch in and remove the knob.

7. On models with a column mounted dimmer switch, remove the actuator arm screw and arm. On models with a tilt column, lift the tilt lever to remove the switch screws.

— CAUTION —

The steering column must be supported at all times to prevent damage.

8. Pull the wiring connector out of the bracket and disconnect it. Wrap it with tape to prevent snagging.

9. Pull the switch straight up and remove it from the housing.

10. Reverse the removal procedures for installation.

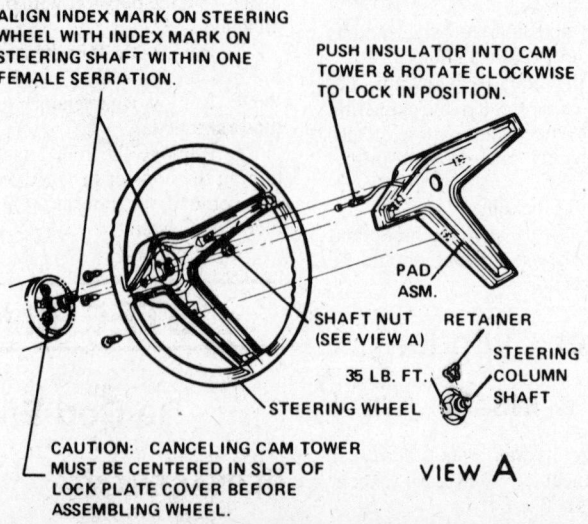

ALIGN INDEX MARK ON STEERING WHEEL WITH INDEX MARK ON STEERING SHAFT WITHIN ONE FEMALE SERRATION.

PUSH INSULATOR INTO CAM TOWER & ROTATE CLOCKWISE TO LOCK IN POSITION.

PAD ASM.

SHAFT NUT (SEE VIEW A)

RETAINER

STEERING COLUMN SHAFT

35 LB. FT.

STEERING WHEEL

CAUTION: CANCELING CAM TOWER MUST BE CENTERED IN SLOT OF LOCK PLATE COVER BEFORE ASSEMBLING WHEEL.

VIEW A

Standard and cushion steering wheel (© Pontiac Div., G.M. Corp.)

Ignition Switch

REPLACEMENT

1. Disconnect the negative battery terminal.
2. Loosen the toe pan screws on the steering column.
3. Remove the column-to-instrument panel trim plates and attaching nuts.
4. Lower the column and disconnect the switch wire connectors.

---------- CAUTION ----------

The steering column must be supported at all times to prevent damage.

---

5. Remove the switch attaching screws and remove the switch.
6. To replace, move the key lock to the LOCK position.

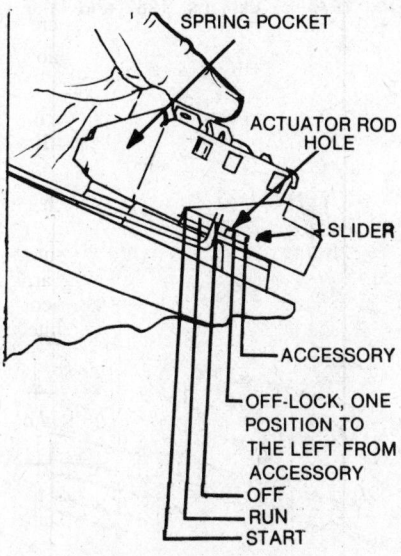

Installing ignition switch

7. Move the actuator rod hole in the switch to the LOCK position.
8. Install the switch with the rod in the hole.
9. Position and reassemble the steering column in the reverse order of the disassembly procedure.

Ignition Switch

ADJUSTMENT

Standard Column

1. Place the switch in the OFF position.
2. Position the switch on the column, then move the slider to the extreme left (toward the wheel).
3. Move the slider back two positions to the right of ACCESSORY position.
4. Place the key in any run position and shift the transmission into any position but Park for automatics. Put it in Reverse for manual.
5. Position the lock toward ACCESSORY with a light finger pressure and secure the switch.

Tilt Column

1. Place the key in ACCESSORY position; leave the key in the lock.
2. Loosen the switch mounting screws.
3. Push the switch upward toward the wheel to make certain it is in ACCESSORY detent.
4. Hold the key in full counterclockwise ACCESSORY position and tighten the switch mounting screws.
5. The switch is properly adjusted if: it will go into ACCESSORY position, the key can be removed when in lock, and the switch will go into START position.

Lock Cylinder

REPLACEMENT

Through 1978

1. Disconnect the negative battery terminal.
2. Remove the steering wheel.
3. Pull the turn signal switch up far enough to allow access to the spring latch slot.
4. Place the key in RUN position, insert a thin screwdriver into the slot next to the switch mounting screw boss and depress the spring latch.

NOTE: There is a casting flash over this slot if the lock has not been removed

before. It is sometimes necessary to use substantial force to remove it. Be careful not to damage anything beneath the flash when penetrating the slot.

5. Remove the lock from housing.
6. To install, first hold the lock cylinder sleeve and rotate the knob clockwise against the stop.

---------- CAUTION ----------

If the lock cylinder is forced beyond its normal latched position, complete disassembly of the upper bearing assembly will be necessary to free it.

---

7. Insert the cylinder into the housing bore, aligning the keyway, and push in the abutment.
8. Rotate the knob counterclockwise, pushing in slightly, until the cylinder mates with the sector.
9. Push in until the spring latch pops into the groove.

1979 and Later

1. Disconnect the negative battery cable.
2. Remove the steering wheel as previously outlined.
3. Place the lock in the Run position.
4. Remove the lock plate, the turn signal switch and the buzzer switch.
5. Remove the lock retaining screw and remove the lock cylinder.
6. To install, hold the replacement cylinder and rotate the key clockwise.
7. Properly align the keyway in the cylinder with the housing and insert the lock cylinder into the lock column.
8. Install the retaining screw. Tighten the screw to 40 in. lbs. on regular columns and 22 in. lbs. on tilt columns.
9. Reverse the remainder of the removal procedure to install.

INSTRUMENT PANEL

Headlamp Switch
REPLACEMENT

1. Disconnect battery.
2. Pull knob to ON position.

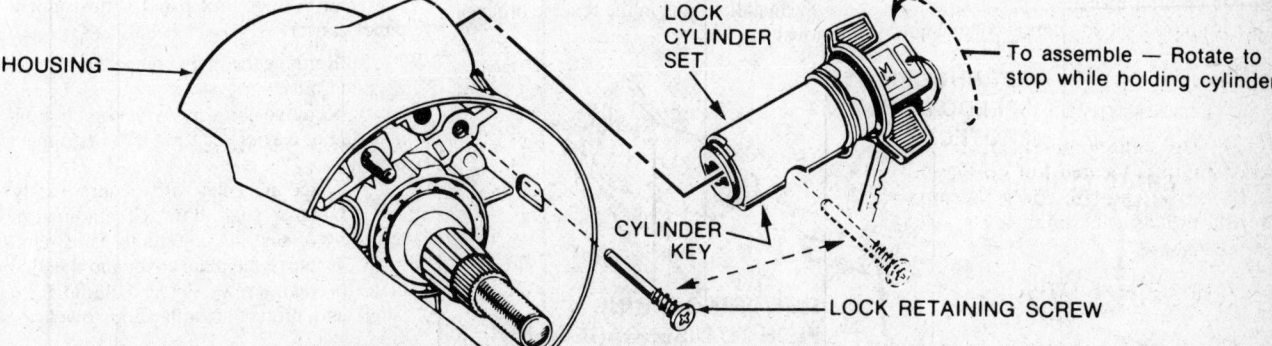

Lock cylinder installation details, 1979 and later (© Pontiac Div., G.M. Corp.)

3. Reach under instrument panel and depress the switch shaft retainer, then remove knob and shaft assembly.

NOTE: Disconnect vacuum hose on vacuum-operated headlamp models.

4. Remove retaining ferrule nut.

5. Remove switch from instrument panel.

6. Disconnect multi-plug connector from switch.

7. Install in reverse of the above. (In checking lights before installation, switch must be grounded to test dome lights on some models).

Speedometer Cable

REMOVAL & INSTALLATION

1. Remove the lower A/C duct or lower instrument panel trimplate, if necessary to gain access.

2. Remove the lower instrument panel trim plates.

3. Reach up behind the speedometer and find where the cable attaches to the speedometer head. Press the retaining clip downward and slide the cable from the head.

4. Slide the old core from the casing. If the core is broken, raise the car and remove the cable retaining clip from the transmission. Pull out the remaining piece of the core.

5. Install in the reverse order of removal. Prior to installing, the core should be wiped clean and the casing flushed out with solvent. Before inserting the core into the case, coat the lower two-thirds of the core with a speedometer cable lubricant. Do not lubricate the upper third.

Instrument Cluster

REMOVAL & INSTALLATION

All Except Phoenix and Parisienne

1. Disconnect the negative battery terminal.

2. Disconnect the shift indicator cable from the column jacket.

3. Remove the two steering column nuts

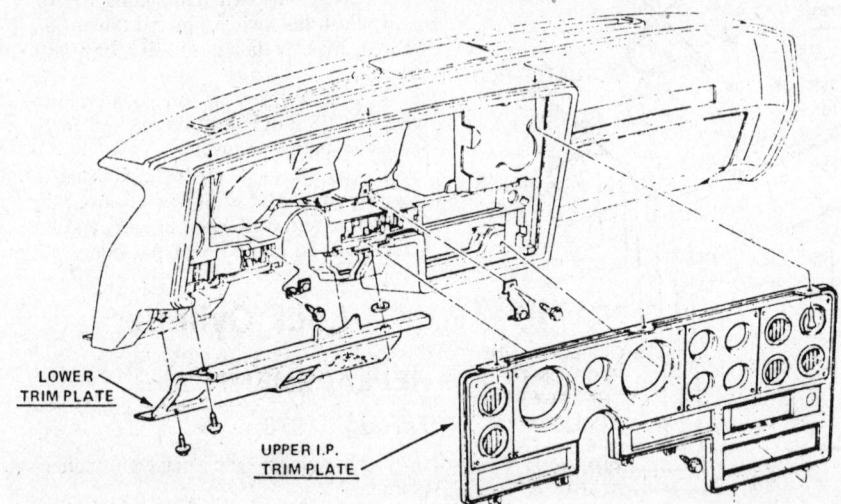

Instrument Cluster—1978 and later Grand Prix, 1978–81 LeMans, 1982 and later Bonneville

Instrument panel trim plate—1978 and later Grand Prix, 1978–81 LeMans, 1982 and later Bonneville

and lower the steering column.

4. Remove the lower trim panel.

5. Remove the cigar lighter retaining nut.

6. Remove the upper trim panel screws and panel.

7. Remove the gauges as needed.

8. Installation is in the reverse order of removal.

Phoenix

1. Disconnect the battery ground cable.

2. Remove the steering column trim panel.

3. Remove hush panel.

4. Remove the three screws retaining heater or A/C control panel to instrument panel carrier.

5. Remove the radio control knobs, bezels and nuts.

6. Remove the screws at top, bottom and side of carrier securing it to instrument panel pad.

7. Disconnect the shift quadrant indicator cable at shaft bowl (if automatic), remove two steering column to panel nuts.

8. Remove toe plate cover and five two plate to cowl screws, lower column from panel and protect it with shop towels or tape.

9. Remove the ground wire screw from under left side of panel pad above kick pad

FERRULE-PILOTS SPEEDO NECK AND PROTECTS TIP

BRAID LINER AND CASING

RETAINING SPRING PUSH TO DISENGAGE

TIP

Speedometer cable attachment details (© Pontiac Div., G.M. Corp.)

and disconnect the speedo cable from under dash.

10. Tilt carrier and cluster rearward, disconnect the printed circuit and cluster ground connectors and rest assembly on top of column.

11. Remove the screws from cluster to carrier assembly and remove cluster.

12. Reverse procedure to install.

Parisienne

1. Disconnect the battery ground cable.

2. Remove the four steering column lower cover screws and cover.

3. If equipped with automatic transmission, disconnect the shift indicator cable from steering column.

4. Remove the two steering column to instrument panel screws and lower steering column.

— CAUTION —

Use extreme care when lowering steering to prevent damage to column assembly.

5. Remove the six screws and three snap-in fasteners from perimeter of instrument cluster lens.

6. Remove the two screws from upper surface of grey sheet metal trim plate.

7. Remove the two stud nuts from lower corner of cluster.

8. Disconnect the speedometer cable and pull cluster from instrument panel.

9. Disconnect the electrical connectors from cluster and remove from vehicle.

10. Reverse procedure to install.

WINDSHIELD WIPERS

Motor

REPLACEMENT

1. Remove hoses and wire terminals that are connected to wiper unit.

2. Remove clip or loosen nut that secures wiper crank to wiper linkage arm.

NOTE: This clip is under leaf screen on depressed-park (hidden wiper) motors, and accessible only after firewall bolts are removed on some standard motors. On some models, the wiper arm must be removed to facilitate motor removal.

3. Remove screws that secure wiper motor assembly to firewall.

4. Position wiper assembly on firewall and secure.

5. Connect wire terminals and hoses.

6. Connect wiper crank with wiper linkage arm.

RADIO

REMOVAL & INSTALLATION

Phoenix

1. Disconnect battery.

2. Remove radio knobs, bezels and hex nuts.

3. Remove support bracket bolt. Remove the Ventura and Phoenix radio side-brace screw.

4. Disconnect electrical and antenna leads; remove radio from under dash.

5. To install, reverse removal procedure.

LeMans, 1982 and Later Bonneville

1. Disconnect the battery.

2. Remove the radio knobs and bezels.

3. Remove the upper and lower instrument panel trim plates.

4. Remove the front radio retaining screws.

5. Open glove box door and lower by releasing spring clips. Pull the radio out after loosening rear, right side nut. Disconnect all wiring and remove the radio.

6. To install, reverse the removal procedure. If the radio is to be replaced, remove the bushing from the rear of the radio and install it on the replacement radio.

Grand Am and Grand LeMans

1. Disconnect the battery.

2. Remove the radio knobs and bezels and the retaining hex nut from the right-hand radio tuning shaft.

3. Remove the four retaining screws and the trim plate.

4. Remove the one front retaining screw and the mounting bracket screw.

5. Remove the radio and the mounting bracket from the dash, disconnecting the electrical connections and the antenna lead.

6. To install, reverse the removal procedure.

1978–'81 Bonneville, Catalina 1984–'85 Parisienne

1. Disconnect the negative battery terminal.

2. Remove the upper trimplate. Remove the radio trimplate by removing the two top screws, the ashtray assembly, disconnecting the lighter, and removing the ashtray bracket.

3. Remove the two radio screws.

4. Remove the radio through the instrument panel and detach all connectors.

5. Reverse the procedure for installation.

Grand Prix

1. Disconnect the negative battery terminal.

2. Remove the knobs, bezels, and right-hand hex nut from the radio. On 1978 and later models, remove the upper and lower instrument panel trimplates.

3. Remove the four retaining screws and the radio trim plate.

4. Remove the one front retaining screw and the radio mounting bracket retaining screw (below radio). On 1978 and later models, open the glove box and loosen the rear nut at the right side of the radio.

5. Remove the radio and bracket as an assembly; disconnect the radio connections and antenna lead-in while the radio is pulled out.

6. Reverse the above steps to install.

FUSES

The fuse block is located beneath the instrument panel above the headlight dimmer floor switch. Fuse holders are labeled as to their service and the correct amperage. Always replace blown fuses with new ones of the correct amperage. Otherwise electrical overloads and possible wiring damage will result.

FUSIBLE LINKS

Fusible links are sections of wire, with special insulation, designed to melt under electrical overload. Replacements are simply spliced into the wire. There may be as many as five of these in the engine compartment wiring harnesses. These are:

1. Horn relay to fuse panel circuit—one link.

2. Charging circuit, from the starter solenoid to the horn relay—two links.

3. Starter solenoid to ammeter circuit—one link.

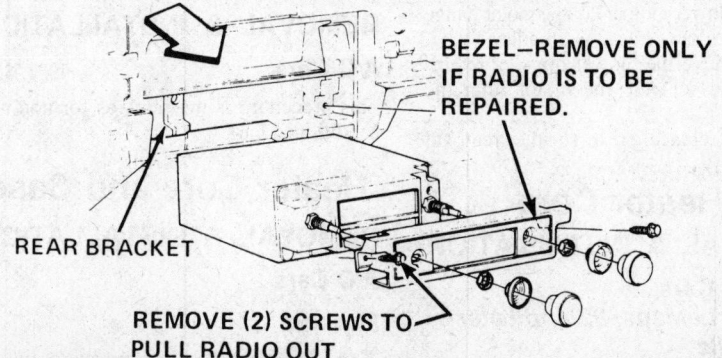

BEZEL—REMOVE ONLY IF RADIO IS TO BE REPAIRED.

REAR BRACKET

REMOVE (2) SCREWS TO PULL RADIO OUT

1978 and later Pontiac radio removal (© Pontiac Div., G.M. Corp.)

4. Horn relay to rear window defroster circuit—one link.

The fusible links are all two wire gauge sizes smaller than the wires they protect.

NOTE: Most models have fusible links at these locations.

REPLACEMENT

1. Disconnect the battery ground cable.
2. Disconnect the fusible link from the junction block or starter solenoid.
3. Cut the harness directly behind the connector to remove the damaged fusible link.
4. Strip the harness wire approximately ½ in.
5. Connect the new fusible link to the harness wire using a crimp on connector. Soder the connection using rosin core solder.
6. Tape all exposed wires with plastic electrical tape.
7. Connect the fusible link to the junction block or starter solenoid and reconnect the battery ground cable.

HEATER

Heater Blower
REMOVAL & INSTALLATION
Non A/C Cars
ALL EXCEPT PHOENIX

1. Disconnect the blower motor feed wire and the ground wire.
2. Remove the blower motor retaining screws and remove the motor.
3. To replace, reverse the removal procedure.

PHOENIX

1. Disconnect the battery.
2. Detach the heater hoses from the clips on the right front fender skirt.
3. Raise the car and remove all fender skirt attaching bolts, except those which attach the skirt to the radiator support.
4. Pull down on the skirt and block the skirt out to provide clearance for removal of the blower motor.
5. Disconnect the electrical wiring from the motor.
6. Remove the attaching screws and remove the blower motor. Pry the motor flange gently if the sealer acts as an adhesive.
7. Remove the blower impeller retaining nut and separate the motor from the impeller.
8. To replace, reverse the removal procedure.

Heater Core
REMOVAL & INSTALLATION
Non A/C Cars
1978–81 LeMans, 82 and Later Bonneville

1. Disconnect the hoses from the core

tubes. Plug them to avoid coolant loss.
2. On the engine side of the firewall, remove the heater core cover from the case.
3. Remove the core bracket and ground screw.
4. Lift out the core.
5. Reverse the procedure for installation.

Phoenix

1. Disconnect battery.
2. Drain radiator, disconnect heater hoses at core and plug core tubes.
3. Remove nuts from core case studs on firewall.
4. Remove glove box and glove box door.
5. From inside car, drill out lower right hand heater case stud with ¼ in. drill.
6. Pull entire heater case, with core, from firewall.
7. Disconnect cables and blower resistor connector, then remove case from car.
8. Remove core from case.
9. To install, reverse removal procedure. Use sealer around core and replace drilled stud with new screw and stamped nut.

1978–81 Bonneville and Catalina

1. Drain the cooling system.
2. Remove the heater hoses from the core tubes.
3. Disconnect the electrical connections.
4. Remove the front module cover screws, and remove the module assembly.
5. Remove the heater core from the module.
6. Reverse the procedure to install the heater core. Use a strip caulk type sealer when installing the module to the firewall.

1984–85 Parisienne
1978 and Later Grand Prix

1. Disconnect the hoses at the core tubes and position them vertically to prevent coolant loss.
2. Remove the core cover from the module.
3. Remove the core bracket and ground screw.
4. Lift out the core.
5. Installation is in the reverse order of removal. Replace any damaged sealer.

Heater Blower
REMOVAL & INSTALLATION
A/C Cars

This procedure is the same as for non air-conditioned cars.

Heater Core and Case
REMOVAL & INSTALLATION
A/C Cars
Phoenix

1. Disconnect the battery and drain the coolant.

2. Disconnect the upper heater hose at the core pipe and remove the accessible heater core and case assembly attaching nuts.
3. Remove the right front fender skirt bolts and lower the skirt to gain access to the lower heater hose clamp. Loosen the clamp and disconnect the hose.
4. Remove the lower right-hand heater core and case assembly attaching nut.
5. Remove the glove compartment and door.
6. Remove the recirculation vacuum diaphragm at the right-hand kick panel.
7. Remove the heater outlet and cold air distributor duct.
8. Disconnect the heater cables and electrical connectors, and remove the case and core as an assembly.
9. Separate the core from the case.
10. Reverse the above steps for installation.

1978 and Later Grand Prix
1978–81 LeMans and Grand Am
1982 and Later Bonneville

1. Position the wipers in the UP position.
2. Disconnect and unplug the heater hoses.
3. Remove the module top cover seals.
4. Remove the module top screens.
5. Disconnect all electrical connectors.
6. Move the lower windshield reverse molding out of the way.
7. Remove the cowl brackets.
8. Tape a strip of wood to the lower edge of the windshield glass, to protect the glass.
9. Remove the top cover screws.
10. Cut the sealing material along the cowl with a knife.
11. Pry the cover off from the side, not from the top.
12. Remove the core and seal.
Installation is in the reverse order of removal. Use all new sealing material.

1978–81 Bonneville and Catalina
1984–85 Parisienne

1. Drain the cooling system.
2. Disconnect the heater hoses.
3. Remove the retaining bracket and the ground strap.
4. Disconnect the module rubber seal and module screen.
5. Remove the right windshield wiper arm.
6. Remove the diaphragm connections, the hi-blower relay, the thermal switch mounting screws, and all the electrical connections from the module top.
7. Remove the module top cover and remove the core.
8. Installation is in the reverse order of removal.
Apply a strip of caulk type sealer when installing the module top.

GM "A" & "X" Body Front Wheel Drive

Celebrity, Century, Cutlass Ciera, 6000, Citation, Omega, Phoenix, Skylark

YEAR IDENTIFICATION

1980 Citation

1981–85 Citation

1980–81 Omega

1982-83 Omega

1984 Omega ES

1984 Omega Sedan

1980 Phoenix

1981 Phoenix

1982 Phoenix

1983 Phoenix

1984 Phoenix LE, SE

1980 Skylark

1981 Skylark

1984–85 Skylark T Type

1981–85 Skylark Sport Coupe

C521

YEAR IDENTIFICATION

1982-83 Celebrity

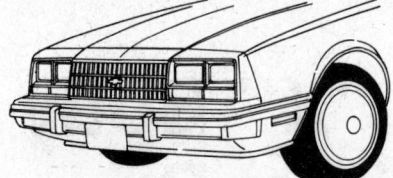

1984–85 Celebrity

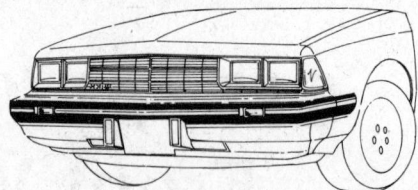

1982-83 Century

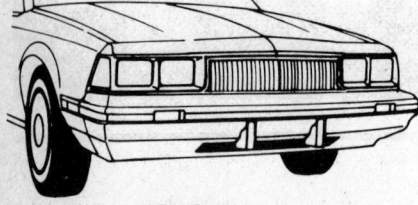

1985 Century

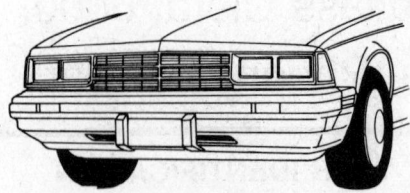

1984 Century T Type

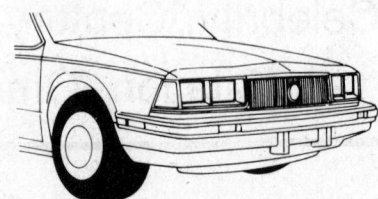

1985 Century T Type

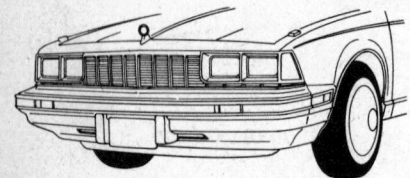

1984 Century Custom, Limited

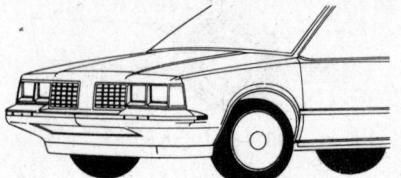

1982-83 Cutlass Ciera

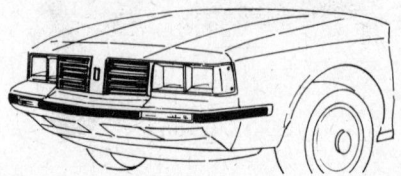

1983 Cutlass Ciera ES

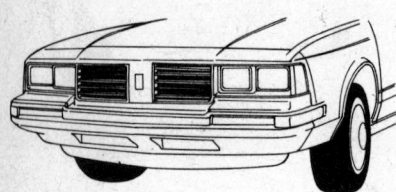

1984 Ciera

1985 Cutlass Ciera

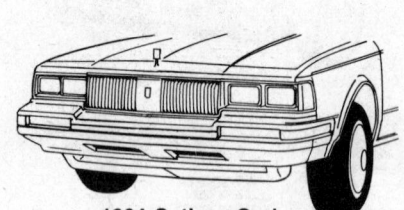

1984 Cutlass Cruiser

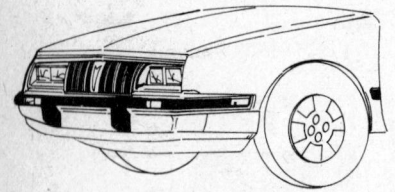

1982-83 6000

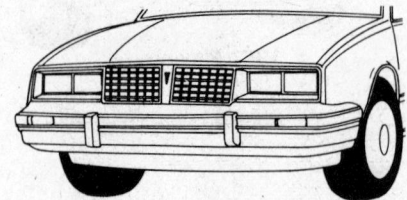

1984 6000, 6000 LE

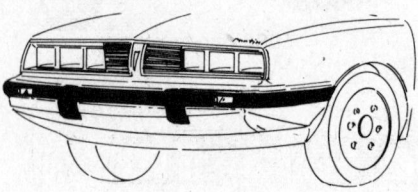

1983–85 6000 STE

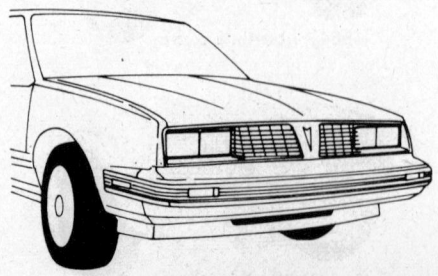

1985 6000, 6000 LE

VEHICLE IDENTIFICATION NUMBER (VIN)

It is important for servicing and ordering parts to be certain of the vehicle and engine identification. The VIN (vehicle identification number) is a 13 or 17 digit number visible through the windshield on the driver's side of the dash and contains the vehicle and engine identification codes. It can be interpreted as follows:

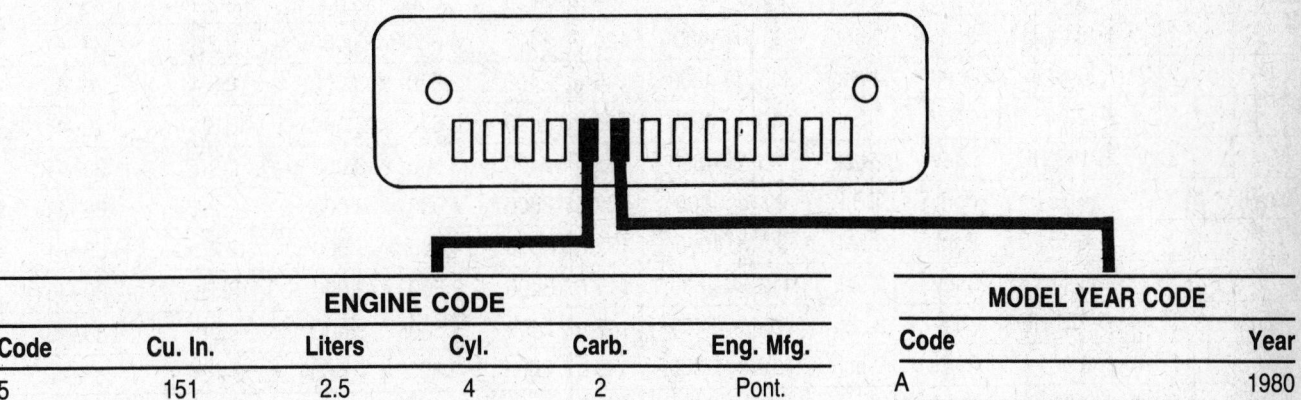

ENGINE CODE						MODEL YEAR CODE	
Code	Cu. In.	Liters	Cyl.	Carb.	Eng. Mfg.	Code	Year
5	151	2.5	4	2	Pont.	A	1980
7	173	2.8	V6	2	Chev.		

The thirteen digit Vehicle Identification Number can be used to determine engine application and model year. The 6th digit indicates the model year, and the 5th digit identifies the factory installed engine.

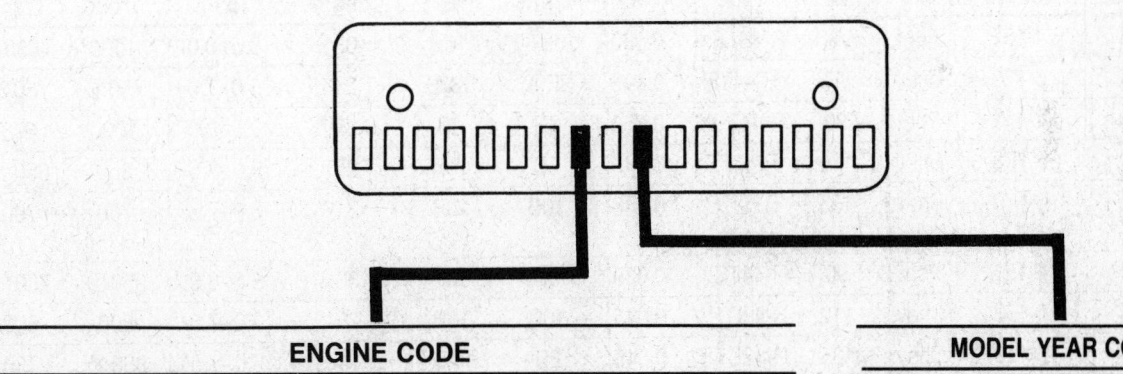

ENGINE CODE						MODEL YEAR CODE	
Code	Cu. In.	Liters	Cyl.	Carb.	Eng. Mfg.	Code	Year
5	151	2.5	4	2	Pont.	B	1981
R	151	2.5	4	TBI	Pont.	C	1982
X	173	2.8	V6	2	Chev.	D	1983
Z	173(HO)	2.8	V6	2	Chev.	E	1984
E	181	3.0	V6	2	Buick	F	1985
3	231	3.8	V6	MFI	Buick		
T	263	4.3	V6	Diesel	Olds		

The seventeen digit Vehicle Identification Number can be used to determine engine application and model year. The 10th digit indicates the model year and the 8th digit identifies the factory installed engine.
T.B.I.: Throttle Body Injection
MFI: Multi-Point Fuel Injection

GENERAL ENGINE SPECIFICATIONS

Year	V.I.N. Code	Engine No. Cyl. Displ. Cu. In.	Eng. Mfg.	Fuel Delivery System	Horsepower @ rpm	Torque @ rpm ft. lb.	Bore × Stroke	Compression Ratio	Oil Pressure 2000 rpm
'80–'81	5	4-151	Pont.	2-bbl.	90 @ 4000	134 @ 2400	4.000 × 3.000	8.2:1	36–41
	5	4-151 Calif.	Pont.	2-bbl.	90 @ 4400	128 @ 2400	4.000 × 3.000	8.2:1	36–41
	X	6-173	Chev.	2-bbl.	115 @ 4800	145 @ 2400	3.500 × 3.000	8.5:1	30–45
	X	6-173 Calif.	Chev.	2-bbl.	110 @ 4800	140 @ 2400	3.500 × 3.000	8.5:1	30–45
	Z	6-173 HO	Chev.	2-bbl.	135 @ 4800	165 @ 2400	3.500 × 3.000	8.9:1	30–45
'82–'85	R	4-151	Pont.	T.B.I.	90 @ 4000	132 @ 2800	4.000 × 3.000	8.2:1	36–41
	5	4-151	Pont.	2-bbl.	90 @ 4000	132 @ 2800	4.000 × 3.000	8.2:1	36–41
	X	6-173	Chev.	2-bbl.	112 @ 4800	145 @ 3400	3.500 × 3.000	8.5:1	30–45
	Z	6-173 HO	Chev.	2-bbl.	135 @ 5400	145 @ 2400	3.500 × 3.000	8.9:1	30–45
	E	6-181	Buick	2-bbl.	110 @ 4800	145 @ 2600	3.800 × 2.660	8.45:1	35–42
	T	6-263	Olds.	Diesel	85 @ 3600	165 @ 1600	4.057 × 3.385	21.6:1	40–45
	3	6-231	Buick	MFI	125 @ 4400	195 @ 2000	3.800 × 3400	8.0:1	35–42

TUNE-UP SPECIFICATIONS

(When analyzing compression test results, look for uniformity among cylinders rather than specific pressures.)

Year	V.I.N. Code	Eng. No. Cyl. Displ. Cu. In.	Eng. Mfg.	hp	Spark Plugs Orig Type	Spark Plugs Gap (in.)	Ignition Timing (deg) ▲ Man Trans	Ignition Timing (deg) ▲ Auto Trans	Intake Valve Opens (deg)■	Fuel Pump Pressure (psi)	Idle Speed (rpm) ▲ Man Trans	Idle Speed (rpm) ▲ Auto Trans
'80	5	4-151	Pont.	All	R-43TSX	0.060	10B③	10B	33	6.5–8.0	1000	650
	X	6-173	Chev.	All	R-44TS	0.045	2B④	6B⑤	25	6.0–7.5	750⑥	750⑥
'81	5	4-151	Pont.	90	R-44TSX	0.060	4B	4B	33	6.5–8.0	1000	675
	X	6-173	Chev.	110	R-43TS	0.045	6B	10B	25	6.0–7.5	850	850⑦
	Z	6-173 HO	Chev.	135	R-42TS	0.045	10B	10B	31	6.0–7.5	700	700
'82–'85	5,R	4-151	Pont.	90	R-44TSX	0.060	8B	8B	33	6.0–8.0	950①	750②
	X	6-173	Chev.	112	R-43CTS	0.045	10B	10B	25	6.0–7.5	800	600
	Z	6-173 HO	Chev.	135	R-42CTS	0.045	6B	10B	31	6.0–7.5	850⑧	750
	E	6-181	Buick	110	R-44TS8	0.080	—	15B	16	6.0–8.0	—	see text
	3	6-231	Buick	125	R-44TS8	0.080	⑨	⑨	4.0–6.5	⑨	⑨	
	T	6-263	Olds.	85	—	—	—	6A	N.A.	5.8–8.7	—	650

NOTE: The underhood specifications sticker often reflects tune-up specification changes made in production. Sticker figures must be used if they disagree with those in this chart.

▲ See text for procedure
■ All figures Before Top Dead Center
B: Before Top Dead Center
A: After Top Dead Center
Part numbers in this chart are not recommendations by Chilton for any product by brand name.

N.A.: Information not available
① Without air conditioning: 850
② Without air conditioning: 680
③ Calif.: 12B
④ Calif.: 6B
⑤ Calif.: 10B
⑥ Calif.: 700

⑦ With A/C: 900
⑧ Calif.: 750
⑨ See underhood specifications sticker

FIRING ORDERS

NOTE: To avoid confusion, always replace sparkplug wires one at a time.

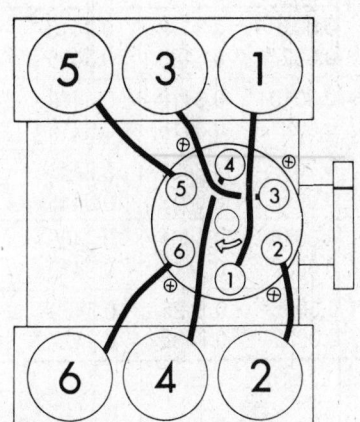

GM (Buick) 183 V6 (3.0 L)
GM (Buick) 231 V6 (3.8 L)
Engine firing order: 1-6-5-4-3-2
Distributor rotation: clockwise

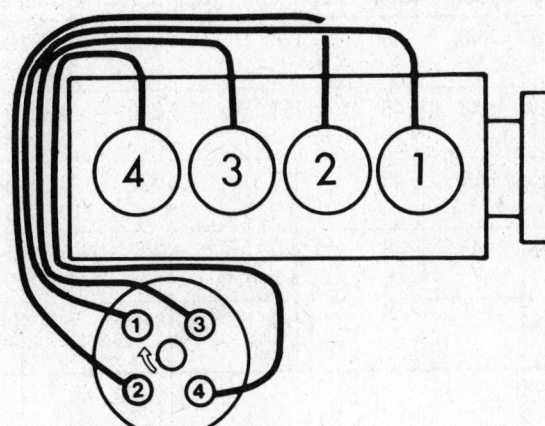

GM (Pontiac) 151-4
Engine firing order: 1-3-4-2
Distributor rotation: clockwise

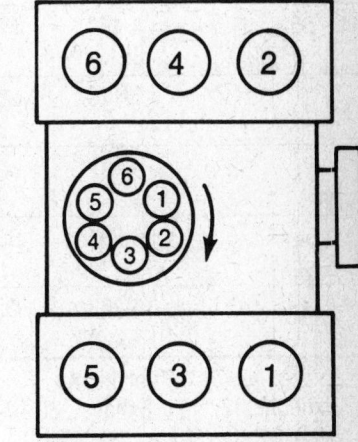

GM (Chevrolet) 173 V6 (2.8 L)
Engine firing order: 1-2-3-4-5-6
Distributor rotation: clockwise

CAPACITIES
A-Body

Year	V.I.N. Code	Engine Displacement Cu. In.	Eng. Mfg.	Crankcase Quarts w/filter	Crankcase Quarts wo/filter	Transaxle Pints 4 speed	Transaxle Pints Auto	Gas Tank Gal	Cooling System Qts w/heater	Cooling System Qts w/AC
'82–'85	R	4-151	Pont.	3.0	2.8	6.0	10.0	16.0	9.5	9.75
	X	6-173	Chev.	4.0	3.0	6.0	10.0	16.0	11.5	11.75
	E	6-181	Buick	4.0	3.0	—	10.0②	16.0	13.5	14.25
	3	6-231	Buick	4.0①	4.0	—	13.0	16.0	12.25	12.75
	T	6-263	Olds.	6.0	5.5	—	10.0②	16.0	13.25	13.75

①Add as necessary to bring to appropriate level.
②13.0 pts w/440T4 transaxle.

CAPACITIES
X-Body

Year	Engine No. Cyl. Displacement (Cu. In.)	Engine Crankcase Add 1 Qt For New Filter ■	Transmission (Pts To Refill After Draining) Manual 3-Speed	Transmission (Pts To Refill After Draining) Manual 4-Speed	Automatic ●	Drive Axle (pts)	Gasoline Tank (gals)	Cooling System (qts) With Heater	Cooling System (qts) With A/C
'80–'81	4-151 Pont.	3	—	5.9	10.5	①	14	8.3	8.6
	6-173 Chev.	4	—	5.9	10.5	①	14	10.2	10.6
'82	4-151 Pont.	3	—	5.9	10.5	①	14	8.3	8.6
	6-173 Chev.	4	—	5.9	10.5	①	14	10.6	10.8
'83–'85	4-151 Pont.	3	—	5.9	10.5	①	14	8.3	8.6
	6-173 Chev.	4	—	5.9	10.5	①	14	10.6	10.8
	6-173 HO Chev.	4	—	5.9	10.5	①	14	10.6	10.8

① Transaxle refill given with transmission capacity

VALVE SPECIFICATIONS

Year	V.I.N. Code	Engine No. Cyl. Displacement (cu. in.)	Eng. Mfg.	Seat Angle (deg)	Face Angle (deg)	Spring Test Pressure (lbs. @ In.)	Spring Installed Height (in.)	Stem-to-Guide Clearance (in.)		Stem Diameter (in.)	
								Intake	Exhaust	Intake	Exhaust
'80–'85	R,5	4-151	Pont.	46	45	176 @ 1.254	1.660	0.0010–0.0027	0.0010–0.0027	0.3418–0.3425	0.3418–0.3425
	X,Z	6-173	Chev.	46	45	155 @ 1.160	1.610	0.0010–0.0027	0.0010–0.0027	0.3410–0.3416	0.3410–0.3416
	E	6-181	Buick	45	45	220 @ 1.340	1.727	0.0015–0.0035	0.0015–0.0032	0.3401–0.3412	0.3402–0.3415
	3	6-231	Buick	45	45	220 @ 1.340	1.727	0.0015–0.0035	0.0015–0.0032	0.3401–0.3412	0.3405–0.3412
	T	6-263	Olds.	①	②	210 @ 1.220	1.670	0.0010–0.0027	0.0015–0.0032	0.3425–0.3432	0.3420–0.3427

① Intake: 45 Exhaust: 32
② Intake: 44 Exhaust: 30

CRANKSHAFT AND CONNECTING ROD SPECIFICATIONS
(All measurements are given in inches)

Year	V.I.N. Code	Engine No. Cyl. Displacement (cu. in.)	Eng. Mfg.	Crankshaft			Thrust on No.	Connecting Rod		
				Main Brg. Journal Dia.	Main Brg. Oil Clearance	Shaft End-Play		Journal Diameter	Oil Clearance	Side Clearance
'80–'85	R,5	4-151	Pont.	2.2995–2.3005	0.0005–0.0022	0.0035–0.0085	5	1.9995–2.0005	0.0005–0.0026	0.006–0.022
	X,Z	6-173	Chev.	2.4937–2.4946	0.0017–0.0030	0.0020–② 0.0067	3	1.9984–1.9994	0.0014–0.0036	0.006–0.017
	E	6-181	Buick	2.4990–2.5000	0.0003–0.0018	0.0030–0.0090	2	2.2487–2.2495	0.0005–0.0026	0.006–0.023
	3	6-231	Buick	2.4995	0.0003–0.0018	0.003–0.011	2	2.2487–2.2495	0.0005–0.0026	0.006–0.023
	T	6-263	Olds.	2.9993–3.0003	①	0.0035–0.0135	4	2.2490–2.2510	0.0003–0.0025	0.008–0.021

① No. 1, 2, 3: 0.0005–0.0021 No. 4: 0.0020–0.0034
② 1980: 0.0020–0.0079

CAMSHAFT SPECIFICATIONS
(All measurements in inches)

Year	V.I.N. Code	Engine	Eng. Mfg.	Journal Diameter					Bearing Clearance	Lobe Lift		Camshaft End Play
				1	2	3	4	5		Intake	Exhaust	
'80–'85	R,5	4-151	Pont.	1.869	1.869	1.869	—	—	0.0007–0.0027	0.398	0.398	0.0015–0.0050
	X	6-173	Chev.	1.869	1.869	1.869	1.869	—	0.0010–0.0040	0.231	0.263	—
	E	6-181	Buick	1.786	1.786	1.786	1.786	1.786	①	0.406	0.406	—
	3	6-231	Buick	1.786	1.786	1.786	1.786	1.786	①	N.A.	N.A.	—
	T	6-263	Olds.	②	2.205	2.185	2.165	—	0.0020–.0059	N.A.	N.A.	0.0008–0.0228

① No. 1: 0.0005–0.0025 No. 2–5: 0.0005–0.0035
② No. 1 bearing is not borable, but must be replaced separately.
N.A. Not available.

PISTON AND RING SPECIFICATIONS

(All measurements are given in inches. To convert inches to metric units, refer to the Metric Information section.)

Year	V.I.N. Code	Engine Type/ Disp. cu. in.	Eng. Mfg.	Piston-to-Bore Clearance	Ring Gap			Ring Side Clearance		
					Top Compression	Bottom Compression	Oil Control	Top Compression	Bottom Compression	Oil Control
'80–'85	R,5	4-151	Pont.	0.0025–0.0033	0.010–① 0.022	0.020–② 0.027	0.015–0.055	0.0015–0.0030	0.0015–0.0030	snug
	X,Z	6-173	Chev.	0.0017–0.0027	0.0098–0.0197	0.0098–0.0197	0.020–③ 0.055	0.0012–④ 0.0028	0.0016–④ 0.0037	0.008 max.
	E	6-181	Buick	0.0008–0.0020	0.013–0.023	0.013–0.023	0.015–0.035	0.0030–0.0050	0.0030–0.0050	0.0035 max.
	3	6-231	Buick	—	0.010–0.020	0.010–0.020	0.015–0.055	0.0030–0.0050	0.0030–0.0050	0.0035 max.
	T	6-263	Olds.	0.0030–0.0040	0.015–0.025	0.015–0.025	0.015–0.055	0.0050–0.0070	0.0030–0.0070	0.001–0.005

① 1980: 0.015–0.025 ③ 1980: 0.015–0.055
② 1980: 0.009–0.019 ④ 1980: 0.012–0.032

TORQUE SPECIFICATIONS

(All readings in ft. lbs.)

Year	V.I.N. Code	Engine No. Cyl. Displacement (cu. in.)	Eng. Mfg.	Cylinder Head Bolts	Rod Bearing Bolts	Main Bearing Bolts	Crankshaft Bolt	Flywheel to Crankshaft Bolts	Manifold	
									Intake	Exhaust
'80–'85	R,5	4-151	Pont.	85③	32	70	200	44	29	44
	X,Z	6-173	Chev.	70	37	68	75	50	23	25
	E	6-181	Buick	80	40	100	225	60	13	25
	3	6-231	Buick	80	40	100	225	60	13	25
	T	6-263	Olds.	①	42	107	255②	76	41	29

① All exc. No. 5, 6, 11, 12, 13, 14: 142
   No. 5, 6, 11, 12, 13, 14: 59
② Range: 160–350 ft. lb.
③ 1980–81: 75
   1984–85: 92

WHEEL ALIGNMENT SPECIFICATIONS

Year	Model	Caster*		Camber		Toe-In (in.)	Steering Axis (deg) Inclination
		Range (deg)	Pref Setting (deg)	Range (deg)	Pref Setting (deg)		
'80–'81	All	2N–2P	0	0–1P	½P	0–3/16	14.5
'82–'85	All	0–4P	2P	½N–½P	0	13/64 out–13/64 in	14.5

*Caster is not adjustable

CHARGING SYSTEM

Alternator and regulator troubleshooting are covered in the "Charging and Starting Systems" Unit Repair section.

Alternator

REMOVAL & INSTALLATION

1. Disconnect battery ground cable to prevent diode damage.
2. Disconnect and label the alternator wiring.
3. Remove the brace bolt. If power steering equipped, loosen pump brace and mount nuts. Detach drive belt(s).
4. On 4-cylinder engines, remove the upper bracket.
5. Support the alternator and remove mount bolt(s). Remove unit from vehicle.
6. Reverse procedure to install. Adjust drive belt to have ¼–½ in. play on longest run of belt.

Integral Voltage Regulator

An alternator with an integral voltage regulator is standard equipment. There are no adjustments possible with this unit; testing procedures will be found in the Charging and Starting Systems Unit Repair Section.

STARTING SYSTEM

Starter motor troubleshooting and repairs are covered in the Charging and Starting Systems Unit Repair Section.

Starter

REMOVAL & INSTALLATION

All except diesel

NOTE: On some models it may be necessary to move the fuel lines out of the way. Remove the fuel lines from the retaining clamp and loosen at the regulator.

— CAUTION —
If equipped with fuel injection, relieve the pressure from the fuel system before disconnecting fuel lines. See Electric Fuel Pump Removal.

1. Disconnect battery ground cable.
2. Raise and support vehicle.
3. Disconnect all wires at solenoid terminals. Note color coding of wires for reinstallation.
4. Remove starter support bracket mount bolts (4 cylinder engines use 2 nuts; V6 engines use 1 nut). On engines with solenoid heat shield, remove front bracket upper bolt and detach bracket from starter motor.
5. Loosen the front bracket bolt or nut and rotate bracket clear. Lower and remove starter. Note the location of any shims so that they may be replaced in the same positions upon installation.
6. Reverse procedure to install.

Diesel

1. Disconnect the negative cable at the battery(s).
2. Raise and support the car on jackstands.
3. Remove the lower starter shield nut and bend the shield out of the way.
4. Disconnect the wires from the starter. It's a good idea to tag the wires.
5. Remove the front starter bolt. Loosen the rear starter bolt and remove the starter with the rear bolt remaining in the starter housing.
6. Installation is the reverse of removal.

IGNITION SYSTEM

All models are equipped with the HEI distributor and ignition system. This system uses no points and is, therefore, relatively maintenance free. See the Electronic Ignition section for unit description.

When using an auxiliary starter switch on HEI systems, the distributor BATT lead must be disconnected. Failure to do this may cause damage to the grounding circuit in the ignition switch.

HEI SYSTEM TACHOMETER HOOKUP

On all 1980 models and all 1981 and later models with the V6 engine, there is a terminal on the distributor cap marked TACH. On all 1981 and later models with the L4 engine, there is a terminal on the ignition coil where the brown wire is connected. Connect one tachometer lead to this terminal and the other lead to a suitable ground. On some tachometers, the leads must be connected to the TACH terminal and then to the positive battery terminal.

— CAUTION —
Never ground the TACH terminal; serious module and ignition coil damage will result. If there is any doubt as to the correct tachometer hookup, check with the tachometer manufacturer.

Distributor

REMOVAL & INSTALLATION

— CAUTION —
On Chevrolet V6 models the distributor body is involved in the engine lubricating system. The lubricating circuit to the right-bank valve train can be interrupted by misalignment of the distributor body. See Firing Order illustrations for correct distributor positioning.

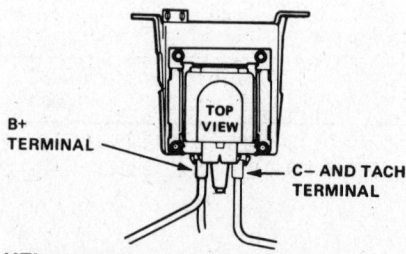

HEI external coil tachometer connection is opposite the BATT (B+) terminal (© Chevrolet Div., G.M. Corp.)

NOTE: On 4 cylinder engines, it may be necessary to remove the 2 rear cradle attaching bolts and lower the cradle enough to allow access to the distributor. If so, also disconnect the brake line support from the floor pan.

1. Disconnect the negative battery cable.
2. Tag and disconnect all wires leading from the distributor cap.
3. Remove the ignition coil on the 1981 and later L4 engine.
4. Remove the distributor cap by turning the four latches counterclockwise. You will need a stubby screwdriver to get at the latches on the four cylinder engine, because there isn't much room between the distributor and the firewall. Remove the distributor cap and set it aside without disconnecting any of the wires.
5. Remove the vacuum hose from the vacuum advance unit. On 1980 models, mark the position of the vacuum advance unit in relation to the engine for correct installation.
6. Remove the hold-down clamp and bolt at the base of the V6 distributor. The four cylinder engine has two bolts and a clamp. Remove the outer bolt first, then loosen, but do not remove, the inner bolt. Slide the clamp back and remove it.
7. Before removing the distributor, note the position of the rotor. Scribe a mark on the distributor body indicating the initial position of the rotor.
8. Remove the distributor from the engine. The drive gear on the distributor shaft is helical, and the shaft will rotate slightly as the distributor is removed. Note and mark the position of the rotor at this second position. Do not crank the engine with the distributor removed.

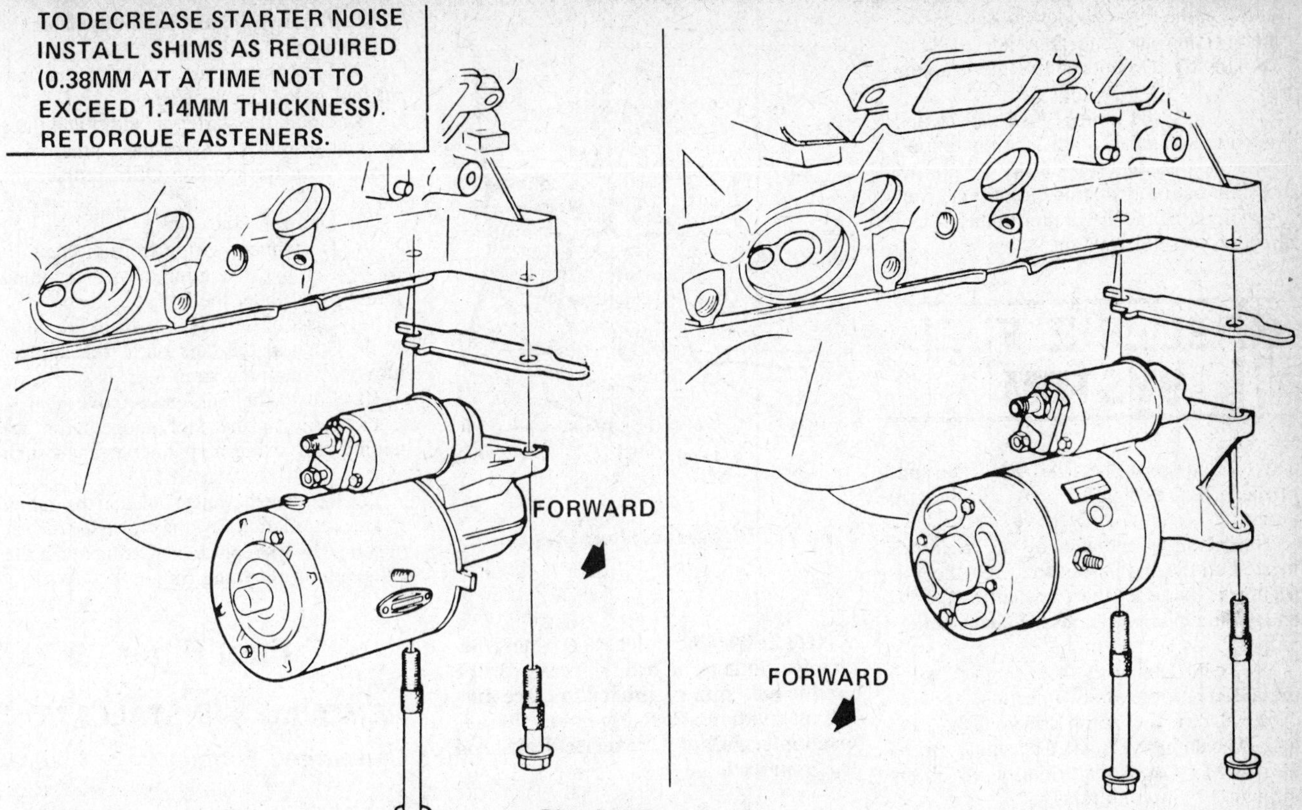

TO DECREASE STARTER NOISE INSTALL SHIMS AS REQUIRED (0.38MM AT A TIME NOT TO EXCEED 1.14MM THICKNESS). RETORQUE FASTENERS.

FORWARD

FORWARD

Diesel starter mounting

9. To install the distributor, rotate the distributor shaft until the rotor aligns with the second mark you made (when the shaft stopped moving). Lubricate the drive gear with clean engine oil, the install the distributor into the engine. On 1980 engines, align the vacuum advance unit with the mark previously made. As the distributor is installed, the rotor should move to the mark you made first, indicating rotor position before the distributor was removed. This will ensure proper timing. If the marks do not align properly, remove the distributor and try again.

10. Install the clamp and hold-down bolt. Tighten them until the distributor can just be moved with a little effort.

11. Connect the ignition wire and tachometer wire, and install the distributor cap. Plug the vacuum advance hose (if so equipped). Set the ignition timing. Connect the vacuum hose.

INSTALLATION IF THE ENGINE WAS DISTURBED

If the engine was cranked while the distributor was removed, you will have to place the engine on TDC of the compression stroke to obtain proper ignition timing.

1. Remove the No. 1 spark plug.
2. Place your thumb over the spark plug hole. Crank the engine slowly until compression is felt. It will be easier if you have someone rotate the engine by hand, using a wrench on the crankshaft pulley.

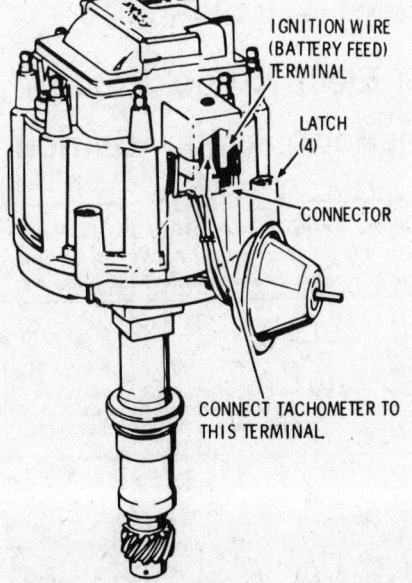

IGNITION WIRE (BATTERY FEED) TERMINAL

LATCH (4)

CONNECTOR

CONNECT TACHOMETER TO THIS TERMINAL

HEI coil-in-cap distributor tachometer hookup

3. Align the timing mark on the crankshaft pulley with the 0° mark on the timing scale attached to the front of the engine. This places the engine at TDC of the compression stroke.

4. Turn the distributor shaft until the rotor points between the No. 1 and No. 3 spark plug towers on the cap for the four cylinder engine, or between the No. 1 and No. 6 spark plug towers for the V6.

5. Install the distributor into the engine. On 1980 models, be sure to align the vacuum advance unit with the mark previously made.

6. Perform Steps 9–11 of the preceding removal and installation procedure.

Ignition Timing

NOTE: Always consult the underhood sticker on your car before adjusting timing. If the sticker differs from these procedures, follow the sticker.

1. Connect a timing light to the No. 1 spark plug wire according to the light manufacturer's instructions. DO NOT PIERCE THE SPARK PLUG WIRE TO CONNECT THE TIMING LIGHT.

2. Disconnect the distributor spark advance hose (if equipped) and plug the vacuum opening.

3. On models with Electronic Spark Timing (EST) distributor, disconnect the 4 terminal plug at the distributor. The EST distributor uses no mechanical or vacuum advance and is easily identified by the absence of a vacuum advance and the presence of a four terminal connector.

4. Start the engine and run it at idle speed.

5. Aim the timing light at the degree scale just over the harmonic balancer.

6. Adjust the timing by loosening the securing clamp and rotating the distributor until the desired ignition advance is achieved, then tighten the clamp.

7. On the four cylinder, loosen the distributor clamp outer bolt, then slide the clamp back slightly. Do not remove the retaining bolt.

8. Adjust the timing, then replace and tighten the clamp. To advance the timing, rotate the distributor opposite the normal direction of rotor rotation. Retard the timing by rotating the distributor in the normal direction of rotor rotation.

GASOLINE FUEL SYSTEM

The fuel pump on the 1980–81 4-151 and on the V6 is the single action AC diaphragm type.

The pump is actuated by an eccentric located on the engine camshaft. On the V6 a pushrod between the camshaft eccentric and the fuel pump actuates the pump rocker arm.

1982 and later 4 cylinder engines with the TBI (Throttle Body Injection) system use an electric fuel pump located in the fuel tank. The pump is activated by signals from the ECM (Electronic Control Module) through a fuel pump relay.

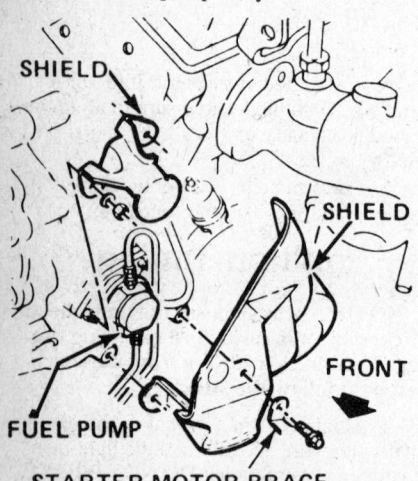

173 V6 fuel pump installation details

Mechanical Fuel Pump

REMOVAL & INSTALLATION

1. Disconnect the negative battery cable. Raise the front of the vehicle and support it on stands.

2. Disconnect fuel inlet and outlet lines at pump and plug pump inlet line.

3. If necessary, on the V6, remove the shields and the oil filter.

4. Remove two pump mounting bolts and lockwashers; remove pump and gasket.

5. Install pump with new gasket coated with sealer. Coat mounting bolt threads with sealer and tighten bolts.

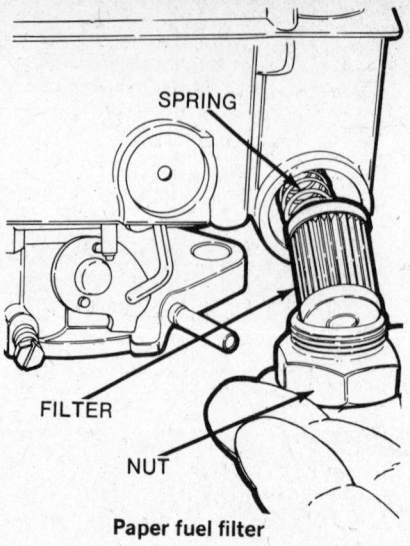

Paper fuel filter

NOTE: On Chevrolet V6 engines, mechanical fingers or heavy grease can be used to hold pump pushrod in place during installation. Coat pipe plug threads or adapter gasket with sealer if pushrod was removed.

6. Install the shields and oil filter on the V6, if removed.

7. Connect inlet and outlet lines, start engine and check for leaks.

Electric Fuel Pump

REMOVAL & INSTALLATION

— CAUTION —
Before opening any part of the fuel system, the pressure must be relieved. Follow the procedure below to relieve the pressure:

1. Remove the fuel pump fuse from the fuse panel.

2. Start the engine and let it run until all fuel in the line is used.

3. Crank the starter an additional three seconds to relieve any residual pressure.

4. With the ignition OFF, replace the fuse.

5. Drain the fuel tank.

6. Disconnect wiring from the tank.

7. Remove the ground wire retaining screw from under the body.

8. Disconnect all hoses from the tank.

9. Support the tank on a jack and remove the retaining strap nuts.

10. Lower the tank and remove it.

11. Remove the fuel gauge/pump retaining ring using a spanner wrench such as tool J-24187.

12. Remove the gauge unit and the pump.

13. Installation is the reverse of removal. Always replace the O-ring under the gauge/pump retaining ring.

Fuel Filter

REMOVAL & INSTALLATION

Carbureted Engines

An in-carburetor filter is used.

1. With the engine cold, disconnect the fuel inlet line at the carburetor. Hold the large nut with a wrench while turning the smaller nut.

2. Remove the large nut from the carburetor inlet.

3. Remove the filter and spring from the carburetor.

4. New filters usually come with a new inlet nut gasket. If not, obtain one. Never reuse the old gasket. Install the new filter, gasket and nut. Do not overtighten the nut.

5. Install the fuel line. Use two wrenches to avoid distorting the fuel pipe.

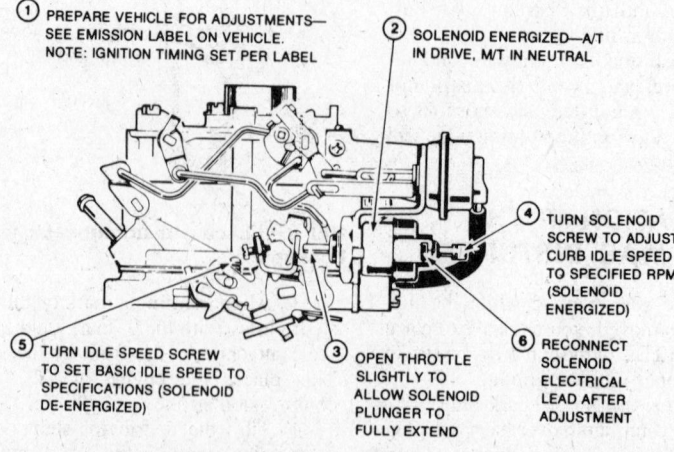

1980 Idle speed adjustment—w/o A/C (© Chevrolet Div., G.M. Corp.)

Fuel Injected Engines

The filter is an inline unit ahead of the TBI unit. To remove the filter, make sure the engine is cold, unclamp and remove the fuel hose, then unscrew the filter from the steel fuel line. Installation is the reverse of removal.

Carburetor

REMOVAL & INSTALLATION

All Models

1. Disconnect the battery.
2. Remove the air cleaner.
3. Disconnect the accelerator linkage.
4. Disconnect the transmission detent cable.
5. If, equipped, disconnect the cruise control cable.
6. Disconnect all electrical connectors at the carburetor, or which might interfere with carburetor removal. Tag the wires for installation.
7. Disconnect and tag all vacuum lines at the carburetor.
8. Disconnect the fuel line at the carburetor inlet.
9. Installation is the reverse of removal. Torque the long bolts to 7 ft. lb.; the short bolts to 11 ft. lb.

Fuel Injection

For all service procedures, including removal and installation of the TBI unit, please refer to the "Fuel Injection" part of the Unit Repair section.

Idle Speed and Mixture Adjustments

CARBURETED MODELS

1980

1. Run the engine to normal operating temperature.
2. Make sure that the choke is fully opened, turn the A/C Off, set the parking brake, block the drive wheels and connect a tachometer to the engine according to the manufacturer's instructions.
3. Disconnect and plug the vacuum hoses at the EGR valve and the vapor canister.
4. Place the transmission in Park (AT) or Neutral (MT).
5. Disconnect and plug the vacuum advance hose at the distributor. Check and adjust the timing.
6. Connect the distributor vacuum line.
7. Manual transmission cars without A/C and without solenoid: place the idle speed screw on the low step of the fast idle cam and turn the screw to achieve the specified idle speed.

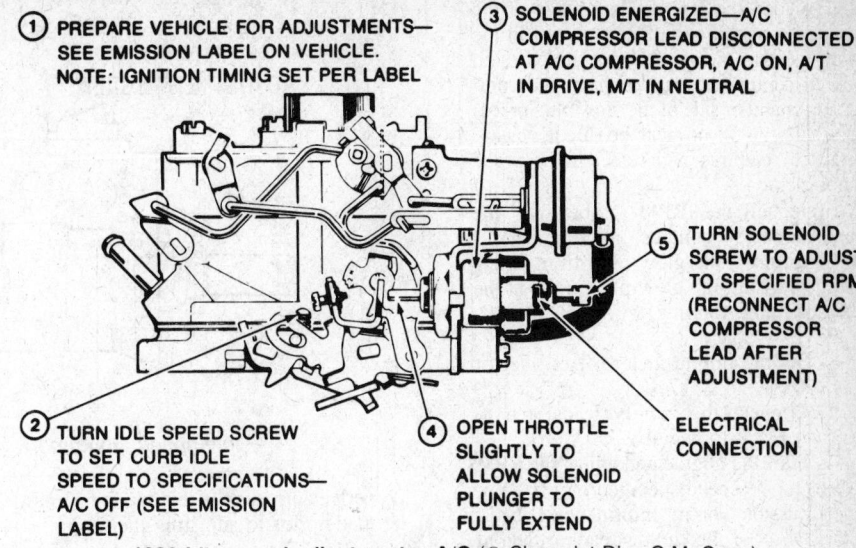

① PREPARE VEHICLE FOR ADJUSTMENTS—SEE EMISSION LABEL ON VEHICLE. NOTE: IGNITION TIMING SET PER LABEL

③ SOLENOID ENERGIZED—A/C COMPRESSOR LEAD DISCONNECTED AT A/C COMPRESSOR, A/C ON, A/T IN DRIVE, M/T IN NEUTRAL

⑤ TURN SOLENOID SCREW TO ADJUST TO SPECIFIED RPM. (RECONNECT A/C COMPRESSOR LEAD AFTER ADJUSTMENT)

② TURN IDLE SPEED SCREW TO SET CURB IDLE SPEED TO SPECIFICATIONS—A/C OFF (SEE EMISSION LABEL)

④ OPEN THROTTLE SLIGHTLY TO ALLOW SOLENOID PLUNGER TO FULLY EXTEND

ELECTRICAL CONNECTION

1980 idle speed adjustment w A/C (© Chevrolet Div., G.M. Corp.)

Cars with A/C: set the idle speed screw to the specified rpm. Disconnect the compressor clutch A/C On. Open the throttle momentarily to extend the solenoid plunger. Turn the solenoid screw to obtain the specified rpm.

Automatic transmission cars without A/C; manual transmission cars without A/C, solenoid-equipped carburetor: momentarily open the throttle to extend the solenoid plunger. Turn the solenoid screw to obtain the specified rpm. Disconnect the solenoid wire and turn the idle speed screw to obtain the slow engine idle speed.

1981–85

Mixture adjustments are a function of the Computer Command Control (CCC) system. See the Emission Control Unit Repair section for more information.

The idle speed on models equipped with an Idle Speed Control (ISC) motor is automatically adjusted by the Computer Command Control System, making manual adjustment unnecessary. The underhood specifications sticker will indicate ISC motor use.

On non-A/C models not equipped with ISC, the idle speed is adjusted at the idle speed screw on the carburetor. Before adjusting, check the underhood sticker for any preparations required.

On A/C equipped models which do not have an ISC motor, an idle speed solenoid similar to the ones on earlier models is used. This solenoid is adjusted at the solenoid screw, using the same procedures as on earlier models. Consult the underhood specifications sticker for special instructions.

FUEL INJECTED MODELS

No idle speed or mixture adjustments are possible on 1982 and later fuel injected engines.

DIESEL FUEL SYSTEM

Injection Timing

CHECKING AND/OR ADJUSTING TIMING USING J-33075 TIMING METER

The timing meter picks up the engine speed and crankshaft position from the crankshaft balancer. It uses a luminosity signal through a glow plug probe to determine combustion timing. Certain engine malfunctions may cause incorrect timing readings. Engine malfunctions should be corrected before a timing adjustment is made. The marks on the pump and adapter flange will normally be aligned within 1.27 mm (.050″).

NOTE: Alignment of timing marks may be used in emergency situations (i.e. timing meter not available). However for optimum engine operation, the timing should be adjusted with the timing meter as soon as possible.

1. Place the transmission selector lever in park, apply the parking brake and block the drive wheels.
2. Start the engine and let it run at idle until fully warmed up. Then shut off the engine.

NOTE: Failure to have the engine fully warmed up will result in incorrect timing reading and adjustments.

3. Remove the air cleaner assembly and install cover J-26996-1. The EGR valve hose must be disconnected.
4. Clean any dirt from the engine probe holder (RPM counter) and crankshaft balancer rim.

5. Clean the lens on both ends of the glow plug probe and clean the lens in the photo-electric pick-up. Use a dulled tooth pick to scrape the carbon from the combustion chamber side of the glow plug probe. Look through the probe to be sure it's clean. Retarded readings will result if the probe is not clean.

6. Install the RPM probe into the crankshaft RPM counter (probe holder).

7. Remove the glow plug from No. 1 cylinder. Install the glow plug probe in the glow opening. Torque the probe to 9 ft. lbs.

8. Set the timing meter offset selector to A (20).

9. Connect the battery leads; red to positive, black to negative.

10. Start the engine and adjust the RPM (speed) to the speed specified on the "Vehicle Emission Control Information Label".

11. Observe the timing reading then at 2 minute intervals, again observe the reading. When the readings stabilize over the 2 minute interval, compare that reading to the one specified on the "Vehicle Emission Control Information Label". The timing reading, when set to specification will be "Negative" (after top dead center).

12. Disconnect the timing meter.

13. Lubricate *only* the threads of the removed glow plug with lubricant 9985462 or equivalent.

NOTE: Failure to apply the correct lubricant can cause engine damage.

14. Install the removed glow plug. Torque the glow plug to 15 ft. lbs.

15. Install the air cleaner being certain to reconnect the EGR valve hose.

ADJUSTMENT

1. Shut off the engine.

2. Note the relative position of the marks on the pump flange and pump intermediate adapter.

3. Loosen the bolts holding the pump to the adapter to a point where the pump can be rotated. Use a 1″ open end wrench. (Tool J-25304 has the proper offset on the handle to clear the fuel return line.

4. Rotate the pump to the left to advance the timing and to the right to retard the timing. The width of the mark on the intermediate adapter is about ⅔ degree. Move the pump the amount that is needed and tighten the pump retaining bolts to 35 ft. lbs.

5. Start the engine and recheck the timing reading as outlined previously. Reset and recheck the timing if needed.

6. Reset the idle speed. Please note the following:

   a. Sooty or dirty probes will result in retarded readings.

   b. The luminosity probe will soot up very fast when used in a cold engine.

   c. Wild needle fluctuations on the timing meter indicate a cylinder not firing

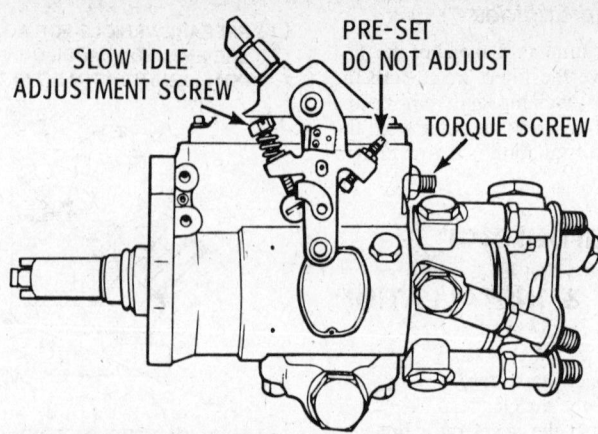

Idle speed adjustment points, CAV pump shown

properly. Correction of this condition must be made prior to adjusting the timing.

Idle Speed

ADJUSTMENT

1. Apply the parking brake, place the transmission selector lever in "**park**" and block the drive wheels.

2. Start engine and allow it to run until warm, usually 10–15 minutes.

3. Shut off the engine, remove the air cleaner assembly.

4. Clean the front cover RPM counter (probe holder) and the crankshaft balancer rim.

5. Install the magnetic pick-up probe of tool J-26925 fully into the RPM counter. Connect the battery leads; red to positive and black to negative.

6. Disconnect the two-lead connector at the generator.

7. Turn off all electrical accessories.

8. Allow no one to touch either the steering wheel or service brake pedal.

9. Start the engine and place the transmission selector lever in "Drive".

10. Check the slow idle speed reading against the one given on the "Vehicle Emission Information Label". Reset if required.

11. Unplug the connector from the fast idle cold advance (engine temp.) switch and install a jumper between the connector terminals—Do not allow the jumper to touch ground.

12. Check the fast idle solenoid speed against the one given on the "Vehicle Emission Information Label." Reset if required.

13. Remove the jumper and reconnect the connector to the temperature switch.

14. Recheck and reset the slow idle speed if necessary.

15. Shut off the engine.

16. Reconnect the lead at the generator.

17. Disconnect and remove the tachometer.

18. If equipped with cruise control adjust the servo throttle cable to minimum slack then install the clip on the servo stud.

Injection Pump

REMOVAL

1. Remove the air cleaner assembly.

2. Remove the crankcase ventilation filter and pipes from the valve cover and air crossover.

3. Remove the air crossover and install intake manifold screened covers J-29657. Remove the fuel lines, filter and fuel pump

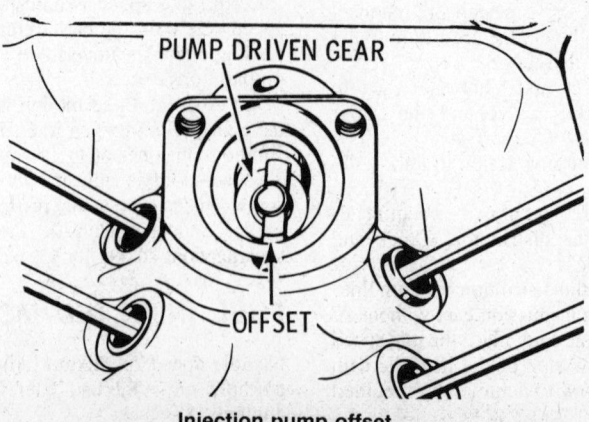

Injection pump offset

as an assembly. Cap all line openings.

4. Disconnect the throttle cable and T.V. cable from the pump throttle lever. Disconnect the throttle return spring.

5. Remove the throttle and T.V./Detent cables from the intake manifold brackets. Position the cables away from the engine.

6. Disconnect the fuel return line from the injection pump.

7. Disconnect the injection line clamps that are closest to the pump.

8. Disconnect the injection lines from the pump and cap all openings. Carefully reposition the lines to gain enough clearance for pump removal.

9. Remove the 2 bolts retaining the injection pump.

10. Remove the pump and discard the pump to adapter O ring.

INSTALLATION

1. Position engine No. 1 cylinder to firing position by aligning the mark on the balancer with zero mark on the indicator located on the front of the engine (the index is offset to the right when number one is at T.D.C.).

2. Line up offset tang on pump driveshaft with the pump driven gear. Install a new pump to adapter O ring, then install the pump fully, seating the pump by hand.

3. If a new or intermediate adapter is installed, set the injection pump at the center of the slots in the pump mounting flange. If the original intermediate adapter is being retained, align the pump timing mark with the mark on the intermediate adapter. Install the 2 bolts and washers retaining the pump and torque to 35 ft. lbs.

4. Remove the caps from the openings and connect the injection lines to the pump. Install the disconnected injection line clamps.

5. Connect the fuel return line.

6. Install the throttle and T.V. cables into the intake manifold bracket.

7. Connect the throttle cable and T.V. cable to the pump throttle lever. Connect the throttle return spring. Adjust the T.V. cable. See the Unit Repair section.

8. Install all remaining fuel lines and fuel filter.

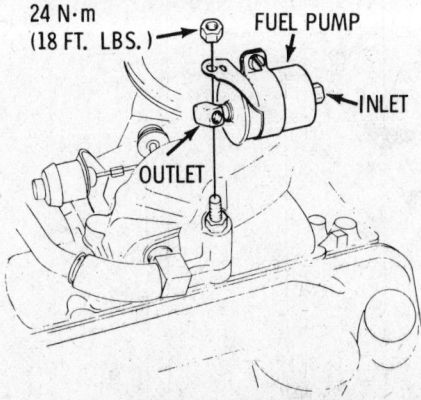

24 N·m
(18 FT. LBS.)
FUEL PUMP
INLET
OUTLET

Diesel fuel transfer pump

9. Start the engine and check for leaks.

10. Check and if necessary reset the pump timing, see "Checking and/or Adjusting Pump Timing."

11. Adjust the vacuum regulator valve. See the Unit Repair Section.

12. Adjust the idle speeds.

13. Remove the screened covers from intake manifold, then install the air crossover.

14. Install tubes and hoses in the air crossover and ventilation filters in the valve cover.

15. Install the air cleaner being certain to reconnect the EGR valve hose.

Electric Fuel Transfer Pump

The pump is located at the front of the engine next to the fuel heater.

REMOVAL & INSTALLATION

1. Place the ignition in the OFF position.

2. Remove the air cleaner.

3. Disconnect the pump electrical supply wire.

4. Using a ¾ in. wrench on the inlet fitting, unscrew the fuel pipe inlet tube.

5. Using the same method, unscrew the outlet pipe.

6. Unbolt the pump mounting bracket and the pump.

7. Installation is the reverse of removal. Using the two wrench method, torque the fuel lines to 19 ft. lb. The pump bracket is torqued to 18 ft. lb. In some cases, it may be necessary to adjust the pump location slightly to get a good alignment on the fuel lines. When the pump is installed, disconnect the fuel line at the filter, and run the pump with the key ON to bleed the lines.

Fuel Injection Pump Lines

REMOVAL & INSTALLATION

1. Remove the air cleaner.

2. Remove the filters and pipes from the valve covers and air crossover.

3. Remove the air crossover and cover the intake opening.

4. Remove the injection pump line clamps, then remove the injection pump lines and cap the opening at once!

NOTE: To remove the right side lines, see the engine lifting procedure outlined under Diesel Engine Right Side Valve Cover, later in this section.

5. Installation is the reverse of removal. Install each line loosely at both ends, then torque each end evenly. If several lines are being replaced, start with the lower lines.

Injection Nozzle

REMOVAL & INSTALLATION

NOTE: Whenever lines are disconnected, use a backup wrench to avoid line distortion.

1. Remove the injection lines as described earlier. When working on the right side, leave the engine in the position described under line removal, for injector removal.

2. Remove the nozzle by applying the wrench to the larger hex on the nozzle.

3. Remove the copper gasket from the head if it did not remain on the nozzle.

4. Installation is the reverse of removal. Use lubricant 9985462 or its equivalent on the nozzle threads. Always use a new copper gasket on each nozzle. Torque the nozzle and the lines to 25 ft. lb. each.

COOLING SYSTEM

Radiator

REMOVAL & INSTALLATION

1. Disconnect the negative battery cable.

2. Drain the cooling system.

3. Remove the forward strut brace for the engine at the radiator. Loosen the bolt to prevent shearing the rubber bushing, then swing the strut rearward.

4. Disconnect the headlamp wiring harness from the fan frame. Unplug the fan electrical connector.

5. Remove the attaching bolts for the fan.

6. Scribe the hood latch location on the radiator support, then remove the latch.

7. Disconnect the coolant hoses from the radiator. Remove the coolant recovery tank hose from the radiator neck. Disconnect and plug the automatic transmission fluid cooler lines from the radiator, if so equipped.

8. Remove the radiator attaching bolts and remove the radiator. If the car has air conditioning, it first may be necessary to raise the left side of the radiator so that the radiator neck will clear the compressor.

To install:

1. Install the radiator in the car, tightening the mounting bolts to 7 in. lbs. Connect the transmission cooler lines and hoses. Install the coolant recovery hose.

2. Install the hood latch. Tighten to 6 ft. lbs.

3. Install the fan, making sure the bottom leg of the frame fits into the rubber grommet at the lower support. Install the fan wires and the headlamp wiring harness.

Swing the strut and brace forward, tightening to 11 ft. lbs. Connect the engine ground strap to the strut brace. Install the negative battery cable, fill the cooling system, and check for leaks.

Water Pump

REMOVAL & INSTALLATION

4-151

1. Disconnect battery negative cable.
2. Remove accessory drive belts.
3. Remove water pump attaching bolts and remove pump.
4. If installing a new water pump, transfer pulley from old unit. With sealing surfaces cleaned, place a 3mm (⅛ in.) bead of sealant #1052289 or equivalent on the water pump sealing surface. While sealer is still wet, install pump and torque bolts to 6 ft. lb.
5. Install accessory drive belts.
6. Connect battery negative cable.

6-173

1. Disconnect battery negative cable.
2. Drain cooling system and remove heater hose.
3. Remove water pump attaching bolts and nut and remove pump.
4. With the sealant surfaces cleaned, place a 2mm (³⁄₃₂ in.) head of sealant #1052357 or equivalent on the water pump sealing surface.
5. Clean old sealant from pump.
6. Coat bolt threads with pipe sealant #1052080 or equivalent.

7. Install pump and torque bolts to 10 ft. lb.
8. Connect battery negative battery cable.

NOTE: When replacing the water pump on a car equipped with the V-6 engine, the timing cover must be clamped to the cylinder block PRIOR TO removing the water pump bolts. Certain bolts holding the water pump pass through the front cover and when removed, may allow the front cover to pull away from the cylinder block, breaking the seal. This may or may not be readily apparent and if left undetected, could allow coolant to enter the crankcase. To prevent this possible separation during water pump removal, Special Tool #J29176 will have to be installed.

6-181

1982–83

1. Disconnect the negative battery cable.
2. Remove accessory drive belts.
3. Remove water pump attaching bolts.
4. Remove the engine support strut.
5. Place a floor jack under the front crossmember of the cradle and raise the jack until the jack just starts to raise the car.
6. Remove the front two body mount bolts with the lower cushions and retainers.
7. Thread the body mount bolts with retainers a minimum of three (3) turns into the cage so that the bolts restrain cradle movement.

8. Release the floor jack slowly until the crossmember contacts the body mount bolt retainers. As the jack is being lowered watch and correct any interference with hoses, lines, pipes and cables.

NOTE: Do not lower the cradle without its being restrained as possible damage can occur to the body and underhood items.

9. Remove water pump from engine.
10. Reverse removal procedure.
11. Install pump and torque to 25 ft. lb.
12. Connect negative battery cable.
13. Fill with coolant and check for leaks.

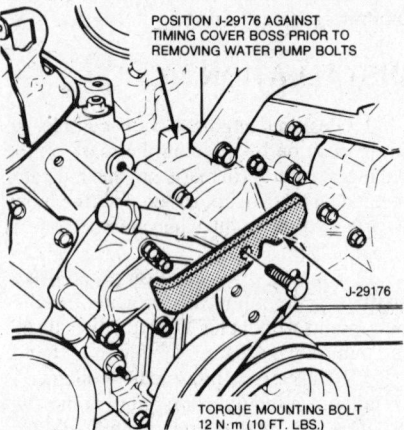

POSITION J-29176 AGAINST TIMING COVER BOSS PRIOR TO REMOVING WATER PUMP BOLTS

J-29176

TORQUE MOUNTING BOLT 12 N·m (10 FT. LBS.)

Install the special tool on the 6-173 to insure that the front cover does not separate from the crankcase when the pump is removed

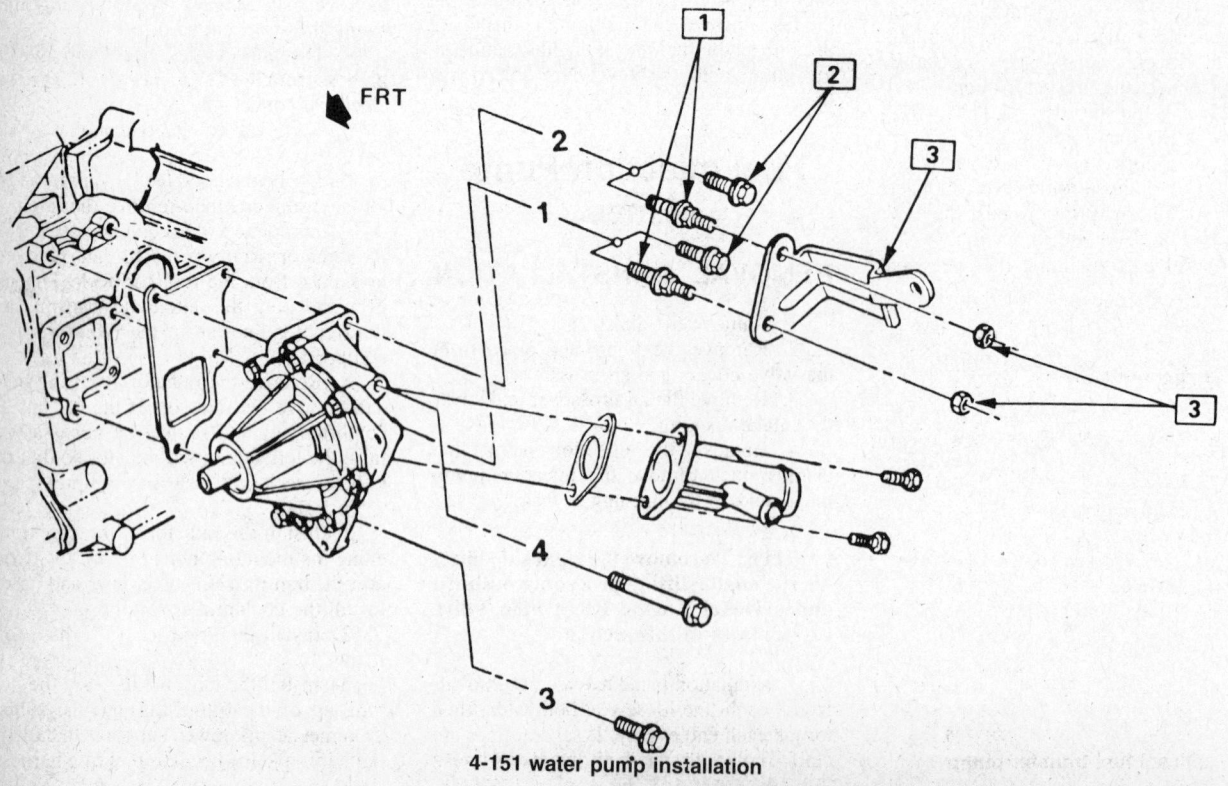

FRT

4-151 water pump installation

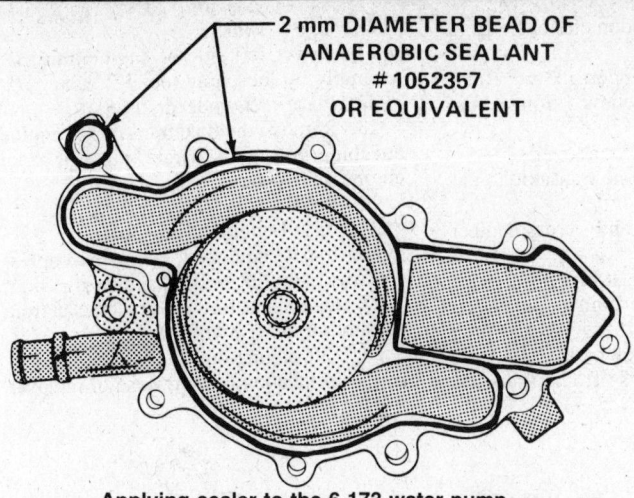

2 mm DIAMETER BEAD OF ANAEROBIC SEALANT # 1052357 OR EQUIVALENT

Applying sealer to the 6-173 water pump

30 N·m (22 FT. LB.)

10 N·m (7 FT. LBS.)

◄ FRT

Water pump installation—6-183 and 6-231

6-181, 231
1984 AND LATER

1. Disconnect the negative cable at the battery.
2. Drain the cooling system.
3. Remove the accessory drive belts.
4. Disconnect the radiator and heater hoses at the water pump.
5. Remove the water pump pulley bolts (long bolt removed through access hole provided in the body side rail), then remove the pulley.
6. Remove the water pump attaching bolts, then remove the water pump.
7. Clean all gasket mating surfaces.
8. Using a new gasket, install the water pump on the engine. Torque the bolts to specifications.
9. Install the water pump pulley, then torque the bolts to specifications. (see illustration.)
10. The remainder of the installation is the reverse of removal.

6-263

1. Drain radiator.
2. Disconnect lower radiator hose at water pump.
3. Disconnect the heater return hose at the water pump, remove the bolt retaining the heater water return pipe to the intake manifold and position the pipe out-of-the-way.
4. If equipped with A/C, remove the vacuum pump drive belt.
5. Remove the serpentine drive belt.
6. Remove the generator, A/C compressor or vacuum pump brackets.
7. Remove the water pump attaching bolts and remove the water pump assembly.
8. Remove the water pump pulley.
9. Clean gasket material from engine block.
10. Apply a thin coat of 1050026 sealer or equivalent to the water pump housing to retain the gasket, then position new gasket on the housing. Also apply sealer to water pump mounting bolts. Torque bolts to 12–15 ft. lb.

Emission Controls

NOTE: The emission systems on your car are listed below. Not all systems will be on each car. For a description of and service for each system, please refer to the "Emission Control" part of the Unit Repair section.

- Positive Crankcase Ventilation
- Evaporative Emission Control
- Early Fuel Evaporation System
- Catalytic Converter
- Exhaust Gas Recirculation
- Computer Command Control
- Deceleration Valve
- Computer Controlled Catalytic Converter
- Air Injection Reactor
- Pulsair System
- Controlled Combustion System

ENGINE

Engine Unit

REMOVAL & INSTALLATION

4-151 with Manual Transaxle

NOTE: Relieve the pressure in the fuel system as described under Fuel Pump.

1. Disconnect battery cables at battery.
2. Hoist car.
3. Remove front mount-to-cradle nuts.
4. Remove forward exhaust pipe.
5. Remove starter assembly (wires attached and swing to side).
6. Remove flywheel inspection cover.
7. Lower car.
8. Remove air cleaner.
9. Remove all bell housing bolts.
10. Remove forward torque reaction rod from engine and core support.
11. If equipped with A/C, remove A/C belt and compressor and swing to side.

12. Remove emission hoses at canister.
13. Remove power steering hose (if so equipped).
14. Remove vacuum hoses and electrical connectors at solenoid.
15. Remove heater blower motor.
16. Disconnect throttle cable.
17. Drain cooling system.
18. Disconnect heater hose.
19. Disconnect radiator hose.
20. Disconnect engine harness at bulkhead connector.
21. With engine lifting tool, hoist engine (remove heater hose at intake manifold and disconnect fuel line).
22. Installation is the reverse of removal.

4-151 with Automatic Transaxle

NOTE: Relieve the pressure in the fuel system as described under Fuel Pump.

1. Disconnect battery cables at battery.
2. Drain cooling system.
3. Remove air cleaner and pre-heat tube.
4. Disconnect engine harness connector.
5. Disconnect all external vacuum hose connections.
6. Remove throttle and transaxle linkage at E.F.I. assembly and intake manifold.
7. Remove upper radiator hose.
8. If equipped with air conditioning, remove A/C compressor from mounting brackets and set aside. Do not disconnect hoses.
9. Remove front engine strut assembly.
10. Disconnect heater hose at intake manifold.
11. Remove transaxle to engine bolts leaving the upper two bolts in place.
12. Remove front mount-to-cradle nuts.
13. Remove forward exhaust pipe.
14. Remove flywheel inspection cover and remove starter motor.
15. Remove torque converter to flywheel bolts.
16. Remove P/S pump and bracket and move to one side.
17. Remove heater hose and lower radiator hose.

18. Remove two rear transaxle support bracket bolts.

19. Remove fuel supply line at fuel filter.

20. Using a floor jack and a block of wood placed under the transaxle, raise engine and transaxle until engine front mount studs clear cradle.

21. Connect engine lift equipment and put tension on engine.

22. Remove two remaining transaxle bolts.

23. Slide engine forward and lift from car. Install engine on stand.

24. Installation is the reverse of removal. Do not completely lower the engine with a jack supporting the transaxle.

6-173 with Manual Transaxle

1. Disconnect cables from battery.
2. Remove air cleaner.
3. Drain cooling system.
4. Disconnect vacuum hosing to all nonengine mounted components.
5. Disconnect accelerator linkage from carburetor.
6. Disconnect engine harness connector.
7. Disconnect radiator hoses from radiator.
8. Disconnect heater hoses from engine.
9. If equipped, remove power steering pump and bracket assembly from engine.
10. Disconnect clutch cable from transaxle.
11. Disconnect shift linkage from transaxle shift levers. Remove cables from transaxle bosses.

12. Disconnect speedometer cable from transaxle.

13. Install engine support fixture. Raise engine until weight is relieved from mount assemblies.

14. Remove exhaust crossover.

15. Remove all but one transaxle to engine retaining bolts.

16. Remove side and crossmember assembly.

17. Disconnect exhaust pipe.

18. Remove all powertrain mount to cradle attachments.

19. Using tool J-28468 or J-33008, pull both axle drive shafts from transaxle assembly.

20. Lower vehicle.

21. Lower left side of engine/transaxle assembly by loosening tool J-22825.

22. Place jack under transaxle.

23. Remove the final transaxle to engine attaching bolt and separate transaxle from engine and lower.

24. Lower vehicle.

25. Install engine lifting fixture.

26. If A/C equipped, remove compressor from mounting bracket and swing aside.

27. Disconnect forward strut bracket from radiator support. Swing aside.

28. Lift engine out of vehicle.

29. Installation is the reverse of removal.

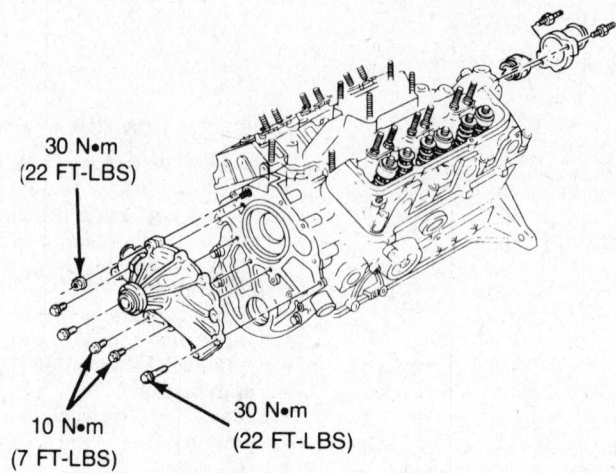

6-173 water pump installation

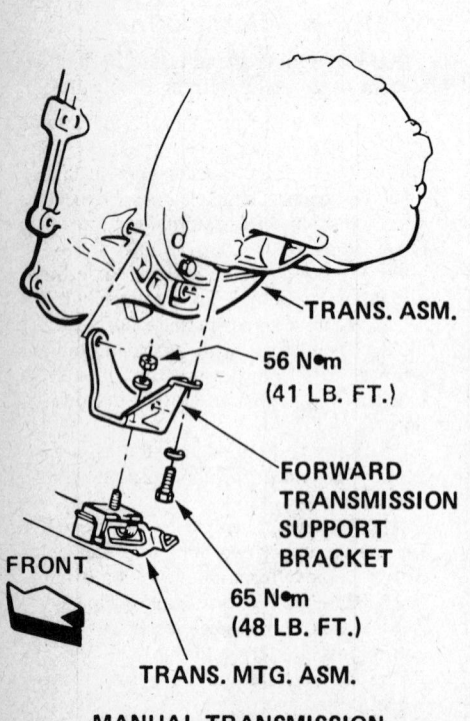

MANUAL TRANSMISSION

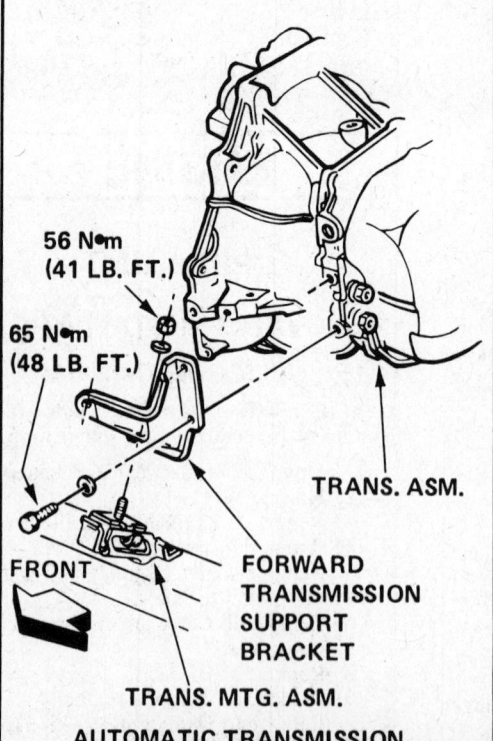

AUTOMATIC TRANSMISSION

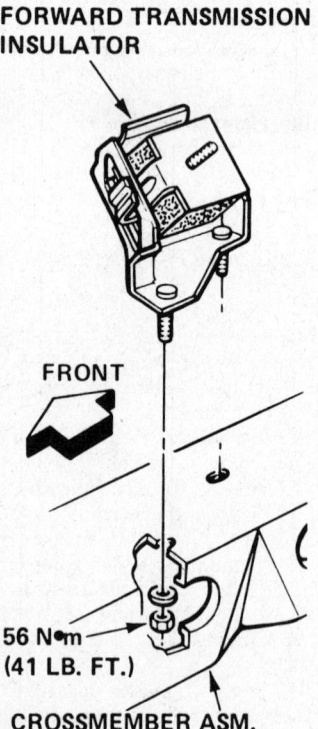

4-151 front mounts

6-173 with Automatic Transaxle

1. Disconnect battery cables from battery.
2. Remove air cleaner.
3. Drain cooling system.
4. Disconnect vacuum hosing to all nonengine mounted components.
5. Disconnect detent cable from carburetor lever.
6. Disconnect accelerator linkage.
7. Disconnect engine harness connector.
8. Disconnect ground strap from engine at engine forward strut.
9. Disconnect radiator hoses from radiator.
10. Disconnect heater hoses from engine.
11. Remove power steering pump and bracket assembly from engine, if equipped.
12. Raise vehicle.
13. Disconnect exhaust pipe.
14. Disconnect fuel lines at rubber hose connections at right side of engine.
15. Remove engine front mount to cradle retaining nuts (right side of vehicle).
16. Disconnect battery cables from engine (Starter and transaxle housing bolt).
17. Remove flex plate cover and disconnect torque convertor from flex plate.
18. Remove transaxle case to cylinder case support bracket bolts.
19. Lower vehicle. Place a support under the transaxle rear extension.
20. Remove engine strut bracket from radiator support and swing rearward.

21. Remove exhaust crossover pipe.
22. Remove transaxle to cylinder case retaining bolts. Make note of ground stud location.
23. If A/C equipped, remove compressor from mounting bracket and lay aside.
24. Install lift fixture to engine and remove engine from vehicle.
25. Installation is the reverse of removal.

6-181 and 231

1. Disconnect battery cables from battery.
2. Remove air cleaner.
3. Drain cooling system.
4. Disconnect vacuum hosing to all nonengine mounted components.
5. Disconnect detent cable from carburetor lever.
6. Disconnect accelerator linkage.
7. Disconnect engine harness connector.
8. Disconnect ground strap from engine at engine forward strut.
9. Disconnect radiator hoses from radiator.
10. Disconnect heater hoses from engine.
11. Remove power steering pump and bracket assembly from engine.
12. Raise vehicle.
13. Disconnect exhaust pipe at manifold.
14. Disconnect fuel lines at rubber hose connections.
15. Remove engine front mount to cradle retaining nuts (right side of vehicle).
16. Disconnect battery cables from engine (Starter and transaxle housing bolt).

17. Remove flex plate cover and disconnect torque converter from flex plate.
18. Remove transaxle case to cylinder case support bracket bolts.
19. Lower vehicle. Place a support under the transaxle rear extension.
20. Remove engine strut bracket from radiator support and swing rearward.
21. Remove transaxle to cylinder case retaining bolts. Make note of ground stud location.
22. If A/C equipped, remove compressor from mounting bracket and lay aside.
23. Install lift fixture to engine and remove engine from vehicle.
24. Installation is the reverse of removal.

6-263

1. Drain the cooling system. Remove the serpentine drive belt (and vacuum pump drive belt, if A/C equipped).
2. Remove air cleaner and install cover J-26996.
3. Disconnect battery negative cable(s) at batteries and ground wires at inner fender panel. Disconnect engine ground strap, rear (right) head to cowl.
4. Hoist car.
5. Remove the flywheel cover.
6. Remove the flywheel to torque converter bolts.
7. Disconnect the exhaust pipe from the rear exhaust manifold.
8. Remove the engine to transaxle brace.
9. Remove the engine mount to cradle retaining nuts and washers.

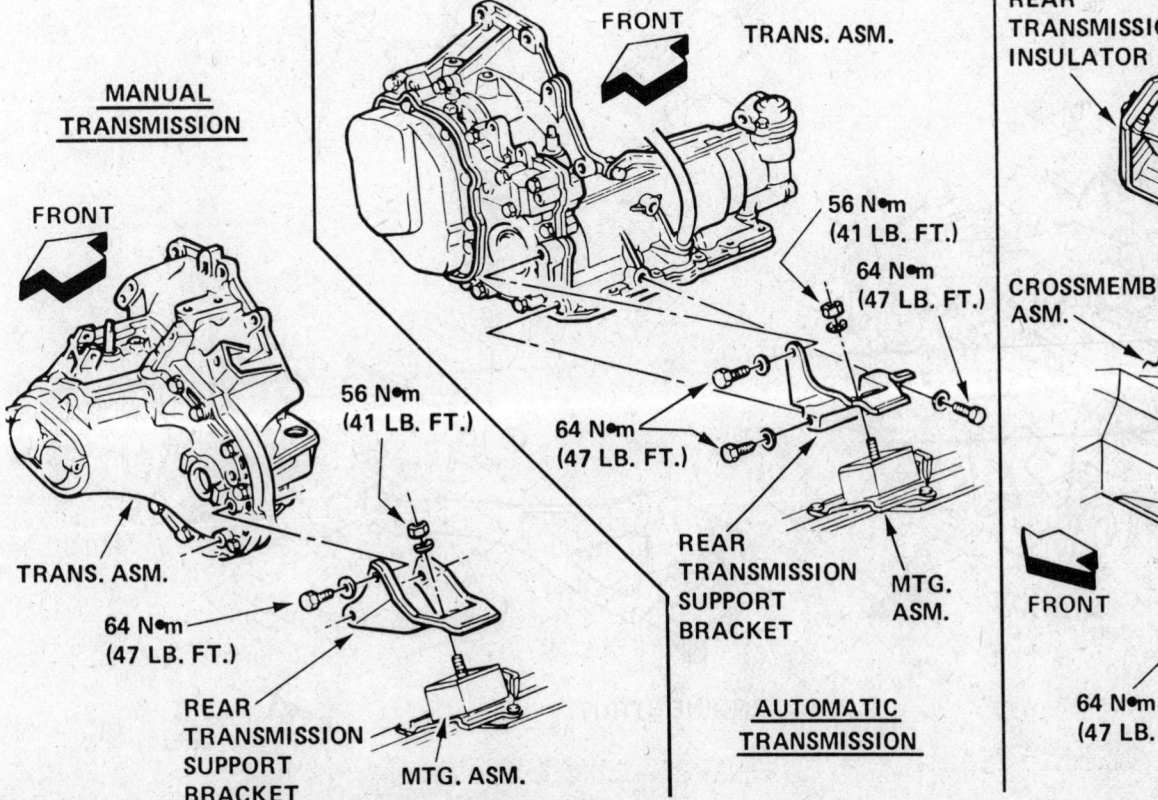

4-151 rear mounts

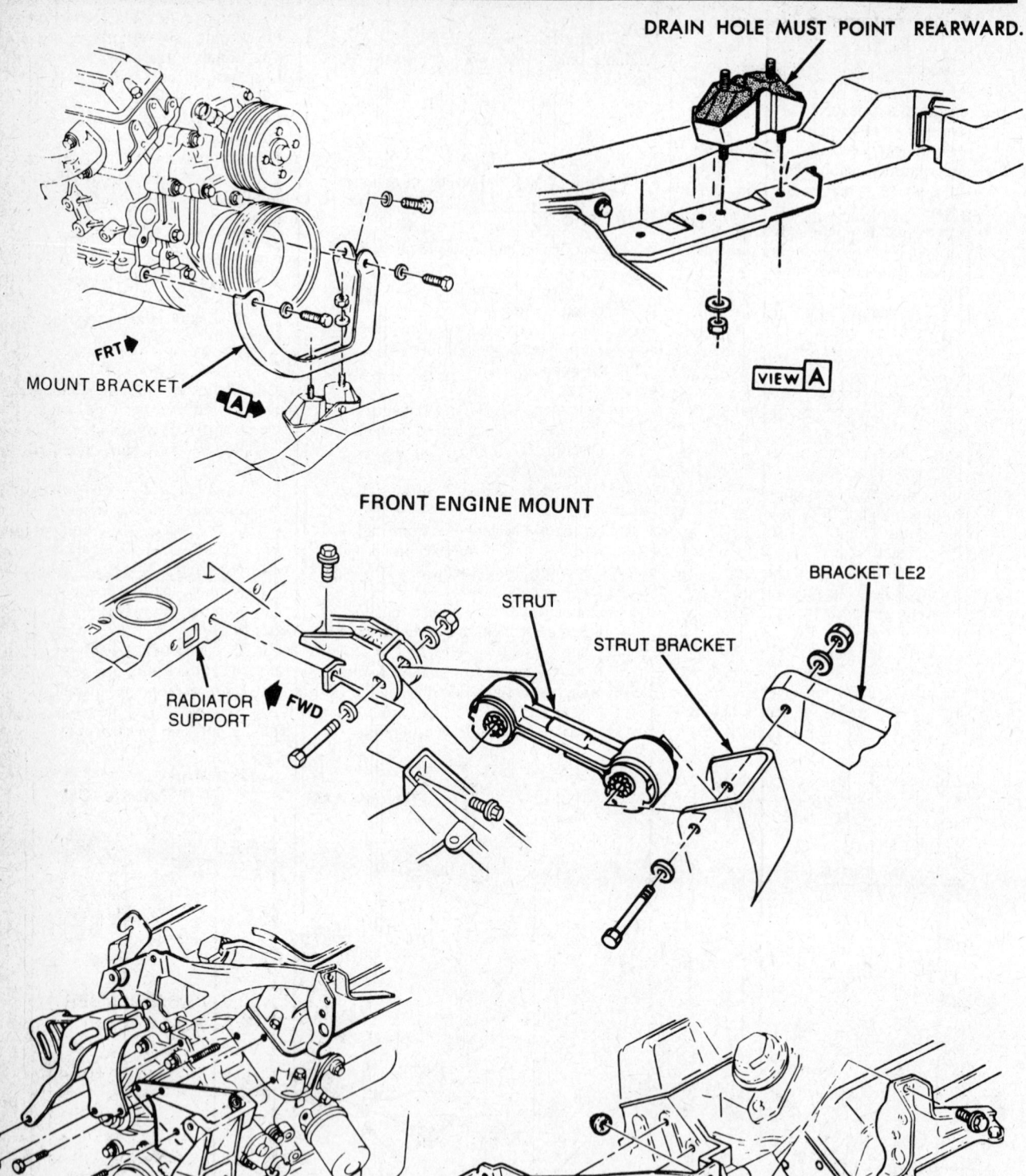

DRAIN HOLE MUST POINT REARWARD.

MOUNT BRACKET

FRT

VIEW A

FRONT ENGINE MOUNT

RADIATOR SUPPORT

FWD

STRUT

STRUT BRACKET

BRACKET LE2

WITH A/C

FRT

ENGINE STRUT

FRT

6-173 mounts

10. Disconnect the leads to the starter motor, #2 cylinder glow plugs and battery ground cable at transaxle to engine bolt.

11. Disconnect the lower oil cooler hose and cap the openings.

12. Remove the accessible power steering pump bracket fasteners.

13. Lower the car.

14. Remove the remaining power steering pump bracket/brace fasteners and lower the power steering pump with hoses out of the way.

15. Remove heater water return pipe.

16. Disconnect all remaining glow plug leads at the glow plugs.

17. Disconnect all other leads at the engine, disconnect the engine harness at the cowl connector and body mounted relays and position the engine harness aside.

18. If A/C equipped, disconnect the compressor with brackets and lines attached and position aside.

19. Disconnect the fuel and vacuum hoses, cap all fuel line openings.

20. Disconnect the throttle and T.V. cables at the injection pump and cable bracket. Position cables aside.

21. Disconnect the upper oil cooler hose and cap the openings.

22. Remove the exhaust crossover pipe heat shield.

23. Disconnect and move aside the transaxle filler tube.

24. Remove the exhaust crossover pipe.

25. Remove the engine mounting strut and strut brackets.

26. Install a suitable engine lifting device. Make certain that when installing chains to the cylinder heads that washers are used under the chains and bolt heads and that the bolts are torqued to 20 ft. lbs.

— CAUTION —
Failure to properly secure the engine lift to the aluminum cylinder heads can result in personal injury.

27. Position a support under the transaxle rear extension. *It may be necessary to raise the support as the engine is being removed.*

28. Remove the engine to transaxle bolts and remove the engine.

29. Installation is the reverse of removal. Note the following:

a. Before installing the flex plate-to-converter bolts, make sure that the weld nuts on the converter are flush with the flex plate, and the converter rotates freely by hand.

b. Use only new O-rings at all connections.

c. Adjust the throttle valve cable as outlined in the Automatic Transmission Unit Repair section.

Intake Manifold

REMOVAL & INSTALLATION

6-181

— CAUTION —
Bleed pressure from the fuel system, if equipped with fuel injection, before servicing.

1. Remove the air cleaner and the PCV valve.

2. Drain the cooling system into a clean container.

3. Disconnect the fuel and vacuum lines and the electrical connections at the carburetor and manifold.

4. Disconnect the throttle linkage at the EFI unit and disconnect the transaxle downshift linkage and cruise control linkage.

5. Remove the carburetor and the spacer.

6. Remove the bell crank and the throttle linkage. Position to the side for clearance.

7. Remove the heater hose at the intake manifold.

8. Remove the pulse air check valve bracket from the manifold.

9. Remove the manifold attaching bolts and remove the manifold.

6-173

1. Remove the rocker covers.

2. Drain the cooling system.

3. If equipped, remove the AIR pump and bracket.

4. Remove the distributor cap. Mark the position of the ignition rotor in relation to the distributor body, and remove the distributor. Do not crank the engine with the distributor removed.

5. Remove the heater and radiator hoses from the intake manifold.

6. Remove the power brake vacuum hose.

7. Disconnect and label the vacuum hoses. Remove the EFE pipe from the rear of the manifold.

8. Remove the carburetor linkage. Disconnect and plug the fuel line.

9. Remove the manifold retaining bolts and nuts.

10. Remove the intake manifold. Remove and discard the gaskets, and scrape off the old silicone seal from the front and rear ridges.

To install:

1. The gaskets are marked for right and left side installation; do not interchange them. Clean the sealing surface of the engine block, and apply a 3/16 in. bead of silicone sealer to each ridge.

2. Install the new gaskets onto the heads. The gaskets will have to be cut slightly to fit past the center pushrods. Do not cut any more material than necessary. Hold the gaskets in place by extending the ridge bead of sealer 1/4 in. onto the gasket ends.

3. Install the intake manifold. The area between the ridges and the manifold should be completely sealed.

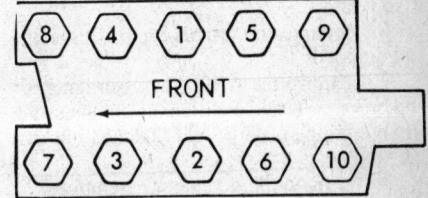

6-173 intake manifold torque sequence

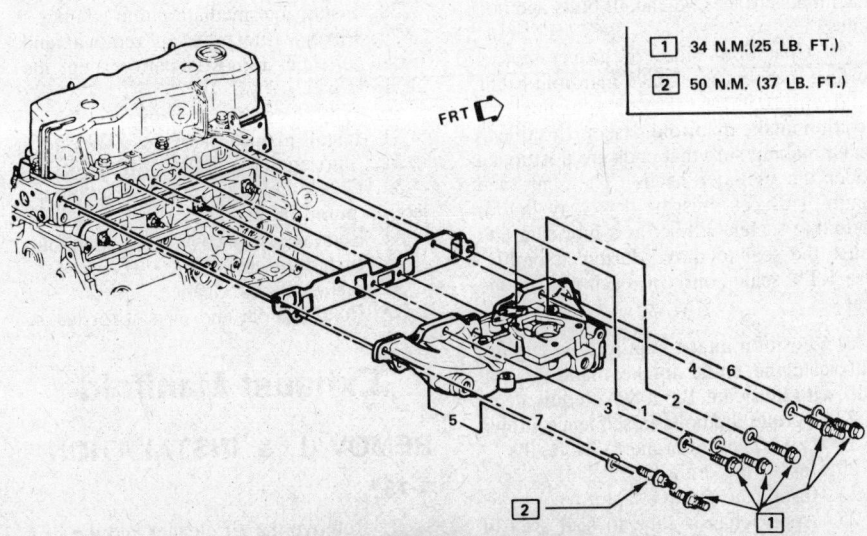

| 1 | 34 N.M. (25 LB. FT.) |
| 2 | 50 N.M. (37 LB. FT.) |

4-151 intake manifold torque sequence

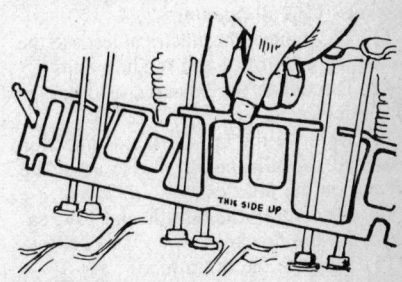

Cut the 6-173 intake manifold gasket as necessary

4. Install the retaining bolts and nuts, and tighten in sequence to 23 ft. lbs. Do not overtighten; the manifold is made from aluminum, and can be warped or cracked with excessive force.

5. The rest of installation is the reverse of removal. Adjust the ignition timing after installation, and check the coolant level after the engine has warmed up.

6-181 and 6-231

1. Disconnect the battery ground.
2. Drain the cooling system.
3. Remove the air cleaner.
4. Disconnect all hoses and wiring from the manifold.
5. Disconnect the accelerator linkage and cruise control chain.
6. Disconnect the fuel line at carburetor.
7. Remove the distributor cap and rotor and remove the Torx® head bolt from the left side of the manifold.
8. Unbolt and remove the manifold.
9. Installation is the reverse of removal. When installing the front and rear seals, make sure that the ends of the seals fit snugly against the block and head. Install nos. 1 & 2 bolts first and tighten them until snug, then install the other bolts in order.

6-263

NOTE: **This procedure requires the removal, disassembly draining and reassembly of the valve lifters. Read that procedure, later on, before continuing.**

1. Remove the air cleaner assembly.
2. Drain the radiator, then disconnect the upper radiator hose from the water outlet.
3. Disconnect the heater inlet hose from the outlet on the intake manifold and disconnect the heater outlet pipe from the intake manifold attachments and move it aside.
4. Remove air crossover and the fuel injection pump.
5. Disconnect wiring as necessary at the generator, A/C compressor and switches, if so equipped.
6. Remove the cruise control servo if so equipped.
7. Remove the A/C compressor bracket and brace bolts and position the compressor (if so equipped) with lines attached out of the way.
8. Remove the generator assembly.
9. Disconnect the engine mounting strut.
10. Remove the fuel lines, filter and brackets. Cap all openings.
11. Disconnect the electrical leads to the glow plug controller and sending units.
12. Disconnect the exhaust crossover pipe heat shield.
13. Remove the left (forward) injection lines and cap all openings. Use a backup wrench on the nozzles.
14. Disconnect the throttle and T.V. cables from the bracket.
15. Remove the drain tube.
16. Remove the intermediate pump adapter.

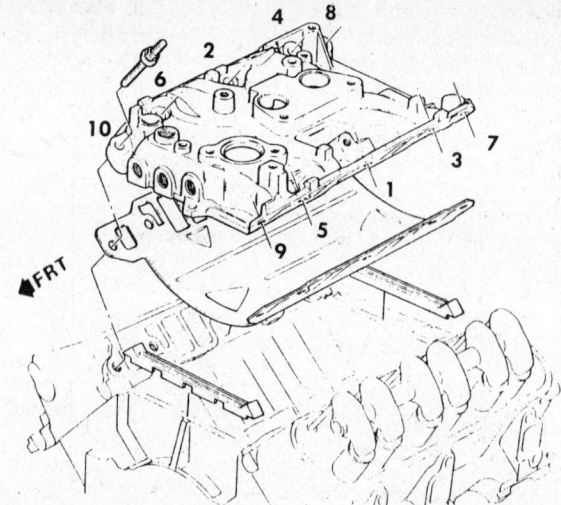

Intake manifold torque sequence—6-183 and 6-231

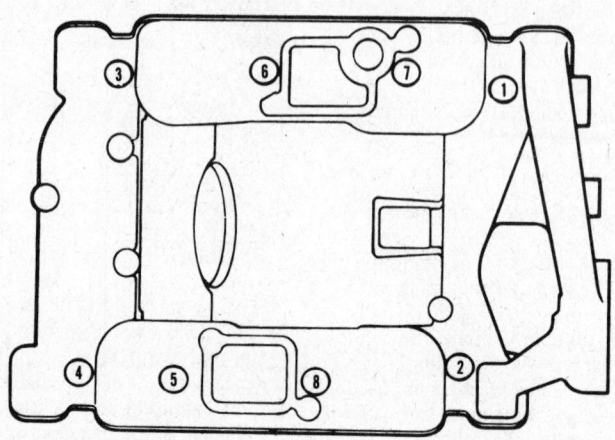

6-263 intake manifold torque sequence

17. Remove pump adapter and seal.
18. Remove the intake manifold.
19. Clean the machined surfaces of cylinder head and intake manifold with a putty knife. Use care not to gouge or scratch the machined surfaces. Clean all bolts and bolt holes.
20. Coat both sides of gasket sealing surface that seal the intake manifold to the head with 1050026 sealer or equivalent and position intake manifold gasket. Install end seals, making sure that ends are positioned under the cylinder heads. The seals and mating surfaces must be dry. Any liquid, including sealer will act as a lubricant and cause the seal to move during assembly. Use RTV sealer only on each end of the seal.
21. Position intake manifold on engine. Lubricate the entire intake manifold bolt (all) with lubricant 1052080 or equivalent.
22. Torque the bolts in sequence shown to 20 ft. lb. Then retorque to 41 ft. lbs.
23. Install the drain tube.
24. Install the pump adapter.
25. Apply chassis lube to seal area of intake manifold and pump adapter.

26. Apply chassis lube to inside and outside diameter of seal and seal area of tool J-28425.
27. Install seal on tool and install the seal.
28. Install intermediate pump adapter.
29. Reverse the order of removal and install all other removed parts except the air crossover.
30. Fill the cooling system.
31. Install manifold covers, J-29657.
32. Start engine and check for leaks.
33. Check and if necessary, reset the injection pump timing.
34. Remove screen covers from manifold.
35. Install air crossover.
36. Install the air cleaner.
37. Road test car and inspect for leaks.

Exhaust Manifold

REMOVAL & INSTALATION

4-151

1. Remove the air cleaner and the EFI pre-heat tube.

2. Remove the manifold strut bolts from the radiator support panel and the cylinder head.

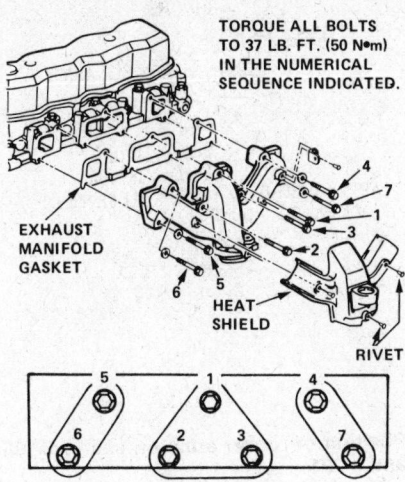

TORQUE ALL BOLTS TO 37 LB. FT. (50 N•m) IN THE NUMERICAL SEQUENCE INDICATED.

EXHAUST MANIFOLD GASKET

HEAT SHIELD

RIVET

BOLT LOCATIONS

4-151 exhaust manifold torque sequence

3. Remove the A/C compressor bracket to one side. Do not disconnect any of the refrigerant lines.
4. If necessary, remove the dipstick tube attaching bolt, and the engine mount bracket from the cylinder head.
5. Raise the car and disconnect the exhaust pipe from the manifold.
6. Remove the manifold attaching bolts and remove the manifold.
7. Reverse to install.

6-173
LEFT SIDE
1. Remove the air cleaner. Remove the carburetor heat stove pipe.
2. Remove the air supply plumbing from the exhaust manifold.
3. Raise and support the car. Unbolt and remove the exhaust pipe at the manifold.
4. Unbolt and remove the manifold.
To install:
1. Clean the mating surfaces of the cylinder head and manifold. Install the manifold onto the head, and install the retaining bolts finger tight.
2. Tighten the manifold bolts in a circular pattern, working from the center to the ends, to 25 ft. lbs. in two stages.
3. Connect the exhaust pipe to the manifold.
4. The remainder of installation is the reverse of removal.

RIGHT SIDE
1. Raise and support the car.
2. Tighten the exhaust pipe-to-manifold flange bolts until they break off. Remove the pipe from the manifold. Later models are equipped with flange bolts.
3. Lower the car. Remove the spark plug wires from the plugs. Number them first if they are not already labeled.

4. Remove the air supply pipes from the manifold. Remove the PULSAIR bracket bolt from the rocker cover, on models so equipped, then remove the pipe assembly.
5. Remove the manifold retaining bolts and remove the manifold.
To install:
1. Clean the mating surfaces of the cylinder head and manifold. Position the manifold against the head and install the retaining bolts finger tight.
2. Tighten the bolts in a circular pattern, working from the center to the ends, to 25 ft. lbs. in two stages.
3. Install the air supply system.
4. Install the spark plug wires.
5. Raise and support the car. Connect the exhaust pipe to the manifold and install new flange bolts.

6-181 and 6-231
RIGHT SIDE
1. Disconnect the battery ground.
2. Remove the pinch bolt at the steering gear intermediate shaft and separate the intermediate shaft from the stub shaft.

— **CAUTION** —
Failure to disconnect the intermediate shaft from the rack and pinion stub shaft can result in damage to the steering gear and/or intermediate shaft. This damage can cause loss of steering control which could result in a vehicle crash with possible bodily injury.

3. Raise and support the car on jackstands.
4. Unbolt the exhaust pipe from the manifold.
5. Lower the car.
6. Remove the upper engine support strut.
7. Place a floor jack under the front crossmember and take up the weight of the car.
8. Remove the two front body mount bolts along with their cushions and retainers.
9. Remove the cushions from the bolts and thread the bolts and their retainers a minimum of three turns into the cradle cage nuts so that the bolts serve to hold the cradle and prevent movement.
10. Lower the floor jack so that the crossmember contacts the body mount bolt retainers. Check for any hose or wire interference problems.
11. Remove the alternator, disconnect the power steering pump and remove its bracket.
12. Disconnect the manifold from the crossover pipe.
13. Unbolt and remove the manifold.
14. Installation is the reverse of removal.

LEFT SIDE
1. Disconnect the battery ground.
2. Unbolt and remove the crossover pipe.
3. Remove the upper engine support strut.

4. Unbolt and remove the manifold.
5. Installation is the reverse of removal.

6-263
LEFT SIDE
1. Remove the crossover pipe from the manifolds.
2. Raise and support the car on jackstands.
3. Unbolt and remove the manifold.
4. Installation is the reverse of removal. Lubricate the entire length of each manifold bolt with lubricant 1052080 or its equivalent.

RIGHT SIDE
1. Remove the engine support strut.
2. Place a floor jack under the front crossmember and take up the weight of the car.
3. Remove the two front body mount bolts. Remove the cushions from the bolts.
4. Thread the body mount bolts with their retainers into the cage nuts so that the bolts restrict movement of the engine cradle.
5. Lower the jack until the crossmember contacts the body mount bolt retainers. Check for any hose or wire interference.
6. Remove the crossover pipe.
7. Raise and support the car on jackstands.
8. Disconnect the exhaust pipe from the manifold.
9. Lower the car.
10. Unbolt and remove the manifold.
11. Installation is the reverse of removal. Lubricate the entire length of each manifold bolt with lubricant 1052080 or its equivalent.

Valve Guides
RECONDITIONING

Valve guides on all engines are integral with the cylinder head. Worn guides can be reamed to accept oversized valve stems, or knurled to retain original sized stems. See the chart at the beginning of this section to determine the original stem diameter.

Rocker Arm, Shaft and Pushrod
REMOVAL & INSTALLATION
4-151
1. Remove the valve cover.
2. On fuel injected engines, see the fuel pump section to relieve pressure in the fuel system before disconnecting any fuel lines.
3. If only the pushrod is being removed, loosen the rocker arm bolt and swing the rocker arm aside.
4. Remove the rocker arm nut and ball.
5. Lift the rocker arm off the stud, keeping rocker arms in order for installation.

C541

6. Installation is the reverse of removal. Tighten the rocker arm bolt to 20 ft. lb.; the rocker cover to 5 ft. lb.

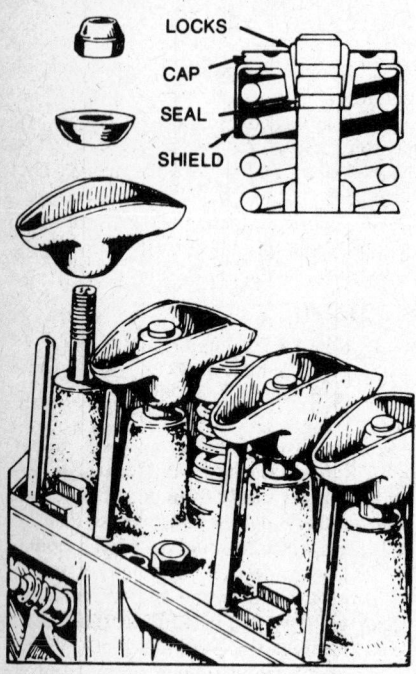

4-151 and 6-173 rocker arm, pivot and nut

6-173

NOTE: Some engines are assembled using RTV (Room Temperature Vulcanizing) silicone sealant in place of rocker arm cover gasket. If the engine was assembled using RTV, never use a gasket when reassembling. Conversely, if the engine was assembled using a rocker arm cover gasket, never replace it with RTV.

When using RTV, an ⅛ in. bead is sufficient. Always run the bead on the inside of the bolt holes.

Rocker arms are removed by removing the adjusting nut. Be sure to adjust valve lash after replacing rocker arms.

NOTE: When replacing an exhaust rocker, move an old intake rocker arm to the exhaust rocker arm stud and install the new rocker arm on the intake stud.

Cylinder heads use threaded rocker arm studs. If the threads in the head are damaged or stripped, the head can be retapped and a helical type insert installed.

NOTE: If engine is equipped with the A.I.R. exhaust emission control system, the interfering components of the system must be removed. Disconnect the lines at the air injection nozzles in the exhaust manifolds.

6-181 and 6-231

1. Remove the rocker arm cover(s).
2. Remove the rocker arm shaft(s).

3. Place the shaft on a clean surface.
4. Remove the nylon rocker arm retainers. A pair of slip joint pliers is good for this.
5. Slide the rocker arms off the shaft and inspect them for wear or damage. Keep them in order!
6. Installation is the reverse of removal. If new rocker arms are being installed, note that they are stamped R (right) or L (left). Each rocker arm must be centered over its oil hole. New nylon retainers must be used.

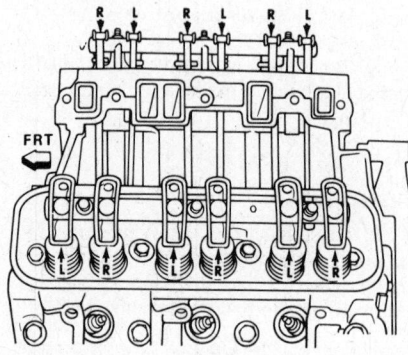

6-263

NOTE: This procedure requires that the valve lifters be bled!

1. Remove the valve cover(s). See the Valve Cover procedure.
2. Remove the rocker arm nuts, pivot and rocker arms.
3. If rocker arms are being replaced, they must be replaced in cylinder sets. Never replace just one rocker arm per cylinder! If a stud was replaced, coat the threads with locking compound and torque it to 11 ft. lb.
4. Installation is the reverse of removal. See the section on Valve lifter bleeddown. This is absolutely necessary! If lifters are not bled, engine damage will be unavoidable! Torque the rocker arm nuts to 28 ft. lbs.; the cover to 5 ft. lb.

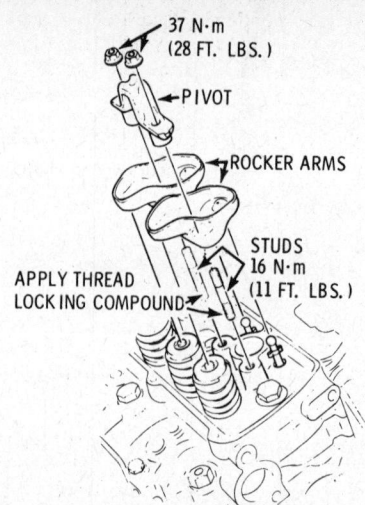

Position of rocker arms on shaft—6-183 and 6-231

Diesel Engine Right Side Valve Cover

REMOVAL & INSTALLATION

1. Remove the injection lines. See the Injection Line procedure, earlier in this section.
2. Disconnect the crankcase ventilation pipes, grommets, filter and crankcase depression regulator valve.
3. Remove the engine support strut.
4. Place a floor jack under the front crossmember and take up the weight of the engine.
5. Remove the two front body mount bolts. Remove the cushions from the bolts and thread the bolts and retainers into the cage nuts to restrict engine cradle movement.
6. Lower the jack until the crossmember contacts the body mount bolt retainers.
7. Remove the valve cover.
8. Installation is the reverse of removal. These covers are installed with a ⅛ in. bead of RTV gasket material in place of a gasket. Coat each bolt with 1052080 lubricant.

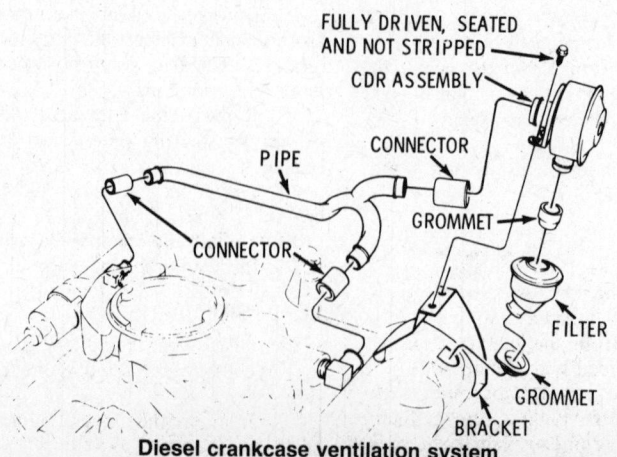

Diesel crankcase ventilation system

Diesel Engine Valve Lifter Bleed-Down

If the intake manifold and valve rocker arms have been removed, it will be necessary to remove, disassemble, drain and reassemble the lifters on that side. If the rocker arms have been loosened or removed, but the intake manifold was not removed, skip down to the Bleed-Down procedure.

REMOVAL

Keep lifters and pushrods in order! This is absolutely necessary for installation, since these parts have differences which could result in engine damage if not installed in their original positions!

1. Remove intake manifold. Refer to "Intake Manifold".
2. Remove valve covers, rocker arm assemblies and pushrods.
3. Remove the valve lifter guide retainer bolts.
4. Remove the retainer guides and valve lifters.

DISASSEMBLY

1. Remove the retainer ring with a small screwdriver.
2. Remove pushrod seat and oil metering valve.
3. Remove plunger and plunger spring.
4. Remove check valve retainer from plunger, then remove valve and spring.

CLEANING & INSPECTION

After lifters are disassembled, all parts should be cleaned in clean solvent. A small particle of foreign material under the check valve will cause malfunctioning of the lifter. Close inspection should be made for nicks, burrs or scoring of parts. If either the roller body or plunger is defective, replace with a new lifter assembly. Whenever lifters are removed, check as follows:

1. Roller should rotate freely, but without excessive play.
2. Check for missing or broken needle bearings.
3. Roller should be free of pits or roughness. If present, check camshaft for similar condition. If pits or roughness are evident replace lifter and camshaft.

ASSEMBLY

1. Coat all lifter parts with a coating of clean kerosene or diesel fuel.
2. Assemble the ball check, spring and retainer into the plunger.
3. Install plunger spring over check retainer.
4. Hold plunger with spring up and insert into lifter body. Hold plunger vertically to prevent cocking spring.

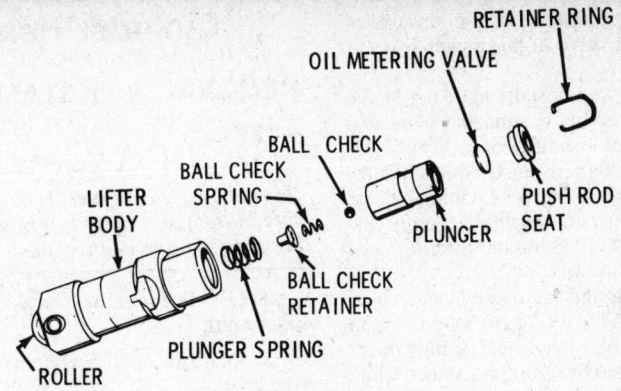

Valve lifter disassembled

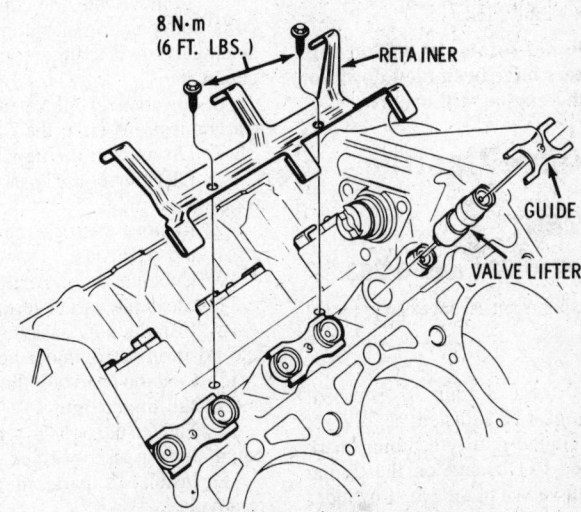

Diesel valve lifters, guides and retainers

5. Submerge the lifter in clean kerosene or diesel fuel.
6. Install oil metering valve and push rod seat into lifter and install retaining ring.

INSTALLATION

Prime new lifters by working lifter plunger while submerged in clean kerosene or diesel fuel. Lifter could be damaged when starting engine if dry.

1. When the rocker arm is loosened or removed, valve lifter bleed down is required. Lifters must be bled down as possible valve to piston interference due to the close tolerances could exist. Before installing a new or used lifter in the engine, lubricate the roller and bearings of the lifter with No. 1052365 lubricant.
2. Install lifters and pushrods into the original position in cylinder block. See note under "Removal."
3. Install manifold gaskets and manifold.
4. Position rocker arms, pivots and bolts on cylinder head.
5. Install valve covers.
6. Install intake manifold assembly.

BLEED–DOWN

1. Before installing any removed rocker arms, rotate the engine crankshaft to a position of No. 1 cylinder being 32° BTDC. This is a 50 mm (2") counterclockwise from the 0° pointer. If only the right valve cover was removed, remove No. 1 cylinder's glow plug to determine if the position of the piston is the correct one. The compression pressure will tell you that you are in the right position.

If the left valve cover was removed, rotate the crankshaft until the number 5 cylinder intake valve pushrod ball is 7.0mm (.28 in.) above the number 5 cylinder exhaust valve pushrod ball.

NOTE: Use only hand wrenches to torque the rocker arm pivot nuts to avoid engine damage.

2. If removed, install the No. 5 cylinder pivot and rocker arms. Torque the nuts alternately between the intake and exhaust valves until the intake valve begins to open, then stop.

3. Install remaining rocker arms except No. 3 exhaust valve (if this rocker arm was removed).

4. If removed, install but do not torque No. 3 valve pivots beyond the point that the valve would be fully open. This is indicated by strong resistance while still turning the pivot retaining bolts. Going beyond this would bend the pushrod. Torque the nuts SLOWLY allowing the lifter to bleed down.

5. Finish torquing No. 5 cylinder rocker arm pivot nut SLOWLY. Do not go beyond the point that the valve would be fully open. This is indicated by strong resistance while still turning the pivot retaining bolts. Going beyond this would bend the pushrod.

6. DO NOT turn the engine crankshaft for at least 45 minutes.

7. Finish reassembling the engine as the lifters are being bled.

NOTE: Do not rotate the engine until the valve lifters have been bled down, or damage to the engine will occur.

Valve Lash

ADJUSTMENT

4-151, 6-181, 6-231 and 6-263

No routine adjustment is necessary.

6-173

Anytime the V6 valve train is disturbed, the valve lash must be adjusted, as follows:

Crank the engine until the timing mark aligns with the "O" mark on the timing scale, and both valves in the No. 1 cylinder are closed. If the valves are moving as the timing marks align, the engine is in the No. 4 firing position. Turn the crankshaft one more revolution. With the engine in the No. 1 firing position, adjust the following valves:

- Exhaust—1,2,3
- Intake—1,5,6

Rotate the crankshaft one full revolution, until it is in the No. 4 firing position. Adjust the following valves:

- Exhaust—4,5,6
- Intake—2,3,4

Adjustment is made by backing off the rocker arm adjusting nut until there is play in the pushrod. Tighten the nut to remove the pushrod clearance (this can be determined by rotating the pushrod with your fingers while tightening the adjusting nut). When the pushrod cannot be freely turned, tighten the nut 1½ additional turns to place the hydraulic lifter in the center of its travel. No further adjustment is required.

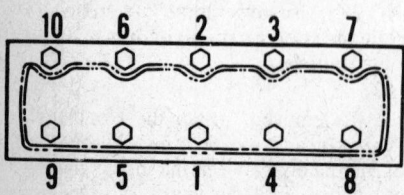

4-151 head bolt torque sequence

Cylinder Head

REMOVAL & INSTALLATION

4-151

---CAUTION---

On fuel injected engines, relieve the pressure in the fuel system before disconnecting any fuel line connections.

NOTE: The engine should be overnight cold.

1. Drain the cooling system into a clean container.
2. Remove the air cleaner.
3. Remove the intake and exhaust manifolds as previously outlined.
4. Remove the alternator bracket bolts.
5. Remove the A/C compressor bracket bolts and position the compressor to one side. Do not disconnect any of the refrigerant lines.
6. Disconnect all vacuum and electrical connections from the cylinder head.
7. Disconnect the upper radiator hose.
8. Disconnect the spark plug wires and remove the plugs.
9. Remove the rocker arm cover, rocker arms, and pushrods.
10. Unbolt and remove the cylinder head.
11. Clean the gasket surfaces thoroughly.
12. Install a new gasket over the dowels and position the cylinder head.
13. Coat the head bolt threads with sealer and install finger tight.
14. Tighten the bolts in sequence, in three equal steps to the specified torque.
15. Install all parts in the reverse of removal.

6-173

LEFT SIDE

1. Raise and support the car.
2. Drain the coolant from the block and lower the car.
3. Remove the intake manifold.
4. Remove the crossover.
5. Remove the alternator and AIR pump brackets.
6. Remove the dipstick tube.
7. Loosen the rocker arm bolts and remove the pushrods. Keep the pushrods in the same order as removed.
8. Remove the cylinder head bolts in stages and in the reverse order of the tightening sequence.
9. Remove the cylinder head. Do not pry on the head to loosen it.
10. Installation is the reverse of removal.

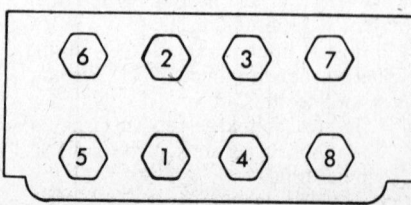

6-173 head bolt torque sequence

The words "This side Up" on the new cylinder head gasket should face upward. Coat the cylinder head bolts with sealer and torque to specifications in the sequence shown. Make sure the pushrods seat in the lifter seats and adjust the valves.

RIGHT SIDE

1. Raise the car and drain the coolant from the block.
2. Disconnect the exhaust pipe and lower the car.
3. If equipped, remove the cruise control servo bracket.
4. Remove the air management valve and hose.
5. Remove the intake manifold.
6. Remove the exhaust crossover.
7. Loosen the rocker arm nuts and remove the pushrods. Keep the pushrods in the order in which they were removed.
8. Remove the cylinder head bolts in stages and in the reverse order of the tightening sequence.
9. Remove the cylinder head. Do not pry on the cylinder head to loosen it.
10. Installation is the reverse of removal. The words "This Side Up" on the new cylinder head gasket should face upwards. Coat the cylinder head bolts with sealer and tighten them to specifications in the sequence shown. Make sure the lower ends of the pushrods seat in the lifter seats and adjust the valves.

6-181 and 6-231

1. Disconnect negative battery cable.
2. Remove intake manifold.
3. Loosen and remove belt(s).
4. When removing LEFT cylinder head;
   a. Remove oil dipstick.
   b. Remove air and vacuum pumps with mounting bracket if present, and move out of the way with hoses attached
5. When removing RIGHT cylinder head;
   a. Remove alternator.
   b. Disconnect power steering gear pump and brackets attached to cylinder head.
6. Disconnect wires from spark plugs, and remove the spark plug wire clips from the rocker arm cover studs.
7. Remove exhaust manifold bolts from head being removed.
8. With air hose and cloths, clean dirt off cylinder head and adjacent area to avoid getting dirt into engine. *It is extremely important to avoid getting dirt into the hydraulic valve lifters.*
9. Remove rocker arm cover and rocker arm and shaft assembly from cylinder head. Lift out pushrods.

If lifters are to be serviced, remove them at this time and place them in a container with numbered holes or a similar device, to keep them identified as to engine position. If they are not to be removed, protect lifters and camshaft from dirt by covering area with a clean cloth.

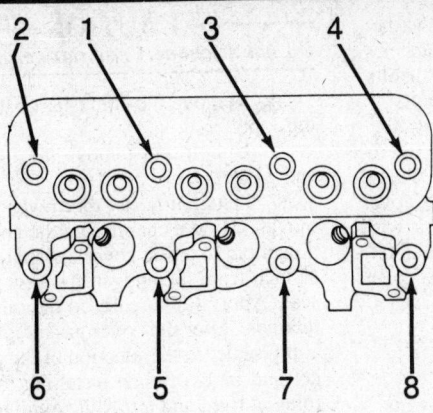

Head bolt torque sequence—6-183 and 6-231

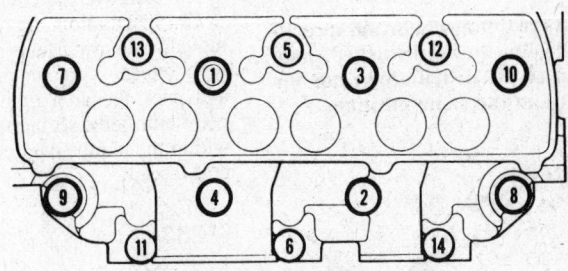

6-263 head bolt torque sequence

10. Loosen all cylinder head bolts, then remove bolts and lift off the cylinder head.

11. With cylinder head on bench, remove all spark plugs for cleaning and to avoid damaging them during work on the head.

12. Installation is the reverse of removal. Clean all gasket surfaces thoroughly. Always use a new head gasket. The head gasket is installed with the bead downward. Coat the head bolt threads with thread sealer. Torque the head bolts in three equal stages. Recheck head bolt torque after the engine has been warmed to operating temperature.

6-263

NOTE: This procedure requires the complete disassembly of the valve lifters as explained under "Diesel Engine Valve Lifter Bleed-Down".

1. Remove intake manifold.
2. Remove valve cover. Loosen or remove any accessory brackets or pipe clamps which interfere.
3. Disconnect glow plug wiring (and block heater lead if so equipped on rear bank).
4. Remove the ground strap from right (rear) cylinder head.
5. Remove rocker arm nuts, pivots, rocker arms and pushrods. Scribe pivots and keep rocker arms separated so they can be installed in their original locations.
6. Disconnect the exhaust crossover pipe from the exhaust manifold on the side being worked on and loosen it on the other.
7. Remove engine block drain plug, from side of the block where head is being removed.
8. Remove the pipe plugs covering the upper cylinder head bolts.
9. Remove all the cylinder head bolts and remove the cylinder head.
10. If necessary to remove the prechamber, remove the glow plug and injection nozzle, then tap out with a small blunt ⅛ in. drift. Do NOT use a tapered drift.

11. Installation is the reverse of removal. Do not use sealer on the head gasket. If a pre-chamber was replaced, measure the chamber height and grind the new one to within 0.001 in. of the old chamber's height, using #80 grit wet sandpaper to polish it. Coat the head bolts with sealer.

Timing Gear Cover

REMOVAL & INSTALLATION
4–151

— CAUTION —

On fuel injected engines, relieve the pressure in the fuel system before disconnecting the fuel line connections.

1. Remove the crankshaft hub. It is necessary to remove the inner fender splash shield.
2. Remove the alternator lower bracket.
3. Remove the front engine mounts.
4. Using a floor jack, raise the engine.
5. Remove the engine mount mounting bracket-to-cylinder block bolts. Remove the bracket and mount as an assembly.
6. Remove the oil pan-to-front cover screws.
7. Remove the front cover-to-block screws.
8. Pull the cover slightly forward, just enough to allow cutting of the oil pan front seal flush with the block on both sides.
9. Remove the front cover and attached portion of the pan seal.
10. Clean the gasket surfaces thoroughly.
11. Cut the tabs from the new oil pan front seal.
12. Install the seal on the front cover, pressing the tips into the holes provided.
13. Coat the new gasket with sealer and position it on the front cover.
14. Apply a ⅛ in. bead of silicone sealer to the joint formed at the oil pan and block.
15. Align the front cover seal with a centering tool and install the front cover. Tighten the screws. Install the hub.

6–173

— CAUTION —

The outer ring (weight) of the harmonic balancer is bonded to the hub with rubber. Breakage may occur if the balancer is hammered back onto the crankshaft. A press or special installation tool is necessary.

1. Remove the water pump.
2. Remove the compressor without disconnecting any A/C lines and lay it aside.
3. Remove harmonic balancer, using a puller.

NOTE: The outer ring (weight) of the harmonic balancer is bonded to the hub with rubber. The balancer must be removed with a puller which acts on the inner hub only. Pulling on the outer portion of the balancer will break the rubber bond or destroy the tuning of the torsional damper.

4. Disconnect the lower radiator hose and heater hose.
5. Remove timing gear cover attaching screws, and cover and gasket.
6. Clean all the gasket mounting surfaces on the front cover and block. Apply a continuous 3/32 in. bead of sealer (1052357 or equivalent) to front cover sealing surface and around coolant passage ports and central bolt holes.
7. Apply a bead of silicone sealer to the oil pan-to-cylinder block joint.
8. Install a centering tool in the crankshaft snout hole in the front cover and install the cover.
9. Install the front cover bolts finger tight, remove the centering tool and tighten the cover bolts. Install the harmonic balancer, pulley, water pump, belts, radiator, and all other parts.

6–181 and 6–231

1. Drain the cooling system.
2. Disconnect the lower radiator hose and the heater hose at the water pump.
3. Remove the two nuts from the front engine mount at the cradle and raise the

engine using a suitable lifting device.

4. Remove the water pump pulley and all drive belts.

5. Remove the alternator and brackets.

6. Remove the distributor.

NOTE: If the timing chain and sprockets are not going to be disturbed, note the position of the distributor rotor for reinstallation in the same position.

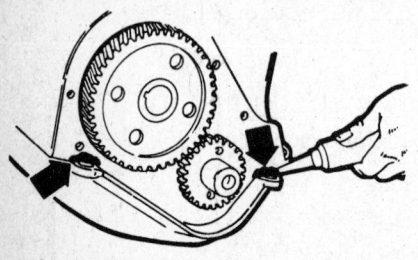

Apply sealant where shown on the 4-151

7. Remove the balancer bolt and washer, and using a puller, remove the balancer.

8. Remove the cover-to-block bolts. Remove the two oil pan-to-cover bolts.

9. Remove the cover and gasket.

10. Installation is the reverse of removal. Always use a new gasket coated with sealer. Remove the oil pump cover and pack the area around the gears with petroleum jelly so that no air space is left within the pump. Apply sealer to the cover bolt threads.

6-263

1. Drain the cooling system.

2. Disconnect the lower radiator hose and the heater hose at the water pump. Disconnect the heater outlet pipe at the manifold.

3. Disconnect the power steering pump, vacuum pump, belt tensioner, air conditioning compressor and alternator brackets.

---- **CAUTION** ----
Do not disconnect any refrigerant lines.

4. Remove the crankshaft balancer using a puller.

5. Unbolt and remove the front cover and gasket.

6. Installation is the reverse of removal. Grind a chamfer on the end of each dowel pin to aid in cover installation. Trim ⅛ inch from the ends of the new front pan seal. Apply RTV sealer to the oil pan seal retainer. After the cover gasket is in place, apply sealer to the junction of the pan, gasket and block. When installing the cover, rotate it right and left while guiding the pan seal into place with a small screwdriver.

Timing Gear and/or Chain

REMOVAL & INSTALLATION
4-151

See the camshaft removal and installation procedure.

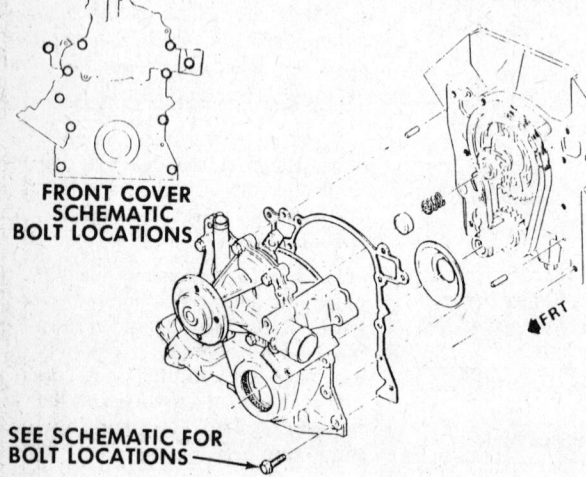

FRONT COVER SCHEMATIC BOLT LOCATIONS

SEE SCHEMATIC FOR BOLT LOCATIONS

Timing cover removal—6-183 and 6-231

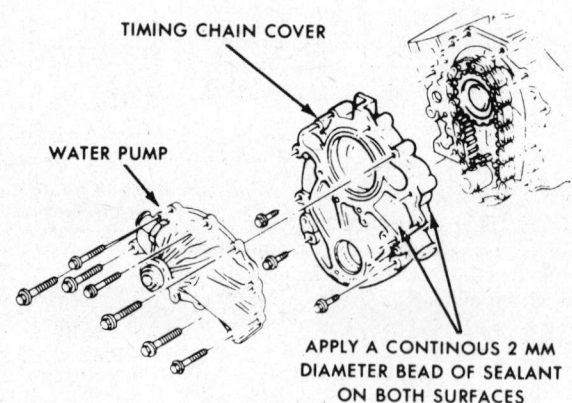

TIMING CHAIN COVER

WATER PUMP

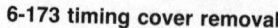

APPLY A CONTINOUS 2 MM DIAMETER BEAD OF SEALANT ON BOTH SURFACES

6-173 timing cover removal

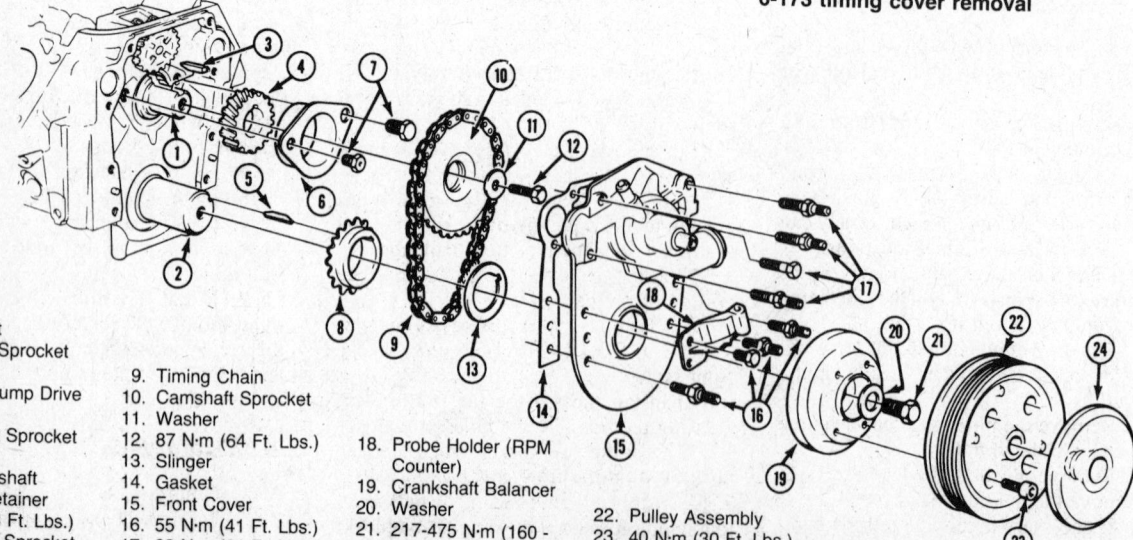

1. Camshaft
2. Crankshaft
3. Camshaft Sprocket Key
4. Injection Pump Drive Gear
5. Crankshaft Sprocket Key
6. Front Camshaft Bearing Retainer
7. 65 N·m (48 Ft. Lbs.)
8. Crankshaft Sprocket

9. Timing Chain
10. Camshaft Sprocket
11. Washer
12. 87 N·m (64 Ft. Lbs.)
13. Slinger
14. Gasket
15. Front Cover
16. 55 N·m (41 Ft. Lbs.)
17. 28 N·m (21 Ft. Lbs.)

18. Probe Holder (RPM Counter)
19. Crankshaft Balancer
20. Washer
21. 217-475 N·m (160 - 350 Ft. Lbs.)

22. Pulley Assembly
23. 40 N·m (30 Ft. Lbs.)
24. Cover

6-263 timing cover and chain removal

6-173

To replace the chain, remove the crankcase front cover. This will allow access to the timing chain. Crank the engine until the marks punched on both sprockets are closest to one another and in line between the shaft centers. Take out the three bolts that hold the camshaft sprocket to the camshaft. This sprocket is a light press fit on the camshaft and will come off readily. It is located by a dowel. The chain comes off with the camshaft sprocket. A gear puller will be required to remove the crankshaft sprocket.

Without disturbing the position of the engine, mount the new crank sprocket on the shaft, then mount the chain over the camshaft sprocket. Arrange the camshaft sprocket in such a way that the timing marks will line up between the shaft centers and the camshaft locating dowel will enter the dowel hole in the cam sprocket.

Place the cam sprocket, with its chain mounted over it, in position on the front of the camshaft and pull up with the three bolts that hold it to the camshaft.

After the sprockets are in place, turn the engine two full revolutions to make certain that the timing marks are in correct alignment between the shaft centers.

6-181 and 6-231

1. Remove the timing chain cover as outlined earlier.
2. Turn the crankshaft so that the timing marks are aligned.
3. Remove the crankshaft oil slinger.
4. Remove the camshaft sprocket bolts.
5. Use two prybars to alternately pry the camshaft and crankshaft sprocket free along with the chain.
6. Installation is the reverse of removal. If the engine was turned, make sure that the No. 1 cylinder is at TDC.

6-263

NOTE: The following procedure requires the bleed-down of the valve lifters. Read that procedure before proceeding.

1. Remove the front cover.
2. Loosen all the rocker arms. See Rocker Arm Removal and Installation.
3. Remove the crankshaft oil slinger.
4. Remove the camshaft sprocket bolt.
5. Using two prybars, work the camshaft and crankshaft sprockets alternately off their shafts along with the chain. It may be necessary to remove the crankshaft sprocket with a puller.

6. Installation is the reverse of removal. If the engine was turned, make sure that the No. 1 piston is at TDC. Bleed the lifters following the procedure under "Diesel Engine Valve Lifter Bleed-Down."

Oil Seal

REMOVAL & INSTALLATION

1. After removing the timing cover, pry oil seal out of front of cover.
2. Install new lip seal with lip (open side of seal) inside and drive or press seal carefully into place.

NOTE: The timing cover oil seal can be replaced without removing the cover. Remove the fan belts, crankshaft pulley and harmonic balancer. Pry the oil seal out the cover working carefully to prevent damage to the seal mating surface. Lubricate the new seal and drive it into place with the open side toward the engine. Use a seal installer to avoid damaging or cocking the seal.

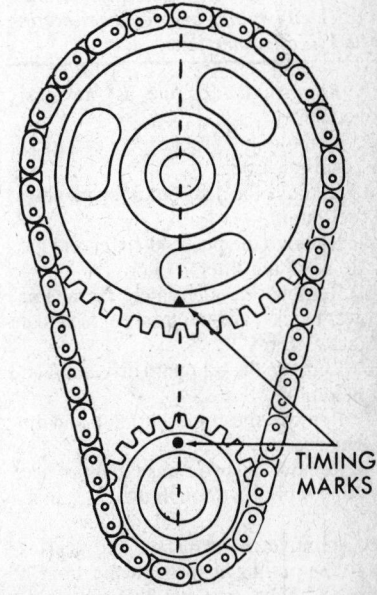

Timing gear alignment—6-183 and 6-231

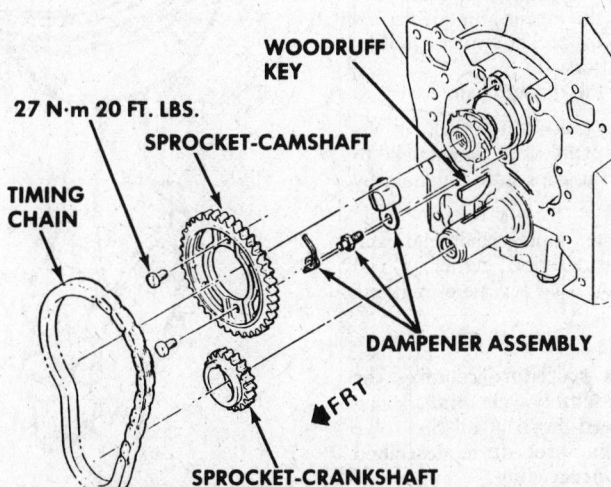

Timing chain and sprockets—6-183 and 6-231

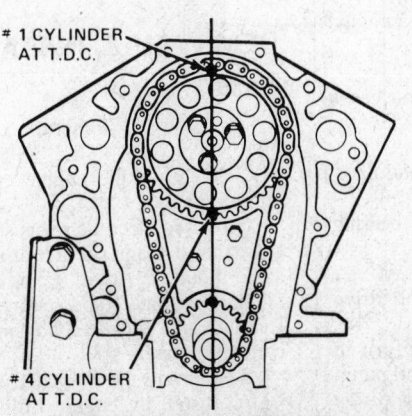

6-173 timing gear alignment

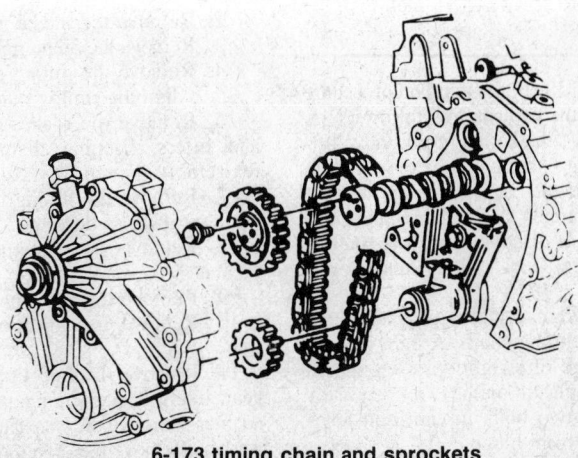

6-173 timing chain and sprockets

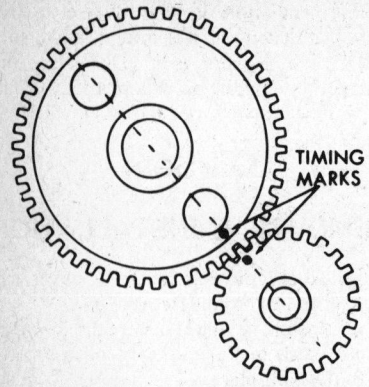

4-151 timing gear alignment

Camshaft

REMOVAL & INSTALLATION

4-151

— CAUTION —

Relieve the pressure in the EFI system on fuel injected engines before disconnecting the fuel line connections.

1. Remove the engine as previously outlined.
2. Remove the rocker cover, rocker arms, and pushrods.
3. Remove the distributor, spark plugs, and fuel pump.
4. Remove the pushrod cover and gasket. Remove the lifters.
5. Remove the alternator, the alternator lower bracket and the front engine mount bracket assembly.
6. Remove the oil pump driveshaft and gear assembly.
7. Remove the crankshaft hub and timing gear cover.
8. Remove the two camshaft thrust plate screws by working through the holes in the gear.
9. Remove the camshaft and gear assembly by pulling it through the front of the block. Take care not to damage the bearings.
10. Install in the reverse order. Torque the thrust plate screws to 75 inch lbs.

6-173

Follow the 6-173 engine removal procedure then remove the camshaft as follows:
1. Remove intake manifold, valve lifters and timing chain cover as described in this section. If the car is equipped with air conditioning, unbolt the condenser and move it aside *without disconnecting any lines*.
2. Remove fuel pump and pump pushrod.
3. Remove camshaft sprocket bolts, sprocket and timing chain. A light blow to the lower edge of a tight sprocket should free it (use a plastic mallet).
4. Install two bolts in cam bolt holes and pull cam from block.

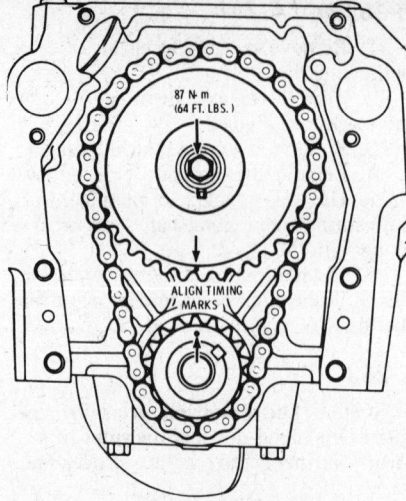

6-263 timing gear alignment

5. To install, reverse removal procedure aligning the sprocket timing marks.

6-181 and 6-231

1. Remove the engine as described earlier.
2. Remove the intake manifold.
3. Remove the rocker arm covers.
4. Remove the rocker arm assemblies, pushrods and lifters.
5. Remove the timing chain cover.

NOTE: Align the timing marks of the camshaft and crankshaft sprockets to avoid burring the camshaft journals by the crankshaft.

6. Remove the timing chain and camshaft sprocket as described earlier.
7. Installation is the reverse of removal.

6-263

NOTE: This procedure requires the removal, disassembly, cleaning, reassembly and bleed-down of all the valve lifters. Read that procedure, described earlier, before proceeding.

1. Remove the engine as described earlier.
2. Remove the intake manifold.
3. Remove the oil pump drive assembly.
4. Remove the timing chain cover.
5. Align the timing marks.
6. Remove the rocker arms, pushrods and lifters, keeping them in order for reassembly.
7. Remove the timing chain and camshaft sprocket as described earlier.
8. Remove the camshaft bearing retainer.
9. Remove the cam sprocket key.
10. Remove the injection pump drive gear.
11. Remove the injection pump driven gear, intermediate pump adapter and pump adapter. Remove the snap ring and selective washer. Remove the driven gear and spring.

12. Carefully slide the camshaft out of the block.
13. If the camshaft bearings are being replaced, you'll have to remove the oil pan.
14. Installation is the reverse of removal. Perform the complete valve lifter bleed-down procedure mentioned earlier.

Piston and Connecting Rod Positioning

See the accompanying illustrations to properly install piston and connecting rod assemblies.

On all engines, the piston assemblies are installed with the notch facing forward

Oil Pan

REMOVAL & INSTALLATION

4-151

1. Raise and support the car. Drain the oil.
2. Remove the engine cradle-to-front engine mounts.
3. Disconnect the exhaust pipe at both the exhaust manifold and at the rear transaxle mount.
4. Disconnect and remove the starter. Remove the flywheel housing or torque converter cover.
5. Remove the alternator upper bracket.
6. Install an engine lifting chain and raise the engine.

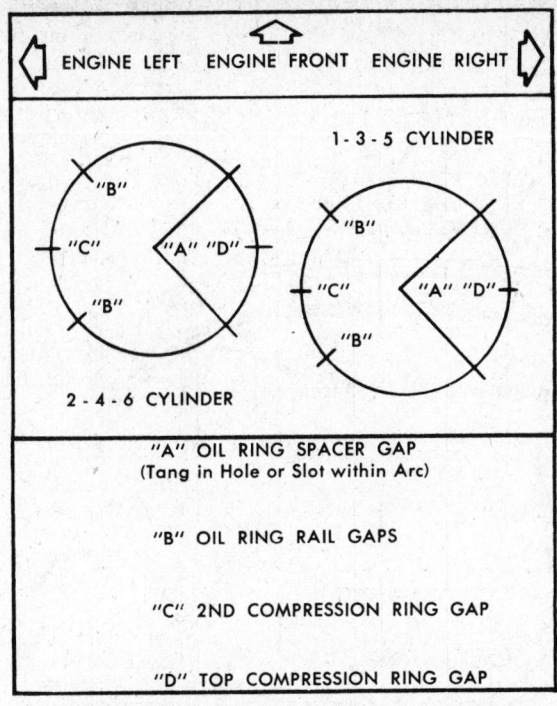

1 - 3 - 5 CYLINDER

2 - 4 - 6 CYLINDER

"A" OIL RING SPACER GAP
(Tang in Hole or Slot within Arc)

"B" OIL RING RAIL GAPS

"C" 2ND COMPRESSION RING GAP

"D" TOP COMPRESSION RING GAP

Arrange the piston rings on all V6 engines as shown

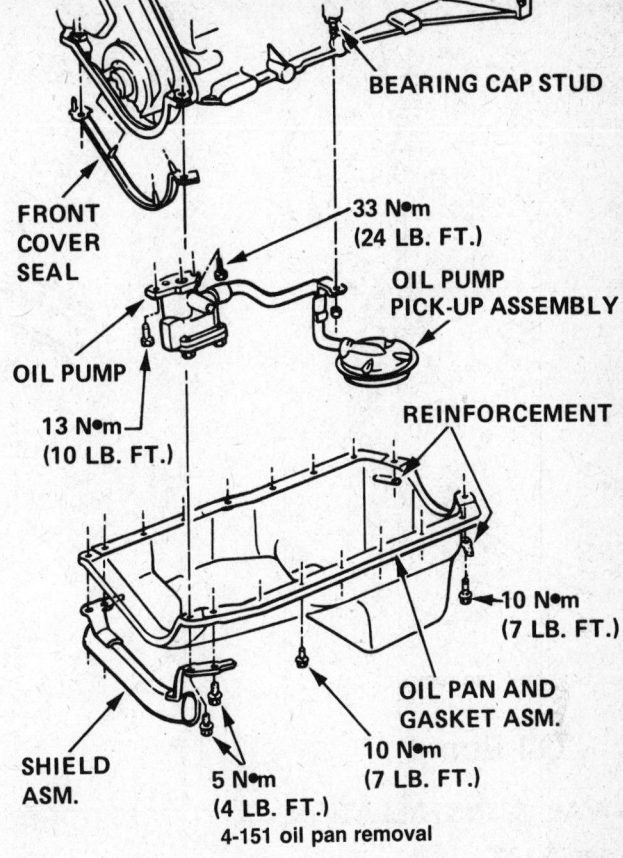

BEARING CAP STUD

FRONT COVER SEAL

33 N•m (24 LB. FT.)

OIL PUMP PICK-UP ASSEMBLY

OIL PUMP

13 N•m (10 LB. FT.)

REINFORCEMENT

10 N•m (7 LB. FT.)

OIL PAN AND GASKET ASM.

SHIELD ASM.

5 N•m (4 LB. FT.)

10 N•m (7 LB. FT.)

4-151 oil pan removal

7. Remove the lower alternator bracket. Remove the engine support bracket.

8. Remove the oil pan retaining bolts and remove the pan.

9. Reverse the procedure to install. Clean all gasket surfaces thoroughly. Install the rear oil pan gasket into the rear main bearing cap, then apply a thin bead of silicone sealer to the pan gasket depressions. Install the front pan gasket into the timing cover. Install the side gaskets onto the pan, not the block. They can be retained in place with grease. Apply a thin bead of silicone sealer to the mating joints of the gaskets. Install the oil pan; install the timing gear bolts last, after the other bolts have been snugged down.

6-173

1. Disconnect the battery ground.
2. Raise and support the car on jackstands.
3. Drain the oil.
4. Remove the bellhousing cover.
5. Remove the starter.
6. Support the engine.
7. Unbolt the engine from its mounts.
8. Remove the oil pan bolts.
9. Raise the engine with a jack, just enough to remove the oil pan.
10. Installation is the reverse of removal. The pan is installed using RTV gasket material in place of a gasket. Make sure that the sealing surfaces are free of old RTV material. Use a ⅛ in. bead of RTV material on the pan sealing flange. Torque the pan bolts to 8–10 ft. lb.

6-181 and 6-231

1. Disconnect the battery ground.

2. Raise and support the car on jackstands.
3. Drain the oil.
4. Remove the bellhousing cover.
5. Unbolt and remove the oil pan.
6. Installation is the reverse of removal. RTV gasket material is used in place of a gasket. Make sure that the sealing surfaces are free of all old RTV material. Use a ⅛ in. bead of RTV material on the oil pan sealing flange. Torque the pan bolts to 10-14 ft. lb.

6-263

— CAUTION —

The following procedure will be personally hazardous unless the procedures are followed exactly.

1. Install the engine support fixture assembly shown in the accompanying illustration. Be certain to arrange washers on the fixture so that the bolt securing the chain to the cylinder head can be torqued to 20 ft. lb. THIS IS ABSOLUTELY NECESSARY!

2. Raise the front and rear of the car and support it on jackstands with the rear slightly lower than the front. The front jackstands should be located at the front lift points shown in your owner's manual.

3. Drain the oil.

4. Remove the left side steering gear cradle bolt and loosen the right side cradle bolts.

5. Remove the front stabilizer bar.

6. Using a ½ in. drill bit, drill through the spot weld located between the rear holes at the left front stabilizer bar mounting.

7. Remove the nuts securing the engine and transaxle to its cradle.

8. Disconnect the left lower ball joint from the knuckle.

9. Place a wood block on a floor jack and raise the transaxle under the pan until the mount studs clear the cradle.

10. Remove the bolts securing the front crossmember to the right side of the cradle.

11. Remove the bolts from the left side front body mounts.

12. Remove the left side and front crossmember assemblies. It will be necessary to lower the rear crossmember below the left side of the body through the careful use of a large prybar.

13. Remove the bellhousing cover.

14. Remove the starter.

15. Remove the engine front mount bracket.

16. Unbolt and remove the oil pan.

17. Installation is the reverse of removal. Apply sealer to both sides of the oil pan gasket and make sure that the tabs on the gaskets are installed in the seal notches. Apply RTV sealer to the front cover oil pan seal retainer, and to each seal where it contacts the block. Wipe the seal area of the pan with clean engine oil before installing the pan. Torque the pan bolts to 10 ft. lb.

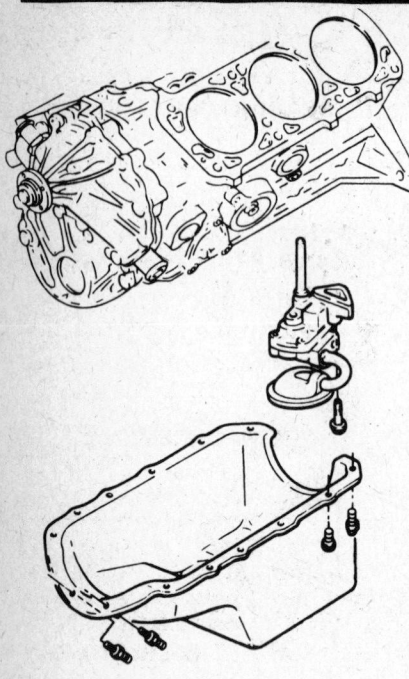

6-173 oil pan removal

Oil Pump

REMOVAL & INSTALLATION

4-151 and 6-173

1. Remove the oil pan as described earlier.

2. Unbolt and remove the oil pump and pickup.

3. Installation is the reverse of removal. Torque the 4-151 pump to 22 ft. lb. and the 6-173 pump bolts to 26–35 ft. lb.

6-181 and 6-231

1. Remove the oil filter.

2. Unbolt the oil pump cover from the timing chain cover.

3. Slide out the oil pump gears. Clean all parts thoroughly in solvent and check for wear. Remove the oil pressure relief valve cap, spring and valve

4. Installation is the reverse of removal. Torque the pressure relief valve cap to 35 ft. lb. Install the pump gears and check their clearances:

   End clearance: 0.002–0.006 in.
   Side clearance: 0.002–0.005 in.

Place a straightedge across the face of the pump cover and check that it is flat to within 0.001 in. Pack the oil pump cavity with petroleum jelly so that there is no air space. Install the cover and torque the bolts to 10 ft. lb.

6-263

1. Remove the oil pan.

2. Unbolt and remove the oil pump and drive extension.

3. Installation is the reverse of removal. Torque the pump bolts to 18 ft. lb.

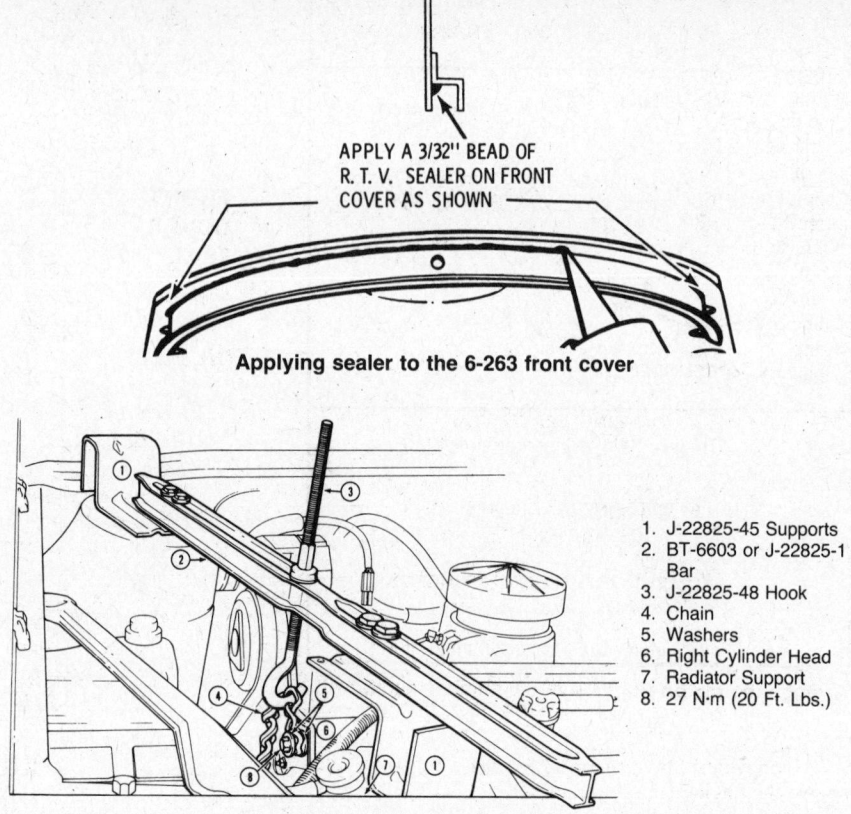

APPLY A 3/32" BEAD OF R. T. V. SEALER ON FRONT COVER AS SHOWN

Applying sealer to the 6-263 front cover

1. J-22825-45 Supports
2. BT-6603 or J-22825-1 Bar
3. J-22825-48 Hook
4. Chain
5. Washers
6. Right Cylinder Head
7. Radiator Support
8. 27 N·m (20 Ft. Lbs.)

6-263 engine support fixture

Rear Main Seal

REMOVAL & INSTALLATION

4-151

1. Remove the transaxle and flywheel.

2. Being careful not to scratch the crankshaft, pry out the old seal with a screwdriver.

3. Coat the new seal with clean engine oil, and install it by hand onto the crankshaft. The seal backing must be flush with the block opening.

4. Install all other parts in reverse of removal.

6-173

1. Remove the oil pan and pump.

2. Remove the rear main bearing cap.

3. Gently pack the upper seal into the groove approximately ¼ in. on each side.

4. Measure the amount the seal was driven in on one side and add ¹⁄₁₆ in. Cut this length from the old lower cap seal. Be sure to get a sharp cut. Repeat for the other side.

5. Place the piece of cut seal into the groove and pack the seal into the block. Do this for each side.

   NOTE: G.M. makes a guide tool (J-29114-1) which bolts to the block via an oil pan bolt hole, and a packing tool (J-29114-2) which are machined to provide

a built-in stop for the installation of the short cut pieces. Using the packing tool, work the short pieces of seal onto the guide tool, then pack them into the block with the packing tool.

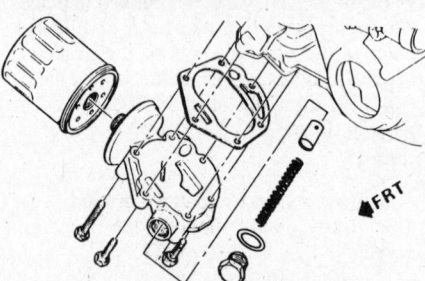

FRT

Oil pump—6-183 and 6-231

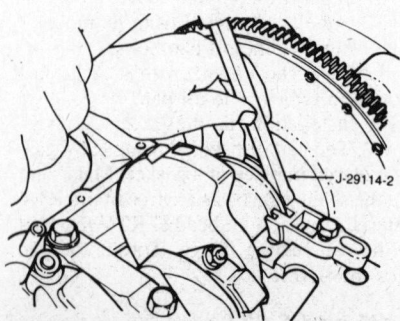

J-29114-2

Installing the upper rear main seal on 6-173 engines

6. Install a new lower seal in the rear main cap.

7. Install a piece of Plastigage or the equivalent on the bearing journal. Install the rear cap and tighten to 70 ft. lbs. Remove the cap and check the gauge for bearing clearance. If out of specification, the ends of the seal may be frayed or not flush, preventing the cap from proper sealing. Correct as required.

8. Clean the journal, and apply a thin film of sealer to the mating surfaces of the cap and block. Do not allow any sealer to get onto the journal or bearing. Install the bearing cap and tighten to 70 ft. lbs. Install the pan and pump.

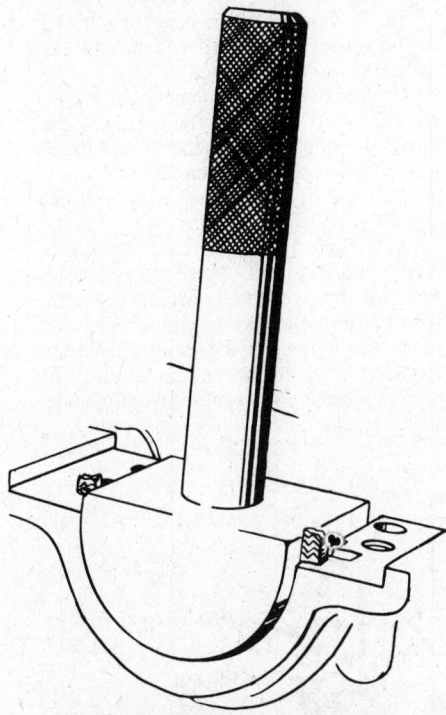

AFTER CORRECTLY POSITIONING SEAL, ROTATE TOOL SLIGHTLY AND CUT OFF EACH END OF SEAL FLUSH WITH BLOCK

Installing the lower seal half

6-181, 6-231 and 6-263

Braided fabric seals are pressed into grooves formed in crankcase and rear bearing cap to rear of the oil collecting groove, to seal against leakage of oil around the crankshaft.

A new braided fabric seal can be installed in crankcase only when crankshaft is removed, but it can be repaired while crankshaft is installed, as outlined under "Rear Main Bearing Upper Oil Seal Repair". The seal can be replaced in cap whenver the cap is removed. Remove old seal and place new seal in groove with both ends projecting above parting surface of cap. Force seal into groove rubbing down with hammer handle or smooth stick until seal projects above the groove not more than 1/16 in. Cut ends off flush with surface of cap, using sharp knife or razor blade.

The engine must be operated at slow speed when first started after a new braided seal is installed.

Neoprene composition seals are placed in grooves in the sides of bearing cap to seal against leakage in the joints between cap and crankcase. The neoprene composition swells in the presence of oil and heat. The seals are undersize when newly installed and may even leak for a short time until the seals have had time to swell and seal the opening.

The neoprene seals are slightly longer than the grooves in the bearing cap. The seals must not be cut to length. Before installation of seals, soak for 1 to 2 minutes in light oil or kerosene. After installation of bearing cap in crankcase, install seal in bearing cap.

To help eliminate oil leakage at the joint where the cap meets the crankcase, apply silicone sealer, or equivalent, to the rear main bearing cap split line. When applying sealer, use only a thin coat as an over abundance will not allow the cap to seat properly.

After seal is installed, force seals up into the cap with a blunt instrument to be sure of a seal at the upper parting line between the cap and case.

REAR MAIN BEARING UPPER OIL SEAL REPAIR

1. Remove oil pan.
2. Insert packing tool (J-21526-2) against one end of the seal in the cylinder block. Drive the old seal gently into the groove until it is packed tight. This varies from 1/4–3/4 in. depending on the amount of pack required.
3. Repeat Step 2 on the other end of the seal in the cylinder block.
4. Measure the amount the seal was driven up on one side and add 1/16 in. Using a single edge razor blade, cut that length from the old seal removed from the rear main bearing cap. Repeat the procedure for the other side. Use the rear main bearing cap as a holding fixture when cutting the seal.

5. Install Guide Tool (J-21526-1) onto cylinder block.
6. Using packing tool, work the short pieces cut in Step 4 into the guide tool and then pack into cylinder block. The guide tool and packing tool have been machined to provide a built-in stop. Use this procedure for both sides. It may help to use oil on the short pieces of the rope seal when packing into the cylinder block.
7. Remove the guide tool.
8. Install a new fabric seal in the rear main bearing cap. Install cap and torque to specifications.
9. Install oil pan.

CLUTCH

The only service adjustment necessary on the clutch is to maintain the correct pedal free play. Clutch pedal free play, or throwout bearing lash, decreases with driven disc wear.

REMOVAL & INSTALLATION

1. Remove the transaxle.
2. Mark the pressure plate assembly and the flywheel so that they can be assembled in the same position. They were balanced as an assembly at the factory.
3. Loosen the attaching bolts one turn at a time until spring tension is relieved.
4. Support the pressure plate and remove the bolts. Remove the pressure plate and clutch disc. Do not disassemble the pressure plate assembly; replace it if defective.
5. Inspect the flywheel, clutch disc, pressure plate, throwout bearing and the clutch fork and pivot shaft assembly for wear. Replace the parts as required. If the flywheel shows any signs of overheating, or if it is badly grooved or scored, it should be replaced.

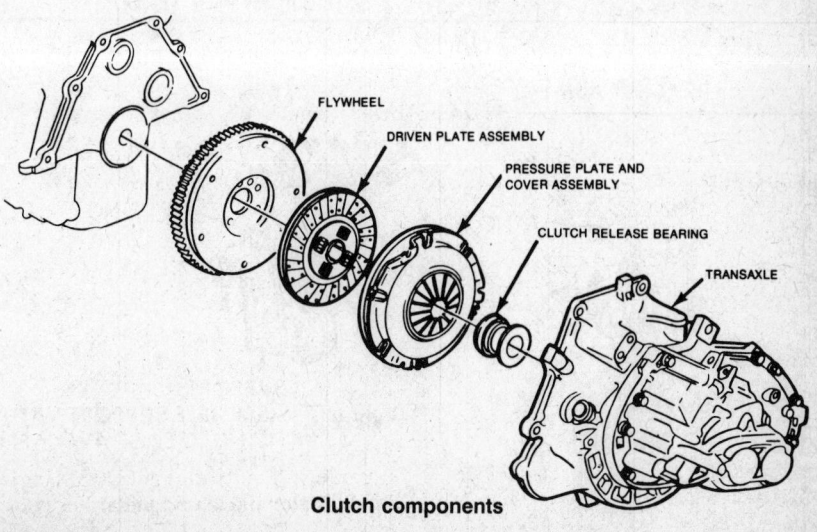

FLYWHEEL
DRIVEN PLATE ASSEMBLY
PRESSURE PLATE AND COVER ASSEMBLY
CLUTCH RELEASE BEARING
TRANSAXLE

Clutch components

6. Clean the pressure plate and flywheel mating surfaces thoroughly. Position the clutch disc and pressure plate into the installed position, and support with a dummy shaft or clutch aligning tool. The clutch plate is assembled with the damper springs offset toward the transaxle. One side of the factory-supplied clutch disc is stamped "Flywheel side".

7. Install the pressure plate-to-flywheel bolts. Tighten them gradually in a criss-cross pattern.

8. Lubricate the outside groove and the inside recess of the release bearing with high temperature grease. Wipe off any excess. Install the release bearing.

9. Install the transaxle.

CLUTCH LINKAGE ADJUSTMENT

All cars use a self-adjusting clutch mechanism which may be checked as follows:

As the clutch friction material wears, the cable must be lengthened. This is accomplished by simply pulling the clutch pedal up to its rubber bumper. This action forces the pawl against its stop and rotates it out of mesh with the quadrant teeth, allowing the cable to play out until the quadrant spring load is balanced against the load applied by the release bearing. This adjustment procedure is required every 5,000 miles or less.

1. With engine running and brake on, hold the clutch pedal approximately ½ in. from floor mat and move shift lever between first and reverse several times. If this can be done smoothly without clashing into reverse, the clutch is fully releasing. If shift is not smooth, clutch is not fully releasing and linkage should be inspected and corrected as necessary.

2. Check clutch pedal bushings for sticking or excessive wear.

3. Have an assistant sit in the driver's seat and fully apply the clutch pedal to the floor. Observe the clutch fork level travel at the transaxle. The end of the clutch fork lever should have a total travel of approximately 1.5–1.7 in.

4. If fork lever is not correct, check the adjusting mechanism by depressing the clutch pedal and looking for pawl to firmly engage with the teeth in the quadrant.

MANUAL TRANSAXLE

All models use a Muncie model MT-125 four speed transaxle. Shifting is controlled by a two cable push-pull arrangement. Final drive is an integral part of the transaxle assembly.

REMOVAL & INSTALLATION

1. Disconnect the negative battery cable from the transaxle case.

2. Remove the two transaxle strut bracket bolts on the left side of the engine compartment, if equipped.

3. On some models equipped with a V6 engine, disconnect the fuel lines and fuel line clamps at the clutch cable bracket.

4. Remove the top four engine-to-transaxle bolts, and the one at the rear near the firewall. The one at the rear is installed from the engine side.

5. Loosen the engine-to-transaxle bolt near the starter, but do not remove.

6. Disconnect the speedometer cable at the transaxle, or at the speed control transducer on cars so equipped.

7. Remove the retaining clip and washer from the shift linkage at the transaxle. Remove the clips holding the cables to the mounting bosses on the case.

8. Support the engine with a lifting chain.

9. Unlock the steering column and raise and support the car. Drain the transaxle. Remove the two nuts attaching the stabilizer bar to the left lower control arm. Remove the four bolts which attach the left retaining plate to the engine cradle. The retaining plate covers and holds the stabilizer bar.

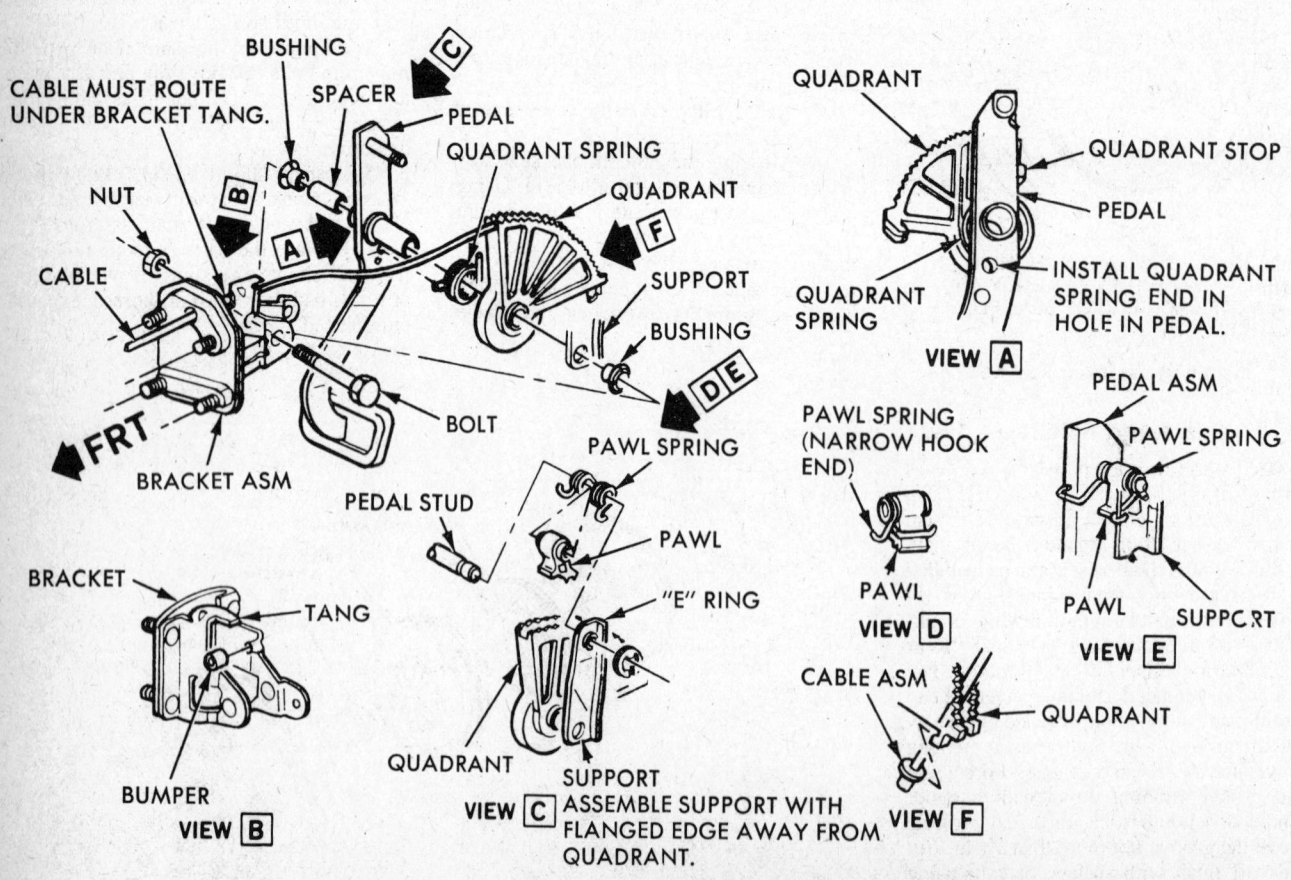

Clutch cable and pedal

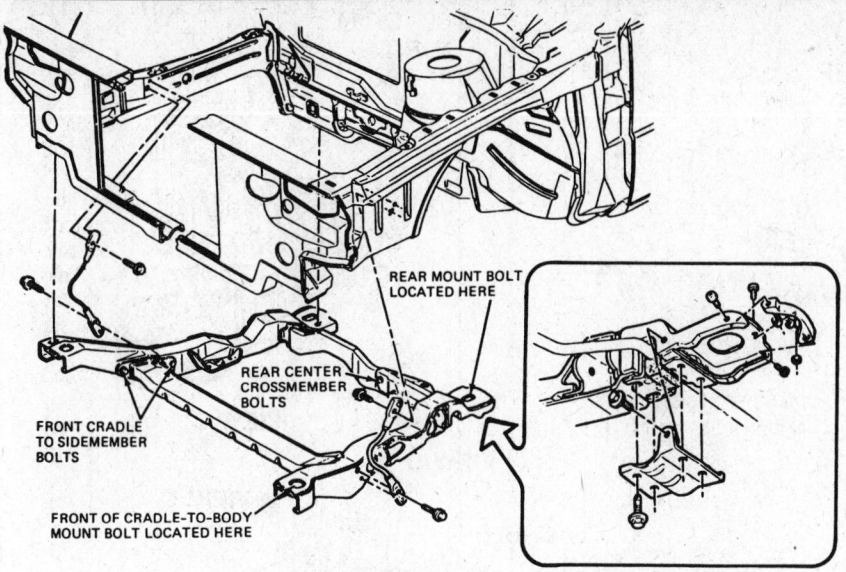

Typical engine/transaxle cradle

REAR MOUNT BOLT
LOCATED HERE

REAR CENTER
CROSSMEMBER
BOLTS

FRONT CRADLE
TO SIDEMEMBER
BOLTS

FRONT OF CRADLE-TO-BODY
MOUNT BOLT LOCATED HERE

SHIFT LINKAGE ADJUSTMENT, BAND ADJUSTMENT, FLUID AND FILTER CHANGE

All automatic transmission service procedures are contained in the "Automatic Transmission" Unit Repair section of this book.

CAUTION

Any inaccuracies in shift linkage adjustments may result in premature failure of the transmission due to operation without the controls in full detent. Such operation results in reduced fluid pressure and in turn, partial engagement of the affected clutches. Partial engagement of the clutches, with sufficient pressure to permit apparently normal vehicle operation will result in failure of the clutches and/or other internal parts after only a few miles of operation.

10. Loosen the four bolts holding the right stabilizer bracket.

11. Disconnect and remove the exhaust pipe and crossover if necessary.

12. Pull the stabilizer bar down on the left side.

13. Remove the four nuts and disconnect the front and rear transaxle mounts from the engine cradle. Remove the two rear center crossmember bolts.

14. Remove the three right side front cradle attaching bolts. They are accessible under the splash shield.

15. Remove the top bolt from the lower front transaxle shock absorber if equipped.

16. Remove the left front wheel. Remove the front cradle-to-body bolts on the left side, and the rear cradle-to-body bolts.

17. Pull the left side drive shaft from the transaxle using G.M. special tool J-28468 or the equivalent. The right side axle shaft will simply disconnect from the case. When the transaxle is removed, the right shaft can be swung out of the way. A boot protector should be used when disconnecting the driveshafts.

18. Swing the cradle to the left side. Secure out of the way, outboard of the fender well.

19. Remove the flywheel and starter shield bolts, and remove the shields.

20. Remove the two transaxle extension bolts from the engine-to-transaxle bracket, if equipped.

21. Place a jack under the transaxle case. Remove the last engine-to-transaxle bolt. Pull the transaxle to the left, away from the engine, then down and out from under the car.

Installation is the reverse.

1. Position the right axle shaft into its bore as the transaxle is being installed.

2. When the transaxle is bolted to the engine, swing the cradle into position and install the cradle-to-body bolts immediately. Be sure to guide the left axle shaft into place as the cradle is moved back into position.

SHIFT LINKAGE ADJUSTMENT

1. Remove the shifter boot and retainer inside the car. Shift into first gear.

2. Install two No. 22 drill bits, or two ⁵⁄₃₂ in. rods, into the two alignment holes in the shifter assembly to hold it in first gear.

3. Place the transaxle into first gear by pushing the rail selector shaft down just to the point of feeling the resistance of the inhibitor spring. Then rotate the shift lever all the way counterclockwise.

4. Install the stud, with the cable attached, into the slotted area of the select lever, while gently pulling on the lever to remove all lash.

5. Remove the two drill bits or pins from the shifter.

6. Check the shifter for proper operation. It may be necessary to fine tune the adjustment after road testing.

AUTOMATIC TRANSMISSION

All models use a Turbo Hydro-Matic 125 or 125C automatic transmission. The 125C is equipped with a torque converter clutch (TCC) which under certain conditions mechanically couples the engine to the transaxle for greater power transfer efficiency and increased fuel mileage. A cable operated throttle valve linkage is used. Automatic transaxle operation is provided through a conventional three element torque converter, a compound planetary gear set, and a dual sprocket and drive link assembly.

REMOVAL & INSTALLATION

1. Disconnect the negative battery cable from the transaxle. Tape the wire to the upper radiator hose to keep it out of the way.

2. Remove the air cleaner and disconnect the detent cable. Slide the detent cable in the opposite direction of the cable to remove it from the carburetor.

3. Unbolt the detent cable attaching bracket at the transaxle.

4. Pull up on the detent cable cover at the transaxle until the cable is exposed. Disconnect the cable from the rod.

5. Remove the two transaxle strut bracket bolts at the transaxle, if equipped.

6. Remove all the engine-to-transaxle bolts except the one near the starter. The one nearest the firewall is installed from the engine side; you will need a short handled box wrench or ratchet to reach it.

7. Loosen, but do not remove the engine-to-transaxle bolt near the starter.

8. Disconnect the speedometer cable at the upper and lower coupling. On cars with cruise control, remove the speedometer cable at the transducer.

9. Remove the retaining clip and washer from the shift linkage at the transaxle. Remove the two shift linkage at the transaxle. Remove the two shift linkage bracket bolts.

10. Disconnect and plug the two fluid cooler lines at the transaxle. These are inch-size fittings (½ and ¹¹⁄₁₆); use a back-up wrench to avoid twisting the lines.

11. Install an engine holding chain or hoist. Raise the engine enough to take its weight off the mounts.

12. Unlock the steering column and raise the car.

13. Remove the two nuts holding the anti-sway (stabilizer) bar to the left lower control arm (driver's side).

14. Remove the four bolts attaching the covering plate over the stabilizer bar to the

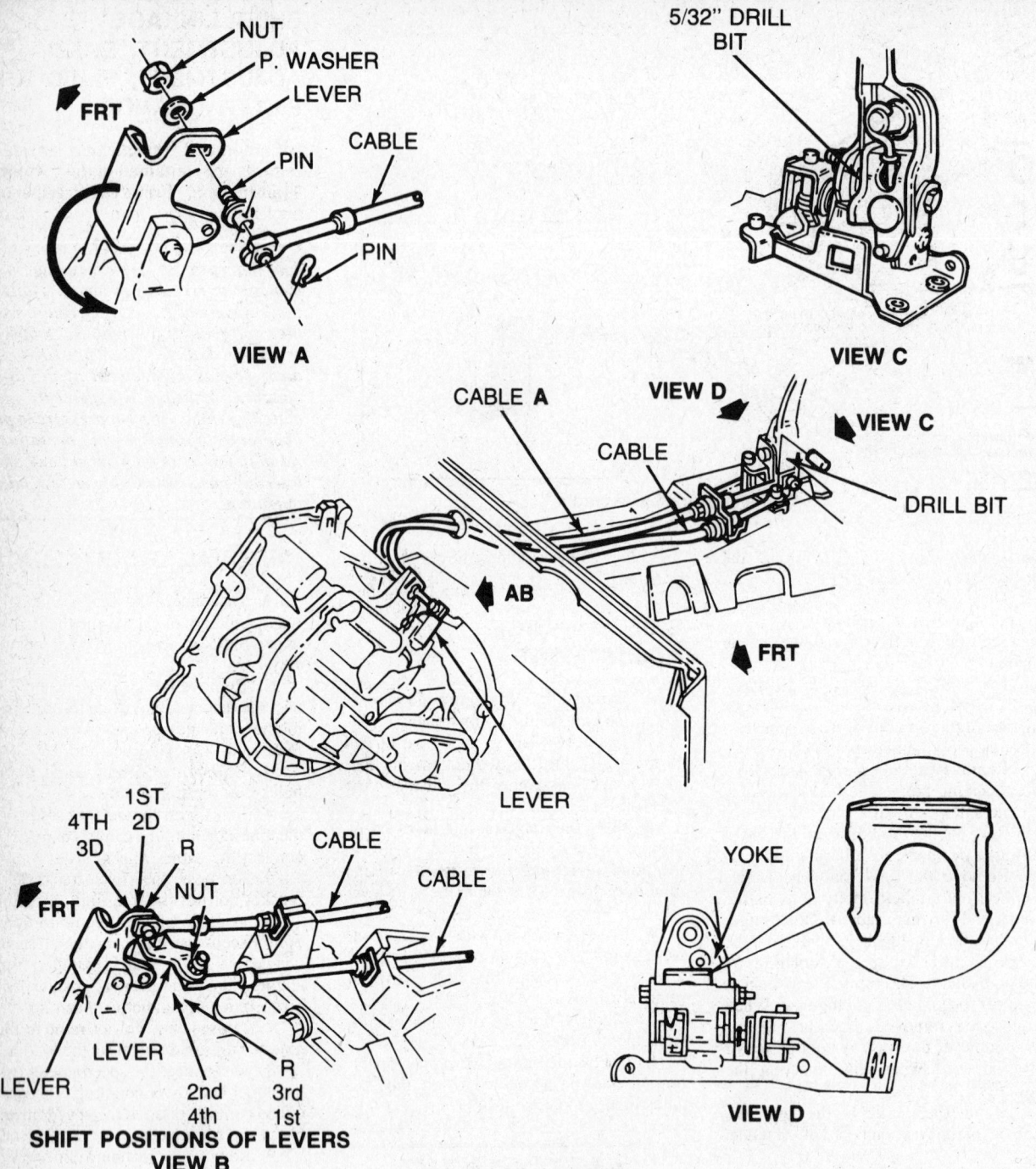

VIEW A

5/32" DRILL BIT

VIEW C

CABLE A

VIEW D

CABLE

VIEW C

DRILL BIT

AB

FRT

LEVER

1ST
2D
4TH
3D
R
FRT
NUT
CABLE
CABLE
LEVER
LEVER
R
2nd
4th
3rd
1st
**SHIFT POSITIONS OF LEVERS
VIEW B**

YOKE

VIEW D

Manual transaxle shift linkage

engine cradle on the left side (driver' side).

15. Loosen but do not remove the four bolts holding the stabilizer bar bracket to the right side (passenger's side) of the engine cradle. Pull the bar down on the driver's side.

16. Disconnect the front and rear transaxle mounts at the engine cradle.

17. Remove the two rear center crossmember bolts.

18. Remove the three right (passenger) side front engine cradle attaching bolts. The nuts are accessible under the splash shield next to the frame rail.

19. Remove the top bolt from the lower front transaxle shock absorber, if equipped (V6 engine only).

20. Remove the left (driver) side front and rear cradle-to-body bolts.

21. Remove the left front wheel. Attach an axle shaft removing tool (G.M. part no. J-28468 or the equivalent) to a slide hammer. Place the tool behind the axle shaft cones and pull the cones out away from the transaxle. Remove the right shaft in the same manner. Set the shafts out of the way. Plug the openings in the transaxle to prevent fluid leakage and the entry of dirt.

22. Swing the partial engine cradle to the left (driver) side and wire it out of the way outboard of the fender well.

23. Remove the four torque converter and starter shield bolts. Remove the two transaxle extension bolts from the engine-to-transaxle bracket.

24. Attach a transaxle jack to the case.

25. Use a felt pen to matchmark the torque converter and flywheel. Remove the three torque converter-to-flywheel bolts.

26. Remove the transaxle-to-engine bolt near the starter. Remove the transaxle by sliding it to the left, away from the engine.

Installation is the reverse. As the transaxle is installed, slide the right axle shaft into the case. Install the cradle-to-body bolts before the stabilizer bar is installed. To aid in stabilizer bar installation, a pry hole has been provided in the engine cradle.

DRIVESHAFTS, DRIVE AXLES AND U-JOINTS

Drive Axle

REMOVAL & INSTALLATION

CAUTION
Use care when removing the drive axle. Tri-pots can be damaged if the drive axle is over extended.

1. Remove the hub nut.
2. Raise the front of the car. Remove the wheel and tire.
3. Install an axle shaft boot seal protector, G.M. special tool no. J-28712 or the equivalent, onto the seal.
4. Disconnect the brake hose clip from the MacPherson strut, but do not disconnect the hose from the caliper. Remove the brake caliper from the spindle, and hang the caliper out of the way by a length of wire. Do not allow the caliper to hang by the brake hose.

5. Mark the camber alignment cam bolt for reassembly. Remove the cam bolt and the upper attaching bolt from the strut and spindle.
6. Pull the steering knuckle assembly from the strut bracket.
7. Using G.M. special tool J-28468 or the equivalent, remove the axle shaft from the transaxle.
8. Using G.M. special tool J-28733 or the equivalent spindle remover, remove the axle shaft from the hub and bearing assembly.

To install:
1. If a new drive axle is to be installed, a new knuckle seal should be installed first.
2. Loosely install the drive axle into the transaxle and steering knuckle.
3. Loosely attach the steering knuckle to the suspension strut.
4. The drive axle is an interference fit in the steering knuckle. Press the axle into place, then install the hub nut. When the shaft begins to turn with the hub, insert a drift through the caliper into one of the cooling slots in the rotor to keep it from turning. Insert a long bolt in the hub flange to prevent the shaft from turning. Tighten the hub nut to 70 ft. lbs. to completely seat the shaft.

5. Install the brake caliper. Tighten the bolts to 30 ft. lbs.
6. Load the hub assembly by lowering it onto a jackstant. Align the camber cam bolt marks made during removal, install the bolt and tighten to 140 ft. lbs. Tighten the upper nut to the same value.
7. Install the axle shaft all the way into the transaxle using a screwdriver inserted into the groove provided on the inner retainer. Tap the screwdriver until the shaft seats in the transaxle. Remove the boot seal protector.
8. Connect the brake hose clip to the strut. Install the tire and wheel, lower the car, and tighten the hub nut to 225 ft. lbs. (1980–82); 185 ft. lbs. (1983 and later).

Constant Velocity Joint

OVERHAUL

Please refer to the "U-Joint/CV-Joint" section of the Unit Repair section.

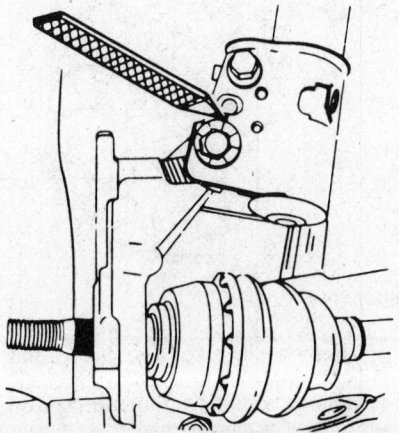

Mark the camber eccentric before removal

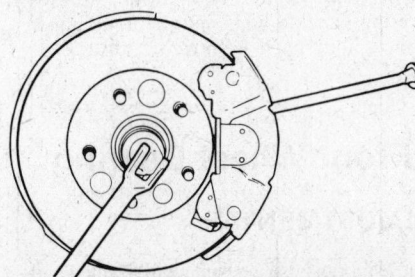

Insert a drift into the caliper when tightening the hub nut

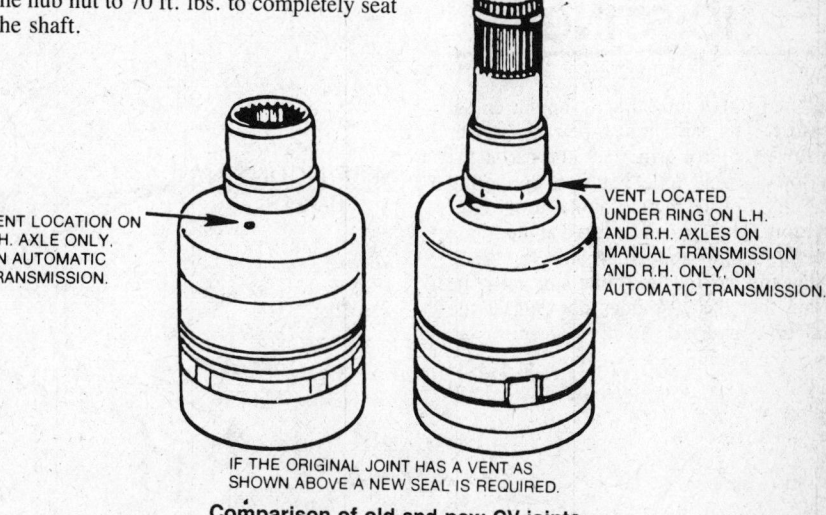

VENT LOCATION ON L.H. AXLE ONLY. ON AUTOMATIC TRANSMISSION.

VENT LOCATED UNDER RING ON L.H. AND R.H. AXLES ON MANUAL TRANSMISSION AND R.H. ONLY, ON AUTOMATIC TRANSMISSION.

IF THE ORIGINAL JOINT HAS A VENT AS SHOWN ABOVE A NEW SEAL IS REQUIRED.

Comparison of old and new CV joints

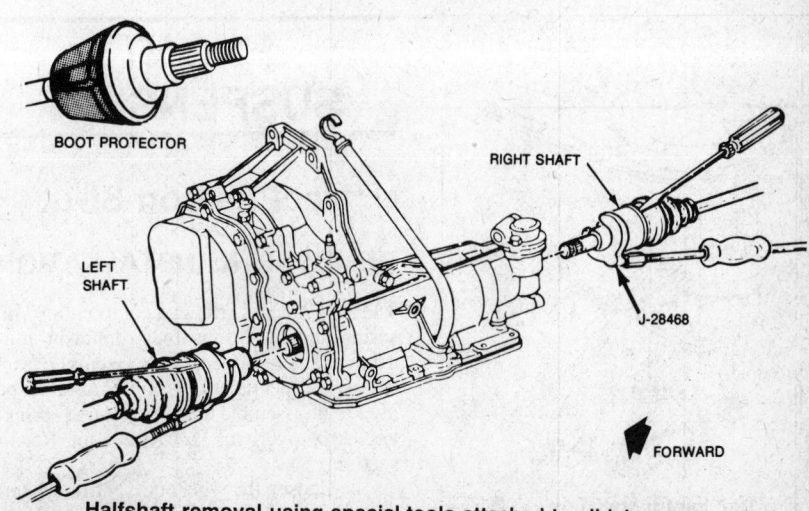

BOOT PROTECTOR

LEFT SHAFT

RIGHT SHAFT

J-28468

FORWARD

Halfshaft removal using special tools attached to slidehammers

REAR AXLE

Hub

REMOVAL & INSTALLATION

A single unit hub and bearing assembly is bolted to both ends of the rear axle assembly. These take the place of "rear axles" used on rear wheel drive cars. The hub and bearing assembly is a sealed unit which requires no maintenance. The unit must be replaced as an assembly and cannot be disassembled or adjusted.

The hub and bearing can be removed by removing the rear brake drum, removing the four hub and bearing-to-axle assembly attaching bolts and pulling the unit out. Installation is the reverse of removal. Tighten the bolts to 35–39 ft. lbs.

JACKING, HOISTING

Jack the front of the car at the engine cradle crossbar. The car can also be raised under the lower control arm. Jack the car at the rear on the rear axle between the spring seats. Do not lift the car by the lower control arms. The car can be lifted at the frame directly behind the front wheels. When raising the car by the frame side rails, be certain that the jack does not contact the catalytic converter.

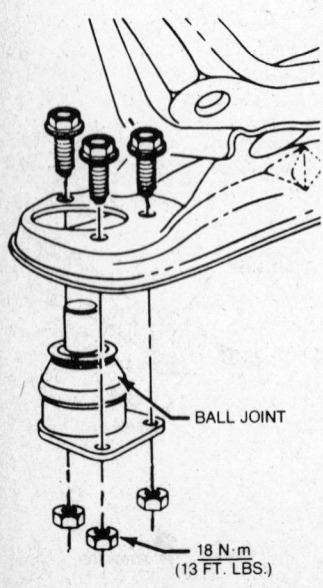

Ball joint installation

Diagram labels: SHOCK NUT, UPPER MOUNT NUT, UPPER MOUNT AND BEARING ASSEMBLY, SPRING SEAT, JOUNCE BUMPER, DUST CAP, SPRING, STRUT ASSEMBLY, LOWER MOUNTING BOLTS

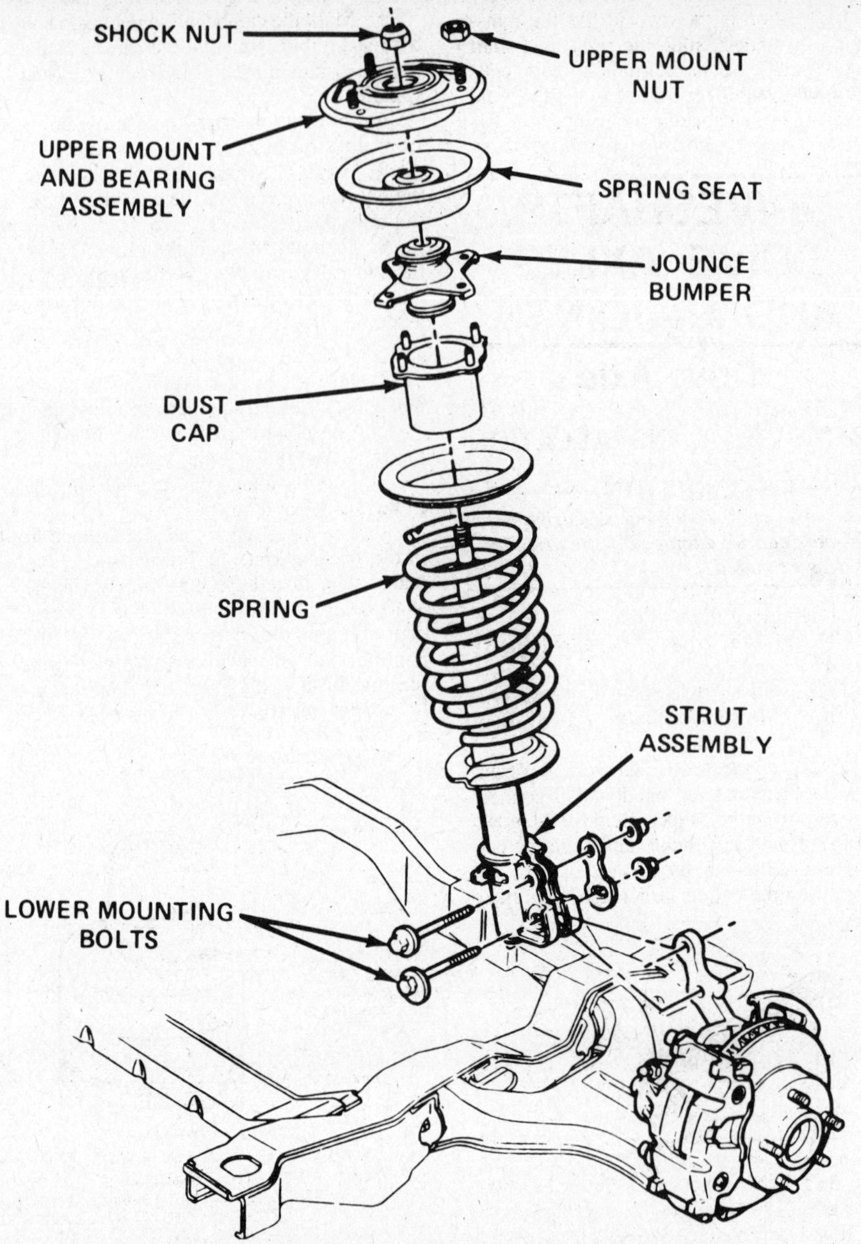

Front suspension components

Ball joint installation labels: BALL JOINT, 18 N·m (13 FT. LBS.)

FRONT SUSPENSION

MacPherson Strut

REMOVAL & INSTALLATION

The MacPherson strut is a combination coil spring and shock absorber (damper) unit. The strut is removed as an assembly from the car. A special strut compressor must be used to disassemble the strut and coil spring. For strut overhaul, see the Unit Repair section.

1. Loosen the wheel nuts, raise the car, and remove the wheel and tire.

2. Remove the brake hose clip-to-strut bolt (if equipped). Do not disconnect the hose from the caliper. Install a drive axle cover to protect the axle boot.

3. Mark the camber cam eccentric adjuster for assembly.

4. Remove the two lower strut-to-steering knuckle bolts and the three upper strut-to-body nuts. Remove the strut.

Front Wheel Bearing

ADJUSTMENT

These models use a permanently sealed and lubricated front wheel bearing assembly. No adjustments are necessary or possible.

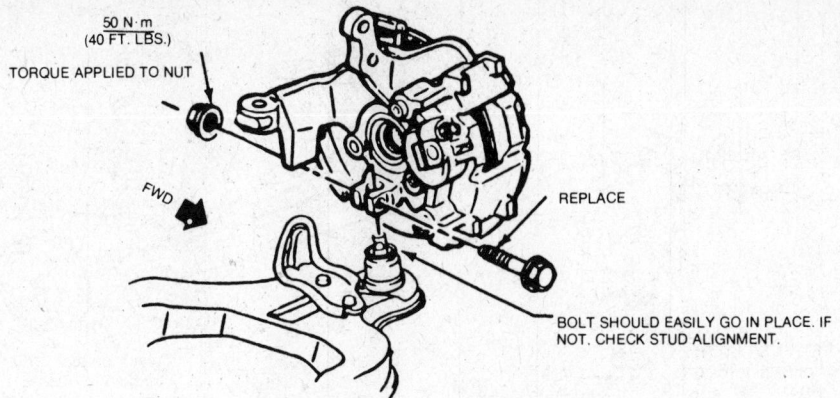

Ball joint stud should go in easily

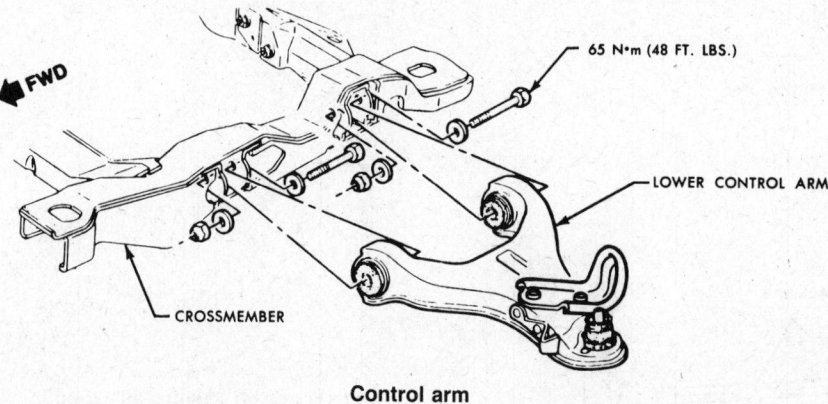

Control arm

6. Insert the ball stud into the pinch bolt fitting. It should go in easily; if not, check the ball joint stud alignment.

7. Install the pinch bolt from the rear to the front. Tighten to 45 ft. lb. on 1980 models and 40 ft. lb. on 1981–85 models.

8. Install the stabilizer bar attachment. Tighten to 35 ft. lbs.

9. Install the wheel and lower the car.

REAR SUSPENSION

Shock Absorber

REMOVAL & INSTALLATION

1. Open the deck or trunk lid, remove the trim cover, and remove the upper shock nut. Remove and replace one shock at a time when replacing both shocks.

2. Jack the car to a convenient working height. Support the rear axle assembly.

3. Remove the lower attaching bolt and remove the shock absorber. On cars equipped with air shocks, disconnect the air line.

NOTE: Purge new shocks of air by repeatedly compressing them while inverted and extending them in their normal installed position.

Install the shock absorber in a reverse of the removal procedure. Torque the lower nuts to 43 ft. lb.; the upper nut to 13 ft. lb.

Spring

REMOVAL & INSTALLATION

1. Raise and support the car on a hoist. Do not use twin-post hoist. The swing arc of the axle may cause it to slip from the hoist when the bolts are removed. If a suitable hoist is not available, raise and support the car on jackstands, and use a jack under the axle.

2. Support the axle with a jack that can be raised and lowered.

3. Remove the brake hose attaching brackets (right and left), allowing the hoses to hang freely. Do not disconnect the hoses.

4. Remove the track bar attaching bolts from the rear axle.

5. Remove both shock absorber lower attaching bolts from the axle.

6. Lower the axle. Remove the coil spring and insulator.

NOTE: Do not suspend rear axle by brake hoses.

7. To install, position the spring and insulator on the axle. The leg on the upper coil of the spring must be parallel to the axle, facing the lefthand side of the car.

Ball Joints

INSPECTION

1. Raise the front of the car with a lift placed under the engine cradle. The front wheels should be clear of the ground.

2. Grasp the wheel at the top and bottom and shake the wheel in and out.

3. If any movement is seen of the steering knuckle relative to the control arm, the ball joints are defective and must be replaced. Note that movement elsewhere may be due to loose wheel bearings or other troubles; watch the knuckle-to-control arm connection.

4. If the ball stud is disconnected from the steering knuckle and any looseness is noted, often the ball joint stud can be twisted in its socket with your fingers, replace the ball joints.

REMOVAL & INSTALLATION

NOTE: These cars use only a lower ball joint.

1. Loosen the wheel nuts, raise the car, and remove the wheel.

2. Use a ⅛ in. drill bit to drill a hole approximately ¼ in. deep in the center of each of the three ball joint rivets.

3. Use a ½ in. drill bit to drill off the rivet heads. Drill only enough to remove the rivet head.

4. Use a hammer and punch to remove the rivets. Drive them out from the bottom.

5. Loosen the ball joint pinch bolt in the steering knuckle.

6. Remove the ball joint.

7. Install the new ball joint in the control arm. Tighten the bolts supplied with the replacement joint to 13 ft. lb.

8. Install the ball stud into the steering knuckle pinch bolt fitting. It should go in easily; if not, check the stud alignment. Install the pinch bolt from the rear to the front. Tighten to 45 ft. lbs.

9. Install the wheel and lower the car.

Lower Control Arm

REMOVAL & INSTALLATION

1. Loosen the wheel nuts, raise the car, and remove the wheel.

2. Remove the stabilizer bar from the control arm.

3. Remove the ball joint from the steering knuckle.

4. Remove the control arm pivot bolts and the control arm.

5. To install, insert the control arm into its fittings. Install the pivot bolts from the rear to the front. Tighten the bolts to 48 ft. lb. on 1980 models and 50 ft. lb. on 1981–85 models.

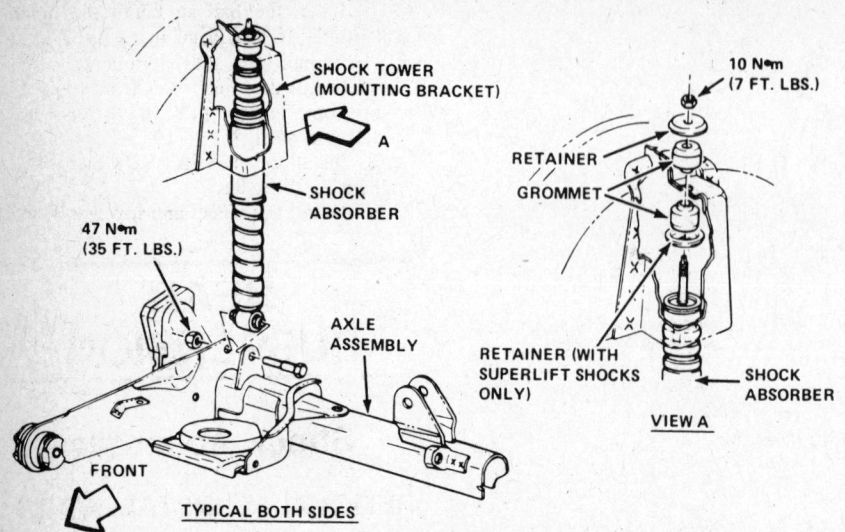

Shock absorber installation

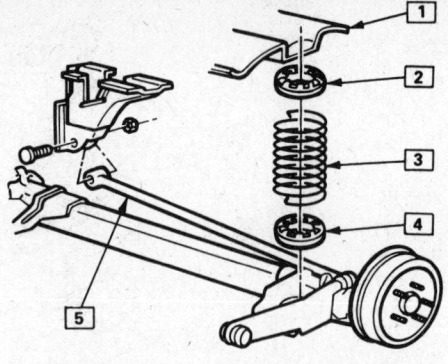

1. Underbody
2. Insulator Upper
3. Spring
4. Lower Insulator on a Series Only
5. Track Bar

A-Body Rear suspension

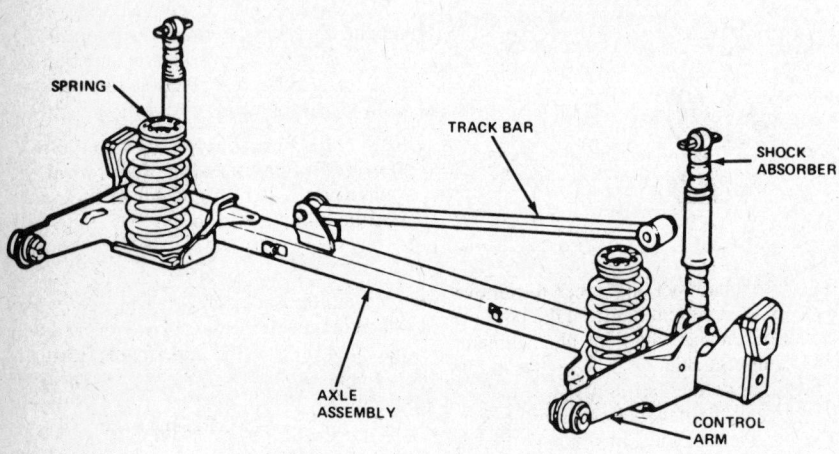

X-Body rear suspension

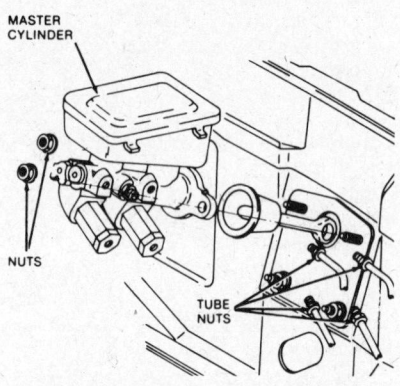

Typical master cylinder installation

8. Install the shock absorber bolts. Tighten to 43 ft. lbs. Install the track bar, if equipped, tightening to 33 ft. lbs. Install the brake line brackets. Tighten to 8 ft. lbs.

BRAKES

Brake lining replacement and adjustment, wheel and master cylinder overhaul and brake bleeding procedures can be found in the "Brakes" section of the Unit Repair section.

Master Cylinder

REMOVAL & INSTALLATION

1. Disconnect hydraulic lines at master cylinder.
2. Remove the retaining nuts and lockwashers that hold cylinder to firewall or the brake booster. Disconnect pushrod at brake pedal (non-power brakes only).
3. Remove the master cylinder, gasket and rubber boot.
4. On non-power brakes, position master cylinder on firewall, making sure pushrod goes through the rubber boot into the

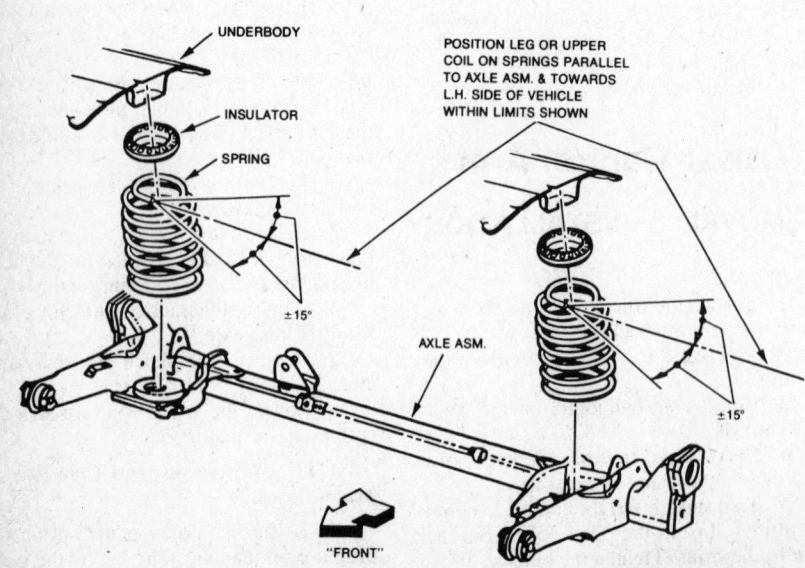

Spring installation

piston. Reconnect pushrod clevis to brake pedal. With power brakes, install the cylinder on the booster. Torque the attaching nuts to 25 ft. lb.

5. Install nuts and lockwashers.

6. Install hydraulic lines then check brake pedal free play.

7. Bleed brakes, as described in Unit Repair section.

NOTE: Cars having disc brakes do not have a check valve in the front outlet port of the master cylinder. If one is installed, front discs will quickly wear out due to residual pressure holding pads against rotor.

Power Brake Booster

REMOVAL & INSTALLATION

1. Disconnect vacuum hose from vacuum check valve.

2. Unbolt the master cylinder and carefully move it aside without disconnecting the hydraulic lines.

3. Disconnect pushrod at brake pedal assembly.

4. Remove nuts and lockwashers that secure booster to firewall and remove booster from engine compartment.

5. Install by reversing removal procedure. Torque the mounting nuts to 25 ft. lbs. Make sure to check operation of stop lights. Allow engine vacuum to build before applying brakes.

Parking Brake

ADJUSTMENT

1. Jack up rear of car and support with both rear wheels off floor.

2. Apply parking brake two ratchet clicks (1980–81); three ratchet clicks (1982 and later) from fully released position.

3. Loosen the equalizer locknut, then tighten the adjusting nut until a light to moderate drag is felt when the rear wheels are rotated.

4. Tight the locknut.

5. Fully release parking brake and rotate rear wheels—no drag should be felt.

STEERING

Tie-Rod

REMOVAL & INSTALLATION

1. Loosen the jam nut on the steering rack (inner tie-rod).

2. Remove the tie-rod end nut. Separate the tie-rod end from the steering knuckle using a puller.

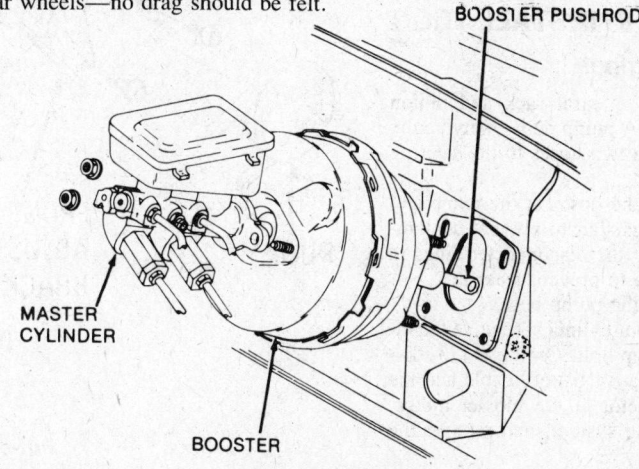

Power booster removal

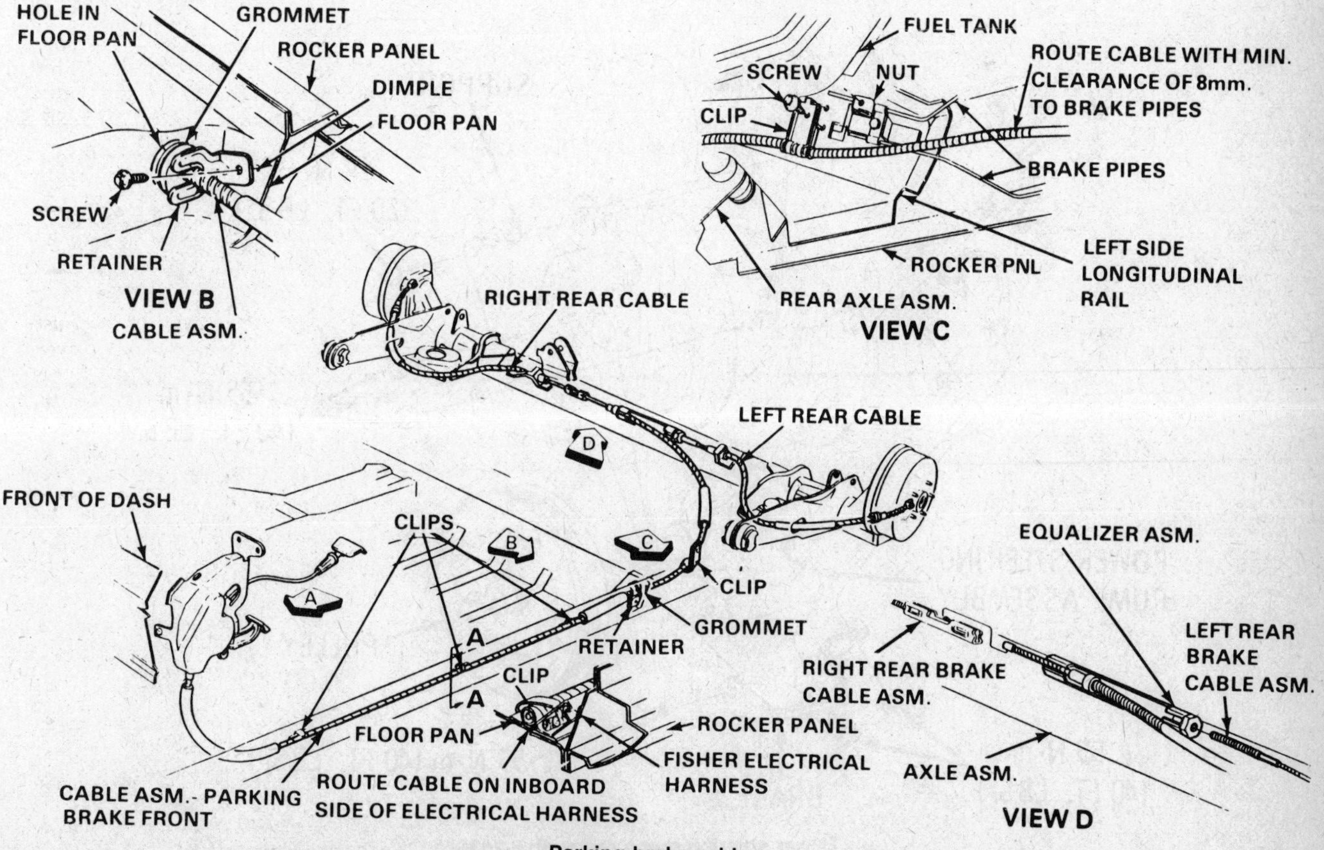

MASTER CYLINDER

BOOSTER

BOOSTER PUSHROD

Parking brake cable

HOLE IN FLOOR PAN

GROMMET

ROCKER PANEL

DIMPLE

FLOOR PAN

SCREW

RETAINER

VIEW B
CABLE ASM.

RIGHT REAR CABLE

FUEL TANK

SCREW   NUT

CLIP

ROUTE CABLE WITH MIN. CLEARANCE OF 8mm. TO BRAKE PIPES

BRAKE PIPES

ROCKER PNL

REAR AXLE ASM.

LEFT SIDE LONGITUDINAL RAIL

VIEW C

LEFT REAR CABLE

FRONT OF DASH

CLIPS

CLIP

GROMMET

RETAINER

CLIP

FLOOR PAN

ROUTE CABLE ON INBOARD SIDE OF ELECTRICAL HARNESS

ROCKER PANEL

FISHER ELECTRICAL HARNESS

CABLE ASM.- PARKING BRAKE FRONT

EQUALIZER ASM.

RIGHT REAR BRAKE CABLE ASM.

AXLE ASM.

LEFT REAR BRAKE CABLE ASM.

VIEW D

3. Unscrew the tie-rod end, counting the number of turns.

4. To install, screw the tie-rod end onto the steering rack (inner tie-rod) the same number of turns as counted for removal. This will give approximately correct toe.

5. Install the tie-rod end into the knuckle. Install the nut and tighten to 40 ft. lbs.

6. If the toe must be adjusted, use pliers to expand the boot clamp. Turn the inner tie-rod to adjust. Replace the clamp.

7. Tighten the jam nut to 50 ft. lbs.

Power Steering Pump

REMOVAL & INSTALLATION

Gasoline Engines

All models use integral rack and pinion power steering. A pump delivers hydraulic pressure through two hoses to the steering gear itself.

1. Remove the hoses at the pump and tape the openings shut to prevent contamination. Position the disconnected lines in a raised position to prevent leakage.

2. Remove the pump belt.

3. On the four cylinder, remove the radiator hose clamp bolt. On the 6-173, disconnect the negative battery cable and the electrical connector at the blower motor, drain the cooling system, and remove the

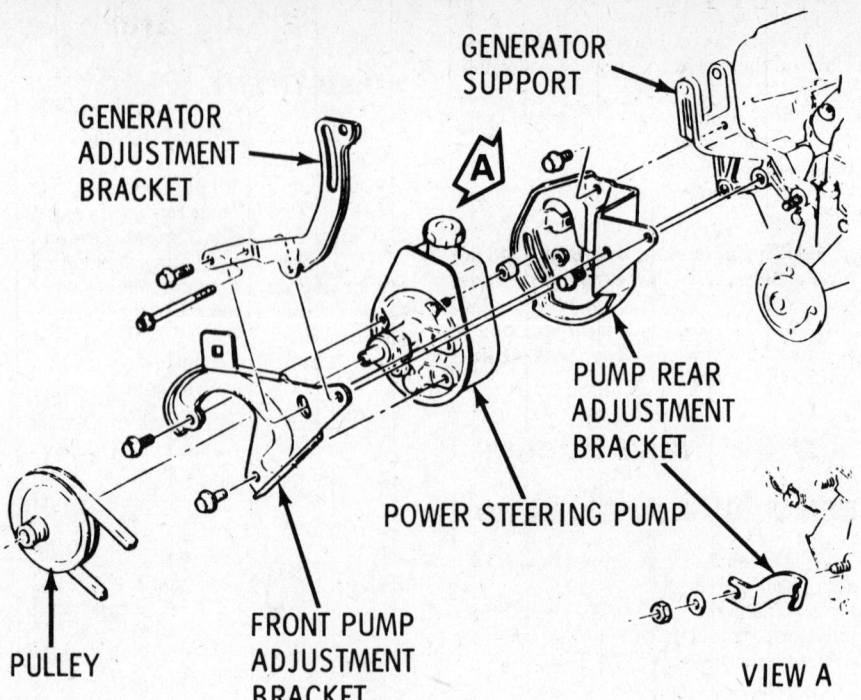

GENERATOR ADJUSTMENT BRACKET

GENERATOR SUPPORT

A

PUMP REAR ADJUSTMENT BRACKET

POWER STEERING PUMP

FRONT PUMP ADJUSTMENT BRACKET

PULLEY

VIEW A

TORQUE ALL FASTENERS SHOWN TO 50 N·m (35 FT. LBS.)

Power steering pump removal, 6-183

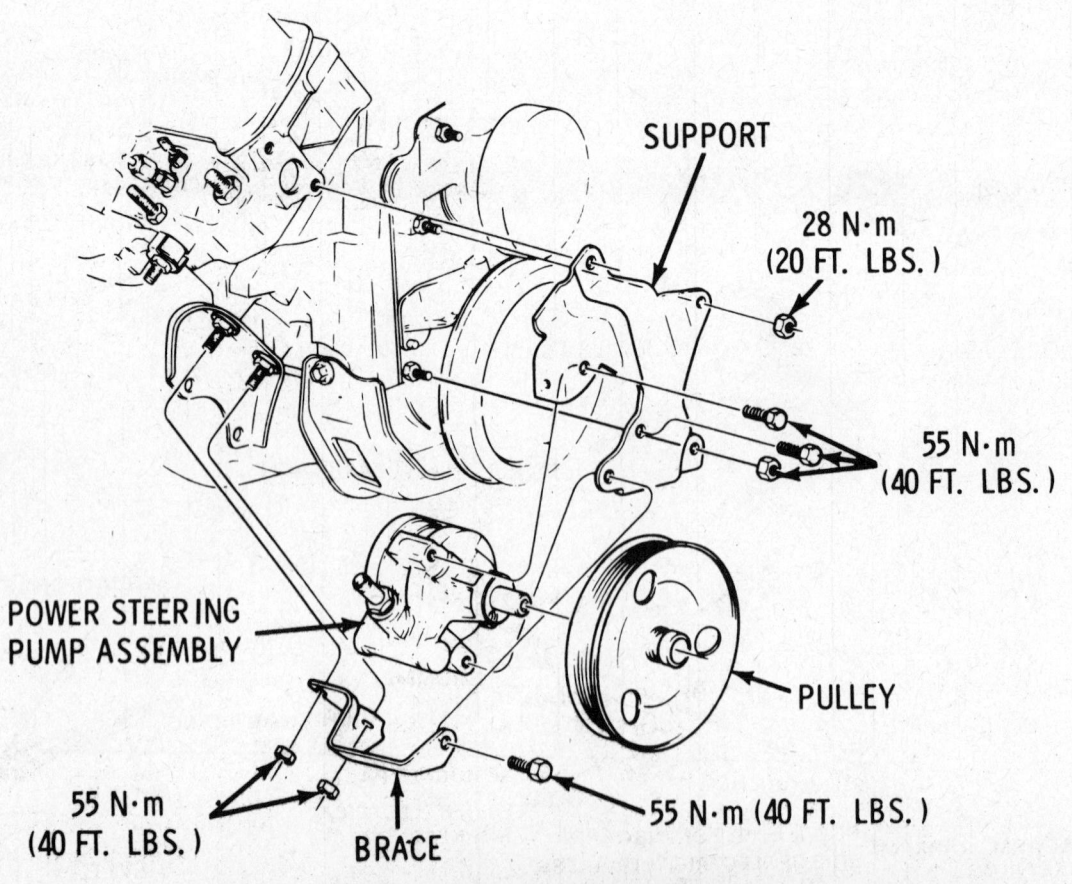

SUPPORT

28 N·m (20 FT. LBS.)

55 N·m (40 FT. LBS.)

POWER STEERING PUMP ASSEMBLY

PULLEY

55 N·m (40 FT. LBS.)

55 N·m (40 FT. LBS.)

BRACE

Power steering pump removal, 6-263

SPACER

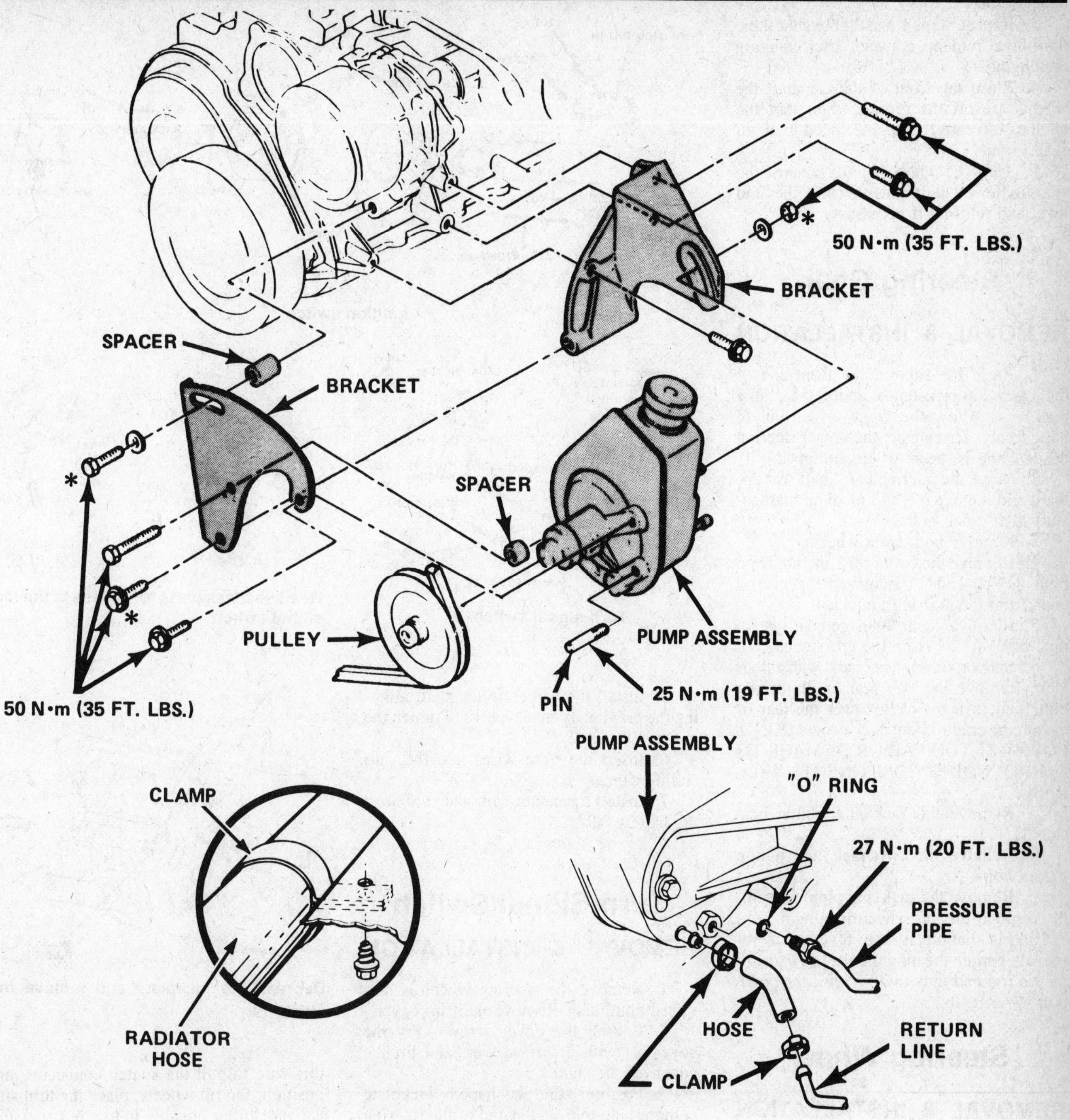

BRACKET

*

50 N·m (35 FT. LBS.)

50 N·m (35 FT. LBS.)

BRACKET

SPACER

PULLEY

PIN

PUMP ASSEMBLY

25 N·m (19 FT. LBS.)

PUMP ASSEMBLY

CLAMP

RADIATOR HOSE

"O" RING

27 N·m (20 FT. LBS.)

PRESSURE PIPE

HOSE

CLAMP

RETURN LINE

Power steering pump removal, 4-151

heater hose at the water pump. On the 6-183, remove the alternator.

4. Loosen the retaining bolts and any braces, and remove the pump.

5. Install the pump on the engine with the retaining bolts handtight.

6. Connect and tighten the hose fittings.

7. Refill the pump with fluid and bleed by turning the pulley counterclockwise (viewed from the front). Stop the bleeding when air bubbles no longer appear.

8. Install the pump belt on the pulley and adjust the tension.

9. Replace all other parts in reverse order of removal.

6-263 Diesel Engine

1. Remove the drive belt.

2. Siphon the fluid from the power steering reservoir.

3. Disconnect the hoses from the pump.

4. Remove the three bolts from the front of the pump through the access holes in the pulley.

5. Remove the two nuts holding the lower brace to the engine. Remove the brace.

6. Remove the pump.

7. Installation is the reverse of removal. Torque the brace nuts to 40 ft. lb.; the pump bolt to 40 ft. lb.

BLEEDING THE POWER STEERING SYSTEM

1. Fill the fluid reservoir.

2. Let the fluid stand undisturbed for two minutes, then crank the engine for about two seconds. Refill reservoir if necessary.

3. Repeat Steps 1 and 2 above until the fluid level remains constant after cranking the engine.

4. Raise the front of the car until the wheels are off the ground, then start the engine. Increase the engine speed to about 1,500 rpm.

5. Turn the wheels lightly against the stops to the left and right, checking the fluid level and refilling if necessary.

Steering Gear

REMOVAL & INSTALLATION

1. Raise tne support the front end of the car with jackstands under the frame members. Allow the front suspension to hang freely. Disconnect the power steering hoses from the gear, where equipped.

2. Move the intermediate shaft seal upward and remove the intermediate shaft-to-stub shaft pinch bolt.

3. Remove both front wheels.

4. Remove the cotter pins and nut from both tie rod ends. Disconnect the tie rod ends from the steering knuckles.

5. Remove the air management system pipe bracket bolt from the crossmember.

6. Support the engine cradle with a floor jack. Remove the two rear cradle mount bolts and, using a jack, lower the rear of the engine cradle about 4–5 inches. DON'T LOWER IT TOO FAR OR DAMAGE TO SURROUNDING COMPONENTS WILL RESULT.

7. Remove the rack and pinion heat shield.

8. Remove the two rack and pinion mount bolts.

9. Remove the rack and pinion assembly through the left wheel opening.

10. Installation is the reverse of removal. Torque the mount bolts to 70 ft. lb.; the tie rod end nuts to 30 ft. lb.; the pinch bolt to 45 ft. lb.

Steering Wheel

REMOVAL & INSTALLATION

——————— CAUTION ———————

Disconnect the battery ground cable before removing the steering wheel. When installing a steering wheel, always make sure that the turn signal lever is in the neutral position.

1. Remove the trim retaining screws from behind the wheel. On wheels with a center cap, pull off the cap.

2. Lift the trim off and pull the horn wires from the turn signal cancelling cam.

3. Remove the retainer and the steering wheel nut.

4. Mark the wheel-to-shaft relationship, and then remove the wheel with a puller.

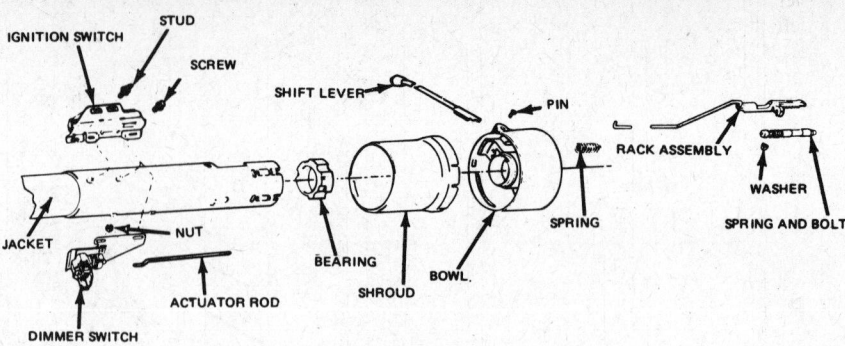

Ignition switch

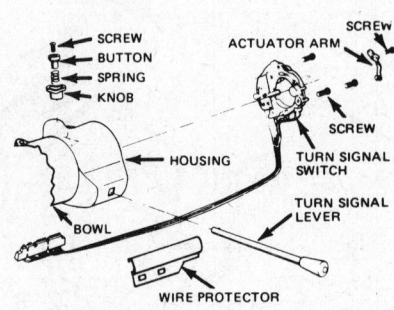

Turn signal switch

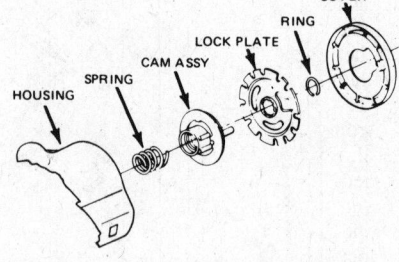

Remove these parts for access to the turn signal switch

5. Install the wheel on the shaft aligning the previously made marks. Tighten the nut to 30 ft. lbs.

6. Insert the horn wires into the cancelling cam.

7. Install the center trim and reconnect the battery cable.

Turn Signal Switch

REMOVAL & INSTALLATION

1. Remove the steering wheel as previously outlined. Remove the trim cover.

2. Loosen the cover screws. Pry the cover off with a screwdriver, and lift the cover off the shaft.

3. Position the U-shaped lockplate compressing tool on the end of the steering shaft and compress the lock plate by turning the shaft nut clockwise. Pry the wire snapring out of the shaft groove.

4. Remove the tool and lift the lockplate off the shaft.

5. Slip the cancelling cam, upper bearing preload spring, and thrust washer off the shaft.

6. Remove the turn signal lever. Push the flasher knob in and unscrew it. Remove the button retaining screw and remove the button, spring and knob.

7. Pull the switch connector out the mast jacket and tape the upper part to facilitate switch removal. Attach a long piece of wire to the turn signal switch connector. When installing the turn signal switch, feed this wire through the column first, and then use

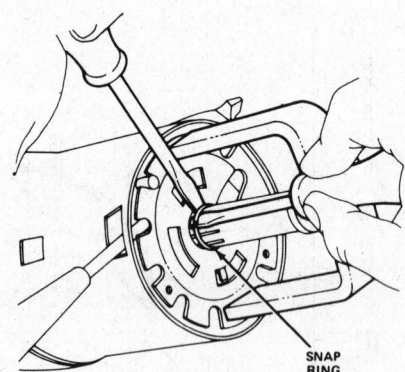

Depress the lockplate and remove the snapring

this wire to pull the switch connector into position. On tilt wheels, place the turn signal and shifter housing in low position and remove the harness cover.

8. Remove the three switch mounting screws. Remove the switch by pulling it straight up while guiding the wiring harness cover through the column.

9. Install the replacement switch by working the connector and cover down through the housing and under the bracket. On tilt models, the connector is worked down through the housing, under the bracket, and then the cover is installed on the harness.

10. Install the switch mounting screws and the connector on the mast jacket bracket. Install the column-to-dash trim plate.

11. Install the flasher knob and the turn signal lever.

12. With the turn signal lever in neutral and the flasher knob out, slide the thrust

washer, upper bearing preload spring, and cancelling cam onto the shaft.

13. Position the lock plate on the shaft and press it down until a new snapring can be inserted in the shaft groove. Always use a new snapring when assembling.

14. Install the cover and the steering wheel.

Ignition Switch

REPLACEMENT

The switch is located inside the channel section of the brake pedal support and is completely inaccessible without first lowering the steering column. The switch is actuated by a rod and rack assembly. A gear on the end of the lock cylinder engages the toothed upper end of the rod.

1. Lower the steering column; be sure to properly support it.

2. Put the switch in the "Off-Unlocked" position. With the cylinder removed, the rod is in "Lock" when it is in the next to the uppermost detent. "Off-Unlocked" is two detents from the top.

3. Remove the two switch screws and remove the switch assembly.

4. Before installing, place the new switch in "Off-Unlocked" position and make sure the lock cylinder and actuating rod are in "Off-Unlocked" (third detent from the top) position.

5. Install the activating rod into the switch and assemble the switch on the column. Tighten the mounting screws. Use only the specified screws since overlength screws could impair the collapsibility of the column.

6. Reinstall the steering column.

Ignition Lock Cylinder

REPLACEMENT

1. Place the lock in the Run position.

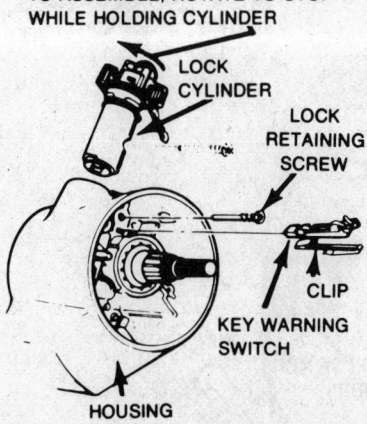

Ignition lock cylinder

TO ASSEMBLE, ROTATE TO STOP WHILE HOLDING CYLINDER

LOCK CYLINDER

LOCK RETAINING SCREW

CLIP

KEY WARNING SWITCH

HOUSING

INSTRUMENT PANEL

FRT

TRIM PLATE

Celebrity headlight switch

2. Remove the lock plate, turn signal switch and buzzer switch.

3. Remove the screw and lock cylinder.

— **CAUTION** —
If the screw is dropped on removal, it could fall into the column, requiring complete disassembly to retrieve the screw.

4. Rotate the cylinder clockwise to align cylinder key with the keyway in the housing.

5. Push the lock all the way in.

6. Install the screw. Tighten the screw to 14 inch lb. for adjustable columns and 25 inch lb. for standard columns.

INSTRUMENT PANEL

Headlight Switch

REPLACEMENT

1980 Citation

1. Disconnect the negative battery cable.
2. Pull the knob out to the ON position.
3. Remove the instrument cluster trim bezel attaching screws.
4. Remove the radio knobs and shaft nuts, and clock knob, if so equipped.
5. Pull the bezel rearward slightly and depress the shaft retaining button. Pull the knob and shaft from the switch.
6. Disconnect the accessory electrical connectors.
7. Remove the bezel.
8. Remove the switch retaining nut and push the switch out from its mounting hole.
9. Disconnect the electrical connector and remove the switch.

1981–85 Citation

1. Disconnect the negative battery cable.

---

2. Pull the headlamp switch knob out to the last detent.
3. Remove the spring clip retainer on the knob shaft and remove the shaft.
4. Disconnect all accessory switch connectors.
5. Remove the headlamp switch ferrule nut and push switch forward out of the mounting hole.
6. Lift the switch up and out through the opening above the switch mounting and disconnect the switch electrical connector.
7. Remove the switch from the instrument panel.
8. Installation is the reverse of removal.

Celebrity

1. Disconnect the battery ground.
2. Remove the headlamp switch knob.
3. Remove the instrument panel trim pad.
4. Unbolt the switch mounting plate from the instrument panel carrier.
5. Disconnect the wiring from the switch.
6. Remove the switch.
7. Installation is the reverse of removal.

Ciera and Omega

1. Remove the left side instrument panel trim pad.
2. Remove the three screws that attach the switch to the instrument panel.
3. Pull the switch rearward and remove it.
4. Installation is the reverse of removal.

6000 and Phoenix

1. Disconnect the battery ground.
2. Remove the steering column trim cover and headlight rod and knob by reaching behind the instrument panel and depressing the lock tab with a screwdriver.
3. Remove the left instrument panel trim plate.
4. Unbolt and remove the switch and bracket assembly from the instrument panel.

C563

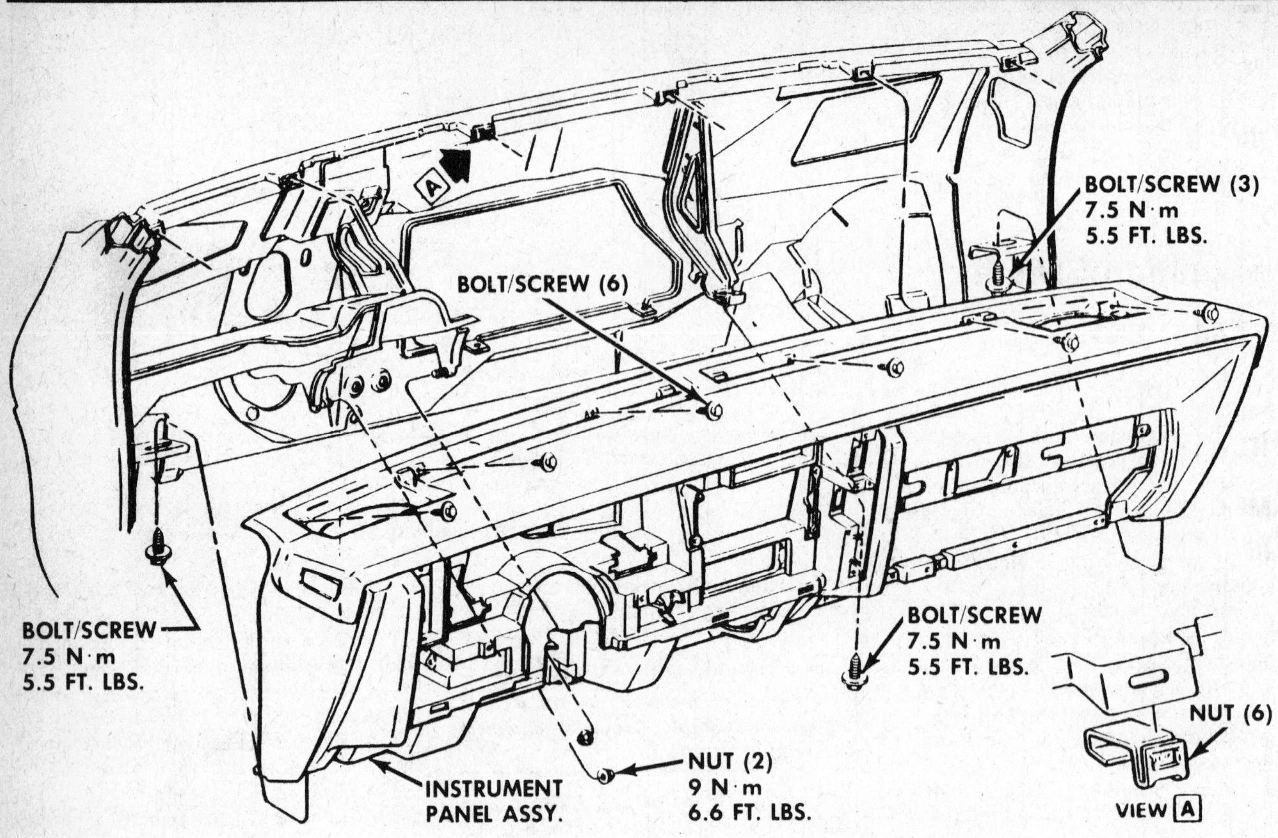

BOLT/SCREW (6)

BOLT/SCREW (3)
7.5 N·m
5.5 FT. LBS.

BOLT/SCREW
7.5 N·m
5.5 FT. LBS.

BOLT/SCREW
7.5 N·m
5.5 FT. LBS.

NUT (6)

VIEW A

INSTRUMENT PANEL ASSY.

NUT (2)
9 N·m
6.6 FT. LBS.

Century instrument panel carrier removal

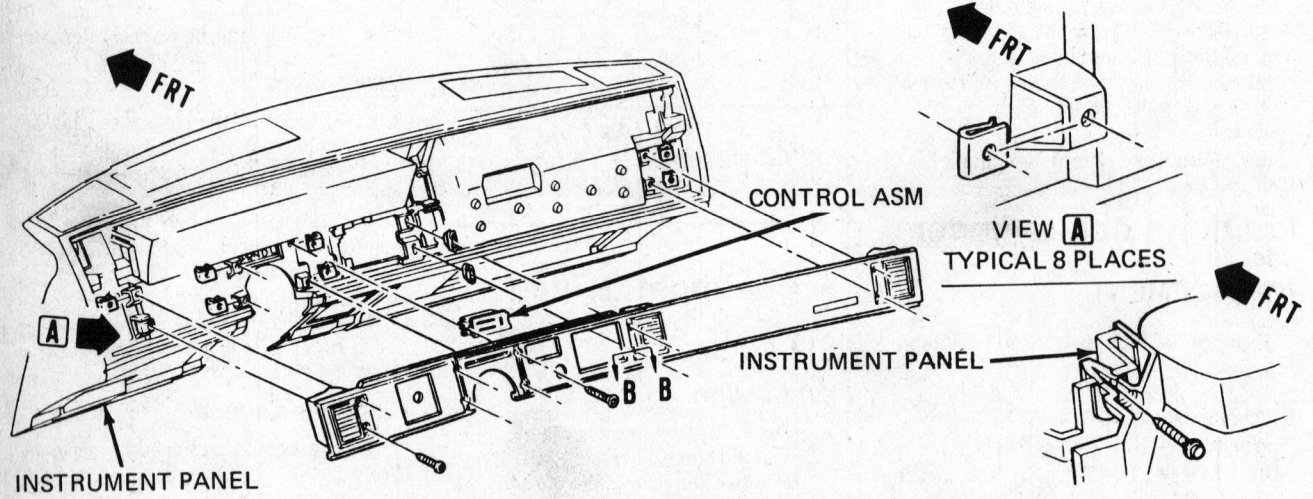

FRT

CONTROL ASM

FRT

VIEW A
TYPICAL 8 PLACES

FRT

A

B B

INSTRUMENT PANEL

INSTRUMENT PANEL

Celebrity instrument cluster trim pad removal

5. Loosen the bezel and remove the switch from the bracket.

6. Installation is the reverse of removal.

Skylark

1. Disconnect the negative battery cable.

2. Remove the light switch knob by depressing the retaining clip behind the knob and removing the knob from the shaft.

3. Turn the sleeve counterclockwise and spin the knob off the shaft.

4. Remove the instrument panel trim plate.

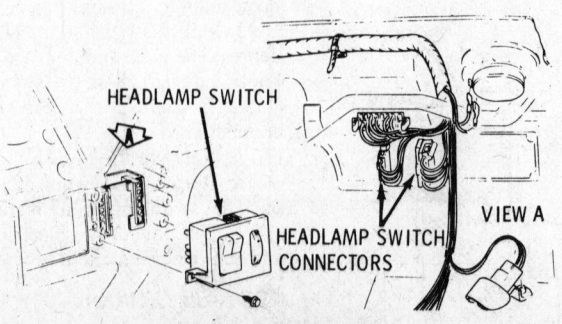

HEADLAMP SWITCH

HEADLAMP SWITCH CONNECTORS

VIEW A

Ciera headlight switch

5. Remove the mounting screws and unplug the switch.

6. Installation is the reverse of removal.

Century

1. Disconnect the battery ground.

2. Remove the instrument panel trim plate.

3. Remove the left side instrument panel switch trim panel by removing the three screws and gently rocking the panel out.

4. Remove the three screws and pull the switch straight out.

5. Installation is the reverse of removal.

Instrument Cluster

REMOVAL & INSTALLATION

Citation

1. Disconnect the negative battery cable.

2. Remove the radio knobs (pull off), the shaft nuts, and the clock knob.

3. Remove the instrument cluster bezel (trim plate) attaching screws; there are three at the top and one each in the two lower corners. Pull the bezel slightly rearward.

4. Remove the headlamp shaft and knob.

5. Disconnect the accessory switch wiring.

6. Remove the bezel.

7. Remove the four screws holding the instrument cluster to the instrument panel.

8. Disconnect the shift indicator cable from the steering column shift bowl on models with automatic transaxle.

• 9. Pull the cluster towards you and disconnect the speedometer cable and instrument electrical connections.

10. Remove the instrument cluster. Installation is the reverse.

Omega

1. Remove the steering column trim cover.

2. Lower the steering column.

3. Remove the four screws holding the instrument panel trim cover to the panel.

4. Pull the trim cover rearward and disconnect the switch wiring, and the remote control mirror cable if your car has one. Remove the trim panel.

5. Remove the four screws holding the instrument cluster to the panel.

6. Disconnect the shift indicator cable from the steering column shift bowl, if your Omega has an automatic transaxle.

7. Pull the cluster towards you and disconnect the speedometer cable and electrical wiring.

8. Remove the instrument cluster. Installation is the reverse.

Phoenix

1. Disconnect the negative battery cable.

2. Remove the speedometer cluster trim plate. There is one screw in each corner.

3. Remove the screws attaching the steering column trim cover to the instrument panel and remove the trim cover.

4. Remove the four cluster attaching screws.

5. With automatic transaxle, disconnect the shift indicator cable, marking the cable location on the steering column shift bowl prior to disconnecting.

6. Disconnect the speedometer cable and pull the cluster toward you. Disconnect the electrical wiring from the back of the cluster and remove the cluster. Installation is the reverse.

Skylark

1. Disconnect the negative battery cable.

2. Remove the radio and accessory switch knobs.

3. Remove the instrument panel trim plate.

4. With automatic transaxle, disconnect the shift indicator cable from the steering column shift bowl.

5. Remove the four cluster attaching screws.

6. Disconnect the speedometer cable and electrical wiring from the back of the cluster. Remove the cluster. Installation is the reverse.

Century

1. Disconnect the battery ground.

2. Disconnect the speedometer cable and pull it through the firewall.

3. Remove the left side hush panel by removing the three 7mm screws and one 11mm nut.

4. Remove the right side hush panel by removing the five 7mm screws and two 11mm nuts.

5. Remove the shift indicator cable clip.

6. Remove the steering column trim plate.

7. Put the gear selector in LOW, remove the nine retaining screws and gently pull out the instrument panel trim plate.

8. Disconnect the parking brake cable at the lever by pushing it forward and sliding it out of its slot.

9. Unbolt and lower the steering column (3 bolts and 1 nut).

10. Remove the gauge cluster by removing the four screws and pulling the cluster out far enough to disconnect any wires, then pull the cluster out.

11. Installation is the reverse of removal.

Celebrity

1. Disconnect battery ground cable.

2. Remove instrument panel hush panel.

3. Remove vent control housing (heater only vehicles).

4. On non A/C cars remove steering column trim cover screws and lower cover with vent cables attached. On A/C equipped vehicles, remove trim cover attaching screws (6) and remove cover.

5. Remove instrument cluster trim pad as outlined in this section.

6. Remove ash tray, retainer and fuse block, disconnect wires as necessary.

7. Remove headlamp switch knob and instrument panel trim plate and disconnect electrical connectors of any accessory switches in trim plate.

8. Remove cluster assembly and disconnect speedometer cable. PRNDL and cluster electrical connectors.

9. Installation is the reverse of removal.

Ciera

1. Remove left instrument panel trim pad.

2. Remove instrument panel cluster trim cover.

3. Disconnect speedometer cable at transmission or cruise control tranducer if equipped.

4. Remove steering column trim cover.

5. Disconnect shift indicator clip from steering column shift bowl.

6. Remove 4 screws attaching cluster assembly to instrument panel.

7. Pull assembly out far enough to reach behind cluster and disconnect speedometer cable.

8. Remove cluster assembly.

9. Installation is the reverse of removal.

6000

1. Remove the center and left-hand lower instrument panel trim plates.

2. Remove 6–8 screws holding instrument cluster to instrument panel carrier.

3. Remove instrument cluster lens to gain access to speedometer head and instruments/gages.

4. Installation is the reverse of removal.

Speedometer Cable

REPLACEMENT

1. Remove the instrument cluster.

2. Slide the cable out from the casing. If the cable is broken, the casing will have to be unscrewed from the transaxle and the broken piece removed from that end.

3. Before installing a new cable, slip a piece of cable into the speedometer and spin it between your fingers in the direction of normal rotation. If the mechanism sticks or binds, the speedometer should be repaired or replaced.

4. Inspect the casing; if it is cracked, kinked, or broken, the casing should be replaced.

5. Slide a new cable into the casing, engaging the transaxle end securely. Sometimes it is easier to unscrew the casing at the transaxle end, install the cable into the transaxle fitting, and screw the casing back into place. Install the instrument cluster.

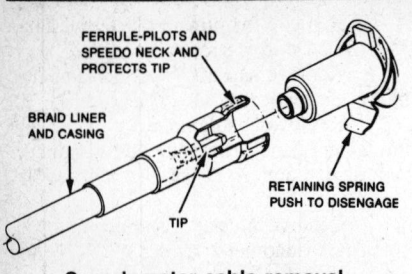

FERRULE-PILOTS AND
SPEEDO NECK AND
PROTECTS TIP

BRAID LINER
AND CASING

TIP

RETAINING SPRING
PUSH TO DISENGAGE

Speedometer cable removal

WINDSHIELD WIPERS

Motor

REMOVAL & INSTALLATION

A–Body Cars

1. Raise the hood.
2. Remove the grille.
3. Loosen the wiper linkage to drive arm attaching nuts.
4. Remove the transmission link from the drive arm.
5. Disconnect the wiring and hoses from the motor.
6. Unbolt and remove the motor.
7. Installation is the reverse of removal.

X–Body Cars

1. Remove the wiper arms.
2. Remove the lower windshield reveal molding, the front cowl panel and the cowl screen. Disconnect the washer hose under the screen.
3. Disconnect the motor electrical leads.
4. Loosen, but do not remove, the transmission drive link attaching nuts to the motor crank arm.
5. Disconnect the drive link from the motor crank arm.
6. Remove the three motor attaching bolts. On models with air conditioning, remove the bolts and while supporting the motor, remove the motor crank arm nut using lock-ring type pliers and a closed end wrench. The motor attaching bolts must be removed first to avoid damage to the nylon gear inside the motor. On all models, rotate the motor up and out to remove.
7. Reverse the procedure to install.

HEATER

Blower

REMOVAL & INSTALLATION

This procedure is for all cars, with or without air conditioning.

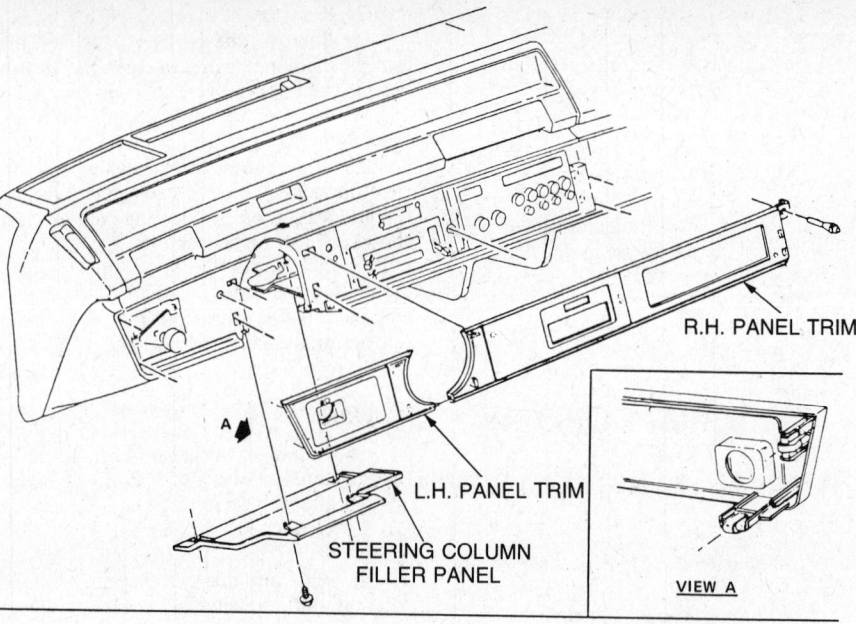

R.H. PANEL TRIM

L.H. PANEL TRIM

STEERING COLUMN
FILLER PANEL

VIEW A

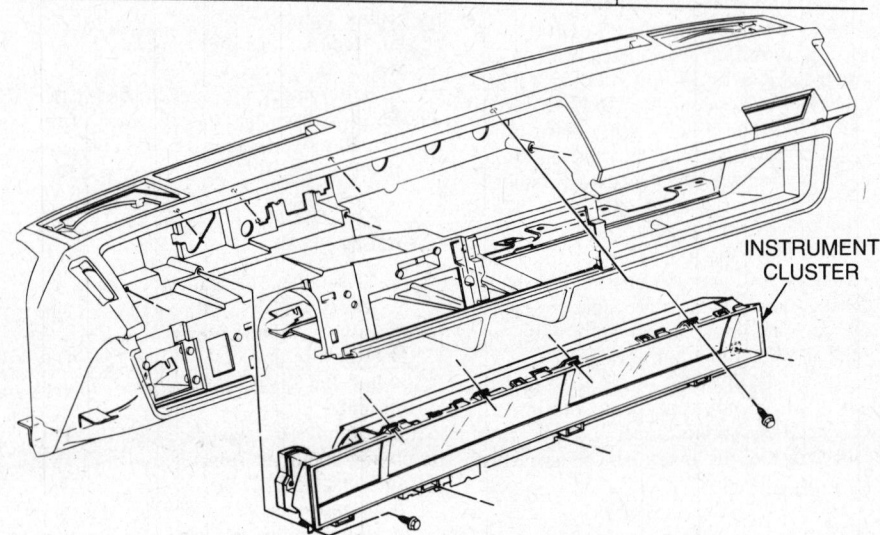

INSTRUMENT CLUSTER

Instrument panel cluster and trim—6000

1. Disconnect the negative cable at the battery.
2. Working inside the engine compartment, disconnect the blower motor electrical leads.
3. Remove the motor retaining screws, and remove the blower motor.
4. Reverse to install.

Heater Core

REMOVAL & INSTALLATION

Cars Without Air Conditioning

1. Drain the cooling system.
2. Remove the heater inlet and outlet hoses at the firewall, inside the engine compartment.
3. Remove the radio noise suppression strap.

4. Remove the heater core cover retaining screws. Remove the cover.
5. Remove the core. Reverse to install.

Cars With Air Conditioning

A–BODY CARS

1. Drain the cooling system.
2. On the diesel, raise and support the car on jackstands.
3. Disconnect the hoses at the core.
4. On the diesel, remove the instrument panel lower sound absorber.
5. Remove the heater duct and lower side covers.
6. Remove the lower heater outlet.
7. Remove the two housing cover-to-air valve housing clips.
8. Remove the housing cover.
9. Remove the core restraining straps.
10. Remove the core tubing retainers and lift out the core.

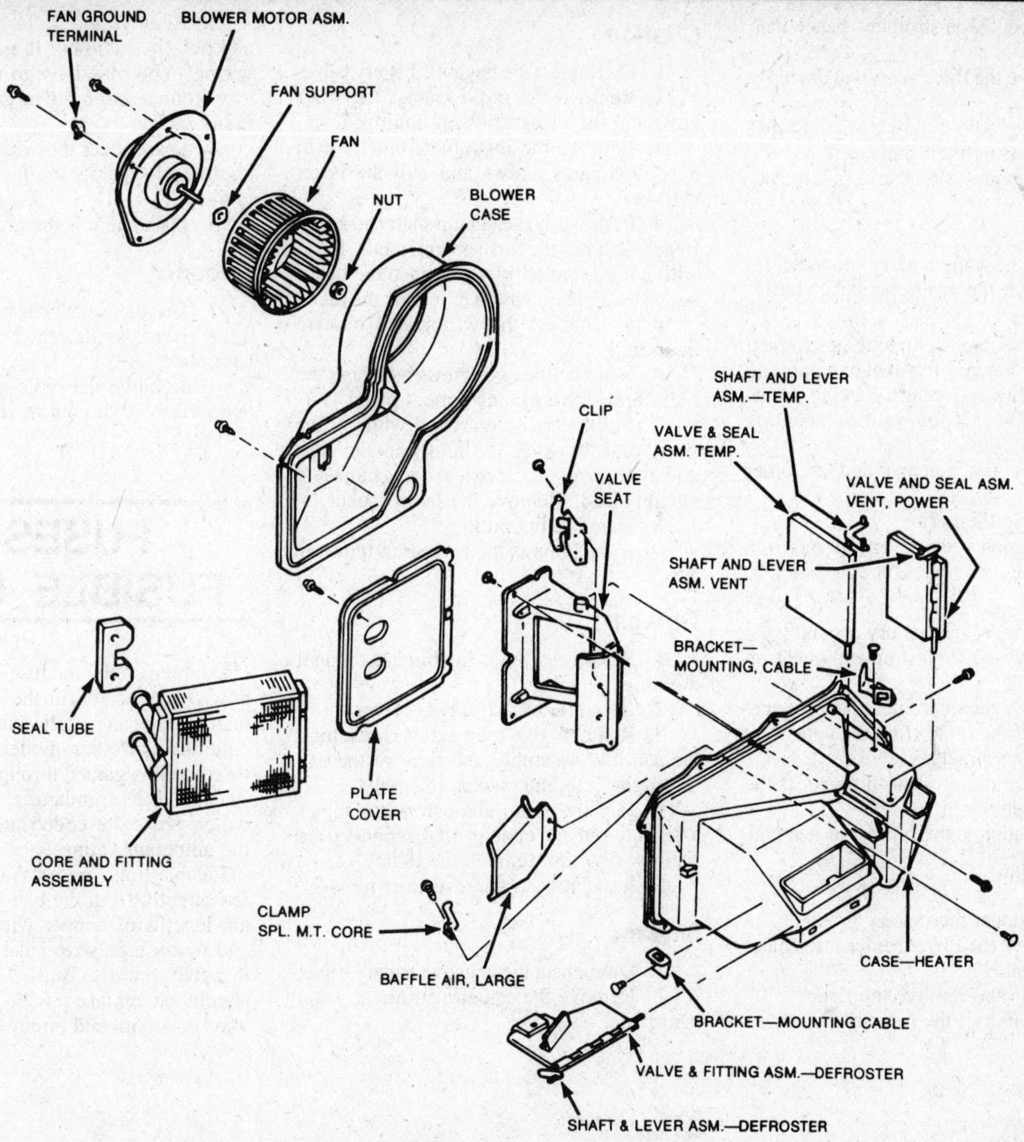

FAN GROUND TERMINAL

BLOWER MOTOR ASM.

FAN SUPPORT

FAN

NUT

BLOWER CASE

SHAFT AND LEVER ASM.—TEMP.

VALVE & SEAL ASM. TEMP.

VALVE AND SEAL ASM. VENT, POWER

CLIP

VALVE SEAT

SHAFT AND LEVER ASM. VENT

BRACKET— MOUNTING, CABLE

SEAL TUBE

CORE AND FITTING ASSEMBLY

PLATE COVER

CLAMP SPL. M.T. CORE

BAFFLE AIR, LARGE

CASE—HEATER

BRACKET—MOUNTING CABLE

VALVE & FITTING ASM.—DEFROSTER

SHAFT & LEVER ASM.—DEFROSTER

Heater assembly, without air conditioning

11. Installation is the reverse of removal.

X–BODY CARS

1. Drain the cooling system.
2. Remove the heater hoses from the core tubes at the firewall.
3. Remove the heater duct and heater case side cover from under the instrument panel.
4. Remove the core retaining clamps. Remove the inlet and outlet tube support clamps.
5. Remove the core. Reverse to install.

RADIO

REMOVAL & INSTALLATION

Celebrity

1. Disconnect the battery ground.

ON STYLES EQUIPPED WITH AIR CONDITIONING, REMOVE MOTOR ATTACHING BOLTS PRIOR TO REMOVING CRANK ARM ATTACHING NUT. CRANK ARM MUST BE REMOVED BEFORE MOTOR CAN BE LIFTED PAST A C EVAPORATOR UNIT.

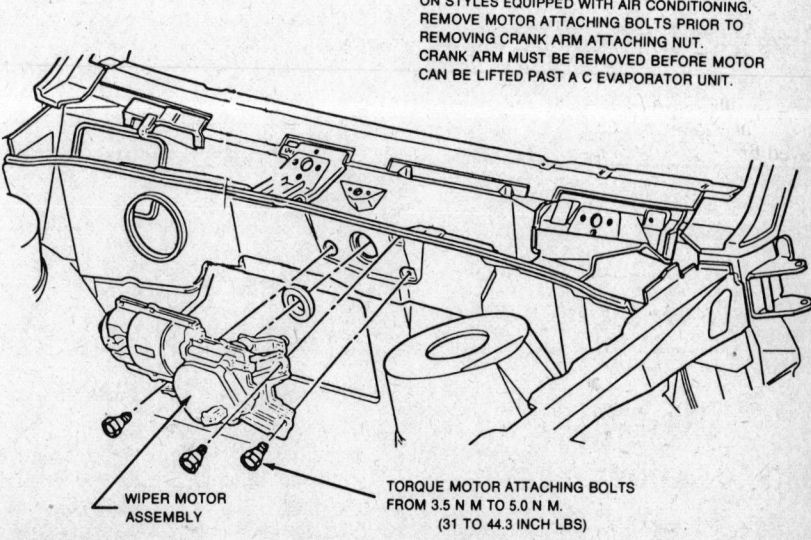

WIPER MOTOR ASSEMBLY

TORQUE MOTOR ATTACHING BOLTS FROM 3.5 N M TO 5.0 N M. (31 TO 44.3 INCH LBS)

Wiper motor removal

2. Remove the instrument panel trim plate.

3. Remove the three screws at the radio brackets.

4. Pull the radio out far enough to disconnect the wiring then remove it.

5. Installation is the reverse of removal.

Century

1. Disconnect the battery ground.

2. Remove the instrument panel trim plate.

3. Remove the right side instrument panel rocker switch trim panel by removing the three screws and gently rocking it out.

4. Remove the four radio mounting screws.

5. Unplug the antenna and all other wires.

6. Remove the radio.

7. Installation is the reverse of removal.

Ciera

1. Disconnect the battery ground.

2. Remove the left instrument panel trim pad.

3. Remove the instrument panel cover.

4. Unbolt the radio from the upper and lower mounting brackets.

5. Pull the radio out to disconnect the wires, then remove it.

6. Installation is the reverse of removal.

6000

1. Disconnect the battery ground.

2. Remove the lower center instrument panel trim plate.

3. Unbolt and remove the radio.

4. Installation is the reverse of removal.

Citation

1. Disconnect the negative battery cable.

2. Remove the radio knobs, the shaft nuts, and the clock knob, if equipped.

3. Remove the instrument cluster trim bezel attaching screws and pull the bezel rearward.

4. Remove the headlamp shaft and knob. Reach behind the instrument panel bezel with a long screwdriver and push the headlamp shaft release button to release the knob.

5. Disconnect the wiring and remove the bezel.

6. Remove the two screws attaching the radio bracket to the instrument panel.

7. Pull the radio rearward while at the same time twisting it slightly to the left, and disconnect the electrical connectors and antenna lead. Remove the lamp socket.

8. Remove the radio.

9. Installation is the reverse of removal.

Omega

1. Remove the instrument panel molding.

2. Remove the ash tray receiver.

3. Remove the four screws attaching the ash tray assembly and remove the ash tray light bulb and socket assembly.

4. Pull the radio and ash tray retainer assembly out far enough to disconnect the radio wiring and remove the radio.

5. Installation is the reverse of removal.

Skylark

1. Disconnect the negative battery cable.

2. Remove the center instrument panel trim plate.

3. Remove the radio attaching screws and pull the radio out to gain access to the wiring. You may have to remove the ashtray retainer assembly to gain access to the radio wiring.

4. Disconnect the wiring. Remove the knobs and separate the face plate from the radio.

5. Installation is the reverse of removal.

Phoenix

1. Disconnect the negative battery cable.

2. Remove the center instrument panel trim plate.

3. Remove the radio attaching screws and pull the radio out to gain access to the wiring.

FUSES & FUSIBLE LINKS

On some models, the fuse block is a swing-down unit located in the underside of the instrument panel, adjacent to the steering column. On other models, access to the fuse block is gained through the glove box. All models use miniaturized plug type fuses which are color-coded and stamped with the amperage rating.

Fusible links are provided in all circuits fed directly from the battery. Fusible links are lengths of copper wire, about 4″ long and four gauge sizes smaller than the wire that they protect. Burned out fusible links should be replaced with the same gauge wire for continued circuit protection.

GM "C" Body

Buick Electra Limited, Park Avenue, T-Type, Cadillac Fleetwood Brougham, DeVille, Oldsmobile 98 Regency, 98 Regency Brougham

YEAR IDENTIFICATION

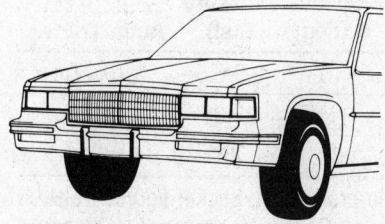

1985 Cadillac DeVille, Fleetwood

1985 Oldsmobile Ninety-Eight Regency Brougham

1985 Buick Electra, Park Avenue

VEHICLE IDENTIFICATION NUMBER (VIN)

It is important for servicing and ordering parts to be certain of the vehicle and engine identification. The VIN (vehicle identification number) is a 17 digit number visable through the windshield on the driver's side of the dash and contains the vehicle and engine identification codes. It can be interpreted as follows:

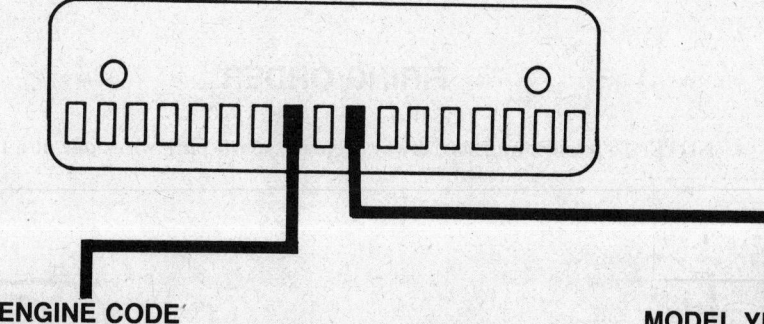

ENGINE CODE

Code	Cu. In.	Liters	Cyl.	Carb.	Eng. Mfg.
E	181	3.0	6	2	Buick
3	231	3.8	6	MFI	Buick
T	263	4.3	6	Diesel	Olds.
8	250	4.1	8	DFI	Cad.

MODEL YEAR CODE

Code	Year
F	85

The seventeen digit Vehicle Identification Number can be used to determine engine application and model year. The 10th digit indicates the model year, and the 8th digit identifies the factory installed engine.

MFI Multi-point Fuel Injection
DFI Digital Fuel Injection

GENERAL ENGINE SPECIFICATIONS

Year	Eng. V.I.N. Code	Engine Displacement Cu. In.	Eng. Mfg.	Fuel Delivery	Horsepower @ rpm ■	Torque @ rpm (ft lbs) ■	Bore x Stroke (in.)	Compression Ratio	Oil Pressure @ 2000 rpm
'85	E	6-181	Buick	2bbl	110 @ 4800	145 @ 2600	3.800 × 2.660	8.4:1	35-42
'85	3	6-231	Buick	MFI	125 @ 4400	195 @ 2000	3.800 × 3.400	8.0:1	35-40
'85	T	6-263	Olds.	Diesel	85 @ 3600	165 @ 1600	4.057 × 3.385	21.6:1	30-45
'85	8	8-250	Cad.	DFL	135 @ 4200	190 @ 2000	3.465 × 3.307	8.5:1	30

■ Horsepower and torque are SAE net figures. They are measured at the rear of the transmission with all accessories installed and operating. Since the figures vary when a given engine is installed in different models, some are representative rather than exact.
MFI Multi-Point Fuel Injection
DFI Digital Fuel Injection

GASOLINE ENGINE TUNE-UP SPECIFICATIONS

(When analyzing compression test results, look for uniformity among cylinders rather than specific pressures.)

Year	Eng. V.I.N. Code	No. Cyl. Displacement (cu. in.)	Eng. Mfg.	Fuel Delivery	Spark Plugs Orig. Type	Spark Plugs Gap (in.)	Distributor Point Dwell (deg)	Distributor Point Gap (in.)	Ignition Timing (deg) ▲ Auto. Trans.	Valves Intake Opens ■ (deg)	Fuel Pump Pressure (psi)	Idle Speed (rpm) ▲ Auto. Trans.
'85	E	6-181	Buick	2 bbl	R44TSX	.060	Electronic		① ②	16	3.9-6.5	① ②
'85	3	6-231	Buick	MFI	R44TS8	.080	Electronic		① ②	NA	28-36	① ②
'85	8	8-250	Cad.	DFI	R42CLTS6	.060	Electronic		① ②	37	40	① ②

NOTE: The underhood specifications sticker often reflects tune-up specification changes made in production. Sticker figures must be used if they disagree with those in this chart. Part numbers in this chart are not recommendations by Chilton for any product by brand name.
▲ See text for procedure.
■ All figures Before Top Dead Center
① See Underhood Specifications Sticker
② Only vehicles equipped with computerized emissions systems (which have no distributor vacuum advance unit), the idle speed and ignition timing are controlled by the emissions computer. These adjustments should be performed professionally on models so equipped.

FIRING ORDER

NOTE: To avoid confusion, always replace spark plug wires one at a time.

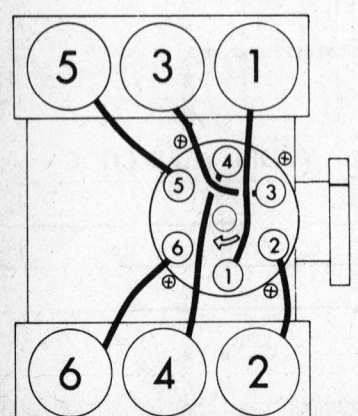

V 6 harmonic balancers have two timing marks: one is ⅛ in. wide. Use the ¹⁄₁₆ in. mark for timing with a hand held light. The ⅛ in. mark is used only with a magnetic timing pick-up probe.

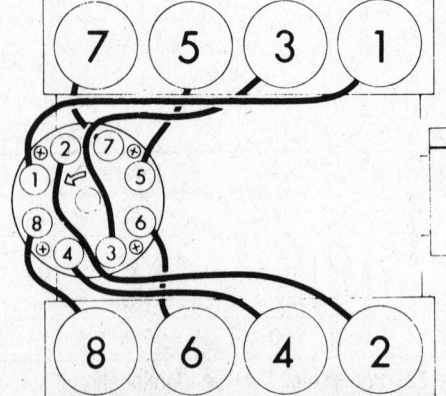

Buick 181, 231 V6 (3.0L, 3.8L) Engine firing order: 1-6-5-4-3-2 Distributor rotation: clockwise.

Cadillac 250 V8 (4.1L) Engine firing order: 1-8-4-3-6-5-7-2 Distributor rotation: counterclockwise

DIESEL ENGINE TUNE-UP SPECIFICATIONS

Year	Engine No. of cyl.- Displacement- Manufacturer	Fuel Pump Pressure (psi)	Compression Pressure (psi)②	Intake Valve Opens (°B.T.D.C.)	Idle Speed (rpm)
'85	6-263-Olds.	5.5-6.5	275 minimum	16	①

① See the Underhood Specifications Sticker

CAPACITIES

Year	Engine No. Cyl. Displacement (Cu. In.)	Engine Crankcase Add 1 Qt For New Filter	Transaxle Automatic Pts To Refill After Draining ●	Gasoline Tank (gals)	Cooling System (qts) With Heater	With A/C
'85	6-181	4.0	13	18	13.3	13.6
'85	6-231	4.0	13	18	13.1	13.2
'85	6-263	5.5	13	18	13.3	13.3
'85	8-250	4	13	NA	NA①	NA①

● Specifications do not include torque converter
NA Not available at time of publication
① The 4.1L V8 uses a coolant solution specifically designed for use in aluminum engines. Be sure that the coolant you choose meets GM spec. #1825M or is labeled for use in aluminum engines.

VALVE SPECIFICATIONS

Year	Engine No. Cyl. Displacement (cu in.)	Seat Angle (deg)	Face Angle (deg)	Spring Test Pressure (lbs @ in.)	Spring Installed Height (in.)	STEM-TO-GUIDE CLEARANCE (in.) Intake	Exhaust	STEM DIAMETER (in.) Intake	Exhaust
'85	6-181	45	45	220 @ 1.340	1.727	0.0015-0.0035	0.0015-0.0032	0.3401-0.3412	0.3405-0.3412
'85	6-231	45	45	220 @ 1.340	1.727	0.0015-0.0035	0.0015-0.0032	0.3401-0.3412	0.3405-0.3412
'85	6-263	①	②	210 @ 1.220	1.670	0.0010-0.0027	0.0015-0.0032	0.3425-0.3432	0.3420-0.3427
'85	8-250	45	44	182 @ 1.280	—	0.001-0.003	0.001-0.003	0.3413-0.3420	0.3411-0.3418

① Intake: 45   ② Intake: 44
  Exhaust: 31   Exhaust: 30

CRANKSHAFT AND CONNECTING ROD SPECIFICATIONS

(All measurements are given in inches)

Year	V.I.N. Code	Engine No. Cyl. Displacement (cu. in.)	Eng. Mfg.	Crankshaft Main Brg. Journal Dia.	Main Brg. Oil Clearance	Shaft End-Play	Thrust on No.	Connecting Rod Journal Diameter	Oil Clearance	Side Clearance
'85	E	6-181	Buick	2.4990-2.5000	0.0003-0.0018	0.0030-0.0110	2	2.2487-2.2495	0.0005-0.0026	0.006-0.023
'85	3	6-231	Buick	2.4990-2.5000	0.0003-0.0018	0.0030-0.0110	2	2.2487-2.2495	0.0005-0.0026	0.006-0.023

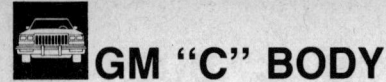

CRANKSHAFT AND CONNECTING ROD SPECIFICATIONS

(All measurements are given in inches)

Year	V.I.N. Code	Engine No. Cyl. Displacement (cu. in.)	Eng. Mfg.	Crankshaft Main Brg. Journal Dia.	Crankshaft Main Brg. Oil Clearance	Crankshaft Shaft End-Play	Thrust on No.	Connecting Rod Journal Diameter	Connecting Rod Oil Clearance	Connecting Rod Side Clearance
'85	T	6-263	Olds.	2.9993–3.0003	①	0.0035–0.0135	4	2.2490–2.2500	0.0005–0.0025	0.008–0.018
'85	8	8-250	Cad.	2.64	0.0004–0.0027	0.0010–0.0070	3	2.0520–2.0540	0.0005–0.0028	0.008–0.020

① No. 1, 2, & 3: 0.0005–0.0020
No. 4: 0.0020–0.0034

CAMSHAFT SPECIFICATIONS

(All measurements in inches)

Year	V.I.N. Code	Engine	Eng. Mfg.	Journal Diameter 1	Journal Diameter 2	Journal Diameter 3	Journal Diameter 4	Journal Diameter 5	Bearing Clearance	Lobe Lift Intake	Lobe Lift Exhaust	Camshaft End Play
'85	E	6-181	Buick	1.786	1.786	1.786	1.786	1.786	①	0.406	0.406	—
'85	3	6-231	Buick	1.786	1.786	1.786	1.786	1.786	①	0.406	0.406	—
'85	T	6-263	Olds.	②	2.015–2.016	1.995–1.996	1.975–1.976	—	0.0020–0.0059	0.252	0.279	0.0008–0.0228
'85	8	8-250	Cad.	—	—	—	—	—	0.0018–0.0037	0.384	0.396	—

① No. 1: 0.0005–0.0025
No. 2-5: 0.0005–0.0035
② No. 1 bearing is not borable, but must be replaced separately.

PISTON AND RING SPECIFICATIONS

(All measurements are given in inches. To convert inches to metric units, refer to the Metric Information section.)

Year	V.I.N. Code	Engine Type/ Disp. cu. in.	Eng. Mfg.	Piston-to-Bore Clearance	Ring Gap Top Compression	Ring Gap Bottom Compression	Ring Gap Oil Control	Ring Side Clearance Top Compression	Ring Side Clearance Bottom Compression	Ring Side Clearance Oil Control
'85	E	6-181	Buick	0.0008–0.0020	0.010–0.020	0.010–0.020	0.015–0.055	0.0030–0.0050	0.0030–0.0050	0.0035 max.
'85	3	6-231	Buick	0.0008–0.0020	0.010–0.020	0.010–0.020	0.015–0.055	0.0030–0.0050	0.0030–0.0050	0.0035 max.
'85	T	6-263	Olds.	0.0035–0.0045	0.019–0.027	0.013–0.021	0.010–0.022	0.005–0.007	0.003–0.005	0.001–0.005
'85	8	8-250	Cad.	0.0010–0.0018	0.023–0.025	0.023–0.025	0.010–0.050	0.0016–0.0037	0.0016–0.0037	None (side sealing)

TORQUE SPECIFICATIONS
(All readings in ft. lbs.)

Year	V.I.N. Code	Engine No. Cyl. Displacement (cu. in.)	Eng. Mfg.	Cylinder Head Bolts	Rod Bearing Bolts	Main Bearing Bolts	Crankshaft Bolt	Flywheel-to-Crankshaft Bolts	Manifold	
									Intake	Exhaust
'85	E	6-181	Buick	80	40	100	200	60	47	25
'85	3	6-231	Buick	80	40	100	200	60	47	25
'85	T	6-263	Olds.	①	42	89	②	76	41	31
'85	8	8-250	Cad.	45③	22	85	18	63	0④	18

① All exc. bolt No. 5, 6, 11, 12, 13, 14: 142 } See text
Bolt No. 5, 6, 11, 12, 13, 14: 59
② Crankshaft balancer to crankshaft bolt: 203-350
Crankshaft pulley to balancer bolts: 30
③ See text for proper tightening sequence
④ Bolts No. 1, 2, 3, 4: 15 }
Bolts No. 5-16: 22
All bolts: 22 } See text
Repeat 3rd step

WHEEL ALIGNMENT SPECIFICATIONS

Year	Model	Caster*		Camber		Toe (in.)	Steering Axis (deg) Inclination
		Range (deg)	Pref Setting (deg)	Range (deg)	Pref Setting (deg)		
'85	All	1¹³⁄₁₆–2¹³⁄₁₆	2⁵⁄₁₆	0-1	½	0	—

CHARGING SYSTEM

For all information on the charging system not detailed below, please refer to "Charging and Starting" in the Unit Repair section.

Alternator

REMOVAL & INSTALLATION

1. Disconnect the negative battery cable.
2. Tag and disconnect the battery charge wire, 3-prong connector and the ground wire at the back of the alternator.
3. Remove the brace at the back of the alternator (if so equipped).
4. Loosen the adjusting bolt, swivel the alternator in and remove the drive belt.
5. Loosen the power steering pump brace mounting bolts.
6. Support the alternator, remove the mounting bolts and then remove the alternator.
7. Installation is in the reverse order of removal. Adjust the drive belt to have ¼–½ in. play midway along the longest free-span of the belt.

Voltage Regulator

An alternator with an integral voltage regulator is standard equipment. There are no adjustments possible with this unit. Testing procedures can be found in the Unit Repair section.

STARTING SYSTEM

For all information concerning the starter which is not detailed below, please refer to "Charging and Starting" in the Unit Repair section.

Starter

REMOVAL & INSTALLATION

All Except Diesel

1. Disconnect the negative battery cable.
2. Raise and support the vehicle on jackstands.
3. Tag and disconnect all wires at the solenoid.

NOTE: On some models it may be necessary to remove the crossover pipe to complete this procedure.

6. Installation is in the reverse order of removal. Don't forget any shims!

Diesel

1. Disconnect the negative battery cable.
2. Raise and support the vehicle on jackstands.
3. Remove the lower starter shield nut and then carefully bend the shield out of the way.
4. Tag and disconnect the starter leads at the starter.
5. Remove the front starter bolt. Loosen

the rear starter mounting bolt and then remove the starter with the rear bolt still in the housing.

6. Installation is in the reverse order of removal.

IGNITION SYSTEM

NOTE: See the "Oldsmobile Rear Wheel Drive" section for a description of the diesel engine compression-ignition process.

All models are equipped with the HEI distributor and ignition system. These models are also equipped with electronic spark timing (EST). The HEI-EST distributor uses no mechanical or vacuum advance and is easily identified by the absence of a vacuum advance unit and the presence of a four terminal connector. There are no contact points or condensor to replace on this distributor, nor any cam or rubbing block to wear out, thus eliminating any normal distributor maintenance.

NOTE: When using an auxiliary starter switch on AEI systems, the distributor BATT lead must be disconnected. Failure to do this may cause damage to the grounding circuit in the ignition switch.

For further information on the ignition system, please refer to "Electronic Ignition Systems" in the Unit Repair section.

HEI SYSTEM TACHOMETER HOOKUP

On all models, there is a terminal on the distributor cap marked TACH (usually next to the BAT terminal). Connect one tachometer lead to this terminal and the other lead to a suitable ground. On some tachometers, the leads must be connected to the TACH terminal and then to the positive battery terminal.

—— CAUTION ——
Never ground the TACH terminal; serious module and ignition coil damage will result. If there is any doubt as to the correct tachometer hookup, check with the tachometer manufacturer.

Distributor

REMOVAL & INSTALLATION

1. Disconnect the negative battery cable.
2. Tag and disconnect all wires leading from the distributor cap. DO NOT use a screwdriver or other tool to release the locking tabs.

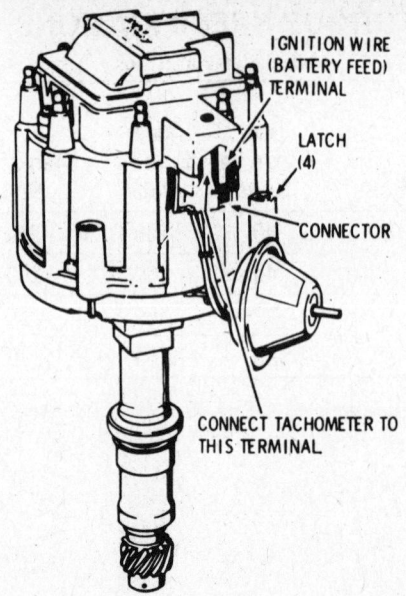

HEI coil-in-cap distributor tachometer hook-up

3. Remove the distributor cap by turning the four latches counterclockwise. Lift off the distributor cap and carefully set it aside.

NOTE: The location of the distributor cap "doghouse" must be in the same position on reinstallation in order to provide sufficient clearance for adjustment.

4. Disconnect the four terminal ECM connector harness from the distributor if not already done.
5. Loosen, but do not remove, the distributor hold-down clamp.

NOTE: On the 8-250 engine, a special tool, #J-29791, will be required to loosen the hold-down clamp bolt.

6. Scribe a mark on the distributor body to note the initial position of the rotor. Pull the distributor upward until the rotor just stops turning (counterclockwise); note the position of the rotor once again. Remove the distributor.

NOTE: Do not crank the engine with the distributor removed.

7. On certain models, a thrust washer is used between the distributor drive gear and the crankcase. This washer may stick to the bottom of the distributor as it is removed. Always make sure that this washer is at the bottom of the distributor bore before installation.

NOTE: On DFI systems (Digital Fuel Injection), the malfunction trouble codes must be cleared after removal or adjustment of the distributor. This is accomplished by removing battery voltage to terminal "R" for 10 seconds. See the CCC system in "Emission Controls" in the Unit Repair section for an explanation.

8. To install the distributor, rotate the distributor shaft until the rotor aligns with the second mark you made (when the shaft stopped moving). Lubricate the drive gear with clean engine oil, and install the distributor into the engine. As the distributor is installed, the rotor should rotate to the first mark you made in Step 6. This will ensure proper timing. If the marks do not align properly, remove the distributor and try again.

NOTE: Don't forget the thrust washer when installing the distributor, if so equipped.

9. Install the clamp and hold-down bolt. Tighten them until the distributor can just be moved with a little effort.
10. Connect all wires and hoses. Install the distributor cap. Check the ignition timing and adjust if necessary.

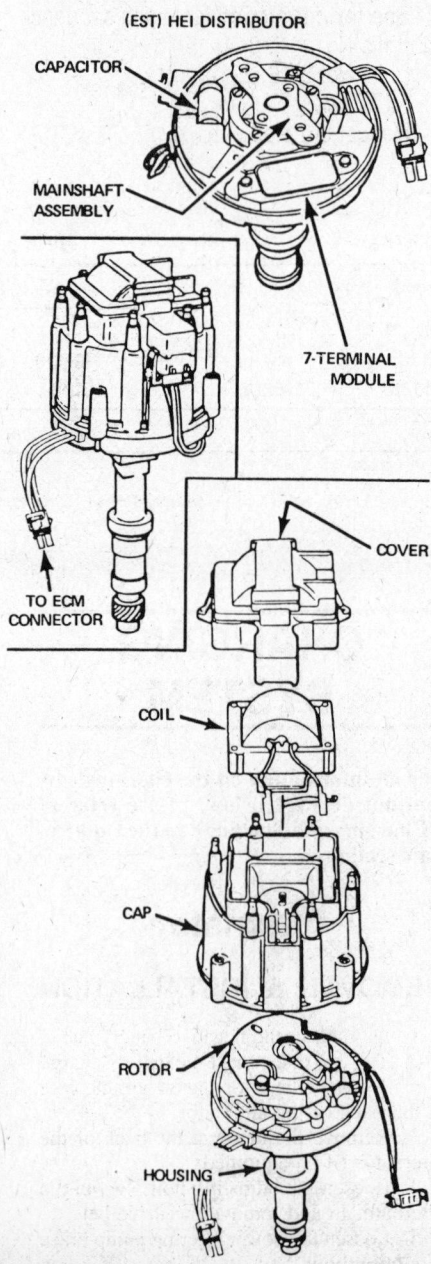

Exploded view of the HEI distributor

INSTALLATION (ENGINE DISTURBED)

If the engine has been disturbed (cranked) after removing the distributor, perform the following procedure for installation:

1. Crank the engine until No. 1 piston is at the top of its compression stroke (TDC). The compression stroke can be determined by removing the spark plug from No. 1 cylinder and placing your thumb over the hole while an assistant slowly cranks the engine. Crank until compression is felt at the hole and then continue cranking slowly until the timing mark on the crankshaft pulley lines up with the zero degrees (0°) timing mark located on the timing chain cover.

2. Position the distributor in the block but do not, at this time, allow it to engage with its drive gear at the base of the mounting hole.

3. Rotate the distributor shaft so that the rotor points between No. 1 and No. 8 spark plug towers on the V8, No. 1 and No. 6 on the V6 and push the distributor down to engage the camshaft. It may be necessary to turn the rotor a small amount in either direction in order to achieve this engagement. The rotor will rotate slightly as the distributor gear engages. If installed correctly, the rotor should point toward the No. 1 spark plug terminal in the distributor cap.

4. Press down firmly on the distributor housing. This will ensure that the distributor shaft engages the oil pump shaft, thereby allowing the distributor to full contact the engine block.

5. Install the hold-down clamp and tighten the bolt until it is snug.

6. Install the distributor cap, making sure that the rotor points to No. 1 terminal in the cap.

7. Attach all wires and hoses.

8. Start the engine. If it fails to start, or runs roughly, the distributor may be 180° out of time. Lift up on the distributor, turn the rotor one-half revolution, and install the distributor. Repeat Steps 1–8 if the engine continues to run poorly.

9. Check the timing and change it as necessary.

Ignition Timing

ADJUSTMENT

NOTE: The 4.1L V8 engine incorporates a magnetic timing probe hole for use with special electronic timing equipment. Consult manufacturer's instructions before using this system.

1. Connect a timing light to the No. 1 spark plug wire according to the light manufacturer's instructions. DO NOT PIERCE THE SPARK PLUG WIRE TO CONNECT THE TIMING LIGHT.

2. Follow the instructions on the tune up label located in the engine compartment.

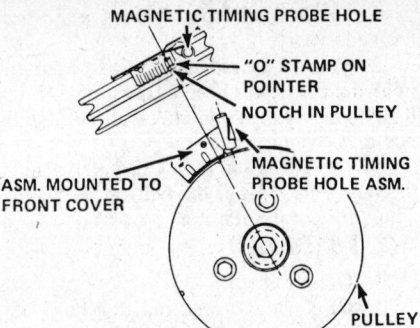

The 4·1L V8 incorporates a special magnetic timing probe hole

3. On models with Electronic Spark Timing (EST) distributor, disconnect the 4 terminal plug at the distributor. Identification of the EST distributor is given in the emission controls part of this car section, under Computer Command Control.

4. Start the engine and run it at idle speed.

5. Aim the timing light at the degree scale just over the harmonic balancer.

6. Adjust the timing by loosening the securing clamp and rotating the distributor until the desired ignition advance is achieved, then tighten the clamp.

NOTE: On the 4.1-250 cu. in. V-8 engine a special tool No. J-29791 is used to loosen the hold down nut.

7. On the four cylinder, loosen the distributor clamp outer bolt, then slide the clamp back slightly. Do not remove the retaining bolt.

8. Adjust the timing, then replace and tighten the clamp. To advance the timing, rotate the distributor opposite the normal direction of rotor rotation. Retard the timing by rotating the distributor in the normal direction of rotor rotation.

NOTE: On DFI systems (Digital Fuel Injection), the malfunction trouble codes must be cleared after removal or adjustment of the distributor. This is accomplished by removing battery voltage to terminal "R" for 10 seconds. See the CCC system in "Emission Controls" in the Unit Repair section for an explanation.

FUEL SYSTEM

NOTE: For service procedures for both the gasoline and diesel engine fuel systems, please refer to the "Buick/Cadillac Rear Wheel Drive" section, or the "GM A and X Body" section.

For further information on fuel injection, please refer to "Fuel Injection" in the Unit Repair section.

For further information on the diesel engine, please refer to "Diesel Maintenance" in the Unit Repair section.

COOLING SYSTEM

RADIATOR

REMOVAL & INSTALLATION

1. Disconnect the negative battery cable.
2. Drain the coolant.

On the 4.1L V8:

3. Detach the electrical connectors, remove the mounting bolts and then remove the left and right cooling fans.

4. Loosen the clamp-screws and remove the coolant reservoir and upper radiator hoses.

5. Disconnect the engine, transaxle and auxiliary oil cooler lines at the radiator. Wire the lines out of the way.

6. Disconnect the lower radiator hose at the radiator.

7. Remove the mounting bolts and lift out the radiator.

On all other engines:

8. Remove the upper fan mounting bolts (the 4.3L diesel engine has two cooling fans like the 4.1L V8).

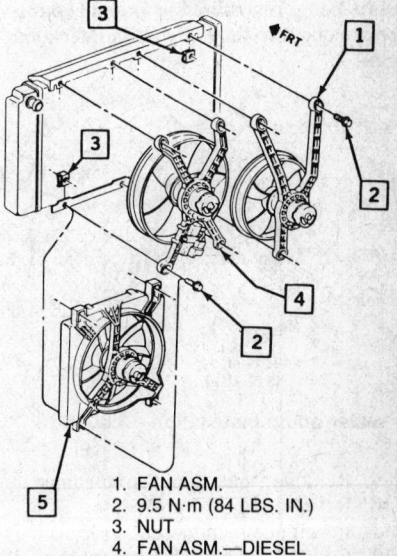

1. FAN ASM.
2. 9.5 N·m (84 LBS. IN.)
3. NUT
4. FAN ASM.—DIESEL
5. FAN ASM.—GAS

Certain models utilize two cooling fans

9. Disconnect the upper air cleaner duct and/or silencer on the Ninety Eight.

10. Unscrew the mounting bolts and remove the upper radiator valance panel.

11. Unscrew the clamp-screws and disconnect the coolant recovery tank hose and the upper radiator hose from the radiator.

12. Disconnect the transaxle and engine (diesel only) oil cooler lines from the radiator side tank. Wire them out of the way.

13. Unscrew the mounting bolts and then lift the radiator from the engine compartment.

14. Installation is in the reverse order of removal.

NOTE: When installing the engine oil cooler lines on the diesel, always use new O-rings. Tighten to 26 ft. lbs. (35 Nm).

Water Pump

REMOVAL & INSTALLATION

3.0L V6

1. Disconnect the negative battery cable.
2. Remove accessory drive belts.
3. Remove water pump attaching bolts.
4. Remove the engine support strut.
5. Place a floor jack under the front crossmember of the cradle and raise the jack until the jack just starts to raise the car.
6. Remove the front two body mount (#1 and #3) bolts with the lower cushions and retainers.
7. Thread the body mount bolts with retainers a minimum of three (3) turns into the cage so that the bolts restrain cradle movement.
8. Release the floor jack slowly until the crossmember contacts the body mount bolt retainers. As the jack is being lowered watch and correct any interference with hoses, lines, pipes and cables.

NOTE: Do not lower the cradle without its being restrained as possible damage can occur to the body and underhood items.

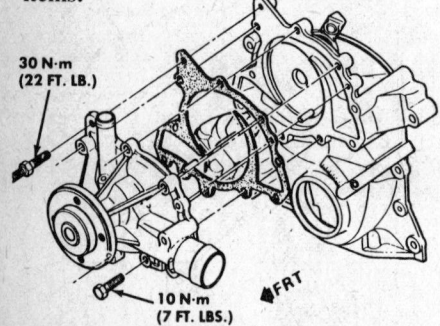

30 N·m
(22 FT. LB.)

10 N·m
(7 FT. LBS.)

◄FRT

Water pump installation—3.0L V6

9. Remove water pump from engine.
10. Reverse removal procedure.
11. Install pump and torque to 25 ft. lb.
12. Connect negative battery cable.
13. Fill with coolant and check for leaks.

3.8L V6

1. Drain the cooling system. Remove the fan shroud, if necessary for clearance.
2. Loosen the belt or belts, then remove the fan blades and pulley or pulleys from the hub on the water pump shaft. Remove the belt or belts.
3. Disconnect the hose from the water pump inlet and the heater hose from the nipple. Remove the bolts, then remove the pump and gasket from the timing case cover or engine block.
To install the pump:
1. Install the pump assembly with a new gasket. Bolts and lock washers must be torqued evenly.
2. Connect the radiator hose to the pump inlet and the heater hose to the nipple. Fill the cooling system and check all points of possible coolant leaks.
3. Install the fan pulley or pulleys and the fan blade. Install the belt or belts and adjust for correct tension.

4.3L V6 (Diesel)

1. Drain radiator.
2. Disconnect lower radiator hose at water pump.
3. Disconnect the heater return hose at the water pump, remove the bolt retaining the heater water return pipe to the intake manifold and position the pipe out-of-the-way.
4. If equipped with A/C, remove the vacuum pump drive belt.
5. Remove the serpentine drive belt.
6. Remove the generator, A/C compressor or vacuum pump brackets.
7. Remove the water pump attaching bolts and remove the water pump assembly.
8. Remove the water pump pulley.
9. Clean gasket material from engine block.
10. Apply a thin coat of 1050026 sealer or equivalent to the water pump housing to retain the gasket, then position new gasket on the housing. Also apply sealer to water pump mounting bolts. Torque bolts to 12–15 ft. lb.

4.1L V8

1. Disconnect the negative battery terminal.
2. Drain the coolant.
3. Disconnect the A/C accumulator from the bracket and then position it out of the way. Disconnect the bracket from the wheel arch.

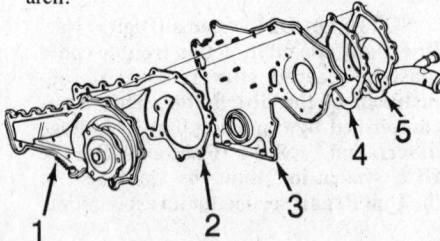

1. WATER PUMP ASSEMBLY
2. WATER PUMP GASKET
3. FRONT COVER
4. WATER PUMP INLET GASKET
5. WATER PUMP INLET

Water pump installation—4.1L V8

4. Remove the right side cross-car brace.
5. Remove the drive belt, the idler pulley and the bracket.
6. Unscrew the three mounting bolts and remove the water pump pulley.
7. Remove the water pump and gasket.
8. Installation is in the reverse order of removal. Always use a new water pump gasket.

Thermostat

REMOVAL & INSTALLATION

To replace the thermostat, drain the cooling system below the level of the thermostat and remove the two bolts holding the water neck in place. Remove the water neck and the thermostat will lift out. Clean the mating surfaces of both the intake manifold and the water neck. Use a new gasket when installing a new thermostat. If only silicone sealer was used from the factory, use only sealer during assembly.

REFER TO FIGURE 1

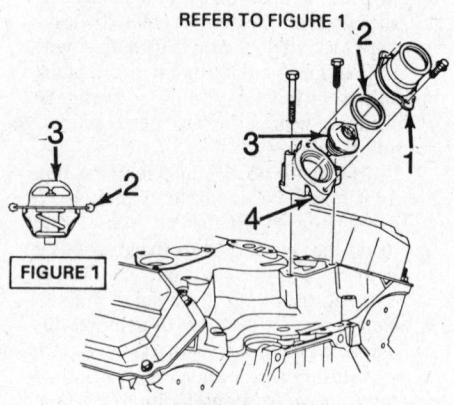

FIGURE 1

1. UPPER HOUSING
2. GASKET
3. THERMOSTAT ASSEMBLY
4. LOWER HOUSING

Thermostat installation—4.L V8

— CAUTION —
Be sure the thermostat is not reversed in its installed position. The spring should be installed toward the engine.

EMISSION CONTROLS

The emission control systems on your car are listed below. For a description of and service for each system, please refer to "Emission Controls" in the Unit Repair section.

- Positive Crankcase Ventilation
- Evaporative Emission Control
- Early Fuel Evaporation System
- Catalytic Converter
- Exhaust Gas Recirculation
- Computer Command Control
- Deceleration Valve
- Computer Controlled Catalytic Converter
- Air Injection Reactor
- Controlled Combustion System
- Transmission Converter Clutch
- Electronic Spark Control
- Electronic Spark Timing
- Thermostatic Air Cleaner

ENGINE

NOTE: For all engine service procedures not detailed below, please refer to the "Buick Rear Wheel Drive" section (3.8L V6), "Cadillac Rear Wheel Drive" section (4.1 V8) or the "GM A & X Body" section (3.0L V6, 4.3L V6).

Engine
REMOVAL & INSTALLATION

3.0L V6 and 3.8L V6

1. Disconnect the negative battery cable.
2. Tag and disconnect the air flow sensor wiring.
3. Disconnect the air intake duct. Drain the engine coolant.
4. Raise the front of the vehicle and support it on jackstands.
5. Unscrew the retaining bolts and separate the exhaust pipe from the manifold.
6. Loosen and remove the engine mount bolts.
7. Remove the bolts and then disconnect the driveline vibration absorber.

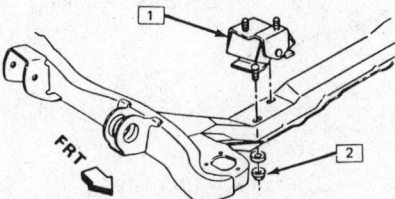

1. ENGINE MOUNT
2. NUT 41 N·m (30 FT. LBS.)

Right side engine mounts—3.0L V6 and 3.8L V6

8. Tag and disconnect the starter wiring and then remove the starter.
9. Disconnect the A/C compressor and position it out of the way. DO NOT disconnect the refrigerant lines.
10. Disconnect the hydraulic lines at the power steering pump and wire them out of the way.
11. Loosen and remove the lower transaxle-to-engine bolts.

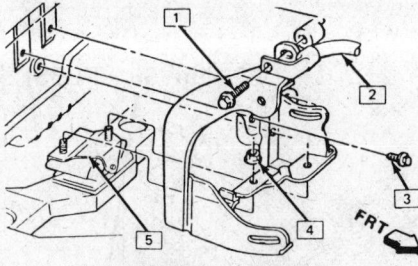

1. BOLT 50 N·m (37 FT. LBS.)
2. NEGATIVE BATTERY CABLE
3. BOLT 95 N·m (70 FT. LBS.)
4. NUT 35 N·m (25 FT. LBS.)
5. ENGINE MOUNT

Left side engine mounts—3.0L V6 and 3.8L V6

NOTE: One bolt is situated between the transaxle case and the engine block. It is installed in the opposite direction of the other bolts.

12. Remove the flexplate cover. Matchmark the flexplate-to-torque converter relationship to insure proper alignment upon installation. Remove the flexplate-to-torque converter bolts.
13. Disconnect the engine support bracket at the transaxle and then lower the vehicle.
14. Disconnect the Radiator and heater hoses at the engine and position them out of the way.

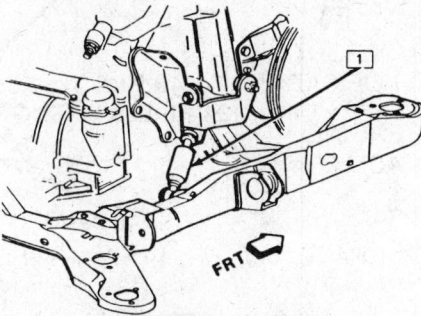

1. DRIVELINE VIBRATION ABSORBER

Typical driveline vibration absorber

15. Remove the alternator and rotate to the cowl.
16. Disconnect the engine wiring harness.
17. Remove the remaining upper transaxle-to-engine bolts.
18. Install a lifting fixture to the engine and remove the engine from the vehicle.
19. Installation is the reverse of the removal procedure.

4.1L V8

1. Disconnect the negative battery cable. Drain the radiator coolant.
2. Remove the air cleaner. Matchmark the hood to the support brackets and remove the hood.
3. Disconnect the A/C hose strap from the strut tower. Disconnect the A/C accumulator from its bracket and position it out of the way.
4. Tag and disconnect the canister hoses and ground wire from the accumulator bracket and then remove the bracket itself from the inner strut tower.
5. Disconnect or remove the cooling fans, the drive belt and the radiator and heater hoses.
6. Tag and disconnect the following:
   a. Oil pressure switch
   b. Coolant temperature sensor
   c. Distributor wires
   d. EGR solenoid
   e. Engine temperature switch
   f. Accelerator cable.
   g. Cruise control linkage
   h. Transmission TV
7. Remove the cruise control diaphragm and its bracket.
8. Remove the vacuum supply hose and the exhaust cross over pipe.

9. Disconnect the oil cooler lines at the oil filter adapter, unscrew their mounting bracket at the transaxle and position them out of the way.
10. Remove the air cleaner mounting bracket.
11. CAREFULLY bleed the fuel pressure at the Schraeder valve and then disconnect the fuel lines at the throttle body.

CAUTION

When bleeding the fuel system, be sure to have a container or rags on hand to catch excess fuel.

12. Unscrew the fuel line bracket at the transaxle and wire the fuel lines out of the way.
13. Tag and disconnect the small vacuum line at the brake booster.
14. Tag and disconnect the AIR solenoid electrical and hose connections. Remove the AIR valves and bracket.
15. Tag and disconnect the wires at the following:
   a. ISC
   b. TPS
   c. Fuel injectors
   d. MAT sensor
   e. Oxygen sensor
   f. Throttle body base warmer
   g. Alternator
16. Remove the idler pulley. Remove the power steering pump hose strap from the stud-headed bolt in front of the right cylinder head. Remove the stud-headed bolt.
17. Remove the AIR pipe clip near the No. 2 spark plug.
18. Remove the power steering pump and belt tensioner (with bracket). Wire them out of the way.
19. Raise the vehicle and support it on jack stands.
20. Tag and disconnect the starter wires and the ground wire at the cylinder block.
21. Remove the two flex plate covers. Remove the starter. Remove the three flexplate-to-converter bolts.
22. Remove the A/C compressor lower dust shield.
23. Remove the right front wheel. Remove the outer wheelhouse plastic shield.
24. Remove the A/C compressor mounting bolts and lower the compressor out of the way.
25. Remove the lower radiator hose.
26. Remove the driveline vibration dampener and its brackets from the lower right front of the engine and cradle.
27. Remove the three right front engine-to-transaxle bracket bolts.
28. Disconnect the exhaust pipe at the manifold. Remove the AIR pipe-to-converter bracket from the exhaust manifold stud.

NOTE: Be careful not to lose the springs when detaching the exhaust pipe.

29. Remove the lower right hand bell housing-to-engine bolt. Support the engine with a jack.
30. Remove the five upper bell housing-

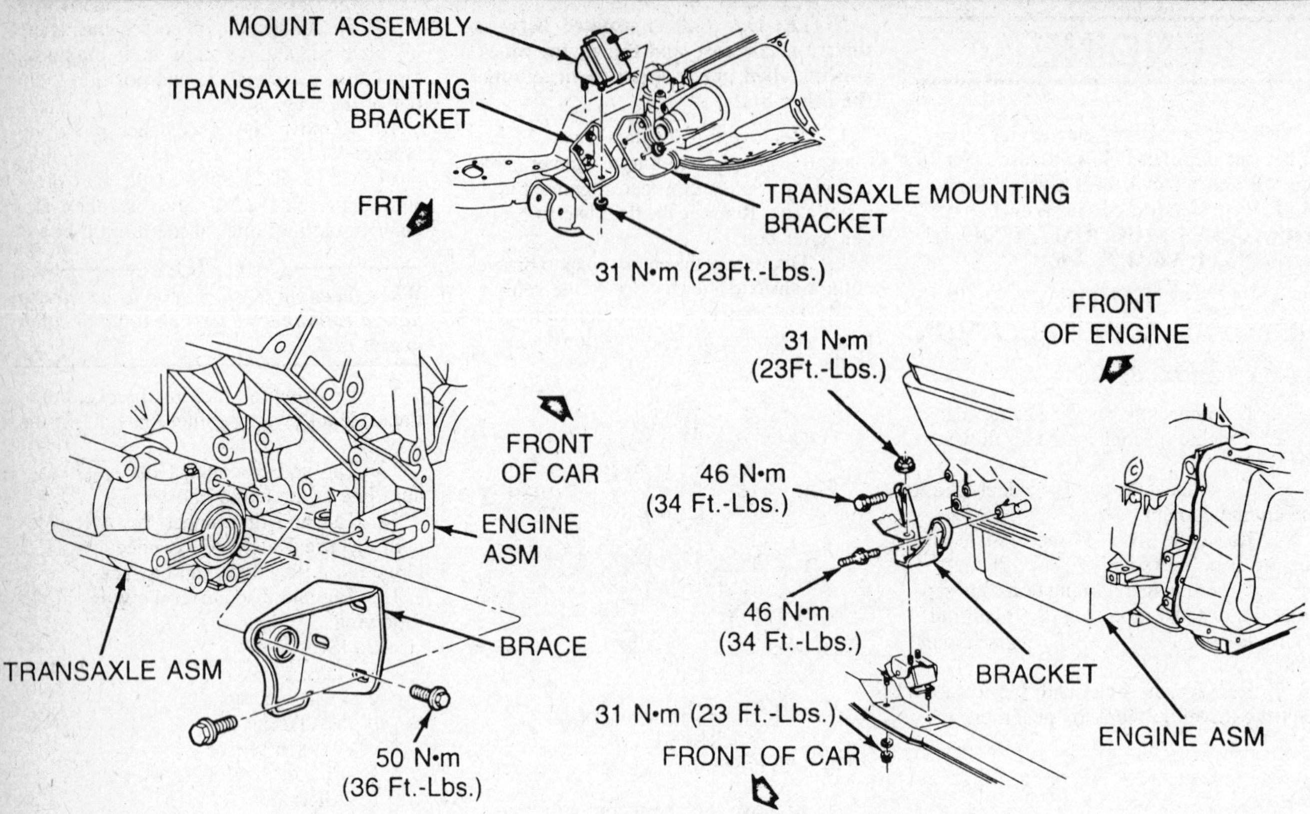

MOUNT ASSEMBLY

TRANSAXLE MOUNTING BRACKET

FRT

TRANSAXLE MOUNTING BRACKET

31 N•m (23Ft.-Lbs.)

FRONT OF ENGINE

31 N•m (23Ft.-Lbs.)

46 N•m (34 Ft.-Lbs.)

46 N•m (34 Ft.-Lbs.)

FRONT OF CAR

ENGINE ASM

BRACE

TRANSAXLE ASM

50 N•m (36 Ft.-Lbs.)

31 N•m (23 Ft.-Lbs.)

FRONT OF CAR

BRACKET

ENGINE ASM

Right side engine, brace and transaxle mounts—4.1L V8

TRANSAXLE MOUNTING BRACKET

31 N•m (23 FT-LBS)

A

B

TRANSAXLE MOUNTING BRACKET

FRT

31 N•m (23 FT-LBS)

FRAME ASM

52 N•m (38 FT-LBS)

FRT

FRT

GUIDE — OIL COOLER PIPES

52 N•m (38 FT-LBS) VIEW A

VIEW B

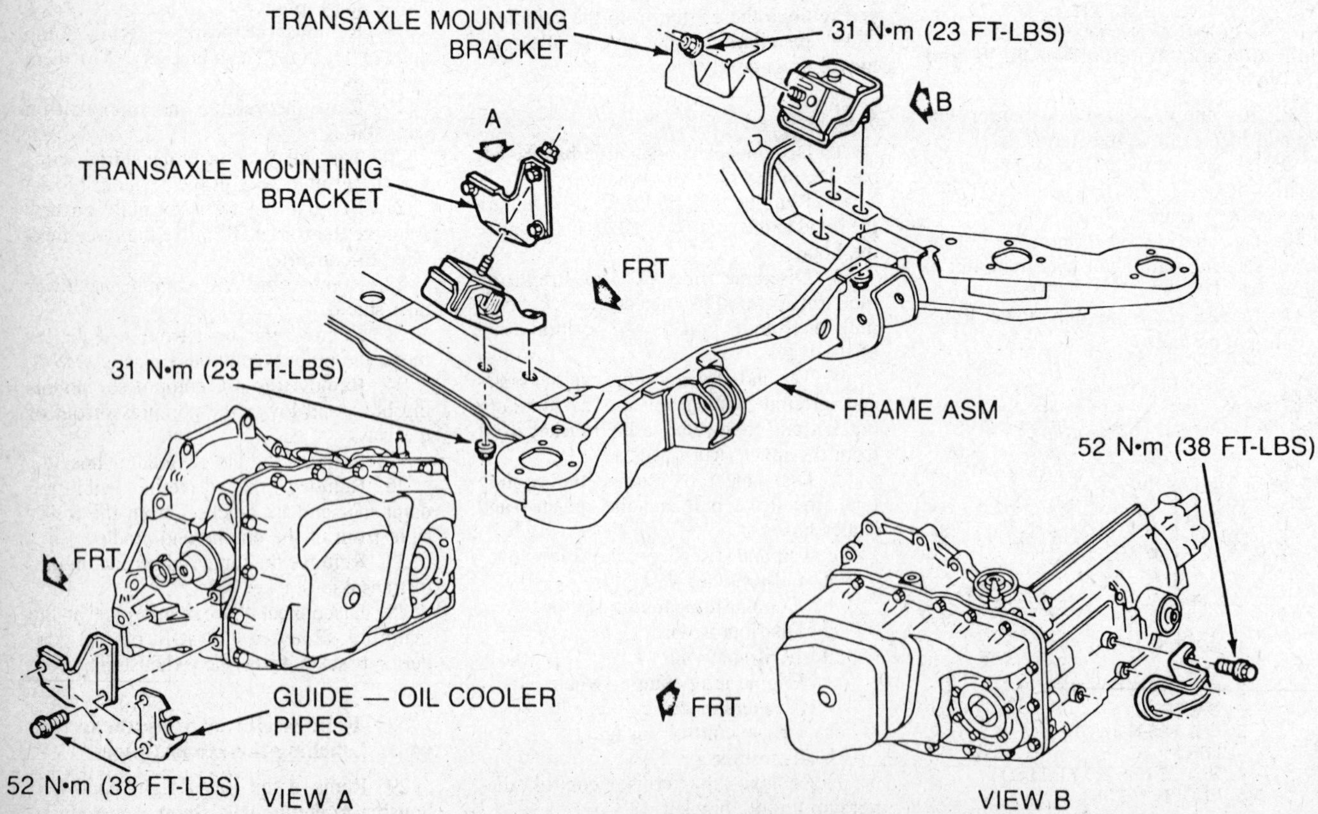

Left side transaxle mounts—4.1L V8

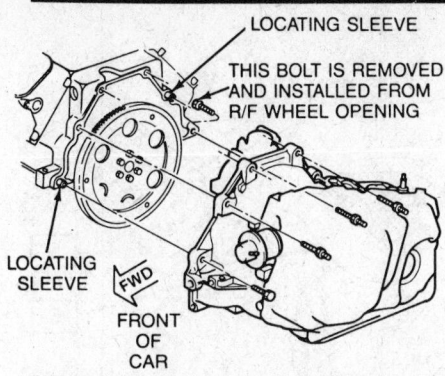

Transaxle-to-engine attaching bolts—4.1L V8

to-engine bolts. Remove the three left front engine mount bracket-to-engine bolts.

31. Attach a suitable lifting fixture and remove the engine.

32. Installation is in the reverse order of removal.

4.3L V6 (Diesel)

1. Disconnect the negative battery cable. Matchmark the hood to the support brackets and then remove the hood. Drain the cooling system.

2. Remove the serpentine drive belt. Remove the vacuum drive belt.

3. Remove the air cleaner. Install an air crossover screen cover (#J-26996-1) or the equivalent.

4. Tag and disconnect the ground wires at the inner fender panel and the engine ground strap.

5. Raise the vehicle and support it on jack stands.

6. Remove the engine-to-transaxle brace.

7. Remove the flywheel cover and then remove the flywheel-to-torque converter bolts.

8. Disconnect the exhaust pipe from the rear exhaust manifold.

9. Remove the engine mount-to-cradle retaining nuts and washers.

10. Remove the engine absorbers assembly from the frame bracket.

11. Tag and disconnect the following:
    a. Starter motor wires
    b. Glow plug wire at No. 2 cylinder
    c. Battery ground cable

12. Disconnect the lower oil cooler hose and cap the opening.

13. Remove the accessible power steering pump bracket fasteners. Lower the vehicle.

14. Remove the remaining power steering pump bracket/brace fasteners and lower the pump (with hoses connected) out of the way.

15. Disconnect the heater water return pipe.

16. Tag and disconnect the remaining glow plug leads and all other electrical leads connected to the engine.

17. Disconnect the engine harness at the cowl connector and body-mounted relays.

18. Remove the A/C compressor with the lines and brackets attached. Wire the compressor out of the way.

19. Disconnect all fuel and vacuum lines.

NOTE: Cap all open fuel lines.

20. Disconnect the throttle and TV cables at the injection pump and cable brackets.

21. Disconnect the upper oil cooler line. Cap the openings.

22. Remove the crossover pipe heat shield and the transaxle filler tube.

23. Remove the exhaust crossover pipe.

24. Install a suitable engine lifting device to the lift hooks on the block.

25. Use a floor jack to support the transaxle under the rear extension housing.

26. Remove the engine-to-transaxle bolts and remove the engine.

27. Installation is in the reverse order of removal.

Exhaust Manifold

REMOVAL & INSTALLATION
3.0L V6 and 3.8L V6

LEFT SIDE

1. Disconnect the negative battery cable.

2. Remove the mass air flow sensor, air intake duct and crankcase ventilation pipe.

3. Remove the two bolts attaching the exhaust crossover pipe to the manifold.

4. Tag and disconnect the spark plug wires.

5. Remove the mounting bolts and remove the manifold.

NOTE: The oil dipstick tube may need to be removed to provide access to the manifold bolts.

6. Installation is in the reverse order of removal.

RIGHT SIDE

1. Disconnect the negative battery cable.

2. Repeat Step 2 of the "Left Side" procedure.

3. Disconnect the IAC connector at the throttle body (3.8L only).

4. Tag and disconnect the spark plug wires and the oxygen sensor lead.

5. Disconnect the heater inlet pipe from the manifold studs.

6. Remove the exhaust crossover pipe.

7. Remove the front alternator support bracket.

8. Remove the exhaust manifold

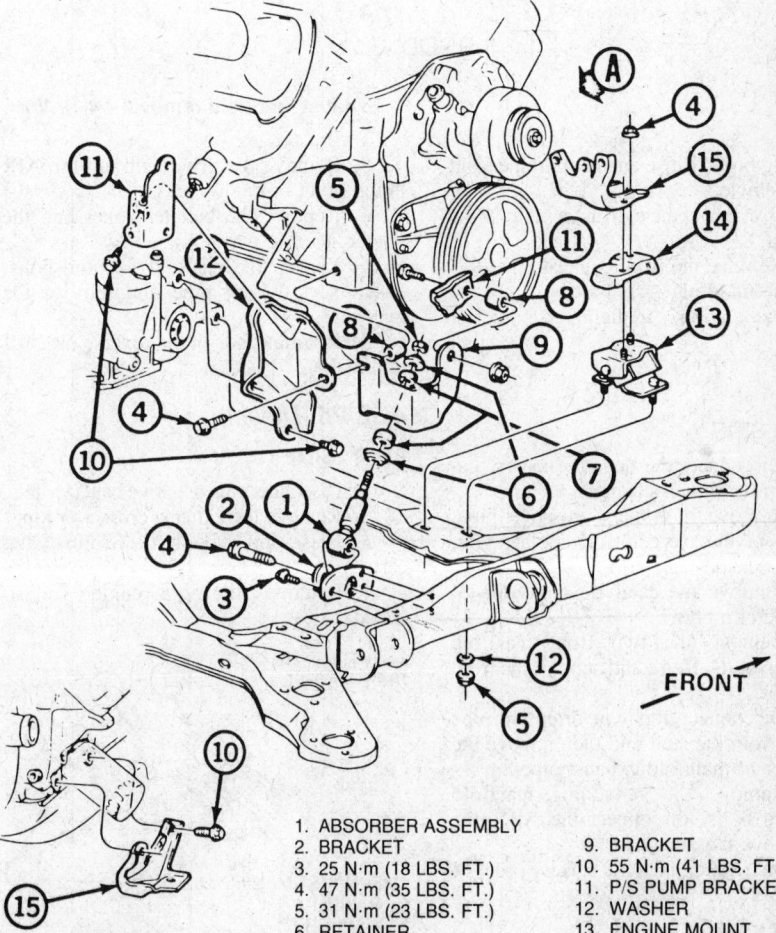

1. ABSORBER ASSEMBLY
2. BRACKET
3. 25 N·m (18 LBS. FT.)
4. 47 N·m (35 LBS. FT.)
5. 31 N·m (23 LBS. FT.)
6. RETAINER
7. INSULATOR
8. SPACER
9. BRACKET
10. 55 N·m (41 LBS. FT.)
11. P/S PUMP BRACKET
12. WASHER
13. ENGINE MOUNT
14. SHIELD
15. BRACKET

Engine mounting—4.3L V6 (diesel)

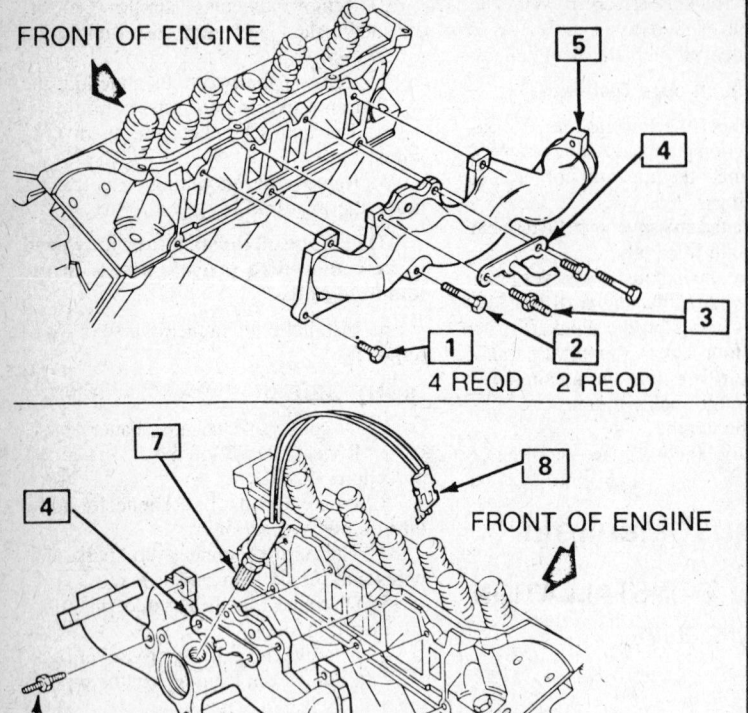

FRONT OF ENGINE

5
4
3
1
2
4 REQD 2 REQD

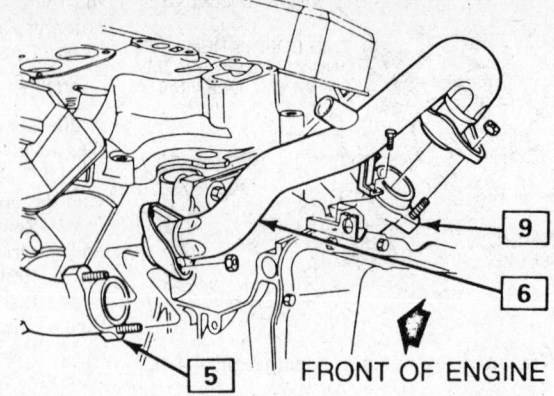

9
6
5
FRONT OF ENGINE

7
4
8
FRONT OF ENGINE
3
2
1 5 REQD
9

Exhaust manifold removal—4.1L V8

1. SHORT BOLT
2. LONG BOLT
3. STUD HEADED BOLT
4. AIR PIPE
5. LEFT EXHAUST MANIFOLD
6. EXHAUST CROSSOVER PIPE
7. OXYGEN SENSOR
8. OXYGEN SENSOR CONNECTOR
9. RIGHT EXHAUST MANIFOLD

mounting bolts. Raise and support the front of the vehicle.

9. Disconnect the exhaust pipe from the manifold.

10. Remove the front exhaust pipe. Remove the manifold.

11. Installation is in the reverse order of removal.

4.1L V8

RIGHT SIDE

1. Disconnect the negative battery cable. Remove the air cleaner.

2. Remove the exhaust crossover pipe. Disconnect the oxygen and coolant temperature sensors.

3. Remove the catalytic converter-to-AIR pipe clip bolt.

4. Remove the two front manifold mounting bolts. Raise and support the front of the car.

5. Disconnect the converter air pipe bracket from the stud and then remove the converter-to-manifold exhaust pipe.

6. Remove the remaining manifold mounting bolts, disconnect the AIR pipe and remove the manifold.

7. Installation is in the reverse order of removal.

LEFT SIDE

1. Disconnect the negative battery cable.

2. Remove both cooling fans and the exhaust crossover pipe.

3. Remove the drive belt and the AIR pump pivot bolt.

4. Remove the belt tensioner and the power steering pump brace.

5. Remove the manifold mounting bolts. Disconnect the air pipe and remove the manifold.

6. Installation is in the reverse order of removal.

4.3L V6 (Diesel)

LEFT SIDE

1. Disconnect the negative battery cable.

2. Remove the exhaust crossover pipe.

3. Raise and support the front of the car.

4. Remove the right engine splash shield.

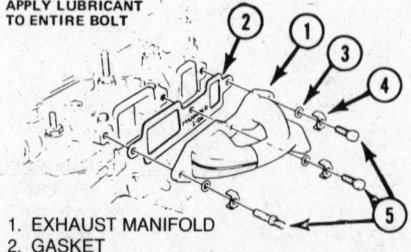

APPLY LUBRICANT TO ENTIRE BOLT

2
1
3
4
5

1. EXHAUST MANIFOLD
2. GASKET
3. WASHER (3)
4. LOCK (3)
5. BOLT-38 N·m (28 LB. FT.)

Left (front) exhaust manifold removal—4.3L V6 (diesel).

5. Remove the vacuum pump-to-exhaust manifold brace.

6. Remove the mounting bolts and remove the manifold.

7. Installation is in the reverse order of removal.

RIGHT SIDE

1. Disconnect the negative battery cable.

2. Remove the exhaust crossover pipe.

3. Raise and support the front of the car.

4. Disconnect the exhaust pipe from the manifold.

5. Remove the mounting bolts and remove the manifold.

6. Installation is in the reverse order of removal.

Camshaft

REMOVAL & INSTALLATION

4.1L V8

1. Remove the engine, timing chain and valve lifters as previously detailed.

2. Temporarily reinstall the camshaft sprocket or a long bolt to use as a handle to slide the camshaft forward until it is out of the engine.

——— CAUTION ———
Extreme care must be exercised to prevent the camshaft lobes from scratching the

camshaft bearings during removal and installation.

3. Installation is in the reverse order of removal. Apply a thin coat of rear axle lubricant or the equivalent to the camshaft lobes, distributor gear teeth and bearing journals.

Oil Pan

REMOVAL & INSTALLATION

4.1L V8

1. Disconnect the negative battery cable.
2. Remove the two flywheel covers.
3. Drain the oil.
4. Remove the mounting bolts and nuts and then remove the oil pan.

NOTE: If the pan is difficult to remove, try tapping the edges lightly with a rubber mallet.

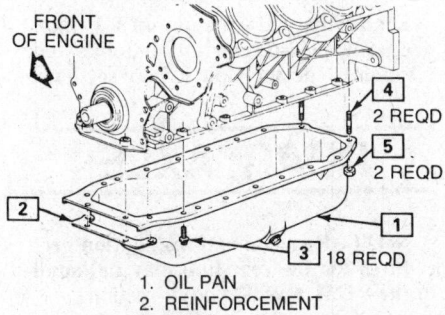

1. OIL PAN
2. REINFORCEMENT
3. BOLT
4. STUD
5. NUT

Oil pan installation—4.1L V8

5. Seal the oil pan to the block with RTV sealant.
6. Install the mounting bolts and nuts and tighten to 12 ft. lbs. (16 Nm).
7. Installation of the remaining components is in the reverse order of removal.

AUTOMATIC TRANSMISSION

For all automatic transmission band and linkage adjustments, and any other service procedures, please refer to "Automatic Transmissions" in the Unit Repair section.

— CAUTION —

Any inaccuracies in shift linkage adjustments may result in premature failure of the transmission due to operation without the controls in full detent. Such operation results in reduced fluid pressure and in turn, partial engagement of the affected clutches. Partial engagement of the clutches, with sufficient pressure to permit

apparently normal vehicle operation will result in failure of the clutches and/or other internal parts after only a few miles of operation.

REMOVAL & INSTALLATION

3.0L V6 and 3.8L V6

1. Disconnect the negative battery cable. Disconnect the wire connector at the mass air flow sensor (3.8L only).
2. Remove the air intake duct and the mass air flow sensor as an assembly.
3. Disconnect the cruise control assembly. Disconnect the shift control linkage.
4. Tag and disconnect the following:
   a. Park/Neutral switch
   b. Torque converter clutch
   c. Vehicle speed sensor
   d. Vacuum modulator hose at the modulator.

NOTE: Care must be exercised on reassembly of the Park/Neutral switch to ensure a proper fit of both the connector and the T-latch. Failure to do so may result in intermittant loss of switch functions.

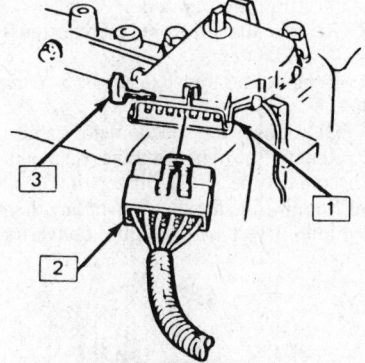

1. PARK/NEUTRAL & BACKUP LAMP SWITCH
2. SWITCH CONN.
3. "T" LATCH

T-latch connector

5. Remove the three top transaxle-to-engine block bolts. Install an engine support fixture.
6. Remove both front wheels and then turn the steering wheel to the full left position.
7. Remove the right front ball joint nut and separate the control arm from the steering knuckle.
8. Remove the right drive axle as detailed later in this section.

NOTE: Be careful not to allow the drive axle splines to contact any portion of the lip seal.

9. Remove the left drive axle using a suitable pry bar. *Be careful not to damage the pan.* Install drive axle boot seal protectors.
10. Remove three bolts at the transaxle and three nuts at the cradle member. Remove the left front transaxle mount.
11. Remove the right front mount-to-cradle nuts. Remove the left rear transaxle mount-to-transaxle bolts.

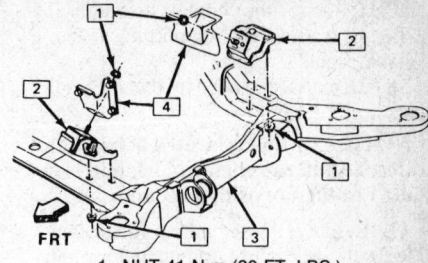

1. NUT 41 N·m (30 FT. LBS.)
2. MOUNT ASM.
3. FRAME ASM.
4. TRANSAXLE MOUNTING BRACKET

Left side transaxle mounts—3.0L V6 and 3.8L V6. 4.3L V6 (diesel) and 4.1L V8 similar

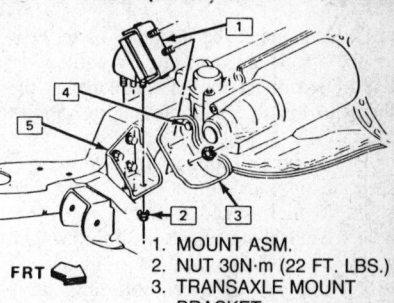

1. MOUNT ASM.
2. NUT 30N·m (22 FT. LBS.)
3. TRANSAXLE MOUNT BRACKET
4. TRANSAXLE TO BRACKET BOLT 55 N·m (40 FT. LBS.)
5. TRANSAXLE MOUNT BRACKET

Right side transaxle mounts—3.0L V6 and 3.8L V6. 4.3L V6 (diesel) and 4.1L V8 similar

12. Remove the right rear transaxle mount as in Step 10. Remove the engine support bracket-to-transaxle case bolts.
13. Remove the flywheel cover. Remove the flywheel-to-converter bolts.

NOTE: Be sure to matchmark the flywheel-to-converter relationship for proper alignment upon reassembly.

14. Remove the bolts attaching the rear cradle member to the front cradle dog leg.
15. Remove the front left cradle-to-body bolt. Remove the front cradle dog leg-to-right cradle member bolts.
16. Install a transaxle support fixture into position.

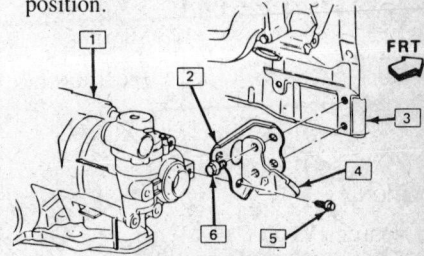

1. TRANSAXLE
2. BRACE—TRANSAXLE
3. ENGINE ASM.
4. BRACKET—DRIVELINE ABSORBER
5. BOLT 45N·m (33 FT. LBS.)
6. BOLT 95N·m (70 FT. LBS.)

Transaxle brace and brackets—3.0L V6 and 3.8L V6. 4.3L V6 (diesel) and 4.3L V8 similar

17. Remove the cradle assembly by swinging it aside and supporting it with a suitable stand.

18. Disconnect and cap the oil cooler lines at the transaxle.

NOTE: One bolt is located between the transaxle and the engine block and is installed in the opposite direction.

19. Remove the remaining lower transaxle-to-engine bolts. And then lower the transaxle assembly away from the car.

20. Installation is in the reverse order of removal. Check the fluid level and all adjustments.

4.1L V8

1. Disconnect the negative battery cable, the air cleaner and the TV cable.

2. Disconnect the shift linkage at the transaxle. Install a suitable engine support fixture.

3. Tag and disconnect the following:
   a. Converter clutch
   b. Vehicle speed sensor
   c. Neutral start/back-up light switch
   d. Vacuum line at the modulator.

4. Remove the upper bolts and studs securing the bell housing to the block.

5. Raise and support the car and remove both front wheels.

6. Disconnect the lower ball joint from the left steering knuckle. Remove both drive axles from the transaxle.

7. Remove the stabilizer bar mounting bolt from the left control arm.

8. Remove the left front cradle assembly.

9. Remove the extension housing-to-engine block support bracket.

10. Disconnect and cap the oil cooler lines at the transaxle case.

11. Remove the right and left transaxle mount attachments.

12. Remove the flexplate splash shield. Remove the converter-to-flexplate bolts.

13. Remove all the lower bell housing bolts except the lower rear one (No. 6).

14. Position a jack under the transaxle and then remove the last bell housing bolt.

POSITION #4
POSITION #5
POSITION #6
FRT
POSITION #3
POSITION #2
POSITION #1
1. BOLT (75 N·m/55 FT. LBS.)
2. STUD (75 N·m/55 FT. LBS.)

Transaxle-to-engine mounting bolts. Remove No. 6 last—4.1L V8

NOTE: To reach the last bell housing bolt, you will need a 3 in. socket wrench extension and you must come through the right wheel arch opening.

15. Remove the transaxle assembly.

16. Installation is in the reverse order of removal. Check the fluid level and all adjustments.

4.3L V6 (Diesel)

1. Disconnect the negative battery cable. Disconnect the TV cable at the injection pump and transaxle.

2. Remove the crossover pipe shield and disconnect the shift control linkage.

3. Tag and disconnect the following:
   a. Park/Neutral switch
   b. Torque converter clutch
   c. Vehicle speed sensor
   d. Vacuum hose at the modulator.

4. Remove the three upper engine-to-transaxle bolts.

5. Loosen, but do not remove, the engine-to-transaxle bolt at the starter.

6. Install a suitable engine support fixture.

7. Raise and support the car. Remove both front wheels and then turn the steering wheel to the full left position.

8. Disconnect the right front ball joint from the steering knuckle. Remove the right drive axle from the transaxle.

9. Remove the left front and rear transaxle-to-cradle mounts.

10. Remove the transaxle brace and its bracket.

11. Disconnect the speedometer cable.

12. Remove the right rear transaxle mount and disconnect the left stabilizer link.

13. Remove the flywheel cover and then remove the flywheel-to-torque converter bolts.

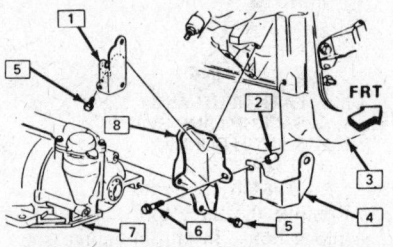

1. POWER STEERING PUMP BRACKET
2. SPACER
3. ENGINE
4. SHOCK ABSORBER BRACKET
5. BOLT 55N·m (40 FT. LBS.)
6. BOLT 45N·m (33 FT. LBS.)
7. TRANSAXLE
8. BRACE

Transaxle brace and brackets—4.3L V6 (diesel)

14. Remove the bolts attaching the rear cradle member to the front cradle dog leg. Remove one stabilizer brace and loosen the other.

15. Remove the front cradle-to-body bolt and the right front motor mount.

16. Remove the wiring harness cover on the cradle and position it out of the way.

17. Install a suitable transmission support fixture.

18. Slide the cradle assembly to one side and support it.

19. Disconnect and cap the oil cooler lines at the transaxle.

20. Remove the exhaust connector pipe and the rear exhaust manifold.

21. Remove the remaining engine-to-transaxle bolts.

NOTE: One engine-to-transaxle bolt is installed in the opposite direction.

22. Lower the transaxle and remove it.

23. Installation is in the reverse order of removal. Check the fluid level and all adjustments.

DRIVESHAFTS, DRIVE AXLES AND U-JOINTS

NOTE: Removal and installation procedures for the front drive axles (half-shafts) and the CV-joints may be found in the "GM A & X Body" section.

For further information on CV-Joint overhaul, please refer to "U-Joints and CV-Joints" in the Unit Repair section.

REAR AXLE

NOTE: Removal and installation procedures for the rear hub may be found in the "GM A & X Body" section.

JACKING AHD HOISTING

Jack the car at the engine cradle crossbar. The car can also be raised under the lower control arms. The car can also be lifted at the frame side rails, directly behind the front wheels and in front of the rear wheels.

— **CAUTION** —
When raising the car by the frame side rails, be certain that the jack does not contact the catalytic converter.

FRONT SUSPENSION

MacPherson Strut

REMOVAL & INSTALLATION

For spring and shock absorber removal and installation, and any other strut overhaul procedures, please refer to

"Strut Overhaul" in the Unit Repair section.

1. Remove the three nuts attaching the top of the strut assembly to the body.

2. Raise the car and support it with jack stands under the engine cradle.

3. Lower the car slightly so that the weight rests on the jack stands.

4. Remove the wheels and tires.

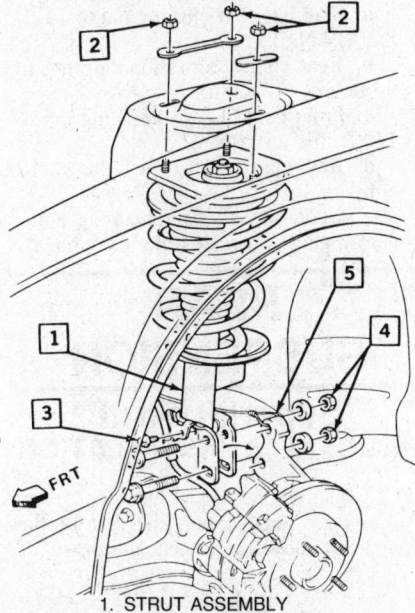

1. STRUT ASSEMBLY
2. STRUT TO BODY NUTS
   24 N·m (18 LBS. FT.)
3. BRAKE LINE BRACKET
   BOLT 17 N·m (13 LBS. FT.)
4. STRUT TO STEERING
   KNUCKLE NUTS 195 N·m
   (144 LBS. FT.)
5. RETAIN STEERING
   KNUCKLE WITH WIRE
   ONCE STRUT ASSEMBLY
   IS REMOVED

Front MacPherson strut assemlby

NOTE: Always install drive axle boot seal protectors. Care must be taken to prevent overextension of the inner Tri-Pot joints.

5. Remove the brake line bracket bolt from the strut assembly. *Do not* disconnect the brake line from the caliper.

6. Remove the strut-to-steering knuckle bolts and then carefully remove the strut assembly.

7. Installation is in the reverse order of removal. Please note the following:

a. Check wheel alignment.

b. Tighten the strut-to-body bolts to 18 ft. lbs. (24 Nm).

c. Tighten the strut-to-steering knuckle bolts to 144 ft. lbs. (195 Nm).

Front Wheel Bearing
ADJUSTMENT

All models covered in this section utilize a permenantly sealed and lubricated front wheel bearing assembly. No adjustments are either necessary or possible.

Ball Joints

INSPECTION

1. Raise the front of the car with a lift placed under the engine cradle. The front wheels should be clear of the ground.

2. Grasp the wheel at the top and bottom and shake the wheel in and out.

3. If any movement is seen of the steering knuckle relative to the control arm, the ball joints are defective and must be replaced. Note that movement elsewhere may be due to loose wheel bearings or other troubles; watch the knuckle-to-control arm connection.

4. If the ball stud is disconnected from the steering knuckle and any looseness is noted, often the ball joint stud can be twisted in its socket with your fingers, replace the ball joints.

REMOVAL & INSTALLATION

1. Raise the front of the car and support it with jackstands underneath the engine cradle. Lower the car slightly so that the weight rests primarily on the jack stands.

2. Remove the wheel and tire assemblies.

3. Install drive axle covers to protect the drive axle boot seals.

4. Pull the cotter pin from the ball joint and install a ball joint separator tool. Turn the castellated nut counterclockwise to separate the ball joint from the steering knuckle.

5. Use a ⅛ in. drill bit to drill a hole approximately ¼ in. deep in the center of each of the three ball joint rivets.

6. Use a ½ in. drill bit to drill off the rivet heads. Drill only enough to remove the rivet head.

7. Use a hammer and punch to remove the rivets. Drive them out from the bottom.

8. Loosen the stabilizer bar bushing assembly nut.

9. Pull down on the control arm and remove the ball joint from the steering knuckle and control arm.

10. Install the new ball joint in the steering knuckle and line up the holes with those in the control arm.

11. Install the three ball joint nuts facing down and tighten the nuts to 50 ft. lbs. (68 Nm).

12. Install the castellated nut and tighten to 81 ft. lbs. (110 Nm).

NOTE: Tightening the nut for cotter pin alignment is allowed, but do not loosen it once the torque value has been reached.

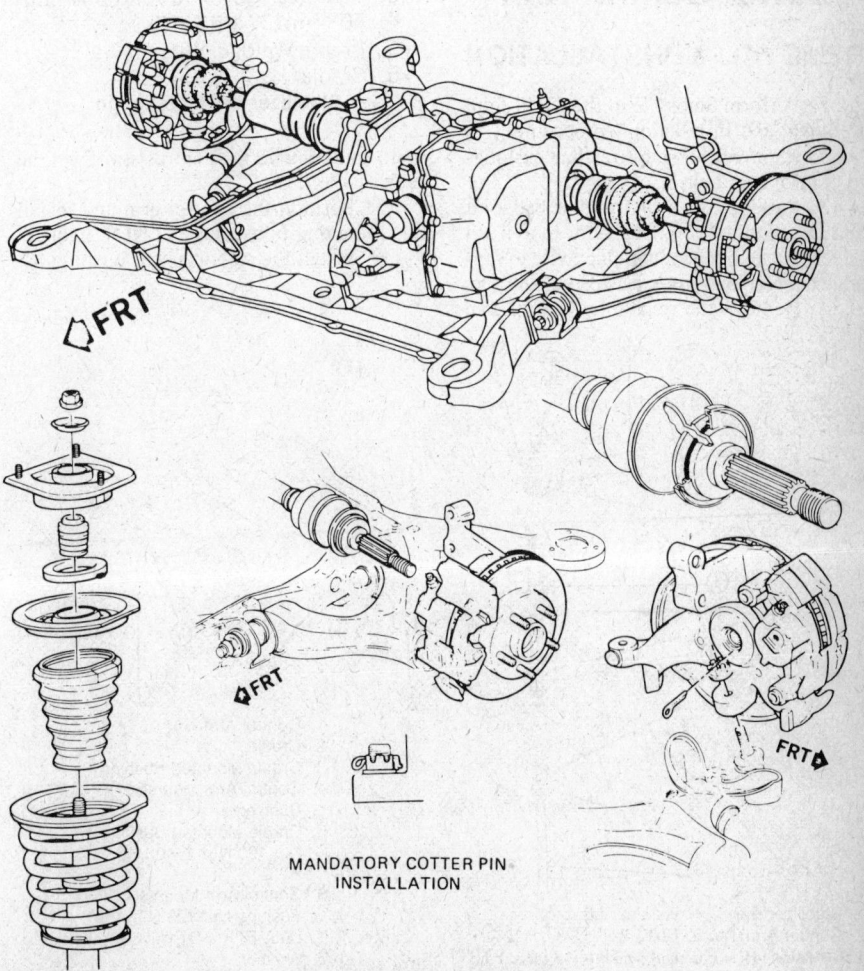

MANDATORY COTTER PIN
INSTALLATION

Front suspension assembly

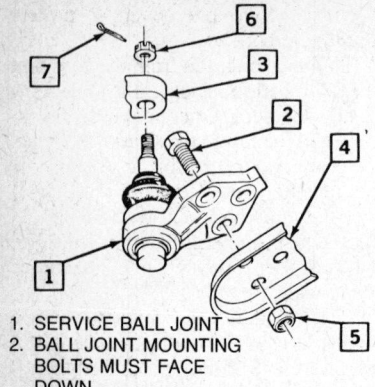

1. SERVICE BALL JOINT
2. BALL JOINT MOUNTING BOLTS MUST FACE DOWN
3. STEERING KNUCKLE
4. CONTROL ARM
5. BALL JOINT MOUNTING NUTS 68 N·m (50 LBS. FT.)
6. BALL JOINT TO STEERING KNUCKLE NUT 110 N·m (81 LBS. FT.) BEFORE COTTER PIN INSTALLATION
7. COTTER PIN

Ball joint installation

13. Install the cotter pin.
14. Installation of the remaining components is in the reverse order of removal.

Lower Control Arm

REMOVAL & INSTALLATION

1. Perform Steps 1-3 of the "Ball Joint Removal and Installation" procedure.
2. Remove the stabilizer bar bushing-to-control arm bolt.
3. Pull the cotter pin from the ball joint and install a ball joint separator tool. Turn the castellated nut counterclockwise to separate the ball joint from the steering knuckle.
4. Remove the remaining control arm

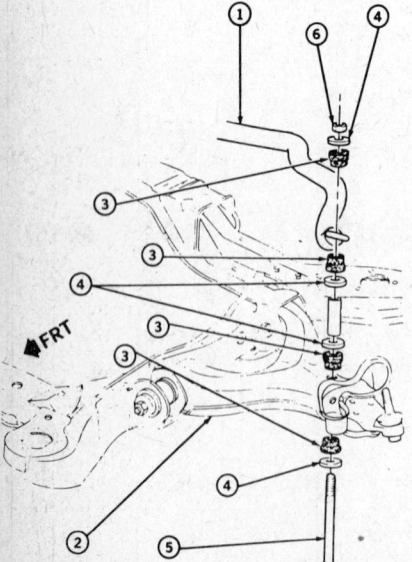

1. Stabilizer Bar   4. Retainer (4)
2. Control Arm   5. Bolt
3. Insulator (4)   6. Nut 17 N·m (13 LBS. FT.)

Stabilizer bar bushing assembly

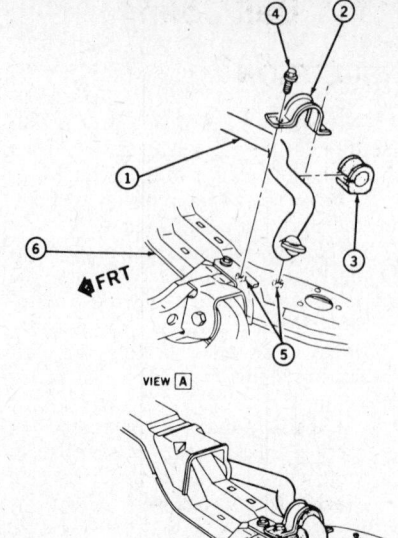

VIEW A

1. Stabilizer Bar
2. Stabilizer Bar Mounting Bracket
3. Stabilizer Bar Mounting Bushing
4. 50 N·m (37 LBS. FT.)
5. Frame Welded Nuts
6. Cradle

Stabilizer bar installation

bolts and remove the control arm from the vehicle.
5. Position the control arm and install the mounting bolts, but DO NOT tighten.
6. Install the stabilizer bar bushing as-

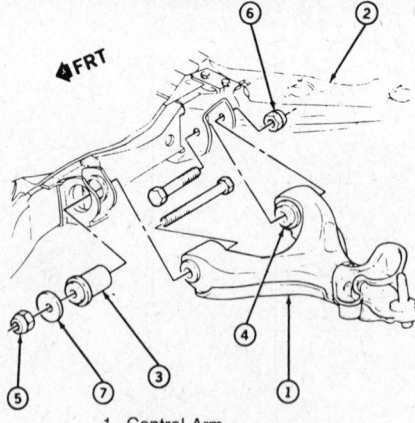

1. Control Arm
2. Cradle
3. Cradle Mounted Bushing
4. Control Arm Mounted Bushing
5. Cradle Mounted Bushing Nut 190 N·m (140 LBS. FT.)
6. Control Arm Mounted Bushing Nut 123 N·m (90 LBS. FT.)
7. Washer

Lower control arm assembly

sembly. Reconnect the ball joint to the steering knuckle.
7. Hoist the vehicle slightly so the weight of the vehicle is supported by the control arms.

NOTE: The weight of the vehicle MUST be supported by the control arms when tightening the mounting nuts.

8. Tighten the:
   a. Stabilizer bar bushing nut to 13 ft. lbs. (17 Nm)
   b. Rear control arm mounting nut to 90 ft. lbs. (123 Nm)
   c. Front control arm mounting nut to 140 ft. lbs. (190 Nm)
   d. Ball joint nut to 81 ft. lbs. (110 Nm).
9. Installation of the remaining components is in the reverse order of removal.

REAR SUSPENSION

Superlift Strut
REMOVAL & INSTALLATION

1. Remove the inner trunk side cover.
2. Raise and support the rear of the vehicle. Remove the wheels and tires.

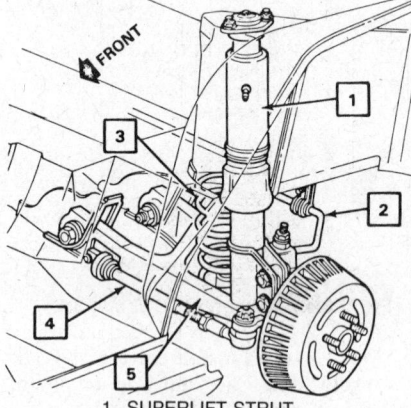

1. SUPERLIFT STRUT
2. STABILIZER BAR
3. COIL SPRING
4. SUSPENSION ADJUSTMENT LINK
5. LOWER CONTROL ARM

Rear suspension

3. Disconnect and plug the ELC air line.
4. Remove the strut tower mounting nuts from inside the trunk.
5. Remove the strut anchor bolts, washers and nuts from the rear knuckle and knuckle bracket.
6. Remove the strut.
7. Installation is in the reverse order of removal. Please note the following:
   a. Tighten the strut tower mounting nuts to 19 ft. lbs. (25 Nm)
   b. Tighten the strut anchor nuts to 144 ft. lbs. (195 Nm)
   c. Lightly pressurize the ELC system by momentarily grounding the compressor test lead in the engine compartment
   d. Check rear wheel alignment.

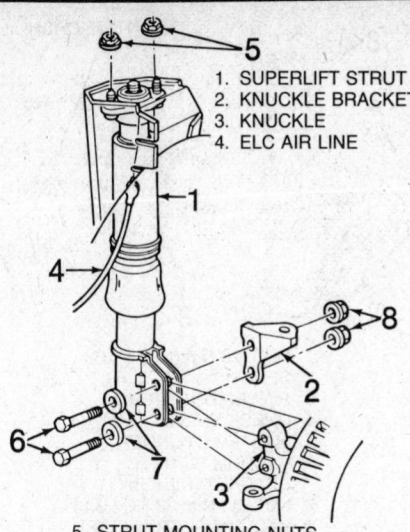

1. SUPERLIFT STRUT
2. KNUCKLE BRACKET
3. KNUCKLE
4. ELC AIR LINE

5. STRUT MOUNTING NUTS (25 N·m/19 FT. LBS.)
6. STRUT ANCHOR BOLTS
7. STRUT ANCHOR WASHERS
8. STRUT ANCHOR NUTS (195 N·m/144 FT. LBS.)

Rear strut installation

Coil Springs

REMOVAL & INSTALLATION

1. Raise the rear of the vehicle and support it so that the control arms hang free. Remove the rear wheels.

2. Separate the rear stabilizer bar from the knuckle bracket and remove it.

3. Disconnect the ELC height sensor link (right control arm) and/or the parking brake cable retaining clip (left control arm).

4. Position the special tool J-23028-01 or its equivalent, so as to cradle the control arm bushings.

NOTE: Special tool J-23028-01 should be secured to a suitable jack.

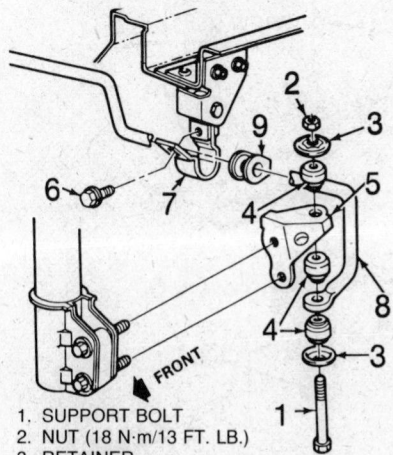

1. SUPPORT BOLT
2. NUT (18 N·m/13 FT. LB.)
3. RETAINER
4. INSULATORS
5. KNUCKLE BRACKET
6. BUSHING CLIP BOLT (50 N·m/37 FT. LB.)
7. SUPPORT ASSEMBLY
8. STABILIZER BAR
9. BUSHING

Rear stabilizer bar bushing assembly

5. Raise the jack to remove the tension from the control arm pivot bolts.

--- **CAUTION** ---

Secure a chain around the spring and through the control arm as a safety precaution.

6. Remove the rear control arm pivot bolt and nut.

7. Slowly maneuver the jack so as to relieve any tension in the front control arm pivot bolt and then remove the bolt and nut.

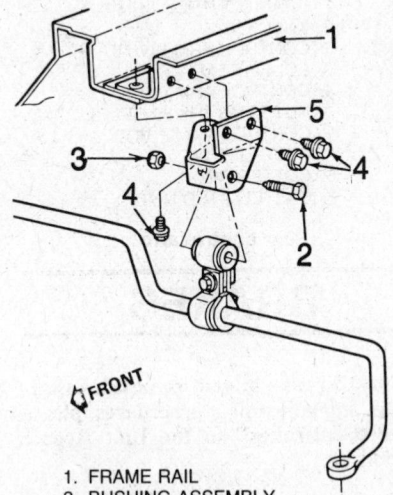

1. FRAME RAIL
2. BUSHING ASSEMBLY BOLT
3. NUT (50 N·m/37 FT. LB.)
4. MOUNTING BRACKET BOLTS (18N·m/13 FT. LB.)
5. MOUNTING BRACKET

Rear stabilizer bar mounting bracket

8. Lower the jack to allow the control arm to pivot downward.

9. When all pressure is removed from the coil spring, remove the safety chain, spring and insulators.

NOTE: The spring insulators should be inspected for cuts or tears. They should be replaced automatically if the vehicle has over 50,000 miles.

10. Snap the upper insulator onto the spring. Position the lower insulator and the spring in the control arm.

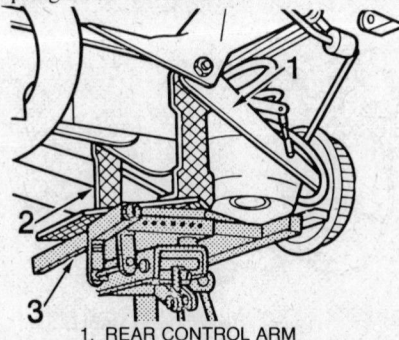

1. REAR CONTROL ARM
2. SPECIAL TOOL J-23028-01
3. TRANSMISSION JACK

Use the special tool and a transmission jack to cradle the control arm

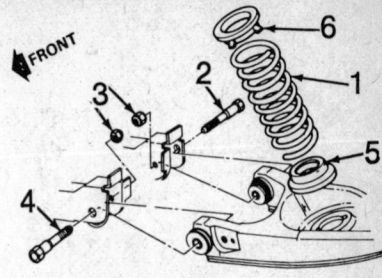

1. COIL SPRING
2. CONTROL ARM PIVOT BOLT-REAR (170 N·m/125 FT. LB.)
3. CONTROL ARM PIVOT NUTS (115 N·m/85 FT. LB.)
4. CONTROL ARM PIVOT BOLT-FRONT (170 N·m/ 125 FT. LB.)
5. LOWER COIL SPRING INSULATOR
6. UPPER COIL SPRING INSULATOR

Rear coil spring installation

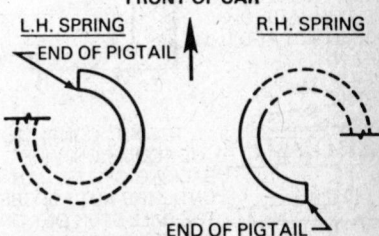

TOP VIEW OF UPPER END OF SPRING

FRONT OF CAR

L.H. SPRING   R.H. SPRING

←END OF PIGTAIL

END OF PIGTAIL→

Rear coil spring positioning

NOTE: Install the coil springs so that the upper ends are positioned as shown in the illustration.

11. Installation of the remaining components is in the reverse order of removal. Control arm mounting nuts should not be tightened until the vehicle is unsupported and resting on its wheels at normal trim height.

Ball Joint
REMOVAL & INSTALLATION

1. Raise and support the rear of the vehicle and remove the wheels.

2. Disconnect the ELC height sensor link (right control arm) and/or the parking brake cable retaining link (left control arm).

3. Remove the cotter pin and castellated nut from the outer suspension adjustment link.

4. Separate the outer suspension link from the knuckle.

5. Support the control arm with a suitable jack. The lower control arm MUST be supported to prevent the coil spring from forcing the control arm downward.

6. Remove the ball stud cotter pin.

7. Remove the castellated nut and then reinstall it with the flat side facing upward. DO NOT tighten the nut.

8. Install a ball joint separator tool and

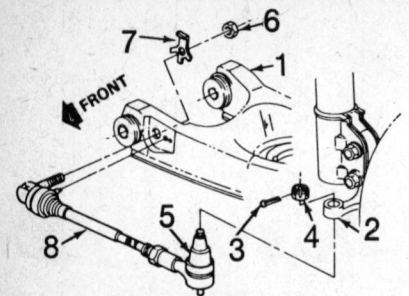

1. REAR CONTROL ARM
2. KNUCKLE
3. COTTER PIN
4. CASTELLATED NUT (50 N·m/37 FT. LB.)
5. OUTER SUSPENSION ADJUSTMENT LINK
6. LINK RETAINING NUT (85 N·m/63 FT. LB.)
7. LINK RETAINER
8. SUSPENSION ADJUSTMENT LINK ASSEMBLY

Rear suspension adjustment link

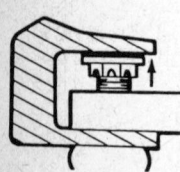

REMOVE CASTELLATED NUT AND REINSTALL WITH FLAT SIDE FACING UPWARD.
PLACE J-34505 INTO POSITION AS SHOWN. LOOSEN NUT AND BACK OFF UNTIL...

...THE NUT CONTACTS THE TOOL. CONTINUE BACKING OFF THE NUT UNTIL THE NUT FORCES THE BALL STUD OUT OF THE KNUCKLE.

Separating the ball joint from the steering knuckle

separate the knuckle from the ball stud by backing off the inverted nut against the tool.

9. Separate the ball joint from the control arm.

10. Installation is in the reverse order of removal. Please note following:

a. Tighten a NEW castellated nut to 7.5 ft. lbs. (10 Nm). Tighten the nut an additional ⅔ of a turn.

b. Align the slot in the nut to the cotter pin hole by tightening only. *Do not loosen the nut to align the holes.*

Control Arm

REMOVAL & INSTALLATION

1. Perform Steps 1-2 of the "Ball Joint Removal and Installation" procedures.

2. Remove the suspension adjustment link retaining nut and retainer.

3. Separate the link assembly from the control arm.

4. Remove the coil spring as detailed previously.

5. Perform Steps 6-9 of the "Ball Joint Removal and Installation" procedure.

6. Remove the control arm.

7. Installation is in the reverse order of removal.

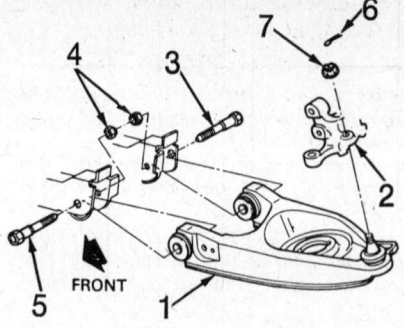

1. REAR CONTROL ARM
2. KNUCKLE
3. CONTROL ARM PIVOT BOLT—REAR
4. CONTROL ARM PIVOT NUTS (115 N·m/85 FT-LB)
5. CONTROL ARM PIVOT BOLT—FRONT
6. COTTER PIN
7. CASTELLATED NUT

Rear control arm

BRAKES

For all brake system removal, installation, and adjustment procedures, please refer to "Brakes" in the Unit Repair section.

Master Cylinder

REMOVAL & INSTALLATION

1. Disconnect and plug hydraulic lines, and drain the cylinder.

1. NUT (20 N·m/14 FT. LB.)
2. SEAL
3. POWER BOOSTER
4. CHECK VALVE
5. MASTER CYLINDER
6. VACUUM SWITCH BRACKET (DIESEL)
7. NUT (30 N·m/22 FT. LB.)
8. VACUUM SWITCH (GAS)

Typical master cylinder and power booster mounting

2. Remove the attaching nuts and remove the master cylinder from the power booster unit.

3. Reverse to install. Bleed the system.

Power Booster

REMOVAL & INSTALLATION

1. From inside the car, detach the brake pushrod from the brake pedal.

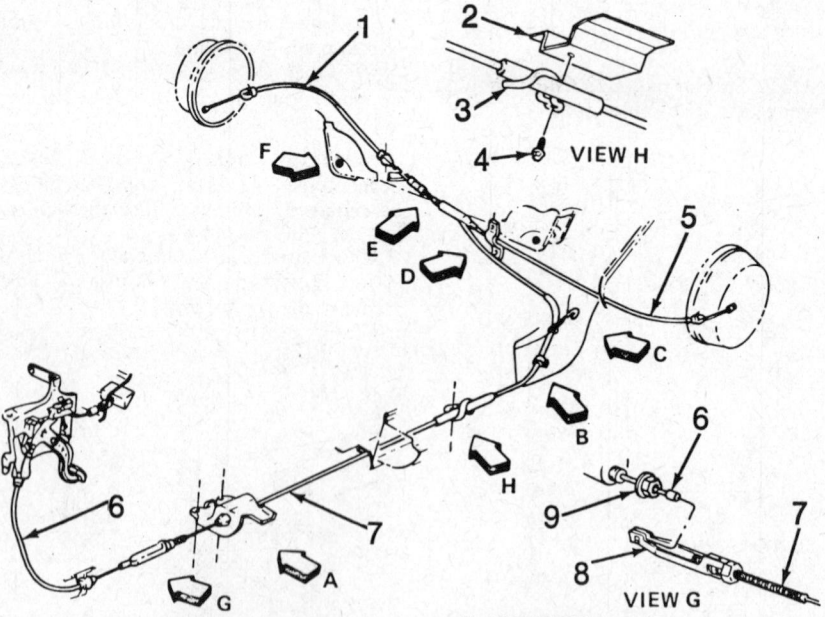

1. RIGHT REAR CABLE
2. UNDERBODY
3. GUIDE
4. BOLT/SCREW 38 N·m (28 FT. LB.)

5. LEFT REAR CABLE
6. CABLE ASM—FRONT
7. CABLE ASM—INTERMEDIATE.
8. EQUALIZER ASM
9. NUT

Parking brake cable routing

2. Disconnect the hydraulic lines from the front of the master cylinder.

3. Remove the nuts from the mounting studs which hold the unit to the dash panel. Remove the unit and clean it prior to installation.

4. Install in reverse order of removal. Bleed system.

Parking Brake

ADJUSTMENT

1. Depress the parking brake pedal 35mm.

2. Raise the vehicle and support it with jack stands.

3. Tighten the adjusting nut until the left rear wheel can just be turned to the rear with both hands, but is locked when forward rotation is attempted.

4. With the mechanisms totally disengaged, both rear wheels should turn freely in either direction with no brake drag.

——— CAUTION ———

Do not adjust the parking brake cables so tight as to cause brake drag.

5. Lower the vehicle.

STEERING

Tie-Rod

REMOVAL & INSTALLATION

1. Loosen the jam nut on the steering rack (inner tie-rod).

2. Rmove the tie-rod end nut. Separate the tie-rod end from the steering knuckle using a puller.

3. Unscrew the tie-rod end, counting the number of turns.

4. To install, screw the tie-rod end onto the steering rack (inner tie-rod) the same number of turns as counted for removal. This will give approximately correct toe.

5. Install the tie-rod end into the knuckle. Install the nut and tighten to 40 ft. lbs.

6. If the toe must be adjusted, use pliers to expand the boot clamp. Turn the inner tie-rod to adjust. Replace the clamp.

7. Tighten the jam nut to 50 ft. lbs.

Steering Gear

REMOVAL & INSTALLATION

1. Raise and support the front end of the car with jackstands under the frame members. Allow the front suspension to hang freely. Disconnect the power steering hoses from the gear, where equipped.

2. Move the intermediate shaft seal upward and remove the intermediate shaft-to-stub shaft pinch bolt.

3. Remove both front wheels.

4. Remove the cotter pins and nut from both tie-rod ends. Disconnect the tie-rod ends from the steering knuckles.

5. Remove the line retainer.

6. Remove the outlet and pressure hose.

7. Remove the five rack and pinion assembly mounting bolts.

8. Loosen the front engine cradle mounting bolts. Install jack stands and then lower the rear of the cradle about 3 in. (76mm).

——— CAUTION ———

Do not lower the rear of the engine cradle too far.

9. Remove the rack and pinion assembly.

10. Installation is in the reverse order of removal. Tighten the rack mounting bolts to 50 ft. lbs. (68 Nm). Tighten the tie-rod end nut to 35–52 ft. lbs. (50–70 Nm). Bleed the power steering system and check for leaks.

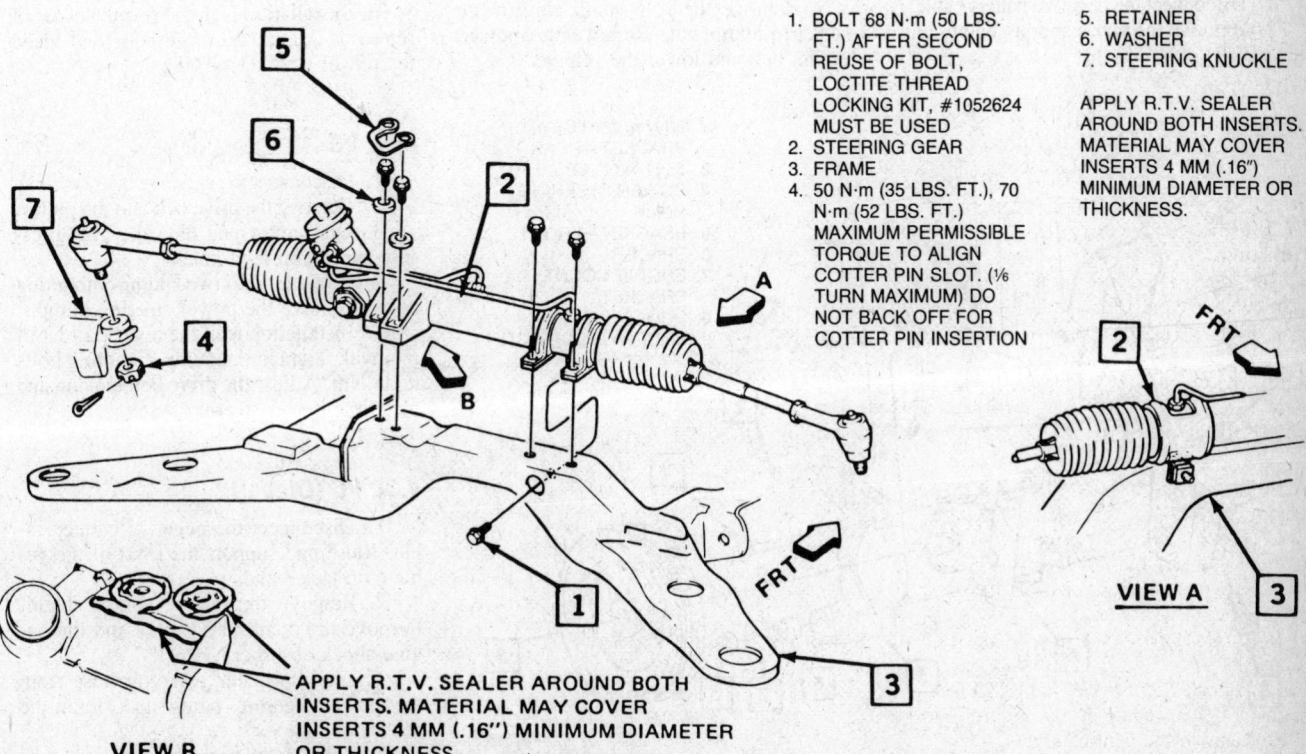

1. BOLT 68 N·m (50 LBS. FT.) AFTER SECOND REUSE OF BOLT, LOCTITE THREAD LOCKING KIT, #1052624 MUST BE USED
2. STEERING GEAR
3. FRAME
4. 50 N·m (35 LBS. FT.), 70 N·m (52 LBS. FT.) MAXIMUM PERMISSIBLE TORQUE TO ALIGN COTTER PIN SLOT. (⅙ TURN MAXIMUM) DO NOT BACK OFF FOR COTTER PIN INSERTION

5. RETAINER
6. WASHER
7. STEERING KNUCKLE

APPLY R.T.V. SEALER AROUND BOTH INSERTS. MATERIAL MAY COVER INSERTS 4 MM (.16") MINIMUM DIAMETER OR THICKNESS.

APPLY R.T.V. SEALER AROUND BOTH INSERTS. MATERIAL MAY COVER INSERTS 4 MM (.16") MINIMUM DIAMETER OR THICKNESS.

VIEW B

VIEW A

Rack and pinion assembly

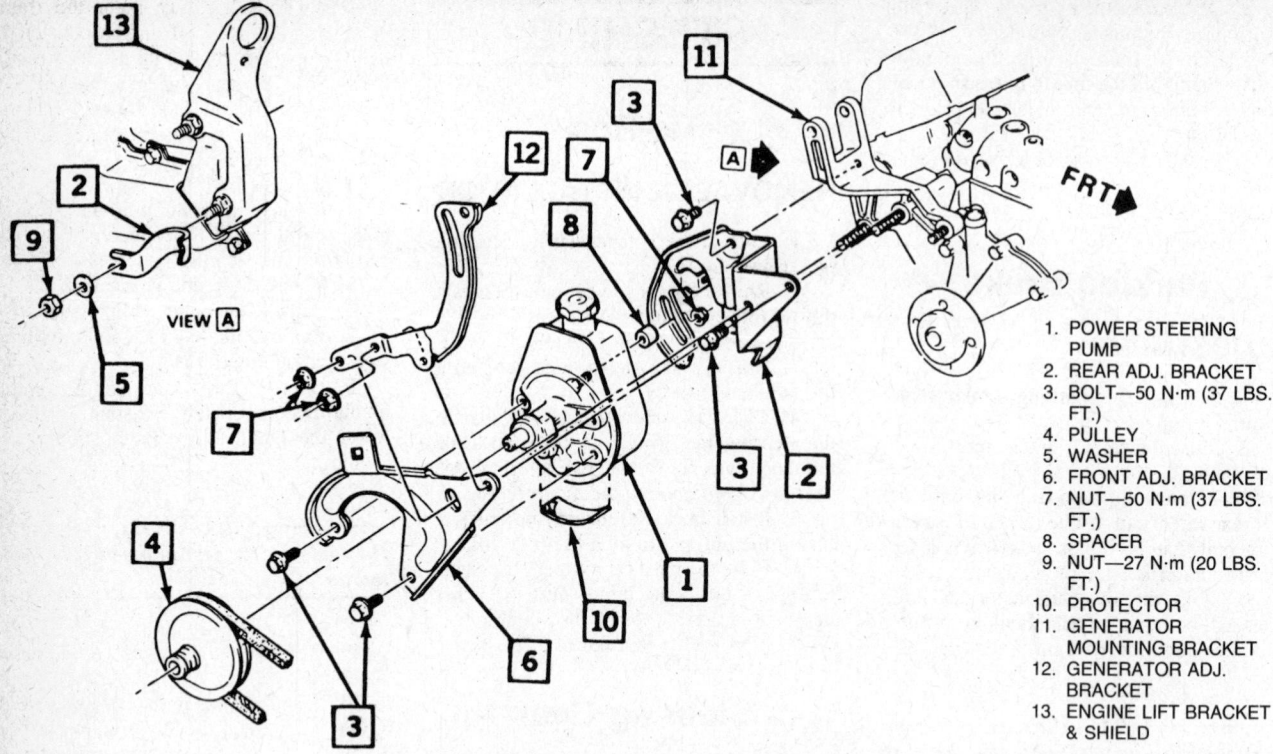

1. POWER STEERING PUMP
2. REAR ADJ. BRACKET
3. BOLT—50 N·m (37 LBS. FT.)
4. PULLEY
5. WASHER
6. FRONT ADJ. BRACKET
7. NUT—50 N·m (37 LBS. FT.)
8. SPACER
9. NUT—27 N·m (20 LBS. FT.)
10. PROTECTOR
11. GENERATOR MOUNTING BRACKET
12. GENERATOR ADJ. BRACKET
13. ENGINE LIFT BRACKET & SHIELD

Power steering pump mounting—3.0L V6 and 3.8L V6

Power Steering Pump

REMOVAL & INSTALLATION

3.0L V6 and 3.8L V6

1. Disconnect the negative battery cable.
2. Remove the air cleaner assembly on the 3.0L.

3. Remove the drive belt and then the alternator itself.
4. Raise the front of the vehicle and support it on jack stands.
5. Disconnect and plug the pressure and return lines at the pump.
6. Remove the rear pump adjustment bracket-to-pump nut. Remove the power steering belt and lower the vehicle.

7. Remove the alternator adjustment bracket and support brace.
8. Remove the rear pump adjustment bracket and then remove the pump assembly.
9. Remove the front pump adjustment bracket and then remove the pulley.
10. Installation is in the reverse order of removal. Adjust the drive belts and bleed the power steering system.

4.1L V8

1. Disconnect the negative battery cable.
2. Remove the drive belt and the pulley.
3. Disconnect and plug the high pressure and pump feed lines.
4. Remove the two pump mounting bolts. Remove the power steering pump.
5. Installation is in the reverse order of removal. Tighten the pump mounting bolts to 25 Nm. Adjust the drive belt tension and bleed the power steering system.

4.3L V6 (Diesel)

1. Disconnect the negative battery cable. Raise and support the front of the vehicle on jack stands.
2. Remove the engine splash shield. Remove the crankshaft pulley and the engine shock absorber.
3. Disconnect the reservoir hose from the power steering pump and drain the reservoir.
4. Remove the high pressure hose support. Disconnect and cap the high pressure hose.

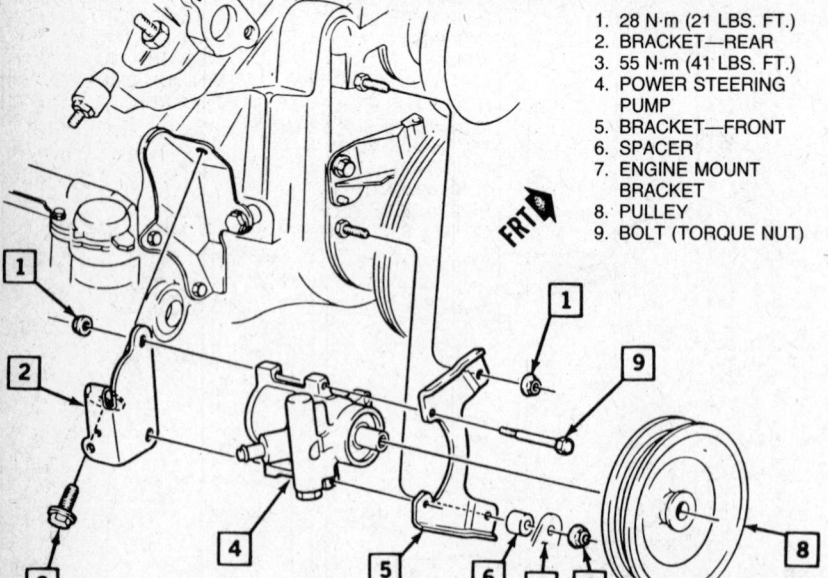

1. 28 N·m (21 LBS. FT.)
2. BRACKET—REAR
3. 55 N·m (41 LBS. FT.)
4. POWER STEERING PUMP
5. BRACKET—FRONT
6. SPACER
7. ENGINE MOUNT BRACKET
8. PULLEY
9. BOLT (TORQUE NUT)

Power steering pump mounting—4.3L V6 (diesel)

5. Remove the three bracket bolts. Remove the pump assembly along with its brackets.

6. Installation is in the reverse order of removal. Adjust the drive belt tension. Bleed the power steering system and check for leaks.

BLEEDING THE POWER STEERING SYSTEM

1. Fill the fluid reservoir.

2. Let the fluid stand undisturbed for two minutes, then crank the engine for about two seconds. Refill reservoir if necessary.

3. Repeat Steps 1 and 2 above until the fluid level remains constant after cranking the engine.

4. Raise the front of the car until the wheels are off the ground, then start the engine. Increase the engine speed to about 1,500 rpm.

5. Turn the wheels lightly against the stops to the left and right, checking the fluid level and refilling if necessary.

Steering Wheel

REMOVAL & INSTALLATION
━━━ CAUTION ━━━
Disconnect the battery ground cable before removing the steering wheel. When installing a steering wheel, always make sure that the turn signal lever is in the neutral position.

1. Remove the trim retaining screws from behind the wheel. On wheels with a center cap, pull off the cap.

2. Lift the trim off and pull the horn wires from the turn signal cancelling cam.

3. Remove the retainer and the steering wheel nut.

4. Mark the wheel-to-shaft relationship, and then remove the wheel with a puller.

5. Install the wheel on the shaft aligning the previously made marks. Tighten the nut.

6. Insert the horn wires into the cancelling cam.

7. Install the center trim and reconnect the battery cable.

Turn Signal Switch

REMOVAL & INSTALLATION

1. Remove the steering wheel as previously outlined. Remove the trim cover.

2. Loosen the cover screws. Pry the cover off with a screwdriver, and lift the cover off the shaft.

3. Position the U-shaped lockplate compressing tool on the end of the steering shaft and compress the lock plate by turning the shaft nut clockwise. Pry the wire snapring out of the shaft groove.

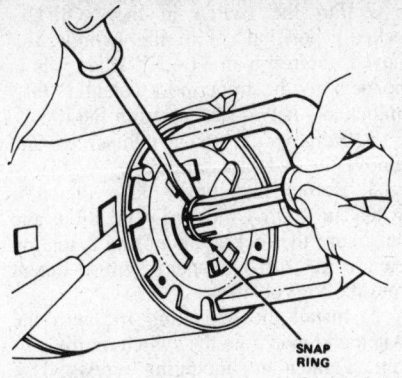

Depress the lockplate and remove the snapring

4. Remove the tool and lift the lockplate off the shaft.

5. Slip the cancelling cam, upper bearing preload spring, and thrust washer off the shaft.

6. Remove the turn signal lever. Push the flasher knob in and unscrew it. Remove the button retaining screw and remove the button, spring and knob.

7. Pull the switch connector out the mast jacket and tape the upper part to facilitate switch removal. Attach a long piece of wire to the turn signal switch connector. When installing the turn signal switch, feed this wire through the column first, and then use this wire to pull the switch connector into position. On tilt wheels, place the turn signal and shifter housing in low position and remove the harness cover.

8. Remove the three switch mounting screws. Remove the switch by pulling it straight up while guiding the wiring harness cover through the column.

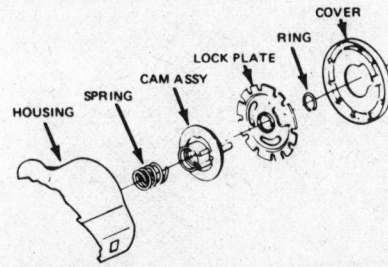

Remove these parts for access to the turn signal switch

9. Install the replacement switch by working the connector and cover down through the housing and under the bracket. On tilt models, the connector is worked down through the housing, under the bracket, and then the cover is installed on the harness.

10. Install the switch mounting screws and the connector on the mast jacket bracket. Install the column-to-dash trim plate.

11. Install the flasher knob and the turn signal lever.

12. With the turn signal lever in neutral and the flasher knob out, slide the thrust washer, upper bearing preload spring, and cancelling cam onto the the shaft.

13. Position the lock plate on the shaft and press it down until a new snapring can be inserted in the shaft groove. Always use a new snapring when assembling.

14. Install the cover and the steering wheel.

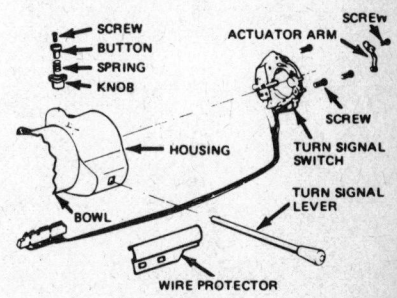

Turn signal switch

Ignition Switch

REMOVAL & INSTALLATION

The switch is located inside the channel section of the brake pedal support and is completely inaccessible without first lowering the steering column. The switch is actuated by a rod and rack assembly. A gear on the end of the lock cylinder engages the toothed upper end of the rod.

1. Lower the steering column; be sure to properly support it.

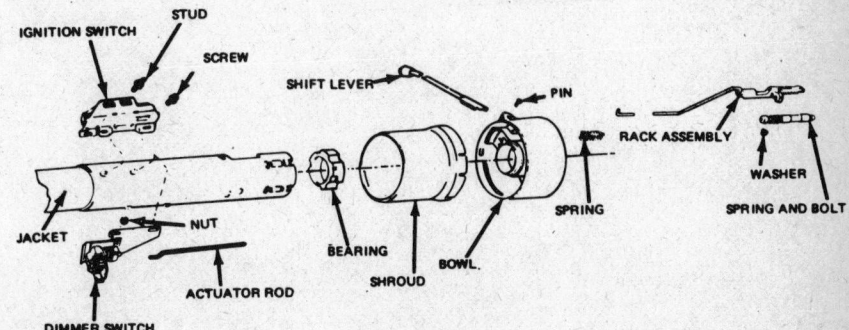

Ignition switch

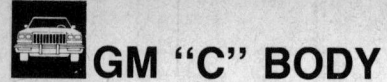
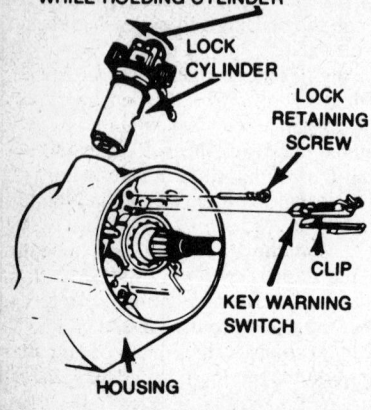

TO ASSEMBLE, ROTATE TO STOP
WHILE HOLDING CYLINDER

LOCK
CYLINDER

LOCK
RETAINING
SCREW

CLIP

KEY WARNING
SWITCH

HOUSING

Ignition lock cylinder

2. Put the switch in the "Off-Unlocked" position. With the cylinder removed, the rod is in "Lock" when it is in the next to the uppermost detent. "Off-Unlocked" is two detents from the top.

3. Remove the two switch screws and remove the switch assembly.

4. Before installing, place the new switch in "Off-Unlocked" position and make sure the lock cylinder and actuating rod are in "Off-Unlocked" (third detent from the top) position.

5. Install the activating rod into the switch and assemble the switch on the column. Tighten the mounting screws. Use only the specified screws since overlength screws could impair the collapsibility of the column.

6. Reinstall the steering column.

Ignition Lock Cylinder
REMOVAL & INSTALLATION

1. Place the lock in the Run position.
2. Remove the lock plate, turn signal switch and buzzer switch.
3. Remove the screw and lock cylinder.

CAUTION

If the screw is dropped on removal, it could fall into the column, requiring complete disassembly to retrieve the screw.

4. Rotate the cylinder clockwise to align cylinder key with the keyway in the housing.
5. Push the lock all the way in.
6. Install the screw. Tighten the screw to 14 in. lb. for adjustable columns and 25 in. lb. for standard columns.

GM "E" & "K" Body Front Wheel Drive
Riviera, Eldorado, Seville, Toronado

YEAR IDENTIFICATION

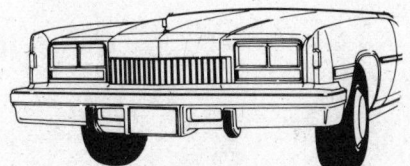

1978 Toronado

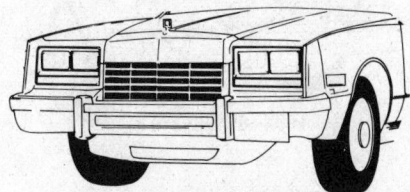

1979 Toronado

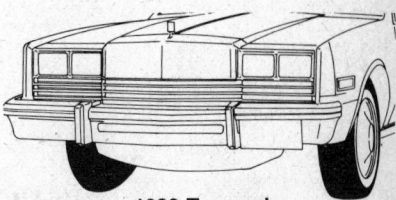

1980 Toronado

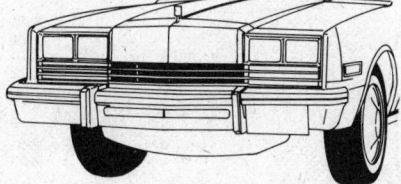

1981–84 Toronado

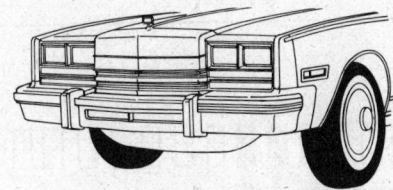

1984–85 Toronado Calienta

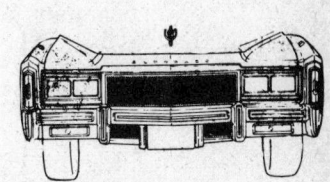

1978 Eldorado

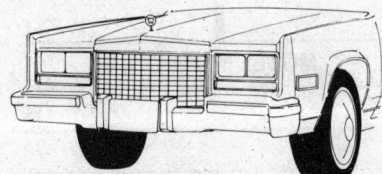

1979 Eldorado

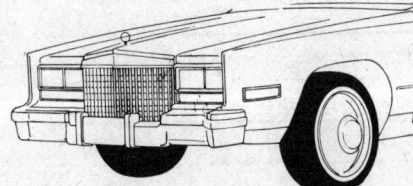

1980 Eldorado

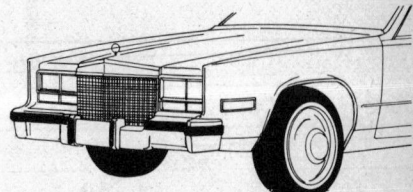

1981 Eldorado

1982–84 Eldorado

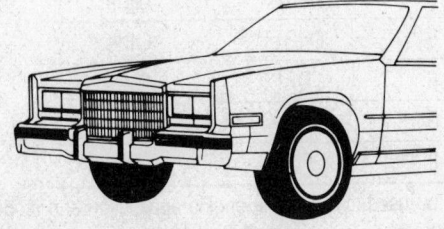

1985 Eldorado

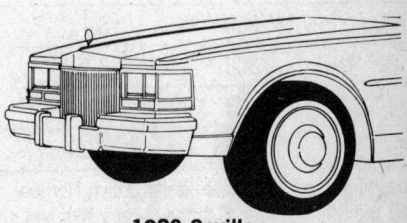

1980 Seville

YEAR IDENTIFICATION

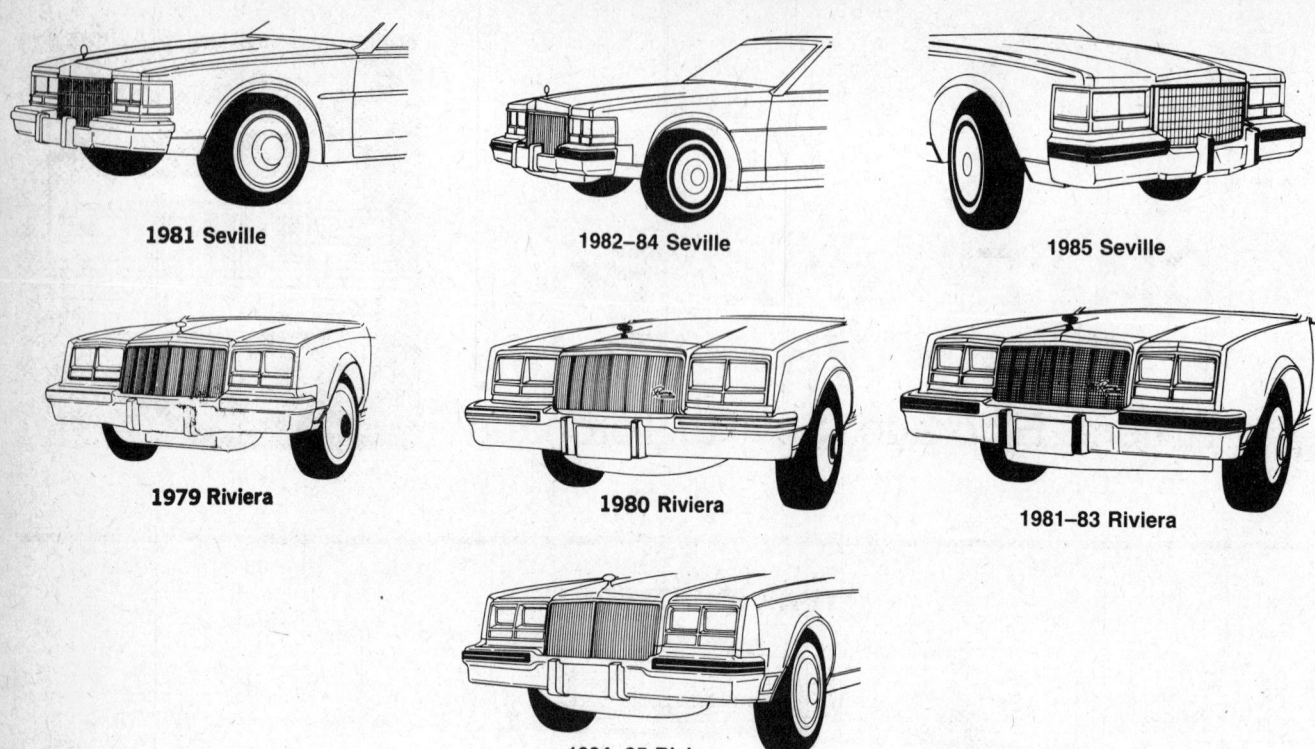

1981 Seville

1982–84 Seville

1985 Seville

1979 Riviera

1980 Riviera

1981–83 Riviera

1984–85 Riviera

VEHICLE IDENTIFICATION NUMBER (VIN)

It is important for servicing and ordering parts to be certain of the vehicle and engine identification. The VIN (vehicle identification number) is a 13 or 17 digit number visible through the windshield on the driver's side of the dash and contains the vehicle and engine identification codes. It can be interpreted as follows:

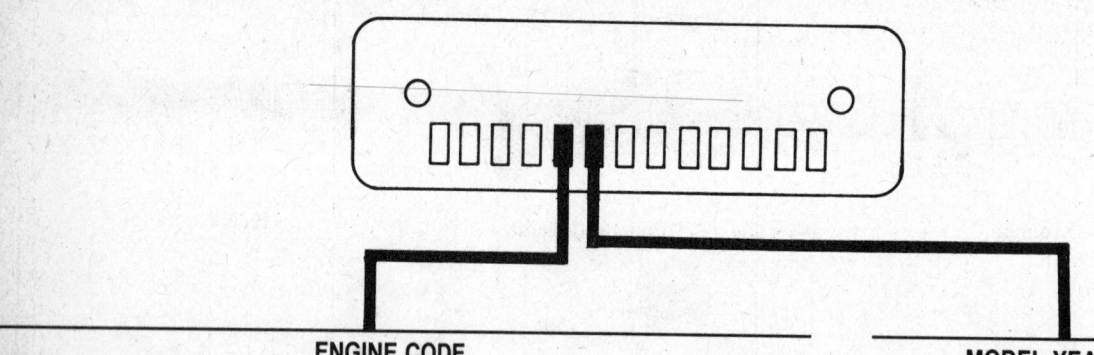

ENGINE CODE							MODEL YEAR CODE	
Code	Cu. In.	Liters	Cyl.	Carb.	Eng. Mfg.		Code	Year
3	231	3.8	6	4	Buick		8	78
Y	307	5.0	8	4	Olds.		9	79
R	350	5.7	8	4	Olds.		A	80
B	350	5.7	8	EFI	Olds.			
N	350	5.7	8	Diesel	Olds.			
9	368	6.0	8	DFI	Cad.			
K	403	6.6	8	4	Olds.			
S	425	7.0	8	4	Cad.			

The thirteen digit Vehicle Identification Number can be used to determine engine application and model year. The 6th digit indicates the model year, and the 5th digit identifies the factory installed body.

VEHICLE IDENTIFICATION NUMBER (VIN)

It is important for servicing and ordering parts to be certain of the vehicle and engine identification. The VIN (vehicle identification number) is a 13 or 17 digit number visible through the windshield on the driver's side of the dash and contains the vehicle and engine identification codes. It can be interpreted as follows:

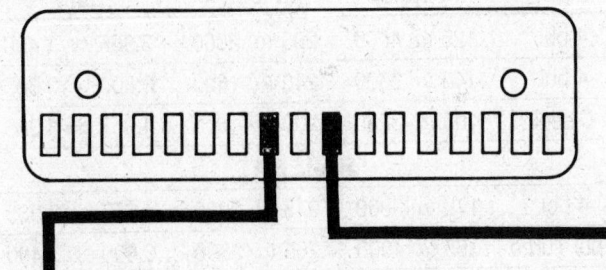

ENGINE CODE

Code	Cu. In.	Liters	Cyl.	Carb.	Eng. Mfg.
8	231	3.8	6	4	Buick
3	231	3.8	6	4	Buick
9	231	3.8	6	FI-Turbo	Buick
8	250	4.1	8	DFI	Cad.
8	250	4.1	8	4	Cad.
4	252	4.1	6	4	Buick
4	252	4.1	6	DFI	Buick
Y	307	5.0	8	4	Olds.
N	350	5.7	8	Diesel	Olds.
9	368	6.0	8	DFI	Cad.

MODEL YEAR CODE

Code	Year
B	81
C	82
D	83
E	84
F	85

The seventeen digit Vehicle Identification Number can be used to determine engine application and model year. The 10th digit indicates the model year, and the 8th digit identifies the factory installed engine.

EFI   Electronic Fuel Injection
DFI   Digital Fuel Injection

GENERAL ENGINE SPECIFICATIONS

Year	Eng. Code	Engine No. Cyl. Displacement Cu. In.	Carburetor Type	Horsepower @ rpm ■	Torque @ rpm (ft. lbs.) ■	Bore × Stroke (in.)	Compression Ratio	Oil Pressure @ 1500 rpm	Eng. Mfg.
				TORONADO					
'78	K	8-403	4 bbl	185 @ 3600	320 @ 2400	4.351 × 3.385	8.0:1	38	Olds.
'79	R	8-350	4 bbl	165 @ 3600	275 @ 2000	4.057 × 3.385	8.0:1	38	Olds.
	N	8-350	Diesel	125 @ 3600	225 @ 1600	4.057 × 3.385	22.5:1	38	Olds.
'80	Y	8-307	4 bbl	148 @ 3800	250 @ 2400	3.800 × 3.385	7.9:1	40	Olds.
	R	8-350	4 bbl	165 @ 3600	275 @ 2400	4.057 × 3.385	8.0:1	38	Olds.
	N	8-350	Diesel	125 @ 3600	225 @ 1600	4.057 × 3.385	22.5:1	38	Olds.
'81-'82	4	6-252	4 bbl	125 @ 4000	205 @ 2000	3.965 × 3.400	8.0:1	37①	Buick
	Y	8-307	4 bbl	148 @ 3800	250 @ 3800	3.800 × 3.385	8.0:1	40	Olds.
	N	8-350	Diesel	125 @ 3600	225 @ 1600	4.057 × 3.385	22.5:1	38	Olds.
'83	4	6-252	4 bbl	125 @ 4000	205 @ 2000	3.965 × 3.400	8.0:1	37①	Buick
	Y	8-307	4 bbl	140 @ 3600	240 @ 1600	3.800 × 3.385	8.0:1	40	Olds.
	N	8-350	Diesel	105 @ 3200	200 @ 1600	4.057 × 3.385	22.5:1	38	Olds.

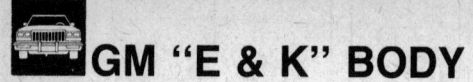

GENERAL ENGINE SPECIFICATIONS

Year	Eng. Code	Engine No. Cyl. Displacement Cu. In.	Carburetor Type	Horsepower @ rpm ■	Torque @ rpm (ft. lbs.) ■	Bore × Stroke (in.)	Compression Ratio	Oil Pressure @ 1500 rpm	Eng. Mfg.
'84–'85	4	6-252	4 bbl	125 @ 4000	205 @ 2000	3.965 × 3.400	8.0:1	37①	Buick
	Y	8-307	4 bbl	140 @ 3600	240 @ 1600	3.800 × 3.385	8.0:1	40	Olds.
	N	8-350	Diesel	105 @ 3200	200 @ 1600	4.057 × 3.385	22.5:1	38	Olds.
RIVIERA									
'79–'80	R	8-350	4 bbl	170 @ 3800	275 @ 2000	4.057 × 3.385	8.5:1	37	Olds.
	3	6-231	4 bbl Turbo	165 @ 4000	265 @ 2800	3.800 × 3.400	8.0:1	37②	Buick
'81	Y	8-307	4 bbl	140 @ 3600	245 @ 1600	3.736 × 3.385	8.0:1	37	Olds.
	4	6-252	4 bbl	125 @ 4000	205 @ 2000	3.965 × 3.400	8.0:1	37②	Buick
	3	6-231	4 bbl Turbo	180 @ 4000	270 @ 2400	3.800 × 3.400	8.0:1	37②	Buick
	N	8-350	Diesel	105 @ 3200	200 @ 1600	4.057 × 3.385	22.5:1	38	Olds.
'82	Y	8-307	4 bbl	140 @ 3600	245 @ 1600	3.736 × 3.385	8.0:1	37	Olds.
	4	6-252	4 bbl	125 @ 3800	210 @ 2000	3.965 × 3.400	8.0:1	35③	Buick
	3	6-231	4 bbl Turbo	180 @ 4000	270 @ 2400	3.800 × 3.400	8.0:1	37②	Buick
	N	8-350	Diesel	105 @ 3200	200 @ 1600	4.057 × 3.385	22.5:1	38	Olds.
'83	Y	8-307	4 bbl	140 @ 3600	240 @ 1600	3.736 × 3.385	8.0:1	37	Olds.
	N	8-350	Diesel	105 @ 3200	200 @ 1600	4.057 × 3.385	22.5:1	38	Olds.
	4	6-252	4 bbl	125 @ 4000	205 @ 2000	3.965 × 3.400	8.0:1	35③	Buick
	8	6-231	4 bbl Turbo	180 @ 4000	290 @ 2400	3.800 × 3.400	8.0:1	37②	Buick
'84–'85	8	6-231	4 bbl Turbo④	190 @ 4000	300 @ 2400	3.800 × 3.400	8.0:1	37②	Buick
	4	6-252	4 bbl	125 @ 4000	205 @ 2000	3.965 × 3.400	8.0:1	35③	Buick
	Y	8-307	4 bbl	140 @ 3600	240 @ 1600	3.736 × 3.385	8.0:1	37	Olds.
	N	8-350	Diesel	105 @ 3200	200 @ 1600	4.057 × 3.385	22.5:1	38	Olds.
SEVILLE									
'80	9	8-368	DFI	145 @ 3800	265 @ 1400	3.800 × 4.060	8.2:1	35③	Cadillac
	N	8-350	Diesel	105 @ 3200	205 @ 1600	4.057 × 3.385	22.5:1	40③	Olds.
'81	9	8-368	DFI	140 @ 3800	265 @ 1400	3.800 × 4.060	8.2:1	35③	Cadillac
	N	8-350	Diesel	105 @ 3200	204 @ 1600	4.057 × 3.385	22.5:1	40③	Olds.
	4	6-252	4 bbl	125 @ 3800	210 @ 2000	3.965 × 3.400	8.0:1	35③	Buick
'82	8	8-250	DFI	135 @ 4200	190 @ 2000	3.465 × 3.307	8.5:1	40	Cadillac
	4	6-252	4 bbl	125 @ 3800	210 @ 2000	3.965 × 3.400	8.0:1	35③	Buick
	N	8-350	Diesel	105 @ 3200	205 @ 1600	4.057 × 3.385	22.5:1	40③	Olds.
'83	8	8-250	DFI	135 @ 4200	190 @ 2000	3.465 × 3.307	8.5:1	40	Cadillac
	N	8-350	Diesel	105 @ 3200	205 @ 1600	4.057 × 3.385	22.5:1	35③	Olds.
'84–'85	8	8-250	DFI	135 @ 4200	200 @ 2000	3.465 × 3.307	8.5:1	40	Cadillac
	N	8-350	Diesel	105 @ 3200	200 @ 1600	4.057 × 3.385	22.5:1	35③	Olds.
ELDORADO									
'78	S	8-425	4 bbl	180 @ 3600	260 @ 2000	4.082 × 4.060	8.5:1	35③	Cadillac
'79	B	8-350	EFI	170 @ 4200	270 @ 2000	4.057 × 3.385	8.5:1	35③	Olds.
	N	8-350	Diesel	120 @ 3600	220 @ 2200	4.057 × 3.385	22.5:1	40③	Olds.

GENERAL ENGINE SPECIFICATIONS

Year	Eng. Code	Engine No. Cyl. Displacement Cu. In.	Carburetor Type	Horsepower @ rpm ■	Torque @ rpm (ft. lbs.) ■	Bore × Stroke (in.)	Compression Ratio	Oil Pressure @ 1500 rpm	Eng. Mfg.
'80	9	8-368	DFI	145 @ 3800	265 @ 1600	3.800 × 4.060	8.2:1	35③	Cadillac
	N	8-350	Diesel	105 @ 3200	205 @ 1600	4.057 × 3.385	22.5:1	40③	Olds.
'81-'82	9	8-368	DFI	140 @ 3800	265 @ 1400	3.800 × 4.060	8.2:1	35③	Cadillac
	N	8-350	Diesel	105 @ 3200	205 @ 1600	4.057 × 3.385	22.5:1	40③	Olds.
	8	8-250	DFI	135 @ 4200	190 @ 2000	3.465 × 3.307	8.5:1	40	Cadillac
	4	6-252	4 bbl	125 @ 3800	210 @ 2000	3.965 × 3.400	8.0:1	35③	Buick
'83	8	8-250	DFI	135 @ 4200	190 @ 2000	3.465 × 3.307	8.5:1	40	Cadillac
	N	8-350	Diesel	105 @ 3200	205 @ 1600	4.057 × 3.385	22.5:1	35③	Olds.
'84–'85	8	8-250	DFI	135 @ 4200	2000 @ 2000	3.465 × 3.307	8.5:1	40	Cadillac
	N	8-350	Diesel	105 @ 3200	200 @ 1600	4.057 × 3.385	22.5:1	35③	Olds.

■Horsepower and torque are SAE net figures. They are measured at the rear of the transmission with all accessories installed and operating. Since the figures vary when a given engine is installed in different models, some are representative rather than exact.

① @ 2400 rpm
② @ 2600 rpm
③ @ 2000 rpm
④ '85-VIN9, Fuel injected Turbo
EFI Electronic Fuel Injection
DFI Digital Fuel Injection

GASOLINE ENGINE TUNE-UP SPECIFICATIONS

(When analyzing compression test results, look for uniformity among cylinders rather than specific pressures.)

Year	Eng. Code	Engine No. Cyl. Displacement (cu. in.)	Eng. Mfg.	Spark Plugs Orig Type	Spark Plugs Gap (in.)	Distributor	Ignition Timing (deg) ▲ *Auto Trans ●	Valves Intake Opens (deg) ●	Fuel Pump Pressure (psi)	Idle Speed (rpm) ▲ Auto Trans ●
				TORONADO						
'78	K	8-403	Olds.	R-46SZ	.060	Electronic	20B(22B)	16B	5.5-6.5	650/550(600)
'79	R	8-350	Olds.	R-46SZ	.060	Electronic	20B	16B	6-7.5	550
'80	Y	8-307	Olds.	R-46SX	.080	Electronic	20B	20	6-7.5	600/500
	R	8-350	Olds.	R-46SX	.080	Electronic	18B(16B)	16	6-7.5	600/500 (650/550)
'81-'82	4	6-252	Buick	R-45TS8	.080	Electronic	15B	16	6-7.5	①
	Y	8-307	Olds.	R-46SX	.080	Electronic	15B	20	6-7.5	①
'83	4	6-252	Buick	R-45TS8	.080	Electronic	15B	16	6-7.5	①
	Y	8-307	Olds.	R-46SX	.080	Electronic	15B	20	6-7.5	①
'84-'85	4	6-252	Buick	R-45TS8	.080	Electronic	①	16	6-7.5	①
	Y	8-307	Olds.	R-46SX	.080	Electronic	①	20	6-7.5	①
				RIVIERA						
'79	3	6-231 Turbo	Buick	R-44TSX	.060	Electronic	15B	16	4.25-5.75	650
	R	8-350	Olds.	R-46SZ	.060	Electronic	15B	16	4.25-5.75	550
'80	3	6-231 Turbo	Buick	R-45TS	.040	Electronic	15B	16	5.0	600
	R	8-350	Olds.	R-46SX	.080	Electronic	18B @ 1100	16	5.5-6.5	500

GASOLINE ENGINE TUNE-UP SPECIFICATIONS

(When analyzing compression test results, look for uniformity among cylinders rather than specific pressures.)

Year	Eng. Code	Engine No. Cyl. Displacement (cu. in.)	Eng. Mfg.	Orig Type	Gap (in.)	Distributor	Ignition Timing (deg) ▲ *Auto Trans ●	Valves Intake Opens (deg) ●	Fuel Pump Pressure (psi)	Idle Speed (rpm) ▲ Auto Trans ●
'81-'82	3	6-231 Turbo	Buick	R-45TS	.040	Electronic	15B	16	4.2-5.8	①
	4	6-252	Buick	R-45TS8	.080	Electronic	15B	16	4.2-5.9	①
	Y	8-307	Olds.	R-45TS4	.060	Electronic	15B @ 1100	20	6-7.5	①
'83	8	6-231 Turbo	Buick	R-45TS	.040	Electronic	15B	16	4.2-5.8	①
	4	6-252	Buick	R-45TS8	.080	Electronic	15B	16	6-7.5	①
	Y	8-307	Olds.	R-46SX	.080	Electronic	15B @ 1100	20	6-7.5	①
'84-'85	8 ⑥	6-231 Turbo	Buick	R-45TS	.040	Electronic	①	16	4.2-5.8	①
	4	6-252	Buick	R-45TS8	.080	Electronic	①	16	6-7.5	①
	Y	8-307	Olds.	R-46SX	.080	Electronic	①	20	6-7.5	①
ELDORADO AND SEVILLE										
'78	S	8-425	Cadillac	R-45NSX	.060	Electronic	18B @ 1400	21	5.25-6.5	650
'79	B	8-350	Olds.	R-47SX	.060	Electronic	10B	22	5.5-6.5	600
'80	9	8-368	Cadillac	R-45NSX	.060	Electronic	18B	11	5.5-6.5	575
'81	4	6-252	Buick	R-45TS8	.060	Electronic	15B	16	4.25-5.75	550 ③
	9	8-368	Cadillac	R-45NSX	.060	Electronic	10B	16	12-14	470 ④
'82	8	8-250	Cadillac	R-43NTS6	.060	Electronic	①	37	40	⑤
	4	6-252	Buick	R-45TSV	.060	Electronic	15B @ 550	16	4.25-5.75	550 ③
'83	8	8-250	Cadillac	R-43NTS6	.060	Electronic	①	37	40	⑤
'84-'85	8	8-250	Cadillac	R-43NTS6 ⑦	.060	Electronic	①	37	40	⑤

*Set timing with carburetor adjusted to 1100 rpm, unless sticker specifies otherwise.

▲ See text for procedure

● Where two figures appear separated by a slash, the first is idle speed with solenoid energized, the second is idle speed with solenoid disconnected. Figure in parentheses indicates California engine.

① See Underhood Sticker

② Solenoid energized (higher) idle speed is set with A/C on and compressor clutch wires disconnected.

③ In Drive; A/C 680

④ Drive or Neutral

⑤ Electronic controlled idle, no adjustment

⑥ '85: VIN9

⑦ R42CLTS6

B   Before Top Dead Center

Part numbers in this chart are not recommendations by Chilton for any product by brand name.

DIESEL TUNE-UP SPECIFICATIONS

Year	Engine No. Cyl Displacement (cu in.)	Fuel Pump Pressure (psi)	Compression (lbs)	Intake Valve Opens (deg)	Idle Speed (rpm) ●
'79	8-350	5.5-6.5	275 min.	16	650/675
'80	8-350	5.5-6.5	275 min.	16	750/600
'81-'85	8-350	5.5-7.0	275 min.	16	①

NOTE: The underhood specifications sticker often reflects tune-up specification changes made in production. Sticker figures must be used if they disagree with those in this chart.

① See underhood specifications sticker

● Where two idle speed figures appear separated by a slash, the first is idle speed with solenoid energized, the second is idle speed with solenoid disconnected.

FIRING ORDERS

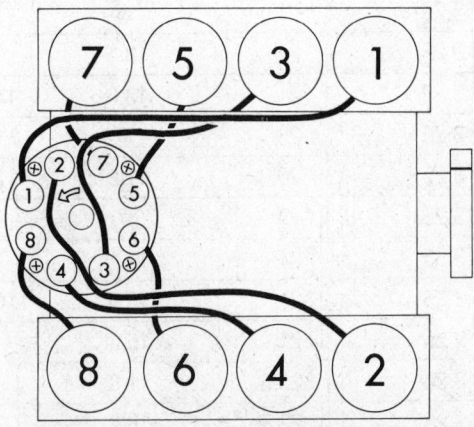

GM 250, 307, 350 V8s, including diesel
Engine firing order: 1-8-4-3-6-5-7-2 Distributor rotation: counterclockwise

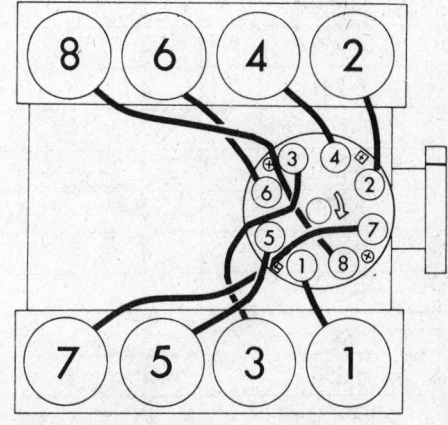

GM 368, 425 V8s
Engine firing order: 1-5-6-3-4-2-7-8 Distributor rotation: clockwise

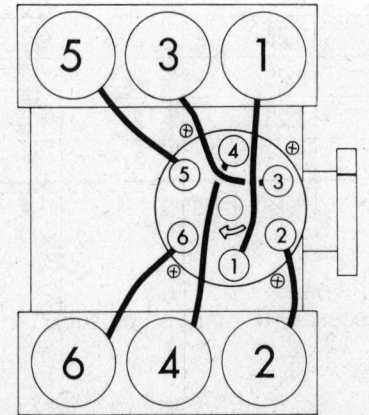

GM (Buick) 231 and 252 V6 (3.8 and 4.1L)
Engine firing order: 1-6-5-4-3-2
Distributor rotation: clockwise
V6 Harmonic balancers have two timing marks: one is ⅛ in. wide, and one is 1/16 in. wide. Use the 1/16 in. mark for timing with a hand held light. The ⅛ in. mark is used only with a magnetic timing pick-up probe.

CAPACITIES
All Models

Year	Engine No. Cyl. Displacement (cu. in.)	Engine Crankcase Add 1 Qt for New Filter	Transmission Pts to Refill After Draining Automatic ●	Drive Axle (pts)	Gasoline Tank (gals)	Cooling Syster (qts)		
						With Heater	With A/C	With Heavy Duty
'78	8-425	4	8	4.25	24		19.8	—
	8-403	4.75	8	4.25	26		17.5	—
'79	8-350 Cadillac	4	9	4.25	25②		17.2	—
	8-350 Olds.	4	10	3.25	20		15	15.5
	8-350 Olds. ③	4	10	3.25	20.7		14.9	15.6
	8-350 Diesel	7①	9	3.25	③		18.5	—
	6-231	4	10	3.25	20.7		14	14.5
'80	8-368	4	④	3.25	20.7		22.4	—
	8-350	4	④	3.25	20.5		15.2	—
	8-350 Diesel	7①	④	3.25	23		18.5	—
	8-307	4	④	3.25	21		16.5	—
	6-231	4	④	3.25	21		13.6	14.1
'81	8-368	4	④	3.25	20.3		22.4	—
	8-307	4	④	3.25	21		16.25	16.25
	8-350 Diesel	7①	④	3.25	⑤		⑥	—
	6-252	4	④	3.25	21		13.1	—
	6-231	4	④	3.25	21		13.6	14.1
'82	8-350 Diesel	7①	④	3.25	23		⑧	⑧
	8-250	4	④	3.25	20.3		11.8	12.5
	8-307	4	④	3.25	21		⑦	—
	6-252	4	④	3.25	21		13.1	—
	6-231	4	④	3.25	21		13.6	14.1
'83	8-307	4	④	3.25	21		16.2	—
	8-250	4	④	3.25	20.3		11.8	—
	8-350 Diesel	7①	④	3.25	22.8		18.2	—
	8-252	4	④	3.25	21.1		13.1	—
	6-231	4	④	3.25	21.1		13.6	14.1
'84-'85	8-307	4	④	3.25	21.1		16.2	—
	8-250	4	④	3.25	20.3		11.8	12.5
	8-350 Diesel	7①	④	3.25	22.8		18.2	—
	6-252	4	④	3.25	21.1		12.5	—
	6-231	5	④	3.25	21.1		12.9	13.7

●Does not include torque converter
①Includes mandatory filter change
②Seville: 21
③Seville: 21, Eldorado: 19.6, Toronado: 22.8
④Add 6 pts; start engine and allow to warm up. Add fluid necessary to mark on dipstick
⑤Riviera: 27, Eldorado/Seville: 22.8, Toronado: 23
⑥Riviera: 18.2, Eldorado/Seville: 18.4, Toronado: 18
⑦Rivivera: 18.9, Toronado: 16.5
⑧Riviera: 23, Eldorado/Seville: 22.8, Toronado: 23

VALVE SPECIFICATIONS
All Models

Year	Engine No. Cyl. Displacement (cu. in.)	Seat Angle (deg)	Face Angle (deg)	Spring Test Pressure (lbs. @ in.)	Spring Installed Height (in.)	Stem to Guide Clearance (in.)		Stem Diameter (in.)	
						Intake	Exhaust	Intake	Exhaust
'78	8-425	45	44	160 @ 1.50	$1\frac{15}{16}$	.0010–.0027	.0010–.0027	.3416	.3416
	8-403	45①	44②	187 @ 1.27	$1\frac{43}{64}$	.0010–.0027	.0015–.0032	.3429	.3424
'79	8-350	45①	44②	187 @ 1.27	$1\frac{43}{64}$	.0010–.0027	.0015–.0032	.3429	.3424
	8-350 Diesel	45①	44②	152 @ 1.30	$1\frac{43}{64}$	.0010–.0027	.0015–.0032	.3429	.3424
	6-231	45	45	164 @ 1.34③	$1\frac{47}{64}$	.0015–.0035	.0015–.0032	.3406	.3408
'80	8-368	45	44	160 @ 1.50	$1\frac{15}{32}$	.0010–.0027	.0012–.0029	.3420	.3418
	8-350 Diesel	45①	44②	152 @ 1.30	$1\frac{43}{64}$	.0010–.0027	.0015–.0032	.3429	.3424
	8-350	45①	44②	187 @ 1.27	$1\frac{43}{64}$	.0010–.0027	.0015–.0032	.3429	.3424
	8-307	45①	44②	187 @ 1.27	$1\frac{43}{64}$	.0010–.0027	.0015–.0032	.3429	.3424
	6-231	45	45	164 @ 1.34③	$1\frac{47}{64}$	.0015–.0035	.0015–.0032	.3406	.3408
'81	8-368	45	44	160 @ 1.50	$1\frac{15}{32}$	.0010–.0027	.0012–.0029	.3420	.3418
	8-350 Diesel	45①	44②	152 @ 1.30④	$1\frac{43}{64}$	.0010–.0027	.0015–.0032	.3429	.3424
	8-307	45①	44②	187 @ 1.270	$1\frac{43}{64}$	.0010–.0027	.0015–.0032	.3429	.3424
	6-252	45	45	182 @ 1.34	$1\frac{47}{64}$	.0015–.0035	.0015–.0032	.3407	.3409
	6-231	45	45	164 @ 1.34③	$1\frac{47}{64}$	.0015–.0035	.0015–.0032	.3406	.3408
'82	8-350 Diesel	45①	44②	152 @ 1.30④	$1\frac{43}{64}$	.0010–.0027	.0015–.0032	.3429	.3424
	8-307	45①	44②	187 @ 1.270	$1\frac{43}{64}$	.0010–.0027	.0015–.0032	.3429	.3424
	8-250	45	44	182 @ 1.28	$1\frac{47}{64}$	.0010–.0027	.0012–.0029	.3420	.3408
	6-252	45	45	220 @ 1.34	$1\frac{47}{64}$	.0015–.0035	.0015–.0032	.3407	.3409
	6-231	45	45	164 @ 1.34③	$1\frac{47}{64}$	.0015–.0035	.0015–.0032	.3406	.3408
'83	6-231	45	45	182 @ 1.34	$1\frac{47}{64}$	.0015–.0035	.0015–.0032	.3401–.3412	.3405–.3412
	6-252	45	45	182 @ 1.34	$1\frac{47}{64}$	.0015–.0035	.0015–.0032	.3401–.3412	.3405–.3412
	8-250	45	44	182 @ 1.28	$1\frac{43}{64}$	.001–.003	.001–.003	.3413–.3420	.3411–.3418
	8-307	45	44	187 @ 1.27	$1\frac{43}{64}$	.0010–.0027	.0015–.0032	.3425–.3432	.3420–.3427
	8-350 Diesel	45①	44②	210 @ 1.22	$1\frac{43}{64}$	.0010–.0027	.0015–.0032	.3425–.3432	.3420–.3427
'84–'85	6-231	45	45	220 @ 1.34	$1\frac{47}{64}$	.0015–.0035	.0015–.0032	.3401–.3412	.3405–.3412
	6-252	45	45	182 @ 1.34	$1\frac{47}{64}$	.0015–.0035	.0015–.0032	.3401–.3412	.3405–.3412
	8-250	45	44	182 @ 1.28	$1\frac{43}{64}$	.001–.003	.001–.003	.3413–.3420	.3411–.3418
	8-307	45	44	187 @ 1.27	$1\frac{43}{64}$	.0010–.0027	.0015–.0032	.3425–.3432	.3420–.3427
	8-350 Diesel	45①	44②	210 @ 1.22	$1\frac{43}{64}$	.0010–.0027	.0015–.0032	.3425–.3432	.3420–.3427

① Exhaust valve seat 31° ③ Exhaust 182 @ 1.34
② Exhaust valve face 30° ④ 210 @ 1.30 1981–82

RING GAP
All Models
(All measurements are given in inches)

Year	Engine	Top Compression	Bottom Compression	Oil Control
'78	8-425	.013–.025	.013–.025	.015–.055
	8-403	.010–.023	.010–.023	.015–.055
'79–'80	8-350	.010–.023	.010–.023	.015–.055
'79–'82	8-350 Diesel	.015–.025	.015–.025	.015–.055
'80–'81	8-368	.013–.023	.013–.023	.015–.055
'80–'82	8-307	.009–.019	.009–.019	.015–.055
'82	8-250	.009–.020	.009–.020	.010–.050
'81–'82	6-252	.013–.023	.013–.023	.015–.035
'79–'82	6-231	.013–.023	.013–.023	.015–.035
'83–'85	6-231	.010–.020	.010–.020	.015–.055
'83–'85	6-252	.010–.020	.010–.020	.015–.055
'83–'85	8-250	.009–.020	.009–.020	.010–.050
'83–'85	8-307	.009–.019	.009–.019	.015–.055
'83–'85	8-350 Diesel	.019–.027	.013–.021	.015–.055

TORQUE SPECIFICATIONS
All Models
(All readings in ft. lbs.)

Year	Engine No. Cyl. Displacement (cu. in.)	Cylinder Head Bolts	Bearing Bolts Rod	Bearing Bolts Main	Crankshaft Bolt	Flywheel to Crankshaft Bolts	Manifold Intake	Manifold Exhaust
'78	8-425	95	40	90	Press fit	75	30	35①
	8-403	130③	42	80②	200–310	60	40	25
'79	8-350	130③	42	80②	200–310	60	40③	25
	8-350 Diesel	130③	42	120	200–310	60	40③	25
	6-231	80	40	100	225	60	45	25
'80	8-368	95③	40	90	Press fit	75	30	35①
	8-350	130③	42	80②	200–310	60	40③	25
	8-350 Diesel	130③	42	120	200–310	60	40③	25
	8-307	130③	42	80②	200–310	60	40③	25
	6-231	80	40	100	225	60	45	25
'81	8-368	95③	40	90	Press fit	75	30	35①
	8-350 Diesel	130③	42	120	200–310	60	40③	25
	8-307	130③	42	80②	200–310	60	40③	25
	6-252	80	40	100	225	60	45	25
	6-231	80	40	100	225	60	45	25

TORQUE SPECIFICATIONS
All Models
(All readings in ft. lbs.)

Year	Engine No. Cyl. Displacement (cu. in.)	Cylinder Head Bolts	Bearing Bolts Rod	Bearing Bolts Main	Crankshaft Bolt	Flywheel to Crankshaft Bolts	Manifold Intake	Manifold Exhaust
'82	8-350 Diesel	130③	42	120	200–310	60	40③	25
	8-307	130③	42	80②	200–310	60	40③	25
	8-250	⑤	22	85	225	75	20	18
	6-252	80	40	100	225	60	45	25
	6-231	80	40	100	225	60	45	25
'83	6-231	80	40	100	225	60	45	25
	6-252	80	40	100	225	60	45	25
	8-250	⑤	20	85	20	35	20	20
	8-307	130③	42	80②	200–310	60	40③	25
	8-350 Diesel	130③	42	120	200–310	60	40③	25
'84–'85	6-231	80	40	100	225	60	45	25
	6-252	80	40	100	225	60	45	25
	8-250	⑤	20	85	20	35	20	20
	8-307	125③	42	80②	200–310	60	40③	25
	8-350 Diesel	130③	42	120	200–310	60	40③	25

① 12 ft. lbs. for short bolt
② 120 on No. 5
③ Bolts must be oiled before tightening
④ Fan pulley to balancer—20 ft. lbs.
⑤ Pull first to 45 ft. lbs. in sequence, then tighten to 90 ft. lbs. in sequence

CRANKSHAFT AND CONNECTING ROD SPECIFICATIONS
All Models
(All measurements are given in inches)

Year	Engine No. Cyl. Displacement (cu. in.)	Crankshaft Main Brg. Journal Dia.	Crankshaft Main Brg. Oil Clearance	Crankshaft Shaft End-Play	Crankshaft Thrust on No.	Connecting Rod Journal Diameter	Connecting Rod Oil Clearance	Connecting Rod Side Clearance
'78	8-425	3.2500	.0003–.0026	.002–.012	3	2.5000	.0005–.0028	.008–.020
	8-403	2.4990②	.0005–.0021③	.004–.019	3	2.1243	.0004–.0033	.006–.020
'79	8-350	2.4995–2.4985④	.0005–.0021③	.0035–.0135	3	2.1243	.0004–.0033	.006–.020
	8-350 Diesel	2.9998	.0005–.0021③	.0035–.0135	3	2.1243	.0004–.0033	.006–.020
	6-231	2.4995	.0003–.0017	.004–.008	2	2.2491	.0005–.0026	.006–.027
'80	8-368	3.2500	.0001–.0026	.002–.012	3	2.5000	.0005–.0028	.008–.020
	8-350	2.4995–2.4985④	.0005–.0021③	.0035–.0135	3	2.1243	.0004–.0033	.006–.020
	8-350 Diesel	2.9998	.0005–.0021③	.0035–.0135	3	2.1243	.0004–.0033	.006–.020
	8-307	2.4995–2.4990⑤	.0005–.0021③	.0035–.0135	3	2.1243	.0004–.0033	.006–.020
	6-231	2.4995	.0003–.0017	.004–.008	2	2.2491	.0005–.0026	.006–.027
'81	8-368	3.2500	.0001–.0026	.002–.012	3	2.5000	.0005–.0028	.008–.020
	8-350 Diesel	2.9998	.0005–.0021③	.0035–.0135	3	2.1243	.0004–.0033	.006–.020
	8-307	2.4995–2.4990⑤	.0005–.0021③	.0035–.0135	3	2.1243	.0004–.0033	.006–.020

CRANKSHAFT AND CONNECTING ROD SPECIFICATIONS
All Models
(All measurements are given in inches)

Year	Engine No. Cyl. Displacement (cu. in.)	Crankshaft				Connecting Rod		
		Main Brg. Journal Dia.	Main Brg. Oil Clearance	Shaft End-Play	Thrust on No.	Journal Diameter	Oil Clearance	Side Clearance
'81	6-252	2.4995	.0003–.0018	.003–.009	2	2.2491	.0005–.0026	.006–.023
	6-231	2.4995	.0003–.0017	.004–.008	2	2.2491	.0005–.0026	.006–.027
'82	8-350 Diesel	2.9998	.0005–.0021 ③	.0035–.0135	3	2.1243	.0004–.0033	.006–.020
	8-307	2.4995–2.4990 ⑤	.0005–.0021 ③	.0035–.0135	3	2.1243	.0004–.0033	.006–.020
	8-250	2.64	.0004–.0030	.001–.007	3	1.929	.0005–.0028	.008–.020
	6-252	2.4995	.0003–.0018	.003–.009	2	2.2491	.0005–.0026	.006–.023
	6-231	2.4995	.0003–.0017	.004–.008	2	2.2491	.0005–.0026	.006–.027
'83	6-231	2.4995	.0003–.0018	.003–.011	2	2.2491	.0005–.0026	.006–.027
	6-252	2.4995	.0003–.0018	.003–.011	2	2.2491	.0005–.0026	.006–.023
	8-250	2.64	.0004–.0027	.001–.007	3	1.929	.0005–.0028	.008–.020
	8-307	2.4995–2.4990 ⑤	.0005–.0021 ③	.0035–.0135	3	2.1238–2.1248	.0004–.0033	.006–.020
	8-350 Diesel	2.9993–3.0003	.0005–.0021 ①	.0035–.0135	3	2.1238–2.1248	.0005–.0026	.006–.020
'84–'85	6-231	2.4995	.0003–.0018	.003–.011	2	2.2491	.0005–.0026	.006–.027
	6-252	2.4995	.0003–.0018	.003–.011	2	2.2491	.0005–.0026	.006–.023
	8-250	2.64	.0004–.0027	.001–.007	3	1.929	.0005–.0028	.008–.020
	8-307	2.4995–2.4990 ⑤	.0005–.0021 ③	.0035–.0135	3	2.1238–2.1248	.0004–.0033	.006–.020
	8-350 Diesel	2.9993–3.0003	.0005–.0021 ①	.0035–.0135	3	2.1238–2.1248	.0005–.0026	.006–.020

① No. 5—.0020–.0034
② No. 1—2.4993
③ No. 5—.0015–.0031
④ No. 1—2.4998–2.4988; 1979–'80 Cadillac 2.4990
⑤ No. 1—2.4998–2.4993

RING SIDE CLEARANCE
All Models
(All measurements are given in inches)

Year	Engine	Top Compression	Bottom Compression	Oil Control
'78	8-425	.0017–.0040	.0017–.0040	None (side sealing)
	8-403	.0020–.0040	.0020–.0040	.0006–.0096
'79–'80	8-350	.0020–.0040	.0020–.0040	.0006–.0096
'79–'85	8-350 Diesel	.0040–.0060 ①	.0018–.0038 ②	.0010–.0050
'80–'81	8-368	.0017–.0040	.0017–.0040	None (side sealing)
'80–'85	8-307	.0020–.0040	.0020–.0040	.015–.055
'82–'85	8-250	.0016–.0037	.0016–.0037	None (side sealing)
'81–'85	6-252	.0030–.0050	.0030–.0050	.0035 max.
'79–'85	6-231	.0030–.0050	.0030–.0050	.0035

① 1979; 83–84; .005–.007
② 83–84—.003–.005

PISTON CLEARANCE
All Models

Year	Engine	Piston-to-bore Clearance (in.)
'78	8-425	.0006–.0014
	8-403	.001–.002
'79–'80	8-350	.0010–.0020
'79–'85	8-350 Diesel	.0005–.0006
'80–'81	8-368	.0006–.0014
'80	8-307	.0005–.0015
'81–'85	8-307	.00075–.00175
'82–'85	8-250	.0010–.0018
'81–'85	6-252	.0008–.0020
'79–'85	6-231	.0008–.0020 ①

① Measured at skirt top   Turbo engines—.0022–.0034 measured at piston pin centerline.

WHEEL ALIGNMENT SPECIFICATIONS

Year	Caster Range (deg)	Caster Pref Setting (deg)	Camber Range (deg)	Camber Pref Setting (deg)	Toe-in (in.)	Steering Axis Inclin. (deg)
TORONADO						
'78	½N to ½P	0	⅕N to ⅘P ① ⅘N to ⅕P ②	⅓P ⅓N	0 ± ¹⁄₁₆	11
'79–'82	2P to 3P	2½P	½N to ½P	0	0 ± ¹⁄₁₆	11
'83–'85	1½P to 3½P	2½P	½N to ½P	0	⅛ in to ⅛ out	—
ELDORADO AND SEVILLE						
'78	½N to ½P	0	⅖N to ⅖P	0	¹⁄₁₆N to ¹⁄₁₆P	11
'79–'82	1½P to 3½P	2½P	³⁄₁₆N to ³⁄₁₆P	0	⅛P to ⅛P	11
'83–'84	2P to 3P	2½P	½N to ½P	0	⅛ in to ⅛ out	—
RIVIERA						
'79–'82	1½P to 3½P	2½P	¹³⁄₁₆N to ¹³⁄₁₆P	0	⅛ in to ⅛ out	—
'83–'85	2P to 3P	2½P	½N to ½P	0	⅛ in to ⅛ out	—

① Left side   ② Right side

NOTE: Service procedures for the Charging System, Starting System, Ignition System, Fuel System, Cooling System, and Emission Controls on the Toronado can be found in the Oldsmobile section.

IGNITION SYSTEM

A high energy ignition (HEI) system is standard on all models. The HEI distributor replaces the points and condenser with a timing wheel, magnetic pick-up, and control module. The coil is built into the distributor cap. For further description, as well as service procedures for HEI, see the Electronic Ignition unit repair section.

Most 1981 and later models use an Electronic Spark Timing (EST) distributor. The EST distributor uses no mechanical or vacuum advance and is easily identified by the absence of a vacuum advance and the presence of a four terminal connector.

Unlike the gasoline engine, which is a spark-ignition design, the diesel engine is a compression-ignition type. When air is compressed to an extreme, high temperatures are produced. At the moment of extreme compression a small quantity of fuel is sprayed, under high pressure, into the compression chambers. The temperature of compression ignites the tiny fuel droplets. A temperature of about 1750°F is needed for the fuel ignition. The use of glow plugs is necessitated because the combustion chambers are cold prior to an initial start-up and the first few revolutions of the engine would not produce sufficiently high combustion chamber temperatures for fuel ignition. The glow plugs warm the chambers for a few seconds, bringing them up to the required temperatures to aid in starting, then automatically shut off.

Distributor

REMOVAL & INSTALLATION

1. Label all hoses and wires before removal. Remove spark plug cables and wire connectors from cap.

2. Remove the cap. Remove the vacuum hose from the vacuum unit.

3. Crank the engine until the rotor points toward the rear of the engine and the No. 1 piston is almost at TDC.

4. Turn the engine until the crankshaft pulley timing mark is at 0. (The white mark on the side of the rotor will be aligned with the white pointer in the distributor.)

5. Remove the distributor clamp and pull the distributor up until the rotor stops turning and note the position of the rotor. Remove the distributor.

6. When installing, make sure that the timing marks are aligned at 0 and the rotor and pointer marks are aligned.

For additional timing and distributor service procedures, see the Emission Control Systems and Electronic Ignition Unit Repair Sections.

ENGINE

NOTE: Please refer to the "Oldsmobile Rear Wheel Drive" or "Cadillac" sections for any engine procedures not included in this section. Service procedures for the Buick built 231 and 252 cu. in. (3.8 and 4.1L) V6 are in the "Buick Rear Wheel Drive Car" section. The 350 cu. in. diesel engine is produced by the General Motors Oldsmobile division; diesel engine service procedures will therefore be found in the "Oldsmobile Rear Wheel Drive" car section.

On the Eldorado and 1980 and later Seville, special mounting brackets are welded to the frame to provide the front attaching points and a special crossmember is used for the rear mount.

Engine

REMOVAL & INSTALLATION

Toronado

1. Drain cooling system.

2. Remove hood, marking hinge for reassembly.

3. If equipped with a fan shroud, unhook the strap and remove the clips holding the seal to the venturi ring. Move the seal toward the radiator.

4. Disconnect battery.

5. Disconnect radiator hoses, oil cooler lines, heater hoses, vacuum hoses, engine-to-body ground strap, fuel hose from fuel pump, wiring and accelerator cable. Remove the air cleaner, hot air pipe, air conditioner compressor and power steering pump

without disconnecting lines and set them aside.

6. Remove the throttle control switch bracket, the radiator support and the radiator.

7. Raise the car.

8. Disconnect exhaust pipes at manifold. Loosen, but do not remove, upper left flywheel cover attaching bolt.

9. Disconnect wires and remove starter.

10. Remove torque converter cover and remove three bolts securing the converter to flywheel. Scribe marks on converter and flywheel for reassembly. Remove the splash shield.

11. Support the final drive assembly.

12. Remove two attaching bolts from right output shaft support bracket and one thru-bolt attaching final drive to engine block on the left side. Scribe around the washers for correct reassembly.

13. Remove engine mount to crossmember nuts and front engine mount nuts. Remove the lower right engine-to-transmission attaching bolt.

14. Support the final drive assembly with a chain stretched under and across the final drive assembly and attached to holes in the frame members.

15. Lower the car.

16. Support engine by using a lifting fixture.

17. Remove the remaining transmission-to-engine bolts.

18. Lift the engine from the car.

--- CAUTION ---
If car is to be moved, install converter holding tool.

19. To install, reverse removal procedure.

1978 Eldorado

--- CAUTION ---
If it is necessary to reposition the air conditioner compressor or the lines, do not disconnect the lines.

1. Matchmark the hood hinges for reasembly. Remove the hood.

2. Drain the cooling system.

3. Disconnect the battery cables and remove the battery.

4. Remove the air cleaner.

5. Disconnect the upper radiator hose at the thermostat housing.

6. Remove the radiator cover screws.

7. Remove the fan blade assembly by loosening the alternator and rotating the fan to gain access to each screw.

8. Disconnect the wiring from the alternator, starter motor, and compressor.

9. Disconnect the water control valve at the rear of the block.

10. Remove the power steering pump and position it out of the way. Do not detach any of the hoses.

11. Disconnect the A/C compressor mounts and position it out of the way. Do not disconnect any of the lines.

12. Disconnect the vacuum lines, cruise control and throttle linkage at the carburetor.

13. Remove the left exhaust manifold flange nuts. Also remove the cooler line bracket screw and the filler pipe nut from the exhaust manifold.

14. Remove the upper screw attaching the steering gear coupling shroud to the frame.

15. Raise the car on a hoist.

16. Remove the remaining screw from the steering gear shroud and remove the shroud.

17. Remove the final drive bracket-to-motor mount attaching screw.

18. Disconnect and plug the fuel lines.

19. Remove the front engine mounts.

20. Remove the lower radiator hose.

21. Remove the right exhaust manifold flange nuts.

22. Remove the starter motor.

23. Remove the flywheel inspection cover and the flywheel-to-converter screws.

24. Remove two transmission-to-engine bolts.

25. Remove the right side output shaft bolts.

26. Remove the two output shaft bracket-to-block bolts and the screw attaching the bracket to the final drive.

27. Loosen the right side shock lower mounting bolt and position the shock outward on the stud.

28. Move the drive axle as far back as possible and remove the output shaft.

29. Lower the car and remove the four transmission-to-engine attaching bolts.

30. Install a lifting chain and remove engine.

31. Reverse to install. Torque the engine mounts to 52 ft. lbs.; the engine-to-transmission bolts to 50 ft. lbs.

1979 And Later Eldorado And 1980 And Later Seville

1. Matchmark the hood hinges for reassembly.

2. Drain the cooling system.

3. Disconnect the battery cables and remove the battery.

4. Remove the air cleaner.

5. Loosely install a special valve compressor tool on the EFI line pressure fitting. Place a towel around the fitting to catch any spray. Slowly tighten the tool to relieve pressure.

6. Raise the car on a hoist and remove the exhaust pipe flange bolts from the manifolds. Separate the left side pipe from the Y pipe and remove the exhaust pipe from the car.

7. Disconnect the shift linkage from the transmission.

8. Disconnect the flexible fuel line from the main fuel pipe. Use a new clamp on installation.

9. Remove the six drive axle-to-output shaft attaching screws from each side.

10. Remove the nuts from the engine and transmission mounts.

11. Remove the lower fan shroud attaching screws and disconnect the lower radiator hose.

12. Lower the car and disconnect the upper radiator hose and the transmission cooler lines.

13. Remove the radiator upper cover and remove the radiator.

14. Remove the four clutch fan nuts and the fan shroud.

15. Disconnect the power steering hoses at the steering gear. Cap the ends to prevent entry of dirt.

16. Disconnect the flexible fuel line from the pressure regulator fuel return pipe. Use a new clamp on installation.

17. If equipped with cruise control, disconnect the vacuum lines from the power unit. Pull the hoses out of the tie-down straps and position them out of the way.

18. Disconnect:
   a. the canister hose
   b. canister vacuum supply hose
   c. throttle cable from the throttle body
   d. heater hoses at the water valve and the water pump
   e. brake vacuum line at the brake pipe
   f. speedometer at the transmission
   g. engine wiring harness at the center bulkhead connector
   h. distributor wiring
   i. heater wire from the water valve.
   j. Wiring at the windshield wiper motor and the washer bottle
   k. engine ground strap from the cowl
   l. wiring at the A/C compressor

19. Remove the coolant reservoir tank.

20. Loosen the A.I.R. pump and remove the belt from the A/C compressor.

21. Remove the compressor-to-bracket screws and position the compressor out of the way. Do not disconnect any of the lines.

22. Install a lifting chain.

23. Remove the engine, transmission and final drives as a unit.

24. Reverse to install. Torque the engine mounts to 65 ft. lbs.; transmission mounts to 48 ft. lbs.; output shaft-to-drive axle attaching screws to 60 ft. lbs.

1979 and Later Riviera

1. Refer to Steps 1-4, 6 and 11-12 of the above procedure.

2. Remove the radiator.

3. Refer to Steps 8-13 of the above procedure.

4. Disconnect the turbo outlet exhaust pipe at the turbocharger assembly.

5. Raise the car and remove the starter motor.

6. Drain the engine oil.

7. Remove the torque convertor cover and remove the converter to flywheel bolts.

8. Remove the transmission to engine bolts.

9. Remove the right output shaft support bolts.

10. Remove the front engine mounts.

11. Install a support chain to the final drive.

12. Remove the final drive to engine bracket.

13. Install a lifting device to the engine

and remove it from the car. Installation is the reverse of removal.

Exhaust Manifold
REMOVAL & INSTALLATION

V8—Left Side

1. Remove the air cleaner and the carburetor heat shroud on the manifold on gasoline engine. Disconnect shift linkage and remove heat shield on diesel engine.

2. Remove the lower alternator bracket; raise the front of the car and support it securely.

3. Disconnect the exhaust pipe.

4. Lower the car and remove the manifold attaching bolts. Remove the manifold from above.

5. To install, reverse the removal procedure using the correct torque for the manifold attaching bolts.

V8—Right Side

1. Raise the car and support it securely.

2. Disconnect the exhaust pipe and then remove the right front wheel.

3. Remove the attaching bolts and lower the manifold down and out from under the vehicle.

4. To install, reverse the removal procedure.

V6—Left Side

1. Raise the front of the car and support it securely.

2. Disconnect the exhaust crossover pipe.

3. Remove the left front engine mount thru-bolt and loosen the thru-bolt on the right mount.

4. Raise the engine slightly, unscrew the manifold mounting bolts and remove the manifold.

5. Installation is in the reverse order of removal.

V6—Right Side

1. Raise the front of the car and support it securely.

2. Disconnect the exhaust pipe from both manifolds and lower it.

3. Unscrew the manifold mounting bolts and remove the manifold from underneath the car.

4. Installation is in the reverse order of removal.

1979 and later Eldorado and 1980 and later Seville

For exhaust manifold procedures for the 350 EFI Cadillac and diesel engines, refer to the "Cadillac" section.

Turbocharger
REMOVAL & INSTALLATION

NOTE: Since turbocharger units are built to extremely high tolerances, we recommend that any internal repairs to

the unit be performed by a professional mechanic familiar with turbochargers.

1. Disconnect the turbocharger exhaust inlet pipe and the exhaust outlet pipe at the turbocharger.

2. Disconnect the oil feed pipe from the center housing.

3. Remove the nut attaching the air intake elbow to the carburetor and remove the elbow, still attached to the flex tube, from the carburetor.

4. Disconnect the accelerator, cruise, and detent linkages at the carburetor. Disconnect the linkage bracket from the plenum.

5. Remove the two bolts attaching the plenum to the side bracket.

6. Disconnect the carburetor fuel line and necessary vacuum hoses.

7. Drain the cooling system.

8. Disconnect the coolant hoses from the front and rear of the plenum.

9. Disconnect the power brake vacuum line at the plenum.

10. Remove the two bolts attaching the turbo housing to the bracket on the intake manifold.

11. Remove the two bolts attaching the EGR valve manifold to the plenum. Loosen the two bolts attaching the EGR valve manifold to the intake manifold.

12. Loosen the clamp attaching the hose from the AIR by-pass to the pipe to the check valve. Remove the hose from the pipe.

13. Remove the three bolts attaching the compressor housing to the intake manifold.

14. Remove the turbocharger and actuator, still attached to the carburetor and plenum assembly, from the engine. Disconnect any vacuum hoses as necessary (after labeling them for later assembly).

15. Remove the six bolts attaching the turbo and actuator unit to the plenum and carburetor assembly.

16. Remove the oil drain from the turbo center housing.

17. Installation is the reverse of removal. Be sure to refill the cooling system.

NOTE: Before installing the turbo unit, make certain that all parts and connections are clean. Serious damage to the turbo unit and engine will result if dirt and/or foreign matter enters into the engine.

Intake Manifold

REMOVAL & INSTALLATION

V8 with Carburetor

1. Remove the negative battery terminal, air cleaner, heat tube and PCV valve.

2. Disconnect the throttle and Cruise Control linkages.

3. Remove the HEI electrical connection from the distributor.

4. Remove the distributor cap and the ignition wires. Mark the wires for easy reinstallation.

5. Disconnect the temperature sending

unit and the electrical connection from the air conditioning compressor.

6. Disconnect the two wires from the downshift switch. Disconnect the throttle return spring and downshift switch bracket. Disconnect the electric choke if so equipped.

7. Remove the plug from the anti dieseling solenoid and any other necessary electrical connections.

8. Disconnect the power brake booster vacuum and vacuum modulator lines. Remove the cruise control mechanism if so equipped. Disconnect the A/C vacuum hose from the rear of the manifold.

9. Disconnect the fuel line from the carburetor.

10. Disconnect the vacuum advance line (if so equipped) and the canister purge hoses and position them out of the way.

11. Remove the air conditioning compressor and position it out of the way. Do not disconnect the refrigerant lines.

12. Disconnect the coolant by-pass hose at the manifold, if so equipped.

13. Remove the carburetor.

14. Remove the manifold bolts and the manifold.

15. Installation is the reverse of removal.

Diesel Engine Or Electronic Fuel Injection (EFI)

For intake manifold removal and installation on models with electronic fuel injection see the "Cadillac" section. For diesel engine servicing refer to the "Oldsmobile" section.

V6

Refer to the "Buick Rear Wheel Drive" section for 231 and 252 V6 intake manifold procedures.

Timing Cover

REMOVAL & INSTALLATION
Toronado V8 and Buick V6

NOTE: Refer to the "Cadillac" section for Cadillac V8 procedures.

1. Drain the cooling system. Disconnect the upper and lower radiator, heater and bypass hoses.

2. Remove the radiator, belts, fan and fan pulley, crankshaft pulley and the harmonic balancer. Remove the fuel lines and pump on the V6.

3. Remove the alternator and brackets on the V6.

4. Remove the distributor on the V6. If timing chain and sprockets are not going to be disturbed, matchmark the distributor rotor and housing to aid installation. On V6, loosen and slide the front clamp on the thermostat by-pass hose rearward.

5. Remove the timing cover attaching bolts and pull off the cover. On the V8, remove the timing pointer and water pump.

6. Remove both front cover dowel pins. Grind a chamfer on one end of each dowel pin. See Step 5 and illustration under "V8 Front Cover Removal and Installation" in the Oldsmobile Rear Wheel Drive section.

7. Before assembly, remove all old gaskets and install a new timing cover gasket. Use sealer around the coolant holes and at the junction of the block, pan and front cover. On the V6, remove the oil pump cover and pack the space around the oil pump gears completely full of petroleum jelly to prime it.

8. Position the front cover, timing pointer and the water pump.

9. Lubricate the attaching bolts and install. Install the fuel pump on V6.

10. Install the harmonic balancer on the crankshaft after lubrication. Replace the engine if removed.

11. Connect all cooling hoses.

12. Install the crankshaft pulley.

13. Install the fan and the fan pulley.

14. Install the drive belts and adjust.

15. Fill the crankcase, if drained, and the radiator.

16. Run the engine and check for leaks.

Timing Chain
REMOVAL & INSTALLATION
V8

Refer to the "Cadillac" or "Oldsmobile Rear Wheel Drive" section for procedures.

V6

Refer to "Buick Rear Wheel Drive" section for procedures.

Camshaft
REMOVAL & INSTALLATION

Refer to the "Cadillac" section, and the "Oldsmobile Rear Wheel Drive Section" for V8 procedures and "Buick Rear Wheel Drive" section for V6 procedures.

Engine Lubrication

Oil Pan

REMOVAL & INSTALLATION
1978 Toronado

The engine must be removed from the vehicle in order to remove the oil pan.

1. Drain the oil and remove the filter.

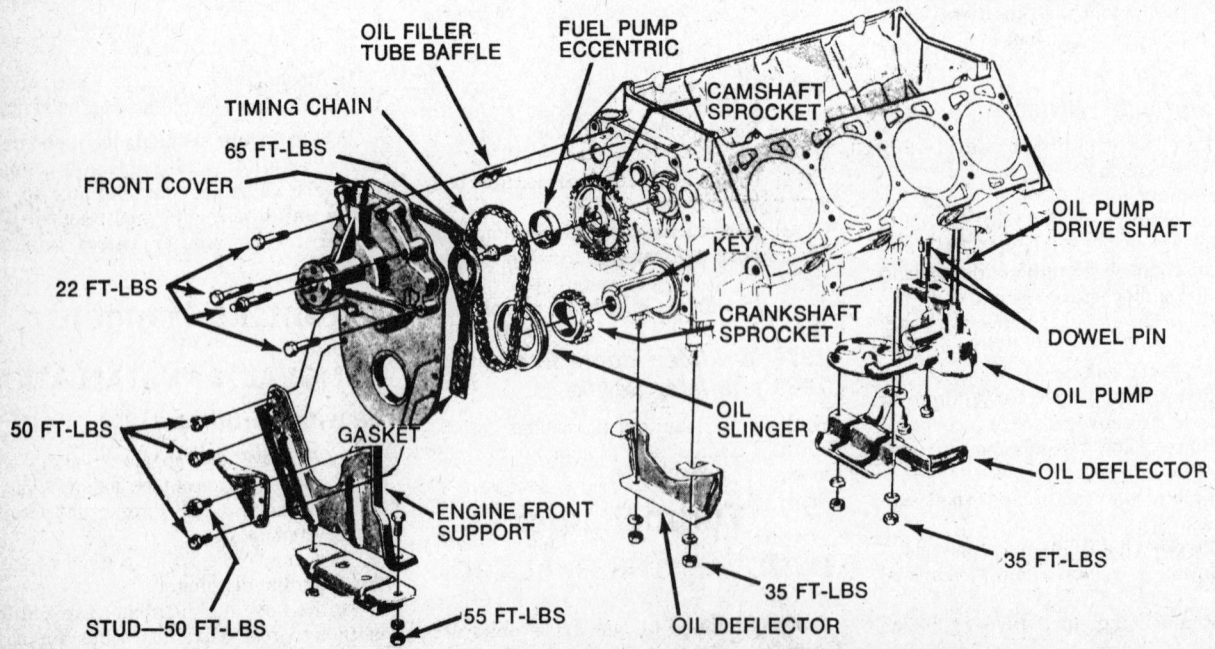

Front cover components, V8 engine. All models similar (© Oldsmobile Div., GM Corp.)

2. Remove engine assembly.

3. Remove dipstick.

4. Remove the front engine mount and bracket.

5. Remove oil pan attaching bolts and remove oil pan.

6. Apply a good sealer to both sides of pan gaskets and install on block.

7. Install front and rear seal.

8. Install the pan. Torque 5/16 in. bolts to 15 ft. lbs and 1/4 in. bolts to 10 ft. lbs.

9. Reinstall mount and oil filter assembly.

10. Reinstall engine and fill crankcase.

1979 and Later Toronado V8

1. Disconnect the negative battery cable.

2. Remove the shroud from the upper radiator support (1979 only). Remove the three final drive-to-transmission bolts (1980 and later).

3. Remove the cotter pin, the retainer and the nut from the right drive axle (1979 only).

4. Raise the front of the car and support it with jackstands. Remove the right wheel (1979 only).

5. Disconnect the right tie rod end (1979 only). Disconnect the two lower frame braces (1980 and later).

6. Disconnect the right side upper ball joint (1979) or the idler and the pitman arms from the relay rod (1980 and later).

7. Remove the bolts attaching the drive axle to the output shaft on the right side and remove the output shaft (1979). Disconnect the right and left side drive axles from their respective output shafts (1980 and later).

8. Disconnect the battery cable bracket from the output shaft support and then disconnect the support itself from the engine block (1980 and later).

9. Remove the remaining final drive-to-transmission bolts, position a transmission jack under the final drive and remove the final drive (1980 and later).

10. Disconnect the starter wiring and remove the starter, remove the splash shield (all models). 1980 and later models should skip to Step 14.

11. Disconnect the pitman and idler arms from the intermediate rod (1979).

12. Remove the front engine mount-to-frame nuts and remove the shroud from the lower radiator support (1979).

13. Raise the engine slightly and remove the right engine mount (1979).

14. Drain the oil, remove the oil pan bolts and remove the oil pan.

15. Installation is in the reverse order of removal. Use sealer on both sides of the new gasket and tighten the oil pan bolts to 10 ft lbs.

Cadillac and Toronado V6

1. Drain the oil pan.

2. Remove the oil pan bolts and remove the oil pan.

Clean gasket surface of pan and block and use new gasket or sealer.

1978 Eldorado

1. Remove engine as previously described in Engine Removal and Installation.

2. Drain engine oil.

3. Remove the transmission lower cover.

4. Remove nuts and cap screws that hold oil pan to cylinder block and engine front cover, then remove the oil pan.

5. Remove side gaskets and rubber front and rear seals from oil pan. Discard the gaskets and seals.

6. Install by reversing the removal procedure. Torque to 10 ft. lbs. Use sealer in the corner notch openings.

1979 And Later Eldorado And 1980 And Later Seville

1. Disconnect the negative battery cable.

2. Raise the car and support safely.

3. Remove the frame brace front attaching bolts from both sides and pivot the braces outward.

4. Remove the six securing bolts from the drive axle to the output shaft on both sides. Separate the flanges of the output shafts and drive axles to gain clearance for removal with the shafts attached.

5. Remove the battery cable-to-output shaft retaining screws and remove the two screws securing the support to the engine block.

6. Remove the final drive-to-transmission screw that holds the front of the shield. Remove the shield.

7. Remove the remaining final drive-to-transmission bolts.

8. Remove the final drive support bracket-to-engine block screw.

9. Using a puller, separate the steering linkage intermediate shaft from the pitman arm and the idler arm. Push the linkage toward the front of the car.

10. With the aid of a helper, slide the final drive assembly forward, off the transmission splined shaft, and remove the unit with the output shaft attached. Do not use the shafts as handles, as damage to the seals will occur.

11. Remove the battery cable and the wiring harness connectors from the starter solenoid BAT terminal.

12. Remove the harness connector from the solenoid S terminal.

13. Remove the harness from the clip on the solenoid and position it out of the way.

14. Remove the starter motor attaching bolts and remove the starter.

15. Drain the engine oil.

16. Remove the oil pan attaching screws and remove the oil pan.

NOTE: On cars equipped with diesel engines it is necessary to loosen the motor mounts and jack up the engine slightly to remove the oil pan.

17. Reverse to install. Torque the oil pan screws to 10 ft. lbs. When installing the final drive, use the following torque values: final drive-to-transmission bolts—30 ft. lbs.; front support bracket-to-block—50 ft. lbs.;

output shaft-to-drive axle—60 ft. lbs.; steering linkage intermediate shaft-to-pitman arm—60 ft. lbs.

1979 Riviera

1. Remove the engine as previously outlined.

2. Remove the oil pan attaching bolts and remove the oil pan.

3. Clean the gasket surfaces on the pan and the block. Apply sealer to a few spots on the new oil pan gasket and install the pan.

4. Torque to 10 ft. lbs. and install the engine.

1980 and Later Riviera

1. Disconnect negative battery cable.

2. Remove top three final drive to transmission bolts.

3. Raise and suitably support car.

4. Disconnect two frame braces.

5. Disconnect idler arm and pitman arm from relay rod.

6. Disconnect drive axles from output shafts.

7. Disconnect battery cable bracket from output shaft support.

8. Disconnect output shaft support from engine block.

9. Remove three final drive to transmission bolts.

10. Install transmission jack and remove final drive.

11. Clean gasket material from mating surfaces.

12. Remove splash shield.

13. Disconnect starter wires.

14. Remove starter.

15. Drain oil pan.

16. Remove oil pan bolts and pan.

17. Installation is the reverse of removal. Tighten pan bolts to 10 ft. lbs.

Oil Pump

REMOVAL & INSTALLATION

Toronado V8

Remove the oil pan. Remove the oil baffle. Remove the oil pump to rear main bearing cap attaching bolts, then remove the pump and drive shaft extension.

Toronado with V6

1. Remove oil pan.

2. Remove screws attaching oil pump pipe and screen assembly to the cylinder block. Remove the oil filter and pump cover, then remove the oil pump gears.

3. On installation, pack the oil pump gears and assembly with petroleum jelly.

1978 Eldorado

1. Raise and support the car with jack stands.

2. Remove the oil filter.

3. Unbolt and remove the pump. The bolt nearest the pressure regulator should be removed last.

4. Remove the pump driveshaft.

5. Installation is the reverse of removal. Use a new gasket. Fill the pump with oil. Torque the bolts to 15 ft. lbs.

1979 and later Eldorado and 1980 and later Seville

ALL EXCEPT 350 CU IN. ENGINE

1. Remove the oil pan as previously outlined.

2. Remove the oil filter.

3. Remove the bolts securing the oil pump to the engine. The screw nearest the pressure regulator should be removed last, allowing the pump to come down with the screw. Always discard the oil pump to crankcase gasket.

4. Remove the oil pump drive shaft.

5. Installation is the reverse of removal.

350 CU IN. ENGINE

1. Remove the oil pan as previously outlined.

2. Remove the bolts attaching the pump to the rear main bearing cup and remove the pump and drive shaft extension.

3. Installation is the reverse of removal. Be sure the shaft is properly mated with the distributor drive gear. Torque the bolts to 35 ft. lbs.

Buick Riviera 1979 and Later

For oil pump procedures, refer to "Buick Rear Wheel Drive" section.

Rear Main Seal

REPLACEMENT

Toronado

See "Oil Pan Removal and Installation". Remove the oil pan and rear main bearing cap. Using a blunt-ended tool, drive the upper seal into its groove on each side until it is tightly packed. This is usually ¼–¾ in. Cut pieces of the old bearing cap seal 1/16 in. longer than the distance each side of the upper seal was compressed. Install these pieces into each side of the upper seal seat, packing them into place. Carefully trim any protruding seal, being sure not to scratch or damage the bearing surface. Install a new seal in the bearing cap and install the cap, tightening bolts to the specified torque. Install the oil pan.

1978 Eldorado

1. Remove the oil pan.

2. Remove the rear main bearing cap and loosen the bolts holding the other four bearings about three turns each. Remove the old rear main bearing seals.

3. Clean the groove in the cap and in the block. Lubricate seals with engine oil.

4. Make an installation tool.

5. Start the upper half into the groove in the block with the lip facing forward and rotate it into position, using the tool as a guide. Press firmly on both ends to be sure it is protruding uniformly on each side.

6. Install the lower half of the seal into the bearing cap with the lip facing forward and one end of the seal over the ridge and flush with the split line. Hold one finger over this end to prevent it from slipping, and push the seal into the seated position by applying pressure to the other end. Be sure the seal is firmly seated and protrudes evenly on each side. Do not apply pressure to the lip. This may damage the effectiveness of the seal.

7. Apply rubber cement to the mating surfaces of the block and cap being careful not to get any cement on the bearing, the crankshaft or the seal. The cement coating should be about .010 in. thick.

8. Install the bearing cap, tightening the bolts with the fingers only.

9. Tighten the bearing bolts to specifications. Be sure to tighten the bolts of the other four bearings also.

10. Reinstall the oil pan.

1979 And Later Eldorado And 1980 And Later Seville

In order to replace the upper main bearing seal, the crankshaft must be removed from the engine. Only the lower rear main oil seal is covered here.

1. Remove the oil pan as previously outlined.

2. Remove the rear main bearing cap.

3. Remove the rear main bearing insert and the old seal. Throughly clean the grooves and inspect it for cracks.

4. Install the new seal into the cap.

5. Cut the seal flush with the mating surface.

6. Clean the bearing insert and install it in the bearing cap.

7. Clean the bearing cap mating surface and apply sealer to the cap.

8. Lubricate the threads of the cap bolts and install the cap. Torque to 120 ft. lbs.

9. Install the oil pan.

Rivera 1979 and later

For rear main bearing oil seal procedures, refer to Buick Rear Wheel Drive section.

AUTOMATIC TRANSMISSION

NOTE: All automatic transmission service procedures are covered in the Unit Repair section.

REMOVAL & INSTALLATION

NOTE: When performing this procedure on the turbocharged Riviera, the turbo must be removed first.

1. Open hood and disconnect negative battery cable (two cables on diesels).

2. Disconnect the speedometer cable at the transmission. Remove transmission oil dipstick tube.

3. Remove the air cleaner.

4. Disconnect the transmission throttle valve (T.V./detent) cable at its upper end. Disconnect the linkage by removing one nut from shaft on left side of transmission, if so equipped.

5. Safely support the engine unit from underneath, or install an engine holding fixture between the cowl and radiator support.

6. Remove the top and two upper left final drive to transmission bolts.

7. Remove the remaining accessible engine-to-transmission bolts (5).

8. Jack up the car and safely support it with jackstands.

9. Remove the starter assembly.

10. Disconnect the transmission converter clutch connector.

11. Disconnect the transmission oil cooler lines and plug the openings.

12. Remove the flywheel inspection cover (loosen top left bolt). Matchmark the flywheel-to-converter relationship for later assembly.

13. On V8s, disconnect the exhaust "Y" pipe connection to the left exhaust pipe. On all, disconnect the right exhaust pipe at the manifold. On gasoline cars, disconnect the catalytic converter hanger bolts (2). On all,

CONVERTER HOLDING CLAMP

CONVERTER

Converter holding clamp. A C-clamp will also work (© Buick Div., GM Corp.)

lower the exhaust system about 5 inches and support the system.

14. Remove the four bolts holding the second frame crossmember.

15. Position a hydraulic floor jack underneath the transmission, with a wooden block on the jack pad to protect the transmission case. Jack up the transmission slightly.

16. Remove the three remaining final drive to transmission bolts.

17. Remove the converter-to-flywheel bolts.

18. Disconnect the shift linkage at the transmissions.

19. Remove the final drive support bracket bolt.

20. Remove the right transmission mount (through bolt and three bracket bolts).

21. Remove the left transmission mount through bolt. Remove the lower bracket-to-transmission bolt. Raise the transmission assembly about two inches for access to the two remaining upper bracket-to-transmission bolts. Remove the remaining transmission-to-engine bolt.

22. Carefully lower the transmission unit while disengaging the final drive.

23. Install a C-clamp or converter holding clamp in front of the torque converter (attached to the bell housing) to hold the converter in place. Remove the transmission from the car.

24. To install the transmission, reverse the removal procedure. Always replace the final drive-to-transmission gasket. Use care when engaging the final drive-to-transmission splines—make sure the final drive-to-transmission mounting faces are in alignment with each other. After the splines are engaged, loosely install the two final drive-to-transmission lower attaching bolts. You can save time here by installing two engine-to-transmission bolts from above first to aid alignment.

25. After the final drive and transmission are mated align the transmission with the engine and install the remaining attaching bolts. Before the flywheel-to-converter bolts, make sure the weld nuts on the converter are flush with the flywheel and that the converter rotates freely by hand in this position. Then hand start all three bolts and tighten finger tight. This will insure proper converter alignment. Torque the transmission-to-engine bolts to 35 ft. lbs., the final drive-to-transmission bolts to 30 ft. lbs., and the final drive support bracket to final drive bolts to 35 ft. lbs.

DRIVE AXLES

Drive axles on these front-wheel drive cars are flexible assemblies and consist of an axle shaft with an inner and outer constant velocity joint. The right axle shaft has a torsional damper mounted in the center. The inner constant velocity joint has complete

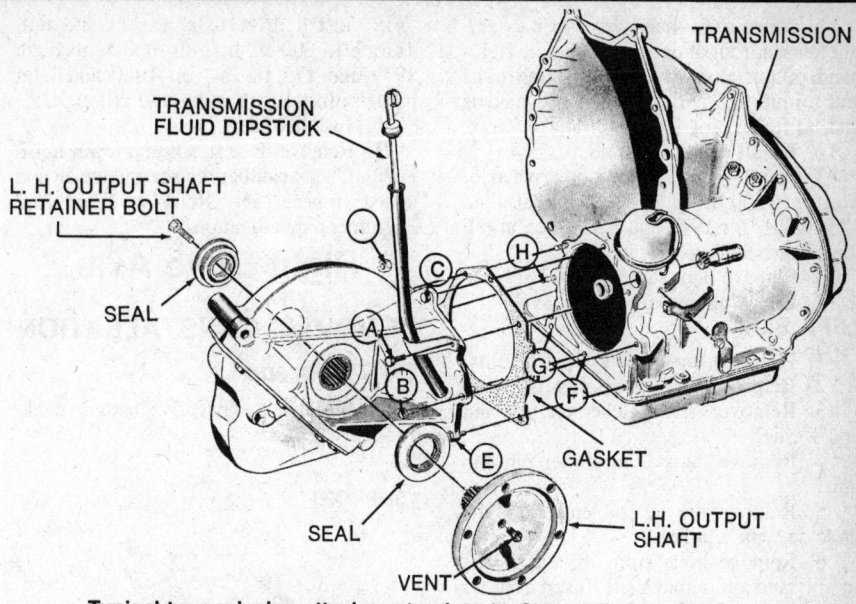

Typical transmission attachment points (© Oldsmobile Div., GM Corp.)

flexibility, plus inward and outward movement. The outer constant velocity joint has complete flexibility but doesn't allow for inward and outward movement. Refer to the Unit Repair section for constant velocity joint service.

REMOVAL & INSTALLATION

Toronado, 1979 and later Riviera, 1979 and later Eldorado and 1980 and later Seville
RIGHT SIDE

1. Hoist car under lower control arms and remove the wheel.

2. Remove drive axle cotter pin, retainer, nut and washer from the wheel hub.

3. Remove oil filter on V8.

4. Remove inner constant velocity joint attaching bolts.

5. Push inner constant velocity joint outward enough to disengage the right-hand final drive output shaft, then move rearward.

6. Remove right-hand output shaft bracket bolts to engine and final drive.

7. Remove right-hand output shaft and drive axle assembly.

— CAUTION —
Care must be exercised so that constant velocity joints do not turn to full extremes, and that seals are not damaged against shock absorber or stabilizer bar.

8. Carefully place right–hand drive axle assembly into lower control arm and enter outer race splines into knuckle.

9. Lubricate final drive output shaft seal, with special seal lubricant.

10. Install right-hand output shaft into final drive and attach the support bolts to engine and brace. Torque the bolts to 50 ft. lbs.

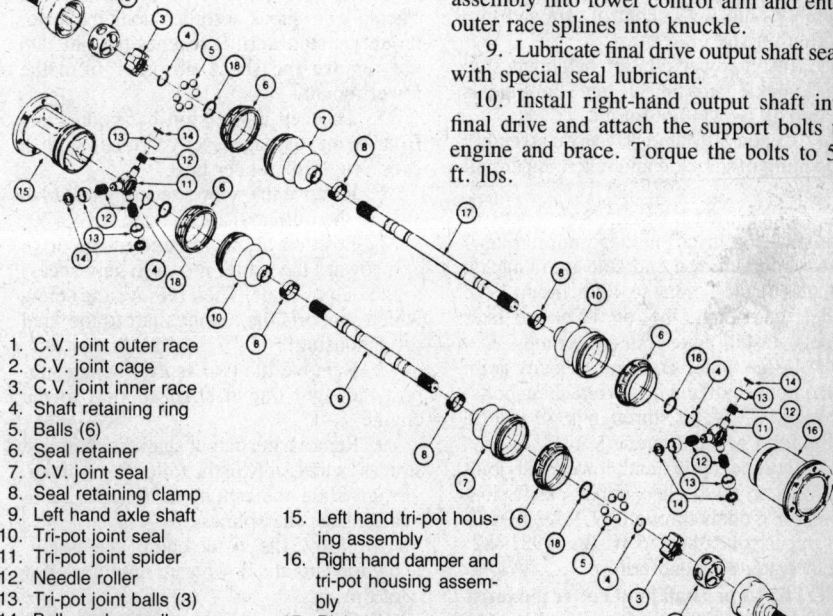

1. C.V. joint outer race
2. C.V. joint cage
3. C.V. joint inner race
4. Shaft retaining ring
5. Balls (6)
6. Seal retainer
7. C.V. joint seal
8. Seal retaining clamp
9. Left hand axle shaft
10. Tri-pot joint seal
11. Tri-pot joint spider
12. Needle roller
13. Tri-pot joint balls (3)
14. Ball and needle retainer (3)
15. Left hand tri-pot housing assembly
16. Right hand damper and tri-pot housing assembly
17. Right hand axle shaft
18. Spacer ring

Exploded view of the drive axle—tri-pot design, first type (© Oldsmobile Div., GM Corp.)

11. Move right-hand drive axle assembly toward front of car and align with right-hand output shaft. Install attaching bolts and torque to 75 ft. lbs. for 1978 models and 60 ft. lbs. for 1979 and later.

12. Install oil filter on V8.

13. Install washer and nut on drive axle. Torque to 200 ft. lbs. for 1978 models, and 175 ft. lbs. for 1979 and later, then install the retainer and cotter pin.

14. Remove floor stands and lower hoist.

15. Check engine oil level on V8.

LEFT SIDE

1. Hoist car under lower control arms.

2. Remove wheel. Remove disc.

3. Remove drive axle cotter pin, nut and washer.

4. Remove tie-rod-end cotter pin and nut.

5. Remove the tie-rod end from the knuckle with a puller.

6. Remove bolts from drive axle assembly and left output shaft. Insert a spacer between the axle shaft and lower control arm.

7. Remove upper control arm ball joint cotter pin and nut.

8. Using hammer and brass drift, drive on knuckle until upper ball joint stud is free.

9. Using puller, remove lower ball joint from knuckle on models through 1979. Care must be exercised so that ball joint does not damage drive axle seal.

10. Remove knuckle and support, so that brake hose is not damaged on models through 1979, support knuckle on 1980 and later.

11. Carefully remove drive axle assembly.

NOTE: Care must be exercised so that constant velocity joints do not turn to full extremes and that seals are not damaged against shock absorber or stabilizer bar.

12. Carefully guide left-hand drive axle assembly onto lower control arm and into position on spacer.

13. Insert lower control ball joint stud into knuckle and attach nut on models through 1979. Do not torque.

14. Center left-hand drive axle assembly in opening of knuckle and insert upper ball joint stud.

15. Place brake hose clip over upper ball joint stud and install nut. Do not torque.

16. Insert tie-rod end into knuckle and attach nut. Torque to 40 ft. lbs on 1978 models and 35 ft. lbs. on 1979 and later models. Install cotter pin and crimp.

17. Align inner constant velocity joint with output shaft and install attaching bolts. Torque to 75 ft. lbs. through 1978 and 60 ft. lbs for 1979 and later.

18. Torque upper and lower ball joint stud nuts to 65 ft. lbs. upper, 95 ft. lbs. lower for models through 1979, and 90 ft. lbs. upper for 1980, 55 ft. lbs. 1981–82. Install cotter pins and crimp.

NOTE: Upper ball joint cotter pin must be crimped toward upper control arm to prevent interference with outer constant velocity joint seal.

19. Install drive axle washer and nut. Torque to 200 ft. lbs. on models through 1979 and 175 ft. lbs. on 1980 and later models. Install cotter pin and crimp.

20. Install wheel.

21. Remove floor stands and lower hoist.

22. Check camber, caster and toe-in and adjust if necessary. Refer to Front End Alignment specifications.

Right Drive Axle

REMOVAL & INSTALLATION

1978 Eldorado

1. Remove the negative battery cable and the wheel disc.

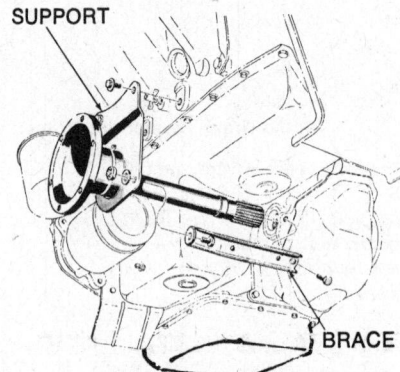

Right-hand output shaft
(© Oldsmobile Div., G.M. Corp)

2. If the drive axle is to be removed, release the cotter pin and loosen but do not remove the spindle nut.

3. Raise the car at the lower control arms.

4. Loosen but do not remove the right front shock absorber lower mounting nut. Then pry the shock absorber along the lower mounting stud until it reaches the nut. Do not remove the shock absorber from the lower mount.

5. To keep the torsion bar connectors from being damaged, cover them with a short length of rubber hose.

6. Remove the screws securing the drive axle to the output shaft.

7. Position the inside end of the drive axle toward the starter motor to gain access to the output shaft. Then remove the screw which supports the output shaft to the final drive housing.

8. Remove the two screws which support the right output shaft support to the engine.

9. Remove the output shaft, support and strut as an assembly in the following manner.

   a. Slide the output shaft outward to disengage the splines.

   b. Move the inside end of the assembly forward and downward until it is clear of the car.

10. If the drive axle is to be removed, use the following procedure.

   a. Using a hammer and a wooden block

tap the end of the drive axle to unseat the axle at the hub.

NOTE: The spindle nut should be loosened but not removed.

   b. Rotate the axle inward and toward the front of the car positioning the axle over the front crossmember and out from under the car.

───────── CAUTION ─────────
Care must be exercised so that constant velocity joints do not turn to full extremes, and that seals are not damaged against shock absorber or stabilizer bar.

11. Carefully place right hand drive axle assembly into lower control arm and enter outer race splines into knuckle.

12. Lubricate final drive output shaft seal with wheel bearing grease.

13. Install right hand output shaft into final drive and attach the support bolts to engine and brace. Torque the bols to 50 ft. lbs.

14. Install brace.

15. Move right-hand drive axle assembly toward front of car and align with right-hand output shaft. Install attaching bolts and torque to 65 ft. lbs.

16. Install washer and nut on drive axle.

17. Remove the jack stands and lower the vehicle.

18. Tighten wheel lugs to 130 ft. lbs.; drive axle nut to 110 ft. lbs. Install cotter pin.

NOTE: Align the hole by tightening the nut.

Left Drive Axle
REMOVAL & INSTALLATION

1978 Eldorado

1. Hoist car under the lower control arms.

2. Remove wheel and tire.

3. Remove drive axle cotter pin, nut and washer.

4. Install a piece of rubber hose over lower control arm torsion bar connector.

5. Remove six drive axle-to-output shaft screws and washers.

6. Loosen upper shock mounting bolt.

7. Remove upper control arm ball joint cotter pin and nut.

8. Using hammer and brass drift, drive on knuckle until upper ball joint stud is free.

9. Remove brake hose bracket.

10. Tip upper part of knuckle and support outward so that brake hose is not damaged.

11. Carefully guide the drive axle assembly outward. Remove left output shaft retaining bolt by installing two screws in the shaft flange to prevent shaft rotation. Pull the shaft straight out toward side of car.

NOTE: Care must be exercised so that constant velocity joints do not turn to full extremes and that seals are not damaged against shock absorber or stabilizer bar.

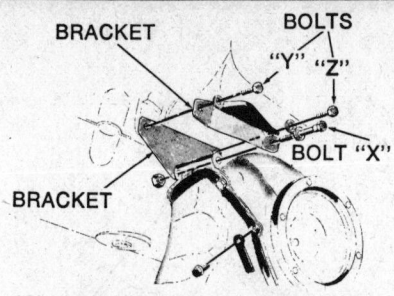

Disconnecting final drive from engine
(© Oldsmobile Div., G.M. Corp)

12. To install, reverse removal procedure. Tighten output shaft retaining bolt to 50 ft. lbs., upper ball joint stud nut to 60 ft. lbs., upper shock absorber bolt to 75 ft. lbs. Tighten wheel lug nuts to 130 ft. lbs. Tighten drive axle nut to 110 ft. lbs.

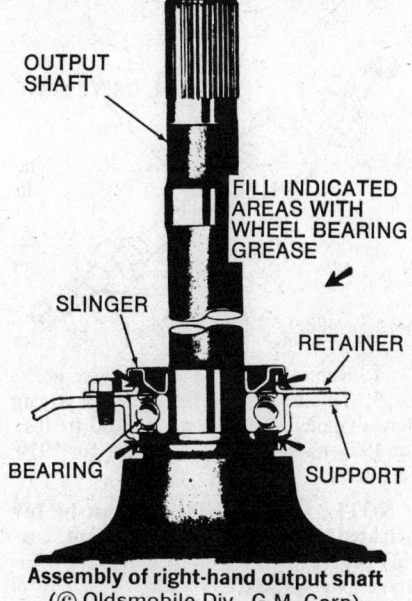

Assembly of right-hand output shaft
(© Oldsmobile Div., G.M. Corp)

FINAL DRIVE

REMOVAL & INSTALLATION

1978

1. Disconnect battery.
2. See illustration. Remove bolts A, B, and C. Nut D must be removed with a special wrench.

NOTE: It may be necessary to remove the transmission filler tube to gain clearance.

3. Hoist the car. If a two post hoist is used, the car must be supported with floor stands at the front frame rails and the front post lowered.
4. Disconnect right and left drive axles from the output shafts.
5. Remove engine oil filter.
6. Disconnect brace from final drive, then disconnect right-hand output shaft assembly from engine.

7. Remove output shaft assembly from final drive.
8. See illustration. Remove bolt X and loosen bolts Y and Z.
9. Remove final drive cover and allow lubricant to drain.
10. Position transmission lift with adapter for final drive. Install an anchor bolt through final drive housing and lift pad.
11. See illustration. Remove bolts E, F, and G, and nut from H.
12. Move transmission lift toward front of car to disengage final drive splines from transmission. Some transmission fluid will be lost.
13. Lower transmission lift and remove final drive from lift.
14. Using a 9/16 in. socket, remove the left output shaft retainer bolt, then pull output shaft from final drive.
15. Remove transmission to final drive gasket.
16. On installation, apply special seal lubricant to both output shaft seals.
17. Install the left output shaft into the final drive. Retain with bolt and torque to 45 ft. lbs.
18. Position final drive on transmission lift and install an anchor bolt through the housing and lift pad.
19. Apply a thin film of special seal lubricant on the transmission side of the new final drive-to-transmission gasket. Then position gasket on the transmission.
20. Raise the transmission lift. Align the two bolt studs D and H on the transmission with their mating holes in the final drive. Move final drive until it mates with the transmission.

NOTE: It may be necessary to rotate the left output shaft to align the splines on the final drive with the splines of the transmission output shaft.

21. Install bolts E, F, and G and nut H finger tight.
22. Install bolt X and torque to 110 ft. lbs. Tighten and torque bolts Y and Z to 55 ft. lbs.
23. Loosen and remove lift from final drive.
24. Position a new cover gasket on the final drive, then install cover. Torque cover bolts to 30 ft. lbs.
25. Install right output shaft into final drive, indexing splines of output shaft with splines of final drive. Install mounting bracket and brace bolts and tighten.
26. Connect drive axles to output shafts using new bolts. Tighten the bolts to 75 ft. lbs.
27. Install oil filter.
28. Raise hoist, remove studs and lower car.
29. If filler tube was removed, attach a new O-ring and install filler tube.
30. Install bolts A, B, and C and nut D. Torque all final drive to transmission bolts to 50 ft. lbs. Torque nuts to 50 ft. lbs.
31. Connect battery.
32. Fill final drive.

33. Check engine oil level. Start engine and check transmission fluid level.
34. Check for any oil leaks.

Toronado, Riviera, Eldorado 1979 and Later; 1980 and Later Seville

1. Disconnect the negative battery cable and raise the car. Place jack stands underneath the front frame horns and the lower front post.
2. Remove the frame brace attaching bolts and pivot the braces outward in order to gain access.
3. With a drain pan under the final drive cover, loosen the final drive cover screws and allow the fluid to drain. Remove the cover and gasket material.
4. Remove the screws on both sides attaching the output shaft to the drive axle. Separate the flanges of the shaft and axle to obtain clearance. The final drive assembly will be removed with the output shafts installed.
5. Remove the battery cable retaining screws from the right output shaft and the screws securing the support to the engine block. Rotate the support downward for clearance.
6. Remove the screws which attach the final drive shield to the transmission and the support bracket. Remove the shield.
7. Remove the remaining final drive screws.
8. Remove the final drive support-to-engine block attaching screws.
9. Using a puller, separate the steering linkage from the pitman arm. Push the linkage toward the front of the car.
10. Slide the final drive assembly forward, off the transmission shaft and remove the unit. Do not hold the unit by the output shafts as the seals or splines could easily be damaged.
11. To install, thoroughly clean all the gasket surfaces and position a new gasket on the final drive. Do not use a sealer on the gasket.
12. Align the final drive assembly, with the output shafts attached, to the transmission and install all the attaching screws except the one used to hold the shield. Torque in rotation to 30 ft. lbs. in two steps.
13. Loosen the front support bracket screws and install the bracket to the engine block while holding the bracket flush on the housing pad. Torque to 50 ft. lbs.
14. Install the final drive shield. Torque the drive-to-transmission screw to 30 ft. lbs. and the bracket-to-housing screws to 34 ft. lbs.
15. Align the right output shaft support with the attaching holes in the engine block. Do not allow the shaft and support assemblies to hang from the drive unit. By moving the flange end of the shaft up and down and installing the screws and washers loosely, locate the centered position. Torque the screws to 50 ft. lbs.
16. Install the battery cable retainer.
17. Align the right drive axle to the out-

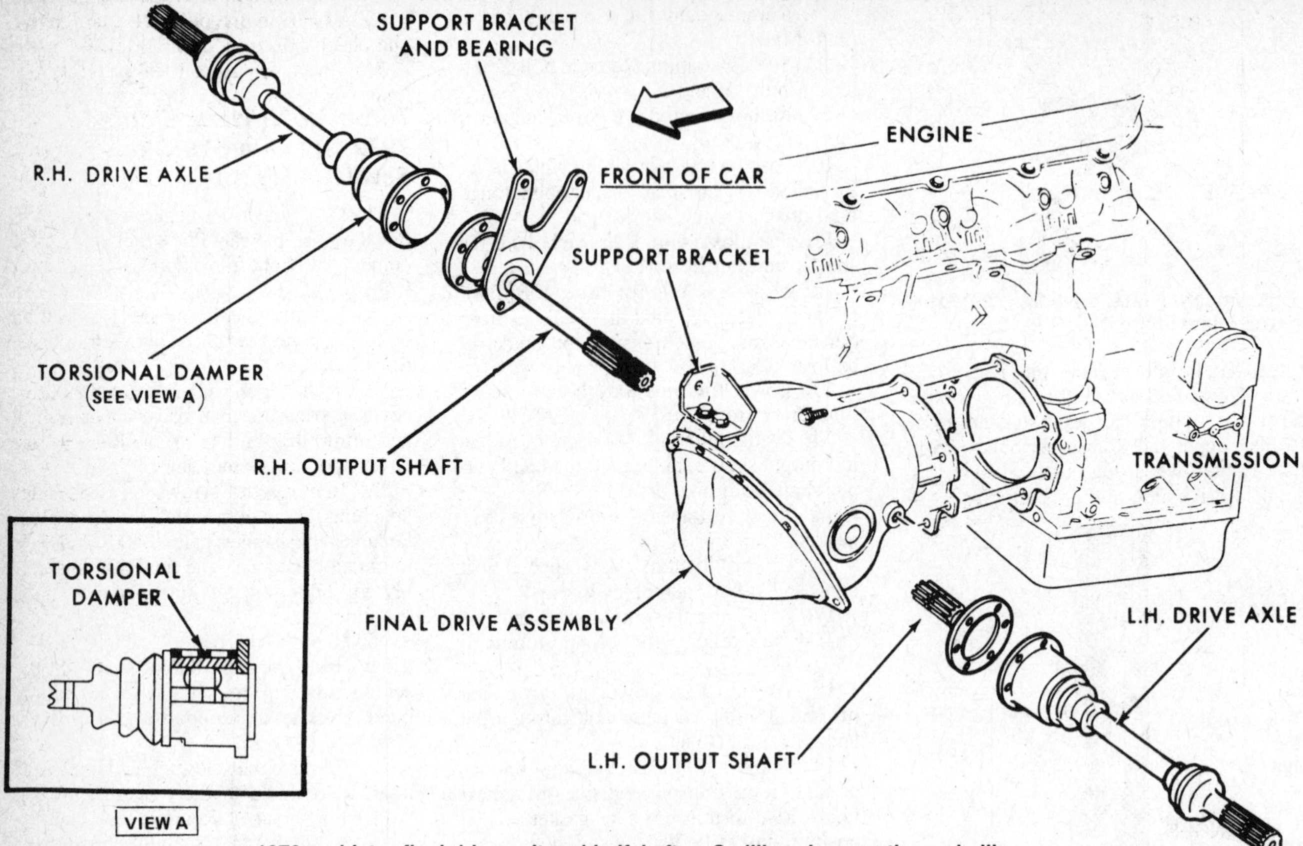

SUPPORT BRACKET
AND BEARING

R.H. DRIVE AXLE

FRONT OF CAR

ENGINE

SUPPORT BRACKET

TORSIONAL DAMPER
(SEE VIEW A)

R.H. OUTPUT SHAFT

TRANSMISSION

TORSIONAL
DAMPER

FINAL DRIVE ASSEMBLY

L.H. DRIVE AXLE

L.H. OUTPUT SHAFT

VIEW A

1979 and later final drive unit and halfshafts—Cadillac shown, others similiar

put shaft and install the attaching screws. Torque the screws to 60 ft. lbs. Repeat for the left side.

18. Position a new cover gasket or apply silicone sealer on the final drive cover. Install the cover and torque the screws to 7 ft. lbs. Refill the unit. Torque the filler plug to 30 ft. lbs.

19. Install the steering linkage to the pitman arm and torque to 60 ft. lbs. If the cotter pin hole does not align properly, tighten the nut slightly. Do not loosen to align. Install a new cotter pin.

20. Install the frame braces and torque the nuts to 50 ft. lbs.

21. Lower the car, connect the battery cable, start the car and check the transmission fluid. When the final drive has reached operating temperature, check it for leaks.

FRONT SUSPENSION

NOTE: See the Unit Repair Section for front end adjustments.

Shock Absorber
REMOVAL & INSTALLATION

Please refer to the Oldsmobile Rear Wheel Drive section for this procedure for all models.

Wheel Hub and Bearing Assembly

REMOVAL & INSTALLATION
Toronado

1. Remove drive axle cotter pin, nut and washer. Remove the lug nuts and wheel. Remove the brake disc.

2. Position access slot in hub assembly so each of the attaching bolts can be removed.

3. Install a front hub puller and slide hammer.

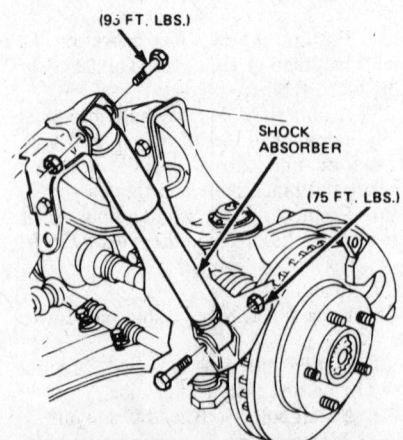

(95 FT. LBS.)

SHOCK ABSORBER

(75 FT. LBS.)

1979 and later Riviera front shock absorber mounting
(© Buick Div., GM Corp.)

4. Remove hub and bearing assembly.

5. To install, reverse removal procedure. Tighten the axle nut to 200 ft. lbs. for 1978 models and 175 ft. lbs. for 1979 and later.

NOTE: O.D. of bearing must be lubricated with E.P. chassis lubricant. Use care when installing hub assembly over drive axle splines.

Eldorado, Riviera, 1980 and Later Seville

1. Remove hub cap, loosen wheel nuts, remove drive axle cotter pin and loosen drive axle nut.

2. Jack up car and place jack stands under lower control arms.

3. Remove axle nut and wheel and tire assembly.

4. Remove brake hose and caliper.

NOTE: Match-mark disc and hub, then remove the disc.

5. Remove the upper ball joint cotter pin and loosen stud nut.

6. Strike steering knuckle near upper joint to separate it from taper.

7. Cover the lower control arm torsion bar connector with a short piece of rubber hose to avoid damaging the inboard tri-pod joint seal when the hub and knuckle are removed.

8. Remove tie-rod end cotter pin and nut.

9. Separate tie-rod end from steering knuckle using a tie-rod splitter.

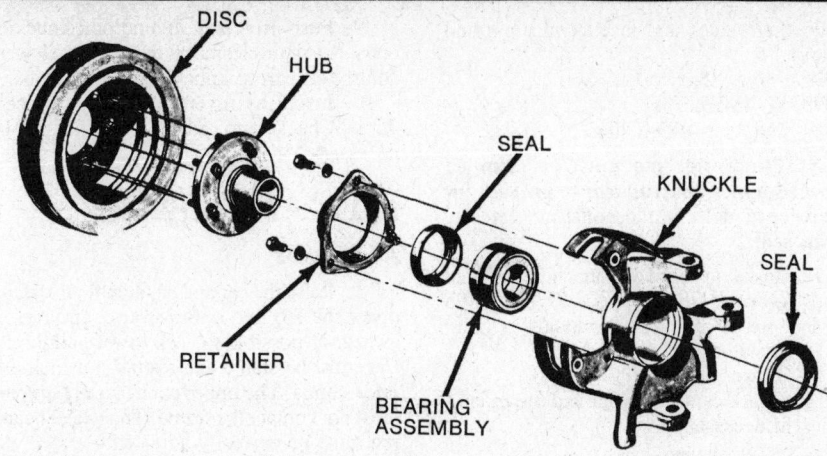

Exploded view of the Toronado and Eldorado hub assembly through 1978 (© Oldsmobile Div., GM Corp.)

10. Remove lower ball joint cotter pin and stud nut.

11. Disconnect lower ball joint.

12. Remove hub, backing plate and steering knuckle as an assembly.

13. To install, reverse removal procedure. Tighten upper ball joint stud to 60 ft. lbs.; tighten lower ball joint stud to 80 ft. lbs. Tighten drive axle nut to 110 ft. lbs. Tighten wheel lug nuts to 130 ft. lbs.

Wheel Bearing

REPLACEMENT

All Models

1. Remove the front brake caliper.

2. Remove the hub and outer bearing assembly.

3. Carefully pry the seal from the hub, then remove the inner bearing assembly.

4. If necessary, remove the outer bearing race.

5. Wash all parts in clean solvent and either blow dry with compressed air or let air dry. Check bearings for cracked cages and worn or pitted rollers. Check the bearing races for cracks, scores, or brinelling.

6. To install the new bearings, drive or press the outer races into the hub (if removed). A large socket (preferably one that's already beat up) can be used with a rubber hammer to drive the bearing in.

7. Thoroughly clean the hub and spindle with clean solvent.

8. Apply a thin wipe of quality, high temperature wheel bearing grease to the spindle at the outer bearing seat and at the inner bearing seat, shoulder and seal seat.

9. Apply a small wipe of grease inboard of each bearing cup in the hub. Pack the bearing cone and roller assemblies full of grease by hand, working the grease thoroughly into the bearings between the rollers, cone, and cage.

10. Place the inner bearing cone and roller assembly in the hub. Then, using your finger, put an additional wipe of grease outboard on the bearing.

11. Install a new grease seal, using a flat plate to seat the seal flush, into the hub.

Lubricate the seal lip with a thin layer of grease.

12. Carefully install the hub and rotor assembly. Place the outer bearing cone and roller assembly in the outer bearing cup. Install the washer and nut and initially tighten the nut to 12 ft. lbs. while turning the wheel assembly forward by hand. Put another wipe of grease outboard of the bearing. This will give the bearings extra grease.

13. Install the brake caliper, then the wheel assembly.

ADJUSTMENT

Tapered Roller Bearings

The proper functioning of the front suspension cannot be maintained unless the front wheel tapered roller bearings are correctly adjusted. Cones must be a slip fit on the spindle and the inside diameter of cones should be lubricated to insure that the cones will creep. Spindle nut must be a free-running fit on threads.

1. Remove cotter pin from spindle and spindle nut.

2. Tighten the spindle nut to 12 ft. lbs. while turning the wheel assembly forward by hand to fully seat the bearings. This will remove any grease or burrs which could cause excessive wheel bearing play later.

3. Back off the nut to the "just loose" position.

4. Hand tighten the spindle nut. Loosen spindle nut until either hole in the spindle lines up with a slot in the nut (not more than ½ flat).

5. Install new cotter pin. Bend the ends of the cotter pin against nut. Cut off extra length to ensure ends will not interfere with the dust cap.

6. Measure the looseness in the hub assembly. There will be from .001–.005 inches end play when properly adjusted.

7. Install dust cap on hub.

Bolt On-Type Bearings

All E and K Series, 1981 and later, have front and rear sealed wheel bearings. The bearings are preadjusted and require no lubrication maintenance or adjustment. There are darkened areas on the bearing assembly. These darkened areas are from a heat treatment process and do not need bearing replacement.

Torsion Bar

REMOVAL & INSTALLATION

Toronado and Cadillac

1. Raise the car and support the frame.

2. Disconnect the parking brake cable at the equalizer and pull it through the support on 1978 models.

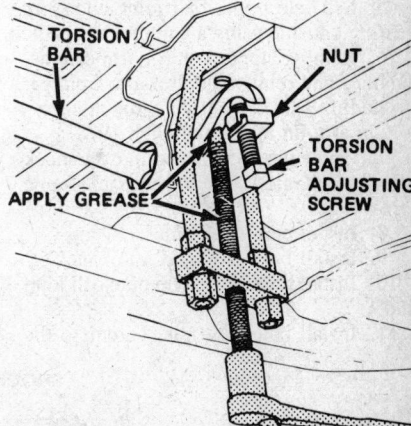

Eldorado and Toronado torsion bar removal through 1978 (© Oldsmobile Div., GM Corp.)

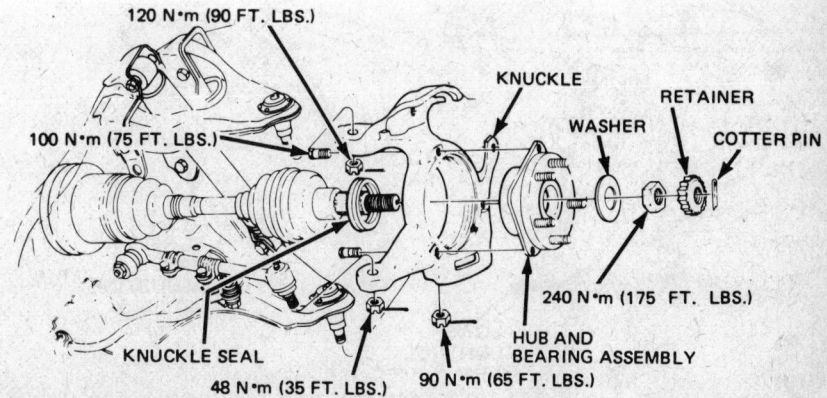

1979 and later hub and bearing assembly (©Oldsmobile Div., G.M. Corp.)

3. Install a torsion bar remover tool, remove the torsion bar adjusting bolt and nut, noting the number of turns to remove, and relax the torsion bar. Do the same on the other torsion bar.

4. Remove the bolts and retainer from the torsion bar crossmember. Move the crossmember back until the bars are free and the adjusting arms can be removed. You may have to slide the torsion bars forward.

5. Reverse the procedure for installation.

Upper Control Arm

REMOVAL & INSTALLATION

All Models

NOTE: The upper control arm is serviced as an assembly, less bushings.

1. Hoist car under lower control arm and remove wheel.

2. Remove upper shock attaching bolt on 1978 models. It is not necessary to remove the upper shock bolt on 1979 and later models, but it does allow more working room.

3. Remove cotter pin and nut on upper ball joint.

4. Disconnect brake hose clamp from ball joint stud.

5. Separate upper ball joint stud from steering knuckle using a hammer and drift.

6. Remove upper control arm cam assemblies and remove control arm from car by guiding shock absorber through access hole in arm on models through 1978.

7. Guide upper control arm over shock absorber and install bushing ends into frame horns.

8. Install cam assemblies.

9. Install ball joint stud into knuckle.

10. Install brake hose clip onto ball joint stud.

11. Install ball joint nut. Torque to the following values and insert cotter pin and crimp.

1978—50 ft. lbs.
1979—80—90 ft. lbs.
1981—and later—55 ft. lbs.

NOTE: Cotter pin must be crimped toward upper control arm to prevent interference with outer constant velocity joint seal.

12. Install upper shock attaching bolt and nut. Torque to 78 ft. lbs for 1978, and 95 ft. lbs. for 1979 and later models.

13. Install wheel.

14. Lower hoist.

15. Check camber, caster and toe-in, and adjust if necessary.

Lower Control Arm

REMOVAL & INSTALLATION

All Models

1. Hoist car and support at lift points. Remove wheel assembly.

2. Place torsion bar remover and installer over crossmember so that center screw is seated in dimple of torsion adjusting arm.

3. Remove torsion bar adjusting bolt and nut, counting the number of turns necessary.

NOTE: This number of turns will be used when installing, to obtain initial ride height.

4. Turn center screw of tool until torsion bar is completely relaxed.

5. Disconnect shock absorber and stabilizer link from lower control arm.

6. Remove drive axle nut. Remove the bolt and nut from the front of the frame brace. Loosen the rear bolt and move the brace out.

7. Remove cotter pin and nut from lower ball joint stud.

8. Remove ball joint stud from knuckle, using puller.

9. Push drive axle in and pull knuckle outward to gain clearance, then remove lower control arm from knuckle and torsion bar.

10. Install by reversing removal procedure. Check and adjust ride height if necessary.

BALL JOINT CHECK

All Models

1. Raise the car and position floor stands under the left and right lower control arm, as near as possible to each lower ball joint. Car must be stable and should not rock on floor stands. The upper control arm bumper must not contact the frame. The wheel bearing must be correctly adjusted.

2. Position the dial indicator to register vertical movement at the base of the tire rim for upper ball joint and at center of hub for lower ball joint.

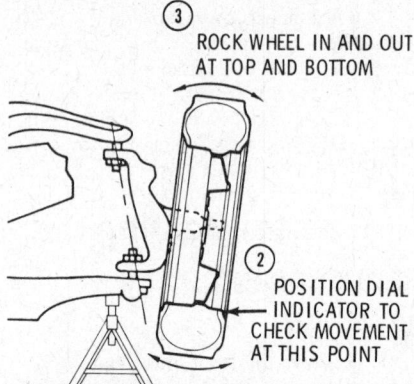

ROCK WHEEL IN AND OUT AT TOP AND BOTTOM

POSITION DIAL INDICATOR TO CHECK MOVEMENT AT THIS POINT

① SUPPORT L. C. ARM AS FAR OUTBOARD AS POSSIBLE.

Upper ball joint check
(© Oldsmobile Div., G.M. Corp.)

3. Grasp the tire at the 12 o'clock and 6 o'clock positions and rock it in and out for upper ball joint. Pry with a pry bar between the lower control arm and the outer race of the CV-joint for lower ball joint. The vertical reading must not exceed .125 in. in either case.

REMOVAL & INSTALLATION

All Models

NOTE: Although not absolutely necessary, removal of the individual control arm will facilitate easier ball joint removal.

1. Remove the steering knuckle.

2. Drill the top rivet head off.

3. Drill the rivets just deep enough to remove the rivet head.

4. Using a hammer and punch, drive the rivets out of the control arm.

5. Install service ball joint into control arm and torque bolts and nut. Side bolts are torqued to 25 ft. lbs. while the upper nut is tightened to 45 ft. lbs. on 1978 models. Torque the bolts to 8 ft. lbs. on 1979 and later models. Stake the upper nut.

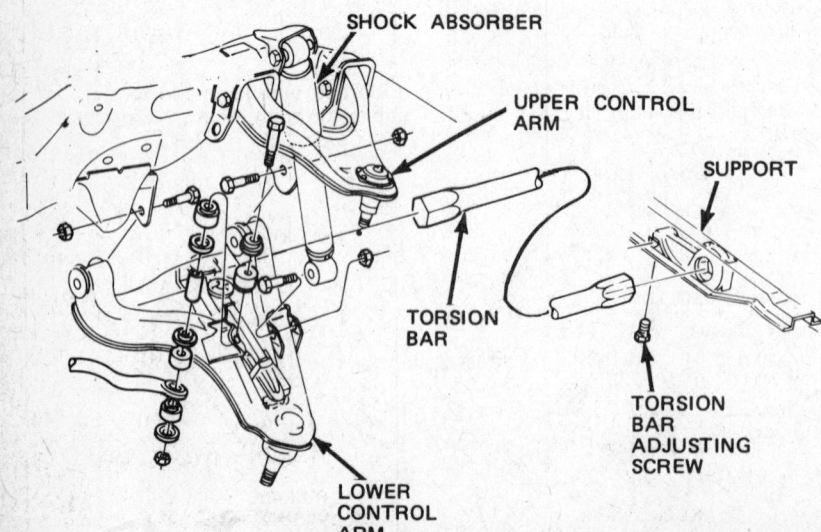

SHOCK ABSORBER

UPPER CONTROL ARM

SUPPORT

TORSION BAR

TORSION BAR ADJUSTING SCREW

LOWER CONTROL ARM

Control arms and related parts—1978 Eldorado and Toronado

6. Install knuckle.

7. Check the nut to drive axle outer joint clearance for models through 1978. If necessary, grind a maximum of 1/16 in. from the nut.

REAR SUSPENSION

All Toronado and Eldorado models through 1978 have a straight tubular axle housing.

Beginning 1979, an independent rear suspension system came into use, incorporating a relatively long control arm for minimum camber change. The hub and wheel bearing is one unit which requires no periodic maintenance or adjustment. The rear suspension on 1980 and later Seville and 1979 and later Riviera is similar.

Spindle

REMOVAL & INSTALLATION

1978

1. Support the rear of the car with stands.
2. Remove the wheel, drum and hub assembly.
3. Disconnect the brake line fitting at the wheel cylinder.
4. Remove the four spindle attaching bolts and tie the backing plate out of the way.
5. Pull the spindle with a slide hammer.
6. To install, reverse the removal procedure. Install spindle with the keyway up, tightening the four bolts progressively one turn at a time. Adjust the rear wheel bearing.

1979 and Later

1. Raise and car and remove the wheel.
2. Remove the brake caliper as outlined in "1979 and Later Rear Control Arm

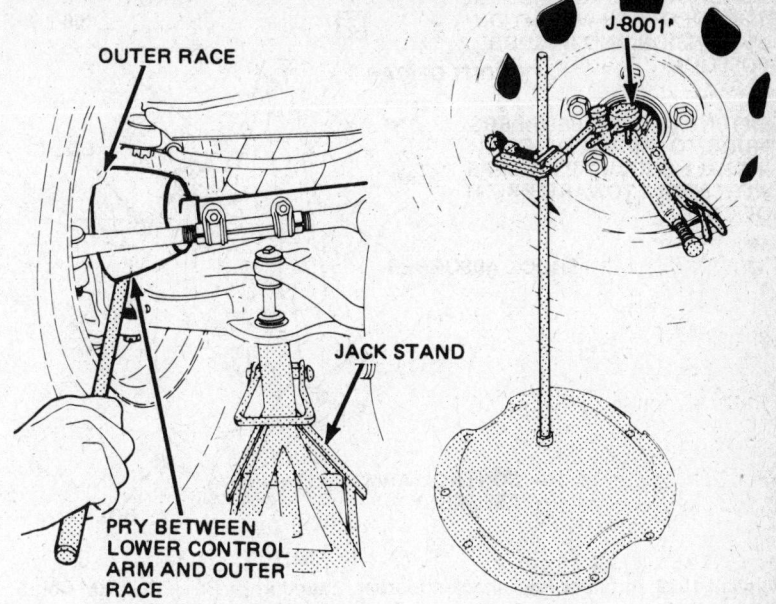

Lower ball joint check (© Oldsmobile Div., G.M. Corp.)

and Spring Removal and Installation," if equipped with disc brakes.

3. Matchmark the rotor or brake drum for reassembly and remove.
4. Remove the four bolts securing the spindle and bearing assembly to the control arm and remove the assembly.
5. Reverse to install. Tighten the spindle bolts to 32 ft. lbs.

Rear Wheel Bearing

ADJUSTMENT

1978 Eldorado and Toronado

For the rear wheel tapered roller bearings to be correctly adjusted, the following precautions should be taken:

1. The cones must be a slip fit on the spindle.
2. Inside of cones should be lubricated to make sure the cone creeps on the spindle.

3. Spindle nut must be a free-running fit on the threads.
4. Adjustment of rear wheel bearings should be made by continuously revolving the wheel forward while torquing the nut as follows:

A. Torque adjusting nut to 25–30 ft. lbs. to seat all components thoroughly.
B. Back off nut one-half turn, then retighten finger tight.
C. If unable to insert cotter pin at this position, back off to nearest castellation.
D. End-play should be 0.001–0.005 in.

1979 and Later

As stated earlier, the hub and wheel bearing is one assembly, thus eliminating the need for wheel bearing adjustments or any other type of periodic maintenance.

Shock Absorber
REMOVAL & INSTALLATION

All Models

Raise the rear of the car and support the control arm with a jack to take the load off of the shock. Unscrew the lower shock retaining bolt and gently tap the shock out of its retainer. Unscrew the upper retaining bolt and remove the shock from the car. Installation is in the reverse order of removal. Tighten the retaining bolts to 65 ft. lbs. Follow any special instructions in the shock absorber packages.

NOTE: If your car is equipped with automatic load control (ALC), disconnect the air lines before removing shocks. Purge the new shocks of air before installing (on all models) by repeatedly extending and compressing them. On ALC-equipped models, the shocks should be fully extended before installing air lines.

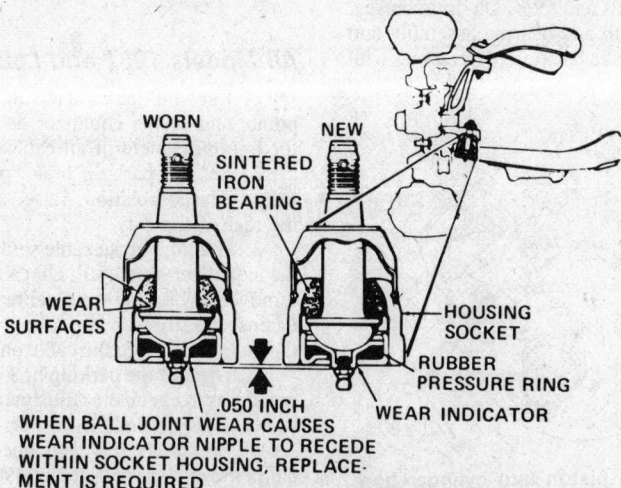

Lower ball joint wear indicator, typical (© Buick Div., GM Corp.)

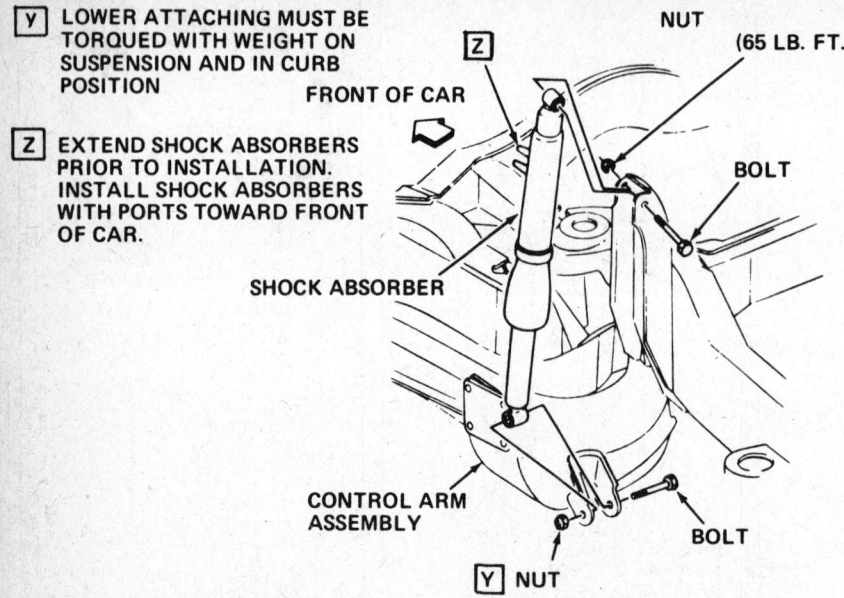

Y LOWER ATTACHING MUST BE TORQUED WITH WEIGHT ON SUSPENSION AND IN CURB POSITION

Z EXTEND SHOCK ABSORBERS PRIOR TO INSTALLATION. INSTALL SHOCK ABSORBERS WITH PORTS TOWARD FRONT OF CAR.

NUT (65 LB. FT.)

FRONT OF CAR

Z

BOLT

SHOCK ABSORBER

CONTROL ARM ASSEMBLY

BOLT

Y NUT

Typical 1979 and later rear shock absorber mounting (© Buick Div., GM Corp.)

Coil Spring

REMOVAL & INSTALLATION

1978 Eldorado and Toronado

1. Raise the car under the tube assembly and support it with stands at the frame lift points. Do not remove the jack.
2. Disconnect the brake line clips.
3. Disconnect the shock absorber at the lower mount.
4. Install a spring compressor and finger tighten the nuts.
5. Disconnect the control arm at the tube assembly.
6. Lower the jack (supporting the control arm, not the frame) and remove the spring.

———— CAUTION ————
Do not stretch the brake hose.

7. When installing, place the insulator on top of the spring and install the spring. The top end of the spring should point to the right side of the car.
8. Hoist the tube assembly and connect the shock absorber.

Rear Control Arm and Coil Spring

REMOVAL & INSTALLATION

All Models

1. Raise the car and remove the wheel.
2. Remove the bolt from each side which secures the front of the stabilizer bar to the control arm.
3. Remove the inner bolt and loosen the outer bolt from each side of the stabilized link.

4. Position the bottom parts of the link to one side and remove the stabilizer bar.
5. Disconnect the brake line bracket from the control arm.
6. Remove about ⅔ of the fluid from the front master cylinder.
7. Loosen the parking brake tension at the cable equalizer.
8. Remove the cable from the parking brake and remove the cable bracket from the caliper or brake drum backing plate.
9. Remove the return spring, lock nut, lever and the anti-friction washer on disc brakes. The lever must be held while removing the nut.
10. Install and tighten a 7 in. C clamp on the caliper as shown to bottom the cylinder pistons.
11. Disconnect the brake line from the brake and plug the openings to prevent the entrance of dirt.
12. With a ⅜ in. allen wrench, remove the two caliper mounting bolts and remove the caliper, pads and rotor. On drum brakes, remove the hub and bearing assembly and remove the brake backing plate, along with the brake shoes.

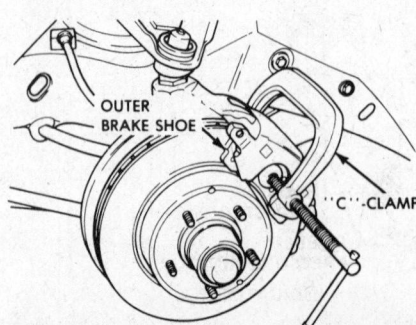

OUTER BRAKE SHOE

"C"-CLAMP

Compressing piston into cylinder bore. All models similar (© Oldsmobile Div., GM Corp.)

13. If working on the left side, snap the Electronic Level Control link off the control arm.
14. Support the bottom of the control arm with a floor jack.
15. Remove the ELC line at the shock.
16. Remove the shock absorber.
17. Lower the control arm to relieve tension on the spring. Remove the spring and the insulators.
18. Remove the two control arm mounting bolts and remove the control arm.
19. Reverse to install. Use the following torque values: control arm-to-frame bolts—98 ft. lbs.; shock absorbers—65 ft. lbs.; brake caliper mounting bolts—30 ft. lbs.; brake lines—15 ft. lbs.; wheel lug nuts—100 ft. lbs.

BRAKES

Brake adjustment, brake lining replacement, hydraulic cylinder overhaul and bleeding procedures for all models covered here can be found in the Brake Unit Repair Section.

Parking Brake

ADJUSTMENT

Models through 1980

1. Depress the parking brake pedal exactly 2 clicks on 1978–79 and 1 click on 1980.
2. Tighten the adjusting nut at the cable equalizer until the left rear wheel can just be turned rearward using 2 hands, but is locked in forward rotation.
3. With the parking brake off, the rear wheels should rotate freely in either direction with no drag.

All Models 1981 and Later

1. Lube the cables at the underbody rub points and at the equalizer hooks. Check for free movement of all cables.
2. Set the parking brake pedal in the fully released position, raise, and support the rear of the car.
3. Hold the brake cable stud and tighten the equalizer nut until all cable slack is removed. Make sure the caliper levers are against the stops on the caliper housing; if they are not, loosen the cable until they are.
4. Operate the parking brake pedal several times to check the adjustment, it should travel approximately 4–5½ in.
5. Lower the car and check that the caliper levers are still on their stops. If not, back off the parking brake adjuster until they are.

Master Cylinder

REMOVAL & INSTALLATION
All Models

1. Disconnect and plug hydraulic lines, and drain the cylinder.
2. Remove the attaching nuts and remove the master cylinder from the power booster unit.
3. Reverse to install. Bleed the system.

Power Booster

REMOVAL & INSTALLATION
All Models

1. From inside the car, detach the brake pushrod from the brake pedal.
2. Detach the vacuum hose at the vacuum cylinder.
3. Remove the nuts from the mounting studs which hold the unit to the dash panel. Remove the unit and clean it prior to installation.
4. Install in reverse order of removal. Bleed system.

Brake Caliper

REMOVAL & INSTALLATION

Please refer to the preceeding "Rear Control Arm and Coil Spring Removal and Installation" procedure.

Brake Disc

REMOVAL & INSTALLATION
All Models

NOTE: Brake disc removal and installation for all models is covered in the Brake Unit Repair Section.

STEERING

All steering system procedures are the same as those given in the Oldsmobile, Buick and Cadillac Rear Wheel Drive sections.

INSTRUMENT PANEL

Headlight Switch

REPLACEMENT
Toronado
1978

1. Disconnect the battery ground.

2. Remove the A/C control, but do not disconnect the hoses or wires.
3. Remove the collar from the headlamp switch with a pair of needlenose pliers.
4. Pull the switch through the A/C control opening far enough to disconnect the wiring.
5. Installation is the reverse of removal.

1979 AND LATER

1. Remove the left hand trim cover:
   a. Remove the headlight switch knob and the radio knobs.
   b. Remove the steering column trim cover and the four screws beneath the cover.
   c. Remove the left hand sound absorber and carefully pull the trim cover rearward to remove.
2. Remove the two screws attaching the switch to the dash frame.
3. Pull the switch rearward to remove.

Riviera
THROUGH 1982

1. Disconnect the negative battery cable.
2. Pull the switch knob to the last notch and depress the spring loaded latch button on top of the switch, while pulling the knob and rod out of the switch.
3. Remove the escutcheon, trim plate and the retaining nut or screws. Remove the switch from the cluster.
4. Disconnect the multiple connector.
5. Installation is the reverse of removal.

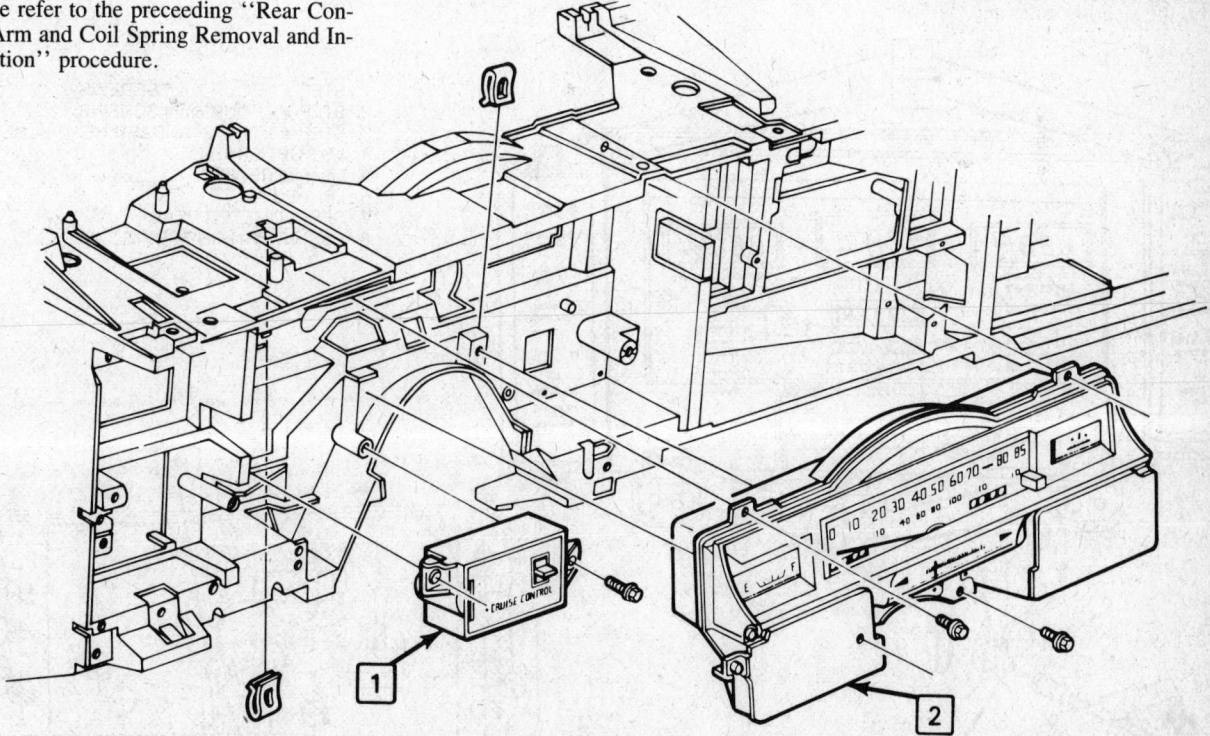

1 CRUISE CONTROL DASH SWITCH   2 INSTRUMENT CLUSTER

Typical instrument cluster (Eldorado and Seville)

1983 AND LATER

1. Disconnect the negative battery cable.
2. Remove the switch trim cover and the left hand trim cover.
3. Remove the headlight switch screws from the instrument panel.
4. Disconnect any electrical connector and pull the switch forward out of the dash panel.

Eldorado and Seville

1. Disconnect negative battery cable. Remove the steering column lower cover.
2. Disconnect wiring harness retainer below headlight switch assembly.
3. Depress spring loaded release button on top of headlight switch and remove switch, knob and rod assembly (switch "on").
4. Remove screw with ground wire at bottom of switch housing and any other mounting screws.
5. Pull assembly down and rearward, disconnect wiring harness connectors, bulb(s) and remove assembly.
6. Install in reverse of above.

Instrument Cluster

REMOVAL & INSTALLATION

Riviera

1. Disconnect the negative battery cable.
2. Slide the steering column collar upward on the steering column.

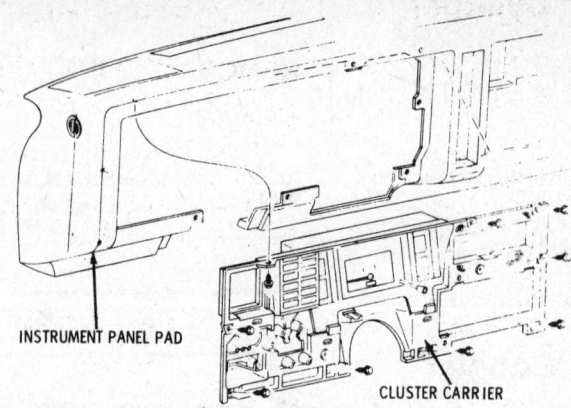

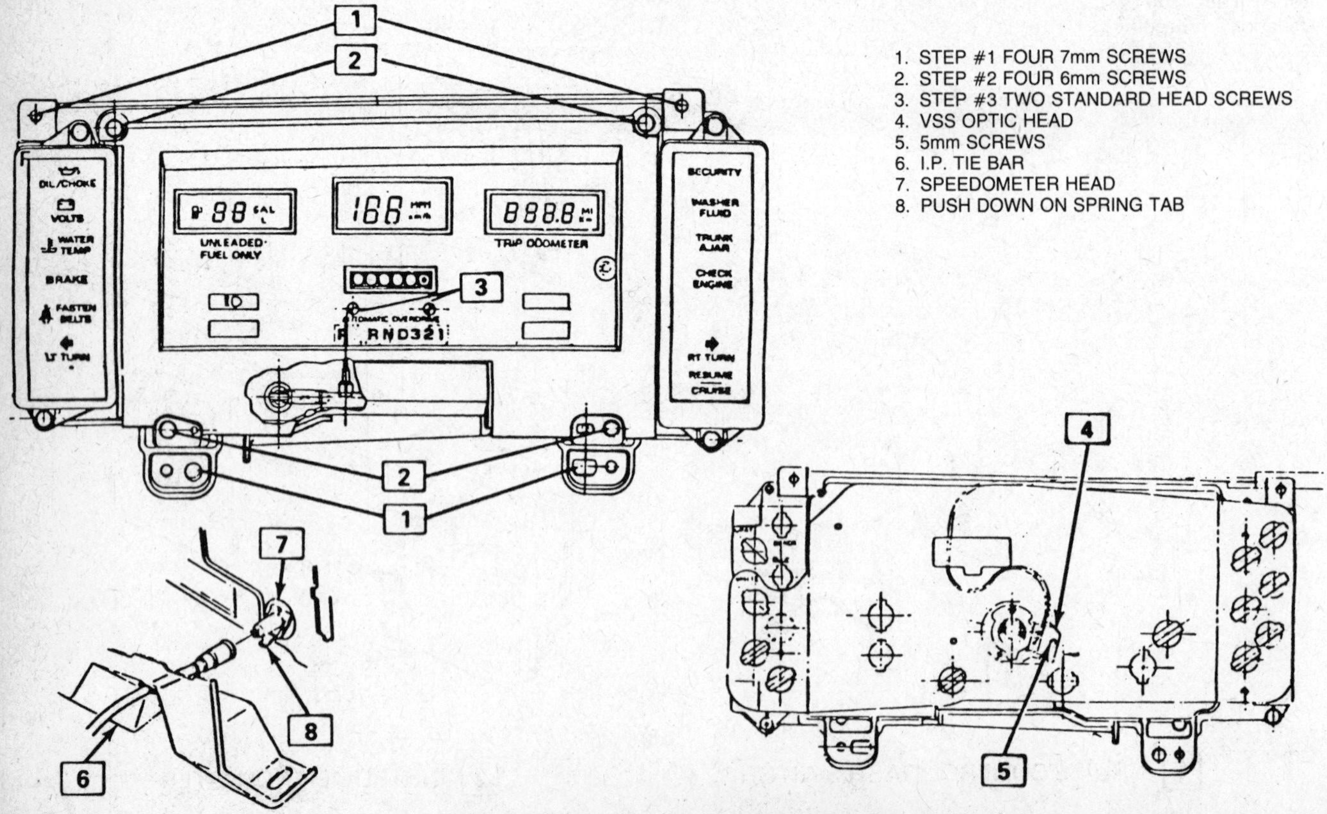

INSTRUMENT PANEL PAD

CLUSTER CARRIER

Toronado instrument cluster

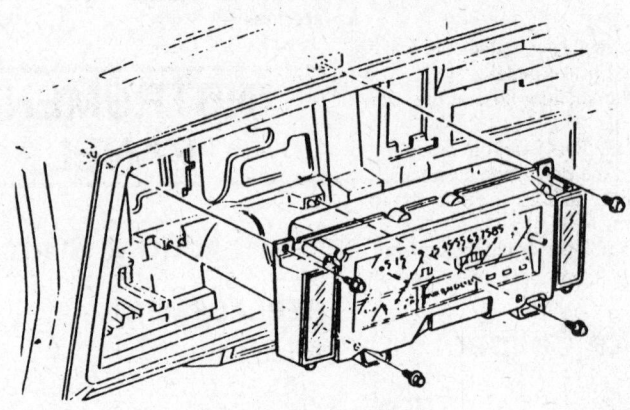

Riviera instrument cluster

1. STEP #1 FOUR 7mm SCREWS
2. STEP #2 FOUR 6mm SCREWS
3. STEP #3 TWO STANDARD HEAD SCREWS
4. VSS OPTIC HEAD
5. 5mm SCREWS
6. I.P. TIE BAR
7. SPEEDOMETER HEAD
8. PUSH DOWN ON SPRING TAB

Typical Riviera digital instrumnet cluster

3. Remove the headlight knob, escutcheon assembly and all remaining knobs.

4. Depending on the car model, pry either the right or left (or both) trim plates from the instrument panel.

NOTE: Remove the center trim plate by first removing the right and left trim plates. Then remove the radio knobs and screws securing the center trim plate.

5. Disconnect the seelite and remove.

6. Remove all cluster retaining screws. Pull the cluster out slightly and disconnect the speedometer cable. Remove the instrument cluster assembly.

7. To install, attach the cluster assembly and speedometer cable. Secure the center trim plate. Hold the left and right trim plates in position, press into place and reposition the rubber filler ring and headlight knob assembly.

1980-81 Seville, to 1981 Eldorado

1. Disconnect the negative battery cable.

2. Remove the top and bottom applique retaining screws.

3. Unsnap the portion of the applique trim below the steering column.

4. If equipped with tilt wheel, place in its lowest position and remove the applique panel.

5. Remove the cluster retaining screws, pull the cluster outward, disconnect the speedometer and circuit board connectors and remove the cluster.

6. The installation is the reverse of the cluster removal.

1982 and later Seville and Eldorado

1. Disconnect the negative battery cable.

2. Remove the left sound insulator.

3. Remove the instrument panel insert and applique trim from the instrument panel.

4. Place the shift lever in the "P" position and remove the shift indicator clip from the steering column.

5. Remove the nuts securing the steering column to the upper mounting bracket and lower the steering column.

6. Remove the screw securing the upper steering column mounting bracket to the cowl and lower the bracket.

7. Remove the cluster retaining screws, disconnect the speedometer cable, printed circuit connector and remove the cluster.

8. The installation is the reverse of the removal procedure. Be sure the shift indicator is properly aligned.

Toronado

NOTE: To remove the left side sound absorber from under the dash take out two screws and one nut. Pull the absorber down to slide from the steering column.

1. Disconnect the A.L.C.L. computer connector, if equipped.

2. remove 4 screws from bottom side of trim cover.

3. Remove steering column trim cover.

4. Remove headlamp switch knob.

5. Remove radio knobs.

6. Carefully pull left hand trim cover rearward to remove. Trim cover is retained by clips. It may be necessary to disconnect the shift indicator clip and lower the steering column slightly to obtain clearance needed for trim cover removal.

7. Remove trip odometer knob by turning counterclockwise.

8. Remove 2 screws attaching cluster lens and face plate to cluster carrier. Remove lens and face plate.

9. Remove 2 screws, attaching gage assembly to cluster housing.

10. Pull gauge assembly rearward to remove.

11. Disconnect shift indicator cable end at shift indicator pointer.

12. Remove 3 screws attaching speedometer to cluster housing.

13. If printed circuit is to be removed, remove both gauge assemblies now by removing 2 screws attaching upper gauge assemblies to cluster housing. Pull assemblies rearward to remove.

14. Remove 2 screws attaching lower cluster housing to cluster carrier.

15. Disconnect speedometer cable at transmission or at transducer on cars equipped with cruise control.

16. Pull cluster housing rearward far enough to reach behind it and disconnect speedometer cable by depressing speedometer cable clip.

17. Remove screw attaching speed sensor pickup to speedometer head and remove pickup, if equipped.

18. Remove cluster housing and speedometer assembly.

19. Remove 2 screws attaching back of cluster housing to speedometer and remove speedometer.

20. Installation is the reverse of removal.

Emissions Indicator

An emissions indicator flag may appear in the odometer window of the speedometer, on some 1980 and later General Motors vehicles. The flag could say "Sensor", "Emissions" or "Catalyst" depending on the part or assembly that is scheduled for regular emissions maintenance replacement. The word "Sensor" indicates a need for oxygen sensor replacement and the words "Emissions" or "Catalyst" indicate the need for catalytic converter catalyst replacement.

RESET PROCEDURE

All Except Eldorado And Seville

1. Remove the instrument panel trim plate.

2. Remove the instrument cluster lens.

3. Locate the flag indicator reset notches at the drivers side of the odometer.

4. Use a pointed tool to apply light downward pressure on the notches, until the indicator is reset.

NOTE: When the indicator is reset an alignment mark will appear in the left center of the odometer window.

Eldorado And Seville

If a vehicle is equipped with an oxygen sensor or an emissions sensor flag in the speedometer, than it should be reset whenever the oxygen sensor or the catalytic converter are replaced.

1. Remove the lower steering column cover.

2. Locate the sensor reset cable at the lower left side of the speedometer cluster. Pull the cable lightly to reset.

3. Reinstall the lower steering column cover.

——————— CAUTION ———————

A minimum of force is required and a maximum of 2 lbs. pull may be used without breaking the cable or damaging the mechanism.

Speedometer Cable

REMOVAL & INSTALLATION

Riviera and Toronado

1. Disconnect the negative battery cable.

2. Remove the speedometer assembly from the instrument cluster.

3. Disconnect the cable casing from the speedometer head.

4. Pull the inner cable from the upper casing.

5. Disconnect the cable from the transaxle. Remove the cable.

6. Installation is the reverse of the removal procedure. Make sure that there are no kinks in the new cable.

Eldorado and Seville

1. Disconnect the negative battery cable.

2. Remove the screws holding the instrument cluster trim plate, left and right teltale lens, instrument cluster lens and the transaxle shift indicator assembly. Remove the lens and retainers.

3. Remove the temperature indicator and the fuel gauge.

4. Remove the screws holding the speedometer assembly to the housing. Pull the speedometer head out and disconnect the screw holding the vehicle speed sensor.

5. Remove the speedometer cable. Remove the speedometer.

6. Installation is the reverse of the removal procedure.

WINDSHIELD WIPERS

Motor

REMOVAL & INSTALLATION

This procedure is the same as given in the Oldsmobile Rear Wheel Drive section. Replacement procedures for the rubber wiper element for all models are given in the Maintenance Section.

RADIO

REMOVAL & INSTALLATION

Toronado

This procedure is the same as given in the "Oldsmobile Rear Wheel Drive" section.

1978 Eldorado

1. Remove the four screws attaching the steering column cover to the reinforcement.

2. Remove the four screws attaching the cover to the instrument panel cross support.

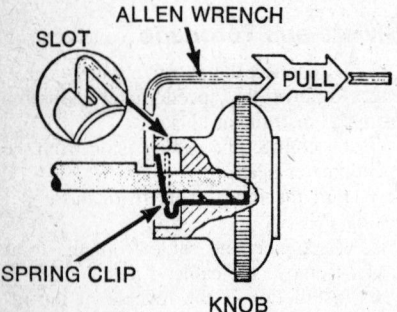

Radio knob removal, most models (© Buick Div., GM Corp.)

3. Remove the ash tray lower bracket screw.

4. Remove the two screws from the left side ash tray mounting bracket.

5. Working from the lower edge of the instrument panel, remove the ash tray right side attaching screw.

6. Remove the ash tray. Disconnect the bulb and the electrical connector.

7. Remove the radio knobs, the anti-rattle spring, the control rings and the retaining nuts.

8. Remove the brace nut at the rear of the radio.

9. Loosen the brace supporting screw and rotate the brace to the right.

10. Slide the radio from the instrument panel and disconnect the wiring.

11. Rotate the dial side downward and remove the radio through the ash tray opening.

12. Reverse to install.

1979 AND LATER ELDORADO AND 1980 AND LATER SEVILLE

1. Disconnect the negative battery cable.

2. Remove the screws from the top of the instrument panel center insert.

3. Remove the radio knobs and remove the insert.

4. Remove the rear window defogger switch to gain access to the left side mounting screw if so equipped.

5. Remove the mounting screw.

6. Remove the radio and disconnect the wiring. Reverse to install.

1979 and Later Riviera

1. Disconnect the battery ground cable.

NOTE: On 1981 and later Rivieras remove the center trim plate by grasping it firmly and pulling out. Be careful not to lose the spring retaining clips.

2. Remove the ashtray and bracket.

3. Pull off the radio knobs and trim washers.

4. Remove the lower left air duct.

5. Remove the two retaining nuts from the control shafts.

6. Unplug the power lead, speaker wire, and antenna lead.

7. Remove the rear radio mounting nut.

FUSES

The fuse block is located beneath the instrument panel above the headlight dimmer floor switch. Fuse holders are labeled as to their service and the correct amperage. Always replace blown fuses with new ones of the correct amperage. Otherwise electrical overloads and possible wiring damage will result.

Electrical Component Location

FUSE PANEL

The fuse panel is located on the left side of the vehicle. It is under the instrument panel assembly. In order to gain access to the fuse panel, it may be necessary to first remove the under dash padding.

ELECTRONIC CONTROL MODULE

The electronic control module is located on the right side of the vehicle. It is positioned in front of the right hand kick panel. In order to gain access to the assembly you must first remove the trim panel.

TURN SIGNAL FLASHER

The turn signal flasher is located directly under the steering column of the vehicle. It is secured in place with a plastic retainer.

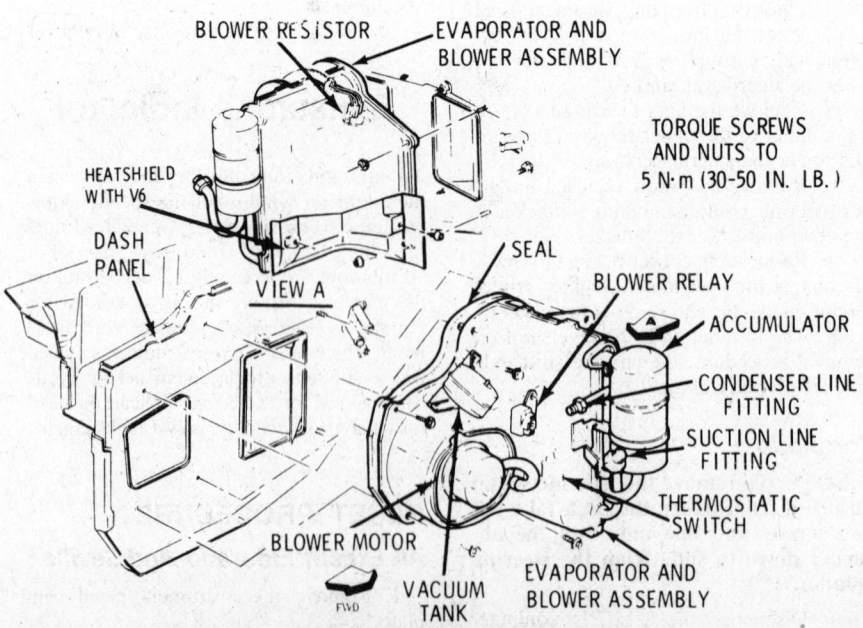

Blower assembly (© Oldsmobile Div., G.M. Corp.)

In order to gain access to the component, it may first be necessary to remove the under dash padding.

CONVENIENCE CENTER

The convenience center is located on the right side of the vehicle. It is positioned under the dash panel. In order to gain access to the convience center it may be needed to remove instrument panel sound absorber.

CIRCUIT BREAKER

A circuit breaker is an electrical switch which breaks the circuit during an electrical overload. The circuit breaker will remain open until the short or overload condition in the circuit is corrected.

FUSIBLE LINKS

Fusible links are sections of wire, with special insulation, designed to melt under electrical overload. Replacements are simply spliced into the wire. There may be as many as five of these in the engine compartment wiring harnesses. These are:

1. Horn relay to fuse panel circuit—one link.
2. Charging circuit, from the starter solenoid to the horn relay—two links.
3. Starter solenoid to ammeter circuit—one link.
4. Horn relay to rear window defroster circuit—one link.

The fusible links are all two wire gauge sizes smaller than the wires they protect.

NOTE: Most models have fusible links at these locations.

REPLACEMENT

1. Disconnect the battery ground cable.
2. Disconnect the fusible link from the junction block or starter solenoid.
3. Cut the harness directly behind the connector to remove the damaged fusible link.
4. Strip the harness wire approximately ½ in.
5. Connect the new fusible link to the harness wire using a crimp on connector. Soder the connection using resin core solder.
6. Tape all exposed wires with plastic electrical tape.
7. Connect the fusible link to the junction block or starter solenoid and reconnect the battery ground cable.

HEATER

Blower Motor

REMOVAL & INSTALLATION
Riviera

1. Disconnect the blower motor wires.

2. On A/C equipped cars, disconnect the cooling tube from the case.
3. Remove the motor attaching screws and lift the motor from the case.
4. Installation is the reverse of removal. Replace any damaged sealer.

1978 And Later Eldorado, 1980 And Later Seville

1. Disconnect the negative battery cable.
2. Disconnect the electrical connections at the blower motor.
3. Disconnect the cooling hose from the blower motor.
4. Remove the mounting screws and remove the motor.
5. Reverse to install. Use a silicone sealer on the blower motor sealing surfaces.

1978 Toronado

1. Raise and support the car; remove the right front wheel.
2. Cut along the inside of the rectangular stamped bead on the right fender filler.
3. Unbolt and remove the blower motor.
4. When installing, fold the flap over and seal it with a sealer.

1979 And Later Toronado

1. Disconnect the battery.
2. Disconnect and remove the Hi-Blower assembly.
3. Remove the blower motor assembly.
4. Installation is the reverse. Be sure the blower mounting has a continuous bead of sealer.

Heater Core

REMOVAL & INSTALLATION
1978 Toronado & Riviera

1. Drain the cooling system.
2. Remove the four heater case attachment nuts.
3. Remove the instrument panel trim cover.
4. Remove the two heater case-to-cowl bolts from inside the car.
5. Remove the lower air duct.
6. Remove the instrument panel pad:
   a. disconnect the battery ground.
   b. remove the courtesy lamps.
   c. carefully pry the speakers from the clips.
   d. remove one screw from each speaker hole.
   e. remove one screw from the left lower outside edge of the instrument panel pad and two screws from the cluster.
   f. open the glovebox and remove one screw from the lower right corner of the glovebox and two screws from the upper edge of the glovebox.
   g. grasp the front center edge of the pad and pull to release the clips at the windshield edge.
7. Disconnect the wiring from the clock and glovebox.

8. Remove the right upper trim panel.
9. Remove the manifold from the heater case.
10. Disconnect the defroster duct from the case.
11. Remove the lower trim panel:
    a. remove the right side screw.
    b. grip the cover with both hands and carefully pull it from the panel.
    c. remove the left side screw.
    d. slide the steering column collar out of the way.
    e. carefully pull the cover from the panel.
    f. disconnect the lower A/C outlet hoses.
    g. remove the cigarette lighter.
    h. disconnect the parking brake cable.
    i. remove the two lower trim panel-to-tie bar screws.
    j. remove the eight trim panel-to-center tie bar screws.
    k. disconnect the ash tray lamp.
    l. remove the trim panel.
12. Remove the heater case.
13. Separate the case halves and remove the core.
14. Installation is the reverse of removal. Replace any damaged sealer.

1979 AND LATER

NOTE: This procedure involves removing the dashboard.

1. Disconnect the negative battery cable.
2. Drain the radiator. Remove the heater hoses from the heater core.
3. Remove the instrument panel sound absorbers which cover the underside of the dash area.
4. Loosen and lower the steering column and remove the left hand trim cover. See Step 1 of "1979 and later Headlight Switch Replacement," above.
5. Remove the instrument cluster:
   a. Remove headlight switch (see above for procedures).
   b. Remove the windshield switch, the radio and the heater/AC control.
   c. Remove all cluster electrical connections and disconnect the speedometer cable.
   d. Remove the nine attaching screws and remove the cluster.
6. Remove the front speakers, the three screws attaching the manifold to the heater case, the four upper and three lower instrument panel retaining screws, and disconnect the brake release cable.
7. Disconnect the instrument panel wiring harness from the dash wiring assembly and disconnect the right hand remote control mirror cable from the instrument panel.
8. Disconnect the speedometer cable from its clip and the heater control cable at the heater case.
9. Disconnect all vacuum lines and wiring necessary to remove the instrument panel. If car is equipped with pulse wipers remove the wiper switch, unlock the connector from the cluster carrier and separate

C621

the pulse jumper harness from the connector.

10. Remove the instrument panel and harness assembly.

11. Remove defroster ducts, disconnect vacuum hoses and temperature cable; remove blower resistor and the three heater assembly retaining nuts.

12. Remove the heater assembly-to-dash screw and clip from inside the car.

13. Remove the heater assembly.

14. Remove the heater core. Reverse procedures to install.

1978 Eldorado & Seville

1. Drain the radiator and remove the hoses from the heater core. Plug the hoses and the nipples to prevent spillage.

2. On the inside of the car, remove the air outlet grilles.

3. Remove the instrument panel fasteners from inside the grille openings.

4. Remove the four attaching screws from the instrument panel cross support and pull the panel pad outward. Disconnect the windshield wiper switch.

5. Remove the center A/C outlet support bracket.

6. Remove the left side A/C outlet hose from the A/C distributor.

7. Remove the center support and attaching braces.

8. Remove the A/C distributor from the heater case.

9. Remove the defroster nozzle.

10. Remove the glove compartment liner.

11. Remove all vacuum and electrical connectors from the programmer.

12. Disconnect the vacuum hoses and position them out of the way.

13. Disconnect and remove the heater case.

14. Remove the rubber seal from around the nipples.

15. Remove the screw and clip from beneath the seal.

16. Remove the core screws and the clip and remove the core.

17. Reverse to install.

1979 AND LATER

1. Drain the radiator.

2. Remove the heater hoses from the core and plug the hoses and the nipples to prevent spillage.

3. Remove the instrument panel.

4. Remove the four defroster nozzle attaching screws at the cowl and the screw on the case and remove the nozzle.

5. Disconnect the vacuum hoses.

6. Disconnect the electrical connector at the programmer.

7. Under the hood, remove the heater case-to-cowl attaching screws.

8. Under the instrument panel, remove the heater case-to-cowl attaching screw.

9. Remove the heater case.

10. Remove the four case-to core screws and remove the core.

11. Reverse to install.

GM "F" Body
Camaro, Firebird

YEAR IDENTIFICATION

1978 Camaro

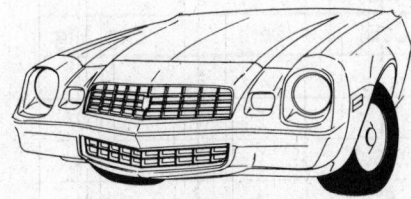

1979 Camaro

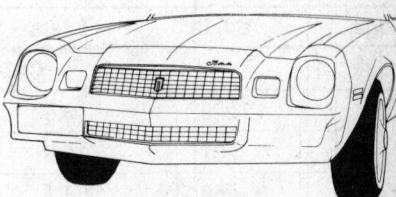

1980 Camaro

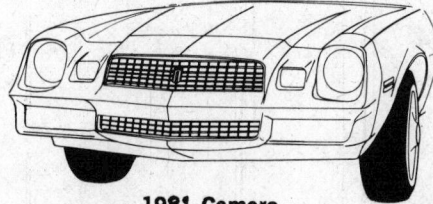

1981 Camaro

1982–85 Camaro

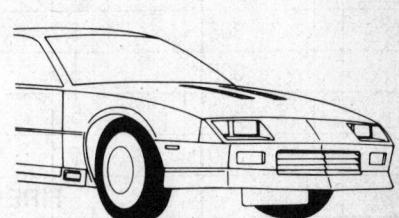

1985 Camaro Z28

1985 Camaro IROC-Z

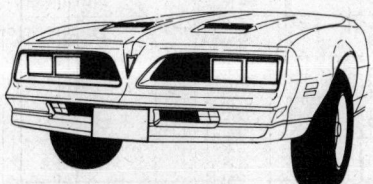

1978 Firebird

1979 Firebird

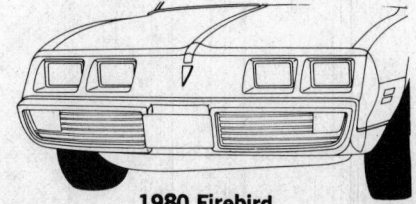

1980 Firebird

1981 Firebird

1982–85 Firebird

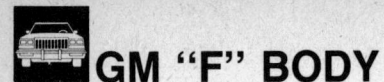

VEHICLE IDENTIFICATION NUMBER (VIN)

It is important for servicing and ordering parts to be certain of the vehicle and engine identification. The VIN (vehicle identification number) is a 13 or 17 digit number visible through the windshield on the driver's side of the dash and contains the vehicle and engine identification codes. It can be interpreted as follows:

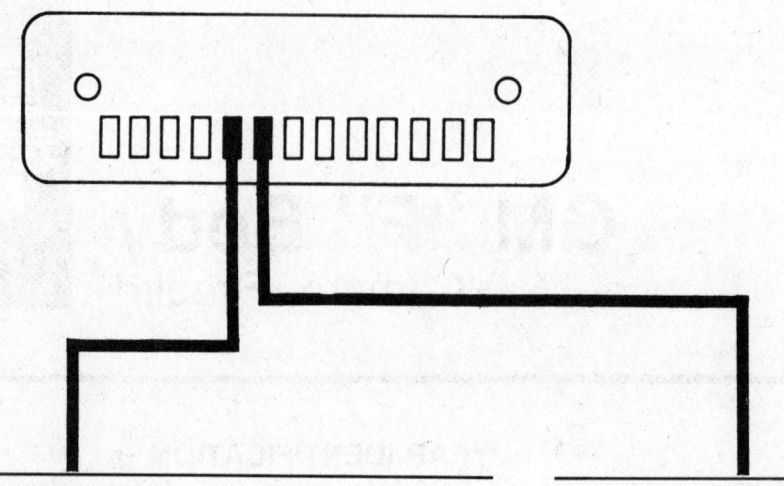

ENGINE CODE							MODEL YEAR CODE	
Code	Cu. In.	Liters	Cyl.	Carb.	Eng. Mfg.		Code	Year
CAMARO							8	1978
K	229	3.8	6	2	Chev.		9	1979
A	231	3.8	V-6	2	Buick		A	1980
D	250	4.1	6	1	Chev.			
J	267	4.4	8	2	Chev.			
U	305	5.0	8	2	Chev.			
G	305	5.0	8	2	Chev.			
H	305	5.0	8	4	Chev.			
L	350	5.7	8	4	Chev.			
FIREBIRD								
A	231	3.8	V-6	2	Buick			
S	265	4.3	8	2	Pont.			
Y	301	4.9	8	2	Pont.			
W	301	4.9	8	4	Pont.			
T	301①	4.9	8	4	Pont.			
U	305	5.0	8	2	Chev.			
G	305	5.0	8	2	Chev.			
H	305	5.0	8	4	Chev.			
P	350	5.7	8	4	Pont.			
R	350	5.7	8	4	Olds.			
L	350	5.7	8	4	Chev.			
Z	400	6.5	8	4	Pont.			
K	403	6.6	8	4	Olds.			

The thirteen digit Vehicle Identification Number can be used to determine engine application and model year. The 6th digit indicates the model year, and the 5th digit identifies the factory installed engine.
① Turbocharged engine

VEHICLE IDENTIFICATION NUMBER (VIN)

It is important for servicing and ordering parts to be certain of the vehicle and engine identification. The VIN (vehicle identification number) is a 13 or 17 digit number visible through the windshield on the driver's side of the dash and contains the vehicle and engine identification codes. It can be interpreted as follows:

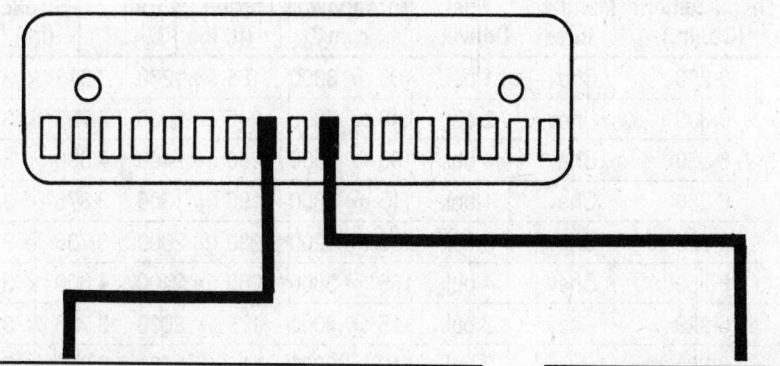

ENGINE CODE

Code	Cu. In.	Liters	Cyl.	Carb.	Eng. Mfg.
CAMARO					
2	151	2.5	4	T.B.I.	Pont.
F	151	2.5	4	2	Pont.
1	173	2.8	V-6	2	Chev.
L	173	2.8	V-6	2	Chev.
K	229	3.8	6	2	Chev.
A	231	3.8	V-6	2	Buick
J	267	4.4	8	2	Chev.
H	305	5.0	8	4	Chev.
7	305	5.0	8	T.B.I.	Chev.
G	305	5.0	8	4	Chev.
S	305	5.0	8	T.B.I.	Chev.
L (81)	350	5.7	8	4	Chev.
FIREBIRD					
2	151	2.5	4	T.B.I.	Pont.
F	151	2.5	4	2	Pont.
1	173	2.8	V-6	2	Chev.
L	173	2.8	V-6	2	Chev.
A	231	3.8	V-6	2	Buick
S (81)	265	4.3	8	2	Pont.
W	301	4.9	8	4	Pont.
T	301①	4.9	8	4	Pont.
H	305	5.0	8	4	Chev.
7	305	5.0	8	T.B.I.	Chev.
G	305	5.0	8	4	Chev.
S	305	5.0	8	T.B.I.	Chev.

MODEL YEAR CODE

Code	Year
B	1981
C	1982
D	1983
E	1984
F	1985

The seventeen digit Vehicle Identification Number can be used to determine engine application and model year. The 10th digit indicates the model year, and the 8th digit identifies the factory installed engine.

① Turbocharged engine

T.B.I.—Throttle body (fuel) injection

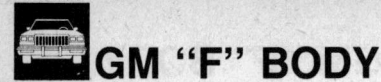

GENERAL ENGINE SPECIFICATIONS
Camaro

Year	Engine V.I.N. Code	Engine No. of Cyl.- Displacement (Cu. In.)	Engine Manufac- turer	Fuel Delivery	Horsepower @ rpm①	Torque @ rpm (ft. lbs.)①	Bore and Stroke (in.)	Compression Ratio	Oil Pressure @ 2000 rpm
'78	D	6-250	Chev.	1 bbl.	105 @ 3800	185 @ 1200	3.875 × 3.530	8.1:1	40
	U	8-305	Chev.	2 bbl.	140 @ 3800	245 @ 2000	3.736 × 3.480	8.0:1	40
	L	8-350	Chev.	4 bbl.	165 @ 3800	260 @ 2400	4.000 × 3.480	8.0:1	40
'79	D	6-250	Chev.	1 bbl.	115 @ 3800	190 @ 1300	3.875 × 3.530	8.0:1	40
	G	8-305	Chev.	2 bbl.	130 @ 3200	230 @ 2000	3.736 × 3.480	8.4:1	45
	L	8-350	Chev.	4 bbl.	165 @ 3800	260 @ 2400	4.000 × 3.480	8.2:1	45
'80	K	6-229	Chev.	2 bbl.	115 @ 4000	175 @ 2000	3.736 × 3.480	8.6:1	45
	A	6-231	Buick	2 bbl.	110 @ 3800	190 @ 1600	3.800 × 3.400	8.0:1	45
	J	8-267	Chev.	2 bbl.	120 @ 3600	215 @ 2000	3.500 × 3.480	8.3:1	45
	H	8-305	Chev.	4 bbl.	155 @ 4000	240 @ 1600	3.736 × 3.480	8.6:1	45
	H	8-305 Calif.	Chev.	4 bbl.	155 @ 4000	230 @ 2400	3.736 × 3.480	8.6:1	45
	H	8-305/Z28	Chev.	4 bbl.	165 @ 4000	245 @ 2400	3.736 × 3.480	8.6:1	45
	L	8-350	Chev.	4 bbl.	190 @ 4200	280 @ 2400	4.000 × 3.480	8.2:1	45
'81	K	6-229	Chev.	2 bbl.	110 @ 4200	170 @ 2000	3.736 × 3.480	8.6:1	45
	A	6-231	Buick	2 bbl.	110 @ 3800	190 @ 1600	3.800 × 3.400	8.0:1	45
	J	8-267	Chev.	2 bbl.	115 @ 4000	200 @ 2400	3.500 × 3.480	8.3:1	45
	H	8-305	Chev.	4 bbl.	150 @ 3800	240 @ 2400	3.736 × 3.480	8.6:1	45
	H	8-305/Z28	Chev.	4 bbl.	165 @ 4000	245 @ 2400	3.736 × 3.480	8.6:1	45
	L	8-350	Chev.	4 bbl.	175 @ 4000	275 @ 2400	4.000 × 3.480	8.2:1	45
'82	2	4-151	Pont.	T.B.I.	90 @ 4000	134 @ 2400	4.000 × 3.000	8.2:1	36–41
	F	4-151	Pont.	2 bbl.	92 @ 4200	130 @ 2800	4.000 × 3.000	8.2:1	36–41
	1	6-173	Chev.	2 bbl.	102 @ 4800	145 @ 2400	3.503 × 2.992	8.5:1	40
	H	8-305	Chev.	4 bbl.	145 @ 4000	240 @ 2400	3.736 × 3.480	8.6:1	40
	7	8-305	Chev.	T.B.I.	165 @ 4200	240 @ 2400	3.736 × 3.480	9.5:1	40
'83	2	4-151	Pont.	T.B.I.	92 @ 4000	134 @ 2400	4.000 × 3.000	8.2:1	36–41
	F	4-151	Pont.	2 bbl.	92 @ 4200	130 @ 2800	4.000 × 3.000	8.2:1	36–41
	1	6-173	Chev.	2 bbl.	102 @ 4800	145 @ 2400	3.503 × 2.992	8.5:1	40
	H	8-305	Chev.	4 bbl.	145 @ 4000	240 @ 2400	3.736 × 3.480	8.6:1	40
	7	8-305	Chev.	4 bbl.	190 @ 4800	240 @ 3200	3.736 × 3.480	9.5:1	40
	S	8-305	Chev.	T.B.I.	175 @ 4200	250 @ 2800	3.736 × 3.480	9.5:1	50–65
'84-'85	2	4-151	Pont.	T.B.I.	90 @ 4000	134 @ 2400	4.000 × 3.000	8.2:1	36–41
	F	4-151	Pont.	2 bbl.	92 @ 4200	130 @ 2800	4.000 × 3.000	9.0:1	36–41
	1	6-173	Chev.	2 bbl.	102 @ 4800	145 @ 2400	3.503 × 2.992	8.5:1	40
	L	6-173	Chev.	2 bbl.	125 @ 5400	145 @ 2400	3.503 × 2.992	8.9:1	40
	H	8-305	Chev.	4 bbl.	145 @ 4000	240 @ 2400	3.736 × 3.480	8.6:1	40
	G	8-305	Chev.	4 bbl.	190 @ 4800	240 @ 3200	3.736 × 3.480	9.5:1	40

① Horsepower and torque are SAE net figures. They are measured at the rear of the transmission with all accessories installed and operating. Since the figures vary when a given engine is installed in different models, some are representative, rather than exact.

GENERAL ENGINE SPECIFICATIONS
Firebird

Year	Engine V.I.N. Code	Engine No. of Cyl. Displacement (Cu. In.)	Engine Manufacturer	Fuel Delivery	Horsepower @ rpm①	Torque @ rpm (ft. lbs.)①	Bore and Stroke (in.)	Compression Ratio	Oil Pressure @ 2050 rpm
'78	A	6-231	Buick	2 bbl.	105 @ 3200	185 @ 2000	3.800 × 3.400	8.0:1	37③
	U	8-305	Chev.	2 bbl.	145 @ 3800	245 @ 2400	3.736 × 3.480	8.4:1	32–40
	L	8-350	Chev.	4 bbl.	170 @ 3800	270 @ 2400	4.000 × 3.480	8.2:1	30–45⑤
	Z	8-400	Pont.	4 bbl.	180 @ 3600	325 @ 1600	4.120 × 3.750	7.7:1	35–40③
	Z	8-400⑦	Pont.	4 bbl.	188 @ 4000	340 @ 1700	4.120 × 3.750	8.1:1	35–40③
	K	8-403	Olds.	4 bbl.	180 @ 3400	315 @ 2200	4.351 × 3.385	7.9:1	30–45⑥
'79	A	6-231	Buick	2 bbl.	115 @ 3800	190 @ 2000	3.800 × 3.400	8.2:1	34
	Y	8-301	Pont.	2 bbl.	140 @ 3600	235 @ 2000	4.000 × 3.000	8.1:1	35–40③
	W	8-301	Pont.	4 bbl.	150 @ 4000	240 @ 2000	4.000 × 3.000	8.1:1	35–40③
	G	8-305	Chev.	2 bbl.	145 @ 3800	270 @ 2400	3.736 × 3.480	8.5:1	40
	L	8-350	Chev.	4 bbl.	160 @ 3800	260 @ 2400	4.000 × 3.480	8.5:1	40
	Z	8-400	Pont.	4 bbl.	220 @ 4000	320 @ 2800	4.120 × 3.750	8.1:1	55–60③
	K	8-403	Olds.	4 bbl.	185 @ 3600	320 @ 2200	4.351 × 3.385	8.0:1	40
'80	A	6-231	Buick	2 bbl.	115 @ 3800	188 @ 2000	3.800 × 3.400	8.0:1	37
	S	8-265	Pont.	2 bbl.	120 @ 3600	210 @ 1600	3.750 × 3.000	8.3:1	37③
	W	8-301	Pont.	4 bbl.	150 @ 4000	240 @ 2000	4.000 × 3.000	8.1:1	38③
	T	8-301⑧	Pont.	4 bbl.	185 @ 4000	280 @ 2000	4.000 × 3.000	7.6:1	55–60③
	H	8-305	Chev.	4 bbl.	150 @ 3800	230 @ 2400	3.736 × 3.480	8.4:1	40
'81	A	6-231	Buick	2 bbl.	115 @ 3800	190 @ 1600	3.800 × 3.400	8.0:1	37⑤
	S	8-265	Pont.	2 bbl.	119 @ 4000	205 @ 2000	3.750 × 3.000	8.3:1	38③
	W	8-301	Pont.	4 bbl.	155 @ 4000	245 @ 2000	4.000 × 3.000	8.1:1	38③
	T	8-301⑧	Pont.	4 bbl.	210 @ 4000	340 @ 2000	4.000 × 3.000	7.5:1	58③
	H	8-305	Chev.	4 bbl.	155 @ 3800	240 @ 2400	3.736 × 3.480	8.6:1	40
'82	2	4-151	Pont.	T.B.I.	90 @ 4000	134 @ 2400	4.000 × 3.000	8.2:1	36–41②
	F	4-151	Pont.	2 bbl.	92 @ 4200	130 @ 2800	4.000 × 3.000	8.2:1	36–41
	1	6-173	Chev.	2 bbl.	102 @ 4800	145 @ 2400	3.503 × 2.992	8.5:1	40
	H	8-305	Chev.	4 bbl.	145 @ 4000	240 @ 2400	3.736 × 3.480	8.6:1	40
	7	8-305	Chev.	T.B.I.	175 @ 4200	240 @ 2400	3.736 × 3.480	9.5:1	40
'83	2	4-151	Pont.	T.B.I.	90 @ 4000	134 @ 2400	4.000 × 3.000	8.2:1	36–41②
	F	4-151	Pont.	2 bbl.	92 @ 4200	130 @ 2800	4.000 × 3.000	8.2:1	36–41
	1	6-173	Chev.	2 bbl.	102 @ 4800	145 @ 2400	3.503 × 2.992	8.5:1	40
	L	6-173	Chev.	2 bbl.	125 @ 5400	145 @ 2400	3.503 × 2.992	8.9:1	50–65
	H	8-305	Chev.	4 bbl.	145 @ 4000	240 @ 2400	3.736 × 3.480	8.6:1	40
	7	8-305	Chev.	4 bbl.	190 @ 4800	240 @ 3200	3.736 × 3.480	9.5:1	40
	S	8-305	Chev.	T.B.I.	175 @ 4200	250 @ 2800	3.736 × 3.480	9.5:1	50–65
'84-'85	2	4-151	Pont.	T.B.I.	90 @ 4000	134 @ 2400	4.000 × 3.000	8.2:1	36–41
	F	4-151	Pont.	2 bbl.	92 @ 4200	130 @ 2800	4.000 × 3.000	9.0:1	36–41
	1	6-173	Chev.	2 bbl.	102 @ 4800	145 @ 2400	3.503 × 2.992	8.5:1	40

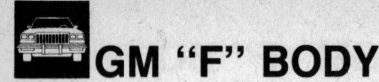
GENERAL ENGINE SPECIFICATIONS
Firebird

Year	Engine V.I.N. Code	Engine No. of Cyl. Displacement (Cu. In.)	Engine Manufacturer	Fuel Delivery	Horsepower @ rpm①	Torque @ rpm (ft. lbs.)①	Bore and Stroke (in.)	Compression Ratio	Oil Pressure @ 2050 rpm
'84-'85	L	6-173HO	Chev.	2 bbl.	125 @ 5400	145 @ 2400	3.503 × 2.992	8.9:1	50-65
	H	8-305	Chev.	4 bbl.	145 @ 4000	240 @ 2400	3.736 × 3.480	8.6:1	40
	G	8-305	Chev.	4 bbl.	190 @ 4800	240 @ 3200	3.736 × 3.480	9.5:1	40
	S	8-305	Chev.	T.B.I.	175 @ 4200	250 @ 2800	3.736 × 3.480	9.5:1	50-65

① Horsepower and torque are SAE net figures. They are measured at the rear of the transmission with all accessories installed and operating. Since the figures vary when a given engine is installed in different models, some are representative, rather than exact.
② Oil pressure at 2000 rpm
③ Oil pressure above 2600 rpm
④ Oil pressure at 1000 rpm
⑤ Oil pressure at 2400 rpm
⑥ Oil pressure at 1500 rpm
⑦ Trans Am only
⑧ Turbocharged engine
T.B.I.—Throttle Body Injection

TUNE-UP SPECIFICATIONS
Camaro

Year	Engine V.I.N. Code	Engine No. of Cyl. Displacement (Cu. In.)	Engine Manufacturer	Spark Plugs Type	Gap (in.)	Ignition Timing (deg)① ② Man Trans	Auto Trans	Intake Valve Opens (deg)③	Fuel Pump Pressure (psi)	Idle Speed (rpm)① ② Man Trans	Auto Trans
'78	D	6-250	Chev.	R-46TS	0.035	6B	10B⑥(6B)	16	4½-6	800	550(600)
	U	8-305	Chev.	R-45TS	0.045	4B	4B(6B)	28	7½-9	600	500
	L	8-350	Chev.	R-45TS	0.045	6B	6B(8B)	28	7½-9	700	500⑤
'79	D	6-250	Chev.	R-46TS	0.035	12B	8B(6B)	16	4½-6	800	675(600)
	G	8-305	Chev.	R-45TS	0.045	4B	4B	28	7½-9	600	500(600)
	L	8-350	Chev.	R-45TS	0.045	6B	6B(8B)	28	7½-9	700	500⑤
'80	K	6-229	Chev.	R-T5TS⑥	0.045	8B	12B	42	4½-6	700	600
	A	6-231	Buick	R-45TSX	0.060	—	15B	16	4¼-5¾	—	600
	J	8-267	Chev.	R-45TS	0.045	—	4B	28	7½-9	—	500
	H	8-305	Chev.	R-45TS	0.045	4B	4B	28	7½-9	700	500(550)
	L	8-350	Chev.	R-45TS	0.045	6B	6B	28	7½-9	700	500
'81	K	6-229	Chev.	R-45TS	0.045	6B	6B	42	4½-6	700⑦	600⑦
	A	6-231	Buick	R-45TS8	0.080	—	15B	16	4¼-5¾	—	500⑦
	J	8-267	Chev.	R-45TS	0.045	—	6B	44	7½-9	—	500⑦
	H	8-305	Chev.	R-45TS	0.045	6B	6B	44	7½-9	700	500
	L	8-350	Chev.	R-45TS	0.045		6B	38	7½-9		500⑦
'82	2	4-151	Pont.	R-44TSX	0.060	⑧	⑧	NA	9-13	⑧	⑧
	F	4-151	Pont.	R-44TSX	0.060	⑧	⑧	NA	5½-6½	⑧	⑧
	1	6-173	Chev.	R-43TS	0.045	⑧	⑧	NA	5½-6½	⑧	⑧
	H	8-305	Chev.	R-45TS	0.045	⑧	⑧	NA	5½-6½	⑧	⑧
	7	8-305	Chev.	R-45TS⑨	0.045	⑧	⑧	NA	9-13	⑧	⑧

TUNE-UP SPECIFICATIONS
Camaro

Year	Engine V.I.N. Code	Engine No. of Cyl. Displacement (Cu. In.)	Engine Manufac-turer	Spark Plugs Type	Gap (in.)	Ignition Timing (deg)① ② Man Trans	Auto Trans	Intake Valve Opens (deg)③	Fuel Pump Pressure (psi)	Idle Speed (rpm)① ② Man Trans	Auto Trans
'83	2	4-151	Pont.	R-44TSX	0.060	⑧	⑧	NA	9–13	⑧	⑧
	F	4-151	Pont.	R-44TSX	0.060	⑧	⑧	NA	5½–6½	⑧	⑧
	1	6-173	Chev.	R-43CTS	0.045	⑧	⑧	NA	5½–6½	⑧	⑧
	H	8-305	Chev.	R-45TS	0.045	⑧	⑧	NA	5½–6½	⑧	⑧
	7	8-305	Chev.	R-45TS	0.045	⑧	⑧	NA	9–13	⑧	⑧
	S	8-305	Chev.	R-45TS	0.045	⑧	⑧	NA	9–13	⑧	⑧
'84-'85	2	4-151	Pont.	R-44TSX	0.060	⑧	⑧	NA	9–13	⑧	⑧
	F	4-151	Pont.	R-44TSX	0.060	⑧	⑧	NA	5½–6½	⑧	⑧
	1	6-173	Chev.	R-43CTS	0.045	⑧	⑧	NA	5½–6½	⑧	⑧
	L	6-173	Chev.	R42CTS	0.045	⑧	⑧	NA	6–7½	⑧	⑧
	H	8-305	Chev.	R-45TS	0.045	⑧	⑧	NA	5½–6½	⑧	⑧
	G	8-305	Chev.	R-45TS	0.045	⑧	⑧	NA	9–13	⑧	⑧
	S	8-305	Chev.	R-45TS	0.045	⑧	⑧	NA	9–13	⑧	⑧

NOTE: The underhood specifications sticker often reflects tune-up specification changes made during the production run. Sticker figures must always be used if they disagree with those in this chart. Part numbers in this chart are not recommendations by Chilton for any product by brand name.

All models use electronic ignition systems.

B Before Top Dead Center

TDC Top Dead Center

—Not applicable

NA—Not available

① See text for procedure

② Figure in parenthesis indicates California engine

③ All figures Before Top Dead Center (B.T.D.C.)

④ 8B with air conditioning

⑤ High altitude engine—600

⑥ With automatic trans.—R-45TS

⑦ Equipped with Idle Speed Control (I.S.C.)

⑧ These functions are controlled by the emissions computer. In rare instances when adjustment is necessary, refer to the underhood emissions sticker for specifications.

⑨ R-44TS if a colder plug is needed

⑩ With air conditioning—750; without air conditioning—800

TUNE-UP SPECIFICATIONS
Firebird

Year	Engine V.I.N. Code	Engine No. of Cyl.-Displacement (Cu. In.)	Engine Manufac-turer	Spark Plugs Type	Gap (in.)	Ignition Timing (deg)③ ④ Man Trans	Auto Trans	Intake Valve Opens (deg)⑤	Fuel Pump Pressure (psi)	Idle Speed (rpm)③ ④ Man Trans	Auto Trans
'78	A	6-231	Buick	R-46TSX	0.060	15B	15B	16	4.5–5.7	800	600
	U	8-305	Chev.	R-45TS	0.045	4B	4B(6B)	29	7–8.5	700	600(650)
	L	8-350	Chev.	R-45TS	0.045	6B	8B	17	4.5–5.7	700	500

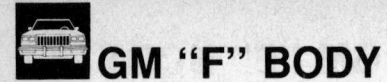
TUNE-UP SPECIFICATIONS
Firebird

Year	Engine V.I.N. Code	Engine No. of Cyl.-Displacement (Cu. In.)	Engine Manufac-turer	Spark Plugs Type	Gap (in.)	Ignition Timing (deg)③④ Man Trans	Auto Trans	Intake Valve Opens (deg)⑤	Fuel Pump Pressure (psi)	Idle Speed (rpm)③④ Man Trans	Auto Trans
'78	Z	8-400	Pont.	R-45TSX	0.060	—	16B	29	7–8.5	—	650
	Z	8-400⑬	Pont.	R-45TSX	0.060	18B	18B	16	7–8.5	775	700
	K	8-403	Olds.	R-46SZ	0.060	—	20B	16	5.5–6.5	—	700(650)
'79	A	6-231	Buick	R-46TSX	0.060	15B	15B	16	4.5–5.5	800	600
	Y	8-301	Pont.	R-46TSX	0.060	—	12B	16	5.5–6.5	—	650
	W	8-301	Pont.	R-45TSX	0.060	14B	12B	16⑥	5.5–6.5	750	650
	G	8-305	Chev.	R-45TS	0.045	—	4B	28	5.5–6.5	—	500
	L	8-350	Chev.	R-45TS	0.045	—	8B	28	5.5–6.5	—	600
	Z	8-400	Pont.	R-45TSX	0.060	18B	—	16	7–8.5	775	—
	K	8-403	Olds.	R-46SZ	0.060	—	18B(20B)	16	5.5–6.5	—	550(500)
'80	A	6-231	Buick	R-45TSX⑦	0.060⑦	15B	15B	16	3–4.5	800/600①	620/550①
	S	8-265	Pont.	R-45TSX	0.060	—	10B	27	7.5–9	—	650/550①
	W	8-301	Pont.	R-45TSX	0.060	—	12B	16	7.5–9	—	650/500①
	W	8-301⑧	Pont.	R-45TSX	0.060	—	12B	17	7.5–9	700	550
	T	8-301⑨	Pont.	R-45TSX	0.060	—	8B	16	7.5–9	—	650/600①
	H	8-305	Chev.	R-45TS	0.045	—	4B	28	7.5–9	—	650/550①
'81	A	6-231	Buick	R-45TS8	0.080	15B	15B	16	4.25–5.75	800	500
	S	8-265	Pont.	R-45TSX	0.060	—	12B	16	7.5–9	—	450 ± 24
	W	8-301	Pont.	R-45TSX	0.060	—	12B	16	7.5–9	—	450 ± 32
	T	8-301⑨	Pont.	R-45TSX	0.060	—	6B	16	7.5–9	—	450 ± 32
	H	8-305	Chev.	R-45TS	0.045	6B	6B	44	7.5–9	800	800
'82	2	4-151	Pont.	R-44TSX	0.060	⑩	⑩	NA	9–13	⑩	⑩
	F	4-151	Pont.	R-44TS	0.060	⑩	⑩	NA	5½–6½	⑨	⑨
	1	6-173	Chev.	R-43TS	0.045	⑩	⑩	NA	5.5–6.5	⑩	⑩
	H	8-305	Chev.	R-45TS	0.045	⑩	⑩	NA	5.5–6.5	⑩	⑩
	7	8-305	Chev.	R-45TS⑯	0.045	⑩	⑩	NA	9–13	⑩	⑩
'83	2	4-151	Pont.	R-44TSX	0.060	⑩	⑩	NA	9–13	⑩	⑩
	F	4-151	Pont.	R-44TS	0.060	⑩	⑩	NA	5½–6½	⑩	⑩
	1	6-173	Chev.	R-43CTS	0.045	⑩	⑩	NA	5.5–6.5	⑩	⑩
	L	6-173HO	Chev.	R-42CTS	0.045	⑩	⑩	NA	6–7½	⑩	⑩
	H	8-305	Chev.	R-45TS	0.045	⑩	⑩	NA	5.5–6.5	⑩	⑩
	7	8-305	Chev.	R-45TS⑯	0.045	⑩	⑩	NA	9–13	⑩	⑩
	S	8-305	Chev.	R-45TS	0.045	⑩	⑩	NA	9–13	⑩	⑩
'84–'85	2	4-151	Pont.	R-44TSX	0.060	⑩	⑩	NA	9–13	⑩	⑩
	F	4-151	Pont.	R-44TSX	0.060	⑩	⑩	NA	5½–6½	⑩	⑩
	1	6-173	Chev.	R-43CTS	0.045	⑩	⑩	NA	5½–6½	⑩	⑩
	L	6-173	Chev.	R-42CTS	0.045	⑩	⑩	NA	6–7½	⑩	⑩
	H	8-305	Chev.	R-45TS	0.045	⑩	⑩	NA	5½–6½	⑩	⑩

TUNE-UP SPECIFICATIONS
Firebird

| Year | Engine V.I.N. Code | Engine No. of Cyl.-Displacement (Cu. In.) | Engine Manufac-turer | Spark Plugs | | Ignition Timing (deg)③④ | | Intake Valve Opens (deg)⑤ | Fuel Pump Pressure (psi) | Idle Speed (rpm)③④ | |
				Type	Gap (in.)	Man Trans	Auto Trans			Man Trans	Auto Trans
'84-'85	G	8-305	Chev.	R-45TS	0.045	⑩	⑩	NA	9–13	⑩	⑩
	S	8-305	Chev.	R-45TS	0.045	⑩	⑩	NA	9–13	⑩	⑩

NOTE: The underhood specifications sticker often reflects tune-up specification changes made during the production run. Sticker figures must always be used if they disagree with those in this chart. Part numbers in this chart are not recommendations by Chilton for any product by brand name.

All models use electronic ignition systems.

B Before Top Dead Center

TDC Top Dead Center

——Not applicable

NA—Not available

① Lower figure indicates idle speed with solenoid disconnected

② High altitude and California R-45TSX

③ See text for procedure

④ Figure in parentheses indicates California engine

⑤ All figures are in degrees Before Top Dead Center. Where two figures appear, the first represents timing with manual transmission, the second with automatic transmission
Auto—29
Trans Am—16

⑥ High performance—27

⑦ All M/T and low altitude A/T—R-45TS, gap 0.040

⑧ With performance package

⑨ Turbocharged engine

⑩ These functions are controlled by the emissions computer. In rare instances when adjustment is necessary, refer to the underhood emissions sticker for specifications.

⑪ R-44TS if a colder plug is needed

⑫ Trans Am only

FIRING ORDER

NOTE: To avoid confusion, replace spark plugs and wires one at a time.

Pontiac-built 151-4 cylinder engine
Engine firing order: 1-3-4-2
Distributor rotation: clockwise

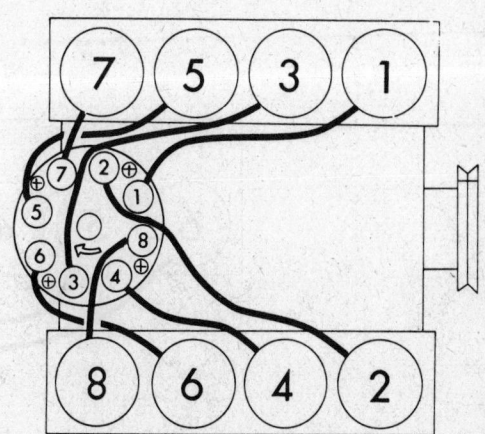

Chevrolet-built V8 engines
Engine firing order: 1-8-4-3-6-5-7-2
Distributor rotation: clockwise

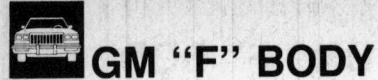

FIRING ORDERS

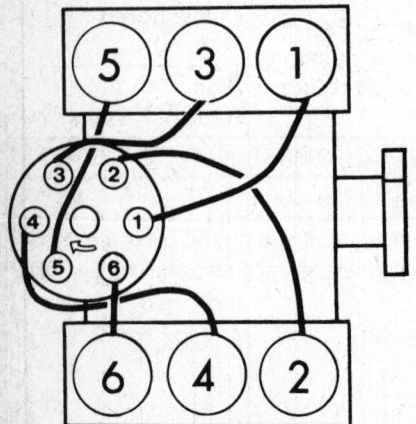

Chevrolet-built 229-V6 engine
Engine firing order: 1-6-5-4-3-2
Distributor rotation: clockwise

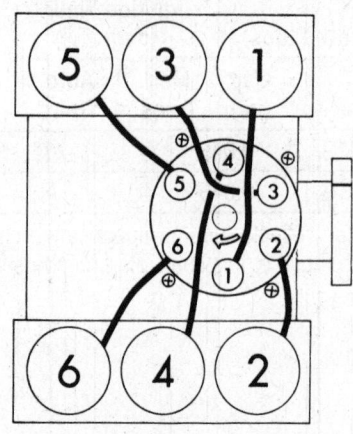

Buick-built 231-V6 engine
Engine firing order: 1-6-5-4-3-2
Distributor rotation: clockwise

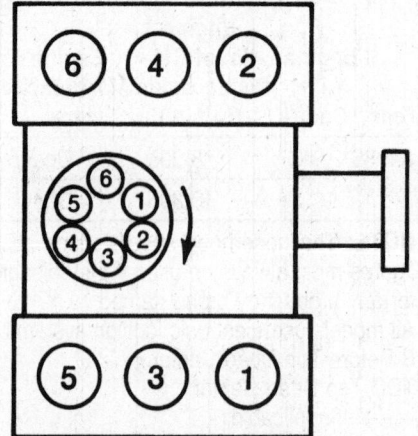

Chevrolet-built 173-V6 engine
Engine firing order: 1-2-3-4-5-6
Distributor rotation: clockwise

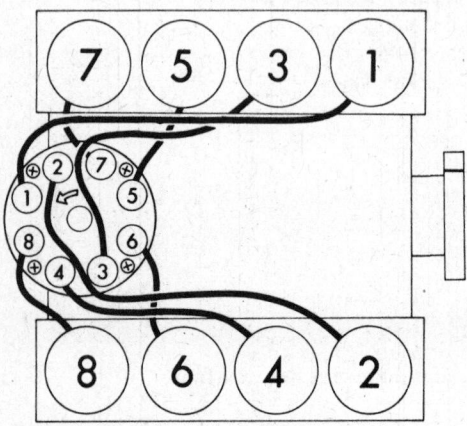

Pontiac-built V8 engines
Engine firing order: 1-8-4-3-6-5-7-2
Distributor rotation: counterclockwise

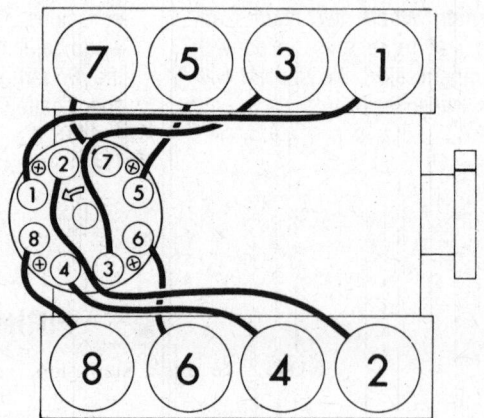

Oldsmobile-built V8 engines
Engine firing order: 1-8-4-3-6-5-7-2
Distributor rotation: counterclockwise

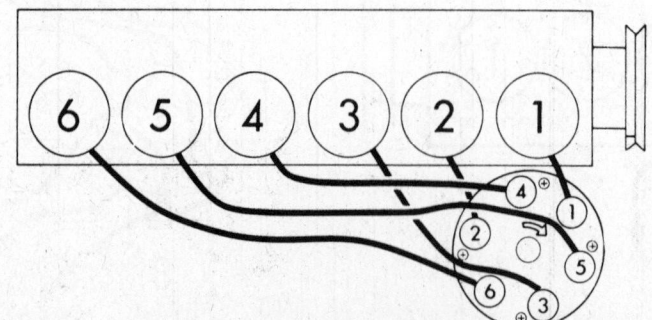

Chevrolet-built 250-6 cylinder engine
Engine firing order: 1-5-3-6-2-4
Distributor rotation: clockwise

CAPACITIES
Camaro

Year	Engine No. Cyl. Displacement (cu. in.)	Engine Crankcase Add 1 qt for New Filter	Transmission Pts to Refill After Draining			Drive Axle (pts)	Gasoline Tank (gals)	Cooling System (qts)	
			Manual		Automatic①			With Heater	With A/C
			3-Speed	4-Speed					
'78	6-250	4	3	—	6	4.25③	21	15.0	16.0
	8-305	4	—	3	6	4.25③	21	17.5	18.5
	8-350	4	—	3	6	4.25③	21	17.5	18.5
'79	6-250	4	3	—	7	4.25③	21	15.0	16.0
	8-305	4	—	3.4	7	4.25③	21	17.5	18.5
	8-350	4	—	3.4	7	4.25③	21	17.5	18.5
'80–'81	6-229	4②	3	—	7④	4.25⑤	21	14.5	15.5
	6-231	4②	—	—	7④	4.25⑤	21	12.0	13.0
	8-267	4	—	—	7④	4.25⑤	21	15.0	16.0
	8-305	4	—	3.4	7④	4.25⑤	21	15.0	16.0
	8-350	4	—	—	7④	4.25⑤	21	16.0	17.0
'82	4-151	3②	—	4.3	8.5	3.5	16	12.8	13.0
	6-173	4②	—	4.3	8.5	3.5	16	12.8	12.8
	8-305⑥	4	—	4.3	8.5	3.5	16	17.2	17.2
	8-305⑦	4	—	4.3	8.5	3.5	16	15.9	15.9
'83	4-151	3②	—	4.3⑧	8.5⑨	3.5	16	12.8	13.0
	6-173	4②	—	4.3⑧	8.5⑨	3.5	16	12.8	12.8
	8-305⑥	4	—	4.3⑧	8.5⑨	3.5	16	17.2	17.2
	8-305⑦	4	—	4.3⑧	8.5⑨	3.5	16	15.9	15.9
'84–'85	4-151	3②	—	3.5⑧	8.5⑨	3.5	16	8.8	9.1
	6-173	4②	—	3.5⑧	8.5⑨	3.5	16	12.5	12.5
	8-305⑥	4	—	3.5⑧	8.5⑨	3.5	16	15.0	15.0
	8-305⑦	4	—	3.5⑧	8.5⑨	3.5	16	15.0	15.0

—Not applicable
① Drain and refill only—does not include torque convertor
② Capacity same with or without filter change
③ With 7½" ring gear—3.5 pints
④ With 350c—6 pints
⑤ With 7½" ring gear—3.5 pints; with 8¾" ring gear—5.4 pints
⑥ With 4 bbl. carburetor
⑦ With throttle body fuel injection
⑧ 5-speed—5.3 pints
⑨ Overdrive transmission—9.9 pints: Add 4 pints, run engine and check dipstick- fill as necessary

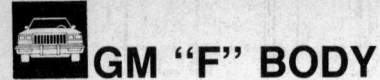

CAPACITIES
Firebird

Year	Engine No. Cyl.- Displacement (Cu. In.)	Engine Crankcase (Add 1 Qt For New Filter)	Transmission (Pts To Refill After Draining)		Automatic (Pts.)①	Drive Axle (pts)	Gasoline Tank (gals)	Cooling System (qts)	
			Manual					With Heater	With Air Cond.
			3 Spd.	4 Spd.					
'78	6-231 Buick	4	3.5	—	7.5	4.25	20.8	14.0	14.0
	8-305 Chev.	4	—	3.5	7.5	4.25	20.8	17.2	17.2
	8-350 Chev.	4	—	3.5	7.5	4.25	20.8	17.2	17.2
	8-400 Pont.	5	—	2.44	7.5	4.25	20.8	19.7	③
	8-403 Olds.	5	—	—	7.5	4.25	20.8	17.4	18.0
'79	6-231 Buick	4	3.5	—	6	4.25	20.8	14.0	14.0
	8-301 Pont.	4	—	3.5	6	4.25	20.8	20.5	20.5
	8-305 Chev.	4	—	—	6	4.25	20.8	17.2	17.2
	8-350 Chev.	4	—	—	7.5	4.25	20.8	17.2	17.8
	8-400 Pont.	5	—	3.5	7.5	4.25	20.8	19.7	20.3
	8-403 Olds.	4	—	—	7.5	4.25	20.8	17.4	18.0
'80	6-231 Buick	4	3.5	3.5	6	4.25	20.8	13.2	13.2
	8-265 Pont.	4②	—	—	6	4.25	20.8	20.4	20.4
	8-301 Pont.	4②	3.5	3.5	6	4.25	20.8	20.4	20.4
	8-301 Pont. Turbo	4②	3.5	3.5	8	4.25	20.8	—	21.4
	8-305 Chev.	4	—	—	6	4.25	20.8	—	16.4
'81	6-231 Buick	4	3.5	—	6	4.25	21.0	20.9	—
	8-265 Pont.	4	—	—	6	4.25	21.0	20.9	—
	8-301 Pont.	4	—	—	6	4.25	21.0	20.9	—
	8-301 Pont. Turbo	4	—	—	6	4.25	21.0	20.9	—
	8-305 Chev.	4	—	—	6	4.25	21.0	20.9	—
'82	4-151 Pont.	3②	—	4.3	8.5	3.5	16.0	12.8	13.0
	6-173 Chev.	4②	—	4.3	8.5	3.5	16.0	12.8	12.8
	8-305 Chev.⑦	4	—	4.3	8.5	3.5	16.0	17.2	17.2
	8-305 Chev.⑧	4	—	4.3	8.5	3.5	16.0	15.9	15.9
'83	4-151 Pont.	3②	—	4.3⑤	8.5⑥	3.5	16.0	12.8	13.0
	6-173 Chev.	4②	—	4.3⑤	8.5⑥	3.5	16.0	12.8	12.8
	8-305 Chev.⑦	4	—	4.3⑤	8.5⑥	3.5	16.0	17.2	17.2
	8-305 Chev.⑧	4	—	4.3⑤	8.5⑥	3.5	16.0	15.9	15.9
'84–'85	4-151 Pont.	3②	—	3.5⑤	8.5⑥	3.5	16.0	8.8	9.1
	6-173 Chev.	4②	—	3.5⑤	8.5⑥	3.5	16.0	12.5	12.5
	8-305 Chev.⑦	4	—	3.5⑤	8.5⑥	3.5	16.0	15.0	15.0
	8-305 Chev.⑧	4	—	3.5⑤	8.5⑥	3.5	16.0	15.0	15.0

—Not applicable
①Drain and refill only—does not include torque convertor.
②Capacity same with or without filter change.
③With manual trans.—20.3; with automatic trans.—22.1

④With manual trans.—22.0; with automatic trans.—21.4
⑤5-speed—5.3 pints
⑥Overdrive transmission—9.9 pints. Add 4 pints, run engine and check dipstick-fill as necessary

⑦With 4 bbl. carburetor
⑧With throttle body injection

VALVE SPECIFICATIONS
Camaro

Year	Engine No. Cyl. Displacement (cu. in.)	Seat Angle (deg)	Face Angle (deg)	Spring Test Pressure (lbs. @ in.)	Spring Installed Height (in.)	Stem to Guide Clearance (in.)		Stem Diameter (in.)	
						Intake	Exhaust	Intake	Exhaust
'78	6-250	46	45	175 @ 1.26	1²³⁄₃₂	.0010–.0027	.0015–.0032	.3414	.3414
	8-305	46	45	200 @ 1.25	1²³⁄₃₂	.0010–.0027	.0010–.0027	.3414	.3414
	8-350	46	45	200 @ 1.25	1²³⁄₃₂	.0010–.0027	.0010–.0027	.3414	.3414
'79	6-250	46	45	175 @ 1.26	1²¹⁄₃₂	.0010–.0027	.0015–.0032	.3414	.3414
	8-305	46	45	200 @ 1.25	1²³⁄₃₂	.0010–.0027	.0010–.0027	.3414	.3414
	8-350	46	45	200 @ 1.25	1²³⁄₃₂	.0010–.0027	.0010–.0027	.3414	.3414
'80–'81	6-229	46	45	200 @ 1.25	1²³⁄₃₂	.0010–.0027	.0010–.0027	.3414	.3414
	6-231	45	45	168 @ 1.33	1⁴⁷⁄₆₄	.0015–.0032	.0015–.0032	.3407	.3409
	8-267	46	45	200 @ 1.25	1²³⁄₃₂	.0010–.0027	.0010–.0027	.3414	.3414
	8-305	46	45	200 @ 1.25	1²³⁄₃₂	.0010–.0027	.0010–.0027	.3414	.3414
	8-350	46	45	200 @ 1.25	1²³⁄₃₂	.0010–.0027	.0010–.0027	.3414	.3414
'82–'83	4-151	46	45	122–180 @ 1.25	1.69	.0010–.0027	.0010–.0027 ②	.3418–.3425	.3418–.3425
	6-173	46	45	194 @ 1.18	1.57	.0010–.0026	.0010–.0026	.3410–.3420	.3410–.3420
	8-305	46	45	194–206 @ 1.25	1²³⁄₃₂	.0010–.0027	.0010–.0027	.3410–.3420	.3410–.3420
'84–'85	4-151	46	45	122–180 @ 1.25	1.69	.0010–.0027	.0010–.0027 ②	.3418–.3425	.3418–.3425
	6-173	46	45	194 @ 1.18	1.57	.0010–.0026	.0010–.0026	.3410–.3420	.3410–.3420
	8-305	46	45	194–206 @ 1.25	1²³⁄₃₂	.0010–.0027	.0010–.0027	.3410–.3420	.3410–.3420

① 1¹⁹⁄₃₂ for the exhaust
② Figure given is measured at the top of the guide; .0020–.0037 is measured at the bottom of the guide.

VALVE SPECIFICATIONS
Firebird

Year	Engine No. Cyl. Displacement (cu. in.)	Seat Angle (deg) ①	Face Angle (deg) ②	Spring Test Pressure (lbs. @ in.)	Spring Installed Height (in.)	Stem to Guide Clearance (in.)		Stem Diameter (in.)	
						Intake	Exhaust	Intake	Exhaust
'78	6-231 Buick	45	45	182 @ 1.34	1⁴⁷⁄₆₄	.0015–.0032	.0015–.0032	.3402–.3412	.3405–.3412
	8-305 Chev.	46 ⑦	45 ⑧	190 @ 1.16	④	.0010–.0037	.0010–.0047	.3414	.3414
	8-350 Chev.	46	45	190 @ 1.16	④	.0010–.0037	.0010–.0047	.3414	.3414
	8-400 Pont.	⑤	⑥	135 @ 1.18	1³⁵⁄₆₄	.0016–.0033	.0021–.0038	.3425	.3425
	8-403 Olds.	③	③	190 @ 1.27	1⁴³⁄₆₄	.0010–.0027	.0015–.0032	.3425–.3432	.3420–.3427

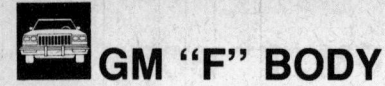

VALVE SPECIFICATIONS
Firebird

Year	Engine No. Cyl. Displacement (cu. in.)	Seat Angle (deg) ①	Face Angle (deg) ②	Spring Test Pressure (lbs. @ in.)	Spring Installed Height (in.)	Stem to Guide Clearance (in.) Intake	Stem to Guide Clearance (in.) Exhaust	Stem Diameter (in.) Intake	Stem Diameter (in.) Exhaust
'79	6-231 Buick	45	45	182 @ 1.34	1^{47}/$_{64}$	.0015–.0032	.0015–.0032	.3402–.3412	.3405–.3412
	8-301 Pont.	46⑦	45⑧	165 @ 1.29	1^{43}/$_{64}$	.0010–.0027	.0010–.0027⑨	.3425	.3425
	8-305 Chev.	46⑦	45⑧	200 @ 1.25	1^{23}/$_{32}$	.0010–.0027	.0010–.0027	.3414	.3414
	8-350 Chev.	46	45	200 @ 1.25	1^{23}/$_{32}$	.0010–.0027	.0010–.0027	.3414	.3414
	8-400 Pont.	⑤	⑥	135 @ 1.18	1^{35}/$_{64}$	.0016–.0033	.0021–.0038	.3425	.3425
	8-403 Olds.	③	③	190 @ 1.27	1^{43}/$_{64}$	.0010–.0027	.0015–.0032	.3425–.3432	.3420–.3427
'80	6-231 Buick	45	45	182 @ 1.34	1^{47}/$_{64}$	.0015–.0032	.0015–.0032	.3402–.3412	.3405–.3412
	8-265 Pont.	46⑦	45⑧	175 @ 1.29	1^{43}/$_{64}$	.0010–.0027	.0010–.0027⑨	.3425	.3425
	8-301 Pont.	46⑦	45⑧	175 @ 1.29	1^{43}/$_{64}$	.0010–.0027	.0010–.0027⑨	.3425	.3425
	8-305 Chev.	46⑦	45⑧	199 @ 1.25	1^{23}/$_{32}$	.0010–.0037	.0010–.0047	.3414	.3414
'81	6-231 Buick	45	44	182 @ 1.34	1^{47}/$_{64}$	.0015–.0035	.0015–.0032	.3401–.3412	.3405–.3412
	8-265 Pont.	46⑦	45⑧	175 @ 1.29	1^{43}/$_{64}$	.0010–.0027	.0010–.0027⑨	.3425	.3425
	8-301 Pont.	46⑦	45⑧	175 @ 1.29	1^{43}/$_{64}$	.0010–.0027	.0010–.0027⑨	.3425	.3425
	8-305 Chev.	46⑦	45⑧	194 @ 1.25	1^{23}/$_{32}$	.0010–.0027	.0010–.0027	.3425–.3432	.3420–.3427
'82–'83	4-151 Pont.	46	45	122–180 @ 1.25	1.69	.0010–.0027	.0010–.0027⑩	.3418–.3425	.3418–.3425
	6-173 Chev.	46	45	194 @ 1.18	1.57	.0010–.0026	.0010–.0026	.3410–.3420	.3410–.3420
	8-305 Chev.	46	45	194–206 @ 1.25	1^{23}/$_{32}$	.0010–.0027	.0010–.0027	.3410–.3420	.3410–.3420
'84–'85	4-151 Pont.	46	45	122–180 @ 1.25	1.69	.0010–.0027	.0010–.0027⑩	.3418–.3425	.3418–.3425
	6-173 Chev.	46	45	194 @ 1.18	1.57	.0010–.0026	.0010–.0026	.3410–.3420	.3410–.3420
	8-305 Chev.	46	45	194–206 @ 1.25	1^{23}/$_{32}$	.0010–.0027	.0010–.0027	.3410–.3420	.3410–.3420

NA: Not available

① Intake valve seat angles are shown. All exhaust valve seat angles are 45° unless otherwise indicated.
② Intake valve face angles are shown. All exhaust valve face angles are 44° unless otherwise indicated.
③ Intake seat 45°, intake face 44° Exhaust seat 31°, exhaust face 30°
④ Intake: 1^{23}/$_{32}$
　 Exhaust: 1^{19}/$_{32}$
⑤ Intake: 30
　 Exhaust: 40
⑥ Intake: 29
　 Exhaust: 44
⑦ Exhaust: 46
⑧ Exhaust: 45
⑨ Bottom exhaust: .0020–.0037
⑩ Figure given is measured at the top of the guide; .0020–.0037 is measured at the bottom of the guide.

TORQUE SPECIFICATIONS
Camaro
(All readings in ft. lbs.)

Year	Engine No. Cyl. Displacement (cu. in.)	Cylinder Head Bolts	Rod Bearing Bolts	Main Bearing Bolts	Crankshaft Pulley Bolts	Flywheel-to-Crankshaft Bolts	Manifold Intake	Manifold Exhaust
All	4-151	85	32	70	160	44	29	44
	6-173	70	37	69	75	50	23	25
	6-229	65	45	70	60	60	30	20
	6-231	80	40	100	175	60	45	25
	6-250	95	35	65	Pressed on	60	25–30①	25③

TORQUE SPECIFICATIONS
Camaro
(All readings in ft. lbs.)

Year	Engine No. Cyl. Displacement (cu. in.)	Cylinder Head Bolts	Rod Bearing Bolts	Main Bearing Bolts	Crankshaft Pulley Bolts	Flywheel-to-Crankshaft Bolts	Manifold	
							Intake	Exhaust
All	8-267, 305, 350	65	45	70	60	60	30②	20

① End bolts—15–20 ft. lbs.
② 20–34 for T.B.I. plate bolts
③ With integral intake manifold cast into head—18–23 for 4 end bolts, 30–35 for all others.

TORQUE SPECIFICATIONS
Firebird
(All readings in ft. lbs.)

Year	Engine No. Cyl. Displacement (cu. in.)	Cylinder Head Bolts	Rod Bearing Bolts	Main Bearing Bolts	Crankshaft Bolt	Flywheel to Crankshaft Bolts	Manifold	
							Intake	Exhaust
'78–'79	6-231 Buick	80	40	100	225	60	45	25
	8-301 Pont.	95	30	70①	160	95	35	40
	8-305 Chev.	65	45	70	60	60	30	20
	8-350 Chev.	65	45	70	60	60	30	20
	8-400 Pont.	95	40	100②	160	95	35	40
	8-403 Olds.	130	42	80②	220	60	40	25
'80–'81	6-231 Buick	80	40	100	225	60	45	25
	8-265 Pont.	95	30	③	160	95	35	40
	8-301 Pont.	95	30	③	160	95	35	40
	8-301 Turbo Pont.	93	28	100	163	—	37	40
	8-305 Chev.	65	45	70	60	60	30	20
'82–'83	4-151 Pont.	85	32	70	160	44	29	44
	6-173 Chev.	65–75	34–40	63–74	66–84	45–55	20–25	22–28
	8-305 Chev.	65	45	70	60	60	30④	20
'84–'85	4-151 Pont.	85	32	70	160	44	29	44
	6-173 Chev.	70	37	69	60	46	30	20
	8-305 Chev.	65	45	70	60	60	30⑧	20

① Rear main—100
② Rear main—120
③ 7/16" bolt—70; 1/2" bolt—100; rear main bearing—100.
④ 20–34 for TBI plate bolts

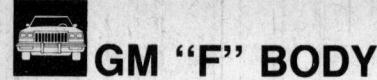

CRANKSHAFT AND CONNECTING ROD SPECIFICATIONS
Camaro
(All measurements are given in inches)

Year	Engine No. Cyl. Displacement (cu. in.)	Crankshaft				Connecting Rod		
		Main Brg Journal Dia.	Main Brg Oil Clearance	Shaft End-Play	Thrust on No.	Journal Diameter	Oil Clearance	Side Clearance
'78	6-250	2.2979–2.2994	.0010–.0024② ④	.0020–.0060	7	1.9928–2.000	.0010–.0026	.0060–.0170
	8-305, 350	①	③	.0020–.0060	5	2.0986–2.0998	.0013–.0035	.0080–.0140
'79	6-250	2.2979–2.2994	.0010–.0024② ④	.0020–.0060	7	1.999–2.000	.0010–.0026	.0060–.0170
	8-305, 350	①	③	.0020–.0060	5	2.0986–2.0998	.0013–.0035	.0060–.0140
'80–'81	6-229	①	③	.0020–.0060	4	2.0986–2.0998	.0013–.0035	.0060–.0140
	6-231	2.4995	.0004–.0015	.0040–.0080	2	2.2495–2.2487	.0005–.0026	.0060–.0270
	8-267	①	③	.0020–.0060	5	2.0986–2.0998	.0013–.0035	.0060–.0140
	8-305	①	③	.0020–.0060	5	2.0986–2.0998	.0013–.0035	.0060–.0140
	8-350	①	③	.0020–.0060	5	2.0986–2.0998	.0013–.0035	.0060–.0140
'82–'83	4-151	2.300	.0005–.0022	.0035–.0085	5	2.000	.0005–.0026	.0060–.0220
	6-173	2.493–2.494	.0017–.0029	.0019–.0066	3	1.998–1.999	.0014–.0035	.0060–.0170
	8-305	①	③	.0020–.0060	5	2.098–2.099	.0018–.0039	.0080–.0140
'84–'85	4-151	2.300	.0005–.0022	.0035–.0085	5	2.000	.0005–.0026	.0060–.0220
	6-173	2.493–2.494	.0017–.0029	.0019–.0066	3	1.998–1.999	.0014–.0035	.0060–.0170
	8-305	①	③	.0020–.0060	5	2.098–2.099	.0018–.0039	.0080–.0140

① No. 1—2.4484–2.4493
   Nos. 2, 3, 4—2.4481–2.4490
   No. 5—2.4479–2.4488
② Auto. trans.: No. 1—0.0019–0.0031
   Nos. 2, 3, 4—0.0013–0.0025
   No. 5—0.0023–0.0033
  Man. trans.: Nos. 1, 2, 3, 4—0.0013–0.0025
   No. 5—0.0023–0.0033

③ No. 1—0.0008–0.0020
   Nos. 2, 3, 4—0.0011–0.0023
   No. 5—0.0017–0.0032

CRANKSHAFT AND CONNECTING ROD SPECIFICATIONS
Firebird
(All measurements are given in inches)

Year	Engine Displacement (cu. in.)	Crankshaft				Connecting Rod		
		Main Brg. Journal Dia.	Main Brg. Oil Clearance	Shaft End-Play	Thrust on No.	Journal Diameter	Oil Clearance	Side Clearance
'78	6-231	2.500	.0003–.0017	.0030–.0090	2	2.000	.0005–.0026	.0060–.0270①
	8-305	④	⑤	.0020–.0070	5	2.099–2.100	.0013–.0035	.0060–.0160
	8-350	④	⑤	.0020–.0070	5	2.099–2.100	.0013–.0035	.0060–.0160
	8-400	3.000	.0002–.0020	.0030–.0090	4	2.250	.0005–.0025	.0060–.0220
	8-403	②	③	.0035–.0135	3	2.120	.0005–.0026	.0060–.0200

CRANKSHAFT AND CONNECTING ROD SPECIFICATIONS
Firebird
(All measurements are given in inches)

Year	Engine Displacement (cu. in.)	Crankshaft				Connecting Rod		
		Main Brg. Journal Dia.	Main Brg. Oil Clearance	Shaft End-Play	Thrust on No.	Journal Diameter	Oil Clearance	Side Clearance
'79	6-231	2.500	.0003–.0018	.0030–.0090	2	2.000	.0005–.0026	.0060–.0270 ①
	8-301	3.000	.0002–.0020	.0030–.0090	4	2.250	.0005–.0025	.0060–.0220 ①
	8-305	⑥	⑤	.0020–.0060	5	2.098–2.099	.0013–.0035	.0060–.0140
	8-350	⑥	⑤	.0020–.0060	5	2.098–2.099	.0013–.0035	.0060–.0140
	8-400	3.000	.0002–.0020	.0030–.0090	4	2.250	.0005–.0025	.0060–.0220
	8-403	②	③	.0035–.0135	3	2.120	.0005–.0026	.0060–.0200
'80–'81	6-231	2.499	.0003–.0018	.0030–.0090	2	2.000	.0005–.0026	.0060–.0230
	8-265	3.000	.0002–.0018	.0030–.0090	4	2.250	.0005–.0025	.0060–.0220 ①
	8-301	3.000	.0002–.0018	.0030–.0090	4	2.250	.0005–.0025	.0060–.0220 ①
	8-305	⑥	⑦	.0020–.0060	5	2.098–2.099	.0030	.0060–.0140
'82–'83	4-151	2.300	.0005–.0022	.0035–.0085	5	2.000	.0005–.0026	.0060–.0220
	6-173	2.493–2.494	.0017–.0029	.0019–.0066	3	1.998–1.999	.0014–.0035	.0060–.0170
	8-305	⑥	⑤	.0020–.0060	5	2.098–2.099	.0018–.0039	.0080–.0140
'84–'85	4-151	2.300	.0005–.0022	.0035–.0085	5	2.000	.0005–.0026	.0060–.0220
	6-173	2.493–2.494	.0017–.0029	.0019–.0066	3	1.998–1.999	.0014–.0035	.0060–.0170
	8-305	⑥	⑤	.0020–.0060	5	2.098–2.099	.0018–.0039	.0080–.0140

① Total for two connecting rods
② No. 1: 2.4988–2.4998
  No.'s 2, 3, 4, 5: 2.4985–2.4995
③ No.'s 1, 2, 3, 4: .0005–.0021
  No. 5: .0031
④ No.'s 1, 2, 3, 4: 2.4502
  No. 5: 2.4508

⑤ No. 1: .0008–.0020
  No.'s 2, 3, 4: .0011–.0023
  No. 5: .0017–.0033
⑥ No. 1: 2.4484–2.4493
  No.'s 2, 3, 4: 2.4481–2.4490
  No. 5: 2.4479–2.4488

⑦ No. 1: .001–.0015
  No.'s 2, 3, 4: .001–.0025
  No. 5: .0025–.0035

CAMSHAFT SPECIFICATIONS
Camaro
(All measurements in inches. To convert inches to metric units, refer to Metric Information section.)

Year	Engine Type/Disp. L(cu in.)	Journal Diameter					Lobe Lift		Camshaft End Play
		1	2	3	4	5	Intake	Exhaust	
'78–'79	4.1(6–250)	All 1.8677–1.8697					0.2217	0.2315	0.003–0.008
	5.0(8–305)	All 1.8682–1.8692					0.2485	0.2733 ①	0.004–0.012
	5.7(8–350)	All 1.8682–1.8692					0.2600	0.2733	0.004–0.012

C639

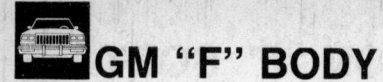

CAMSHAFT SPECIFICATIONS
Camaro
(All measurements in inches. To convert inches to metric units, refer to Metric Information section.)

Year	Engine Type/Disp. L(cu in.)	Journal Diameter					Lobe Lift		Camshaft End Play
		1	2	3	4	5	Intake	Exhaust	
'80–'81	3.8(6–229)	All 1.8682–1.8692					0.3570	0.3900	0.004–0.012
	3.8(6–231)	All 1.7850–1.7860					NA	NA	NA
	4.4(8–267)	All 1.8682–1.8692					0.3570	0.3900	0.004–0.012
	5.0(8–305)	All 1.8682–1.8692					0.2484	0.2667	0.004–0.012
	5.7(8–350)	All 1.8682–1.8692					0.2600	0.2733	0.004–0.012
'82	2.5(4–151)	All 1.8690					0.3980	0.3980	0.0015–0.0050
	2.8(6–173)	All 1.8976–1.8996					0.2350	0.2660	NA
	5.0(8–305)	All 1.8682–1.8692					0.2380②	0.2600②	0.004–0.012
'83	2.5(4–151)	All 1.8690					0.3980	0.3980	0.0015–0.0050
	2.8(6–173)	All 1.8976–1.8996					0.2350	0.2660	NA
	5.0(8–305)	All 1.8682–1.8692					0.2340③④	0.2570③④	0.004–0.012
'84–'85	2.5(4–151)	All 1.8690					0.3980	0.3980	0.0015–0.0050
	2.8(6–173)	All 1.8976–1.8996					0.2350	0.2660	NA
	5.0(8–305)	All 1.8682–1.8692					0.2340③④	0.2570③④	0.004–0.012

NA—Not available
① '78–'79 0.2267
② TBI engine 0.2600 intake—0.2730 exhaust
③ TBI engine 0.2570 intake—0.2690 exhaust
④ 4–bbl. High Output engine 0.2690 intake—0.2760 exhaust

CAMSHAFT SPECIFICATIONS
Firebird
(All measurements in inches. To convert inches to metric units, refer to Metric Information section.)

Year	Engine Type/Disp. L(cu in.)	Journal Diameter					Lobe Lift		Camshaft End Play
		1	2	3	4	5	Intake	Exhaust	
'78–'79	3.8(6–231)	All 1.7850–1.7860					NA	NA	NA
	4.9(8–301)	All 1.9000					NA	NA	NA
	5.0(8–305)	All 1.8682–1.8692					0.2485	0.2733①	0.004–0.012
	5.7(8–350)Pont.	All 1.7850–1.7860					NA	NA	NA
	5.7(8–350)Olds.	2.0357–2.0365	2.0157–2.0165	1.9957–1.9965	1.9757–1.9765	1.9557–1.9565	NA	NA	0.011–0.077
	5.7(8–350)Chev.	All 1.8682–1.8692					0.2600	0.2733	0.004–0.012
	6.4(8–400)	All 1.9000					NA	NA	NA
	6.6(8–403)	2.0357–2.0365	2.0157–2.0165	1.9957–1.9965	1.9757–1.9765	1.9557–1.9565	NA	NA	0.011–0.077
'80–'81	3.8(6–231)	All 1.7850–1.7860					NA	NA	NA
	4.3(8–265)	All 1.9000					NA	NA	NA
	4.9(8–301)	All 1.9000					NA	NA	NA
	5.0(8–305)	All 1.8682–1.8692					0.2484	0.2667	0.004–0.012

CAMSHAFT SPECIFICATIONS
Firebird
(All measurements in inches. To convert inches to metric units, refer to Metric Information section.)

Year	Engine Type/Disp. L(cu in.)	Journal Diameter					Lobe Lift		Camshaft End Play
		1	2	3	4	5	Intake	Exhaust	
'82	2.5(4–151)	All 1.8690					0.3980	0.3980	0.0015–0.0050
	2.8(6–173)	All 1.8976–1.8996					0.2350	0.2660	NA
	5.0(8–305)	All 1.8682–1.8692					0.2380②	0.2600②	0.004–0.012
'83	2.5(4–151)	All 1.8690					0.3980	0.3980	0.0015–0.0050
	2.8(6–173)	All 1.8976–1.8996					0.2350	0.2660	NA
	5.0(8–305)	All 1.8682–1.8692					0.2340③④	0.2570③④	0.004–0.012
'84–'85	2.5(4–151)	All 1.8690					0.3980	0.3980	0.0015–0.0050
	2.8(6–173)	All 1.8976–1.8996					0.2350	0.2660	NA
	5.0(8–305)	All 1.8682–1.8692					0.2340③④	0.2570③④	0.004–0.012

NA—Not available
① '78–'79 0.2267
② TBI engine 0.2600 intake—0.2730 exhaust
③ TBI engine 0.2570 intake—0.2690 exhaust
④ 4–bbl. High Output engine 0.2690 intake—0.2760 exhaust

RING SPECIFICATIONS
Camaro
(All measurements are given in inches)

Year	Engine No. of Cyl.- Displacement (Cu. In.)	Ring Gap			Ring Side Clearance		
		Top Compression	Bottom Compression	Oil Control	Top Compression	Bottom Compression	Oil Control
'82–'83	4-151	.0100–.0220	.0100–.0270	.0150–.0550	.0015–.0030	.0015–.0030	.0010–.0050
'82–'83	6-173	.0098–.0196	.0098–.0196	.0020–.0550	.0011–.0027	.0015–.0037	.0078 max.
'80–'81	6-229	.0100–.0200	.0100–.0250	.0150–.0550	.0012–.0032	.0012–.0032	.0020–.0070
'80–'81	6-231	.0100–.0200	.0100–.0200	.0150–.0350	.0030–.0050	.0030–.0050	.0035 max.
'78–'79	6-250	.0100–.0200	.0100–.0200	.0150–.0550	.0012–.0027	.0012–.0032	.0000–.0050
'80–'83	8-267, 305	.0100–.0200	.0100–.0250	.0150–.0550	.0012–.0032	.0012–.0032	.0020–.0070
'78–'81	8-350	.0100–.0200	.0100–.0250	.0150–.0550	.0012–.0032	.0012–.0032	.0020–.0070
'84–'85	4-151	.0100–.0220	.0100–.0270	.0150–.0550	.0015–.0030	.0015–.0030	.0010–.0050
	6-173	.0098–.0196	.0098–.0196	.0020–.0550	.0011–.0027	.0015–.0037	.0078 max.
	8-305	.0100–.0200	.0100–.0250	.0150–.0550	.0012–.0032	.0012–.0032	.0020–.0070

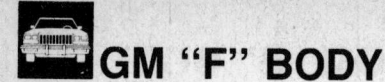

RING SPECIFICATIONS
Firebird
(All measurements are given in inches)

Year	Engine No. of Cyl.- Displacement (Cu. In.)	Ring Gap			Ring Side Clearance		
		Top Compression	Bottom Compression	Oil Control	Top Compression	Bottom Compression	Oil Control
'78	8-305, 350 Chev.	.0100–.0200	.0100–.0250	.0100–.0350	.0012–.0032	.0012–.0027	.0000–.0050
'79–'83	8-305, 350 Chev.	.0100–.0200	.0100–.0250	.0150–.0550	.0012–.0032	.0012–.0032	.0020–.0070
'78	8-400 Pont.	.0100–.0200	.0100–.0200	.0150–.0550	.0015–.0035	.0015–.0035	.0015–.0035
'79	8-400 Pont.	.0090–.0190	.0050–.0150	.0150–.0350	.0015–.0035	.0015–.0035	.0015–.0035
'79–'81	8-265, 301 Pont.	.0100–.0200	.0100–.0200	.0150–.0550	.0015–.0035	.0015–.0035	.0015–.0035
'78–'79	8-403 Olds.	.0100–.0200	.0100–.0200	.0150–.0550	.0020–.0040	.0020–.0040	.0006–.0096
'78	6-231 Buick	.0100–.0200	.0100–.0200	.0150–.0350	.0030–.0050	.0030–.0050	.0035 max.

PISTON CLEARANCE
Camaro

Year	Engine No. Cyl.- Displacement (cu. in.)	Piston-to-Bore Clearance (in.)
'78–'79	6-250	.0010–.0020
	8-305, 350	.0007–.0017①
'80–'81	6-229	.0007–.0017①
	6-231	.0008–.0020②
	8-267	.0007–.0017①
	8-305	.0007–.0017①
	8-350	.0007–.0017①
'82–'83	4-151	.0017–.0033③
	6-173	.0016–.0027
	8-305	.0007–.0027①
'84–'85	4-151	.0017–.0033③
	6-173	.0016–.0027
	8-305	.0007–.0027①

① .75" below piston pin centerline
② 2.5" from top of cylinder (bore); across piston pin centerline (piston)
③ 2.25" from top of cylinder (bore); 1¹³⁄₁₆" from top of piston

RING SPECIFICATIONS
Firebird
(All measurements are given in inches)

Year	Engine No. of Cyl.- Displacement (Cu. In.)	Ring Gap			Ring Side Clearance		
		Top Compression	Bottom Compression	Oil Control	Top Compression	Bottom Compression	Oil Control
'79–'81	6-231 Buick	.0130– .0230	.0130– .0230	.0150– .0350	.0030– .0050	.0030– .0050	.0035 max.
'82–'83	4-151 Pont.	.0100– .0220	.0100– .0270	.0150– .0550	.0015– .0030	.0015– .0030	.0010– .0050
'82–'83	6-173 Chev.	.0098– .0196	.0098– .0196	.0200– .0550	.0011– .0027	.0015– .0037	.0078 max.
'84–'85	4-151	.0100– .0220	.0100– .0270	.0150– .0550	.0015– .0030	.0015– .0030	.0010– .0050
	6-173	.0098– .0196	.0098– .0196	.0020– .0550	.0011– .0027	.0015– .0037	.0078 max.
	8-305	.0100– .0200	.0100– .0250	.0150– .0550	.0012– .0032	.0012– .0032	.0020– .0070

PISTON CLEARANCE
Firebird

Year	Engine	Piston-to-Bore Clearance (in.)
'78–'79	6-231 Buick	.0008–.0020④
	8-301 Pont.	.0025–.0033④
	8-305 Chev.	.0007–.0027①
	8-350 Chev.	.0007–.0027①
	8-400 Pont.	.0025–.0033④
	8-403 Olds.	.0008–.0018②
'80–'81	6-231 Buick	.0008–.0020④
	8-265 Pont.	.0017–.0025④
	8-301 Pont.	.0017–.0025④
	8-305 Chev.	.0007–.0027
'82–'83	4-151 Pont.	.0017–.0033⑤
	6-173 Chev.	.0016–.0027
	8-305 Chev.	.0007–.0027④
'84–'85	4-151	.0017–.0033③
	6-173	.0016–.0027
	8-305	.0007–.0027①

① .75" below piston pin C/L
② 1.11" from top of piston
③ Top of skirt
④ 2.5" from top of cylinder (bore); across piston pin centerline (piston)
⑤ 2.25" from top of cylinder (bore); 1¹³/₁₆" from top of piston

WHEEL ALIGNMENT SPECIFICATIONS
Firebird

Year	Caster		Camber		Toe-in (in.)	Steering Axis Inclin.
	Range (deg)	Pref Setting (deg)	Range (deg)	Pref Setting (deg)		
'78	½P to 1½P	1P	½P to 1½P	1P	1/16 to 3/16	10.50
'79–'81	½P to 1½P	1P	½P to 1½P	1P	1/16 to 3/16	10.35
'82–'83	2½P to 3½P	3P	½P to 1½P	1P	①	NA
'84–'85	2½P to 3½P	3P	½P to 1½P	1P	①	NA

① Except Trans Am—.2° ± .05°; Trans Am—.15° ± .05°
N—Negative
P—Positive
NA—Not available

WHEEL ALIGNMENT SPECIFICATIONS
Camaro

Year	Caster		Camber		Toe-in (in.)	Steering Axis Inclin (deg)
	Range(deg)	Pref Setting (deg)	Range (deg)	Pref Setting (deg)		
'78	1N to 3P	1P	½N to 2½P	1P	1/16–3/16	10½
'79–'81	0 to 2P	1P	1/5N to 1⅘P	1P	1/16–¼	10.35①
'82–'83	2½P to 3½P	3P	½P to 1½P	1P	②	NA
'84–'85	2½P to 3½P	3P	½P to 1½P	1P	②	NA

① At 1° camber
② Except Z28—.2° ± 0.5°; Z-28—.15° ± .05°
N—Negative
P—Positive
NA—Not available

CHARGING SYSTEM

Alternator

REMOVAL & INSTALLATION

NOTE: For alternator testing and diagnosis, refer to "Charging and Starting" of the Unit Repair section.

1. Disconnect the battery ground cable to prevent diode damage.
2. Tag and disconnect the alternator wiring.
3. Remove the alternator brace bolt. If the car is equipped with power steering, loosen the pump brace and mount nuts. Detach the drive belt(s).
4. Support the alternator and remove the mount bolt(s). Remove the unit from the vehicle.
5. Installation is the reverse of the previous steps. Tighten belt enough to allow approximately ½ in. of play on the longest run between pulleys.

Voltage Regulator

The voltage regulator is electronic and is housed within the alternator. Adjustments to the regulator are not possible. Should replacement of the regulator become necessary, the alternator must be disassembled.

STARTING SYSTEM

Starter

REMOVAL & INSTALLATION

NOTE: For starter overhaul procedures, refer to "Charging and Starting" in the Unit Repair section.

1. Disconnect the battery cable.
2. Raise the car to a convenient working height, and support with jackstands.
3. Disconnect all wiring from the starter solenoid. Replace each nut as the connector

is removed, as thread sizes differ from connector to connector. Note or tag the wiring positions for installation.

4. Remove the front bracket from the starter and the two mounting bolts. On engines with a solenoid heat shield, remove the front bracket upper bolt and detach the bracket from the starter.

NOTE: Starter removal on certain models may necessitate the removal of the frame support. This support runs from the corner of the frame to the front crossmember. To remove:

a. Loosen the mounting bolt that attaches the support to the corner of the frame.

b. Loosen and remove the mounting bolt that attaches the support to the front crossmember and then swing the support out of the way.

c. Installation is in the reverse order of removal.

5. Remove the front bracket bolt or nut. Lower the starter front end first, and then remove the unit from the car.

6. Reverse the removal procedures to install the starter. Torque the two mounting bolts to 25–35 ft. lbs.

NOTE: If shims were placed between the starter and engine block, they must be replaced in their original locations.

Starter Solenoid

REMOVAL & INSTALLATION

1. Remove the starter assembly as previously outlined.

2. Remove the fastener which attaches the field strap to the solenoid.

3. Remove the solenoid attaching screws.

4. Twist the solenoid and remove it from the starter.

5. Installation is the reverse of the previous steps.

IGNITION SYSTEM

All models use High Energy Ignition systems (electronic). Periodic adjustments to the distributor are not required, since no breaker points are used.

NOTE: For electronic ignition system description, testing and service, refer to "Electronic Ignition Systems" in the Unit Repair section.

Distributor

REMOVAL & INSTALLATION

1. Disconnect the ground cable from the battery.

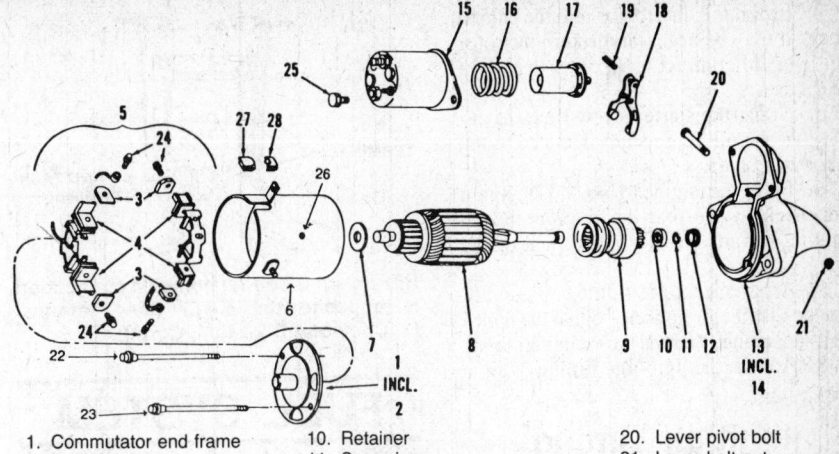

1. Commutator end frame
2. Bushing (not pictured)
3. Brush
4. Brush holder
5. Brush and holder package
6. Field and frame assembly
7. Washer
8. Armature
9. Drive assembly
10. Retainer
11. Snap-ring
12. Thrust washer
13. Drive end housing
14. Bushing (not pictured)
15. Solenoid assembly
16. Plunger spring
17. Plunger
18. Lever
19. Roll pin
20. Lever pivot bolt
21. Lever bolt nut
22. Through bolt
23. Through bolt
24. Brush screw
25. Bolt
26. Field retaining screw
27. Plug
28. Grommet

Exploded view of a typical starter

2. Tag and disconnect the feed and module terminal connectors from the distributor cap.

3. Disconnect the hose at the vacuum advance unit, if so equipped

4. Depress and release the 4 distributor cap-to-housing retainers and lift off the cap assembly.

5. Using crayon or chalk, make locating marks on the rotor and module and on the distributor housing and engine for installation purposes.

6. Loosen and remove the distributor clamp bolt and clamp, and lift the distributor out of the engine. Noting the relative position of the rotor and module alignment marks, make a second mark on the rotor to align it with the one mark on the module.

7. With a new O-ring on the distributor housing and the second mark on the rotor aligned with the mark on the module, install the distributor, taking care to align the mark on the housing with the one on the engine. It may be necessary to lift the distributor and turn the rotor slightly to align the gears and the oil pump driveshaft.

8. With the respective marks aligned, install the clamp and bolt finger-tight.

9. Install and secure the distributor cap.

10. Connect the feed and module connectors to the distributor cap.

11. Connect a timing light to the engine and plug the vacuum hose, if so equipped.

12. Connect the ground cable to the battery.

13. Start the engine and set the timing.

NOTE: If equipped with electronic spark timing (EST) which is note equipped with a vacuum advance, the four wire connector must be separated before initial timing can be adjusted.

14. Turn the engine off and tighten the distributor clamp bolt. Disconnect the timing light and unplug and connect the hose

to the vacuum advance. If the engine was disturbed with the distributor removed, install the distributor in the following manner:

1. Turn the engine to bring No. 1 piston to the top of its compression stroke. This may be determined by inserting a rag into the No. 1 spark plug hole and slowly turning the engine over. When the timing mark on the crankshaft pulley aligns with the 0 on the timing scale and the rag is blown out by compression, No. 1 piston is at top-dead-center (TDC).

2. Install the distributor to the engine block so that the vacuum advance unit points in the correct direction.

3. Turn the rotor so that it will point to the No. 1 terminal in the cap.

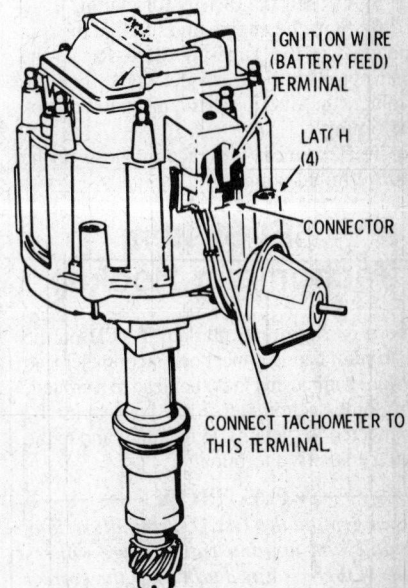

IGNITION WIRE (BATTERY FEED) TERMINAL

LATCH (4)

CONNECTOR

CONNECT TACHOMETER TO THIS TERMINAL

HEI coil-in-cap distributor tachometer hookup

4. Install the distributor into the engine block. It may be necessary to turn the rotor a little in either direction in order to engage the gears.

5. Crank the starter a few times to ensure that the oil pump shaft is mated to the distributor shaft.

6. Bring the engine to No. 1 TDC again and check to see that the rotor is indeed pointing toward the No. 1 terminal of the cap.

7. After correct positioning is assured, turn the distributor housing so that the points are just opening. Tighten the retaining clamp.

8. Adjust the ignition timing with a timing light.

Ignition Timing

ADJUSTMENT

Timing marks are located on the front engine cover and on the harmonic balancer or pulley.

1. Disconnect the distributor vacuum advance hose from the distributor and plug the hose.

2. On most 1981 and later models with the EST distributor disconnect the four terminal connector from the wiring harness.

NOTE: If the instructions on your underhood sticker differ from these procedures, follow your underhood sticker's directions.

3. Make sure the timing marks are clean and readable. The engine must be at normal operating temperature.

NOTE: It may be necessary to put a small amount of white paint or chalk on the timing marks to make them more visible.

4. Connect a timing light to No. 1 cylinder.

5. Loosen the distributor clamp.

6. Start the engine and run it at the rpm specified in the Tune-up chart. Rotate the distributor until the correct marks line up. Tighten the distributor clamp and recheck the timing.

7. Reconnect the vacuum hose or the four terminal connector.

HEI System Tachometer Hookup

There is a terminal marked TACH on the distributor cap. Connect one tachometer lead to this terminal and the other lead to a ground. On some tachometers, the leads must be connected to the TACH terminal and to the battery positive terminal.

CAUTION

Never ground the TACH terminal; serious module and ignition coil damage will result. If there is any doubt as to the correct tachometer hookup, check with the tachometer manufacturer.

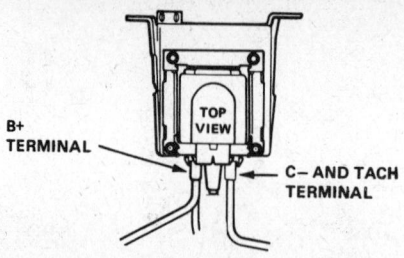

B+ TERMINAL

TOP VIEW

C− AND TACH TERMINAL

HEI external coil tachometer connection is opposite the BATT (B+) terminal (© Chevrolet Div., G.M. Corp.)

FUEL SYSTEM

Information on the fuel gauge, carburetor, and carburetor specifications can be found in the Unit Repair section.

Carburetors

REMOVAL & INSTALLATION

1. Remove the air cleaner and its gasket.
2. Disconnect the fuel and vacuum lines from the carburetor.
3. Disconnect the choke electrical connector.
4. Disconnect the throttle linkage.
5. On automatic transmission cars, disconnect the throttle valve linkage if so equipped.
6. Disconnect the EGR line, if so equipped.
7. Remove the idle stop solenoid, if so equipped.
8. Remove the carburetor attaching nuts and/or bolts, gasket or insulator, and remove the carburetor.
9. Install the carburetor using the reverse of the removal procedure. Use a new gasket.

Idle Speed Adjustments

CAMARO

Through 81

All models have sealed idle mixture screws; in most cases these are concealed under staked-in plugs. Idle mixture is adjustable only during carburetor overhaul, and requires the addition of propane as an artificial mixture enrichener.

See the emission control label in the engine compartment for procedures and specifications not supplied here. Prepare the car for adjustment (engine warm, choke open, fast idle screw off the fast idle cam) as per the label instructions.

1 BBL

1. Run the engine to normal operating temperature.
2. Make sure that the choke is fully opened.

3. Turn the A/C Off and disconnect the vacuum line at the vapor canister. Plug the line.

4. Set the parking brake, block the drive wheels and place the transmission in Drive (AT) or Neutral (MT). Connect a tachometer to the engine according to the manufacturer's instructions.

5. Turn the solenoid assembly to achieve the solenoid-on speed.

6. Disconnect the solenoid wire and turn the 1/8 inch hex screw in the solenoid end, to achieve the solenoid-off speed.

7. Remove the tachometer, connect the canister vacuum line and shut off the engine.

2 BBL AND 4 BBL (ALL BUT V8-350)

1. Run the engine to normal operating temperature.

2. Make sure that the choke is fully opened, turn the A/C Off, set the parking brake, block the drive wheels and connect a tachometer to the engine according to the manufacturer's instructions.

3. Disconnect and plug the vacuum hoses at the EGR valve and the vapor canister.

4. Place the transmission in Park (AT) or Neutral (MT).

5. Disconnect and plug the vacuum advance hose at the distributor. Check and adjust the timing.

6. Connect the distributor vacuum line.

7. Manual transmission cars without A/C and without solenoid: place the idle speed screw on the low step of the fast idle cam and turn the screw to achieve the specified idle speed.

Cars with A/C: set the idle speed screw to the specified rpm. Disconnect the compressor clutch wire and turn the A/C On. Open the throttle momentarily to extend the solenoid plunger. Turn the solenoid screw to obtain the specified rpm.

Automatic transmission cars without A/C; manual transmission cars without A/C, solenoid-equipped carburetor: momentarily open the throttle to extend the solenoid plunger. Turn the solenoid screw to obtain the specified rpm. Disconnect the solenoid wire and turn the idle speed screw to obtain the slow engine idle speed.

V8-350

1. Run the engine to normal operating temperature.

2. Set the parking brake and block the drive wheels.

3. Connect a tachometer to the engine according to the manufacturer's instructions.

4. Disconnect and plug the purge hose at the vapor canister. Disconnect and plug the EGR vacuum hose at the EGR valve.

5. Turn the A/C Off.

6. Place the transmission in Park (AT) or Neutral (MT).

7. Disconnect and plug the vacuum advance line at the distributor. Check and adjust the timing.

8. Connect the vacuum advance line.

Place the automatic transmission in Drive.

9. Manual transmission cars without A/C: adjust the idle stop screw to obtain the specified rpm. Cars with A/C: with the A/C off, adjust the idle stop screw to obtain the specified rpm. Disconnect the compressor clutch wire and turn the A/C on. Open the throttle slightly to allow the solenoid plunger to extend. Turn the solenoid screw to obtain the solenoid rpm listed on the underhood emission sticker.

10. Connect all hoses and remove the tachometer.

1982 and Later

Refer to the underhood specifications sticker for procedures regarding specific models. Idle mixture adjustments should not be attempted, except by professional service personnel.

——— **CAUTION** ———

Block the drive wheels and set the parking brake before performing idle adjustments.

WITH A/C

1. Turn the base idle speed screw to obtain the specified rpm.

2. Disconnect the A/C solenoid lead and open the throttle slightly to extend the solenoid plunger.

3. Turn the solenoid screw to the specified solenoid rpm.

WITHOUT A/C

1. Open the throttle slightly to fully extend the solenoid plunger if equipped.

2. Turn the solenoid screw to obtain the specified rpm (solenoid energized—if equipped).

3. Disconnect the solenoid electrical lead and turn the base idle speed screw to the specified base rpm.

FIREBIRD

Through 1981

231 V6 AND 305 V8

1. Run the engine until it reaches normal operating temperature. Make sure that the choke is open and the air conditioning is off.

2. Connect a tachometer and a timing light as detailed earlier in this chapter.

3. Set the parking brake and block the wheels.

4. Tag, disconnect and plug all vapor canister and EGR vacuum hoses.

5. Start the engine and place the transmission in Drive or Neutral.

6. Disconnect the vacuum advance hose and then set the timing as detailed earlier in this chapter.

7. Reconnect the vacuum advance hose and set the idle speed to specifications.

8. Connect all hoses and stop the engine.

301 V8

1. Run the engine until it reaches normal operating temperature. Make sure that the choke is fully open and the air conditioning is Off.

2. Connect a tachometer and a timing light as detailed earlier in this chapter.

3. Set the parking brake and block the wheels.

4. Disconnect the air conditioner compressor clutch lead wire.

5. Start the engine and place the transmission in Drive or Neutral.

6. Check and adjust the ignition timing.

7. Disconnect the purge hose at the vapor canister.

8. On cars with air conditioning: set the idle speed screw to obtain the specified rpm. Turn the A/C On. Open the throttle momentarily to ensure that the solenoid plunger is fully extended. Adjust the idle speed solenoid to the speed given on the underhood sticker. Turn the A/C Off.

9. On cars without air conditioning: turn the idle speed screw until you obtain the specified rpm.

10. Place the automatic transmission in Park.

11. Disconnect and plug the vacuum hose running from the EGR valve.

12. Adjust the fast idle screw on the second step of the fast idle cam until you obtain the specified rpm.

13. Stop the engine and reconnect the EGR vacuum hose, the vapor canister hose and the A/C compressor clutch connector.

350, 400 AND 403 V8's

1. Follow Steps 1–3 of the preceeding "301 V8" procedure.

2. Disconnect the purge hose from the vapor canister. On the 350 engine, you must plug the hose.

3. Disconnect and plug the vacuum hose leading from the EGR valve.

4. Start the engine and place the transmission in Park or Neutral.

5. Check and adjust the ignition timing.

NOTE: After checking the timing on the 400 engine with a manual transmission, do not reconnect the vacuum advance line.

6. Place the automatic transmission in Drive.

7. On models equipped with air conditioning: Turn the A/C On and then disconnect the electrical connector at the compressor clutch. Open the throttle momentarily to ensure that the solenoid plunger is fully extended. Adjust the solenoid screw to the specified rpm. Reconnect the compressor clutch connector and turn the A/C Off.

8. On models without air conditioning: turn the idle screw to obtain the specified rpm.

9. Reconnect any hoses previously disconnected and then shut off the engine.

1982 and Later

Refer to the underhood specifications sticker for procedures regarding specific models. Idle mixture adjustments should not be attempted, except by professional service personnel.

——— **CAUTION** ———

Block the drive wheels and set the parking brake before performing idle adjustment.

WITH A/C

1. Turn the base idle speed screw to obtain the specified rpm.

2. Disconnect the A/C solenoid lead and open the throttle slightly to extend the solenoid plunger.

3. Turn the solenoid screw to the specified solenoid rpm.

WITHOUT A/C

1. Open the throttle slightly to fully extend the solenoid plunger if equipped.

2. Turn the solenoid screw to obtain the specified rpm (solenoid energized—if equipped).

3. Disconnect the solenoid electrical lead and turn the base idle speed screw to the specified base rpm.

MIXTURE ADJUSTMENT—ALL MODELS

All models have sealed idle mixture screws; in most cases these are concealed under staked-in plugs. Idle mixture is adjustable only during carburetor overhaul, and requires the addition of propane as an artificial enrichener. The equipment necessary for this procedure is not readily available to the general public.

Throttle Body (Fuel) Injection (TBI)

NOTE: T.B.I. descriptions and service are found in "Fuel Injection" in the Unit Repair section.

Fuel Pump

REMOVAL & INSTALLATION

NOTE: Fuel pumps are not rebuildable—if defective, they must be replaced.

Carbureted Engines— Mechanical Pump

NOTE: When you connect the fuel pump outlet fitting, always use 2 wrenches to avoid damaging the pump.

1. Disconnect the negative battery cable at the battery.

2. Disconnect the fuel intake and outlet lines at the pump and plug the pump intake line.

3. On Chevrolet V6 and V8 engines, remove the upper bolt from the right front mounting boss. Insert a longer bolt (³⁄₈–16 × 2 in.) in this hole to hold the fuel pump pushrod.

4. Remove the two pump mounting bolts and lockwashers; remove the pump and its gasket.

C647

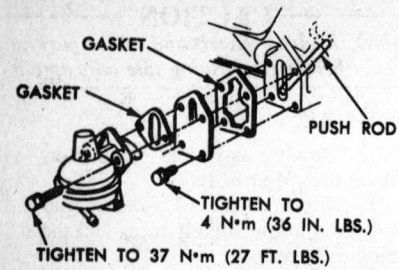

Typical mechanical fuel pump installation on a V8 engine (© Chevrolet Div., G.M. Corp.)

5. If the rocker arm pushrod is to be removed from V6 or V8, remove the two adapter bolts and lockwashers and remove the adaptor and its gasket.

6. Install the fuel pump with a new gasket reversing the removal procedure. Coat the mating surfaces with sealer.

7. Connect the fuel lines and check for leaks.

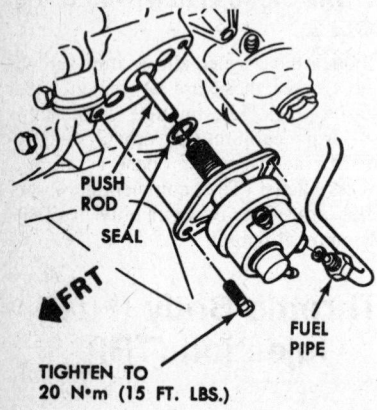

Mechanical fuel pump installation on the 173-V6 engine (© Chevrolet Div., G.M. Corp.)

Fuel Injected (TBI) Engines— Electric Pump

The electric pump used with fuel injected models is an integral part of the fuel tank (gauge) sending unit. The pump may be serviced separately after the pump/sending unit assembly is removed from the tank.

1. Relieve the fuel pressure from the fuel system as follows:

a. Remove the fuel pump fuse from the fuse block located in the passenger compartment.

b. Start the engine and allow it to run until it stalls due to lack of fuel.

c. Engage the starter for a few seconds to make sure that all pressure has been relieved.

d. Turn the ignition Off and reinstall the fuel pump fuse.

2. Disconnect the negative battery cable at the battery.

3. Remove the fuel filler cap and drain the fuel from the fuel tank.

4. Disconnect the exhaust pipe at the catalytic convertor and the rear hanger. Allow the exhaust system to hang over the rear axle assembly.

5. Remove the tailpipe and muffler heat shields.

6. Remove the fuel filler neck shield from behind the left rear tire.

7. Remove the rear suspension track bar and the track bar brace.

8. Disconnect the fuel pump/sending unit electrical connector, at the body harness connector.

CAUTION
DO NOT pry up on the cover connector, as the pump/sending unit wiring harness is an integral part of the sending unit.

9. Disconnect the flexible fuel lines from the metal fuel pipes at the tank.

10. Remove the fuel pipe retaining bracket on the left side and the brake line clip from the retaining bracket.

11. Position a jack under the rear axle assembly in order to support the rear axle.

12. Disconnect the lower ends of the shock absorbers, lower the axle assembly enough to release the tension on the coil springs. Remove the coil springs.

13. Lower the rear axle assembly as far as possible without causing damage to the brake lines and cables.

14. Remove the fuel tank strap bolts.

15. Remove the tank by rotating the front of the tank downward and sliding it to the right side.

16. Remove the fuel pump/sending unit from the tank, by loosening the cam nut (refer to the CAUTION, below). Remove the O-ring from beneath the unit. Replace the O-ring if defective.

CAUTION
Use EXTREME care when working around fuel. Do not smoke or use a drop light in the area. When removing the cam nut, use brass tools to tap the nut loose. DO NOT use standard metal tools, as sparks could be generated.

17. Separate the fuel pump from the sending unit and install the new pump in the same manner.

18. Installation of the fuel pump/send-

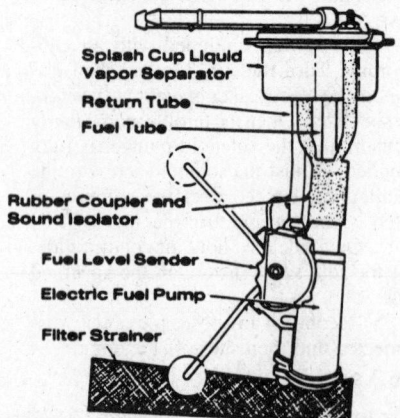

Electric fuel pump and fuel gauge meter assembly of a TBI-equipped engine (© Chevrolet Div., G.M. Corp.)

ing unit is performed in the reverse of Steps 1–17.

Fuel Filter

REPLACEMENT
Carbureted Engines

1. Disconnect the fuel line connection at the intake fuel filter nut. Plug the opening to prevent loss of fuel.

2. Remove the intake fuel filter nut from the carburetor with a box wrench or socket.

3. Remove the filter element and spring.

4. Check the element for restrictions by blowing on the cone end. Air should pass freely.

5. Clean or replace the element, as necessary.

6. Install the element spring, then the filter elements in the carburetor. Bronze filters should have the small section of the cone facing out.

7. Install a new gasket on the intake fuel nut. Install the nut in the carburetor body and tighten securely.

8. Install the fuel line and tighten the connector.

9. Check for leaks with the engine idling.

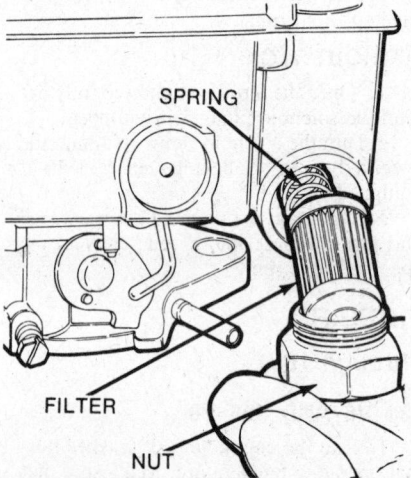

Typical fuel filter of carbureted engines (© Chevrolet Div., G.M. Corp.)

Fuel Injected Engines (TBI Equipped)

1. Relieve the system of pressure by following Step 1 of the fuel pump replacement procedure for TBI-equipped models.

2. Disconnect the fuel feed pipe nut from the fuel filter upper fitting.

3. Disconnect the remaining fuel line from the fuel filter.

4. On four cylinder models, loosen the filter bracket nut and remove the filter from the bracket. On eight cylinder models, lift the filter out of the filter bracket.

5. Installation is performed in the reverse order of the previous steps. Check for leaks after starting.

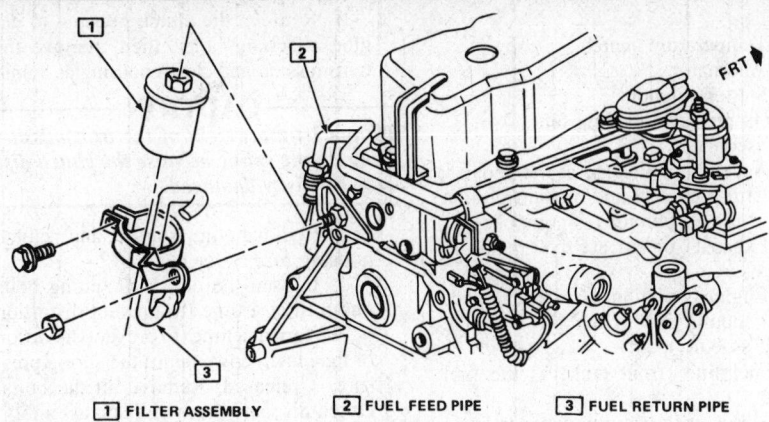

1 FILTER ASSEMBLY   **2** FUEL FEED PIPE   **3** FUEL RETURN PIPE

Fuel filter mounting on a TBI-equipped 151-4 cylinder engine (© Chevrolet Div., G.M. Corp.)

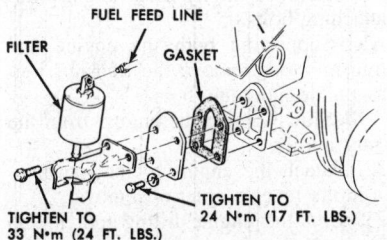

Fuel filter mounting on a TBI-equipped V8 engine. Note that the mounting location is the same as that for the fuel pump on carbureted engines (© Chevrolet Div., G.M. Corp.)

COOLING SYSTEM

Thermostat

REPLACEMENT

1. Drain the cooling system until the coolant level is below the thermostat.
2. Remove the air cleaner assembly (except on four cylinder models).
3. On four cylinder models, remove the upper radiator hose. It is not necessary to remove the hose on six and eight cylinder models, move the thermostat housing away from the thermostat, then lift the thermostat from the engine.
4. Clean the gasket mating surfaces of both the engine and the thermostat housing.
5. On models which use a housing-to-engine gasket, replace the thermostat and housing using a new gasket. Make sure that the thermostat spring is installed towards the engine; NOT the radiator.

— CAUTION —
DO NOT use sealant in place of the gasket on four cylinder models.

7. On models which use sealer in place of a gasket, apply a ⅛ in. bead of RTV

(Room Temperature Vulcanizing) sealer around the thermostat housing sealing surface of the engine. Be sure to run the RTV on the INSIDE of the housing bolt holes. Install the thermostat in the same manner as in step 6, then attach the thermostat housing.

8. On models with a gasket, torque the housing retaining bolts to approximately 20 ft. lbs.; on models with RTV only, torque the housing bolts to approximately 30 ft. lbs.

9. Start the engine, replenish the cooling system, and check for leakage.

Water Pump

REPLACEMENT

1. Drain the cooling system.
2. Loosen the fan pulley bolts.
3. Disconnect the heater hose(s) and lower radiator hose, at the water pump.
4. Loosen the alternator swivel bolt (remove the upper brace on V8s) and remove the alternator drive belt.
5. Disconnect the power steering and air conditioning belts.
6. Remove the fan and pulley.

NOTE: Viscous drive fans should not be stored horizontally. The silicone fluid can leak out of the fan assembly if it is not kept upright.

7. Remove the water pump-to-cylinder block bolts and the power steering-to-pump bolts (if so equipped). Remove the water pump. On four cylinder and inline-six engines, remove the pump by pulling it straight out of the block.

8. Install the pump on the block with a new gasket.
9. Install the pump pulley and the fan onto the pump.
10. Connect the hoses and refill the cooling system. Install the remaining components, bolts, and belts.
11. Start the engine, replenish the cooling system, and check for leaks.

Radiator

REMOVAL & INSTALLATION

Camaro to 1981

1. Disconnect the battery.
2. Drain the cooling system.
3. Disconnect the radiator upper and lower hoses and, if applicable, the transmission coolant lines. Remove the coolant recovery system line, if so equipped.
4. Remove the radiator upper panel if so equipped.
5. If there is a radiator shroud in front of the radiator, the radiator and shroud are removed as an assembly.
6. If there is a fan shroud, remove the shroud attaching screws and let the shroud hang on the fan.
7. Remove the radiator attaching bolts and remove the radiator.
8. Installation is the reverse of the removal procedure.

Firebird to 1981

1. Disconnect the battery.
2. Drain the coolant, then disconnect the upper and lower hoses.
3. Disconnect and plug the oil cooler lines, if equipped with automatic transmission.
4. Remove the upper fan shield (six-cylinder) or upper shroud bracket (V8). Remove the radiator hold-down bolts and lift the radiator and shroud assembly from the car.
6. To install, reverse the removal procedure, making sure that the automatic transmission fluid level is correct. Tighten the hold-down bolts to 12 ft. lbs.

1982 and Later All

1. Disconnect the negative battery cable at the battery.
2. Drain the radiator.
3. Remove the engine cooling fan. On models equipped with a fan clutch, the clutch must be set aside in an upright position to prevent seal leakage.
4. Disconnect the radiator hoses from the radiator.
5. If equipped with an automatic transmission, disconnect the transmission cooler lines from the radiator, then plug the lines to prevent the entrance of dirt.
6. Remove the fan shield assembly, if so equipped.
7. Unbolt and remove the radiator and shroud assembly by lifting the assembly straight up.

NOTE: The radiator assembly is held at the bottom by two cradles which are secured to the radiator support.

8. If a new radiator is to be installed, transfer the fittings from the old radiator to the new one.
9. Installation of the radiator is the reverse of Steps 1–7. Replenish the cooling system and check for leakage after the en-

gine has been started. If the vehicle has an automatic transmission, check the transmission fluid level and adjust the level as required.

EMISSION CONTROLS

NOTE: For information of the following emission control systems please refer to "Emission Controls" in the Unit Repair section.

- Positive Crankcase Ventilation
- Air Injection Reactor
- Pulsair
- Controlled Combustion System
- Evaportive Emission Control
- Early Fuel Evaporation System
- Catalytic Converter
- Exhaust Gas Recirculation
- Computer Controlled Catalytic Converter System (C-4)
- Computer Command Control (CCC)
- Deceleration Valve

ENGINE MECHANICAL

Engine

REMOVAL & INSTALLATION

The factory recommended procedure for engine removal is to remove the engine/transmission as a unit and then separate them outside of the car. In the process of removing the engine you will come across a number of steps which call for the removal of a separate component or system, i.e. "Disconnect the exhaust system" or "Remove the radiator." In all of these instances, a detailed removal procedure can be found elsewhere in this section.

It is virtually impossible to list each individual wire and hose which must be disconnected, simply because so many different model and engine combinations have been manufactured. Careful observation and common sense are the best possible additions to any repair procedure. Be absolutely sure to tag any wire or hose before disconnecting it, so that it may be reconnected properly during installation.

1. Remove the hood. Scribe lines around the hinges so that the hood can be installed in its original location.
2. Remove the air cleaner.
3. Disconnect the battery cables at the battery.
4. Remove the radiator and shroud.
5. Remove the fan blade and pulley.
6. Disconnect and label wires at:
    a. Emission control components
    b. Coil.
    c. Temperature switch.
    d. Alternator.
    e. Starter solenoid.
    f. Oil pressure sending unit.
7. Disconnect:
    a. Accelerator linkage at the pedal.
    b. Cruise control and/or transmission cable at the carburetor (as equipped).
    c. Exhaust pipes at the manifold flanges.
    d. Engine cooler lines, if so equipped.
    e. Vacuum line to the power brake unit, if so equipped.
    f. Fuel line (front tank) as the fuel pump.
    g. Hoses at the carbon canister.
8. If the car has air conditioning, unbolt the compressor, leaving the hoses attached. Set the compressor out of the way. *Do not disconnect any air conditioning refrigerant lines unless you are familiar with discharge procedures.* Escaping refrigerant can freeze any surface it contacts, including your skin and eyes.
9. Remove the power steering pump, leaving the hoses attached to the pump. Set the pump aside, out of the way.
10. Raise the car on a hoist.
11. Drain the crankcase.
12. Remove the driveshaft.

NOTE: If a plug for the driveshaft opening in the transmission is not available, drain the transmission.

13. Disconnect:
    a. Shift linkage at the transmission.
    b. Speedometer cable at the transmission.
    c. Transmission cooler lines, if so equipped.
    d. TCS switch at the transmission.
14. On vehicles with manual transmissions, disconnect the clutch linkage at the cross-shaft then remove the cross-shaft at the frame bracket.
15. Lower the vehicle, remove the rocker arm covers and install an engine lifting adapter on the cylinder heads.
16. Raise the engine enough to take the weight off the front mounts, then remove the front mount thru-bolts.
17. Remove the rear mount to crossmember bolts.

NOTE: Make sure, that the same number of transmission mount shims are reinstalled. These are used to adjust driveshaft angle.

18. Raise the engine enough to take the weight off the rear mount, then remove the crossmember.

NOTE: It is necessary to remove the mount from the transmission before the crossmember can be removed.

19. Remove the engine/transmission assembly as a unit.
20. To remove the clutch and manual transmission from the engine:
    a. Remove the clutch housing cover plate screws.
    b. Remove the clutch housing to engine attaching bolts, then, remove the transmission and clutch housing as a unit.

--- CAUTION ---
Do not let the weight of the transmission hang on the spline because the clutch disc may be easily damaged.

    c. Remove the starter and clutch housing rear cover plate.
    d. Loosen the clutch mounting bolts one turn at a time (to prevent distortion of one turn at a time (to prevent distortion of the clutch cover) until the spring pressure is released. Remove all the bolts, clutch disc and pressure plate assembly.
21. To remove the automatic transmission:
    a. Remove the starter and the converter housing underpan.
    b. Remove the flywheel to converter attaching bolts.
    c. Supporting both the engine and transmission, remove the transmission-to-engine mounting bolts.
    d. Slowly guide the engine from the transmission.
22. Attach the engine to the transmission in the reverse order of removal.
23. Bolt the engine lifting tool to the engine and then lower the engine and the transmission into the chassis as a unit. Guide the engine so as to align the front engine mounts with the mounts on the frame.
24. Install one rear transmission crossmember side bolt, swing the crossmember up under the transmission mount and install the bolt in the opposite side rail.
25. Align and install the rear mount bolts.
26. Install the engine front mount bolts and then remove the lifting tool from the engine.
27. Installation of the remaining components is in the reverse order of removal.

Exhaust Manifold

REMOVAL & INSTALLATION

Through 1981
INLINE SIX (250)

1. Disconnect negative (−) battery cable and remove air cleaner.
2. Remove the power steering and/or AIR pumps and brackets, where they are present. (You need not disconnect power-steering hoses—just support pump out of the way.)
3. Working from below, with the vehicle safely supported, disconnect the exhaust pipe at the manifold and at the catalytic converter bracket near the transmission mount. If the car uses an exhaust manifold mounted converter, disconnect the pipe at the bottom of the converter, and then remove the converter.
4. Working from above, remove the rear heat shield and accelerator cable bracket.
5. Remove the exhaust manifold bolts, and pull off the manifold.

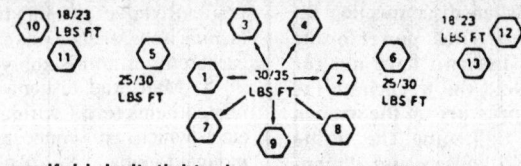
6. If the manifold is to be replaced, transfer the EFE valve, actuator, and rod assembly to the new part. Otherwise, inspect the manifold as described in Step 7.

7. Clean and then inspect the manifold carefully for cracks, and for free operation of the EFE valve. Repair or replace parts, and free up the EFE valve with solvent, if necessary.

8. Make sure the gasket surface is clean and free of deep scratches. Position a new gasket on the manifold, and then put the manifold in position on the block, and install the bolts hand tight.

9. Torque all bolts *in the proper order* to the specified torque (see illustration).

10. Install the rear heat shield and the accelerator cable bracket.

11. Working from underneath, connect the exhaust pipe at the manifold flange and connect the converter bracket at the transmission mount. If the car has an exhaust manifold converter, first install the converter to the manifold loosely; then attach the exhaust pipe to the converter and align the exhaust system; finally, torque the converter mounting bolts to 15 ft. lbs., in an X pattern, and torquing in several stages.

12. Working from above, install the power steering and A.I.R. pumps as necessary. Then, install the air cleaner and connect the battery ground cable.

V6 AND V8

1. If equipped with AIR, remove the air injector manifold assembly. The ¼ in. pipe threads in the manifold are straight threads. Do not use a ¼ in. tapered pipe tap to clean the threads.

2. Disconnect the battery.

3. If applicable, remove the air cleaner pre-heater shroud.

4. Remove the spark plug wire heat shields.

5. On the left exhaust manifold, disconnect and remove the alternator.

6. Disconnect the exhaust pipe from the manifold and hang it from the frame out of the way.

7. Bend the locktabs and remove the end bolts, then the center bolts. Remove the manifold.

NOTE: A ⁹⁄₁₆ in. thin wall 6-point socket, sharpened at the leading edge and tapped onto the head of the bolt, simplifies bending the locktabs.

When installing a new manifold on the right side on 1978 and later V8s you must transfer the heat stove from the old manifold to the new one.

8. Installation is the reverse of removal. Clean all mating surfaces and use new gaskets. Torque all bolts to specifications from the inside working out.

1982 and Later
FOUR CYLINDER ENGINE

1. Disconnect the negative battery cable at the battery.

2. Remove the air cleaner assembly,

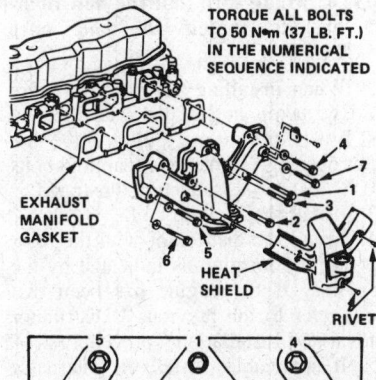

Exhaust manifold bolt tightening sequence—250-6 cylinder engine

being sure to mark any disconnected hoses for proper reinstallation.

3. Remove the E.F.I. preheat tube.

4. Remove the oxygen sensor and disconnect the exhaust pipe from the exhaust manifold.

5. Remove the engine oil level dipstick and tube.

6. Remove the exhaust manifold attaching bolts and remove the manifold.

7. Installation of the manifold is performed in the reverse of the previous steps. When torquing the bolts, follow the sequence in the accompanying diagram and tighten each bolt to 44 ft. lbs.

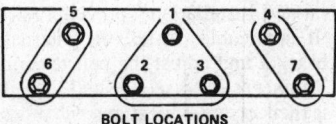

Exhaust manifold bolt tightening sequence—151-4 cylinder engine (© Chevrolet Div., G.M. Corp.)

V6 ENGINE—LEFT SIDE

1. Disconnect the negative battery cable at the battery.

2. Raise the vehicle and support it safely with jackstands.

3. Disconnect the exhaust pipe from the exhaust manifold.

4. Remove the four rear manifold bolts and the one nut, then lower the vehicle.

5. Disconnect the air management hoses and wires.

6. Remove the power steering bracket.

7. Remove the manifold attaching bolts and remove the manifold.

8. Installation is performed in the reverse of removal. Torque the manifold bolts from the inside working outward to 25 ft. lbs.

V6 ENGINE—RIGHT SIDE

1. Disconnect the negative battery cable at the battery.

2. Raise the vehicle and support it safely with jackstands.

3. Disconnect the exhaust pipe from the exhaust manifold.

4. Lower the vehicle and remove the exhaust manifold bolts.

5. Disconnect the air management hose and remove the manifold.

6. Installation is performed in the reverse of the previous steps. Tighten the manifold bolts in the same manner as that for the left side.

V8 ENGINE—LEFT SIDE

1. Disconnect the negative battery cable at the battery.

2. Mark and disconnect the spark plug wires from the spark plugs.

3. Disconnect the air injection system hoses.

4. On air conditioned models, unbolt the air conditioning compressor (without disconnecting the refrigerant hoses) and move it aside.

5. Unbolt the power steering pump (without disconnecting the hydraulic lines) and move it aside.

6. Remove the following brackets:
   a. Rear A/C and power steering adjusting bracket
   b. Lower power steering adjusting bracket

7. Raise the vehicle and support it safely with jackstands.

8. Disconnect the exhaust pipe from the exhaust manifold, then lower the vehicle.

9. Remove the manifold attaching bolts, then remove the manifold.

10. Installation is the reverse of the previous steps. Torque the manifold bolts to 20 ft. lbs., working from the inside bolts towards the outer bolts. Make sure that the mating surfaces are clean before installing the manifold.

V8 ENGINE—RIGHT SIDE

1. Disconnect the negative battery cable at the battery.

2. Mark and disconnect the spark plug wires from the spark plugs.

3. Disconnect the air injection system hoses and remove the air management valve.

4. Raise the vehicle and support it safely with jackstands.

5. Disconnect the exhaust pipe from the exhaust manifold, then lower the vehicle.

6. Remove the manifold attaching bolts, then remove the manifold. See step 10 of the previous procedure.

Intake Manifold

REMOVAL & INSTALLATION

NOTE: When servicing late model vehicles, be absolutely sure to mark vacuum hoses and wiring so that these items may be properly reconnected during in-

stallation. Also, when disconnecting fittings of metal lines (fuel, power brake vacuum), always use two flare nut (or line) wrenches. Hold the wrench on the large fitting with pressure on the wrench as if you were tightening the fitting (clockwise), THEN loosen and disconnect the smaller fitting from the larger fitting. If this is not done, damage to the line will result.

Through 1981
INLINE SIX CYLINDER ENGINE

The inline six uses an intake manifold which is cast as an integral part of the cylinder head. Refer to the "Cylinder Head Removal and Installation" procedure to remove the head/manifold unit.

CAMARO V6 AND V8 MODELS— EXCEPT THE 231 V6

1. Remove the air cleaner.
2. Drain the radiator.
3. Disconnect:
   a. Battery cables at the battery.
   b. Upper radiator and heater hoses at the manifold.
   c. Crankcase ventilation hoses as required.
   d. Fuel line at the carburetor.
   e. Accelerator linkage.
   f. Vacuum hose at the distributor.
   g. Power brake hose at the carburetor base or manifold, if applicable.
   h. Ignition coil and temperature sending switch wires.
4. Remove the distributor cap and scribe the rotor position relative to the distributor body.
5. Remove the distributor.
6. If applicable, remove the alternator upper bracket. As required, remove the air cleaner bracket, and accelerator bellcrank.

7. Remove the manifold-to-head attaching bolts, then remove the manifold and carburetor as an assembly.
8. Mark and disconnect all emission-related items (e.q.- wiring, vacuum hoses, etc.) which are connected to manifold-mounted items.
9. If the manifold is to be replaced, transfer the carburetor (and mounting studs), water outlet and thermostat (use a new gasket) heater hose adapter, EGR valve (use new gasket) and, if applicable, TVS switch(s) and the choke coil. Most engines use a carburetor heat choke tube which must be transferred to a new manifold.
10. Before installing the manifold, thoroughly clean the gasket and seal surfaces of the cylinder heads and manifold.
11. Install the manifold end seals, folding the tabs if applicable, and the manifold/head gaskets, using a sealing compound around the water passages.

NOTE: Make sure that the new manifold gaskets match the old ones EXACTLY.

12. When installing the manifold, care should be taken not to dislocate the end seals. It is helpful to use a pilot in the distributor opening. Tighten the manifold bolts to 30 ft. lbs. in the sequence illustrated.
13. Install the ignition coil.
14. Install the distributor with the rotor in its original location as indicated by the scribe line. If the engine has been disturbed, refer to the previous "Distributor Removal and Installation" procedure.
15. If applicable, install the alternator upper bracket and adjust the belt tension.
16. Connect all disconnected components at their original locations.
17. Fill the cooling system, start the engine, check for leaks and adjust the ignition timing and carburetor idle speed and mixture.

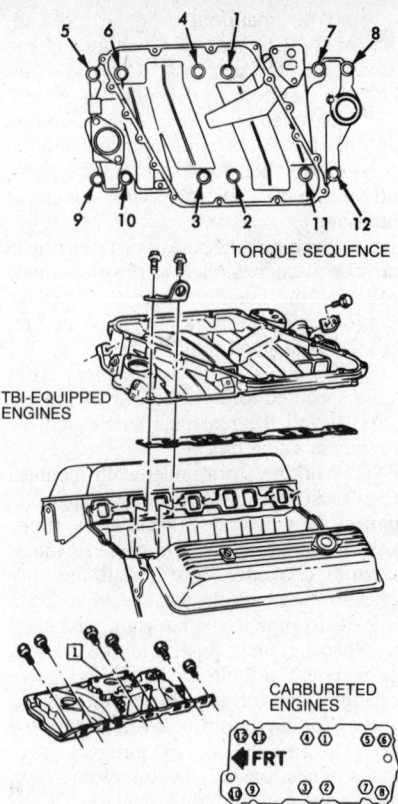

TORQUE SEQUENCE

Intake manifold bolt tightening sequence of all Chevrolet-built V8 engines. Note that the lower sequence is used for all carbureted engines, whereas the upper sequence is used for all TBI-equipped engines. (© Chevrolet Div., G.M. Corp.)

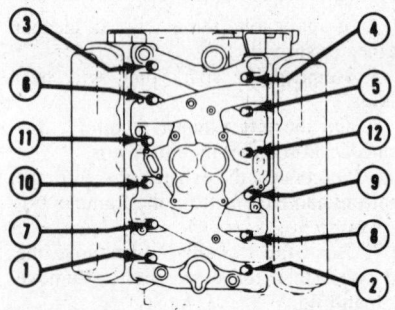

Intake manifold bolt tightening sequence for the Oldsmobile-built V8 engines

FIREBIRD V8 MODELS

NOTE: Refer to the previous Camaro procedure to service Chevrolet-built engines.

1. Drain the cooling system.
2. Remove the air cleaner assembly.
3. Remove the water outlet fitting allowing the radiator hose to remain attached.
4. As necessary, disconnect the heater hose from its fitting.
5. Disconnect the wire from the temperature gauge sending unit.
6. Remove the spark plug wire bracket.
7. If equipped with power brakes, remove the vacuum pipe from the carburetor.

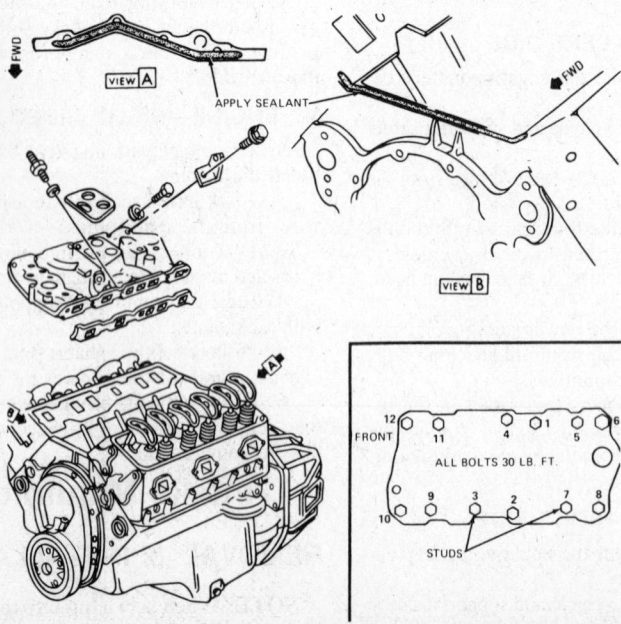

Intake manifold bolt tightening sequence for the Chevrolet-built 229-V6 engine (© Chevrolet Div., G.M. Corp.)

8. Disconnect the fuel line and the vacuum hoses.

9. Disconnect the crankcase vent hose from the manifold.

10. Disconnect the throttle linkage from the carburetor.

NOTE: If your car is equipped with a turbocharger, before proceeding any further you must remove the turbocharger and actuator assembly as detailed later in this chapter.

11. Remove the screws from the throttle control bracket.

12. Remove the EGR valve.

13. Remove the manifold bolts and lift off the manifold.

NOTE: It may be necessary to remove the distributor for clearance.

14. Install new gaskets on the heads keeping them in position with plastic gasket retainers.

15. Lower the intake manifold onto the engine and then install the O-ring seal.

16. Loosely install the bolts and nuts.

17. Install the throttle control bracket assembly.

18. Install a new O-ring seal (use the old one if undamaged) between the timing chain cover and the intake manifold and tighten the bolt to 15 ft. lbs.

19. Tighten all bolts and nuts evenly to 40 ft. lbs., starting from the center and working out.

20. To complete the installation, reverse the removal procedures.

ALL MODELS WITH THE 231 V6

NOTE: For these models, refer to the "Buick Rear Wheel Drive" car section for the appropriate procedure.

1982 and Later

151 FOUR CYLINDER ENGINE

1. Disconnect the negative battery cable at the battery.

2. Remove the air cleaner assembly.

3. Remove the PCV valve and hose.

4. Drain the cooling system.

5. Disconnect the fuel lines from the Throttle Body Injection (TBI) unit.

6. Mark and disconnect the vacuum lines and the electrical connections from the TBI unit.

7. Disconnect the linkage from the TBI unit (throttle, downshift, and/or cruise control, as applicable).

8. Remove the ignition coil (2 nuts, 1 bolt).

9. Disconnect the coolant inlet and outlet hoses from the intake manifold.

10. Remove the air conditioning compressor support brackets and the compressor. DO NOT disconnect the refrigerant lines from the compressor. Lay the compressor aside.

11. Remove the manifold attaching bolts and remove the manifold.

12. Installation is performed in the reverse of the previous steps. Be sure to torque

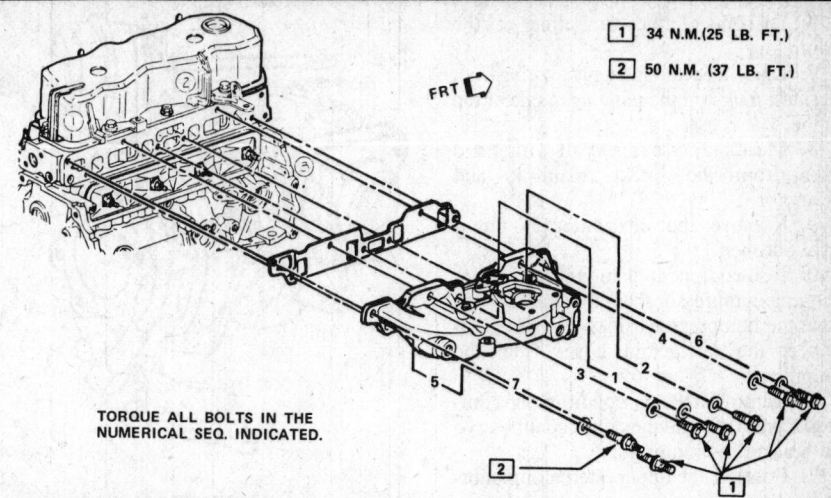

TORQUE ALL BOLTS IN THE NUMERICAL SEQ. INDICATED.

Intake manifold bolt tightening sequence for the 151-4 cylinder engine (© Pontiac Div., G.M. Corp.)

the manifold bolts to 29 ft. lbs., following the sequence in the accompanying illustration. Replenish the cooling system and check for leaks after the engine is started.

173 V6 ENGINE

1. Disconnect the negative battery cable at the battery.

2. Remove the air cleaner assembly.

3. Drain the cooling system.

4. Mark and disconnect all wiring and hoses from the carburetor.

5. Disconnect the fuel line at the carburetor.

6. Disconnect the cables at the carburetor (throttle, downshift, and/or cruise control, as equipped).

7. Mark and disconnect all wiring from the ignition coil.

8. Remove the ignition distributor as previously outlined.

9. Remove the air management hose.

10. Mark and disconnect the hoses from the emission canister. Remove the pipe bracket from the drivers side valve cover.

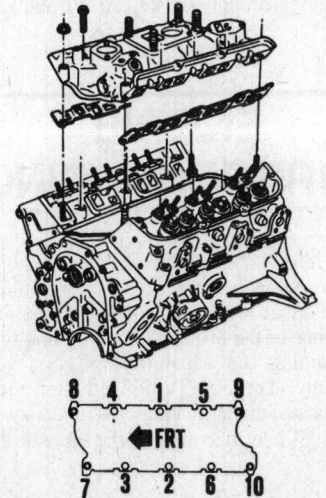

Intake manifold bolt tightening sequence for the 173-V6 engine (© Chevrolet Div., G.M. Corp.)

11. Remove the drivers side valve cover.

12. Remove the air management bracket from the passenger side valve cover.

13. Remove the passenger side valve cover.

14. Remove the upper radiator hose and disconnect the heater hose from the intake manifold.

15. Disconnect the wiring from the coolant switches.

16. Remove the manifold attaching bolts and lift the manifold off of the engine.

17. Installation is performed in the reverse of the previous steps. Note the following points before installing the manifold:

a. Be sure that the new manifold gaskets match the old gaskets EXACTLY.

b. Note that the manifold gaskets are different for the right and left sides of the engine and are marked as such.

c. It is not necessary to remove all of the RTV sealant from the manifold and the cylinder block; just remove the loose RTV.

d. Apply a ³⁄₁₆ in. bead of RTV over all existing RTV.

e. After installing the new gaskets on the cylinder heads, hold them in place by extending an RTV ridge about ³⁄₁₆ in. to the gasket ends.

f. To install the new intake gaskets behind the pushrods, carefully cut the gaskets where indicated, only as required.

g. The manifold retaining bolts must be torqued to 23 ft. lbs. in the sequence shown in the accompanying illustration.

h. Replenish the cooling system and check for leaks after the engine is started.

CARBURETED V8 ENGINES

1. Disconnect the negative battery cable at the battery.

2. Remove the air cleaner assembly.

3. Drain the cooling system.

4. Disconnect the upper radiator hose and the heater hose from the intake manifold.

5. Disconnect the linkage from the carburetor (throttle, downshift, and/or cruise control, as equipped).

6. Disconnect the fuel line at the carburetor.

7. Disconnect the spark plug wiring from the spark plugs on the passenger side of the engine.

8. Mark and disconnect all wiring and hoses from the intake manifold and carburetor.

9. Remove the distributor as previously outlined.

10. If so equipped, dismount the air conditioning compressor from the brackets and move the compressor aside. DO NOT disconnect the refrigerant hoses from the compressor.

11. Remove the air conditioning compressor brackets, and the cruise control servo and bracket, as required.

12. Remove the upper alternator mounting bracket.

13. Remove the EGR solenoid and the bracket.

14. Remove the vacuum line (for the power brake booster) from the intake manifold/carburetor connection.

15. Remove the manifold mounting bolts and lift the manifold off of the engine.

16. Refer to Steps 17 of the previous V6 ENGINE procedure (Disregard 17b and 17f).

TBI EQUIPPED V8 ENGINES

1. Disconnect the negative battery cable at the battery.

2. Remove the air cleaner assembly.

3. Drain the cooling system.

4. Disconnect the fuel inlet line at the front Throttle Body Injection (TBI) unit.

5. Remove the exhaust gas recirculation (EGR) solenoid.

6. Disconnect the wiring from the idle air motors, injectors, and the throttle position sensor (TPS).

7. Disconnect the fuel return line at the rear TBI unit.

8. Remove the power brake booster line.

9. Disconnect the accelerator and cruise control cables, unbolt the cable bracket from the manifold and tie the cable and bracket assembly out of the way.

10. Disconnect the air injection hose at the check valve and the air control valve.

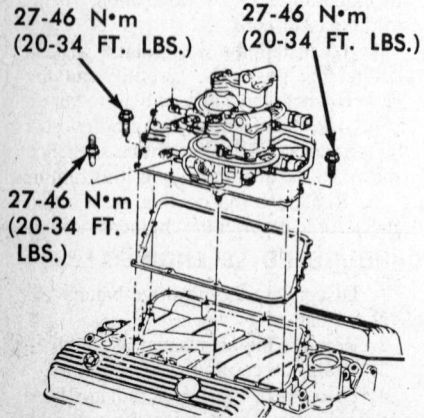

27-46 N•m (20-34 FT. LBS.)
27-46 N•m (20-34 FT. LBS.)
27-46 N•m (20-34 FT. LBS.)

TBI plate and gasket installation on V8 engines so equipped (© Chevrolet Div., G.M. Corp.)

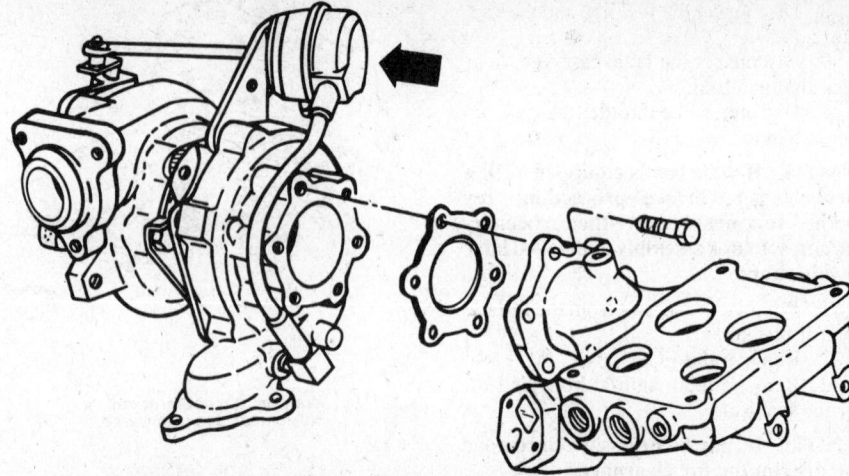

Turbocharger to plenum mounting position. Arrow points to actuator (© Pontiac Div., G.M. Corp.)

11. Unbolt the air injection pump and move it out of the way.

12. Disconnect the positive crankcase ventilation valve hose at the manifold and move the hose aside.

13. Mark and disconnect any vacuum hoses which will interfere with removal of the manifold.

14. If you plan on removing the TBI units from the upper manifold plate, remove the fuel balance tube (connecting the units) at this time.

15. Remove the bolts which attach the upper manifold plate (or TBI plate) to the intake manifold. Lift the TBI and plate assembly off of the intake manifold.

16. Remove the distributor as previously outlined.

17. Disconnect the upper radiator hose from the thermostat housing.

18. Disconnect the heater hose from the intake manifold.

19. Remove the intake manifold-to-cylinder head bolts and lift the intake manifold assembly off of the engine.

20. Refer to Step 17 of the previous V6 ENGINE procedure (Disregard 17b and 17f).

ENGINE TURBOCHARGING

For 1980–81, turbocharing was an option for the 301 V8 engine. With this application, Pontiac was able to improve the performance of the 301 while at the same time maintaining the capability of good fuel economy. The 301 Turbo, although more complicated than its naturally-aspirated twin, continues to utilize most of the same design features.

PRECAUTIONS

Before beginning any turbocharger disassembly procedures, the following general precautions should be considered.

1. Clean the area around the turbocharger with non-caustic solution before removal of the assembly.

2. When removing the turbocharger assembly, take special care not to bend, nick or in any way damage the compressor or turbine wheels. The turbine and compressor wheels routinely reach 130,000 rpm during boost, at which speeds the slightest imbalance can be destructive.

3. Before disconnecting the center housing rotating assembly from either compressor housing or turbine housing, scribe the components and make sure they are reassembled in the same order.

4. Any time the center housing rotating assembly or any part of the turbocharger assembly which includes the center housing assembly is being replaced, the oil and oil filter should be changed as part of the repair procedure.

Wastegate Actuator

REMOVAL & INSTALLATION

1. Disconnect the two hoses from the actuator.

2. Remove the waste gate linkage-to-actuator rod clip.

3. Remove the two bolts attaching the actuator to the compressor housing.

4. Installation is the reverse of removal.

Turbocharger and Actuator Assembly

REMOVAL & INSTALLATION

The carburetor and plenum are removed as a unit with the turbocharger.

1. Disconnect the turbocharger exhaust inlet and outlet pipes at the turbocharger. Remove the air cleaner.

2. Disconnect all carburetor and transmission control linkages at the carburetor.

Disconnect and plug the carburetor fuel line and necessary vacuum lines.

3. Drain about 3 quarts of coolant from the radiator. Disconnect the coolant hoses from the front and rear of the plenum.

4. Disconnect the EGR pipe at the intake manifold fitting. Remove the two bolts attaching the turbine housing to the bracket on the intake manifold.

5. Remove the three bolts attaching the compressor housing to the intake manifold.

6. Remove the turbocharger, actuator, carburetor and plenum as an assembly. Disconnect vacuum hoses as necessary.

7. Remove the six bolts attaching the turbocharger to the carburetor/plenum to separate the components if necessary.

Valve System

All engines use hydraulic valve lifters, which eliminate the need for periodic valve adjustments. If the rocker arms and/or cylinder heads have been removed or replaced, the rocker arms must be adjusted for zero lash.

For all valve system information, refer to the following sections:

Pontiac-built 4-cylinder	— GM H-body section
Chevrolet-built engines (except the 173 V6)	— Chevrolet Rear Wheel Drive section
Chevrolet 173 V6 engine	— GM X-body section
Buick 231 V6 engine	— Buick Rear Wheel Drive section
Pontiac-built V8 engine	— Pontiac Rear Wheel Drive section
Oldsmobile-built V8 engine	— Oldsmobile Rear Wheel Drive section

Cylinder Head
REMOVAL & INSTALLATION

NOTE: When servicing late model vehicles, be absolutely sure to mark vacuum hoses and wiring so that these items may be properly reconnected during installation. Also, when disconnecting fittings of metal lines (fuel, power brake vacuum), always use two flare nut (or line) wrenches. Hold the wrench on the large fitting with pressure on the wrench as if you were tightening the fitting (clockwise), THEN loosen and disconnect the smaller fitting from the larger fitting. If this is not done, damage to the line will result.

1. Disconnect the battery cables at the battery.

2. Drain the engine block of coolant.

3. Remove the intake manifold as previously described. Dismount the alternator

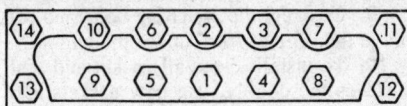

Inline six cylinder head torque sequence

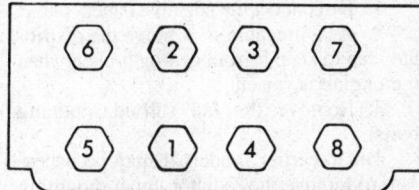

173 V6 cylinder head torque sequence

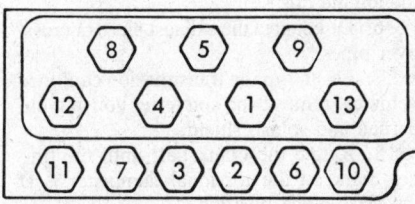

Chevrolet-built 229-V6 cylinder head bolt torque sequence

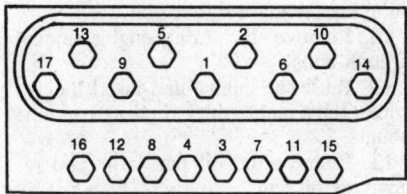

Chevrolet-built V8 engine cylinder head bolt torque sequence

and lay the unit aside. If necessary, remove the alternator brackets.

4. Remove the exhaust manifold(s). If the vehicle has air conditioning, dismount the compressor and position it out of the way. Do not disconnect the refrigerant lines.

5. Back off the rocker arm nuts and pivot the rocker arms out of the way so that the pushrods can be removed. Identify the pushrods so that they can be reinstalled in their original locations.

6. Remove the cylinder head bolts and cylinder head(s).

NOTE: On inline six cylinder engines, it is recommended that you use a hoist to lift the cylinder head.

7. Install using new gaskets. The head gasket is installed with the bead up.

NOTE: Coat a steel gasket, thinly and evenly, on both sides with sealer. If a steel asbestos gasket is used, do not apply sealer. Clean the bolt threads, apply sealing compound and install the bolts finger tight.

8. Tighten the head bolts a little at a time in the sequence illustrated to the specified torque.

9. Install the exhaust and intake manifolds as previously outlined.

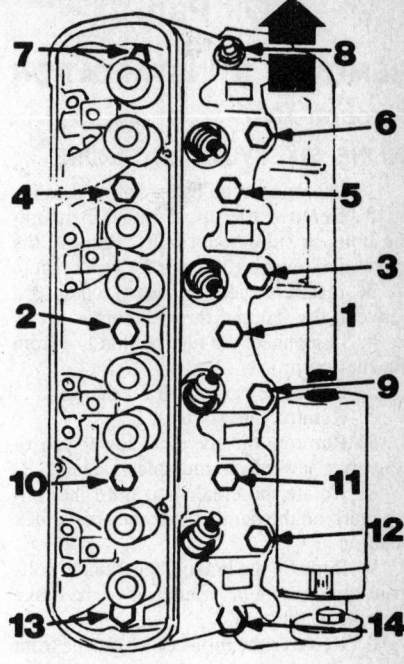

Pontiac-built V8 engine cylinder head bolt torque sequence

10. Adjust the valves (See the note under "Valve System").

Timing Components, Camshaft, and Pistons

Refer to the necessary engine section according to the chart under "Valve System" for these service procedures.

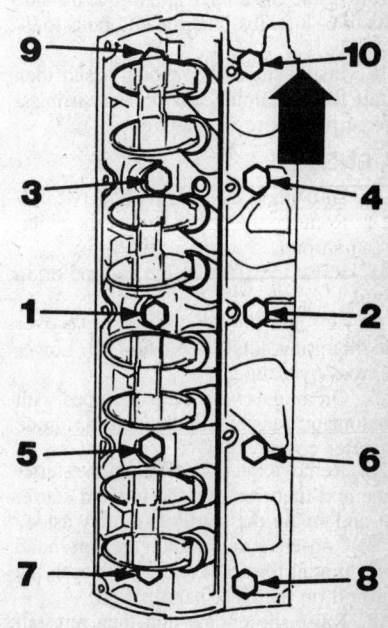

Oldsmobile-built V8 engine cylinder head bolt torque sequence

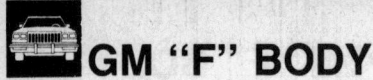

GM "F" BODY

Oil Pan

REMOVAL & INSTALLATION

Through 1981

INLINE SIX CYLINDER ENGINE

1. Disconnect the battery ground cable.
2. Remove the upper radiator mounting bolts or side mount bolts. Remove the upper and lower hoses from the water pump.
3. Install a piece of heavy cardboard between the fan and the radiator.
4. Disconnect the fuel suction line from the fuel pump.
5. Raise the car and drain the oil.
6. Remove the starter.
7. Remove the flywheel lower pan or converter lower pan and splash shield.
8. Rotate the crankshaft until the timing mark on the damper is at the six o'clock position.
9. Remove the brake line retaining bolts from the crossmember and move the brake line out of the way.
10. Remove the thru-bolts from the front motor mounts.
11. Remove the oil pan bolts.
12. Slowly raise the engine until the motor mounts can be removed from the frame brackets.
13. Remove the mounts and continue to raise the engine until it has been raised three inches.
14. Remove the oil pan by pulling it down from the engine and then twisting it into the opening left by the removal of the left engine mount.
15. When the pan is clear of the engine, tilt the front up and remove it by pulling it down and to the rear.
16. Install the oil pan gaskets to the engine block.
17. Install the oil pan and torque the side bolts to 6–8 ft. lbs. and the end bolts to 9–12 ft. lbs.
18. Install the motor mounts, and then install the remaining components using a reverse procedure of removal.

V6 ENGINE

1. Disconnect the negative battery cable.
2. Remove the upper half of the radiator fan shroud.
3. Raise the front of the car and drain the oil.
4. Unscrew the exhaust pipe cross-over tube mounting nuts at the manifold. Lower the cross-over tube.
5. On models which are equipped with an automatic transmission, remove the torque converter cover.
6. Remove the upper bolt on the starter brace and then remove the inboard starter bolt and swing the starter assembly aside.
7. Loosen and remove the left hand motor mount thru-bolt and then loosen the thru-bolt on the right hand mount.
8. Raise the engine and then reinstall the thru-bolt in the left-hand motor mount. *Do not tighten the bolt.*

9. Unscrew the attaching bolts and remove the oil pan from under the engine.
10. To install, clean all gasket and seal surfaces thoroughly, use new gaskets and seals and reverse the removal procedure.

V8 ENGINE

1. Disconnect the negative battery cable.
2. As a precaution, remove the distributor cap to keep it from getting broken when the engine is raised.
3. Remove the fan shroud retaining bolts.
4. On earlier models it may be necessary to remove the radiator upper mounting panel.
5. Raise the vehicle on a hoist and drain the engine oil.
6. Disconnect the exhaust pipes or cross-over pipes.
7. On automatic transmission equipped vehicles, remove the converter housing underpan and splash shield.
8. Rotate the crankshaft until the timing mark on the torsional dampener is at the six o'clock position.
9. The starter can be swung out of the way be disconnecting the brace at the starter, removing the inboard starter bolt and loosening the outboard starter bolt.
10. Remove the front engine mount through-bolts.
11. Raise the engine and insert blocks, at least three inches thick, under the engine mounts.
12. Remove the oil pan bolts and remove the oil pan.
13. To install, clean all gasket and seal surfaces thoroughly, use new gaskets and seals, and reverse the removal procedure.

NOTE: If the crankshaft was rotated while the pan was off, place the timing mark at the six o'clock position.

1982 And Later

FOUR CYLINDER ENGINE

1. Disconnect the negative battery cable at the battery.
2. Raise the vehicle and support it safely with jackstands.
3. Drain the engine oil.
4. Disconnect the exhaust pipe at the manifold.
5. Loosen the exhaust pipe hanger bracket.
6. Remove the starter assembly.
7. Remove the flywheel dust cover.
8. Remove the front engine mount through-bolts.
9. Carefully raise the engine enough to provide sufficient clearance to lower the oil pan.
10. Remove the oil pan retaining bolts and remove the oil pan.
11. Clean all old RTV from the mating surfaces.
12. Install the rear gasket into the rear main bearing cap and apply a small amount of RTV where the gasket engages into the engine block.

13. Install the front gasket.
14. Install the side gaskets, using grease as a retainer. Apply a small amount of RTV where the side gaskets meet the front gasket.
15. Install the oil pan.

NOTE: Install the oil pan-to-timing cover bolts last, as these holes will not align until the other pan bolts are snug.

16. The remainder of the installation procedure is performed in the reverse of Steps 1–9.

V6 and V8 ENGINES

1. Disconnect the negative battery cable at the battery.
2. Remove the fan shroud assembly.
3. Raise the vehicle and support it safely with jackstands.
4. Drain the engine oil.

——— CAUTION ———
Be sure that the catalytic convertor is cool before proceeding.

5. Remove the air injection pipe at the catalytic convertor.
6. Remove the catalytic convertor hanger bolts.
7. Remove the starter bolts, loosen the starter brace, then lay the starter aside.
8. Remove the front engine mount through-bolts.
9. Raise the engine enough to provide sufficient clearance for oil pan removal.
10. Remove the oil pan bolts.

NOTE: If the front crankshaft throw prohibits removal of the pan, turn the crankshaft to position the throw horizontally.

11. Remove the oil pan from the vehicle.
12. Remove all old RTV from the oil pan and engine block.
13. Run a 1/8 in. bead of RTV around the oil pan sealing surface. Remember to keep the RTV on the INSIDE of the bolt holes.
14. Install the pan and reverse the removal steps to complete the operation.

Oil Pump

NOTE: On all engines except the 231 V6, remove the oil pan (as previously outlined) in order to gain access to the oil pump bolts. On the 231 V6, remove the pump according to the following procedure.

REMOVAL & INSTALLATION

The oil pump is located in the timing chain cover and is connected by a drilled passage to the oil screen housing and pipe assembly in the oil pan. All oil is discharged from the pump to the oil pump cover assembly, on which the oil filter is mounted.

1. To remove the oil pump cover and gears, first remove the oil filter.
2. Remove the screws which attach the

oil pump cover assembly to the timing chain cover.

3. Remove the cover assembly and slide out the oil pump gears. Clean the gears and inspect them for any obvious defects such as chipping or scoring.

4. Remove the oil pressure relief valve cap, spring and valve. Clean them and inspect them for wear or scoring. Check the relief valve spring so that it is not worn on its side or collapsed. Replace the spring if it seems questionable.

5. Check the relief valve for a correct fit in its bore. It should be an easy slip fit and no more. If any perceptible shake can be felt, the valve and/or the cover should be replaced.

6. To install, lubricate the pressure relief valve and spring and place them in the cover. Install the cap and the gasket. Torque the cap to 35 ft. lbs.

7. Pack the oil pump gear cavity full of petroleum jelly. Do not use gear lube. Reinstall the oil pump gears so that the petroleum jelly is forced into every cavity of the gear pocket, and between the gear teeth. There must be no air spaces. This step is very important. Unless the pump is packed, it may not begin to pump oil as soon as the engine is started.

8. Install the cover assembly using a new gasket and sealer. Tighten the screws to 10 ft. lbs.

9. Install the oil filter.

Rear Main Seal

REMOVAL & INSTALLATION

Refer to the note under "Valve System" to determine the car section which includes your engine. Refer to the appropriate car section for the service procedure.

CLUTCH

The only required adjustment of the clutch is to maintain the proper clutch pedal free-play. This adjustment is very important, as it determines the engaging and disengaging characteristics of the clutch assembly.

Clutch Assembly

REMOVAL

1. Support engine and remove the transmission (as outlined later in this section).

2. Disconnect the clutch fork push rod and spring.

3. Remove the flywheel housing.

4. Slide the clutch fork from the ball stud and remove the fork from the dust boot. The ball stud is threaded into the clutch housing and may be replaced, if necessary.

5. Install an alignment tool to support the clutch assembly during removal. Mark the flywheel and clutch cover for reinstallation, if they do not already have "X" marks.

6. Loosen the clutch-to-flywheel attaching bolts evenly, one turn at a time, until spring pressure is released. Remove the bolts and clutch assembly.

INSTALLATION

1. Clean the pressure plate and flywheel face.

2. Support the clutch disc and pressure plate with an alignment tool. The driven disc is installed with the damper springs on the transmission side.

3. Turn the clutch assembly until the mark on the cover lines up with the mark on the flywheel, then install the bolts. Tighten down evenly and gradually to avoid distortion.

4. Remove the alignment tool.

5. Lubricate the ball socket and fork fingers at the release bearing end with high melting-point grease. Lubricate the recess on the inside of the throwout bearing and throwout fork groove with a light coat of graphite grease.

6. Install the clutch fork and dust boot into the housing. Install the throwout bearing to the throwout fork. Install the flywheel housing. Install the transmission.

7. Connect the fork push rod and spring. Lubricate the spring and pushrod ends.

8. Adjust the shift linkage and clutch pedal free-play.

PEDAL FREE-PLAY ADJUSTMENT

1. Disconnect the return spring at the clutch fork.

2. Hold the pedal against the rubber bumper on the dash brace.

3. Push the clutch fork so that the throwout bearing lightly contacts the pressure plate fingers.

4. Loosen the locknut and adjust the length of the rod so that the swivel or rod can slip freely into the gauge hole in the lever. Increase the length of the rod until all free-play is removed.

5. Remove the rod or swivel from the gauge hole and insert it in the other (original) hole on the lever. Install the retainer and tighten the locknut.

6. Install the return spring and check free-play measurement from the floor mat to top of the pedal pad. It should measure: $\frac{7}{8}$–$1\frac{1}{2}$ in. through 1981; $\frac{7}{8}$–$1\frac{1}{8}$ in. for 1982 and later.

MANUAL TRANSMISSION

Refer to the Manual Transmission segment of the Unit Repair Section for identification and overhaul information.

REMOVAL & INSTALLATION

Through 1981

1. On the floor-shift models, remove the shift knob and console trim plate.

2. Raise the car and support it with floor stands.

3. Disconnect the speedometer cable and the TCS switch wiring, if so equipped.

4. Remove the driveshaft as outlined in the next Chapter.

5. Remove the bolts securing the transmission mounts to the crossmember and also those bolts securing the cross-member to the frame. Remove the cross-member.

6. Remove the shift levers from the side of the transmission.

7. Disconnect the back drive rod from the bellcrank.

8. Remove the bolts from the shift control assembly and carefully lower the assembly until the shift lever clears the rubber shift boot. Remove the assembly from the car.

9. Remove the transmission-to-bell-housing bolts and lift the transmission from the car.

10. Lift the transmission and insert the mainshaft into the bellhousing.

11. Install and torque the transmission-to-clutch housing bolts and lock-washers.

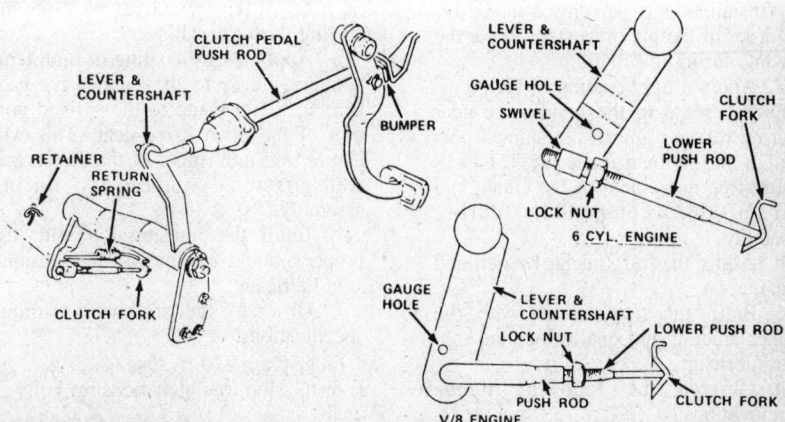

Typical clutch linkage and adjustment points (© Pontiac Div., G.M. Corp.)

C657

12. Install the shift lever.

13. Install the shift levers to the transmission side cover.

14. Connect the back drive rod to the bellcrank.

15. Raise the engine high enough to position the crossmember. Install and tighten the crossmember-to-frame bolts and transmission mounts to crossmember bolts.

16. Install the driveshaft.

17. Connect the speedometer cable and TCS wiring, if so equipped.

18. Fill the transmission with the specified lubricant. If applicable, install the console trim plate and shift knob. Adjust the linkage.

1982 and Later
4-SPEED

1. Disconnect the negative battery cable at the battery.

2. Raise the vehicle and support it safely with jackstands.

3. Drain the lubricant from the transmission.

4. Remove the torque arm from the vehicle as outlined under "Rear Suspension".

5. Mark the driveshaft and the rear axle pinion flange to indicate their relationship. Unbolt the rear universal joint straps. Lower the rear of the driveshaft, being careful to keep the universal joint caps in place. Withdraw the driveshaft from the transmission and remove it from the vehicle.

6. Disconnect the speedometer cable and the electrical connectors from the transmission.

7. Remove the exhaust pipe brace.

8. Remove the transmission shifter support attaching bolts from the transmission.

9. Disconnect the shift linkage at the shifter.

10. Raise the transmission slightly with a jack, then remove the crossmember attaching bolts.

11. Remove the transmission mount attaching bolts and remove the mount and crossmember from the vehicle.

12. Remove the transmission attaching bolts, and with the aid of an assistant, move the transmission rearward and downward out of the vehicle.

13. Installation is performed in the reverse order of the previous steps. Note the following during installation:

    a. Apply a light coating of high temperature grease to the main drive gear bearing retainer and to the splined portion of the main drive gear. This will assure free movement of the clutch and transmission components during assembly.

    b. Adjust the shift linkage (as outlined later).

    c. Refill the transmission with the proper amount and quality of transmission lubricant.

    d. Observe the following torque specifications:

Filler plug—15 ft. lbs.

Transmission–to–clutch housing bolts—55 ft. lbs.

Crossmember–to–body bolts—35 ft. lbs.

Mount–to–crossmember bolts—35 ft. lbs.

Mount–to–transmission bolts—35 ft. lbs.

Shifter bracket–to–extension housing—25 ft. lbs.

5-Speed

1. Disconnect the negative battery cable at the battery.

2. Remove the shift lever boot attaching screws and slide the boot up the shift lever.

3. Remove the shift lever from the transmission.

4. Raise the vehicle and support it safely with jackstands.

5. Drain the lubricant from the transmission.

6. Remove the torque arm from the vehicle as outlined under "Rear Suspension".

7. Mark the driveshaft and the rear axle pinion flange to indicate their relationship. Unbolt the rear universal joint straps. Lower the rear of the driveshaft, being careful to keep the universal joint caps in place. Withdraw the driveshaft from the transmission and remove it from the vehicle.

8. Disconnect the speedometer cable and the electrical connectors from the transmission.

9. Disconnect the clutch cable at the transmission.

10. Remove the catalytic converter hanger.

11. Remove the exhaust pipe brace.

12. Remove the transmission shifter support attaching bolts from the transmission.

13. Disconnect the shift linkage at the shifter.

14. Raise the transmission slightly with a jack, then remove the crossmember attaching bolts.

15. Remove the transmission mount attaching bolts and remove the mount and crossmember from the vehicle.

16. Remove the transmission attaching bolts, and with the aid of an assistant, move the transmission rearward and downward out of the vehicle.

17. Installation is performed in the reverse order of the previous steps. Note the following during installation:

    a. Apply a light coating of high temperature grease to the main drive gear bearing retainer and to the splined portion of the main drive gear. This will assure free movement of the clutch and transmission components during assembly.

    b. Refill the transmission with the proper amount and quality of transmission lubricant.

    c. Observe the following torque specifications:

Filler plug—20 ft. lbs.

Transmission-to-clutch housing bolts—55 ft.lbs.

Crossmember-to-body bolts—35 ft. lbs.

Mount-to-crossmember bolts—35 ft. lbs.

Mount-to-transmission bolts—35 ft. lbs.

Shift Linkage

NOTE: The 5-speed 77mm transmission gearshift lever is floor-mounted and is located on top of the extension housing. The shift mechanism does not require any adjustment.

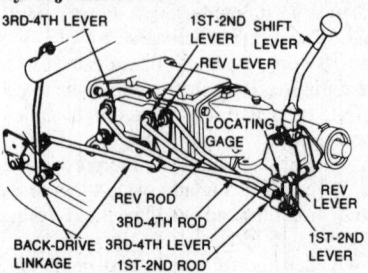

Typical 4 speed transmission shift linkage—through 1981

ADJUSTMENT
Through 1981

1. Turn the ignition switch Off, raise the car, and support it on jackstands.

2. Loosen the swivel locknuts on all shift rods and on the back drive control rod.

3. Place the transmission shift levers (on the side of the transmission) in neutral (centered).

4. Place the floor shift lever in neutral and lock it in this position by installing a pin into the lever bracket assembly directly below the shift lever.

5. Move the shift rod nut up against the swivel on each shift rod and hold it in place by tightening the locknuts.

6. Remove the locating pin from the control bracket assembly and shift the transmission into reverse. Place the ignition key in "lock." To remove any slack in the steering column mechanism, pull down on the back drive rod and tighten the nut. When in reverse, it must be possible to easily turn the ignition key in and out of the "lock" position. If any binding exists, leave the key in "lock" and readjust the back drive control rod.

7. Check the shifting operation and readjust if necessary.

1982 and Later

NOTE: All terms used in the following procedure match those which are used in the accompanying illustration.

1. Disconnect the negative battery cable at the battery.

2. Place the shift control lever (F) in Neutral.

3. Raise the vehicle and support it safely with jackstands.

4. Remove the swivel retainers (P) from the levers (E,H, and J).

5. Remove the swivels (S) from the

shifter assembly (G), and loosen the swivel locknuts (R and T).

6. Make sure that levers L,M, and N are in their Neutral positions (center detents).

7. Align the holes of levers E,H, and J with the notch in the shifter assembly (G). Insert an alignment gauge (J-33195) to hold the levers in this position.

8. Insert swivel S into lever E and install washer Q. Secure with retainer P.

9. Apply rearward pressure (Z) to lever N. Tighten locknuts R and T (at the same time) against swivel S to 25 ft. lbs.

10. Repeat Steps 8 and 9 for rod D and levers J and M.

11. Repeat steps 8 and 9 for rod K and levers H and L.

12. Remove the alignment gauge, lower the vehicle, and check the operation of the shifting mechanism.

13. Reconnect the negative battery cable.

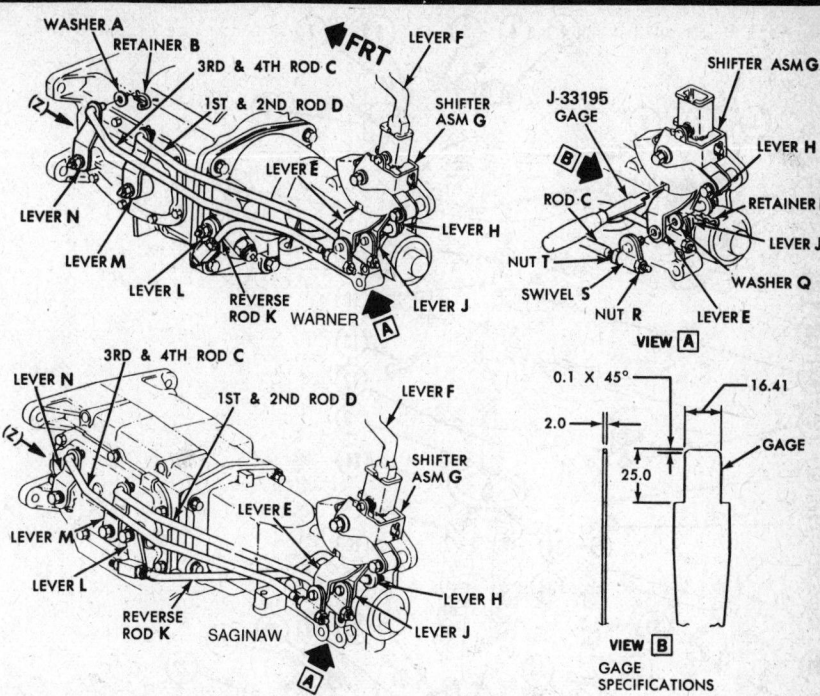

Transmission shift linkage adjustment on 1982 and later models. Note that all component references in the illustration match those in the text and that dimensions are expressed in millimeters. (© Chevrolet Div., G.M. Corp.)

AUTOMATIC TRANSMISSION

TRANSMISSION REMOVAL & INSTALLATION

Through 1981

NOTE: For these models, refer to the "Chevrolet Rear Wheel Drive" car section for the appropriate procedure.

1982 and Later

1. Disconnect the negative battery cable at the battery.

2. Remove the air cleaner assembly.

3. Disconnect the throttle valve (TV) control cable at the carburetor.

4. Remove the transmission oil dipstick. Unbolt and remove the dipstick tube.

5. Raise the vehicle and support it safely with jackstands.

NOTE: In order to provide adequate clearance for transmission removal, it may be necessary to raise both the front and the rear of the vehicle.

6. Mark the relationship between the driveshaft and the rear pinion flange so that the driveshaft may be reinstalled in its original position.

7. Unbolt the universal joint straps from the pinion flange (use care to keep the universal joint caps in place), lower and remove the driveshaft from the vehicle.

8. Disconnect the catalytic convertor support bracket at the transmission.

9. Disconnect the speedometer cable, electrical connectors and the shift control cable from the transmission.

—— CAUTION ——

During the next step, rear spring force will cause the torque arm to move toward the floor pan. When disconnecting the arm from the transmission, carefully place a

piece of wood between the floor pan and the torque arm. This will prevent possible personal injury and/or floor pan damage.

10. Remove the torque arm-to-transmission bolts.

11. Remove the flywheel cover, then mark the relationship between the torque convertor and the flywheel so that these parts may be reassembled in the same relationship.

12. Remove the torque convertor-to-flywheel attaching bolts.

13. Support the transmission with a jack, then remove the transmission mount bolt.

14. Unbolt and remove the transmission crossmember.

15. Lower the transmission slightly. Disconnect the TV cable and oil cooler lines from the transmission.

16. Support the engine using Chevrolet special tool BT-6424 or its equivalent. Remove the transmission-to-engine mounting bolts.

—— CAUTION ——

The transmission must be secured to the transmission jack.

17. Remove the transmission from the vehicle. Be careful not to damage the oil cooler lines, TV cable, or the shift control cable. Also, keep the rear of the transmission lower than the front to avoid the possibility of the torque convertor disengaging from the transmission.

18. Installation is performed in the reverse of the previous steps. Note the following points during installation:

a. Before installing the convertor-to-

flywheel bolts, be sure that the weld nuts on the convertor are flush with the flywheel, and that the convertor rotates freely by hand in this position.

b. Install a NEW dipstick tube O-ring before installing the tube.

c. Refer to the installation points listed with the previous procedure (through 1981).

LINKAGE ADJUSTMENTS, FLUID AND FILTER CHANGE

Refer to the Automatic Transmission segment of the Unit Repair Section for information on these services.

DRIVESHAFT AND UNIVERSAL JOINTS

The universal joints are lubricated and sealed at the factory and require no periodic maintenance. Two basic universal joints are used. The Dana or Cleveland type uses snap-ring bearing cap retainers. The Saginaw uses injection molded plastic to retain the bearing caps. On the Saginaw type there is a snap-ring groove in the bearing housing inboard of the yoke to facilitate installation of a repair kit.

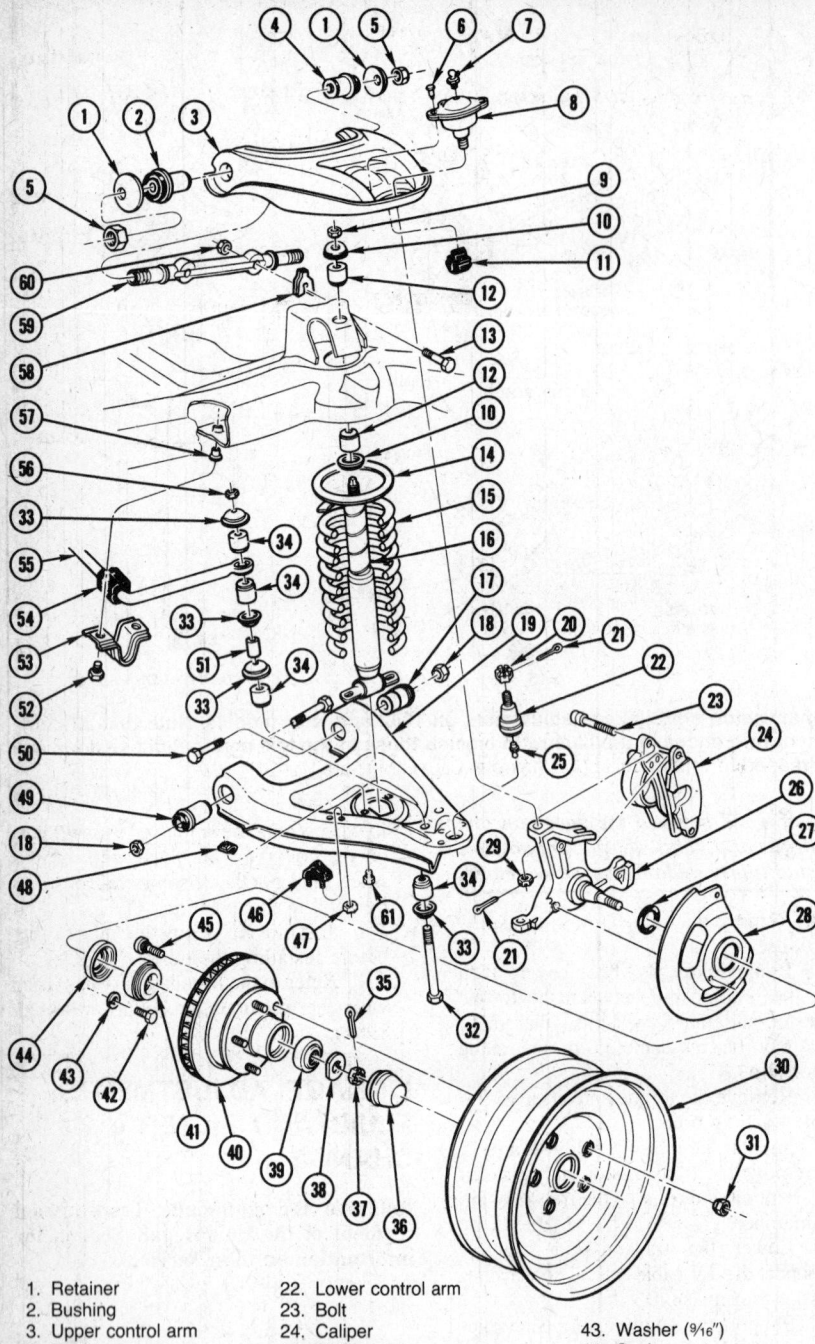

NOTE: For driveshaft removal, refer to the procedure listed in the "Chevrolet Rear Wheel Drive" car section. For all universal joint information refer to the "U–Joints/CV–Joints" segment of the Unit Repair section.

REAR DRIVE AXLE

Axle Shaft

NOTE: Refer to the procedure listed in the "Chevrolet Rear Wheel Drive" section to remove and install the axle shaft. On models with rear disc brakes, remove the calipers and rotors according to the "Brakes" segment of the Unit Repair section.

JACKING HOISTING

── CAUTION ──

Use extreme care to avoid damage to the catalytic convertor, oil pan, brackets, lines, etc. while raising the vehicle with a jack.

The front of the car may be raised with the jack positioned under the front A-frame spring seats or from the front subframe, in front of the transmission crossmember.

The rear may be raised anywhere along the drive axle, or at the rear subframe, just inboard of the forward spring mounts.

── CAUTION ──

DO NOT position the jack under the rear axle if equipped with a rear stabilizer bar, unless the jack is made to clear the bar.

FRONT SUSPENSION

Coil Spring

REMOVAL & INSTALLATION

Through 1981

1. Remove the shock absorber. Disconnect the stabilizer bar.
2. Support the car at the frame so the control arms hang free.
3. Support the inner end of the control arm with a floor jack. (Dealers have a device that cradles the inner bushings).
4. Raise the jack enough to take the tension off the lower control arm pivot bolts.

1. Retainer
2. Bushing
3. Upper control arm
4. Bushing
5. Nut (⅝"-18)
6. Rivet
7. Fitting
8. Upper ball joint
9. Nut (⅜"-16)
10. Retainer
11. Bumper
12. Grommet
13. Bolt
14. Insulator
15. Spring
16. Shock Absorber
17. Bushing
18. Nut (½"-13)
19. Lower control arm
20. Nut
21. Cotter pin (⅛" × 1¼")
22. Lower control arm
23. Bolt
24. Caliper
25. Fittings
26. Steering knuckle
27. Gasket
28. Shield
29. Nut
30. Wheel
31. Nut (½"-20)
32. Stabilizer link kit
33. Retainer
34. Grommet
35. Cotter pin (¼" × 1¼")
36. Cap
37. Nut (¾"-20)
38. Washer
39. Bearing
40. Hub
41. Inner front wheel bearing
42. Bolt
43. Washer (⁹⁄₁₆")
44. Seal
45. Bolt
46. Bumper
47. Nut (⅜"-16)
48. Nut
49. Bushing
50. Bolt (½"-13 × 3¾")
51. Spacer
52. Screw
53. Bracket
54. Bushing
55. Front stabilizer shaft
56. Nut (⁵⁄₁₆"-18)
57. Nut (⅜"-16)
58. Shim
59. Shaft Kit
60. Nut (½"-13)
61. Bolt

Exploded view of the front suspension used on models through 1981

5. Chain the spring to the lower control arm, for safety's sake.

6. Remove first the rear, then the front pivot bolt.

7. Cautiously lower the jack until all spring tension is released.

8. Note the way in which the spring is installed to the control arm and remove it.

9. On installation, position the spring to the control arm and raise it into place.

10. Install the pivot bolts and torque the nuts to 90 ft. lbs.

11. Replace the shock absorber and stabilizer bar.

1982 and Later

1. Raise the front of the vehicle and support it on jack stands.

2. Remove the road wheel(s).

3. Disconnect the stabilizer link from the lower control arm.

4. If the steering gear hinders removal procedures, disattach the unit and move it out of the way.

5. Disconnect the tie-rod from the steering knuckle using a ball joint remover.

6. Using an internal-fit coil spring compressor, compress the coil spring so that it is loose in its seat.

---- **CAUTION** ----

Be sure to follow manufacturer's instructions when using spring compressor. Coil springs in a compressed state contain enormous energy which, if released accidentally, could cause serious injury.

---

7. To remove the coil spring, disconnect the lower control arm from the crossmember at the pivot bolts. If additional clearance is necessary, disconnect the lower control arm from the steering knuckle at the ball joint.

8. To install, compress the coil spring until spring height is the same as when removed, then position the spring on the control arm. Make sure the lower end of the coil spring is properly positioned in the lower control arm and that the upper end fits correctly in its pad.

9. Remaining installation is the reverse of removal.

Shock Absorber

REMOVAL & INSTALLATION

Through 1981

1. Remove the upper stem nut while holding the stem to keep it from turning.

2. Remove the two bolts holding the shock absorber to the lower control arm, and pull the shock through the arm.

3. Extend the new shock absorber and insert it up through the lower control arm. Make sure that the upper stem goes through the hole in the upper control arm frame bracket.

NOTE: Purge new shocks of air by repeatedly compressing them while in-

verted and extending them in their normal installed position.

4. Install the grommet, retainer cup and nut to the shock absorber upper stem.

5. Hold the shock absorber stem and tighten the upper nut to 8 ft. lbs.

6. Install the lower control arm retaining bolts and tighten to 20 ft. lbs.

1982 and Later

1. Place the ignition key in the unlocked position so that the front wheels can be moved.

MacPherson Strut

REMOVAL & INSTALLATION

1982 and Later

1. Place the ignition key in the unlocked position so that the front wheels can be moved.

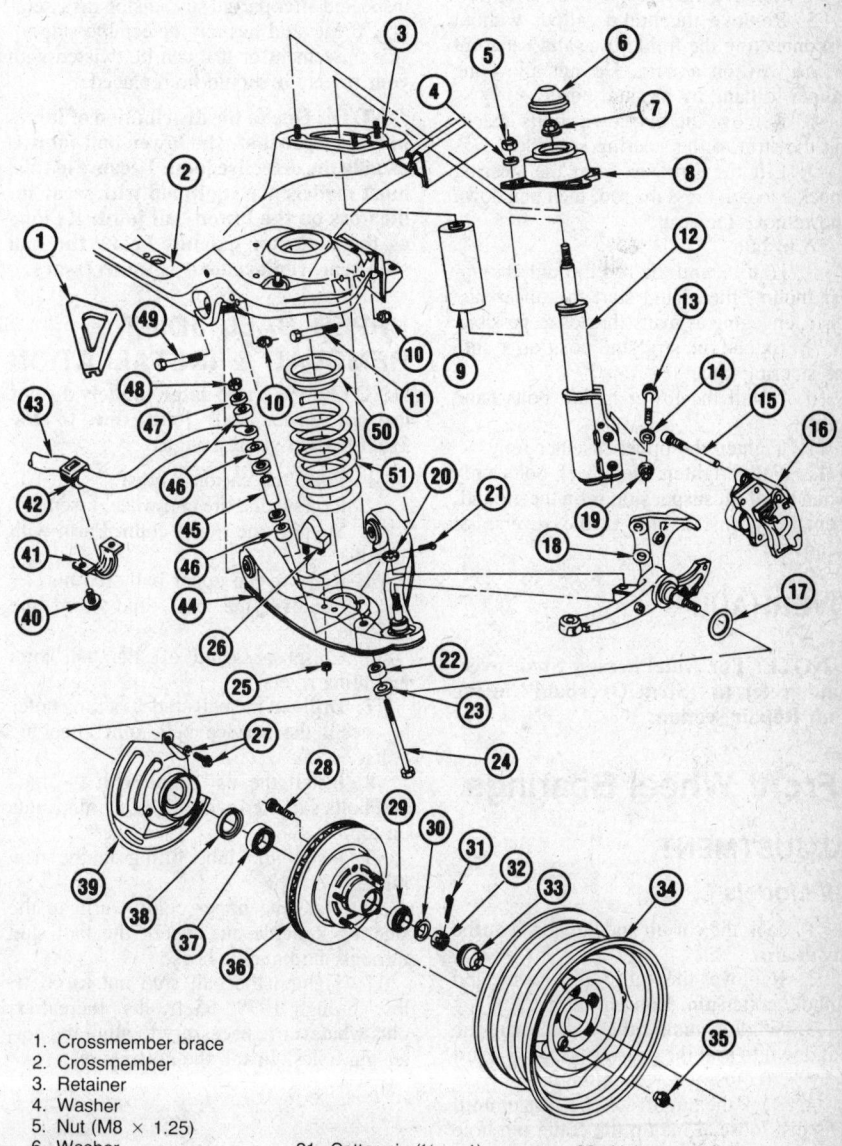

1. Crossmember brace
2. Crossmember
3. Retainer
4. Washer
5. Nut (M8 × 1.25)
6. Washer
7. Nut (M14 × 2)
8. Mount
9. Shield
10. Nut (M12 × 1.75)
11. Bolt (M12 × 1.75 × 95)
12. Absorber w/strut
13. Bolt
14. Washer
15. Bolt
16. Caliper
17. Gasket
18. Knuckle
19. Nut (M16 × 2)
20. Nut (9/16-18)
21. Cotter pin (1/8 × 1)
22. Grommet
23. Retainer
24. Bolt(5/16-18 × 7)
25. Nut (7/16-14)
26. Bumper
27. Bolt
28. Bolt
29. Outer front wheel bearing
30. Washer
31. Cotter pin (M3.2 × 25)
32. Nut
33. Cap
34. Wheel
35. Nut
36. Hub
37. Inner front wheel bearing
38. Seal
39. Shield
40. Bolt (M10 × 1.5 × 30)
41. Bracket
42. Insulator
43. Front stabilizer shaft
44. Lower control arm
45. Spacer
46. Grommet
47. Retainer
48. Nut
49. Bolt (M12 × 1.75 × 115)
50. Insulator

Exploded view of the front suspension used on 1982 and later models (© Chevrolet Div., G.M. Corp.)

2. From in the engine compartment, remove the upper strut to upper mount fastener.

— CAUTION —

Do not attempt to move the vehicle with the upper strut fastener disconnected.

3. Raise the front of the vehicle by the lower control arms, and position safety stands under the vehicle.

4. Remove the wheel and tire assembly.

5. Remove the brake caliper without disconnecting the fluid hose, and hang out of the way on a wire. Do not allow the caliper to hang by its fluid hose.

6. Remove the two lower bolts attaching the strut to the steering knuckle.

7. Lift the strut up from the steering knuckle to compress the rod, then pull down and remove the strut.

To Install:

8. Half extend the rod through the upper mount, then hand start the upper fastener, engaging as many threads as possible.

9. Extend the strut and position it onto the steering knuckle.

10. Install the lower mount bolts hand tight.

11. Tighten the upper fastener fully.

12. Fully tighten the lower bolts only when the front suspension is on the ground. Remaining installation is the reverse of removal.

OVERHAUL

NOTE: For MacPherson Strut overhaul, refer to "Strut Overhaul" in the Unit Repair section.

Front Wheel Bearings

ADJUSTMENT

All Models

1. Jack the car up and support it at the lower arm.

2. Remove the hub dust cover and spindle cotter pin. Loosen the nut.

3. While spinning the wheel, snug the nut down to seat the bearings. Do not exert over 12 ft. lbs of force on the nut.

4. Back the nut off ¼–½ a turn or until it is just loose. Line up the cotter pin hole in the spindle with the hole in the nut.

5. Insert a new cotter pin. Endplay should be between 0.001 and 0.005 in. If play exceeds this tolerance, the wheel bearings should be replaced.

Ball Joints

INSPECTION

NOTE: Before performing this inspection, make sure the wheel bearings are adjusted correctly and that the control arm bushings are in good condition.

1. Jack the car up under the front lower control arm at the spring seat.

2. Raise the car until there is 1-2 in. of clearance under the wheel.

3. Insert a bar under the wheel and pry upward. If the wheel raises more than ⅛ in., the ball joints are worn. Determine if the upper or lower ball joint is worn by visual inspection while prying on the wheel.

4. The upper ball joint can be further inspected after partial suspension disassembly. If the stud has any detectable side-to-side movement or if it can be twisted with your fingers it should be replaced.

NOTE: Due to the distribution of forces in the suspension, the lower ball joint is usually the defective joint. Because of this, most models are equipped with wear indicators on the lower ball joint. As long as the indicator extends below the ball stud seat, replacement is unnecessary.

UPPER BALL JOINT REMOVAL & INSTALLATION

NOTE: 1982 and later models do not use an upper ball joint due to the MacPherson strut design.

1. Raise the car on a hoist.

2. Remove the tire and wheel assembly.

3. Support the lower control arm with a jack.

4. Remove the upper ball stud nut.

5. Remove the ball stud from the knuckle.

6. Chisel or grind off the ball joint mounting rivets.

7. Drill out the ball stud attaching holes to accept the service ball joint attaching bolts.

8. Install the ball joint with the nuts and bolts supplied with the new joint, nuts on top.

9. Install the lube fitting in the new joint.

10. Mate the upper control arm to the steering knuckle and install the ball stud through the knuckle boss.

11. Tighten the ball stud nut to 60 ft. lbs. through 1979, 65 ft. lbs. thereafter, plus whatever is necessary to align the cotter pin holes. Install the cotter pin.

— CAUTION —

Do not back off on the nut to align the cotter pin.

12. Install the wheel and lower the vehicle.

LOWER BALL JOINT REMOVAL & INSTALLATION

NOTE: To prevent component damage, an on-car ball joint press, such as Kent-Moore tool J-9519-03 should be used.

1. Raise the vehicle on a hoist and remove the wheel.

2. Support the lower control arm with a jack.

3. Loosen the lower ball stud nut. Break the ball stud loose. Remove the ball stud nut.

4. Remove the ball stud from the steering knuckle.

5. The ball joint is pressed in and must be pressed out.

6. Install the new ball joint, using the bolts supplied with the service ball joint. The thick-headed bolt is installed on the forward side of control arm. Press in the ball joint.

7. Install the ball stud in the steering knuckle boss. This may be done by raising the lower control arm with the jack.

8. Install the nut on the ball stud, tightening to 83 ft. lbs. on all models. Continue to tighten the nut until the cotter pin holes align and install the pin. Do not back off the nut to align the holes.

9. Install the lube fitting.

Lower Control Arm

REMOVAL & INSTALLATION

1. Remove the spring as described earlier.

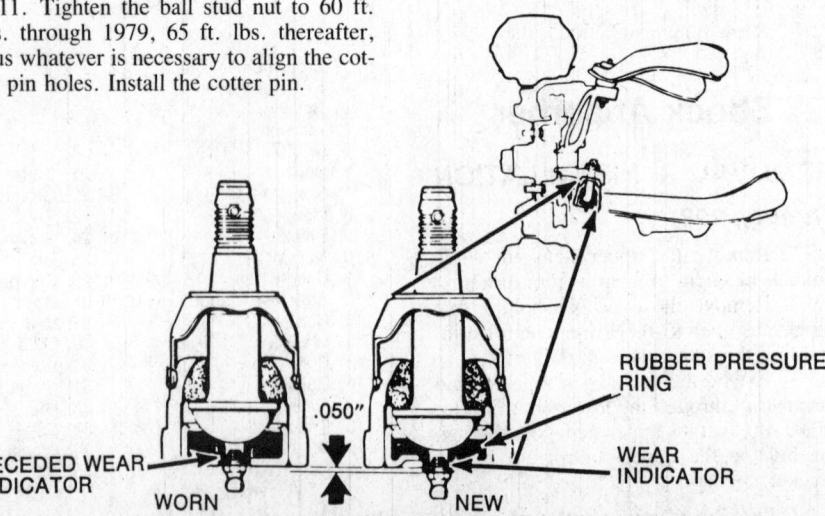

Wear indicator used on the lower ball joints—all models (© Chevrolet Div., G.M. Corp.)

2. Remove the ball stud from the steering knuckle.

3. Remove the control arm.

4. To install, reverse the above procedure.

Upper Control Arm

REMOVAL & INSTALLATION

Through 1981

1. Raise the vehicle on a hoist.

2. Support the outer end of the lower control arm with a jack.

3. Remove the wheel. Support the hub assembly to prevent its weight from damaging the brake hose when the upper ball joint is removed.

4. Separate the upper ball joint from the steering knuckle as described above under Upper Ball Joint Removal and Installation.

5. Remove the control arm shaft to frame nuts.

NOTE: Tape the shims together and identify them so that they can be installed in the position from which they were removed.

6. Remove the bolts which attach the control arm shaft to the frame and remove the control arm. Note the positions of the bolts.

7. Install in the reverse order of removal. Make sure the shaft to frame bolts are installed in the same position they were in before removal and that the shims are in their original positions. Tighten the shaft to frame bolts to 75 ft. lbs.

REAR SUSPENSION

All models through 1981 use a leaf spring rear suspension, whereas 1982 and later models use a coil spring rear suspension having a torque arm and a track bar to stabilize the axle assembly. Anti-sway (stabilizer) bars are optional equipment on all models.

Shock Absorber

REMOVAL & INSTALLATION

1. Jack the car to a convenient working height. Support the rear axle assembly.

2. If the car is equipped with Superlift shock absorbers, disconnect the air line.

3. On models through 1981, remove the lower shock absorber nut, retainer, and grommet. Remove the upper bolts, and remove the shock.

4. On 1982 and later models, disconnect the upper shock attaching nut, remove

the lower shock to axle mounting bolt, then remove the shock absorber.

5. Install the shock absorbers in the reverse of the previous steps. On models through 1981, torque the upper fasteners to 18 ft. lbs.; lower to 7 ft. lbs. On 1982 and later models, torque the upper fasteners to 13 ft. lbs.; the lower to 70 ft. lbs.

Springs

REMOVAL & INSTALLATION

Through 1981

1. Raise the car by the frame so that the rear axle can be independently raised and lowered.

2. Support the rear axle with a floor jack.

3. Disconnect the shock absorber lower mount.

4. Loosen the retaining bolt through the front spring eye. Unbolt the front bracket from the body.

5. Lower the axle enough to remove the bracket and retaining bolt from the front spring eye.

6. Pry the parking brake cable from the spring mounting plate retainer.

7. Remove the U-bolt nuts, the spring plate, and the upper and lower spring pads.

8. Support the spring. Remove the lower rear shackle bolt. Remove the spring.

9. On installation, install the front bracket to the spring eye, install the rear shackle, bolt the front bracket in place, install the U-bolts, and replace the shock absorber. Tighten the bolts with the weight of the car on the springs. Torque the front bracket mounting bolt to 25–30 ft. lbs., the front eye bolt to 75 ft. lbs., the U-bolts to 40 ft. lbs., and the rear shackle bolts to 50 ft. lbs.

1982 and Later

1. Raise the car by the frame so that the rear axle can be independently raised and lowered.

2. Support the rear axle with a floor jack.

3. If equipped with brake hose attaching brackets, disconnect the brackets allowing the hoses to hang free. Do not disconnect the hoses. Perform this step only if the hoses will be unduly stretched when the axle is lowered.

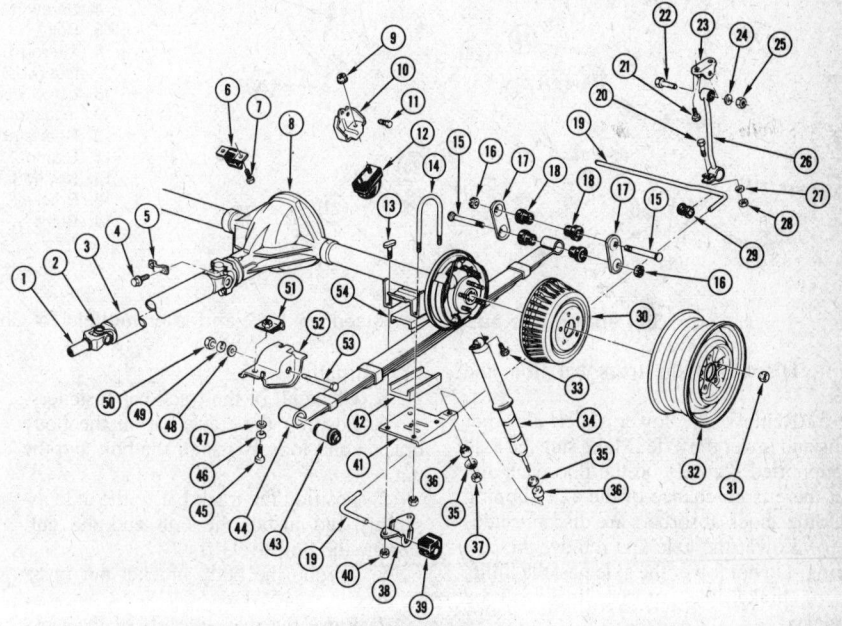

1. Universal joint yoke	19. Rear stabilizer shaft	37. Nut
2. Universal joint	20. Bolt (5/16"-18 × 3/8")	38. Bracket
3. Driveshaft	21. Screw (3/8"-16 × 1 1/8")	39. Bushing
4. Bolt (5/16"-24 × 1 7/16")	22. Bolt (3/8"-16 × 2 1/4")	40. Nut
5. Strap	23. Bracket	41. Plate
6. Bumper	24. Washer (1" × 25/64")	42. Cushion
7. Bolt (5/16"-12 × 3/4")	25. Nut (3/8"-16)	43. Bushing ASM
8. Housing	26. Support	44. Rear Leaf Spring
9. Nut	27. Washer (1/4")	45. Bolt
10. Bracket	28. Nut (5/16"-18)	46. Washer (3/8")
11. Screw (3/8"-16 × 1 1/8")	29. Bushing	47. Washer
12. Bumper ASM	30. Brake Drum	48. Washer
13. Bolt (7/16"-20 × 1 5/16")	31. Nut	49. Washer (1/2")
14. Bolt (7/16"-20 U-shape)	32. Wheel	50. Nut (1/2"-20)
15. Pin	33. Screw (5/16"-18 × 1")	51. Nut (3/8"-16)
16. Nut (7/16"-20)	34. Shock Absorber	52. Bracket
17. Shackle unit	35. Retainer	53. Bolt (1/2"-20 × 4 7/8")
18. Bushing	36. Grommet	54. Cushion

Leaf spring rear suspension used on models through 1981

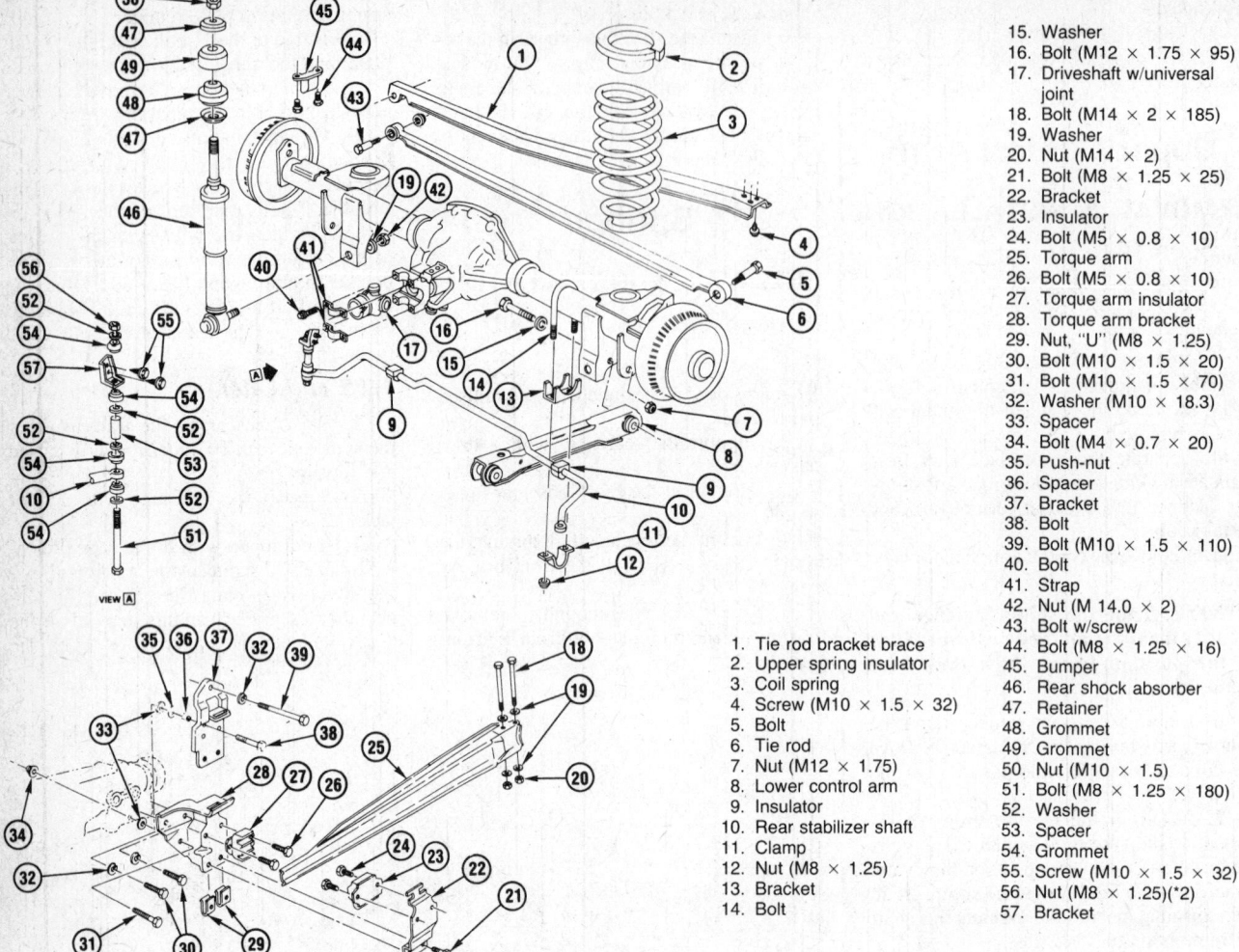

15. Washer
16. Bolt (M12 × 1.75 × 95)
17. Driveshaft w/universal joint
18. Bolt (M14 × 2 × 185)
19. Washer
20. Nut (M14 × 2)
21. Bolt (M8 × 1.25 × 25)
22. Bracket
23. Insulator
24. Bolt (M5 × 0.8 × 10)
25. Torque arm
26. Bolt (M5 × 0.8 × 10)
27. Torque arm insulator
28. Torque arm bracket
29. Nut, "U" (M8 × 1.25)
30. Bolt (M10 × 1.5 × 20)
31. Bolt (M10 × 1.5 × 70)
32. Washer (M10 × 18.3)
33. Spacer
34. Bolt (M4 × 0.7 × 20)
35. Push-nut
36. Spacer
37. Bracket
38. Bolt
39. Bolt (M10 × 1.5 × 110)
40. Bolt
41. Strap
42. Nut (M 14.0 × 2)
43. Bolt w/screw
44. Bolt (M8 × 1.25 × 16)
45. Bumper
46. Rear shock absorber
47. Retainer
48. Grommet
49. Grommet
50. Nut (M10 × 1.5)
51. Bolt (M8 × 1.25 × 180)
52. Washer
53. Spacer
54. Grommet
55. Screw (M10 × 1.5 × 32)
56. Nut (M8 × 1.25)(*2)
57. Bracket

1. Tie rod bracket brace
2. Upper spring insulator
3. Coil spring
4. Screw (M10 × 1.5 × 32)
5. Bolt
6. Tie rod
7. Nut (M12 × 1.75)
8. Lower control arm
9. Insulator
10. Rear stabilizer shaft
11. Clamp
12. Nut (M8 × 1.25)
13. Bracket
14. Bolt

Coil spring rear suspension used on 1982 and later models (© Chevrolet Div., G.M. Corp.)

4. Disconnect the track bar from the axle.

5. Remove the lower shock absorber bolts and lower the axle. Make sure the axle is supported securely on the floor jack and that there is no chance of the axle slipping after the shock absorbers are disconnected.

6. Lower the axle and remove the coil spring. Do not lower the axle past the limits of the brake lines or the lines will be damaged.

7. Installation is the reverse of removal. Make sure the spring is seated in the same position as before removal.

Track Bar

REMOVAL & INSTALLATION

1982 and Later

1. Raise the rear of the vehicle, place jackstands under the rear axle, then lower the jack so that the stands are supporting all of the weight.

2. Remove the track bar mounting fasteners.

To install:

3. Clean all of the track bar fasteners.

4. Position the track bar in the body bracket and loosely install the bolt and the nut.

5. Position the track bar to the axle assembly and install the bolt and the nut. Torque the bolt to 93 ft. lbs.

6. Torque the body bracket nut to 58 ft. lbs.

7. Raise the rear axle off of the jackstands, remove the jackstands, then lower the vehicle.

Track Bar Brace

REMOVAL & INSTALLATION

1982 and Later

1. Raise the rear of the vehicle, place jackstands under the rear axle, then lower the jack so that the stands are supporting all of the weight.

2. Remove the heat shield screws from the track bar brace.

3. Remove the three track bar brace-to-body brace screws.

4. Remove the track bar-to-body bracket fasteners and remove the track bar brace.

5. Installation is performed in the reverse of the previous steps. Torque the body brace fasteners to 58 ft. lbs., and the body bracket fasteners to 34 ft. lbs.

Rear Lower Control Arm

REMOVAL & INSTALLATION

1982 and Later

NOTE: Remove/reinstall only one lower control arm at a time. If both arms are removed at the same time, the axle could roll or slip sideways, making reinstallation of the arms very difficult.

1. Raise the rear of the vehicle, place jackstands under the rear axle, then lower the jack so that the stands are supporting all of the weight.

2. Remove the control arm attaching fasteners, then remove the control arm.

3. Installation is a simple matter of

bolting the arm into place. Torque the fasteners to 68 ft. lbs.

Torque Arm

REMOVAL & INSTALLATION

1982 and Later

NOTE: The coil springs must be removed BEFORE the torque arm. If the torque arm is removed first, vehicle damage will result.

NOTE: In order to proceed, the vehicle must be supported in a manner which will allow the rear axle height to be adjusted independently of the body height.

1. Remove the track bar mounting bolt at the axle assembly, then loosen the track bar bolt at the body brace.
2. Disconnect the rear brake hose clip at the axle assembly, which will allow additional drop of the axle.
3. Remove the lower attaching nuts from both rear shock absorbers.
4. Disconnect the shock absorbers from their lower attaching points.
5. On models with four cylinder engines, remove the driveshaft.
6. Carefully lower the rear axle assembly and remove the rear coil springs.

—————— CAUTION ——————
DO NOT overstress the brake hose when lowering the axle—damage to the hose will result.

7. Remove the torque arm rear attaching bolts.
8. Remove the front torque arm outer bracket.
9. Remove the torque arm from the vehicle.
To install:
10. Place the torque arm in position and loosely install the rear torque arm bolts.
11. Install the front torque arm bracket and torque the nuts to 20 ft. lbs.
12. Torque the rear torque arm nuts to 100 ft. lbs.
13. Place the rear springs and insulators in position, then raise the rear axle assembly until all of the weight is supported by the spring.
14. Attach the shock absorbers to the rear axle and torque the fasteners to 70 ft. lbs.
15. Clean and reinstall the track bar mounting bolt at the axle. Torque the bolt to 93 ft. lbs.
16. Clean and reinstall the track bar-to-body bracket nut. Torque the nut to 58 ft. lbs.
17. Install the brake line clip to the underbody.
18. On four cylinder models, reinstall the driveshaft.
19. Lower the vehicle.

BRAKES

Refer to the "Brakes" segment of the Unit Repair section for brake services not listed here.

Master Cylinder

NOTE: For master cylinder removal, refer to the procedure listed in the "Chevrolet Rear Wheel Drive" car section.

Vacuum Power Brake Booster

NOTE: For vacuum power brake booster removal, refer to the procedure listed in the "Chevrolet Rear Wheel Drive" car section.

Parking Brake

ADJUSTMENT

Models With Rear Drum Brakes

1. Depress the parking brake pedal exactly two ratchet clicks.
2. Raise the rear of the vehicle and support safely with jackstands.
3. Tighten the brake cable adjusting nut until the left rear wheel can be turned rearward with both hands, but locks when forward rotation is attempted.
4. Release the parking brake pedal; both rear wheels must turn freely in either direction without brake drag.
5. Lower the vehicle.

Models With Rear Disc Brakes

1. Check for free movement of the parking brake cables and lubricate the underbody rub points of the cables. Also lubricate the equalizer hooks.
2. Release the parking brake pedal completely.
3. Raise the rear of the vehicle and support it safely with jackstands.
4. Hold the brake cable stud from turning, then tighten the adjusting nut until all cable slack is taken up.

NOTE: Check that the parking brake levers on the rear calipers are against the stops on the caliper housing. If the levers are not contacting the stops, loosen the cable adjusting nut until the levers just contact the stops.

5. Operate the parking brake cable several times. Parking brake pedal travel should be 5¼–6¾ in. (models through 1981) or 14 clicks (1982 and later) with approximately 125–130 lbs. of force applied to the pedal.

6. Readjust if necessary.
7. Make sure that the levers contact the caliper stops after adjustments.
8. Lower the vehicle.

STEERING

Tie–Rod Ends

REMOVAL & INSTALLATION

1. Raise the vehicle and support securely.
2. Remove the cotter pins from the ball studs and remove the castellated nuts.
3. Remove the outer ball stud by tapping on the steering arm at the tie-rod end with a heavy hammer on the other side of the steering arm as a backing. If necessary, pull downward on the tie-rod to disconnect it from the steering arm.
4. Remove the inner ball stud from the relay rod using a similar procedure.
5. Remove the tie-rod end or ends to be replaced by loosening the clamp bolt and unscrewing them.
6. Lubricate tie-rod threads with chassis grease and install new tie-rod(s). Make sure both ends are an equal distance from the tie-rod and tighten clamp bolts.
7. Make sure ball studs, tapered surfaces, and all threaded surfaces are clean and smooth, and free of grease. Install seals on ball studs. Install ball stud in steering arm and relay rod.
8. Rotate both inner and outer tie-rod housings rearward to the limit of ball joint travel before tightening clamps. Make sure clamp slots and sleeve slots are aligned before tightening clamps. Make sure tightened bolts will be in horizontal position to 45 degrees upward (in the forward direction) when the tie-rod is in its normal position. Make sure the tie-rod end stays in position relative to the rod during the tightening operation. Tighten the clamps, and then return the assembly to the center of its travel.
9. Install ball stud nuts and torque to 35 ft. lbs. Then tighten (*do not loosen*) further as required to align cotter pin holes in studs and nuts. Install new cotter pins.
10. Lubricate new tie-rod ends and lower the vehicle.

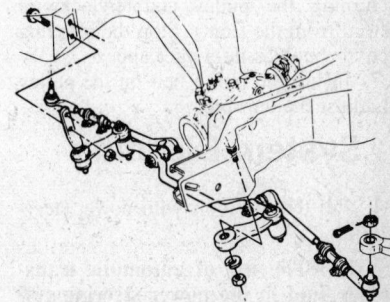

Steering linkage—typical of all models

Steering Gear (Manual and/or Power)

REMOVAL & INSTALLATION

1. Disconnect the negative battery cable. Remove the coupling shield.
2. Remove the retaining bolts at the steering coupling to steering shaft flange.
3. Remove the pitman arm nut and washer. Mark the relation of the arm position to the shaft.
4. Remove pitman arm using special tool J-6632 or its equal.
5. Remove the steering box to frame bolts. Remove the steering box.
6. Installation is the reverse of removal.

NOTE: On vehicles with power steering remove the fluid hoses and cap them to prevent foreign material from entering the system.

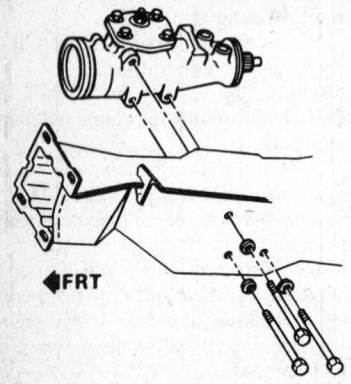

Power steering gear mounting—typical of all models (© Chevrolet Div., G.M. Corp.)

Power Steering Pump

REMOVAL & INSTALLATION

1. Remove the hoses at the pump and tape the openings shut to prevent contamination. Position the disconnected lines in a raised position to prevent leakage.
2. Remove the pump belt.
3. Loosen the retaining bolts and any braces, and remove the pump.
4. Install the pump on the engine with the retaining bolt handtight.
5. Connect and tighten the hose fittings.
6. Refill the pump with fluid and bleed by turning the pulley counterclockwise (viewed from the front). Stop the bleeding when air bubbles no longer appear.
7. Install the pump belt on the pulley and adjust the tension.

System Bleeding

1. Fill the reservoir with power steering fluid.

NOTE: The use of automatic transmission fluid in the power steering system is NOT recommended.

2. Allow the reservoir and fluid to sit undisturbed for a few minutes.
3. Start the engine, allow it to run for a moment, then turn if off.
4. Check the reservoir fluid level and add fluid if necessary.
5. Repeat the above steps until the fluid level stabilizes.
6. Raise the front of the vehicle so that the wheels are off of the ground.
7. Start the engine and increase the engine speed to about 1500 rpm.
8. Turn the front wheels right to left (and back) several times, lightly contacting the wheel stops at the ends of travel.
9. Check the reservoir fluid level. Add fluid as required.
10. Repeat Step 8 until the fluid level in the reservoir stabilizes.
11. Lower the vehicle and repeat Steps 8 and 9.

Steering Wheel

REMOVAL & INSTALLATION

——— CAUTION ———
Disconnect the battery ground cable before removing the steering wheel. When installing a steering wheel, always make sure that the turn signal lever is in the neutral position.

Standard Wheel

1. Remove the trim retaining screws from behind the wheel. On wheels with a center cap, pull off the cap.
2. Lift the trim off and pull the horn wires from the turn signal cancelling cam.

NOTE: On the tilt-telescope wheel, remove the three upper contact retaining screws, the contact and shim if used. Then remove the center star screw and lever.

3. Remove the shaft snap-ring. Remove the steering wheel nut.
4. Mark the wheel-to-shaft relationship, and then remove the wheel with a puller.
5. Install the wheel on the shaft aligning the previously made marks. Tighten the nut to 30 ft. lbs.
6. Insert the horn wires into the cancelling cam.

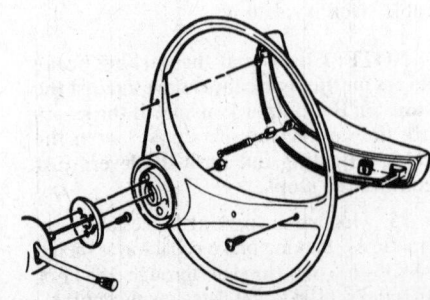

Standard steering wheel (©Chevrolet Div., G.M. Corp)

7. Install the center trim and reconnect the battery cable.

Padded Rim Wheel

1. Pry out the center cap and retainer. Remove the shaft snap-ring.

NOTE: On the tilt-telescope wheel, remove the three upper contact retaining screws, the contact and shim if used. Then remove the center star screw and lever.

2. Remove the steering wheel nut and washer.
3. Remove the three receiving cup screws and remove the cup belleville spring, bushing, and pivot ring.
4. Mark the wheel-to-shaft relationship, and then remove the wheel with a puller.
5. Install the wheel on the shaft, aligning the previously made marks. Tighten the nut to 30 ft. lbs.
6. Install the belleville spring (dished side up), pivot ring, bushing, and receiving cup. Install the center cap and reconnect the battery.

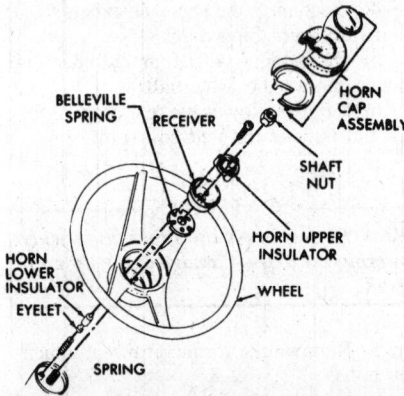

Cushioned rim steering wheel assembly (© Chevrolet Div., G.M. Corp)

Turn Signal Switch

REMOVAL & INSTALLATION

1. Remove the steering wheel as previously outlined. Remove the trim cover.
2. Pry the cover off with a screwdriver, and lift the cover off the shaft.
3. Position the U-shaped lockplate compressing tool on the end of the steering shaft and compress the lock plate by turning the shaft nut clockwise. Pry the wire snap-ring out of the shaft groove.
4. Remove the tool and lift the lockplate off the shaft.
5. Slip the cancelling cam, upper bearing preload spring, and thrust washer off the shaft.
6. Remove the turn signal lever. Push the flasher knob in and unscrew it. On models equipped with a button and a knob, remove the button retaining screw, then remove the button, spring, and knob.
7. Pull the switch connector out the mast jacket and tape the upper part to facilitate

Depressing lock cylinder spring latch (© Chevrolet Motor Division, G.M. Corp.)

switch removal. Attach a long piece of wire to the turn signal switch connector. When installing the turn signal switch, feed this wire through the column first, and then use this wire to pull the switch connector into position. On tilt wheels, place the turn signal and shifter housing in low position and remove the harness cover.

8. Remove the three switch mounting screws. Remove the switch by pulling it straight up while guiding the wiring harness cover through the column.

9. Install the replacement switch by working the connector and cover down through the housing and under the bracket. On tilt models, the connector is worked down through the housing, under the bracket, and then the cover is installed on the harness.

10. Install the switch mounting screws and the connector on the mast jacket bracket. Install the column-to-dash trim plate.

11. Install the flasher knob and the turn signal lever.

12. With the turn signal lever in neutral and the flasher knob out, slide the thrust washer, upper bearing preload spring, and cancelling cam onto the shaft.

13. Position the lock plate on the shaft and press it down until a new snap–ring can be inserted in the shaft groove. Always use a new snap–ring when assembling.

14. Install the cover and the steering wheel.

Ignition Switch

REPLACEMENT

The switch is located inside the channel section of the brake pedal support and is completely inaccessible without first lowering the steering column. The switch is actuated by a rod and rack assembly. A gear on the end of the lock cylinder engages the toothed upper end of the rod.

1. Lower the steering column; be sure to properly support it.

2. Put the switch in the "Off-Unlocked" position. With the cylinder removed, the rod is in "Off-Unlocked" which is two detents from the top.

3. Remove the two switch screws and remove the switch assembly.

4. Before installing, place the new switch in the "Off-Unlocked" position and make sure the lock cylinder and actuating rod are in the "Off-Unlocked" (third detent from the top) position.

5. Install the activating rod into the switch and assemble the switch on the column. Tighten the mounting screws. Use only the specified screws since overlength screws could impair the collapsibility of the column.

6. Reinstall the steering column.

Ignition Lock Cylinder

REPLACEMENT

1978

1. Remove the steering wheel as previously described.

2. Remove the turn signal switch as previously described.

3. Do not remove the buzzer switch or lock damage will result.

4. Place the cylinder in the Lock position. Insert a small screwdriver or similar tool into the turn signal housing slot. Keep the tool to the right of the slot, break the housing slot loose and at the same time, depress the spring latch at the lower end of the cylinder. With the latch depressed, the lock cylinder can be removed from the housing.

5. Hold the lock cylinder sleeve and rotate the knob clockwise against the stop. Insert the cylinder into the housing bore with the key on the cylinder sleeve aligned with the keyway in the housing. Push the cylinder into the abutment of the sector and cylinder.

6. Rotate the cylinder counterclockwise, maintaining a light pressure until the drive section of the cylinder mates with the sector.

7. Push in until the snap ring pops into the grooves and the lock cylinder is secured in the housing. Check for free rotation.

8. Install the turn signal and steering wheel.

1979 and Later

1. Place the lock in the Run position.

2. Remove the lock plate, turn signal switch and buzzer switch.

3. Remove the screw and lock cylinder.

------- CAUTION -------

If the screw is dropped on removal, it could fall into the column, requiring complete disassembly to retrieve the screw.

4. Rotate the cylinder clockwise to align cylinder key with the keyway in the housing.

5. Push the lock all the way in.

6. Install the screw. Tighten the screw to 14 in. lb. for adjustable columns and 25 in. lb. for standard columns.

INSTRUMENT PANEL

Headlamp Switch

REMOVAL & INSTALLATION

Camaro—Through 1981

1. Disconnect battery negative cable.

2. Remove steering column lower cover (six screws).

3. Reach up under cluster on the left side and depress light switch shaft retainer, while pulling gently on shaft.

4. Remove nut that secures switch to cluster carrier.

5. Remove four cluster carrier screws in front and two from rear, then tilt right side of cluster out. Cigarette lighter grounding ring may have to be freed.

6. Unplug harness connector from switch.

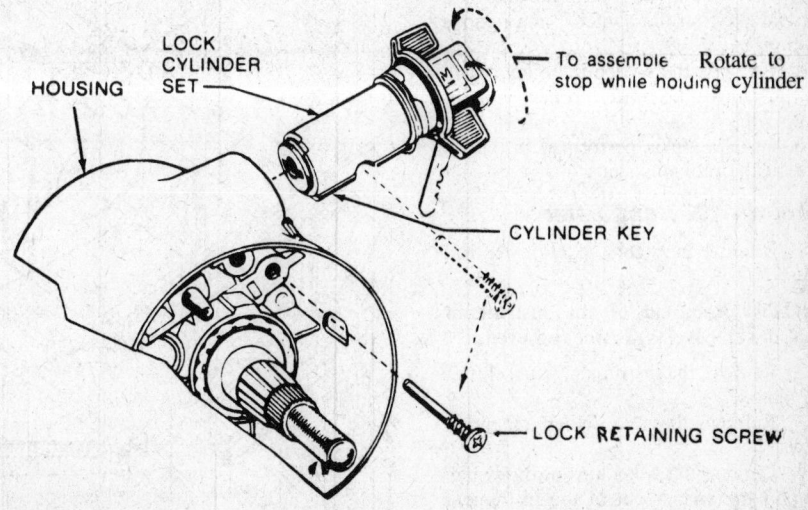

1979 and later ignition lock cylinder replacement (© Chevrolet Div., G.M. Corp.)

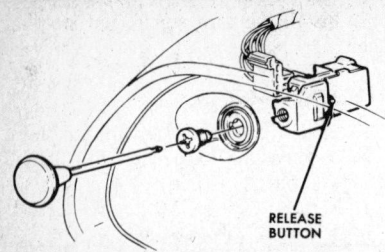

Typical headlamp switch. Note the positioning of the knob and shaft release button (© Chevrolet Div., G.M. Corp.)

7. Remove switch.

8. To install, reverse removal procedure. Make sure all ground connections are refastened.

Camaro—1982 and Later

1. Disconnect the negative battery cable at the battery.

2. Remove the four screws from inside the defroster duct (instrument panel pad securing screws).

3. Remove the screws which are under the lip of the instrument panel pad.

4. Remove the instrument panel pad.

5. On models equipped with air conditioning, remove the instrument panel cluster bezel and the cluster.

6. Remove the radio speaker bracket.

7. Pull the headlamp switch knob to the On position, depress the locking button for the knob and shaft (located on the switch), and remove the knob and shaft.

8. Remove the switch bezel (retainer).

9. Disconnect the wiring from the switch and remove the switch.

10. Installation is performed in the reverse of the previous steps.

Firebird—Through 1981

1. Disconnect the negative battery cable at the battery.

2. Pull the headlamp switch knob to the On position.

3. Reach under the instrument panel and depress the locking button for the knob and shaft (located on the switch), and remove the knob and shaft.

4. Remove the switch retaining nut.

5. Remove the switch from the instrument panel.

6. Installation is performed in the reverse of the previous steps.

Firebird—1982 and Later

1. Remove the right and left lower trim plates.

NOTE: Removal of the instrument panel lower cover(s) is not required.

2. Remove the instrument panel cluster trim plate.

3. Remove the two switch mounting screws.

4. Depress the side tangs of the switch and pull the switch out of the instrument panel.

5. The individual switches of the headlamp switch assembly are now serviceable. Installation of the switch is performed in the reverse order of the previous steps.

Speedometer Cable
REMOVAL & INSTALLATION
Through 1981

1. Disconnect the battery ground cable.

2. Reach up behind the speedometer and depress the retaining tab while pushing in, then out on the cable end.

3. Remove the firewall panel sealing plug to allow movement of the cable.

4. Pull the core from the casing. If the core is broken, it will be necessary to raise the car and disconnect the cable from the transmission.

5. Lubricate the core with cable lubricant and insert it into the casing. Connect the case to the speedometer and install the dash sealing plug.

1982 and Later

1. Disconnect the negative battery cable at the battery.

2. On Firebird models, remove the upper and lower instrument panel trim plates.

3. On models without cruise control, disconnect the speedometer cable strap at the power brake booster. On models with power brakes, disconnect the speedometer cable at the cruise control transducer.

4. On Camaro models, remove the instrument cluster bezel.

5. Remove the six instrument cluster attachment screws and pull the cluster out far enough to gain access to the rear of the speedometer head.

6. Reach beneath the cable connection at the speedometer head, push in on the cabel retaining spring, and disconnect the cable from the speedometer.

7. Slide the old cable out of the speedometer cable casing. If the cable is broken, remove the cable from both ends of the casing. Using a short piece of the old cable to fit the speedometer connection, turn the speedometer to increase the speed indicated on the dial and check for any binding during rotation. If binding is noted, the speedometer must be removed for repair or replacement. Check the entire cable casing for extreme bends, chafing, breaks, etc., and replace if necessary.

To install:

8. Wipe the cable clean using a lint-free cloth.

9. If the old casing is to be reused, flush the casing with petroleum spirits and blow dry with compressed air.

10. Lubricate the speedometer cable with an appropriate lubricant, being sure to cover the lower two-thirds of the cable.

11. Insert the cable into the casing, then connect the cable and casing assembly to the speedometer.

12. The remainder of the procedure is the reverse of Steps 1–5.

Instrument Cluster
REMOVAL & INSTALLATION
Camaro—Through 1981

1. Disconnect the battery ground cable.

2. Remove the six screws holding the trim cover beneath the steering column. Remember to remove the two screws above the ashtray.

3. Reach behind the cluster and press in the retainer button on the headlamp switch shaft while pulling on the switch knob.

4. Remove the retaining nut from the switch.

5. Remove the cigarette lighter element, disconnect the lighter wire, and unscrew the retainer from the housing.

6. Look up under the lower edge of the cluster and remove the screw from either side of the steering column.

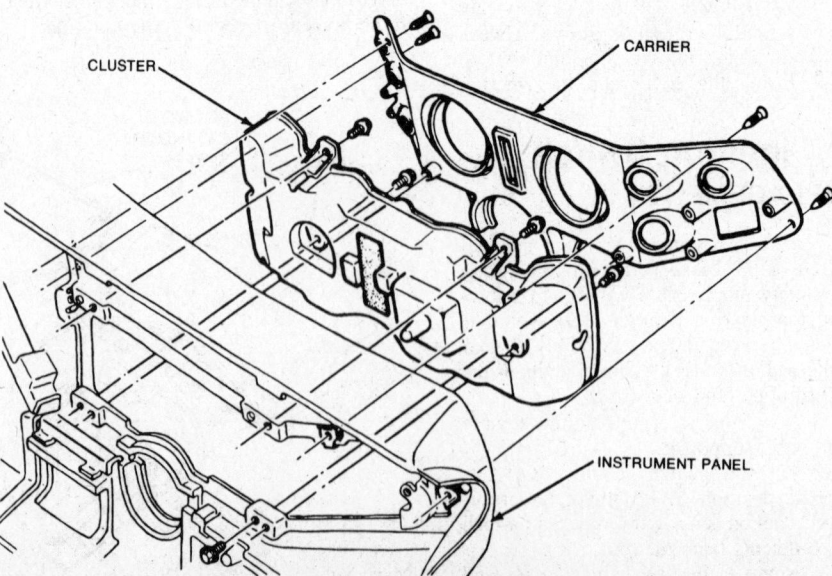

Typical instrument cluster mounting—models through 1981

7. Remove the four screws from the front of the carrier.

8. Remove the screw holding the wiper switch ground wire. It is located under the wiper switch.

9. Detach the connector plugs and remove the carrier.

10. Remove the eight lens screws and the four cluster screws.

11. Disconnect the transmission indicator (PRNDL) from the column.

12. Depress the speedometer cable housing tang on the rear of the cluster and tilt the cluster forward.

13. Remove the connectors from the printed circuit and clock, and free the wiring harness from the cluster.

14. Lift out the cluster.

15. To install, reverse the removal procedure, making sure that all connections are clean and tight, and that the printed circuits are placed with the metallic side to the bulb sockets. It would be a good idea to lubricate the speedometer cable at this time.

OPTIONAL INSTRUMENT CLUSTER

To remove all bulbs, instruments (except speedometer), and printed circuits, it is not necessary (unless air-conditioned) to remove the cluster. The instruments are installed and removed from the rear of the cluster. On cars with air-conditioning, it will be necessary to remove the cluster to remove the ammeter, fuel, and temperature gauges.

NOTE: When performing any operation behind the cluster, disconnect the battery ground cable first.

Firebird—Through 1981

1. Disconnect the battery ground cable.
2. Remove the upper instrument panel trim plate.
3. Remove the lower instrument panel trim and bracket at the steering column.
4. Loosen the two steering column nuts and carefully lower the column.
5. Remove the cluster screws, pull out the cluster and disconnect the speedometer and wiring for the printed circuit.
6. Remove the cluster. To install, reverse the removal procedure.

Camaro—1982 and Later

1. Disconnect the negative battery cable.
2. Remove the instrument cluster bezel.
3. Remove the cluster attachment screws.
4. Pull the cluster out. Disconnect the speedometer cable and electrical connections.
5. Remove the cluster lens.
6. Installation is the reverse of removal.

Firebird—1982 and Later

1. Disconnect the negative battery cable.
2. Remove the right and left lower trim plates.

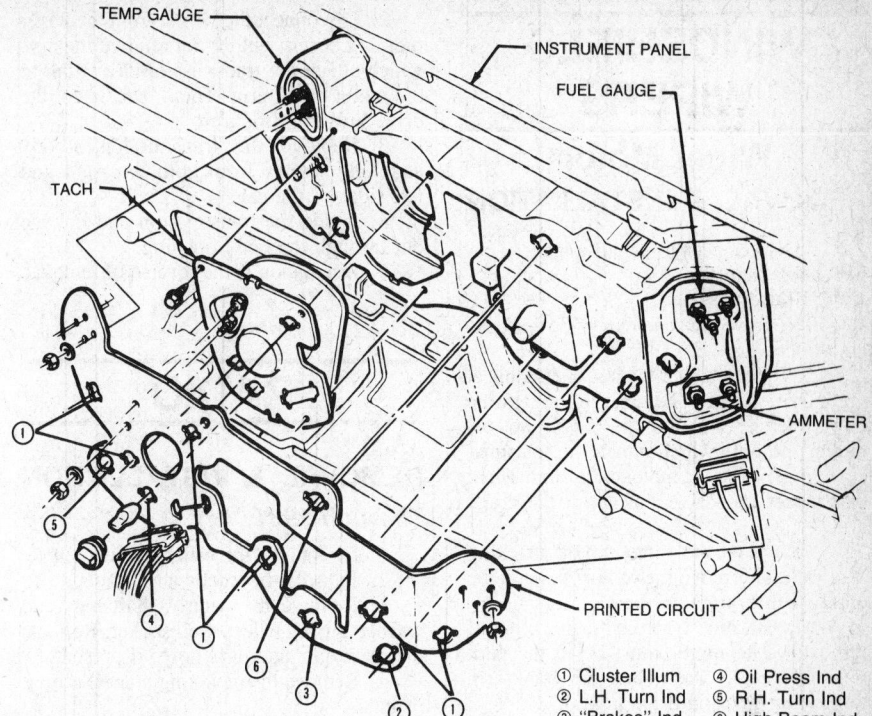

Typical optional instrument panel cluster mounting—models through 1981

① Cluster Illum   ④ Oil Press Ind
② L.H. Turn Ind   ⑤ R.H. Turn Ind
③ "Brakes" Ind   ⑥ High Beam Ind

3. Remove the instrument cluster trim plate.

4. Remove the cluster attachment screws, pull the cluster back and disconnect the speed cable and the electrical connections.

5. Remove the trip odometer, reset knob (if so equipped) and the cluster lens.

6. Installation is the reverse of removal.

EMISSIONS INDICATOR

An emissions indicator flag may appear in the odometer window of the speedometer, on some 1980 and later General Motors vehicles. The flag could say "Sensor" "Emissions" or "Catalyst" depending on the part or assembly that is scheduled for regular emissions maintenance replacement. The word "Sensor" indicates a need for oxygen sensor replacement and the words "Emissions" or "Catalyst" indicate the need for catalytic converter catalyst replacement.

Reset

1. Remove the instrument panel trim plate.

2. Remove the instrument cluster lens.

3. Locate the flag indicator reset notches at the drivers side of the odometer.

4. Use a pointed tool to apply light downward pressure on the notches, until the indictor is reset.

NOTE: When the indicator is reset an alignment mark will appear in the left center of the odometer window.

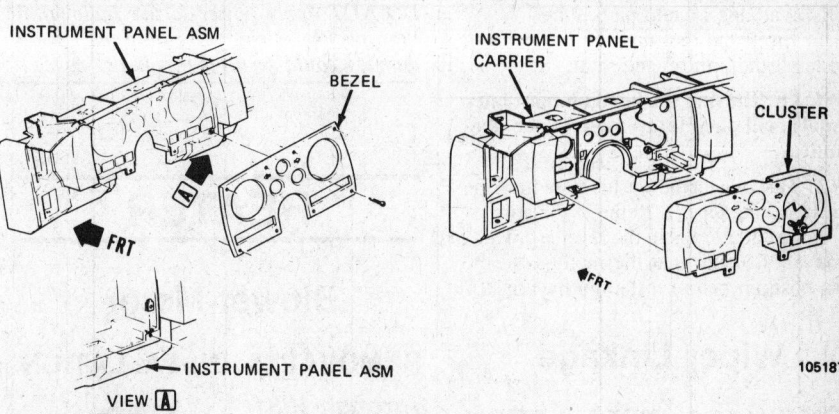

Typical instrument panel cluster and bezel—1982 and later (© Chevrolet Div., G.M. Corp.)

WINDSHIELD WIPERS

Wiper Motor

REMOVAL & INSTALLATION

1. Disconnect the negative battery cable at the battery.
2. Raise the hood.
3. Remove the screen or grille that covers the cowl area.
4. Working under the hood, disconnect the motor wiring. Then, reach through the cowl opening and loosen, but do not remove, the nuts which attach the transmission drive link to the motor crank arm. Then, disconnect the drive link from the crank arm.
5. Remove the three motor attaching screws, and remove the motor, guiding the crank arm through the hole.
6. Installation is in the reverse order of removal. The motor must be in the park position before assembling the crank arm to the transmission drive link(s).

Wiper Arms and Blades

REMOVAL & INSTALLATION

If the wiper assembly has a press type release tab at the center, simply depress the tab and remove the blade. If the blade has no release tab, use a screwdriver to depress the spring at the center. This will release the assembly. To install the assembly, position the blade over the pin at the tip of the arm and press until the spring retainer engages the groove in the pin.

To remove the element, either depress the release button or squeeze the spring type retainer clip at the outer end together, and slide the blade element out. Just slide the new element in until it latches.

Removal of the wiper arms requires the use of a special tool, G.M. J8966 or its equivalent. Versions of this tool are generally available in auto parts stores.

1. Insert the tool under the wiper arm and lever the arm off the shaft.

NOTE: Raising the hood on most later models will facilitate easier wiper arm removal.

2. Disconnect the washer hose from the arm (if so equipped). Remove the arm.
3. Installation is in the reverse order of removal. Be sure that the motor is in the park position before installing the arms.

Wiper Linkage

REMOVAL & INSTALLATION

1. Remove the wiper arms and blades. Remove the cowl screen or grille.

2. Disconnect the wiring from the wiper motor. Loosen, but do not remove the nuts which attach the transmission drive link to the motor crank arm. Then, disconnect the drive link from the arm.
3. Remove the transmission-to-body attaching screws from both the right and left sides of the car.
4. Guide the transmission and linkage out through the cowl opening.
5. Installation is the reverse of removal.

RADIO

REMOVAL & INSTALLATION

Through 1981

1. Disconnect the battery ground cable.
2. Pull off the knobs and bezels.
3. Remove the control shaft nuts and washers, using a deep well socket. Remove the center air duct and hose, if present.
4. Remove the mounting bracket screws or nuts.
5. Move the radio back until the shafts clear the instrument panel. Lower it and disconnect the antenna, speaker, and power wires.
6. Remove the radio. Reverse the procedure for installation. Make sure to hook up the speaker leads before turning the radio on; operating without a speaker will damage the transistors.

1982 and Later

1. Disconnect the negative battery cable at the battery.
2. Remove the three console bezel screws and the console bezel.
3. Remove the four radio-to-console attaching screws.
4. Remove the radio and disconnect the electrical connector.
5. Installation is performed in the reverse of the previous steps.

--- CAUTION ---

DO NOT apply power to the radio until the speaker wiring is connected; radio damage could result if this is not done.

HEATER

Blower Motor

REMOVAL & INSTALLATION

Through 1981

1. Disconnect the negative battery cable.
2. Tag and disconnect any electrical connections at the motor.

3. Remove the heater front module screws and nuts.
4. Lift off the front module and the motor.
5. Installation is in the reverse order of removal. Replace all sealer.

1982 and Later

1. Disconnect the negative battery cable at the battery.
2. Tag and disconnect the wiring from the blower motor and the resistor.
3. Remove the blower motor cooling tube.
4. Remove the blower motor retaining screws.
5. Remove the blower motor and fan assembly from the case.
6. Installation of the motor is performed in the reverse of the previous steps.

Heater Core

REMOVAL & INSTALLATION

Through 1981—Without Air Conditioning

1. Disconnect the negative battery cable. Drain the radiator. Disconnect heater hoses.
2. Remove the nuts that attach the heater case to the firewall from the firewall side. Then, remove the screws from inside the car.
3. Remove the glovebox and door. Remove the screws attaching the heater outlet duct to the heater case, and remove the duct.
4. Remove the defroster screw. Pull the heater case out. The core may now be pulled out of the case.
5. Reverse the removal procedure to install. Use new seals between the heater case and the firewall.

1982 and Later—Without Air Conditioning

1. Disconnect the negative battery cable at the battery.
2. Drain the cooling system.
3. Disconnect the coolant (heater) hoses from the heater core.
4. Remove the right side lower hush panel (see accompanying illustration).
5. Remove the right side lower instrument panel trim panel.
6. On fuel-injected V8 models, remove the electronic spark control (ESC) module from under the right side of the instrument panel.
7. Remove the right side lower instrument panel carrier-to-cowl screw.
8. Remove the four heater case cover screws.

NOTE: The upper left heater case cover screw may be reached with a long socket extension placed through the instrument panel openings which were exposed by the removal of the lower instrument panel

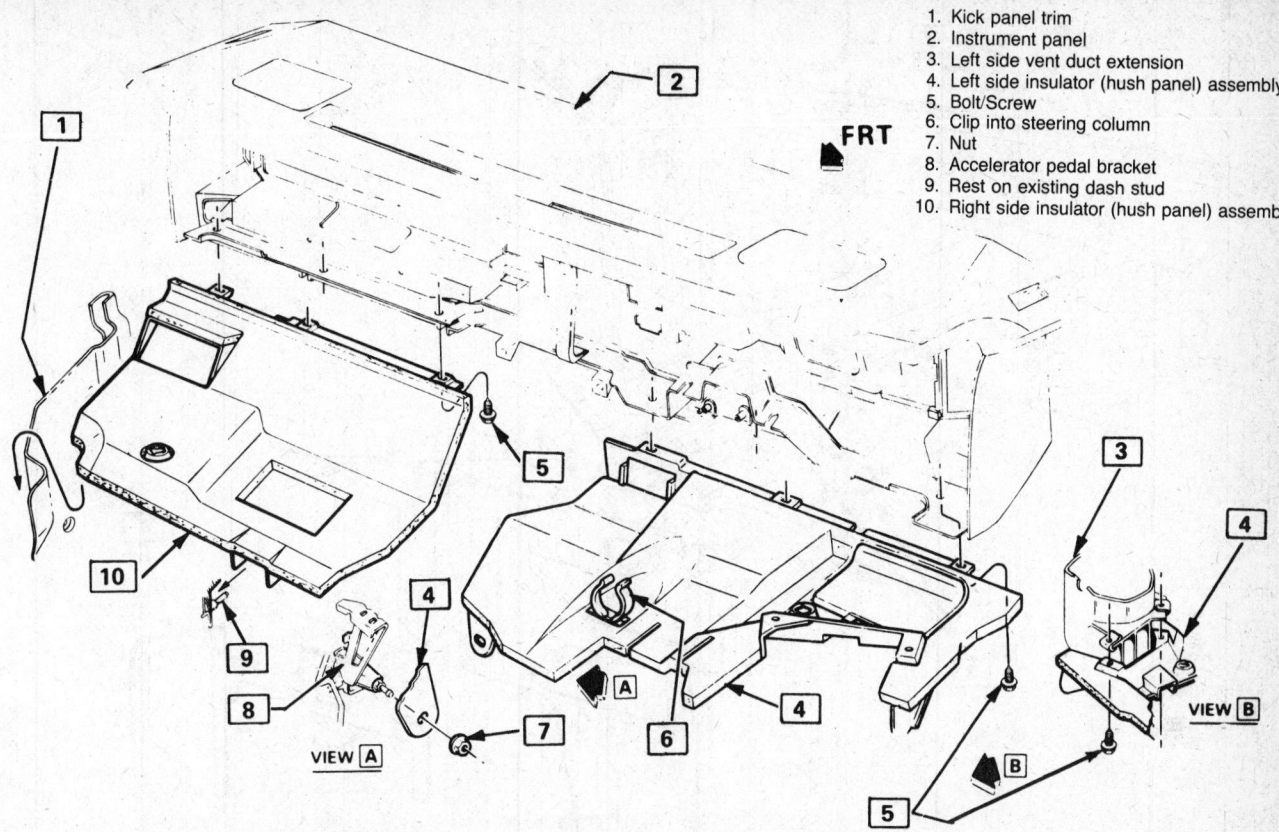

1. Kick panel trim
2. Instrument panel
3. Left side vent duct extension
4. Left side insulator (hush panel) assembly
5. Bolt/Screw
6. Clip into steering column
7. Nut
8. Accelerator pedal bracket
9. Rest on existing dash stud
10. Right side insulator (hush panel) assembly

Hush panel mounting on 1982 and later models without air conditioning (© Pontiac Div., G.M. Corp.)

trim panel. Carefully lift the lower right corner of the instrument panel to align the socket extension.

9. Remove the heater case cover.

10. Remove the heater core support plate and the baffle screws.

11. Remove the heater core, support plate, and baffle from the heater case.

12. Installation of the core is performed in the reverse of the previous steps. Refill the cooling system and check for leaks after the engine has been started.

All Air Conditioned Models

Because removal of the heater core on these models requires that the air conditioning system be discharged, replacement of the core should be referred to a qualified, professional technician.

CIRCUIT PROTECTION

Circuit Breakers

A circuit breaker in the light switch protects the headlight circuit. A separate 30 amp breaker mounted on the firewall protects the

power window, seat, and power top circuits. On 1982 and later models this is located in the fuse box. Circuit breakers open and close rapidly to protect the circuit if current is excessive.

Fuses and Flashers

The fuse box is located under the instrument panel on the left side. The turn signal flasher is under the dash to the right of the steering column. The hazard flasher is under the dash, to the left of the steering column. On all 1980–81 models, both the turn signal flasher and the hazard flasher are located at the lower left hand and the upper right hand corners of the fuse box respectively. On the 1982 and later models, the hazard flasher is located in the convenience center which is on the underside of the instrument panel, to the right of the steering column. The turn signal flasher is located in a clip behind the instrument panel to the right of the steering column. There is an inline fuse for the underhood/spotlamp circuit. The fuse box is marked to indicate fuse size and the circuit(s) protected.

Fusible Links

In addition to circuit breakers and fuses,

the wiring harness incorporates fusible links to protect the wiring. Links are used rather than a fuse, in wiring circuits that are not normally fused, such as the ignition circuit. Fusible links are color coded red in the charging and load circuits to match the color coding of the circuits they protect. Each link is four gauges smaller than the cable it protects, and is marked on the insulation with the gauge size because the insulation makes it appear heavier than it really is.

The engine compartment wiring harness has several fusible links. The same size wire with a special hypalon insulation must be used when replacing a fusible link.

The links are typically located in the following areas:

1. A molded splice at the starter solenoid "Bat" terminal, a 14 gauge red wire.

2. A 16 gauge red fusible link at the junction block to protect the unfused wiring of 12 gauge or larger wire. This link stops at the bulkhead connector.

3. The alternator warning light and field circuitry is protected by a 20 gauge red wire fusible link used in the "battery feed to voltage regulator No. 3 terminal." The link is installed as a molded splice in the circuit at the junction block.

4. The ammeter circuit is protected by two 20 gauge fusible links installed as molded splices in the circuit at the junction block and battery to starter circuit.

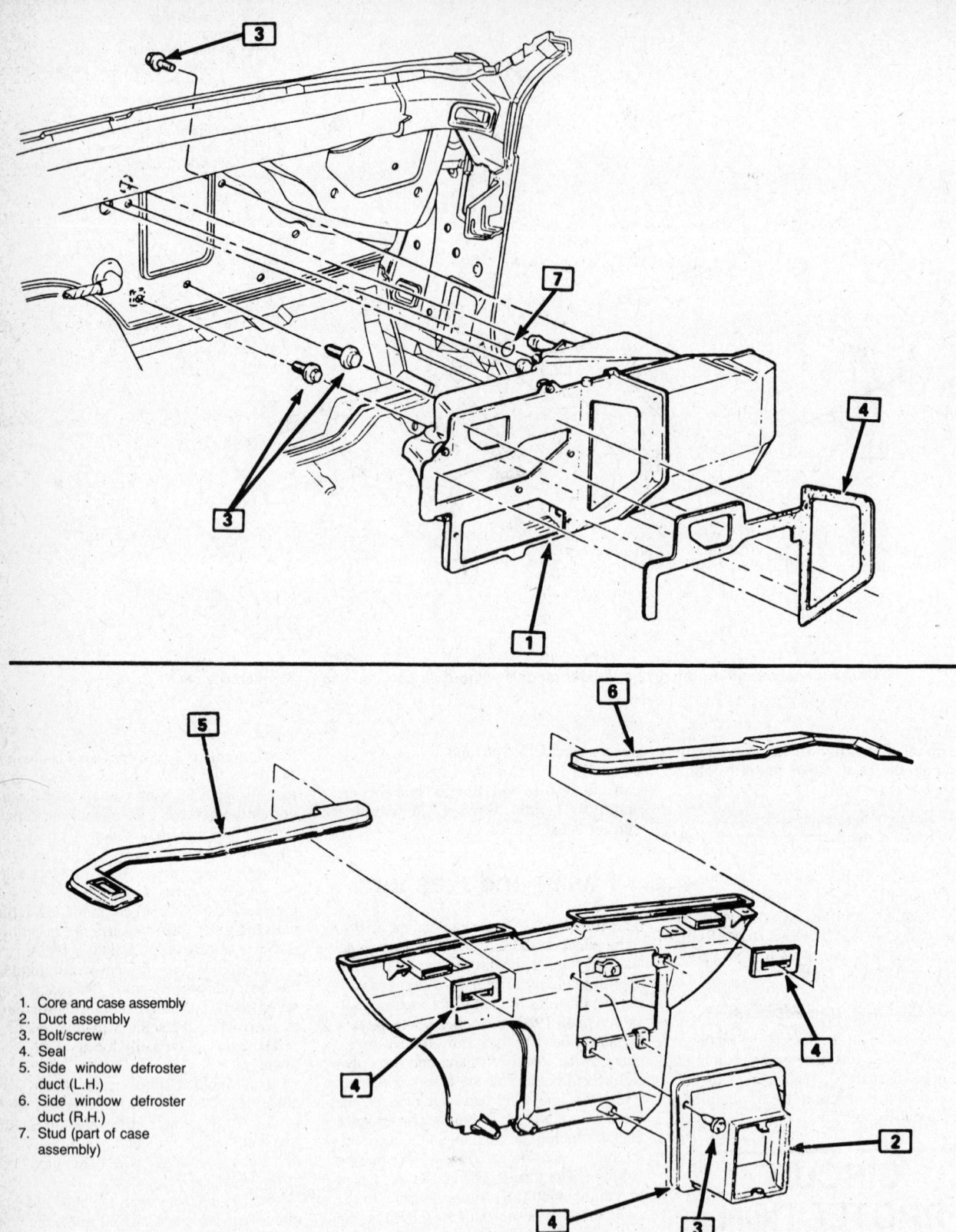

1. Core and case assembly
2. Duct assembly
3. Bolt/screw
4. Seal
5. Side window defroster duct (L.H.)
6. Side window defroster duct (R.H.)
7. Stud (part of case assembly)

Heater assembly duct work—1982 and later (© Chevrolet Div., G.M. Corp.)

GM "H" Body
Astre, Monza, Starfire,
'78–'80 Skyhawk, 1978–80 Sunbird

YEAR IDENTIFICATION

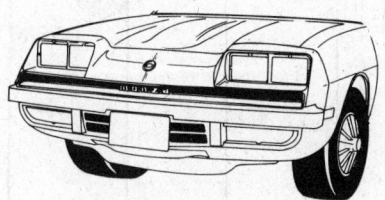

1977 Monza

1978 Monza Town Coupe

1979 Monza

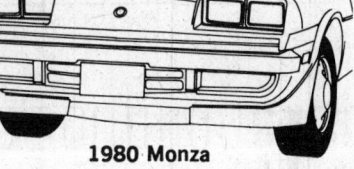

1980 Monza

1978 Starfire

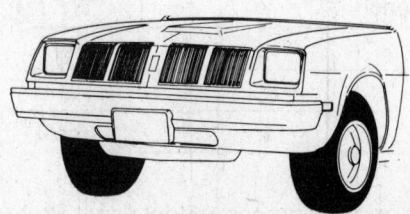

1979 Starfire

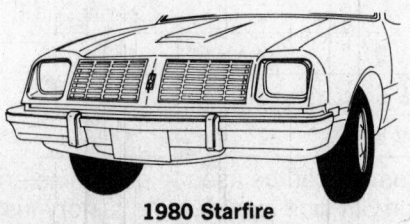

1980 Starfire

1978 Skyhawk

C673

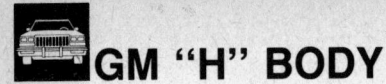

YEAR IDENTIFICATION

1979 Skyhawk

1980 Skyhawk

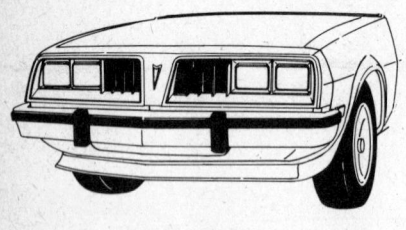

1978 Sunbird

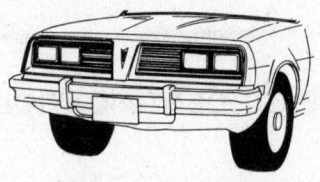

1979 Sunbird

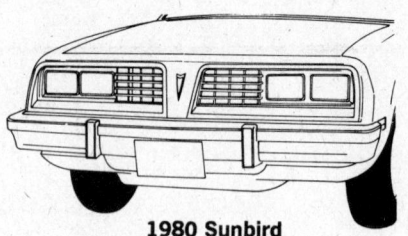

1980 Sunbird

VEHICLE IDENTIFICATION NUMBER (VIN)

It is important for servicing and ordering parts to be certain of the vehicle and engine identification. The VIN (vehicle identification number) is a 13 or 17 digit number visible through the windshield on the driver's side of the dash and contains the vehicle and engine identification codes. It can be interpreted as follows:

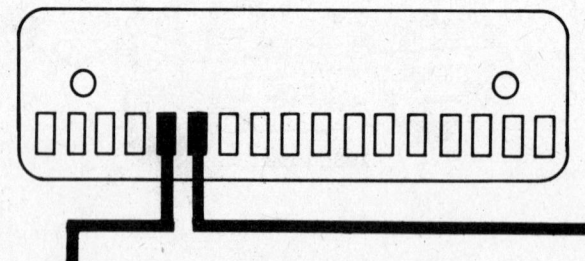

Engine Code						Model Year Code	
Code	Cu. in.	Liters	Cyl.	Carb.	Eng. Mfg.	Code	Year
V	151	2.5	4	2	Pont.	8	1978
C	196	3.2	V-6	2	Buick	9	1979
A	231	3.8	V-6	2	Buick	A	1980
G	305	5.0	V-8	2	Chev.		

The thirteen digit Vehicle Identification Number can be used to determine engine application and model year. The 6th digit indicates the model year, and the 5th digit identifies the factory installed engine.

GENERAL ENGINE SPECIFICATIONS

Year	Eng. V.I.N. Code	Engine Displacement Cu In. (cc)	Eng. Mfg.	Carburetor Type	Horsepower (@ rpm)■	Torque @ rpm (ft lbs)■	Bore × Stroke (in.)	Compression Ratio	Oil Pressure @ rpm (psi)
'78	V	4-151①	Pont.	2 bbl	85 @ 4400	123 @ 2800	4.000 × 3.000	8.3:1	36–41
	V	4-151②	Pont.	2 bbl	87 @ 4400	128 @ 2400	4.000 × 3.000	8.3:1	36–41
	V	4-151③	Pont.	2 bbl	90 @ 4400	130 @ 2400	4.000 × 3.000	8.3:1	40
	C	6-196	Buick	2 bbl	90 @ 3600	165 @ 2000	3.500 × 3.400	8.0:1	37
	A	6-231	Buick	2 bbl	105 @ 3400	185 @ 2000	3.800 × 3.400	8.0:1	37
	G	8-305	Chev.	2 bbl	145 @ 3800	245 @ 2400	3.736 × 3.480	8.4:1	32–70
'79	V	4-151④	Pont.	2 bbl	85 @ 4400	123 @ 2800	4.000 × 3.000	8.3:1	36–41
	V	4-151⑤	Pont.	2 bbl	90 @ 4400	128 @ 2400	4.000 × 3.000	8.3:1	36–41
	C	4-196	Buick	2 bbl	105 @ 4000	160 @ 2000	3.500 × 3.400	8.0:1	37
	A	6-231	Buick	2 bbl	115 @ 3600	190 @ 2000	3.800 × 3.400	8.0:1	37
	G	8-305	Chev.	2 bbl	130 @ 3200	245 @ 2400	3.736 × 3.480	8.4:1	45
'80	V	4-151	Pont.	2 bbl	90 @ 4400⑥	128 @ 2400⑦	4.000 × 3.000	8.2:1	37–41
	A	6-231	Buick	2 bbl	110 @ 3800	190 @ 1600	3.800 × 3.400	8.0:1	37

■Horsepower and torque are SAE net figures. They are measured at the rear of the transmission with all accessories installed and operating. Since the figures vary when a given engine is installed in different models, some are representative rather than exact.
EFI—Electronic Fuel Injection
① Monza
② Sunbird
③ Starfire
④ All exc. Calif.—Starfire
⑤ All exc. Calif.—Monza, Sunbird
⑥ Calif.—85 @ 4400
⑦ Calif.—123 @ 2800

TUNE-UP SPECIFICATIONS

Year	Model	Eng. V.I.N. Code	Engine No. Cyl. Displacement (cu. in.)	Eng. Mfg.	(hp)	Spark Plugs Orig. Type	Spark Plugs Gap (in.)	Distributor (deg) (in.)	Ignition Timing (deg) Man	Ignition Timing (deg) Auto	Intake Valve Opens (deg)	Fuel Pump Pressure (psi)	Idle Speed (rpm) ▲ Man	Idle Speed (rpm) ▲ Auto
'78	Monza	V	4-151	Pont.	85	R43TSX	0.060	Electronic	14B	14B⑥	33	4–5½	1000/500	③
	Starfire	V	4-151	Pont.	90	R43TSX	0.060	Electronic	14B	14B	33	4–5	②	③
	Sunbird	V	4-151	Pont.	87	R43TSX	0.060	Electronic	14B	12B④	33	4–5½	②	⑤
	Monza	C	6-196	Buick	90	R46TSX	0.060	Electronic	15B	15B	17	5–6	800	600
	All	A	6-231	Buick	105	R46TSX	0.060	Electronic	15B	15B	17	3–4½	800⑦	600
	Monza	G	8-305	Chev.	145	R45TS	0.045	Electronic	4B	6B⑧	28	4–5	600	500⑨
'79	Starfire	V	4-151	Pont.	85	R44TSX	0.060	Electronic	14B	14B①	33	4–5½	1000	650
	Sunbird	V	4-151	Pont.	85	R44TSX	0.060	Electronic	12B④	12B④	33	5–6½	1000	650
	Monza	V	4-151	Pont.	85	R43TSX	0.060	Electronic	12B④	12B④	33	4–5.5	1000	650
	Monza	C	6-196	Buick	90	R46TSX	0.060	Electronic	15B	15B	16	4.5–7.5	800	670/550
	All	A	6-231	Buick	115	R46TSX	0.060	Electronic	15B	15B	16	4–6.5	800	600
	Monza	G	8-305	Chev.	130	R45TS	0.045	Electronic	4B	4B	28	7.5–9	700/600	600/500⑧

TUNE-UP SPECIFICATIONS

Year	Model	Eng. V.I.N. Code	Engine No. Cyl. Displacement (cu. in.)	Eng. Mfg.	(hp)	Spark Plugs		Distributor		Ignition Timing (deg)		Intake Valve Opens (deg)	Fuel Pump Pressure (psi)	Idle Speed (rpm) ▲	
						Orig. Type	Gap (in.)	(deg)	(in.)	Man	Auto			Man	Auto
'80	All	V	4-151	Pont.	85	R43TSX⑭	0.060	Electronic		12B	12B	33	4.5–5	1000/550 ⑨ ⑩	650/550 ⑪ ⑫
	All	A	6-231	Buick	115	R46TSX	0.060	Electronic		15B	15B	16	4.5–7.5	800/600	650/550⑬

▲ Lines separated by a slash show solenoid on/off

NOTE: The underhood specifications sticker often reflects tune-up specification changes made in production. Sticker figures must be used if they disagree with those in this chart.

NOTE: Where two figures are separated by a slash, the first figure is for idle speed with the solenoid connected, while the second is for the idle speed with the solenoid disconnected.

① Without a/c—1000/500. With a/c—1200/1000
② Calif.—14B
③ With a/c—650, Without a/c—500
④ Calif. without EGR valve—12B
⑤ 600—Skyhawk, Starfire exc. Calif.
⑥ 8B—Calf.
⑦ 600—High Altitude
⑧ Calif.—650/600
⑨ 49 States with a/c—1250/1000
⑩ Calif. without a/c—1000/500, Calif. with a/c—1200/1000
⑪ 49 State with a/c—850/650
⑫ Calif. without a/c—650/550, Calif. with a/c—850/650
⑬ Calif. with a/c—670/620
⑭ Calif. Monza—R44TSX, Sunbird, Starfire—R44TSX

FIRING ORDERS

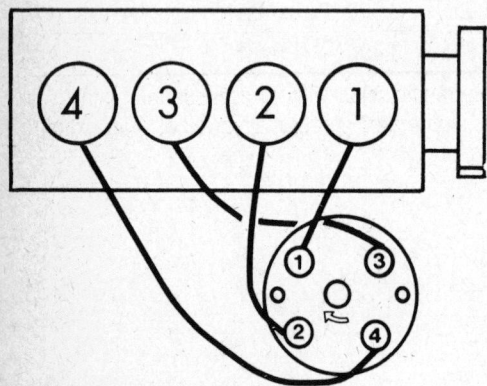

GM Pontiac 151 4 cyl. (1978)
Engine firing order: 1-3-4-2
Distributor rotation: clockwise

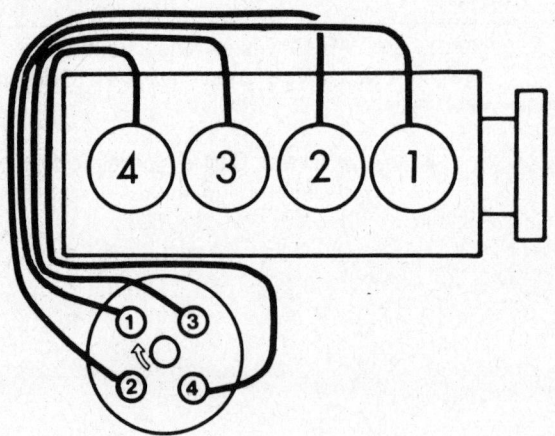

GM Pontiac 151 4-cyl. (1979-80)
Engine firing order: 1-3-4-2
Distributor rotation: clockwise

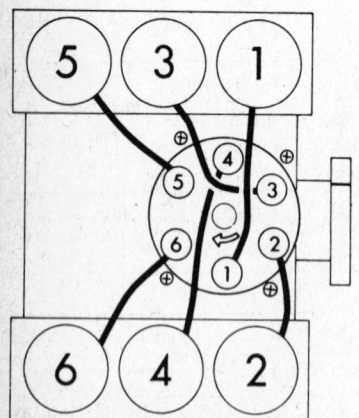

GM (Buick) 196, 231 V6
Engine firing order: 1-6-5-4-3-2
Distributor rotation: clockwise

V6 harmonic balancers have two timing marks: one is 1/8 in. wide, and one is 1/16 in. wide. Use the 1/16 in. mark for timing with a hand held light. The 1/8 in. mark is used only with a magnetic timing pick-up probe.

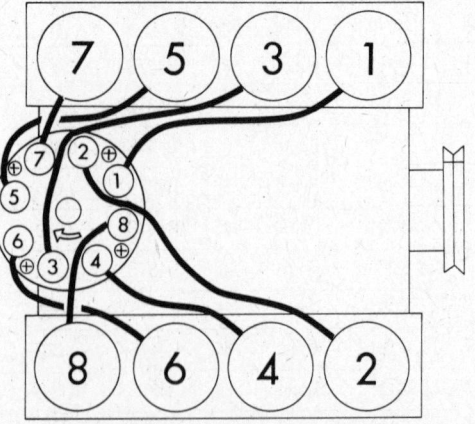

GM (Chevrolet) 305 V8
Engine firing order: 1-8-4-3-6-5-7-2
Distributor rotation: Clockwise

CAPACITIES

Year	Model	Engine Displacement Cu In. (cc)	Engine Crankcase (qts)		Transmission (pts) ▲			Drive Axle (pts)	Gasoline Tank (gals)	Cooling System (qts)	
					Manual		Automatic ●				
			With Filter	Without Filter	3-spd	4-5 spd				W/ AC	W/O AC
'78-'79	Monza	4-151	4	3	—	3①	6	2.8	18.5②	10.8	10.8
	Sunbird	4-151	4	3	—	3.5	6	3.5	18.5③	④	⑤
	Starfire	4-151	4	3	—	3.5	6	3.5	18.5	11.5	11.0
	Monza	6-196	5	4	—	3①	6	2.8	18.5②	11.6	11.6
	Monza	6-231	5	4	—	3①	6	2.8	18.5②	11.6	11.6
	Sunbird	6-231	5	4	—	3.5	7.5	3.5	18.5③	12.8	12.7
	Starfire	6-231	5	4	—	3.5	6	3.5	18.5	12.25	11.75
	Skyhawk	6-231	5	4	—	3.5①	6	3.75	18.5	1.21	11.8
	All	8-305	5	4	—	3①	8	2.8	18.5	18.0	18.0
'80	Monza	4-151	4	3	3.4	—	7.5	3.5	18.5	11.5	11.6
		6-231	5	4	3.4	—	7.0	3.5	18.5	11.9	11.9
	Sunbird	4-151	4	3	3.0	3.5	8.0	3.5	18.5⑥	11.5	11.0
		6-231	5	4	3.4	—	7.0	3.5	18.5⑥	11.9	11.9
	Starfire	4-151	4	3	3.0	—	6.0	3.5	18.5	11.5	11.0
		6-231	5	4	3.0	—	6.0	3.5	18.5	12.4	11.9
	Skyhawk	6-231	5	4	3.0	—	6.0	3.5	18.5	12.2	12.3

● Specifications do not include torque converter
▲ Pints to refill after draining

① 5-speed uses Dexron® II Auto. Trans. Fluid
② Sta. wag. and Monza "S" hatchback—15.0
③ Sta. wag: early production—15.9, late production—15.0
④ Man. trans.—10.9, Auto. trans.—11.6
⑤ Man. trans—10.9, Auto. trans.—11.4
⑥ Sta. wag.—15.0

VALVE SPECIFICATIONS

Year	Engine No. Cyl. Displacement (cu in.)	Seat Angle (deg)	Face Angle (deg)	Spring Test Pressure (lbs @ in.)	Spring Installed Height (in.)	Stem-to-Guide Clearance (in.)		Stem Diameter (in.)	
						Intake	Exhaust	Intake	Exhaust
'78-'79	8-305	46	45	200 @ 1.25②	1²³⁄₃₂	.0010-.0027	.0010-.0027	.3414	.3414
'78-'80	4-151	46	45	176 @ 1.254	1.69	.0010-.0027	.0010-.0027①	.3400	.3400
'78-'80	6-196, 231	45	45	168 @ 1.327	1.727	.0015-.0032	.0015-.0032	.3408	.3408

① Figure given is at top of stem; bottom of stem: .0020-.0037
② 1.16 Exhaust

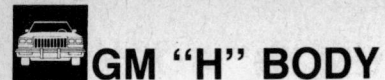

CRANKSHAFT AND CONNECTING ROD SPECIFICATIONS

(All measurements are given in inches)

Year	Engine No. Cyl. Displacement (cu in.)	Crankshaft				Connecting Rod		
		Main Brg. Journal Dia	Main Brg. Oil Clearance	Shaft End-Play	Thrust on No.	Journal Diameter	Oil Clearance	Side Clearance
'78-'80	4-151	2.3000③	.0002-.0022	.0035-.0085	5	2.0000	.0005-.0026	.006-.022
'78-'80	6-196, 231	2.4995	.0003-.0017	.004-.008	2	2.2487-2.2495	.0005-.0026	.006-.027④
'78-'79	8-305	②	①	.002-.006	5	2.0988-2.0998	.0013-.0035	.008-.014

① No. 1—.0008-.0020 in.
No. 2, 3, 4—.0011-.0023 in.
No. 5—.0017-.0033 in.
② No. 1: 2.4484-2.4493
Nos. 2, 3, 4: 2.4481-2.4490
No. 5: 2.4479-2.4488
③ 1979-80: 2.2988
④ 1979-80: .006-.023

TORQUE SPECIFICATIONS

(All readings in ft lbs)

Year	Engine No. Cyl. Displacement (cu in.)	Cylinder Head Bolts	Rod Bearing Bolts	Main Bearing Bolts	Crankshaft Pulley Bolt	Flywheel to Crankshaft Bolts	Manifold	
							Intake	Exhaust
'78-'79	8-305	65	45	80	60	60	30	20①
'78-'80	4-151	85④	30	65	160	55	②	②
'78-'80	6-196, 231	80	40	100	225③	60	45	25

① Inside bolts—30 ft. lbs
② Bolt—40; Nut—30
③ Harmonic balancer; not the pulley
④ 1979 California and all 1980 engines require that the head bolt threads be coated with non-hardening sealer

PISTON AND RING SPECIFICATIONS

(All measurements are given in inches. To convert inches to metric units, refer to the Metric Information section.)

Year	V.I.N. Code	Engine Type/ Disp. cu. in.	Eng. Mfg.	Piston-to-Bore Clearance	Ring Gap			Ring Side Clearance		
					Top Compression	Bottom Compression	Oil Control	Top Compression	Bottom Compression	Oil Control
'78	V	151	Pont.	.0025-.0033②	.010-.020	.010-.020	.015-.035	.0015-.0035	.0015-.0035	.0015-.0035
'79-'80	V	151	Pont.	.0025-.0033②	.016-.026	.009-.019	.015-.055	.0015-.0035	.0015-.0035	.0015-.0035
'78	C	196	Buick	.0008-.0020	.010-.020	.010-.020	.015-.035	.0030-.0050	.0030-.0050	.0035 Max.
'79	C	196	Buick	.0008-.0020	.013-.023	.013-.023	.015-.035	.0030-.0050	.0030-.0050	.0035 Max.
'78	A	231	Buick	.0008-.0020	.010-.020	.010-.020	.015-.035	.0030-.0050	.0030-.0050	.0035 Max.
'79-'80	A	231	Buick	.0008-.0020	.013-.023	.013-.023	.015-.035	.0030-.0050	.0030-.0050	.0035 Max.

PISTON AND RING SPECIFICATIONS

(All measurements are given in inches. To convert inches to metric units, refer to the Metric Information section.)

Year	V.I.N. Code	Engine Type/ Disp. cu. in.	Eng. Mfg.	Piston-to-Bore Clearance	Ring Gap			Ring Side Clearance		
					Top Compression	Bottom Compression	Oil Control	Top Compression	Bottom Compression	Oil Control
'78-'79	G	305	Chev.	.0007–.0017	.010–.020	.010–.025	.010–.035	.0012–.0032	.0012–.0032	.002–.007

① Measured 1.50 in. from top of piston
② Measured 1.11 in. from top of piston

WHEEL ALIGNMENT SPECIFICATIONS

Year	Model	Caster		Camber		Toe-out (in.)	Steering Axis Inclin. (deg)
		Range (deg)	Pref Setting (deg)	Range (deg)	Pref Setting (deg)		
'78	All	⅓N to 1⅓N	⅘N	⅓N to ⁷⁄₁₀P	⅕P	0 to ⅛	8.55
'79-'80	All	⅓N to 1⅓N	⅘N	³⁄₁₀N to ⁷⁄₁₀P	⅕P	0 to ¹⁄₁₆	8.55

CHARGING SYSTEM

A 10-SI Series Delcotron alternator is used. This unit features a non-adjustable, integral solid-state regulator mounted inside the slipring end frame.

For further information on the charging system, please refer to "Charging and Starting" in the Unit Repair section.

Alternator

REMOVAL & INSTALLATION

1. Disconnect the battery.
2. Disconnect the alternator wiring.
3. Remove the alternator brace bolt and V-belt.
4. Remove the pivot mount bolt and the alternator.
5. Installation is the reverse of the removal procedure.
6. Adjust the belt to have ¼-½ inch play on the longest span of the belt. If a tensioning gauge is available, adjust the belt to 80 lbs.

STARTING SYSTEM

The starter is a solenoid actuated Delco-Remy unit. The starter has no R terminal.

The HEI system does not use the solenoid-to-coil wire.

For further information on the starting system, please refer to "Charging and Starting" in the Unit Repair section.

Starter

REMOVAL & INSTALLATION

1. Disconnect the battery ground cable and all the wiring at the solenoid terminals. Install each nut on the terminal from which it was removed, as these nuts are not interchangeable.
2. Loosen the front starter bracket and remove the two mounting bolts.
3. Remove the front bracket bolt and rotate the bracket out of the way.
4. Remove the starter from the car, lowering the front end first.
5. To install, reverse the removal procedure. Tighten the mounting bolts, and then install the brace.

IGNITION SYSTEM

The V8 distributor is mounted at the rear of the engine, gear driven off the camshaft.

The V6 distributor is camshaft driven, and mounted at the front of the engine.

The 151 cu. in. distributor is mounted at the front right side of the engine through 1978, and at the right rear, 1979–80.

Electronic ignition is standard equipment on all models, eliminating the points and

condensor. Two types of HEI distributors are used. 4-151, V6 and V8 distributors combine all ignition components in one unit. The coil is in the distributor cap and connects directly to the rotor.

TIMING LIGHT CONNECTIONS—HEI SYSTEM

Timing light connections should be made in parallel using an adapter at the distributor No. 1 terminal.

TACHOMETER CONNECTIONS—HEI SYSTEM

NOTE: There is a tachometer connecting terminal next to the ignition switch connector on the V8, 151 4 cylinder and V6 HEI distributor cap. Most tachometers will work when connected to this terminal to the positive battery terminal. Some tachometers won't work at all with this system or may require a special hookup. Never ground the tachometer terminal; the system will be damaged.

Distributor

REMOVAL

1. Disconnect the wiring harness connectors at the side of the cap and remove the cap.
2. Disconnect the vacuum line and the primary lead.
3. Mark the distributor housing and the

TIME SAVER

To gain working clearance to remove the number three spark plug on Monza V8s with power steering, perform the following procedure.

1. Raise the car on a lift or jack stands to gain working clearance.
2. Loosen the engine mount to frame bracket bolts on both sides, and the transmission mount to support bolts, but do not remove them.
3. Position a jack under the engine oil pan and while protecting the oil pan from damage, lift the engine to remove weight from the engine mounts.

4. Pry the engine to the right as far as it will go and tighten the right front engine mount to frame bolts to 35-40 ft lbs.
5. With a combination of engine lifting and mount prying, move the left mount bolts toward the inboard side of the mount bracket as far as possible. Torque the mount bolts to 35-40 ft lbs.
6. Torque the transmission mount bolts to 21-31 ft lbs.
7. Because of the relocation of the engine, exhaust vibrations may occur. To avoid this problem, loosen the exhaust system clamps and brackets. Start the engine. While the system is warm, tighten the clamps and brackets to neutralize the system in its new location.

engine in line with the rotor centerline with chalk. This must be done to insure correct distributor installation.

4. Remove the hold-down clamp and distributor.

NOTE: Avoid turning the engine while the distributor is removed.

INSTALLATION

1. Turn the rotor approximately ⅛ turn clockwise past the alignment mark.
2. Push the distributor into position, moving the rotor to mesh the gears.
3. Install the clamp bolt.
4. Connect the vacuum line and the wiring harness.
5. Install the cap and adjust the timing.

INSTALLATION—ENGINE DISTURBED

1. Remove No. 1 spark plug and place a finger over the plug hole. Remove the center coil wire and crank the engine until compression is felt in No. 1 cylinder. Rotate the engine until the timing pointer is aligned with the proper mark.
2. Line up the rotor and the mark made on the distributor housing with the mark made on the engine, then turn the rotor clockwise about ⅛ turn past the marks and install the distributor. As the rotor gear engages the drive gear the rotor should rotate back into line with the marks. If not, repeat procedure until it does. Tighten the clamp bolt.
3. Install the rotor, cap and vacuum line.
4. Connect the wiring harness.
5. Check and adjust the ignition timing.

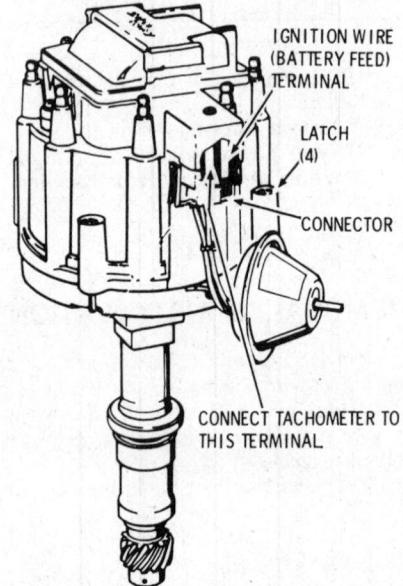

HEI distributor tachometer connecion

Ignition Timing

The timing marks are on a plate mounted on the front of the block and the timing notch is on the crankshaft pulley.

Timing is set as follows:

1. Bring the engine to normal operating temperature, shut the engine off, and connect a timing light according to the manufacturer's instructions. Clean the timing plate and mark the notch in the pulley with chalk.
2. Disconnect and plug the vacuum line to the distributor.
3. See the underhood sticker for the latest certified information on preparing the engine for ignition timing.
4. Set the idle speed to specifications, following the procedure outlined in the Fuel System section.
5. Aim the timing light at the timing marks. If the notch does not align with the correct value on the scale, loosen the distributor clamp locknut and slowly turn the distributor to adjust.
6. Tighten the clamp locknut. Adjust the carburetor idle speed screw to give the specified idle speed with the solenoid disconnected.
7. Reconnect the idle stop solenoid lead. Increase the engine speed to allow the solenoid to extend and then adjust the solenoid plunger screw to obtain the idle speed specified with the solenoid connected.
8. Shut the engine off and connect the vacuum and evaporative emission line.

FUEL SYSTEM

The Holley 5210-C, 6510-C and Rochester 2SE are used on the 4-151. The Rochester 2GE and 2GC are used on the 6-196 and 6-231 through 1978. In 1979 the Rochester M2ME and M2MC replaced the 2GE. The Rochester 2GC is used on the 8-305 through

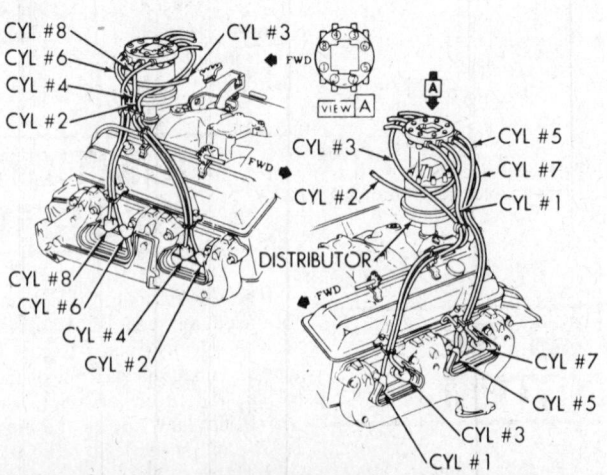

V8 HEI ignition wiring (© Chevrolet Div., G.M. Corp)

1978 and 8-350. On 1979 305 engines, the Rochester M2MC is used.

The electric fuel pump used with all engines except the 4-151 is an integral part of the fuel tank unit assembly, which includes the fuel gauge metering unit. The fuel pump is energized by the ignition switch when the key is in the start or on position. After the engine starts, the pump receives current through the oil pressure safety switch as long as there is approximately 2 psi oil pressure.

Fuel Pump

REMOVAL & INSTALLATION

Electric Fuel Pump

NOTE: It is not necessary to raise the car for tank removal.

1. Disconnect the battery ground cable and siphon the fuel from the tank.
2. Disconnect the gauge sending-unit and pump wires at the rear harness connector.
3. Thoroughly clean and disconnect the fuel line and tank vent line at the tank. These connectors are short pieces of rubber hose secured by squeeze clamps. They are located adjacent to the top of the right rear tire. Wear eye protective goggles when working in this area as the lines and connectors are covered with road dirt. A pair of angled slip-joint pliers will be necessary to reach the clamps.
4. Thoroughly clean the area around the filler neck where it enters the rubber connector pipe. Remove the clamp. Remove the three filler pipe-to-body screws.
5. Place a floor jack under the fuel tank to take up the weight. Remove the nuts from the tank straps and slowly lower the tank until the wire connectors in the top of the tank are visible. Reach up and disconnect the wires. At this point it will probably be necessary to pull the filler tube from the rubber connector pipe. This requires considerable twisting and maneuvering. Take care to avoid getting dirt in the tank.
6. Lower the tank the rest of the way and remove it. The tank may stick to the straps which are coated with a sticky anti-squeak compound.

7. A special wrench is available to remove the lock ring from the gauge pickup unit. If this is not available, use a brass drift. Always use a plastic or hardwood mallet.
8. Spray the area with penetrating oil and very carefully tap the ears of the lock-ring around, alternating ears, until it is free.
9. Carefully remove the pump and sending unit from the tank. Remove the rubber gasket from the lockring.
10. Remove the nut or screw securing the pump ground wire to the bracket. Remove the two wire connector nuts from the pump, making sure you know which wire is which for replacement. Slide the pump and hose connector from the pickup tube.
11. Install the new pump. A filter screen should be supplied with the new pump. Do not overtighten the nuts securing the wires to the pump motor.
12. Carefully lower the assembly into position in the tank. The pickup screen should lie flat along the bottom of the tank facing forward.
13. The rubber gasket is reusable if not damaged. Coat it with lithium-based grease prior to installation to avoid twisting and to ease installation.
14. If the special removal tool was not used, carefully tap the lock ring around until it contacts the tab stops. The lock ring will tend to move to one side when tapping it. Be certain that the gasket is centered at all times or leakage will result. Alternating the points at which you tap will help prevent cocking, but time and care are necessary.
15. The tank is installed by reversing the removal procedure. Care should be taken to avoid getting dirt in the tank when installing the filler pipe. Refill the tank and check the pump operation and for leaks.

Mechanical Fuel Pump

4 CYL. 151 ENGINE

All four cylinder 151 engines use a mechanical fuel pump.

1. Disconnect the negative battery cable.
2. Disconnect the fuel inlet hose from the pump.
3. Disconnect the vapor return hose, if so equipped.
4. Disconnect the fuel outlet pipe.

5. Remove the pump mounting bolts.
6. Remove the fuel pump.
7. To install, position the new pump using a new gasket.
8. Install the bolts and tighten evenly.
9. Install the fuel outlet pipe.

NOTE: If you have difficulty starting the fitting on the outlet pipe it might make it easier if you disconnect the upper end of the pipe from the carburetor then hold the fuel pump nut with a wrench and tighten the fitting securely. Reconnect and tighten the fitting at the carburetor.

10. Install the fuel inlet hose.
11. Install the vapor return hose, if so equipped.
12. Connect the negative battery cable.
13. Start the engine and check for leaks.

Fuel Filter

REMOVAL & INSTALLATION

Either a paper or a bronze filter may be used, depending on the carburetor model.

1. Disconnect the fuel line at the intake fuel filter nut on the carburetor.

CAUTION
Two wrenches, one on the line nut and one on the filter nut are necessary to avoid damage to the line and/or threads.

---

2. Remove the intake fuel filter nut.
3. Remove the filter element and spring.
4. Install the element spring and element. Bronze filters are installed with the conical section facing out and with a gasket between the filter element and the fuel intake nut.
5. Install the nut using a new gasket and tighten. Do not overtighten this nut, as it is easily stripped.
6. Install fuel line and tighten the connector.

Carburetor

REMOVAL & INSTALLATION

1. Remove the air cleaner and gasket.
2. Disconnect the fuel and vacuum lines.
3. Disconnect the choke rod, or on an early model two-barrel, remove the choke water cover by removing the three attaching screws. Disconnect all electrical connections.
4. Disconnect the accelerator linkage.
5. Disconnect the Powerglide throttle valve linkage or Turbo Hydra-Matic detent cable.
6. Unbolt the carburetor and remove the carburetor and solenoid assembly.
7. Remove the insulator gasket, air cleaner bracket, and flange gasket.
8. Before installation, make sure that the carburetor and manifold sealing surfaces are clean.

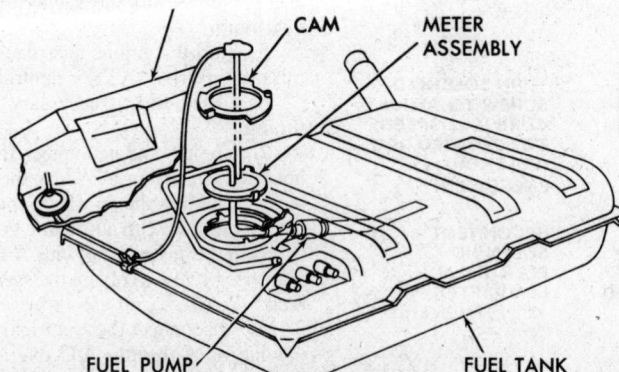

Electric fuel pump installation (© Chevrolet Div., G.M. Corp.)

CAM   METER ASSEMBLY

FUEL PUMP   FUEL TANK

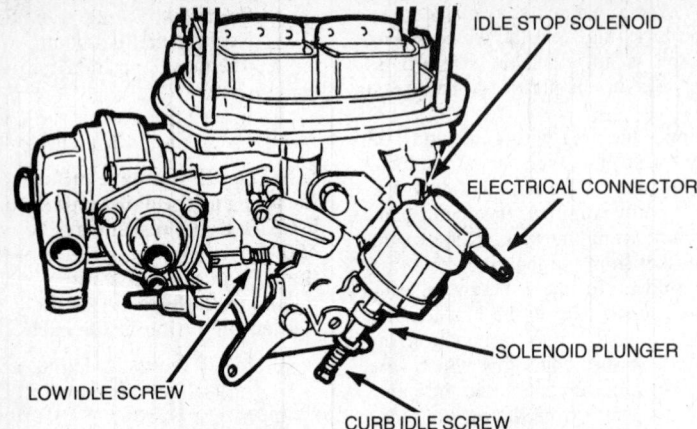

Holley 5210-C, 6510-C idle speed adjustment

NOTE: To reduce the possibility of backfiring fill the carburetor bowl with a small amount of fuel.

9. Install a new carburetor base gasket.

10. Install the air cleaner brace and the insulator.

11. Install the carburetor and start the fuel and vacuum lines.

12. Bolt down the carburetor evenly.

13. Tighten the fuel and vacuum lines.

14. Connect and adjust the accelerator and automatic transmission linkage.

15. Connect the choke rod or water cover if so equipped.

Install the air cleaner. Adjust the idle speed. Do not tamper with the idle mixture screw unless the carburetor has been repaired, overhauled, or replaced.

For carburetor adjustments and specifications, refer to "Carburetors" in the Unit Repair section.

IDLE SPEED ADJUSTMENT

1978

4-151

Refer to the underhood sticker for the latest certification information.

1. Run the engine to normal operating temperature.

2. Make sure that the choke is fully opened, set the parking brake, block the drive wheels and turn the air conditioning off.

3. Connect a timing light and tachometer to the engine according to their manufacturers' instructions.

4. Disconnect and plug the PCV hose at the vapor canister. Disconnect and plug the vacuum advance hose at the distributor.

5. Place the transmission in Drive (AT) or Neutral (MT).

6. Check and adjust timing.

7. Connect the vacuum advance line.

8. On manual transmission cars without A/C: Turn the idle speed screw to achieve the specified rpm. On automatic transmission cars or manual transmission cars with A/C: Turn the idle speed screw to obtain the specified rpm. Disconnect the wire at the wide open throttle A/C override switch. The switch is located on the accelerator linkage bracket. Turn the A/C on. Momentarily open the throttle to extend the solenoid plunger. Adjust the solenoid screw to the rpm specified on the underhood sticker. Connect the override switch and turn the A/C off.

9. Connect all hoses and remove the timing light and tachometer.

6-196, 231, AND V8-305

Refer to the underhood sticker for the latest certification information.

1. Run the engine to normal operating temperature.

2. Make sure that the choke is fully opened, set the parking brake, block the drive wheels and turn the A/C off.

3. Connect a timing light and tachometer to the engine according to their manufacturers' instructions.

4. Disconnect and plug the vacuum hoses at the vapor canister and EGR valve.

5. Place the transmission in Park (AT) or Neutral (MT).

6. Disconnect the vacuum advance hose and set the timing.

7. On manual transmission without A/C: Adjust the idle speed screw to obtain the specified rpm. On automatic transmission cars without A/C: Open the throttle slightly to fully extend the solenoid plunger. Turn the idle speed screw to obtain the specified rpm. Disconnect the solenoid and turn the solenoid screw to obtain the rpm specified on the underhood sticker.

On cars with A/C: Turn the idle speed screw to obtain the specified rpm. Momentarily open the throttle to extend the solenoid plunger. Disconnect the A/C compressor clutch wire. Turn the A/C on. Place the AT in Drive, the MT in Neutral. Turn the solenoid screw to obtain the rpm specified on the underhood sticker.

1979–80

4-151

Check the Vehicle Emission Control Information label for the latest certified information.

1. Run the engine to normal operating temperature with the choke fully open. The air conditioning should be off.

2. Connect a tachometer and a timing light according to the manufacturer's instructions.

3. Set the parking brake and block the drive wheels.

4. Disconnect and plug the PCV hose at the canister and the vacuum hose at the distributor.

5. Start the engine and place the transmission in drive (AT) or neutral (MT).

6. Check and, if necessary, adjust the timing.

7. Unplug and reconnect the vacuum hose at the distributor. Adjust the idle speed screw to obtain the specified rpm.

8. On cars with automatic transmission or manual transmission with A/C, turn the idle speed screw to obtain the specified rpm, then:

a. disconnect the electrical line at the wide open throttle A/C override switch located on the accelerator linkage bracket.

b. turn the A/C on.

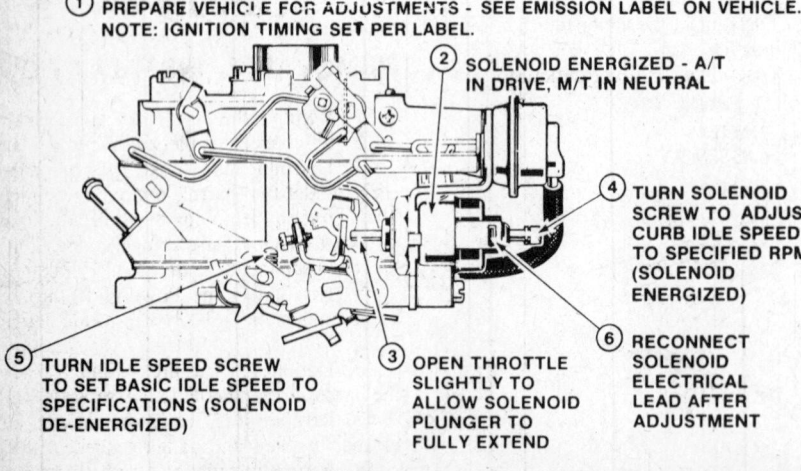

Rochester 2SE idle speed adjustment
(© Chevrolet Div., G.M. Corp.)

c. momentarily open the throttle to allow the solenoid plunger to extend.

d. adjust the solenoid screw to the rpm specified in the Tune-Up table.

e. reconnect the electrical connector.

f. turn the A/C off.

g. reconnect the PCV hose at the canister.

V6 AND V8

1. Prepare the vehicle according to the instructions found on the Emission label.

2. Turn the idle speed screw to obtain the rpm specified in the Tune-Up table. Follow steps 3–6 if the car is equipped with air conditioning.

3. Disconnect the A/C lead at the compressor clutch.

4. Turn the A/C on. Open the throttle slightly to extend the solenoid plunger.

5. Turn the solenoid screw to obtain the rpm specified in the Tune-Up table.

6. Reconnect the A/C lead.

IDLE MIXTURE ADJUSTMENT

Changes in the mixture system have made the adjustment of the air/fuel mixture impossible without a propane enrichment system not available to the general public.

COOLING SYSTEM

The intake manifold is water heated to provide an even intake temperature. All models have a radiator drain petcock.

All models are equipped with a coolant recovery system reservoir. A translucent plastic reservoir allows for hot coolant expansion. When the engine cools, coolant is drawn into the radiator by vacuum. Additional coolant should be added to the reservoir, not the radiator.

The Monza with V8 engine and air conditioning has an auxiliary fan installed forward of the radiator. The fan is operated by a thermostatic switch located on the right rear side of the cylinder head. If engine temperature exceeds approximately 235°F, the switch will close to operate the fan.

Radiator

REMOVAL & INSTALLATION

1. Drain the radiator.

2. On models with the heavy duty radiator, remove the fan shroud.

3. Disconnect the intake and outlet hoses.

4. Remove the front lighting wiring harness from the clips on the fanguard. Remove the two screws which secure the fan guard to the radiator support, then remove the support and the two radiator pads.

NOTE: On vehicles with the heavy duty radiator, remove the two upper brackets (instead of the single support).

5. Lift the radiator up and out of the lower brackets.

6. To install, reverse the removal procedure.

Water Pump

REMOVAL & INSTALLATION

1. Drain the coolant from the radiator.

2. Loosen the fan pulley bolts.

3. If necessary, remove the alternator with the drive belt and brackets.

4. If necessary, remove the air pump with the drive belt and brackets.

5. Disconnect the lower radiator hose and the heater hose at the water pump.

6. Remove the fan and pulley.

7. Remove the pump-to-cylinder block and power steering-to-pump bolts and remove the water pump and old gasket.

8. Installation is the reverse of removal. Use a new gasket coated with sealer. Adjust the alternator and air pump drive belt tension. Fill the cooling system, run the engine and check for leaks.

Thermostat

REMOVAL & INSTALLATION

The 4-151 thermostat is located in a housing at the cylinder head water outlet adjacent to the intake manifold. On the V6 and V8 engines, the thermostat is in the water outlet housing in the front of the intake manifold.

1. Drain the coolant to a level below that of the water outlet housing.

2. Remove the radiator upper hose.

3. Remove the housing bolts and remove the water outlet housing and gasket.

4. Remove the thermostat.

5. Installation is the reverse of removal. Use a new gasket.

EMISSION CONTROLS

The following emission control systems have been used on the GM "H" bodies. Please refer to the "Emission Control" section of the Unit Repair Section for a description and service of these systems:

- Positive Crankcase Ventilation
- Evaporative Emission Control
- Controlled Combustion System
- Air Injection Reactor System
- Pulsair Injection Reaction System
- Exhaust Gas Recirculation (EGR)
- Catalytic Converter System
- Electronic Fuel Control (EFC)
- Computer Controlled Catalytic Converter (C-4)
- Early Fuel Evaporation (EFE)

ENGINE

Four Cylinder

The 151 is a cast iron push rod type. It has overhead valves with very long connecting rods. Using a short stroke (3 in.) and long connecting rods minimizes roughness. In 1979, the 151 cylinder head configuration was changed to a crossflow design, and the distributor was moved to the rear left-hand side of the block.

NOTE: Service procedures for the Pontiac built 151 cu. in. four cylinder engine may be found in the "Pontiac Rear Wheel Drive" section of this book.

NOTE: The use of anti-seize compound is recommended on all bolts installed in aluminum engine blocks.

V6 and V8

The Buick built V6-196,231 engines and the Chevrolet built V8-262,305,350 engines are very simular in design.

The nodular cast iron crankshaft is supported by five bearings (V8), four bearings (V6). The crankshaft is counterbalanced by

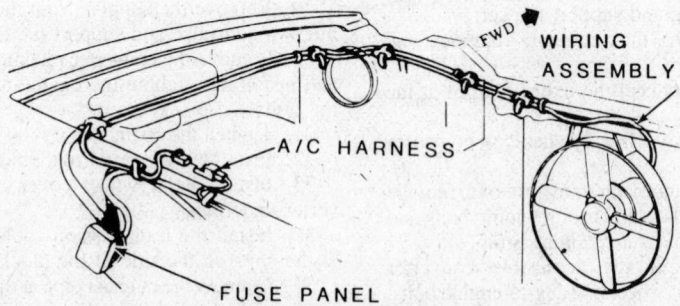

Auxiliary cooling fan-Monza V8 with air conditioning (© Chevrolet Div. G.M. Ccrp.)

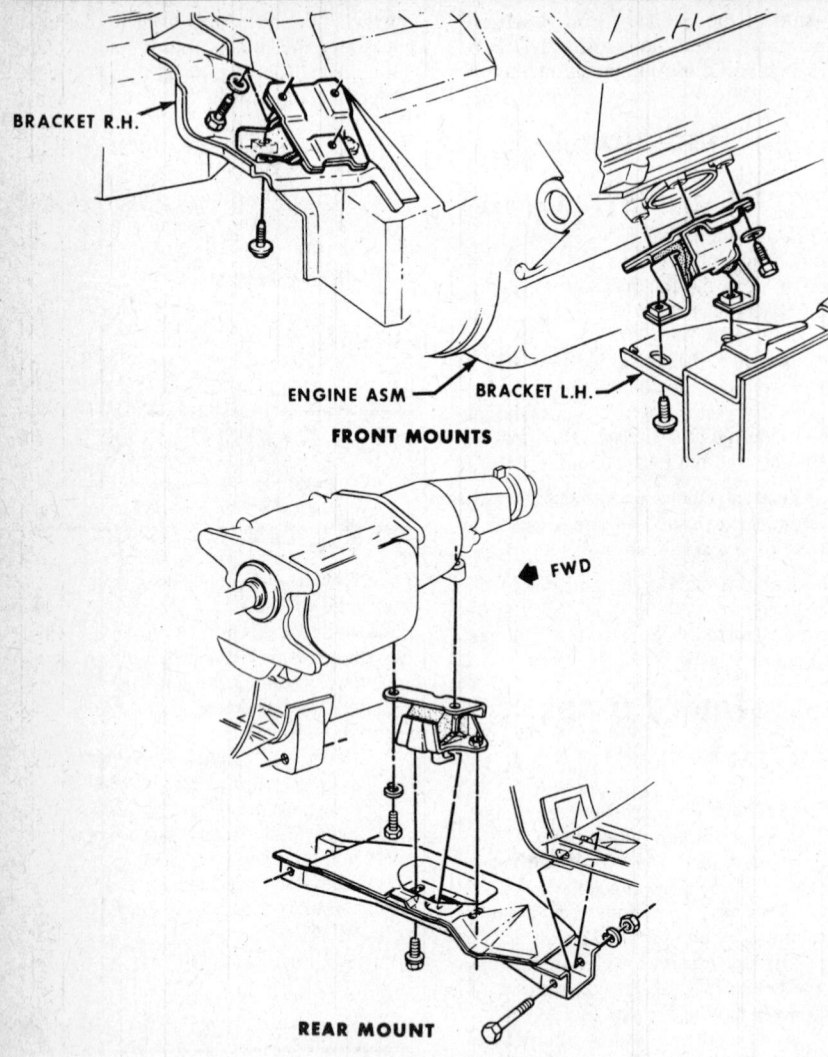

BRACKET R.H.

ENGINE ASM — **BRACKET L.H.**

FRONT MOUNTS

FWD

REAR MOUNT

V8 engine mounts
(© Chevrolet Div., G.M. Corp)

weights cast integral with the crankshaft. Additional counterbalancing is obtained from the flywheel and harmonic balancer. The pistons are tin plated aluminum alloy and full skirts and are cam ground.

The camshaft is supported in the crankcase by five steel backed babbit lined bearings. It is driven from the crankshaft by sprockets and chain. The cylinder heads are cast iron. The V6 rocker arms are mounted on tubular steel shafts supported on the cylinder head by three pedestals. On the V8 engines the rocker arms are individually mounted. Hydraulic valve lifters and tubular push rods are used to operate the overhead rocker arms and valves of both banks of cylinders from a single camshaft. This system requires no lash adjustment.

NOTE: Service procedures for the Buick built 196 and 231 cu. in. engines may be found in the "Buick Rear Wheel Drive" section of this book.

Engine

REMOVAL & INSTALLATION
V8

1. Raise and support the hood.
2. Disconnect the battery cables.
3. Raise and support the car.
4. Drain the coolant, engine and transmission.
5. Disconnect the exhaust pipes at the manifold.
6. Remove the flywheel or converter underpan.
7. On automatic transmissions, remove the converter-to-flywheel retaining bolts and install a converter retaining strap.
8. Remove the accessible converter housing or flywheel housing-to-engine bolts.
9. Remove the transmission cooler lines from the retaining clips on the side of the engine.

10. Remove the engine front mounting bolts at the frame brackets and lower the car.
11. Remove the radiator panel or shroud.
12. Remove the radiator and fan.
13. Disconnect the heater hose from the water pump and manifold.
14. Remove the air cleaner.
15. Disconnect the electrical leads from:
    a. alternator
    b. distributor
    c. starter solenoid
    d. oil pressure switch
    e. engine temperature switch
    f. temperature gauge switch
    g. choke secondary pull-off solenoid
16. Unclip the wiring harness from the rocker cover and position it out of the way.
17. Disconnect the automatic transmission vacuum modulator and air conditioning vacuum line from the manifold.
18. Disconnect the rubber fuel line at the rear of the engine.
19. Disconnect the following:
    a. canister vacuum hose at the carburetor
    b. accelerator at the carburetor and manifold bracket
    c. air conditioning blower delay lead at the rear of the engine.
20. On air conditioned cars, remove the compressor from its mount. Do not disconnect any fittings. Secure the compressor to the fender.
21. Disconnect the power steering pump and lay it aside.
22. Install a floor jack under the transmission.
23. Install a hoist on the engine and raise the engine slightly to take the weight off the engine mounts. Remove the remaining engine to transmission bolts.
24. Remove the engine from the car.
To install the engine:
25. Install transmission-to-engine guide pins, made from ⅜ in. bolts with the heads cut off, into the engine.
26. Install the engine, aligning the engine with the transmission housing.
27. Align the engine mounts with the frame brackets and lower the engine onto the brackets. Loosely install the engine mount bolts.
28. Remove the guide pins and install the engine-to-housing bolts. Remove the lifting equipment.
29. Remove the support from the transmission and raise and support the car.
30. Remove the converter retaining strap and install and tighten the engine-to-housing bolts.
31. Tighten the engine front mount bolts.
32. Install the converter to the flywheel.
33. Install the flywheel cover or converter underpan.
34. Install the transmission cooler lines in the clips on the side of the block.
35. Connect the exhaust pipe at the manifold and lower the car.
36. Install the air conditioning compressor and power steering pump. Adjust

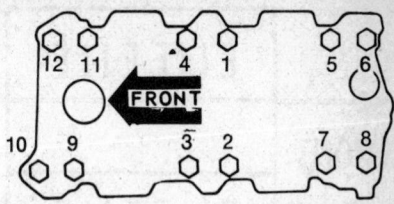
the drive belts.

37. Connect the following:
  a. canister vacuum hose to carburetor
  b. accelerator cable at carburetor and manifold bracket
  c. air conditioning blower delay lead at side of engine
  d. fuel line to rubber hose at rear of engine
  e. air conditioning vacuum line.

38. Install the electrical harness in the clip in the rocker cover and connect the following:
  a. alternator
  b. distributor
  c. starter solenoid
  d. oil pressure switch
  e. engine temperature switch
  f. temperature gauge switch
  g. choke secondary pull-off solenoid.

39. Connect the heater hose at the water pump and at the manifold.

40. Install the radiator, fan, radiator panel or shroud, fill the cooling system, add engine oil and fill the transmission.

41. Install the air cleaner.

42. Connect the battery cables, start the engine and check for leaks.

Intake Manifold

REMOVAL & INSTALLATION

V8

1. Remove the air cleaner.
2. Drain the radiator.
3. Disconnect:
  a. Battery cables at the battery.
  b. Upper radiator and heater hoses at the manifold.
  c. Crankcase ventilation hoses as required.
  d. Fuel line at the rubber hose.
  e. Accelerator linkage at the pedal lever.
  f. Vacuum hose at the distributor.
  g. Power brake hose at the accelerator bracket.
  h. Ignition coil and temperature sending switch wires.
  i. Air diverter valve line.
  j. Choke pull-off lead.
  k. Air conditioning bracket or power steering brace.
  l. Choke hot and cold air pipes.

4. Remove the distributor cap and scribe the rotor position relative to distributor body.

5. Remove the distributor.

6. If applicable, remove the alternator upper bracket.

7. Remove the air pump.

8. Remove the manifold to head attaching bolts, then remove the manifold and carburetor as an assembly.

9. If the manifold is to be replaced, transfer the carburetor (and mounting studs), and other applicable equipment to the new manifold.

10. Before installing the manifold, thoroughly clean the gasket and seal surfaces of the cylinder heads and manifold.

11. Install the manifold end seals, folding the tabs if applicable, and the manifold/head gaskets, using a sealing compound around the water passages. Make sure the gaskets are firmly cemented in place before installing the manifold.

12. When installing the manifold, care should be taken not to dislocate the end seals, it is helpful to use a pilot in the distributor opening. Tighten the manifold bolts to the proper torque in the sequence illustrated.

13. Install the distributor with the rotor in its original location as indicated by the scribe line. If the engine has been disturbed, refer to Distributor Removal and Installation.

14. If applicable, install the alternator and adjust the belt tension.

15. Install the air pump. Adjust all drive belts.

16. Connect all components disconnected in Step 3 above.

17. Fill the cooling system, start the engine, check for leaks and adjust the ignition timing and carburetor idle speed and mixture.

Exhaust Manifold

REMOVAL & INSTALLATION

V8 Right Side

1. Disconnect the negative battery cable.

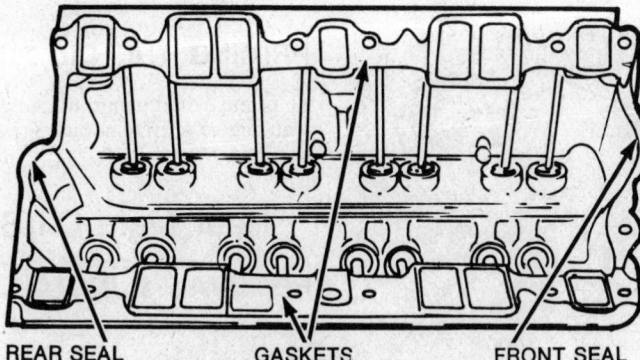

V8 intake manifold gasket and seals
(© Chevrolet Div., G.M. Corp)

REAR SEAL   GASKETS   FRONT SEAL

Intake manifold torque sequence—V8

2. On air conditioned cars, remove the emission vapor canister. Without disconnecting any lines, remove the air conditioning compressor and place it out of the way.

3. Raise the car and disconnect the exhaust pipe from the manifold. Remove the engine mount-to-frame bolts and slide the engine to the left.

4. Lower the car and disconnect the spark plug wires and temperature sender wire. Remove the alternator and alternator bracket from the exhaust manifold.

5. Remove No. 6 and 8 spark plugs and the six manifold attaching bolts. Remove the spark plug shields from the brackets and bend the brackets upward.

6. Remove the exhaust manifold and EFE valve as an assembly.

7. Installation is the reverse of removal. On installation, be sure to clean the mating surfaces of the manifold and cylinder head, adjust bent tension where necessary, and align the engine.

V8 Left Side

1. Disconnect the negative battery cable.

2. Raise the car and disconnect the exhaust pipe from the manifold.

3. Remove the engine mount-to-frame bolts and slide the engine to the right.

4. Remove the two rear manifold bolts, then raise the engine and place a 6 in. piece of 2 × 4 wood block under the left engine mount.

5. Lower the car, remove the air cleaner and dipstick tube bracket nut, and move the dipstick tube aside.

6. Remove the remaining attaching bolts and remove the manifold.

7. To install, clean the mating surfaces of the manifold and cylinder head, install the manifold and the front four attaching bolts, and start the two rear bolts.

8. Install the dipstick tube bracket and air cleaner. Raise the car and remove the block from under the left engine mount.

9. Tighten the two rear manifold attaching bolts and connect the exhaust pipe to the manifold. Align and install the engine mount-to-frame bolts.

10. Lower the car and connect the negative battery cable.

Valve System

All engines are equipped with hydraulic lifters. No periodic adjustment is necessary.

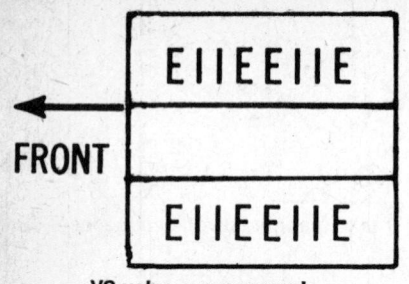

V8 valve arrangement

Valve Guides

V8

Valve guides are integral with the cylinder head. Valve guide bores may be reamed to accommodate oversize valve stems or the guides may be knurled (if wear permits) to allow the retention of standard size valves.

Cylinder Head

REMOVAL & INSTALLATION
V8

1. Drain the coolant.
2. Remove the intake manifold.
3. Remove the exhaust manifolds.
4. Back off the rocker arm nuts and pivot the rocker arms out of the way so that the pushrods can be removed. Identify the pushrods so that they can be reinstalled in their original locations.
5. Remove the cylinder head bolts and cylinder heads.
6. Install using new gaskets. The head gasket is installed with the bead up.

NOTE: Coat a steel gasket on both sides with sealer. If a steel/asbestos gasket is used, do not apply sealer. Clean the bolt threads, apply sealing compound and install the bolts finger tight.

7. Tighten the head bolts a little at a time in the sequence illustrated.
8. Install the exhaust and intake manifolds as described previously.
9. Adjust the valves as explained in the Camaro section. Fill the cooling system.

V8 cylinder head torque sequence

Rocker Arm

REMOVAL & INSTALLATION
V8

Rocker arms are removed by removing the adjusting nut. Be sure to adjust valve lash after replacing rocker arms.

Rocker arm studs that have damaged threads or are loose in the cylinder heads may be replaced with new studs available in 0.003 in. and 0.013 in. oversize or the bores may be tapped and screw-in replacement studs used. Do not attempt to install an oversize stud without reaming the stud bore. Studs are press-fit. Lubricate the press-fit area of the stud with hypoid axle lubricant.

NOTE: If engine is equipped with the AIR exhaust emission control system, the interfering components of the system must be removed. Disconnect the lines at the air injection nozzles in the exhaust manifolds.

Front Cover

REMOVAL & INSTALLATION
V8

Front cover removal and installation procedures are given in the Chevrolet Car section.

Timing Chain

Replacement

Timing chain and sprocket removal and installation procedures are given in the "Chevrolet Rear Wheel Drive" car section.

Camshaft

REMOVAL & INSTALLATION
V8

Camshaft removal and installation procedures are given in the "Chevrolet Rear Wheel Drive" car section.

Piston and Rod

INSTALLATION

On V8s, install the piston with the tang on the connecting rod bearing on the side away from the camshaft. Be sure that the pistons and rods are installed in their original locations.

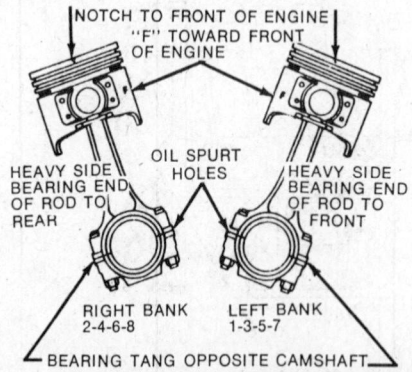

NOTCH TO FRONT OF ENGINE
"F" TOWARD FRONT OF ENGINE

HEAVY SIDE BEARING END OF ROD TO REAR

OIL SPURT HOLES

HEAVY SIDE BEARING END OF ROD TO FRONT

RIGHT BANK 2-4-6-8

LEFT BANK 1-3-5-7

BEARING TANG OPPOSITE CAMSHAFT

Piston-to-rod relationship—V8

Oil Pan

REMOVAL & INSTALLATION
V8

1. Disconnect the battery.
2. Raise the car and drain the oil.
3. Disconnect the exhaust crossover pipe.
4. Remove the converter housing underpan and splash shield.
5. Scribe marks on each side of the frame crossmember and support the engine. Remove the frame crossmember.
6. Disconnect the steering idler arm at the frame side rail.
7. Disconnect the starter brace and remove the starter.
8. Remove the oil pan bolts and remove the oil pan.
9. Installation is the reverse of removal. Use new gaskets with sealer as a retainer and be sure to match the scribe marks when installing the crossmember. Fill the engine with oil.

Oil Pump

REMOVAL & INSTALLATION
V8

1. Remove the oil pan.
2. Remove the bolt holding the oil pump to the rear main bearing cap.
3. Remove the pump and the extension shaft.
4. Installation is the reverse of removal. Align the slot on the top of the extension shaft with the drive tang on the lower end of the distributor driveshaft. The installed position of the oil pump screen should be parallel to the oil pan rails.

PRIMING THE OIL PUMP

To prime the oil pump, fill the gear cavity with engine oil. Do not use grease.

Rear Main Oil Seal

REMOVAL & INSTALLATION
V8

Rear main oil seal replacement procedures are given in the "Chevrolet Rear Wheel Drive" car section.

CLUTCH

The clutch assembly consists of a driven plate, a pressure plate, and a release bearing, and is connected to the clutch pedal by a cable.

Clutch Pedal Free Travel

ADJUSTMENT

1. Remove the ball stud cap and loosen the locknut on the ball stud end, located to the left of the transmission, on the clutch housing.
2. Adjust the ball stud to obtain ⅛ inch clearance between the release bearing face and the pressure plate release fingers.
3. Tighten the ball stud locknut to 25 ft. lbs., being careful not to change the adjustment, and install the ball stud cap.
4. Pull the cable at the clutch fork until the clutch pedal is firmly against the rubber bumper.
5. Push the clutch fork forward until the release bearing contacts the pressure plate fingers, and screw the pin on the cable forward until it contacts the fork. Turn the pin ¼ turn clockwise, and seat the pin in its seat on the clutch fork.
6. Attach the cable return spring and install the clutch fork cover.
7. Check the clutch pedal free play. This procedure should provide .90 ± .25 inch lash at the clutch pedal.

NOTE: When the adjustment of the ball stud and the cable have been completed, verify the clearance between the pressure plate fingers and the release bearing. The release bearing should not be in constant contact with the pressure plate fingers.

Clutch Disc

REMOVAL & INSTALLATION

1. Raise the vehicle on a hoist.
2. Remove the transmission as outlined in this section.
3. Remove the clutch fork cover, then disconnect the clutch return spring and control cable from the clutch fork.
4. Remove the input shaft oil seal from the clutch release bearing sleeve.
5. Remove the flywheel housing lower cover.
6. Remove the flywheel housing from the engine.
7. To remove the release bearing from the clutch fork and sleeve, slide the lever off the ball stud against the spring action. If necessary to replace the ball stud, remove the cap, locknut and stud from the housing.

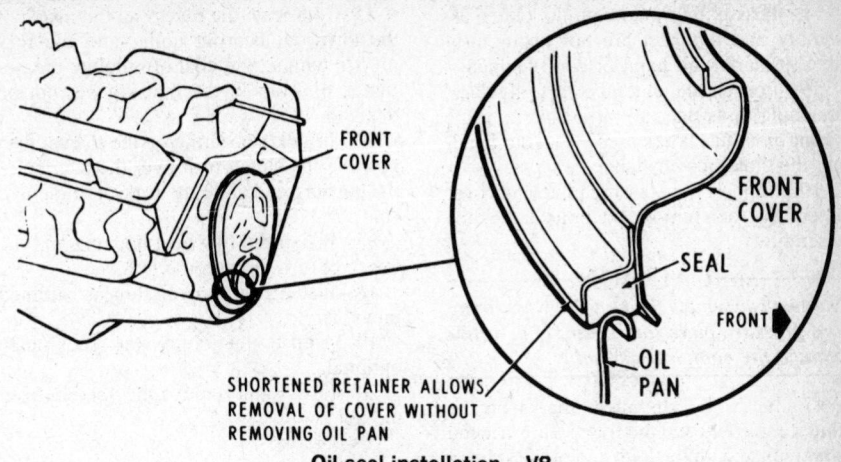

SHORTENED RETAINER ALLOWS REMOVAL OF COVER WITHOUT REMOVING OIL PAN

Oil seal installation—V8
(© Chevrolet Div., G.M. Corp)

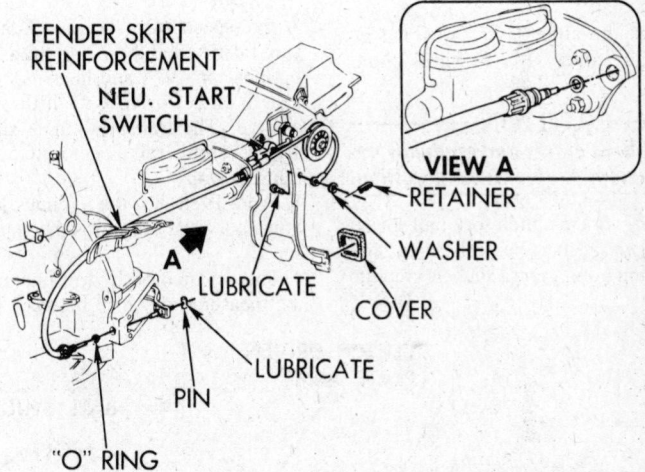

Clutch control cable (© Chevrolet Div., G.M. Corp)

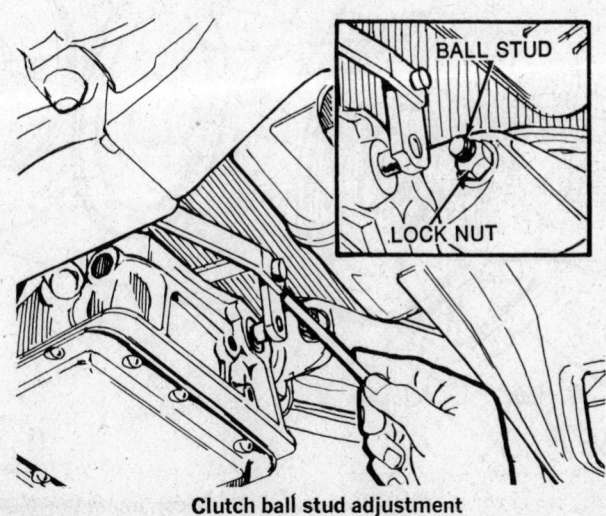

Clutch ball stud adjustment

8. If assembly marks on the clutch assembly and flywheel are not distinguishable, remark with paint or center-punch.

9. Loosen the clutch cover to flywheel attaching bolts one turn at a time until the spring pressure is released, to avoid bending the clutch cover flange.

10. Support the pressure plate and cover assembly, then remove the bolts and clutch assembly.

— CAUTION —
Do not disassemble the clutch cover, spring and pressure plate for repair. If defective replace the complete assembly.

11. Index the alignment marks on the clutch assembly and the flywheel. Place the driven plate with the long end of the splined end facing forward, the plate damper springs facing the pressure plate, and insert a dummy input shaft or aligning tool through the cover and the driven plate.

12. Position the complete assembly against the flywheel and insert the dummy shaft or aligning tool into the pilot bearing in the crankshaft.

13. Index the alignment marks and install clutch cover to flywheel bolts fingertight.

— CAUTION —
Tighten all bolts evenly and gradually until tight to avoid possible clutch distortion.

14. Lubricate the clutch fork ball socket and the fingers at the release bearing with a high melting point grease such as graphite grease.

15. Lubricate the recess on the inside of the throwout bearing collar and the fork groove with a light coat of graphite grease. Install the fork in the housing but not on the stud.

16. Install the bearing on the sleeve, then position the clutch fork over the bearing in the housing and slide the fork onto the ball stud.

17. Install the flywheel housing and the lower cover. Tighten the bolts.

18. Install the transmission as outlined previously.

19. Adjust the clutch as previously outlined.

20. Lower and remove the vehicle from the hoist.

MANUAL TRANSMISSION

A five-speed Borg-Warner T-50 transmission (also called the 77mm transmission) is optional on 1978 and later models. Fourth gear is direct drive with fifth gear an overdrive. The transmission is shifted by a single shift rail enclosed within the transmission.

From 1978–80, the Saginaw four-speed, now called the 76mm, is the standard four-speed.

The designation by millimeters refers to the measured distance between the center-lines of the transmission's mainshaft and countershaft.

LINKAGE ADJUSTMENT

Saginaw Four-Speed

1. Turn the ignition switch to Off and place the shift lever in Neutral.
2. Raise the car.
3. Loosen the lock nuts on the control rods. Position the transmission side cover levers in their neutral detents.
4. With the floor shift lever in Neutral, align the shifter levers and insert a gauge pin into the levers and bracket.
5. Tighten the First/Reverse (First/Second on four-speed) control rod lock nut against its swivel.
6. Tighten the Second/Third (Third/Fourth on four-speed) control rod lock nut against its swivel.
7. On four-speeds, tighten the Reverse control rod lock nut against its swivel.
8. Remove the gauge pin and check shifter operation.

Transmission

REMOVAL & INSTALLATION

Four-Speed

NOTE: Transmission removal will require additional work due to the torque arm rear suspension. The torque arm serves as an upper control arm, is rigidly mounted to the differential, and is mounted to the transmission through a

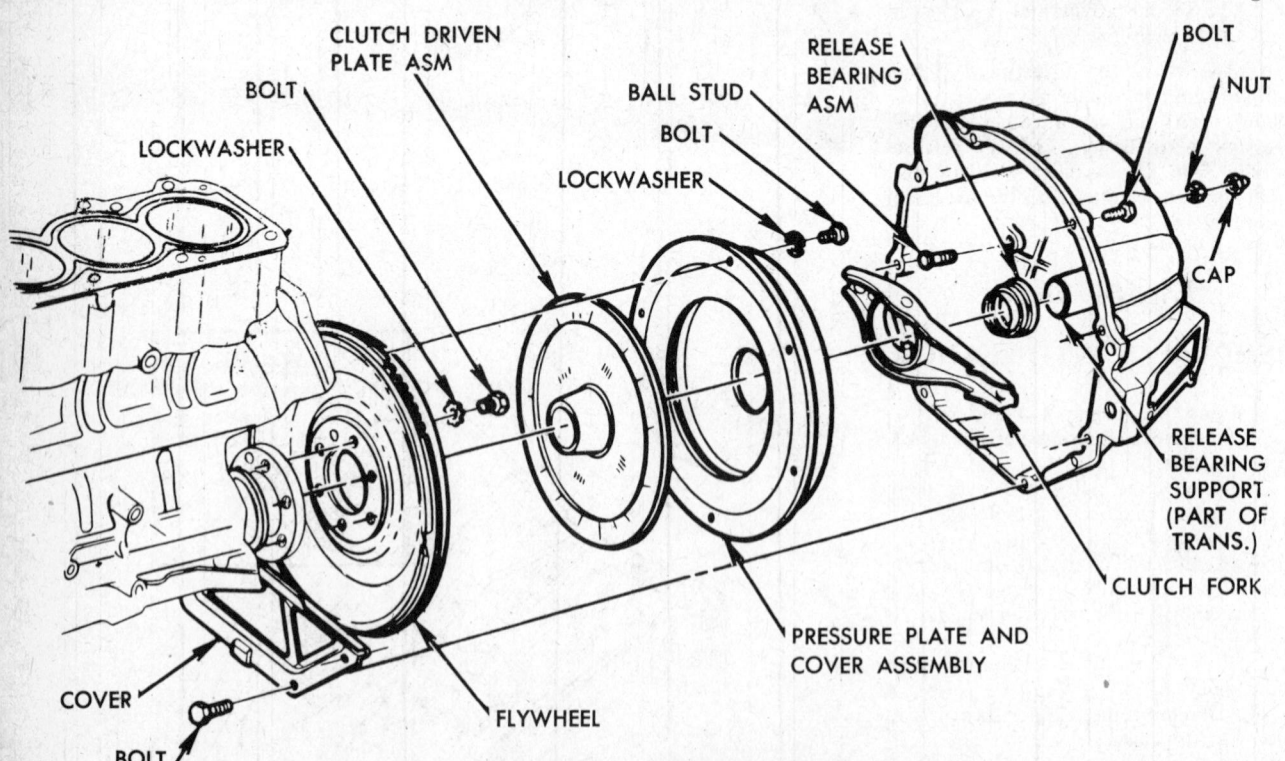

Exploded view of clutch components (© Chevrolet Div., G.M. Corp)

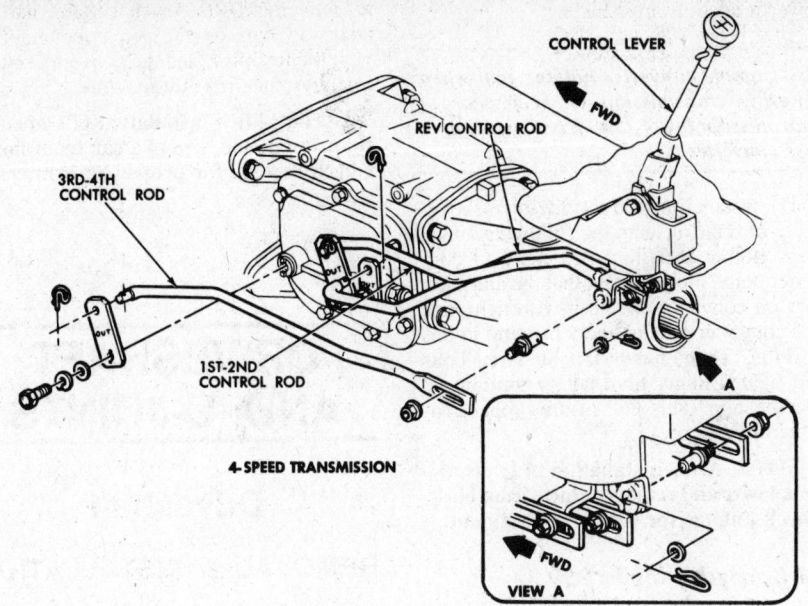

Saginaw four speed inkage

rubber bushing. See "Rear Suspension" for torque arm removal procedures.

1. Raise the car and support it on four jackstands placed under the lower control arms and the rear axle.

2. Match-mark the driveshaft to differential flange and driveshaft to transmission case. Remove the driveshaft. Stuff the output shaft opening with rags to prevent fluid loss.

3. Disconnect the speedometer cable, TCS switch, and the backup light switch. Remove the damper.

4. Mark the position of the control rods on the shift levers. Detach the control rods and levers from the transmission, tie them together, and position them out of the way.

5. Position a jack under the transmission to take up the weight. Remove the crossmember-to-transmission mounting bolts.

6. Support the engine and remove the crossmember-to-frame bolts. Remove the crossmember.

7. Remove the top transmission-to-clutch housing bolts and install guide pins in the holes.

8. Remove the lower bolts and pull the transmission back and out of the car.

9. Guide the input shaft through the throwout bearing and into the pilot bearing.

10. Install the transmission retaining bolts and lockwashers. Tighten the bolts to 40 ft. lbs.

11. Position the crossmember on the frame and install the retaining bolts handtight.

12. Install the crossmember-to-transmission bolts and then tighten all bolts to 28 ft. lbs.

13. Remove the engine support.

14. Install the transmission control rods to the shifter. Adjust the linkage as previously outlined.

15. Connect the speedometer cable, TCS switch, and back-up light switch.

16. Install the driveshaft.

17. Fill the transmission to the level of the filler plug.

18. Lower the car and check the transmission operation.

Five-Speed

1. Remove the shift lever boot bezel and slide the shift boot upward on the shift lever.

2. Remove the foam insulator over the shift lever bolts. Remove the four shift lever bolts and remove the shift lever.

3. Raise the car and remove the driveshaft.

4. Remove the damper assembly, converter bracket, and torque arm bracket. Disconnect the speedometer cable and backup light switch.

5. Support the transmission with a jack and remove the transmission support.

6. Remove the transmission-to-clutch housing bolts and slide the exhaust bracket forward. Slide the transmission to the rear and remove it.

7. To install, make sure that the main drive gear splines are clean and dry. Position the transmission to the clutch housing and slide it forward.

8. Slide the exhaust bracket into place and install the transmission-to-clutch housing attaching bolts.

9. Install the rear transmission mount and transmission support. Install the converter bracket, damper, and torque arm.

10. Install the driveshaft, connect the speedometer cable and back-up light switch.

11. Fill the transmission with 3 pints of Dexron® II automatic transmission fluid.

12. Lower the car and install the shift lever and foam insulator. Install the shift lever boot and bezel.

13. Check the transmission for proper operation.

OVERHAUL

For all overhaul procedures, please refer to "Manual Transmission Overhaul" in the Unit Repair section.

AUTOMATIC TRANSMISSION

Several automatic transmissions have been available. A three-speed Turbo Hydra-Matic 250 transmission was used through 1979 on some models. The 250 is similar to the 350, except that the intermediate clutch assembly has been replaced by an externally adjustable intermediate band assembly. The 250 can be identified by the band adjusting screw and locknut on the right side of the case. Some V8 models used the Turbo Hydra-Matic 350. Starting 1976, a new three-speed transmission is offered: Turbo Hydra-Matic 200. The light weight Turbo Hydra-Matic 200 transmission can sometimes be identified by the word METRIC stamped into the bottom of the fluid pan. The 200 has 10 pan bolts; the 350 has 13.

For adjustments and service, see "Automatic Transmissions" in the Unit Repair Section.

Transmission

REMOVAL & INSTALLATION
Turbo Hydra-Matic 200

1. Before raising the car, disconnect the negative battery cable and the detent cable at the bracket and carburetor.

2. Remove the air cleaner and dip stick.

3. On vehicles with air conditioning, remove the (5) five heater core cover screws from the heater assembly. Disconnect the wire connector and with hoses attached, place the heater core cover out of the way.

4. Raise vehicle on hoist and remove propeller shafts as outlined in Section 4.

5. Disconnect speedometer cable, electrical lead to case connector and oil cooler pipes.

6. Disconnect shift control linkage.

7. Support transmission with suitable transmission jack and remove the four (4) rear transmission support bolts.

8. Remove the nuts holding the converter bracket to the support.

9. Disconnect the exhaust pipe at the rear of the catalytic converter.

10. Disconnect exhaust pipe at manifold and remove the exhaust pipe, catalytic con-

verter and converter bracket as an assembly.

11. Remove the torque converter under pan.

12. Remove converter to flywheel bolts.

13. Lower transmission until jack is barely supporting it and remove transmission to engine mounting bolts.

14. Raise transmission to its normal position, support engine with jack and slide transmission rearward from engine and lower it away from vehicle.

— CAUTION —

Use converter holding Tool J-5384 when lowering transmission or keep rear of transmission lower than front so not to lose converter.

The installation of the transmission is the reverse of the removal with the following added steps.

1. Place a 2″ block between the rack and pinion housing assembly and the engine oil pan. This will permit correct alignment of the engine and transmission.

2. Before installing the flexplate to converter bolts, make certain that the welded brackets on the converter are flush with the flexplate and the converter rotates freely by hand in this position. Then, hand start all bolts and tighten finger tight before torquing to 27-41 Nm (20-30 ft. lbs.). This insures proper converter alignment.

3. After installation of transmission, remove car from hoist. Check linkage for proper adjustment.

Turbo Hydra-Matic 250

1. Remove air cleaner, disconnect negative battery cable, detent downshift cable at carburetor and release parking brake.

2. Raise vehicle on hoist.

3. Remove torque arm.

4. Remove propeller shaft.

5. Remove converter bracket to transmission and disconnect exhaust pipe and converter.

6. Disconnect speedometer cable and modulator vacuum line at transmission.

7. Disconnect shift control cable.

8. Support transmission with suitable transmission jack.

9. Disconnect transmission rear mount from frame crossmember.

10. Remove two bolts at each end of frame crossmember. Remove crossmember.

11. Remove converter under-pan.

12. Remove converter to flywheel bolts.

13. Lower transmission until jack is barely supporting it.

14. Remove transmission-to-engine mounting bolts and remove oil filler tube at transmission.

15. Disconnect oil cooler lines (V8 models only).

16. Disconnect detent downshift cable at transmission.

17. Raise transmission to its normal position, support engine with jack and slide transmission rearward from the engine and

lower it away from vehicle.

— CAUTION —

Use suitable converter holding tool when lowering transmission or keep rear of transmission lower than front so as not to lose converter.

The installation of transmission is the reverse of removal with the following added step. Before installing flex plate to converter bolts, make certain that the attaching lugs on converter are flush with flex plate and converter rotates freely by hand in this position. Then, hand start all three bolts and tighten finger tight before torquing to specification. This will insure proper converter alignment.

NOTE: After installation of transmission, lower and remove vehicle from hoist. Check linkage for proper adjustment.

Turbo Hydra-Matic 350

Before raising the vehicle, disconnect the negative battery cable, detent downshift cable at carburetor and release the parking brake.

1. Raise vehicle on hoist.

2. Remove propeller shaft.

3. Disconnect speedometer cable, detent downshift cable, modulator vacuum line and oil cooler pipes at transmission.

4. Disconnect shift control linkage. ·

5. Support transmission with suitable transmission jack.

6. Disconnect rear mount from frame crossmember.

7. Remove two bolts at each end of frame crossmember. Remove crossmember.

8. Remove converter under pan.

9. Remove converter to flexplate bolts.

10. Loosen exhaust pipe to manifold bolts approximately ¼ inch. Lower transmission until jack is barely supporting it.

— CAUTION —

Care must be taken not to lower rear of transmission too far as the distributor housing may be forced against the dash causing damage to the distributor. It is best to have an assistant observe clearance of all upper engine components while the transmission rear end is being lowered.

11. Remove transmission-to-engine mounting bolts and remove oil filler tube at transmission.

12. Raise transmission to its normal position, support engine with jack and slide transmission rearward from engine and lower it away from vehicle.

— CAUTION —

Use suitable converter holding tool when lowering transmission or keep rear of transmission lower than front so as not to lose converter.

The installation of the transmission is the reverse of the removal with the following added step. Before installing the flex plate

to converter bolts, make certain that the attaching lugs on the converter are flush with the flex plate and the converter rotates freely by hand in this position.

NOTE: After installation of transmission, lower car, remove car from hoist. Check linkage for proper adjustment.

DRIVESHAFT AND U-JOINTS

Driveshaft

REMOVAL & INSTALLATION

1. Raise and support the car with jack stands. Mark the relationship of the shaft to the companion flange and disconnect the rear universal joint by removing the trunnion bearing U-bolts. Tape the bearing cups to the trunnion to prevent loss of the bearing rollers.

2. Withdraw the driveshaft front yoke from the transmission by moving the shaft rearward and passing it under the axle housing. Plug the transmission opening with rags to prevent fluid or oil loss.

3. Inspect the yoke seal in the transmission extension; replace if necessary.

4. Insert the driveshaft front yoke into transmission extension, making sure that the output shaft splines mate with the driveshaft yoke splines.

5. Align the driveshaft with the companion flange using the reference marks established in the removal procedure. Remove the tape from the U-joint, install the U-bolts to the rear axle flange, and torque them to 15 ft. lbs.

Universal Joint

OVERHAUL

For U-joint overhaul see "U-Joint/CV-Joint Overhaul" in the Unit Repair section.

REAR AXLE

All axles are the C-lock type with C-locks retaining the axle shafts. All axles are hypoid type, semi-floating with an integral gear carrier and a removable cover plate.

All models use either a 6½ in. or 7½ in. diameter ring gear.

Axle Shaft, Bearing and Seal

REMOVAL & INSTALLATION

See the "Chevrolet Rear Wheel Drive" car section for the proper procedures.

JACKING, HOISTING

The illustration shows the correct jacking and hoist lifting positions.

FRONT SUSPENSION

The independent front suspension, like the rear, is very similar to that used on some larger GM vehicles. Each wheel is suspended by unequal length control arms. The steering knuckle, which supports the wheel, is attached to the upper and lower control arms by ball joints. The coil spring is located between the lower control arm and the frame. The tubular shock absorber is mounted inside the spring. Vehicles equipped with the optional ride and handling package (standard on GT) have a stabilizer bar mounted in rubber bushings to the body and connecting the lower control arms.

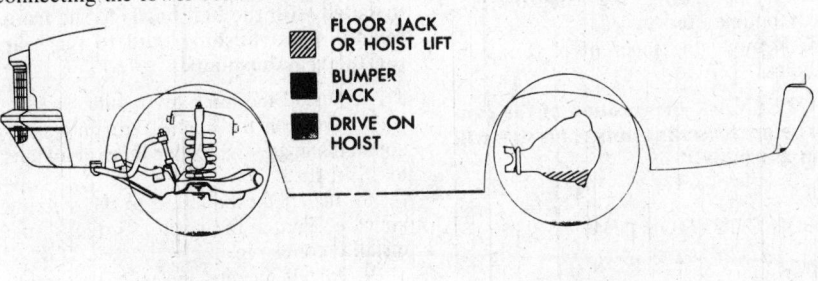

- ▨ FLOOR JACK OR HOIST LIFT
- ■ BUMPER JACK
- ■ DRIVE ON HOIST

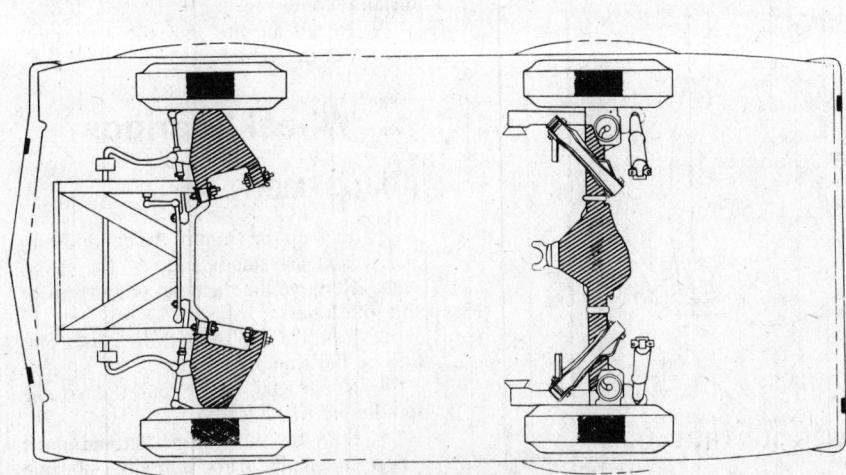

Lift points (© Chevrolet Div., G.M. Corp)

Shock Absorber

REMOVAL & INSTALLATION

NOTE: To purge air from the shock absorber before installation, extend the shock fully and invert it. Compress the shock, and return it to its upright position. Repeat this operation several times. Do not extend the shock absorber while it is inverted.

1. Pry out the access plug in the engine compartment so that the upper mount is visible.
2. Raise the front of the car and support it with jack stands.
3. Turn the wheels for clearance.
4. Hold the upper shock stud with a wrench. Loosen and remove the locknut.
5. Unbolt the lower end and pull the shock down and out.

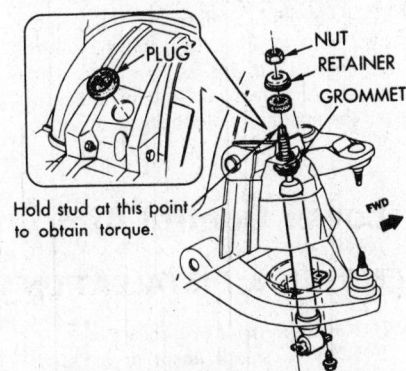

Front shock absorber mounting
(© Chevrolet Div., G.M. Corp)

6. Place the lower retainer and rubber grommet on the shock stud.
7. Put the shock in place and tighten the lower bolts. Torque to 20 ft. lbs.
8. Place the upper grommet, retainer, and nut on the shock stud.
9. Hold the stud with a wrench and tighten the nut. Torque to 120 in. lbs., or just enough to avoid distorting the rubber grommets.

Ball Joint

INSPECTION

Upper

To check the ball joints for excessive wear:
1. Place jackstands under the lower control arms.
2. Turn the wheels straight ahead.
3. Lift and shake the wheel up and down vertically. If there is noticeable looseness, the ball joints are worn.
4. Grasp the top and bottom of the tire and rock it by pushing in on the top and pulling out on the bottom, then pulling out on the top and pushing in on the bottom. A ¼ in. play indicates worn ball joints. Make sure that loose wheel bearings do not result in a false reading.

Lower

The lower ball joints incorporate wear indicators. They can be inspected visually; when the ½ in. diameter grease fitting is flush with, or inside the cover surface, replace the ball joint. Inspect the grease fitting with the car supported on its wheels so that the lower ball joint is in a loaded condition. Normal protrusion of the grease fitting is .050 in. beyond the cover surface.

Ball joint tightness can also be checked using the preceding procedure.

REMOVAL & INSTALLATION

Upper

1. Jack up the front of the car and support it under the crossmember braces. Remove the wheel.
2. Place a hydraulic jack under the lower control arm.
3. Remove the cotter pin from the ball joint stud. Loosen, but do not remove the nut.
4. The stud may now be pressed out of the steering knuckle. There is a special tool available to do this.
5. Remove the ball joint by grinding off the rivets, or removing the heads of the rivets with a chisel.
6. Bolt the new ball joint on, using the nuts and bolts supplied with the replacement joint.
7. Install the stud to the steering knuckle and torque the nut to 30 ft. lbs. If the cotter pin hole does not align, tighten the nut ½ of a turn further to line it up. Install a new cotter pin.
8. Install the wheel and lower the car.

C691

Lower

1. Repeat steps one through three of the upper ball joint procedure.
2. The stud may now be pressed out of the steering knuckle.
3. The old ball joint must be pressed out of the control arm. A special tool is available for this purpose.
4. Press in the new joint, positioning it so that the grease bleed vent in the rubber boot is facing inward.
5. Install a lubrication fitting in the new joint.
6. Install the stud to the steering knuckle and torque the nut to 60 ft. lbs. If the cotter pin hole does not align, tighten it ⅙ of a turn further. Do not loosen the nut to install the cotter pin.
7. Install the wheel and lower the car.

Spring

REMOVAL & INSTALLATION

1. Raise the front of the car and support it with jackstands placed under the front crossmember braces.
2. Remove the wheel, shock absorbers, and stabilizer bar.
3. Support the lower control arm outer end with a hydraulic floor jack and a block of wood.
4. Securely fasten the spring to the lower control arm with a heavy chain.
5. To detach the tie rod, remove the cotter pin and nut, and tap on the steering arm (not the tie rod end) with a hammer. Hold another hammer behind the steering arm to take the force of the tapping. The tie rod should then fall free.
6. Remove the lower ball joint stud from the steering knuckle as described in the "Lower Ball Joint Removal and Installation" procedure.
7. Very cautiously lower the jack until the spring is fully expanded.

8. Place the spring in its pads on the lower control arm and shock tower. Spring insulators are used on 1978 and later models. On these models, make sure that the insulator is indexed with its closed end located at the high point in the spring seat. Secure the spring with a safety chain as in Step 4.
9. Carefully raise the jack.
10. Place the lower ball joint stud in the steering knuckle. Torque the stud nut to 60 ft. lbs. If the cotter pin does not align, tighten it 1/16 of a turn further and insert a new cotter pin.
11. Install the tie rod end to the steering arm. Torque the nut to 35 ft. lbs. If the cotter pin hole does not align, tighten further up to a maximum of 50 ft. lbs. Insert a new cotter pin.
12. Replace the shock absorber as described in "Shock Absorber Removal and Installation." Do not attach the top end of the shock at this point.
13. Install the stabilizer bar. Tighten the bracket bolts to 30 ft. lbs. and the control arm bolts to 10 ft. lbs.
14. Replace the wheel and lower the car. Install the upper end of the shock absorber.

Lower Control Arm

REMOVAL & INSTALLATION

1. Raise the front of the car.
2. Remove shock absorber as previously outlined.
3. Remove ball stud from steering knuckle.
4. Remove coil spring using the previously outlined procedure.
5. Remove the inner pivot cam nuts and bolts.

NOTE: Mark the position of the cam bolts before loosening nuts. This step will aid in assembly.

6. Remove the control arm.
7. Install the control arm.

NOTE: Be sure that the control arm bushings have the metal caps installed.

8. Install the cam bolts through the control arm bushings.

NOTE: The front cam bolt (camber) must be installed with the head toward the front of the vehicle and the rear cam bolt (caster) must be installed with the head toward the rear of the vehicle.

9. Install the inner cams to the cam bolt.
10. Install the lockwasher and nut. Torque the nut to 49 ft. lbs.
11. Align the cam bolts with the marks made before removal.
12. Install the coil spring.
13. Install the shock absorber.
14. Lower vehicle to the floor.
15. Check front alignment.

Upper Control Arm

REMOVAL & INSTALLATION

1. Raise the vehicle on a hoist and remove the wheel.
2. Support the lower control arm with a floor jack.
3. Remove the upper ball stud nut and remove the ball stud from the steering knuckle.
4. Remove the control arm pivot bolts and remove the control arm from the vehicle.
5. Install the upper control arm to the vehicle at the inner pivot.

NOTE: The inner pivot bolts must be installed with the bolt heads to the front (on the front bushing) and to the rear (on the rear bushing).

6. Install the inner pivot nuts.
7. Position the control arm in a horizontal plane and tighten the inner pivot nuts to 48 ft. lbs.
8. Install the ball stud to the steering knuckle. Torque the nut to 30 ft. lbs. and install a cotter pin.
9. Install the tire and wheel assembly and lower the vehicle.

Wheel Bearings

ADJUSTMENT

1. Jack up the front of the car and support it with jackstands.
2. Remove the dust cap with a pair of slip-joint pliers.
3. Remove and discard the cotter pin. Loosen the spindle nut.
4. Rotate the wheel and tighten the spindle nut to 12 ft. lbs.
5. Back the nut off one flat and insert a new cotter pin. If the hole does not line up, back the nut off ½ flat or less to align the hole.

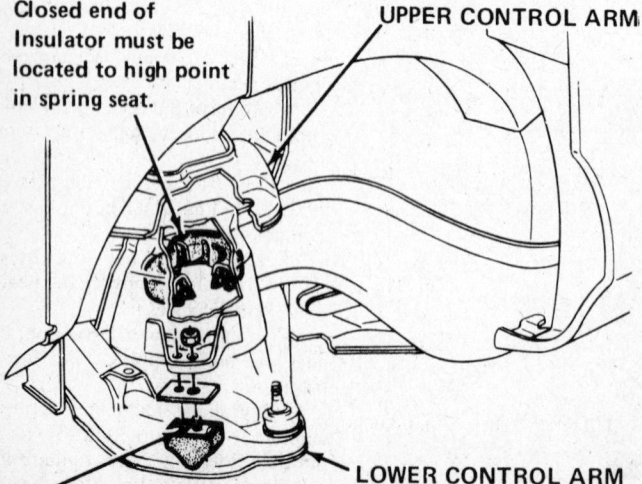

Closed end of Insulator must be located to high point in spring seat.

UPPER CONTROL ARM

LOWER CONTROL ARM

ANTI-ROTATION TAB

Position spring insulators as shown (© Chevrolet Div., G.M. Corp)

6. Check that the wheel turns freely, and then lock the cotter pin.

7. Bearing end-play should be between 0.001–0.005 in. Tap the dust cap back on and lower the car.

REAR SUSPENSION

A torque arm rear suspension is used on all models. The suspension consist of lower control arms and a track bar to control lateral movement. A torque arm is used to control rear axle wind-up. A stabilizer bar is standard and the upper control arms have been eliminated.

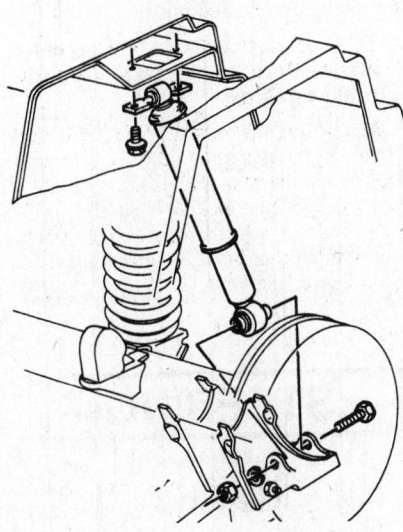

Rear shock absorber mounting
(© Chevrolet Div., G.M. Corp)

Shock Absorber

REMOVAL & INSTALLATION

NOTE: To purge air from the shock absorber before installation, extend the shock fully and invert it. Compress the shock, and return it to its upright position. Repeat this operation several times. Do not extend the shock absorber while it is inverted.

1. Raise the vehicle and support the rear axle.

2. Remove the upper attaching bolts and lower through-bolt.

3. Remove the shock absorber.

4. Install the retainer and the rubber grommet onto the shock.

5. Place the shock absorber into the installed position and install the upper retaining bolts. Torque to 18 ft. lbs.

6. Coat the through-bolt shank with chassis lube and install it and a rubber grommet on each side of the shock eye. Torque the nut to 42 ft. lbs.

7. Lower the car.

Rear Spring

REMOVAL & INSTALLATION

1. Raise the vehicle and support the rear axle, with a hydraulic jack.

2. Disconnect the shock absorber lower bolt, only on one side at a time.

3. Mark the position of the spring ends on their pads, if the springs are being reused. Lower the axle and remove the spring and spring insulators.

— CAUTION —
When lowering the axle, do not stretch the brake hose running from frame to axle.

4. Install the insulators on the top and bottom of the spring and position it on the axle.

5. Raise the axle and reconnect the shock absorber. Torque the bottom stud or bolt nuts to 42 ft. lbs.

6. Lower the vehicle.

Lower Control Arm

REMOVAL & INSTALLATION

— CAUTION —
If both control arms are to be replaced, remove and replace one control arm at a time to prevent the axle from rolling or slipping sideways.

1. Raise the vehicle on a hoist.

2. Support the rear axle.

3. Disconnect the stabilizer bar if so equipped.

4. Remove the control arm front and rear attaching bolts and remove the control arm.

5. Replacement of these bushings is the same procedure as that described for the upper control arm.

6. Place the control arm into position and install the front and rear bolts. Torque to 80 ft. lbs. with the weight of the car on the suspension.

7. Attach the stabilizer bar and the restraint cable, if so equipped.

8. Remove the support from the axle.

9. Lower the vehicle.

Torque Arm

REMOVAL & INSTALLATION

1. Raise and support the car at the rear axle.

2. Remove the torque arm mounting bracket from the transmission, then remove the through bolt at the bracket.

3. Remove the mounting bolts at the rear axle.

4. Installation is the reverse of removal. See the torque figures in the accompanying illustration.

Track Rod (Tie-Rod)

REMOVAL & INSTALLATION

1. Raise and support the car at the rear axle.

2. Remove the track rod mounting bolt at the underbody point, then remove the mounting bolt at the rear axle.

3. Installation is the reverse of removal. Lubricate the track rod bushings, prior to installation, with clean brake fluid. This will prevent squeaking and cracking. Note the torque figures in the accompanying illustration.

NOTE: It is important to use shims as shown to position the axle assembly so that equal clearance exists between the tire and wheelhouse on both sides of the vehicle.

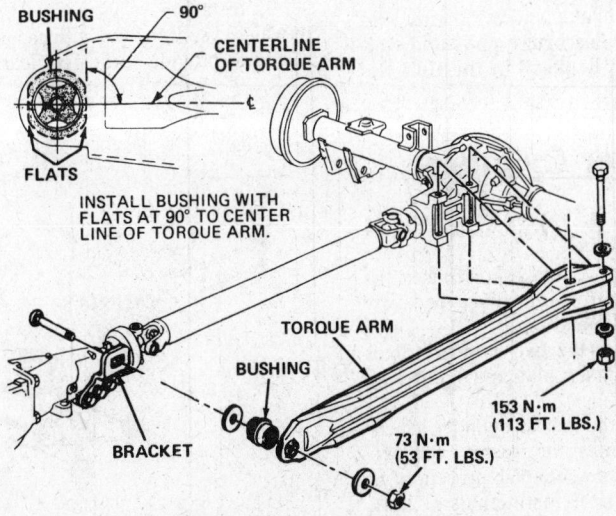

BUSHING 90°
CENTERLINE OF TORQUE ARM
FLATS
INSTALL BUSHING WITH FLATS AT 90° TO CENTER LINE OF TORQUE ARM.
TORQUE ARM
BUSHING
BRACKET
153 N·m (113 FT. LBS.)
73 N·m (53 FT. LBS.)

Torque arm removal and installation
(© Chevrolet Div., G.M. Corp.)

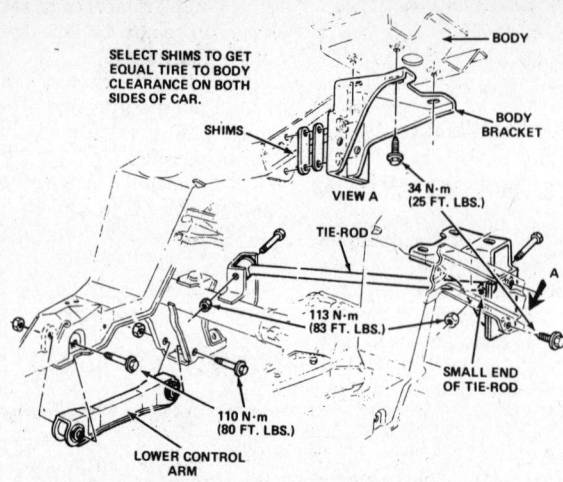

Track rod and lower control arm installation
(© Chevrolet Div., G.M. Corp)

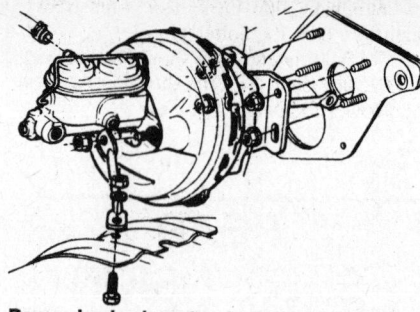

Power brake booster installation details
(© Chevrolet Div., G.M. Corp.)

BRAKES

Front disc brakes are standard equipment on all models, with power brakes optional. Hub and disc are one-piece and the assembly is mounted to a one-piece steering knuckle and steering arm. The disc caliper design is similar to the single-piston Delco-Moraine disc brake used on other Chevrolet vehicles.

Rear brakes are drum-type. Adjustment occurs automatically when the brakes are applied during a reverse stop.

The tandem master cylinder pushrod is not adjustable, thus eliminating a pedal free travel adjustment.

Both front and rear hydraulic systems are routed to and from a distribution valve. Any significant change in the pressure difference between the front and rear systems moves a piston which activates a warning light switch, indicating pressure failure in one of the systems.

To service brake shoes, drums and wheel cylinders or brake pads and calipers, refer to "Brakes" in the Unit Repair section.

Master Cylinder

REMOVAL & INSTALLATION

1. On non-power brakes, disconnect the master cylinder from the brake pedal by detaching the clip and pin.
2. Disconnect the two hydraulic lines at the master cylinder, plugging or covering the ends of the lines.
3. Remove the master cylinder attaching nuts and remove the master cylinder.
4. Reverse the removal procedure to install. Torque the mounting nuts to 24 ft. lbs.
5. Bleed the hydraulic system.

Power Booster

REMOVAL & INSTALLATION

1. Remove the vacuum hose from the check valve.
2. Remove the master cylinder-to-power booster nuts.
3. Remove the brake line distribution and switch mounting bolt from the fender skirt.
4. Pull forward on the master cylinder until the cylinder clears the power booster.
5. Carefully remove the master cylinder with the brake lines attached and set the master cylinder aside. Support the cylinder so that there is no stress on the brake lines. The master cylinder should be moved the minimum distance necessary.
6. Unbolt the power booster from the firewall.
7. Remove the brake pedal pushrod from the pedal pin.
8. Remove the power brake booster.
9. Installation is the reverse of removal. Be sure the brake lines are properly routed to provide sufficient clearance.

Parking Brake

ADJUSTMENT

1. Raise and support the rear of the car.
2. Apply the parking brake one notch from the fully released position.

NOTE: It may be necessary to remove the driveshaft to gain access to the parking brake equilizer.

3. Loosen the adjusting locknut and tighten the adjusting nut until a slight drag is felt when the rear wheels are rotated.
4. Tighten the locknut securely.
5. The rear wheels should rotate freely when the parking brake is fully released.
6. Lower the vehicle.

STEERING

Tie-Rod

REMOVAL & INSTALLATION

1. Place the vehicle on a hoist.
2. Remove the cotter pins from the ball studs and remove the special nuts.
3. To remove the outer ball stud, tap on the steering arm at the tie-rod end with

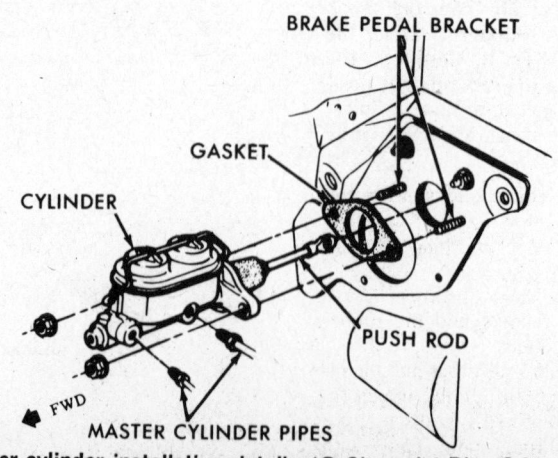

Master cylinder installation details (© Chevrolet Div., G.M. Corp.)

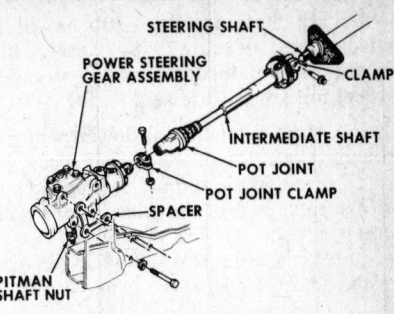

a hammer while using a heavy hammer or similar tool as a backing.

4. Remove the inner ball stud from the relay rod using the same procedure as described in Step 3.

5. To remove the tie-rod ends from the tie-rod, loosen the clamp bolts and unscrew the end assemblies.

6. If the tie-rod ends were removed, lubricate the tie-rod threads with chassis lube and install the ends on the tie-rod making sure that both ends are threaded an equal distance from the tie-rod.

7. Make sure that the threads on the ball studs and in the ball stud nuts are perfectly clean and smooth. Check the condition of the ball stud seals; replace if necessary.

NOTE: If threads are not clean and smooth, the ball studs may turn in the tie rod ends when attempting to tighten nut.

8. Install the ball studs in the steering arms and the relay rod.

9. Install the ball stud nut, tighten and install new cotter pins. Lubricate the tie rod ends.

10. Remove the vehicle from the hoist.

11. Adjust toe-in.

Manual Steering Gear

REMOVAL & INSTALLATION

1. Remove the pot joint coupling clamp bolt at the steering gear wormshaft.

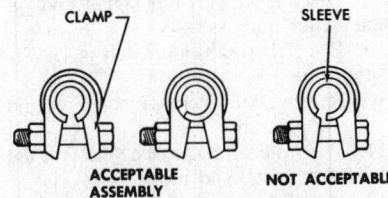

Tie-rod clamp installation
(© Chevrolet Div., G.M. Corp)

2. Raise the vehicle and support it with jack stands.

3. Remove the "K" brace.

4. Remove the pitman arm nut and washer from the pitman shaft and mark the relation of the arm position to the shaft.

5. Remove the pitman arm. G.M. recommends the use of tool No. J-6632 for this procedure.

6. Remove the bolts retaining the steering gear to the frame and remove the gear from the vehicle.

7. Installation is the reverse of removal.

Power Steering Gear

REMOVAL

1. To provide access to the steering gear remove the battery.

2. Remove the clamp which secures the intermediate shaft to the steering shaft.

3. Disconnect both hydraulic lines at the steering gear and allow to drain. Position the lines out of the way.

4. Raise the vehicle and support it with jack stands.

5. Remove the clamps at the stabilizer ban.

6. Remove the left front crossmember and bolts.

7. Remove the pitman shaft nut.

8. Remove the pitman arm from the pitman shaft. G.M. recommends using tool J-6632 or J-5504 for this procedure.

9. Remove the three steering gear mounting bolts and lock washers.

10. Lift the steering gear, remove the pitman arm, and position to provide clearance for removal.

11. Remove the steering gear and intermediate shaft as an assembly from the vehicle.

12. Remove the plastic shield.

13. Remove the pot joint clamp and separate the steering gear from the pot joint.

Power steering gear

INSTALLATION

1. Install the pot joint to the intermediate shaft.

2. Position the pot joint to the steering gear and install the pot joint clamp and torque to 30 ft. lbs.

3. Install the plastic shield.

4. Install the steering gear and intermediate shaft assembly to the steering column. Torque to 30 ft. lbs.

NOTE: Make sure the flat on the steering shaft is properly aligned. Also the steering gear can rotate three (3) full turns from lock to lock, therefore, it is important for proper installation that the steering gear be centrally positioned (1-1/2 turns) when installing the pot joint and intermediate shaft assembly.

5. Install the hydraulic lines to the steering gear.

6. Raise the vehicle and support it with jack stands.

7. Lift the steering gear and position the pitman arm to the pitman shaft.

8. Install the spacer and the three (3) steering gear mounting bolts and lock washers to 70 ft. lbs.

9. Install the pitman shaft nut and lock washer and torque to 185 ft. lbs.

10. Install the left front crossmember and bolts.

11. Install the stablizer bar clamps.

12. Lower the vehicle, install the battery and check the level of the power steering fluid.

Steering Wheel

REMOVAL & INSTALLATION
Standard Wheel

1. Disconnect the battery ground cable.

2. Remove the two screws from the back of the wheel, allowing the shroud (horn actuator bar) to be removed.

3. Set the wheel straight ahead. Mark the relationship of the wheel to the shaft and remove the snap-ring and nut.

4. Remove the steering wheel with a puller, using the two threaded holes in the wheel.

5. Install the wheel, aligning the previously made marks. Make sure that the turn signal switch is in the neutral position. Torque the nut to 30 ft. lbs.

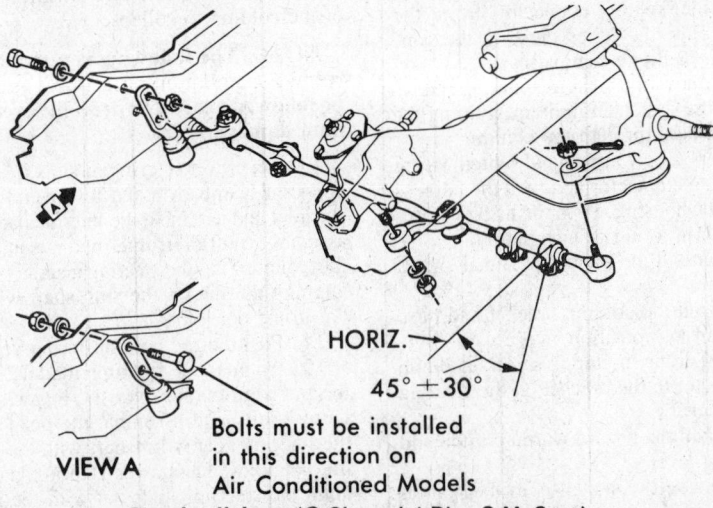

VIEW A

HORIZ.

45° ± 30°

Bolts must be installed in this direction on Air Conditioned Models

Steering linkage (© Chevrolet Div., G.M. Corp)

NOTE: Steering wheel rub has been encountered on some 1978–79 cars. This is due to over-torquing of the steering wheel nut by as little as 2 ft. lb.

6. Make sure that the lower horn insulator, eyelet, and spring are in place.

7. Position the shroud, seating the pin on the right side of the wheel in the hole in the shroud.

8. Replace the two screws in the rear of the wheel. Connect the battery cable.

GT and Sport Wheel

1. Disconnect the battery ground cable.

2. Pry off the horn button. Set the wheel in the straight ahead position.

3. Mark the relationship of the wheel to the shaft.

4. Remove the three screws and the upper horn insulator, receiver, and round belleville spring. Remove the snap-ring and nut.

5. Remove the steering wheel with a puller, utilizing the two threaded holes in the wheel.

6. Replace the wheel, aligning the marks previously made. Make sure that the turn signal switch is in the neutral position. Torque the nut to 30 ft. lbs.

NOTE: Steering wheel rub has been encountered on some 1978–79 cars. This is due to over-torquing of the steering wheel nut by as little as 2 ft. lb.

7. Make sure that the lower horn insulator, eyelet, and spring are in place.

8. Install the belleville spring, receiver, upper horn insulator, and three screws.

9. Install the horn button and connect the battery cable.

Turn Signal Switch

REMOVAL & INSTALLATION

Standard Column

1. Remove the steering wheel as outlined above.

2. On 1978 models loosen the three captive screws and lift the cover off the shaft. On 1979–80 models the cover can be pried off with a screwdriver.

3. The lockplate must be depressed with a special tool. Depress the lockplate and remove the wire snap-ring from the shaft.

4. Remove the cancelling cam, upper bearing pre-load spring, and thrust washer from the shaft.

5. Remove the turn signal lever screw and the lever.

6. Push the hazard knob in and unscrew it.

7. Unplug the switch connector from the column and wrap the upper part of the connector with tape.

8. Remove the three switch mounting screws and pull the switch straight up. Guide the wiring connector through the column.

9. Tape the new switch connector. Feed the connector down through the column housing and under the mounting bracket.

10. Install the three switch mounting screws.

─── CAUTION ───

It is extremely important that only the specified length fasteners be used. Use of overlength fasteners could prevent designed collapse of the steering column during impact.

11. Replace the hazard flasher knob and the turn signal lever. The turn signal switch should be in Neutral and the hazard flasher knob out.

12. Place the thrust washer, upper bearing preload spring, and cancelling cam on the shaft.

13. Place the lockplate and a new snap-ring on the shaft. Press the lockplate down as in Step three and install the new snap-ring.

14. Replace the cover and its three screws.

15. Install the steering wheel.

Tilt Column

1. Remove the steering wheel.

2. Remove the cover from the steering shaft. The screws have plastic retainers on the back of the cover. It is not necessary to completely remove the screws.

3. Remove the turn signal lever screw and lever.

4. Push the hazard warning knob in and remove the knob.

5. Depress the shaft lockplate and remove the retaining snap-ring. Remove the lockplate.

6. Slide the turn signal cancelling cam and upper bearing preload spring off the end of the shaft.

7. Remove the column mounting bracket and gently lower the column. Support the column.

8. Remove the signal switch wire protective cover and strip the wires from the protector. Do not damage the wires. Disconnect the switch connector from the bracket. Tape the wires close to the connectors to facilitate removal.

9. Remove the switch mounting screws and pull the switch straight up, guiding the wiring harness through the column.

10. Tape a new turn signal switch wiring harness and connector and feed the harness through the housing. Push the hazard warning switch in to aid in installation.

11. Reinstall the protective signal switch wire cover.

12. Install the column bracket and raise the column into position.

13. Install the mounting screws and clip the connector to the bracket on the steering column jacket.

14. Install the hazard warning knob and turn signal lever.

15. Be sure the switch is in the neutral position and the hazard warning knob is

out. Slide the upper bearing preload spring and cancelling cam onto the shaft.

16. Install the lockplate on the end of the shaft. Compress the lockplate and install a new snap-ring.

17. Reinstall the cover on the end of the shaft.

18. Install the steering wheel.

Ignition Switch

REMOVAL & INSTALLATION

The ignition switch is mounted on top of the column jacket under the dashboard, completely inaccessible unless the steering column is lowered. The energy-absorbing column is fragile when disconnected and should not be subjected to any shock or excess pressure. Since the column will distort under its own weight, make sure that it is fully supported along its entire length while it is disconnected from the dashboard.

1. Disconnect the battery ground cable.

2. Remove the steering wheel.

3. On manual steering columns, remove the pot joint coupling clamp bolt.

4. On power steering columns, remove the flexible coupling pinch bolt.

5. Move the front seat back out of the way.

6. Remove the three floor pan bracket screws.

7. Remove the two column-to-instrument panel nuts and carefully lower the column far enough to allow the harness plugs to be disconnected.

8. Disconnect the turn signal and ignition switch harnesses.

9. Place the ignition switch in LOCK position.

10. Remove the two switch screws and the switch assembly.

11. When installing, make sure that the switch is in LOCK position.

12. Install the rod to the switch and the switch to the column. Do not use mounting screws longer than the original ones because they could interfere with the ability of the column to collapse.

NOTE: The following is a mandatory column installation procedure, and must be followed exactly to prevent severe column damage.

13. On power steering models, place the pot joint clamp over the lower end of the pot joint and assemble the intermediate shaft assembly (pot joint, intermediate shaft and flex coupling) to the steering gear stub shaft, aligning the flat on the stub shaft with the flat in the pot joint.

14. Position the column in the vehicle.

15. On manual steering models, place the pot joint clamp over the lower end of the pot joint and assemble the pot joint to the steering gear wormshaft with the flat in the pot joint. On power steering models, align the steering shaft flat with the flat in the flex coupling. When the shaft is bot-

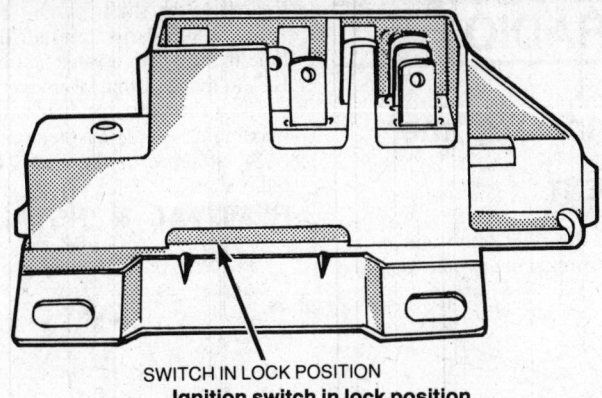

SWITCH IN LOCK POSITION
Ignition switch in lock position

tomed against the coupling reinforcement, install and tighten bolt to 30 ft. lbs.

16. Connect the turn signal and ignition switch wiring harnesses.

17. Loosely install the steering column bracket to instrument panel stud nuts.

18. Align the pot joint clamp with the groove across the end of the pot joint. Install bolt and nut, tightening nut to 55 ft. lbs.

NOTE: The bolt must pass through the shaft undercut.

19. With the vehicle on the ground, tighten instrument panel nuts to 19 ft. lbs.

20. Slide the toe plate down the column to the floorboard and install the three screws.

NOTE: On power steering models, alignment flange on the toe plate must be engaged with the front of the toe pan before driving screws. On manual steering models, no side load is allowed during installation of the attaching screws. A side load could cause misalignment.

21. On manual steering models: remove the alignment spacers. The minimum allowable clearance between the O.D. of the steering shaft and the I.D. of the column jacket lower plastic bushing after installation is 0.18 in.

22. Install the steering wheel.

23. Connect the battery ground cable.

Ignition Lock Cylinder

REMOVAL & INSTALLATION

Through Mid-1978

1. Place the lock cylinder in the On position.

2. Remove the turn signal switch and steering wheel as previously described.

3. Insert a thin-bladed screwdriver into the rectangular slot inside the column housing. Keep the screwdriver to the right side of the slot and break the housing casting flash loose. Depress the spring latch at the lower end of the lock cylinder. The lock cylinder can be removed with the latch depressed.

4. Place the key part way into the new lock cylinder assembly. If the key is in all the way, the sleeve assembly cannot be installed. Place the wave washer and antitheft ring onto the cylinder.

5. Make sure that the plastic keeper in the sleeve assembly is protruding. Align the lock cylinder lock bolt, the antitheft ring tab, and the slot in the sleeve.

6. Push the sleeve onto the cylinder. Push the key all the way in and rotate the cylinder clockwise.

7. Clamp the tabs of the lock in a padded vise.

8. Place the adapter ring on the cylinder with the serrations out. The adapter ring tab should be against the step in the sleeve. The key must be free to rotate 120°.

9. Tap the adapter into place so that the cylinder extends through it about 1/16 in.

10. Use a small, flat-tipped punch, at least 1/8 in. in diameter, to stake the cylinder over the adapter ring in four places just outside the four dimples.

11. Check the lock for proper operation.

12. Hold the sleeve and turn the tabs clockwise against the stop. Insert the assembly into the housing, aligning the key on the sleeve with the slot in the housing bore.

13. Hold a 0.070 in. drill bit between the lock rim and the housing. Turn the cylinder counterclockwise while pushing in lightly.

14. When the cylinder is felt to go into place, push the cylinder in until the retainer pops into place, securing the cylinder.

15. Remove the drill. Check the operation of the lock.

16. Install the turn signal switch and the steering wheel.

Mid-1978 and Later

1. Place the lock in the Run position.

2. Remove the lock plate, turn signal switch and buzzer switch.

3. Remove the screw and lock cylinder.

--- **CAUTION** ---

If the screw is dropped on removal, it could fall into the column, requiring complete disassembly to retrieve the screw.

4. Rotate the cylinder clockwise to align the cylinder key with the keyway in the housing.

5. Push the lock all the way in.

6. Install the screw. Tighten the screw to 14 in. lb. for adjustable columns and 25 in. lb. for standard columns.

Power Steering Pump

REMOVAL & INSTALLATION

1. Disconnect the hoses at the pump. Secure the hose ends in a raised position and cap the ends. Cap the pump openings as well.

2. Remove the pump adjusting nut and remove the drive belt.

3. Using a puller, remove the pump pulley.

4. Unbolt the pump from the brackets and lift it out of the car.

5. Installation is the reverse of removal. Adjust the drive belt, fill the reservoir and bleed the system.

INSTRUMENT PANEL

Speedometer Cable and Instrument Cluster

REMOVAL & INSTALLATION

The speedometer and the instruments are removed from the front of the panel by removing the bezel and the lens.

Lift the speedometer away from the panel and disconnect the speedometer cable and wiring from the rear of the cluster. The cable core can then be removed with the aid of a pair of needle nose pliers. If the cable core is broken, it may be necessary to remove the broken piece from the transmission end of the cable. The cable is easily unscrewed from the left side of the transmission case. When installing a new cable, liberally lubricate it with graphite base speedometer cable lubricant.

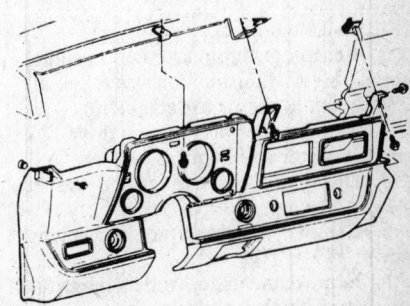

Standard instrument cluster, except station wagons—typical

All of the indicator bulbs are of the quarter twist type and are removed from the rear of the instrument cluster.

Headlight Switch

REMOVAL & INSTALLATION

1. Disconnect the battery ground cable.
2. Pull the light switch to ON position.
3. Reach up under the instrument panel and depress the switch retainer button while pulling on the knob.
4. Remove the knob and shaft, then remove the ferrule nut with a large screwdriver.
5. Disconnect the multi-contact connector, prying gently with a small screwdriver.
6. Connect the new switch and reverse the removal procedure to complete the replacement.

WINDSHIELD WIPERS

Wiper Blade

REMOVAL & INSTALLATION

Three methods of blade attachment may be used. If there is a small tab on top of the blade, depress it and slide the blade off. If there is a small spring visible in the top of the blade, insert a screwdriver in the opening, press down and slide the blade off. If there is a clip on the underside of the arm, press down on the clip and slide the blade off.

Motor

REMOVAL & INSTALLATION

1. Raise the hood.
2. Reaching through cowl opening, loosen the two transmission drive link attaching nuts to the motor crankarm.
3. Remove the transmission drive link from the motor crankarm.
4. Disconnect the wiring, and washer hoses.
5. Remove the three motor attaching screws.
6. Remove the motor while guiding the crankarm through the hole.
7. To install, reverse the removal procedure.

RADIO

Antenna Trimmer

ADJUSTMENT

1. Remove the right knob and bezel, and locate the trimmer screw above and to the left of the shaft.
2. Temporarily reinstall the knob and tune the radio to a weak station near 1400 KC on the AM dial. Remove the knob.
3. Adjust the trimmer screw until the maximum volume has been reached.
4. Replace the knob and bezel on the radio shaft.

REMOVAL & INSTALLATION

1. Remove the battery ground cable.

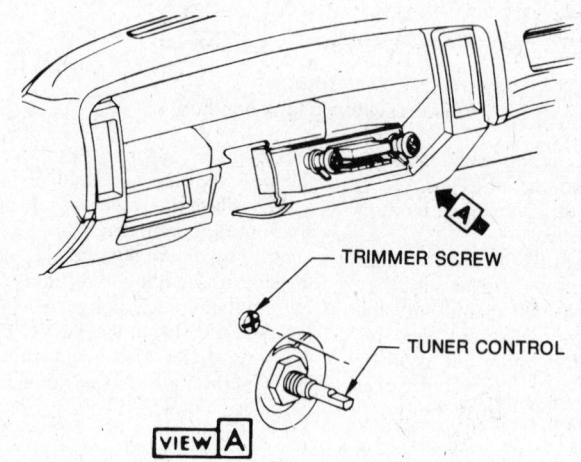

TRIMMER SCREW

TUNER CONTROL

VIEW A

Antenna trimmer screw location (© Chevrolet Div., G.M. Corp.)

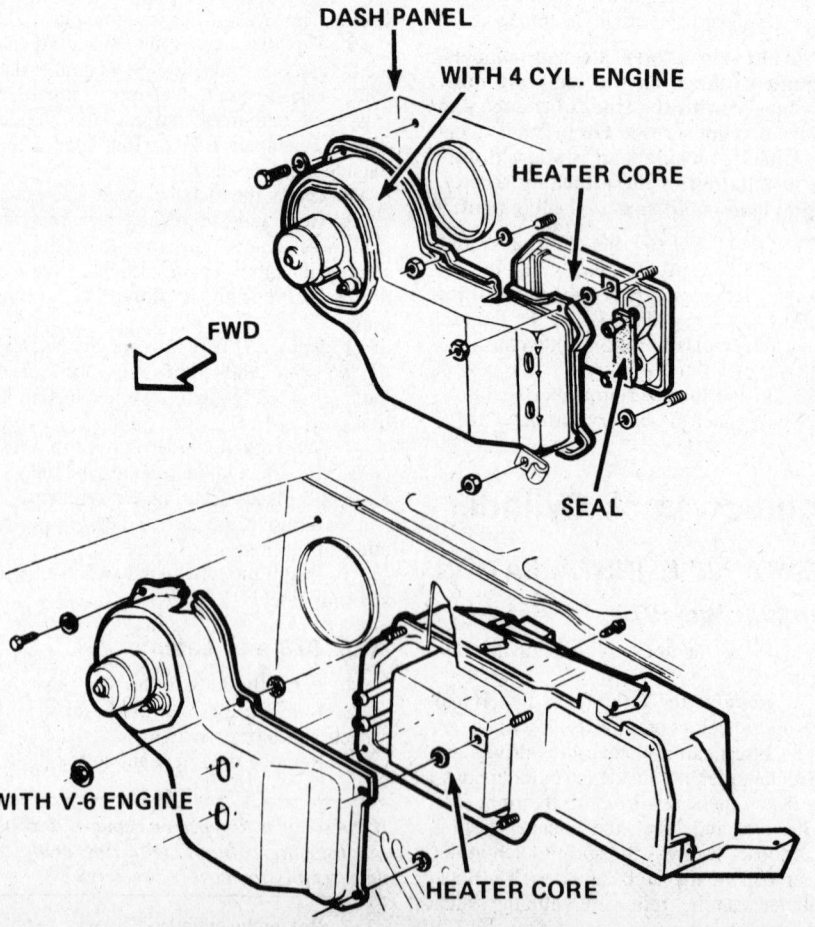

DASH PANEL

WITH 4 CYL. ENGINE

HEATER CORE

FWD

SEAL

WITH V-6 ENGINE

HEATER CORE

Blower motor and case assembly without A/C (© Chevrolet Div., G.M. Corp.)

2. Remove the knobs, controls, washers and nuts from the radio bushings.

3. On some models it may be necessary to remove the heater outlet duct on cars with air conditioning.

4. Disconnect the antenna lead, power connector, and speaker connectors from the rear of the receiver.

5. Remove the two screws securing the radio mounting bracket to the instrument panel lower reinforcement and lift out the radio receiver.

6. To install, reverse the removal procedure.

HEATER

Blower Motor

REMOVAL & INSTALLATION

1. Disconnect the battery ground cable.

2. Remove the coolant recovery tank attaching screws and move the tank aside; draining the tank is unnecessary.

3. Disconnect the blower motor lead wire. Disconnect the motor cooling tube on air-conditioned models.

4. Scribe the blower motor flange to case position.

5. Remove the blower to case attaching screws and remove the blower wheel and motor assembly. Pry the flange gently if the sealer is retaining the assembly.

6. Remove the blower wheel retaining nut and separate the motor and wheel.

7. To install, reverse Steps 1–5, lining up the match-marks on the motor flange and case which were made at removal.

NOTE: Assemble the blower wheel to the motor with the open end of the blower away from the motor. Reseal the motor flange, if necessary.

Heater Core

REMOVAL & INSTALLATION

All Models Without Air Conditioning

1. Disconnect the battery ground cable.

2. Disconnect the blower motor lead wire.

3. Place a pan under the vehicle. Disconnect the heater hoses at the core connections and secure the ends of the hoses in a raised position.

4. Remove the coil bracket to firewall stud nut and move the coil out of the way.

5. Remove the blower intake to firewall screws and nuts and remove the blower intake, blower motor and wheel as an assembly.

6. Remove the core retaining strap screws and remove the core from the vehicle.

7. To install, reverse Steps 1–6.

NOTE: Be sure that the blower intake sealer is intact, replace if necessary.

1978–80 Monza "S" Hatchback and Station Wagon With Air Conditioning

1. Disconnect the battery ground.

2. Disconnect the hoses at the core tubes and place in a raised position.

3. Remove the nuts from the selector duct studs in the engine compartment.

4. Remove the glove box and door.

5. Remove the right outlet to instrument panel screws and remove the outlet and hose.

6. Remove the intermediate duct leading to the left outlet.

7. Lower the steering column as described in Ignition Switch Removal and Installation.

8. Remove the instrument panel bezel. Remove the ashtray and retainer.

9. Remove the screws securing the A/C control head to the instrument panel.

10. Disconnect the radio leads and antenna wire.

11. Remove the instrument cluster screws and allow the entire cluster, including the radio, to rest on the steering column.

12. Disconnect the speedometer cable and remove the A/C control head.

13. Remove the center duct screws, then slide it first to the left, then to the right then remove it.

14. Remove the defroster duct and remaining selector ducts.

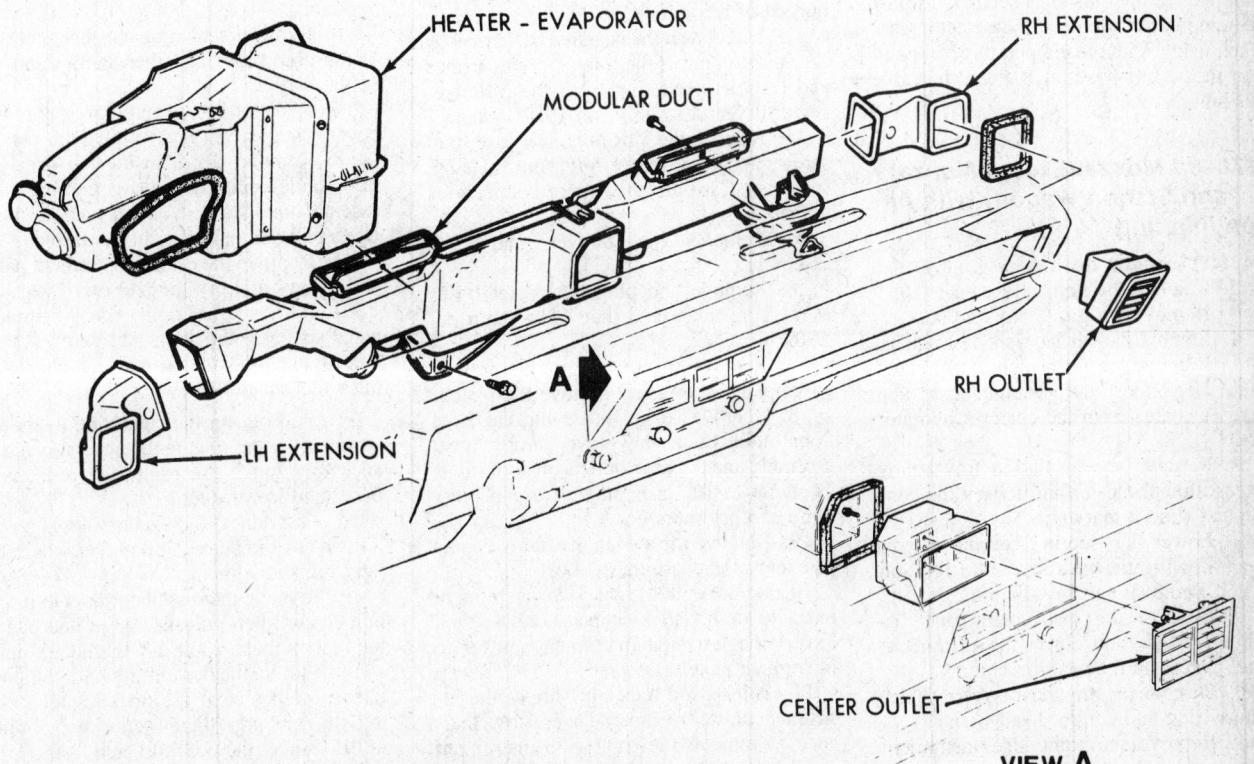

HEATER - EVAPORATOR

MODULAR DUCT

RH EXTENSION

RH OUTLET

LH EXTENSION

A

CENTER OUTLET

VIEW A

A/C Air Distribution Ducts (© Chevrolet Div., G.M. Corp.)

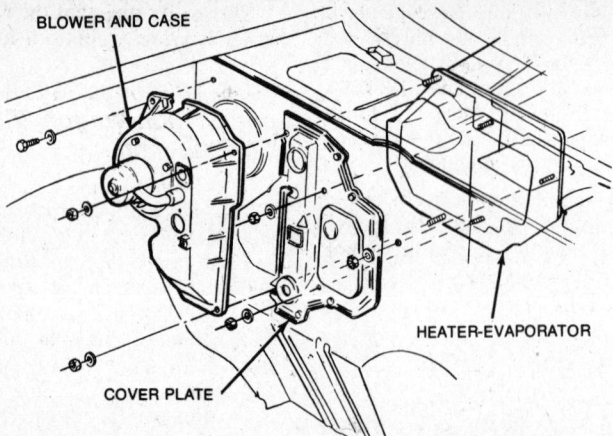

Heater core case installation (© Chevrolet Div., G.M. Corp.)

Labels in figure: BLOWER AND CASE, HEATER-EVAPORATOR, COVER PLATE

15. Disconnect all electrical and vacuum lines from the evaporator.

16. Disconnect the temperature door cables.

17. Pry off or punch out the temperature door bell crank.

18. Remove the temperature door.

19. Remove the screws securing the temperature door cable retainer and backing plate.

20. Remove the heater core and backing plate assembly and remove the straps from the core.

21. Installation is the reverse of removal. When installing the ducts, make sure the firewall seals are positioned correctly. When installing the cluster, position the A/C control head and connect the speedometer cable before the cluster is secured. Adjust the temperature door at the selector duct attachment. With the temperature lever and door in the Off position, tighten the cable attaching screw.

1978–80 Monza (Except Monza "S" and Station Wagon) With Air Conditioning

1. Disconnect the battery ground.
2. Remove the floor outlet duct.
3. Remove the glove box and door.
4. Remove the left and right dash outlets.
5. Remove the instrument panel pad.
6. Disconnect the vacuum hoses and electrical wires from the heater-evaporator case.
7. Remove the insulation tray below the instrument cluster and loosen the console and slide it rearward.
8. Lower the steering column assembly, following the instructions in Ignition Switch Removal and Installation.
9. Remove the instrument panel attaching screws and allow the instrument panel to rest on the steering column.
10. Disconnect the speedometer cable, radio wiring and control head wiring.
11. Remove the right side instrument panel and lap duct.
12. Remove the modular duct from the case.

13. Disconnect the temperature door cable and the wiring harness.

14. Remove the heater hoses from the core tubes and position them upright to avoid coolant loss.

15. Remove the three heater case stud nuts.

16. Remove the heater core case-to-evaporator core case screws.

17. Hammer on the studs, carefully, to break loose the heater core case.

18. Unbolt the core from the case.

19. Installation is the reverse of removal. Replace any damaged sealer.

Sunbird with Air Conditioning.

1. Have the air conditioning system purged of refrigerant.
2. Disconnect the negative battery cable.
3. Disconnect the inlet and outlet lines and the oil bleed line from the VIR (receiver-dryer) assembly, on 1977 systems.
4. Remove the VIR to blower case strap screw, and remove the VIR unit on 1977 systems. Cap all the open connections immediately.
5. Remove the blower and case assembly.
6. Remove and plug the heater hoses at the core tubes and then hang them out of the way.
7. Remove the evaporator to firewall cover plate screws and remove the plate.
8. Remove (from inside the car), the floor outlet duct, the glove compartment assembly and the dash outlets on both sides. To remove the dash outlets, use a putty knife and pry them out.
9. Remove the eleven instrument panel pad screws and pry the pad off.
10. Remove the right side instrument panel to dash and kick pad screws, then loosen the left side instrument cluster to instrument panel screws.
11. Pull out on the right side of the instrument cluster to gain the necessary clearance to remove the right side instrument panel and lower duct.
12. Disconnect the vacuum hoses on the left side of the heater unit and tag them for

later reinstallation.

13. Remove the modulator duct to heater unit screw, then pull the carpet and pad to the rear to make room for the heater unit removal.

14. Pull the heater unit toward you until the core tubes clear the firewall, then pull it to the right until there is enough clearance to disconnect the control cable.

15. After disconnecting the control cable, disconnect the wiring harness and remove the heater assembly.

16. Remove the screws and separate the heater case, then remove the core to case screws and remove the core.

17. Installation is the reverse of the above procedure, but before assembly, add 3 oz. of refrigerant oil to the evaporator core.

18. When installing the refrigerant lines, coat all the O-rings with refrigerant oil.

Skyhawk with Air Conditioning

NOTE: This procedure requires purging the air conditioning system of refrigerant. Do not attempt this unless you are a qualified air conditioning technician.

1. Have the air conditioning system purged of refrigerant.
2. Disconnect the negative battery cable.
3. Disconnect the inlet and outlet lines and the oil bleed line from the accumulator assembly.
4. Remove the accumulator to blower case strap screw, and remove the accumulator unit. Cap all the open connections immediately.
5. Remove the blower and case assembly.
6. Remove and plug the heater hoses at the core tubes and then hang them out of the way.
7. Remove the evaporator to firewall cover plate screws and remove the plate.
8. Remove (from inside the car), the floor outlet duct, the glove compartment assembly and the dash outlets on both sides. Use a putty knife to pry out the dash outlets.
9. Remove the eleven instrument panel pad screws and pry the pad off.
10. Remove the right side instrument panel to dash and kick pad screws, then loosen the left side instrument cluster to instrument panel screws.
11. Pull out on the right side of the instrument cluster to gain the necessary clearance to remove the right side instrument panel and lower duct.
12. Disconnect the vacuum hoses on the left side of the heater unit and tag them for later reinstallation.
13. Remove the modulator duct to heater unit screw, then pull the carpet and pad to the rear to make room for the heater unit.
14. Pull the heater unit toward you until the core tubes clear the firewall, then pull it to the right until there is enough clearance to disconnect the control cable.
15. After disconnecting the control cable, disconnect the wiring harness and remove the heater assembly.

16. Remove the screws and separate the heater case, then remove the core to case screws and remove the core.

17. Installation is the reverse of the above procedure, but before assembly, add 3 oz. of refrigerant oil to the evaporator core.

18. When installing the refrigerant lines, coat all the O-rings with refrigerant oil.

Starfire with Air Conditioning

1. Disconnect the negative battery cable.

2. Remove the three nuts from the engine compartment side of the cover plate.

3. Disconnect the heater hoses and fasten them in a raised position to prevent coolant loss. Plug the core tubes.

4. Remove the heater floor outlet.

5. Remove the glove box and door.

6. Remove the right and left air outlets.

7. Unscrew and move the console back.

8. Remove the column nuts and let the wheel rest on the seat. Remove the instrument panel screws and lower the panel onto the steering column.

9. Remove the right instrument panel and the lower outlet as an assembly.

10. Disconnect the vacuum hoses at the left end of the heater case.

11. Remove the modular duct to heater case screw and the two heater case to evaporator case screws. Pry off the retaining clips at the defroster outlets and move the duct back.

12. Pull the heater case away from the firewall until the core tubes clear, then disconnect the temperature cable.

13. Remove the core to case screws and remove the core.

14. Reverse the procedures for installation. Torque the steering column nuts to 25 ft. lbs.

FUSES AND FUSIBLE LINKS, CIRCUIT BREAKERS

Fuses

The fuse block is located beneath the instrument panel above the headlight dimmer floor switch. Fuse holders are labeled as to their service and the correct amperage. Always replace blown fuses with new ones of the correct amperage. Otherwise electrical overloads and possible wiring damage will result.

Circuit Breaker

A circuit breaker is an electrical switch which breaks the circuit during an electrical overload. The circuit breaker will remain open until the short or overload condition in the circuit is corrected.

Fusible Links

Fusible links are sections of wire, with special insulation, designed to melt under electrical overload. Replacements are simply spliced into the wire. There may be as many as five of these in the engine compartment wiring harnesses. These are:

1. Horn relay to fuse panel circuit—one link.

2. Charging circuit, from the starter solenoid to the horn relay—two links.

3. Starter solenoid to ammeter circuit—one link.

4. Horn relay to rear window defroster circuit—one link.

The fusible links are all two wire gauge sizes smaller than the wires they protect.

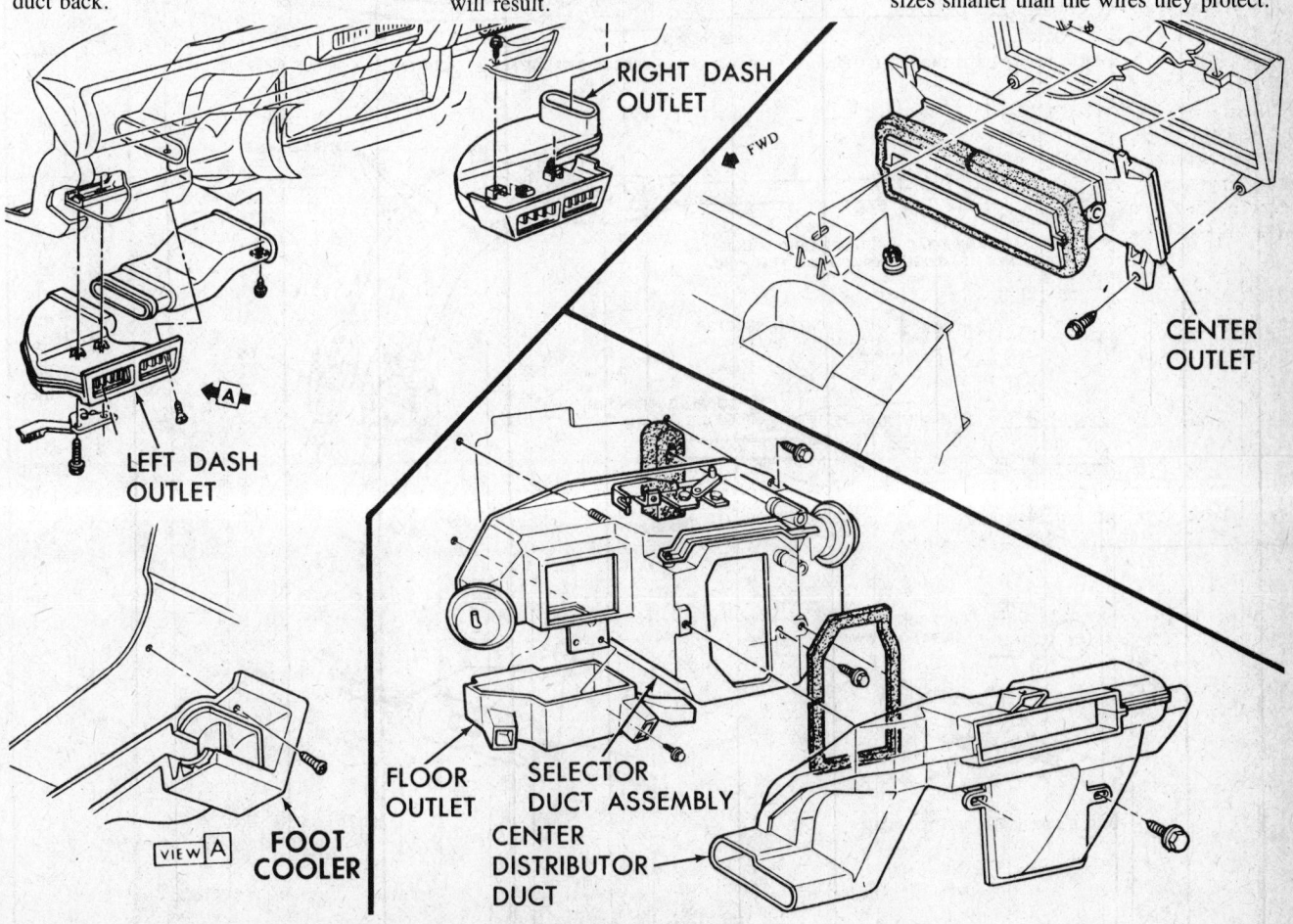

RIGHT DASH OUTLET

FWD

CENTER OUTLET

LEFT DASH OUTLET

VIEW A FOOT COOLER

FLOOR OUTLET SELECTOR DUCT ASSEMBLY CENTER DISTRIBUTOR DUCT

Air distributor and ducts

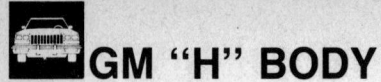

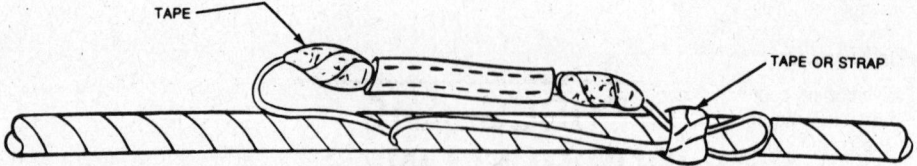

REMOVE EXISTING VINYL TUBE SHIELDING
REINSTALL OVER FUSE LINK BEFORE CRIMPING
FUSE LINK TO WIRE ENDS

TAPE

TAPE OR STRAP

TYPICAL REPAIR USING THE SPECIAL #17 GA. (9.00" LONG-YELLOW) FUSE LINK REQUIRED FOR THE AIR/COND.
CIRCUITS (2) #687E and #261A LOCATED IN THE ENGINE COMPARTMENT

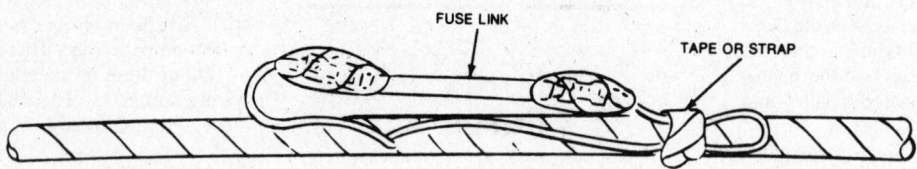

FUSE LINK

TAPE OR STRAP

TYPICAL REPAIR FOR ANY IN-LINE FUSE LINK USING THE SPECIFIED GAUGE FUSE LINK FOR THE SPECIFIC CIRCUIT

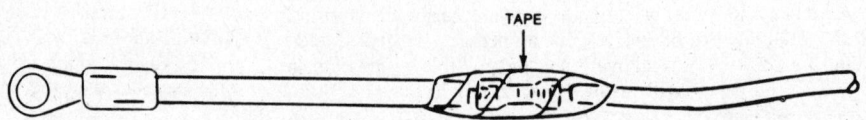

TAPE

TYPICAL REPAIR USING THE EYELET TERMINAL FUSE LINK OF THE SPECIFIED GAUGE FOR ATTACHMENT TO A CIRCUIT WIRE END

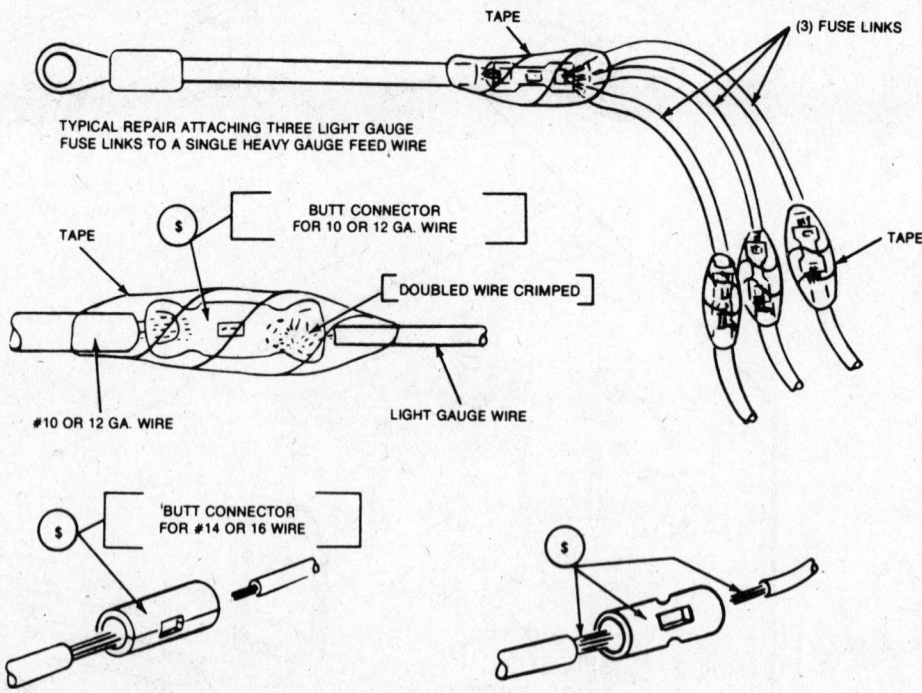

TAPE

(3) FUSE LINKS

TYPICAL REPAIR ATTACHING THREE LIGHT GAUGE
FUSE LINKS TO A SINGLE HEAVY GAUGE FEED WIRE

TAPE

BUTT CONNECTOR
FOR 10 OR 12 GA. WIRE

DOUBLED WIRE CRIMPED

TAPE

#10 OR 12 GA. WIRE

LIGHT GAUGE WIRE

BUTT CONNECTOR
FOR #14 OR 16 WIRE

FUSIBLE LINK REPAIR PROCEDURE

General fusible link repair procedure

GM "J" Body
Cavalier, Cimarron, Firenza, 2000 Sunbird, '82–'85 Skyhawk

YEAR IDENTIFICATION

1982–83 Cavalier

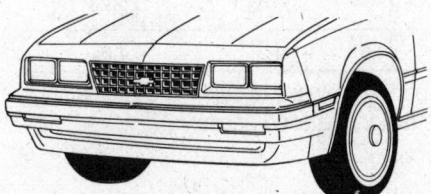

1984–85 Cavalier

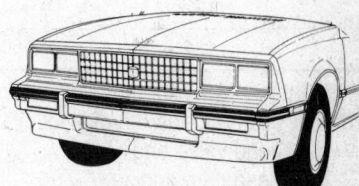

1982–83 Cimarron

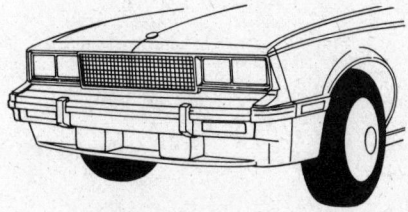

1984 Cimarron

1982–83 Firenza

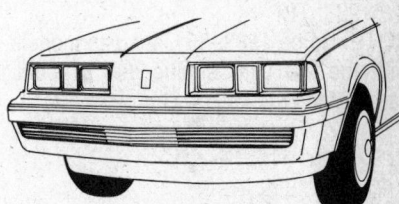

1984 Firenza

1984–85 Firenza GT

1982–83 2000

1984 2000 Sunbird

1984 2000 Sunbird LE, SE

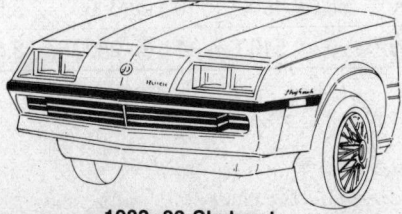

1982–83 Skyhawk

1984–85 Skyhawk

C703

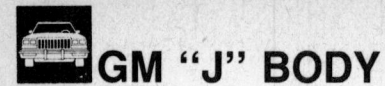

VEHICLE IDENTIFICATION NUMBER (VIN)

It is important for servicing and ordering parts to be certain of the vehicle and engine identification. The VIN (vehicle identification number) is a 13 or 17 digit number visible through the windshield on the driver's side of the dash and contains the vehicle and engine identification codes. It can be interpeted as follows:

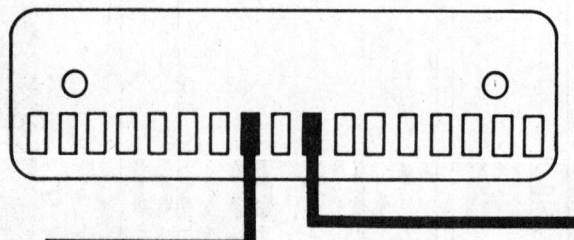

ENGINE CODE

Code	Cu. In.	Liters	Cyl.	Carb.	Eng. Mfg.
G	110 (OHV)	1.8	4	2 bbl	Chev.
O	110 (OHC)	1.8	4	TBI	Pontiac
J	110 (OHC)	1.8	4	MFI (Turbo)	Pontiac
B	122	2.0	4	①	Chev.
P	122	2.0	4	TBI	Chev.

MODEL YEAR CODE

Code	Year
C	1982
D	1983
E	1984
F	1985

The seventeen digit Vehicle Identification Number can be used to determine engine application and model year. The 10th digit indicates the model year, and the 8th digit identifies the factory installed engine.

OHV–Overhead valve engine
OHC–Overhead cam engine
TBI–Throttle Body Injection
MFI–Multi-Port Fuel Injection
①–1982: 2 bbl.
   1983: TBI
NOTE: Some 1983–85 Canadian models with the 2.0 Liter engine use a 2 bbl. carburetor

GENERAL ENGINE SPECIFICATIONS

Year	Engine No. Cyl. Displ. Cu. in.	Engine V.I.N. Code	Fuel Delivery System	Engine Mfg.	Horsepower @ rpm	Torque @ rpm (ft. lb.)	Bore × Stroke	Compression Ratio	Oil Pressure 2400 rpm
1982–85	4-110	G	2-bbl	Chev.	88 @ 5100	100 @ 2800	3.50 × 2.91	9.0:1	45
	4-110	O	TBI	Pont.	84 @ 5200	102 @ 2800	3.34 × 3.13	8.8:1	45
	4-110	J	MFI②	Pont.	150 @ 5600	150 @ 2800	3.34 × 3.13	8.0:1	65④
	4-122	P	TBI	Chev.	86 @ 4900	100 @ 3000	3.50 × 3.15	9.3:1	68③
	4-122	B	①	Chev.	90 @ 5100	111 @ 2800	3.50 × 3.15	9.0:1	45

① 1982: 2 bbl
   1983: TBI
② Turbocharged
③ @ 1200 rpm
④ @ 2500 rpm

TUNE-UP SPECIFICATIONS

(When analyzing compression test results, look for uniformity among cylinders rather than specific pressures.)

Year	Eng. V.I.N. Code	Engine No. Cyl. Displacement (cu. in.)	Eng. Mfg.	hp	Spark Plugs Orig Type	Spark Plugs Gap (in.)	Ignition Timing (deg)▲● Man Trans	Ignition Timing (deg)▲● Auto Trans	Valves Intake Opens (deg)■	Fuel Pump Pressure (psi)	Idle Speed (rpm)▲● Man Trans	Idle Speed (rpm)▲● Auto Trans
1982–'85	G	4-110	Chev.	88	R-42TS	0.045①	12B	12B	30	4.5–6.0	②	②
	0	4-110	Pont.	84	R-42XLS6④	0.060	8B	8B	N.A.	9–13	②	②
	B	4-122	Chev.	90	R-42CTS	0.035	—	12B	30	4.5–6.0③	②	②
	P	4-122	Chev	86	R-42CTS	0.035	②	②	N.A.	12	②	②
	J	4-110	Pont.	150	R-42CXLS	0.035	②	②	N.A.	12	②	②

NOTE: The underhood specifications sticker often reflects tune-up specification changes made in production. Sticker figures must be used if they disagree with those in this chart.
▲See text for procedure
●Figure in parenthesis indicates California and High Altitude engine
■All figures Before Top Dead Center
B Before Top Dead Center
Part numbers in this chart are not recommendations by Chilton for any product by brand name.
①Certain models may use 0.035 in. Gap— see underhood specifications sticker to be sure
②See underhood specifications sticker
③1983–84 w/T.B.I—12 psi
④1984–85—R44XLS
N.A.: Not Available

FIRING ORDERS

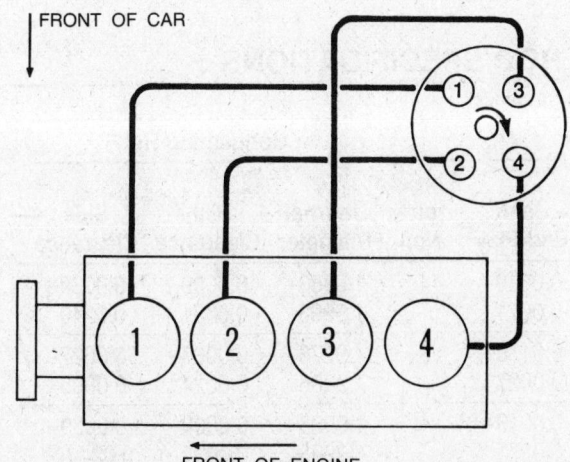

GM (Chevrolet) 110 and 122 overhead valve (OHV)
Engine firing order: 1-3-4-2
Distributor rotation: clockwise

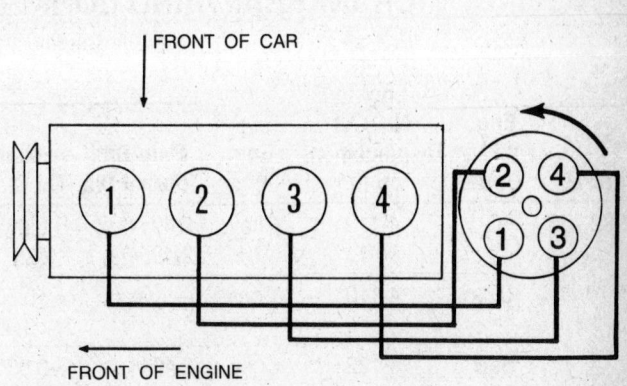

GM (Pontiac) 110 overhead camshaft (OHC)
Engine firing order: 1-3-4-2
Distributor rotation: counterclockwise

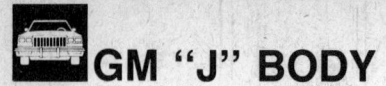

CAPACITIES

Year	Eng. V.I.N. Code	Engine Displacement (Cu. In.)	Eng. Mfg.	Crankcase Quarts (Liters) w/filter	Crankcase Quarts (Liters) wo/filter	Transaxle Pints (L) 4 speed	Transaxle Pints (L) 5 speed	Transaxle Pints (L) Auto	Gas Tank Gal (L)	Cooling System Qts (L) w/heater	Cooling System Qts (L) w/AC
1982–'85	G	110	Chev.	4.0 (3.8)	4.0 (3.8)	5.9 (2.8)	—	10.5 (5.0)	14 (53)	8.0 (7.57)	8.0 (7.57)
	0, J	110	Pont.	①	①	—	2.5 (5.3)	10.5 (5.0)	14 (53)	7.8 (7.4)	7.9 (7.5)
	B, P	122	Chev.	4.0 (3.8)	4.0 (3.8)	5.9 (2.8)	—	10.5 (5.0)	14 (53)	8.3 (7.7)	8.3 (7.7)

①Add 3 qts, check oil level at dipstick and add as necessary.

VALVE SPECIFICATIONS

Year	Eng. V.I.N. Code	Engine No. Cyl. Displacement (cu. in.)	Eng. Mfg.	Seat Angle (deg)	Face Angle (deg)	Spring Test Pressure (lbs. @ In.)	Spring Installed Height (in.)	Stem to Guide Clearance (in.) Intake	Stem to Guide Clearance (in.) Exhaust	Stem Diameter (in.) Intake	Stem Diameter (in.) Exhaust
1982–'85	G	4-110	Chev.	46	45	183 @ 1.33	1.60	0.0011–0.0026	0.0014–0.0031	0.3139–0.3144	0.3129–0.3136
	0, J	4-110	Pont.	46	46	N.A.	N.A.	0.0006–0.0016	0.0012–0.0024	N.A.	N.A.
	B, P	4-122	Chev.	46	45	183 @ 1.33	1.60	0.0011–0.0026	0.0014–0.0031	0.3139–0.3144	0.3129–0.3136

N.A.: Not Available

CAMSHAFT SPECIFICATIONS

(All measurements in inches)

Year	Eng. V.I.N. Code	Engine	Eng. Mfg.	Journal Diameter 1	Journal Diameter 2	Journal Diameter 3	Journal Diameter 4	Journal Diameter 5	Bearing Clearance	Lobe Lift Intake	Lobe Lift Exhaust	Camshaft End Play
1982–'85	G	4-110	Chev.	1.8677–1.8696	1.8677–1.8696	1.8677–1.8696	1.8677–1.8696	1.8677–1.8696	0.0010–0.0039	0.2625	0.2625	N.A.
	0, J	4-110	Pont.	1.6714–1.6720	1.6812–1.6816	1.6911–1.6917	1.7009–1.7015	1.7108–1.7114	N.A.	0.2409	0.2409	0.016–0.064
	B, P	4-122	Chev.	1.8677–1.8696	1.8677–1.8696	1.8677–1.8696	1.8677–1.8696	1.8677–1.8696	0.0010–0.0039	0.2625	0.2625	N.A.

N.A.: Not Available

CRANKSHAFT AND CONNECTING ROD SPECIFICATIONS

(All measurements are given in inches)

Year	Eng. V.I.N. Code	Engine No. Cyl Displacement (cu in.)	Eng. Mfg.	Crankshaft Main Brg Journal Dia	Crankshaft Main Brg Oil Clearance	Crankshaft Shaft End-Play	Thrust on No.	Connecting Rod Journal Diameter	Connecting Rod Oil Clearance	Connecting Rod Side Clearance
1982–'85	G	4-110	Chev.	2.4944–2.4954②	0.0006–0.0018③	0.0019–0.0071	4	1.9983–1.9993	0.0009–0.0031	0.0039–0.0240
	0, J	4-110	Pont.	①	0.0006–0.0016	0.0118–0.0027	3	1.9278–1.9286	0.0007–0.0024	0.0027–0.0095
	B, P	4-122	Chev.	2.4944–2.4954②	0.0006–0.0018③	0.0019–0.0071	4	1.9983–1.9993	0.0009–0.0031	0.0039–0.0240④

①Bearings are identified by color:
  Brown 2.2830–2.2832
  Green 2.2827–2.2830

② #5: 2.4936–2.4946
③ #5: 0.0014–0.0027
④ '84–'85: .004–.015

PISTON AND RING SPECIFICATIONS

(All measurements are given in inches.)

Year	Eng. V.I.N. Code	Engine No. Cyl. Disp. (cu in.)	Eng. Mfg.	Piston-to-Bore Clearance	Ring Gap: Top Compression	Ring Gap: Botton Compression	Ring Gap: Oil Control	Ring Side Clearance: Top Compression	Ring Side Clearance: Bottom Compression	Ring Side Clearance: Oil Control
1982–'85	G	4-110	Chev.	0.0008–0.0018	0.0098–0.0197	0.0098–0.0197	snug	0.0012–0.0027	0.0012–0.0034	0.0078
	0, J	4-110	Pont.	0.0008①	0.0010–0.0020	0.0010–0.0020	0.0010–0.0020	0.0020–0.0030	0.0010–0.0024	snug
	B, P	4-122	Chev.	0.0008–② 0.0018	0.0098–0.0197	0.0098–0.0197	snug	0.0012–0.0027	0.0012–0.0034	0.0078

①Code J: 0.0004–0.0012
②1984–85: 0.0007–0.0017

TORQUE SPECIFICATIONS

(All readings in ft. lbs.)

Year	Eng. V.I.N. Code	Engine No. Cyl Displacement (cu in.)	Eng. Mfg.	Cylinder Head Bolts	Rod Bearing Bold	Main Bearing Bolt	Crankshaft Pulley Bolt	Flywheel to Crankshaft Bolts	Manifold: Intake	Manifold: Exhaust
1982–'85	G	4-110	Chev.	65–75	34–40	63–74	66–84	45–55	20–25	22–28
	O,J	4-110	Pont.	①	39	57	115	45	25	16
	B,P	4-122	Chev.	65–75	34–43	63–77	66–89	②45–63	18–25	20–30

①Torque bolts to 18 ft. lb., then turn each bolt 60°, in sequence, 3 times for a 180° rotation, then run the engine to normal operating temperature and turn each bolt, in sequence, an additional 30°–50°.
② Auto. trans.: 45–59.

WHEEL ALIGNMENT SPECIFICATIONS

Year	Camber (positive): Range (degrees)	Camber (positive): Preferred (degrees)	Toe: Range (degrees)	Toe: Preferred (degrees)
'82	$\frac{1}{16}$ to $1\frac{1}{16}$	$\frac{9}{16}$	$\frac{1}{4}$ to 0	$\frac{1}{8}$①
'83	$\frac{7}{32}$ to $1\frac{7}{32}$	$\frac{23}{32}$	$\frac{5}{16}$ to $\frac{1}{16}$	$\frac{1}{8}$①
'84–'85	$\frac{3}{16}$ to $1\frac{3}{16}$	$\frac{11}{16}$	$\frac{1}{4}$ to 0	$\frac{1}{8}$①

①Out

CHARGING SYSTEM

Alternator

For further information on the charging system, please refer to "Charging and Starting" in the Unit Repair section.

PRECAUTIONS

1. When installing a battery, make sure that the positive and negative cables are not reversed.

2. When jump-starting the car, be sure that like terminals are connected. This also applies to using a battery charger. Reversed polarity will burn out the alternator and regulator in a matter of seconds.

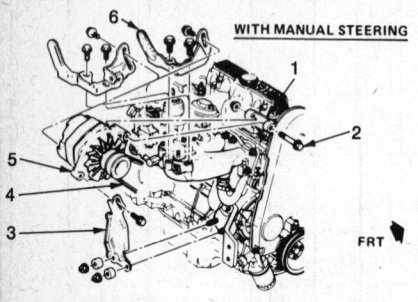

WITH MANUAL STEERING

1. Bracket
2. Bolt
3. Bracket
4. Belt
5. Alternator
6. Bracket

Alternator installation, OHC engines with manual steering

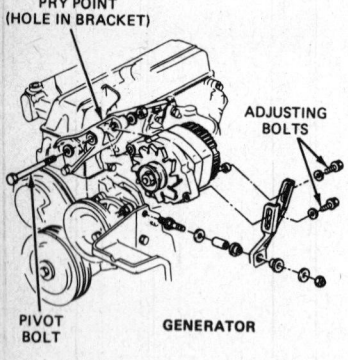

PRY POINT (HOLE IN BRACKET)

ADJUSTING BOLTS

PIVOT BOLT

GENERATOR

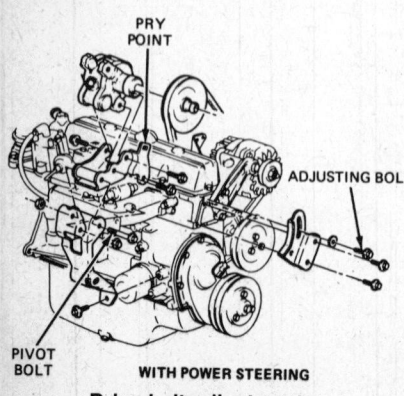

PRY POINT

ADJUSTING BOLT

PIVOT BOLT

WITH POWER STEERING

Drive belt adjustments

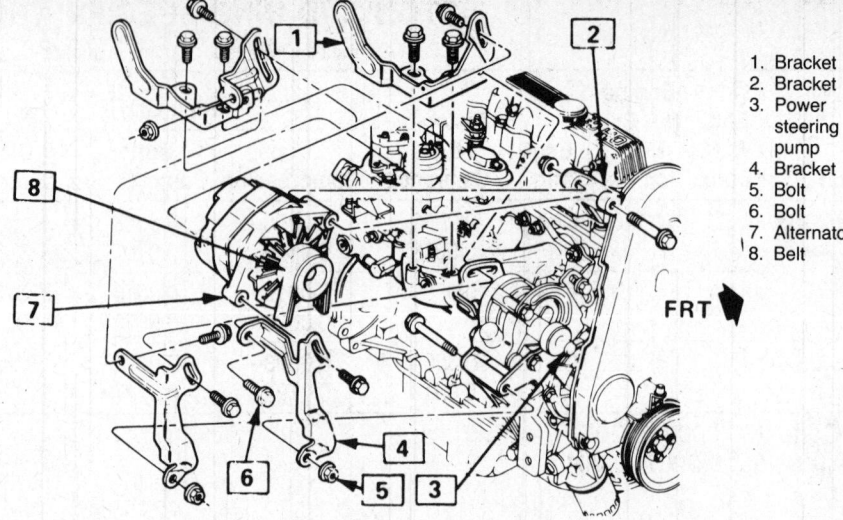

1. Bracket
2. Bracket
3. Power steering pump
4. Bracket
5. Bolt
6. Bolt
7. Alternator
8. Belt

FRT

Alternator installation, OHC engines with power steering

3. Never operate the alternator with the battery disconnected or on an otherwise uncontrolled open circuit.

4. Do not short across or ground any alternator or regulator terminals.

5. Do not try to polarize the alternator.

6. Do not apply full battery voltage to the field (brown) connector.

7. Always disconnect the battery ground cable before disconnecting the alternator lead.

8. Always disconnect the battery (negative cable first) when charging it.

9. Never subject the alternator to excessive heat or dampness. If you are steam-cleaning the engine, cover the alternator.

10. Never use arc-welding equipment on the car with the alternator connected.

REMOVAL & INSTALLATION

1. Disconnect the negative battery cable at the battery.

CAUTION

Failure to disconnect the negative cable may result in injury from the positive battery lead at the alternator, and may short the alternator and regulator during the removal process.

2. Disconnect and label the two terminal plug and the battery leads from the rear of the alternator.

3. Loosen the mounting bolts. Push the alternator inwards and slip the drive belt off the pulley.

4. Remove the mounting bolts and remove the alternator.

5. To install, place the alternator in its brackets and install the mounting bolts. Do not tighten them yet.

6. Slip the belt back over the pulley. Pull outwards on the unit and adjust the belt tension. Tighten the mounting and adjusting bolts.

7. Install the electrical leads.

8. Install the negative battery cable.

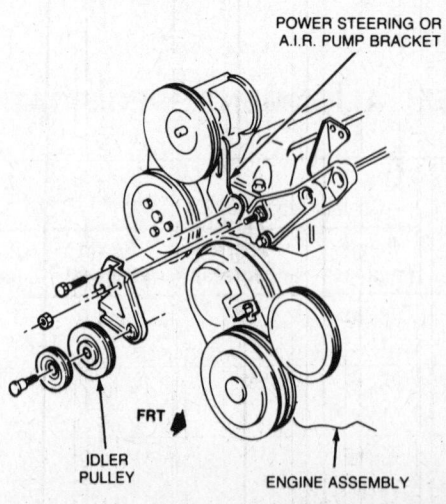

POWER STEERING OR A.I.R. PUMP BRACKET

FRT

IDLER PULLEY

ENGINE ASSEMBLY

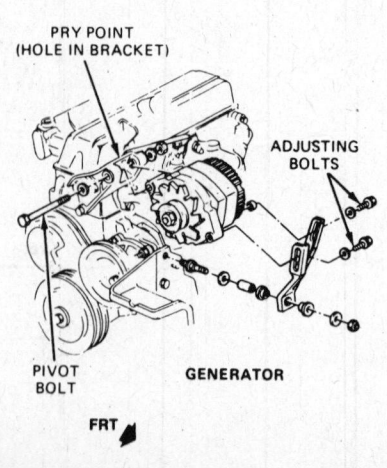

PRY POINT (HOLE IN BRACKET)

ADJUSTING BOLTS

PIVOT BOLT

GENERATOR

FRT

Alternator installation, OHV engines

Regulator

A solid state regulator is mounted within the alternator. All regulator components are enclosed in a solid mold. The regulator is non-adjustable and requires no maintenance.

STARTING SYSTEM

For further information on the starting system, please refer to "Charging and Starting" in the Unit Repair section.

Starter

REMOVAL & INSTALLATION

OHV Engine

1. Disconnect the negative battery cable at the battery.
2. Label and disconnect the solenoid wires and battery cable.
3. Remove the rear motor support bracket. Remove the A/C compressor support rod (if so equipped).
4. Working under the car, remove the two starter-to-engine bolts, and allow the starter to drop down. Note the location and number of any shims. Remove the starter.
5. Installation is the reverse. Tighten the mounting bolts to 25–35 ft. lbs.

OHC Engines

1. Disconnect the battery ground cable.
2. Remove the air cleaner.
3. Remove the lower starter bolt.
4. Remove the rear starter brace.
5. Remove the wiring from the starter
6. Remove the upper starter bolt.
7. Raise and support the car on jackstands.
8. Disconnect the speedometer cable.
9. Push the shifter cable up and guide

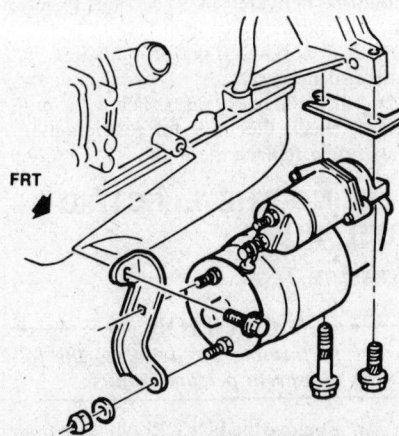

Starter mounting, OHV engines

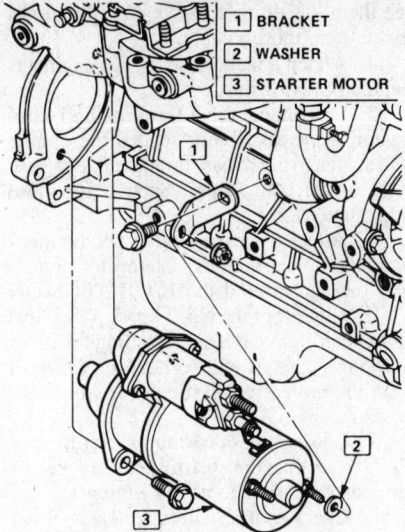

1 BRACKET
2 WASHER
3 STARTER MOTOR

Starter mounting, OHC engines

the starter, armature end first, down between the stabilizer bar and the engine.
10. Installation is the reverse of removal.

IGNITION SYSTEM

For further information on the ignition system, please refer to "Electronic Ignition Systems" in the Unit Repair section.

REMOVAL & INSTALLATION

OHV Engines

1. Disconnect the negative battery cable.
2. Tag and disconnect all wires leading from the distributor cap.
3. Remove the air cleaner housing as previously detailed.
4. Remove the distributor cap.
5. Disconnect the AIR pipe-to-exhaust manifold hose at the air management valve.
6. Unscrew the rear engine lift bracket bolt and nut, lift it off the stud and then position the entire assembly out of the way to facilitate better access to the distributor.
7. Mark the position of the distributor, relative to the engine block and then scribe a mark on the distributor body indicating the initial position of the rotor.
8. Remove the hold-down nut and clamp from the base of the distributor. Remove the distributor from the engine. The drive gear on the distributor shaft is helical and the shaft will rotate slightly as the distributor is removed. Note and mark the position of the rotor at this second position. *Do not crank the engine while the distributor is removed.*

9. To install the distributor, rotate the shaft until the rotor aligns with the second mark you made (when the shaft stopped moving). Lubricate the drive gear with clean engine oil and install the distributor into the engine. As the distributor is installed, the rotor should move to the first mark that you made. This will ensure proper timing. If the marks do not align properly, remove the distributor and try again.
10. Install the clamp and hold-down nut.

NOTE: You may wish to use a magnet attached to an extension bar to position the clamp on the stud.

11. Installation of the remaining components is in the reverse order of removal. Check the ignition timing.

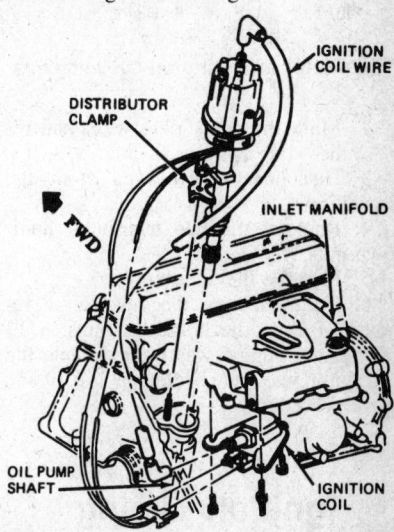

IGNITION COIL WIRE
DISTRIBUTOR CLAMP
FWD
INLET MANIFOLD
OIL PUMP SHAFT
IGNITION COIL

Removing the distributor from OHV engines

INSTALLATION IF THE ENGINE WAS DISTURBED

If the engine was cranked while the distributor was removed, you will have to place the engine on TDC of the compression stroke to obtain proper ignition timing.

1. Remove the No. 1 spark plug.
2. Place your thumb over the spark plug hole. Crank the engine slowly until compression is felt. It will be easier if you have someone rotate the engine by hand, using a wrench on the crankshaft pulley.
3. Align the timing mark on the crankshaft pulley with the 0° mark on the timing scale attached to the front of the engine. This places the engine at TDC of the compression stroke.
4. Turn the distributor shaft until the rotor points to the No. 1 spark plug tower on the cap.
5. Install the distributor into the engine. Be sure to align the distributor-to-engine block mark made earlier.
6. Perform Steps 10–11 of the preceeding removal and installation procedure.

OHC Engines

1. Disconnect the battery ground.

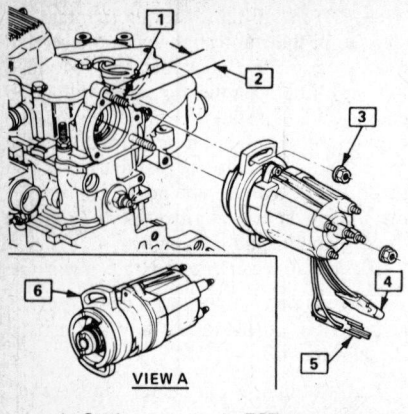

1. Stud
2. 20 ± 1.0
3. Nut
4. EST connector
5. Coil Connector
6. Distributor

Distributor mounting on OHC engines

2. Mark the spark plug wires and remove the wires and coil.

3. Disconnect the wiring from the distributor.

4. Remove the two distributor hold-down nuts.

5. Remove the distributor.

6. Installation is the reverse of removal. Torque the holddown nuts to 13 ft.lb. If the engine was rotated while the distributor was out, see steps 1–5 of the above procedure.

Ignition Timing

ADJUSTMENT

1. Refer to the instructions on the emission control sticker inside the engine compartment. Follow all instructions on the label.

2. Locate the timing marks on the crankshaft pulley and the front of the engine.

3. Clean off the marks so that you can see them. Chalk or white paint will help to make them more visible.

4. Attach a tachometer to the engine as detailed previously.

5. Disconnect the 4-terminal EST connector at the distributor so that the engine will switch to the bypass timing mode (please refer to the Unit Repair Section for more information).

6. Attach a timing light as per the manufacturer's instructions. Clamp the inductive pick-up around the HIGH TENSION COIL WIRE (not the No. 1 spark plug wire) at the distributor. Before installing the pick-up on the wire, it will be necessary to peel back the protective plastic cover which encases the wire.

7. Loosen the distributor clamp bolt slightly so that the distributor may be rotated as necessary to adjust timing.

8. Check that all wires are clear of the fan and then start the engine. Allow the engine to reach normal operating temperature.

9. Aim the timing light at the marks. A slight jiggling of the notch on the pulley may appear due to the fact that each cylinder is being displayed as it fires. The apparent notch 'width' *cannot* be reduced by a timing adjustment.

10. Center the total apparent notch 'width' about the correct timing mark on the indicator by rotating the distributor housing. This will insure that the average cylinder timing is as close to specifications as possible. Once again, the apparent notch 'width' *cannot* be reduced by timing adjustment.

11. Turn off the engine and tighten the distributor lock bolt. Start the engine and recheck the timing. Sometimes the distributor will move a little during the tightening process. If the ignition timing is within 1° of the correct setting, that is close enough; a tolerance of up to 2° is permitted by the manufacturer.

12. Turn off the engine and disconnect the timing light and the tachometer. Reconnect the 4-terminal EST connector.

FUEL SYSTEM

Fuel Pump

A mechanical fuel pump is used on carbureted engines. It is of the diaphragm-type and because of the design is serviced by replacement only. No adjustments or repairs are possible. The pump is operated by an eccentric on the camshaft. An electric, in-tank fuel pump is used with fuel injected engines. No adjustments or repairs are possible.

TESTING THE MECHANICAL FUEL PUMP

To determine if the pump is in good condition, tests for both volume and pressure should be performed. The tests are made with the pump installed, and the engine at normal operating temperature and idle speed. Never replace a fuel pump without first performing these simple tests.

Be sure that the fuel filter has been changed at the specified interval. If in doubt, install a new filter first.

Pressure Test

1. Disconnect the fuel line at the carburetor and connect a fuel pump pressure gauge. Fill the carburetor float bowl with gasoline.

2. Start the engine and check the pressure with the engine at idle. If the pump has a vapor return hose, squeeze it off so that an accurate reading can be obtained. Pressure should not be below 4.5 psi.

3. If the pressure is incorrect, replace the pump. If it is ok, go on to the volume test.

Volume Test

4. Disconnect the pressure gauge. Run the fuel line into a graduated container.

5. Run the engine at idle until one pint of gasoline has been pumped. One pint should be delivered in 30 seconds or less. There is normally enough fuel in the carburetor float bowl to perform this test, but refill it if necessary.

6. If the delivery rate is below the minimum, check the lines for restrictions or leaks, then replace the pump

TESTING THE ELECTRIC FUEL PUMP

Pressure Test

— CAUTION —

Before performing any tests, do the following to prevent personal injury:

a. Remove the FUEL PUMP fuse from the fuse panel in the passenger compartment.

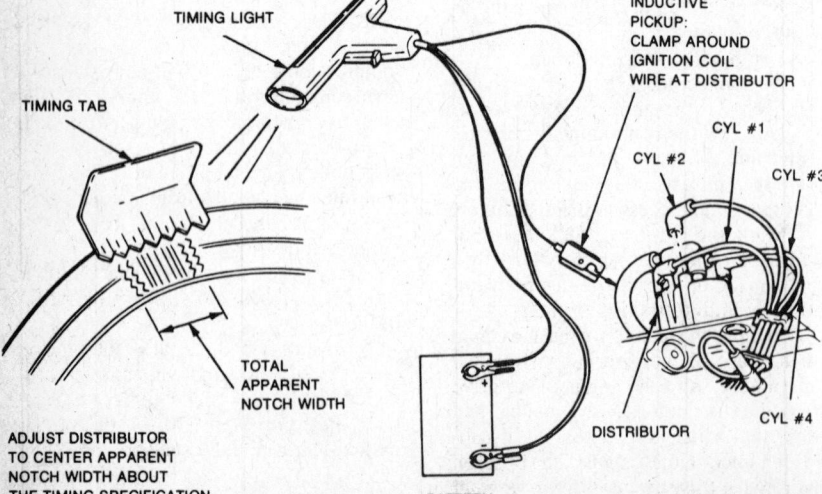

Ignition timing is accomplished by using the averaging method; see the text

b. Start the engine and run it until all fuel in the system is used.

c. Crank the engine for an additional 3 seconds to relieve any residual pressure.

d. Turn the ignition to OFF and replace the fuse.

1. Remove the air cleaner and plug the thermal vacuum port on the throttle body unit.

2. Remove the steel fuel line from between the throttle body unit and the fuel filter.

3. Install a fuel pressure gauge with at least a 15 psi capacity between the throttle body and the filter.

4. Start the engine and observe the pressure reading. pressure should be 9–13 psi. If the pressure is not within these limits, one or more of the following could be at fault:

a. A short in the system

b. A clogged fuel filter

c. A shorted or defective oil pressure switch

d. Defective fuel pump relay

e. Defective fuel pump

Check each of these components in turn to diagnose the problem before replacing the pump.

5. Follow the Cautions at the start of this procedure to depressurize the system, then remove the pressure gauge and install the fuel line. Torque the nuts to 19–25 ft.lb.

6. Start the engine and check for leaks.

7. Unplug the thermal vacuum port on the throttle body.

Volume Test

1. Disconnect the fuel feed line from the throttle body.

2. Using an extension, connect a length of hose to the fuel feed line and into a measured container.

3. Using a watch with a sweep second hand, apply voltage to the fuel pump test terminal (terminal g of the ALCL (Assembly Line Communication Link) until there is one pint of fuel in the container. One pint should flow in 25 seconds or less. If not, check the components listed in the Pressure Test procedure above.

REMOVAL & INSTALLATION

Mechanical Pump

The fuel pump is located at the center rear of the engine.

1. Disconnect the negative cable at the battery. Raise and support the car.

2. Disconnect the inlet hose from the pump. Disconnect the vapor return hose, if equipped.

3. Loosen the fuel line at the carburetor, then disconnect the outlet pipe from the pump.

4. Remove the two mounting bolts and remove the pump from the engine.

5. To install, place a new gasket on the pump and install the pump on the engine.

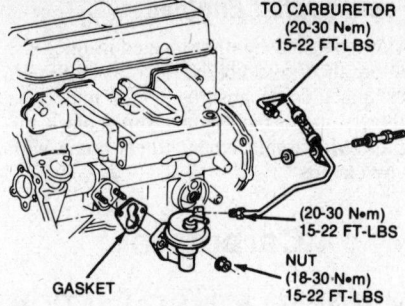

TO CARBURETOR
(20-30 N•m)
15-22 FT-LBS

(20-30 N•m)
15-22 FT-LBS

NUT
(18-30 N•m)
15-22 FT-LBS

GASKET

Fuel pump mounting on carbureted engines

Tighten the two mounting bolts alternately and evenly.

6. Install the pump outlet pipe. This is easier if the pipe is disconnected from the carburetor. Tighten the fitting while backing up the pump nut with another wrench. Install the pipe at the carburetor.

7. Install the inlet and vapor hoses. Lower the car, connect the negative battery cable, start the engine, and check for leaks.

Electric Pump

1. Depressurize the system. See the Pressure Test procedure above.

2. Disconnect the battery ground.

3. Raise and support the car on jackstands.

4. Remove the fuel filler cap.

5. Drain the fuel tank. Due to a restrictor in the fuel filler neck, a siphon cannot be used to drain the tank. Disconnect the fuel feed hose from the chassis feed pipe at the rear of the car. Connect a length of hose to the feed line and into a container. Apply voltage to the pump at the pump test lead (terminal G on the ALCL (Assembly Line Communication Link) and run the pump until the tank is empty. DO NOT RUN THE PUMP AFTER THE TANK IS EMPTIED, AS THIS WILL DAMAGE THE PUMP!

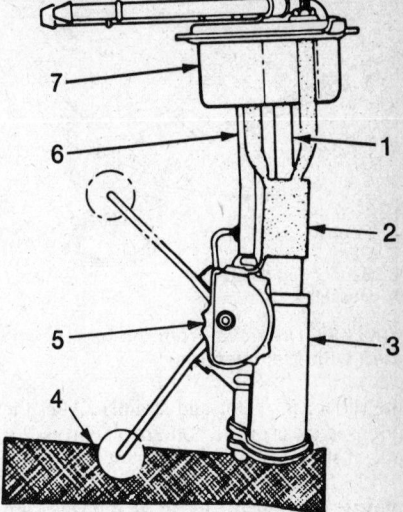

1. Fuel line
2. Rubber coupler and sound insulator
3. Electric fuel pump
4. Filter/strainer
5. Fuel level sender
6. Return tube
7. Splash cup liquid/vapor separator

Fuel injected engine fuel pump

6. Disconnect the wiring from the tank.

7. Disconnect the filler neck hose and the vent hose.

8. Remove the fuel tank strap rear support bolts and lower the tank on a jack, just enough to disconnect the fuel feed line, return and vapor lines from the fuel meter.

9. Remove the tank.

10. Remove the fuel meter/pump assembly by turning the cam lockring counterclockwise. Lift the assembly from the tank and remove the pump from the meter.

11. Pull the pump up onto the attaching hose while pulling outward from the bottom support. Take care that you don't damage

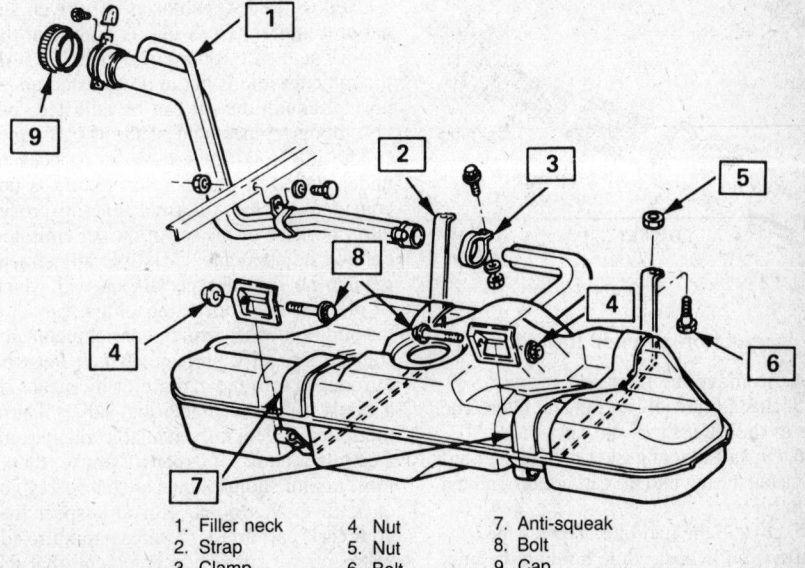

1. Filler neck
2. Strap
3. Clamp
4. Nut
5. Nut
6. Bolt
7. Anti-squeak
8. Bolt
9. Cap

Fuel tank mounting on cars with fuel injection. The tank must be removed to remove the electric fuel pump

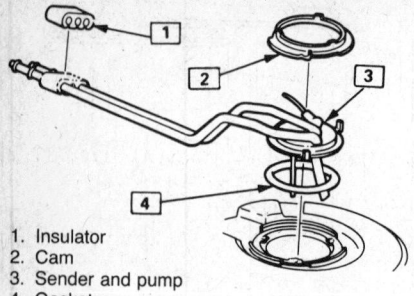

1. Insulator
2. Cam
3. Sender and pump
4. Gasket

Fuel meter removal from the fuel tank on cars with fuel injection

the rubber insulator and strainer. After the pump is clear of the bottom support pull it out of the rubber connector.

12. Installation is the reverse of removal. Use a new O-ring on the tank cam lockring.

Fuel Filter

REMOVAL & INSTALLATION
Carburetted Engines

All models have a fuel filter located within the carburetor body. The fuel filter has a check valve to prevent fuel spillage in the event of an accident. When the filter is replaced, make sure the new one is of the same type. All filters are of the paper element type. Replace the filter every 15,000 miles.

1. Place a few absorbent rages underneath the fuel line where it joins the carburetor.
2. Disconnect the fuel line connection at the fuel inlet nut.
3. Unscrew the fuel inlet nut from the carburetor. As the nut is removed, the filter will be pushed partway out by spring pressure.

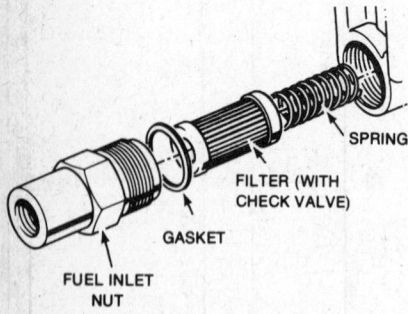

SPRING

FILTER (WITH CHECK VALVE)

GASKET

FUEL INLET NUT

Carburetor-mounted fuel filter

4. Remove the filter and spring.
5. Install the new spring and filter. The hole in the filter faces the nut.
6. Install a new gasket on the inlet nut and install the nut into the carburetor. Tighten securely.
7. Install the fuel line. Tighten the connector to 18 ft. lbs. while holding the inlet nut with a wrench.
8. Start the engine and check for leaks.

Fuel Injected Engines

All models have a filter located in-line, just before the throttle body. To replace the filter, place some absorbant rags under the filter, remove the clamps and replace the filter. Most replacement filters come with new clamps.

Carburetor

REMOVAL & INSTALLATION

1. Remove the air cleaner and gasket.
2. Disconnect the fuel pipe and all vacuum lines.
3. Tag and disconnect all electrical connections.
4. Disconnect the downshift cable.
5. If equipped with cruise control, disconnect the linkage.
6. Unscrew the carburetor mounting bolts and remove the carburetor.
7. Before installing the carburetor, fill the float bowl with gasoline to reduce the battery strain and the possibility of backfiring when the engine is started again.
8. Inspect the EFE heater for damage. Be sure that the throttle body and EFE mating surfaces are clean.
9. Install the carburetor and tighten the nuts alternately.
10. Installation of the remaining components is in the reverse order of removal.

IDLE SPEED AND MIXTURE ADJUSTMENT— CARBURETED ENGINES

All carbureted J-cars are equipped with an Idle Speed Control (ISC) motor which is in turn controlled by the Electronic Control Module (ECM). All idle speeds are programmed into the ECM's memory and then relayed to the ISC motor as any given situation requires. Curb idle is pre-set at the factory and not routinely adjustable. Although curb idle is not to be adjusted under normal conditions, it can be adjusted, but only upon replacement of the ISC.

The idle mixture screws are concealed under staked-in plugs. Idle mixture is not considered to be a normal tune-up procedure, because of the sensitivity of emission control adjustments. Mixture adjustment requires not only the special tools with which to remove the concealing plugs, but also the addition of an artificial enrichment substance (generally propane) which must be introduced into the carburetor by means of a finely calibrated metering valve. These tools are not generally available and require a certain amount of expertise to use, therefore, mixture adjustments are purposely not covered in this book. If you suspect that your car's carburetor requires a mixture adjustment, we strongly recommend that the job be referred to a qualified service technician.

Fuel Injection

NOTE: For all fuel injection system services, see the "Fuel Injection" part of the Unit Repair section.

COOLING SYSTEM

Radiator

REMOVAL & INSTALLATION

1. Disconnect the negative battery cable.
2. Drain the cooling system.
3. Disconnect the electrical lead at the fan motor.
4. Remove the fan frame-to-radiator support attaching bolts and then remove the fan assembly.
5. Disconnect the upper and lower radiator hoses and the coolant recovery hose from the radiator.
6. Disconnect the transmission oil cooler lines from the radiator and wire them out of the way.
7. Remove the radiator-to-radiator support attaching bolts and clamps. Remove the radiator.
8. Place the radiator in the vehicle so that the bottom is located in the lower mounting pads. Tighten the attaching bolts and clamps.
9. Connect the transmission oil cooler lines and tighten the bolts to 20 ft. lbs.
10. Installation of the remaining components is in the reverse order of removal.

Water Pump

REMOVAL & INSTALLATION
OHV Engines

1. Disconnect the negative battery cable.
2. Drain the cooling system.
3. Remove all accessory drive belts.
4. Remove the alternator.
5. Unscrew the water pump pulley mounting bolts and then pull off the pulley.
6. Remove the mounting bolts and remove the water pump.
7. Place a 1/8 in. bead of RTV sealant on the water pump sealing surface. While the sealer is still wet, install the pump and tighten the bolts to 13–18 ft. lbs.
8. Installation of the remaining components is in the reverse order of removal.

OHC Engines

1. Remove the timing belt as described later.
2. Remove the timing belt rear protective covers.

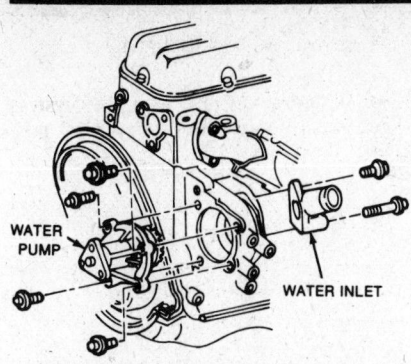

OHV engine water pump installation

3. Remove the hose from the pump.

4. Unbolt and remove the pump

5. Installation is the reverse of removal. Torque the bolts to 19 ft. lb.

Thermostat

REMOVAL & INSTALLATION

OHV Engines

The thermostat is located inside a housing on the back of the cylinder head. It is not necessary to remove the radiator hose from the thermostat housing when removing the thermostat.

1. Disconnect the negative battery cable.

2. Drain the cooling system and remove the air cleaner.

3. Disconnect the A.I.R. pipe at the upper check valve and the bracket at the water outlet.

4. Disconnect the electrical lead.

5. Remove the two retaining bolts from the thermostat housing and lift up the housing with the house attached. Lift out the thermostat.

6. Insert the new thermostat, spring end down. Apply a thin bead of silicone sealer to the housing mating surface and install the housing while the sealer is still wet. Tighten the housing retaining bolts to 6 ft. lbs.

NOTE: Poor heater output and slow warmup is often caused by a thermostat stuck in the open position; occasionally one sticks shut causing immediate over-

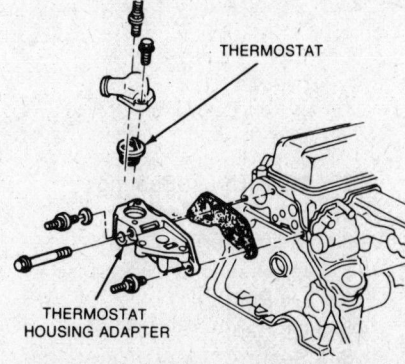

OHV engine thermostat mounting

1. Thermostat housing cap
2. Thermostat
3. Thermostat housing assembly
4. Cylinder head

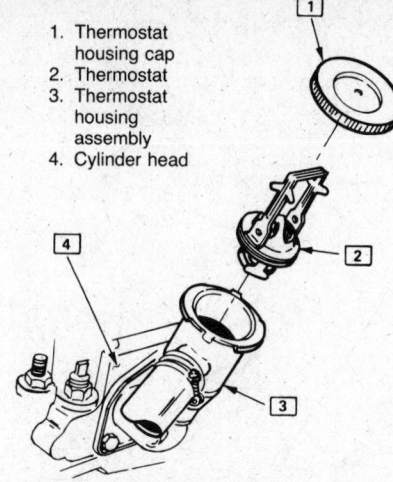

OHC engine thermostat mounting

heating. Do not attempt to correct a chronic overheating condition by permanently removing the thermostat. Thermostat flow restriction is designed into the system; without it, localized overheating (due to coolant turbulence) may occur, causing expensive troubles.

7. Installation of the remaining components is in the reverse order of removal.

OHC Engines

1. Remove the thermostat housing.

2. Grasp the handle of the thermostat and pull it from the housing.

3. Install the thermostat in the housing, pushing it down as far as it will go to make sure it's seated.

4. Install the housing on the engine, using a new gasket coated with sealer.

EMISSION CONTROL SYSTEMS

NOTE: The following emission control devices may be found on your car. Not every car will have all of these devices. For a description of and service on these devices, see the "Emission Contol" part of the Unit Repair section.

- Positive Crankcase Ventilation
- Evaporative Emission Control
- Exhaust Emission Controls
- Thermostatic Air Cleaner
- Air Management System
- Early Fuel Evaporation
- Exhaust Gas Recirculation
- Computer Command Control System
- Deceleration Valve
- Mixture Control Solenoid
- Throttle Position Sensor
- Idle Speed Control
- Electronic Spark Timing
- Transmission Converter Clutch
- Catalytic Converter
- Oxygen Sensor

ENGINE MECHANICAL

NOTE: J-Cars use three different four cylinder engines. Two are built by Chevrolet, a 1.8L (112 cid) and a 2.0L (122 cid). Both of these Chevrolet-built engines are of the overhead valve configuration (OHV). That means that the camshaft is in the block and the rest of the valve train is on top of the head. The other engine is a Pontiac-built 1.8L (112 cid) overhead cam engine (OHC). This means that the camshaft and valve components are all located in the engine head. The two Chevrolet-built engines are virtually indentical in all aspects except cubic inch displacement.

The Pontiac-built engine is quite different in most respects.

Engine

REMOVAL & INSTALLATION

OHV Engines

NOTE: This procedure will require the use of a special powertrain alignment tool #M6X1X65.

1. Disconnect the battery cables at the battery, negative cable first.

2. Remove the air cleaner. Drain the cooling system.

3. Remove the power steering pump (if so equipped) and position it out of the way. Leave the lines connected. Remove the windshield washer bottle.

4. If the car is equipped with A/C, remove the relay bracket at the bulkhead connector. Remove the bulkhead connector and then separate the wiring harness connections.

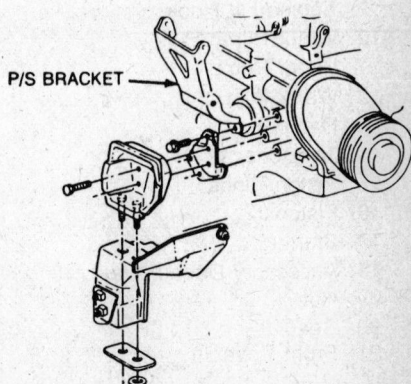

Rear engine mounts on OHV engines

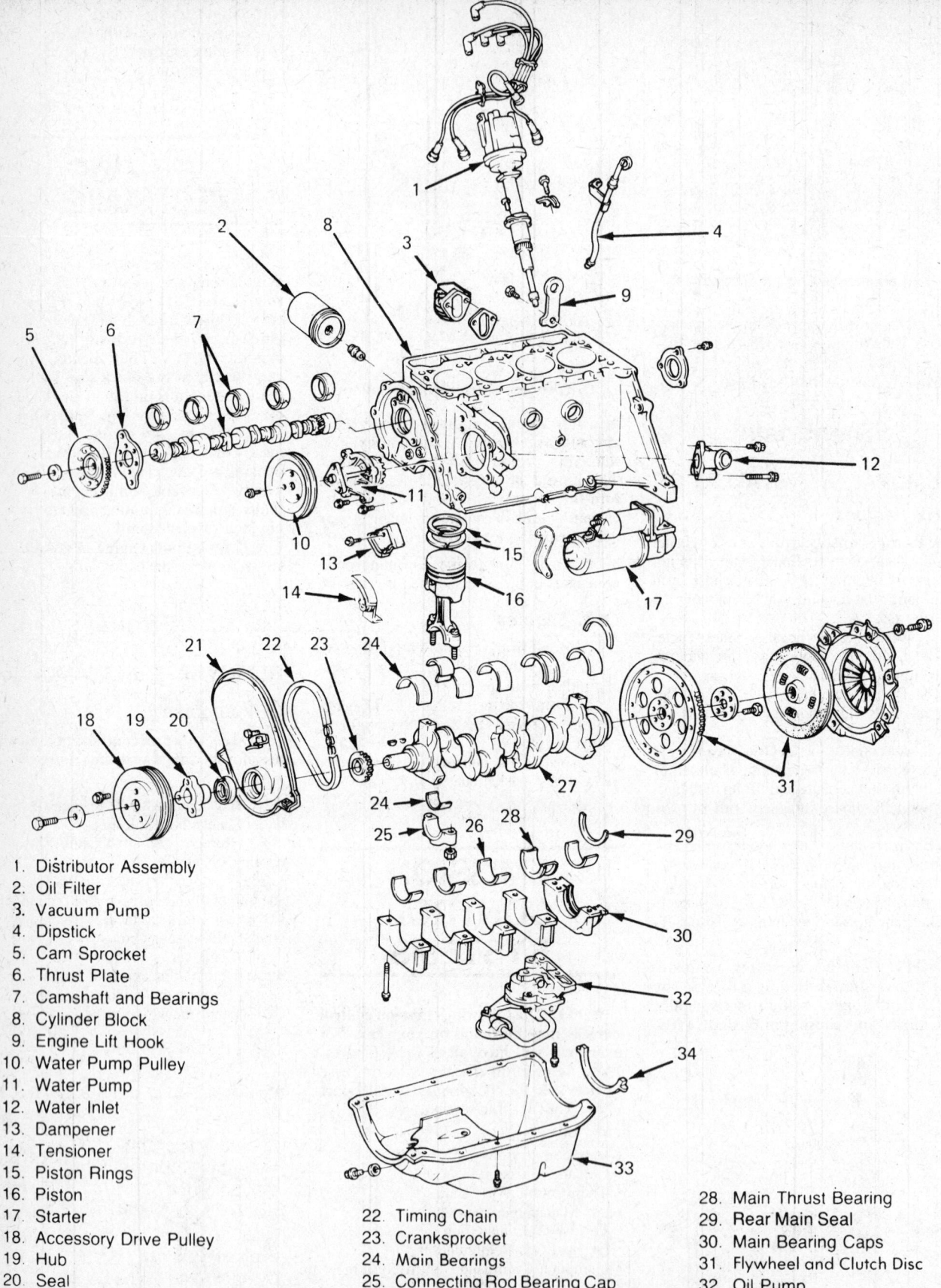

1. Distributor Assembly
2. Oil Filter
3. Vacuum Pump
4. Dipstick
5. Cam Sprocket
6. Thrust Plate
7. Camshaft and Bearings
8. Cylinder Block
9. Engine Lift Hook
10. Water Pump Pulley
11. Water Pump
12. Water Inlet
13. Dampener
14. Tensioner
15. Piston Rings
16. Piston
17. Starter
18. Accessory Drive Pulley
19. Hub
20. Seal
21. Front Cover
22. Timing Chain
23. Cranksprocket
24. Main Bearings
25. Connecting Rod Bearing Cap
26. Main Bearings
27. Crankshaft
28. Main Thrust Bearing
29. Rear Main Seal
30. Main Bearing Caps
31. Flywheel and Clutch Disc
32. Oil Pump
33. Oil Pan
34. Seal

Exploded view of the cylinder block—2.0L

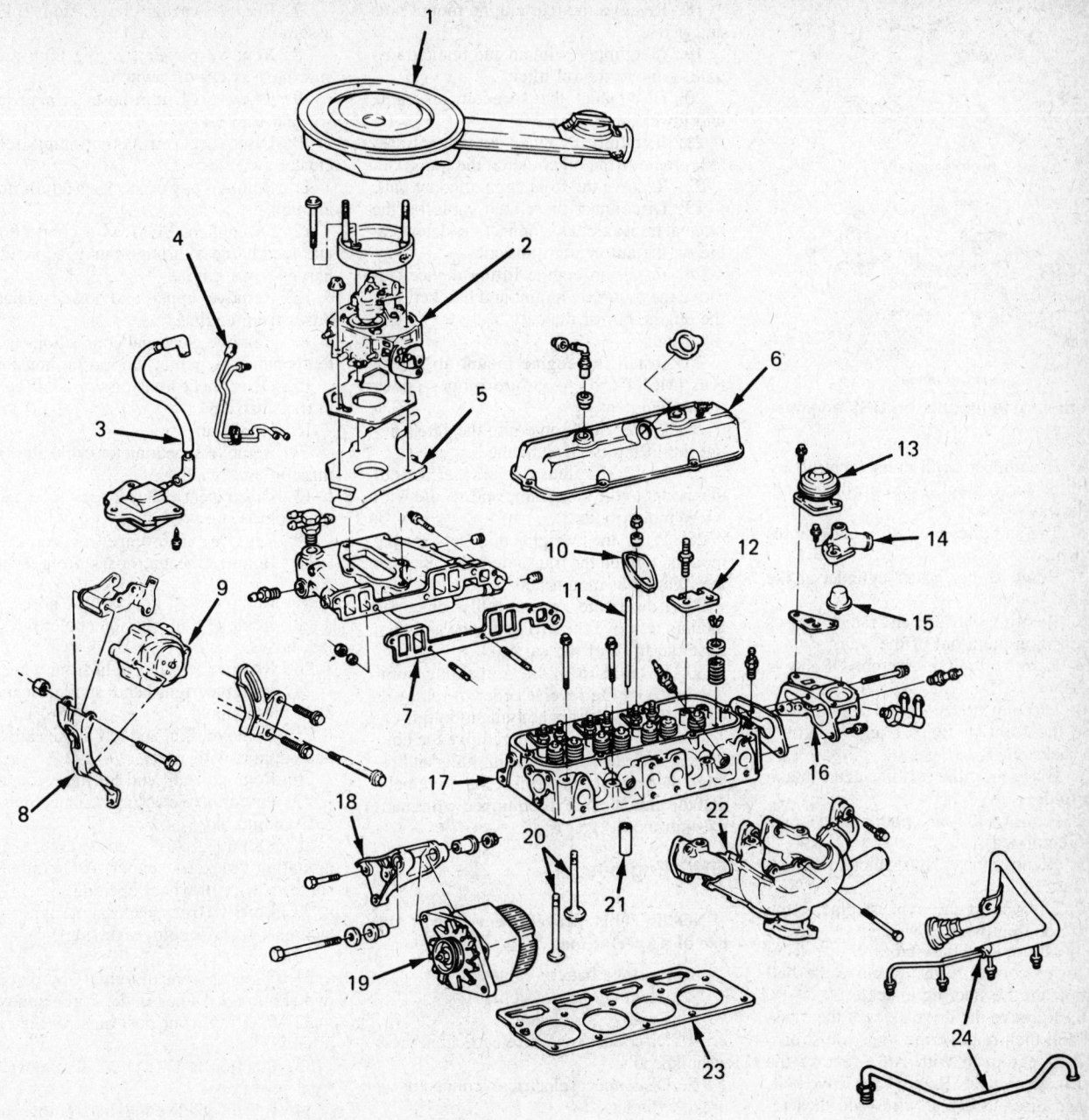

1. Air Cleaner
2. TBI Unit
3. Coil and Coil Wire
4. Fuel Line
5. E.F.E. Grid
6. Rocker Arm Cover
7. Intake Manifold & Gasket
8. A.I.R. Mounting Bracket
9. A.I.R. Pump
10. Rocker Arm
11. Push Rod
12. Push Rod Guide
13. E.G.R. Valve
14. Thermostat Outlet
15. Thermostat
16. Adapter
17. Cylinder Head
18. Generator Bracket
19. Generator
20. Valves
21. Lifter
22. Exhaust Manifold
23. Cylinder Head Gasket
24. A.I.R. or Pulsair Pipe

Exploded view of the cylinder head—2.0L

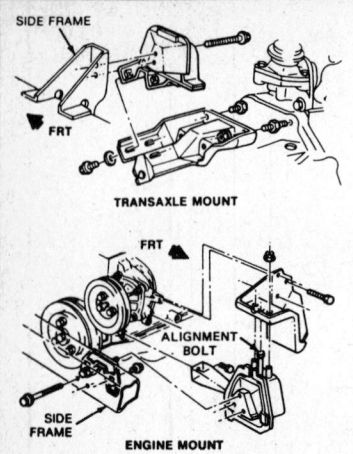

Front engine mounts on OHV engines

5. If equipped with cruise control, remove the servo bracket and position it out of the way.

6. Tag and disconnect all vacuum hoses and wires.

7. Remove the master cylinder at the vacuum booster.

8. Remove all heater and radiator hoses and position them out of the way.

9. Remove the fan assembly. Remove the horn.

10. Disconnect the carburetor linkage. Raise the front of the car and support it with jackstands.

11. Disconnect the fuel line at the intake manifold.

12. Remove the air conditioning brace (if so equipped).

13. Remove the exhaust shield. Remove the starter.

14. Disconnect the exhaust pipe at the manifold. Remove the wheels.

15. Disconnect the stabilizer bar from the lower control arms. Remove the ball joints from the steering knuckle.

16. Remove the drive axles at the transaxle and then remove the transaxle strut.

17. If equipped with A/C, remove the inner fender shield. Remove the drive belt, tag and disconnect the wires and then remove the compressor. *Do not disconnect any of the refrigerant lines.*

18. Remove the rear engine mount nuts and plate.

19. If equipped with an automatic transaxle, remove the oil filter.

20. Disconnect the speedometer cable and lower the vehicle.

21. If equipped with an automatic transaxle, remove the oil cooler at the transaxle.

22. Remove the front engine mount nuts.

23. Disconnect the clutch cable on the manual transaxle. Disconnect the detent cable on the automatic transaxle.

24. Install an engine lifting device, remove the transaxle mount and bracket. Lift the engine out of the car.

To install:

25. Install the engine mount alignment bolt (M6X1X65) to ensure proper power train alignment.

26. Lower the engine into the car, leaving the lifting device attached.

27. Install the transaxle bracket. Install the mount to the side frame and secure with NEW mount bolts.

28. With the weight not yet on the mounts, tighten the transaxle bolts. Tighten the right front mount nuts.

29. Lower the engine fully onto the mounts, remove the lifting device and then raise the front of the car.

30. Installation of the remaining components is in the reverse order of removal. Check the powertrain alignment bolt; if excessive force is required to remove the bolt, loosen the transaxle adjusting bolts and realign the powertrain. Adjust the drive belts and the clutch cable (if equipped with manual transaxle).

OHC Engines

NOTE: This procedure requires the use of a special tool.

1. Remove battery cables.
2. Drain cooling system.
3. Remove air cleaner.
4. Disconnect engine electrical harness at bulkhead.
5. Disconnect electrical connector at brake cylinder.
6. Remove throttle cable from bracket and E.F.I. assembly.

7. Remove vacuum hoses from E.F.I. assembly.

8. Remove power steering high pressure hose at cut-off switch.

9. Remove vacuum hoses at map sensor and canister.

10. Disconnect air conditioning relay cluster switches.

11. Remove power steering return hose at pump.

12. Disconnect ECM wire connections and feed harness through bulkhead and lay harness over engine.

13. Remove upper and lower radiator hoses from engine.

14. Remove electrical connections from temperature switch at thermostat housing.

15. Disconnect transmission shift cable at transmission.

16. Hoist car.

17. Remove speedometer cable at transmission and bracket.

18. Disconnect exhaust pipe at exhaust manifold.

19. Remove exhaust pipe from converter.

20. Remove heater hoses from heater core.

21. Remove fuel lines at flex hoses.

22. Remove transmission cooler lines at flex hoses.

23. Remove left and right front wheels.

24. Remove right-hand spoiler section and splash shield.

25. Remove right and left brake calipers and support with wire.

26. Remove right and left tie rod ends.

27. Disconnect electrical connections at A/C compressor.

28. Remove A/C compressor and mounting brackets, support A/C compressor with wire in wheel opening.

29. Remove front suspension support attachment bolts (6 bolts each side).

30. Lower car.

31. Support front of vehicle by placing two short jack stands under core support.

32. Position front post hoist to the rear of cowl.

33. Position a 4'' x 4'' x 6' timber on front post hoist.

34. Raise vehicle enough to remove jack stands.

35. Position a 4-wheel dolly under engine and transaxle assembly.

36. Position three (3) 4'' x 4'' x 12'' blocks under "engine and transaxle" assembly only, letting support rails hang free.

37. Lower vehicle onto 4-wheel dolly "slightly."

38. Remove rear transaxle mount attachment bolts (2).

39. Remove left front engine mount attachment bolts (3).

40. Remove two (2) engine support to body attachment bolts behind right-hand inner axle U-joint.

41. Remove one (1) attaching bolt and nut from right-hand chassis side rail to engine mount bracket.

42. Remove six (6) strut attachment nuts.

43. Raise vehicle letting engine, transaxle and suspension resting on 4-wheel dolly.

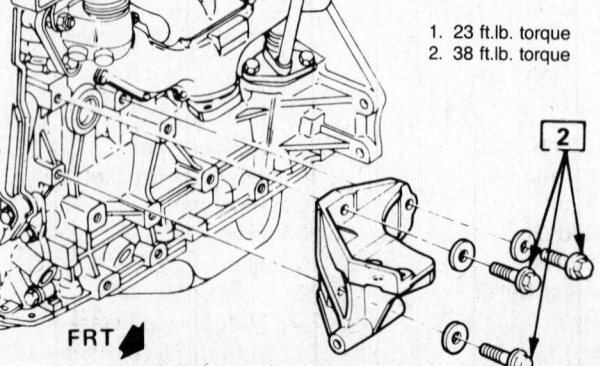

1. 23 ft.lb. torque
2. 38 ft.lb. torque

RIGHT HAND FRONT W/A.C.

Front right engine mount on OHC engines with air conditioning

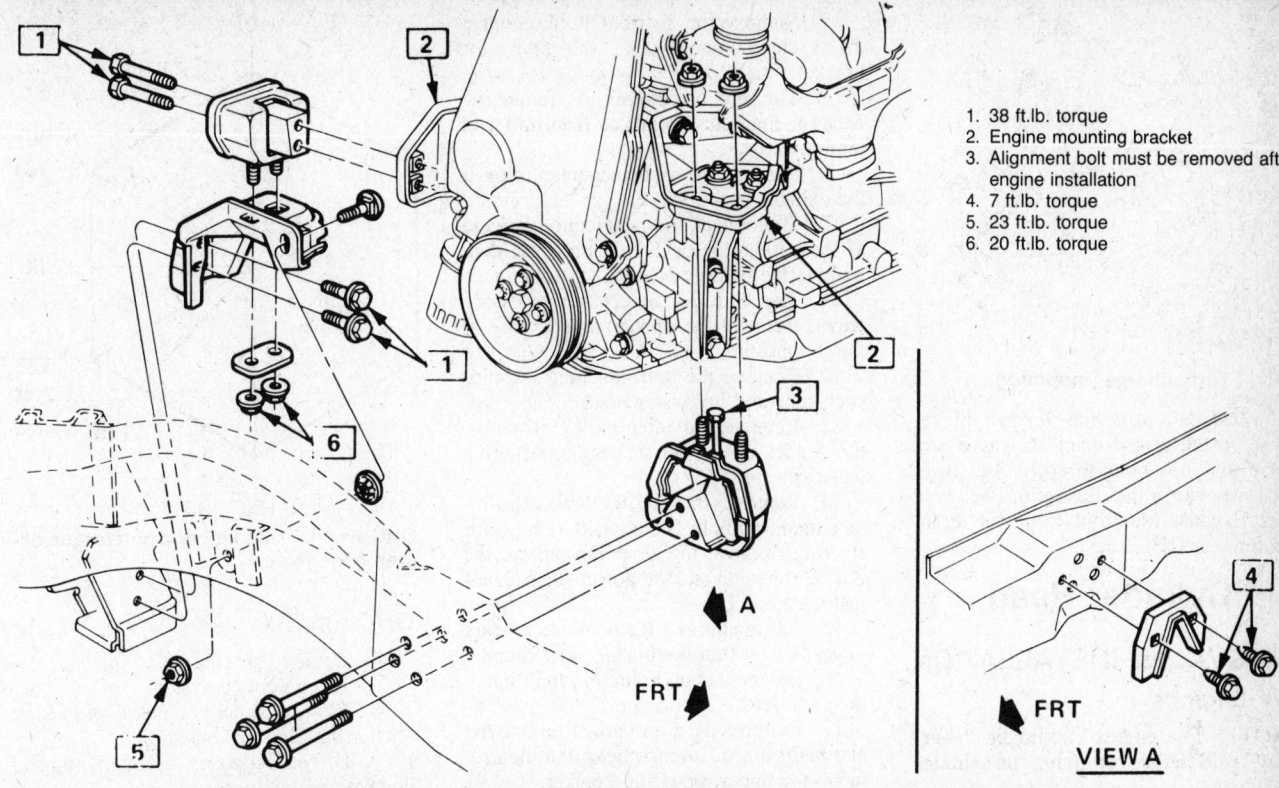

1. 38 ft.lb. torque
2. Engine mounting bracket
3. Alignment bolt must be removed after engine installation
4. 7 ft.lb. torque
5. 23 ft.lb. torque
6. 20 ft.lb. torque

VIEW A

Front engine mounts on OHC engines. The right mount is for cars without air conditioning

Reverse removal procedure for engine installation with the following exceptions.

1. With one man's assistance, position engine and transaxle assembly in chassis.

2. Install transaxle and left front mounts to side rail bolts loosely.

3. Install M6X1X65 alignment bolt in left front mount to prevent powertrain misalignment.

4. Torque transaxle mount bolts to 42 lb. ft. and left front mount bolts to 18 lb. ft.

5. Install right rear mount to body bolts and torque to 38 lb. ft.

6. Install right rear mount to chassis side rail bolt and nut torque to 38 lb. ft.

7. Place a floor jack under control arms, jack struts into position and install retaining nuts.

8. Raise vehicle.

9. Using a transmission jack or suitable lifting equipment, raise control arms and attach tie rod ends.

Turbocharger

REMOVAL & INSTALLATION

1. Raise the car and support it with jack stands.

2. Remove the lower fan retaining screw.

3. Disconnect the exhaust pipe.

4. Remove the rear A/C support bracket and loosen the remaining bolts.

5. Remove the turbo support bracket bolt to the engine.

6. Disconnect the oil drain hose at the turbo.

7. Lower the vehicle.

8. Disconnect the coolant recovery pipe and move to one side.

9. Disconnect the induction tube.

10. Disconnect the cooling fan.

11. DIsconnect the oxygen sensor.

12. Disconnect the oil feed pipe at the union.

13. Disconnect the air intake duct and vacuum hose at the actuator.

14. Remove the exhaust manifold retaining nuts and remove the exhaust manifold and turbocharger.

TORQUE #2 AND #3 MANIFOLD RUNNER PRIOR TO #1 AND #4 RUNNERS.

Exhaust manifold torque sequence—1.8 turbocharged engine

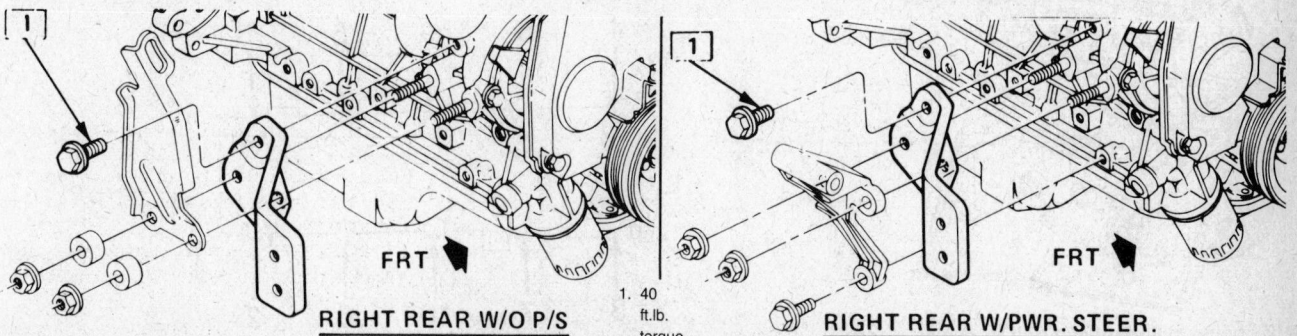

RIGHT REAR W/O P/S

1. 40 ft.lb. torque

RIGHT REAR W/PWR. STEER.

Rear engine mounts on OHC engines

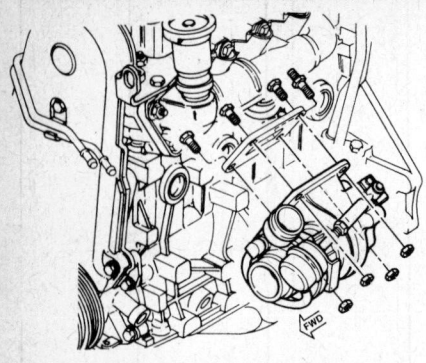

Turbocharger mounting

15. Installation is the reverse of removal. Install a new manifold gasket and tighten retaining bolts to 16 ft. lbs. in sequence shown in the illustration. See note under Exhaust Manifold Removal & Installation for OHC engs.

Cylinder Head

REMOVAL & INSTALLATION
OHV Engines

NOTE: The engine should be "overnight" cold before removing the cylinder head.

1. Disconnect the negative battery cable.
2. Drain the cooling system into a clean container; the coolant can be reused if it is still good.
3. Remove the air cleaner. Raise and support the front of the vehicle.
4. Remove the exhaust shield. Disconnect the exhaust pipe.
5. Remove the heater hose from the intake manifold and then lower the car.
6. Unscrew the mounting bolts and remove the engine lift bracket (includes air management).

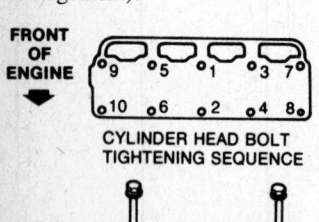

CYLINDER HEAD BOLT TIGHTENING SEQUENCE

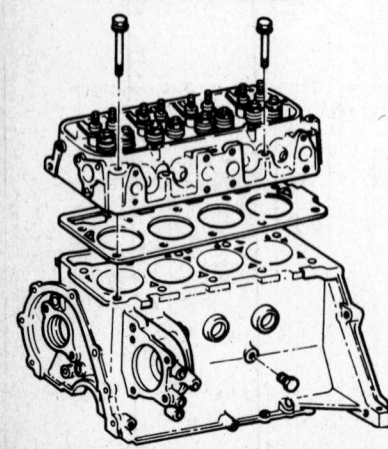

OHV engine cylinder head bolt torque sequence

7. Remove the distributor. Disconnect the vacuum manifold at the alternator bracket.
8. Tag and disconnect the remaining vacuum lines at the intake manifold and thermostat.
9. Remove the air management pipe at the exhaust check valve.
10. Disconnect the accelerator linkage at the carburetor or T.B.I. unit and then remove the linkage bracket.
11. Tag and disconnect all necessary wires. Remove the upper radiator hose at the thermostat.
12. Remove the bolt attaching the dipstick tube and hot water bracket.
13. Remove the idler pulley. Remove the A.I.R. and power steering pump drive belts.
14. Remove the A.I.R. bracket-to-intake manifold bolt. If equipped with power steering, remove the air pump pulley, the A.I.R. thru-bolt and the power steering adjusting bracket.
15. Loosen the A.I.R. mounting bracket lower bolt so that the bracket will rotate.
16. Disconnect and plug the fuel line at the carburetor.
17. Remove the alternator. Remove the alternator brace from the head and then remove the upper mounting bracket.
18. Remove the cylinder head cover. Remove the rocker arms and push rods.
19. Remove the cylinder head bolts in the order given in the illustration. Remove the cylinder head with the carburetor or T.B.I. unit, intake and exhaust manifolds still attached.
To install, the gasket surfaces on both the head and the block must be clean of any foreign matter and free of any nicks or heavy scratches. Cylinder bolt threads in the block and the bolt must be clean.
20. Place a new cylinder head gasket in position over the dowel pins on the block. Carefully guide the cylinder head into position.
21. Coat the cylinder bolts with sealing compound and install them finger tight.
22. Using a torque wrench, gradually tighten the bolts in the sequence shown in the illustration to the proper specifications.
23. Installation of the remaining components is in the reverse order of removal.

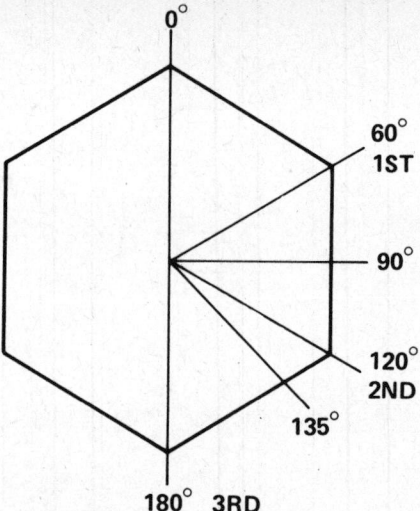

OHC engine cylinder head bolt torque degree sequence

OHC Engine

1. Remove air cleaner.
2. Drain cooling system.
3. Remove generator and pivot bracket at camshaft carrier housing.
4. Disconnect power steering pump and bracket and lay to one side.
5. Disconnect ignition coil electrical connections and remove coil.
6. Disconnect spark plug wires and distributor cap and remove.
7. Remove throttle cable from bracket at intake manifold.
8. Disconnect throttle cable, downshift cable and T.V. cable from E.F.I. assembly.
9. Disconnect E.C.M. connectors from E.F.I. assembly.
10. Remove vacuum brake hose at filter.
11. Disconnect inlet and return fuel lines at flex joints.
12. Remove water pump bypass hose at intake manifold and water pump.
13. Disconnect ECM harness connectors at intake manifold.
14. Disconnect heater hose from intake manifold.
15. Disconnect exhaust pipe at exhaust manifold.
16. Disconnect breather hose at camshaft carrier.

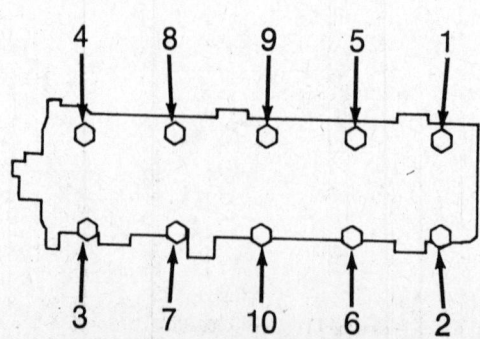

OHC engine camshaft carrier and head bolt loosening sequence

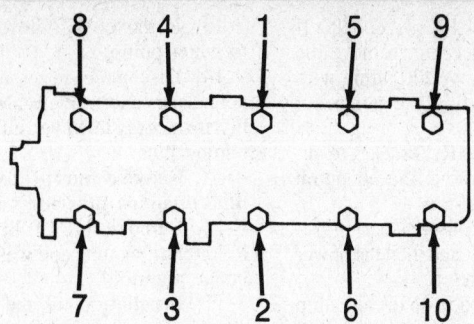

17. Remove upper radiator hose.

18. Disconnect engine electrical harness and wires from thermostat housing.

19. Remove timing cover.

20. Remove timing probe holder.

21. Loosen water pump retaining bolts and remove timing belt.

22. Loosen camshaft carrier and cylinder head attaching bolts a little at a time in sequence shown.

NOTE: Camshaft carrier and cylinder head bolts should only be removed when engine is cold.

23. Remove camshaft carrier assembly.

24. Remove cylinder head, intake manifold and exhaust manifold as an assembly.

25. Installation is the reverse of removal. Torque head bolts in the sequence shown. Make sure that you follow the note on torquing, at the bottom of the Torque Chart.

Rocker Arms and Push Rods

REMOVAL, INSTALLATION AND ADJUSTMENT

OHV Engines

1. Remove the air cleaner. Remove the cylinder head cover.

2. Remove the rocker arm nut and ball. Lift the rocker arm off the stud. *Always keep the rocker arm assemblies together and install them on the same stud.* Remove the push rrods.
To install:

3. Coat the bearing surfaces of the rocker arms and the rocker arm balls with "Molykote" or its equivalent.

4. Install the push rods making sure that they seat properly in the lifter.

5. Install the rocker arms, balls and nuts. Tighten the rocker arm nuts until all lash is eliminated.

6. Adjust the valves when the lifter is on the base circle of a camshaft lobe:

   a. Crank the engine until the mark on the crankshaft pulley lines up with the '0' mark on the timing tab. Make sure that the engine is in the No. 1 firing position. Place your fingers on the No. 1 rocker arms as the mark on the crank pulley comes near the '0' mark. If the valves are not moving, the engine is in the No. 1 firing position. If the valves move, the engine is in the No. 4 firing position; rotate the engine one complete revolution and it will be in the No. 1 position.

   b. When the engine is in the No. 1 firing position, adjust the following valves:

   Exhaust—1,3
   Intake—1,2

   c. Back the adjusting nut out until lash can be felt at the push rod, then turn the nut until all lash is removed (this can be determined by rotating the push rod while

turning the adjusting nut). When all lash has been removed, turn the nut in 1½ additional turns, this will center the lifter plunger.

   d. Crank the engine one complete revolution until the timing tab and the '0' mark are again in alignment. Now the engine is in the No. 4 firing position. Adjust the following valves:

   Exhaust—2,4
   Intake—3,4

7. Installation of the remaining components is in the reverse order of removal.

OHC engine camshaft carrier and head bolt tightening sequence

NOTE: AT TIME OF INSTALLATION, FLANGES MUST BE FREE OF OIL. A ⅛ BEAD OF SEALANT MUST BE APPLIED TO FLANGES AND SEALANT MUST BE WET TO TOUCH WHEN BOLTS ARE TORQUED.

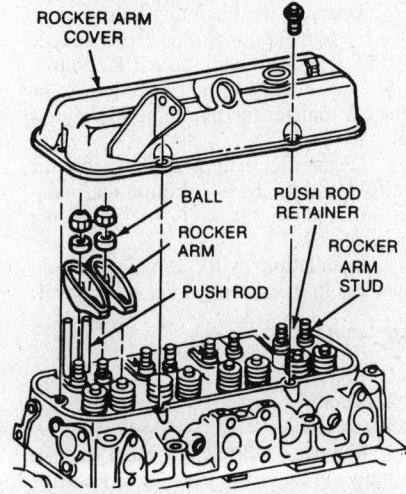

OHV engine rocker arm assembly

OHC Engines

NOTE: A special tool is required for this procedure.

1. Remove the camshaft carrier cover.

2. Using a valve train compressing fixture, tool J-33302, depress all the lifters at once.

3. Remove the rocker arms, placing them on the workbench in the same order that they were removed.

4. Remove the hydraulic valve lash compensators keeping them in the order in which they were removed.

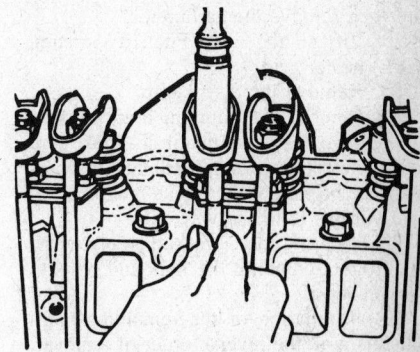

On OHV engines, tighten the rocker arm nut until the pushrod can't be rotated between your fingers

5. Installation is the reverse of removal. Rocker arms and compensators must be replaced in the exact same position as when they were removed.

Intake Manifold

REMOVAL & INSTALLATION

OHV Engines

1. Disconnect the negative battery cable.

2. Remove the air cleaner. Drain the cooling system.

3. Tag and disconnect all necessary vacuum lines and wires. Remove the idler pulley.

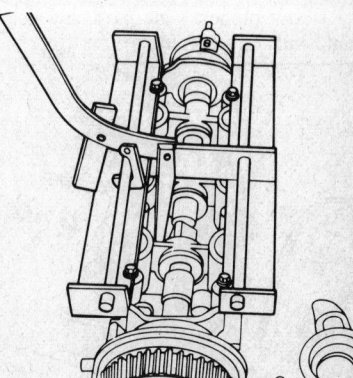

Compressing the valve spring using the valve train compressing tool J-33302, on OHC engines

C719

4. Remove the A.I.R. drive belt. If equipped with power steering, remove the drive belt and then remove the pump with the lines attached. Position the pump out of the way.

5. Remove the A.I.R. bracket-to-intake manifold bolt. Remove the air pump pulley.

6. If equipped with power steering, remove the A.I.R. thru-bolt and then the power steering adjusting bracket.

7. Loosen the lower bolt on the air pump mounting bracket so that the bracket will rotate.

8. Disconnect the fuel line at the carburetor. Disconnect the carburetor linkage and then remove the carburetor.

9. Lift off the Early Fuel Evaporation (EFE) heater grid.

10. Remove the distributor.

11. Remove the mounting bolts and nuts and remove the intake manifold. Make sure to disconnect the heater hose and condenser from the bottom of the intake manifold before you lift it all the way out.

12. Using a new gasket, replace the manifold, tightening the nuts and bolts to specification.

13. Installation of the remaining components is in the reverse order of removal. Adjust all necessary drive belts and check the ignition timing.

OHC Engines

1. Remove air cleaner.

2. Drain cooling system.

3. Remove generator and generator bracket at camshaft carrier.

4. Remove power steering pump and lay to one side.

5. Remove power steering bracket at intake manifold.

6. Remove ignition coil.

7. Remove throttle cable from bracket at intake manifold.

8. Disconnect throttle, downshift and TV cables from EFI assembly.

9. Disconnect wire harness connectors from TBI assembly.

10. Remove vacuum brake hose at filter.

11. Disconnect inlet and return fuel lines at flex joints.

12. Remove preheat water hose at water pump and intake manifold.

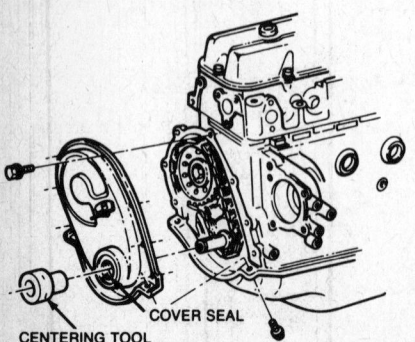

COVER SEAL
CENTERING TOOL

Front cover installation on OHV engines; a centering tool will aid in positioning

13. Remove "S" hose from inlet tube to water pump.

14. Disconnect necessary ECM harness connectors and move ECM harness assembly for access to lower intake manifold retaining nuts.

15. Remove four (4) lower intake manifold retaining nuts and washers.

16. Remove five (5) upper intake manifold retaining nuts and washers and remove intake manifold.

17. Installation is the reverse of removal. Torque the bolts to 16 ft. lb.

Exhaust Manifold

REMOVAL & INSTALLATION

OHV Engines

1. Disconnect the negative battery cable.

2. Remove the air cleaner. Remove the exhaust manifold shield. Raise and support the front of the vehicle.

3. Disconnect the exhaust pipe at the manifold and then lower the vehicle.

4. Disconnect the air management-to-check valve hose and remove the bracket. Disconnect the oxygen sensor lead wire.

5. Remove the alternator belt. Remove the alternator adjusting bolts, loosen the pivot bolt and pivot the alternator upward.

6. Remove the alternator brace and the A.I.R. pipes bracket bolt.

7. Unscrew the mounting bolts and remove the exhaust manifold. The manifold should be removed with the A.I.R. plumbing as an assembly. If the manifold is to be replaced, transfer the plumbing to the new one.

8. Clean the mating surfaces on the manifold and the head, position the manifold and tighten the bolts to the proper specifications.

9. Installation of the remaining components is in the reverse order of removal.

OHC Engines

1. Remove air cleaner.

2. Remove spark plug wires and retainers.

3. Remove oil dipstick tube and breather assembly.

4. Disconnect oxygen sensor wire.

5. Disconnect exhaust pipe from manifold flange.

6. Remove exhaust manifold to cylinder head attaching nuts and remove manifold and gasket.

7. Installation is the reverse of removal. Torque the bolts to 16–19 ft. lb.

NOTE: Before installing a new gasket on the 1.8L MFI Turbo engine (code J), check for the location of the stamped part number on the surface. This gasket should be installed with this number toward the manifold. The gasket appears to be the same in either direction but it is not. Installing the gasket backwards will result in a leak.

Crankcase Front Cover

REMOVAL & INSTALLATION

OHV Engines Only

NOTE: The following procedure requires the use of a special tool.

1. Remove the engine drive belts.

2. Although not absolutely necessary, removal of the right front inner fender splash shield will facilitate access to the front cover.

3. Unscrew the center bolt from the crankshaft pulley and slide the pulley and hub from the crankshaft.

4. Remove the alternator lower bracket.

5. Remove the oil pan-to-front cover bolts.

6. Remove the front cover-to-block bolts and then remove the front cover. If the front cover is difficult to remove, use a plastic mallet.

7. The surfaces of the block and front cover must be clean and free of oil. Apply a ⅛ in. bead of RTV sealant to the cover. The sealant must be wet to the touch when the bolts are torqued down.

NOTE: When applying RTV sealant to the front cover, be sure to keep it out of the bolt holes.

8. Position the front cover on the block using a centering tool (J-23042) and tighten the screws.

9. Installation of the remaining components is in the reverse order of removal.

TIMING COVER OIL SEAL

OHV Engines Only

The oil seal can be replaced with the cover either on or off the engine. If the cover is on the engine, remove the crankshaft pulley and hub first. Pry out the seal using a large screwdriver, being careful not to distort the seal mating surface. Install the new seal so that the open side or helical side is towards the engine. Press it into place with a seal driver made for the purpose. Install the hub if removed.

Timing Chain and Sprockets

REMOVAL & INSTALLATION

OHV Engines Only

1. Remove the front cover as previously detailed.

2. Place the No. 1 piston at TDC of the compression stroke so that the marks on the camshaft and crankshaft sprockets are in alignment (see illustration).

3. Loosen the timing chain tensioner nut as far as possible without actually removing it.

4. Remove the camshaft sprocket bolts and remove the sprocket and chain together. If the sprocket does not slide from

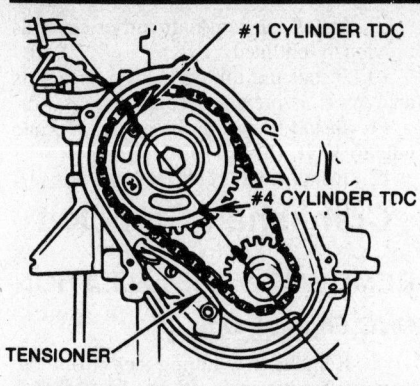

Timing mark alignment on OHV engines

the camshaft easily, a light blow with a soft mallet at the lower edge of the sprocket will dislodge it.

5. Use a gear puller (J-2288-8-20) and remove the crankshaft sprocket.

6. Press the crankshaft sprocket back onto the crankshaft.

7. Install the timing chain over the camshaft sprocket and then around the crankshaft sprocket. Make sure that the marks on the two sprockets are in alignment (see illustration). Lubricate the thrust surface with Molykote or its equivalent.

8. Align the dowel in the camshaft with the dowel hole in the sprocket and then install the sprocket onto the camshaft. Use the mounting bolts to draw the sprocket onto the camshaft and then tighten them to 27–33 ft. lb.

9. Lubricate the timing chain with clean engine oil. Tighten the chain tensioner.

10. Installation of the remaining components is in the reverse order of removal.

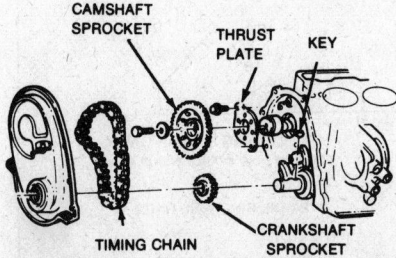

Timing chain and sprocket installation on OHV engines

Timing Belt

REMOVAL & INSTALLATION

OHC Engine Only

NOTE: The following procedure requires the use of a special tool.

1. Remove the timing belt front cover.

2. Rotate the crankshaft so that the timing mark on the crankshaft pulley lines up with the 10° BTDC mark on the indicator scale. The mark on the camshaft sprocket must line up with mark on the camshaft carrier.

3. Remove the crankshaft pulley as previously described.

4. Remove timing probe holder.

5. Loosen the water pump retaining bolts and rotate the water pump to loosen the timing belt.

6. Remove the timing belt.

7. Install timing belt on sprockets.

8. Install the crankshaft pulley.

9. Check if the mark on the camshaft sprocket lines up with mark on the camshaft carrier. The timing mark on the crankshaft pulley should line up at 10° BTDC on the indicator scale.

10. Rotate the water pump clockwise using Tool J-33039 until all slack is removed from the belt. Slightly tighten the water pump retaining bolts.

11. Install Tool J-26486 between the water pump and camshaft sprockets so that the pointer is midway between the sprockets.

NOTE: Whenever a timing belt is replaced on a 1.8L OHC (code O, J) engine it must be adjusted when the engine is at normal operating temperature (Thermostat Open).

Belt Size	19mm
INITIAL ADJUSTMENT	
New Belt	22 lbs.
Used Belt	18 lbs
CHECKING VALUE	
New Belt	18-27 lbs.
Used Belt	13-22 lbs.

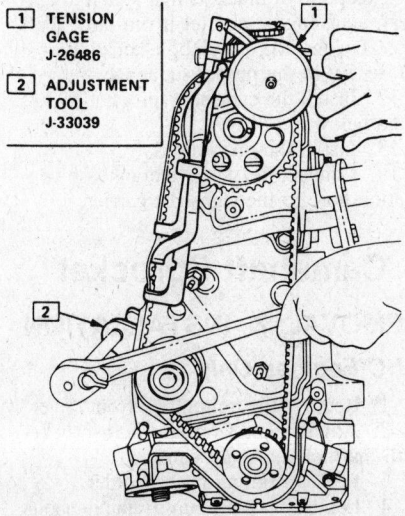

Timing belt tension adjustment on OHC engines

12. If the tension is incorrect, loosen the water pump and rotate it using Tool J-33039 until the proper tension is obtained.

13. Fully torque the water pump retaining bolts to 19 ft. lb. taking care not to further rotate the water pump.

14. Install timing probe holder. Torque nuts to 19 ft. lb.

15. Install the timing belt front cover and torque the attaching bolts to 5 ft. lb.

16. Install and adjust the generator and

power steering belt. Refill the cooling system, if necessary.

Timing Belt Rear Cover

REMOVAL & INSTALLATION

OHC Engines Only

1. Remove the timing belt from the crankshaft sprocket as previously outlined.

2. Remove the timing belt rear covers attaching bolts and the rear covers.

3. Install the rear covers and torque the attaching bolts to 19 ft. lb.

4. Install the timing belt and adjust as previously outlined.

Camshaft

REMOVAL & INSTALLATION

OHV Engines

1. Remove the engine.

2. Remove the intake manifold.

3. Remove the cylinder head cover, pivot the rocker arms to the sides, and remove the pushrods, keeping them in order. Remove the valve lifters, keeping them in order. There are special tools which make lifter removal easier.

4. Remove the front cover.

5. Remove the distributor.

6. Remove the fuel pump and its pushrod.

7. Remove the timing chain and sprocket as described earlier in this chapter.

8. Carefully pull the camshaft from the block, being sure that the camshaft lobes do not contact the bearings.

9. To install, lubricate the camshaft journals with clean engine oil. Lubricate the lobes with Molykote or the equivalent. Install the camshaft into the engine, being extremely careful not to contact the bearings with the cam lobes.

10. Install the timing chain and sprocket. Install the fuel pump and pushrod. Install the timing cover. Install the distributor.

11. Install the valve lifters. If a new camshaft has been installed, new lifters should be used to ensure durability of the cam lobes.

12. Install the pushrods and rocker arms and the intake manifold. Adjust the valve lash after installing the engine. Install the cylinder head cover.

OHC Engines

NOTE: The following procedure requires the use of a special tool.

1. Remove camshaft carrier cover.

2. Using valve train compressing Fixture J-33302, compress valve springs and remove rocker arms.

3. Remove timing belt front cover.

4. Remove timing belt as previously outlined.

5. Remove camshaft sprocket as previously outlined.

6. Remove distributor.

7. Remove camshaft thrust plate from rear of camshaft carrier.

8. Slide camshaft rearward and remove it from the carrier.

9. Install a new camshaft carrier front oil seal using Tool J-33085

10. Place camshaft in the carrier.

Camshaft sprocket removal on OHC engines

NOTE: Take care not to damage the carrier front oil seal when installing the camshaft.

11. Install camshaft thrust plate retaining bolts. Torque bolts to 70 inch lb.

12. Check camshaft end play, which should be within 0.016-0.064mm (0.04-0.16).

13. Install distributor.

14. Install camshaft sprocket as previously described.

15. Install timing belt as previously described.

16. Install timing belt front cover.

17. Using valve train compressing fixture J-33302, compress valve springs and replace rocker arms.

18. Install camshaft carrier cover as previously described.

Camshaft Carrier

REMOVAL & INSTALLATION

OHC Engines Only

NOTE: Whenever the camshaft carrier bolts are loosened, it is necessary to replace the cylinder head gasket. To do this, see the previous instructions under Cylinder Head Removal and Installation.

1. Disconnect the positive crankcase ventilation hose from the camshaft carrier.

2. Remove the distributor.

3. Remove the camshaft sprocket as previously outlined.

4. Loosen the camshaft carrier and cylinder head attaching bolts a little at a time in the sequence shown in the Cylinder Head Removal and Installation procedure.

NOTE: Camshaft carrier and cylinder head bolts should be loosened only when the engine is cold.

5. Remove the camshaft carrier.

6. Remove the camshaft thrust plate from the rear of the camshaft carrier.

7. Slide the camshaft rearward and remove it from the carrier.

8. Remove the carrier front oil seal.

9. Install a new carrier front oil seal using Tool J-33085.

10. Place the camshaft in the carrier.

NOTE: Take care not to damage the carrier front oil seal when installing the camshaft.

11. Install the camshaft thrust plate and the retaining bolts. Torque the bolts to 70 inch lb.

12. Check the camshaft end-play which should be within 0.016-0.064 in. (0.04-0.16mm).

13. Clean the sealing surfaces on cylinder head and carrier. Apply a continuous 3mm bead of RTV sealer.

14. Install the camshaft carrier on the cylinder head.

15. Install the camshaft carrier and cylinder head attaching bolts.

16. Torque the bolts a little at a time in the proper sequence, to 18 ft. lb. Then turn each bolt 60° clockwise in the proper sequence for three times until a 180° rotation is obtained, or equivalent to $\frac{1}{2}$ turn. After remainder of installation is completed (with the exception of brackets that attach to carrier), start engine and let it run until thermostat opens. Torque all bolts an additional 30° to 50° in the proper sequence.

17. Install camshaft sprocket as outlined below.

18. Install the distributor.

19. Connect the positive crankcase ventilation hose to the camshaft carrier.

Camshaft Sprocket

REMOVAL & INSTALLATION

OHC Engines Only

1. Remove the timing belt front cover.

2. Align the mark on camshaft sprocket with mark on camshaft carrier.

3. Remove timing probe holder.

4. Loosen the water pump retaining bolts and remove the timing belt from the camshaft sprocket.

5. Remove the camshaft carrier cover as previously outlined.

6. Hold the camshaft with a open-end wrench. For this purpose a hexagonal is provided in the camshaft. Remove the camshaft sprocket retaining bolt and washer and then the sprocket.

7. Install the camshaft sprocket and align marks on camshaft sprocket and camshaft carrier.

8. Hold the camshaft with a hexagonal open-end wrench. Install the sprocket washer and retaining bolt. Torque to 34 ft. lb.

9. Install the camshaft carrier cover as previously outlined.

10. Install the timing belt on sprockets and adjust as previously outlined.

11. Install timing probe holder. Torque nuts to 19 ft. lb.

12. Install timing belt front cover.

Crankshaft Sprocket

REMOVAL & INSTALLATION

OHC Engines Only

1. Remove the timing belt from the crankshaft sprocket as previously described.

2. Remove the crankshaft sprocket to crankshaft attaching bolt and the thrust washer.

3. Remove the sprocket.

4. Position the sprocket over the key on end of crankshaft.

5. Install the thrust washer and the attaching bolt. Torque to 115 ft. lb.

6. Install the timing belt and adjust as previously described.

Piston and Ring Installation

Pistons are installed with the notch in the top of the piston facing the front end of the engine. See the accompanying illustration for ring positioning.

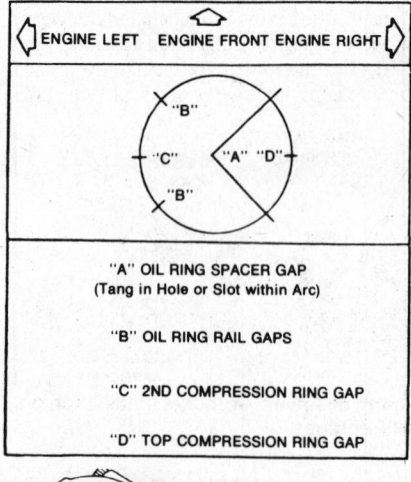

"A" OIL RING SPACER GAP
(Tang in Hole or Slot within Arc)

"B" OIL RING RAIL GAPS

"C" 2ND COMPRESSION RING GAP

"D" TOP COMPRESSION RING GAP

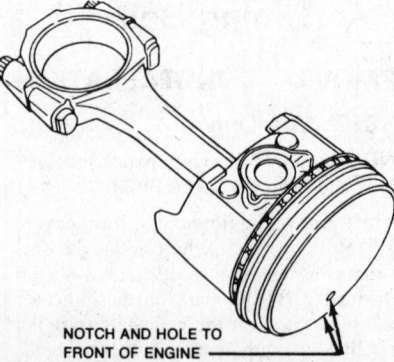

NOTCH AND HOLE TO
FRONT OF ENGINE

Install the piston and rod with the notch and/or hole facing front (engine's front end)

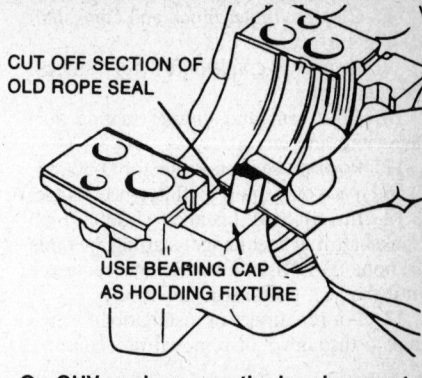

For engine overhaul procedures, see the Engine Unit Repair Section.

LUBRICATION SYSTEM

Oil Pan

REMOVAL & INSTALLATION

OHV Engines

1. Disconnect the negative battery cable.
2. Drain the crankcase. Raise and support the front of the vehicle.
3. Remove the A/C brace if so equipped.
4. Remove the exhaust shield and disconnect the exhaust pipe at the manifold.
5. Remove the starter motor and position it out of the way.
6. Remove the flywheel cover. Remove the oil pan.

NOTE: Prior to oil pan installation, check that the sealing surfaces on the pan, cylinder block and front cover are clean and free of oil. If installing the old pan, be sure that all old RTV has been removed.

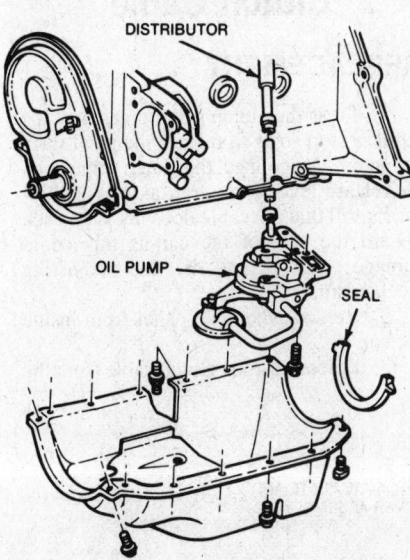

DISTRIBUTOR

OIL PUMP

SEAL

OHV engine oil pan and pump mounting

7. Apply a ⅛ in. bead of RTV sealant to the oil pan sealing surface. Use a new oil pan rear seal and install the pan in place. Tighten the bolts to 9-13 ft. lbs.
8. Installation of the remaining components is in the reverse order of removal.

OHC Engines

1. Hoist vehicle.
2. If a twin-post hoist is being used, position jack stands at jacking points and lower hoist.

3. Remove right front wheel.
4. Remove right-hand splash shield.
5. Remove lower A/C bracket strut rod attachment bolt and swing aside.
6. Remove flywheel dust cover.
7. Remove exhaust pipe to manifold attachment bolts.
8. Drain engine oil.
9. Remove oil pan.
10. Installation is the reverse of removal. Torque the pan bolts to 4 ft. lb. (48 in. lb.).

APPLY RTV SEALER BETWEEN OIL PAN GASKET AND OIL PUMP GASKET

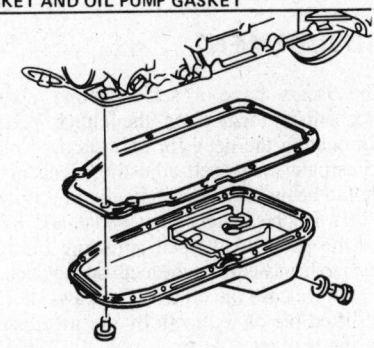

OHC engine oil pan mounting

Rear Main Oil Seal

REMOVAL & INSTALLATION

OHV Engines

1. Remove the oil pan and pump.
2. Remove the rear main bearing cap.
3. Gently pack the upper seal into the groove approximately ¼ inch on each side.
4. Measure the amount the seal was driven in on one side and add $\frac{1}{16}$ in. Cut this length from the old lower cap seal. Be sure to get a sharp cut. Repeat for the other side.
5. Place the piece of cut seal into the groove and pack the seal into the block. Do this for each side.
6. Install a piece of Plastigage or the equivalent on the bearing journal. Install

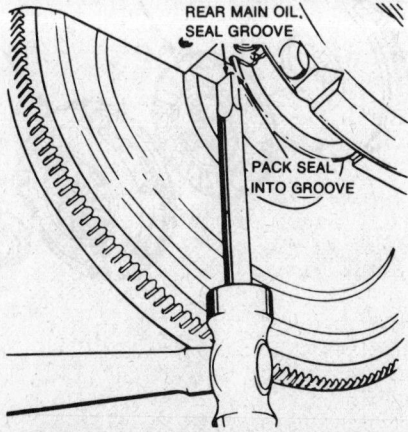

REAR MAIN OIL SEAL GROOVE

PACK SEAL INTO GROOVE

On OHV engines, pack the upper seal into its groove, ¼ inch on each side

CUT OFF SECTION OF OLD ROPE SEAL

USE BEARING CAP AS HOLDING FIXTURE

On OHV engines, use the bearing cap to hold the lower seal while you cut it

the rear cap and tighten to 75 ft. lbs. Remove the cap and check the gauge for bearing clearance. If out of specification, the ends of the seal may be frayed or not flush, preventing the cap from proper seating. Correct as required.

8. Clean the journal, and apply a thin film of sealer to the mating surfaces of the cap and tighten to 70 ft. lbs. Install the pan and pump.

NOTE: Some 1982 1.8L engines (Code G), experience a rear main seal oil leak. To correct this condition a new crankshaft part No. 14086053 and a one piece rear main seal kit part No. 14081761 has been released for service. The one piece seal kit contains an installation tool, rear main seal, and an instruction sheet.

COATED AREA INDICATED WITH #1052357 SEALER OR EQUIVALENT.

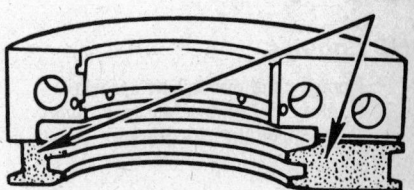

SEALER

Applying sealer to the rear cap on OHV engines

OHC Engines

NOTE: The following requires the use of special tools.

1. Remove engine as previously outlined.
2. Remove flywheel dust cover.
3. Remove flexplate to torque converter attachment bolts on automatic vehicles.
4. Remove bellhousing bolts and separate engine from transaxle assembly.
5. Remove flexplate on automatic transaxle vehicles.
6. Remove pressure plate, clutch disc and flywheel on manual transaxle vehicles.
7. Using a screwdriver or suitable tool, remove rear main oil seal.

8. Clean cylinder block and crankshaft sealing surface.

9. Inspect crankshaft for nicks, scratches, etc.

10. Coat seal and engine mating surfaces with engine oil.

11. Position seal on Protector (J-33084-2) and place onto crankshaft flywheel flange.

12. Install Seal Installer (J-33084) on crankshaft flywheel flange, starting the three (3) bolts EVENLY in a rotational sequence until the seal bottoms in the block.

13. For remainder of installation reverse steps 6 through 1 of removal procedure.

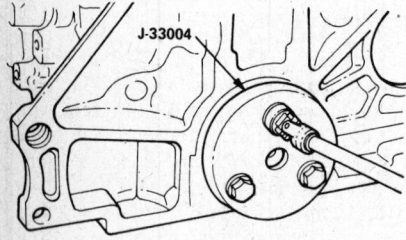

Rear main seal installation on OHC engines

Oil Pump

REMOVAL & INSTALLATION

OHV Engines

1. Remove the engine oil pan.

2. Remove the pump attaching bolts and carefully lower the pump.

3. Install in reverse order. To ensure immediate oil pressure on start-up, the oil pump gear cavity should be packed with petroleum jelly. Installation torque is 26-35 ft. lbs.

OHC Engines

1. Remove the crankshaft sprocket.

2. Remove the timing belt rear covers.

3. Disconnect the oil pressure switch wires.

4. Remove the oil pan.

5. Remove the oil filter

6. Unbolt and remove the oil pick-up tube.

7. Unbolt and remove the oil pump.

8. Installation is the reverse of removal. Use new gaskets in all instances. Torque the oil pump bolts to 5 ft. lb. Torque the oil pan bolts to 4 ft. lb., and the oil pick-up tube bolts to 5 ft. lb.

CLUTCH

ADJUSTMENT

The J-cars have a self-adjusting clutch mechanism located on the clutch pedal, eliminating the need for periodic free play adjustments. The self-adjusting mechanism should be inspected periodically as follows:

1. Depress the clutch pedal and look for the pawl on the self-adjusting mechanism to firmly engage the teeth on the ratchet.

2. Release the clutch. The pawl should be lifted off of the teeth by the metal stop on the bracket.

CLUTCH REMOVAL & INSTALLATION

1. Remove the transaxle.

2. Mark the pressure plate assembly and the flywheel so that they can be assembled in the same position. They were balanced as an assembly at the factory.

3. Loosen the attaching bolts one turn at a time until spring tension is relieved.

4. Support the pressure plate and remove the bolts. Remove the pressure plate and clutch disc. Do not disassemble the pressure plate assembly; replace it if defective.

5. Inspect the flywheel, clutch disc, pressure plate, throwout bearing and the clutch fork and pivot shaft assembly for

wear. Replace the parts as required. If the flywheel shows any signs of overheating, or if it is badly grooved or scored, it should be refaced or replaced.

6. Clean the pressure plate and flywheel mating surfaces thoroughly. Position the clutch disc and pressure plate into the installed position, and support with a dummy shaft or clutch aligning tool. The clutch plate is assembled with the damper springs offset toward the transaxle. One side of the factory-supplied clutch disc is stamped "Flywheel Side."

7. Install the pressure plate-to-flywheel bolts. Tighten them gradually in a criss-cross pattern.

8. Lubricate the outside groove and the inside recess of the release bearing with high temperature grease. Wipe off any excess. Install the release bearing.

9. Install the transaxle.

Neutral Start Switch

A neutral start switch is located on the clutch pedal assembly; the switch prevents the engine from starting unless the clutch is depressed. If the switch is faulty, it can be unbolted and replaced without removing the pedal assembly from the car. No adjustments for the switch are provided.

Clutch Cable

REPLACEMENT

1. Press the clutch pedal up against the bumper stop so as to release the pawl from the detent. Disconnect the clutch cable from the release lever at the transaxle assembly. Be careful that the cable does not snap back toward the rear of the car as this could damage the detent in the adjusting mechanism.

2. Remove the hush panel from inside the car.

3. Disconnect the clutch cable from the

1. Pick-up screen
2. Pump cover
3. Drive gear and shaft
4. Idler gear
5. Pump body
6. Pressure regulator spring
7. Pressure regulator valve
8. Retaining pin
9. Gasket
10. Bolts

OHV engine oil pump

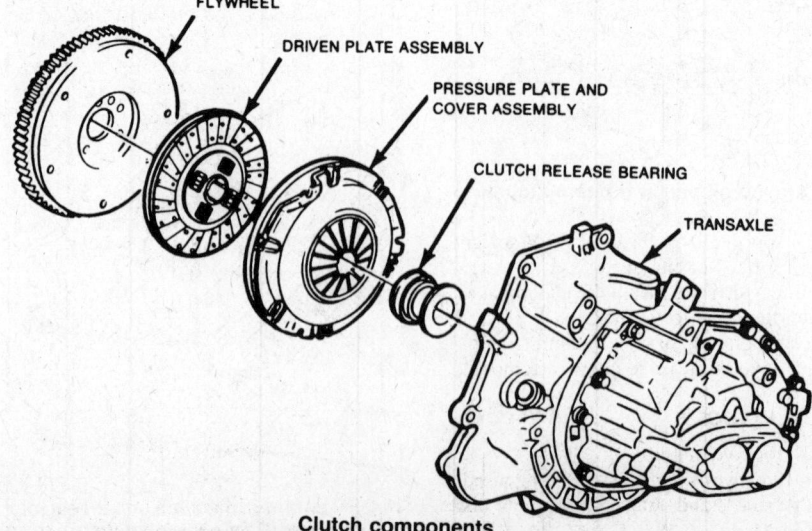

Clutch components

detent end tangs. Lift the locking pawl away from the detent and then pull the cable forward between the detent and the pawl.

4. Remove the windshield washer bottle.

5. From the engine side of the cowl, pull the clutch cable out to disengage it from the clutch pedal mounting bracket. The insulators, dampener and washers may separate from the cable in the process.

6. Disconnect the cable from the transaxle mounting bracket and remove it.

7. Install the cable into both insulators, damper and washer. Lubricate the rear insulator with tire mounting lube or the like to ease installation into the pedal mounting bracket.

8. From inside the car, attach the end of the cable to the detent. Be sure to route the cable underneath the pawl and into the detent cable groove.

9. Press the clutch pedal up against the bumper stop to release the pawl from the detent. Install the other end of the cable at the release lever and the transaxle mount bracket.

10. Install the hush panel and the windshield washer bottle.

11. Check the clutch operation.

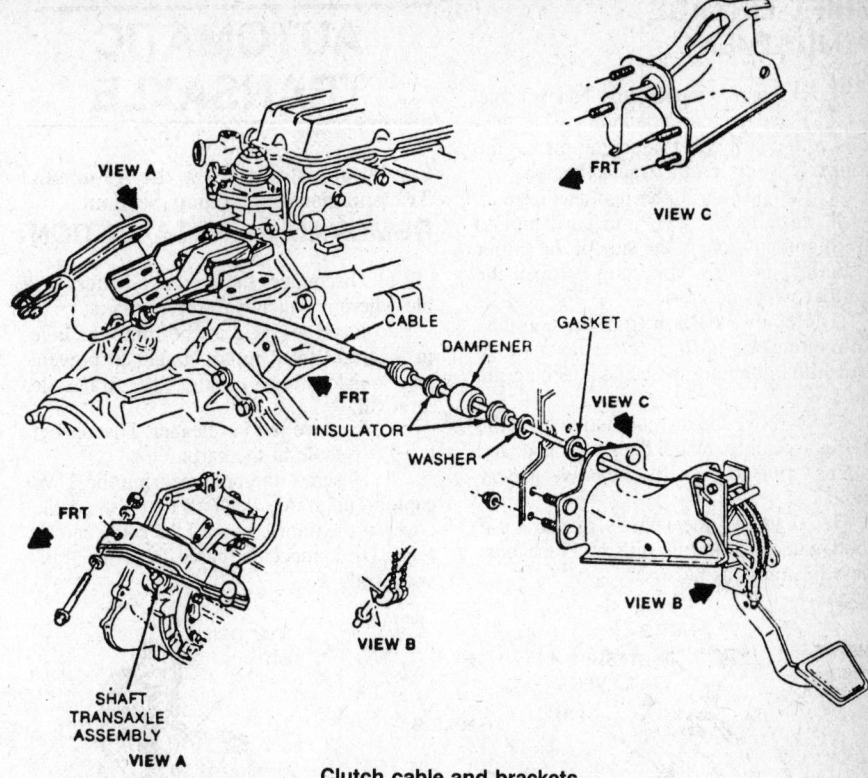

Clutch cable and brackets

MANUAL TRANSAXLE

REMOVAL & INSTALLATION

1. Disconnect the negative battery cable.

2. Install an engine holding bar so that one end is supported on the cowl tray over the wiper motor and the other end rests on the radiator support. Use padding and be careful not to damage the paint or body work with the bar. Attach a lifting hook to the engine lift ring and to the bar and raise the engine enough to take the pressure off the motor mounts.

NOTE: If a lifting bar and hook is not available, a chain hoist can be used, however, during the procedure the vehicle must be raised, at which time the chain hoist must be adjusted to keep tension on the engine/transaxle assembly.

3. Remove the heater hose clamp at the transaxle mount bracket. Disconnect the electrical connector and remove the horn assembly.

4. Remove the transaxle mount attaching bolts. Discard the bolts attaching the mount to the side frame: *New bolts must be used at installation.*

5. Disconnect the clutch cable from the clutch release lever. Remove the transaxle mount bracket attaching bolts and nuts.

6. Disconnect the shift cables and retaining clips at the transaxle. Disconnect the ground cables at the transaxle mounting stud.

7. Remove the four upper transaxle-to-engine mounting bolts.

8. Raise the vehicle and support it on stands. Remove the left front wheel.

9. Remove the left front inner splash shield. Remove the transaxle strut and bracket.

10. Remove the clutch housing cover bolts.

11. Disconnect the speedometer cable at the transaxle.

12. Disconnect the stabilizer bar at the left suspension support and control arm.

13. Disconnect the ball joint from the steering knuckle.

14. Remove the left suspension support attaching bolts and remove the support and control arm as an assembly.

15. Install boot protectors and disengage the drive axles at the transaxle. Remove the left side shaft from the transaxle.

16. Position a jack under the transaxle case, remove the lower two transaxle-to-engine mounting bolts and remove the

transaxle by sliding it towards the driver's side, away from the engine. Carefully lower the jack, guiding the right shaft out the transaxle.

17. When installing the transaxle, guide the right drive axle into its bore as the transaxle is being raised. The right drive axle CANNOT be readily installed after the transaxle is connected to the engine. Installation of the remaining components is in the reverse order of removal with the following notes: Tighten the transaxle-to-engine mounting bolts to 55 ft. lbs. Tighten the suspension support-to-body attaching bolts to 75 ft. lbs. and the clutch housing cover bolts to 10 ft. lbs. Using new bolts, install and tighten the transaxle mount-to-side frame to 40 ft. lbs. When installing the bolts attaching the mount-to-transaxle bracket, check the alignment bolt at the engine mount. If excessive effort is required to remove the alignment bolt, realign the powertrain components and tighten the bolts to 40 ft. lbs., and then remove the alignment bolt.

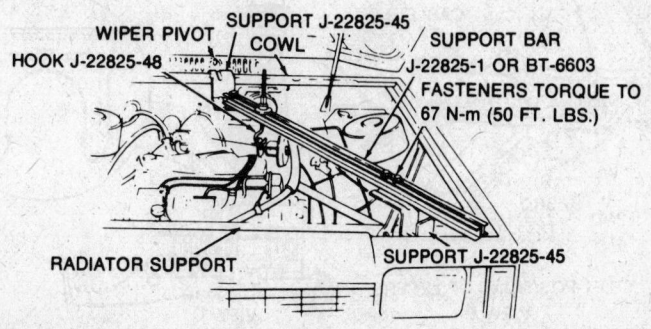

Install an engine holding bar when removing the manual transmission

SHIFT LINKAGE ADJUSTMENT

1. Disconnect the negative battery cable.

2. Place the transaxle in first gear, then loosen the shift cable attaching pins at the transaxle levers on the transaxle case.

3. Remove the shifter boot and retainer.

4. Install a No. 22 (5/32 in.) drill bit into the alignment hole at the side of the shifter assembly. Install a yoke clip between the shifter tower and carrier.

5. Remove the lash from the transaxle by rotating the upright select lever (lever D) while tightening the cable attaching pin nut.

6. Remove the drill bit and yoke at the shifter assembly, install the shifter boot and retainer and connect the negative battery cable.

7. Road test the vehicle to check for good gate feel during shifting. Fine tune the adjustment as necessary.

AUTOMATIC TRANSAXLE

For all adjustments, see the Automatic Transmission Unit Repair Section.

REMOVAL & INSTALLATION

1. Disconnect the negative battery cable where it attaches to the transaxle.

2. Insert a ¼ x 2 in. bolt into the hole in the right front motor mount to prevent any mislocation during the transaxle removal.

3. Remove the air cleaner. Disconnect the T.V. cable at the carburetor.

4. Unscrew the bolt securing the T.V. cable to the transaxle. Pull up on the cable cover at the transaxle until the cable can be seen. Disconnect the cable from the transaxle rod.

5. Remove the wiring harness retaining bolt at the top of the transaxle.

6. Remove the hose from the air management valve and then pull the wiring harness up and out of the way.

7. Install an engine support bar as shown in the illustration. Raise the engine just enough to take the pressure off the motor mounts.

— **CAUTION** —
The engine support bar must be located in the center of the cowl and the bolts must be tightened before attempting to support the engine.

8. Remove the transaxle mount and bracket assembly. It may be necessary to raise the engine slightly to aid in removal.

9. Disconnect the shift control linkage from the transaxle.

10. Remove the top transaxle-to-engine mounting bolts. Loosen, but do not remove, the transaxle-to-engine bolt nearest to the starter.

11. Unlock the steering column. Raise and support the front of the car. Remove the front wheels.

12. Pull out the cotter pin and loosen the castellated ball joint nut until the ball joint separates from the control arm. Repeat on the other side of the car.

13. Disconnect the stabilizer bar from the left lower control arm.

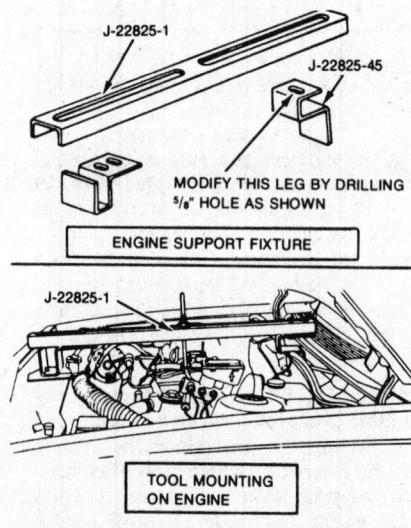

Supporting the engine with a holding bar when removing the automatic transmission

14. Remove the six bolts that secure the left front suspension support assembly.

15. Connect an axle shaft removal tool (J-28468) to a slide hammer (J-23907).

16. Position the tool behind the axle shaft cones and then pull the cones out and away from the transaxle. Remove the axle shafts and plug the transaxle bores to reduce fluid leakage.

17. Remove the nut that secures the transaxle control cable bracket to the transaxle, then remove the engine-to-transaxle stud.

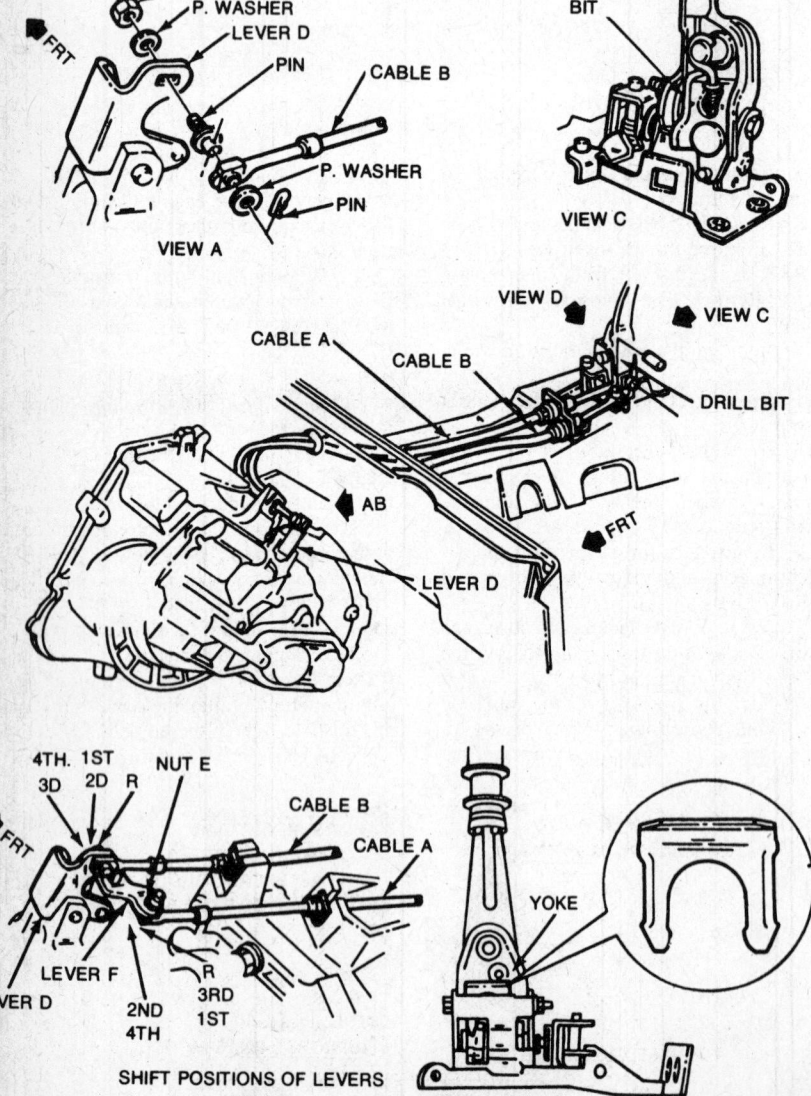

Shift linkage adjustment

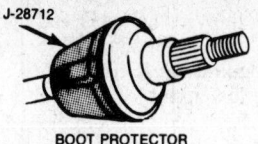

18. Disconnect the speedometer cable at the transaxle.

19. Disconnect the transaxle strut (stabilizer) at the transaxle.

20. Remove the four retaining screws and remove the torque converter shield.

21. Remove the three bolts securing the torque converter to the flex plate.

22. Disconnect and plug the oil cooler lines at the transaxle. Remove the starter.

23. Remove the screws that hold the brake and fuel line brackets to the left side of the underbody. This will allow the lines to be moved slightly for clearance during transaxle removal.

24. Remove the bolt that was loosened in Step 10.

25. Remove the transaxle to the left.

Installation is in the reverse order of removal. Please note the following:

1. Reinstall both axle shafts AFTER the transaxle is in position.

2. When installing the front suspension support assembly you must follow the tightening sequence shown in the illustration.

3. Check alignment when installation is complete.

HALFSHAFTS

The J-cars use unequal-length halfshafts, with specific application for automatic and manual transaxle use. All halfshafts except the left-hand inboard joint of the automatic transaxle incorporate a male spline; the shafts interlock with the transaxle gears through the use of barrel-type snap rings. The left-hand inboard shaft on the automatic transaxle uses a female spline which installs over a stub shaft protruding from the transaxle. Four constant velocity joints are used, two on each shaft. The inner joints are of the double offset design; the outer joints are Rzeppa-type.

REMOVAL & INSTALLATION

NOTE: This procedure requires the use of special tools.

1. Remove the hub nut.

2. Raise the front of the car. Remove the wheel and tire.

3. Install an axle shaft boot seal protector, G.M. special tool no. J-28712 or the equivalent, onto the seal.

4. Disconnect the brake hose clip from the MacPherson strut, but do not disconnect the hose from the caliper. Remove the brake caliper from the spindle, and hang the caliper out of the way by a length of wire. *Do not allow the caliper to hang by the brake hose.*

5. Mark the camber alignment cam bolt for reassembly. Remove the cam bolt and the upper attaching bolt from the strut and spindle.

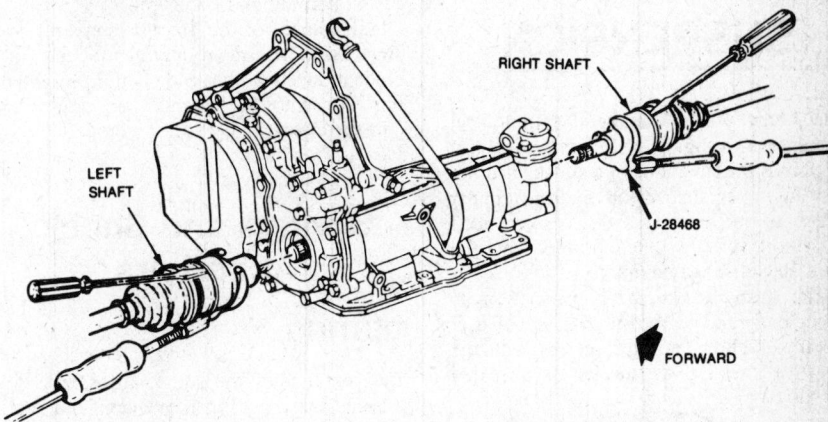

Halfshaft removal; the special tools are attached to slide hammers in this diagram

6. Pull the steering knuckle assembly from the strut bracket.

7. Using G.M. special tool J-28468 or the equivalent, remove the axle shaft from the transaxle.

8. Using G.M. special tool J-28733 or the equivaelent spindle remover, remove the axle shaft from the hub and bearing assembly.

To install:

1. If a new drive axle is to be installed, a new knuckle seal should be installed first.

2. Loosely install the drive axle into the transaxle and steering knuckle.

3. Loosely attach the steering knuckle to the suspension strut.

4. Install the brake caliper. Tighten the bolts to 30 ft. lbs. (40 Nm.).

5. The drive axle is an interference fit in the steering knuckle. Press the axle into place, then install the hub nut. When the shaft begins to turn with the hub, insert a drift through the caliper into one of the cooling slots in the rotor to keep it from turning. Tighten the hub nut to 70 ft. lbs. (100 Nm.) to completely seat the shaft.

6. Load the hub assembly by lowering it onto a jackstand. Align the camber cam bolt marks made during removal, install the

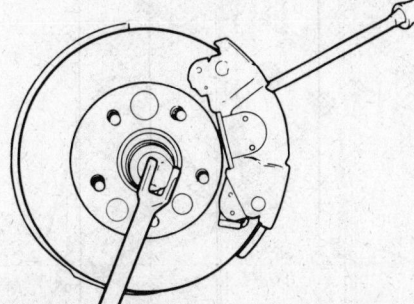

Insert a holding tool, such as a drift or punch into the caliper when tightening the hub nut

bolt and tighten to 140 ft. lbs. (190 Nm). Tighten the upper nut to the same value.

7. Install the axle shaft all the way into the transaxle using a screwdriver inserted into the groove provided on the inner retainer. Tap the screwdriver until the shaft seats in the transaxle.

8. Connect the brake hose clip to the strut. Install the tire and wheel, lower the car, and tighten the hub nut to 225 ft. lbs. (305 Nm).

JACKING AND HOISTING

The J-cars are supplied with a jack for changing tires. This is a bumper jack, engaging slots in the bumpers by means of a hook. This jack is satisfactory for its intended purpose; it is not meant to support the car while you go crawling around underneath it. *Never* crawl under the car when it is supported by only the bumper jack.

The car may also be jacked at the rear axle between the spring seats, or at the front end at the engine cradle crossbar or lower control arm. The car must never be lifted by the rear lower control arms.

The car can be raised on a four point hoist which contacts the chassis at points just behind the front wheels and just ahead of the rear wheels, as shown in the accompanying diagram. Be certain that the lift pads do not contact the catalytic converter.

It is imperative that strict safety precautions be observed both while raising the car and in the subsequent support after the car is raised. If a jack is used to raise the car, the transaxle should be shifted to Park (automatic) or First (manual), the parking brake should be set, and the opposite wheel should be blocked. Jacking should only be attempted on a hard level surface.

FRONT SUSPENSION

The J-cars use a MacPherson strut front suspension design. A MacPherson strut combines the functions of a shock absorber and an upper suspension member (upper arm) into one unit. The strut is surrounded by a coil spring, which provides normal front suspension functions.

The strut bolts to the body shell at its upper end, and to the steering knuckle at the lower end. The strut pivots with the steering knuckle by means of a sealed

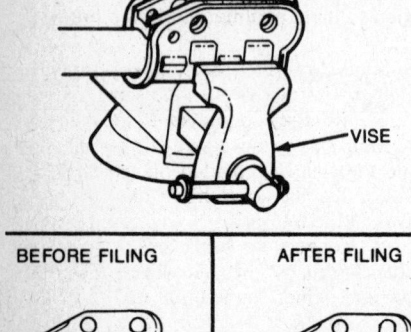

BEFORE FILING   **AFTER FILING**

Modifying the strut mounting holes

mounting assembly at the upper end which contains a preloaded, non-adjustable bearing.

The steering knuckle is connected to the chassis at the lower end by a conventional lower control arm, and pivots in the arm in a preloaded ball joint stud by means of a castellated nut and cotter pin.

Advantages of the MacPherson strut design, aside from its relative simplicity, include reduced weight and friction, minimal intrusion into the engine and passenger compartments, and ease of service.

Springs and Shock Absorbers

TESTING

The function of the shock absorber is to dampen harsh spring movement and provide a means of dissipating the motion of the wheels so that the shocks encountered by the wheels are not totally transmitted to the body and, therefore, to you and your passengers. As the wheel moves up and down, the shock absorber shortens and lengthens, thereby imposing a restraint on movement by its hydraulic action.

A good way to see if your shock absorbers are functioning correctly is to push one corner of the car until it is moving up and down for almost the full suspension travel, then release it and watch its recovery. If the car bounces slightly about one more time and then comes to a rest, the shock is alright. If the car continues to bounce excessively, the shocks will probably require replacement.

MacPherson Struts

REMOVAL & INSTALLATION

The struts are precious parts and retain the springs under tremendous pressure even when removed from the car. For these reasons, several expensive special tools and substantial specialized knowledge are required to safely and effectively work on these parts. We recommend that if spring or shock absorber repair work is required, you remove the strut or struts involved and take them to a repair facility which is fully equipped and familiar with the car.

1. Working under the hood, pry off the shock cover and then unscrew the upper strut-to-body nuts.

2. Loosen the wheel nuts, raise and support the car and then remove the wheel and tire.

3. Install a drive axle protective cover (J28712).

4. Use a two-armed puller and press the tie rod out of the strut bracket.

5. Remove both strut-to-steering knuckle bolts and carefully lift out the strut.

6. Installation is in the reverse order of removal. Be sure that the flat sides of the strut-to-knuckle bolt heads are horizontal (see illustration).

STRUT MODIFICATION

This modification is made only if a camber adjustment is anticipated.

1. Place the strut in a vise. This step is not absolutely necessary; filing can be accomplished by disconnecting the strut from the steering knuckle.

FRONT SUSPENSION SUPPORT ATTACHING BOLT/SCREW SEQUENCE

1. INSTALL LOOSELY, THE CENTER SCREW INTO HOLE **A**.

2. INSTALL LOOSELY, THE TIE BAR SCREW INTO THE SMALL SLOTTED OUTBOARD HOLE.

3. INSTALL AND TORQUE BOTH BOLTS IN THE REAR HOLES.

4. INSTALL AND TORQUE 2ND CENTER HOLE **D** BOLT/SCREW.

5. TORQUE CENTER HOLE **A** BOLT.

6. INSTALL OTHER TIE BAR BOLT (FRONT HOLE **E**) AND TORQUE.

7. TORQUE 2ND BOLT/SCREW IN THE (FRONT HOLE **B**).

FRONT SUSPENSION SUPPORT

88 N·m (65 FT. LBS.)

FRONT OF CAR

LOWER CONTROL ARM

88 N·m (65 FT. LBS.)

88 N·m (65 FT. LBS.)

88 N·m (65 FT. LBS.)

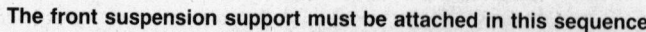

The front suspension support must be attached in this sequence

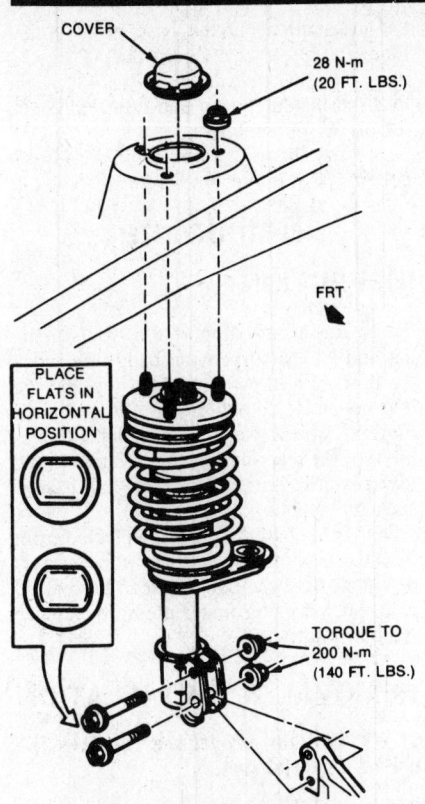

COVER

28 N·m (20 FT. LBS.)

FRT

PLACE FLATS IN HORIZONTAL POSITION

TORQUE TO 200 N·m (140 FT. LBS.)

Strut assembly mounting

2. File the holes in the outer flanges so as to enlarge the bottom holes until they match the slots already in the inner flanges.

3. Camber adjustment procedures are detailed later in this chapter.

Coil Springs

REMOVAL & INSTALLATION

NOTE: This procedure requires the use of special tools.

> ── CAUTION ──
> *The coil springs are retained under considerable pressure. They can exert enough force to cause serious injury. Exercise extreme caution when disassembling the strut for coil spring removal.*

This procedure requires the use of a spring compressor and several other special tools. It cannot be performed without them. If you do not have access to these tools, DO NOT attempt to disassemble the strut.

1. Remove the strut assembly.

2. Clamp the spring compressor (J26584) in a vise. Position the strut assembly in the bottom adapter of the compresser and install the special tool J26584-86 (see illustration). Be sure that the adapter captures the strut and that the locating pins are engaged.

3. Rotate the strut assembly so that the top mounting assembly lip aligns with the compressor support notch. Insert two top adapters (J26584-88) between the top mounting assembly and the top spring seat. Position the adapters so that the split lines are in the 3 o'clock and 9 o'clock positions.

4. Using a 1 in. socket, turn the screw on top of the compressor clockwise until the top support flange contacts the adapters. Continue turning the screw until the coil spring is compressed approximately ½ in. (4 complete turns). *Never bottom the spring or the strut damper rod.*

5. Unscrew the nut from the strut damper shaft and then lift off the top mounting assembly.

6. Turn the compressor adjusting screw counterclockwise until the spring tension has been relieved. Remove the adapters and then remove the coil spring.

7. When installing a new spring, NEVER place a hard tool such as pliers or screwdriver against the polished surface of the damper shaft. The shaft can be held up with your fingers or an extension in order to prevent it from receding into the strut assembly while the spring is being compressed.

8. Installation is in the reverse order of removal.

Shock Absorbers

REMOVAL & INSTALLATION

The internal piston rod, cylinder assembly and fluid can be replaced utilizing a service cartridge and nut. Internal threads are located inside the tube immediately below a cut line groove.

1. Remove the strut and the coil springs. Clamp the strut in a vise. Do not overtighten it as this will cause damage to the strut tube.

2. Locate the cut line groove just below the top edge of the strut tube. It is imperative that the groove be accurately located as any mislocation will cause inner thread damage. Using pipe cutters, cut around the groove until the tube is completely cut through.

3. Remove and discard the end cap, the cylinder and the piston rod assembly. Remove the strut assembly from the vise and pour out the old fluid.

4. Reclamp the strut in the vise. A flaring cup tool is included in the replacement cartridge kit to flare and deburr the edge that was cut on the strut tube. Place the flaring cup on the open edge of the tube and strike it with a mallet until its flat outer surface rests on the top edge of the tube. Remove the cup and discard it.

5. Try the new nut to make sure that it threads properly. If not, use the flaring cup again until it does.

6. Place the new strut cartridge into the tube. Turn the cartridge until it settles into

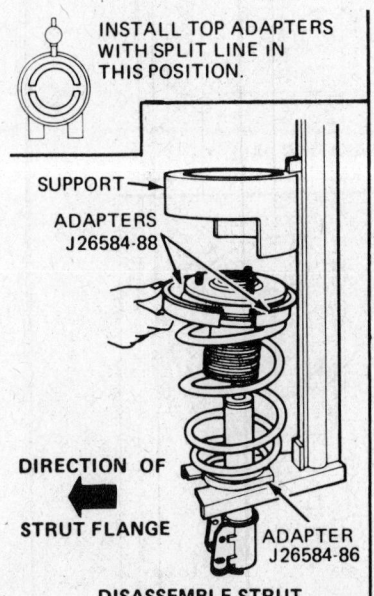

INSTALL TOP ADAPTERS WITH SPLIT LINE IN THIS POSITION.

SUPPORT

ADAPTERS J26584-88

DIRECTION OF STRUT FLANGE

ADAPTER J26584-86

DISASSEMBLE STRUT

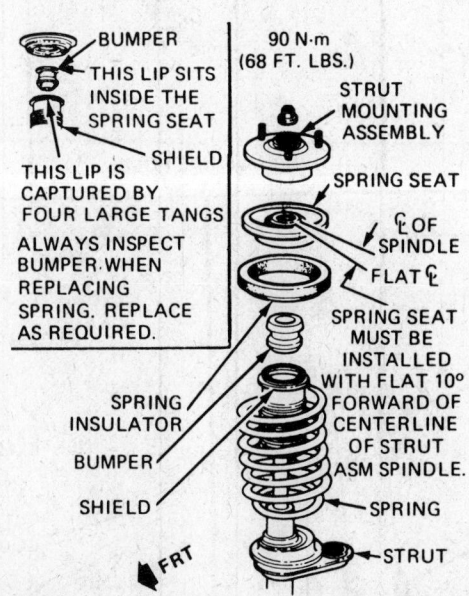

BUMPER

THIS LIP SITS INSIDE THE SPRING SEAT

SHIELD

THIS LIP IS CAPTURED BY FOUR LARGE TANGS

ALWAYS INSPECT BUMPER WHEN REPLACING SPRING. REPLACE AS REQUIRED.

90 N·m (68 FT. LBS.)

STRUT MOUNTING ASSEMBLY

SPRING SEAT

₵ OF SPINDLE

FLAT ₵

SPRING SEAT MUST BE INSTALLED WITH FLAT 10° FORWARD OF CENTERLINE OF STRUT ASM SPINDLE.

SPRING INSULATOR

BUMPER

SHIELD

SPRING

STRUT

FRT

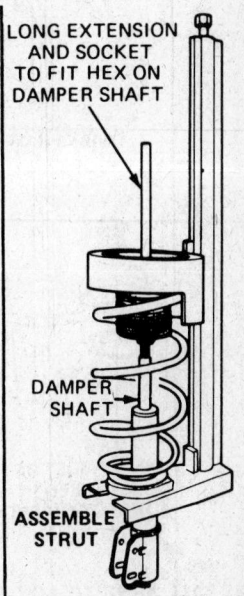

LONG EXTENSION AND SOCKET TO FIT HEX ON DAMPER SHAFT

DAMPER SHAFT

ASSEMBLE STRUT

Coil spring removal and installation

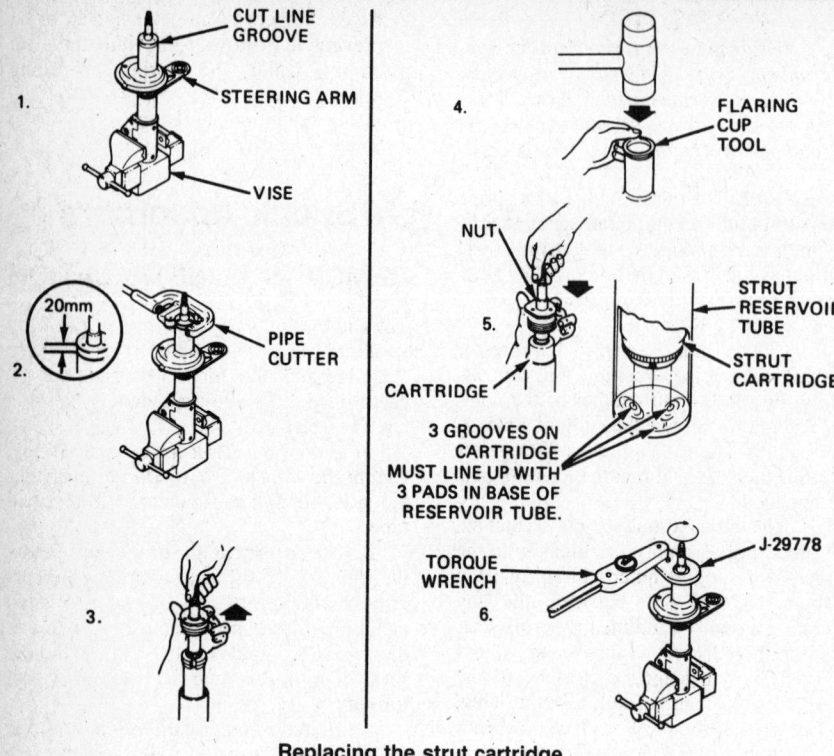

the indentations at the base of the tube. Place the nut over the cartridge.

7. Tighten the nut to 140-170 ft. lbs. Pull the piston rod up and down to check for proper operation.

8. Installation of the remaining components is in the reverse order of removal.

Replacing the strut cartridge

Ball Joints

INSPECTION

1. Raise and support the front of the car and let the suspension hang free.

2. Grasp the wheel at the top and the bottom and shake it in an "in-and-out" motion. Check for any horizontal movement of the steering knuckle relative to the lower control arm. Replace the ball joint if such movement is noted.

3. If the ball stud is disconnected from the steering knuckle and any looseness is detected, or if the ball stud can be twisted in its socket using finger pressure, replace the ball joint.

REMOVAL & INSTALLATION

NOTE: This procedure requires the use of a special tool.

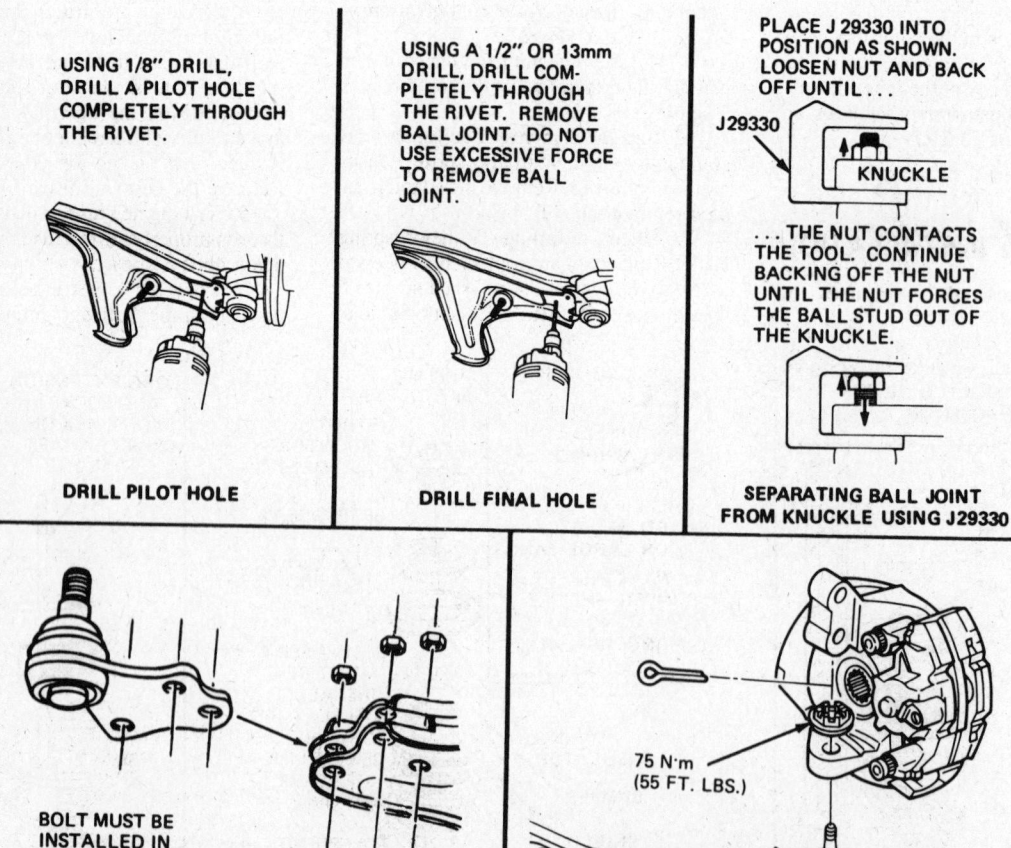

USING 1/8" DRILL, DRILL A PILOT HOLE COMPLETELY THROUGH THE RIVET.

DRILL PILOT HOLE

USING A 1/2" OR 13mm DRILL, DRILL COMPLETELY THROUGH THE RIVET. REMOVE BALL JOINT. DO NOT USE EXCESSIVE FORCE TO REMOVE BALL JOINT.

DRILL FINAL HOLE

PLACE J 29330 INTO POSITION AS SHOWN. LOOSEN NUT AND BACK OFF UNTIL...

... THE NUT CONTACTS THE TOOL. CONTINUE BACKING OFF THE NUT UNTIL THE NUT FORCES THE BALL STUD OUT OF THE KNUCKLE.

SEPARATING BALL JOINT FROM KNUCKLE USING J29330

BOLT MUST BE INSTALLED IN DIRECTION SHOWN

INSTALL BALL JOINT TO CONTROL ARM

75 N·m (55 FT. LBS.)

Ball joint removal and installation

Only one ball joint is used in each lower arm. The MacPherson strut design does not use an upper ball joint.

1. Loosen the wheel nuts, raise the car, and remove the wheel.

2. Use a ⅛ in. drill bit to drill a hole through the center of each of the three ball joint rivets.

3. Use a ½ in. drill bit to drill completely through the rivet.

4. Use a hammer and punch to remove the rivets. Drive them out from the bottom.

5. Use the special tool J29330 or a ball joint removal tool to separate the ball joint from the steering knuckle (see illustration). Don't forget to remove the cotter pin.

6. Disconnect the stabilizer bar from the lower control arm. Remove the ball joint.

7. Install the new ball joint into the control arm with the three bolts supplied as shown. Installation of the remaining components is in the reverse order of removal. Use a new cotter pin when installing the castellated nut on the ball joint. Check the toe setting and adjust as necessary.

Control Arm

REMOVAL & INSTALLATION

1. Raise and support the front of the car. Remove the wheel.

2. Disconnect the stabilizer bar from the control arm and/or support.

3. Separate the ball joint from the steering knuckle as previously detailed.

4. Remove the two control arm-to-support bolts and remove the control arm.

5. If control arm support bar removal is necessary, unscrew the six mounting bolts and remove the support.

6. Installation is in the reverse order of removal. Tighten the control arm support rail bolts in the sequence shown. Check the toe and adjust as necessary.

Wheel Bearings

The front wheel bearings are sealed, non-adjustable units which require no periodic attention. They are bolted to the steering knuckle by means of an integral flange.

REPLACEMENT

NOTE: This procedure requires the use of special tools.

You will need a special tool to pull the bearing free of the halfshaft, G.M. tool no. J-28733 or the equivalent. You should also use a halfshaft boot protector, G.M. tool no. J-28712 or the equivalent to protect the parts from damage.

1. Remove the wheel cover, loosen the hub nut, and raise and support the car. Remove the front wheel.

2. Install the boot cover, G.M. part no. J-28712 or the equivalent.

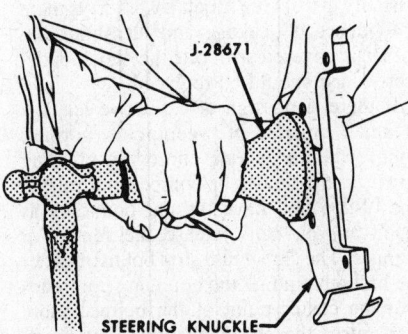

Use a seal driver when installing the new seal into the knuckle

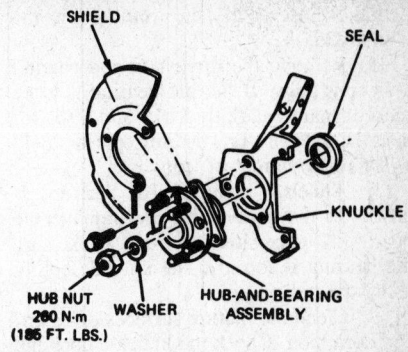

Hub and bearing attachment to the knuckle

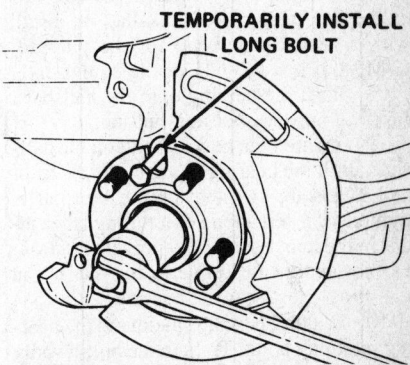

Insert a bolt into the rotor when tightening the hub nut

3. Remove and discard the hub nut. Be sure to use a new one on assembly, not the old one.

4. Remove the brake caliper and rotor:

a. Remove the allen head caliper mounting bolts;

b. Remove the caliper from the knuckle and suspend from a length of wire. Do not allow the caliper to hang from the

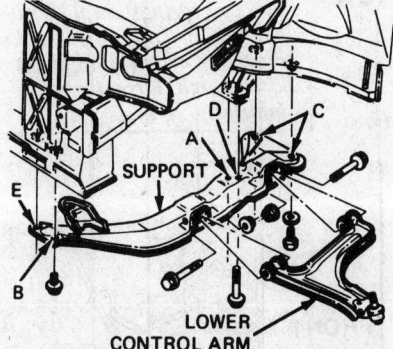

FRONT SUSP SUPPORT ASM ATTACHING BOLT/SCREW SEQUENCE

1. LOOSELY INSTALL CENTER BOLT INTO HOLE (A).
2. LOOSELY INSTALL TIE BAR BOLT INTO OUTBOARD HOLE (B).
3. INSTALL BOTH REAR BOLTS INTO HOLES (C) TORQUE REAR BOLTS.
4. INSTALL BOLT INTO CENTER HOLE (D), THEN TORQUE.
5. TORQUE BOLT IN HOLE (A).
6. INSTALL BOLT INTO FRONT HOLE (E), THEN TORQUE.
7. TORQUE BOLT IN HOLE (B).

SUPPORT-TO-BODY BOLTS . . . . . . .90 N·m (63 FT. LBS.)
LCA PIVOT BOLTS . . . . .95 N·m (67 FT. LBS.)

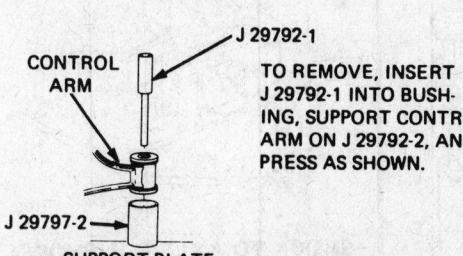

TO REMOVE, INSERT J 29792-1 INTO BUSHING, SUPPORT CONTROL ARM ON J 29792-2, AND PRESS AS SHOWN.

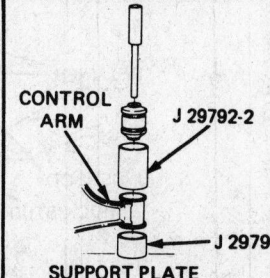

TO INSTALL, SUPPORT CONTROL ARM ON J 29792-3, PLACE BUSHING INTO J 29792-2, AND PRESS BUSING INTO CONTROL ARM USING J 29792-1. LUBRICATE BUSHING.

Installing the front suspension (control arm) support rail; be sure to follow the tightening sequence exactly

brake hose. Pull the rotor from the knuckle.

5. Remove the three hub and bearing attaching bolts. If the old bearing is to be reused, match mark the bolts and holes for installation. The brake rotor splash shield will have to come off, too.

6. Attach a puller, G.M. part no. J-28733 or the equivalent, and remove the bearing. If corrosion is present, make sure the bearing is loose in the knuckle before using the puller.

7. Clean the mating surfaces of all dirt and corrosion. Check the knuckle bore and knuckle seal for damage. If a new bearing is to be installed, remove the old knuckle seal and install a new one. Grease the lips of the new seal before installation; install with a seal driver made for the purpose, G.M. tool no. J-28671 or the equivalent.

8. Push the bearing onto the halfshaft. Install a new washer and hub nut.

9. Tighten the new hub nut on the halfshaft until the bearing is seated. If the rotor and hub start to rotate as the hub nut is tightened, insert a long bolt through the cut-out in the hub assembly to prevent rotation. Do not apply full torque to the hub nut at this time—just seat the bearing.

10. Install the brake shield and the bearing retaining bolts. Tighten the bolts evenly to 40 ft. lbs.

11. Install the caliper and rotor. Be sure that the caliper hose isn't twisted. Install the caliper bolts and tighten to 21-35 ft. lbs.

12. Install the wheel. Lower the car. Tighten the hub nut to 185 ft. lbs.

REAR SUSPENSION

J-cars have a semi-independent rear suspension system which consists of an axle with trailing arms and a twisting cross beam, two coil springs and two shock absorbers. The axle assembly attaches to the body through a rubber bushing located at the front of each control arm. A stabilizer bar is available as an option.

Two coil springs are used, each being retained between a seat in the underbody and one on the control arm. A rubber cushion is used to isolate the coil spring upper end from the underbody seat, while the lower end sits on a combination bumper and spring insulator.

The double acting shock absorbers are filled with a calibrated amount of fluid and sealed during production. They are non-adjustable, non-refillable and cannot be disassembled.

A single unit hub and bearing assembly is bolted to both ends of the rear axle assembly; it is a sealed unit and must be replaced as one if found to be defective.

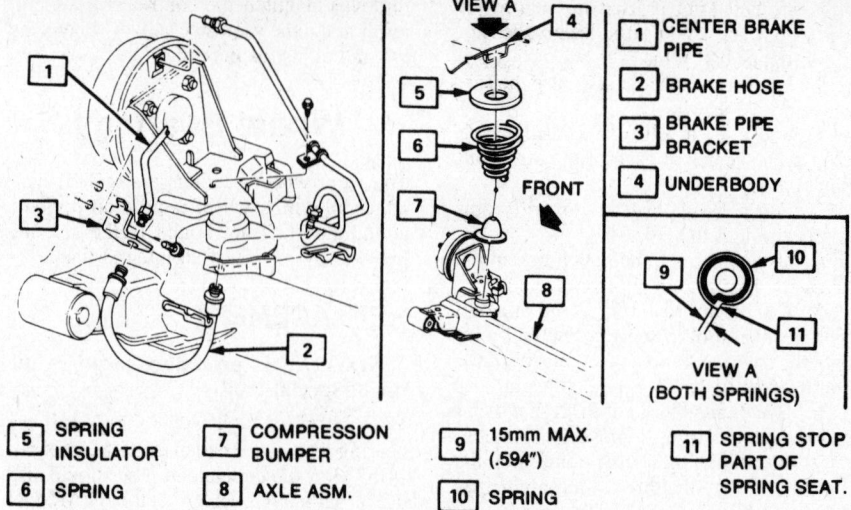

1	CENTER BRAKE PIPE
2	BRAKE HOSE
3	BRAKE PIPE BRACKET
4	UNDERBODY

5	SPRING INSULATOR
6	SPRING
7	COMPRESSION BUMPER
8	AXLE ASM.
9	15mm MAX. (.594")
10	SPRING
11	SPRING STOP PART OF SPRING SEAT.

Rear spring mounting

Shock Absorbers

TESTING

Visually inspect the shock absorber. If there is evidence of leakage and the shock absorber is covered with oil, the shock is defective and should be replaced.

If there is no sign of excessive leakage (a small amount of weeping is normal) bounce the car at one corner by pressing down on the fender or bumper and releasing. When you have the car bouncing as much as you can, release the fender or bumper. The car should stop bouncing after the first rebound. If the bouncing continues past the center point of the bounce more than once, the shock absorbers are worn and should be replaced.

REMOVAL & INSTALLATION

1. Open the hatch or trunk lid, remove the trim cover if present, and remove the upper shock absorber nut.

2. Raise and support the car at a con-

venient working height if you desire. It is not necessary to remove the weight of the car from the shock absorbers, however, so you can leave the car on the ground if you prefer.

3. Remove the lower attaching bolt and remove the shock.

4. If new shock absorbers are being installed, repeatedly compress them while inverted and extend them in their normal upright position. This will purge them of air.

5. Install the shocks in the reverse order of removal. Tighten the lower mount nut and bolt to 55 ft. lbs. the upper to 13 ft. lbs.

Springs

REMOVAL & INSTALLATION

— CAUTION —

The coil springs are under a considerable amount of tension. Be very careful when removing or installing them; they can exert enough force to cause very serious injuries.

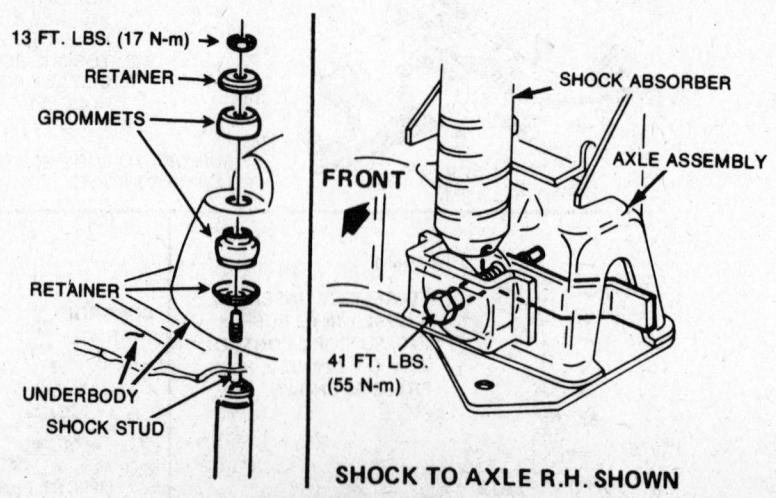

SHOCK TO AXLE R.H. SHOWN
Shock absorber mounting

1. Raise and support the car on a hoist. Do not use a twin-post hoist. The swing arc of the axle may cause it to slip from the hoist when the bolts are removed. If a suitable hoist is not available, raise and support the car on jackstands, and use a jack under the axle.

2. Support the axle with a jack that can be raised and lowered.

3. Remove the brake hose attaching brackets (right and left), allowing the hoses to hang freely. Do not disconnect the hoses.

4. Remove both shock absorber lower attaching bolts from the axle.

5. Lower the axle. Remove the coil spring and insulator.

6. To install, position the spring and insulator on the axle. The leg on the upper coil of the spring must be parallel to the axle, facing the lefthand side of the car.

7. Install the shock absorber bolts. Tighten to 41 ft. lbs. Install the brake line brackets. Tighten to 8 ft. lbs.

Rear Hub and Bearing

REMOVAL & INSTALLATION

1. Loosen the wheel lug nuts. Raise and support the car and remove the wheel.
2. Remove the brake drum.

NOTE: Do not hammer on the brake drum to remove; damage to the bearing will result.

3. Remove the four hub and bearing retaining bolts and remove the assembly from the axle. The top rear attaching bolt will not clear the brake shoe when removing the hub and bearing assembly. Partially remove the hub and bearing assembly prior to removing this bolt.

4. Installation is the reverse. Hub and bearing bolt torque is 39 ft. lbs.

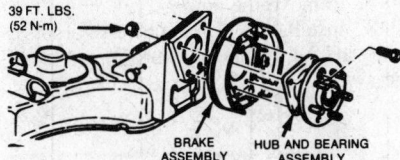

Rear hub and bearing

STEERING

All J-cars except the Cimarron use an aluminum-housed Saginaw manual rack and pinion steering gear as standard equipment. The pinion is supported by and turns in a sealed ball bearing at the top and a pressed-in roller bearing at the bottom. The rack moves in bushings pressed into each end of the rack housing.

Wear compensation occurs through the action of an adjuster spring which forces the rack against the pinion teeth. This adjuster eliminates the need for periodic pin-ion preload adjustments. Preload is adjustable only at overhaul.

The inner tie rod assemblies are bolted to the front of the rack. A special bushing is used, allowing both rocking and rotating motion of the tie rods.

Any service other than replacement of the outer tie rods or the boots requires removal of the unit from the car.

The power rack and pinion steering gear is optional on the Cavalier, J-2000, Skyhawk and Firenza while it is standard equipment on the Cavalier CL and the Cimarron; it is an integral unit and shares most features with the manual gear. A rotary control valve directs the hydraulic fluid to either side of the rack piston. The integral rack piston is attached to the rack and converts the hydraulic pressure into left or right linear motion. A vane-type constant displacement pump with integral reservoir provides hydraulic pressure. No in-car adjustments are necessary or possible on the system, except for periodic belt tension checks and adjustments for the pump.

Steering Wheel

REMOVAL & INSTALLATION

Standard Wheel

1. Disconnect the negative cable at the battery.

2. Pull the pad from the wheel. The horn lead is attached to the pad at one end; the other end of the pad has a wire with a spade connector. The horn lead is disconnected by pushing and turning; the spade connector is simply unplugged.

3. Remove the retainer under the pad (if so equipped).

4. Remove the steering shaft nut.

5. There should be alignment marks already present on the wheel and shaft. If not, matchmark the parts.

6. Remove the wheel with a puller.

7. Install the wheel on the shaft, aligning the matchmarks. Install the shaft nut and tighten to 30 ft. lbs.

8. Install the retainer.

9. Plug in the spade connector, and push and turn the horn lead to connect. Install the pad. Connect the negative battery cable.

Sport Wheel

1. Disconnect the negative cable at the battery.

2. Pry the center cap from the wheel.

3. Remove the retainer (if so equipped).

4. Remove the shaft nut.

5. If the wheel and shaft do not have factory-installed alignment marks, matchmark the parts before removal of the wheel.

6. Install a puller and remove the wheel. A horn spring, eyelet and insulator are underneath; don't lose the parts.

7. Install the spring, eyelet and insulator into the tower on the column.

8. Align the matchmarks and install the wheel onto the shaft. Install the retaining nut and tighten to 30 ft. lbs.

9. Install the retainer. Install the center cap. Connect the negative battery cable.

Turn Signal Switch

REMOVAL & INSTALLATION

1. Remove the steering wheel. Remove the trim cover.

2. Pry the cover from the steering column.

3. Position a U-shaped lockplate compressing tool on the end of the steering shaft and compress the lock plate by turning the shaft nut clockwise. Pry the wire snap-ring out of the shaft groove.

4. Remove the tool and lift the lockplate off the shaft.

5. Slip the cancelling cam, upper bearing preload spring, and thrust washer off the shaft.

6. Remove the turn signal lever. Remove the hazard flasher button retaining screw and remove the button, spring and knob.

7. Pull the switch connector out of the mast jacket and tape the upper part to facilitate switch removal. Attach a long piece of wire to the turn signal switch connector. When installing the turn signal switch, feed this wire through the column first, and then use this wire to pull the switch connector into position. On tilt wheels, place the turn signal and shifter housing in low position and remove the harness cover.

8. Remove the three switch mounting screws. Remove the switch by pulling it

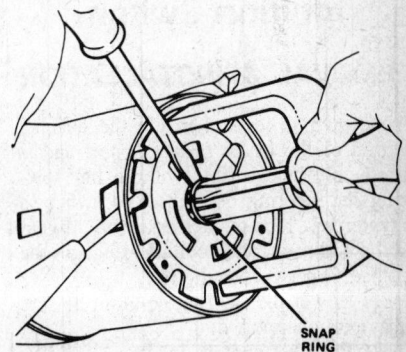

Depress the lockplate and remove the snap ring

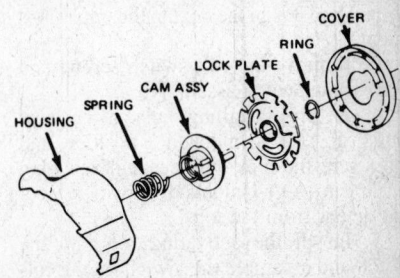

Remove these parts to get at the turn signal switch

straight up while guiding the wiring harness cover through the column.

9. Install the replacement switch by working the connector and cover down through the housing and under the bracket. On tilt models, the connector is worked down through the housing, under the bracket, and then the cover is installed on the harness.

10. Install the switch mounting screws and the connector on the mast jacket bracket. Install the column-to-dash trim plate.

11. Install the flasher knob and the turn signal lever.

12. With the turn signal lever in neutral and the flasher knob out, slide the thrust washer, upper bearing preload spring, and cancelling cam onto the shaft.

13. Position the lock plate on the shaft and press it down until a new snap-ring can be inserted in the shaft groove. Always use a new snap-ring when assembling.

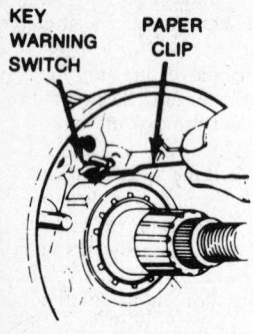

Remove the key warning buzzer switch with a paper clip

14. Install the cover and the steering wheel.

Ignition Switch

REMOVAL & INSTALLATION

The switch is located inside the channel section of the brake pedal support and is completely inaccessible without first lowering the steering column. The switch is actuated by a rod and rack assembly. A gear on the end of the lock cylinder engages the toothed upper end of the rod.

1. Lower the steering column; be sure to properly support it.

2. Put the switch in the "Off-Unlocked" position. With the cylinder removed, the rod is in "Off-Unlocked" position when it is in the next to the uppermost detent.

3. Remove the two switch screws and remove the switch assembly.

4. Before installing, place the new switch in "Off-Unlocked" position and make sure the lock cylinder and actuating rod are in "Off-Unlocked" position (second detent from the top).

5. Install the activating rod into the switch and assemble the switch on the column. Tighten the mounting screws. Use only the specified screws, since overlength

screws could impair the collapsibility of the column.

6. Reinstall the steering column.

Ignition Lock Cylinder

REMOVAL & INSTALLATION

1. Remove the steering wheel.

2. Turn the lock to the Run position.

3. Remove the lock plate, turn signal switch or combination switch, and the key warning buzzer switch. The warning buzzer switch can be fished out with a bent paper clip.

4. Remove the lock cylinder retaining screw and lock cylinder.

— CAUTION —

If the screw is dropped on removal, it could fall into the column, requiring complete disassembly to retrieve the screw.

5. Rotate the cylinder clockwise to align the cylinder key with the keyway in the housing.

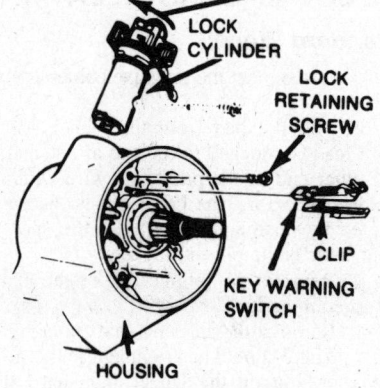

Lock cylinder installation

6. Push the lock all the way in.

7. Install the screw. Tighten to 15 in. lbs.

8. The rest of installation is the reverse of removal. Turn the lock to Run to install the key warning buzzer switch, which is simply pushed down into place.

Tie-Rod Ends

REMOVAL & INSTALLATION

1. Loosen both pinch bolts at the outer tie-rod.

2. Remove the tie-rod end from the strut assembly using a suitable removal tool.

3. Unscrew the outer tie-rod end from the tie-rod adjuster, counting the number of revolutions required before they are disconnected.

4. Install the new tie-rod end, screwing it on the same number of revolutions as

counted in Step 3. When the tie-rod end is installed, the tie-rod adjuster must be centered between the tie-rod and the tie-rod end, with an equal number of threads exposed on both sides of the adjuster nut. Tighten the pinch bolts to 20 ft. lbs.

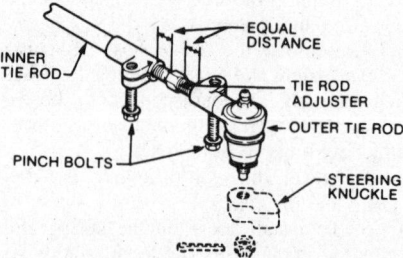

Tie rod end removal and installation

5. Install the tie-rod end to the strut assembly and tighten to 50 ft. lbs. If the cotter pin cannot be installed, tighten the nut up to $\frac{1}{16}$ in. further. *Never back off the nut to align the holes for the cotter pin.*

6. Have the front end alignment adjusted.

Power Steering Pump

REMOVAL & INSTALLATION

1. Disconnect the negative battery cable.

2. Disconnect the vent hose at the carburetor.

3. Loosen the adjusting bolt and pivot bolt on the pump, then remove the pump's drive belt.

4. Remove the three pump-to-bracket bolts and remove the adjusting bolt.

5. Remove the high pressure fitting from the pump.

6. Disconnect the reservoir-to-pump hose from the pump.

7. Remove the pump.

8. Installation is in the reverse order of removal. Adjust the belt tension and bleed the system.

Rack and Pinion Unit

REMOVAL & INSTALLATION

1. From the driver's side, remove the sound insulator.

2. From under the instrument panel, pull the seal assembly down from the steering column and remove the upper pinch bolt from the flexible coupling.

3. Remove the air cleaner and the windshield washer jar.

4. On power steering models: disconnect the pressure line from the steering gear and remove the screw securing the pressure line bracket to the cowl. Move the pressure line aside.

5. Raise and support the car on jackstands.

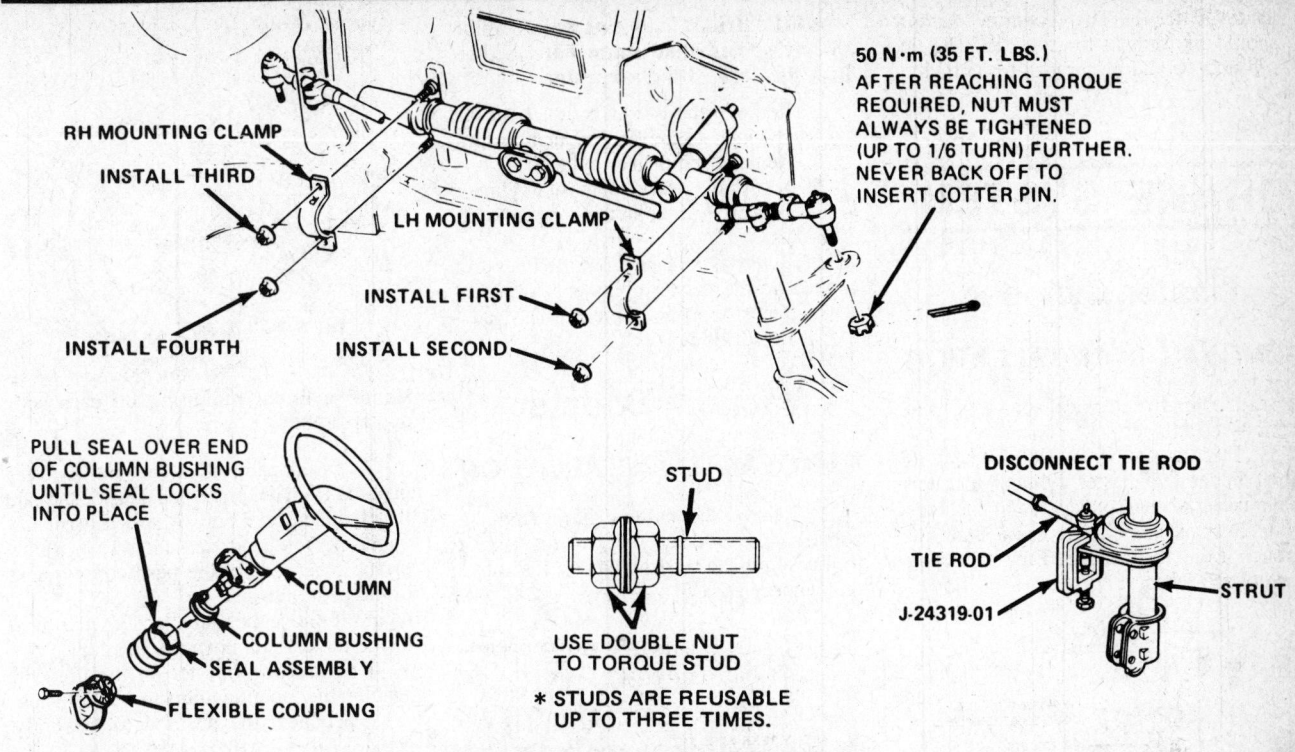

Manual rack and pinion unit mounting

6. Remove both front wheels.
7. Disconnect both tie rods from the struts.
8. Lower the car.
9. Remove the right side rack mounting clamp.
10. Remove the left side rack mounting clamp.
11. Move the gear forward slightly. On power steering models, disconnect the fluid return pipe from the gear.
12. Remove the lower pinch bolt from the flexible coupling and separate the rack from the coupling.
13. Remove the dash seal from the rack assembly.
14. Raise and support the car on jackstands.
15. Remove the splash shield from the inner, left fender.
16. Turn the left knuckle and hub assembly to the full left turn position and remove the rack and pinion assembly through the access hole on the left fender.

17. Installation is the reverse of removal. Note the following points:
   a. If the mounting studs backed out during removal, it will be necessary to reposition them prior to rack installation. Double-nut the stud so that it can be torqued to 15 ft. lb.
   b. It will be good to have a helper inside the car to guide the flexible coupling onto the stub shaft and onto the steering column.
   c. Both pinch bolts should be torqued

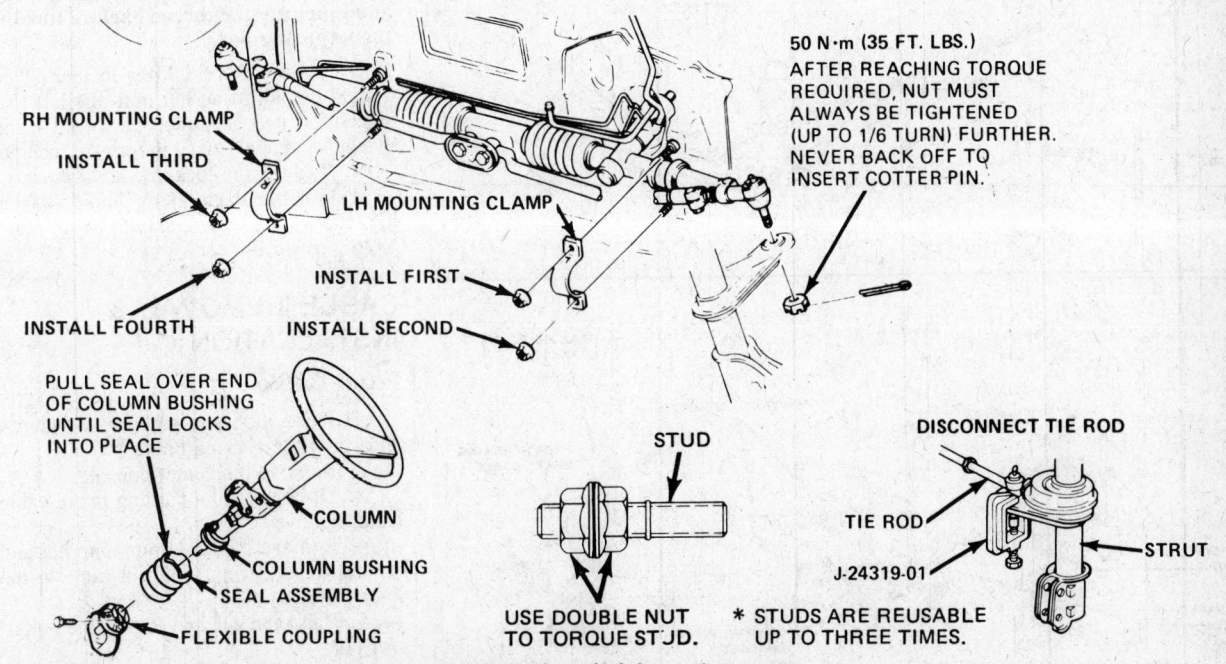

Power rack and pinion unit mounting

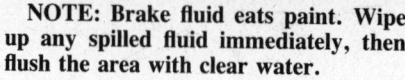
to 29-30 ft. lb. The mounting clamps should be torqued to 28 ft. lb. The tie rod nuts should be torqued to 35 ft. lb.

BRAKE SYSTEM

Master Cylinder

REMOVAL & INSTALLATION

1. Unplug the electrical connector from the master cylinder.
2. Place a number of cloths or a container under the master cylinder to catch the brake fluid. Disconnect the brake tubes from the master cylinder; use a flare nut wrench if one is available. Tape over open ends of the tubes.

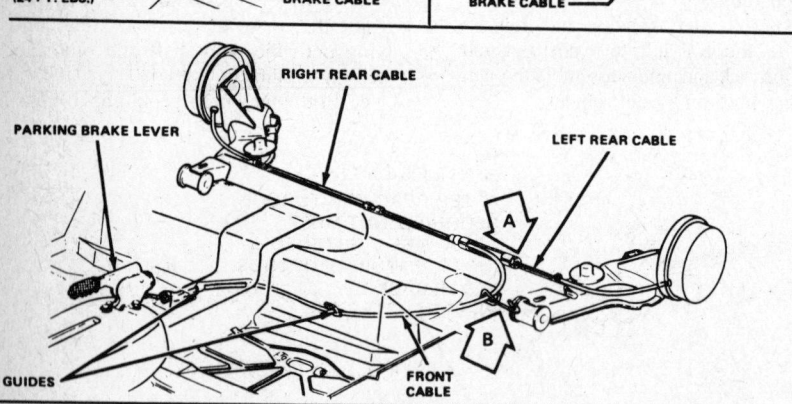

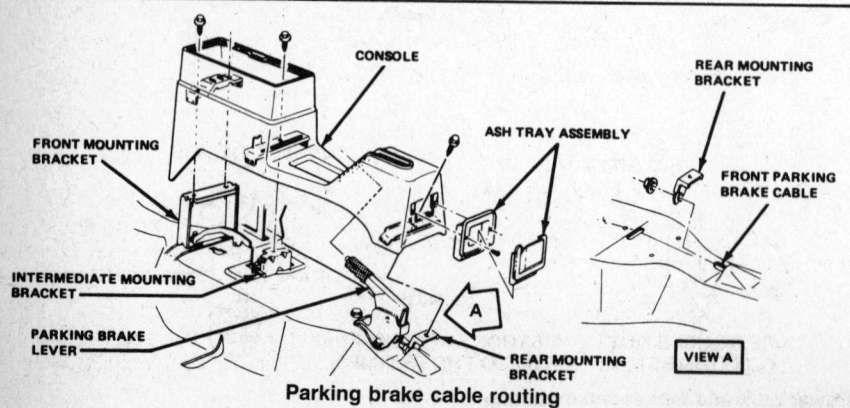

Parking brake cable routing

NOTE: Brake fluid eats paint. Wipe up any spilled fluid immediately, then flush the area with clear water.

3. Remove the two nuts attaching the master cylinder to the booster or firewall.
4. Remove the master cylinder.
5. To install, attach the master cylinder to the booster with the nuts. Torque to 22-30 ft. lbs.
6. Remove the tape from the lines and connect to the master cylinder. Torque to 10-15 ft. lbs. Connect the electrical lead.
7. Bleed the brakes.

Vacuum Booster

REMOVAL & INSTALLATION

1. Remove the master cylinder from the booster. It is not necessary to disconnect the lines from the master cylinder. Just move the cylinder aside.

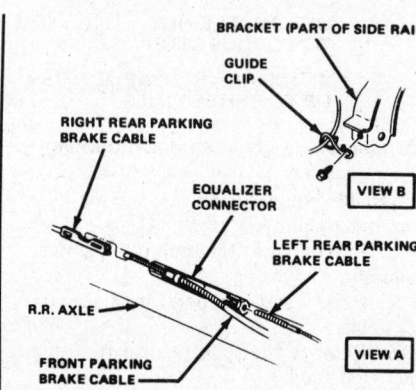

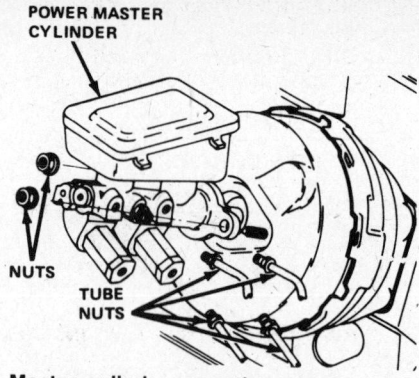

Master cylinder mounting on cars with power brakes

2. Disconnect the vacuum booster pushrod from the brake pedal inside the car. It is retained by a bolt. A spring washer is under the bolt head, and a flat washer goes on the other side of the pushrod eye, next to the pedal arm.
3. Remove the four attaching nuts from inside the car. Remove the booster.
4. Install the booster on the firewall. Tighten the mounting nuts to 22-33 ft. lbs.
5. Connect the pushrod to the brake pedal.
6. Install the master cylinder. Mounting torque is 22-33 ft. lbs.

Parking Brake

ADJUSTMENT

1. Raise and support the car with both rear wheels off the ground.
2. Pull the parking brake lever exactly two ratchet clicks.

NOTE: To prevent damage to the threaded adjusting rod, thoroughly clean and lubricate the threads before turning the adjusting nut.

3. Loosen the equalizer locknut, then tighten the adjusting nut until the left rear wheel can just be turned backward using two hands, but is locked in forward rotation.
4. Tighten the locknut.
5. Release the parking brake. Rotate the rear wheels—there should be no drag.
6. Lower the car.

CABLE REMOVAL & INSTALLATION

Front Cable

1. Place the gear selector in Neutral and apply the parking brake.
2. Remove the center console.
3. Disconnect the parking brake cable from the lever.
4. Remove the cable retaining nut and the bracket securing the front cable to the floor panel.
5. Raise the car and loosen the equalizer nut.
6. Loosen the catalytic converter shield

and then remove the parking brake cable from the body.

7. Disconnect the cable from the equalizer and then remove the cable from the guide and the underbody clips.

8. Reverse the procedure and adjust the ceble.

Right and Left Rear Cables

1. Raise and support the rear of the car.

2. Back off the equalizer nut until the cable tension is eliminated.

3. Remove the tires, wheels and brake drums.

4. Insert a screwdriver between the brake shoe and the top part of the brake adjuster bracket. Push the bracket to the front and then release the top brake adjuster rod.

5. Remove the rear hold down spring. Remove the actuator lever and the lever return spring.

6. Remove the adjuster screw spring.

7. Remove the top rear brake shoe return spring.

8. Unhook the parking brake cable from the parking brake lever.

9. Depress the conduit fitting retaining tangs and then remove the conduit fitting from the backing plate.

10. Remove the cable end button from the connector.

11. Depress the conduit fitting retaining tangs and remove the conduit fitting from the axle bracket.

12. Reverse the procedure to install and adjust the cable.

INSTRUMENT PANEL

Instrument Cluster

REMOVAL & INSTALLATION

1. Disconnect the negative battery cable.

2. Remove the right and left hush panels and the steering column trim cover. Disconnect the vent panels from the bottom of the panel (if so equipped).

3. Remove the glove box. Disconnect the temperature and mode control cables on cars without air conditioning. On cars with air conditioning, remove the lower A/C duct.

4. Remove the three steering column retaining bolts (two at the instrument panel pad and one at the cowl) and lower the steering column.

5. Remove the lower right hand trim plate. Disconnect the cigar lighter and accessory switches.

6. Pull the heater or A/C control head out far enough to disconnect any wiring or vacuum harnesses, then remove the head.

7. Disconnect the front end and engine

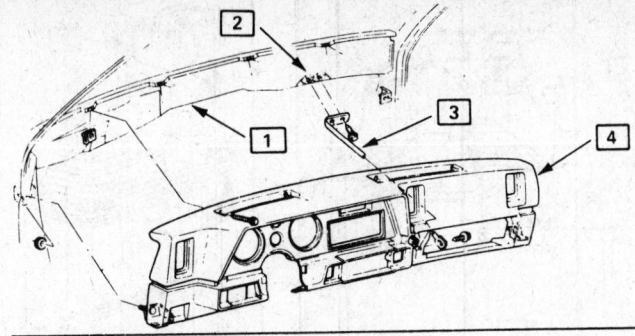

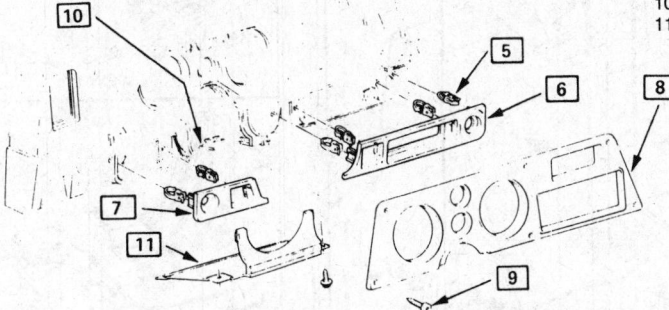

Instrument panel and trim plate mounting

1. Dash panel
2. Weld nuts
3. Center reinforcement
4. Pad
5. Snap-in clips
6. Right lower instrument panel trim plate
7. Left lower instrument panel trim plate
8. Instrument panel trim plate
9. Torx screw
10. Hush panel
11. Steering column trim cover

harnesses from the bulkhead connector in the engine compartment and then remove the bulkhead connector from the cowl (2) screws.

8. Loosen the set screw and remove the hood release handle. Unscrew the retaining nut and pull the hood release cable loose.

9. Unscrew the four upper instrument panel retaining screws (in the defroster duct openings).

10. Unscrew the two lower corner instrument panel retaining nuts. Remove the screw to the instrument panel brace from the left side of the glove box opening.

11. Pull the instrument panel out far enough to disconnect the ignition, the headlight dimmer switch and the turn signal switch. Tag and disconnect all other wiring and vacuum lines.

12. Remove the instrument panel with the wiring harness intact.

13. Installation is in the reverse order of removal.

Center Console

REMOVAL & INSTALLATION

Manual Transmission

1. Place the gear selector in Neutral and apply the parking brake.

2. Lift the ashtray out of the console and then remove the two screws in the opening.

3. Loosen the set screw underneath the shifter knob and remove the knob.

4. Remove the screw under the parking brake handle. Remove the two screws at the rear of the console and lift it off.

5. Installation is in the reverse order of removal.

Automatic Transmission

1. Place the gear selector in Neutral and apply the parking brake.

2. Lift out the ashtray from the front of the console and remove the two screws from the opening.

3. Gently pry the emblem out of the center of the shift knob and remove the snap ring that secures the knob. Remove the knob.

4. Lift the trim plate assembly out by pulling the front end up first. Disconnect the wiring harness.

5. Remove the three screws under the trim plate and then lift out the rear ashtray and remove the screw under it. Remove the console.

6. Installation is in the reverse order of removal.

Speedometer Cable

REPLACEMENT

1. Reach behind the instrument cluster and push the speedometer cable casing toward the speedometer while depressing the retaining spring on the back of the instrument cluster case. Once the retaining spring has released, hold it in while pulling outward on the casing to disconnect the casing from the speedometer.

NOTE: Removal of the steering column trim plate and/or the speedo cluster may provide better access to the cable.

2. Remove the cable casing sealing plug from the dash panel. Then, pull the casing down from behind the dash and remove the cable.

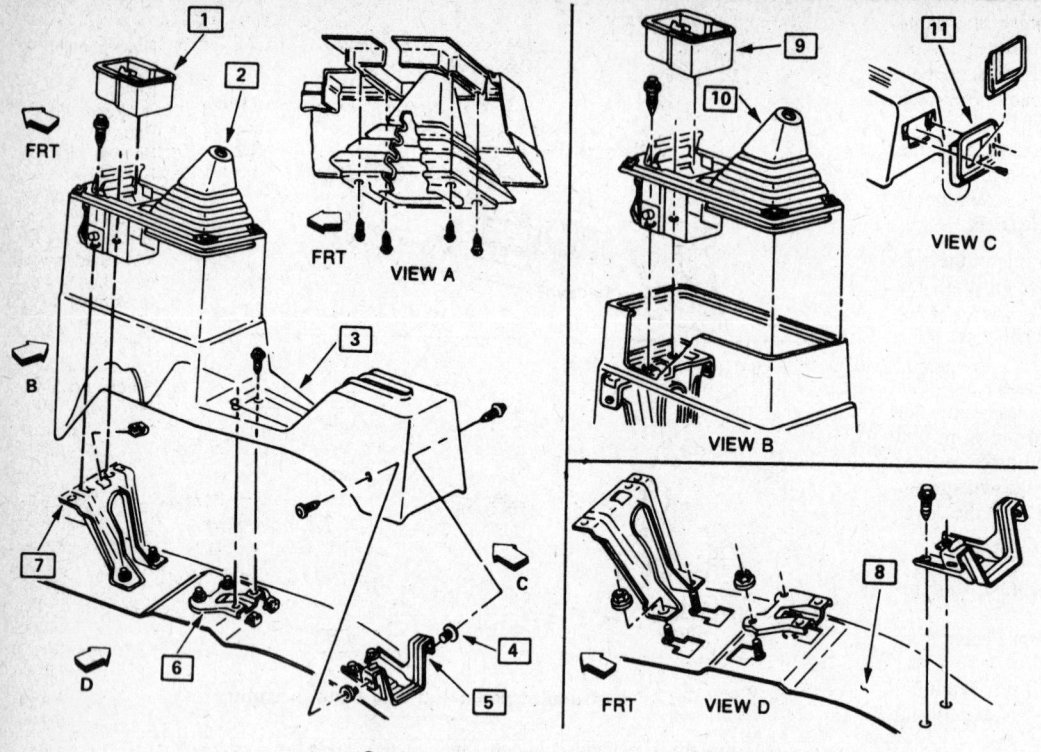

Center console mounting on cars with manual transaxle

1. Ash tray
2. Boot
3. Console
4. Push nut
5. Rear mounting bracket
6. Center mounting bracket
7. Front mounting bracket
8. Floor panel
9. Ash tray
10. Trimplate
11. Rear ash tray

VIEW C

VIEW B

FRT   VIEW D

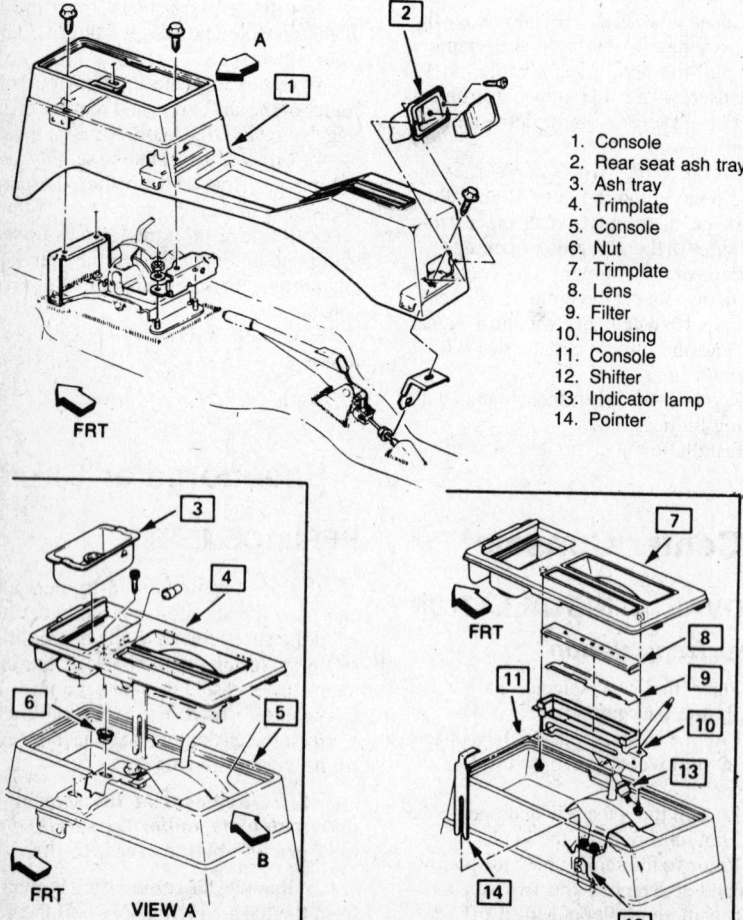

Center console mounting on cars with automatic transaxle

1. Console
2. Rear seat ash tray
3. Ash tray
4. Trimplate
5. Console
6. Nut
7. Trimplate
8. Lens
9. Filter
10. Housing
11. Console
12. Shifter
13. Indicator lamp
14. Pointer

VIEW A

VIEW B

3. If the cable is broken and cannot be entirely removed from the top, support the car securely, and then unscrew the cable casing connector at the transmission. Pull the bottom part of the cable out, and then screw the connector back onto the transmission.

4. Lubricate the new cable. Insert it into the casing until it bottoms. Push inward while rotating it until the square portion at the bottom engages with the coupling in the transmission, permitting the cable to move in another inch or so. Then, reconnect the cable casing to the speedometer and install the sealing plug into the dash panel.

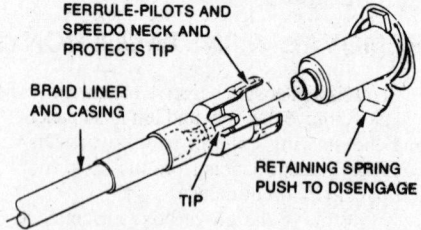

FERRULE-PILOTS AND SPEEDO NECK AND PROTECTS TIP

BRAID LINER AND CASING

RETAINING SPRING PUSH TO DISENGAGE

TIP

Speedometer cable attachment at the speedometer

WINDSHIELD WIPERS

Blade and Arm

REPLACEMENT

Removal of the wiper arms requires the use

of a special tool, G.M. J8966 or its equivalent. Versions of this tool are generally available in auto parts stores.

1. Insert the tool under the wiper arm and lever the arm off the shaft.

2. Disconnect the washer hose from the arm (if so equipped). Remove the arm.

3. Installation is in the reverse order of removal.

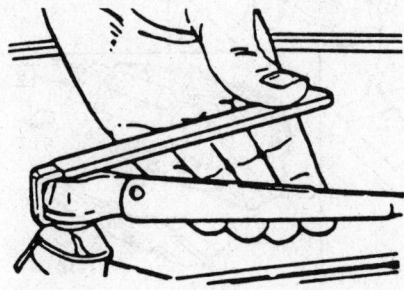

Removing the wiper arm with a special tool

The proper park position is at the top of the blackout line on the glass. If the wiper arms and blades were in the proper position prior to removal, adjustment should not be required.

ADJUSTMENT

The only adjustment for the wiper arms is to remove an arm from the transmission shaft, rotate the arm the required distance and direction and then install the arm back in position so it is in line with the blackout line on the glass. The wiper motor must be in the park position.

The correct blade-out wipe position on the driver's side is $1\frac{3}{32}$ in. (28mm) from the tip of the blade to the left windshield pillar moulding. The correct blade-down wipe position on the passenger side of the car is in line with the blackout line at the bottom of the glass.

Linkage

REMOVAL & INSTALLATION

1. Remove the wiper arms.
2. Remove the shroud top vent grille.
3. Loosen (but do not remove) the drive link-to-crank arm attaching nuts.
4. Unscrew the linkage-to-cowl panel retaining screws and remove the linkage.
5. Installation is in the reverse order of removal.

Wiper Motor

REMOVAL & INSTALLATION

1. Loosen (but do not remove) the drive

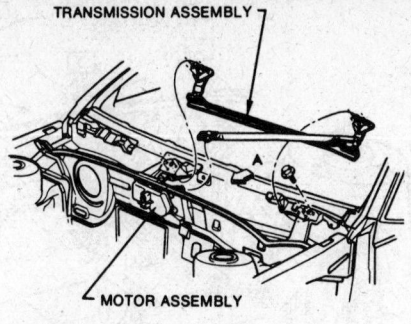

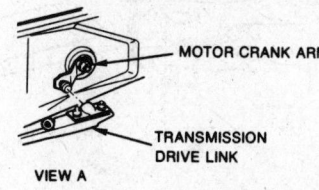

Wiper motor and linkage

link-to-crank arm attaching nuts and detach the drive link from the motor crank arm.

2. Tag and disconnect all electrical leads from the wiper motor.

3. Unscrew the mounting bolts, rotate the motor up and outward and remove it.

4. Guide the crank arm though the opening in the body and then tighten the mounting bolts to 4-6 ft. lbs.

5. Install the drive link to the crank arm with the motor in the park position.

6. Installation of the remaining components is in the reverse order of removal.

RADIO

REMOVAL & INSTALLATION

NOTE: Do not operate the radio with the speaker leads disconnected. Operating the radio without an electrical load will damage the output transistors.

1. Disconnect the negative battery cable.
2. Remove the instrument panel trim plate.
3. Check the right side of the radio to determine whether a nut or a stud is used for side retention.
4. If a nut is used, remove the hush panel and then loosen the nut from below on cars without air conditioning. On cars with air conditioning, remove the hush panel, the A/C duct and the A/C control head for access to the nut. Do not remove the nut; loosen it just enough to pull the radio out. If a rubber stud is used, go on to Step 5.
5. Remove the two radio bracket-to-instrument panel attaching screws. Pull the radio forward far enough to disconnect the wiring and antenna and then remove the radio.
6. Installation is in the reverse order of removal.

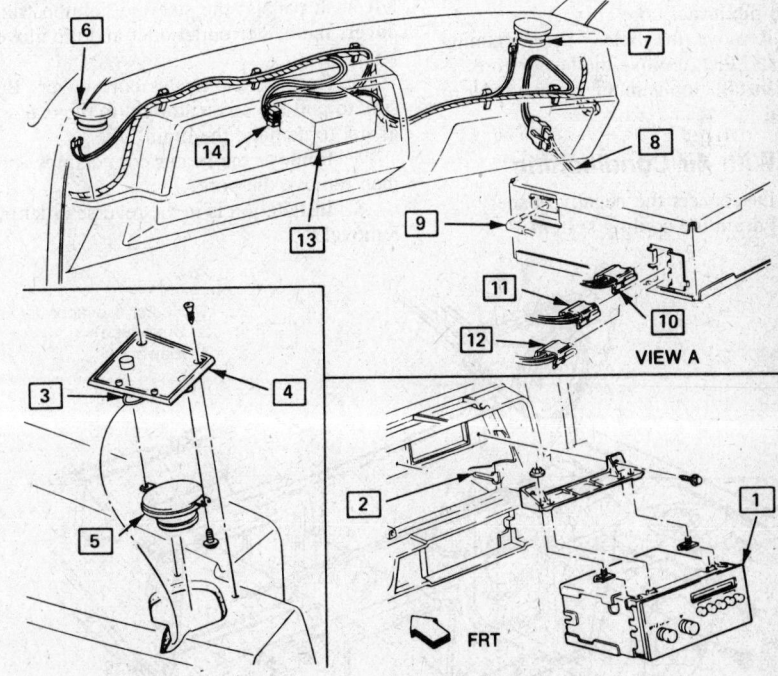

1. Radio
2. Screw on side of radio fits here
3. Retainer
4. Grille
5. Speaker
6. Front speaker
7. Front speaker
8. Rear speaker wire
9. Antenna
10. Rear speakers
11. Front speakers
12. Instrument panel harness
13. Receiver
14. Instrument panel harness

Radio removal and installation

HEATER

Blower Motor

REMOVAL & INSTALLATION

1. Disconnect the negative battery cable.
2. Disconnect the electrical connections at the blower motor and blower resistor.
3. Remove the plastic water shield from the right side of the cowl.
4. Remove the blower motor retaining screws and then pull the blower motor and cage out.
5. Hold the blower motor cage and remove the cage retaining nut from the blower motor shaft.
6. Remove the blower motor and cage.
7. Installation is in the reverse order of removal.

Heater Core

REMOVAL & INSTALLATION

Cars Without Air Conditioning

1. Disconnect the negative battery cable and drain the cooling system.
2. Remove the heater inlet and outlet hoses from the heater core.
3. Remove the heater outlet deflector.
4. Remove the retaining screws and then remove the heater core cover.
5. Remove the heater core retaining straps and then remove the heater core.
6. Installation is in the reverse order of removal.

Cars With Air Conditioning

1. Disconnect the negative battery cable and drain the cooling system.

1. Heater case
2. Stud dash panel
3. Locating studs dash panel
4. Heater core
5. Heater module
6. Module cover

Heater assembly on models without air conditioning

2. Raise and support the front of the vehicle.
3. Disconnect the drain tube from the heater case.
4. Remove the heater hoses from the heater core.
5. Lower the car. Remove the right and left hush panels, the steering column trim cover, the heater outlet duct and the glove box.
6. Remove the heater core cover. Be sure to pull the cover straight to the rear so as not to damage the drain tube.
7. Remove the heater core clamps and then remove the core.
8. Installation is in the reverse order of removal.

1. Heater & evaporator
2. Drain tube
3. Blower

Heater assembly on models with air conditioning

CIRCUIT PROTECTION

Fuses

All major electrical systems are protected by fuses. In the event of an overload, the fuse melts, protecting the component. If a fuse blows, the cause should be investigated before replacing the fuse. The fuse box is located under the left side of the instrument panel. The amperage of each fuse and the circuit it protects is stamped on the fuse box.

Fusible Links

A fusible link is a length (usually about 4 inches) of wire located in the circuit it protects. The wire is usually 4 gauge sizes smaller than the circuit wire it protects. In the event of a short or overload, the fusible link melts and stops the flow of current. Components fed directly from the battery are protected by a fusible link. Use only a fusible link of the correct gauge size when replacing a melted link.

Circuit Breakers

The headlights, windshield wipers, power door locks and power windows are protected by circuit breakers. The CB for the headlights is located in the headlight switch; the one for the wipers is located in the wiper switch; the ones for the power door locks and power windows are located in the fuse box. Breakers reset themselves automatically when the problem is relieved.

GM "P" Body
Pontiac Fiero

YEAR IDENTIFICATION

1984–85 Fiero

VEHICLE IDENTIFICATION NUMBER (VIN)

It is important for servicing and ordering parts to be certain of the vehicle and engine identification. The VIN (vehicle identification number) is a 17 digit number visible through the windshield on the driver's side of the dash and contains the vehicle and engine identification codes. It can be interpreted as follows:

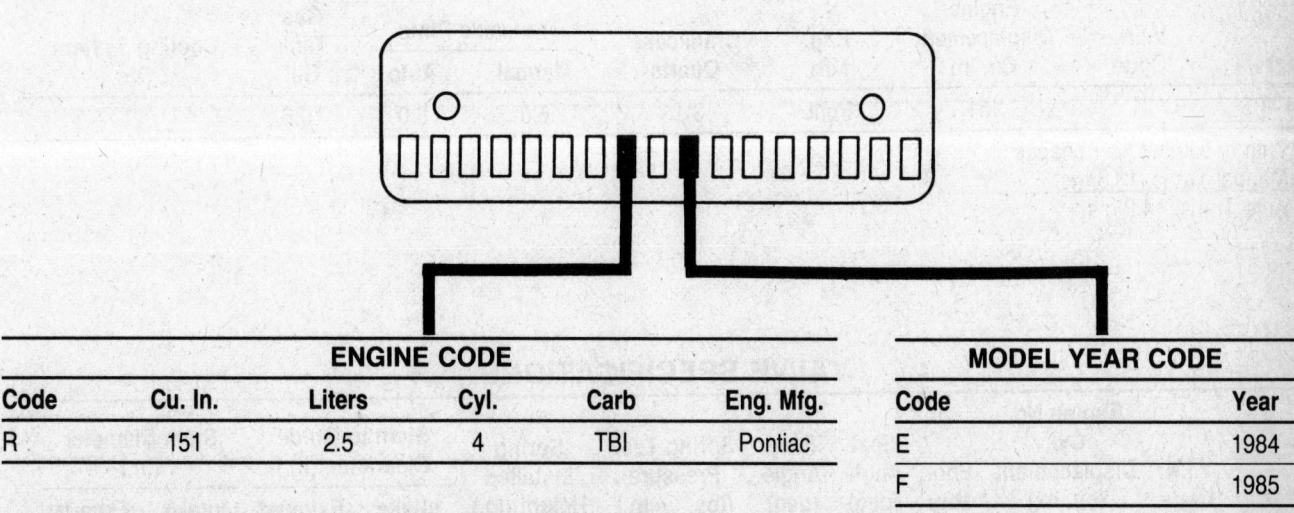

ENGINE CODE						MODEL YEAR CODE	
Code	Cu. In.	Liters	Cyl.	Carb	Eng. Mfg.	Code	Year
R	151	2.5	4	TBI	Pontiac	E	1984
						F	1985

The seventeen digit Vehicle Identification Number can be used to determine engine application and model year. The 10th digit indicates the model year, and the 8th digit identifies the factory installed engine.
TBI (Throttle body injection)

GENERAL ENGINE SPECIFICATIONS

Year	Eng. V.I.N. Code	Engine Displacement Cu. In.	Eng. Mfg.	Fuel Delivery	Horsepower @ rpm ■	Torque @ rpm (ft·lbs) ■	Bore × Stroke (in.)	Compression Ratio	Oil Pressure @ 2000 rpm
'84–'85	R	151	Pont.	TBI	90 @ 4000	132 @ 2800	4.000 × 3.000	9.0:1	36-41

TUNE-UP SPECIFICATIONS

(When analyzing compression test results, look for uniformity among cylinders rather than specific pressures.)

Year	V.I.N. Code	Eng. No. Cyl. Displ. Cu. in.	Eng. Mfg.	hp	Spark Plugs Orig Type	Gap (in.)	Ignition Timing (deg)▲ Man Trans	Auto Trans	Intake Valve Opens (deg)■	Fuel Pump Pressure (psi)	Idle Speed (rpm)▲ Man Trans	Auto Trans
'84–'85	R	151	Pont.	90	R44TSX	.060	①	①	33	6-8	①	①

NOTE: The underhood specifications sticker often reflects tune-up specification changes made in production. Sticker figures must be used if they disagree with those in this chart.

① See underhood sticker

FIRING ORDER

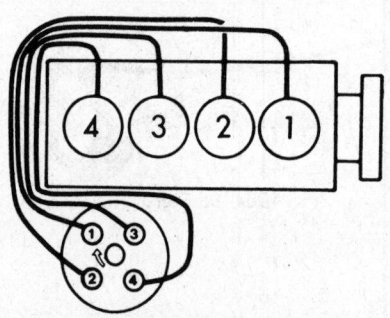

GM (Pontiac) 151-4 engine firing order: 1-3-4-2 Distributor rotation: clockwise

CAPACITIES

Year	V.I.N. Code	Engine Displacement Cu. In.	Eng. Mfg.	Crankcase Quarts	Transaxle Pints Manual	Auto	Gas Tank Gal	Cooling System Qts
'84–'85	R	151	Pont.	3①	6.0	8.0	10.5	②

① With or without filter change
② Manual Trans. 13.8 qts.
Auto Trans. 14.2 qts.

VALVE SPECIFICATIONS

Year	V.I.N. Code	Engine No. Cyl. Displacement (cu. in.)	Eng. Mfg.	Seat Angle (deg)	Face Angle (deg)	Spring Test Pressure (lbs. @ In.)	Spring Installed Height (in.)	Stem to Guide Clearance (in.) Intake	Exhaust	Stem Diameter (in.) Intake	Exhaust
'84–'85	R	4-151	Pont.	45	45	176 @ 1.254	1.69	0.0010–0.0027	0.0010–0.0027	0.3418–0.3425	0.3418–0.3425

CRANKSHAFT AND CONNECTING ROD SPECIFICATIONS

(All measurements are given in inches)

Year	V.I.N. Code	Engine No. Cyl. Displacement (cu. in.)	Eng. Mfg.	Main Brg. Journal Dia.	Main Brg. Oil Clearance	Shaft End-Play	Thrust on No.	Journal Diameter	Oil Clearance	Side Clearance
'84–'85	R	4-151	Pont.	2.2995–2.3005	0.0005–0.0022	0.0035–0.0085	5	1.9995–2.0005	0.0005–0.0026	0.006–0.022

CAMSHAFT SPECIFICATIONS

(All measurements in inches)

Year	V.I.N. Code	Engine	Eng. Mfg.	Journal Diameter 1	2	3	4	5	Bearing Clearance	Lobe Lift Intake	Exhaust	Camshaft End Play
'84–'85	R	4-151	Pont.	1.869	1.869	1.869	—	—	0.0007–0.0027	0.398	0.398	0.0015–0.0050

PISTON AND RING SPECIFICATIONS

(All measurements are given in inches. To convert inches to metric units, refer to the Metric Information section.)

Year	V.I.N. Code	Engine Type/ Disp. cu. in.	Eng. Mfg.	Piston-to-Bore Clearance	Ring Gap Top Compression	Bottom Compression	Oil Control	Ring Side Clearance Top Compression	Bottom Compression	Oil Control
'84–'85	R	4-151	Pont.	0.0025–0.0033	0.010–0.022	0.010–0.027	0.015–0.055	0.002–0.003	0.002–0.003	snug

TORQUE SPECIFICATIONS

(All readings in ft. lbs.)

Year	V.I.N. Code	Engine No. Cyl. Displacement (cu. in.)	Eng. Mfg.	Cylinder Head Bolts	Rod Bearing Bolts	Main Bearing Bolts	Crankshaft Bolt	Flywheel to Crankshaft Bolts	Manifold Intake	Exhaust
'84–'85	R	4-151	Pont.	92	32	70	200	44	29	44

WHEEL ALIGNMENT SPECIFICATIONS

Year	Model	Caster Range (deg)	Pref Setting (deg)	Camber Range (deg)	Pref Setting (deg)	Toe-In (in.)	Steering Axis (deg) Inclination
'84–'85	All	3N-7P	5P	5/16N–1 5/16P	1/2P	1/16 ± 1/32	—

CHARGING SYSTEM

Test details can be found in the Charging and Starting Systems Unit Repair Section. The voltage regulator is a solid-state, non-adjustable unit integral with the alternator. The alternator must be disassembled to remove the regulator.

Refer to the Charging System segment of the Unit Repair Section for further information.

Alternator

REMOVAL & INSTALLATION

1. Disconnect the negative battery cable.
2. Remove the air cleaner.
3. Disconnect the upper strut mount.
4. Disconnect the generator adjusting bolts, upper adjusting bracket and drive belt.
5. Disconnect the wiring from the back of the generator.
6. Lower the generator mounting bracket and remove the generator from the bottom of the vehicle.
7. Installation is the reverse of removal.

STARTING SYSTEM

Starter motor troubleshooting and repairs are covered in "Charging and Starting" in the Unit Repair Section.

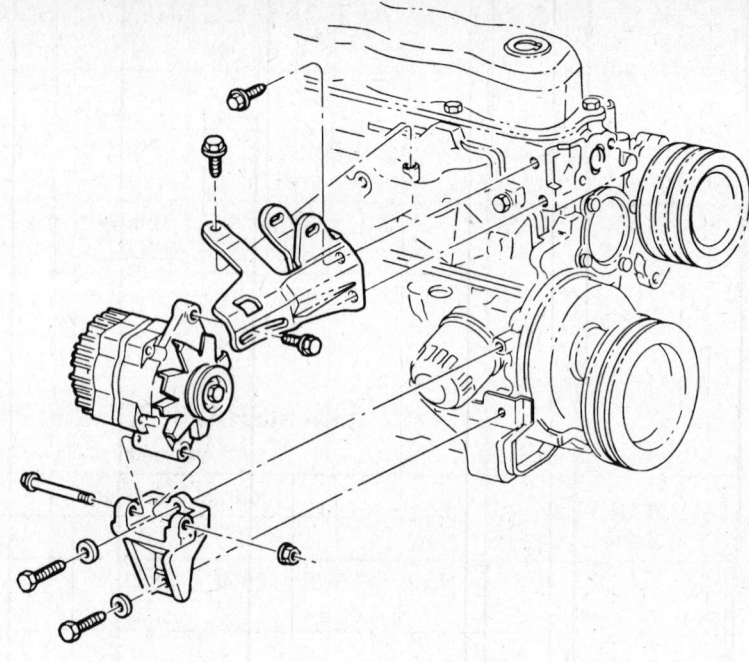

Generator mounting

Starter

REMOVAL & INSTALLATION

1. Disconnect battery ground cable.
2. Raise and support vehicle.
3. Disconnect all wires at solenoid terminals. Note color coding of wires for reinstallation.
4. Remove starter support mount bolts.
5. Loosen the front bracket bolt or nut and rotate bracket clear. Lower and remove starter. Note the location of any shims so that they may be replaced in the same positions upon installation.
6. Reverse procedure to install.

INTEGRAL VOLTAGE REGULATOR

An alternator with an integral voltage regulator is standard equipment. There are no adjustments possible with this unit; testing procedures will be found in the "Charging and Starting Systems" Unit Repair Section.

IGNITION SYSTEM

All models with gasoline engines are equipped with the HEI distributor and ignition system. This system uses no points and is, therefore, relatively maintenance free. See the Electronic Ignition section for unit description.

When using an auxiliary starter switch on HEI systems, the distributor BATT lead must be disconnected. Failure to do this may cause damage to the grounding circuit in the ignition switch.

Tachometer Hookup

The tachometer (TACH) terminal is next to the ignition switch (BAT) connector on the distributor cap.

— **CAUTION** —
Never ground the TACH terminal; serious module and ignition coil damage will result. If there is any doubt as to the correct tachometer hookup, check with the tachometer manufacturer.

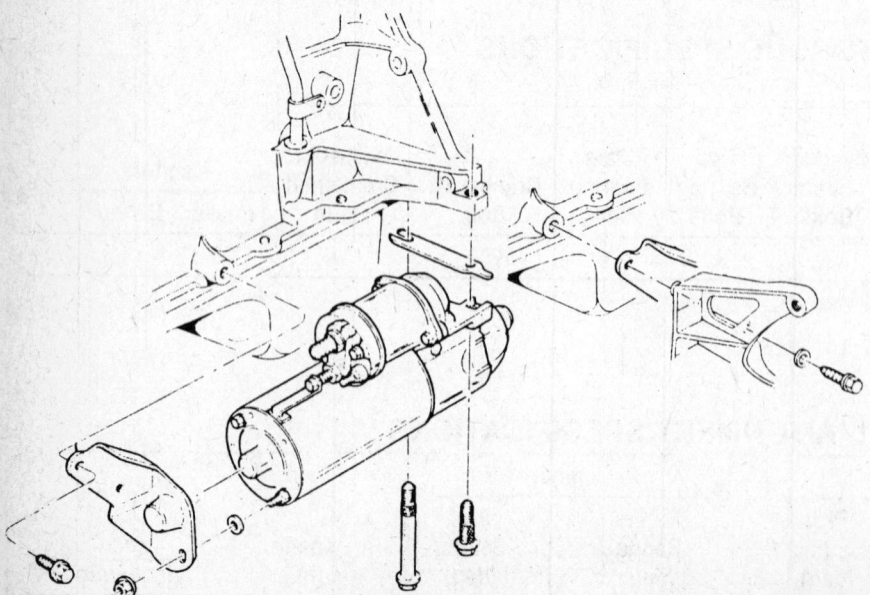

Starter motor mounting

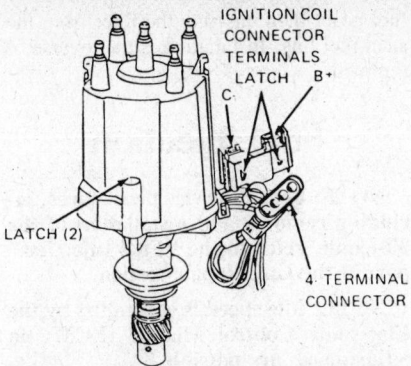

Typical distributor used with a separately mounted coil

Distributor

REMOVAL & INSTALLATION

1. Disconnect the negative battery cable.
2. Tag and disconnect all wires leading from the distributor cap.
3. Remove the external ignition coil.
4. Remove the distributor cap by turning the four latches counterclockwise. You will need a stubby screwdriver to get at the latches on the four cylinder engine, because there isn't much room between the distributor and the firewall. Remove the distributor cap and set it aside without disconnecting any of the wires.
5. Remove the vacuum hose from the vacuum advance unit. On 1980 models, mark the position of the vacuum advance unit in relation to the engine for correct installation.
6. The four cylinder engine has two bolts and a clamp. Remove the outer bolt first, then loosen, but do not remove, the inner bolt. Slide the clamp back and remove it.
7. Before removing the distributor, note the position of the rotor. Scribe a mark on the distributor body indicating the initial position of the rotor.
8. Remove the distributor from the engine. The drive gear on the distributor shaft is helical, and the shaft will rotate slightly as the distributor is removed. Note and mark the position of the rotor at this second position. Do not crank the engine with the distributor removed.
9. To install the distributor, rotate the distributor shaft until the rotor aligns with the second mark you made (when the shaft stopped moving). Lubricate the drive gear with clean engine oil, then install the distributor into the engine.
10. Install the clamp and hold-down bolt. Tighten them until the distributor can just be moved with a little effort.
11. Connect the ignition wire and tachometer wire, and install the distributor cap.
12. Set the timing.

INSTALLATION IF THE ENGINE WAS DISTURBED

If the engine was cranked while the dis-tributor was removed, you will have to place the engine on TDC of the compression stroke to obtain proper ignition timing.

1. Remove the No. 1 spark plug.
2. Place your thumb over the spark plug hole. Crank the engine slowly until compression is felt. It will be easier if you have someone rotate the engine by hand, using a wrench on the crankshaft pulley.
3. Align the timing mark on the crankshaft pulley with the 0° mark on the timing scale attached to the front of the engine. This places the engine at TDC of the compression stroke.
4. Turn the distributor shaft until the rotor points between the No. 1 and No. 3 spark plug towers on the cap for the four cylinder engine.
5. Install the distributor into the engine.
6. Perform Steps 9–11 of the preceding removal and installation procedure.

Ignition Timing

1. Connect a timing light to the No. 1 spark plug wire according to the light manufacturer's instructions. DO NOT PIERCE THE SPARK PLUG WIRE TO CONNECT THE TIMING LIGHT.
2. Follow the instructions on the underhood engine decal.
3. Disconnect the 4 terminal connector at the distributor.
4. Start the engine and run it at idle speed.
5. Aim the timing light at the degree scale just over the harmonic balancer.
6. Adjust the timing by loosening the securing clamp and rotating the distributor until the desired ignition advance is achieved, then tighten the clamp.
7. Loosen the distributor clamp outer bolt, the slide the clamp back slightly. Do not remove the retaining bolt.
8. Adjust the timing, then replace and tighten the clamp. To advance the timing, rotate the distributor opposite the normal direction of rotor rotation. Retard the timing by rotating the distributor in the normal direction of rotor rotation.

FUEL SYSTEM

The TBI (Throttle Body Injection) system used by the Fiero uses an electric fuel pump. This pump is located in the gas tank.

Fuel Pressure Relief Procedure

— CAUTION —

Before opening any part of the fuel system, the pressure must be relieved. Follow the procedure below to relieve the pressure:

1. Remove the fuel pump fuse from the fuse panel.
2. Start the engine and let it run until all fuel in the line is used.
3. Crank the starter an additional three seconds to relieve any residual pressure.
4. With the ignition OFF, replace the fuse.

Electric Fuel Pump

REMOVAL & INSTALLATION

1. Relieve the fuel system pressure (refer to procedure above).
2. Drain the fuel tank.
3. Disconnect wiring from the tank.
4. Remove the ground wire retaining screw from under the body.
5. Disconnect all hoses from the tank.

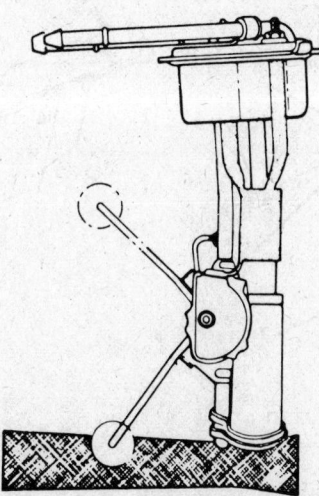

Typical electric fuel pump and sending unit

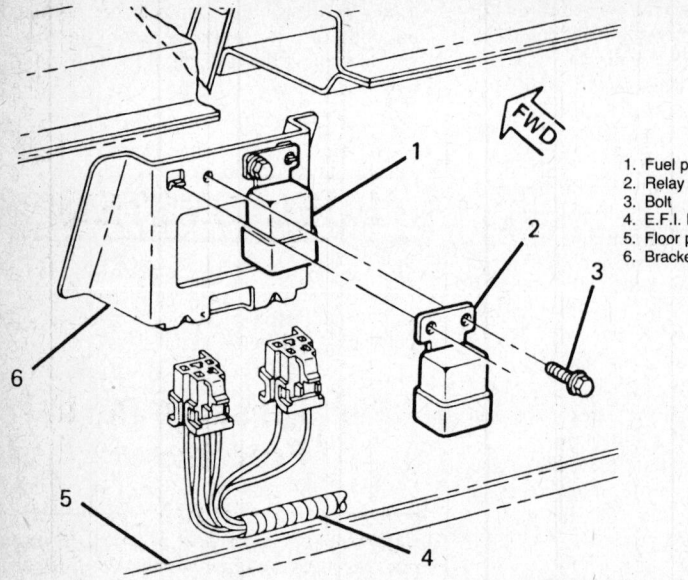

1. Fuel pump relay
2. Relay assy. (ac clutch control)
3. Bolt
4. E.F.I. harness
5. Floor pan
6. Bracket

Fuel pump relay location

6. Support the tank on a jack and remove the retaining strap nuts.
7. Lower the tank and remove it.
8. Remove the fuel gauge/pump retaining ring using a spanner wrench such as tool J-24187.
9. Remove the gauge unit and the pump.

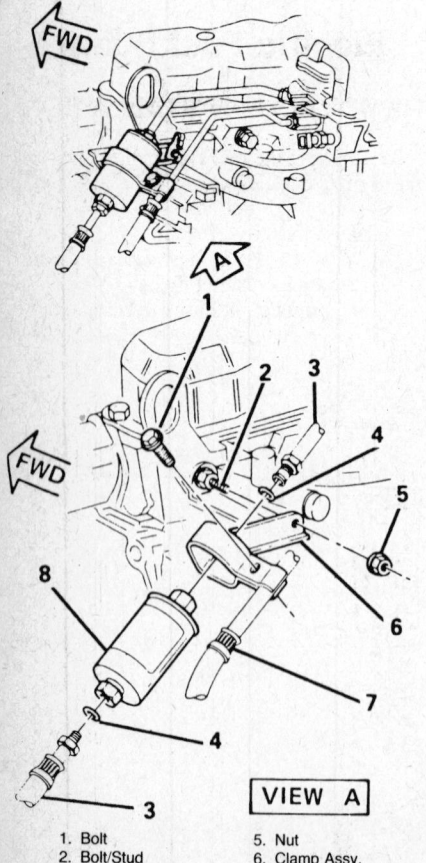

1. Bolt
2. Bolt/Stud
3. Fuel feed pipe
4. "O-ring
5. Nut
6. Clamp Assy.
7. Pipe Assy.
8. Filter Assy.

VIEW A

Fuel filter

10. Installation is the reverse of removal. Always replace the O-ring under the gauge/pump retaining ring.

Fuel Filter

REMOVAL & INSTALLATION

NOTE: Relieve fuel pressure (see caution above).

The filter is an inline unit ahead of the TBI unit. To remove the filter, make sure the engine is cold, unclamp and remove the fuel hose, then unscrew the filter from the steel fuel line. Installation is the reverse of removal.

Fuel Injection

NOTE: For all service procedures, including removal and installation of the TBI unit, refer to the "Fuel Injection" part of the Unit Repair section.

NOTE: Idle speed is controlled by the Electronic Control Module (ECM) no adjustments are possible.

COOLING SYSTEM

— CAUTION —
Keep hands, tools, and clothing away from engine cooling fan to help prevent personal injury. This fan is electric and can come on whether or not the engine is running. The fan can start automatically in response to a heat sensor with the ignition in the "On" position.

Radiator

REMOVAL & INSTALLATION

1. Drain the engine coolant.
2. Disconnect the wiring harness from the fan and fan frame.

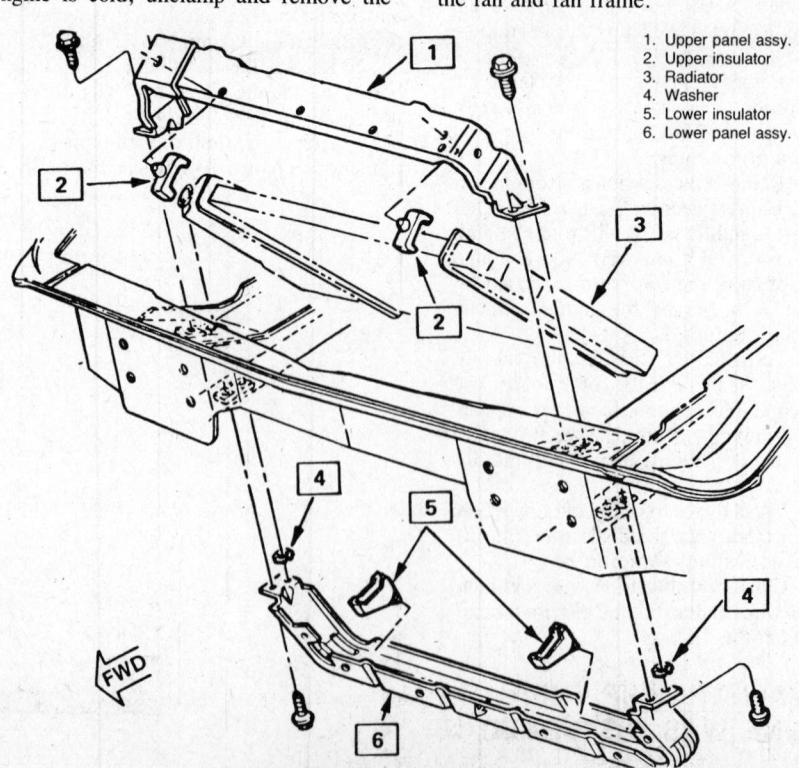

1. Upper panel assy.
2. Upper insulator
3. Radiator
4. Washer
5. Lower insulator
6. Lower panel assy.

Radiator and support

3. Remove the fan and frame assembly.

4. Disconnect the upper radiator support bracket.

5. Disconnect the coolant hoses at the radiator.

6. Disconnect the transmission/engine oil cooler lines at the radiator.

7. Remove the radiator from the car.

8. Installation is the reverse of removal. After installation run the engine and check for leaks.

Water Pump

REMOVAL & INSTALLATION

1. Disconnect battery negative cable.

2. Remove accessory drive belts.

3. Remove water pump attaching bolts and remove pump.

4. If installing a new water pump, transfer pulley from old unit. With sealing surfaces cleaned, place a ⅛ in. (3mm) bead of sealant #1052289 or equivalent on the water pump sealing surface. While sealer is still wet, install pump and torque bolts to 6 ft. lb.

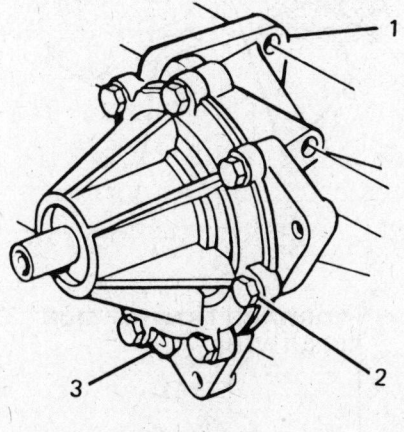

1. Body
2. Bolt
3. Housing

Water pump mounting

5. Install accessory drive belts.

6. Connect battery negative cable.

Thermostat

REMOVAL & INSTALLATION

1. Remove the thermostat cap.

2. Grasp the thermostat handle and gently pull up.

3. Before installing, clean the thermostat housing and O-ring. Apply a suitable lubricant to the O-ring for easier installation.

4. Push the thermostat down into the housing until it is properly seated and install the cap.

EMISSION CONTROLS

NOTE: For a description and service procedures for the following emission control systems, please refer to the Emission Control section of the Unit Repair section.

- Computer System
- Exhaust Gas Recirculation System
- Fuel Vapor Control System
- Exhaust Oxygen Sensor
- Coolant Sensor
- Manifold Pressure Sensor

ENGINE

REMOVAL & INSTALLATION

NOTE: The engine assembly is removed from underneath the vehicle.

1. Disconnect the battery cables.

2. Drain the engine coolant.

3. Remove the rear compartment lid.

NOTE: Do not remove the torsion rod retaining bolts.

4. Remove the air cleaner assembly.

5. Disconnect the throttle and shift cables.

6. Disconnect the heater hose at the intake manifold.

7. Disconnect vacuum hoses from all non engine components.

8. Disconnect the fuel lines and filter.

9. Disconnect the fuel pump relay and the oxygen sensor.

10. On models equipped with automatic transaxle, disconnect the transaxle cooler lines.

11. Disconnect the slave cylinder from the manual transaxle equipped vehicles.

12. Disconnect the engine to chassis ground strap.

13. Discharge the A/C system if so equipped then disconnect the A/C lines at the compressor and seal.

— CAUTION —
Do not disconnect any refrigerant lines unless you have experience with air conditioning systems. Escaping refrigerant will freeze any surface it contacts, including your skin and eyes.

14. Remove the rear console.

15. Remove the E.C.M. harness through the bulkhead panel.

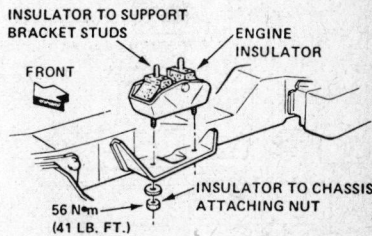

Engine mount to crossmember

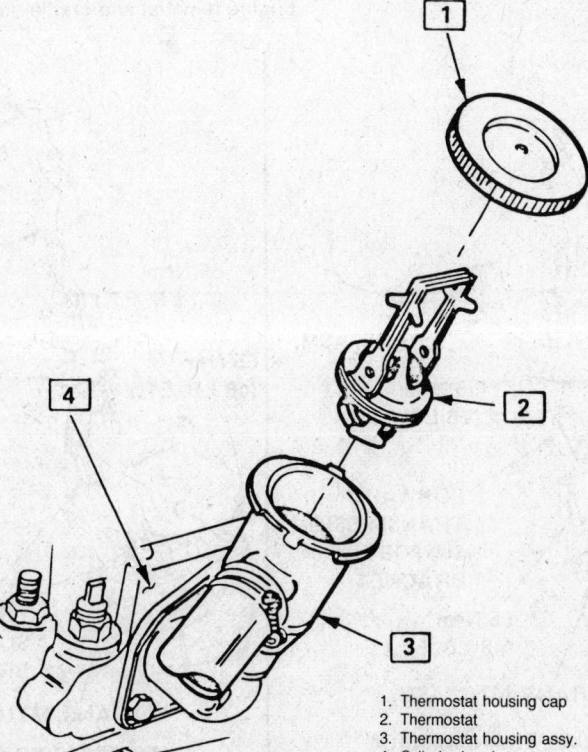

1. Thermostat housing cap
2. Thermostat
3. Thermostat housing assy.
4. Cylinder head

Thermostat and housing

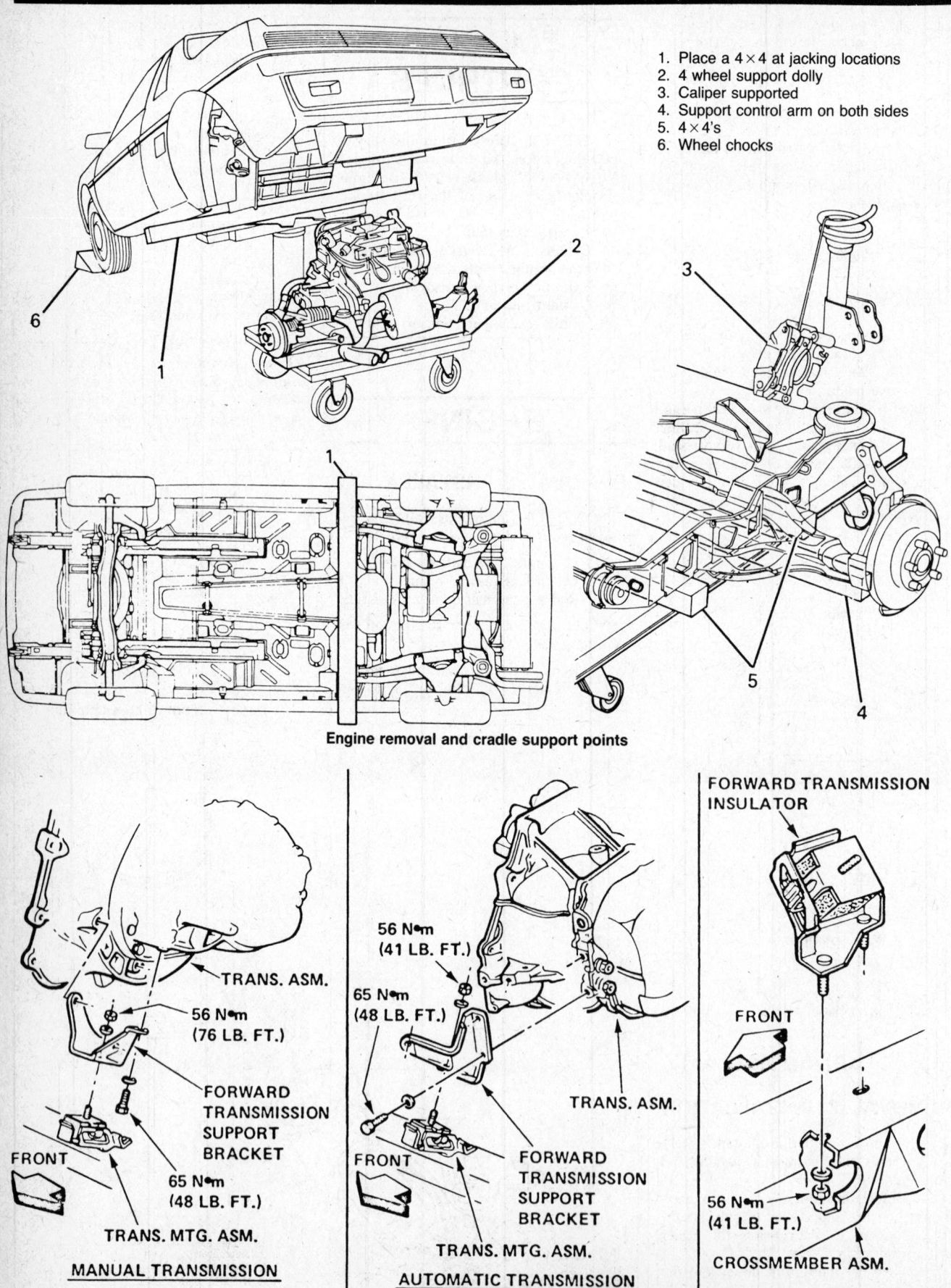

1. Place a 4 × 4 at jacking locations
2. 4 wheel support dolly
3. Caliper supported
4. Support control arm on both sides
5. 4 × 4's
6. Wheel chocks

Engine removal and cradle support points

TRANS. ASM.

56 N•m
(76 LB. FT.)

FORWARD
TRANSMISSION
SUPPORT
BRACKET

FRONT

65 N•m
(48 LB. FT.)

TRANS. MTG. ASM.

MANUAL TRANSMISSION

56 N•m
(41 LB. FT.)

65 N•m
(48 LB. FT.)

FRONT

TRANS. ASM.

FORWARD
TRANSMISSION
SUPPORT
BRACKET

TRANS. MTG. ASM.

AUTOMATIC TRANSMISSION

FORWARD TRANSMISSION
INSULATOR

FRONT

56 N•m
(41 LB. FT.)

CROSSMEMBER ASM.

Forward transaxle mount and mounting brackets

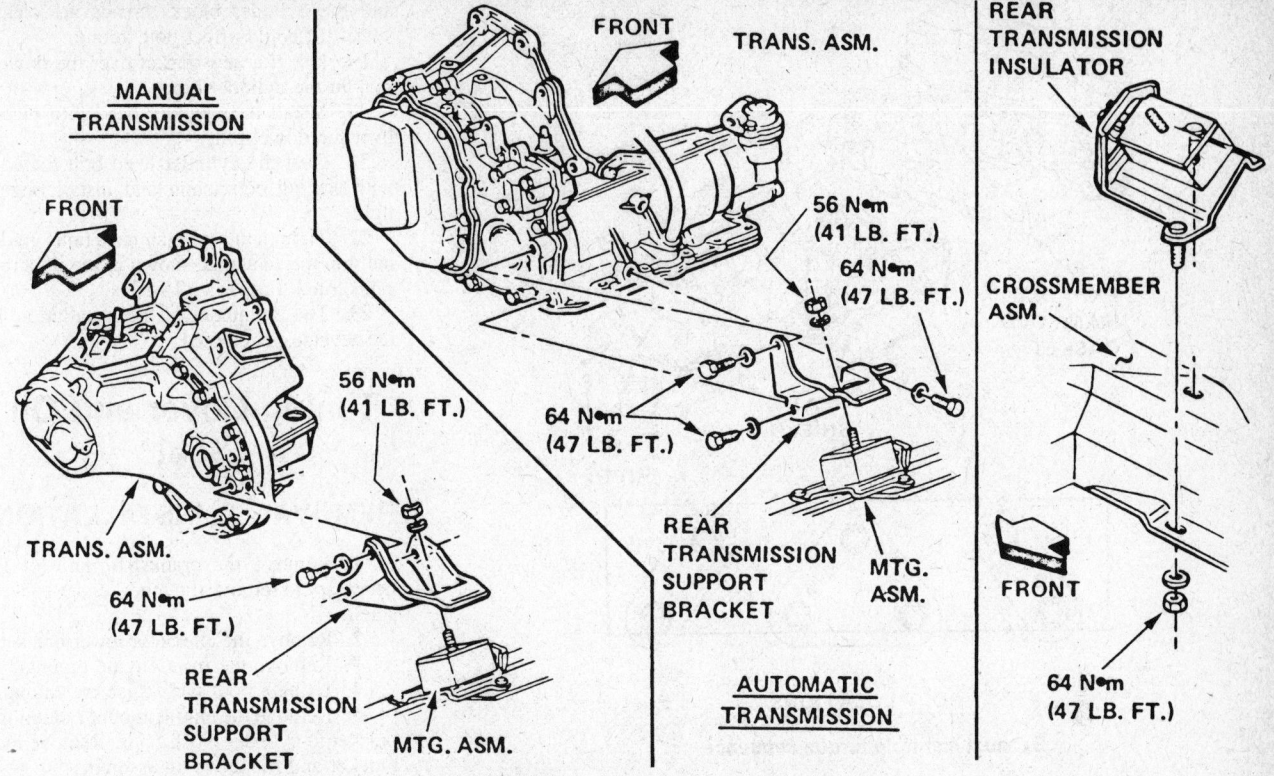

MANUAL TRANSMISSION

FRONT

TRANS. ASM.

56 N•m
(41 LB. FT.)

64 N•m
(47 LB. FT.)

REAR TRANSMISSION SUPPORT BRACKET

MTG. ASM.

FRONT

TRANS. ASM.

56 N•m
(41 LB. FT.)

64 N•m
(47 LB. FT.)

REAR TRANSMISSION SUPPORT BRACKET

MTG. ASM.

AUTOMATIC TRANSMISSION

REAR TRANSMISSION INSULATOR

CROSSMEMBER ASM.

FRONT

64 N•m
(47 LB. FT.)

Rear transaxle mount and mounting brackets

16. Install a engine support fixture.

17. Remove the engine strut bracket and mark the bolt and bracket for reassembly.

18. Raise the vehicle (see illustration).

19. Remove the rear wheels.

20. On models equipped with automatic transaxle, remove the torque converter bolts.

21. Remove the parking brake cable and calipers.

NOTE: Do not disconnect the brake hoses. Support the caliper out of the way.

22. Remove the strut bolts and mark the struts for realignment (refer to the "Strut Removal and Installation" procedure in the Front Suspension section).

23. Disconnect the A/C wiring, if so equipped.

24. Remove the four cradle bolts.

25. Use tool J-34065 to release the parking brake cables at the cradle.

─────── **CAUTION** ───────

Support the engine/transaxle and cradle assembly on a dolly. Be sure to support the outboard ends of the lower control arms. Disconnect the engine support fixture.

26. Raise the vehicle leaving the engine/transaxle and cradle assembly on the dolly.

27. Separate the engine and transaxle.

28. Installation is the reverse of removal.

Intake Manifold

REMOVAL & INSTALLATION

─────── **CAUTION** ───────

Relieve the pressure from the fuel system before disconnecting any fuel lines (refer to the Fuel System section).

1. Remove the air cleaner assembly.

2. Remove the PCV valve and hose.

3. Drain the cooling system.

4. Relieve the fuel system pressure and disconnect the fuel lines.

5. Disconnect the vacuum hoses.

6. Disconnect the wiring and the throttle linkage from the throttle body assembly.

7. Disconnect the cruise control and linkage, if so equipped.

8. Disconnect the throttle linkage and bell crank and place to one side.

9. Disconnect the heater hose.

10. Remove the generator upper bracket.

11. Remove the ignition coil.

12. Remove the retaining bolts and remove the manifold.

13. Installation is the reverse of removal. Torque all bolts in the sequence shown in the illustration. Torque the No. 7 bolt to 37 ft. lbs. and all others to 25 ft. lbs.

Exhaust Manifold

REMOVAL & INSTALLATION

1. Remove the air cleaner and the EFI bracket tube.

2. Raise the vehicle and support it with jack stands.

3. Remove the exhaust pipe and lower the vehicle.

4. Remove the retaining bolts and washers and remove the exhaust manifold and gasket.

5. Installation is the reverse of re-

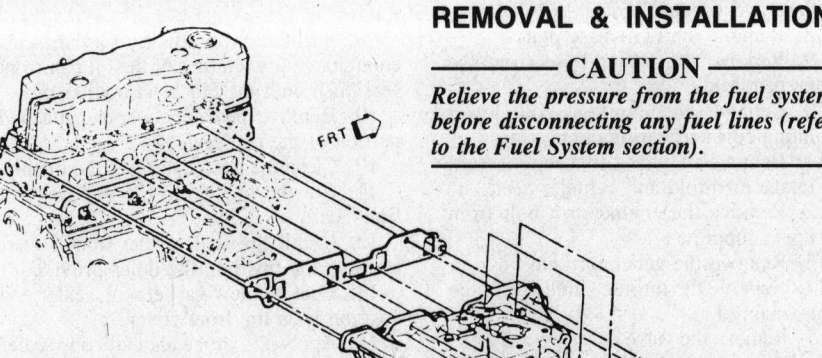

FRT

Intake manifold torque sequence

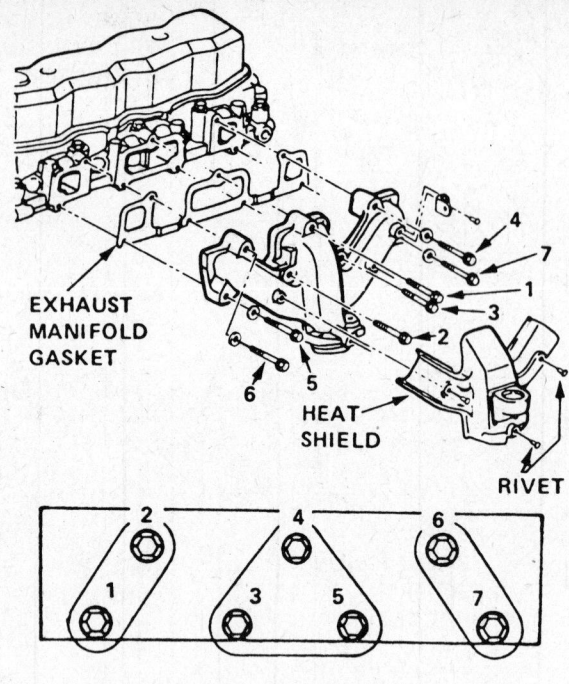

EXHAUST MANIFOLD GASKET

HEAT SHIELD

RIVET

BOLT LOCATIONS

Exhaust manifold torque sequence

moval. Clean the sealing surfaces and use a new gasket. Torque the retaining bolts to the sequence shown in the illustration. Torque bolts No. 3,4 and 5 to 37 ft. lbs. Torque bolts No. 1,2,6 and 7 to 16. ft. lbs.

Rocker Arm And Push Rod

REMOVAL & INSTALLATION

1. Remove the air cleaner.
2. Remove the PCV valve and hose.
3. Remove the valve cover bolts.
4. Disconnect the wires from the spark plugs and clips.
5. Remove the valve cover by tapping lightly with a rubber hammer.

NOTE: Prying on the cover could cause damage to the sealing surfaces.

6. Remove the rocker arm bolt and ball.
7. If replacing the push rod only, loosen the rocker arm bolt and swing the arm clear of the push rod.
8. Remove the rocker arm and push rod.
9. Installation is the reverse of removal. Torque the rocker arm bolt to 20 ft. lbs. Apply a continuous 3/16 in. diameter bead of RTV sealant or equivalent around the cylinder head sealant surfaces inboard at the bolt holes.

NOTE: Keep the sealant out of the bolt holes.

Valve Lash

No routine adjustment is necessary.

Cylinder Head

REMOVAL & INSTALLATION

1. Drain the cooling system.
2. Raise the vehicle and support safely with jack stands.
3. Remove the exhaust pipe.
4. Lower the vehicle.
5. Remove the oil level indicator tube.
6. Remove the air cleaner assembly.
7. Disconnect the E.F.I. electrical connections and vacuum hoses.
8. Remove the EGR base plate.
9. Remove the heater hose from the intake manifold.
10. Remove the ignition coil lower mounting bolt and wiring connections.
11. Remove all wiring connections from the intake manifold and cylinder head.
12. Remove the engine strut bolt from the upper support.
13. Remove the generator belt.
14. Remove the throttle cables from the intake manifold.
15. Remove the valve cover, rocker arms and push rods.
16. Remove the cylinder head bolts and remove the cylinder head.
17. Before installing, clean the gasket surfaces of the head and block.
18. Make sure the retaining bolt threads

and the cylinder block threads are clean since dirt could affect bolt torque.
19. Install a new gasket over the dowel pins in the cylinder block.
20. Install the cylinder head into place over the dowel pins.
21. Coat the cylinder head bolt threads with sealing compound and install finger tight.
22. Tighten the cylinder head bolts gradually in the sequence shown in the illustration. Final torque is 92 ft. lbs.
23. The remainder of the installation is the reverse of removal.

Timing Cover and Oil Seal

REMOVAL & INSTALLATION

1. Remove the crankshaft hub. It is necessary to remove the inner fender splash shield.
2. Remove the alternator lower bracket.
3. Remove the front engine mounts.
4. Using a floor jack, raise the engine.
5. Remove the engine mount mounting bracket-to-cylinder block bolts. Remove the bracket and mount as an assembly.
6. Remove the oil pan-to-front cover screws.

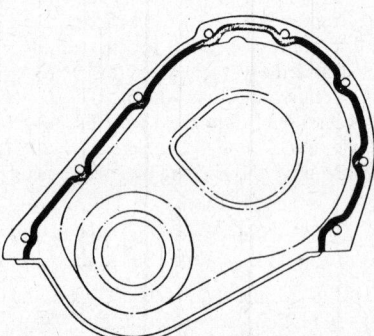

Timing cover sealer application

7. Remove the front cover-to-block screws.
8. Pull the cover slightly forward, just enough to allow cutting of the oil pan front seal flush with the block on both sides.
9. Remove the front cover and attached portion of the pan seal.
10. Clean the gasket surfaces thoroughly.
11. Cut the tabs from the new oil pan front seal.
12. Install the seal on the front cover, pressing the tips into the holes provided.
13. Coat the new gasket with sealer and position it on the front cover.
14. Apply a 1/8 in. bead of silicone sealer to the joint formed at the oil pan and block.
15. Align the front cover seal with a centering tool and install the front cover. Tighten the screws.
16. Install the hub and torque the hub bolt to 160 ft. lbs.

APPLY SEALING COMPOUND PART NUMBER 1052080 OR EQUIVALENT TO THREADS ON BOLTS SHOWN.

MOUNTING SURFACES OF BLOCK ASM., HEAD ASM. AND BOTH SIDES OF GASKET MUST BE FREE OF OIL AND FOREIGN MATERIAL.

NUMBERS SHOWN DESIGNATE BOLT POSITIONS AND BOLT TIGHTENING SEQUENCE.

FRONT

LOCATING PINS

Cylinder head torque sequence

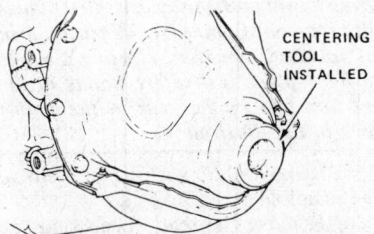

Front cover centering tool installed

CENTERING TOOL INSTALLED

NOTE: Coat the pulley to hub bolts with a locking sealant.

Camshaft And Timing Gear

REMOVAL

1. Remove the engine as previously described.
2. Install the engine on a stand.
3. Remove the rocker arm cover, loosen valve rocker arm bolts and pivot rocker arms clear of push rods.
4. Remove the distributor, and fuel pump.
5. Remove the push rod cover, push rods and valve lifters.
6. Remove the generator, lower generator bracket and front engine mount bracket assembly.
7. Remove the oil pump drive shaft and gear assembly.

8. Remove the front pulley hub and timing gear cover.
9. Remove the two camshaft thrust plate screws by working through holes in the camshaft gear.
10. Remove the camshaft and gear assembly by pulling it out through the front of the block. (Support shaft carefully when removing so as not to damage camshaft bearings.)
11. If the gear must be removed from the shaft, use press plate and adaptor J-971 on press.
12. Place tools on table of a press. Place the camshaft through the opening in the tools. Press shaft out of gear using socket or other suitable tool. Thrust plate must be so positioned that woodruff key in shaft does not damage it when the shaft is pressed out of gear.

INSTALLATION

1. To assemble camshaft gear, thrust

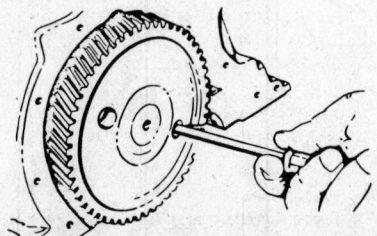

Removing camshaft thrust screws

plate and gear spacer ring to camshaft, proceed as follows:

   a. Firmly support shaft at back of front journal in an arbor press using press plate adaptors.

   b. Place gear spacer ring and thrust plate over end of shaft, and install woodruff key in shaft keyway.

   c. Install camshaft gear and press it onto the shaft until it bottoms against the gear spacer ring. The end clearance of the thrust plate should be 0.0015-0.0050 in. If less than .0015 in., the spacer ring should be replaced. If more than .0050 in., the thrust plate should be replaced.

2. Thoroughly coat the camshaft journals with a high quality engine oil supplement.
3. Install the camshaft assembly in the engine block, being careful not to damage bearings or cam.
4. Turn crankshaft and camshaft so that the valve timing marks on the gear teeth will line up. Engine is now in the number 4 cylinder firing position. Install camshaft thrust plate to block screws and tighten to 75 inch lbs. (10 Nm).
5. Install the timing gear cover and gasket.
6. Line up the keyway in hub with key on crankshaft and slide hub onto shaft. Install the center bolt and torque to 160 ft. lbs. (212 Nm).
7. Install as previously described valve lifters, push rods, push rod cover, oil pump shaft and gear assembly and fuel pump.

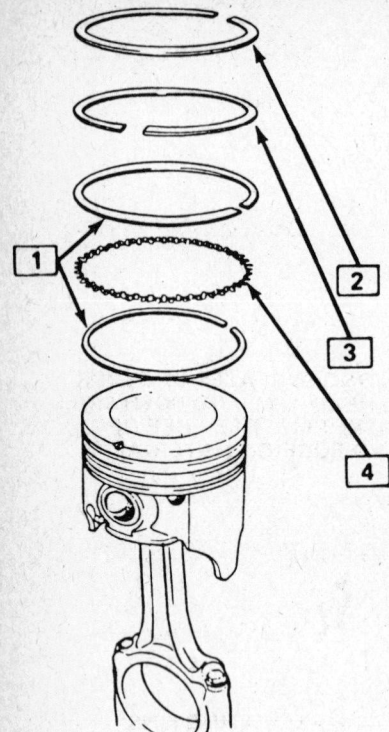

1. Oil rings
2. Top compression ring
3. Second compression ring
4. Expander

Typical piston and rod assembly

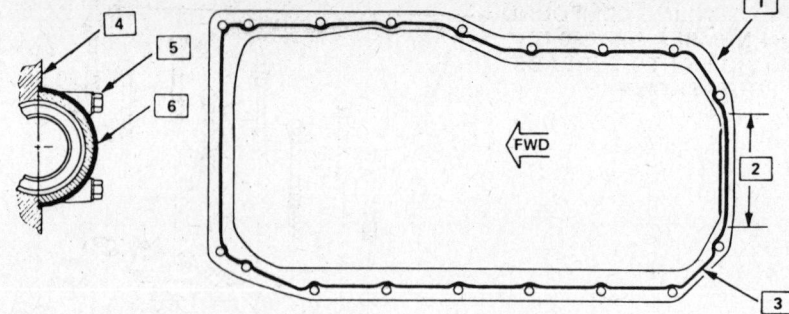

1. Oil pan
2. Apply a ⅜" thick bead of RTV sealer in area indicated
3. Apply a ³⁄₁₆" wide by ⅛" thick bead of RTV sealer in area indicated

4. Engine block assy.
5. Rear bearing
6. Groove in main bearing cap must be filled flush to ⅛" above surface with RTV

Oil pan sealer application

8. Install the distributor as follows:

a. Turn the crankshaft 360° to firing position of number one cylinder (number one exhaust and intake valve lifters both on base circle of camshaft and timing mark on harmonic balancer indexed with top dead center mark on timing pad).

b. Install the distributor in its original position and align shaft so that rotor arm points toward number one cylinder spark plug contact.

9. Pivot the rocker arms over push rods. With lifters on base circle of camshaft, tighten rocker arm bolt to 20 ft. lbs. (27 Nm). Do not over torque.

10. Install the front mount assembly lower generator bracket and generator.

11. Complete the engine installation as described earlier.

Piston and Connecting Rod Position

See the accompanying illustrations to properly install piston and connecting rod assemblies.

Align the piston and connecting rod assembly with the piston mark (notch) toward the front of the engine.

Oil Pan

REMOVAL & INSTALLATION

1. Remove the engine cradle.

NOTE: The cradle can be removed from the car without removing the engine or transaxle.

a. Using engine support fixture J-28467 or equivalent, raise the engine enough to take tension off of the engine mounts.

b. Raise the vehicle and support safely with jack stands.

—— CAUTION ——

If using a twin post hoist place safety stands at the rear most point (see illustration in the "Jacking" Section). If using a single post hoist place two safety stands in the front and two in the rear at the points shown in the illustration.

c. Remove the exhaust pipe bolts at the manifold.

d. Remove the rear wheels and tire assemblies.

e. Remove both lower control arms at the knuckle.

f. Remove both toe-link rods at the knuckle.

g. Remove the emergency brake cable at the cradle.

h. Remove the engine and transmission mounting bolts.

j. Remove the cradle bolts and remove the cradle assembly.

2. Drain the engine oil.

3. Remove the nuts from the engine mount to the support bracket.

4. Disconnect the exhaust pipe at the manifold and the rear transaxle mount.

5. Remove the starter and flywheel cover.

6. Remove the upper generator bracket.

7. Support the engine with Tool J28467 or equivalent.

8. Remove the lower generator bracket and engine support bracket.

9. Remove the oil pan retaining bolts and remove the oil pan.

10. Installation is the reverse of removal. Apply RTV sealer or equivalent as

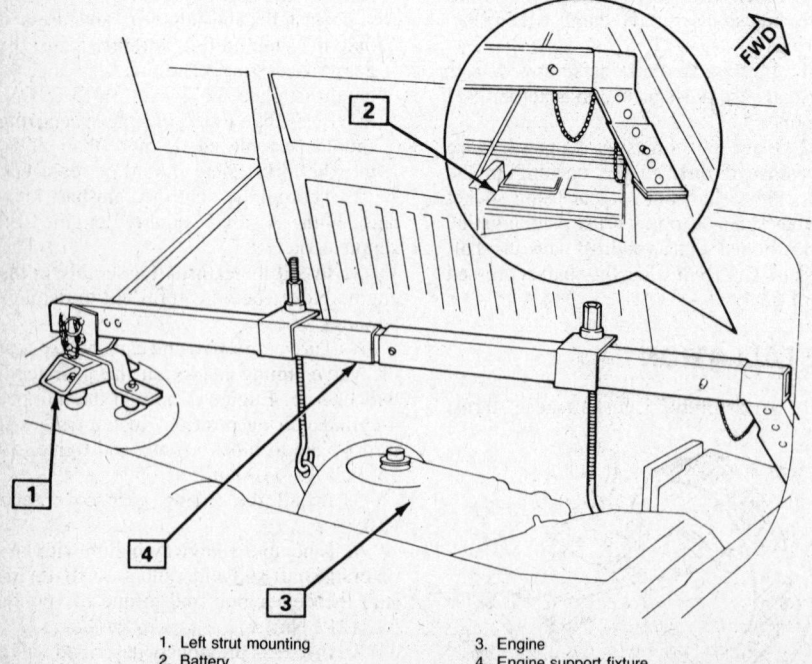

1. Left strut mounting
2. Battery
3. Engine
4. Engine support fixture

Engine holding fixture mounting

shown in the illustration. The two bolts in the timing gear cover should be installed last after the pan bolts are tight.

NOTE: When installing the engine cradle torque the following as indicated:
Rear cradle bolts 76 ft. lbs. (103 Nm).
Front cradle nut 67 ft. lbs. (90 Nm).
Engine mount assembly 42 ft. lbs. (57 Nm).
Rear mount assembly 18 ft. lbs. (24 Nm).
Front mount assembly 36 ft. lbs. (48 Nm).
Lower control arm at knuckle 33 ft. lbs. (45 Nm).
Lower control arm at cradle 69 ft. lbs. (93 Nm).

Oil Pump

REMOVAL & INSTALLATION

1. Remove the oil pan as described earlier.
2. Remove the two flange mounting bolts and the nut from the main bearing cap bolt.
3. Remove the pump and screen as an assembly.
4. Installation is the reverse of removal. Align the pump shaft with the drive shaft tang. Torque the pump retaining bolts to 20 ft. lbs.

Rear Main Oil Seal

REMOVAL & INSTALLATION

NOTE: This is a one piece seal and can be replaced without removal of the oil pan or crankshaft.

1. Remove the transaxle assembly.
2. Remove the flywheel.
3. If equipped with a manual transaxle, remove the pressure plate and disc.
4. Pry out the rear main seal.
5. Before installing, clean the block and crankshaft to seal mating surfaces.

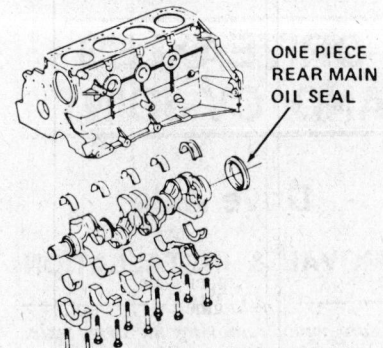

ONE PIECE REAR MAIN OIL SEAL

Crankshaft bearings and rear seal

6. Lubricate the outside of the seal for ease of installation and press into the block with fingers.

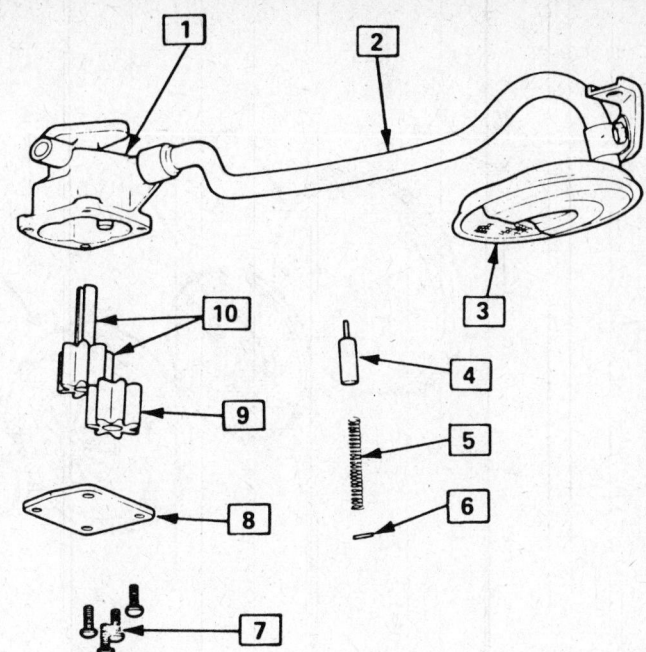

1. Pump body
2. Pickup tube
3. Pickup screen assy.
4. Pressure regulator valve
5. Pressure regulator spring
6. Spring retainer
7. Cover Screws
8. Cover
9. Idler gear
10. Drive gear and shaft

Oil pump - exploded view

7. Install the flywheel and torque the bolts to 44 ft. lbs.
8. Install the transaxle assembly.

Clutch

REMOVAL & INSTALLATION

1. Remove the transaxle.
2. Mark the pressure plate assembly and the flywheel so that they can be assembled in the same position. They were balanced as an assembly at the factory.
3. Loosen the attaching bolts one turn at a time until spring tension is relieved.
4. Support the pressure plate and remove the bolts. Remove the pressure plate and clutch disc. Do not disassemble the pressure plate assembly; replace it if defective.
5. Inspect the flywheel, clutch disc, pressure plate, throwout bearing and the clutch fork and pivot shaft assembly for wear. Replace the parts as required. If the flywheel shows any signs of overheating, or if it is badly grooved or scored, it should be replaced.
6. Clean the pressure plate and flywheel mating surfaces thoroughly. Position the clutch disc and pressure plate into the installed position, and support with a dummy shaft or clutch aligning tool. The clutch plate is assembled with the damper springs offset toward the transaxle. One side of the

factory-supplied clutch disc is stamped "Flywheel side".

7. Install the pressure plate-to-flywheel bolts. Tighten them gradually in a criss-cross pattern.
8. Lubricate the outside groove and the inside recess of the release bearing with high temperature grease. Wipe off any excess. Install the release bearing.
9. Install the transaxle.

Manual and Automatic Transaxle

REMOVAL & INSTALLATION

1. Remove the air cleaner assembly.
2. Disconnect the negative battery cable.
3. Disconnect the ground cable at the transaxle.
4. Disconnect the shift and select cable at the transaxle.
5. Remove the upper transaxle to engine bolts.
6. Install an engine support fixture J-28467 or equivalent.
7. Hoist the car and support if safely with jack stands.
8. Remove the rear wheels and tires.
9. Remove the axle shafts.
10. Remove the heat shield from the catalytic converter.

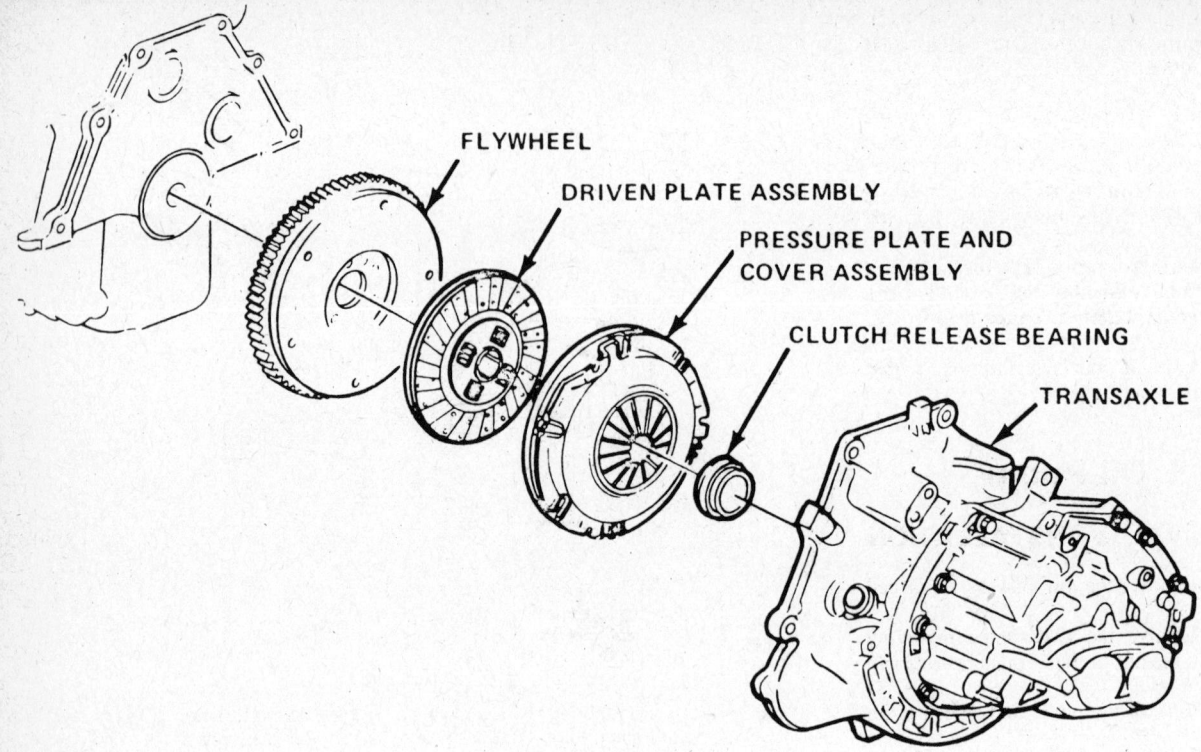

Exploded view of clutch assembly

FLYWHEEL

DRIVEN PLATE ASSEMBLY

PRESSURE PLATE AND
COVER ASSEMBLY

CLUTCH RELEASE BEARING

TRANSAXLE

11. Disconnect the exhaust pipe at the exhaust manifold.

12. Remove the engine mount to cradle nuts.

13. Support the cradle with an adjustable stand.

14. Remove the rear cradle to body bolts.

15. Remove the forward cradle to body through bolts.

16. Lower the cradle and move out of the way.

17. Remove the starter and inspection cover shields and remove the starter.

18. Remove the flywheel to converter bolts.

19. Disconnect and plug cooler lines, if equipped with Automatic Transaxle.

20. Position a transmission stand under the transaxle.

21. On manual transaxles, remove the lower transaxle to engine bolts and remove the transaxle.

22. On Automatic transaxles, remove the transaxle to support mounting bolts on the right side.
To install:

1. Install the starter and the inspection cover shields.

2. Hoist the cradle into position.

NOTE: Lower the cradle at the front and raise the car. Work cradle at rear into position on mounts then raise the front into position.

3. The remainder of the installation is the reverse of removal.
Torque the retaining nuts to the following specifications:
Starter to engine—32 ft. lbs. (43 Nm).

Front cradle to body nuts—67 ft. lbs. (90 Nm).
Rear cradle to body bolts—76 ft. lbs. (103 Nm).
Exhaust pipe to exhaust manifold—25 ft. lbs. (33 Nm).
Transaxle mounts to cradle nuts, rear—8 ft. lbs. (24 Nm), front—36 ft. lbs. (48 Nm).
Engine mount to cradle nuts—40 ft. lbs. (55 Nm).
Upper transaxle to engine bolts—55 ft. lbs. (75 Nm).
Cooler lines—20 ft. lbs. (27 Nm).
Support bracket-to-transaxle (automatic)—37 ft. lbs. (50 Nm).

MANUAL TRANSAXLE CABLE ADJUSTMENT

1. Disconnect the negative (1) battery cable.

2. Place the transaxle in first gear.

3. Loosen the shift cable attaching nuts (E) at transaxle levers (D) and (F).

4. Remove the console and trim plates as required for access to shifter.

5. With the shifter lever in first gear position (pulled to left and held against stop), insert alignment pins F and G as shown in view D.

6. Remove the lash from transaxle by first compressing select cable (B) and then tightening nut (E). Levers (D) and (F) should be kept from moving during this process. Similarly, shift cable (A) is first compressed and nut (E) then tightened. Again levers (D) and (F) remain stationary. Nut

(E) on levers (D) and (F) tightened to 20 ft. lbs. (27 Nm).

7. Ensure that the reverse inhibit cam is against roller and align if necessary.

8. Remove the alignment pins F and G at shifter assembly.

NOTE: While cycling from 1 to 2 and 2 to 1, the select cable should not move. Difficulty in shifting transaxle to reverse may be corrected by biasing select lever (D) inboard toward 1-3-R position during shift cable (A) adjustment.

NOTE: For linkage adjustment and fluid and filter change for automatic transaxles, please refer to Automatic Transmission in the Unit Repair section.

DRIVEAXLES AND CV-JOINT

Drive Axle

REMOVAL & INSTALLATION
———— CAUTION ————
Use care when removing the drive axle. Tri-pots can be damaged if the drive axle is over extended.

1. Remove the hub nut and discard.

2. Raise the car and remove the wheel and tire.

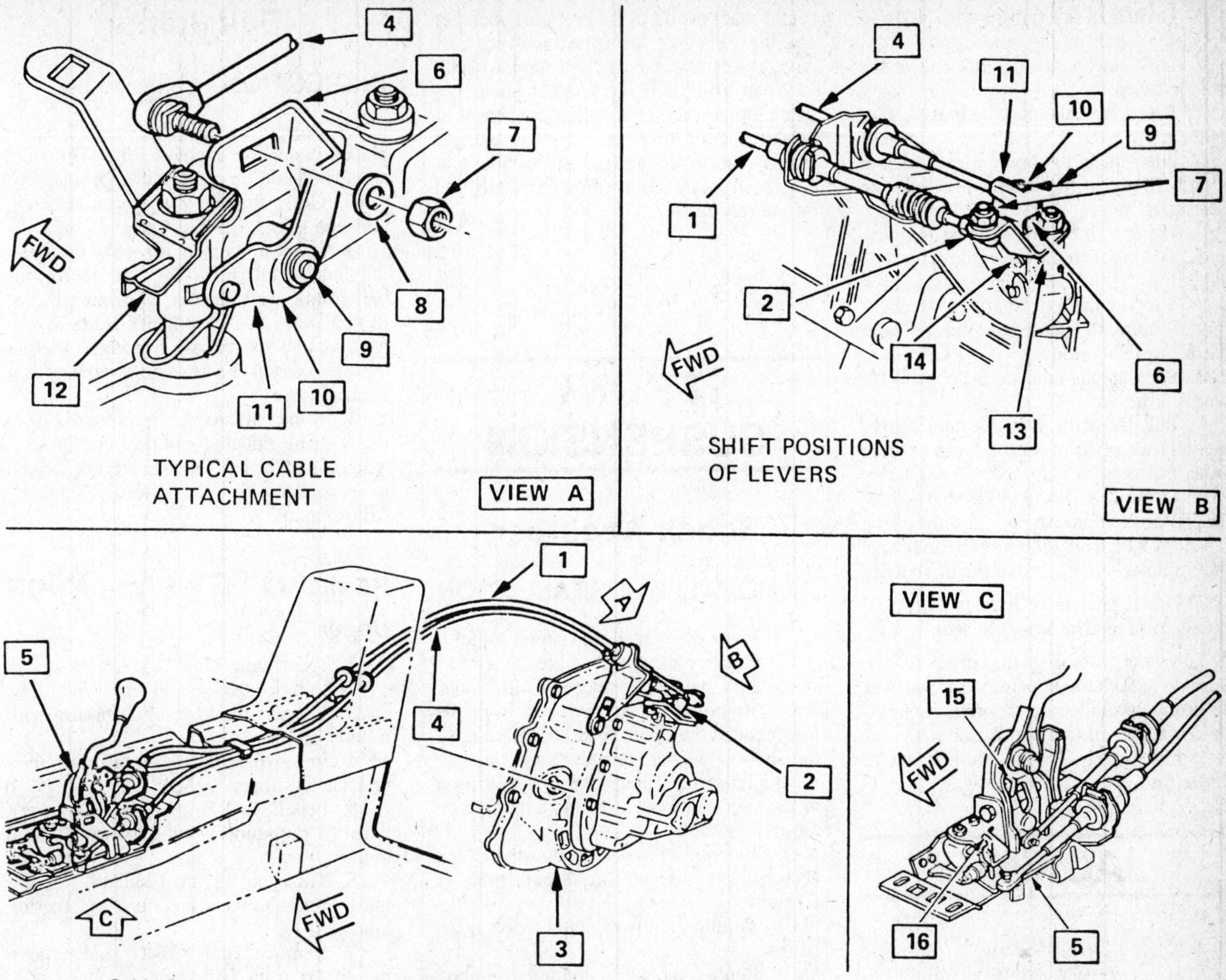

4
6
7
8
9
10
11
12
FWD
TYPICAL CABLE ATTACHMENT
VIEW A
4
11
10
9
7
1
2
14
6
13
FWD
SHIFT POSITIONS OF LEVERS
VIEW B
1
A
B
5
4
2
3
C
FWD
VIEW C
15
FWD
16
5

1. Cable A
2. Lever F
3. Tansaxle assy.
4. Cable B
5. Trans. control assy.
6. Lever D
7. Nut E
8. Washer P
9. R
10. 1st/2nd
11. 4th/3rd
12. Retainer clip J
13. R/3rd/1st
14. 2nd/4th
15. Alignment pin F
16. Alignment pin G

Manual transaxle cable adjustment

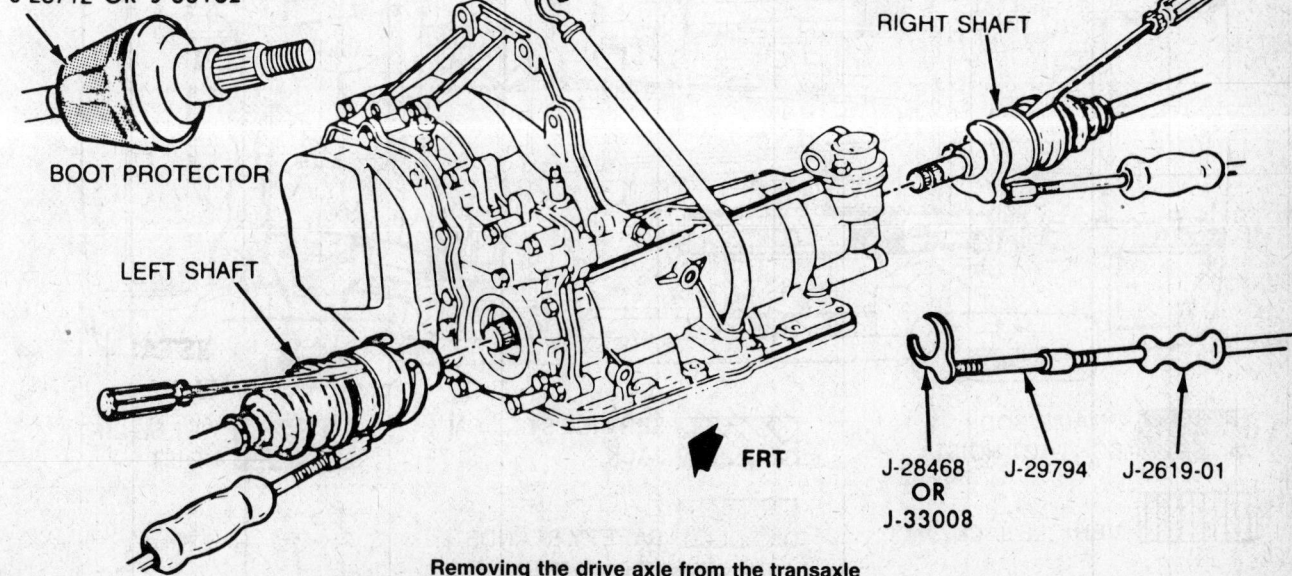

J-28712 OR J-33162
BOOT PROTECTOR
RIGHT SHAFT
LEFT SHAFT
FRT
J-28468
OR
J-33008
J-29794
J-2619-01

Removing the drive axle from the transaxle

3. Drive boot seal protector No. J-28712 or its equivalent on the outer seal.

4. Disconnect the toe link rod at the knuckle assembly.

5. Disconnect the parking brake cables at the cradle.

6. Disconnect the brake line bracket at the underbody in the inner wheel housing opening.

7. Using tool No. J-28733 or its equivalent, hub spindle remover, remove the axle shaft from the hub and bearing assembly.

8. Support the axle shaft.

9. Remove the clamp bolt from the lower control arm ball stud.

10. Separate the knuckle from the lower control arm.

11. Pull the strut, knuckle and caliper assembly away from the body and secure in this position.

12. Using tool No. J33008 and No. J-2619-01 or their equivalents, disengage the snap rings which are retaining the drive axle at the transaxle and remove the drive axle.

NOTE: If the drive axle is being replaced, replace the knuckle seal.

13. When installing the drive to the transaxle seat the axle using a screwdriver and groove provided on the inner retainer. The remainder of the installation is the reverse of removal. Torque the hub nut to 225 ft. lbs.

JACKING

When using a floor jack, lift on the center of the front and rear control arms, on the center rear portion of the rear crossmember and the center of the front crossmember. Always set parking brake and block wheels.

When using a frame contact hoist, position either rearward of the front wheel or forward of the rear wheel. When using a suspension contact hoist, position either under the front lower control arm or lifting on the rear tires.

FRONT SUSPENSION

Shock Absorber

REMOVAL & INSTALLATION

1. Raise the vehicle and support safely.
2. Remove the wheel and tire assembly.
3. Remove the two upper retaining bolts.
4. Remove the nut and bolt from the lower end of the shock absorber and remove the shock absorber from the vechicle.
5. To install, place the lower portion of the shock into position and hand tighten the nut and bolt.
6. Extend the shock up into the shock absorber support and torque both bolts to 20 ft. lbs.
7. Torque the lower nut and bolt to 20 ft. lbs.
8. Replace the wheel and tire assembly.

Ball Joints

INSPECTION

1. Raise the front of the car with a lift placed under the engine cradle. The front wheels should be clear of the ground.

2. Grasp the wheel at the top and bottom and shake the wheel in and out.

3. If any movement is seen of the steering knuckle relative to the control arm, the ball joints are defective and must be replaced. Note that movement elsewhere may be due to loose wheel bearings or other troubles; watch the knuckle-to-control arm connection.

4. If the ball stud is disconnected from the steering knuckle and any looseness is noted, often the ball joint stud can be twisted in its socket with your fingers, replace the ball joints.

REMOVAL & INSTALLATION
Upper

1. Raise the vehicle and support safely.
2. Remove the tire and wheel assembly.
3. Support the lower control arm with a floor jack.
4. Remove upper ball stud nut, then reinstall nut finger tight.
5. Install Tool J-26407 or equivalent with the cup end over the lower ball stud nut.
6. Turn the threaded end of J-26407 until upper ball stud is free of steering knuckle.
7. Remove Tool J-26407 and remove the nut from the ball stud.

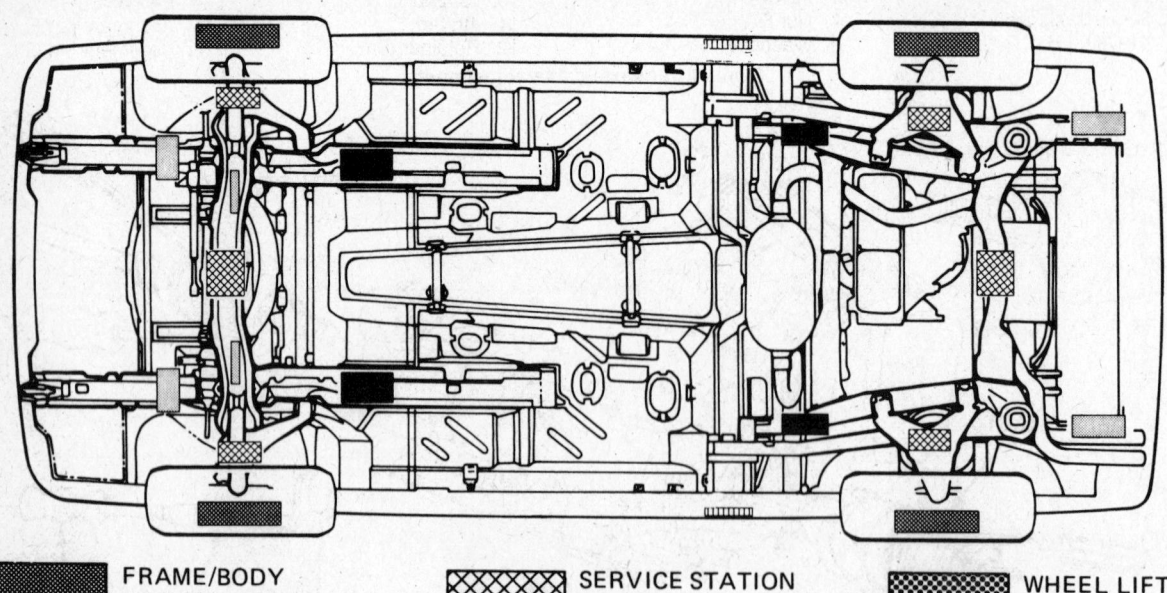

▮ FRAME/BODY CONTACT HOIST	▨ SERVICE STATION JACK	▨ WHEEL LIFT HOIST
▮ VEHICLE JACK	▨ SAFETY STANDS	

Body lifting points

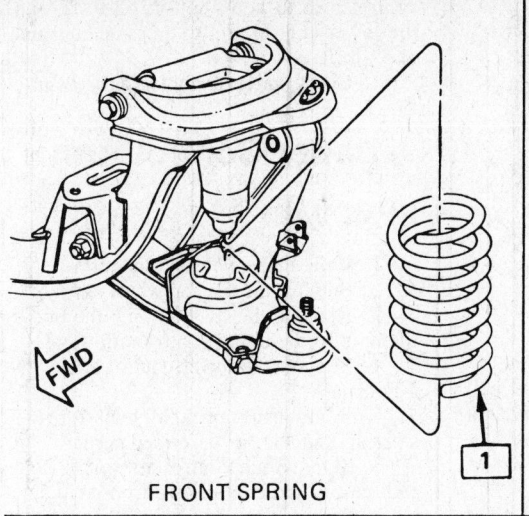

FRONT SPRING

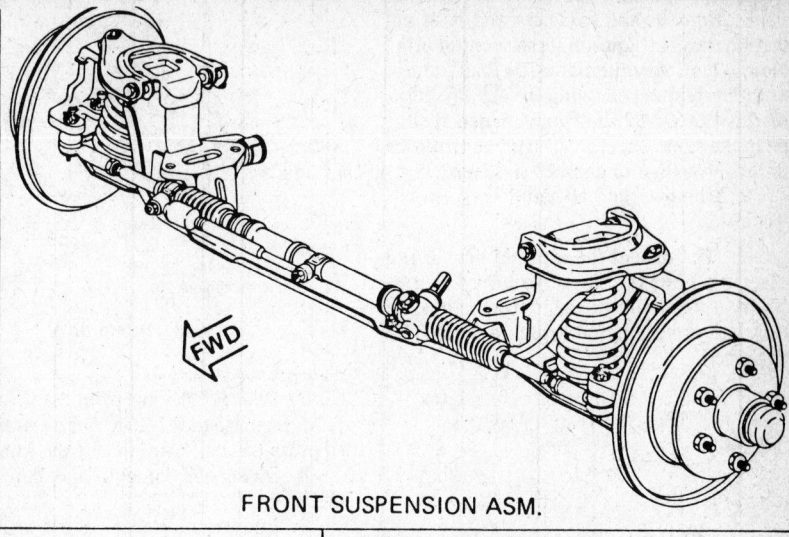

FRONT SUSPENSION ASM.

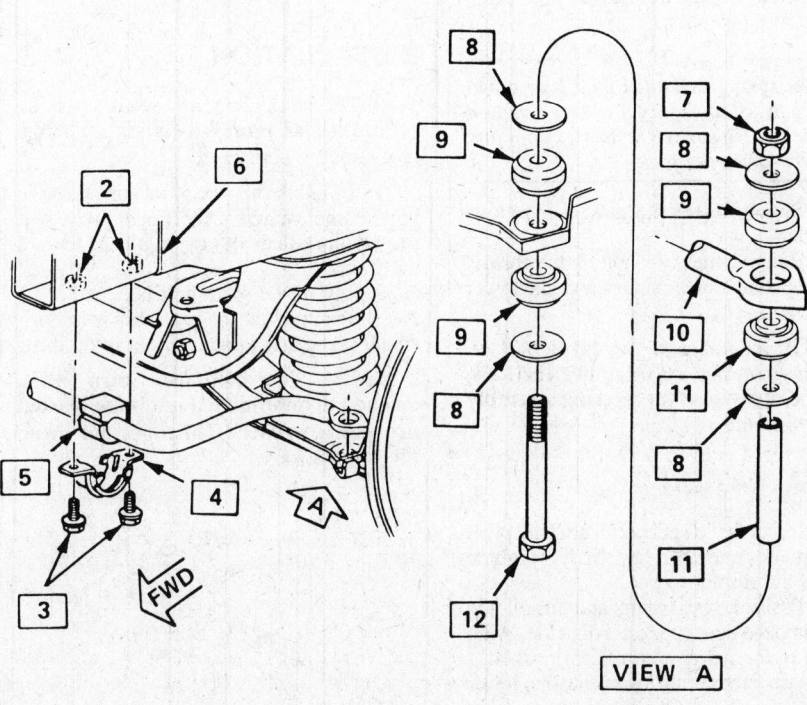

VIEW A

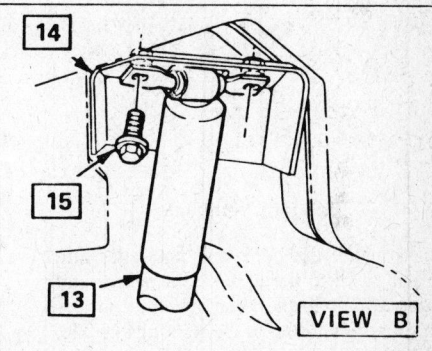

VIEW B

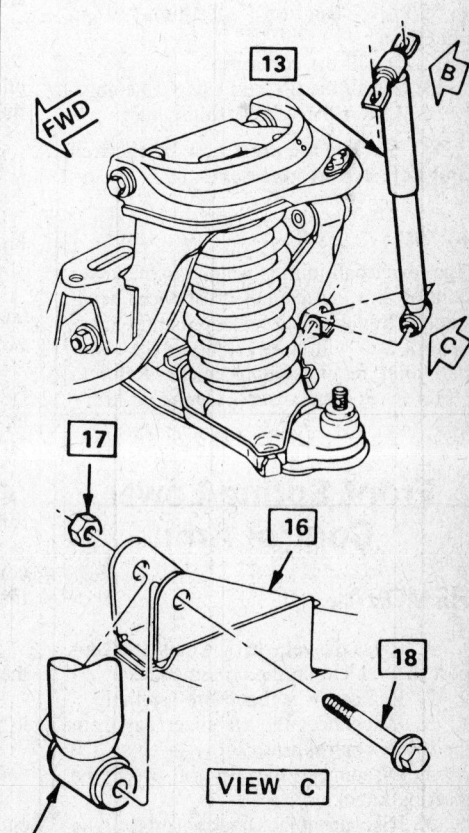

VIEW C

FRONT SHOCK ABSORBER
ASSEMBLY

1. Spring
2. Weld nuts
3. Bolt/screw (15 ft. lbs.)
4. Clamp
5. Bushing
6. Front rail
7. Tighten until nut bottoms on end of bolt thread
8. Washer
9. Grommet
10. Shaft front stabilizer
11. Spacer
12. Torque from this end 13 ft. lbs.
13. Shock absorber
14. Shock absorber support
15. Bolt
16. Control arm
17. Nut
18. Bolt

Front suspension

8. Remove the two nuts and bolts attaching the ball joint to upper control arm. Note which way the flat of the ball joint is pointing before removing it. The direction of this flat on the ball joint flange should be in the same direction as the one removed unless a change in camber is desired.

9. Remove the ball joint.

To install:

NOTE: Inspect the tapered hole in the steering knuckle. Remove any dirt and if any out-of-roundness, deformation, or damage is noted, the knuckle MUST be replaced.

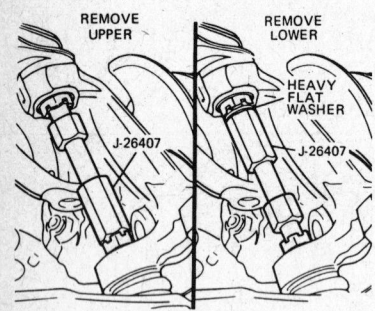

Ball joint removal

10. Install the bolts and nuts attaching the ball joint to the upper control arm and torque to 28 lb.ft., then mate the upper control arm ball stud to the steering knuckle.

11. Install the ball stud nut and torque to 35 lb.ft. Then turn ⅙ of a turn to align cotter pin.

12. Install the cotter pin.

13. Install the tire and wheel assembly.

14. Lower the vehicle to the floor.

NOTE: The toe must now be checked and adjusted as necessary.

Lower

The lower ball joint is welded to the lower control arm and cannot be serviced separately. Replacement of the entire lower control arm will be necessary if the lower ball joint requires replacement. Refer to "Front Spring/Lower Control Arm" removal.

Front Spring/Lower Control Arm

REMOVAL

1. Raise the vehicle on a hoist and support the vehicle on the crossmember.

2. Remove wheel and tire assembly.

3. Disconnect the stabilizer bar from the lower control arm.

4. Disconnect the tie rod from the steering knuckle.

5. Disconnect the shock absorber at the lower control arm.

6. Support the lower control arm with a jack.

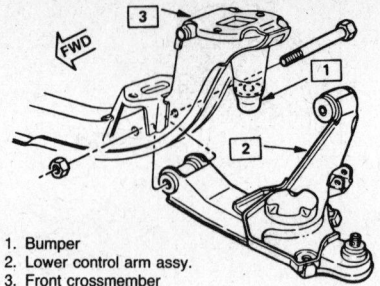

1. Bumper
2. Lower control arm assy.
3. Front crossmember

Lower control arm

7. Remove the nut from the lower ball joint, then use tool J-26407 or its equivalent to press the ball joint out of the knuckle.

8. Swing the knuckle and hub out of the way.

9. Loosen the lower control arm pivot bolts.

10. Install a chain through the coil spring as a safety precaution.

——————— CAUTION ———————

The coil spring is under load and could result in personal injury if it were released too quickly. Be sure to install a chain and to slowly lower the jack.

11. Slowly lower the jack and remove the spring.

12. Remove the pivot bolts at the chassis and the crossmember and remove the lower control arm.

NOTE: Removal of the pivot bolt at the crossmember may require the loosening or removal of the steering assembly mounting bolts.

INSTALLATION

1. Install the lower control arm and pivot bolts at crossmember and body. Tighten slightly but do not torque.

2. Position the spring and install the spring into the upper pocket. Align the spring bottom to the lower control arm pocket.

3. Install the spring lower end onto lower control arm. It may be necessary to have an assistant help you compress the spring far enough to slide it over the raised area of the lower control arm seat.

4. Use a jack to raise the lower control arm and compress the coil spring.

5. Install the ball joint through the lower control arm and into the steering knuckle. Install nut to ball joint stud and torque to 55 lb.ft. Install a new cotter pin.

6. Connect the stablizer bar and torque the bolt to 16 lb.ft.

7. Connect the tie rod and torque to 29 lb.ft.

8. Install the shock absorber to the lower control arm and torque the bolt to 35 lb.ft.

9. If the bolts were removed or loosened at the steering assembly replace with new bolts and torque to 21 lb.ft.

10. With the suspension system in its normal standing height, torque the lower

control arm to body bolt at 62 lb.ft. and the lower control arm to crossmember nut at 52 lb.ft.

11. Check and set alignment as necessary.

Upper Control Arm

REMOVAL

1. Raise the vehicle and support safely.

2. Remove the tire and wheel assembly.

3. Remove the rivet holding the brake line clip to the upper control arm.

4. Support the lower control arm with a floor jack.

5. Remove the upper ball joint from the steering knuckle, as described earlier.

6. Remove the control arm pivot bolt and remove the control arm from vehicle.

7. Transfer the ball joint if not damaged or worn.

INSTALLATION

NOTE: Washers and shims must be reinstalled as removed unless a change in geometry is desired.

1. Install the upper control arm and pivot bolt to the vehicle. The inner pivot bolt must be installed with the bolt head toward the front.

2. Install the pivot bolt nut.

3. Position the control arm in a horizontal plane and torque the nut to 66 lb.ft.

NOTE: The bolt may turn when torqued to minumum if nut is not backed up with a wrench. This does not mean the joint is loose.

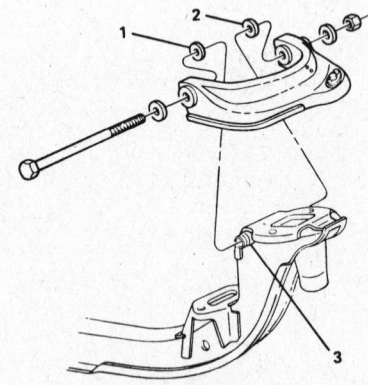

1. Front washer
2. Rear washer
3. Support bracket

Upper control arm

4. Install the ball joint to the upper control arm and to steering knuckle, as described earlier. Install the nut, torque to 35 lb.ft. Install a new cotter pin.

5. Install the wheel and tire.

6. Lower the vehicle to the floor.

Steering Knuckle

REMOVAL

1. Raise vehicle on a hoist and support the lower control arm with a jackstand.

—— CAUTION ——
This keeps the coil spring compressed. Use care to support adequately, or personal injury could result.

2. Remove the tire and wheel assembly.
3. Remove the disc brake caliper. Secure the caliper to the suspension using wire. Do not allow the caliper to hang by the brake hose. Insert a piece of wood between the shoes to hold the piston in the caliper bore. (The block of wood should be about the same thickness as the brake disc.)
4. Remove the hub and disc.
5. Remove the splash shield.
6. Remove both ball stud nuts (See Ball Joint Removal).
7. Remove the tie rod end from the steering knuckle.
8. Using Tool J-26407, or its equivalent press the upper ball stud from the steering knuckle.
9. Reverse Tool J-26407 to the other ball stud and press the lower ball stud from the steering knuckle.
10. Remove the ball stud nuts and remove the steering knuckle.

INSTALLATION

1. Place the steering knuckle in position and insert the upper and lower ball studs into knuckle bosses.
2. Install the ball stud nuts and tighten to specifications. Lower, torque to 55 lb.ft. upper, torque to 35 lb.ft. Install new cotter pins.
3. Install the splash shield to the steering knuckle. Torque to 7 lb.ft.
4. Install the tie rod end to the steering knuckle. Torque to 29 lb.ft., and install the cotter pin.
5. Repack the wheel bearings. Then install the hub and disc, bearings and nut. Torque to specifications.
6. Install the brake caliper.
7. Install the tire wheel assembly.
8. Remove the jackstand and lower the vehicle to the floor.

Front Wheel Bearing Adjustment

1. Raise the vehicle and support with jack stands.
2. Remove the wheel.
3. Remove the dust cap from the hub.
4. Remove cotter pin from spindle and spindle nut.
5. Tighten the spindle nut to 12 lb.ft. while turning the wheel assembly forward by hand to fully seat the bearings. This will remove any grease or burrs which could cause excessive wheel bearing play later.
6. Back off the nut to the "just loose" position.
7. Hand tighten the spindle nut. Loosen the spindle nut until either hole in the spindle lines up with a slot in the nut. (Not more than ½ flat.)
8. Install new cotter pin. Bend the ends of the cotter pin against nut, cut off extra length to ensure ends will not interfere with the dust cap.
9. Measure the looseness in the hub assembly. There will be from .001" to .005" end play when properly adjusted.
10. Install the dust cap on the hub.
11. Replace the wheel cover or hub cap.
12. Lower the vehicle to the floor.
13. Perform the same operation for each front wheel.

REAR SUSPENSION

MacPherson Strut

REMOVAL & INSTALLATION

1. Remove the engine compartment cover.
2. Remove the three upper strut nuts and washers.
3. Loosen the wheel lug nuts.
4. Raise the vehicle and support the rear control arm.
5. Remove the wheel and tire.
6. Remove the brake line clip.
7. Scribe the strut and knuckle.
   a. Using a sharp tool, scribe the knuckle along the lower outboard strut radius, as in view A.
   b. Scribe the strut flange on the inboard side, along the curve of the knuckle, as in view B.
   c. Make a chisel mark across the strut/knuckle interface, as shown in view C.
8. Remove the two strut mounting nuts and bolts and remove the strut assembly and spacer plate.
9. Installation is the reverse of removal. Align the scribe marks on the strut and knuckle and replace the bolts in the same order in which they were removed.

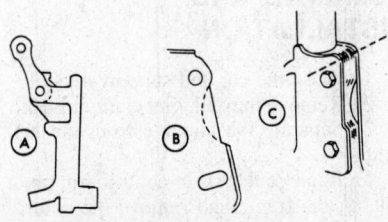

Scribing strut and knuckle

Tighten the strut mounting nuts to 140 ft. lbs. and the upper strut nuts to 18 ft. lbs.

Coil Spring

REMOVAL

NOTE: Special tool No. J-26584 or its equivalent must be used to disassemble and assemble strut damper. Care must be used not to damage the special coating on the coil springs, or damage could occur to the coils.

1. Clamp Tool No. J-26584 Strut Compressor in vise.
2. Place the strut assembly in bottom adapter of compressor and install Tool No. J-26584-89 (make sure adapter captures the strut and locating pins are engaged).
3. Rotate the strut assembly to align the top mounting assembly lip with strut compressor support notch.
4. Insert Tool No. J-26584-430 top adapter on the top spring seal. Postion top adapters so that the long stud is at high location to strut flange.
5. Using a ratchet with 1 in. socket, turn the compressor forcing screw clockwise until the top support flange contacts the Tool No. J-26584-430 top adapter. Continue turning the screw compressing the strut spring.
6. Place Tool No. J-26584-430 top adapter over the spring seat assembly.
7. Turn the strut compressor forcing the screw counterclockwise until the strut spring tension is relieved. Remove the top adapters, bottom adapter, then remove the strut.

INSTALLATION

1. Clamp the strut compressor body Tool No. J-26584 in vise.
2. Place the strut assembly in bottom adapter of compressor and install Tool No. J-26584-89 (make sure adapter captures strut and locating pins are engaged).
3. Rotate the strut assembly until the mounting flange is facing out, directly opposite the compressor forcing screw.
4. Position the spring and components on the strut, as shown below. Make sure the spring is properly seated on the bottom spring plate.
5. Install the strut spring seat assembly on top of the spring. The long stud must be 180° from the strut mounting flange.
6. Place Tool No. J-26584-403 top adapter over the spring seat assembly.
7. Turn the compressor forcing screw until the compressor top support just contacts the top adapters (do not compress spring at this time).
8. Install Tool No. J-26584-27 Strut Alignment Rod through the top spring seat and thread the rod onto the damper shaft, hand tight.
9. Compress the spring by turning the screw clockwise until enough of the damper

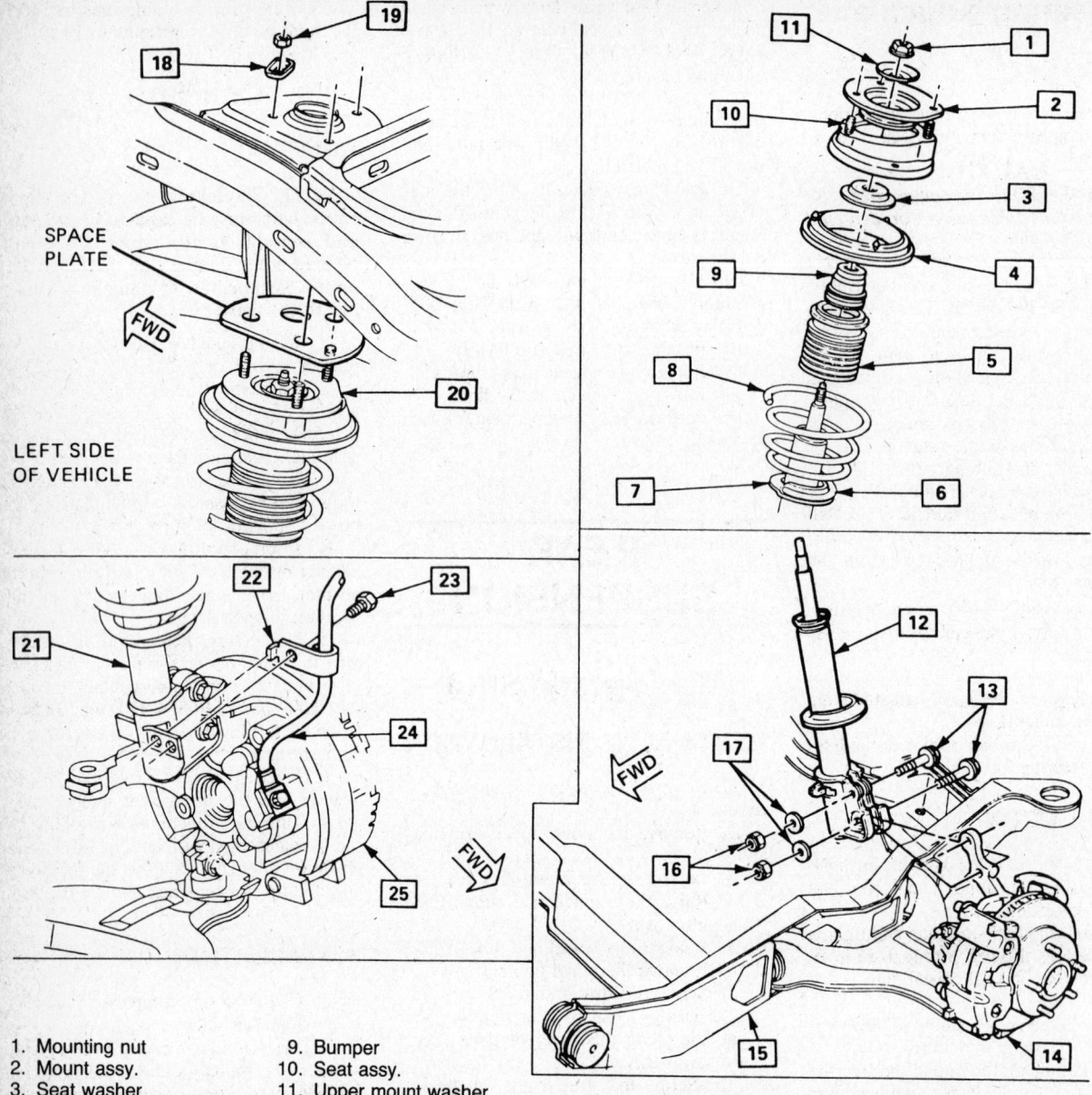

SPACE PLATE

FWD

LEFT SIDE OF VEHICLE

1. Mounting nut
2. Mount assy.
3. Seat washer
4. Upper spring insulator
5. Shield
6. Lower spring insulator
7. Lower spring seat
8. Spring
9. Bumper
10. Seat assy.
11. Upper mount washer
12. Strut assy.
13. Strut mounting bolts
14. Knuckle and hub assy.
15. Cradle assy.
16. Strut mounting nuts
17. Strut lower washers
18. Strut upper washers
19. Strut upper nuts
20. Rear strut mount assy.
21. Strut assy.
22. Brake line clip
23. Brake line clip bolt
24. Rear brake hose
25. Caliper assy.

Exploded view of strut assembly

shaft is exposed to where the nut can be threaded securely, and thread nut on the damper shaft.

NOTE: Do not compress spring until it bottoms. Be sure that the damper shaft comes through the CENTER of the spring seat opening, or damage could occur.

10. Remove the alignment rod and position the strut mount over the damper shaft and spring seat studs. Install the washer and nut.

11. Turn the forcing screw counterclockwise to back off support and remove the strut assembly from the compressor.

Lower Control Arm

REMOVAL AND INSTALLATION

1. Raise the car and support it safely.
2. Remove the ball joint clamping bolt.
3. Separate the knuckle from the ball joint.
4. Remove the lower control arm pivot bolts at the frame and remove the control arm.
5. Installation is the reverse of removal.

NOTE: The toe-in and camber settings should be checked and adjusted as required.

Lower Ball Joint

REMOVAL AND INSTALLATION

1. Raise the car, support it safely and remove the wheel.
2. Remove the clamp bolt from the lower control arm ball stud.

3. Disconnect the ball joint from the knuckle.

NOTE: It may be necessary to tap the ball stud with a mallet.

4. Using a ⅛ in. drill, drill the rivets approximately ¼ in. deep in the center of the rivet.

5. Use a ½ in. drill and drill just deep enough to remove the rivet head.

6. Remove the rivets using a hammer and a punch.

7. The ball joint is replaced using nuts and bolts. Torque to 13 ft. lbs. Check the toe-in setting and adjust as necessary.

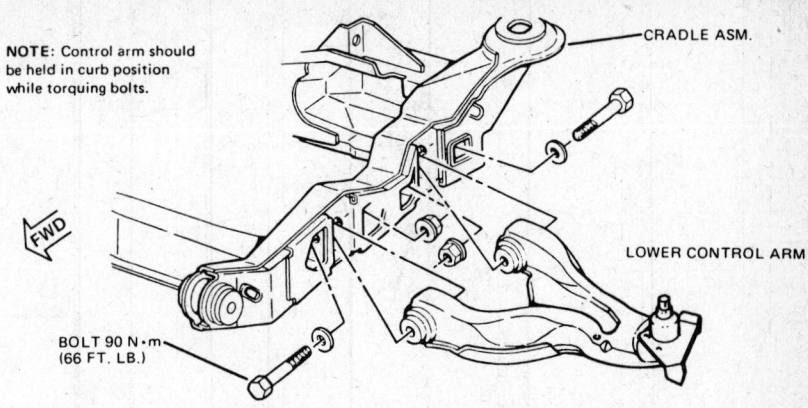

NOTE: Control arm should be held in curb position while torquing bolts.

CRADLE ASM.

LOWER CONTROL ARM

BOLT 90 N·m (66 FT. LB.)

Lower control arm removal

BRAKES

NOTE: To service brake shoes, drums and wheel cylinders or brake pads and calipers, please refer to "Brakes" in the Unit Repair Section.

Master Clyinder

REMOVAL & INSTALLATION

1. Disconnect the hydraulic lines at the master cylinder.

1. Place a number of cloths or a container under the master cylinder to catch the brake fluid. Disconnect the brake tubes from the master cylinder; use a flare nut wrench if one is available. Tape over open ends of the tubes.

NOTE: Brake fluid eats paint. Wipe up any spilled fluid immediately, then flush the area with clear water.

2. Remove the two nuts attaching the master cylinder to the booster or firewall.

3. Remove the master cylinder.

4. To install, attach the master cylinder to the booster with the nuts. Torque to 22–30 ft. lbs.

5. Remove the tape from the lines and connect to the master cylinder. Torque to 10–15 ft. lbs. Connect the electrical lead.

6. Bleed the brakes.

PARKING BRAKE ADJUSTMENT

Adjustment of parking brake cable is necessary whenever the rear brake cables have been disconnected. Need for parking brake adjustment is indicated if the hydraulic brake system operates with good reserve, but the parking brake hand level travel is more than 9 ratchet clicks.

1. Place the parking brake hand lever in the unapplied positon.

2. Raise the rear wheels off floor and support safely.

3. Apply lubricant to groove in the equalizer nut.

4. Hold the brake cable stud from turning and tighten the equalizer nut until cable slack is removed.

5. Make sure the caliper levers are against the stops on the caliper housing after tightening the equalizer nut.

6. If the levers are off the stops, loosen the cable until the levers do return to the stops.

7. Operate the parking brake lever several times to check adjustment. Properly adjusted parking brake shoes and properly adjusted parking brake cable will result in a parking brake handle movement of five (5) to eight (8) notches when a force is applied perpendicularly at the handle grip mid-point.

8. Lower the rear wheels.

NOTE: The levers must be on the caliper stops after completion of adjustment. Back off the parking brake adjuster if necessary to keep the levers on the stops.

STEERING

Rack and Pinion Assembly

REMOVAL & INSTALLATION

1. Raise the vehicle and support it safely.

2. Disconnect both front cross member braces.

3. Disconnect the flexible coupling pinch bolt to the shaft.

4. Remove the outer tie rod cotter pins and nuts on the left and right sides.

5. Disconnect the tie rods from the steering knuckle.

6. Remove the four bolts retaining the steering assembly to the cross member and remove the steering assembly.

7. Installation is the reverse of removal. Tighten the flexible coupling bolt to 46 ft. lbs., the four new steering assembly bolts to 21 ft. lbs., the four cross mem-

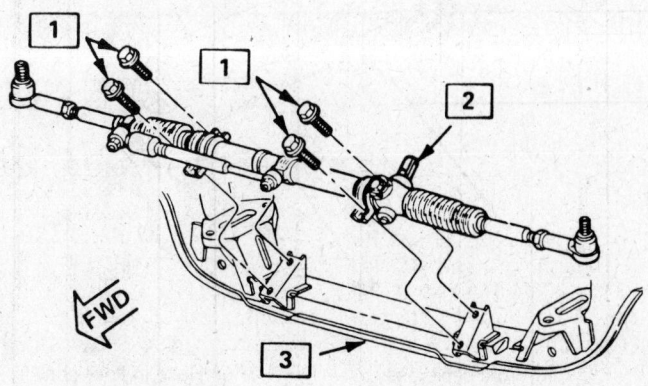

1. Bolt (21 ft. lbs.)
2. Steering assy.
3. Cross member
4. Nut (32 ft. lbs.)
5. Washer
6. Stud assy (36 ft. lbs.)
7. Steering link damper

Rack and pinion assembly

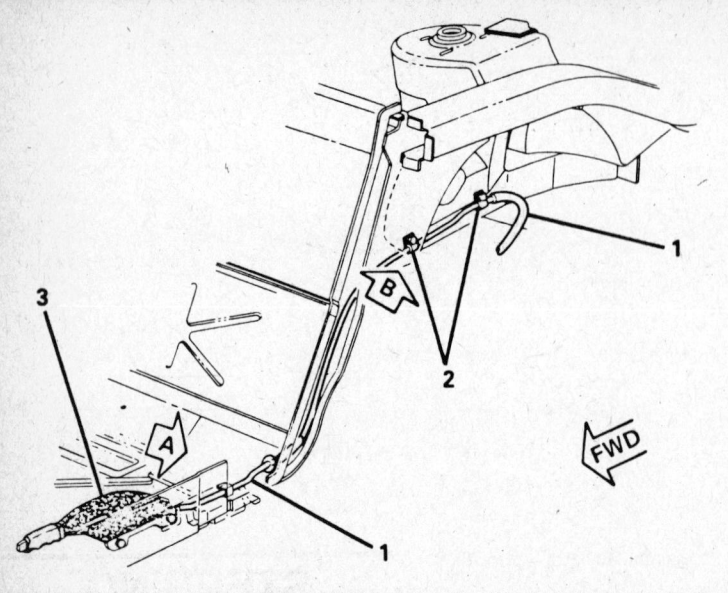

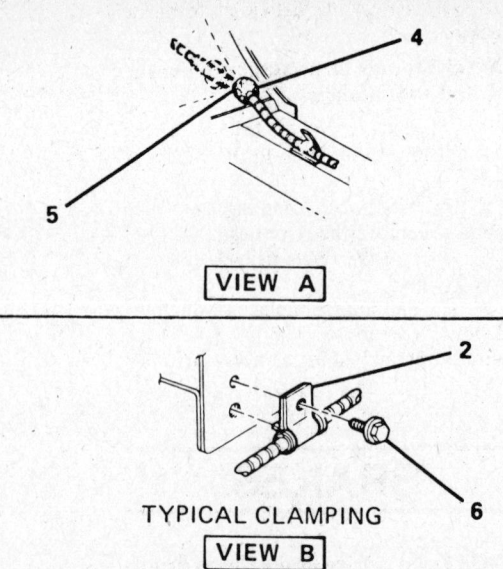

VIEW A

TYPICAL CLAMPING

VIEW B

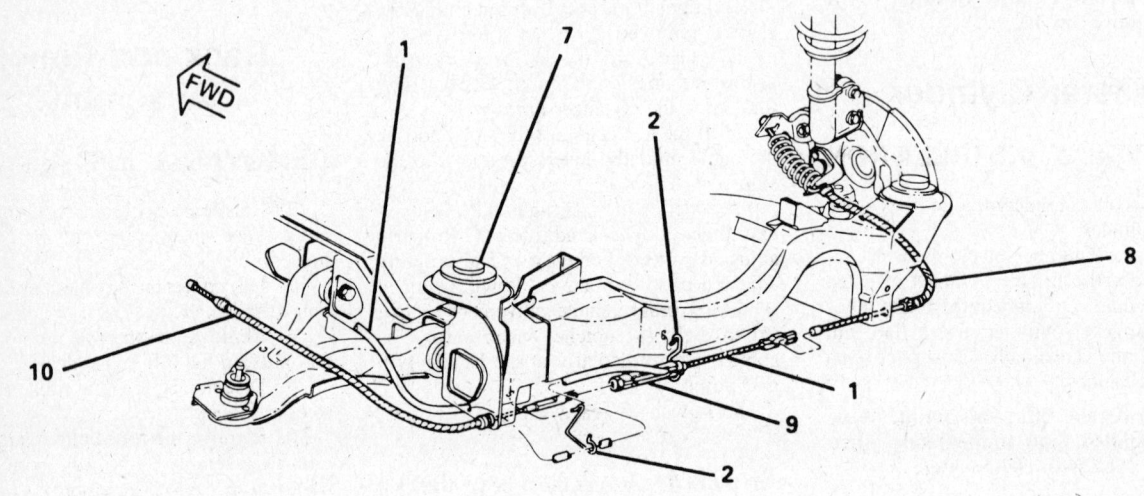

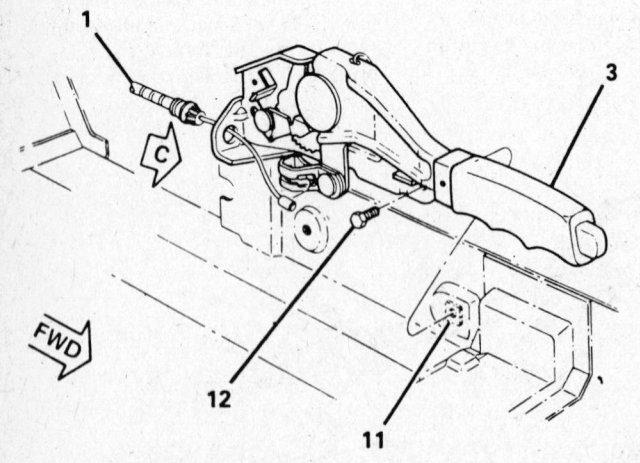

VIEW C

1. Front cable assy.	5. Hose in floor pan	9. Equalizer
2. Clip	6. Bolt	10. L.H. cable assy.
3. Lever assy.	7. Frame assy.	11. Weld nut
4. Grommet	8. R.H. cable assy.	12. Bolt/Screw

Parking brake assembly

ber brace bolts to 20 ft. lbs., and the tie rod nut at each knuckle to 29 ft. lbs. then ⅙ turn to align the cotter pin.

Outer Tie-Rod

REMOVAL & INSTALLATION

1. Loosen the jam nut and remove the tie-rod from the steering knuckle.

NOTE: GM recommends a special tool for this procedure. Tool No. J-24319-01 or BT 7101.

2. Remove the outer tie-rod.
3. Install the outer tie-rod in the reverse of removal. Do not tighten the jam nut.
4. Adjust the toe-in by turning the inner tie-rod.
5. Make sure the boot is not twisted then torque the jam nut to 50 ft. lbs.

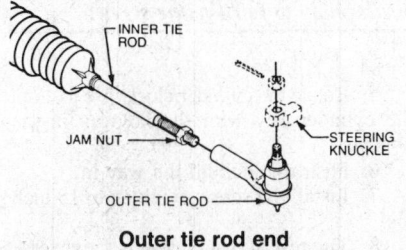

Outer tie rod end

Steering Wheel

REMOVAL & INSTALLATION

1. Pry off the center cap and remove the retainer clip and nut.
2. Remove the wheel using a steering wheel puller.
3. When installing align the index mark on the steering wheel with the index mark on the steering shaft. Torque the retaining nut to 35 ft. lbs.

———— **CAUTION** ————
The cancelling cam tower must be centered in the slot of the lock plate cover before assembling the wheel.

Turn Signal Switch

REMOVAL & INSTALLATION

1. Remove the steering wheel. Remove the trim cover.
2. Pry the cover from the steering column.
3. Position a U-shaped lockplate compressing tool on the end of the steering shaft and compress the lock plate by turning the shaft nut clockwise. Pry the wire snap-ring out of the shaft groove.
4. Remove the tool and lift the lockplate off the shaft.
5. Slip the cancelling cam, upper bear-

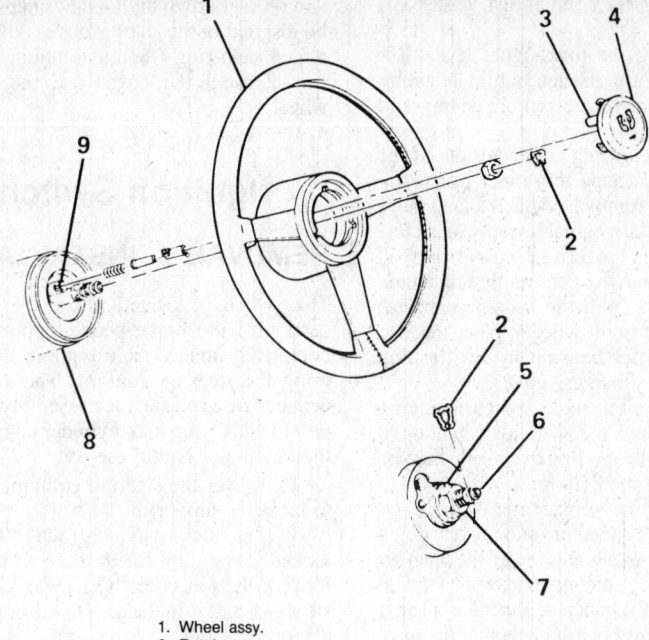

1. Wheel assy.
2. Retainer
3. Nylon shrink tube
4. Cap assy.
5. Index mark
6. Steering column shaft
7. Nut (35 ft. lbs.)
8. Steering column
9. Canceling cam tower centered in slot of lock plate

Steering wheel removal

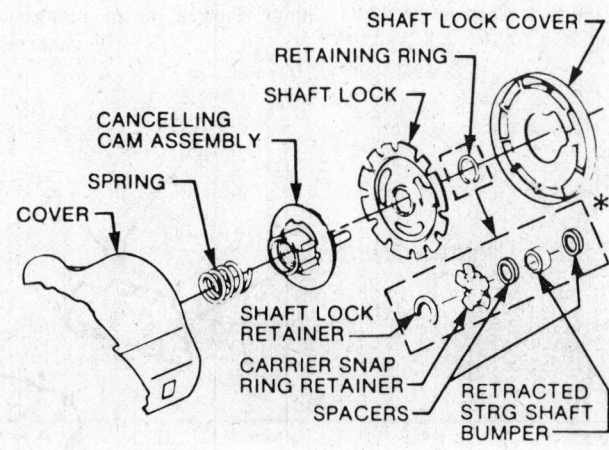

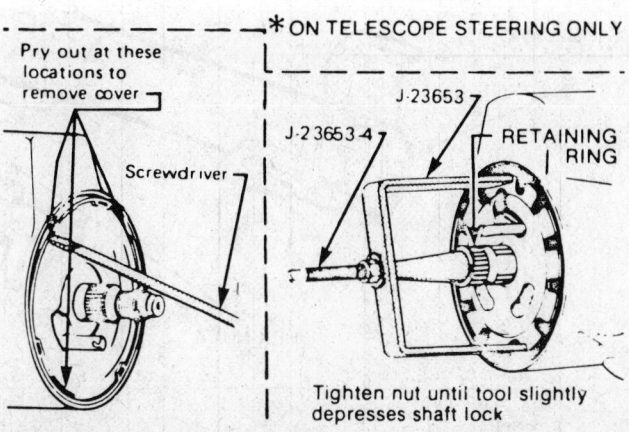

These parts must be removed to remove the turn signal switch

ing preload spring, and thrust washer off the shaft.

6. Remove the turn signal lever. Remove the hazard flasher button retaining screw and remove the button, spring and knob.

7. Pull the switch connector out of the mast jacket and tape the upper part to facilitate switch removal. Attach a long piece of wire to the turn signal switch connector. When installing the turn signal switch, feed this wire through the column first, and then use this wire to pull the switch connector into position. On tilt wheels, place the turn signal and shifter housing in low position and remove the harness cover.

8. Remove the three switch mounting screws. Remove the switch by pulling it straight up while guiding the wiring harness cover through the column.

9. Install the replacement switch by working the connector and cover down through the housing and under the bracket. On tilt models, the connector is worked down through the housing, under the bracket, and then the cover is installed on the harness.

10. Install the switch mounting screws and the connector on the mast jacket bracket. Install the column-to-dash trim plate.

11. Install the flasher knob and the turn signal lever.

12. With the turn signal lever in neutral and the flasher knob out, slide the thrust washer, upper bearing preload spring, and cancelling cam onto the shaft.

13. Position the lock plate on the shaft and press it down until a new snap-ring can be inserted in the shaft groove. Always use a new snap-ring when assembling.

14. Install the cover and the steering wheel.

Ignition Switch

REMOVAL & INSTALLATION

The switch is located inside the channel section of the brake pedal support and is completely inaccessible without first lowering the steering column. The switch is actuated by a rod and rack assembly. A gear on the end of the lock cylinder engages the toothed upper end of the rod.

1. Lower the steering column; be sure to properly support it.

2. Put the switch in the "Off-Unlocked" position. With the cylinder removed, the rod is in "Off-Unlocked" position when it is in the next to the uppermost detent.

3. Remove the two switch screws and remove the switch assembly.

4. Before installing, place the new switch in "Off-Unlocked" position and make sure the lock cylinder and actuating rod are in "Off-Unlocked" position (second detent from the top).

5. Install the activating rod into the switch and assemble the switch on the column. Tighten the mounting screws. Use only the specified screws, since overlength screws could impair the collapsibility of the column.

6. Reinstall the steering column.

Ignition Lock Cylinder

REMOVAL & INSTALLATION

1. Remove the steering wheel.

2. Turn the lock to the Run position.

3. Remove the lock plate, turn signal switch or combination switch, and the key warning buzzer switch. The warning buzzer switch can be fished out with a bent paper clip.

4. Remove the lock cylinder retaining screw and lock cylinder.

CAUTION
If the screw is dropped on removal, it could fall into the column, requiring complete disassembly to retrieve the screw.

---

5. Rotate the cylinder clockwise to align the cylinder key with the keyway in the housing.

6. Push the lock all the way in.

7. Install the screw. Tighten to 15 inch lbs.

8. The rest of installation is the reverse of removal. Turn the lock to Run to install the key warning buzzer switch, which is simply pushed down into place.

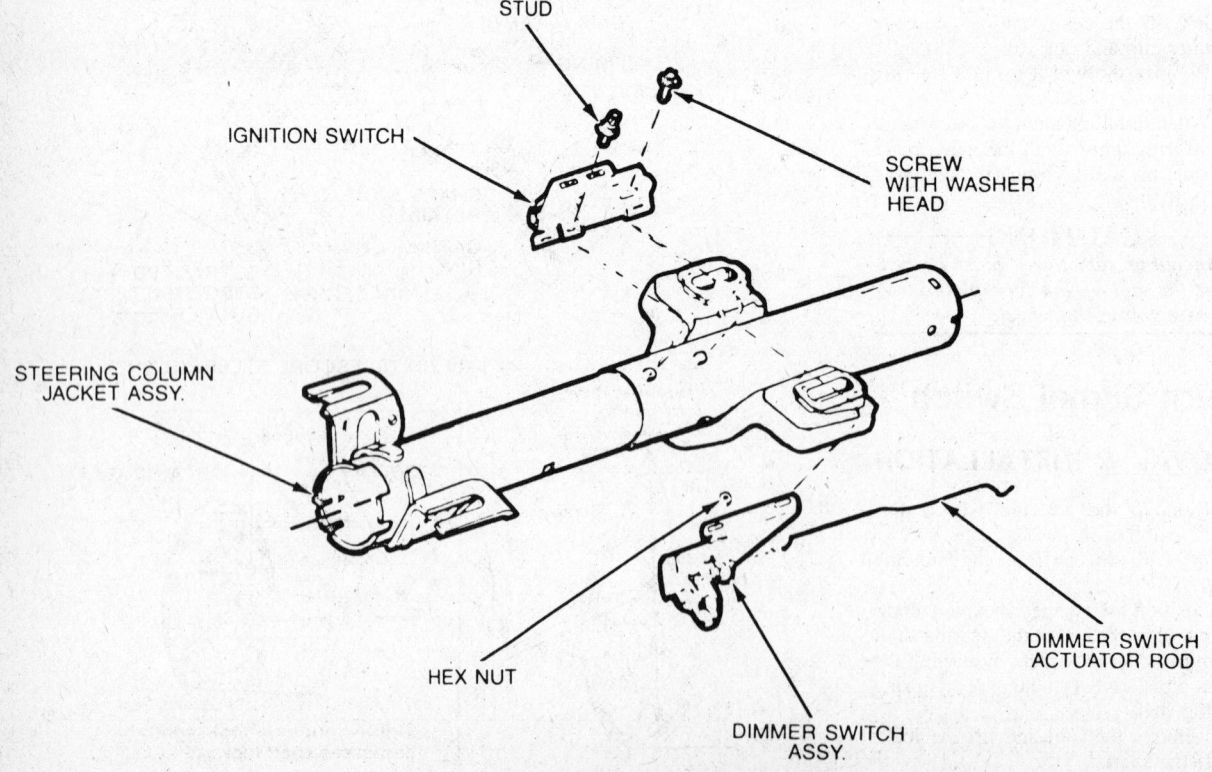

Ignition switch removal

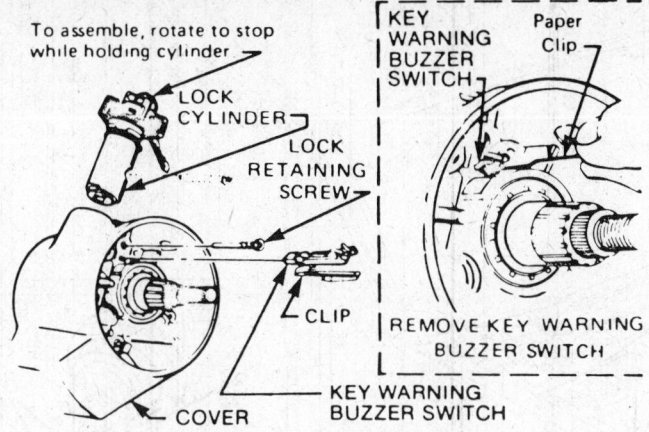

To assemble, rotate to stop while holding cylinder

LOCK CYLINDER
LOCK RETAINING SCREW
CLIP
KEY WARNING BUZZER SWITCH
COVER

KEY WARNING BUZZER SWITCH
Paper Clip
REMOVE KEY WARNING BUZZER SWITCH

Ignition lock cylinder removal

2. Remove the rear cluster cover.
3. Remove the front trim plate.
4. Remove the steering column cover.
5. Remove the cluster attaching screws, disconnect the wiring harness and remove the cluster assembly.

NOTE: The speedometer, tach, and gauges may be serviced be removing the front cluster lens.

INSTRUMENT PANEL

Headlight Switch

REMOVAL & INSTALLATION

1. Disconnect the negative battery cable.

2. Remove the headlight/dimmer switch trim plate screws.
3. Disconnect the electrical connector and remove the switch assembly.
4. Installation is the reverse of removal.

Instrument Cluster

REMOVAL & INSTALLATION

1. Disconnect the negative battery cable.

WINDSHIELD WIPERS

Motor

REMOVAL & INSTALLATION

1. Remove the wiper arms.
2. Remove the shroud top vent screen.
3. Remove the drive link from the crank arm.
4. Disconnect the electrical leads.
5. Remove the three attaching screws and remove the wiper motor.
6. Installation is the reverse of removal. Make sure the wiper motor is in the

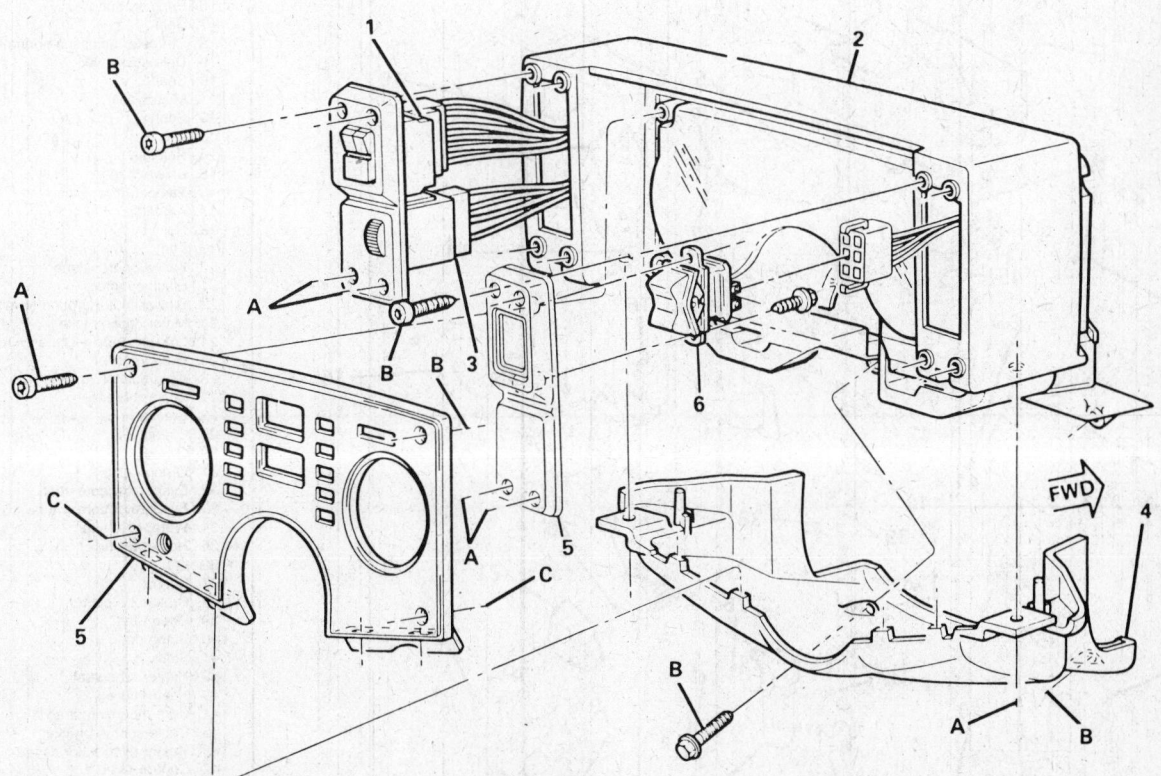

1. Headlamp switch
2. Cluster pad assy.
3. Dimmer switch
4. Cover assy.
5. Trim plate
6. Deck lid switch
A. Install these bolts/screws first
B. Install these bolts/screws 2nd
C. Install these bolts/screws last

Instrument cluster trim plates

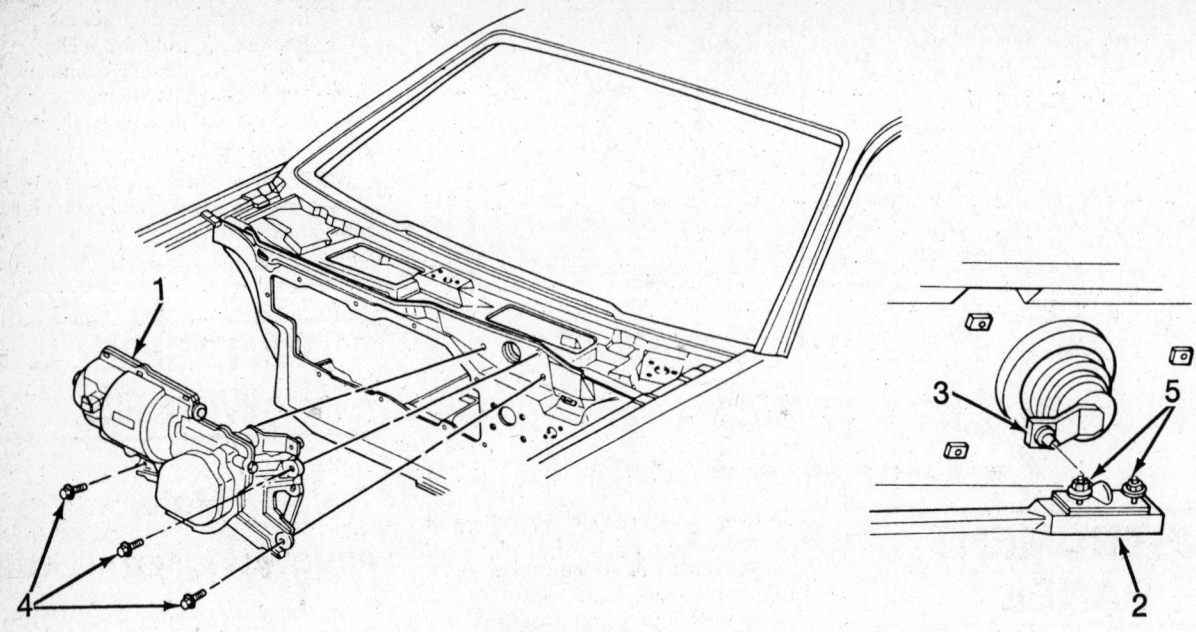

1. Wiper motor
2. Drive link
3. Crank arm
4. Wiper motor attaching screws
5. Drive link attaching nut

Wiper motor removal

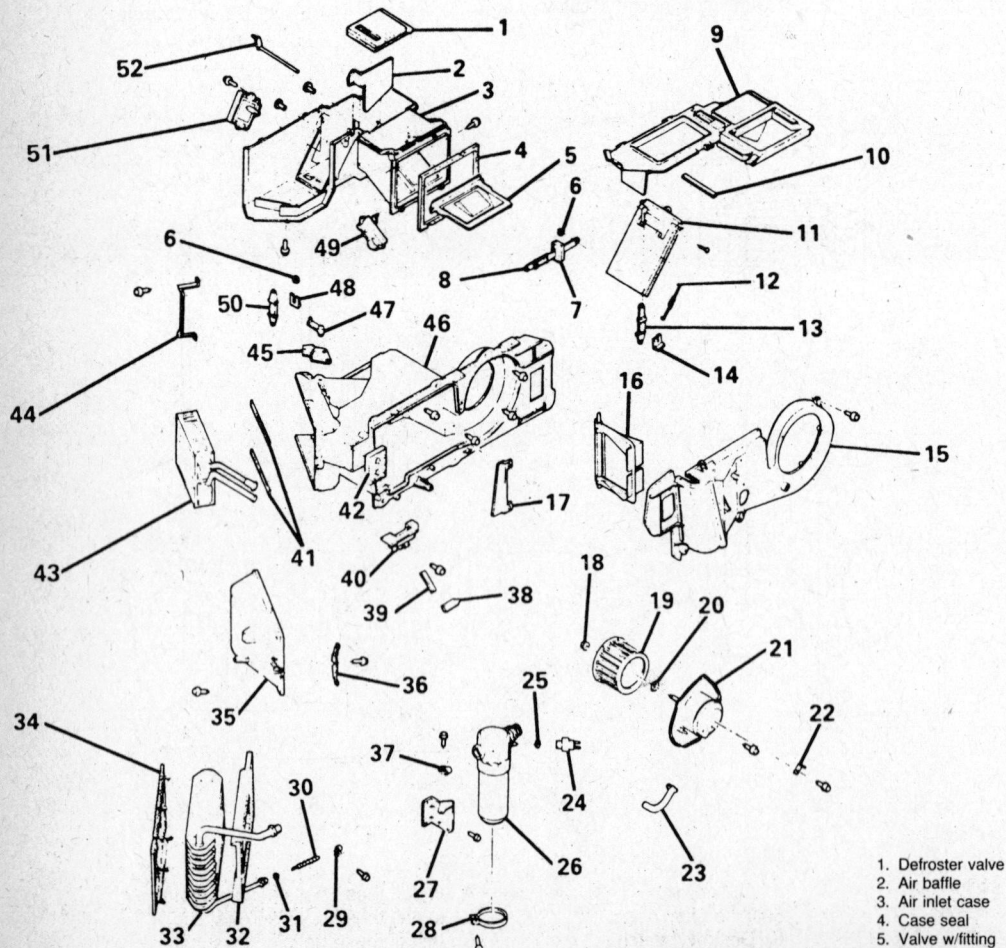

6. Push on nut
7. Seal
8. Defroster adjusting spring link
9. Defroster cover
10. Seal
11. Mode valve
12. Spring
13. Link
14. Retainer
15. Blower case
16. Temperature valve
17. Air baffle
18. Nut
19. Fan
20. Fan support washer
21. Electric motor
22. Blower motor ground terminal
23. Motor cooling tube
24. Low pressure electric switch
25. O-ring gasket
26. Accumulator w/fitting
27. Support bracket
28. Bracket
29. Clamp
30. Orifice
31. O-ring gasket
32. Evaporator core seal
33. Evaporator core w/tube
34. Water core filter
35. Heater cover
36. Clip
37. Clamp
38. Drain tube clamp
39. Drain tube
40. Sump drain
41. Seal
42. Heater tube seal
43. Heater core
44. Core mounting strap
45. Cable control bracket
46. Heater evaporator case
47. Control lever
48. Clip
49. Actuator
50. Link
51. Electric mode actuator
52. Defroster shaft w/lever

1. Defroster valve
2. Air baffle
3. Air inlet case
4. Case seal
5. Valve w/fitting

Exploded view of a/c module

park position before installing the wiper arms and the shroud top screen.

Wiper Blade

REMOVAL & INSTALLATION

1. The blade assembly is removed by depressing the lever on the side of the blade.
2. To install, position the blade over the pin on the arm and press the release lever until it engages with the groove in the pin.

HEATER

Blower Motor

REMOVAL & INSTALLATION

1. Disconnect the negative battery cable.
2. Remove the cooling tube.
3. Disconnect all electrical connections.
4. Remove the heater retaining screws and remove the heater and cage assembly.
5. Installation is the reverse of removal.

Heater Core

REMOVAL & INSTALLATION

With A/C

1. Under the hood, disconnect and plug the heater hoses at the heater.
2. Remove the speaker grille and the speaker.
3. Remove the heater core cover, retainers and the heater core.
4. Installation is the reverse of removal. Refill the cooling system as required.

Without A/C

1. Disconnect the negative battery cable.
2. Disconnect the following wire connections.
   a. Heater relay
   b. Heat blower resistor
   c. Heater blower switch
   d. Heater ground connection
   e. Forward courtesy lamp socket
3. Remove the windshield washer fluid container.
4. Disconnect the heater core inlet and outlet hoses.
5. Remove the heater core grommets.
6. Remove the heater case cover.
7. Remove the heater core retainer and remove the heater core.
8. Installation is the reverse of removal. Refill the cooling system as required.

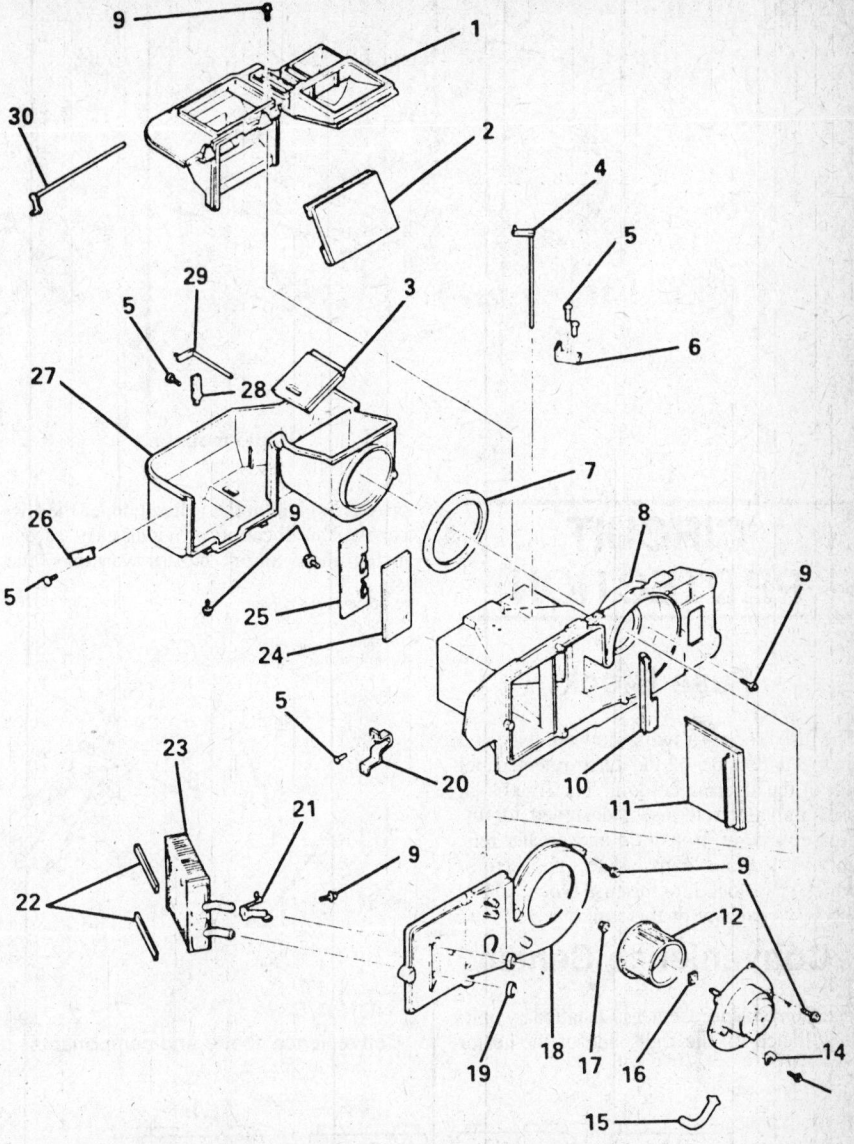

1.	Air inlet and distributor cover	16.	Fan support washer
2.	Vent valve	17.	Nut
3.	Defroster valve	18.	Blower cover
4.	Temperature valve shaft w/lever	19.	Heater core tube seal
5.	Rivet	20.	Mounting bracket
6.	Cable mounting bracket	21.	Core mounting clamp
7.	Heater and blower case seal	22.	Heater core seal
8.	Heater case	23.	Heater core
9.	Screw	24.	Heater core case seal
10.	Air baffle	25.	Clip
11.	Temperature valve	26.	Bracket
12.	Blower fan	27.	Air inlet and distribution case
13.	Screw	28.	Cable mounting bracket
14.	Blower motor ground terminal	29.	Defroster valve shaft w/lever
15.	Tube	30.	Vent valve shaft w/lever

Exploded view of heater module

Radio

REMOVAL & INSTALLATION

1. Remove the console trim plate assembly.
2. Disconnect the side retaining nuts and the rear retaining bolt.
3. Disconnect the electrical and antenna connections.
4. Remove the radio out the front of the console.
5. Installation is the reverse of removal.

NOTE: It is important when doing any radio work to avoid pinching the speaker wires. A short circuit to ground from either wire will cause damage to the output circuit of the radio.

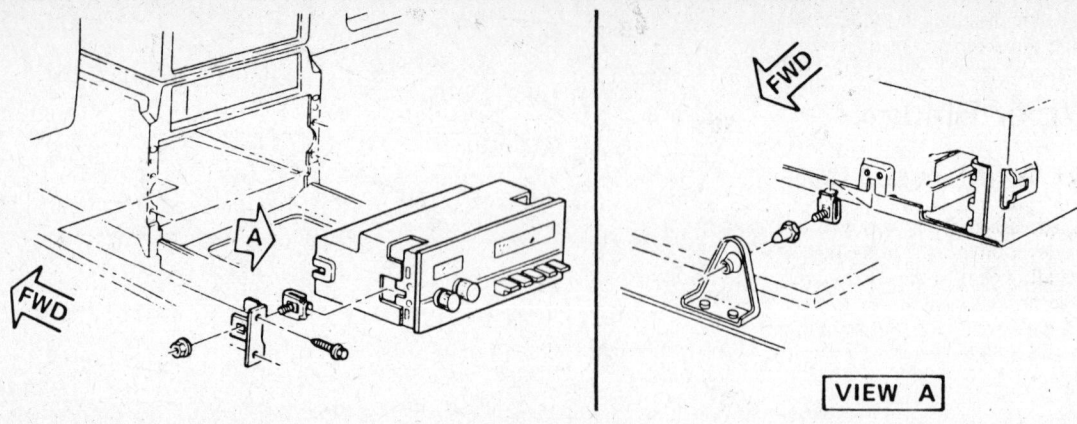

Radio mounting

VIEW A

CIRCUIT PROTECTION

Fuse Block

The fuse block is a swing-down unit located in the underside of the intstrument panel left of the steering column. The fuse block uses miniaturized fuses, designed for increased circuit protection and greater reliability. Various convenience connectors, which snap-lock into the fuse block, add to the serviceability of this unit.

Convenience Center

The Convenience Center is a stationary unit. It is locted on the right side of the heater or A/C module in the vehicle under the I.P. panel. This location provides easy access to the audio alarm, hazard warnings, the

1. Convenience center
2. Screw
3. Alarm
4. Horn relay
5. 4-way flasher
6. Bracket
7. Heater and A/C Module

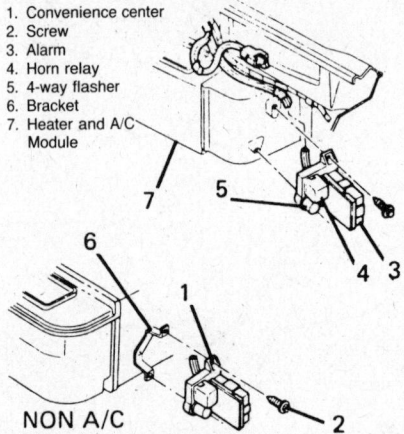

NON A/C

Convenience center and components

horn relay and the seatbelt key and headlamp warning alarm. All units are serviced by plug-in replacement.

Fusible Link

Added protection is provided in all battery feed circuits and other selected circuits by a fusible link. This link is a short piece of copper wire approximately 4″ long inserted in series with the circuit and acts as a fuse. The link is two (2) or more gages smaller in size than the circuit wire it is protecting and will burn out without damage to the circuit in case of current overload.

FUSIBLE LINK-REPLACEMENT

1. Disconnect the battery.
2. Locate the burned out link.
3. Strip away all melted harness insulation.
4. Cut the burned link ends from the circuit wire.
5. Strip the circuit wire back approximately ½ in. to allow soldering of new link.
6. Using fusible link four (4) gages smaller than protected the circuit (approximately 10″ long), solder a new link into circuit.

NOTE: Use only resin core solder. Under no circumstances should an acid solder be used nor should link be connected in any other manner except by soldering. Use of acid core solder may result in corrosion.

7. Tape the soldered ends securely using suitable electrical tape.
8. After taping wire, tape the harness leaving an exposed loop of wire approximately 5 in. in length.
9. Reconnect the battery.

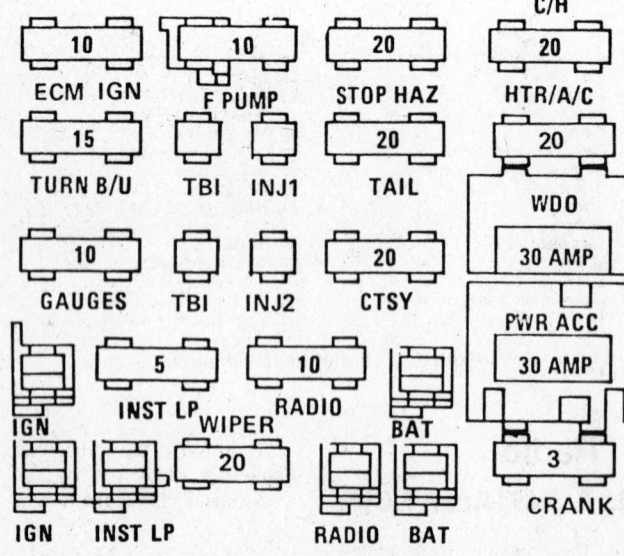

Front face of fuse block

GM "T" Body
Chevette, Pontiac T1000

YEAR IDENTIFICATION

1978

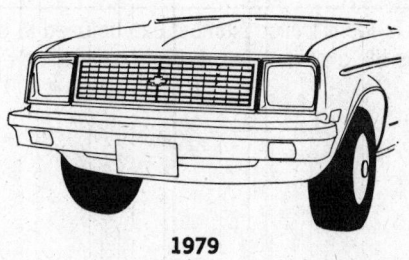

1979

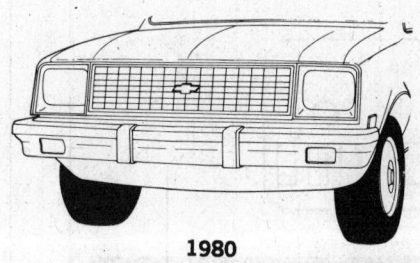

1980

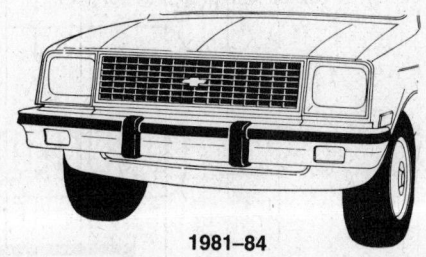

1981–84

1982–83 1000

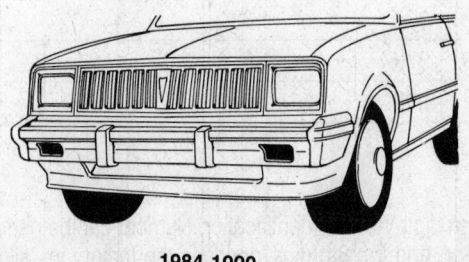

1984 1000

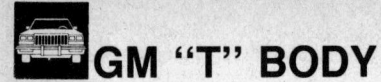

VEHICLE IDENTIFICATION NUMBER (VIN)

It is important for servicing and ordering parts to be certain of the vehicle and engine identification. The VIN (vehicle identification number) is a 13 or 17 digit number visible through the windshield on the driver's side of the dash and contains the vehicle and engine identification codes. It can be interpreted as follows:

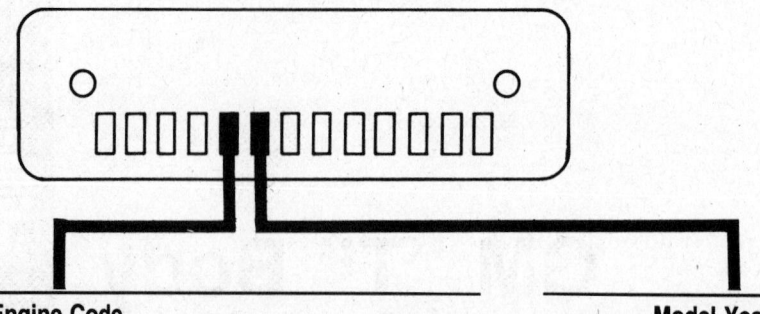

Engine Code						Model Year Code	
Code	Cu. In.	Liters	Cyl.	Carb.	Eng. Mfg.	Code	Year
E	97.6	1.6	4	1	Chev.	8	1978
J	97.6	1.6	4	1	Chev.	9	1979
E('79)	97.6	1.6	4	2	Chev.	A	1980
0	97.6	1.6	4	2	Chev.		
9	97.6	1.6	4	2	Chev.		

The thirteen digit Vehicle Identification Number can be used to determine engine application and model year. The 6th digit indicates the model year, and the 5th digit identifies the factory installed engine.

VEHICLE IDENTIFICATION NUMBER (VIN)

It is important for servicing and ordering parts to be certain of the vehicle and engine identification. The VIN (vehicle identification number) is a 13 or 17 digit number visible through the windshield on the driver's side of the dash and contains the vehicle and engine identification codes. It can be interpreted as follows:

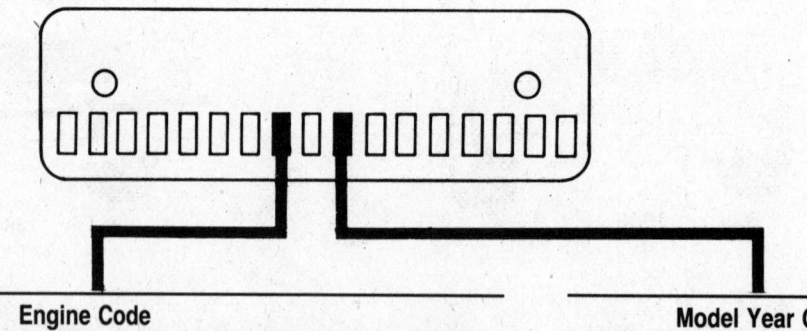

Engine Code						Model Year Code	
Code	Cu. In.	Liters	Cyl.	Carb	Eng. Mfg.	Code	Year
9	97.6	1.6	4	2	Chev.	B	1981
C	97.6	1.6	4	2	Chev.	C	1982
D	111	1.8	4	FI	Isuzu	D	1983
						E	1984
						F	1985

The seventeen digit Vehicle Identification Number can be used to determine engine application and model year. The 10th digit indicates the model year, and the 8th digit identifies the factory installed engine.

GENERAL ENGINE SPECIFICATIONS

Year	Eng. V.I.N. Code	Engine No. Cyl. Displacement liters (cu in.)	Mfg.	Carburetor Type	Horsepower @ rpm ■	Torque @ rpm (ft lbs)■	Bore × Stroke (in.)	Compression Ratio	Oil Pressure @ 2000 rpm
'78	E	4-1.6 (97.6)	Chev.	1 bbl	63 @ 4800	82 @ 3200	3.228 × 2.980	8.6:1	34-42
	J	4-1.6 (97.6)	Chev.	1 bbl HO	68 @ 5000	84 @ 3200	3.228 × 2.980	8.6:1	34-42
'79	E	4-1.6 (97.6)	Chev.	2 bbl	70 @ 5200	82 @ 2400	3.228 × 2.980	8.5:1	55
'80	9	4-1.6 (97.6)	Chev.	2 bbl	70 @ 5200	82 @ 2400	3.228 × 2.980	8.5:1	55
'79-'80	0	4-1.6 (97.6)	Chev.	2 bbl HO	74 @ 5200	88 @ 2800	3.228 × 2.980	8.5:1	55
'81-'85	9	4-1.6 (98)	Chev.	2 bbl	65 @ 5200③	80 @ 2400④	3.228 × 2.980	9.0:1①	55
'81-'85 Diesel	D	4-1.8 (111)	Isuzu	Fuel Injection	51 @ 5000	72 @ 2000	3.310 × 3.230	22.0:1	64②

■ Horsepower and torque are SAE net figures. They are measured at the rear of the transmission with all accessories installed and operating. Since the figures vary when a given engine is installed in different models, some are representative rather than exact.
① '81—8.5:1
② @ 5000
③ '81—70 @ 5200
④ '81—82 @ 2400

TUNE-UP SPECIFICATIONS

(When analyzing compression test results, look for uniformity among cylinders rather than specific pressures.)

Year	Eng. V.I.N. Code	Engine No. Cyl. Displacement (liters)	Mfg.	SPARK PLUGS Orig. Type	SPARK PLUGS Gap (in.)	DISTRIBUTOR Point Dwell (deg)	DISTRIBUTOR Point Gap (in.)	IGNITION TIMING (deg) ▲ Man Trans	IGNITION TIMING (deg) ▲ Auto Trans	Valves Intake Opens ■ (deg)	Fuel Pump Pressure (psi)	IDLE SPEED (rpm) ▲ Man Trans ●	IDLE SPEED (rpm) ▲ Auto Trans.
'78	E	4-1.6 base	Chev.	R-43TS	.035	Electronic		8B	8B	28	5-6.5	800	800
	0	4-1.6 HO	Chev.	R-43TS	.035	Electronic		8B	8B	31	5-6.5	800	800
'79	E	4-1.6 base	Chev.	R-42TS	.035	Electronic		12B	18B①	28	5-6.5	800	750
	0	4-1.6 HO	Chev.	R-42TS	.035	Electronic		12B	18B②	31	5-6.5	800	750
'80	9	4-1.6 base	Chev.	R42TS	.035	Electronic		12B	18B	28	5-6.5	800	750③
	0	4-1.6 HO	Chev.	R42TS	.035	Electronic		12B	18B	31	5-6.5	800	750
'81	9	4-1.6	Chev.	R42TS	.035	Electronic		18B	18B	28	2.5-6.5	800	700
'82-'85		4-1.6				See Underhood Specification Sticker							

NOTE: The underhood specifications sticker often reflects tune-up specification changes made in production. Sticker figures must be used if they disagree with those in this chart. Product numbers in this chart are not recommendations by Chilton for any product by brand name.
▲ See text for procedure
● Figure in parentheses indicates California engine
■ All figures Before Top Dead Center
B Before Top Dead Center
HO High Output
① Calif.—16B
② Calif.—12B
③ Calif.—800

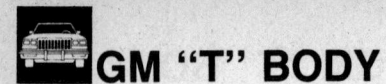

DIESEL TUNE-UP SPECIFICATIONS

Year	Engine No. Cyl. Displacement (liters)	Static Injection Timing	Fuel Injection Order	Compression (lbs)	Injection Nozzle Opening Pressure (psi)	Intake Valve Opens (deg)	IDLE SPEED ▲ (rpm) Man.	IDLE SPEED ▲ (rpm) Auto.
'81-'82	L-4 (1.8)	18°B	1-3-4-2	441①	1707	32	625	725
'83-'85	L-4 (1.8)	11°B	1-3-4-2	441①	1707	32	620	720

NOTE: The underhood specifications sticker often reflects changes made in production. Sticker figures must be used if they disagree with those in the above chart.
▲ See underhood sticker for fast idle speed.
① At 200 rpm

FIRING ORDER

NOTE: To avoid confusion, replace spark plugs and wires one at a time.

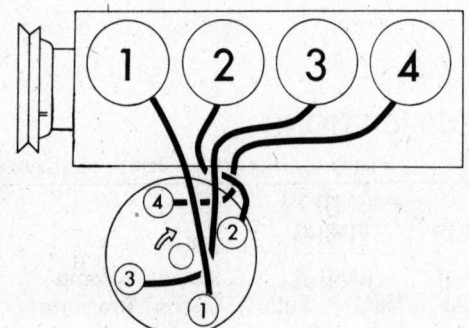

Chevrolet 98 cu. in. (1.6 liter) 4 cyl.
Engine firing order: 1-3-4-2
Distributor rotation: clockwise

CAPACITIES

Year	Engine No. Cyl. Displacement (liters)	Engine Crankcase	TRANSMISSION PTS TO REFILL AFTER DRAINING Manual 4-Speed	TRANSMISSION PTS TO REFILL AFTER DRAINING Manual 5-Speed	Automatic ●	Drive Axle (pts)	Gasoline Tank (gals)	COOLING SYSTEM (qts) With Heater	COOLING SYSTEM (qts) With A/C
'78	4-1.6	4	3	—	10	2	12.5	8.5	9.0
'79	4-1.6	4	3	—	10	1.75	12.5	8.5	9.0
'80-'85	4-1.6	4	3	4	6	1¾	12.5	9	9¼
'81-'85	4-1.8 Diesel	6①	3	3¼	6	1¾	12.5	8.5	9.0

● Specifications do not include torque converter
① With filter change

VALVE SPECIFICATIONS

Year	Engine No. Cyl. Displacement (liters)	Seat Angle (deg)	Face Angle (deg)	Spring Test Pressure (lbs @ in.)	Spring Installed Height (in.)	STEM TO GUIDE CLEARANCE (in.)		STEM DIAMETER (in.)	
						Intake	Exhaust	Intake	Exhaust
'78-'85	4-1.6	45	46	173 @ .886	1.25	.0006-.0017	.0014-.0025	.3141	.3133
'81-'85	4-1.8 Diesel	45	45	108 @ 1.24①	1.61	.0015-.0028	.0018-.0030	.3128-.3134	.3126-.3132

① Exhaust 112 @ 1.22; Inner spring test
pressures—intake 58 @ 1.14
   exhaust 60 @ 1.12

CRANKSHAFT AND CONNECTING ROD SPECIFICATIONS

(All measurements are given in inches)

Year	Engine No. Cyl. Displacement (liters)	CRANKSHAFT				CONNECTING ROD		
		Main Brg. Journal Dia	Main Brg. Oil Clearance	Shaft End-Play	Thrust on No.	Journal Diameter	Oil Clearance	Side Clearance
'78	4-1.6	2.0078-2.0088	.0009-.0026	.004-.008	4	1.809-1.810	.0014-.0031	.004-.012
'79-'85	4-1.6	2.0078-2.0088	①	.004-.008	4	1.809-1.810	.0014-.0031	.004-.012
'81-'85	4-1.8 Diesel	2.2010-2.2020	.0015-.0027	.0024-.0094	3	1.927-1.928	.0016-.0032	N.A.

N.A.—Not Applicable
① #5—.0009-.0026
   All others—.0005-.0018

CAMSHAFT SPECIFICATIONS

(All measurements in inches. To convert inches to metric units, refer to Metric Information section.)

Year	Engine Type/ Disp. L(cu in.)	Journal Diameter					Bearing Clearance	Lobe Lift		Camshaft End Play
		1	2	3	4	5		Intake	Exhaust	
'78-'85	4-1.6(98)	1.7682-1.7697	1.7584-1.7598	1.7485-1.7500	1.7387-1.7402	1.1816-1.1837	.0020-.0044	.2410	.2410	.0067-.0169
'81-'85	4-1.8(111)			NA			.0008-.0035	NA	NA	NA

NA—Not Available

TORQUE SPECIFICATIONS

(All readings in ft. lbs.)

Year	Engine No. Cyl. Displacement (liters)	Cylinder Head Bolts	Rod Bearing Bolts	Main Bearing Bolts	Crankshaft Pulley Bolt	Flywheel to Crankshaft Bolts	MANIFOLD	
							Intake	Exhaust
'78-'84	4-1.4, 1.6	70-80	34-40	40-52	75-100	40-52	13-18	①
'81-'85	4-1.8 Diesel	②	65	75	N/A	N/A	30	N/A

N/A Not available
① Center bolts—13-18; end bolts—19-25
② First tighten to 21-36 ft. lbs. then retighten to 83-98 (new bolt), 90-105 (reused bolt)

PISTON AND RING SPECIFICATIONS

(All measurements are given in inches. To convert inches to metric units, refer to the Metric Information section.)

Year	Engine Type/ Disp. L(cu in.)	Piston-to-Bore Clearance	Ring Gap			Ring Side Clearance		
			Top Compression	Bottom Compression	Oil Control	Top Compression	Bottom Compression	Oil Control
'78-'85	4-1.6	.0008-.0016	.009-.019	.008-.018	.015-.055	.0012-.0027	.0012-.0032	.0000-.0050
'81-'82	4-1.8 Diesel	.0006-.0014	.0078-.0157	.0078-.0157	.0078-.0157	.0035-.0049	.0014-.0020	.0012-.0028
'83-'85	4-1.8 Diesel	.0002-.0017	.0078-.0157	.0078-.0157	.0078-.0157	.0035-.0049	.0019-.0033	.0012-.0028

WHEEL ALIGNMENT SPECIFICATIONS

Year	Model	CASTER		CAMBER		Toe-in (in.)	Steering Axis Inclination (deg)
		Range (deg)	Pref Setting (deg)	Range (deg)	Pref Setting (deg)		
'78-'81	All	3½P-5½P	4½P	¼P-½P	¼P	1/16P	—
'82-'85	All	4P-6P	5P	¼P-½P	¼P	1/16P	—

N Negative
P Positive

CHARGING SYSTEM

A Delcotron 10-SI series alternator is used on gasoline engines. This unit contains a solid state, integrated circuit voltage regulator. The alternator is non-adjustable and requires no periodic maintenance.

The diesel engine is fitted with an Hitachi alternator, which is equipped with an IC regulator and drives a vacuum pump mounted at its rear.

For further testing and overhaul procedures, please refer to "Charging and Starting" in the Unit Repair section.

Alternator

REMOVAL & INSTALLATION

1. Disconnect the negative battery cable.
2. Disconnect the alternator wiring. On the Chevette diesel, remove the fan shroud and fresh air duct, then disconnect the oil and vacuum lines at the vacuum pump.
3. Remove the brace bolt and the drive belt.
4. Support the alternator, remove the mounting bolt, and remove the alternator.

NOTE: On the diesel, the mount bolts are removed from below the car.

5. Installation is the reverse of removal. Adjust drive belt deflection to ½ in. under moderate thumb pressure.

STARTING SYSTEM

Engine cranking is accomplished by a solenoid-actuated starter motor powered by the vehicle battery. The motor on the gasoline engine is a Delco-Remy unit similar to other GM starters. No periodic lubrication of the motor or solenoid is necessary.

The diesel engine is equipped with an Hitachi reduction gear starter motor which is solenoid activated.

For further testing and overhaul procedures, please refer to "Charging and Starting" in the Unit Repair section.

Starter

REMOVAL & INSTALLATION
Gasoline Engine
1978–79 WITHOUT POWER BRAKES

1. Disconnect the negative battery cable and remove the air cleaner.
2. Disconnect and remove the oil pressure sending unit.

NOTE: The oil pressure sending unit has a harness lock. To disconnect the electrical connector, lift the tab on the collar of the lock and remove the lock assembly.

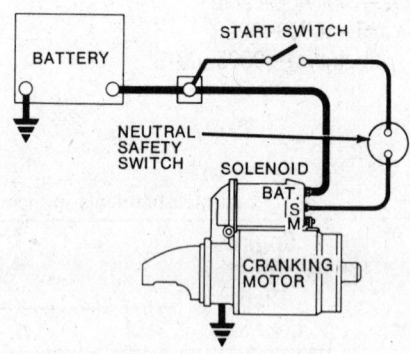

Typical gasoline engine starting system (© Chevrolet Div., G.M. Corp.)

3. Disconnect the starter solenoid.
4. Remove the brace screw from the bottom of the starter housing.
5. Remove the two starter-to-fly-wheel housing mounting screws.
6. Hold the starter with both hands and tip it past the engine mount bracket, then upward between the intake manifold and wheel arch.
7. Installation is the reverse of removal.

1980 AND LATER WITHOUT POWER BRAKES

1. Disconnect the battery negative cable.
2. Remove the air cleaner.
3. Disconnect the gas line at the carburetor and move to one side.
4. Disconnect the vacuum hose at the carburetor.
5. Remove the splash shield from the distributor coil and move to one side.

6. Using a 6 inch and 12 inch extension with a universal socket, remove the upper starter bolt.

7. Remove the lower starter bolt.

8. Disconnect the starter wiring.

9. Remove the master cylinder mounting nuts to gain access for removing the starter.

10. Installation is the reverse of removal.

1978–79 WITH POWER BRAKES (WITHOUT AIR CONDITIONING)

1. Disconnect the battery negative cable and remove the air cleaner.

2. Remove the distributor cap.

3. Remove the fuel line from the carburetor.

4. Disconnect the electrical connector from the ignition coil. Remove the three coil bracket retaining screws and remove the coil with bracket.

5. Disconnect the vacuum hose at the distributor.

6. Disconnect and remove the oil pressure sending unit. See the preceding "Note" concerning the oil pressure sender harness lock.

7. Disconnect the wires from the starter solenoid.

8. Remove the brace screw from the bottom of the starter housing.

9. Remove the two starter-to-fly-wheel housing mounting screws.

10. Hold the starter with both hands and remove it by sliding it toward the front of the car.

11. Installation is the reverse of removal.

1978–79 WITH POWER BRAKES (WITH AIR CONDITIONING)

1. Disconnect the negative battery cable and remove the air cleaner.

2. Remove the upper starter-to-fly-wheel housing mounting screw.

3. Remove the two steering column lever cover screws.

4. Remove the mast jacket lower bracket screw.

5. Remove the upper steering column mounting bracket.

6. Disconnect the four electrical connectors from the steering column.

7. Raise the car on a hoist.

8. Disconnect the steering flexible coupling (rag joint) and push it aside.

9. Disconnect the wires from the starter solenoid.

10. Remove the brace screw from the bottom of the starter housing.

11. Remove the lower starter-to-fly-wheel housing mounting screw.

12. To gain clearance, raise the engine ½ in. with a jack placed under the left-side of the engine.

13. Remove the starter by lowering it through the opening at the bottom of the engine.

14. Installation is the reverse of removal.

1980 AND LATER WITH POWER BRAKES

1. Disconnect the battery ground cable.

2. Remove the air cleaner.

3. Disconnect the gas line at the carburetor and move to one side.

4. Remove the splash shield from the distributor coil and move to one side.

5. Using a 6 inch and 12 inch extension with a universal socket, remove the upper starter bolt.

6. Remove the steering column cover screws and remove the cover.

7. Remove the steering column upper nuts and toe pan screw.

8. Raise the vehicle on a hoist and remove the steering shaft from the steering coupling.

9. Lower the vehicle and move the steering column from inside the car to gain access to the starter.

10. Disconnect the starter wiring.

11. Remove the starter lower bolt and remove the starter.

12. Installation is the reverse of removal.

Diesel Engine

1. Disconnect the negative battery cable.

2. Disconnect the starter wiring after labeling. The starter is located at the right rear of the engine.

3. Remove the upper mounting nut and the lower mounting bolt, then remove the starter.

4. Installation is the reverse of removal.

IGNITION SYSTEM

All gasoline engine models are equipped with High Energy Ignition (HEI). This is a pulse triggered, transistor-controlled, inductive discharge ignition system that uses no breaker points. The HEI distributor contains a pick-up assembly and an electronic module which perform the function of breaker points. Centrifugal and vacuum advance mechanisms are basically the same as those in breaker point distributors. 1981 and later models are equipped with EST (Electronic Spark Timing) distributors which have no mechanical or vacuum advance mechanisms. The ignition coil is mounted externally, on the left side of the engine, beneath the intake manifold, and is not visible on A/C equipped cars. The coil has a plastic cover.

A conventional ignition system is not needed on the diesel engine, because it uses compression heat rather than a manufactured spark to ignite its air/fuel mixture. An electrically operated glow plug system is used on the diesel engine to pre-heat the combustion chambers for easy cold startup.

See the Diesel Maintenance Unit Repair Section for additional diesel engine information.

For further information on the ignition system, please refer to "Electronic Ignition Systems" in the Unit Repair section.

HEI System Tachometer Hookup

Connect a tachometer to the negative terminal on the coil and to a ground. However, some tachometers must connect to the negative terminal and the battery positive terminal. Some old tachometers, without a relay, won't work at all with HEI. Check the tachometer manufacturer's instructions.

Distributor

REMOVAL & INSTALLATION

1. Disconnect the negative battery cable.

2. If the vehicle is air conditioned: Disconnect the electrical lead at the air conditioning compressor. Remove the compressor mounting thru bolt and two adjusting bolts. Remove two bolts and remove the compressor upper mounting bracket. Raise the vehicle on a hoist. Remove the two bolts securing the compressor lower mounting bracket and pull the bracket outward for clearance. Lower the vehicle.

Do not disconnect refrigerant lines.

3. Remove the air cleaner.

4. Remove the distributor cap and place it aside.

5. Remove the ignition coil cover by prying on the flat on the front edge of the cover.

6. Remove the ignition coil mounting bracket bolts.

7. Disconnect the electrical connector with red and brown wires that goes from the ignition coil to the distributor.

8. Remove the fuel pump, gasket, and push rod, noting the direction in which push rod was installed.

NOTE: It is important that the push rod be installed in exactly the same direction as removed.

9. Scribe a mark on the engine in line with the distributor rotor. Note the approximate position of the distributor housing in relation to the engine.

10. Remove the distributor hold-down bolt and clamp and remove the distributor.

11. If the engine has not been disturbed with the distributor removed, simply reverse the installation procedure to install, aligning the marks made during removal. If the engine has been disturbed, remove the No. 1 spark plug and place your thumb or finger over the spark plug hole. Manually turn the engine in the normal direction of operation until compression is felt and the

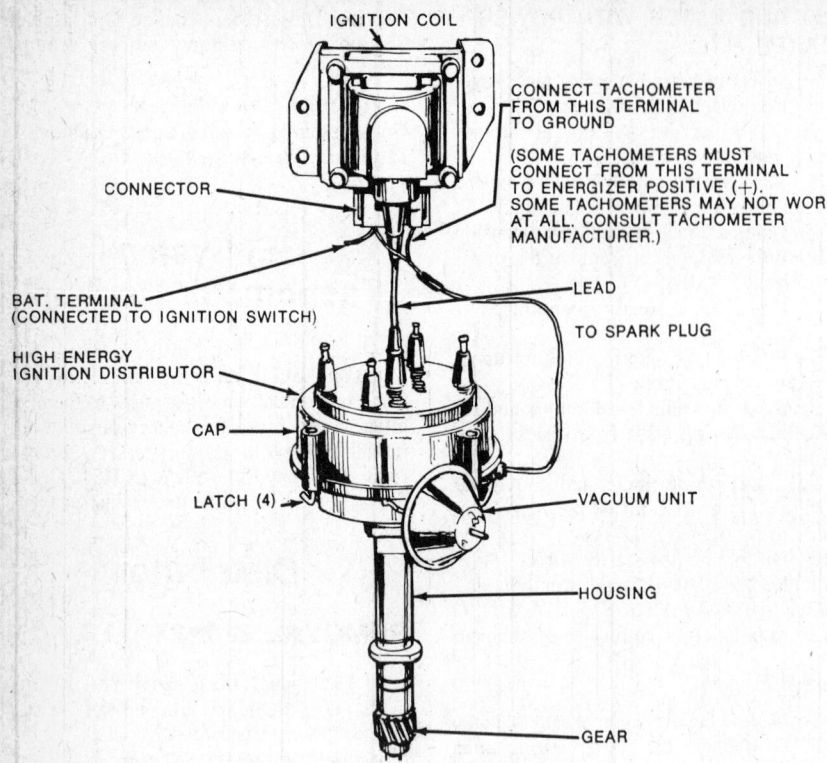

IGNITION COIL

CONNECT TACHOMETER FROM THIS TERMINAL TO GROUND

(SOME TACHOMETERS MUST CONNECT FROM THIS TERMINAL TO ENERGIZER POSITIVE (+). SOME TACHOMETERS MAY NOT WORK AT ALL. CONSULT TACHOMETER MANUFACTURER.)

CONNECTOR

BAT. TERMINAL (CONNECTED TO IGNITION SWITCH)

HIGH ENERGY IGNITION DISTRIBUTOR

CAP

LATCH (4)

LEAD

TO SPARK PLUG

VACUUM UNIT

HOUSING

GEAR

HEI tachometer hookup

NOTE: Steps 3-4 are important, because if the engine is at idle and not warm enough, when the EST terminal is disconnected, the oxygen sensor could cool off, putting the system into an open loop operation resulting in the engine shutting off.

5. With the engine running, aim the timing light at the timing mark.

6. If a change is necessary, loosen the distributor hold-down clamp bolt at the base of the distributor. While observing the mark with the timing light, slightly rotate the distributor until the correct timing is indicated. Tighten the hold-down bolt, and recheck the timing.

7. Turn off the engine and reconnect all wires.

NOTE: Models with air conditioning require removal of the compressor since it is mounted directly above the distributor. Do not disconnect the refrigerant lines. Move the compressor and bracket to one side.

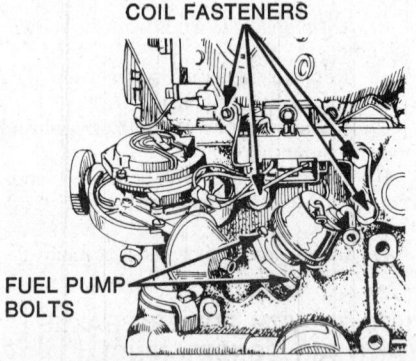

COIL FASTENERS

FUEL PUMP BOLTS

Fuel pump and coil bolt locations

timing marks point to Top Dead Center. Align the marks made during removal and install the distributor.

Ignition Timing

ADJUSTMENT

Models Without EST Distributor

NOTE: Use an adapter to make timing light connections at the distributor No. 1 terminal.

NOTE: Follow all the instructions on the Vehicle Emissions Control Information label located on the radiator support panel.

1. Bring the engine to normal operating temperature. Stop the engine and connect a tachometer. Disconnect and plug the PCV hose at the vapor canister and the vacuum hose at the distributor vacuum advance unit (on models so equipped). Start the engine and check curb idle speed. Adjust as necessary.

2. Stop the engine, clean the timing marks and mark them with chalk to make them more visible. Connect a timing light.

3. Start the engine and aim the timing light at the timing marks. If the marks align, stop the engine, reconnect the PCV and vacuum hoses, and remove the timing light.

4. If adjustment is necessary, loosen the distributor clamp and rotate the distributor to align the marks. Tighten the clamp and recheck the timing.

NOTE: Air conditioned models require removal of the compressor, bracket, and belt to reach the distributor clamp.

Do not disconnect refrigerant lines. Move compressor and bracket to one side.

5. Reset the curb idle speed if necessary, stop the engine, and remove the tachometer and timing light. Reconnect the PCV and vacuum hoses.

Models With EST Distributor

NOTE: Engines with Electronic Spark Timing (EST) can be identified by the absence of a vacuum and a mechanical spark advance on the distributor. EST allows continuous spark timing adjustments to be made by the ECM (Electronic Control Module).

1. Follow all instructions on the Vehicle Emissions Control information label located on the radiator support panel.

2. Connect the pick-up lead of the timing light to the number one spark plug. Use a jumper lead or adapter between the wire and plug, better yet use a timing light with an inductive type pick-up.

NOTE: Do not pierce the wire or attempt to insert a wire between the boot and the wire. Connect the timing light power leads according to the manufacturer's instructions.

3. Start the engine and make sure it is operating at normal operating temperature.

4. Increase idle and disconnect the four (4) terminal EST connector at the distributor. This will cause the engine to operate in the bypass timing mode.

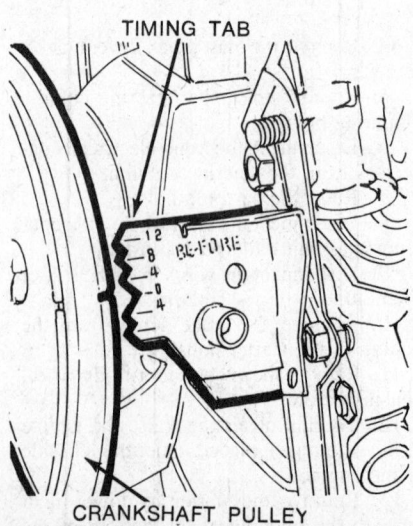

TIMING TAB

BEFORE

CRANKSHAFT PULLEY

Ignition timing marks
(© Chevrolet Div., G.M. Corp)

GASOLINE FUEL SYSTEM

All 1978 Chevettes use a Rochester 1ME carburetor. The unit incorporates an automatic choke with an electronically heated choke coil. The choke coil is heated in a housing which is mounted on a bracket connected to the fuel bowl.

The internal fuel filter is made of pleated paper and is located in the fuel bowl behind the fuel inlet nut. The throttle body of the 1ME is made of aluminum for better heat dispersement.

The carburetor identification number is stamped on the float bowl, right next to the fuel inlet nut. When replacing the fuel bowl, be sure to transfer the identification number to the new bowl.

All 1979 Chevettes are equipped with a 2-bbl Holley carburetor, model number 5210-C. This provides a slight increase in horsepower and at the same time, improves the fuel economy. Like the 1 bbl carburetor, this carburetor is also equipped with an internal fuel filter.

1980 models are equipped with either the 5210-C carburetor or the 6510-C model. 1981 and later models use only the 6510-C. Both are staged, two barrel models which are very similar to one another.

Fuel Pump

REMOVAL & INSTALLATION

NOTE: Air conditioned cars require the removal of the rear compressor bracket to gain working room.

1. Disconnect the negative battery cable.
2. Remove the distributor cap and the spark plug wire retaining clips.
3. Remove the coil wire and the coil assembly.
4. It may be necessary to remove the air cleaner on some models.
5. Disconnect the fuel pump hoses and remove the pump.
6. Remove the fuel pump push rod.
7. Reverse the above to install.

Fuel Filter

REMOVAL & INSTALLATION

NOTE: Do not perform this operation on a hot engine. Place some rags under the fuel fitting to catch any spilled fuel.

1. Disconnect the small fuel line connection nut, using a flare nut wrench, while holding the large fitting nut with a standard open end wrench.

NOTE: A flared nut wrench is preferred over a standard open end wrench

since it will not slip off and round off the corners of the tubing nut.

2. Remove the large filter retaining nut from the carburetor. There is a spring behind the filter. Remove the filter and spring.
3. Install the spring and the filter element.
4. Install the new gasket on the retaining nut and screw it into place. Do not overtighten; the threads are rather soft.
5. Install the fuel line.
6. Discard the gas-soaked rag safely.

Carburetor

REMOVAL & INSTALLATION

1. Remove air cleaner and gasket.
2. Disconnect the fuel and vacuum lines from the carburetor.
3. Disconnect the accelerator linkage and the electrical connectors.
4. Remove the carburetor attaching nuts and remove the carburetor.
5. Remove the electric EFE heater (if so equipped) and the insulator gasket.

6. Be sure the throttle body and intake manifold sealing surfaces are clean.

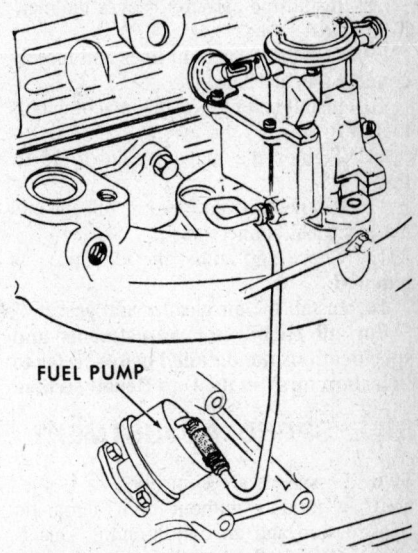

FUEL PUMP

Chevette fuel pump location (© Chevrolet Div., G.M. Corp.)

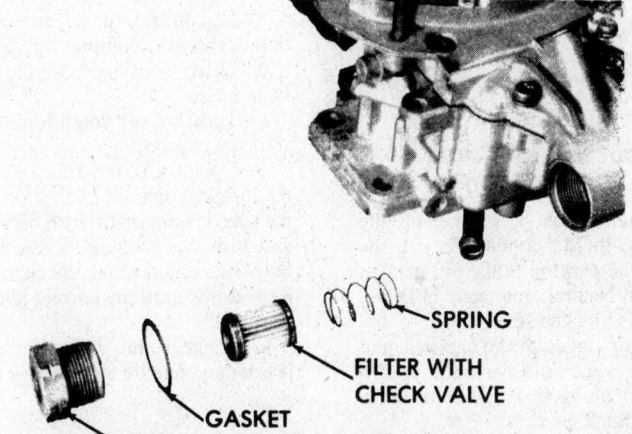

SPRING
FILTER WITH CHECK VALVE
GASKET
NUT

Fuel filter assembly—2 bbl (© Chevrolet Div., G.M. Corp.)

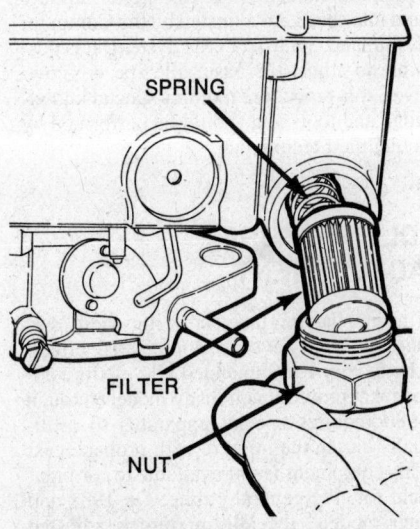

SPRING
FILTER
NUT

Fuel filter assembly—Rochester 1 bbl (© Chevrolet Div., G.M. Corp.)

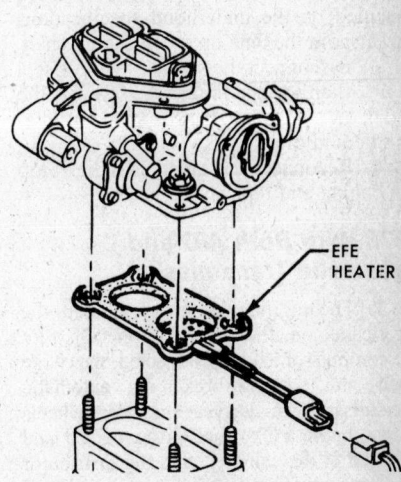

EFE HEATER

EFE heater and insulator gasket location (© Chevrolet Div., G.M. Corp.)

7. Install a new EFE heater (if so equipped) and an insulator gasket on the manifold.

8. Install the carburetor over the manifold studs.

9. Install the vacuum lines and loosely connect the fuel line.

10. Install and tighten the attaching nuts to 144 in. lbs.

11. Tighten the fuel inlet nut to 25 ft. lbs.

12. Connect the accelerator linkage and the electrical connectors.

13. Check and adjust the idle speed as required.

14. Install the air cleaner and gasket.

For all carburetor adjustments and specifications not detailed below, refer to "Carburetors" in the Unit Repair section.

IDLE SPEED ADJUSTMENT

Two idle speeds are controlled by a solenoid on models without both automatic transmission and air conditioning. One is normal curb idle speed (solenoid energized). The second is low idle speed (solenoid de-energized) which prevents dieseling when the ignition is turned off. On cars with both automatic transmission and air conditioning the solenoid is energized when air conditioning is on to maintain curb idle speed.

1978 Without Both A/C and Automatic Transmission

1. The engine must be warmed up, the air cleaner on, the air conditioner off, the choke open, the parking brake on, manual transmission in Neutral, automatic in Drive, the rear wheels blocked, the PCV hose disconnected and plugged at the canister, and the distributor vacuum advance hose disconnected and plugged at the distributor. Connect a tachometer.

2. Open the throttle momentarily to let the solenoid plunger extend. Turn the solenoid body nut to get the curb idle speed specified on the underhood specifications sticker or in the tune-up specifications chart.

3. Disconnect the solenoid wire. Use a ⅛ in. Allen wrench to turn the screw in the end of the solenoid to the specified low idle, or solenoid off, speed.

4. Reconnect the solenoid wire. Stop the engine and replace the hoses.

1978 With Both A/C and Automatic Transmission

1. The engine must be warmed up, the air cleaner on, the air conditioner on with the compressor lead disconnected, the choke open, the parking brake on, automatic transmission in Drive, the rear wheels blocked, the PCV hose disconnected and plugged at the canister, and the distributor vacuum advance hose disconnected and plugged at the distributor. Connect a tachometer. Open the throttle momentarily to let the solenoid plunger extend.

2. Turn the solenoid body nut to get an idle speed of 950 rpm.

3. Reconnect the compressor lead, and turn the air conditioner off.

4. Adjust the curb idle speed by turning the ⅛ in. Allen screw in the end of the solenoid.

5. Stop the engine and replace the hoses.

1979 and Later 5210-C Carburetor

Refer to the emission label on the car for the proper idle speed adjustment procedure.

1980 Models With 6510-C Carburetor

1. Adjust the timing as previously outlined.

2. On non-air conditioned models, connect the PCV and the vacuum advance hoses and adjust the idle speed to specification using the idle speed adjusting screw on the carburetor.

3. If the car is equipped with air conditioning:

a. Disconnect the electrical connection at the A/C compressor.

b. Disconnect and plug the EGR and PCV hoses.

c. Turn the air conditioning On and start the engine.

d. Open the throttle slightly to extend the throttle solenoid on the carburetor. If the speed is incorrect, turn off the engine and turn the solenoid screw to adjust. Start the engine and check the speed. Repeat this until the correct idle speed is obtained.

e. Connect the wiring at the compressor and unplug and connect the hoses.

1981 and Later Models

On these models, the carburetor mixture and idle speed are adjusted by the Computer Command Control (CCC) System. It is possible to adjust the basic idle speed—however, this procedure requires special knowledge and tools and should be performed by a qualified technician.

IDLE MIXTURE ADJUSTMENT

Turning the mixture screw on these carburetors will have no appreciable effect. The factory-recommended idle mixture adjustment procedure on many models through 1980 requires special apparatus to artificially enrich the mixture with propane gas. This equipment is not available to, or practical for, the general public. On 1981 and later models, the idle mixture is adjusted by the CCC system and requires no manual adjustment.

DIESEL FUEL SYSTEM

The diesel fuel system consists of a high pressure fuel injection pump driven by the camshaft timing belt, four pressure activated fuel injectors installed in the cylinder head and connected by fuel lines to the pump, a fuel filter with built in water separator, drain and hand primer, a fuel tank and connecting fuel feed and return lines. The injection pump is equipped with an electrically operated fuel cut-off solenoid which halts fuel flow (and the engine) whenever the ignition key is turned to the "Off" position.

For further information on diesel engines, please refer to "Diesel Maintenance" in the Unit Repair section.

Fuel Filter

REMOVAL & INSTALLATION

1. Disconnect the negative battery cable.

2. Disconnect the water sensor lead at the bottom of the filter, then disconnect the water filter to main body hose.

3. Remove the filter element by turning it counterclockwise using a filter strap wrench. Be careful not to spill any fuel.

4. After draining the filter, unscrew the water sensor from the bottom of the element.

5. Install the sensor in the new filter after applying a thin film of diesel fuel to the sensor O-ring.

6. Clean the filter mounting surface, apply a thin film of diesel fuel to the gasket on the new filter and install the filter. Continue turning the filter an additional ⅔ turn after it contacts the filter main body.

7. Connect the sensor wire. Disconnect the fuel outlet hose from the injector pump and place in a suitable container, then operate the priming pump handle several times to fill the filter with fuel. Reconnect the hose to the injector pump and start the engine to check for leaks.

Idle Speed

ADJUSTMENT

1. Set the parking brake and block the wheels.

2. Place the transmission in Neutral. Connect a tachometer as per the manufacturer's instructions.

3. Start the engine and allow it to reach normal operating temperature.

4. Loosen the lock nut on the idle speed adjusting screw and turn the screw to obtain the correct idle speed (see underhood specifications sticker).

5. Tighten the lock nut, turn the engine off and disconnect the tachometer.

Fast Idle Speed

ADJUSTMENT

1. Set the parking brake and block the wheels.
2. Place the transmission in neutral.
3. Connect a tachometer.
4. Start the engine and allow it to run until it reaches normal operating temperature.
5. Apply vacuum to the fast idle actuator.
6. Loosen the lock nut on the fast idle adjusting screw and adjust the knurled nut to obtain the fast idle speed specified on the emission label. After adjusting, re-tighten the lock nut.

Injection Pump

REMOVAL & INSTALLATION

NOTE: This procedure will require the use of two special tools: a gear puller (J-22888), and a fixing plate (J-29761). It is a long and complicated procedure and must be performed in conjunction with the following "injection timing" procedure. We do not suggest that the average amateur mechanic perform these procedures.

1. Disconnect the negative battery cable.
2. Drain the cooling system. Remove the fan shroud, radiator and coolant recovery tank.
3. Disconnect the bypass hose leading from the front cover and then remove the upper half of the front cover.

NOTE: Fan removal may facilitate better access to certain front cover retaining bolts.

4. Loosen the timing belt tension pulley and plate bolts. Slide the tensioner over.
5. Unscrew the two retaining bolts and

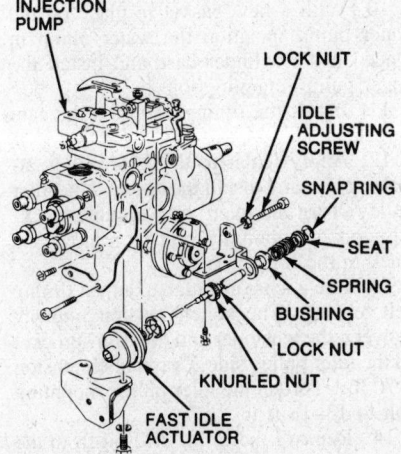

Exploded view of diesel injection pump linkage showing idle adjusting screw and fast idle adjuster (knurled nut) (© Chevrolet Div., G.M. Corp.)

remove the tension spring from behind the front plate, by the injection pump.

6. Remove the injection pump gear retaining nut and then remove the gear with a gear puller.
7. Tag and disconnect any wires, hoses or cables leading from the pump. Disconnect and plug the fuel feed lines.
8. Remove the fuel filter. Disconnect the injector lines at the pump and at the injector nozzles and remove the lines.
9. Unscrew the four retaining bolts and remove the pump rear bracket.
10. Unscrew the nuts attaching the pump flange to the front plate and then remove the pump complete with the fast idle device and return spring. To install:

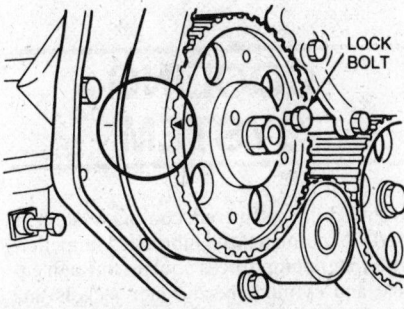

Use a lockbolt to ensure that the index marks on the injection pump gear and the front plate stay in alignment—diesel (© Chevrolet Div., G.M. Corp.)

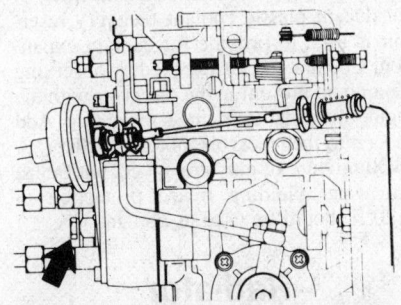

Remove the distributor head screw and washer (© Chevrolet Div., G.M. Corp.)

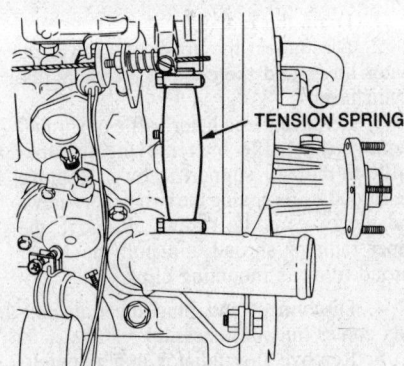

Tension spring, located behind the front plate beside the injection pump on diesel engine (© Chevrolet Div., G.M. Corp.)

11. Place the pump in position and tighten the flange bolts. Position the rear bracket and tighten the bracket-to-block bolts, then tighten the bracket-to-pump bolts. There should be no clearance between the rear bracket and the pump bracket.
12. Reconnect all wires, hoses and cables.
13. Slide the pump gear onto its shaft, making sure that it is aligned with the key groove. Turn the gear until the notch mark aligns with the index mark on the front plate. Thread a lock bolt (8mm × 1.25) through the gear and into the front plate and then tighten the retaining nut to 45 ft lbs.
14. Remove the cylinder head cover. Position the No. 1 piston at TDC of the compression stroke and install the fixing plate into the slot in the rear of the camshaft to prevent it from rotating.
15. Unscrew the cam gear retaining bolt and, using a puller, remove the gear. Reinstall the gear loosely so that it can be turned smoothly by hand.
16. Grasp the timing belt on each side near the lower half of the front cover; move it back and forth until the cogs on the belt engage with those on the lower gears. Slide the belt over the pump gear and then over the cam gear (you may need to turn the cam gear slightly to facilitate proper engagement of the cogs).
17. Make sure that any slack in the belt is concentrated around the tension pulley and NOT around or between the two upper gears. Depress the tension pulley with your finger and then install the tension spring.
18. Partially tighten the tension pulley bolts; first the upper, then the lower. Tighten the cam gear retaining bolt to 45 ft lbs.
19. Remove the pump gear lock bolt. Remove the fixing plate from the end of the camshaft.
20. Check that the No. 1 piston is still at TDC. Check that the marks on the front plate and the pump gear are still aligned. Check that the fixing plate still fits properly into the rear of the camshaft.

NOTE: If these three steps do not check out correctly, repeat the entire procedure, DO NOT attempt to compensate by moving the camshaft, pump gear or crankshaft.

21. Loosen the tension pulley and plate bolts. Make sure the belt slack is concentrated around the pulley and then tighten the bolts in the same manner as before. Belt tension should be checked at a point between the cam gear and the pump gear.
22. Installation of the remaining components is in the reverse order of removal.
23. Check the injection timing.

Injection Timing

1. Check that the No. 1 piston is at TDC of the compression stroke. Make sure that the timing belt is properly tensioned and the timing marks are aligned.

2. Remove the cylinder head cover and check that the fixing plate used in the previous section will still fit smoothly into the slot at the rear of the camshaft.

3. Remove the injection lines as detailed earlier and then remove the distributor head screw and washer.

4. Position a Static Timing Gauge (J-29763) and a dial indicator in the distributor head hole. Set the lift approximately 0.04 in. (1 mm) from the end of the plunger.

5. Turn the crankshaft until the No. 1 piston is 45-60 degrees BTDC and then zero the dial indicator.

NOTE: The damper pulley is notched with eleven lines; four in one position, seven in another. The group of four are to be used for static timing.

6. Turn the crankshaft until the 18° notch on the damper pulley is aligned with the timing pointer.

7. The dial indicator should read 0.02 in. (0.05mm). If it does not, hold the crankshaft in the 18° position, loosen the two nuts on the injection pump flange and move the pump until the proper reading is achieved. Swivel the pump up to retard the timing and down to advance the timing. When adjustment is correct, retighten the pump flange nuts.

8. Remove the dial indicator and install the distributor head screw and washer.

9. Install the cylinder head cover, injection lines and fuel filter.

10. Reconnect all necessary wires and hoses. Installation of the remaining components is in the reverse order of removal.

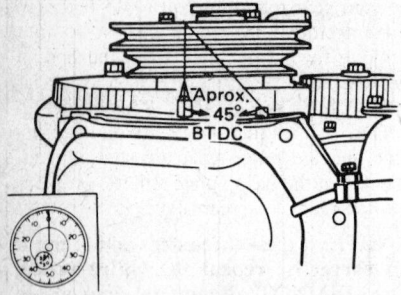

Zeroing the dial indicator (© Chevrolet Div., G.M. Corp.)

Fuel Injector Nozzle

REMOVAL & INSTALLATION

NOTE: The primary function of an injection nozzle is to distribute fuel in the combustion chamber. Do not, under any circumstances, crank the engine while an injection line or injector is disconnected.

1. Disconnect the negative battery cable.
2. Remove the fresh air duct and disconnect the PCV hose.
3. Disconnect the injection line at the injector nozzle and then loosen it at the injection pump. Carefully move it out of the way.

4. Remove the fuel return line.
5. Unscrew and remove the injector.
6. Installation is in the reverse order of removal.

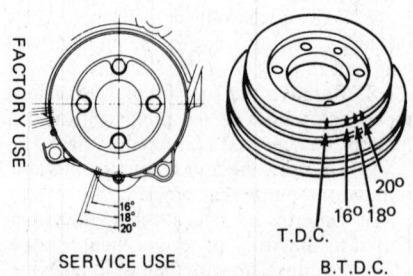

Static timing notches on the damper pulley (© Chevrolet Div., G.M. Corp.)

COOLING SYSTEM

A standard pressurized cooling system is used. A permanently lubricated impeller-type water pump forces coolant through engine and cylinder head water jackets and into a cross-flow radiator. Some models use a heavy-duty radiator with a fan shroud. The pressure-type radiator cap pressurizes the cooling system to 15 psi. A 190°F (180°F on Diesel) thermostat in the coolant outlet passage is used to control coolant flow. A translucent plastic coolant recovery reservoir is used to provide for coolant expansion. Coolant level is checked by observing the amount present in the reservoir with the engine at normal operating temperature. Add coolant to the reservoir, not the radiator. A 50/50 mixture of ethylene glycol antifreeze and water yielding freeze protection to −20°F should be used as coolant.

Radiator

REMOVAL & INSTALLATION
1978

1. Drain the radiator.
2. Disconnect the upper and lower radiator hoses and the coolant recovery reservoir hose.
3. Remove the radiator baffle or shroud. Remove the baffle by removing the four baffle-to-radiator support screws. Remove the shroud by removing the two upper screws and the two middle screws. Remove the upper radiator shroud and pull the lower shroud from its mounting clips.
4. Disconnect and plug the transmission cooler lines if necessary.
5. Remove the radiator upper mounting panel or brackets and lift the radiator out of the lower brackets.
6. To install, reverse the removal procedure. Fill the system and run the engine

with the heater on until the thermostat opens. Recheck the level.

1979 and Later

1. Disconnect the negative battery cable.
2. Drain the cooling system.
3. Remove the upper radiator support or the upper fan shroud, as necessary.
4. Disconnect the coolant hoses and the automatic transmission cooler lines from the radiator.
5. Remove the radiator.
6. Reverse to install.

Water Pump

REMOVAL & INSTALLATION
Gasoline Engine

1. Disconnect the battery negative cable and remove the alternator, and A/C compressor drive belts.
2. Remove the engine fan, spacer (air conditioned models), and the pulley.
3. Remove the timing belt front cover by removing the two upper bolts, center bolt, and two lower nuts. Remove the timing belt lower cover retaining nut and remove the cover.
4. Drain the coolant from the engine.
5. Remove the lower radiator hose and the heater hose at the water pump.
6. Turn the crankshaft pulley so that the mark on the pulley is aligned with the 0 mark on the timing scale and that a ⅛ in. drill bit can be inserted through the timing belt upper rear cover and camshaft sprocket.
7. Remove the idler pulley and pull the timing belt off the sprocket. Don't disturb crankshaft position.
8. Remove the water pump retaining bolts and remove the pump and gasket from the engine.
9. Clean all the old gasket material from the cylinder case.
10. With a new gasket in place on the water pump, position the water pump in place on the cylinder case and install the water pump retaining bolts.
11. Install the timing belt onto the cam sprocket.
12. Apply sealer to the idler pulley attaching bolt and install the bolt and the idler pulley. Turn the idler pulley counterclockwise on its mounting bolt to remove the slack in the timing belt.
13. Use a tension gauge to adjust timing belt tension. Check belt tension midway between the tensioner and the cam sprocket on the idler pulley side. Correct belt tension is 70 lbs. Torque the idler pulley mounting bolt to 13–18 ft lbs.
14. Remove the ⅛ in. drill bit from the upper rear timing belt cover and cam sprocket.
15. Install the lower radiator hose and the heater hose to the water pump.
16. Install the timing belt front covers.

17. Install the water pump pulley, spacer (if equipped), and engine fan.

18. Install the engine drive belt(s).

19. Refill the cooling system.

20. Connect the battery negative cable.

21. Start the engine and check for leaks. Run the engine with the heater on until the thermostat opens, then recheck the coolant level.

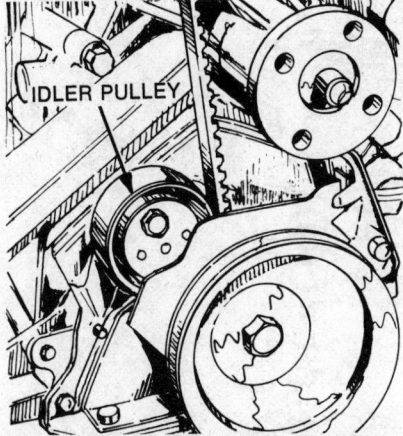

Gasoline engine timing belt idler pulley

Diesel Engine

1. Disconnect the negative battery cable and drain the cooling system.

2. Remove the fan shroud, fan assembly and the accessory drive belt.

3. Unscrew the retaining bolts and remove the damper pulley.

4. Remove the upper and lower halves of the front cover and then remove the bypass hose at the pump.

5. Unscrew the pump retaining bolts and remove the pump assembly.

6. Installation is in the reverse order of removal.

Thermostat

REMOVAL & INSTALLATION

1. Drain the radiator and remove the radiator hose at the water outlet.

2. Remove the thermostat housing bolts and remove the housing, gasket, and thermostat.

3. Install the thermostat. Use a new gasket on the thermostat housing and install the thermostat housing bolts.

4. Install the radiator hose at the water outlet.

5. Fill the cooling system. Run the engine with the heater on until the thermostat opens, then recheck the coolant level.

EMISSION CONTROLS

For a description and service procedures for the following emission control systems, please refer to "Emission Control" in the Unit Repair section.

- Positive Crankcase Ventilation
- Exhaust Gas Recirculation
- Pulse Air System
- Evaporative Emission Control
- Controled Combustion System
- Thermostatic Air Cleaner
- Catalytic Converter
- Computer Controled Catalytic Converter (C-4) System
- Computer Command Control (CCC) System
- Resetting emissions indicator flag in speedometer.

ENGINE

All gasoline engine models are powered by a 1.6 liter inline four-cylinder overhead camshaft, 98 cu. in. engine.

The belt-driven camshaft is supported on five bearing surfaces in an aluminum carrier on top of the cast iron cylinder head. The crossflow cylinder head has induction-hardened exhaust valve seats for greater durability. Rocker arms bridge hydraulic valve adjusters and the valve stems and open the valves via camshaft depression.

The distributor and oil pump are simultaneously driven by a gear on the crankshaft next to the front main bearing. An eccentric on the distributor shaft drives the fuel pump.

The cast iron cylinder block supports the crankshaft in five main bearings. The aluminum intake manifold is heated by engine coolant.

Beginning in 1981, the Chevette, and in 1982 the T1000 offers an optional diesel engine. This is a 1.8 liter inline four-cylinder overhead camshaft engine on which the belt-driven camshaft rides in five bearings. The valves are operated by direct acting rocker arms, while adjustment is manually obtained through lash adjusters on the opposite end of each rocker arm. The cast iron, cross-flow cylinder head incorporates a pre-combustion chamber which adds to smooth performance and easy start-up characteristics.

The injection pump and the oil pump are also driven off of a cog belt by means of the crankshaft. The crankshaft is supported in the cast iron cylinder block by five main bearings with the thrust being taken on the center bearing.

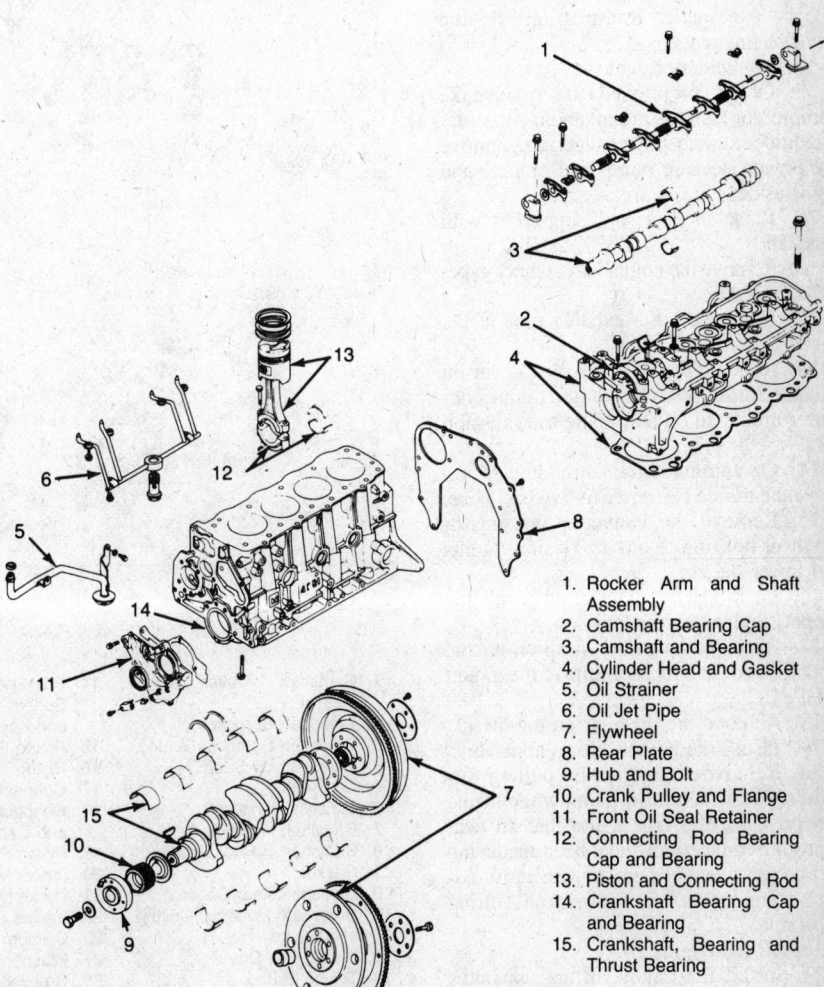

1. Rocker Arm and Shaft Assembly
2. Camshaft Bearing Cap
3. Camshaft and Bearing
4. Cylinder Head and Gasket
5. Oil Strainer
6. Oil Jet Pipe
7. Flywheel
8. Rear Plate
9. Hub and Bolt
10. Crank Pulley and Flange
11. Front Oil Seal Retainer
12. Connecting Rod Bearing Cap and Bearing
13. Piston and Connecting Rod
14. Crankshaft Bearing Cap and Bearing
15. Crankshaft, Bearing and Thrust Bearing

Exploded view of the diesel engine

REMOVAL & INSTALLATION

CAUTION

Do not discharge the air conditioning compressor or disconnect any of the refrigerant lines unless you have the skill and experience necessary to do so. Personal injury from the freon gas may result.

1. Remove the engine hood from the car.

2. Disconnect the battery cables.

3. Remove the battery cable clips from the frame rail.

4. Drain the cooling system. Disconnect the radiator hoses from the engine and the heater hoses at the heater.

5. Tag and disconnect any wires leading from the engine.

6. Remove the radiator upper support and remove the radiator and engine fan. On the diesel, you must also remove the oil cooler.

7. Remove the air cleaner assembly.

8. Disconnect the following items:

a. Fuel line at the rubber hose along the left frame rail. On the diesel, disconnect and plug the fuel lines at the injector pump and position them out of the way.

b. Automatic transmission throttle valve linkage.

c. Accelerator cable.

9. On air conditioned cars, remove the compressor from its mount and lay it aside. If equipped with power steering, remove the power steering pump and bracket and lay it aside.

10. Raise the car and support it with jackstands.

11. Remove the engine strut (shock-type) on the diesel.

12. Disconnect the exhaust pipe at the exhaust manifold.

13. Remove the flywheel dust cover on manual transmission cars or the torque converter underpan on automatic transmission cars.

14. On automatic transmission cars, remove the torque converter-to-flywheel bolts.

15. Remove the converter housing or flywheel housing-to-engine retaining bolts and lower the car.

16. Position a floor jack or other suitable support under the transmission.

17. Remove the safety straps from the front engine mounts and remove the mount nuts.

18. Remove the oil filter on the diesel.

19. Install the engine lifting apparatus.

20. Remove the engine by pulling forward to clear the transmission while lifting slowly. Check to make sure that all necessary disconnections have been made and that proper clearance exists with surrounding components. Remove the lifting apparatus.

To install the engine:

21. Install the engine lifting apparatus and install guide pins in the engine block.

22. Install the engine in the car by align-

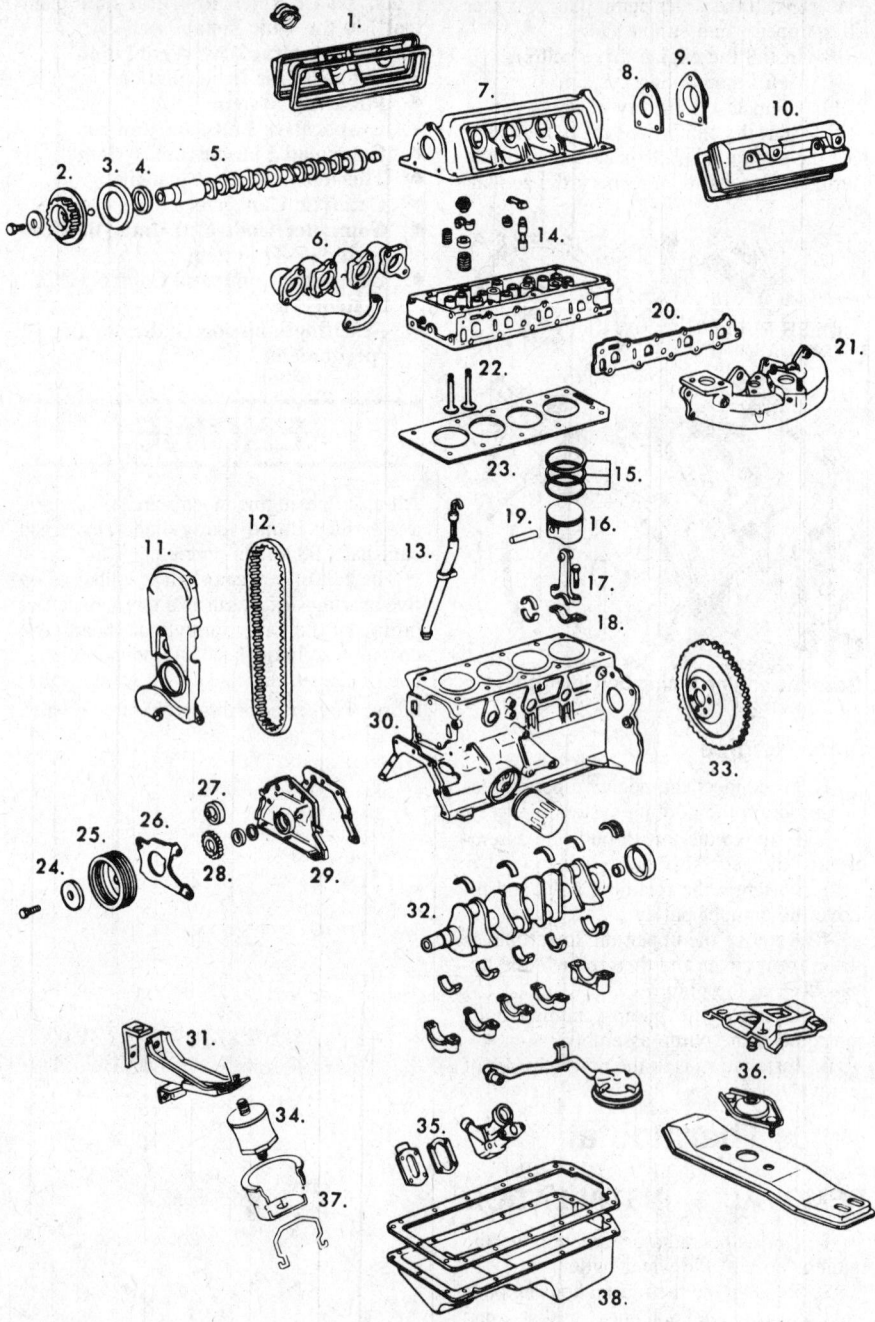

1. Camshaft Cover and Gasket	14. Rocker Arm, Adjuster, Valve Springs, Valve Spring Cap, and Keys	26. Lower Cover
2. Camshaft Sprocket	15. Piston Rings	27. Idler
3. Camshaft Sprocket Guide	16. Piston	28. Crankshaft Sprocket
4. Camshaft Oil Seal	17. Connecting Rod	29. Crankcase Front Cover
5. Camshaft	18. Connecting Rod Bearing and Cap	30. Cylinder Block
6. Exhaust Manifold	19. Piston Pin	31. Engine Mounting Bracket
7. Camshaft Housing	20. Intake Manifold Gasket	32. Crankshaft and Bearings
8. Camshaft Rear Cover Gasket	21. Intake Manifold	33. Flywheel
9. Camshaft Rear Cover	22. Valves	34. Engine Mount
10. Camshaft Housing Cover and Gasket	23. Cylinder Head Gasket	35. Oil Pump Assembly
11. Timing Belt Cover	24. Washer	36. Transmission Mounting and Support
12. Timing Belt	25. Crankshaft Pulley	37. Engine Mounting Plate and Spring
13. Oil Dipstick and Tube		38. Oil Pan and Gasket

Exploded view of the gasoline engine

ing the engine with the transmission housing.

23. Install the front engine mount nuts and safety straps.

24. Raise the car and support it with jackstands.

25. Install the engine-to-transmission housing bolts. Tighten to 25 ft. lbs.

26. On automatic transmission cars, install the torque converter to the flywheel. Torque the bolts to 35 ft. lbs.

27. Install the flywheel dust cover or torque converter underpan as applicable.

28. Install the engine strut on the diesel.

29. Install the exhaust pipe to the exhaust manifold and lower the car.

30. Install the air conditioning compressor or the power steering pump if necessary, and adjust drive belt tension.

31. Connect the following items:

  a. Fuel lines.

  b. Automatic transmission throttle valve linkage.

  c. Accelerator cable.

32. Install the air cleaner.

33. Install the engine fan, radiator, and radiator upper support. Install the oil cooler if so equipped.

34. Connect all wires previously disconnected.

35. Connect the radiator and heater hoses and fill the cooling system.

36. Install the battery cable clips along the frame rail.

37. Install the engine hood.

38. Connect the battery cables, start the engine and check for leaks.

Intake Manifold

REMOVAL & INSTALLATION

Gasoline Engine

1. Disconnect the battery ground.

2. Drain the cooling system.

3. Remove the air cleaner.

4. Disconnect the upper radiator and heater hoses.

5. Remove the EGR valve.

6. Disconnect all electrical wiring, vacuum hoses and the accelerator linkage from the carburetor.

7. Disconnect the fuel line from the carburetor.

8. On 1978 models equipped with A/C: A/C:

  a. Remove the upper radiator support.

  b. Remove the alternator and compressor drive belts and the compressor adjusting bolts.

  c. Remove the fan and pulley.

  d. Remove the timing belt cover.

  e. Move the compressor out of the way *without disconnecting the refrigerant lines.*

  f. Raise the car and remove the lower compressor brackets.

  g. Lower the car and remove the upper compressor brackets.

9. Remove the coil.

10. Remove the manifold.

11. If installing a new manifold, transfer all good parts. Always use a new gasket.

Installation is the reverse of removal. Torque all bracket bolts to 30 ft lbs, and intake manifold bolts to 15 ft. lbs.

Diesel Engine

1. Disconnect the negative battery cable.

2. Disconnect the fresh air hose and the vent hose. Remove the fuel separator.

3. Tag and disconnect all electrical

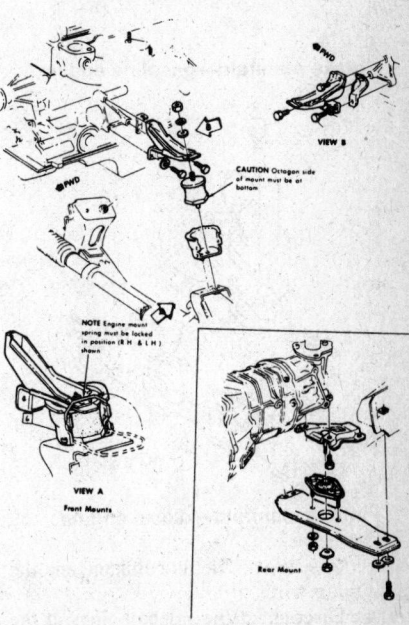

Engine mounts—gasoline engine

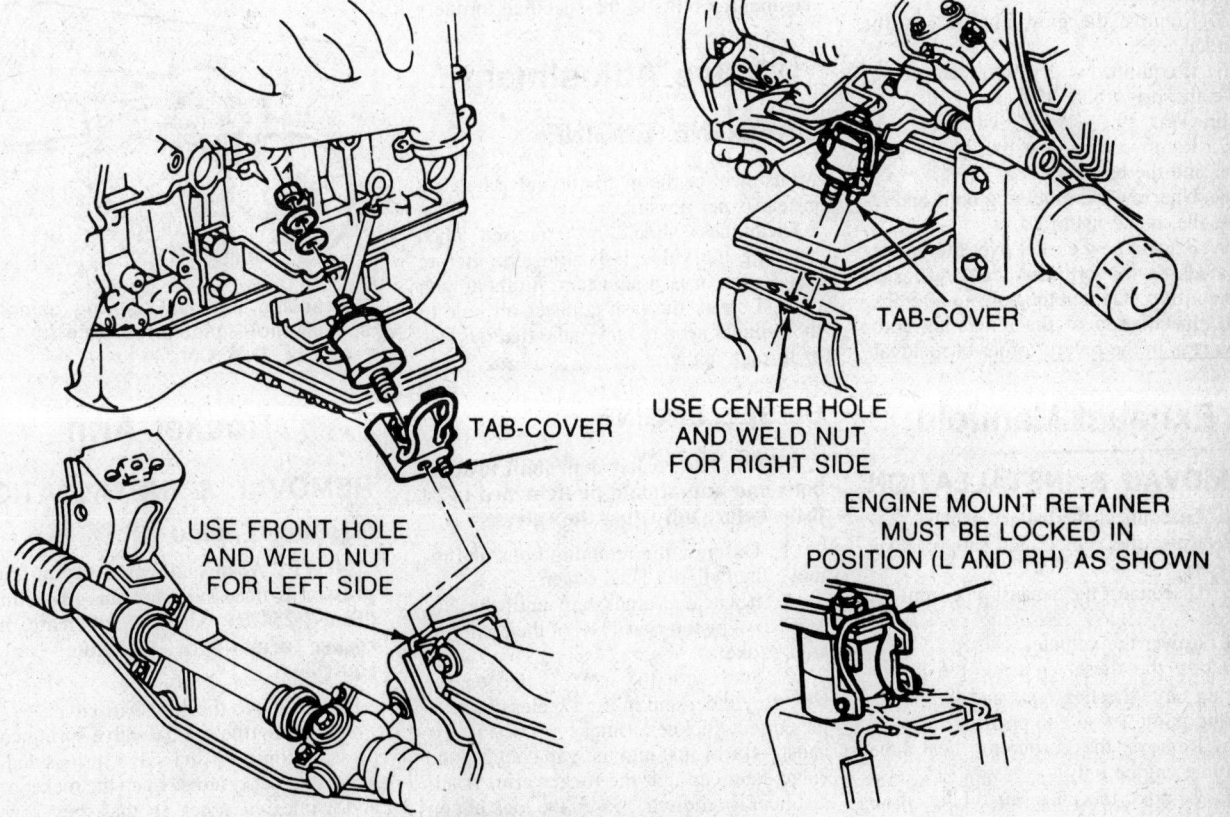

Engine mounts—diesel engine

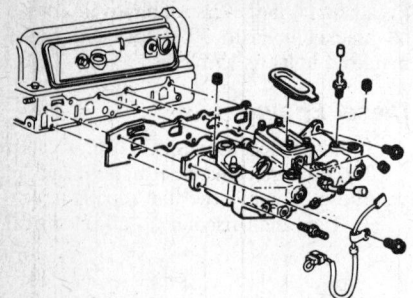

Intake manifold—gasoline engine

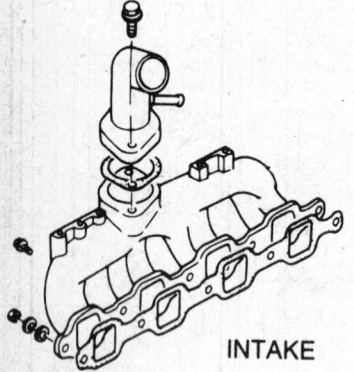

INTAKE

Intake manifold—diesel engine

connectors, the accelerator linkage and the glow plug wires.

4. Disconnect the injector lines at the injection pump and at the injector nozzles. Remove the injector lines and the hold-down clamps.

5. Remove the glow plug line at the cylinder head.

6. If equipped with power steering, remove the drive belt, the idler pulley and the bracket.

7. Remove the upper half of the front cover and the bracket.

8. Unscrew the mounting bolts and remove the intake manifold.

9. Place a new gasket over the mounting studs on the cylinder head and install the manifold. Tighten the bolts to 30 ft lbs.

10. Installation of the remaining components is in the reverse order of removal.

Exhaust Manifold

REMOVAL & INSTALLATION

1. Disconnect the battery ground.
2. Raise the vehicle and support it on stands.
3. Disconnect the exhaust pipe from the flange.
4. Lower the vehicle.
5. On the diesel, remove the power steering belt, the flex hose and the power steering pump (if so equipped).
6. Remove the carburetor heat tube (gasoline engine only).
7. Remove the pulse air tubing, if so equipped.

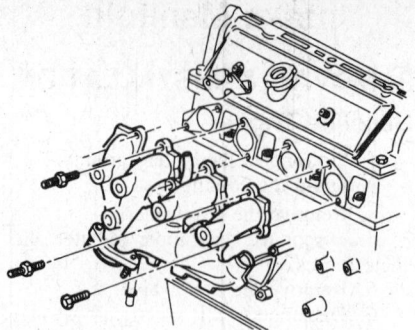

Exhaust manifold—gasoline engine

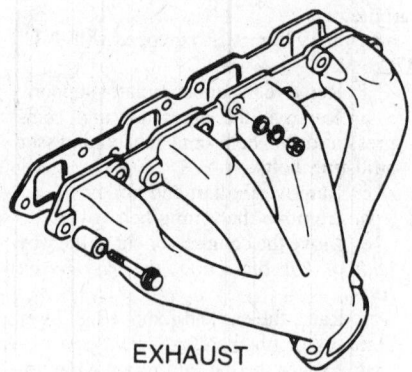

EXHAUST

Exhaust manifold—diesel engine

8. Remove the manifold.
9. Installation is the reverse of removal. Install the two upper inner bolts first, to properly position the manifold. Tighten the bolts to the specified torque.

Valve Adjustment

GASOLINE ENGINE

Adjustment of the hydraulic valve lash adjusters is not possible.

Cleanliness should be exercised when handling the valve lash adjusters. Before installation of lash adjusters, fill them with oil and check the lash adjuster oil hole in the cylinder head to make sure that it is free of foreign matter.

DIESEL ENGINE

NOTE: The rocker arm shaft bracket bolts and nuts should be tightened to 20 ft lbs before adjusting the valves.

1. Unscrew the retaining bolts and remove the cylinder head cover.
2. Rotate the crankshaft until the No. 1 or No. 4 piston is at TDC of the compression stroke.
3. Start with the intake valve on the NO. 1 cylinder and insert a feeler gauge of the correct thickness (intake—0.01 in., exhaust—0.014 in.) into the gap between the valve stem cap and the rocker arm. If adjustment is required, loosen the lock nut on top of the rocker arm and turn the adjusting

screw clockwise to decrease the gap and counterclockwise to increase it. When the proper clearance is reached, tighten the lock nut and then recheck the gap. Adjust the remaining three valves in this step (see illustration) in the same manner.

4. Rotate the crankshaft one complete revolution and then adjust the remaining valves accordingly (see illustration).

CYLINDER NO.	1		2		3		4	
VALVES	I	E	I	E	I	E	I	E
STEP. 1	○	○	○			○		
STEP. 2				○	○		○	○

I : INTAKE VALVE
E : EXHAUST VALVE

Valve adjustment sequence for the diesel engine (© Chevrolet Div., G.M. Corp.)

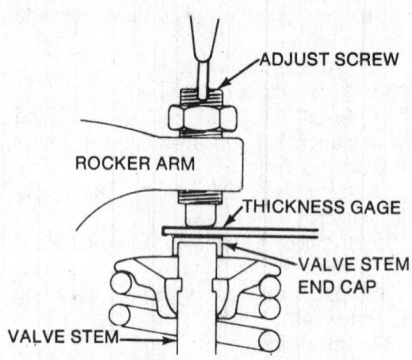

ADJUST SCREW
ROCKER ARM
THICKNESS GAGE
VALVE STEM END CAP
VALVE STEM

Valve adjustment—diesel engine

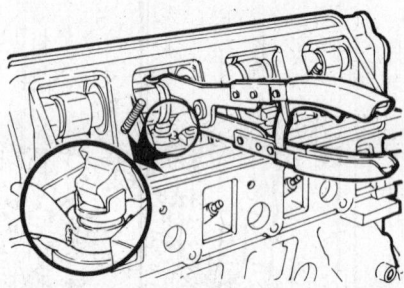

Depressing the valve spring using the special tool—gasoline engine (© Chevrolet Div., G.M. Corp.)

Rocker Arm

REMOVAL & INSTALLATION

Gasoline Engine

NOTE: A special valve spring compressor is necessary for this procedure. (Tool-J-25477) Also prelubricate new rocker arms with Molykote® or its equivalent.

1. Remove the camshaft cover.
2. Using the special valve spring compressor, compress the valve springs and remove the rocker arms. Keep the rocker arms and guides in order so that they can be installed in their original locations.

3. To install the rocker arms, compress the valve springs and install the rocker arm guides.

4. Position the rocker arms in the guides and on the valve lash adjusters.

5. Install the camshaft cover.

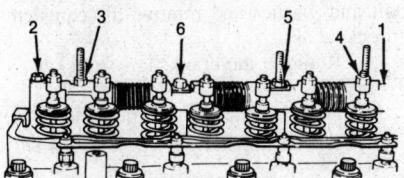

Loosening and tightening sequence for the rocker arm shaft bracket bolts and nuts—Diesel engine

Diesel Engine

1. Disconnect the negative battery cable.
2. Remove the cylinder head cover.
3. Remove the rocker arm shaft bracket bolts and nuts in sequence (see illustration). Remove the rocker arm shaft bracket and the rocker arm assembly.
4. Remove the rocker arms.
5. Apply a generous amount of clean engine oil to the rocker arm shaft, rocker arms and the valve stem end caps.
6. Install the rocker arm shaft assembly and then tighten the bolts to 20 ft lbs in the same sequence as removal.
7. Adjust the valves as previously detailed and reinstall the cylinder head cover.

Cylinder Head

REMOVAL & INSTALLATION

Gasoline Engine

1. Disconnect the negative battery cable.
2. Remove all accessory drive belts.
3. Remove the engine fan, timing belt cover and the timing belt, as outlined later in this section.
4. Remove the air cleaner and snorkel (silencer) assembly.
5. Drain the cooling system and disconnect the upper radiator hose and heater hose at the intake manifold.
6. Remove the accelerator cable support bracket.
7. Disconnect and label the spark plug wires.
8. Disconnect and label the wires from the idle solenoid, choke, temperature sender, and alternator.
9. Disconnect the exhaust pipe from the exhaust manifold.
10. Remove the dipstick tube bracket-to-manifold attaching bolt.
11. Disconnect the fuel line at the carburetor.
12. Take off the coil cover. Remove the coil bracket bolts and lay the coil aside.
13. Remove the camshaft cover.
14. Remove the camshaft cover-to-camshaft housing attaching studs.

15. Remove the rocker arms, rocker arm guides, and valve lash adjusters. Keep the parts in order so that they can be installed in their original locations.

16. Remove the camshaft carrier bolts and remove the camshaft carrier. A sharp wedge may be necessary to separate the camshaft carrier from the cylinder head. *Be very cautious not to damage the mating surfaces.*

17. Remove the manifold and cylinder head assembly.

To install the cylinder head:

18. Install a new cylinder head gasket with the words This Side Up facing up over dowel pins in the block. Make sure that the gasket is absolutely clean.

19. Install the manifold and cylinder head assembly.

20. Apply a light, thin continuous bead of sealant to the joining surfaces of the cylinder head and the camshaft carrier and install the camshaft carrier. Clean any excess sealer from the cylinder head. Apply sealing compound to the camshaft carrier/cylinder head bolts and install the bolts finger-tight. Tighten the bolts a little at a time and in the proper sequence until the final specified torque figure is reached.

21. Install the camshaft cover-to-camshaft housing attaching studs.

22. Install the valve lash adjusters and rocker arm guides. Prelube the rocker arms with engine assembly lubricant and install the rocker arms.

23. Using new gaskets, install the camshaft covers.

24. Install the coil bracket mounting bolt.

25. Connect the fuel line to the carburetor.

26. Install the dipstick tube bracket-to-manifold attaching bolt.

27. Attach the exhaust pipe to the exhaust manifold.

28. Connect the wires to the idle solenoid, choke, temperature sender, and alternator.

29. Connect the spark plug wires.

30. Apply Teflon tape or its equivalent to the threads of the accelerator cable support bracket attaching bolts and install the bracket.

31. Install the air cleaner and snorkel (silencer) assembly.

32. Connect the upper radiator hose and heater hose to the intake manifold.

33. Fill the cooling system.

34. Install the timing belt, timing belt cover, engine fan, drive belts and connect the negative battery cable.

Diesel Engine

1. Disconnect the negative battery cable.
2. Drain the cooling system.
3. Remove the cylinder head cover.
4. Disconnect the bypass hose. Remove the upper half of the front cover.
5. Loosen the tension pulley bolts and slide the timing belt off of the two upper gears.
6. Unscrew the bearing cap bolts and then remove the camshaft as detailed later in this section.
7. Tag and disconnect the glow plug resistor wire.
8. Disconnect the injector lines at the injector pump and at the injector nozzles and then remove the injector lines. Disconnect and plug the fuel leak-off hose.
9. Disconnect the exhaust pipe at the manifold.
10. Remove the oil feed pipe from the rear of the cylinder head.
11. Disconnect the upper radiator hose and position it out of the way.
12. Remove the head bolts in the sequence shown and then remove the cylinder head with the intake and exhaust manifolds installed.

To install:

NOTE: The gasket surfaces on both the head and the block must be clean of any foreign matter and free of nicks or heavy scratches. Cylinder bolt threads in the block and on the bolt must also be clean.

13. Place a new gasket over the dowel pins with the word "TOP" facing up.

14. Apply engine oil to the threads and the seating face of the cylinder head bolts, install them and then tighten them in the proper sequence.

15. Install the camshaft and rocker arm assembly. Loosen the adjusting screws so that the entire rocker arm assembly is held in a free state.

16. Reinstall the timing belt as outlined later in this section.

17. Connect the upper radiator hose and the oil feed pipe.

18. Connect the exhaust pipe to the manifold.

19. Install the fuel leak-off hose. Connect the injector lines.

20. Connect the glow plug resistor wire.

21. Adjust the valve clearance as previously detailed. Install the cylinder head cover.

22. Refill the cooling system.

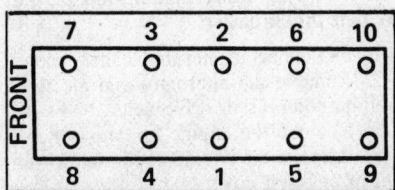

1.4 and 1.6 liter cylinder head torque sequence (© Chevrolet Div., G.M. Corp)

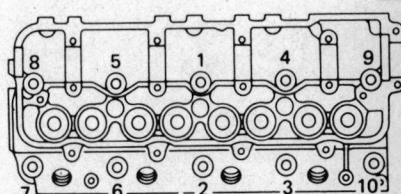

Diesel engine cylinder head torque sequence (© Chevrolet Div., G.M. Corp.)

Timing Belt Cover

REMOVAL & INSTALLATION

Upper Front Cover

1. Disconnect the negative battery cable. Remove the radiator upper mounting panel on models without A/C or fan shroud on models with A/C.
2. Remove engine accessory drive belts on the gasoline engine. Remove the bypass hose on the diesel engine.
3. Remove the engine fan.
4. Remove the cover retaining screws and nuts and remove the cover.
To install the cover:
5. Align the screw slots on the upper and lower parts of the cover.
6. Install the cover retaining screws and nuts.
7. Install the engine fan.
8. Install the engine accessory drive belts or the bypass hose.
9. Connect the negative battery cable.

Lower Front Cover

1. Disconnect the negative battery cable.
2. Loosen the alternator and the A/C compressor bolts, if so equipped. Remove the drive belt.
3. Remove the damper pulley-to-crankshaft bolt and washer and remove the pulley.
4. Remove the upper front timing belt cover as outlined previously.
5. Remove the lower cover retaining nut (gasoline) or bolts (diesel). Remove the lower cover.
6. To install the cover, align the cover with the studs on the engine block.
7. Install the lower front cover retaining nut or bolts.
8. Install the upper front timing belt cover.
9. Install the crankshaft damper pulley. Torque the retaining bolt to the specified torque.
10. Install the drive belt and tighten the alternator and compressor mounting bolts.
11. Connect the negative battery cable.

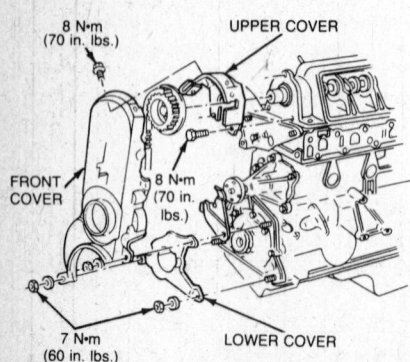

Timing belt front cover fasteners—gasoline engine

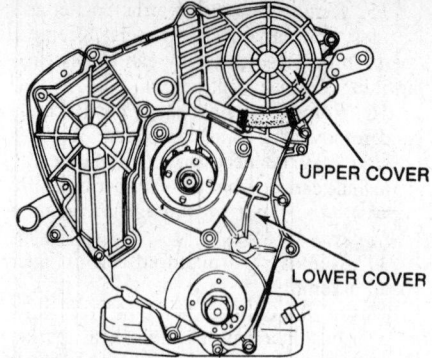

Timing belt covers—diesel engine

Upper Rear Cover—Gasoline Engine

1. Crank the engine so that No. 1 cylinder is at TDC of the compression stroke.
2. Disconnect the negative battery cable.
3. Remove the upper and lower front cover, the timing belt, and the camshaft timing sprocket.
4. Remove the three screws retaining the camshaft sprocket cover to the camshaft carrier.
5. Inspect the condition of the cam seal.
6. Position and align a new gasket over the end of the camshaft and against the camshaft carrier.
7. Install the three camshaft sprocket cover retaining screws.
8. Install the camshaft sprocket, timing belt, and the upper and lower front covers.
9. Connect the negative battery cable.

Timing Belt & Sprockets

REMOVAL & INSTALLATION

Gasoline Engine

—— CAUTION ——

Do not discharge the air conditioning compressor or disconnect the air conditioning lines. Personal injury could result.

NOTE: Rotate the engine to bring No. 1 cylinder to TDC. The timing mark should be at the 0° mark on the timing scale. With No. 1 cylinder at TDC, a 1/8 in. drill bit may be inserted through a hole in the timing belt upper rear cover into a hole in the camshaft drive sprocket. These holes are provided to facilitate and verify camshaft timing. Aligning these holes now will make installation of the new belt much easier.

1. Disconnect the negative battery cable.
2. Remove the alternator and air conditioning compressor drive belts.
3. Remove the engine fan and pulley.
4. Remove the engine upper and lower front timing belt covers.
5. Remove the timing belt idler pulley.
6. Remove the timing belt from the camshaft and crankshaft timing sprockets.
7. With the distributor cap off, mark the location of the rotor in the No. 1 spark plug firing position on the distributor housing. On air conditioned cars, remove the compressor and lower its mounting bracket.
8. Remove the camshaft timing sprocket bolt and washer and remove the camshaft sprocket.
9. Remove the crankshaft sprocket.
To install:
10. Place the crankshaft sprocket on the crankshaft making sure that the locating tabs face outward.

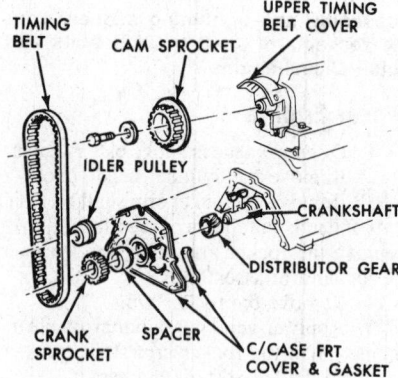

Timing belt and gears—gasoline engine

11. Install the crankshaft sprocket.
12. Align the camshaft sprocket dowel with the hole in the end of the camshaft and install the sprocket on the camshaft.
13. Apply thread locking compound to the camshaft sprocket retaining bolt and washer and torque to 65–85 ft lbs.
14. Position the timing belt over the crankshaft sprocket.
15. Install the crankshaft pulley.
16. Align the crankshaft pulley timing mark with the 0 mark on the timing scale and the distributor rotor with the scribed mark on the distributor housing.
17. Align the hole in the camshaft sprocket with the hole in the upper rear timing belt cover. Insert a 1/8 in. drill bit to hold the sprocket in alignment.
18. Install the timing belt on the camshaft and crankshaft sprockets.
19. To adjust timing belt tension see "Timing Belt Adjustment."
20. Install the distributor cap. On air conditioned cars, install the lower compressor bracket and the compressor.
21. Install the upper and lower front timing belt covers.
22. Install the engine fan and pulley.
23. Install the alternator and, if necessary, the air conditioning compressor drive belts.
24. Connect the negative battery cable.

Diesel Engine

NOTE: In order to complete this procedure you will need three special tools. A gear puller (J-22888), a fixing plate (J-29761) and a belt tension gauge (J-26486).

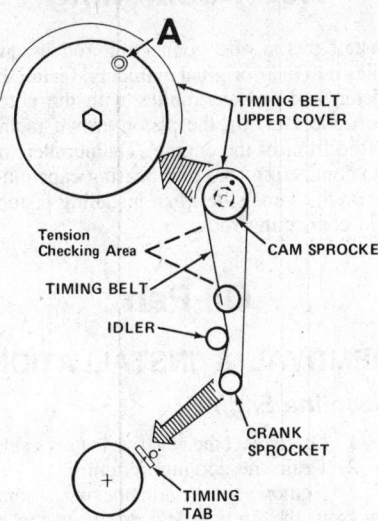

Quick Check Hole (In Sprocket) should align with hole in Timing Belt Upper Cover (A) when #1 Cyl. is at T.D.C.

Pulley timing mark should align with 0° mark on timing tab.

Timing belt installation—1.6 L Chevette. When camshaft is aligned at No. 1 cylinder TDC compression stroke, a 1/8 in. drill bit should fit through rear timing belt cover and into quick check hole in sprocket. (© Chevrolet Div., G.M. Corp.)

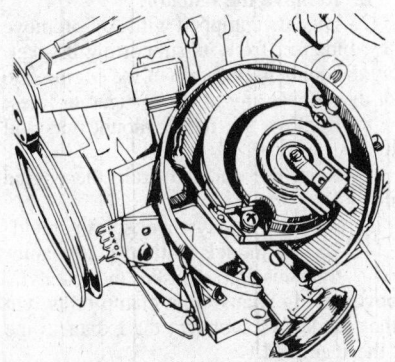

Correct distributor rotor alignment for timing belt installation

1. Disconnect the negative battery cable.
2. Drain the cooling system.
3. Remove the fan shroud, cooling fan and the pulley.
4. Disconnect the bypass hose and then remove the upper half of the front cover.
5. With the No. 1 piston at TDC of the compression stroke, make sure that the notch mark on the injection pump gear is aligned with the index mark on the front plate. If so, thread a lock bolt (8mm × 1.25) through the gear and into the front plate.
6. Remove the cylinder head cover and install a fixing plate (J-29761) in the slot at the rear of the cam. This will prevent the cam from rotating during the procedure.
7. Remove the crankshaft damper pulley and check to make sure that the No. 1 piston is still at TDC.
8. Remove the lower half of the front cover and then remove the timing belt holder

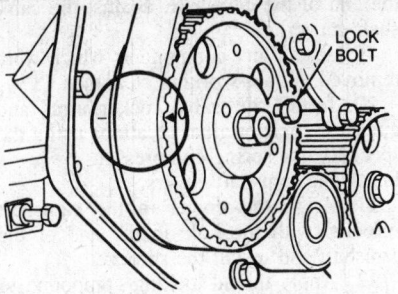

Injection gear setting mark—diesel engine

from the bottom of the front plate.

9. Remove the tension spring behind the front plate, next to the injection pump.
10. Loosen the tension pulley and slide the timing belt off the pulleys.
11. Remove the camshaft gear retaining bolt, install a gear puller and remove the gear.

To Install:

12. Reinstall the cam gear loosely so that it can be turned smoothly by hand.
13. Slide the timing belt back over the gears and note the following: the belt should be properly tensioned between the pulleys, the cogs on the belt and the gears should be properly engaged, the crankshaft should not be turned and the belt slack should be concentrated at the two tension pulleys. Push the tension pulley in with your finger and install the tension spring.
14. Partially tighten the tension pulley bolts in sequence (top first, bottom second) so as to prevent any movement of the pulley.
15. Tighten the camshaft gear retaining bolt to 45 ft lbs. Remove the injection pump gear lock bolt.
16. Remove the fixing plate from the end of the cam.
17. Install the crankshaft damper pulley and then check that the No. 1 piston is still at TDC. *Do not try to adjust it by moving the crankshaft.*

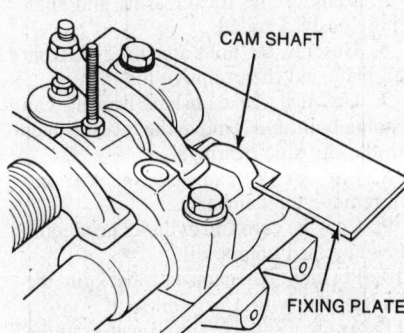

Camshaft fixing plate—diesel engine

18. Check that the marks on the injection pump gear and the front plate are still aligned and that the fixing plate still fits properly into the slot on the camshaft.
19. Loosen the tensioner pulley and plate bolts, concentrate the looseness of the timing belt around the tensioner and then tighten the bolts.

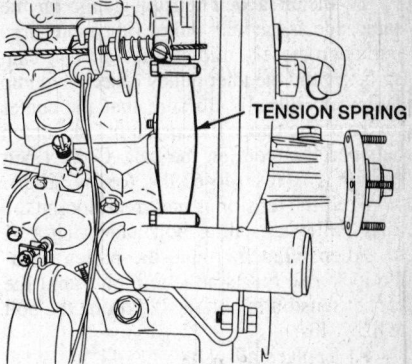

Tension spring—diesel engine

Tighten the tension pulley bolts in sequence—diesel engin

20. Belt tension should be 46–63 lbs, checked at a point midway between the upper two pulleys.
21. Remove the damper pulley again and install the belt holder in position away from the timing belt.
22. Installation of the remaining components is in the reverse order of removal.

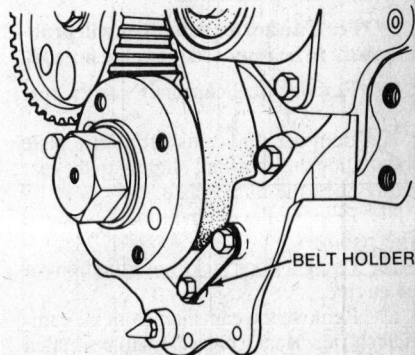

Diesel engine: the timing belt holder must be removed before the timing belt can be taken off (© Chevrolet Div., G.M. Corp.)

TIMING BELT ADJUSTMENT

1. Remove the fan, fan belt, water pump pulley and upper cam belt cover.
2. Rotate the crankshaft clockwise a minimum of one revolution. Stop with No. 1 piston at TDC. **DO NOT TURN THE ENGINE BACKWARD!**

3. Install a belt tension gauge on the same side as the idler pulley (injection pump pulley on diesel), midway between the cam sprocket and the idler pulley (injection pump pulley on diesel). Be sure that the center finger of the gauge extension fits in a notch between the teeth on the belt. Correct belt tension is 70 lbs. (46-63 lbs. for the diesel).

4. If the tension is incorrect, loosen the idler pulley attaching bolt and using a ¼ in. Allen wrench, rotate the pulley counterclockwise on its attaching bolt until the proper tension is obtained. Torque the bolt to 15 ft lbs.

5. Replace all parts.

Camshaft

REMOVAL & INSTALLATION

Gasoline Engine

NOTE: A special valve spring compressor (tool no. J-25477) is necessary for this procedure. If replacing the camshaft or rocker arms, prelube new parts with engine assembly lubricant.

1. Disconnect the negative battery cable.
2. Remove engine accessory drive belts.
3. Remove the engine fan and pulley.
4. Remove the upper and lower front timing belt covers.
5. Loosen the idler pulley and remove the timing belt from the camshaft sprocket.
6. Remove the camshaft sprocket attaching bolt and washer and remove the camshaft sprocket.
7. Remove the camshaft cover. Using the special valve spring compressor, remove the rocker arms and guides. Keep the rocker arms and guides in order so that they can be installed in their original locations.
8. Remove any components necessary to gain working clearance.

NOTE: The heater assembly will probably have to be removed from the firewall.

9. Remove the camshaft carrier rear cover.
10. Remove the camshaft thrust plate bolts. Slide the camshaft slightly to the rear and remove the thrust plate.
11. Remove the engine mount nuts and wire retainers.
12. Using a floor jack, raise the front of the engine.
13. Remove the camshaft from the camshaft carrier. Heavy pressure will be needed to pull the camshaft and seal forward.
To install:
14. Install the camshaft into the camshaft carrier.
15. Lower the engine.
16. Install the engine mount nuts and attach the retaining wires.
17. Slide the camshaft slightly to the rear and install the thrust plate. Slide the camshaft forward and install the carrier rear cover.
18. Position and align a new gasket over

the end of the camshaft, against the camshaft carrier.
19. Install any components which were removed to gain working clearance.
20. Install the valve rocker arms and guides in their original locations using the special valve spring compressor. Install the camshaft covers.
21. Align the dowel in the camshaft sprocket with the hole in the end of the camshaft and install the sprocket.
22. Apply thread locking compound to the sprocket retaining bolt threads and install the bolt and washer. Torque the sprocket retaining bolt to 65–85 ft lbs.
23. Turn the crankshaft clockwise to bring the No. 1 cylinder to top dead center. Make sure that the distributor rotor is in position to fire the No. 1 spark plug. Align the hole in the camshaft sprocket with the hole in the upper rear timing belt cover and install the timing belt on the camshaft sprocket.
24. Adjust timing belt tension as previously outlined.
25. Install the upper and lower front timing belt covers.
26. Install the engine fan and pulley.
27. Install the engine accessory drive belts.
28. Connect the negative battery cable.

Diesel Engine

NOTE: In order to complete this procedure you will need a gear puller (J-22888) and a fixing plate (J-29761).

1. Remove the cylinder head cover.
2. Remove the timing belt as previously detailed. Remove the plug.
3. Install the fixing plate into the slot at the rear of the camshaft.
4. Remove the camshaft gear retaining bolt and then use a puller to remove the cam gear.
5. Remove the rocker arms and shaft as previously detailed.
6. Unscrew the bolts attaching the front head plate and then remove the plate.
7. Unscrew the camshaft bearing cap retaining bolts and remove the bearing caps with the cap side bearings.
8. Lift out the camshaft oil seal and then remove the camshaft.
9. Coat the cam and cylinder head journals with clean engine oil.
10. Position the camshaft back in the cylinder head with a new oil seal.
11. Apply a suitable liquid gasket to the cylinder head face of the No. 1 camshaft bearing cap.
12. Install the remaining bearing caps. Install the rocker arm shaft assembly, leaving the adjusting screws loose.
13. Install the front head plate.
14. Install the timing belt as previously detailed.
15. Adjust the valve clearance to specifications and then install the cylinder head cover.

Piston and Connecting Rod Positioning

Install piston and connecting rod assemblies into their original cylinders. Install the piston and rod assemblies with the notch (arrow-diesel) on the piston crown facing to the front of the engine. The numbers on the connecting rods and bearing caps must be on the same side when installing pistons and connecting rods.

Oil Pan

REMOVAL & INSTALLATION

Gasoline Engine

1. Disconnect the negative battery cable.
2. Drain the cooling system.
3. Remove the heater housing assembly from the firewall and rest it on top of the engine.
4. Remove the upper radiator support. On cars with A/C, remove the upper half of the fan shroud.
5. Remove the radiator hoses and on cars with automatic transmission, disconnect and plug the cooler lines from the radiator.
6. Remove the radiator.
7. On cars equipped with A/C, remove the condenser from its supporting bracket. Lay the condenser on top of the engine. Do not disconnect any of the refrigerant lines.
8. Remove the motor mount nuts and clips.
9. Raise the car and drain the engine oil.
10. Remove the flywheel splash shield.
11. On all models with the 200 automatic transmission, loosen the catalytic converter-to-exhaust pipe clamp bolts. On other models, disconnect the exhaust pipe at the manifold.
12. Remove the body-to-crossmember braces, if so equipped.
13. Remove the rack and pinion unit from the crossmember and the steering shaft. Pull the unit down and out of the way.
14. With a floor jack and a lifting adapter, raise the front of the engine.
15. Remove the oil pan bolts.
16. Pull the oil pan down and remove the oil pump suction pipe and the screen.
17. Remove the oil pan.
18. Clean all of the old sealer that is loose off the oil pan mating surface. It is not necessary to clean all of the sealer material off. Reverse the above procedure to install. Tighten the oil pan attaching bolts to 55 in. lbs.

Diesel Engine

1. Remove the engine as detailed earlier in this section.
2. Support the engine in a stand.
3. Unscrew the nuts and bolts attaching

the oil pan to the crankcase and then remove the pan.

4. Clean the mating surfaces of the oil pan and the block. Apply a suitable liquid gasket to the front and rear mating surfaces and then install a new gasket.

5. Install the oil pan retaining bolts and tighten them to 5 ft. lbs.

6. Reinstall the engine.

Oil Pump

REMOVAL & INSTALLATION

Gasoline Engine

1. Remove the ignition coil attaching bolts and lay the coil aside.

2. Raise the car and remove the fuel pump, pushrod, and gasket.

3. Lower the car and remove the distributor. On air conditioned cars, remove the compressor mounting bolts and lay it aside. Do not disconnect any refrigerant lines.

4. Raise the car and remove the oil pan as previously outlined.

5. Remove the oil pump pipe and screen assembly clamp and remove the bolts attaching the pipe and screen assembly.

6. Remove the pipe and screen assembly from the oil pump.

7. Remove the pick-up tube seal from the oil pump.

8. Remove the oil pump attaching bolts and remove the oil pump.

To install:

9. Install the oil pump. Torque the oil pump bolts to 15 ft. lbs.

NOTE: Make certain that the pilot on the oil pump engages the case.

10. Install the pick-up tube seal in the oil pump.

11. Install the pick-up pipe and screen assembly in the oil pump and install the pick-up pipe and screen clamp. Torque the clamp bolt to 70–95 in. lbs. Torque the pick-up tube and screen mounting bolt to 19–25 ft. lbs.

12. Install the oil pan.

13. Install the fuel pump with gasket and pushrod.

14. Lower the car and install the distributor and the ignition coil.

Diesel Engine

1. Remove the timing belt as previously detailed.

2. Unscrew the four allen bolts attaching the oil pump to the front plate and remove the pump complete with the pulley.

3. Coat the vane with clean engine oil and then install it with the taper side toward the cylinder body.

4. Install a new O-ring, coated with engine oil, into the pump housing.

5. Position the rotor in the vane and then install the pump body together with

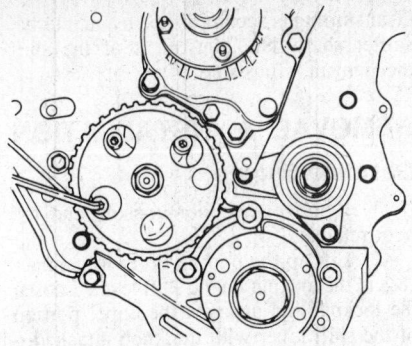

Removing the allen bolts attaching the oil pump to the front pate—diesel engine

the pulley. Tighten the Allen bolts to 15 ft. lbs.

6. Install the timing belt as previously detailed.

Rear Main Oil Seal

REPLACEMENT

Gasoline Engine

1. Remove the engine from the car and place it in a stand.

2. Remove the flywheel or flexplate (A.T).

3. Remove the oil pan.

4. Remove the rear main bearing cap.

5. Clean the bearing cap and case.

6. Check the crankshaft seal for excessive wear, etc.

7. Install a new crankshaft seal. Make sure that it is properly seated against the rear main bearing seal bulkhead.

8. Apply RTV sealer or its equivalent to the bearing cap horizontal split line.

9. With the sealer still wet, install the rear main bearing cap. Tighten the bearing bolts to 10–12 ft. lbs. Tap the crankshaft toward the rear, then toward the front to be sure everything is properly seated. Retorque the cap bolts to the specified torque.

10. Apply RTV sealer or its equivalent in the vertical grooves of the rear main bearing cap.

11. Remove any excess sealer and install the oil pan. Torque the oil pan bolts to 45–60 in. lbs.

12. Install the engine in the car.

Diesel Engine

1. Remove the transmission as detailed later in this section. If equipped with a manual transmission remove the clutch.

2. Unscrew the flywheel retaining bolts in a diagonal pattern and then remove the flywheel.

3. Pry off the old oil seal.

4. Coat the lipped portion and the fitting face of the new oil seal with engine oil and install it into the crankshaft bearing. Make sure that the seal is properly seated.

5. Coat the threads of the new mounting bolts with Loctite® and install the fly-

wheel. Tighten the bolts to 40 ft. lbs. in a diagonal sequence. Do not reuse the old bolts, they must be new.

6. Installation of the remaining components is in the reverse order of removal.

CLUTCH

All manual transmission models use a cable-operated diaphragm spring-type clutch. The clutch cable is attached to the clutch pedal at its upper end and is threaded at its lower end where it attaches to the clutch fork. The clutch release fork pivots on a ball stud located opposite the clutch cable attaching point. The pressure plate, clutch disc, and throwout bearing are of conventional design.

When the clutch pedal is depressed, the clutch release fork pivots on the ball stud and pushes the throwout bearing forward. The throwout bearing presses against the inner ends of the pressure plate diaphragm spring fingers to release pressure on the clutch disc, disengaging the clutch. The return spring preloads the clutch release mechanism to remove any looseness. Clutch pedal free-play will increase with release mechanism wear and will decrease with clutch disc wear.

Clutch

REMOVAL & INSTALLATION

1. Raise the car on a hoist.

2. Remove the transmission.

3. Remove the throwout bearing from the clutch fork by sliding the fork off the ball stud against spring tension. If the ball stud is to be replaced, remove the locknut and stud from the bellhousing.

4. If the balance marks on the pressure plate and the flywheel are not easily seen, remark them with paint or a centerpunch.

5. Alternately loosen the pressure plate-to-flywheel attaching bolts one turn at a time until spring tension is released.

6. Support the pressure plate and cover assembly, then remove the bolts and the clutch assembly.

— CAUTION —

Do not disassemble the clutch cover and pressure plate for repair. If defective, replace the assembly.

7. Check the pressure plate, clutch plate and flywheel for wear. If the flywheel is scored, worn or discolored from overheating, it should be either refaced or replaced. Replace the clutch plate as necessary.

8. Align the balance marks on the clutch assembly and the flywheel. Place the clutch disc on the pressure plate with the long end of the splined hub facing forward and the damper springs inside the pressure plate.

Insert a dummy shaft through the cover and clutch disc.

9. Position the assembly against the flywheel and insert the dummy shaft into the pilot bearing in the crankshaft.

10. Align the balance marks and install the pressure plate-to-flywheel bolts finger-tight.

CAUTION
Tighten all bolts evenly and gradually until tight to avoid possible clutch distortion. Torque the bolts to 18 ft lbs (14 ft lbs on diesel engine) and remove the dummy shaft.

11. Pack the groove on the inside of the throwout bearing with graphite grease. Also coat the fork groove and ball stud depression with the lubricant.

12. Install the throwout bearing and release fork assembly in the bellhousing with the fork spring hooked under the ball stud and the fork spring fingers inside the bearing groove.

13. Position the transmission and clutch housing and install the clutch housing attaching bolts and lockwashers. Torque the bolts to 25 ft. lbs.

14. Complete the transmission installation.

CAUTION
Check the position of the engine in the front mounts and realign as necessary.

NOTE: A special gauge (J-23644) is necessary to adjust ball stud position if it has been removed.

15. Adjust clutch pedal free-play if necessary.

16. Lower the car and check operation of the clutch and transmission.

CLUTCH PEDAL FREE-PLAY ADJUSTMENT

1978 and Later

Adjustment is made at the firewall end of the outer clutch cable. Pedal free-play should be ½ to 1 in. at the pedal.

1. Pull the adjusting ring clip from the cable at the firewall.

2. To increase free-play, move the cable into the firewall, one notch at a time, and replace the clip.

3. To decrease free-play, pull the cable out, one notch at a time, and replace the clip.

4. If, after the adjustment, the pedal won't return tight against the bumper, the ball stud will have to be adjusted. Use the special gauge mentioned in the clutch replacement procedure.

MANUAL TRANSMISSION

Chevettes and T1000's use either a four or five speed fully syncronized transmission.

Gear shifting is accomplished by an internal shifter shaft. No adjustment of the shift mechanism is possible.

REMOVAL & INSTALLATION

Gasoline Engine

1. Remove the floor console and the boot retainer.

2. Lift up the boot in order to gain access to the locknut on the shift lever. Loosen the locknut and unscrew the upper portion of the shift lever with the knob attached.

3. Remove the foam insulator.

4. Remove the three bolts on the extension and remove the control assembly.

5. Carefully remove the retaining clip.

6. Remove the locknut, the boot retainer and the seat from the threaded end of the control lever.

7. Remove the spring and the guide from the forked end of the control lever.

8. Raise the car on a hoist and drain the lubricant from the transmission.

9. Remove the driveshaft.

10. Disconnect the speedometer cable and back-up light switch.

11. Disconnect the return spring and clutch cable at the clutch release fork.

12. Remove the crossmember-to-transmission mount bolts.

13. Remove the exhaust manifold nuts and converter-to-tailpipe bolts and nuts. Remove the converter-to-transmission bracket bolts and remove the converter.

14. Remove the crossmember-to-frame bolts and remove the crossmember.

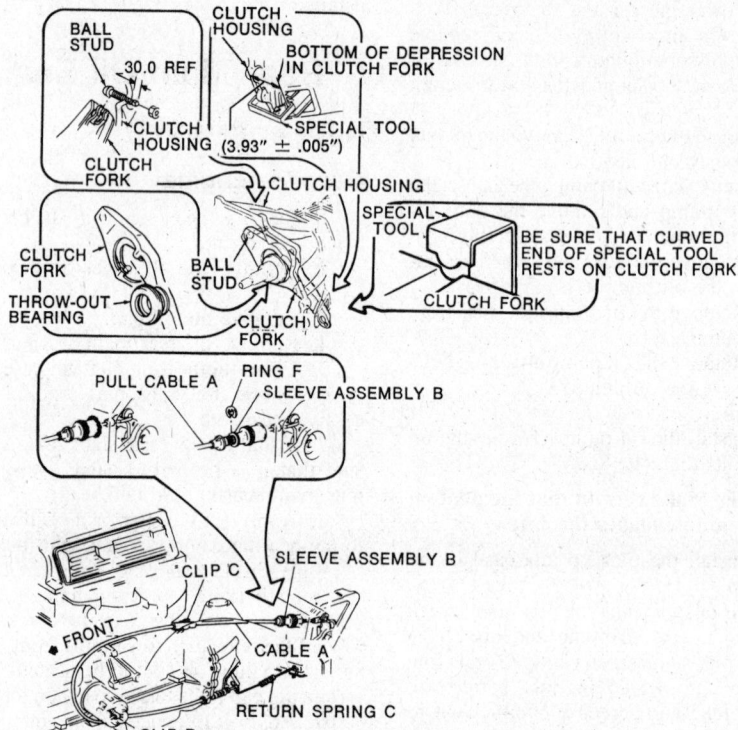

1978 and later clutch cable and ball stud adjustment details
(© Chevrolet Div., G.M. Corp.)

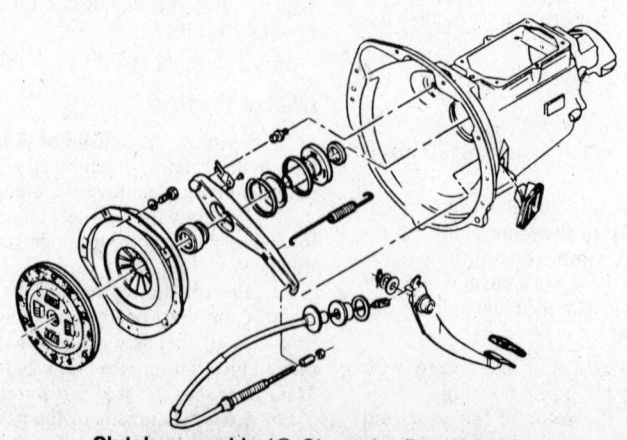

Clutch assembly (© Chevrolet Div., G.M. Corp)

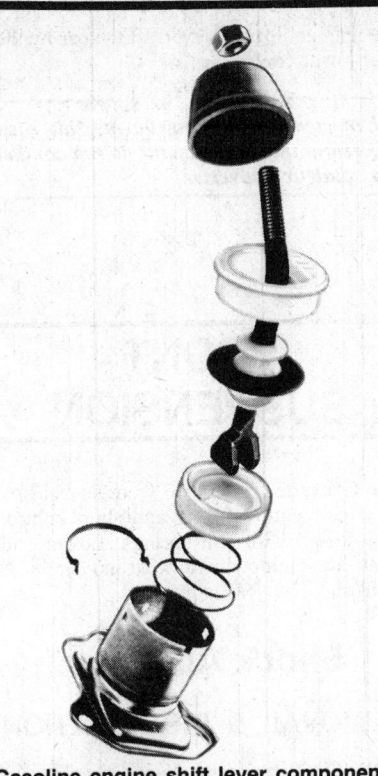

Gasoline engine shift lever components (© Chevrolet Div., G.M. Corp.)

15. Remove the dust cover.

16. Remove the clutch housing-to-engine retaining bolts, slide the transmission and clutch housing to the rear, and remove the transmission.

To install:

17. Place the transmission in gear, position the transmission and clutch housing, and slide forward. Turn the output shaft to align the input shaft splines with the clutch hub.

18. Install the clutch housing retaining bolts and lockwashers. Torque the bolts to 25 ft lbs.

19. Install the dust cover.

20. Position the crossmember to the frame and loosely install the retaining bolts. Install the crossmember-to-transmission mounting bolts. Torque the center nuts to 33 ft. lbs; the end nuts to 21 ft. lbs. Torque the crossmember-to-frame bolts to 40 ft. lbs.

21. Install the exhaust pipe to the manifold and the converter bracket on the transmission.

22. Connect the clutch cable. Adjust clutch pedal free-play.

23. Connect the speedometer cable and back-up light switch.

24. Install the driveshaft.

25. Fill the transmission to the correct level with SAE 80W or SAE 80W-90 GL-5 gear lubricant. Lower the car.

26. Install the shift lever and check operation of the transmission.

Diesel Engine

1. Disconnect the negative battery cable.

2. Unscrew the retaining screws and then remove the shift lever console.

3. Remove the mounting screws and remove the shift lever assembly.

4. Unscrew and remove the upper starter mounting bolts.

5. Raise the front of the car and drain the lubricant from the transmission.

6. Remove the drive shaft as detailed later in this section.

7. Disconnect the speedometer and the back-up light switch wires.

8. Disconnect the return spring and clutch cable at the clutch release fork.

9. Remove the starter lower bolt and support the starter.

10. Unscrew the retaining bolts and disconnect the exhaust pipe from the manifold.

11. Remove the flywheel inspection cover.

12. Unscrew the rear transmission support mounting bolt. Support the transmission underneath the case and then remove the rear support from the frame.

13. Lower the transmission approximately four (4) in.

14. Remove the transmission housing-to-engine block bolts. Pull the transmission straight back and away from the engine.

15. Installation of the remaining components is in the reverse order of removal. Please note the following:

   a. Be sure to lubricate the drive gear shaft with a light coat of grease before installing the transmission.

   b. After installation, fill the transmission to the level of the filler hole with 5W-30SF engine oil.

OVERHAUL

For all overhaul procedures, please refer to "Manual Transmission Overhaul" in the Unit Repair section.

AUTOMATIC TRANSMISSION

All Chevettes and T1000's use either the Turbo Hydra—Matic 180 or 200 transmission.

For all identification and service procedures, please refer to "Automatic Transmissions" in the Unit Repair section.

REMOVAL & INSTALLATION

1. Before raising the car, disconnect the negative battery cable and the T.V./detent cable at the bracket and carburetor or pump.

2. Remove the air cleaner and dipstick.

3. On vehicles with air conditioning, remove the heater core cover screws from the heater assembly. Disconnect the wire connector and with hoses attached, place the heater core cover out of the way.

4. Raise vehicle on hoist and remove propeller shaft.

5. Disconnect speedometer cable, electrical lead to case connector and oil cooler pipes.

6. Disconnect shift control linkage.

7. Support transmission with suitable transmission jack and remove the rear transmission support bolts.

8. Remove the nuts holding the converter bracket to the support.

9. Disconnect exhaust pipe at the rear of the catalytic converter.

10. Disconnect exhaust pipe at manifold and remove the exhaust pipe, catalytic converter and converter bracket as an assembly.

11. Remove the torque converter under pan.

12. Remove converter to flexplate bolts.

13. Lower transmission until jack is barely supporting it and remove transmission to engine mounting bolts.

14. Raise transmission to its normal position, then place a 2" block of wood between the rack-and-pinion housing and the engine oil pan, then support engine with jack and slide transmission rearward from engine and lower it away from vehicle.

NOTE: The use of a converter holding tool J-5384 is necessary when lowering the transmission or keep the rear of the transmission lower than the front so not to lose the converter.

15. Installation is the reverse of removal and include the following:

Before installing the flex plate to converter bolts, make certain that the weld nuts on the converter are flush with the flex plate and the converter rotates freely by hand in this position. Hand start the three bolts and tighten finger tight, then torque to specifications. This will insure proper converter alignment. Install new oil seal on oil filler tube before installing tube.

Make all linkage adjustments. See the Unit Repair Section.

DRIVESHAFT AND U-JOINTS

A one-piece driveshaft is mounted to the companion flange with a conventional universal joint at the rear. The driveshaft is connected to the transmission output shaft with a splined slip yoke. The slip yoke contains a thrust spring which seats against the end of the transmission output shaft. The thrust spring must be installed for proper operation.

The universal joints are of the long-life design and do not require periodic inspection or lubrication. When the joints are disassembled, repack the bearings and lubricate the reservoirs at the end of the trunnions with chassis grease and replace the dust seals.

For all U-Joint overhaul procedures, please refer to "U-Joint/CV-Joint Overhaul" in the Unit Repair section.

Driveshaft

REMOVAL & INSTALLATION

1. Raise the car on a hoist. Scribe matchmarks on the driveshaft and the companion flange and disconnect the rear universal joint by removing the trunnion bearing straps.
2. Move the driveshaft to the rear under the axle to remove the slip yoke from the transmission. Watch for leakage from the transmission output shaft housing.
3. Install the driveshaft in the reverse order of removal. Tighten the trunnion strap bolts to 16 ft lbs.

REAR AXLE

Axle Shaft, Bearing, and Seal

For further information on the rear axle, please refer to "Drive Axles" in the Unit Repair section.

REMOVAL & INSTALLATION

1. Raise the car on a hoist. Remove the wheel and tire assembly and the brake drum.
2. Clean the area around the differential carrier cover.
3. Remove the differential carrier cover to drain the rear axle lubricant.
4. Use a metric Allen wrench to unscrew the differential pinion shaft lockscrew and remove the differential pinion shaft. It may be necessary to shorten the Allen wrench to do this.
5. Push the flanged end of the axle shaft toward the center of the car and remove the C-lock from the inner end of the shaft.
6. Remove the axle shaft from the housing making sure not to damage the oil seal.

7. If replacing the seal only, remove the oil seal by using the inner end of the axle shaft. Insert the end of the shaft behind the steel case of the oil seal and carefully pry the seal out of the bore.
8. To remove bearings, insert a bearing and seal remover into the bore so that the tool head grasps behind the bearing. Slide the washer against the seal or bearing and turn the nut against the washer. Attach a slide hammer and remove the bearing.
9. Lubricate a new bearing with hypoid lubricant and install it into the housing with a bearing installer tool. Make sure that the tool contacts the end of the axle tube to ensure that the bearing is at the proper depth.
10. Lubricate the cavity between the seal lips with a high melting point wheel bearing grease. Place a new oil seal on the seal installation tool and position the seal in the axle housing bore. Tap the seal into the bore flush with the end of the housing.
11. To install the axle shaft, slide the axle shaft into place making sure that the splines on the end of the shaft do not damage the oil seal and that they engage the splines of the differential side gear. Install the C-lock on the inner end of the axle shaft and push the shaft outward so that the shaft lock seats in the counterbore of the differential side gear.
12. Position the differential pinion shaft through the case and pinions, aligning the hole in the shaft with the lockscrew hole. Install the lockscrew.
13. Clean the gasket mounting surfaces on the differential carrier and the carrier cover. Install the carrier cover using a new gasket and tighten the cover bolts in a crosswise pattern to 22 ft. lbs.
14. Fill the rear axle with lubricant to the bottom of the filler hole.
15. Install the brake drum and the wheel and tire assembly.
16. Lower the car.

JACKING, HOISTING

The illustration shows the recommended areas for jacking and hoisting. When using a twin post hoist, be sure that it is positioned properly on the rear axle to avoid damaging

the rear stabilizer. Never lift the car by the rear lower control arms.

— CAUTION —
When jacking or lifting on the side rails be certain that the lift pads do not contact the catalytic converter.

FRONT SUSPENSION

The Chevette and T1000 front suspension is of conventional long and short control arm design with coil springs. Lower ball joints are equipped with wear indicators. A front stabilizer bar is used.

Shock Absorber

REMOVAL & INSTALLATION

NOTE: Purge new shock absorbers of air by repeatedly extending in the normal position and compressing while inverted.

1. Hold the shock absorber upper stem and remove the nut, upper retainer, and rubber grommet.
2. Raise the car on a hoist.
3. Remove the bolt from the lower end of the shock absorber and remove the shock absorber.
To install:
4. With the lower retainer and rubber grommet in position, extend the shock absorber stem and install the stem through the wheelhouse opening.
5. Install and torque the lower bolt to 35–50 ft. lbs. through 1979, 22 ft. lbs. for 1980 and 35–50 ft. lbs. for 1981 and later.
6. Lower the car.
7. Install the upper rubber grommet, retainer, and nut to the shock absorber stem.
8. Hold the shock absorber upper stem and torque the nut to 7 ft. lbs.

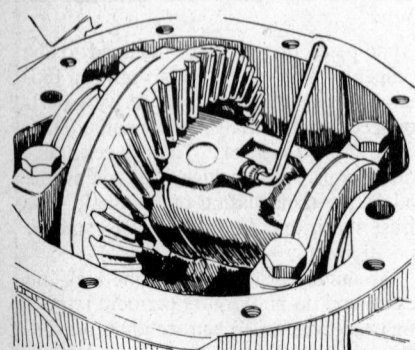

Removing the differential pinion shaft lockscrew

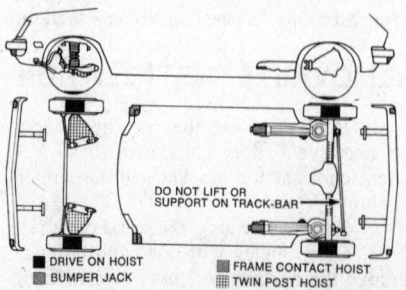

■ DRIVE ON HOIST
□ BUMPER JACK
▨ FRAME CONTACT HOIST
▧ TWIN POST HOIST

DO NOT LIFT OR SUPPORT ON TRACK-BAR

Lift points (© Chevrolet Div., G.M. Corp.)

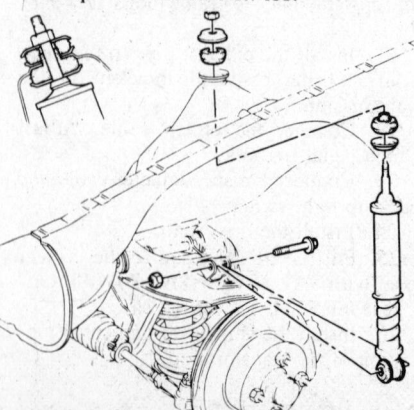

Front shock absorber mounting
(© Chevrolet Div., G.M. Corp)

Lower Ball Joint

REMOVAL & INSTALLATION

NOTE: The ball joint studs use a special nut which must be discarded whenever loosened and removed. On assembly, use a standard nut to draw the ball joint into position on the knuckle, then remove the standard nut and install a new special nut for final installation.

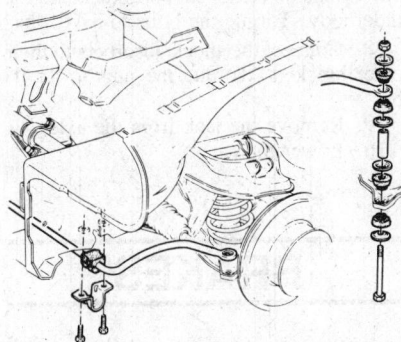

Front suspension stabilizer bar attachment (© Chevrolet Div., G.M. Corp.)

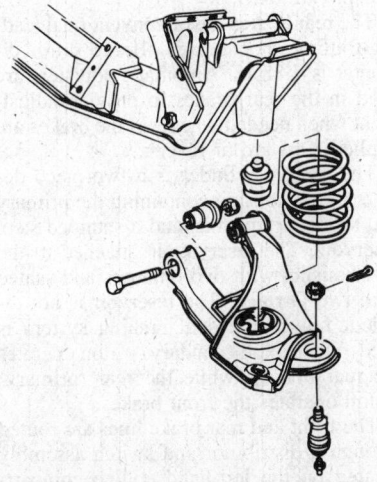

Correct position for front spring installation (© Chevrolet Div., G.M. Corp)

1. Raise the car on a hoist.
2. Remove the tire and wheel.
3. Support the lower control arm with a hydraulic floor jack.
4. Loosen, but do not remove the lower ball stud nut.
5. Install a ball joint removal tool with the cup end over the upper ball stud nut.
6. Turn the threaded end of the ball joint removal tool until the ball stud is free of the steering knuckle.
7. Remove the ball joint removal tool and remove the nut from the ball stud.
8. Remove the ball joint.

NOTE: Inspect the tapered hole in the steering knuckle. Clean the area. If any out-of-roundness, deformation, or damage is found, the steering knuckle must be replaced.

9. To install the lower ball joint, mate the ball stud through the lower control arm and into the steering knuckle.
10. Install and torque the ball stud nut to 41–54 ft. lbs.
11. Install the tire and wheel.
12. Lower the car.

Lower Control Arm and Coil Spring

REMOVAL & INSTALLATION

NOTE: The ball joint studs use a special nut which must be discarded whenever loosened and removed. On assembly, use a standard nut to draw the ball joint into position on the knuckle, then remove the standard nut and install a new special nut for final installation.

1. Raise the car on a frame contact hoist.
2. Remove the wheel and tire.
3. Disconnect the stabilizer bar from the lower control arm and disconnect the tie-rod from the steering knuckle.
4. Support the lower control arm with a jack.
5. Remove the nut from the lower ball joint, then use a ball joint removal tool to press out the lower ball joint.
6. Swing the knuckle and hub aside and attach them securely with wire.
7. Loosen the lower control arm pivot bolts.
8. As a safety precaution, install a chain through the coil spring.
9. Slowly lower the jack.
10. When the spring is extended as far as possible, use a pry bar to carefully lift the spring over the lower control arm seat. Remove the spring.
11. Remove the pivot bolts and remove the lower control arm.
To install:
12. Install the lower control arm and pivot bolts to the underbody brackets. Torque the lower control arm pivot bolts to 49 ft. lbs.
13. Position in spring correctly and install it in the upper pocket. Use tape to hold the insulator onto the spring.
14. Install the lower end of the spring onto the lower control arm. An assistant may be necessary to compress the spring far enough to slide it over the raised area of the lower control arm seat.
15. Use a jack to raise the lower control arm and compress the coil spring.
16. Install the ball joint through the lower control arm and into the steering knuckle. Install the nut on the ball stud and torque to 41–54 ft. lbs.
17. Connect the stabilizer bar to the lower control arm. Connect the tie-rod to the steering knuckle. Install the wheel and tire.
18. Lower the car.

Upper Ball Joint

REMOVAL & INSTALLATION

NOTE: The ball joint studs use a special nut which must be discarded whenever loosened and removed. On assembly, use a standard nut to draw the ball joint into position on the knuckle, then remove the standard nut and install a new special nut for final installation.

1. Raise the car on a hoist.
2. Remove the tire and wheel.
3. Support the lower control arm with a floor jack.
4. Loosen, but do not remove the upper ball stud nut.
5. Install a ball joint removal tool with the cup end over the lower ball stud nut.
6. Turn the threaded end of the ball joint removal tool until the upper ball stud is free of the steering knuckle.
7. Remove the ball joint removal tool and remove the nut from the ball stud.
8. Remove the two nuts and bolts attaching the ball joint to the upper control arm and remove the ball joint.

NOTE: Inspect the tapered hole in the steering knuckle. Clean the area. If any out-of-roundness, deformation, or damage is found, the steering knuckle must be replaced.

9. To install the upper ball joint, install the nuts and bolts attaching the ball joint to the upper control arm. Torque the nuts to 29 ft. lbs. Then mate the upper control arm ball stud to the steering knuckle.
10. Install and torque the ball stud nut to 29–36 ft. lbs.
11. Install the tire and wheel.
12. Lower the car.

Upper Control Arm

REMOVAL & INSTALLATION

NOTE: The ball joint studs use a special nut which must be discarded whenever loosened and removed. On assembly, use a standard nut to draw the ball joint into position on the knuckle, then remove the standard nut and install a new special nut for final installation.

1. Raise the car on a hoist.
2. Remove the tire and wheel.
3. Support the lower control arm with a floor jack.
4. Remove the upper ball joint from the steering knuckle as previously described.
5. Remove the upper control arm pivot bolts and remove the upper control arm.
6. To install the upper control arm, install the upper control arm with its pivot bolts.

NOTE: The inner pivot bolt must be installed with the bolt head toward the front.

7. Install the pivot bolt nut.

8. Position the upper control arm in a horizontal plane and torque the nut to 43–50 ft. lbs.

9. Install the ball joint to the upper control arm and to the steering knuckle as previously described. Torque the ball joint-to-upper control arm attaching bolts to 29 ft. lbs. Torque the ball stud nut to 29–36 ft. lbs.

10. Install the tire and wheel.

11. Lower the car.

FRONT WHEEL BEARING ADJUSTMENT

1. Raise the car and support at the front lower control arm.

2. Remove the hub cap or wheel cover from the wheel. Remove the dust cap from the hub.

3. Remove the cotter pin from the spindle and spindle nut.

4. Spin the wheel forward by hand and tighten the spindle nut to 12 ft. lbs. This will fully seat the bearings.

5. Back off the nut to a just loose position.

6. Hand-tighten the spindle nut. Loosen the spindle nut until either hole in the spindle aligns with a slot in the nut, but not more than ½ flat.

7. Install a new cotter pin, bend the ends of the pin against the nut, and cut off any extra length to avoid interference with the dust cap.

8. Proper bearing adjustment should give 0.001–0.005 in. of end-play.

9. Install the dust cap on the hub and the hub cap or wheel cover on the wheel.

10. Lower the car.

11. Adjust the opposite front wheel bearings.

REAR SUSPENSION

When using a hoist contacting the rear axle, be sure that the stabilizer links and the track rod are not damaged.

Shock Absorber

REMOVAL & INSTALLATION

NOTE: Purge new shock absorbers of air by repeatedly extending in the normal position and compressing while inverted.

1. Raise the car on a hoist.

2. Support the rear axle.

3. Remove the shock absorber upper attaching nut and lower attaching bolt and nut, and remove the shock absorber.

To install:

4. Install the retainer and the rubber grommet onto the shock absorber.

5. Place the shock absorber into its installed position and install and tighten the upper retaining nut to 7 ft. lbs.

6. Install the lower shock absorber nut and bolt and torque to 21 ft. lbs.

7. Remove the rear axle supports and lower the car.

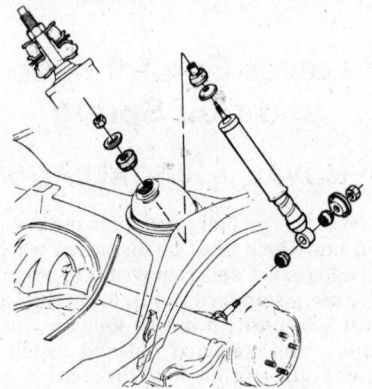

Rear shock absorber mounting
(© Chevrolet Div., G.M. Corp)

Rear Spring

REMOVAL & INSTALLATION

1. Raise the car on a hoist.

2. Support the rear axle with a floor jack.

3. Disconnect both shock absorbers from their lower brackets.

4. Disconnect the rear axle extension center support bracket from the underbody. Use caution when disconnecting the exten-

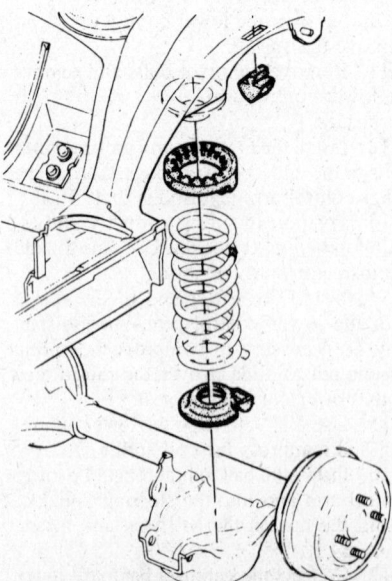

Rear spring installation—position both insulators as shown
(© Chevrolet Div., G.M. Corp)

sion and safely support it when disconnected.

5. Lower the rear axle and remove the springs and spring insulators.

— CAUTION —
Do not stretch the rear brake hoses when lowering the rear axle.

6. To install, place the insulators on top and on the bottom of the springs and position the springs between their upper and lower seats.

7. Raise the rear axle. Connect the rear axle extension center support bracket to the underbody. Torque the bolts to 37 ft. lbs.

8. Connect the shock absorbers to their lower brackets. Torque the nuts to 21 ft. lbs.

9. Remove the jack from the axle.

10. Lower the car.

BRAKES

Front disc brakes are standard equipment. Power brakes are available as an option. The 9.68 in. diameter disc is a one-piece casting with the hub. Single-piston sliding calipers are used.

The rear brakes are of conventional leading-trailing shoe design. Brake drum diameter is 7.88 in. Automatic adjusters are used in the rear brakes to provide adjustment when needed whenever the brakes are applied, forward or reverse.

The master cylinder is a two-piece design: a cast housing containing the primary and secondary pistons and a stamped steel reservoir. The reservoir is attached to the cast housing with two retainers and sealed with two O-rings. The reservoir is not divided, however a dual braking system is used. The front (secondary) piston operates the rear brakes, while the rear (primary) piston operates the front brakes.

The front and rear brake lines are routed through a distributor and switch assembly located on the left-hand engine compartment side panel. The switch is a pressure differential type which lights the brake warning light on the instrument panel if either the front or rear hydraulic system fails. It automatically resets after repair. The switch is nonadjustable and nonserviceable; it must be replaced if defective.

To service brake shoes, drums and wheel cylinders or brake pads and calipers, see "Brakes" in the Unit Repair section.

Master Cylinder

REMOVAL & INSTALLATION

1. Disconnect the master cylinder pushrod from the brake pedal.

2. Remove the pushrod boot.

3. Remove the air cleaner.

4. Thoroughly clean all dirt from the master cylinder and the brake lines. Disconnect the brake lines from the master cylinder and plug them to prevent the entry of dirt.

5. Remove the master cylinder securing nuts and remove the master cylinder.

6. Install the master cylinder with its spacer. Tighten the securing nuts.

7. Connect the brake lines to their ports.

8. Place the pushrod boot over the end of the pushrod. Secure the pushrod to the brake pedal with the pin and clip.

9. Fill the master cylinder and bleed the entire hydraulic system. After bleeding, fill the master cylinder to within ¼ in. from the top of the reservoir. Check for leaks.

10. Install the air cleaner.

11. Check brake operation before moving the car.

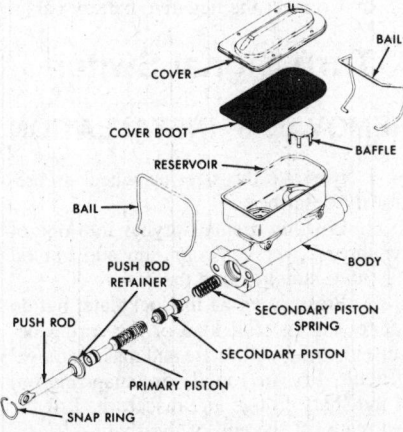

Dual piston master cylinder with common reservoir—through 1978 (© Chevrolet Div., G.M. Corp.)

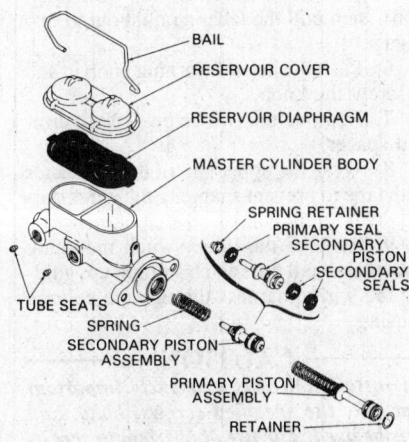

Dual piston master cylinder with common reservoir—1979 and later (© Chevrolet Div., G.M. Corp.)

PARKING BRAKE ADJUSTMENT

1. Raise the car on a hoist.

2. Apply the parking brake one notch from the fully released position on models through 1979 and three notches from the fully released position on 1980 and later models.

3. Tighten the parking brake cable equalizer adjusting nut under the car until a light drag is felt when the rear wheels are rotated forward.

4. Fully release the parking brake and rotate the rear wheels. There should be no drag.

5. Lower the car.

Power Brake Booster

REMOVAL & INSTALLATION

1. Remove the air cleaner.

2. Disconnect the vacuum hose from the check valve.

3. Remove the master cylinder brace.

4. Remove the master cylinder-to-power cylinder nut, and pull forward on the master cylinder until it clears the power cylinder mounting studs. Move the master cylinder aside and support it, being careful of the brake lines.

5. Remove the nuts securing the power cylinder to the firewall.

6. Remove the pushrod-to-pedal retainer and slip the pushrod off the pedal pin. Remove the power cylinder.

7. Installation is the reverse of removal.

STEERING

All models use manual rack and pinion steering which encloses the steering gear and linkage in one unit. Power steering is available as an option in all 1981 and later models with an automatic transmission.

Tie-Rod

REMOVAL & INSTALLATION

1. Loosen the jam nut located on the inner tie-rod.

2. Remove the outer tie-rod cotter pin and nut.

3. Using a tie-rod end separating tool, remove the tie-rod from the steering knuckle.

4. Remove the outer tie-rod from the inner tie-rod assembly.

5. Install the new outer tie-rod end onto the inner tie-rod assembly. Do not tighten the jam nut.

6. Install the outer tie-rod into the steering knuckle and torque the nut to 32 ft. lbs. Install a new cotter pin.

7. Set toe-in adjustment to specification by turning the inner tie-rod. Be sure not to twist the boot when making the adjustment.

8. Torque the jam nut to 50 ft. lbs.

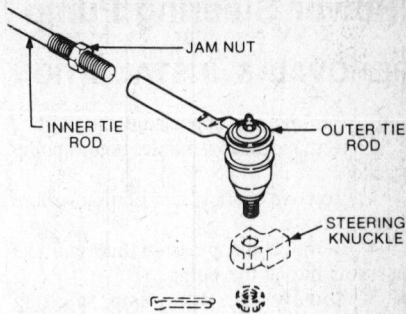

Tie rod end assembly (© Chevrolet Div., G.M. Corp.)

Steering Gear

REMOVAL & INSTALLATION

1. Raise the vehicle and support it with jackstands.

2. Remove the bolts and shield.

3. Remove the outer tie-rod cotter pins and nuts on both sides.

4. Using a tie-rod separating tool, disconnect the tie-rods from the steering knuckles.

5. On power steering models remove the two hydraulic lines from the steering gear.

6. Remove the flexible coupling pinch bolt to the shaft.

7. Remove the four bolts at the clamps, and remove the assembly from the vehicle.
Installation:

8. Position the assembly to the vehicle with the stub shaft in position with the flexible coupling, and install the clamps and four new bolts.

9. Install the flexible coupling pinch bolt to the shaft.

10. Install the tie-rods into the steering knuckles and torque the nuts to 30 ft. lbs. Install a new cotter pin.

11. On power steering models install the two hydraulic hoses and bleed the system.

12. Install the bolts and shield. Remove the jackstands and lower the vehicle.

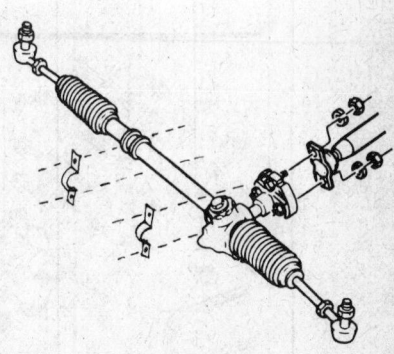

Manual rack and pinion assembly (© Chevrolet Div., G.M. Corp.)

Power Steering Pump

REMOVAL & INSTALLATION

1. Remove the upper adjusting bolt.
2. Remove the lower brace bolt-to-pump bracket.
3. Remove the left hand crossmember brace to body.
4. Remove the pressure line and the reservoir line at the pump.
5. Remove the rear pump adjusting bracket.
6. Remove the front pivot bolt at the pump and remove the bolt.
7. Remove the front pump bracket at the bolt-to-engine. Remove the bracket and pump.
8. Installation is the reverse of the removal procedure. In addition, adjust the belt tension, fill the reservoir and bleed the system.

BLEEDING THE POWER STEERING SYSTEM

NOTE: When checking or adjusting the fluid level after the system has been serviced, air must be bled from the system, as follows:

1. Install the pump, bracket and all hoses and lines to specifications, EXCEPT the pressure line at the pump outlet.

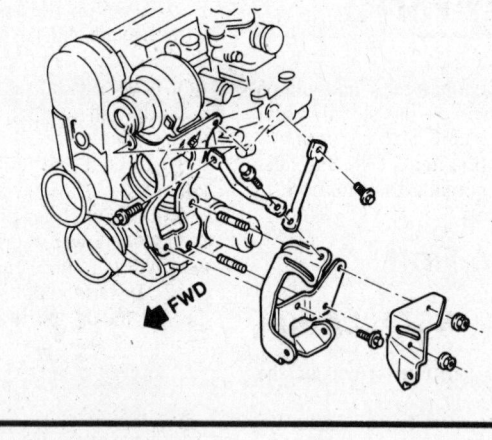

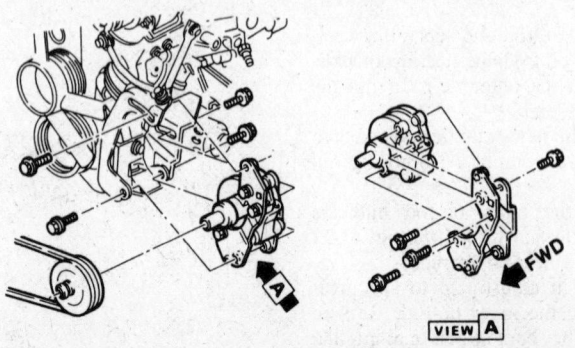

Power steering pump mounting—gasoline engine (© Chevrolet Div., G.M. Corp.)

2. Add fluid to the reservoir until fluid begins leaving the pump at the pressure fittings.
3. Attach the pressure line to the pump.
4. Continue filling the reservoir until the proper level is reached.
5. Road test the car to make sure the steering system functions normally.
6. Re-check the fluid level. If fluid level is low, add fluid to the proper level, and install cap.

Steering Wheel

REMOVAL & INSTALLATION

1. Disconnect the negative battery cable.
2. On 1978 models remove the two steering wheel shroud screws at the underside of the steering wheel and remove the shroud. On 1979 and later models, pull up on the horn cap to remove it. Remove the horn ring-to-steering wheel attaching screws and remove the ring.
3. Remove the wheel nut retainer and the wheel nut.

— CAUTION —
Do not overexpand the retainer.

4. Using a steering wheel puller, thread the puller anchor screws into the threaded holes in the steering wheel. With the center bolt of the puller butting against the steering shaft, turn the center bolt to remove the

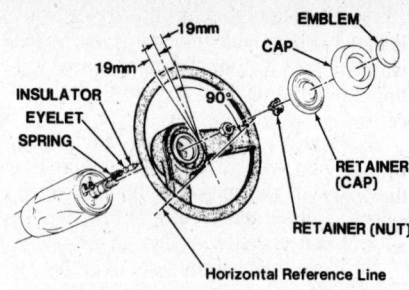

Chevette steering wheel assembly (© Chevrolet Div., G.M. Corp.)

steering wheel.
5. To install, place the turn signal lever in the neutral position and install the steering wheel. Torque the steering wheel nut to 30 ft lbs and install the nut retainer. Use caution not to overexpand the nut retainer.
6. Connect the negative battery cable.

Turn Signal Switch

REMOVAL & INSTALLATION

1. Remove the steering wheel as previously described.
2. Position a small prybar into one of the three cover slots. Pry up and out (at least two slots) to free the cover.
3. Press down on the lockplate, but do not relieve the full load of the spring because the ring will rotate and make removal difficult. Pry the round wire snap-ring out of the shaft groove and discard it. Lift the lockplate off the end of the shaft.
4. Slide the turn signal cancelling cam, upper bearing preload spring, and thrust washer off the end of the shaft.
5. Remove the multi-function lever by rotating it clockwise to its stop (off position), then pull the lever straight out to disengage it.
6. Push the hazard warning knob in and unscrew the knob.
7. Remove the two screws, pivot arm, and spacer.
8. Wrap the upper part of the connector with tape to prevent snagging the wires during switch removal.
9. Remove the three switch mounting screws and pull the switch straight up, guiding the wiring harness through the column housing.

— CAUTION —
On installation it is extremely important that only the specified screws, bolts, and nuts be used. The use of overlength screws could prevent the steering column from compressing under impact.

10. Position the switch into the housing.
11. Install the three switch mounting screws. Replace the spacer and pivot arm. Be sure that the spacer protrudes through the hole in the arm and that the arm finger encloses the turn signal switch frame.
12. Install the hazard warning knob.

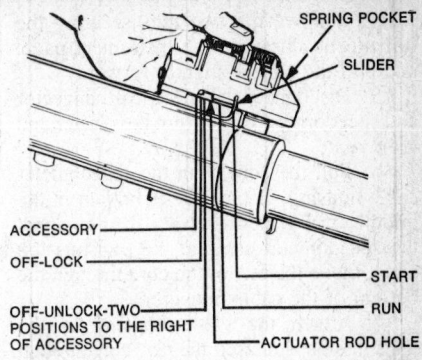

Postioning the ignition switch for installation

13. Make sure that the turn signal switch is in the neutral position and that the hazard warning knob is out. Slide the thrust washer, upper bearing preload spring, and the cancelling cam into the upper end of the shaft.

14. Place the lockplate and a new snapring onto the end of the shaft. Compress the lockplate as far as possible. Slide the new snap-ring into the shaft groove and remove the lockplate compressor tool.

— **CAUTION** —
On assembly, always use a new snap-ring.

15. Install the multi-function lever, guiding the wire harness through the column housing. Align the lever pin with the switch slot. Push on the end of the lever until it is seated securely.

16. Install the steering wheel as previously described.

Lock Cylinder

REMOVAL & INSTALLATION

The lock cylinder is located on the right-side of the steering column and should be removed only in the Run position. Removal in any other position will damage the key buzzer switch. The lock cylinder cannot be disassembled; if replacement is required, a new cylinder coded to the old key must be installed.

1. Remove the steering wheel and turn signal switch as previously described.

2. Do not remove the buzzer switch or damage to the lock cylinder will result.

3. On 1978 models, insert a small pry bar or similar tool into the turn signal housing slot to the upper right of the steering shaft. Keep the tool to the right side of the slot and depress the retainer at the bottom to release the lock cylinder. Remove the lock cylinder. On 1979 and later models, place the lock cylinder in the RUN position. Remove the securing screw and remove the cylinder.

4. To install the lock cylinder, hold the cylinder sleeve and rotate knob (key in) clockwise to stop. (This retracts the actuator). Insert the cylinder into the housing bore with the key on the cylinder sleeve aligned with the keyway in the housing. Push the cylinder in until it bottoms. On 1978 models, rotate the knob counterclockwise while maintaining a light pressure inward until the drive section of the cylinder mates with the sector. Push the cylinder in fully until the retainer pops into the housing groove. On 1979 and later models, install the retaining screw.

5. Install the turn signal switch and the steering wheel as previously described.

Ignition Switch and Dimmer Switch

REMOVAL & INSTALLATION

The ignition switch is mounted on top of the mast jacket near the front of the instrument panel. The switch is located inside the channel section of the brake pedal support and is completely inaccessible without first lowering the steering column.

1. Disconnect the negative battery cable.
2. Remove the steering wheel as previously described.
3. Move the driver's seat as far back as possible.
4. Remove the floor pan bracket screw.
5. Remove the two column bracket-to-instrument panel nuts and lower the column far enough to disconnect the ignition switch wiring harness.

— **CAUTION** —
Be sure that the steering column is properly supported before proceeding.

6. The switch should be in the Lock position before removal. If the lock cylinder has already been removed, the actuating rod to the switch should be pulled up until there is a definite stop, then moved down one detent to the Lock position.

7. Remove the two mounting screws and remove the ignition and dimmer switch.

8. Refer to the lock cylinder installation procedure previously described in Lock Cylinder Removal and Installation.

9. Turn the cylinder clockwise to stop and then counterclockwise to stop, then counterclockwise again to stop (Off-Unlock position).

10. Place the ignition switch in the Off-Unlock position. Move the slider two positions to the right from Accessory to the Off-Unlock position.

11. Fit the actuator rod into the slider hole and install the switch on the column. Be sure to use only the correct screws. Be careful not to move the switch out of its detent.

12. Check the dimmer switch adjustment.

13. Connect the ignition switch wiring harness.

14. Loosely install the column bracket-to-instrument panel nuts.

15. Install the floor pan bracket screw and tighten it to 20 ft. lbs.

16. Tighten the column bracket-to-instrument panel nuts to 22 ft. lbs.

17. Install the steering wheel as previously outlined.

18. Connect the battery negative cable.

INSTRUMENT PANEL

Instrument Cluster and Speedometer Cable

REPLACEMENT

The instrument cluster must be removed to replace light bulbs, gauges, and printed circuit.

1. Disconnect the negative battery cable.
2. Remove the clock stem knob.
3. Remove the four screws and remove the instrument cluster bezel and lens.

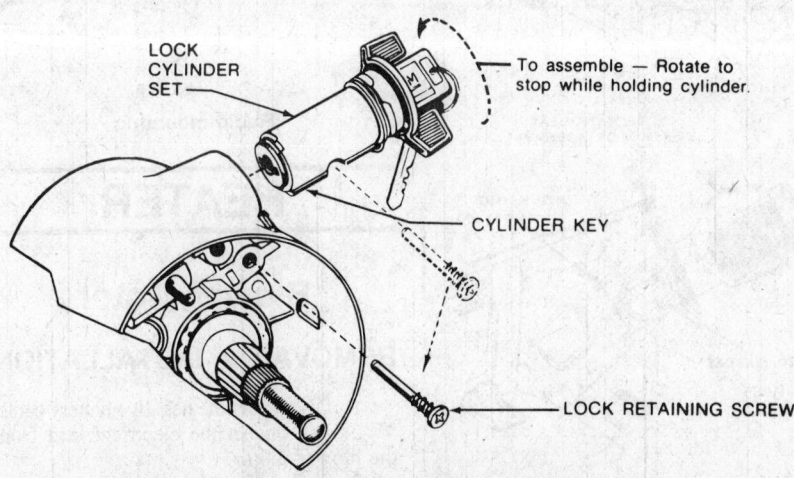

Lock cylinder installation details (© Chevrolet Div., G.M. Corp.)

4. Remove the two nuts securing the instrument cluster to the instrument panel and pull the cluster slightly forward.

5. Disconnect the electrical connector and speedometer cable from the cluster and remove it.

6. Pull the core from the speedometer cable housing. If the core is broken in the middle, it will be necessary to disconnect the speedometer cable at the transmission and remove the rest of the core through the bottom of the cable housing.

7. Attach the cable housing to the transmission and insert the new core through the top of the housing.

8. Attach the speedometer cable to the rear of the speedometer.

9. Reverse to install.

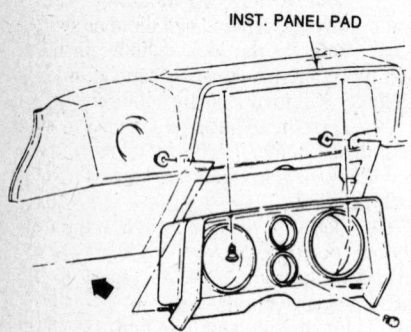

Instrument cluster mounting

Headlight Switch

REMOVAL & INSTALLATION

1. Disconnect the negative battery cable.
2. Pull the headlight switch control knob to the On position.
3. Reach up under the instrument panel and depress the switch shaft retainer button while pulling on the switch control shaft knob.
4. Remove the three screws and remove the headlight switch trim plate.

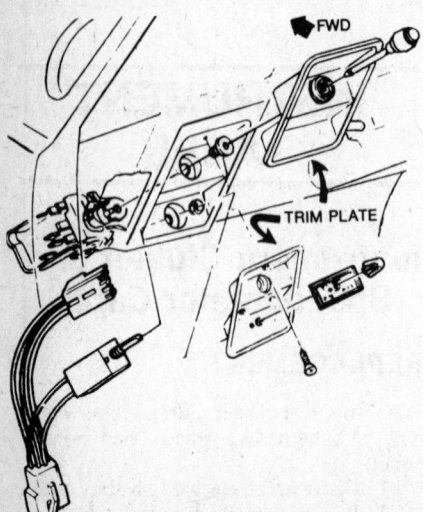

Headlight switch mounting

5. Remove the light switch ferrule nut from the front of the instrument panel.
6. Disconnect the multi-contact connector from the bottom of the headlight switch.
7. Installation is the reverse of removal.

WINDSHIELD WIPERS

Motor

REMOVAL & INSTALLATION

1. Working inside the car, reach up under the instrument panel above the steering column and loosen, but do not remove, the transmission drive link-to-motor crank arm attaching nuts.
2. Disconnect the transmission drive link from the wiper motor crank arm.
3. Raise the hood and disconnect the wiper motor wiring.
4. Remove the three motor attaching bolts.
5. Remove the motor while guiding the crank arm through the hole.
6. To install, align the sealing gasket to the base of the motor and reverse the rest of the removal procedure.

NOTE: If the wiper motor-to-firewall sealing gasket is damaged during removal, it should be replaced with a new gasket to prevent possible water leaks.

Wiper Blade
REPLACEMENT

To remove the blade from the arm, depress

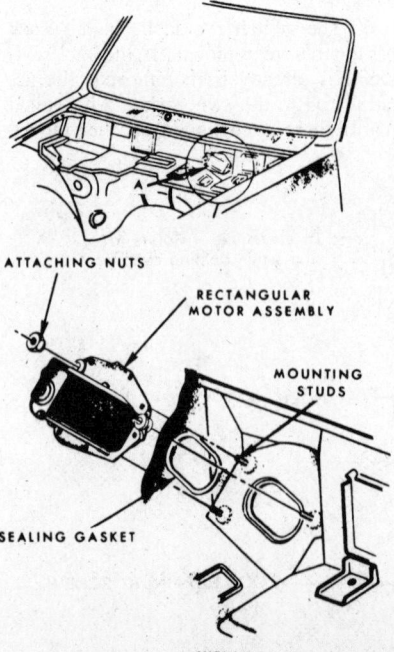

Wiper motor mounting

the spring type blade clip away from the underside of the arm and slide the arm out of the blade clip. To install the blade, slide the tip end of the arm into the blade clip until the pin on the tip end engages the hole in the clip. The rubber wiper element can be replaced separately from the blade; see the Maintenance Section in this book for details.

RADIO

REMOVAL & INSTALLATION

1. Disconnect the negative battery cable.
2. Remove the nut from the mounting stud on the bottom of the radio.
3. Remove all control knobs and/or spacers from the right and left radio control shafts.
4. Remove the four screws from the center trim plate and pull the trim plate and the radio forward slightly.
5. Disconnect the antenna lead from the rear of the radio.
6. Disconnect the speaker and electrical connectors from the radio harness.
7. Disconnect the electrical connectors from the rear window defogger and cigarette lighter.
8. Use a deep well socket to remove the retaining nuts from both control shafts and remove the radio.
9. To install, reverse the removal procedure.

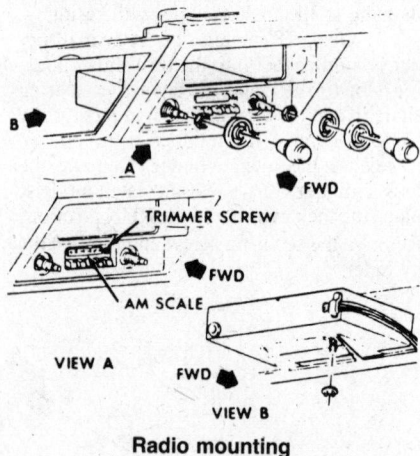

Radio mounting

HEATER

Blower Motor

REMOVAL & INSTALLATION

1. Disconnect the negative battery cable.
2. Disconnect the electrical lead from the blower motor.
3. Scribe a mark to reference the blower motor flange-to-case position.

4. Remove the blower motor-to-case attaching screws and remove the blower motor and wheel as an assembly. Pry the flange gently if the sealer acts as an adhesive.

5. Remove the blower wheel retaining nut and separate the motor and wheel.

6. Reverse Steps 1–5 to install. Be sure to align the scribe marks made during removal.

NOTE: Assemble the blower wheel to the motor with the open end of the wheel away from the motor. If necessary, replace the sealer at the motor flange.

Heater Core

REMOVAL & INSTALLATION

Without Air Conditioning

1. Disconnect the negative battery cable.
2. Drain the radiator.
3. Disconnect the heater hoses at the heater core tube connections. Use care when removing the hoses as the core tube attachment seams can be easily damaged if too much force is used on them. When the hoses are removed, install plugs in the core tubes to avoid spilling coolant when removing the core.

NOTE: The larger diameter hose goes to the water pump; the smaller diameter hose goes to the thermostat housing.

4. Remove the screws around the perimeter of the heater core cover on the engine side of the firewall.

5. Pull the heater core cover from its mounting in the firewall.

6. Remove the core from the distributor assembly.

7. Reverse the removal procedure to install. Be sure that the core-to-case sealer is intact before replacing the core; use new sealer if necessary. When installation is complete, check for coolant leaks.

With Air Conditioning

1. Disconnect the negative battery cable.
2. Disconnect the heater hoses at the core with a drain pan under the car. Plug the hoses to prevent spillage.
3. Remove the A/C hose bracket.
4. Remove the heater core case cover and remove the core from the case.
5. Reverse to install.

CIRCUIT PROTECTION

Fuses & Circuit Breakers

The fuse panel is located under the left-hand side of the instrument panel. The fuse amperage and the circuit protected is marked on the fuse panel. The headlight circuit is protected by a circuit breaker in the light switch. An electrical overload will cause the lights to go on and off, or in some cases to remain off. If this condition develops, check the wiring circuits immediately. An air conditioning high blower speed fuse, 30 amp, is located in an in-line fuse holder running from the junction block to the air conditioning relay.

Fusible Link

A Fusible link is incorporated into the wiring system. This is a wire of such a gauge that it will fuse (or melt) before damage occurs to the wiring harness in the event of an electrical overload. The fusible link is a 16 gauge red wire located at the battery terminal of the starter solenoid. Also, on diesel models a 14 gauge brown fusible link is located between the battery and the glow plug relay.

Flashers

The hazard warning flasher is located in the fuse box. The directional signal flasher is located above the brake pedal bracket, to the left of the steering column.

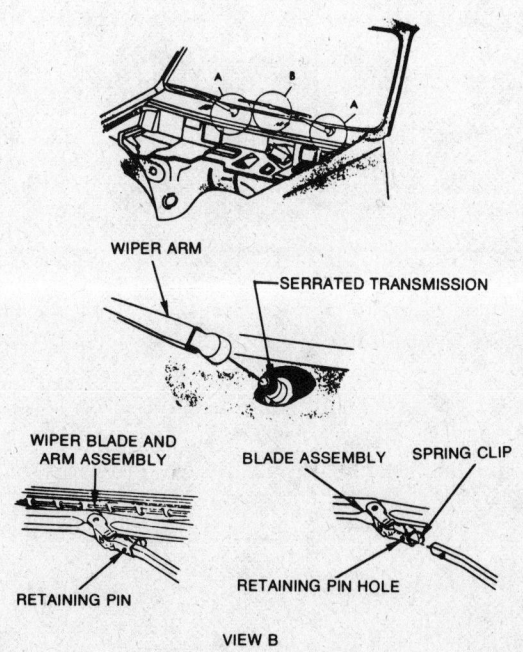

Wiper blade and arm installation

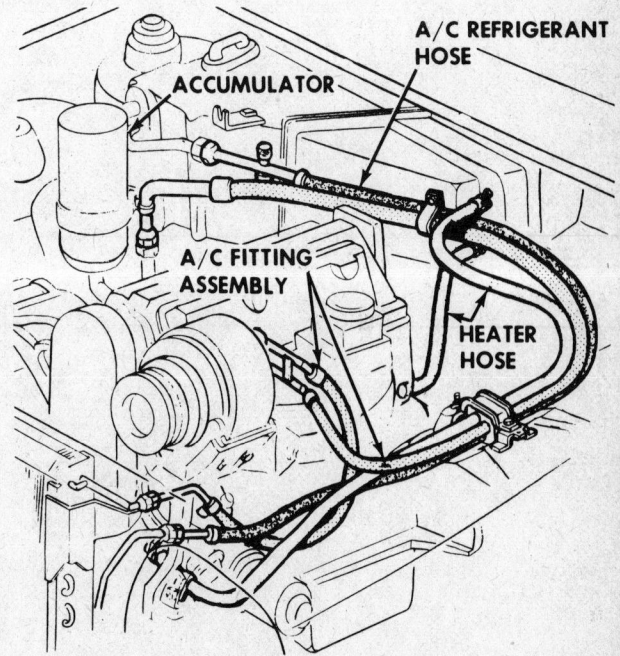

A/C refrigerant hose routing

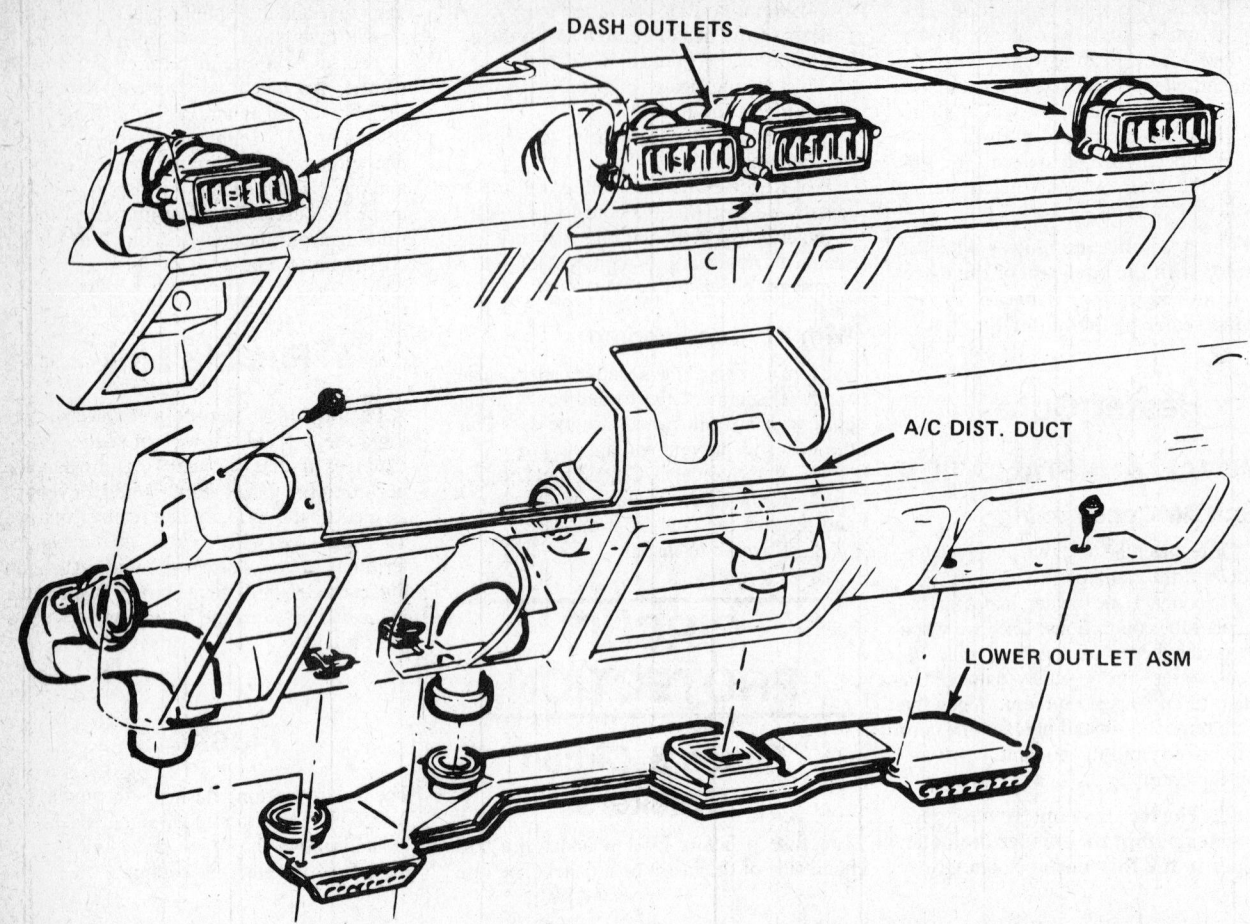

DASH OUTLETS

A/C DIST. DUCT

LOWER OUTLET ASM

Air conditioner ducts and dash outlets

Chevrolet Sprint

1985 Sprint

VEHICLE IDENTIFICATION NUMBER (VIN)

It is important for servicing and ordering parts to be certain of the vehicle and engine identification. The VIN (vehicle identification number) is a 17 digit number visible through the windshield on the driver's side of the dash and contains the vehicle and engine identification codes. It can be interpreted as follows:

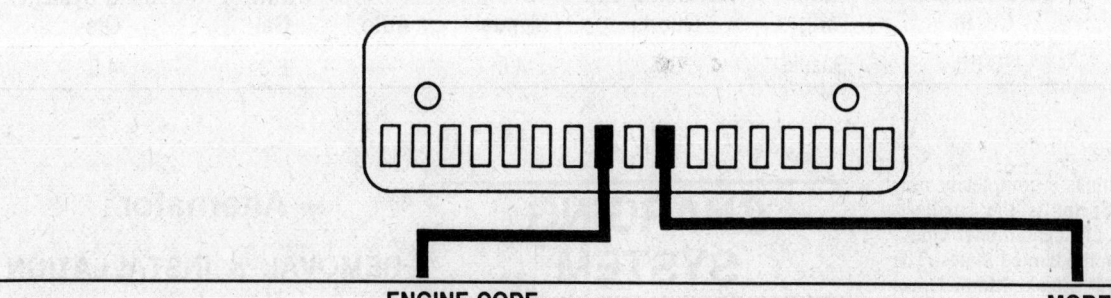

ENGINE CODE						MODEL YEAR CODE	
Code	Cu. In.	Liters	Cyl.	Carb.	Eng. Mfg.	Code	Year
N.A.	61	1.0	3	2bbl	Suzuki	F	1985

The seventeen digit Vehicle Identification Number can be used to determine engine application and model year. The 10th digit indicates the model year, and the 8th digit identifies the factory installed engine.
N.A.—Not Available

GENERAL ENGINE SPECIFICATIONS

Year	Engine No. Cyl. Displ. Cu. in.	Engine V.I.N. Code	Fuel Delivery System	Engine Mfg.	Horsepower @ rpm	Torque @ rpm (ft. lb.)	Bore × Stroke	Compression Ratio	Oil Pressure 2400 rpm
'85	3-61	N.A.	2bbl	Suzuki	48 @ 5100	57 @ 3200	2.91 × 3.03	9.5:1	N.A.

N.A.—Not Available

TUNE-UP SPECIFICATIONS

(When analyzing compression test results, look for uniformity among cylinders rather than specific pressures.)

Year	Eng. V.I.N. Code	Engine No. Cyl. Displacement (cu. in.)	Eng. Mfg.	hp	Spark Plugs Orig Type	Spark Plugs Gap (in.)	Ignition Timing (deg)▲● Man Trans	Ignition Timing (deg)▲● Auto Trans	Valves Intake Opens (deg)■	Fuel Pump Pressure (psi)	Idle Speed (rpm) ▲● Man Trans	Idle Speed (rpm) ▲● Auto Trans
'85	N.A.	3-61	Suzuki	48	①	③	③	③	N.A.	3.5②	③	③

① NGK:BPRGES-11 or Nippondenso WIGEXR-U11
② @ 5,000 rpm
③ Refer to underhood specifications sticker

FIRING ORDERS

NOTE: To avoid confusion, replace spark plugs and wires one at a time.

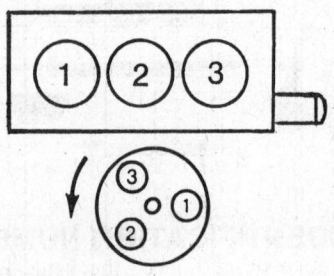

FIRING ORDER
Firing Order: 1-3-2
Distributor rotation: counterclockwise

CAPACITIES

Year	V.I.N. Code	Engine Displacement Cu. In.	Eng. Mfg.	Crankcase Quarts	Transaxle Pints Manual	Transaxle Pints Auto	Gas Tank Gal	Cooling System Qts
'85		3-61	Suzuki	3.7	4.8	—	8.3	4.5

The Chevrolet Sprint is a completely new model for 1985. Sprint is the smallest, lightest, most fuel efficient model Chevrolet has available in the United States. The Sprint is built by the Suzuki Motor Company Limited of Japan. The front wheel drive Sprint features a 48 horsepower three-cylinder engine which is aluminum with cast iron cylinder sleeves and hollow cam and crankshaft segments. The total "dressed" weight of the engine is 150 pounds. All models are equipped with a five-speed transaxle.

CHARGING SYSTEM

Alternator and regulator troubleshooting are covered in the "Charging and Starting Systems" Unit Repair section.

Alternator

REMOVAL & INSTALLATION

1. Disconnect the negative battery cable from the battery.
2. Disconnect the wiring harness plug from the back of the alternator.
3. Remove the heat shield from the side of the alternator.
4. Loosen the adjusting bracket to alternator end frame bolt. Loosen the lower

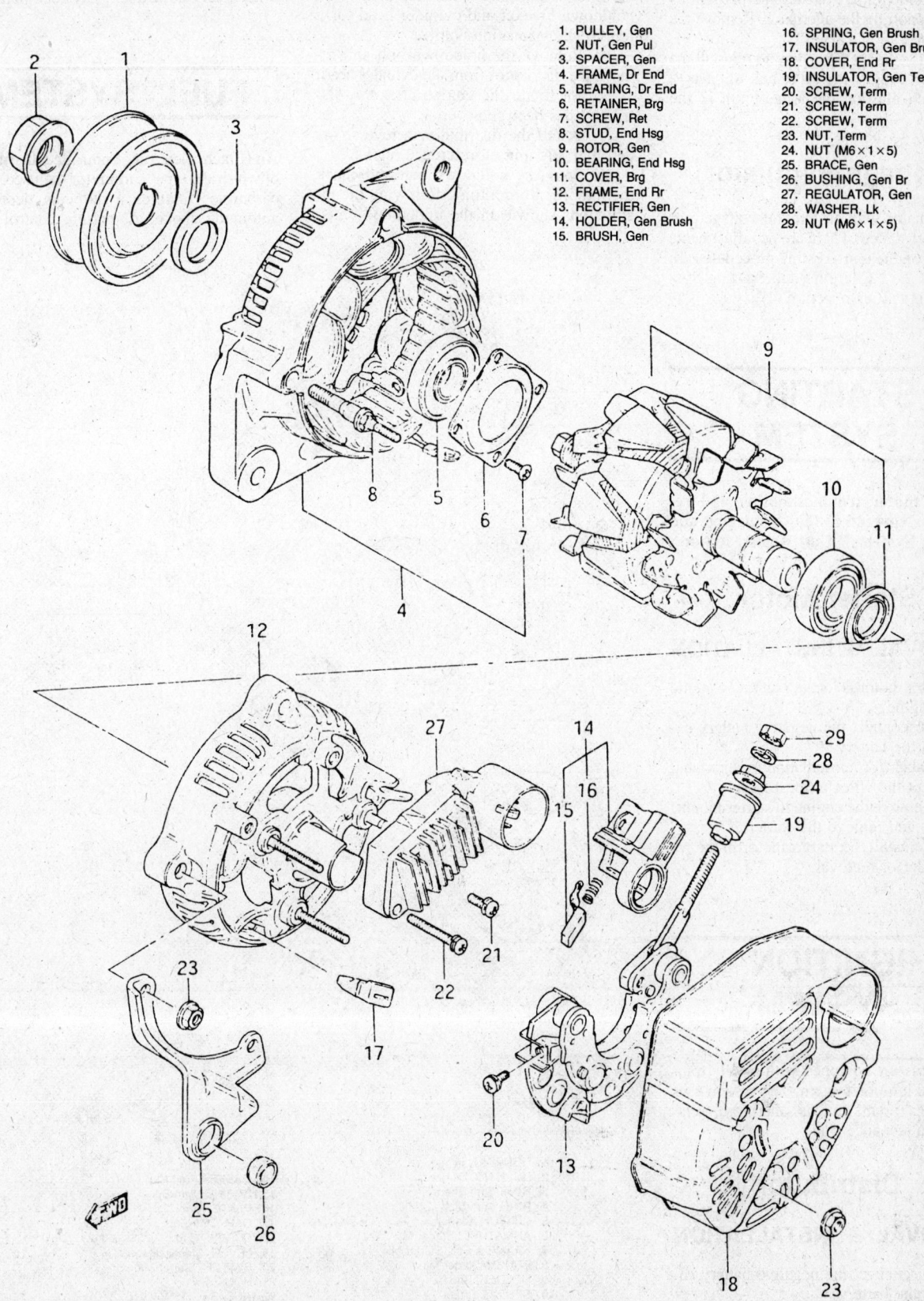

1. PULLEY, Gen
2. NUT, Gen Pul
3. SPACER, Gen
4. FRAME, Dr End
5. BEARING, Dr End
6. RETAINER, Brg
7. SCREW, Ret
8. STUD, End Hsg
9. ROTOR, Gen
10. BEARING, End Hsg
11. COVER, Brg
12. FRAME, End Rr
13. RECTIFIER, Gen
14. HOLDER, Gen Brush
15. BRUSH, Gen
16. SPRING, Gen Brush
17. INSULATOR, Gen Brush
18. COVER, End Rr
19. INSULATOR, Gen Term
20. SCREW, Term
21. SCREW, Term
22. SCREW, Term
23. NUT, Term
24. NUT (M6×1×5)
25. BRACE, Gen
26. BUSHING, Gen Br
27. REGULATOR, Gen
28. WASHER, Lk
29. NUT (M6×1×5)

Exploded view of the alternator

pivot bolt and remove the drive belt.

5. Remove the adjuster and pivot bolts while supporting the alternator. Remove the alternator.

6. Reverse the procedure to reinstall the alternator. Adjust the drive belt to have ¼ to ½ inch play on the longest run of the drive belt.

Voltage Regulator

An alternator with an integral voltage regulator is installed. There are no adjustments possible on the unit. Testing procedures are found in the ''Charging and Starting Systems'' Unit Repair section.

STARTING SYSTEM

Starter motor troubleshooting and repairs are covered in the ''Charging and Starting Systems'' Unit Repair section.

Starter Motor

REMOVAL & INSTALLATION

The starter motor is located on the rear side of the engine.

1. Disconnect the negative battery cable from the battery.

2. Label (for reinstallation location) and disconnect the wires at the solenoid.

3. Remove the engine to starter mounting bolts and remove the starter.

4. Reinstall the starter motor in the reverse order of removal.

IGNITION SYSTEM

All models are equipped with a fully transistorized ignition system. The system uses no contact points and is, therefore, relatively maintenance free.

Distributor

REMOVAL & INSTALLATION

1. Disconnect the negative battery cable from the battery.

2. Disconnect the wiring harness plug at the distributor. Disconnect the vacuum line at the distributor vacuum unit.

3. Remove the distributor cap. Mark

the distributor body in reference to where the rotor is pointing. Mark the distributor holddown bracket and cylinder head for a reinstallation location point.

4. Remove the holddown bolt and remove the distributor from the cylinder head.

Do not rotate the engine after the distributor has been removed.

5. Install the distributor in reverse order after aligning all reference marks.

6. Snug the holddown bolt and check the initial ignition timing following the instructions shown on the underhood emissions label. Tighten the holddown bolt after a necessary adjustment has been made.

FUEL SYSTEM

An Hitachi electronic controlled dual-barrel down-draft type carburetor is used. The carburetor features a no-pedal depressed automatic choke. A mixture control sole-

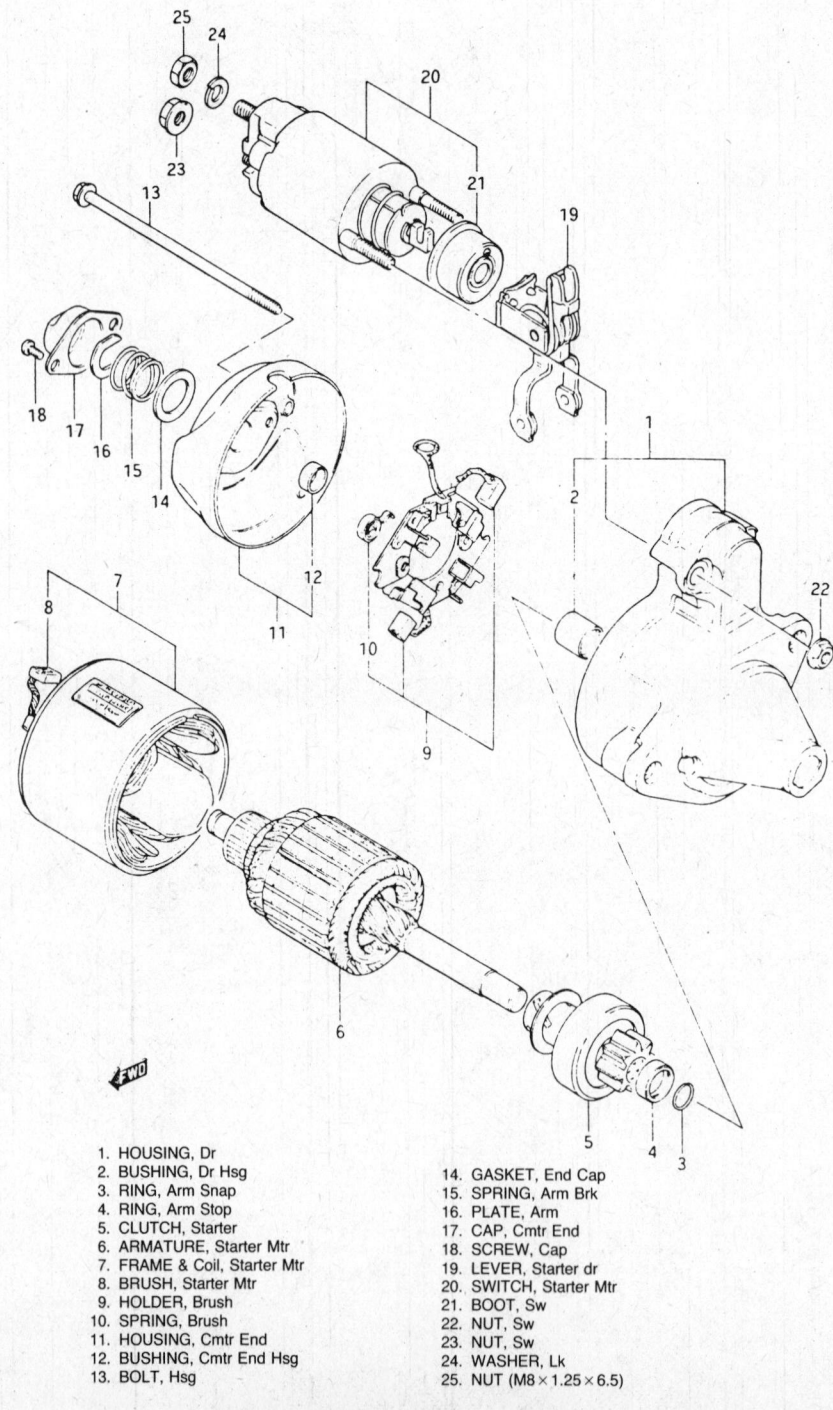

1. HOUSING, Dr
2. BUSHING, Dr Hsg
3. RING, Arm Snap
4. RING, Arm Stop
5. CLUTCH, Starter
6. ARMATURE, Starter Mtr
7. FRAME & Coil, Starter Mtr
8. BRUSH, Starter Mtr
9. HOLDER, Brush
10. SPRING, Brush
11. HOUSING, Cmtr End
12. BUSHING, Cmtr End Hsg
13. BOLT, Hsg
14. GASKET, End Cap
15. SPRING, Arm Brk
16. PLATE, Arm
17. CAP, Cmtr End
18. SCREW, Cap
19. LEVER, Starter dr
20. SWITCH, Starter Mtr
21. BOOT, Sw
22. NUT, Sw
23. NUT, Sw
24. WASHER, Lk
25. NUT (M8 × 1.25 × 6.5)

Exploded view of the starter motor

noid is incorporated which controls the primary slow and primary main system to maintain the correct air/fuel mixture under all engine operating conditions.

A mechanical fuel pump is located on the right side of the cylinder head which supplies fuel at a rate of 3.5 psi at 5,000 rpm.

The air cleaner uses a replaceable, and washable dry unwoven cloth filter element.

COOLING SYSTEM

The radiator is a single row type and consists of copper corrugated fins, brass tubes and plastic tanks. A fan shroud is attached to the radiator lower tank by two 6mm bolts. The radiator is attached at the front end of the upper tank to the body and fan shroud by two 6mm bolts. The lower part of the radiator is supported by two rubber cushions. An electric cooling fan is mounted on the radator shroud, the fan and shroud may

Water Pump

REMOVAL & INSTALLATION

1. Drain the cooling system. A plug at the bottom of the radiator is provided for this purpose.
2. Disconnect the negative battery cable.

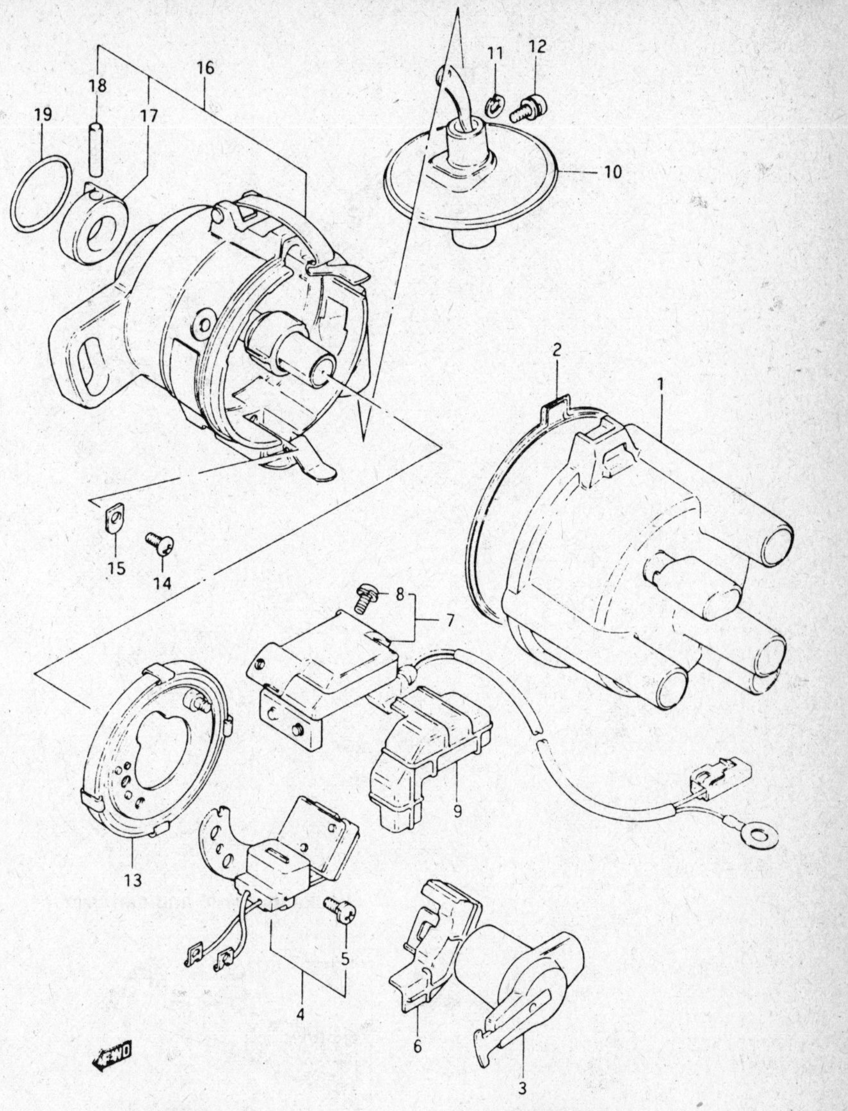

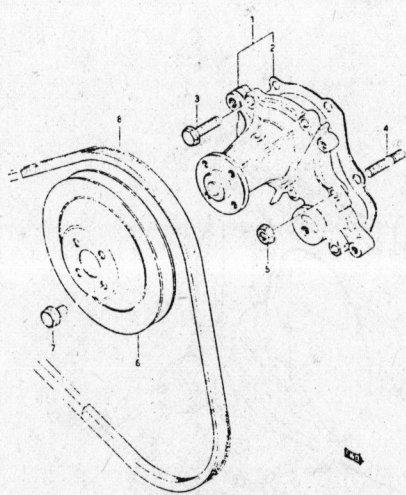

1. PUMP SET, Wat
2. GASKET, Wat Pump
3. BOLT, Wat Pump
4. STUD, Wat Pump
5. NUT (M6 × 1 × 6.5)
6. PULLEY, Wat Pump
7. BOLT, Pul
8. BELY, Wat Pump

Water pump mounting

1. CAP, Distr	11. RETAINER, Cont
2. SEAL, Distr Cap	12. SCREW, Cont
3. ROTOR, Distr	13. PLATE, Gen Base
4. GENERATOR, Distr	14. SCREW, Base Plate
5. SCREW, Distr Gen	15. WASHER, Base Plate
6. COVER, Signal Gen Dust	16. HOUSING, Distr (Exc Canadian)
7. IGNITER, Distr	17. COUPLING, Distr
8. SCREW, Distr Ign	18. PIN, Distr Cplg
9. COVER, Ign Dust	19. SEAL, Distr Hsg
10. CONTROLLER, Vac (Exc Canadian)	

Exploded view of the distributor

3. Remove the water pump drive belt. Remove the water pump drive pulley.
4. Remove any accessory drive brackets attached to the water pump.
5. Remove the pump mounting bolt(s) and nut(s) and remove the water pump.
6. Clean all gasket mounting surfaces.
7. Install the water pump, with a new gasket, in the reverse order of removal. Fill the cooling system with the correct mixture of anti-freeze and water. Start the engine and run at idle until the normal operating temperature is reached. Check for leaks.

Thermostat

REMOVAL & INSTALLATION

1. The thermostat is located under housing which is attached to the intake manifold.
2. Drain the cooling system to a level below the thermostat. Disconnect the negative battery cable.
3. Remove the thermostat housing mounting bolts and remove the thermostat.

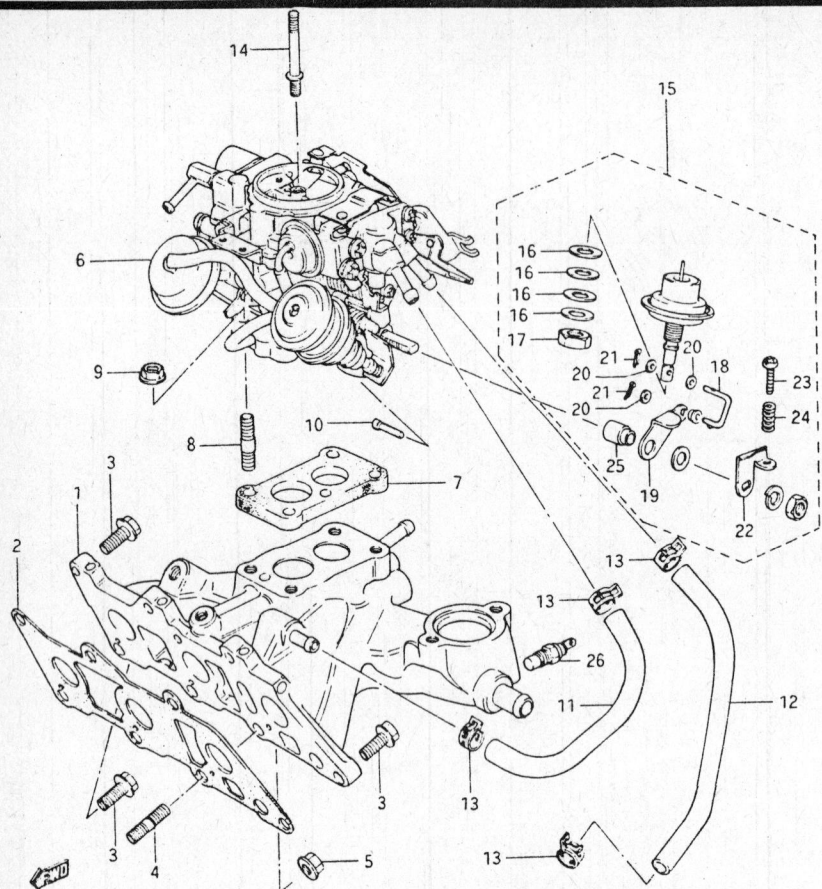

1. MANIFOLD, Int
2. GASKET, Int Manif
3. BOLT, Manif
4. STUD, Int. Manif
5. NUT (M8 × 1.25 × 7.5)
6. CARBURETOR
7. INSULATOR, Carb
8. STUD
9. NUT (M8 × 1 × 1.125 × 7.5)
10. PIN, Mixture Adj Screw
11. HOSE, Carb Choke No. 1
12. HOSE, Carb Choke No. 2
13. CLIP, Hose
14. STUD, A/Clnr(Exc Canadian)
15. ACTUATOR, Carb, Idle, Up, W/A.C.
16. WASHER, Actr, Idle Up, W/A.C.
17. NUT, Actr, Idle Up, W/A.C.
18. ROD, Servo, Idle Up, W/A.C.
19. LEVER, Idle Up, W/A.C.
20. WASHER, Idle Up, W/A.C.
21. PIN, Idle Up, W/A.C.
22. LEVER, Idle Up, W/A.C.
23. SCREW, Idle Adj, W/A.C.
24. SPRING, Adj Screw, W/A.C.
25. SLEEVE, Idle Up, W/A.C.
26. SWITCH (GAUGE), Wat Temp

Intake manifold and carburetor

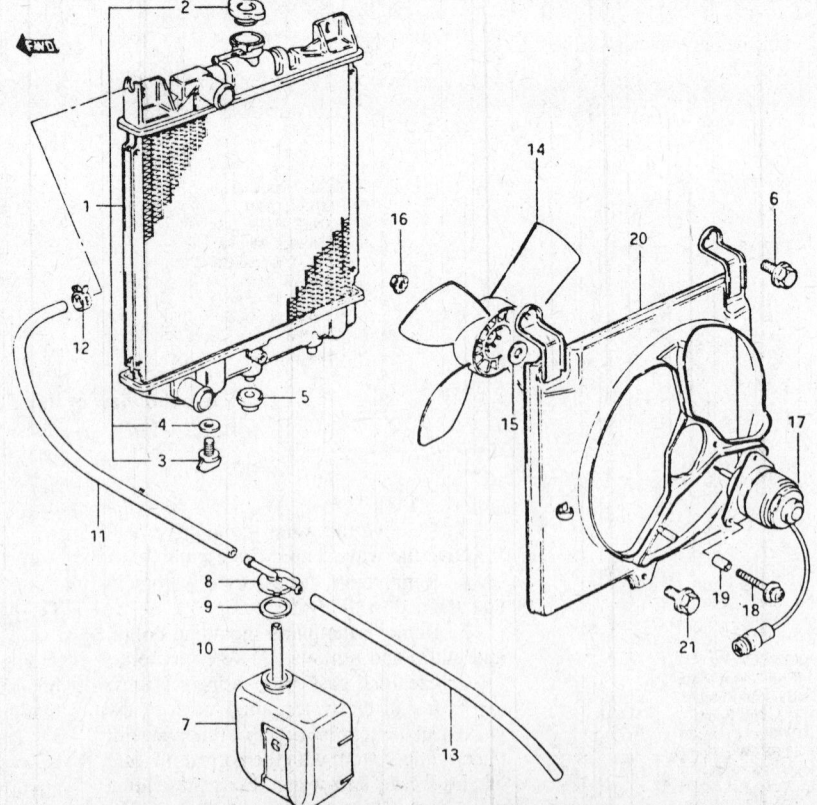

1. RADIATOR
2. CAP, Rad
3. PLUG, Rad Drn
4. SEAL, Rad Drn Plug
5. BUSHING, Rad Supt
6. BOLT, Rad
7. TANK, Wat Resvr
8. CAP, Wat Resvr Tank
9. RUBBER, Wat Resvr Tank Cap
10. HOSE (5/16 × 24)
11. HOSE (5/16 × 24)
12. CLAMP (CLIP), Worm Dr (.750/.310)
13. HOSE (5/16 × 24)
14. FAN, Eng Clg (Exc A.C.)
    FAN, Eng Clg (W/A.C.)
15. WASHER, Clg Fan No. 1
16. NUT (M6 × 1 × 6)
17. MOTOR, Eng Clg (Exc A.C.)
    MOTOR, Eng Clg (W/A.C.)
18. SCREW, Clg Mtr
19. BUSHING, Clg Mtr Rub
20. SHROUD, Eng Clg Fan (Exc A.C.)
    SHROUD, Eng Clg Fan (W/A.C.)
21. BOLT, Shrd

Radiator and fan mounting

4. Clean all gasket mounting surfaces.

5. Install the thermostat, with a new gasket, in the reverse order of removal.

6. Fill the cooling system to the correct level. Run the engine at idle until normal operating temperature is reached. Check for leaks.

EMMISSION CONTROLS

The crankcase emission control system is of the closed dual return type. The system has two passages. The first passage connects the rocker cover and the intake manifold through the PCV valve. The second passage connects the rocker cover to the filtered side of the air cleaner.

The engine is equipped with an air jet quick combustion system. A jet of air located near the intake valve is synchronized to the intake stroke and drawn into the combustion chamber through an induction air nozzle. This action causes a swirl in the chamber which promotes cleaner burning of the air/fuel mixture.

System Controls

TESTING

Operation of the feedback system can be checked by using the oxygen sensor lamp on the instrument panel and its cancel switch (located underneath the panel on the driver's side) as a test device.

When the cancel switch is turned on, flashing of the sensor lamp indicates proper functioning of the feedback system. Steady glow of the signal lamp indicates failure in the system and that the system is not functioning properly.

The oxygen sensor lamp is also linked with the odometer and lights automatically every 30,000 miles. Observe and confirm the sensor lamp indication of normal feedback operation, and reset the cancel switch for the next 30,000 miles of operation.

There is no diagnostic circuitry in the ECM (electronic control module) other than the feedback system test.

The purpose of the ECM/feedback system is to maintain a controlled air/fuel ratio, allowing the catalyst to reduce oxides of nitrogen, hydrocarbons, carbon monoxide and to improve fuel economy simultaneously.

An oxygen sensor mounted on the exhaust manifold monitors the exhaust gases, air/fuel mixture and transmits an electrical signal to the ECM. The ECM processes the signal and controls the air/fuel mixture by operating the carburetor mounted mixture control solenoid. The ECM also controls the pulse air system, fuel cut system, idle up system and the bowl vent system.

Input signals from a variety of sensors are fed to the ECM, which in return generates an output signal for all of the controlled functions.

Fuel Cut System

The fuel cut system consists of an idle solenoid, a throttle valve switch, an ECM, a clutch linkage switch and a coolant temperature switch. The system operates when the engine speed is higher than a preset level, the throttle valve opening is small and the coolant temeprature is within normal operating range. The carburetor slow passage is closed cutting off the current to the idle solenoid. The system is also activated when the ignition is shut off to prevent run-on (dieseling). The system is deactivated when the clutch pedal is depressed.

Temperature Controlled Air Cleaner

The air cleaner is equipped with a bimetal type temperature sensor and a vacuum motor. The temperature sensor detects the temperature inside the air cleaner and regulates the vacuum to the vacuum motor. The vacuum motor is linked with a hot air control valve which controls the hot air from the heat stove located on the exhaust manifold, the intake air temperature is kept nearly constant by this method. A hot idle compensator is also incorporated on the inside of the air cleaner for maintaining the proper idle speed under hot operation.

Exhaust Gas Recirculation (EGR) System

The EGR valve is located on the side face of the intake manifold and connected to the exhaust manifold through a passage cast inside the cylinder head and intake mani-

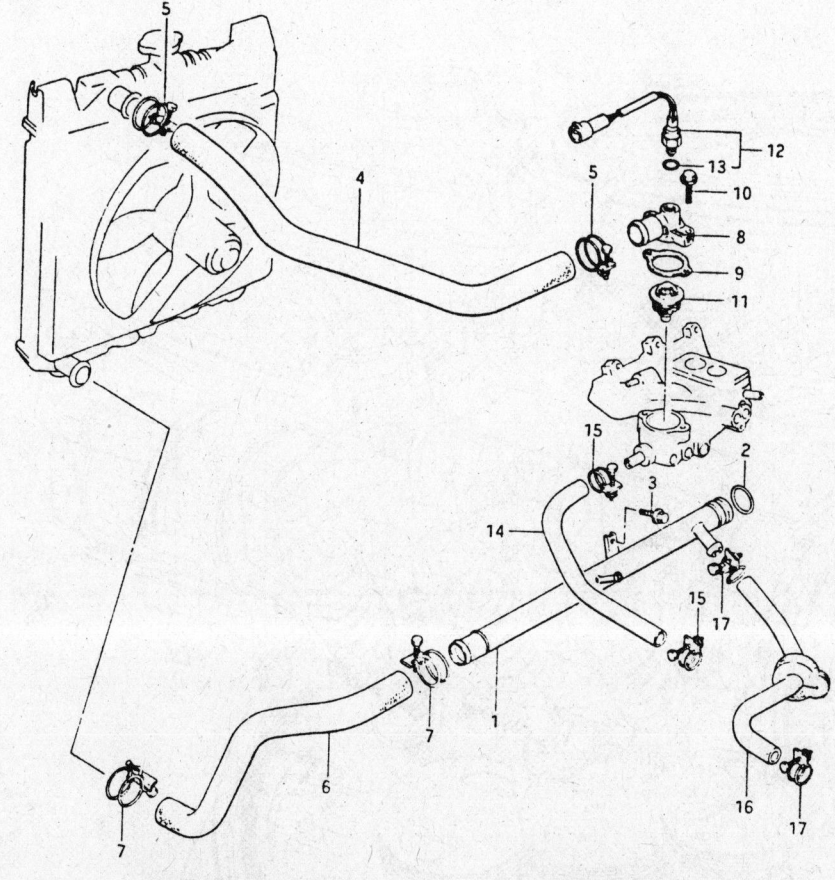

1. PIPE, Wat Int (Exc Canadian)
   PIPE, Wat Int (W/Z49, Canadian)
2. SEAL, Wat Int Pipe
3. BOLT, Pipe
4. HOSE, Rad Inl
5. CLAMP, Rad Inl Hose
6. HOSE, Rad Otlt
7. CLAMP, Rad Otlt Hose
8. CAP, Wat Therm
9. GASKET, Wat Therm Cap
10. BOLT, Cap
11. THERMOSTAT, Wat (88 Deg C, R)
12. SWITCH, Fan Therm
13. SEAL, Fan Therm Sw
14. HOSE, Htr Inl
15. CLAMP, Gr Type (3/4 × 1 3/4)
16. HOSE, Htr Otlt
17. CLAMP, Gr Type (3/4 × 1 3/4)

Thermostat and hoses

fold. A vacuum signal modulated by the EGR modulator causes the EGR valve to open allowing the exhaust gases to be introduced into the intake manifold. EGR operation is restricted when the coolant is lower than normal operating temperature.

Pulse Air System

Secondary air is drawn from the clean side of the air cleaner into the exhaust manifold through the air control and air induction valves. The secondary air is introduced when the coolant temperature is below a pre-set level or when decelerating from high engine rpm.

Fuel Evaporation Control

Fuel vapors form the gas tank are stored in a canister after passing through a two-way valve. The fuel vapor from the carburetor is also stored in the canister after passing through a bowl vent solenoid when the ig-

nition switch is in the OFF position. The fuel vapor is drawn from the canister into the intake manifold when the engine is running, after passing through a purge control valve.

ENGINE

Removal & Installation

Engine removal and installation is fairly simple and straight forward, refer to the other GM front wheel drive sections. Procedures are similar with some slight differences.

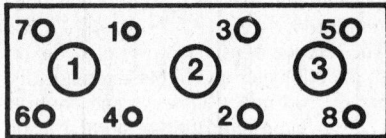

Cylinder head torque sequence

TRANSAXLE

REMOVAL & INSTALLATION

The Sprint is equipped with a five speed manual transaxle. Refer to the other GM front wheel drive sections. Procedures are similar with some slight differences.

DRIVEAXLES

REMOVAL & INSTALLATION

Refer to the other GM front wheel drive sections. Procedures are similar with some slight differences. Also refer to the "Constant Velocity Joint" Unit Repair section.

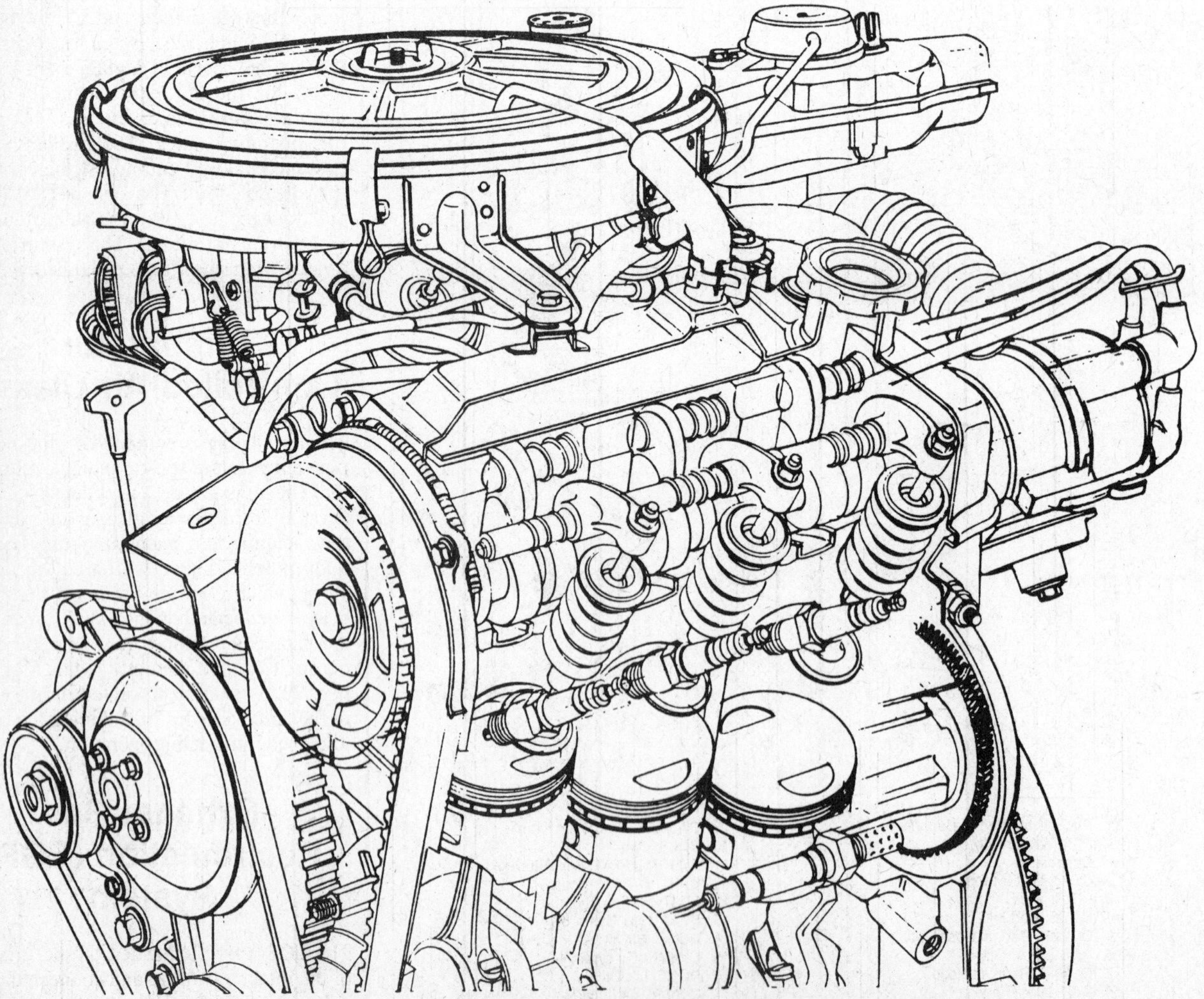

Cutaway view of the engine

1. MOUNT, Eng Frt
2. WASHER, Mt Lk
3. NUT, Frt Mt
4. INSULATOR, Eng Frt Mt Ht
5. BRACKET, Eng Frt Mt
6. BOLT, Brkt
7. WASHER, Brkt Mt
8. BRACKET, Frt Mt Body
9. BOLT, Brkt
10. WASHER, Brkt Lk
11. MOUNT, Trans
12. NUT, Trans Mt
13. BOLT (M8 × 1.25 × 20)
14. WASHER
15. MEMBER, Trans Mt
16. CUSHION, Mt Mbr Upr
17. CUSHION, Mt Mbr Lwr
18. WASHER, Mt Mbr
19. SPACER, Mbr
20. WASHER, Mt Mbr Lk
21. BOLT, Mbr
22. MOUNT, Eng Rr
23. WASHER, Mt
24. NUT (M10 × 1.25 × 8)
25. BRACKET, Eng Rr Mt
26. BOLT, Brkt
27. WASHER, Brkt Lk
28. BRACKET, Rr Mt Body
29. BOLT, Brkt
30. WASHER, Brkt Lk
31. STUD, Brkt
32. WASHER, Brkt Lk
33. NUT, Brkt
34. BRACKET, Eng Si Mt
35. BOLT, Si Brkt
36. WASHER, Brkt Lk
37. BUSHING, Eng Si Mt
38. BOLT, Mt Bush
39. NUT, Mt Bush
40. BOLT, Mt Bush
41. WASHER, Lk
42. WASHER, Bush
43. ROD, Eng Frt Torq
44. STUD, Frt Rod
45. WASHER, Frt Rod
46. WASHER, Rod Lk
47. NUT, Frt Rod
48. BOLT, Frt Rod
49. NUT, Frt Rod
50. BRACKET, Rr Torq Rod
51. BOLT, Rod Brkt
52. WASHER, Brkt Lk
53. ROD, Eng Rr Torq
54. BOLT, Rr Rod
55. PLATE, Rr Torq Stopper
56. WASHER, Rr Rod Lk
57. NUT, Rr Rod
58. BOLT, Rr Rod
59. NUT, Rr Rod

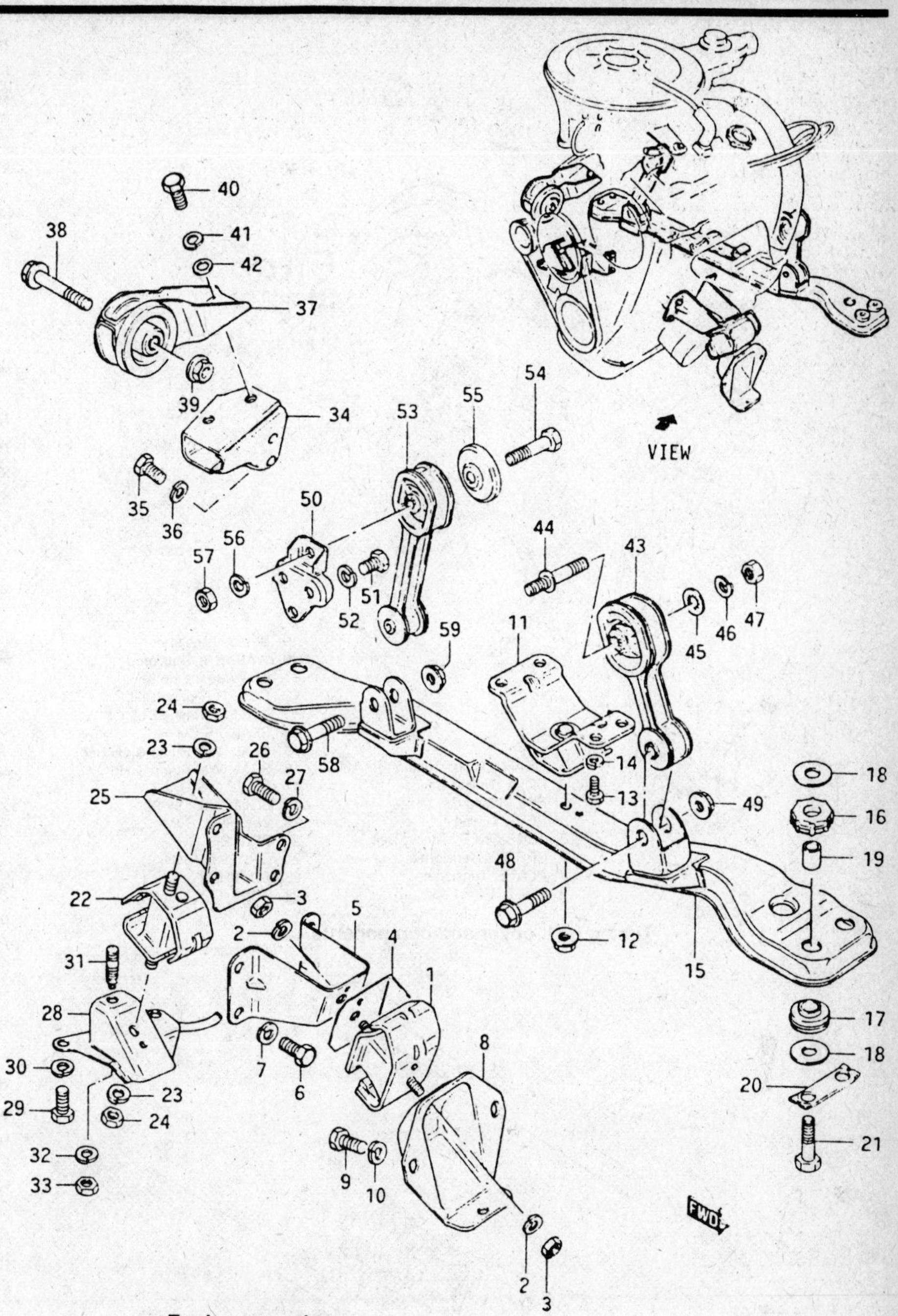

Engine mounting

FRONT SUSPENSION

The front suspension, on the Sprint, is MacPherson strut independent type. The upper strut is attached to the body through the strut mount, and the lower strut is attached to the steering knuckle by two bolts. For servicing or removal and installation refer to the other GM front wheel drive sections. Procedures are similar with some slight differences.

REAR SUSPENSION

The rear suspension is a rigid axle type. One tapered leaf spring is longitudinally slung under each side of the axle. The front end of the spring is attached to the body bracket through a rubber bushing, and the rear end of the spring is attached to the body hanger through a rubber bushing and shackle assembly. A shock absorber is positioned inboard of the spring and slanted toward the rear of the car. For removal and installation and servicing procedures for the rear leaf springs and shock absorbers refer to the GM "F" body section. Procedures are similar with some slight differences.

BRAKES

Service brakes are vacuum hydraulic and self-adjusting with power assist. A single piston, self-adjusting, floating caliper disc brake is used on the front. A leading-trail-

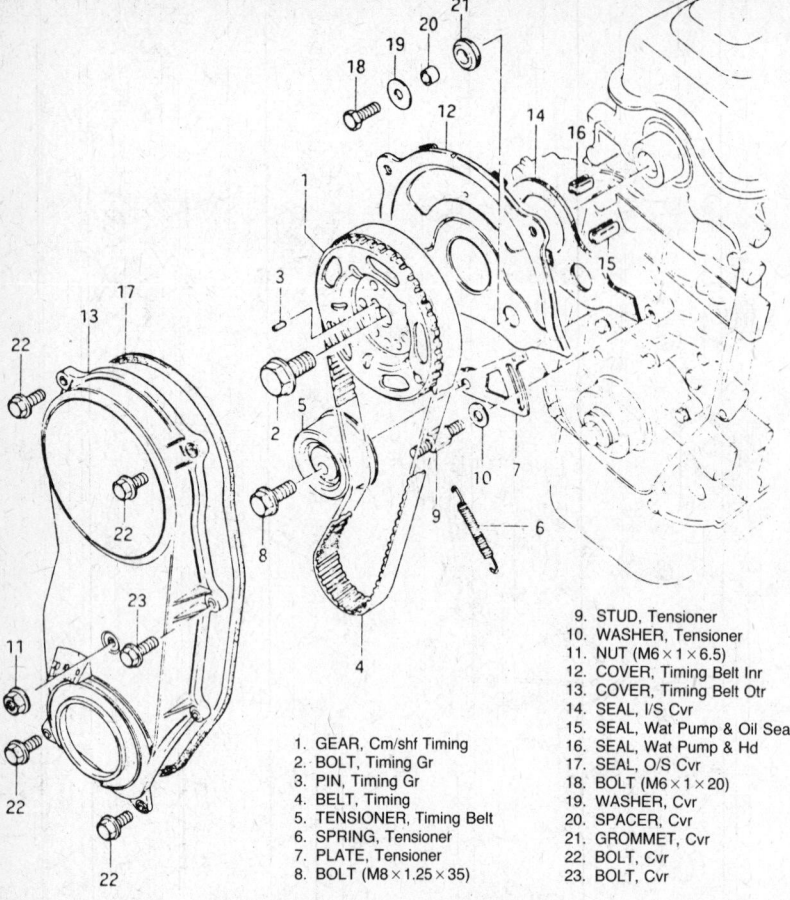

9. STUD, Tensioner
10. WASHER, Tensioner
11. NUT (M6 × 1 × 6.5)
12. COVER, Timing Belt Inr
13. COVER, Timing Belt Otr
14. SEAL, I/S Cvr
15. SEAL, Wat Pump & Oil Seal
16. SEAL, Wat Pump & Hd
17. SEAL, O/S Cvr
18. BOLT (M6 × 1 × 20)
19. WASHER, Cvr
20. SPACER, Cvr
21. GROMMET, Cvr
22. BOLT, Cvr
23. BOLT, Cvr

1. GEAR, Cm/shf Timing
2. BOLT, Timing Gr
3. PIN, Timing Gr
4. BELT, Timing
5. TENSIONER, Timing Belt
6. SPRING, Tensioner
7. PLATE, Tensioner
8. BOLT (M8 × 1.25 × 35)

Timing belt, cover and components

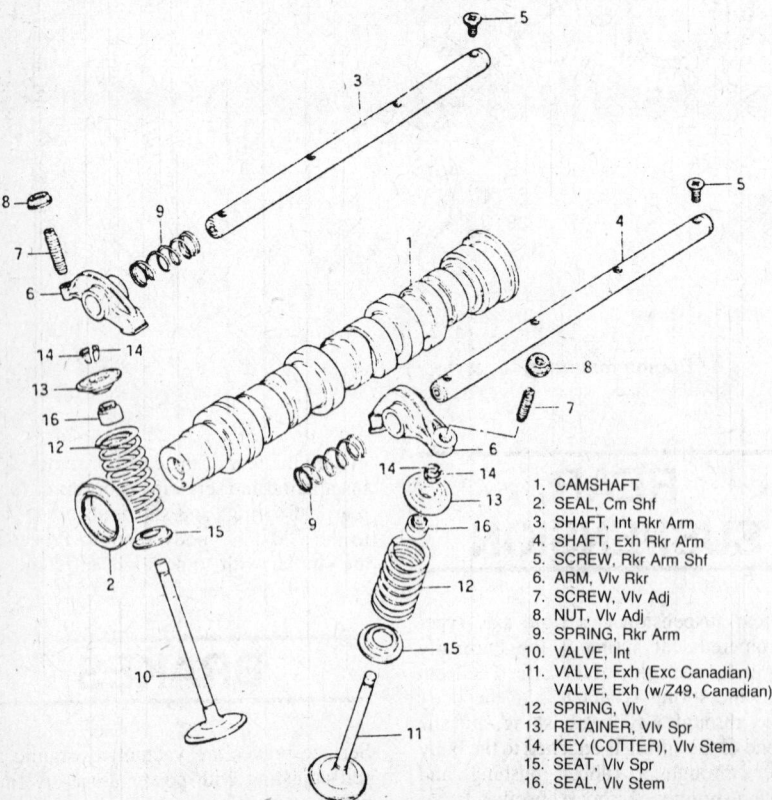

1. CAMSHAFT
2. SEAL, Cm Shf
3. SHAFT, Int Rkr Arm
4. SHAFT, Exh Rkr Arm
5. SCREW, Rkr Arm Shf
6. ARM, Vlv Rkr
7. SCREW, Vlv Adj
8. NUT, Vlv Adj
9. SPRING, Rkr Arm
10. VALVE, Int
11. VALVE, Exh (Exc Canadian)
   VALVE, Exh (w/Z49, Canadian)
12. SPRING, Vlv
13. RETAINER, Vlv Spr
14. KEY (COTTER), Vlv Stem
15. SEAT, Vlv Spr
16. SEAL, Vlv Stem

Camshaft and valve train

ing self-adjusting drum brake is used on the rear. Wear indicators are installed on the front brake pads. For wheel bearing service refer to the other GM front wheel drive sections. Procedures are similar with some slight differences.

STEERING

Rack and pinion steering is used on all models. Refer to the other GM sections for servicing. Procedures are similar with some slight differences.

CHASSIS ELECTRICAL

Battery

All models are equipped with a maintenance-free battery of the top post design. An over-size battery tray is provided for aftermarket heavy duty replacement.

Front Lamps

Single seal-beam rectangular head-lamps with ABS plastic headlamp body colored bezels are located on both sides of the grill. Headlamp adjustment with two screws can be accomplished without removing the covers. Two front combination amber park, turn signal/hazard lamps are integrated into the front bumper. An amber side marker is snapped into each fender.

Rear Lamps and Reflectors

The rear combination lamps are of wrap around design, having three sections. Tail and stop lamps with red lens and red reflectors are located in the upper section. Tail and stops lamps with red lens and back-up lights are located in the middle section. An amber turn signal light is located in the lower section.

Flasher

An electronic flasher is used, combining the turn signal and hazard warning functions.

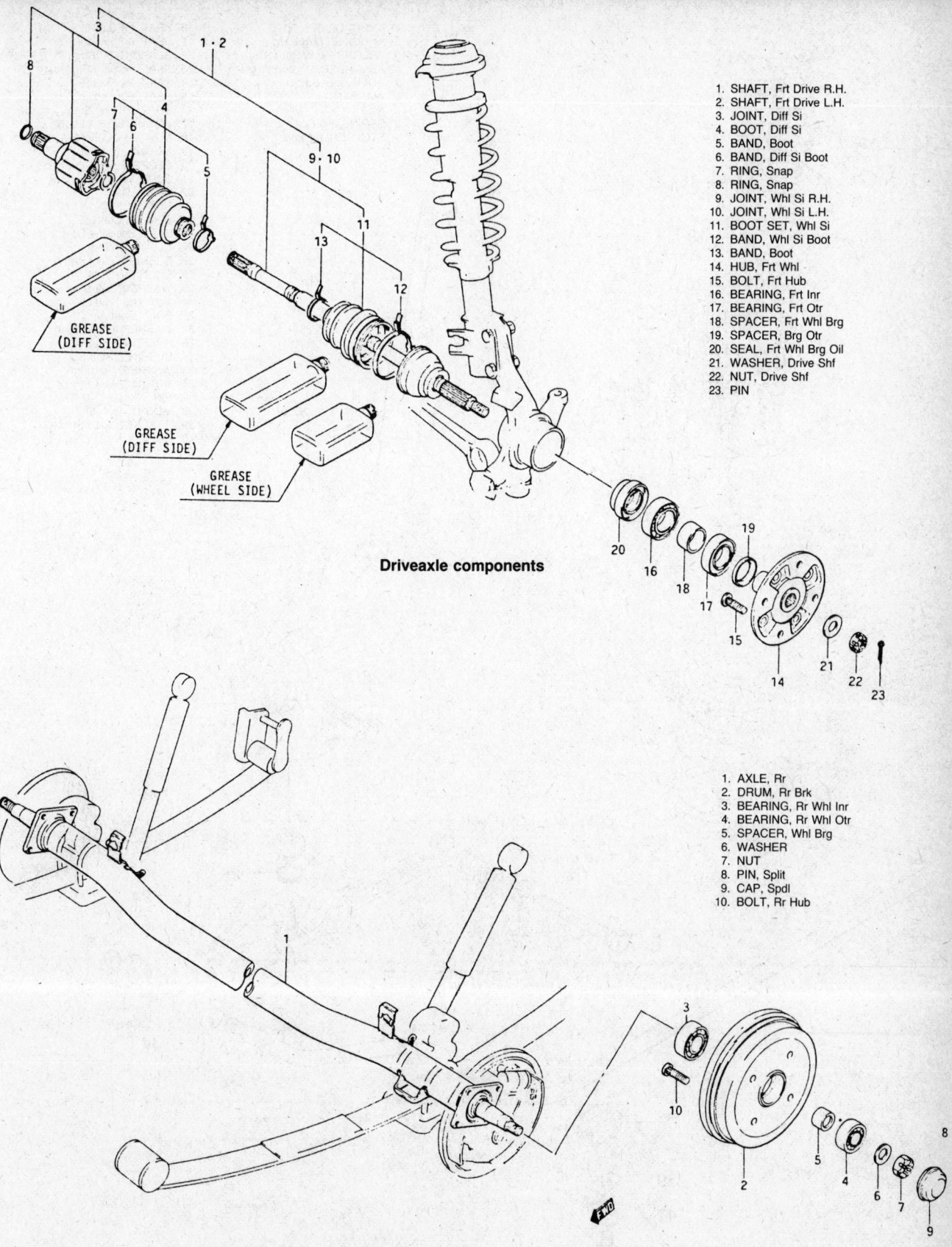

1. SHAFT, Frt Drive R.H.
2. SHAFT, Frt Drive L.H.
3. JOINT, Diff Si
4. BOOT, Diff Si
5. BAND, Boot
6. BAND, Diff Si Boot
7. RING, Snap
8. RING, Snap
9. JOINT, Whl Si R.H.
10. JOINT, Whl Si L.H.
11. BOOT SET, Whl Si
12. BAND, Whl Si Boot
13. BAND, Boot
14. HUB, Frt Whl
15. BOLT, Frt Hub
16. BEARING, Frt Inr
17. BEARING, Frt Otr
18. SPACER, Frt Whl Brg
19. SPACER, Brg Otr
20. SEAL, Frt Whl Brg Oil
21. WASHER, Drive Shf
22. NUT, Drive Shf
23. PIN

GREASE
(DIFF SIDE)

GREASE
(DIFF SIDE)

GREASE
(WHEEL SIDE)

Driveaxle components

1. AXLE, Rr
2. DRUM, Rr Brk
3. BEARING, Rr Whl Inr
4. BEARING, Rr Whl Otr
5. SPACER, Whl Brg
6. WASHER
7. NUT
8. PIN, Split
9. CAP, Spdl
10. BOLT, Rr Hub

Rear suspension

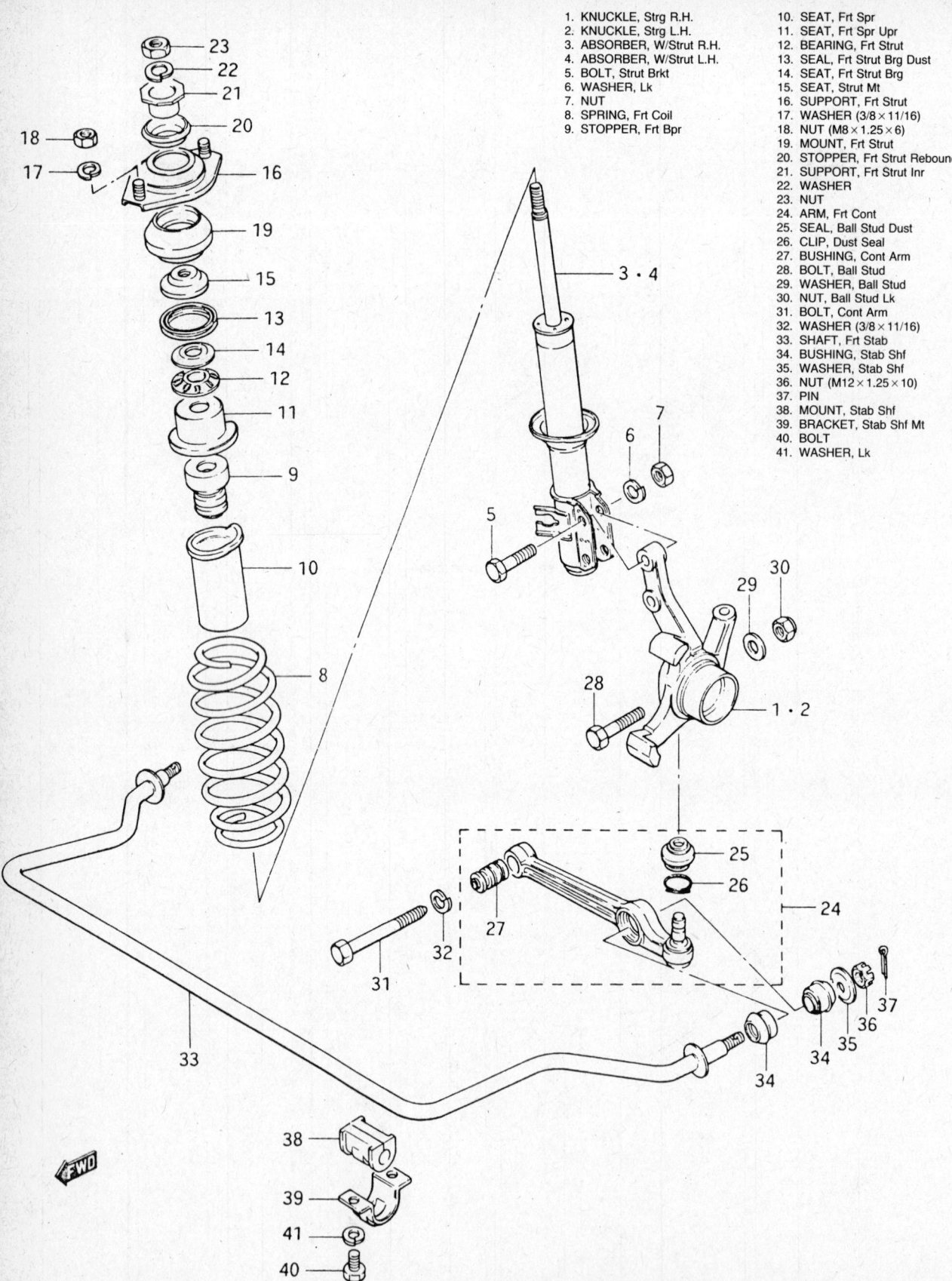

1. KNUCKLE, Strg R.H.
2. KNUCKLE, Strg L.H.
3. ABSORBER, W/Strut R.H.
4. ABSORBER, W/Strut L.H.
5. BOLT, Strut Brkt
6. WASHER, Lk
7. NUT
8. SPRING, Frt Coil
9. STOPPER, Frt Bpr
10. SEAT, Frt Spr
11. SEAT, Frt Spr Upr
12. BEARING, Frt Strut
13. SEAL, Frt Strut Brg Dust
14. SEAT, Frt Strut Brg
15. SEAT, Strut Mt
16. SUPPORT, Frt Strut
17. WASHER (3/8 × 11/16)
18. NUT (M8 × 1.25 × 6)
19. MOUNT, Frt Strut
20. STOPPER, Frt Strut Rebound
21. SUPPORT, Frt Strut Inr
22. WASHER
23. NUT
24. ARM, Frt Cont
25. SEAL, Ball Stud Dust
26. CLIP, Dust Seal
27. BUSHING, Cont Arm
28. BOLT, Ball Stud
29. WASHER, Ball Stud
30. NUT, Ball Stud Lk
31. BOLT, Cont Arm
32. WASHER (3/8 × 11/16)
33. SHAFT, Frt Stab
34. BUSHING, Stab Shf
35. WASHER, Stab Shf
36. NUT (M12 × 1.25 × 10)
37. PIN
38. MOUNT, Stab Shf
39. BRACKET, Stab Shf Mt
40. BOLT
41. WASHER, Lk

Front suspension

1. PLATE, Backing R.H.
2. PLATE, Backing L.H.
3. BOLT, Bkg Plt
4. BOLT, Whl Cyl
5. PLUG, Bkg Plt
6. SHOE, Brk
7. SPRING, Shoe Rtn
8. PIN, Shoe Holdn
9. SPRING, Shoe Holdn
10. SPRING, Shoe Holdn R.H.
11. SPRING, Shoe Holdn L.H.
12. CYLINDER, Rr Whl
13. CUP SET, Whl Cyl
14. SPRING, Whl Cyl

15. PLUG, Bleeder
16. CAP, Bleeder Plug
17. GASKET, Whl Cyl
18. STRUT, Brk R.H.
19. STRUT, Brk L.H.
20. SPRING, Quadrant
21. SPRING, Anti-Rattle
22. LEVER, Pk Shoe R.H.
23. LEVER, Pk Shoe L.H.
24. RETAINER, Pk Lvr
25. NUT
26. WASHER (8.2 × 15.6 × 2.5)
27. PLUG, Bkg Plt #2

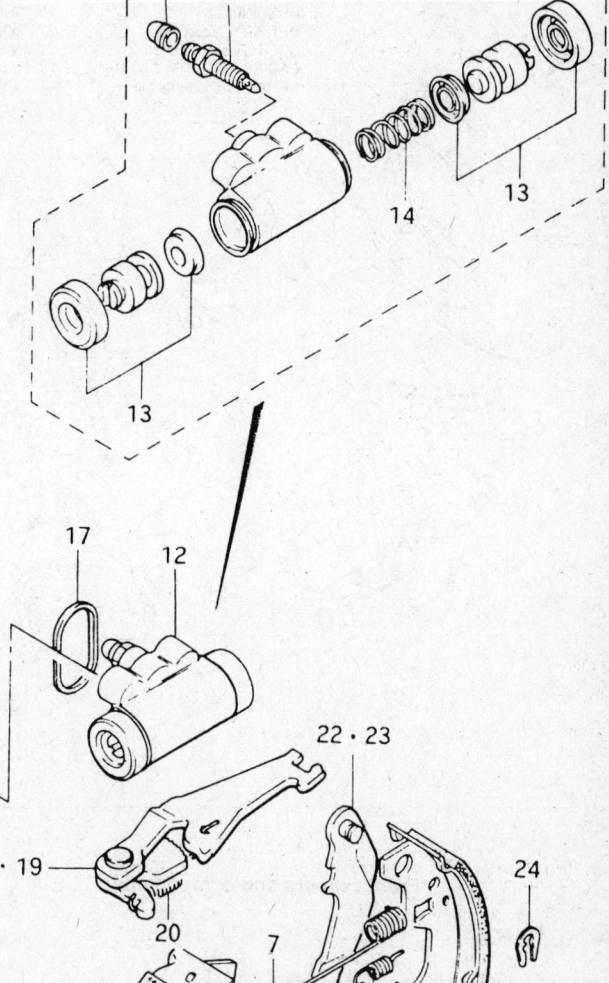

Rear drum brakes

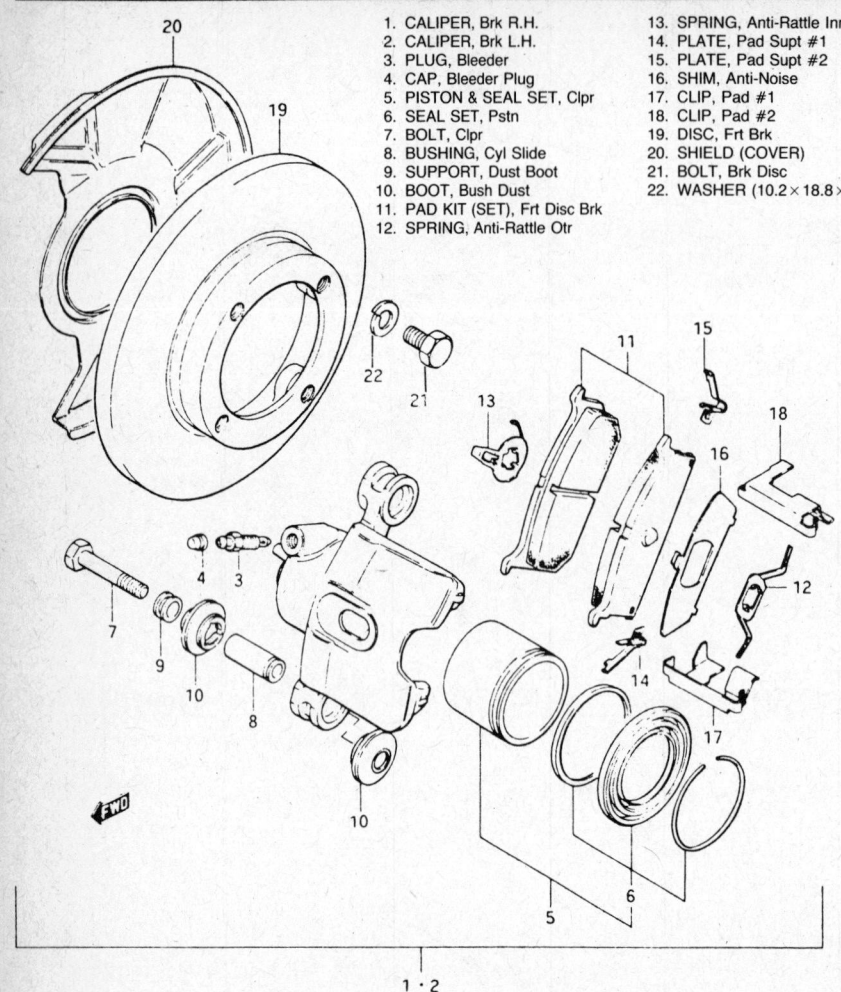

1. CALIPER, Brk R.H.
2. CALIPER, Brk L.H.
3. PLUG, Bleeder
4. CAP, Bleeder Plug
5. PISTON & SEAL SET, Clpr
6. SEAL SET, Pstn
7. BOLT, Clpr
8. BUSHING, Cyl Slide
9. SUPPORT, Dust Boot
10. BOOT, Bush Dust
11. PAD KIT (SET), Frt Disc Brk
12. SPRING, Anti-Rattle Otr
13. SPRING, Anti-Rattle Inr
14. PLATE, Pad Supt #1
15. PLATE, Pad Supt #2
16. SHIM, Anti-Noise
17. CLIP, Pad #1
18. CLIP, Pad #2
19. DISC, Frt Brk
20. SHIELD (COVER)
21. BOLT, Brk Disc
22. WASHER (10.2 × 18.8 × 3)

Front calipers and components

Instrument Panel

The instrument cluster consists of a speedometer, odometer, trip meter, coolant temperature gauge and a fuel gauge. Warning lamps are used for low oil pressure, alternator, parking brake "on", brake failure warning, high coolant temperature, fasten seat belt, highbeam indicator and oxygen sensor/ECM check.

Refer to the other GM sections for servicing. Procedures are similar with some differences.

Fusible Link and Fuses

The main fuse at the battery is a fusible link. The wiring circuits are protected by fourteen fuses in the fuse block. The fuse block is located at the lower left of the instrument panel. The cover is built into the instrument panel.

Unit Repair Sections

General Maintenance

INTRODUCTION

Routine maintenance is probably the most important part of automobile care and the easiest to neglect. A regular program aimed at monitoring essential systems ensures that all components are in good and safe working order, and can prevent small problems from developing into major headaches. Routine maintenance also pays off big dividends in keeping major repair costs at a minimum and extending the life of the car.

The owner's manual that came with your car includes a maintenance schedule, indicating service intervals in numbers of months or thousands of miles. This schedule should always be followed, if possible. We have provided, in each section, a guide to service intervals based on an averaging of manufacturer's recommendations. In most cases, the suggested interval offered here will be close to that given by the manufacturer of your car, but the manufacturer's schedule should always take precedence.

We have divided the maintenance work to be done into three categories: Under Hood, Under Car, and Exterior. The checks in each section require only a few minutes of attention every few weeks; the services to be performed can be easily accomplished in a morning. The most important part of any maintenance program is regularity. The few minutes or occasional morning spent on these seemingly trivial tasks will forestall or eliminate major problems later.

UNDER HOOD

Automatic Transmission, Automatic Transaxle

The fluid level in the automatic transmission or transaxle should be checked every three months or 6000 miles. All automatic transmissions have a dipstick for fluid level checks.

1. Drive the car until it is at normal operating temperature. The level should not be checked immediately after the car has been driven for a long time at high speed, or in city traffic in hot weather; in those cases, the transmission should be given a half hour to cool down.

2. Stop the car, apply the parking brake,

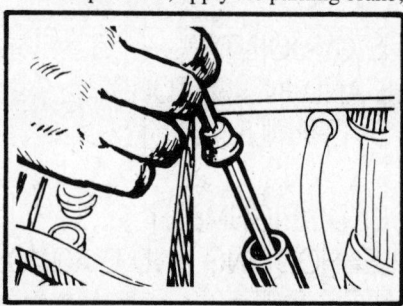

Check the automatic transmission fluid level with the dipstick provided

then shift slowly through all gear positions, ending in Park. Leave the engine running.

3. Remove the dipstick, wipe it clean, then reinsert it, pushing it fully home.

4. Pull the dipstick again and, holding it horizontally, read the fluid level.

5. Cautiously feel the end of the dipstick to determine the temperature. Most dipsticks are marked with both cool and hot levels. If the fluid is not up to the correct level, more will have to be added.

NOTE: On 1980 and later Citation, Omega, Phoenix, Skylark, Cavalier, Cimarron, J2000, Celebrity, Cierra and 6000, the "Cold" level marks (dimples) are above the "Hot" level area.

6. Fluid is added through the dipstick tube. You will probably need the aid of a spout or a long-necked funnel. Be sure that whatever you pour through is perfectly clean and dry. Fluid recommendations can be found in the owner's manual or the Automatic Transmission Unit Repair Section in this book.

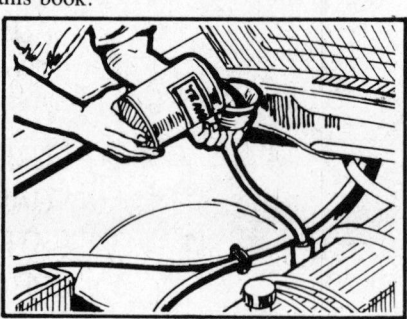

Fill the automatic transmission through the dipstick tube

Add fluid slowly, and in small amounts, checking the level frequently between additions. Do not overfill, which will cause foaming, fluid loss, slippage, and possible transmission damage.

Battery

FLUID LEVEL (EXCEPT "MAINTENANCE FREE" BATTERIES)

Check the battery electrolyte level at least once a month, or more often in hot weather or during periods of extended car operation. The level can be checked through the case on translucent polypropylene batteries; the cell caps must be removed on other models. The electrolyte level in each cell should be kept filled to the split ring inside, or the line marked on the outside of the case.

If the level is low, add only distilled water, or colorless, odorless drinking water, through the opening until the level is correct. Each cell is completely separate from the others, so each must be checked and filled individually.

If water is added in freezing weather, the car should be driven several miles to allow the water to mix with the electrolyte. Otherwise, the battery could freeze.

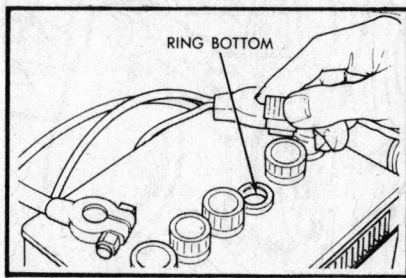

Fill the battery cell to the bottom of the split ring

SPECIFIC GRAVITY (EXCEPT "MAINTENANCE FREE" BATTERIES)

At least once a year, check the specific gravity of the battery. It should be between 1.20 and 1.26 at room temperature. See the "Charging and Starting Systems" Section in this book for details.

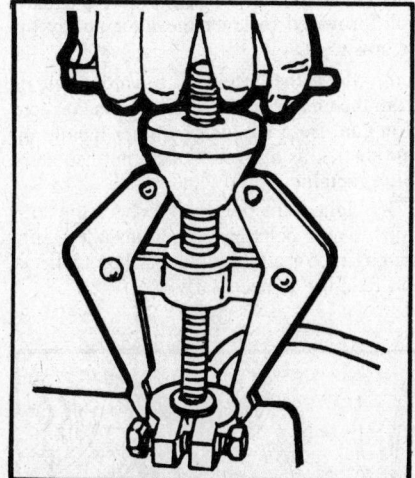

Use a puller to remove the clamp on post-type batteries

CABLES AND CLAMPS

Once a year, the battery terminals and the cable clamps should be cleaned. Loosen the clamps and remove the cables, negative cable first. On batteries with posts on top, the use of a puller specially made for the purpose is recommended. These are inexpensive, and available in auto parts stores. Side terminal battery cables are secured with a bolt.

Clean the cable clamps and the battery terminal with a wire brush, until all corrosion, grease, etc. is removed and the metal is shiny. It is especially important to clean the inside of the clamp thoroughly, since a small deposit of foreign material or oxi-

dation there will prevent a sound electrical connection and inhibit either starting or charging. Special tools are available for

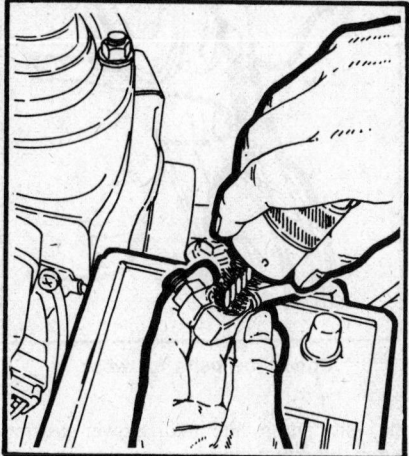

Clean the clamp with a wire brush

cleaning these parts, one type for conventional batteries and another type for side terminal batteries.

Before installing the cables, loosen the battery hold-down clamp or strap, remove the battery and check the battery tray. Clear it of any debris, and check it for soundness. Rust should be wire brushed away, and the metal given a coat of anti-rust paint. Replace the battery and tighten the hold-down clamp or strap securely, but be careful not to overtighten, which will crack the battery case.

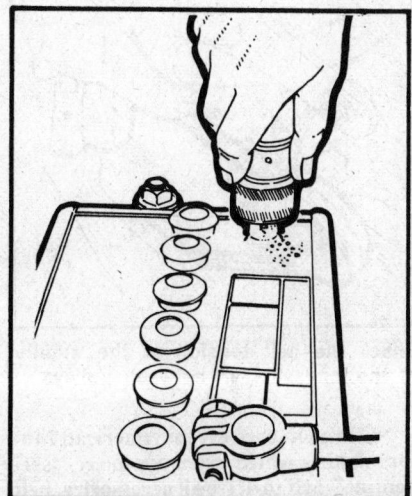

The posts are easily cleaned with a wire brush, or the battery post tool shown

After the clamps and terminals are clean, reinstall the cables, negative cable last; do not hammer on the clamps to install. Tighten the clamps securely, but do not distort them. Give the clamps and terminals a thin external coat of grease after installation, to retard corrosion.

Check the cables at the same time that the terminals are cleaned. If the cable insulation is cracked or broken, or if the ends

are frayed, the cable should be replaced with a new cable of the same length and gauge.

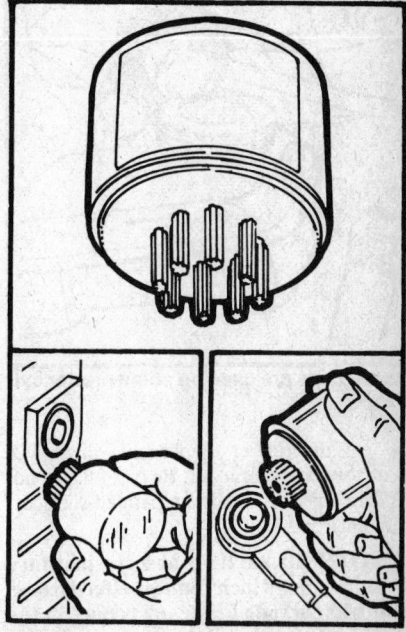

A special tool is required to clean the terminals and clamps on side terminal batteries

NOTE: Keep flame or sparks away from the battery; it gives off explosive hydrogen gas. Battery electrolyte contains sulphuric acid. If you should splash any on your skin or in your eyes, flush the affected area with plenty of clear water; if it lands in your eyes, get medical help immediately.

Brake Fluid

Once a month, the fluid level in the brake master cylinder should be checked.

1. Park the car on a level surface.
2. Clean off the master cylinder cover before removal. Most covers are held on by a wire bail, which can be pushed aside with thumb pressure, or levered off with a screwdriver. Some covers are retained by a bolt. Some of the newer master cylinders with plastic reservoirs have screw caps. Remove the cover, being careful not to drop

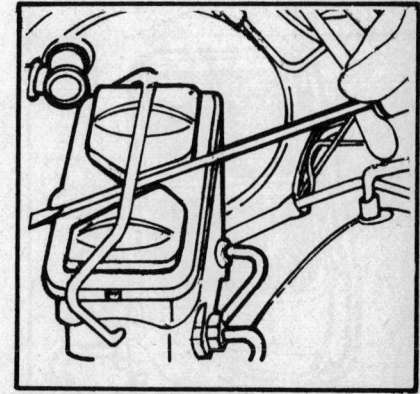

Lever the bail off the master cylinder cap with a screwdriver

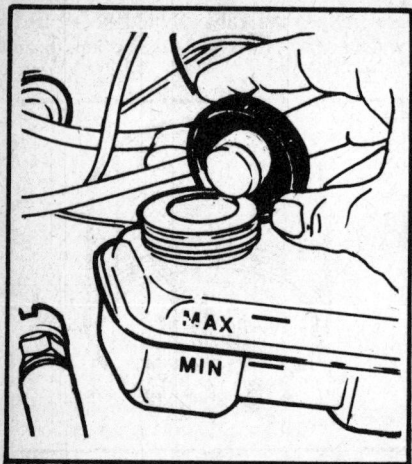

Screw caps are used on some master cylinders

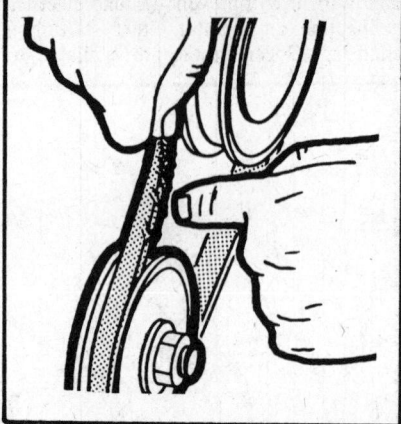

Check the belts for wear

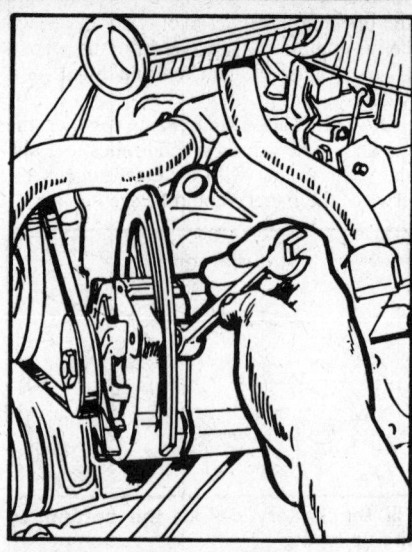

To either adjust or remove a belt, loosen the driven component's adjusting bolt

or tear the rubber diaphragm which will probably be underneath. Be careful also not to drip any brake fluid on painted surfaces; the stuff eats paint.

NOTE: Brake fluid absorbs moisture from the air, which reduces effectiveness and will corrode brake parts once in the system. Never leave the master cylinder or the brake fluid container uncovered for any longer than necessary.

3. The fluid level should be about ¼ inch below the lip of the master cylinder well.

4. If fluid addition is necessary, use only extra heavy duty disc brake fluid meeting DOT 3 specifications. The fluid should be reasonably fresh, because brake fluid deteriorates with age.

5. Replace the cover, making sure that the diaphragm is correctly seated.

If the brake fluid level is constantly low, the system should be checked for leaks. However, it is normal for the fluid level to fall gradually as the disc brake pads wear; expect the fluid level to drop about ⅛ inch for every 10,000 miles of wear.

Belt Tension

Every six months or 12,000 miles, check

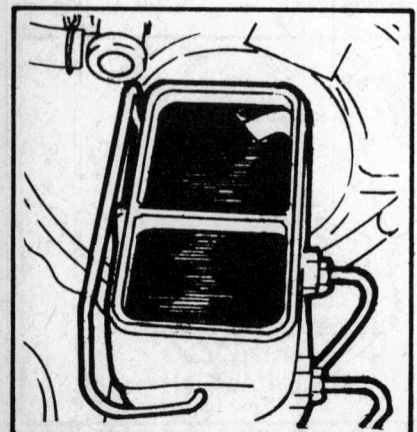

Proper brake fluid level

the water pump, alternator, power steering pump, air pump, and air conditioning compressor drive belts for proper tension. Also look for signs of wear, fraying, separation, glazing and so on, and replace the belts as required.

Belt tension should be checked with a gauge made for the purpose. If a gauge is not available, tension can be checked with moderate thumb pressure applied to the belt at its longest span midway between pulleys. If the belt has a free span less than twelve inches, it should deflect approximately ⅛–¼ inch. If the span is longer than twelve inches, deflection can range between ⅛ and ⅜ inches.

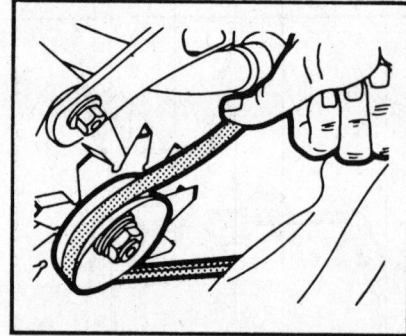

Check the belt tension at the middle of the longest span between pulleys

NOTE: On cars except American Motors models which use a one-piece "serpentine" belt to drive all accessories, belt tension is automatically adjusted. On cars which have two "serpentine" belts, or one "serpentine" belt as well as conventional V-belts, and on all American Motors models with the "serpentine" belt, belt tensions usually must be checked and adjusted. Belt tension is higher on "serpentine" belts and cannot be tested with thumb pressure. Some Ford models (Thunderbird/XR-7 with AOD transmission) require special tools for adjustment. American Motors "serpentine" belts are adjusted at the alternator.

To adjust or replace belts:

1. Loosen the driven accessory's pivot and mounting bolts. Some air conditioning compressor belts are tensioned by an idler pulley; in this case, loosen the idler pulley and use a ½ in. drive ratchet in the square hole provided to lever the idler pulley up or down.

2. Move the accessory toward or away from the engine until the tension is correct. You can use a wooden hammer handle or broomstick as a lever, but do not use anything metallic.

3. Tighten the bolts and recheck the tension. If new belts have been installed, run the engine for a few minutes, then recheck and readjust as necessary.

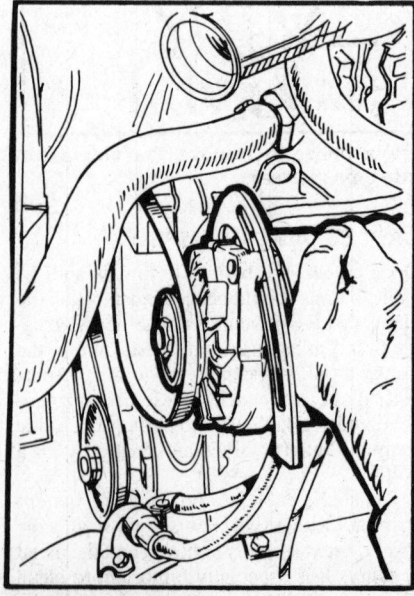

Push the component toward the engine to remove the belt

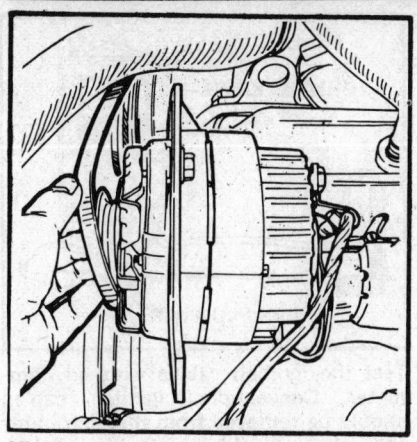

Slip the replacement belt over the pulley

NOTE: If the driven component has two drive belts, the belts should be replaced in pairs to maintain proper tension.

It is better to have belts too loose than too tight, because overtight belts will lead to bearing failure, particularly in the water pump and alternator. However, loose belts place an extremely high impact load on the driven component due to the whipping action of the belt.

Carburetor and Choke Linkage

Every 12 months or 6000 miles, examine the carburetor linkage and choke plate for free movement. The choke plate action can generally be freed, if necessary, with the application of a solvent made for the purpose to the ends of the choke shaft. This solvent will also clean grease and dirt from the throttle linkage.

Cooling System

Once a month, the engine coolant level should be checked. On cars without a coolant recovery system, this should only be done when the engine is cold. Remove the radiator cap; the coolant level should be about one inch below the radiator filler neck.

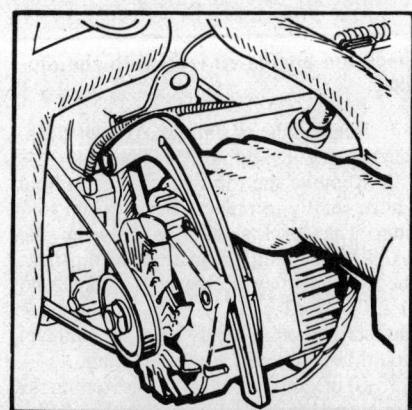

Pull outwards on the component to tension the belt, then tighten the bolts; recheck the belt tension after tightening

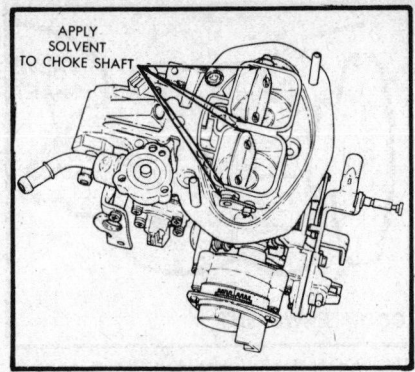

APPLY SOLVENT TO CHOKE SHAFT

Use a spray solvent on the choke shaft, but do not apply any lubricants

——— CAUTION ———

To avoid injury when working with a hot engine, cover the radiator cap with a thick cloth. Wear a heavy glove to protect your hand. Turn the radiator cap slowly to the first stop, and allow all the pressure to vent (indicated when the hissing noise stops). When the pressure has been released, remove the cap the rest of the way.

On cars with a coolant recovery tank, coolant should be visible within the tank;

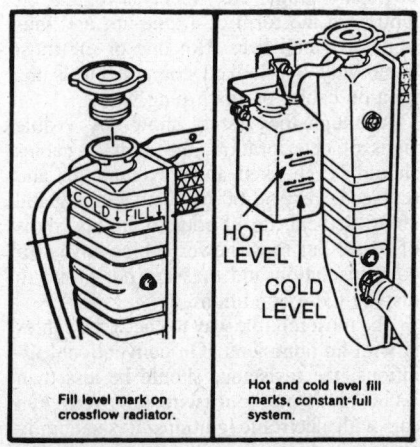

COLD FILL

HOT LEVEL

COLD LEVEL

Fill level mark on crossflow radiator.

Hot and cold level fill marks, constant-full system.

Proper coolant level is about one inch below the radiator neck, or between the lines on the recovery tank

Some caps have a lever to vent pressure. The lever must be pulled up before unscrewing the cap

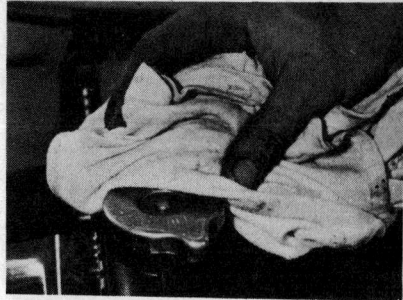

If the engine is hot, place a rag over the radiator cap

as long as the coolant is between the markings on the tank, the level is correct.

If coolant is needed, a 50/50 mix of ethylene glycol-based antifreeze and water should always be used, both winter and summer. This is imperative on cars with air conditioning; without the antifreeze, the heater core could freeze when the air conditioning is used. Add coolant to the radiator if the car does not have a coolant recovery system. Add coolant to the recovery tank on cars so equipped.

The radiator hoses and clamps and the radiator cap should be checked at the same time as the coolant level. Hoses which are brittle, cracked, or swollen should be replaced. Clamps should be checked for tightness (screwdriver tight only—do not allow the clamp to cut into the hose or crush the fitting). The radiator cap gasket should be checked for any obvious tears, cracks or swelling, or any signs of incorrect seating in the radiator neck.

The cooling system should be drained, flushed and refilled after the first 24 months or 24,000 miles, and every year thereafter.

1. Drain the radiator by opening the drain cock at the bottom. Some radiators do not have these; the lower radiator hose must be disconnected at the radiator instead. If the engine block has drain plugs, they should be opened to speed draining.

2. Close the drain cocks and fill the system with clear water. A cooling system flushing additive can be used, if desired.

3. Run the engine until it is hot. The heater should be turned on to its maximum heat position so that the core is flushed out.

4. Drain the system, then flush with water until it runs clear.

5. Clean out the coolant recovery tank, if equipped.

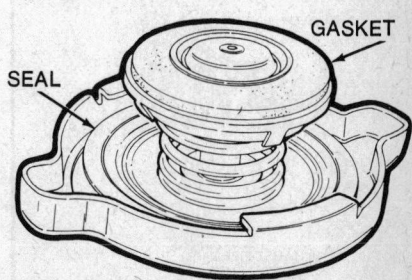

GASKET

SEAL

Check the radiator cap gasket and sealing surface

Most radiators have a drain cock at the bottom; unscrew to drain

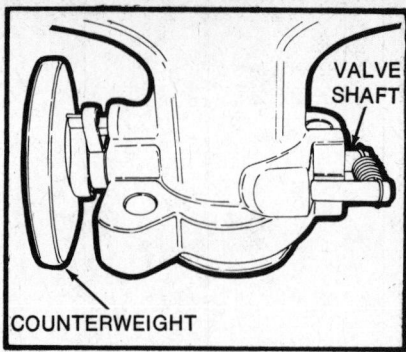

Thermostatically-operated heat control valve

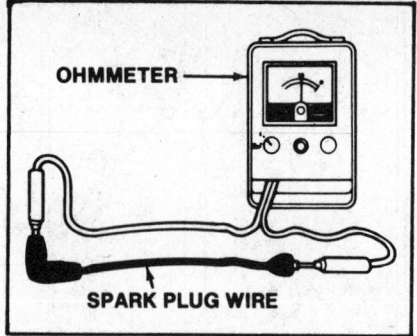

Test the ignition cables with an ohmmeter. Conventional ignition cables should be removed from the distributor cap, but electronic ignition wires should first be tested through the cap

6. Fill the system with a 50/50 mix of ethylene glycol-based antifreeze and water. Fill the coolant recovery tank midway between the marks with this mixture also (except G.M. cars, which should be filled to the "Full Cold" mark).

7. Run the engine until it is hot, then let it cool and top up the radiator or coolant recovery tank as necessary with the antifreeze/water mixture.

Heat Riser

The heat riser is a thermostatically or vacuum operated valve in the exhaust manifold. (Not all cars have one.) it closes when the engine is warming up, to direct hot exhaust gases to the intake manifold, in order to preheat the incoming fuel/air mixture. If it sticks open, the result will be frequent stalling during warmup, especially in cold and damp weather. If it sticks shut, the result will be a rough idle after the engine is warm.

NOTE: Some 1981 and later GM engines are equipped with an electrically heated ceramic grid mounted below the carburetor which takes the place of a heat riser.

The heat riser should move freely. It can be checked easily when the engine is cold by giving the counterweight on the valve shaft a twirl, or pulling the vacuum rod to

open and shut the valve. If the valve is sticking or binding, a quick shot of solvent made for the purpose will free it up. This solvent should be applied every six months or 6000 miles to keep the valve free. If the valve is still stuck after application of the solvent, sometimes rapping the end of the shaft lightly with a hammer will break it loose. Otherwise, the components will have to be removed for further repairs.

Ignition Cables

The ignition system (points, condenser, rotor, spark plugs, etc.) receives regular attention in the form of a tune-up, and thus is not covered here. But one of the most commonly overlooked components is the ignition cable, or spark plug wire.

Although they rarely show any visible signs of deterioration, the ignition cables should be checked at every tune-up, and replaced every 50,000 miles. Cracking and embrittlement are of course obvious signs of wear, but most newer cables have silicone insulation and thus are not prone to display these conditions.

The most reliable way to check the cables is with an ohmmeter. On conventional ignitions, the resistance should be less than 7,000 ohms per foot (wire removed). On cars with electronic ignitions, it is generally recommended to leave the wire attached to the distributor cap; test with one lead from the ohmmeter connected to the corresponding terminal in the distributor cap, the other lead touched to the disconnected end of the cable at the spark plug. Then, if resistance seems close to the limit, remove the wire from the cap and retest. In general, the

spark plug wires on electronic ignitions should be replaced if the total resistance is over 36,000 ohms (50,000 ohms on Ford and Chrysler products).

Always replace the cables with new ones of the same type. Replace the wires one at a time, working from the longest to the shortest.

Oil Level

The engine oil should be checked on a regular basis, ideally at each fuel stop, or once a week. It is best to check when the engine is at operating temperature, but checking the level immediately after shutting off the engine will give a false reading, because all of the oil will not yet have drained back into the crankcase. The car should be parked on a level surface to obtain an accurate reading.

Check the engine oil level with the dipstick

1. Remove the oil dipstick. Wipe it clean, then replace it, seating it firmly.

2. Remove the dipstick again and hold it horizontally to prevent the oil from running. The level should be between the "Add" and "Full" marks on the dipstick. The dipstick may be marked "Add" and "Full", "Add" and "Safe", or may have lines scribed on it; in any case, the oil level should be above the lower marking.

3. If the oil is below the lower mark, enough oil should be added to the engine to raise the level to the upper mark. The markings are usually spaced so that one-half to one quart of oil will raise the level

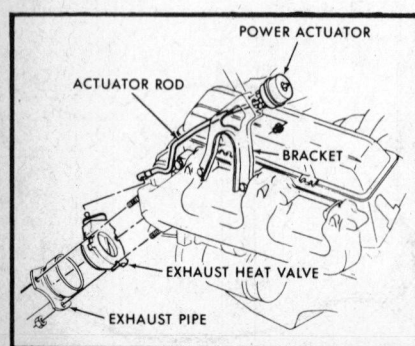

Exploded view of a vacuum-operated heat riser

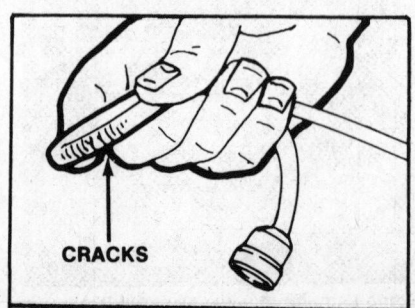

Inspect the ignition cables for cracks or breaks in the insulation

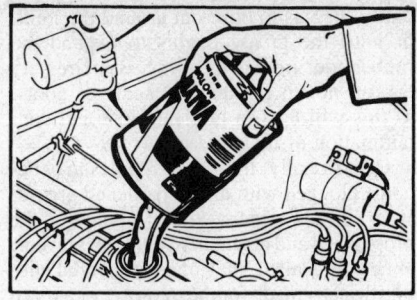

Add oil through the valve cover

from the "Add" mark to the "Full" mark. Oil is added through the capped opening in the valve cover. Only oils labeled SE or SF should be used; select a viscosity that will be compatible with the temperatures expected until the next drain interval.

NOTE: The diesel engines used in G.M. cars require the use of SF/CC or SF/CD type oils only. Do not use oil which is rated for SE or SF use only, or which is rated for CD use. Do not use the oil if the rating CD appears anywhere on the can, either alone or in combination with ratings other than SF, such as SE/CD. The use of CD type oil will void the manufacturer's warranty, and may cause expensive engine damage and leakage.

4. Replace the dipstick, then check the level again after any additions of oil. Be careful not to overfill, which will lead to leakage and seal damage.

Power Steering

The power steering fluid level is checked with a dipstick inserted into the pump reservoir. The dipstick may be attached to the reservoir cap, or inserted into a tube on the pump body. The level should be checked at every oil change. On all cars except Ford products, the level can be checked with the fluid either warm or cold; on Fords, the engine must be at operating temperature.

1. On Ford products, with the engine hot

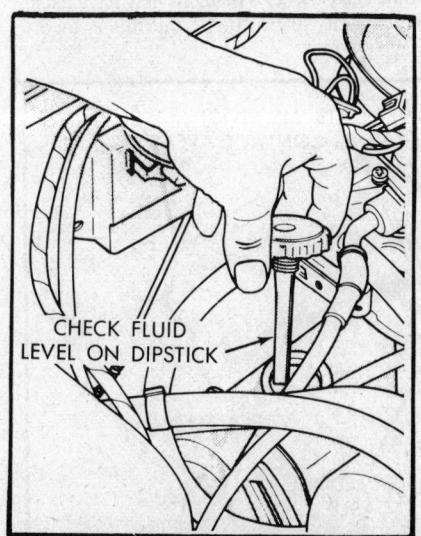

The power steering level is checked with the dipstick installed in the reservoir

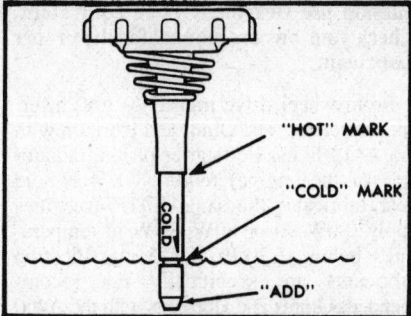

Power steering dipstick markings, typical of all types except Ford

and idling, turn the steering wheel back and forth to the full right and full left stops several times, then center the wheels and shut off the engine.

2. On all cars, with the engine off, pull or unscrew the dipstick and check the level. If the engine is warm, the level should be between the "Hot" and "Cold" marks on the dipstick; on Fords, the level should be between the "Cold Full" and "Hot Full" marks. If the engine is cold, the fluid should be between the "Add" and "Cold" marks; this does not apply to Ford products.

3. If the level is low, add power steering fluid until correct. Be careful not to overfill, which will cause fluid loss and seal damage.

Windshield Washer Fluid

Check the fluid level in the windshield washer tank at every oil level check. The fluid can be mixed in a 50% solution with water, if desired, as long as temperatures remain above freezing. Below freezing, the fluid should be used full strength. Never add engine coolant antifreeze to the washer fluid, because it will damage the car's paint.

UNDER CAR

Axle

The fluid level in the drive axle should be checked every 12 months or 12,000 miles. On the front wheel drive Omni, Horizon, Aries, Reliant LeBaron and Dodge 400 with automatic transmission, the drive axle lubricant is separate from the automatic fluid and must be checked separately. The level can be checked through the fill plug in the drive axle housing.

On the American Motors Eagle, SX/4 and Kammback, both drive axles should be checked. Both assemblies have fill plugs for this purpose.

1. With the car parked on a level surface, remove the filler plug. The plug can be found either in the rear cover of the differential, or on the front of the pinion housing.

2. If lubricant dribbles out when the plug is removed, the level is correct. Otherwise, stick in your finger (watch out for sharp threads); the fluid should be even with or just a little below the filler hole.

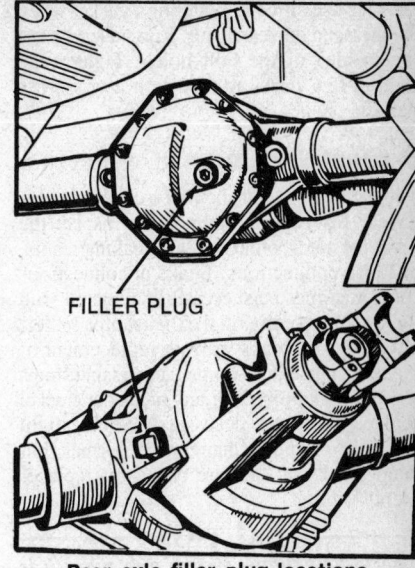

FILLER PLUG

Rear axle filler plug locations

3. If lubricant is needed, use SAE 80W-90 GL-5 gear oil (SAE 80W GL-5 in very cold climates) to fill standard axles. Limited slip axles require a special lubricant, available in auto parts stores. The Omni, Horizon, Aries, Reliant Dodge 400 and LeBaron drive axles should be filled with DEXRON® II ATF fluid.

4. When the level is correct, install the plug and tighten until snug. Do not overtighten.

Drive axles should be drained and refilled according to the manufacturer's maintenance schedule, usually found in the owner's manual. If the unit is used in severe driving conditions (trailer towing, etc.) the lubricant should be changed more often. Some later model drive axles do not require regular draining and refilling. Refer to the owner's manual for information on this subject. The axle may be drained by removing the drain plug at the bottom of the axle housing, if present. Otherwise the rear cover (if equipped) must be removed or a suction gun used through the filler hole.

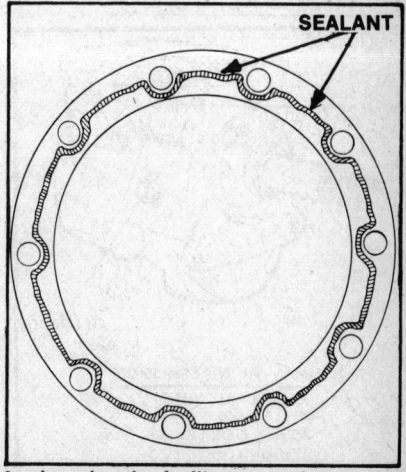

SEALANT

Apply a bead of silicone sealer to the rear cover if no gasket is used

Always use silicone sealer or a gasket when re-installing the rear cover. Run sealer around the insides of the bolt holes. Tighten the bolts a few turns at a time in a crisscross pattern.

Exhaust System

The exhaust system should be checked twice a year for general soundness. Inspect the pipes for holes, broken welds, leaking seams, or loose connections. Leaks at connections can sometimes be successfully repaired with the use of a commercial exhaust pipe sealer, but holes or breaks warrant replacement of the part. The exhaust pipe hangers and straps should be examined for any breaks or cracks; replace these as necessary. Some slight cracking of rubber hangers is normal, but deep cracks or cuts are cause for replacement.

--- **CAUTION** ---
Check the exhaust system only when it is cold. The temperature on an exhaust system using a catalytic converter can reach 1000°F after only a short period of engine operation.

Manual Transmission, Manual Transaxle

The fluid level in the manual transmission (or transaxle on front wheel drive cars) should be checked twice a year, or every 6000 miles.

1. Park the car on a level surface. The transmission should be cool to the touch.

2. Remove the filler plug from the side of the transmission or transaxle. If lubricant trickles out as the plug is removed, the fluid level is correct. If not, stick in your finger (watch out for sharp threads); the lubricant should be right up to the edge of the filler hole.

3. If lubricant is needed, use SAE 80W-90 GL-5 gear lubricant (SAE 80W GL-5 in extremely cold climates) in manual transmissions.

NOTE: Some 1979 and earlier GM cars equipped with a five speed manual transmission use Dexron ® II or equivalent. Check your owners manual for the proper Lubricant.

Front wheel drive transaxles use different lubricants. The Omni and Horizon with the A412 transaxle (starter on the radiator side of the engine) require GL-4 hypoid gear lubricant; the same SAE viscosities apply (80W-90 or 80W; 75W in temperatures below −30°F). GL-5 classification lubricants are specifically *not* recommended. Omnis and Horizons with the A460 transaxle (starter on the firewall side of the engine), and all Aires, Reliant LeBaron and Dodge 400 models use DEXRON® II automatic transmission fluid.

The front wheel drive Citation, Omega, Phoenix, Skylark Cavalier, J2000, Cimarron, Celebrity, Cierra and 6000 require DEXRON® II automatic transmission fluid. The use of a manual transmission lubricant is specifically *not* recommended.

The Ford Escort, EXP, and Mercury Lynx and LN-7 use Ford Type F automatic transmission fluid. The use of a manual transmission lubricant is specifically *not* recommended.

4. When the level is correct, install the filler plug and tighten until snug.

Parking Brake Linkage

The parking brake cable assembly should be inspected twice a year for fraying, kinks, and binding. A smooth white waterproof lubricant should be applied at the same time to all pivot points and areas in sliding contact.

Suspension Lubrication

Depending on the year of manufacture, there may be as many as twelve grease fittings on the suspension parts, or as few as two. Typical locations for grease nipples are on the ball joints, control arm pivot points, steering linkage, and the tie-rod ends.

Lubricate these fittings with a small hand operated grease gun filled with EP chassis lubricant. Pump grease into the fitting slowly, until it begins to ooze out around the joint, or until the grease begins to expand the rubber boot around the fitting. Be extremely careful not to rupture any seals or boots, as this will lead to lubricant loss and contamination of the parts involved.

Occasionally, the grease nipples may become clogged with dirt or hardened grease. If so, unscrew them with a wrench of the proper size and clean them out with solvent. When reinstalled, they may be covered with plastic caps made for the purpose, or a piece of aluminum foil.

The chassis and suspension parts should be lubricated once a year, or every 7500 miles, whichever comes first.

Transfer Case

If you have a four-wheel drive AMC car, you should check the transfer case lubricant level every 5000 miles.

1. Park the car on a level surface.

2. Check the build date tag on the rear of the transfer case.

3. If the transfer case was built after March 1980, the fill plug will be at location "A" in the illustration. Remove the fill plug. The lubricant should be right up to the edge of the filler hole. Check and correct as necessary.

4. If the transfer case was built before March, 1980, the filler plug may be in any one of the four locations shown in the illustration. Check to see which one you have, then remove the filler plug. Use a length of wire to measure the distance from the bottom edge of the fill hole to the lubricant. The correct distance depends on the location of the hole:

"A" 0.56 inch
"B" 1.13 inch
"C" 1.20 inch
"D" 0.56 inch

Check and correct as necessary.

5. The correct fluid to use is 10W-30 SE or SF motor oil. Capacity is 4.0 pints, regardless of when the transfer case was built. Some early owner's manuals may have listed the capacity as 3.0 pints, but this is incor-

MANUAL TRANSMISSION
FILL TO BOTTOM OF FILLER HOLE WITH VEHICLE ON LEVEL GROUND.

Typical manual transmission filler plug location

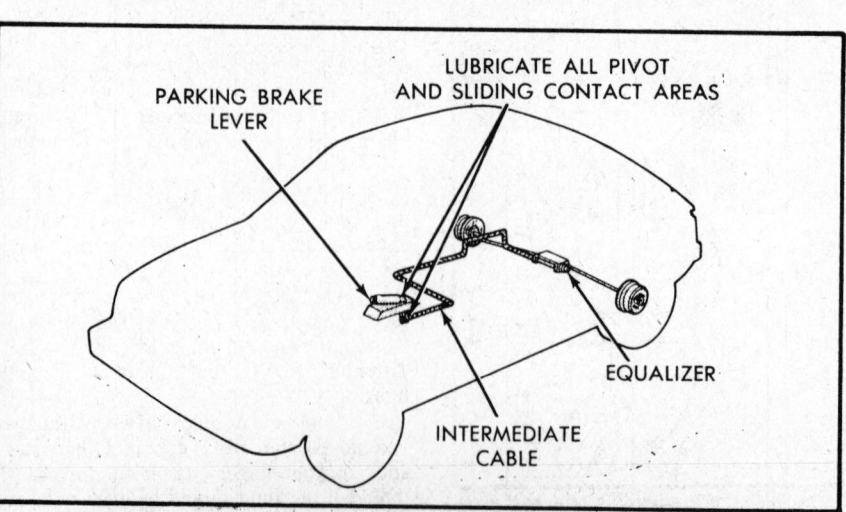

Lubricate the parking brake cable with white waterproof grease

rect; revised publications call for a capacity of 4.0 pints.

The transfer case should be drained and refilled every 15,000 miles. The drain plug is located at the lower edge of the rear face of the case. Installation torque for the plugs is 18 ft. lbs. The case is made from aluminum, so this figure should not be exceeded.

EXTERIOR

Drain Holes and Underbody

Most cars have drain holes spaced along the lower edge of the rocker panels and doors. These holes should be cleared of any debris or rust twice a year. A small screwdriver can be used to open plugged drain holes.

Every spring, the underbody should be flushed with clear water to remove deposits of mud, road salt, and debris. It is advisable to loosen any packed-in sediment before flushing to assure a more thorough cleaning.

Hinges and Locks

Once a year, the door, hood, and trunk hinges, and all locks should be lubricated to ensure smooth operation. The hinge points should be lightly oiled. Lock cylinders may be easily lubricated with a shot of silicone spray directed into the keyhole. Silicone lubricant also works well on the door latch mechanisms, and keeps the door, trunk, and window weatherseals pliable when applied in a light film.

Tires

Tires should be checked weekly for proper air pressure. A chart, located either in the glove compartment or on the driver's or passenger's door, gives the recommended inflation pressures. Maximum fuel economy and tire life will result if the pressure is maintained at the highest figure given on the chart. Pressures should be checked before driving since pressure can increase as much as six pounds per square inch (psi) due to heat buildup. It is a good idea to have your own accurate pressure gauge, because not all gauges on service station

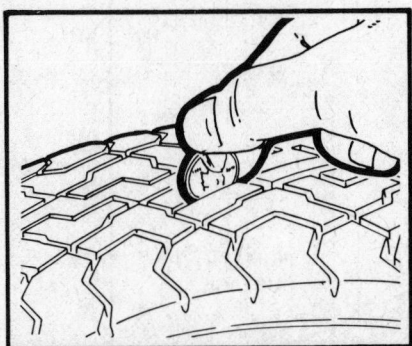

Tire tread depth can be checked with a penny. If the top of Lincoln's head is visible, the tires are due for replacement

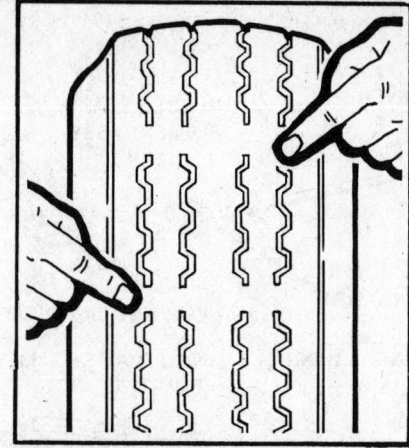

Tread wear indicators will appear as a band across the tire when the tread has worn out.

air pumps can be trusted. When checking pressures, do not neglect the spare tire. Note that some spare tires require pressures considerably higher than those used in the other tires.

While you are about the task of checking air pressure, inspect the tire treads for cuts, bruises and other damage. Check the air valves to be sure that they are tight. Replace any missing valve caps.

Check the tires for uneven wear that might indicate the need for front end alignment or tire rotation. Tires should be replaced when a tread wear indicator appears as a solid band across the tread.

When buying new tires, give some thought to the following points, especially if you are considering a switch to larger tires or a different profile series:

1. All four tires must be of the same construction type. This rule cannot be violated. Radial, bias, and bias-belted tires must not be mixed.

2. The wheels should be the correct width for the tire. Tire dealers have charts of tire and rim compatibility. A mismatch will cause sloppy handling and rapid tire wear. The tread width should match the rim width (inside bead to inside bead) within an inch. For radial tires, the rim width should be 80% or less of the tire (not tread) width.

3. The height (mounted diameter) of the new tires can change speedometer accuracy, engine speed at a given road speed, fuel mileage, acceleration, and ground clearance. Tire manufacturers furnish full measurement specifications.

4. The spare tire should be usable, at least for short distance and low speed operation, with the new tires.

5. There shouldn't be any body interference when loaded, on bumps, or in turns.

TIRE ROTATION

Tire rotation is recommended every 6000 miles or so, to obtain maximum tire wear. The pattern you use depends on whether or not your car has a usable spare. Radial tires should not be cross-switched (from one side

of the car to the other); they last longer if their direction of rotation is not changed. Snow tires sometimes have directional arrows molded into the side of the carcass; the arrow shows the direction of rotation. They will wear very rapidly if the rotation is reversed. Studded tires will lose their studs if their rotational direction is reversed.

NOTE: Mark the wheel position or direction of rotation on radial tires or studded snow tires before removing them.

STORAGE

Store the tires at the proper inflation pressure if they are mounted on wheels. Keep them in a cool dry place, laid on their sides. If the tires are stored in the garage or basement, do not let them stand on a concrete floor; set them on strips of wood.

Windshield Wipers and Washers

For maximum effectiveness and longest element life, the windshield and wiper blades should be kept clean. Dirt, tree sap, road tar and so on will cause streaking, smearing and blade deterioration if left on the glass. It is advisable to wash the windshield carefully with a commercial glass cleaner at least once a month. Wipe off the rubber blades with the wet rag afterwards. For access to the blades on wiper systems which park below the hood line, turn the ignition key to "On" and run the wipers to the center of the windshield. Shut the wipers off with the ignition key, not the wiper switch. Do not attempt to move the wipers by hand; damage to the motor and drive mechanism will result.

If the blades are found to be cracked, broken or torn, they should be replaced immediately. Replacement intervals will vary with usage, although ozone deterioration usually limits blade life to about one year. If the wiper pattern is smeared or streaked, or if the blade chatters across the glass, the elements should be replaced. It is easiest and most sensible to replace the elements in pairs.

There are basically three different types of refills, which differ in their method of replacement. One type has two release buttons, approximately one-third of the way up from the ends of the blade frame. Pushing the buttons down releases a lock and allows the rubber filler to be removed from the frame. The new filler slides back into the frame and locks in place.

The second type of refill has two metal tabs which are unlocked by squeezing them together. The rubber filler can then be withdrawn from the frame jaws. A new refill is installed by inserting the refill into the front frame jaws and sliding it rearward to engage the remaining frame jaws. There are usually four jaws; be certain when installing that the refill is engaged in all of them. At the end of its travel, the tabs will lock into place on the front jaws of the wiper blade frame.

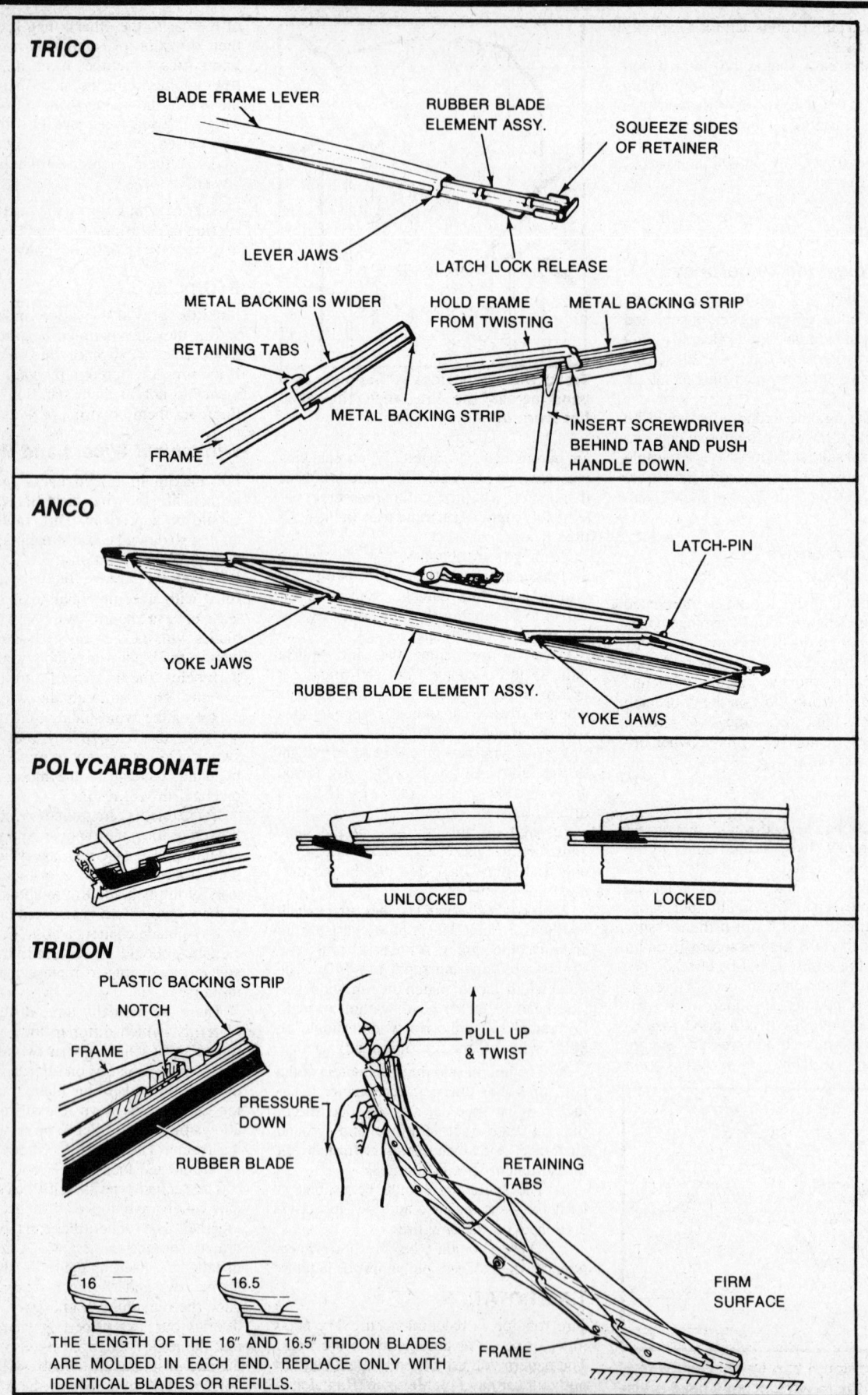

TRICO

BLADE FRAME LEVER

RUBBER BLADE ELEMENT ASSY.

SQUEEZE SIDES OF RETAINER

LEVER JAWS

LATCH LOCK RELEASE

METAL BACKING IS WIDER

HOLD FRAME FROM TWISTING

METAL BACKING STRIP

RETAINING TABS

METAL BACKING STRIP

FRAME

INSERT SCREWDRIVER BEHIND TAB AND PUSH HANDLE DOWN.

ANCO

LATCH-PIN

YOKE JAWS

RUBBER BLADE ELEMENT ASSY.

YOKE JAWS

POLYCARBONATE

UNLOCKED

LOCKED

TRIDON

PLASTIC BACKING STRIP

NOTCH

FRAME

PULL UP & TWIST

PRESSURE DOWN

RUBBER BLADE

RETAINING TABS

16

16.5

FIRM SURFACE

FRAME

THE LENGTH OF THE 16" AND 16.5" TRIDON BLADES ARE MOLDED IN EACH END. REPLACE ONLY WITH IDENTICAL BLADES OR REFILLS.

Windshield wiper blade replacement methods

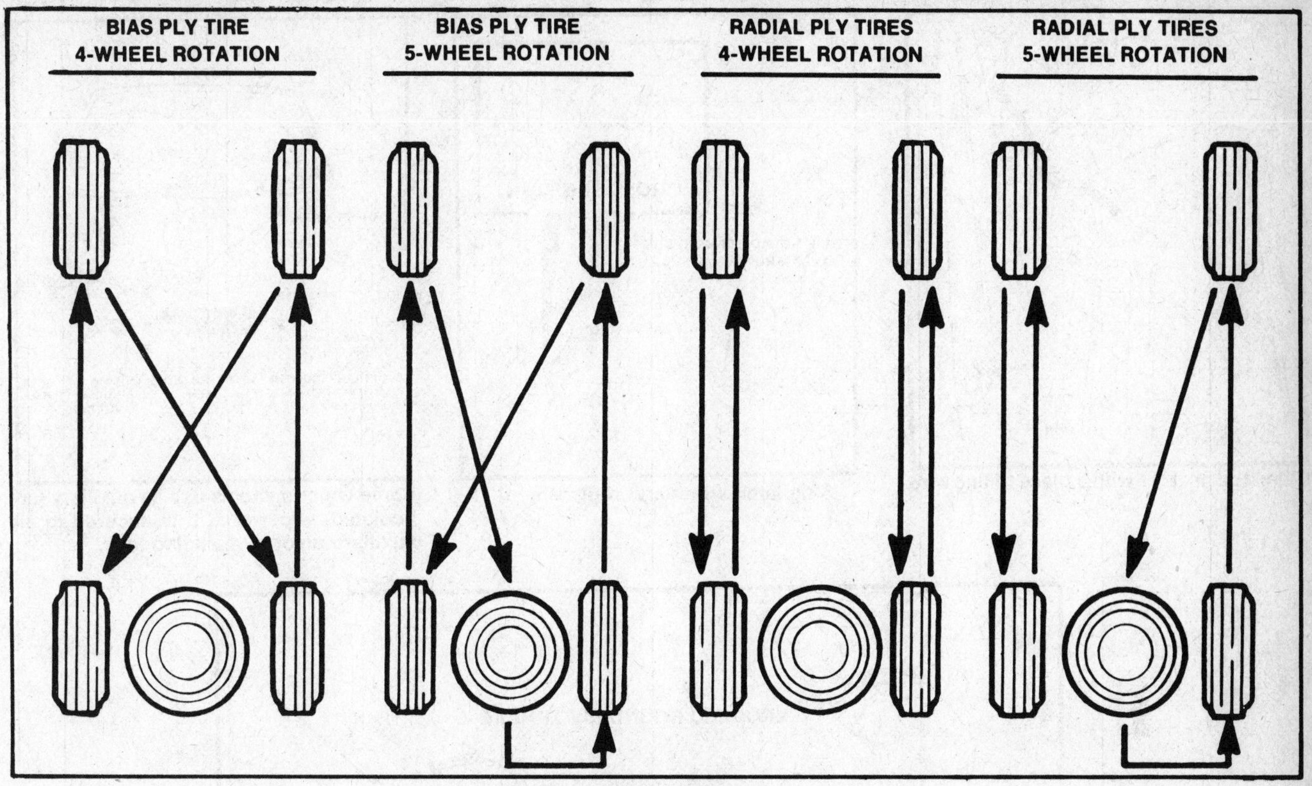

BIAS PLY TIRE 4-WHEEL ROTATION	BIAS PLY TIRE 5-WHEEL ROTATION	RADIAL PLY TIRES 4-WHEEL ROTATION	RADIAL PLY TIRES 5-WHEEL ROTATION

Tire rotation diagrams

The third type is a refill made from polycarbonate. The refill has a simple locking device at one end which flexes downward out of the groove into which the jaws of the holder fit, allowing easy release. By sliding the new refill through all the jaws and pushing through the slight resistance when it reaches the end of its travel, the refill will lock into position.

Regardless of the type of refill used, make sure that all of the frame jaws are engaged as the refill is pushed into place and locked. The metal blade holder and frame will scratch the glass if allowed to touch it.

Washer Nozzle Adjustment
CENTERED SINGLE POST—NON-ADJUSTABLE NOZZLES

This type is usually located on the rear center of the hood panel, directly in front of the windshield. By loosening the body retaining nut from under the hood, the nozzle body can be turned to provide the best spray discharge to cover the windshield. Tighten the retaining nut while holding the nozzle body in position.

CENTERED SINGLE POST—ADJUSTABLE NOZZLES

This nozzle is adjusted with a wrench, screwdriver, or pliers. If the nozzle has no gripping area, the adjustment is made by inserting a stiff wire into the nozzle opening and moving the nozzle in the direction desired. When using the wire as an adjuster tool, do not force the nozzle; the wire can be broken within the nozzle opening.

INDIVIDUAL NOZZLES

A tab is usually fastened to the nozzle stem to assist in turning the nozzle in the desired direction. If a tab is not present, use a pair of pliers to gently move the nozzle.

WIPER ARM NOZZLES

No adjustment is necessary on this type of nozzle, because the opening is centered on the wiper arm and moves along with the arm.

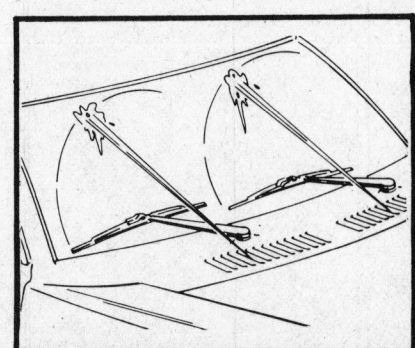

Washer nozzles should be adjusted to hit the windshield above center

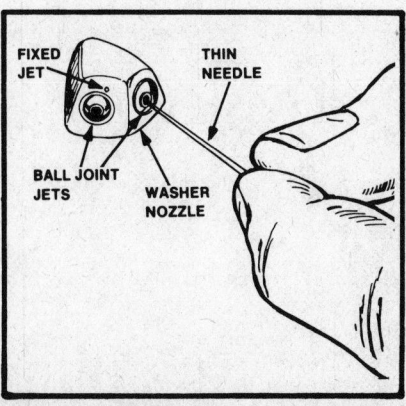

FIXED JET — THIN NEEDLE — BALL JOINT JETS — WASHER NOZZLE

Some jets can be adjusted with a piece of fine wire or a thin needle

This type of jet is adjusted with pliers or by hand

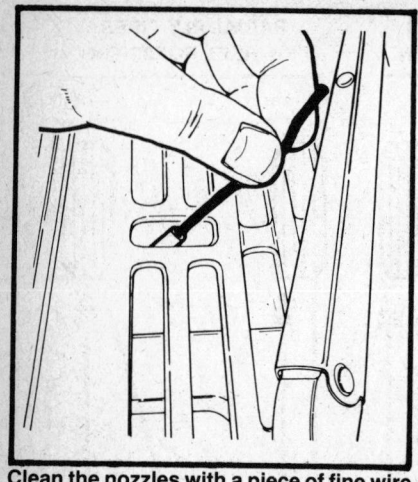

Clean the nozzles with a piece of fine wire

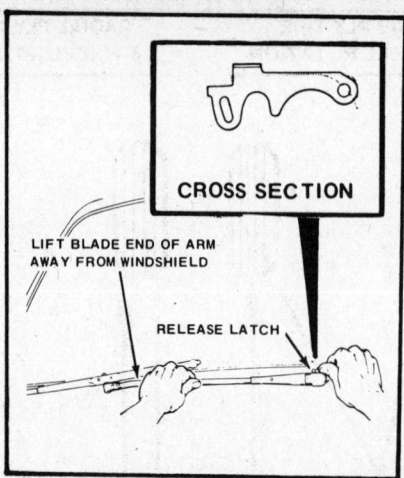

CROSS SECTION

LIFT BLADE END OF ARM
AWAY FROM WINDSHIELD

RELEASE LATCH

Side latch wiper arm replacement

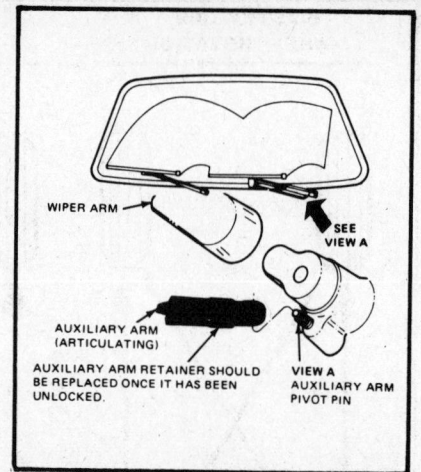

WIPER ARM

SEE VIEW A

AUXILIARY ARM
(ARTICULATING)

AUXILIARY ARM RETAINER SHOULD
BE REPLACED ONCE IT HAS BEEN
UNLOCKED.

VIEW A
AUXILIARY ARM
PIVOT PIN

Some wiper systems use an auxiliary (articulated) wiper arm. It is secured to an auxiliary pivot by a sliding lock.

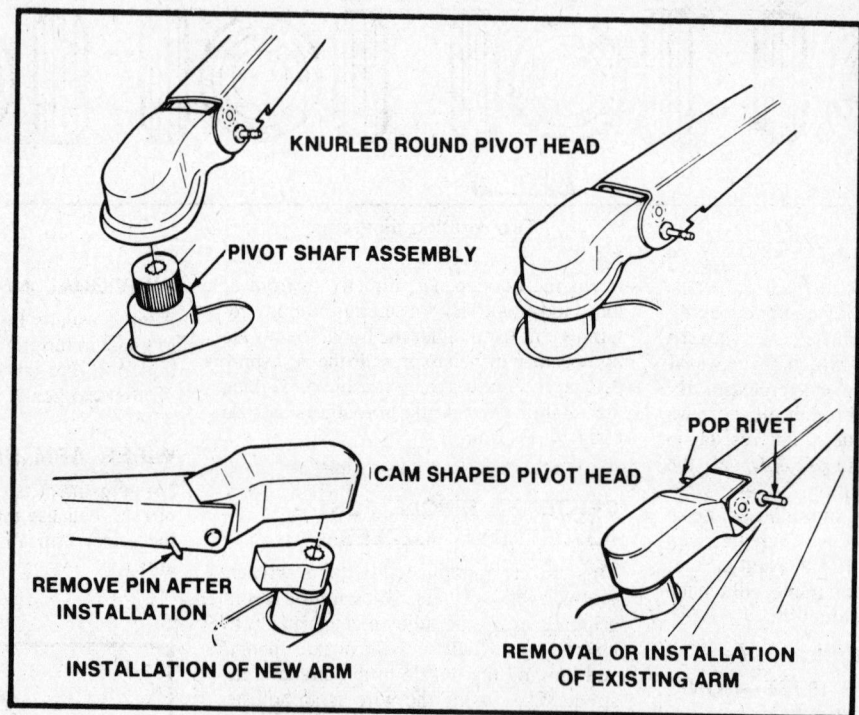

KNURLED ROUND PIVOT HEAD

PIVOT SHAFT ASSEMBLY

CAM SHAPED PIVOT HEAD

REMOVE PIN AFTER INSTALLATION

INSTALLATION OF NEW ARM

POP RIVET

REMOVAL OR INSTALLATION
OF EXISTING ARM

Pin and hole type wiper arm replacement

Diesel Maintenance

NOTE: Standard maintenance procedures are given here while component removal, installation and adjustment procedures are given in the appropriate car section.

HOW THE DIESEL ENGINE WORKS

Four-stroke diesels require four piston strokes for the complete cycle of actions, exactly like a gasoline engine. The difference lies in how the fuel mixture is ignited. A diesel engine does not rely on a conventional spark ignition to ignite the fuel mixture for the power stroke. Instead, a diesel relies on the heat produced by compressing air in the combustion chamber to ignite the fuel and produce a power stroke. This is known as a compression-ignition engine. No fuel enters the cylinder on the intake stroke, only air. At the end of the compression stroke, fuel is sprayed into the precombustion chamber (prechamber). The mixture ignites and spreads out into the main combustion chamber, forcing the piston downward (power stroke). The fuel/air mixture ignites because of the very high combustion chamber temperatures generated by the extraordinarily high compression ratios used in diesel engines. Typically, the compression ratios used in automotive diesels run anywhere from 16:1 to 23:1. A typical spark-ignition engine has a ratio of about 8:1. This is why a spark-ignition engine which continues to run after you have shut off the engine is said to be "dieseling". It is running on combustion chamber heat alone.

Designing an engine to ignite on its own combustion chamber heat poses certain problems. For instance, although a diesel engine has no need for a coil, spark plugs, or a distributor, it does need what are known as "glow plugs". These superficially resemble spark plugs, but are only used to warm the combustion chambers when the engine is cold. Without these plugs, cold starting would be impossible, due to the enormously high compression ratios and the characteristics of the diesel fuel itself.

All diesel engines use fuel injection, because unlike spark-ignited engines, the fuel cannot be drawn through the intake tract and into the cylinders. The introduction of fuel into a diesel engine must be precisely timed so that each cylinder "fires" at the

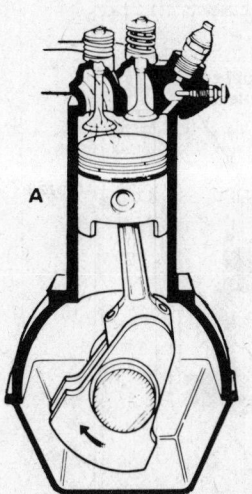
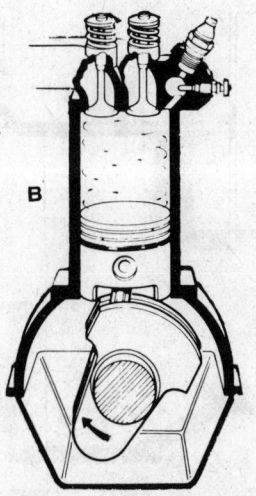
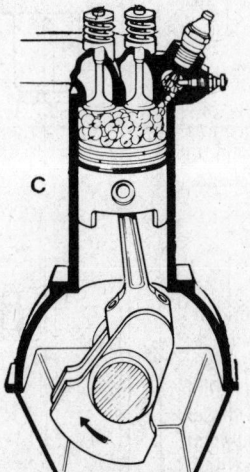
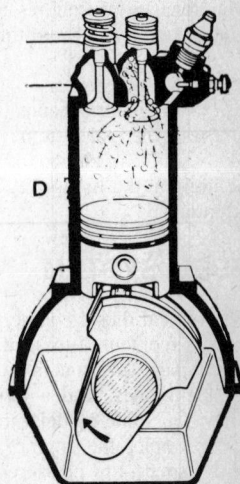

Cycles of a four-stroke cycle diesel engine. (A) Intake stroke: The downward movement of the piston draws air into the cylinder through the open intake valve. (B) Compression: The intake valve closes and the piston moves upward, compressing the air in the cylinder. (C) Ignition: While the piston is at approximately top dead center, fuel is injected into the cylinder. The superheated air (from compression) ignites the fuel, causing an explosion which forces the piston downward. (D) Exhaust: The piston begins moving upward, forcing the exhaust gas out of the cylinder, through the open exhaust valve.

proper moment. Also, the fuel injection pressure (at the cylinder) must be great enough to overcome the high compression pressures, and properly atomize the fuel without the aid of a moving air mass (as in a carbureted gas engine). It is not uncommon for diesel engine fuel injection pressures to be set at 1500–1700 psi.

Diesel engines share many of their basic mechanical components with gasoline engines, though the cylinder block, head(s), crankshaft, connecting rods, pistons, etc., are manufactured to be much stronger for use in diesel engines. The additional strength of the components is necessary due to the very high cylinder pressure generated within the diesel engine.

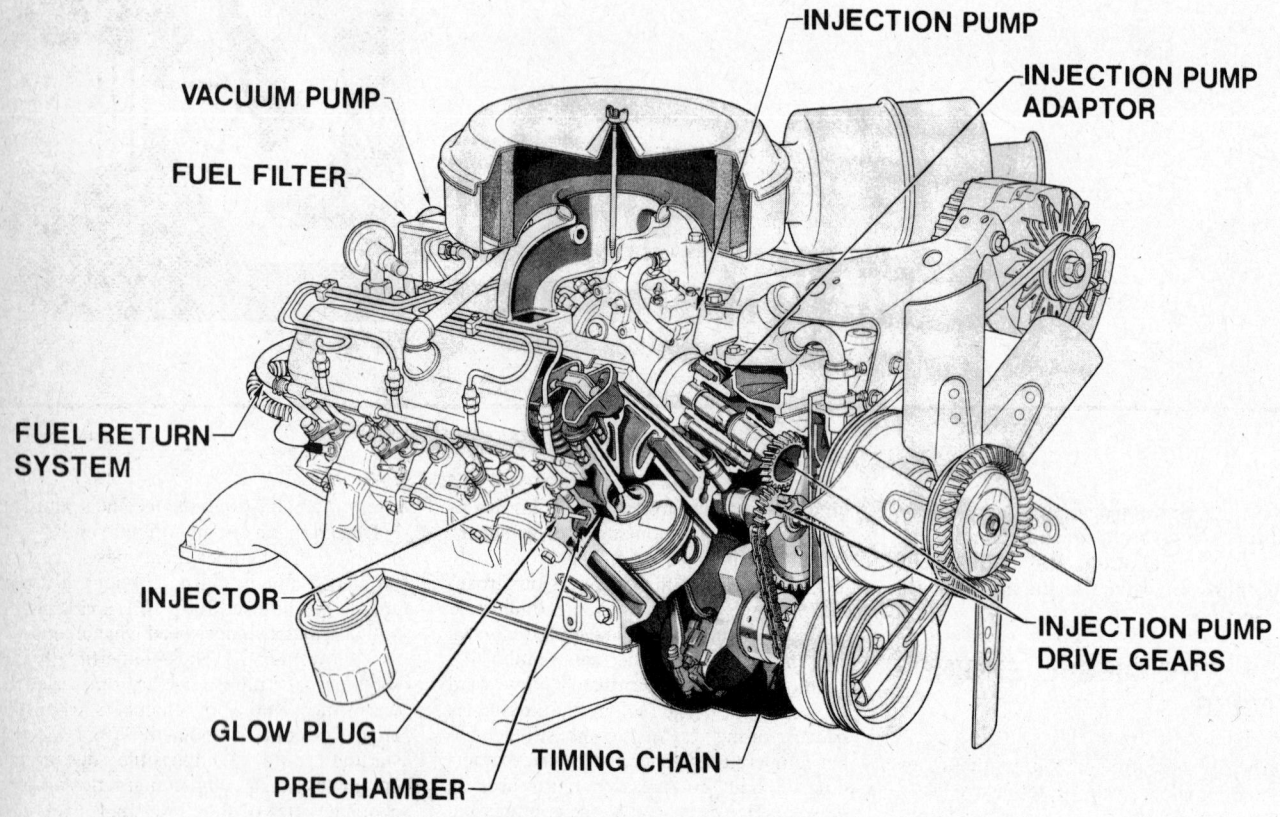

GM V8 diesel engine—1978 model shown (© Oldsmobile division, GM Corp.)

Maintenance Procedures

Maintenance procedures for the diesel engine generally fall into three categories:
1. Fuel system
2. Starting system
3. Engine mechanical systems

Of these, the fuel system is usually the most likely source of engine troubles, and should be high on the list for regular maintenance attention.

FUEL SYSTEM

The typical diesel engine fuel system consists of fuel tank, fuel feed and return lines, mechanical fuel injection pump, fuel injectors and lines, and a large capacity fuel filter. On some models, the GM V8 diesel for example, the engine is also equipped with a small, low pressure fuel pump which feeds the injection pump.

In addition to these, the air intake system (air cleaner, inlet manifold) should be checked over regularly to insure unrestricted air flow into the cylinders.

In operation, fuel is sucked out of the

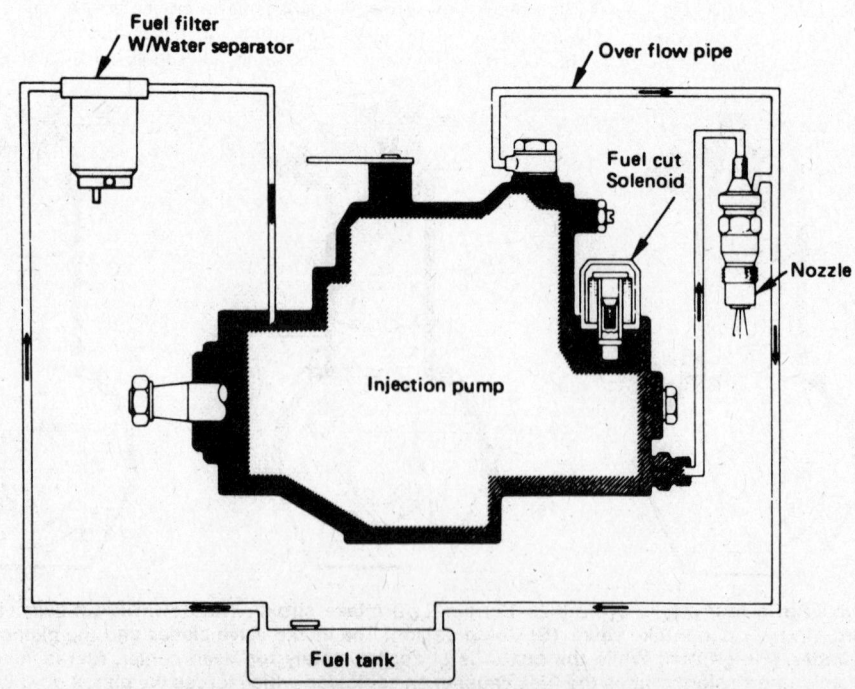

Chevette diesel fuel system schematic (© Chevrolet division, GM Corp.)

fuel tank by the injection pump (or its feed pump) and fed by the injection pump to the injectors in the cylinder head at a very high pressure. Before the fuel is allowed to enter the main injection pump, it passes through a specially built fuel filter which traps solid particles (and water on some models) in the fuel. Fuel that is not used is pumped back to the fuel tank through the fuel return lines. This recirculated fuel helps cool the injection pump.

Air Cleaner

On a gasoline engine, the volume of air taken in by the engine is controlled by throttle valves. When the throttle valves are closed (engine idling), air intake is restricted. When the throttle valves are wide open (accelerator pedal to the floor), the engine draws in the maximum amount of air it possibly can. This applies to both carbureted and fuel injected gasoline engines.

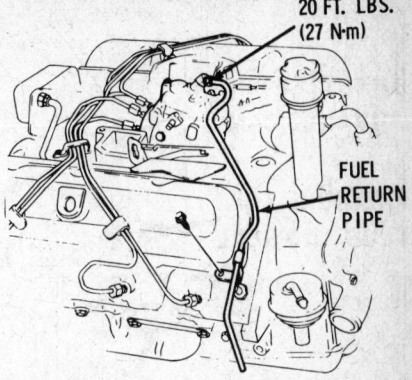

20 FT. LBS. (27 N·m)

FUEL RETURN PIPE

Fuel return pipe (© Oldsmobile Div., G.M. Corp)

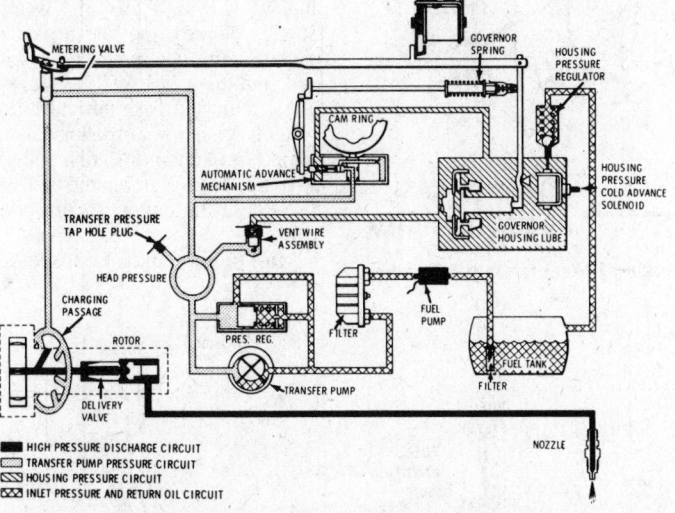

HIGH PRESSURE DISCHARGE CIRCUIT
TRANSFER PUMP PRESSURE CIRCUIT
HOUSING PRESSURE CIRCUIT
INLET PRESSURE AND RETURN OIL CIRCUIT

GM V8 diesel fuel system schematic (© Chevrolet division, GM Corp.)

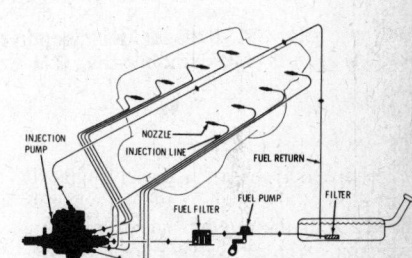

GM V8 diesel fuel system components (© Oldsmobile Div., G.M. Corp)

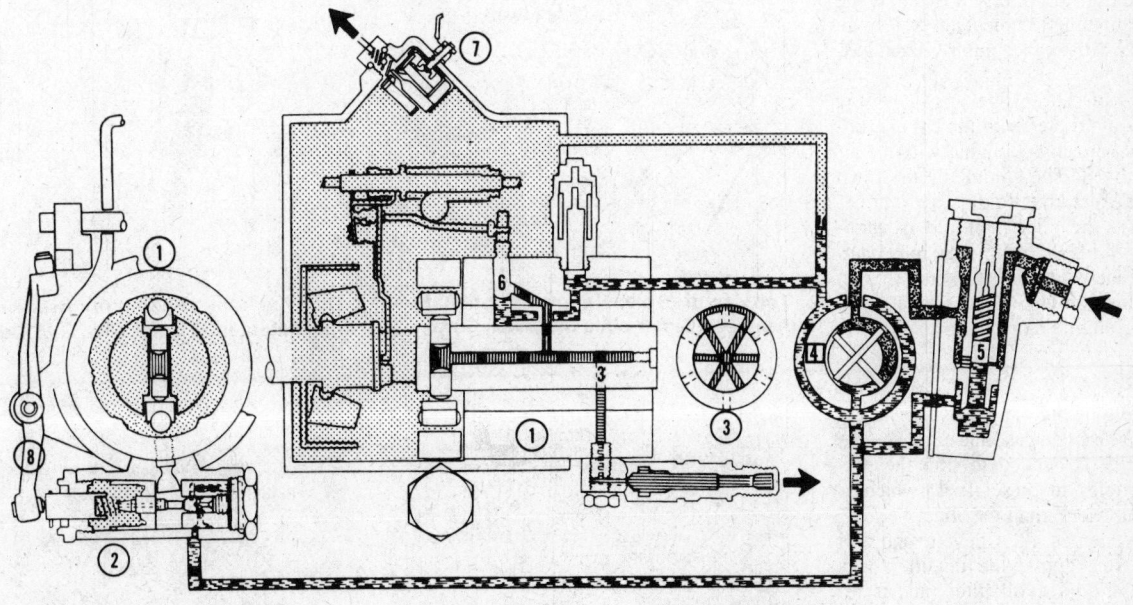

TRANSFER PRESSURE
FEED PRESSURE
METERING PRESSURE
INJECTION PRESSURE
HOUSING PRESSURE

1. Head and rotor
2. Auto-advance unit
3. Charging passage
4. Transfer pump
5. Pressure regulator
6. Metering passage
7. Housing pressure cold advance unit
8. Light load advance arm

GM V6 diesel fuel injection schematic (© Chevrolet division, GM Corp.)

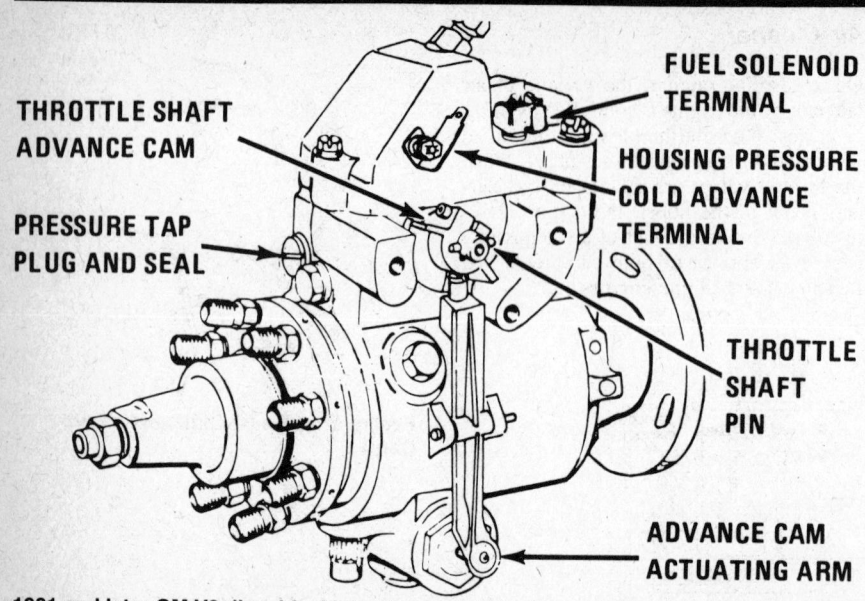

FUEL SOLENOID TERMINAL

THROTTLE SHAFT ADVANCE CAM

HOUSING PRESSURE COLD ADVANCE TERMINAL

PRESSURE TAP PLUG AND SEAL

THROTTLE SHAFT PIN

ADVANCE CAM ACTUATING ARM

1981 and later GM V8 diesel fuel injection pump with Housing Pressure Cold Advance (HPCA) system (© Oldsmobile Div., G.M. Corp)

After installing the fuel filter on GM V8s, start the engine and check for leaks. Run the engine for about two minutes, then stop the engine for the same amount of time to allow any air trapped in the injection system to bleed off.

Many diesels also have a small, in-tank filter which is usually maintenance-free.

Water In Fuel

Diesel fuel is a hydrophilic fluid, that is, it naturally attracts water. Since diesel fuel and water do not mix, the water remains floating beneath the fuel at the bottom of the tank. This water must be removed every now and then, or it will be sucked into the fuel circuit and pass through the injection system, causing corrosion and possible component failure (injection pumps can cost up to $1,000). Water in the fuel system will also cause the engine to run poorly, if at all.

Most diesel fuel tanks are equipped with

The speed (rpm) of a diesel engine is controlled by the quantity of fuel which is injected into the engine; no air metering restrictions (throttle valves) are used. Because of this, diesel engines ingest as much air as they possibly can under all conditions. A much greater volume of air passes through the air cleaner of a diesel per mile, therefore, diesel air filters must either be larger or the filter replacement intervals more frequent than those of a similarly sized gasoline engine.

One word of caution: never remove the air cleaner on a diesel with the engine running, and never run the engine with the air cleaner removed. The volume of air drawn through the inlet manifold is very great, and, because the inlet manifold is unobstructed, anything drawn into the inlet manifold (air cleaner wing nut, etc.) goes straight to the combustion chambers, where it can cause major engine damage.

Fuel Filter

The diesel engine fuel filter is usually larger than the filter used on gasoline engines. The extra capacity is needed to trap the suspended particles in diesel fuel, which is generally "dirtier" than gasoline.

On some engines, the Chevette and GM V6 diesels, for example, the fuel filter looks like a second engine oil filter, and is removed and installed in the same manner as the canister-type oil filter. On GM V8 engines, the fuel filter is located at the rear of the engine and is unbolted from its bracket after its fuel lines are disconnected. See the Chevette car section for diesel fuel filter removal and installation.

The fuel filter must be changed according to the manufacturer's suggested interval. See the owner's manual for information.

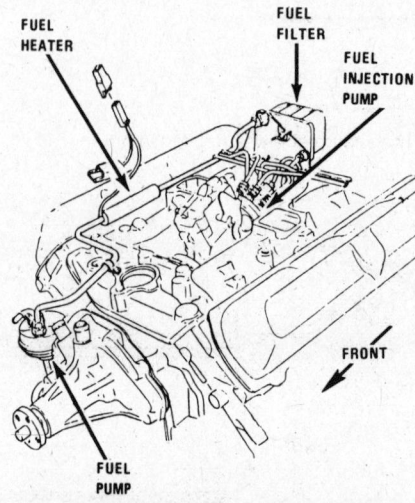

FUEL HEATER

FUEL FILTER

FUEL INJECTION PUMP

FRONT

FUEL PUMP

Top view of V8 diesel showing optional fuel heater (© Oldsmobile Div., G.M. Corp)

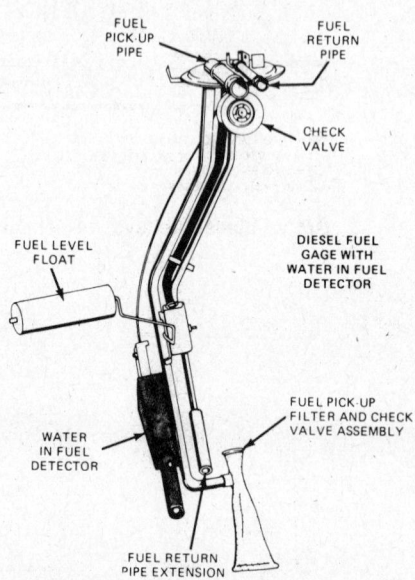

FUEL PICK-UP PIPE

FUEL RETURN PIPE

CHECK VALVE

FUEL LEVEL FLOAT

DIESEL FUEL GAGE WITH WATER IN FUEL DETECTOR

WATER IN FUEL DETECTOR

FUEL PICK-UP FILTER AND CHECK VALVE ASSEMBLY

FUEL RETURN PIPE EXTENSION

G.M. fuel tank sending unit with water in fuel detector (© Buick Div., G.M. Corp.)

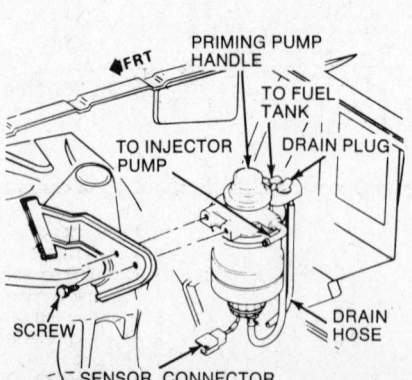

FRT

PRIMING PUMP HANDLE

TO FUEL TANK

TO INJECTOR PUMP

DRAIN PLUG

SCREW

SENSOR CONNECTOR

DRAIN HOSE

Chevette diesel fuel filter assembly, showing drain plug and hose and fuel priming pump (© Chevrolet Div., G.M. Corp.)

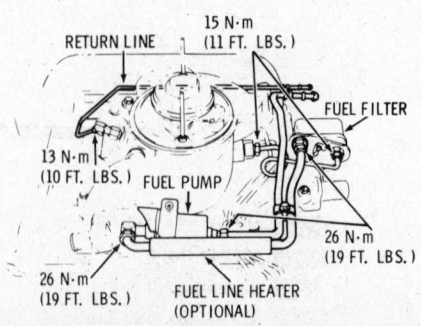

RETURN LINE

15 N·m (11 FT. LBS.)

FUEL FILTER

13 N·m (10 FT. LBS.)

FUEL PUMP

26 N·m (19 FT. LBS.)

26 N·m (19 FT. LBS.)

FUEL LINE HEATER (OPTIONAL)

Top view of the GM V6 diesel engine. Note the location of the fuel filter. (© Chevrolet division, GM Corp.)

a separator which can isolate from 1 to 3 gallons of water from the fuel.

Many GM diesels are also equipped with "Water in Fuel" lights in the dashboard which warn of the presence of H_2O in the fuel tank. These warning systems can be installed by the dealer on GM models not so equipped.

On some diesels, such as the Chevette, there is a water catcher in the bottom of the fuel filter which can easily be bled off. In addition, there are several bolt-on water filters on the market which attach to the fuel line under the hood and separate water from the fuel. Depending on which kind you buy, draining water from the system is simply a matter of opening the petcock in the bottom of the filter and letting the water drain out, or, if money is no object, a separator is available on which water is drained from the filter simply by activating a switch on the dashboard.

BLEEDING WATER FROM THE CHEVETTE DIESEL FUEL FILTER

1. Place a 4 pint see-through container at the end of the vinyl hose beneath the drain plug on the filter.

2. Open the drain plug approximately 4 turns.

3. Operate the priming pump handle at the top of the filter by pumping it about 10 times or until all of the water is drained out. The water will collect at the bottom of the see-through container and the diesel fuel will float on top of it. When the pump is pushing through nothing but diesel fuel system bleeding is complete.

4. Close the drain plug and again operate the pump handle up and down several times to prime the fuel system.

5. Start the engine and check for leaks. Make sure the "Water in Fuel" light in the instrument panel goes off. If it doesn't the water in the fuel tank will have to be drained. See procedure below.

REMOVING WATER FROM THE FUEL TANK

Treat diesel fuel with the same respect you would gasoline, and after the procedure, properly dispose of the fuel.

1. Remove the fuel tank cap.

2. Connect a pump or siphon hose to the ¼ in. fuel return hose (smaller of the two fuel hoses) above the rear axle, or under the hood near the fuel pump (on the passenger's side of the engine, near the front).

3. Siphon until all water is removed from the tank. Do not use your mouth to create siphon vacuum, EVER! The best method is to siphon the water into a large capacity see-through container. The water will collect at the bottom of the container.

4. When all water has been removed from the tank, be sure to reinstall the fuel return hose and fuel cap.

NOTE: If the entire fuel system (not just the tank) is contaminated by water,

the vehicle must be stopped immediately and the fuel system must be purged. This includes draining and removing the fuel tank, blowing low pressure compressed air backwards through the fuel feed and return lines, and bleeding the water out of all injection components. This job should be referred to a qualified technician.

Cold Weather Fuel System Maintenance

—————— CAUTION ——————
NEVER use "starting aids" (e.g.—ether) to help start a GM diesel engine—serious engine damage will result.

As will be explained later under "Fuel Recommendations", diesel fuel tends to become "cloudy", or thicker, as the temperature drops. The thicker the diesel fuel becomes, the slower it flows through the fuel system, until finally it stops flowing altogether somewhere near the bottom of the thermometer.

One way to fight sluggish fuel flow is to use winterized blends of diesel fuel or straight No. 1 diesel fuel.

Another way is to install an aftermarket fuel system pre-heater. These are generally canisters which connect into the fuel line and use coolant from the engine cooling system to heat the fuel before it reaches the injection pump. The one drawback with this system is the engine must be started before the pre-heater begins to work. Also available are electric fuel warmers. These pre-heat the fuel going into the filter and can be used in conjunction with the coolant-type fuel heater.

For 1981 and later Diesels, GM offers an optional electric diesel fuel heater (V6 and V8 only) and an engine block heater (all GM diesels). The fuel heater is thermostatically controlled to heat the fuel before it enters the fuel filter when fuel temperature is 20°F or lower. The fuel heater works only when the ignition key is in the RUN position. On these models, the fuel tank filter has a bypass valve which allows fuel to flow to the heater when the tank filter is covered with fuel wax. The engine block heater is equipped with an electrical cord wrapped up on the right side of the engine compartment. The cord plugs into regular 110 volt household current. The block heater can be used, according to the type of oil in the crankcase, up to eight hours or overnight to warm up the block. Consult the manufacturer's Diesel Engine Supplement for more information.

1981 and later GM V6 and V8 diesel engine fuel injection pumps are equipped with a Housing Pressure Cold Advance (HPCA) system which advances the injection timing about 3° during cold operation to promote easier cold starts, better idle and less noise when cold. The system should be maintenance free.

STARTING SYSTEM

The diesel starting system includes one (sometimes two) heavy duty battery, the starter, and the glow plug circuit. In addition to the heavy duty battery(ies), the majority of diesel engines also have starters and battery cables designed specifically as heavy duty items for diesel usage only. Because of the high compression of any diesel, the torque required to turn the engine is much greater than a gasoline engine. The starter must be powerful enough to handle the increased load; the battery cables must be thick enough to withstand the heat generated by the starter load.

For battery maintenance, see the regular "Maintenance" section. Jump starting procedures for a dual battery car are given below. Starter maintenance is included in the appropriate car section, or the "Charging and Starting Systems" section.

The glow plug circuit is used on the diesel to initially start the engine. When the ignition switch is turned to the ON position, a light will come on in the instrument panel signalling that the glow plugs are preheating the combustion chambers. After a certain interval (depending on how cold the engine is), the light will go off. This signals that the starter may be engaged and the engine started. If the glow plug circuit malfunctions, especially in cold weather, the engine will be almost impossible to start.

—————— CAUTION ——————
NEVER use "starting aids" (e.g.—ether) to help start a GM diesel engine—serious engine damage will result.

Glow Plug Testing
EXCEPT CHEVETTE

To test each individual glow plug, discon-

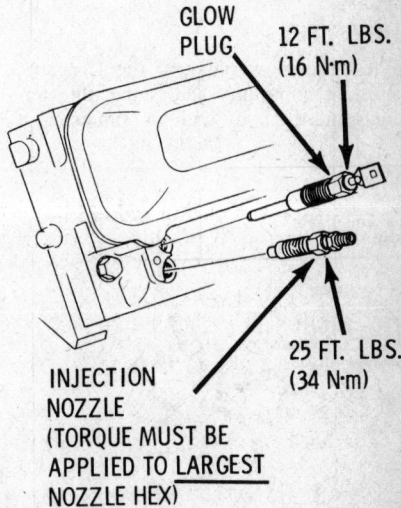

GLOW PLUG — 12 FT. LBS. (16 N·m)

25 FT. LBS. (34 N·m)

INJECTION NOZZLE (TORQUE MUST BE APPLIED TO LARGEST NOZZLE HEX)

GM V8 diesel engine glow plug and injection nozzle—1980 and later models shown. Nozzles of 1978–79 models are retained by a collar clamp and bolt. (© Oldsmobile division, GM Corp.)

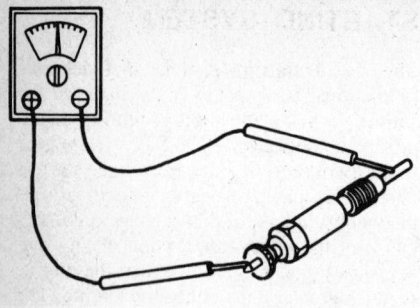

Testing the Chevette diesel glow plug with an ohmmeter (© Chevrolet division, GM Corp.)

nect the busbar and/or wire connector from the glow plug and connect a test light between the glow plug terminal and the positive battery terminal. If the test light lights, the glow plug is working. Replace individual glow plugs which do not work. See the appropriate car sections for removal and installation procedures.

NOTE: GM V8 diesel engines are equipped with either "slow glow" or "fast glow" glow plugs. See the Oldsmobile 88 car section for information on these two systems. Do not attempt to interchange any parts of these two glow plug systems. The GM V6 diesel uses the "fast glow" style glow plugs exclusively.

To test the glow plug circuit, connect a test light to the terminal of one of the glow plugs (glow plug wiring still attached) and turn the ignition to the heating position. The test light should light for a short while. If not, the glow plug circuit is malfunctioning and must be diagnosed and repaired.

NOTE: Perform this operation on a cold engine only.

CHEVETTE

To test the glow plugs of the Chevette, check for continuity across the plug terminals and the body with an ohmmeter. If there is continuity between these points, the glow plug is okay; if not, replace the glow plug.

Jump-Starting a Dual Battery Diesel

Many GM diesels are equipped with two 12 volt batteries. The batteries are connected in parallel circuit (positive terminal to positive terminal, negative terminal to negative terminal). Hooking the batteries up in parallel circuit increases battery cranking power without increasing total battery voltage output (12 volts). On the other hand, hooking two 12 volt batteries up in a series circuit (positive terminal to negative terminal, positive terminal to negative terminal) increases total battery output to 24 volts (12 volts + 12 volts).

— CAUTION —

NEVER hook the batteries up in a series circuit; SEVERE electrical system damage will result.

In the event that a dual battery diesel must be jumped started, use the following procedure.

1. Open the hood and locate the batteries. On GM diesels, the manufacturer usually suggests using the battery on the driver's side of the car to make the connection.

2. Position the donor car so that the jumper cables will reach from its battery (must be 12 volt, negative ground) to the appropriate battery in the diesel. Do not allow the cars to touch.

3. Shut off all electrical equipment on both vehicles. Turn off the engine of the donor car, set the parking brakes on both vehicles and block the wheels. Also, make sure both vehicles are in Neutral (manual transmission models) or Park (automatic transmission models).

4. Using the jumper cables, connect the positive (+) terminal of the donor car battery to the positive terminal of one (not both) of the diesel batteries.

5. Using the second jumper cable, con-

nect the negative (−) terminal of the donor battery to a solid, stationary, metallic point on the diesel (alternator bracket, engine block, etc.). Be very careful to keep the jumper cables away from moving parts (cooling fan, alternator belt, etc.) on both vehicles.

6. Start the engine of the donor car and run it at moderate speed.

7. Start the engine of the diesel.

8. When the diesel starts, disconnect the battery cables in the reverse order of attachment.

ENGINE MECHANICAL SYSTEMS

Included are engine lubrication and engine compression.

Although diesel engines are very low in carbon monoxide (CO) and hydrocarbon (HC) emissions, "particulate" emission output is very high from diesel engines. This is evident from the black smoke emitted by diesels, which is most noticeable during hard acceleration or high engine loads. The particulates are made up of mostly soot (carbon) and sulpher particles. The majority of these particulates are released into the atmosphere. However, some of the particulate matter, because it is produced within the engines cylinders, is left inside the engine and gradually contaminates the engine oil. This contamination makes the oil corrosive, due to the sulpher, and abrasive, due to the carbon. Serious engine damage will result if these contaminants continue to accumulate in the oil. Engine oil and filters of diesel engines must be changed more frequently than those of gasoline engines, due to the increased rate at which the contaminants form in the diesel. Consult the "Maintenance" section for oil and filter change procedures. The manufacturer's recommended oil change interval will be given in the owner's manual. An explanation of diesel engine oils is given at the end of this section.

As explained earlier, very high cylinder

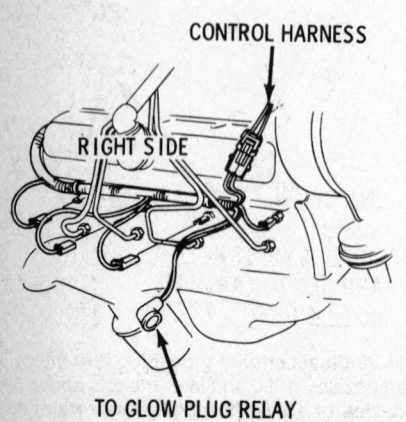

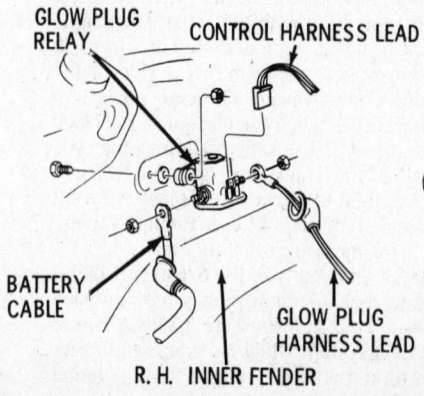

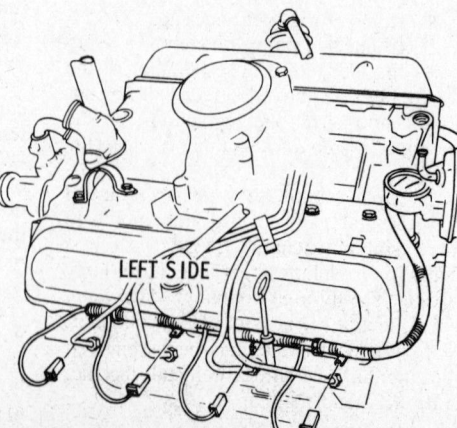

Typical GM V8 diesel glow plug harness arrangement—V6 similar. (© Oldsmobile division, GM Corp.)

compression is the key to the operation of the diesel engine. The normal compression of most gasoline engines will rarely exceed 180 psi; whereas with diesel engines, compression pressures of 350–400 psi are commonplace.

—————— CAUTION ——————

DO NOT attempt to check the compression of a diesel engine with a standard compression gauge—personal injury could result. A special, high pressure compression gauge is needed to safely check the compression of any diesel.

Compression Test

GM V6 AND V8 DIESEL ENGINES

1. Remove the air cleaner and install air crossover cover (Tool No. J-26996-1).
2. Disconnect the wire from the fuel shutoff solenoid terminal of the injection pump.
3. Disconnect the wires from the glow plugs and remove all glow plugs.
4. Screw compression gauge J-26999 into the glow plug hole in the cylinder being checked.
5. Crank the engine, allowing six "puffs" for each cylinder.

The lowest reading cylinder should not be less than 70% of the highest, and no cylinder should be less than 275 pounds.

CHEVETTE DIESEL

1. Start the engine and bring it to normal operating temperature.
2. Disconnect or remove the following:
   a. Sensing resistor
   b. Glow plug connector
   c. Glow plugs (4)
   d. Fuel cut-off solenoid connector
   e. Disconnect the in-line fusible link wire of Q.S.S.(Quick Start and Silent idling) system at the connector
3. Install an adapter (special tool J-29762) into the glow plug hole, then hook a compression gauge (must read to 600 psi) to the adapter.
4. Engage the starter motor to take the reading. Standard compression is 441 psi at 200 rpm or more. Limit is 370 psi at 200 rpm or less.

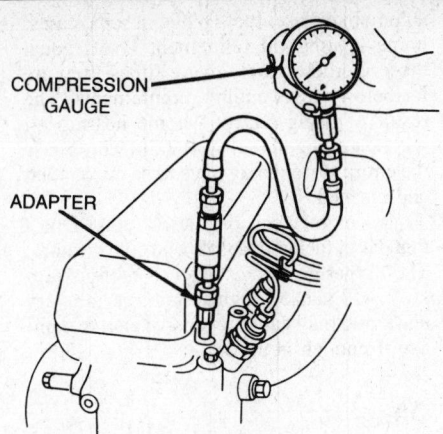

Compression test arrangement for a Chevette diesel (© Chevrolet division, GM Corp.)

Connecting a Tachometer to a Diesel Engine

As mentioned earlier, the diesel engine does not require an electrical ignition system. Because of this, problems arise when attempts are made to connect a tachometer to the engine for the purpose of idle adjustments, etc. The average gasoline engine tachometer senses the ignition spark pulses and converts them into a readable engine rpm signal. This type of tachometer is useless on the diesel engine, as you may have guessed, because of the diesel's compression ignition system.

There are several magnetic and photoelectric tachometers available from various tool manufacturers (Kent-Moore Corp., Snap-on Tools, etc.) which were designed specifically for use with the diesel engine. These units can run into a little more money than the average do-it-yourselfer may be willing to spend, in which case any adjustments requiring the monitoring of engine rpm should be performed by a competent service technician.

Diesel Engine Precautions

- Never run the engine with the air cleaner removed: if anything is sucked into the inlet manifold it will go straight to the combustion chambers, or jam behind a valve.
- Never wash a diesel engine: the reaction of a warm fuel injection pump to cold (or even warm) water can ruin the pump.
- Never operate a diesel engine with one or more fuel injectors removed unless fully familiar with injector testing procedures: some diesel injection pumps spray fuel at up to 1400 psi—enough pressure to allow the fuel to penetrate your skin.
- Do not skip engine oil and filter changes.
- Strictly follow the manufacturer's oil and fuel recommendations as given in the owner's manual.
- Do not use home heating oil as fuel for your diesel unless it's a *dire* emergency.
- Do not use "starting aids" (e.g.—ether) in the automotive diesel engine, as these "aids" can cause severe internal engine damage.
- Do not run a diesel engine with the "Water in Fuel" warning light on in the dashboard.
- If removing water from the fuel tank yourself, use the same caution you would use when working around gasoline engine fuel components.
- Do not allow diesel fuel to come in contact with rubber hoses or components on the engine, as it can damage them.

Fuel and Oil Recommendations

FUEL

Fuel makers produce two grades of diesel fuel, No. 1 and No. 2, for use in automotive diesel engines. Generally speaking, No. 2

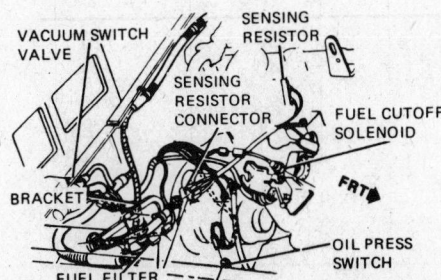

Chevette underhood wiring, showing relative locations of fuel cutoff solenoid and sensing resistor (© Chevrolet Div., G.M. Corp.)

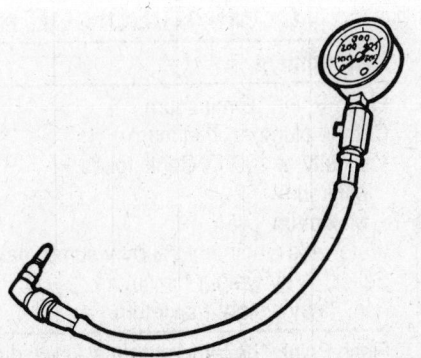
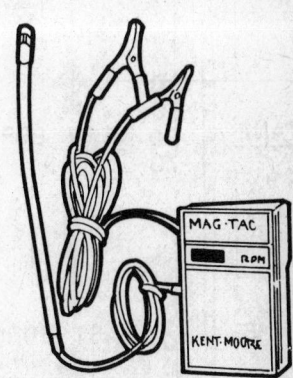

GM V6 and V8 diesel engine compression gauge with adapter (left—Kent-Moore #J-26999 shown), and digital tachometer with electromagnetic pick-up probe which counts crankshafts revolutions (right—Kent-Moore #J-26925).

fuel is recommended over No. 1 for driving in temperatures above 20°F. In fact, in many areas, No. 2 diesel is the only fuel available. By comparison, No. 2 diesel fuel is less volatile than No. 1 fuel, and gives better fuel economy. No. 2 fuel is also a better injection pump lubricant.

Two important characteristics of diesel fuel are its cetane number and its viscosity.

The cetane number of a diesel fuel refers to the ease with which a diesel fuel ignites. High cetane numbers mean that the fuel will ignite with relative ease or that it ignites well at low temperatures. Naturally, the lower the cetane number, the higher the temperature must be to ignite the fuel. Most commercial fuels have cetane numbers that range from 35 to 65. No. 1 diesel fuel generally has a higher cetane rating than No. 2 fuel.

Viscosity is the ability of a liquid, in this case diesel fuel, to flow. Using straight No. 2 diesel fuel below 20°F can cause problems, because this fuel tends to become cloudy, meaning wax crystals begin forming in the fuel. In extreme cold weather, No. 2 fuel can stop flowing altogether. In either case, fuel flow is restricted, which can result in a "no start" condition or poor engine performance. Fuel manufacturers often "winterize" No. 2 diesel fuel by using various fuel additives and blends (No. 1 diesel fuel, kerosene, etc.) to lower its winter-time viscosity. Generally speaking, though, No. 1 diesel fuel is more satisfactory in extremely cold weather.

NOTE: No. 1 and No. 2 diesel fuels will mix and burn with no ill effects, although the engine manufacturer will undoubtedly recommend one or the other. Consult the owner's manual for information.

Depending on local climate, most fuel manufacturers make winterized No. 2 fuel available seasonally.

Many automobile manufacturers (Oldsmobile, for example) publish pamphlets giving the locations of diesel fuel stations nationwide. Contact the local dealer for information.

Do not substitute home heating oil for automotive diesel fuel. While in some cases, home heating oil refinement levels equal those of diesel fuel, many times they are far below diesel engine requirements. The result of using "dirty" home heating oil will be a clogged fuel system, in which case the entire system may have to be dismantled and cleaned.

One more word on diesel fuels. Don't thin diesel fuel with gasoline in cold weather. The lighter gasoline, which is more explosive, will cause rough running at the very least, and may cause extensive engine damage if enough is used.

OIL

Diesel engines require different engine oil from those used in gasoline engines. Besides doing the things gasoline engine oil does, diesel oil must also deal with increased engine heat and the diesel blow-by gases, which create sulphuric acid, a high corrosive.

Under the American Petroleum Institute (API) classifications, gasoline engine oil codes begin with an "S", and diesel engine oil codes begin with a "C". This first letter designation is followed by a second letter code which explains what type of service (heavy, moderate, light) the oil is meant for. For example, the top of a typical oil can will include: "API SERVICES SC, SD, SE, CA, CB, CC". This means the oil in the can is a good, moderate duty engine oil when used in a diesel engine.

It should be noted here that the further down the alphabet the second letter of the API classification is, the greater the oil's protective qualities are (CD is the severest duty diesel engine oil, CA is the lightest duty oil, etc.). The same is true for gasoline engine oil classifications (SF is the severest duty gasoline engine oil, SA is the lightest duty oil, etc.).

Many diesel manufacturers recommend an oil with both gasoline and diesel engine API classifications. Consult the owner's manual for specifications.

The top of the oil can will also contain an SAE (Society of Automotive Engineers) designation, which gives the oil's viscosity. A typical designation will be: SAE 10W-30, which means the oil is a "winter" viscosity oil, meaning it will flow and give protection at low temperatures.

On the diesel engine, oil viscosity is critical, because the diesel is much harder to start (due to its higher compression) than a gasoline engine. Obviously, if you fill the crankcase with a very heavy oil during winter (SAE 20W-50, for example), the starter is going to require a lot of current from the battery to turn the engine. And, since batteries don't function well in cold weather in the first place, you may find yourself stranded some morning. Consult the owner's manual for recommended oil specifications for the climate you live in.

Aftermarket Fuel System Accessories

Due to reasons described previously, most diesel engine problems can be attributed to either fuel contamination or cold weather fuel performance characteristics. Diesel-engined vehicle manufacturers have designed and installed various systems to combat these problems, but ultimately, their best efforts are limited by cost.

Inconvenience is a major concern to diesel owners. Excepting the Chevette, for example, if water accumulates (in substantial quantities) in the diesel fuel system, the fuel and water must be siphoned from the fuel tank and purged from the remainder of the fuel system. It goes without saying that this operation is a messy, time-consuming process. Even if the vehicle is equipped with a water/fuel separator having a drain valve, the owner must manually open the valve from either under the hood or beneath the vehicle.

Although the fuel filter installed by the manufacturer offers adequate performance when maintained properly, the addition of another, separate diesel fuel filter is a wise improvement.

If you live in an extremely cold climate, you've probably experienced cold starting

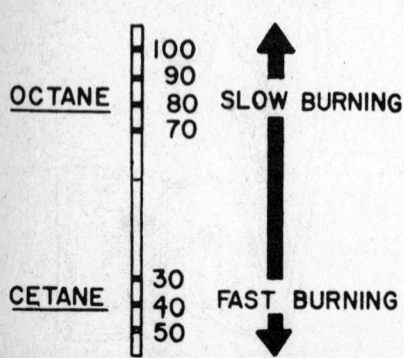

Diesel engine cetane versus gasoline engine octane ratings. The higher the cetane number, the faster the fuel burns

COMPARISON OF #1 AND #2 DIESEL FUEL

Requirement	1-D	2-D
Flash Point, °F minimum	100	125
Cetane Number, minimum	40	40
Viscosity at 100°F, Centistokes		
Minimum	1.4	2.0
Maximum	2.5	4.3
Water and Sediment, % by volume maximum	Trace	0.05
Sulfur, % by weight maximum	0.5	0.5
Ash, % by weight maximum	0.01	0.01

Flash Point: The temperature at which diesel fuel ignites when exposed to a flame *in the open air.*

Cetane Number: See text

problems due to fuel "waxing", plugged filters, "gelled" fuel, etc. If your vehicle is not factory-equipped with the optional fuel line or cylinder block heaters, these heaters can be purchased from the aftermarket (retail auto parts manufacturers). The installation of either of these items can improve cold-starting dramatically.

WATER/FUEL SEPARATORS

Centrifugal Action

Sometimes referred to as a "cyclonic" water/fuel separator, this device uses baffles which spin the fuel as it comes through the separator inlet. Since water is heavier than diesel fuel, the water will spin away from the fuel, sink to the bottom of the separator, and collect in the sediment bowl.

This type of separator is most efficient in dealing with large water droplets. If the water is in emulsion with the fuel, that is, if the water is equally dispersed through the fuel in very small droplets, some of the water will remain with the fuel to travel through the fuel system.

Coalescing Action

In this type of separator, the fuel must pass through a coalescent filtering media before proceeding through the fuel system. The idea behind the coalescent media is to trap even the smallest droplets of water on the media. As the small droplets combine into larger, heavier droplets, gravity acts on the droplets to pull them downward, off of the media and into the sediment bowl.

FUEL FILTER/SEPARATOR COMBINATION UNITS

Most separators of either the centrifugal or coalescent types are available with disposeable fuel filtering elements which are built into the separator unit. If your car already has a large, disposeable filter, it would probably be more cost-effective to stay with a separator only, and to change the factory-equipped filter at the recommended intervals. Should your vehicle have a fairly small filter, and/or an inconveniently located water drain (or none at all), choose the filter/separator combination. The filter/separator offers both increased fuel filtering ability and efficient water separation.

CONVENIENCE ADD-ONS

Available with many separators and filter/separators are items such as dash-mounted water-in-fuel indicator lamps, audible water-in-fuel alarms, and dash-controlled water ejection systems. A properly chosen system would warn you of water in the fuel, and allow you to eject the water by simply "flipping" a dash-mounted switch.

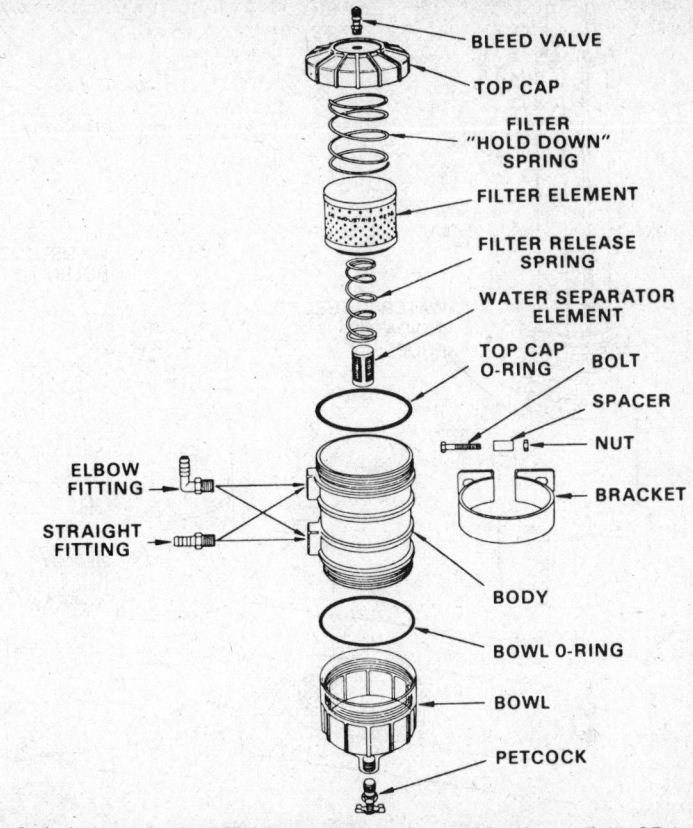

Exploded view of a fuel filter/water separator combination unit (© CR Industries)

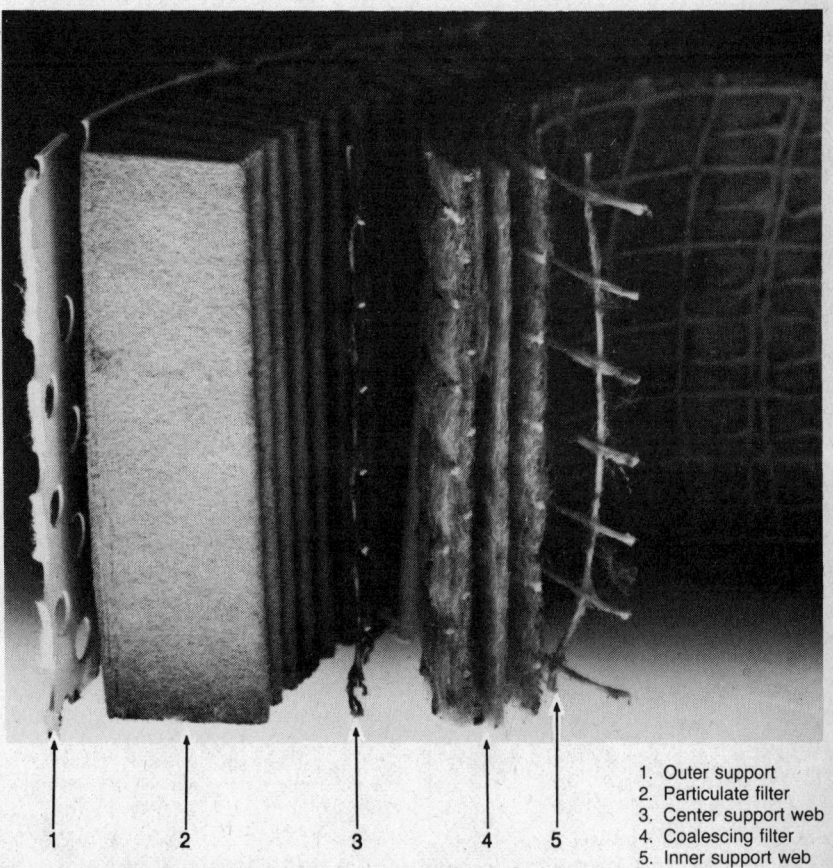

1. Outer support
2. Particulate filter
3. Center support web
4. Coalescing filter
5. Inner support web

Cross section of a coalescing filter/fuel filter combination (© CR Industries)

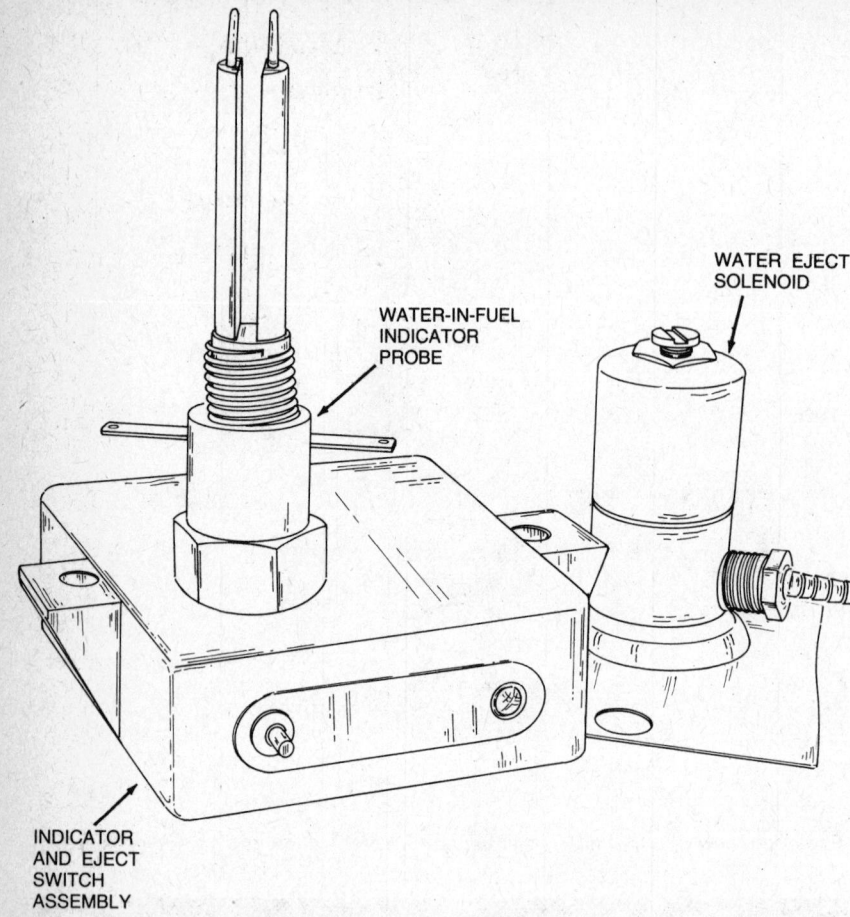

WATER-IN-FUEL INDICATOR PROBE

WATER EJECT SOLENOID

INDICATOR AND EJECT SWITCH ASSEMBLY

Typical convenience accessories for a water-in-fuel detection system (© CR Industries)

Installing a Separator

Clear installation instructions and the necessary installation parts will be provided with the separator kit. Follow those instructions exactly. A general list of suggestions follows:

1. Fuel additives should not be used unless approved by the separator manufacturer.

2. Do not install a separator less than 4″ away from any exhaust system component.

3. If plastic fittings are supplied with the kit, do not replace them with metal fittings. Also, use extreme caution when tightening the fittings, especially those made of plastic.

4. Use a fuel-proof sealer on all fitting threads, only if the threads are not factory-coated with sealer.

5. Use only fuel-proof hoses for the installation.

6. Do not eliminate the original equipment fuel filter, even if a filter/separator is installed.

7. For new car warranty purposes, a filter/separator should be located BEFORE the original equipment filter. The fuel must pass through the original filter last, before entering the fuel injection pump.

8. If any type of fuel line heater is installed, it is best to position the heater between the fuel tank and the separator inlet.

9. To ease the job of the separator, the separator should be installed between the fuel transfer pump and the tank (unless the separator manufacturer specifies otherwise). Fuel and water which have been churned through the fuel transfer pump will be more difficult to separate.

10. Be sure that any wiring (for warning lamps, water ejection, etc.) is routed and connected properly. If the wiring must pass through a drilled hole, be sure to use a rubber grommet between the drilled component(s) and the wire to prevent damage to the wire.

FUEL LINE HEATERS

Two popular types of fuel line heaters are available for diesel passenger cars. Both types raise the temperature of the fuel to prevent ''waxing'' and ''gelling'' of the fuel in the lines during cold weather operation. One type uses engine coolant as a heating source. In order for this type to heat the fuel, the engine must first be started and allowed to run until the coolant temperature increases. Though this type of heater will usually increase fuel mileage, it offers no aid in starting ability.

The other type of heater uses a 12VDC electric heating element. This type is recommended, due to its ability to warm the fuel BEFORE the engine is started. This type of heater will also usually increase the overall fuel mileage.

Installation

Follow the manufacturer's instructions exactly. Also, see suggestions 5, 8, and 9 under Separator Installation.

CYLINDER BLOCK HEATERS

A cylinder block heater electrically (usually 110V house current) heats the engine coolant, which in turn warms the cylinder block, heads, and engine oil. In this case, the warmth is not used to alter the characteristics of the fuel. Block heaters offer two main advantages when starting a diesel in cold weather:

1. The reduced viscosity (thinning) of the engine oil from the warmth allows the engine to be ''turned over'' easier (and faster) by the starter. Less strain is imposed on the starting system.

2. Because the diesel relies on the heat of compression to ignite the fuel, the increase in the base combustion chamber temperature results in a higher tempeature during compression. This allows the fuel to ignite easier than if just the glow plugs were used.

Installation

Most cylinder block heaters replace one of the existing freeze (or expansion) plugs of the cylinder block. Follow the manufacturers installation instructions exactly. Also, refer to the manufacturers recommendations for usage.

Tools and Equipment

In addition to the normal assortment of screwdrivers and pliers, automotive service work requires an investment in wrenches, sockets and the handles needed to drive them, and various measuring tools such as torque wrenches and feeler gauges.

The best approach to gathering the required equipment is to proceed slowly, buying high-quality tools as they are needed. An initial investment should be made in a set of quality wrenches, ranging in size from ¼ inch to one inch, if your car has standard bolts, or from 5 mm to 19 mm if your car has metric fasteners. High quality forged wrenches are available in three styles: open end, box end, and combination open/box end. The combination tools are generally the most desirable as a starter set; the wrenches shown in the illustration are of the combination type.

NOTE: Many later model American cars use both metric and standard nuts and bolts.

The other set of tools inevitably required is a ratchet handle and socket set. This set should have the same size range as your wrench set. The ratchet, extension, and flex drives for the sockets are available in many sizes; it is advisable to choose a ⅜ inch drive set initially. One break in the inch/metric sizing war is that metric-sized sockets sold in the U.S. have inch-sized drive (¼, ⅜, ½, etc.). Sockets are available in six and twelve point versions: six point types are generally cheaper and are a good choice for a first set. The choice of a drive handle for the sockets should be made with some care. If this is your first set, take the plunge and invest in a flex-head ratchet; it will get into many places otherwise accessible only through a long chain of universal joints, extensions and adapters. An alternative is a flex handle; such a tool is shown in the illustration, below the ratchet handle. In addition to the range of sockets mentioned, a rubber-lined spark plug socket should be purchased. Spark plugs have either a ¹³⁄₁₆ or a ⅝ inch hex; get the correct socket for the plugs in your car.

The most important thing to consider when purchasing hand tools is quality. Don't be misled by the low cost of ''bargain'' tools. Forged wrenches, tempered screwdriver blades, and fine tooth ratchets are a much better investment than their less expensive counterparts. The skinned knuckles and frustration inflicted by poor quality tools make any job an unhappy chore. Another consideration is that quality tools sold by reputable firms come with an on-the-spot replacement guarantee—if the tool breaks, you get a new one, no questions asked.

The tools needed for basic maintenance jobs, in addition to those just mentioned, include:

1. Jackstands, for support;
2. Oil filter wrench;
3. Oil filler spout or funnel;
4. Grease gun;
5. Battery hydrometer;
6. Battery post and clamp cleaner;
7. Container for draining oil;
8. Many rags for the inevitable spills.

In addition to these items there are several others which are not absolutely necessary, but handy to have around. These include a transmission funnel and filler tube, a drop (trouble) light on a long cord, an adjustable wrench (crescent wrench), and slip joint pliers.

A more extensive list of tools, suitable for tune-up work, can be drawn up easily. While the tools involved are slightly more sophisticated, they need not be outrageously expensive. For example, there are several inexpensive tach/dwell meters on the market that are every bit as good for the average mechanic as a $100.00 professional model. The key to these purchases is to make them with an eye towards adaptability and wide range. Using the tach/dwell meter example again, if the model you buy runs up to at least 1,500 rpm on the tachometer scale, the dwell meter works on 4, 6, or 8 cylinder engines, and the tachometer unit is adaptable to both conventional and electronic ignitions, it will serve for a long time on a variety of automobiles. A basic list of tune-up tools could include:

1. A tach/dwell meter;
2. Spark plug gauge and gapping tool;
3. Feeler blades;
4. Timing light.

In this list, the choice of a timing light should be made carefully. A light which works on the DC current supplied by the car battery is the best choice; it should have a xenon tube for brightness. If your car has electronic ignition, the light should have an inductive pick-up (the timing light illustrated has one of these), and since nearly all cars will have electronic ignition in the future, this feature is a reasonable one to look for.

In addition to these basic tools, there are several other tools and gauges you may find useful. These include:

1. A compression gauge. The screw-in type is slower to use, but eliminates the possibility of a faulty reading due to escaping pressure.
2. A manifold vacuum gauge.
3. A test light.
4. An induction meter. This is used to determine whether or not there is current flowing in a wire, and thus is extremely helpful in electrical troubleshooting.

Finally, you will probably find a torque wrench necessary for all but the most basic of work. The beam type models are perfectly adequate, although the newer click (breakaway) type are more precise. Whichever type you choose, plan on having it recalibrated every once in a while.

SPECIAL TOOLS

Several procedures in this manual refer to special tools needed to make repairs or adjustments. These tools can be purchased from the following companies:

AMC, GM	Special Tool Division Kent-Moore Corp. 1501 South Jackson St. Jackson, MI 49203
Ford	Owatonna Tool Co. Owatonna, MN 55060
Chrysler	Miller Special Tools A Division of Utica Tool Co. 32615 Park Lane Garden City, MI 48135

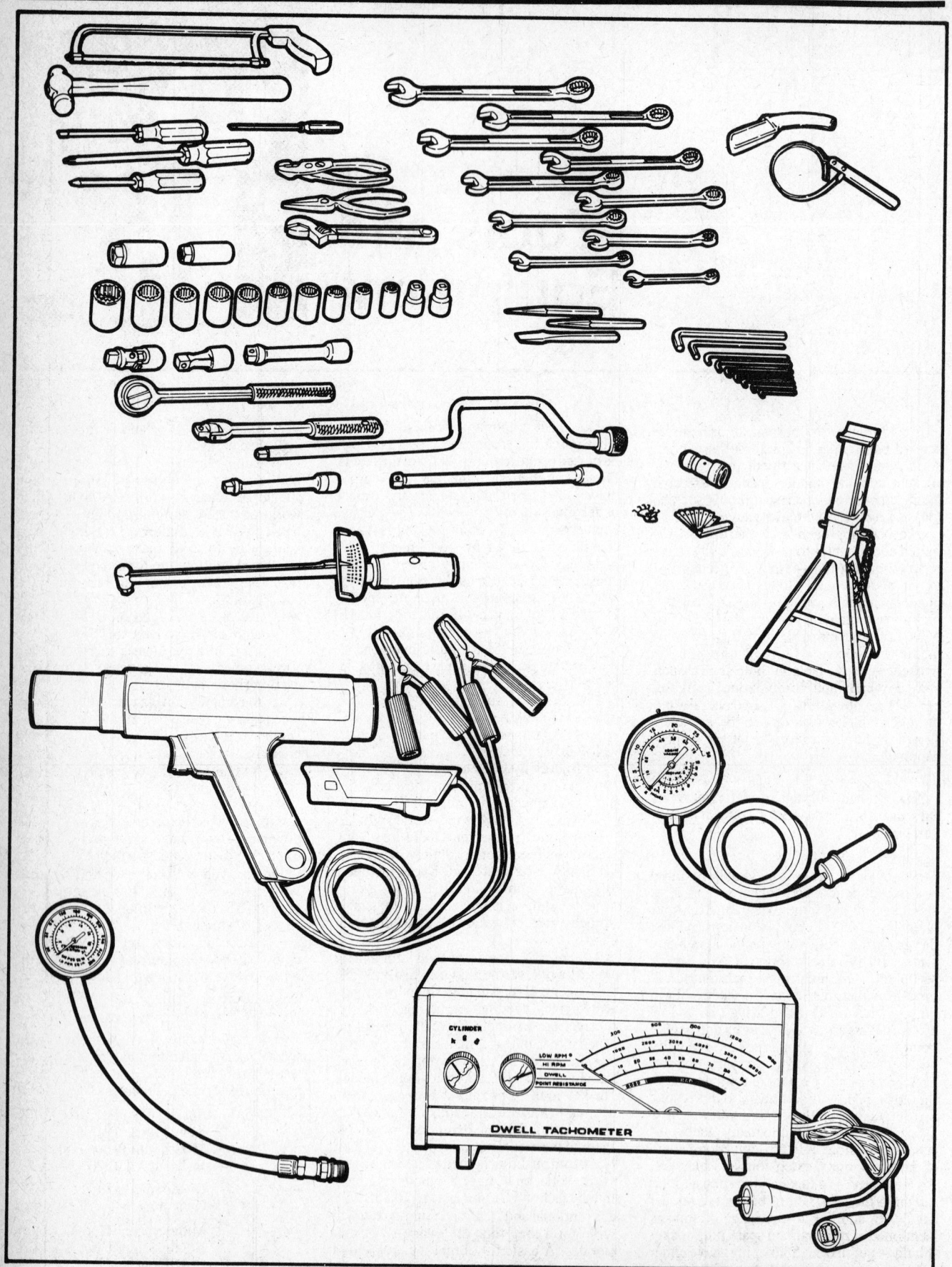

A basic tool collection will handle almost any automotive repair work

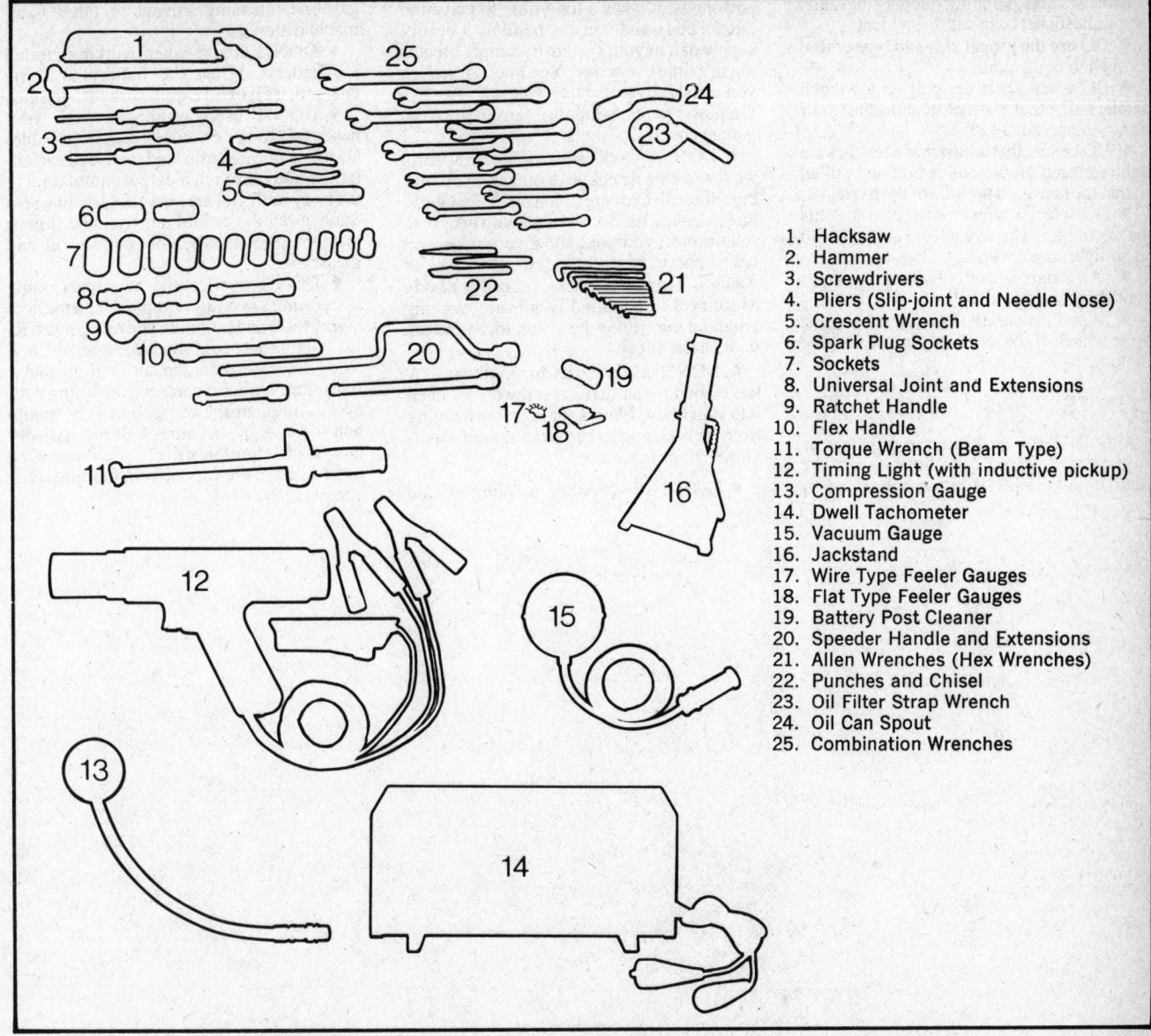

1. Hacksaw
2. Hammer
3. Screwdrivers
4. Pliers (Slip-joint and Needle Nose)
5. Crescent Wrench
6. Spark Plug Sockets
7. Sockets
8. Universal Joint and Extensions
9. Ratchet Handle
10. Flex Handle
11. Torque Wrench (Beam Type)
12. Timing Light (with inductive pickup)
13. Compression Gauge
14. Dwell Tachometer
15. Vacuum Gauge
16. Jackstand
17. Wire Type Feeler Gauges
18. Flat Type Feeler Gauges
19. Battery Post Cleaner
20. Speeder Handle and Extensions
21. Allen Wrenches (Hex Wrenches)
22. Punches and Chisel
23. Oil Filter Strap Wrench
24. Oil Can Spout
25. Combination Wrenches

SERVICING YOUR CAR SAFELY

It is virtually impossible to anticipate all of the hazards involved with automotive maintenance and service, but care and common sense will prevent most accidents.

The rules of safety for mechanics range from ''don't smoke around gasoline,'' to ''use the proper tool for the job.'' The trick to avoiding injuries is to develop safe work habits and take every possible precaution.

DO'S

● DO keep a fire extinguisher and first aid kit within easy reach.

● DO wear safety glasses or goggles when cutting, drilling, grinding or prying, even if you have 20-20 vision. If you wear glasses for the sake of vision, they should be made of hardened glass that can serve also as safety glasses, or wear safety goggles over your regular glasses.

● DO shield your eyes whenever you work around the battery. Batteries contain sulphuric acid. In case of contact with the eyes or skin, flush the area with water or a mixture of water and baking soda and get medical attention immediately.

● DO use safety stands for any undercar service. Jacks are for raising vehicles; safety stands are for making sure the vehicle stays raised until you want it to come down. Whenever the car is raised, block the wheels remaining on the ground and set the parking brake.

● DO use adequate ventilation when working with any chemicals or hazardous materials. Follow the manufacturer's directions for usage. Brake fluid, anti-freeze, sol-

vents, paints, etc. are all deadly poisons if taken internally. Seal the containers tightly after use and store them safely, out of the reach of children.

● DO use caution when working on clutches or brakes. The asbestos used in the friction material will cause lung cancer if inhaled. Wipe the component with a damp rag to remove dust, and dispose of the rag after use.

● DO disconnect the negative battery cable when working on the electrical system. The secondary ignition system can contain up to 40,000 volts.

● DO properly maintain your tools. Loose hammberheads, mushroomed punches and chisels, frayed or poorly grounded electrical cords, excessively worn screwdrivers, spread open-end wrenches, cracked sockets, slipping ratchets, or faulty droplight sockets can cause accidents.

- DO use the proper size and type of tool for the job being done.
- DO when possible, pull on a wrench handle rather than push on it, and adjust your stance to prevent a fall.
- DO be sure that adjustable wrenches are tightly closed on the nut or bolt and pulled so that the face is on the side of the fixed jaw.
- DO select a wrench or socket that fits the nut or bolt. The wrench or socket should sit straight, not cocked.
- DO strike squarely with a hammer; avoid glancing blows.
- DO set the parking brake and block the drive wheels if the work requires the engine running.

DON'TS

- DON'T run an engine in a garage or anywhere else without proper ventilation—EVER! Carbon monoxide is poisonous; it takes a long time to leave the human body and you can build up a deadly supply of it in your system by simply breathing in a little every day. You may not realize you are slowly poisoning yourself. Always use power vents, windows, fans or open the garage doors.
- DON'T work around moving parts while wearing a necktie or other loose clothing. Short sleeves are much safer than long, loose sleeves; hard-toed shoes with neoprene soles protect your toes and give a better grip on slippery surfaces. Jewelry such as watches, fancy belt buckles, beads or body adornment of any kind is not safe working around a car. Long hair should be hidden under a hat or cap.
- DON'T use pockets for toolboxes. A fall or bump can drive a screwdriver deep into your body. Even a wiping cloth hanging from the back pocket can wrap around a spinning shaft or fan.
- DON'T smoke when working around gasoline, cleaning solvent or other flammable material.
- DON'T smoke when working around the battery. When the battery is being charged, it gives off explosive hydrogen gas.
- DON'T use gasoline to wash your hands; there are excellent soaps available. Gasoline may contain lead, and lead can enter the body through a cut, accumulating in the body until you are very ill. Gasoline also removes all the natural oils from the skin so that bone dry hands will suck up oil and grease.
- DON'T service the air conditioning system unless you are equipped with the necessary tools and training. The refrigerant, R-12, is extremely cold when compressed, and when released into the air will instantly freeze any surface it contacts, including your eyes. Although the refrigerant is normally non-toxic, R-12 becomes a deadly poisonous gas in the presence of an open flame. One good whiff of the vapors from burning refrigerant can be fatal.

Air Conditioning

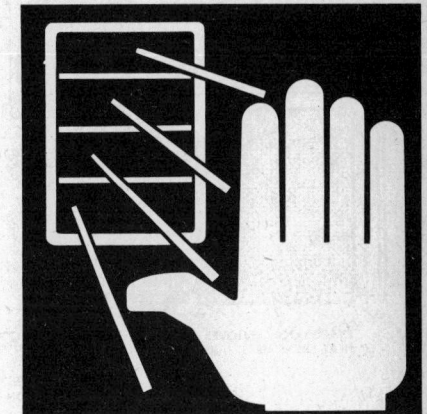

AIR CONDITIONING SYSTEMS

Automotive air conditioning systems are basic in design and operation, but many different components are used by the vehicle manufacturers to operate and control the systems to their specifications.

Basic System

The basic air conditioning system utilizes the compressor, condenser, evaporator, receiver-drier, expansion valve and a thermostatic or ambient type switch to control evaporator freeze-up. The controls are manually operated and the unit is basic in design. This system is usually installed as an add-on or after-market unit. A sight glass may be used in the system.

P.O.A. System

The P.O.A. (pilot operated absolute) suction throttling valve system contains the compressor, condenser, evaporator, receiver-drier, expansion valve and a suction throttling valve. The suction throttling valve is used to keep the refrigerant gas in the evaporator at a pressure which will not allow the temperature of the evaporator core surface to go below 32 degrees F., thus preventing evaporator freeze-up. For the system to operate effectively, an equalizer line is connected between the suction side of the suction throttling valve and the expansion valve diaphragm. This modifies the operation of the expansion valve which now is controlled by the evaporator outlet temperature and compression suction pressure.

When a crank type compressor is used with the P.O.A. system, an accumulator is placed between the evaporator and the compressor. The accumulator operates as its name implies, accumulating any liquid refrigerant that may have passed from the evaporator and to prevent its moving to the compressor as a liquid, which may, in its form, cause internal compressor damage. A sight glass is normally used in this system.

V.I.R. System

The V.I.R. system contains the compressor, evaporator, condenser, muffler and a unit containing the P.O.A. valve, expansion valve and the receiver-drier. This unit is called the V.I.R. (valves in receiver) assembly. A muffler is normally used with this system and is located between the com-

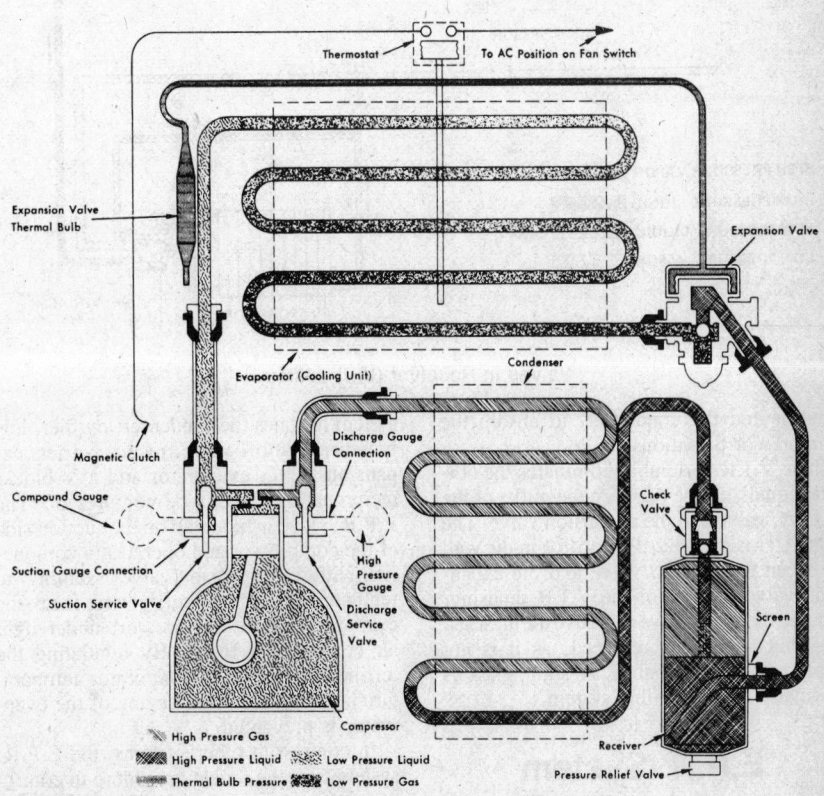

Basic air conditioning system

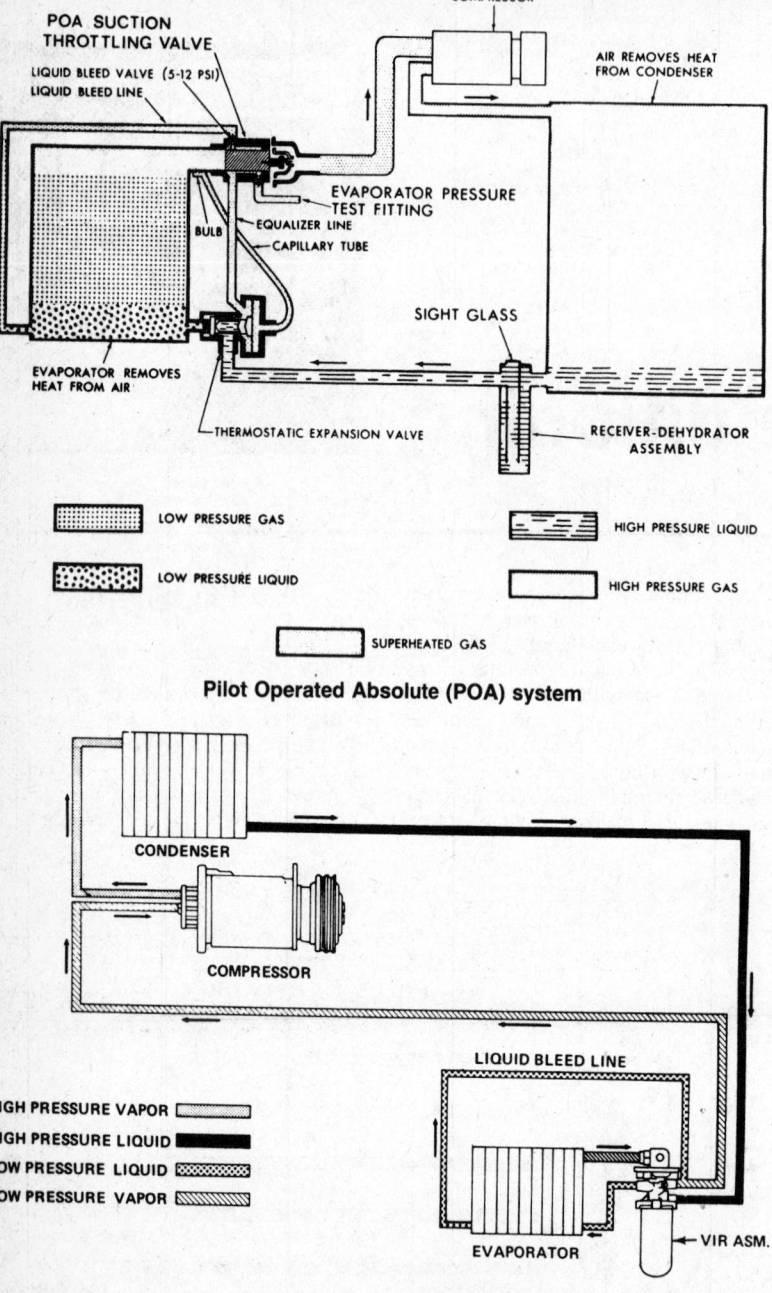

Pilot Operated Absolute (POA) system

POA SUCTION THROTTLING VALVE

LIQUID BLEED VALVE (5-12 PSI)
LIQUID BLEED LINE

COMPRESSOR

AIR REMOVES HEAT FROM CONDENSER

EVAPORATOR PRESSURE TEST FITTING

EQUALIZER LINE

CAPILLARY TUBE

BULB

SIGHT GLASS

EVAPORATOR REMOVES HEAT FROM AIR

THERMOSTATIC EXPANSION VALVE

RECEIVER-DEHYDRATOR ASSEMBLY

LOW PRESSURE GAS

LOW PRESSURE LIQUID

HIGH PRESSURE LIQUID

HIGH PRESSURE GAS

SUPERHEATED GAS

Valves In Receiver (VIR) system

CONDENSER

COMPRESSOR

LIQUID BLEED LINE

HIGH PRESSURE VAPOR
HIGH PRESSURE LIQUID
LOW PRESSURE LIQUID
LOW PRESSURE VAPOR

EVAPORATOR

VIR ASM.

pressor and the condenser, to absorb the compressor pulsations.

The V.I.R. assembly eliminates the outside equalizer line between the outlet of the P.O.A. valve and the expansion valve. The equalizer is now a drilled orifice in the wall between the P.O.A. valve and the expansion valve cavities of the V.I.R. housing. Should the valve prove defective during tests, the unit should be replaced, as it is not repairable or adjustable. A sight glass is normally used with this system.

E.P.R. System

The E.P.R. (evaporator pressure regulator)

system includes the condenser, muffler, low pressure shut off valve, receiver-drier, expansion valve, evaporator and a V-block, reciprocating crank type compressor. The E.P.R. valve is mounted on the suction side of the compressor and operates in conjunction with the expansion valve assembly, to regulate the flow of refrigerant from the evaporator to the compressor, under light air conditioning loads. By regulating the refrigerant flow, the evaporator temperature is controlled and freezing of the evaporator is prevented.

In contrast to other systems, the E.P.R. system uses the reheat procedure to control the temperature of the air, after it is cooled by passing through the evaporator fins. A

manually controlled operating lever is connected to the heater water flow control valve and to a blend air door and the opening of the blend air door proportions the amount of air around and through the heater core to control the mix of the cool and hot air for the desired inside temperature. A sight glass is used with this system.

Two types of expansion valves are used with this system. The first type has a capillary tube, mounted in a well on the suction line. The second type has no capillary tube, but senses the need to meter refrigerant into the evaporator by an internal sensing tube. This type of expansion valve is called the "H" type.

"H" Valve System

As was described in the E.P.R. system, the "H" expansion valve can be used with the E.P.R. valve, located in the V-block, reciprocating crank type compressor, to control the amount of refrigerant metered into the evaporator and to control the temperature of the evaporator coils to prevent freeze-up of the condensed moisture. However, when the "H" valve is used with the three piston, axial compressor, a cycling switch is used to control the temperature of the evaporator to prevent freeze-up, rather than the E.P.R. valve, as used with the reciprocating crank type compressor. This can be called the "H" valve system for explanation purposes only and should be recognized as such. The "H" system uses the same components as the other systems, basically the compressor (axial type), condenser, evaporator, expansion valve without a capillary tub ("H" type), receiver-drier, muffler and a low pressure shut off valve. The cycling clutch switch uses a capillary tube, attached to the surface of the suction line, to sense the need for refrigerant movement and compressor operation, therefore, causing the electrical clutch pulley and coil to operate the compressor on demand from the cycling switch and to open the circuit to the coil when the demand is not needed. A sight glass is used with this system.

CCOT System

The CCOT (cycling clutch orifice tube) system includes the compressor, condenser, evaporator, an accumulator-drier, a clutch cycling switch with a capillary tube, and a fixed orifice tube, mounted to the evaporator, replacing the expansion valve.

The clutch cycling switch with a temperature probing capillary tube, cycles the compressor clutch off and on as required to maintain a selected comfortable temperature within the vehicle, while preventing evaporator freeze-up. Full control of the system is maintained through the use of a selector control, mounted in the dash assembly. The selector control makes use of

Evaporator pressure can only be measured on this system and a special type connector must be used to attach the high pressure gauge line to the service gauge port.

When either of the external type expansion valves are used, separate suction throttling valves are used. The operation of each is basically the same as the components of the combination valve assembly.

The type of external expansion valve used with the system will dictate either low suction or evaporator pressure measurements from the gauge service ports. To determine the pressure measurement that may be obtained from the system, examine the external expansion valve for one of the following conditions:

a. Should the expansion valve have one capillary tube and one equalizer line, it is of the conventional externally equalizer type and low pressure suction would be measured at the service port, normally located on the suction line. A second gauge port may be located on the POA valve body and an evaporator pressure reading can be obtained from this port.

b. If the expansion valve has only one capillary tube, it is the by-pass orifice (BPO) type and only evaporator pressure will be measured at the service port valve, located on the STV assembly.

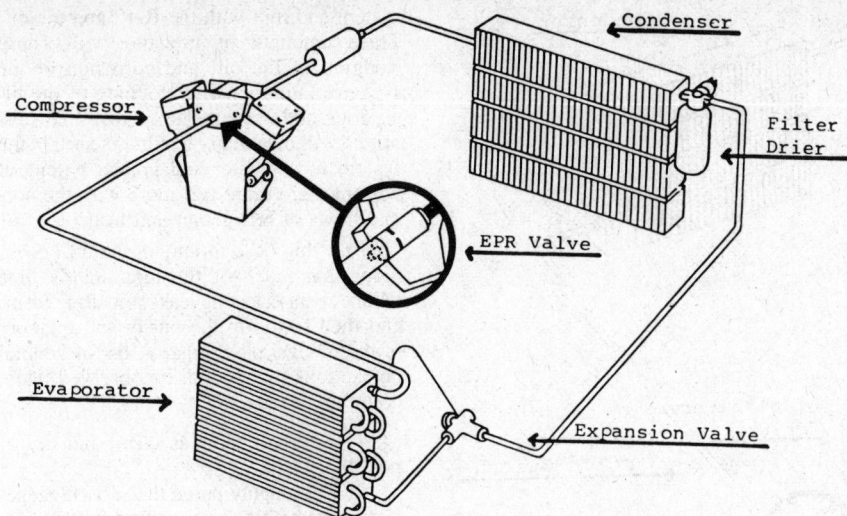

Evaporator Pressure Regulator (EPR) system

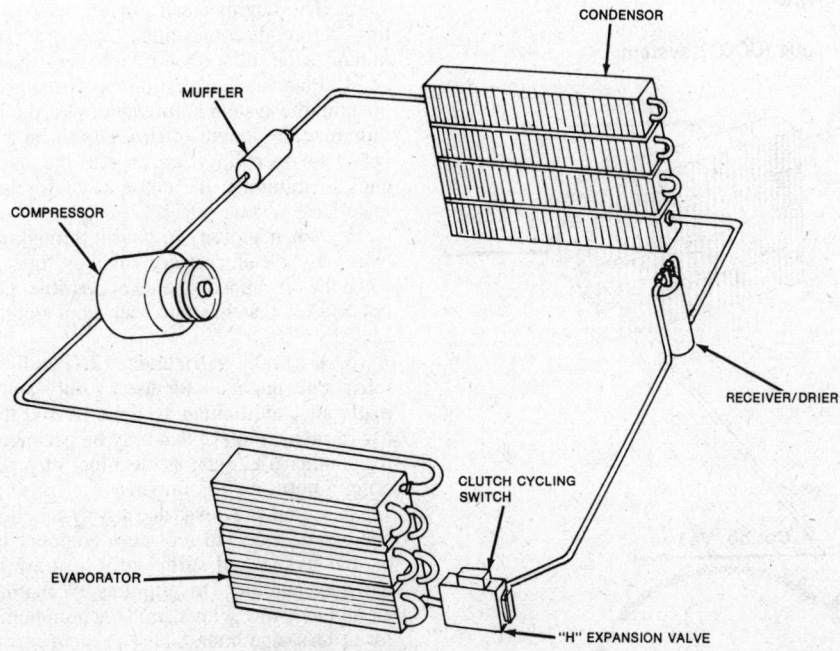

H type expansion valve system

a vacuum supply and electrical switches to operate mode doors and the blower motor. A sight glass is not used in this system and one should not be installed. When charging the system, the correct quantity of refrigerant must be installed by measurement.

STV/BPO System

The STV/BPO (suction throttling valve/by-pass orifice) system uses either two types of external expansion valves or a mini-combination valve assembly. The mini-combination valve assembly contains an expansion valve, suction throttling valve and a service port. The expansion valve is of the "H" block design and is used to regulate the flow of refrigerant into the evap-

orator core. It is also the dividing point for the high and low pressure within the system. The suction throttling valve is used to control the evaporator pressure and to prevent coil freeze-up. The suction throttling starts when the compressor suction pressure decreases below the valve setting. The compressor suction pressure can continue to drop, but the evaporator pressure is held steady by the controlling or throttling action of the STV. A pressure differential valve is used within the combination valve assembly, to allow oil laden refrigerant to by-pass the restriction formed when the STV assembly is closed, to assure oil return to the compressor during times of reduced heat loads on the system. The by-pass valve remains closed under high heat loads since ample oil is moving through the system and compressor.

GENERAL SERVICING PROCEDURES

The most important aspect of air conditioning service is the maintenance of a pure and adequate charge of refrigerant in the system. A refrigeration system cannot function properly if a significant percentage of the charge is lost. Leaks are common because the severe vibration encountered in an automobile can easily cause a sufficient cracking or loosening of the air conditioning fittings; as a result, the extreme operating pressures of the system force refrigerant out.

The problem can be understood by considering what happens to the system as it is operated with a continuous leak. Because the expansion valve regulates the flow of refrigerant to the evaporator, the level of refrigerant there is fairly constant. The receiver-drier stores any excess of refrigerant, and so a loss will first appear there as a reduction in the level of liquid. As this level nears the bottom of the vessel, some refrigerant vapor bubbles will begin to appear in the stream of liquid supplied to the expansion valve. This vapor decreases the capacity of the expansion valve very little as the valve opens to compensate for its presence. As the quantity of liquid in the

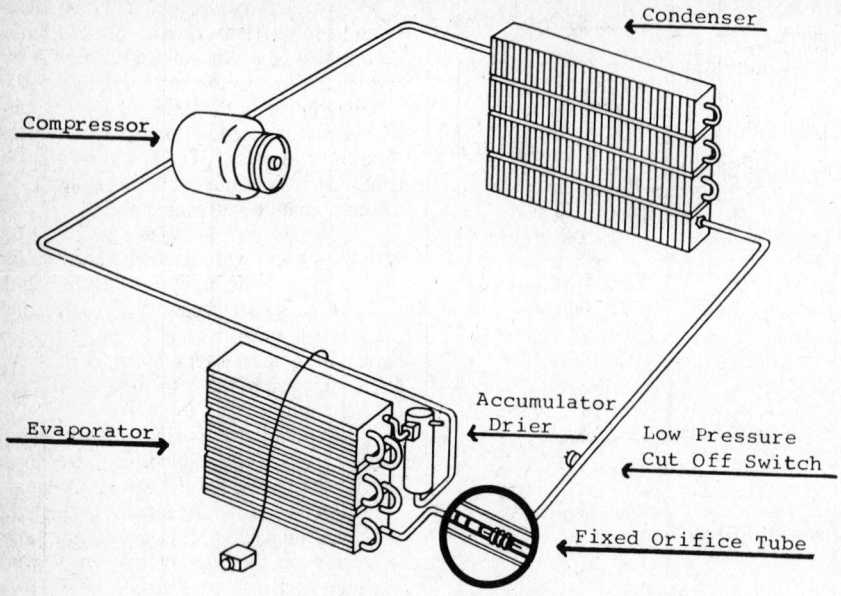

Cycling Clutch Orifice Tube (CCOT) system

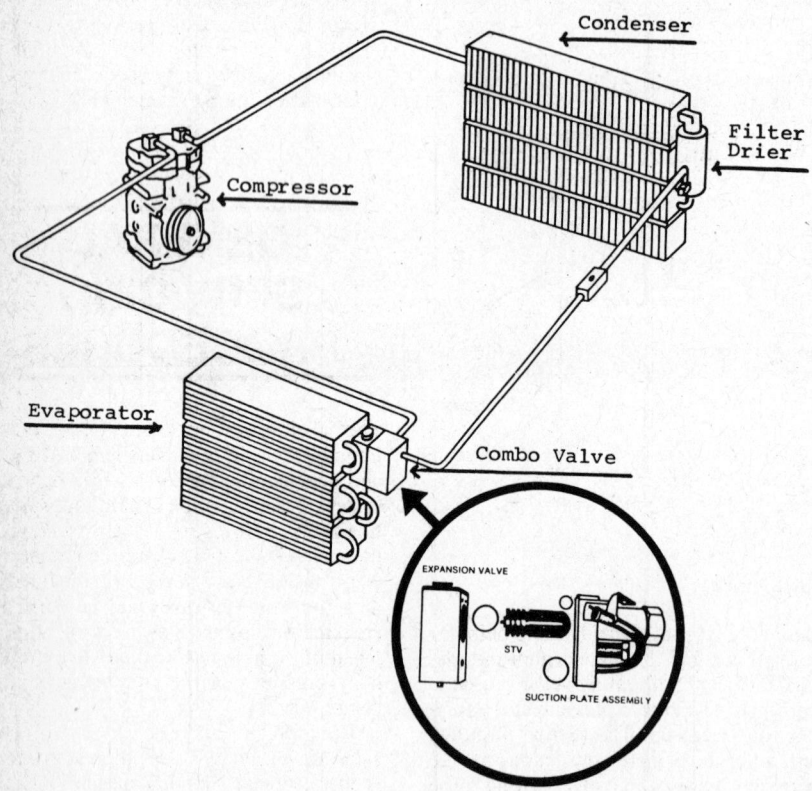

Suction Throttling Valve/By-Pass Orifice (STV/BPO) system

system and mix with the R-12 and the oil. Trace amounts of moisture will cause sludging of the oil, and corrosion of the system. Saturation and clogging of the filter-drier, and freezing of the expansion valve orifice will eventually result. As air fills the system to a greater and greater extent, it will interfere more and more with the normal flows of refrigerant and heat.

From this description, it should be obvious that much of the repairman's time will be spent detecting leaks, repairing them, and then restoring the purity and quantity of the refrigerant charge. A list of general precautions that should be observed while doing this follows:

1. Keep all tools as clean and dry as possible.

2. Thoroughly purge the service gauges and hoses of air and moisture before connecting them to the system. Keep them capped when not in use.

3. Thoroughly clean any refrigerant fitting before disconnecting it, in order to minimize the entrance of dirt into the system.

4. Plan any operation that requires opening the system beforehand, in order to minimize the length of time it will be exposed to open air. Cap or seal the open ends to minimize the entrance of foreign material.

5. When adding oil, pour it through an extremely clean and dry tube or funnel. Keep the oil capped whenever possible. Do not use oil that has not been kept tightly sealed.

6. Use only refrigerant 12. Purchase refrigerant intended for use in only automatic air conditioning systems. Avoid the use of refrigerant-12 that may be packaged for another use, such as cleaning, or powering a horn, as it is impure.

7. Completely evacuate any system that has been opened to replace a component, or that has leaked sufficiently to draw in moisture and air. This requires evacuating air and moisture with a good vacuum pump for at least one hour.

If a system has been open for a considerable length of time it may be advisable to evacuate the system for up to 12 hours (overnight).

8. Use a wrench on both halves of a fitting that is to be disconnected, so as to avoid placing torque on any of the refrigerant lines.

9. When overhauling a compressor, pour some of the oil into a clean glass and inspect it. If there is evidence of dirt or metal particles, or both, flush all refrigerant components with clean refrigerant before evacuating and recharging the system. In addition, if metal particles are present, the compressor should be replaced.

10. Schrader valves may leak only when under full operating pressure. Therefore, if leakage is suspected but cannot be located, operate the system with a full charge of refrigerant and look for leaks from all Schrader valves. Replace any faulty valves.

condenser decreases, the operating pressure will drop there and throughout the high side of the system. As the R-12 continues to be expelled, the pressure available to force the liquid through the expansion valve will continue to decrease, and, eventually, the valve's orifice will prove to be too much of a restriction for adequate flow even with the needle fully withdrawn.

At this point, low side pressure will start to drop, and severe reduction in cooling capacity, marked by freeze-up of the evaporator coil, will result. Eventually, the operating pressure of the evaporator will be lower than the pressure of the atmosphere surrounding it, and air will be drawn into the system wherever there are leaks in the low side.

Because all atmospheric air contains at least some moisture, water will enter the

Additional Preventive Maintenance Checks

ANTIFREEZE

In order to prevent heater core freeze-up during A/C operation, it is necessary to maintain permanent type antifreeze protection of + 15 degrees F. or lower. A reading of − 15 degrees F. is ideal since this protection also supplies sufficient corrosion inhibitors for the protection of the engine cooling system.

NOTE: The same antifreeze should not be used longer than the manufacturer specifies.

RADIATOR CAP

For efficient operation of an air conditioned car's cooling system, the radiator cap should have a holding pressure which meets manufacturer's specifications. A cap which fails to hold these pressures should be replaced.

CONDENSER

Any obstruction of or damage to the condenser configuration will restrict the air flow which is essential to its efficient operation. It is therefore a good rule to keep this unit clean and in proper physical shape.

NOTE: Bug screens are regarded as obstructions.

CONDENSATION DRAIN TUBE

This single molded drain tube expels the condensation, which accumulates on the bottom of the evaporator housing, into the engine compartment.

If this tube is obstructed, the air conditioning performance can be restricted and condensation buildup can spill over onto the vehicle's floor.

Safety Precautions

Because of the importance of the necessary safety precautions that must be exercised when working with air conditioning sytems and R-12 refrigerant, a recap of the safety precautions are outlined.

1. Avoid contact with a charged refrigeration system, even when working on another part of the air conditioning system or vehicle. If a heavy tool comes into contact with a section of copper tubing or a heat exchanger, it can easily cause the relatively soft material to rupture.

2. When it is necessary to apply force to a fitting which contains refrigerant, as when checking that all system couplings are securely tightened, use a wrench on both parts of the fitting involved, if possible.

This will avoid putting torque on refrigerant tubing.

(It is advisable, when possible, to use tube or line wrenches when tightening these flare nut fittings.)

3. Do not attempt to discharge the system by merely loosening a fitting, or removing the service valve caps and cracking these valves. Precise control is possible only when using the service gauges. Place a rag under the open end of the center charging hose while discharging the system to catch any drops of liquid that might escape. Wear protective gloves when connecting or disconnecting service gauge hoses.

4. Discharge the system only in a well ventilated area, as high concentrations of the gas can exclude oxygen and act as an anaesthetic. When leak testing or soldering, this is particularly important, as toxic gas is formed when R-12 contacts any flame.

5. Never start a system without first verifying that both service valves are backseated, if equipped, and that all fittings throughout the system are snugly connected.

6. Avoid applying heat to any refrigerant line or storage vessel. Charging may be aided by using water heated to less than 125° to warm the refrigerant container. Never allow a refrigerant storage container to sit out in the sun, or near any other source of heat, such as a radiator.

7. Always wear goggles when working on a system to protect the eyes. If refrigerant contacts the eyes, it is advisable in all cases to see a physician as soon as possible.

8. Frostbite from liquid refrigerant should be treated by first gradually warming the area with cool water, and then gently applying petroleum jelly. A physician should be consulted.

9. Always keep refrigerant drum fittings capped when not in use. Avoid sudden shock to the drum, which might occur from dropping it, or from banging a heavy tool against it. Never carry a drum in the passenger compartment of a car.

10. Always completely discharge the system before painting the vehicle (if the paint is to be baked on), or before welding anywhere near refrigerant lines.

AIR CONDITIONING TOOLS AND GAUGES

Test Gauges

Most of the service work performed in air conditioning requires the use of a set of two gauges, one for the high (head) pressure side of the system, the other for the low (suction) side.

The low side gauge records both pressure and vacuum. Vacuum readings are calibrated from 0 to 30 inches and the pressure graduations read from 0 to no less than 60 psi.

The high side gauge measures pressure from 0 to at least 600 psi.

Both gauges are threaded into a manifold that contains two hand shut-off valves. Proper manipulation of these valves and the use of the attached test hoses allow the user to perform the following services:

1. Test high and low side pressures.
2. Remove air, moisture, and contaminated refrigerant.
3. Purge the system (of refrigerant).
4. Charge the system (with refrigerant).

NOTE: Chrysler Corp. requires the use of a third gauge on those units that have an evaporator pressure regulator (EPR) valve mounted on the suction side of the compressor.

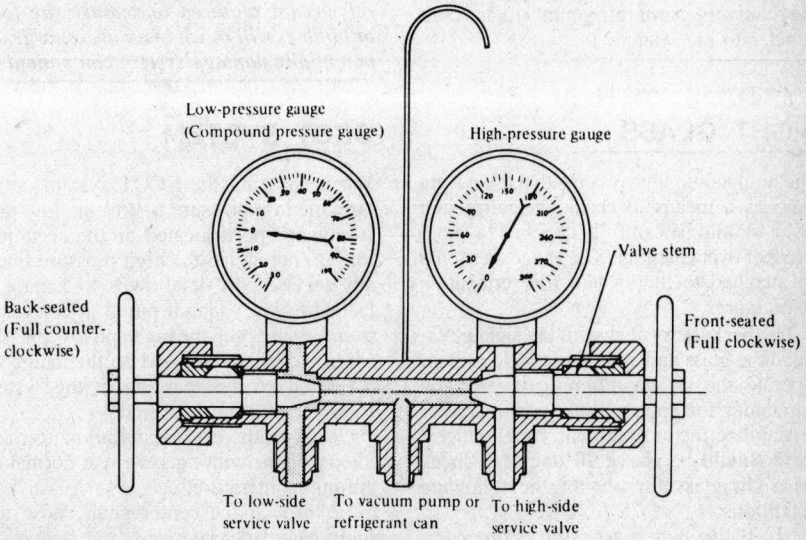

Typical manifold gauge set

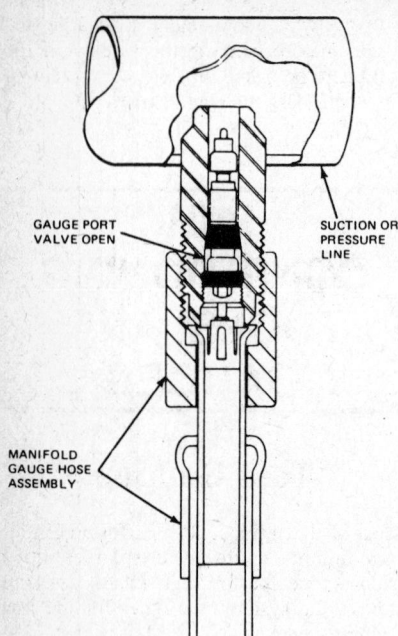

Manifold gauge hose connected to a Schraeder type service port

The manifold valves are designed so they have no direct effect on gauge readings, but serve only to provide for, or cut off, flow of refrigerant through the manifold. During all testing and hook-up operations, the valves are kept in a closed position to avoid disturbing the refrigeration system. The valves are opened only to purge the system of refrigerant or to charge it.

When purging the system, the center hose is uncapped at the lower end, and both valves are cracked open slightly. This allows refrigerant pressure to force the entire contents of the system out through the center hose. During charging, the valve on the high side of the manifold is closed, and the valve on the low side is cracked open. Under these conditions, the low pressure in the evaporator will draw refrigerant from the relatively warm refrigerant storage container into the system.

SYSTEMS WITH A SIGHT GLASS

The air conditioning systems that use a sight glass as a means to check the refrigerant level, should be carefully checked to avoid under or over charging. The gauge set should be attached to the system for verification of pressures.

To check the system with the sight glass, clean the glass and start the vehicle engine. Operate the air conditioning controls on maximum for approximately five minutes to stabilize the system. The room temperature should be above 70 degrees. Check the sight glass for one of the following conditions:

1. If the sight glass is clear, the compressor clutch is engaged, the compressor discharge line is warm and the compressor inlet line is cool, the system has a full charge of refrigerant.

2. If the sight glass is clear, the compressor clutch is engaged and there is no significant temperature difference between the compressor inlet and discharge lines, the system is empty or nearly empty. By having the gauge set attached to the system, a measurement can be taken. If the gauge reads less than 25 psi, the low pressure cut-off protection switch has failed.

3. If the sight glass is clear and the compressor clutch is disengaged, the clutch is defective, or the clutch circuit is open, or the system is out of refrigerant. By-pass the low pressure cut-off switch momentarily to determine the cause.

4. If the sight glass shows foam or bubbles, the system can be low on refrigerant. Occasional foam or bubbles is normal when the air temperature is above 110 degrees or below 70 degrees. To verify, increase the engine speed to approximately 1500 rpm and block the airflow through the condenser to increase the compressor discharge pressure to between 225 to 250 psi. If the sight glass still shows bubbles or foam, the refrigerant level is low.

CAUTION

Do not operate the vehicle engine any longer than necessary with the condenser airflow blocked. This blocking action also blocks the cooling system radiator and will cause the system to overheat rapidly.

When the system is low on refrigerant, a leak is present or the system was not properly charged. Use a leak detector and locate the problem area and repair. If no leakage is found, charge the system to its capacity. (Refer to the refrigerant capacity chart at the end of this section).

CAUTION

It is not advisable to add refrigerant to a system utilizing the suction throttling valve and a sight glass, because the amount of refrigerant required to remove the foam or bubbles will result in an overcharge and potentially damage system components.

CCOT SYSTEM

When charging the CCOT system, attach only the low pressure line to the low pressure gauge port, located on the accumulator. Do not attach the high pressure line to any service port or allow it to remain attached to the vacuum pump after evacuation. Be sure both the high and low pressure control valves are closed on the gauge set. To complete the charging of the system, follow the outline supplied.

1. Start the engine and allow to run at idle, with the cooling system at normal operating temperature.

2. Attach the center gauge hose to a multi-can dispenser.

3. Allow one pound or the contents of one or two 14 oz. cans to enter the system through the low pressure side by opening the gauge low pressure control valve.

4. Close the low pressure gauge control valve and turn the A/C system on to engage the compressor. Place the blower motor in its high mode.

5. Open the low pressure gauge control valve and draw the remaining charge into the system. Refer to the capacity chart at the end of this section for the individual vehicle or system capacity.

6. Close the low pressure gauge control valve and the refrigerant source valve on the multi-can dispenser. Remove the low pressure hose from the accumulator quickly to avoid loss of refrigerant through the Schrader valve.

7. Install the protective cap on the gauge port and check the system for leakage.

8. Test the system for proper operation.

Leak Testing the System

There are several methods of detecting leaks in an air conditioning system; among them, the two most popular are (1) halide leak-detection or the "open flame method," and (2) electronic leak-detection.

The halide leak detection is a torch like device which produces a yellow-green color when refrigerant is introduced into the flame at the burner. A brilliant blue or violet color indicates the presence of large amounts of refrigerant at the burner. A small leak will cause the flame to turn a yellow-green color.

An electronic leak detector is a small portable electronic device with an extended probe. With the unit activated the probe is passed along those components of the system which contain refrigerant. If a leak is detected, the unit will sound an alarm signal or activate a display signal depending on the manufacturer's design. It is advisable to follow the manufacturer's instructions as the design and function of the detection may vary significantly.

NOTE: Caution should be taken to operate either type of detector in well ventilated areas, so as to reduce the chance of personal injury, which may result from coming in contact with poisonous gases produced when R-12 is exposed to flame or electric spark.

Service Valves

For the user to diagnose an air conditioning system he or she must gain "entrance" to the system in order to observe the pressures. There are two types of terminals for this purpose, the hand shut off type and the familiar Schrader valve.

The Schrader valve is similar to a tire valve stem and the process of connecting the test hoses is the same as threading a

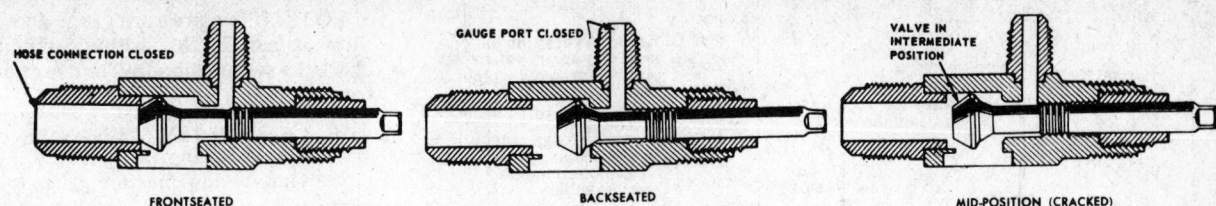

Manual service valve positions

hand pump outlet hose to a bicycle tire. As the test hose is threaded to the service port the valve core is depressed, allowing the refrigerant to enter the test hose outlet. Removal of the test hose automatically closes the system.

Extreme caution must be observed when removing test hoses from the Schrader valves as some refrigerant will normally escape, usually under high pressure. (Observe safety precautions.)

Some systems have hand shut-off valves (the stem can be rotated with a special ratcheting box wrench) that can be positioned in the following three ways:

1. FRONT SEATED—Rotated to full clockwise position.

a. Refrigerant will not flow to compressor, but will reach test gauge port. COMPRESSOR WILL BE DAMAGED IF SYSTEM IS TURNED ON IN THIS POSITION.

b. The compressor is now isolated and ready for service. However, care must be exercised when removing service valves from the compressor as a residue of refrigerant may still be present within the compressor. Therefore, remove service valves slowly observing all safety precautions.

2. BACK SEATED—Rotated to full counter clockwise position. Normal position for system while in operation. Refrigerant flows to compressor but not to test gauge.

3. MID-POSITION (CRACKED)—Refrigerant flows to entire system. Gauge port (with hose connected) open for testing.

USING THE MANIFOLD GAUGES

The following are step-by-step procedures to guide the user to correct gauge usage.

1. WEAR GOGGLES OR FACE SHIELD DURING ALL TESTING OPERATIONS. BACKSEAT HAND SHUT-OFF TYPE SERVICE VALVES.

2. Remove caps from high and low side service ports. Make sure both gauge valves are closed.

3. Connect low side test hose to service valve that leads to the evaporator (located between the evaporator outlet and the compressor).

4. Attach high side test hose to service valve that leads to the condenser.

5. Mid-position hand shutoff type service valves.

6. Start engine and allow for warm-up. All testing and charging of the system should be done after engine and system have reached normal operation temperatures (except when using certain charging stations).

7. Adjust air conditioner controls to maximum cold.

8. Observe gauge readings.

When the gauges are not being used it is a good idea to:

a. Keep both hand valves in the closed position.

b. Attach both ends of the high and low service hoses to the manifold, if extra outlets are present on the manifold, or plug them if not. Also, keep the center charging hose attached to an empty re-

frigerant can. This extra precaution will reduce the possibility of moisture entering the gauges. If air and moisture have gotten into the gauges, purge the hoses by supplying refrigerant under pressure to the center hose with both gauge valves open and all openings unplugged.

DISCHARGING, EVACUATING AND CHARGING

Discharging the System

——— CAUTION ———
Perform operation in a well-ventilated area.

When it is necessary to remove (purge) the refrigerant pressurized in the system, follow this procedure:

1. Operate air conditioner for at least 10 minutes.

2. Attach gauges, shut off engine and air conditioner.

3. Place a container or rag at the outlet of the center charging hose on the gauge. The refrigerant will be discharged there and this precaution will avoid its uncontrolled exposure.

4. Open low side hand valve on gauge slightly.

5. Open high side hand valve slightly.

NOTE: Too rapid a purging process will be identified by the appearance of an oily foam. If this occurs, close the hand valves a little more until this condition stops.

6. Close both hand valves on the gauge set when the pressures read 0 and all the refrigerant has left the system.

Evacuating the System

Before charging any system it is necessary to purge the refrigerant and draw out the trapped moisture with a suitable vacuum pump. Failure to do so will result in ineffective charging and possible damage to the system.

BAR GAUGE MANIFOLD AND COMPRESSOR SERVICE VALVE SETTINGS

Condition	Manifold Valves	Compressor Valves
Testing System	Both fully closed	Both cracked off backseat
Depressurizing System	Both cracked open	Both at mid position
Evacuating the system	Both wide open	Both at mid position
Charging in gas form with compressor running	High pressure valve closed	High pressure valve cracked off backseat
	Low pressure valve cracked	Low pressure valve at mid position
Charging in liquid form with compressor off	Low pressure valve closed	Both valves mid positioned
	High pressure valve wide open	

Note: A very small leak, causing system discharge about every two weeks, can be caused by a leaky Schrader type service valve. Check these valves with extra care when testing for a small leak.

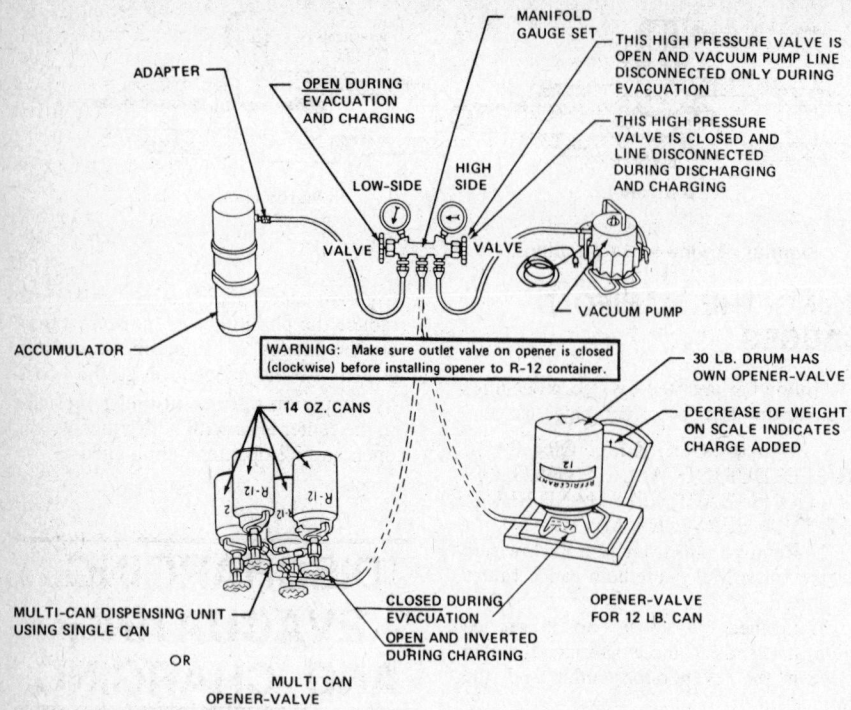

Typical gauge connections for discharge, evacuation and charging the system

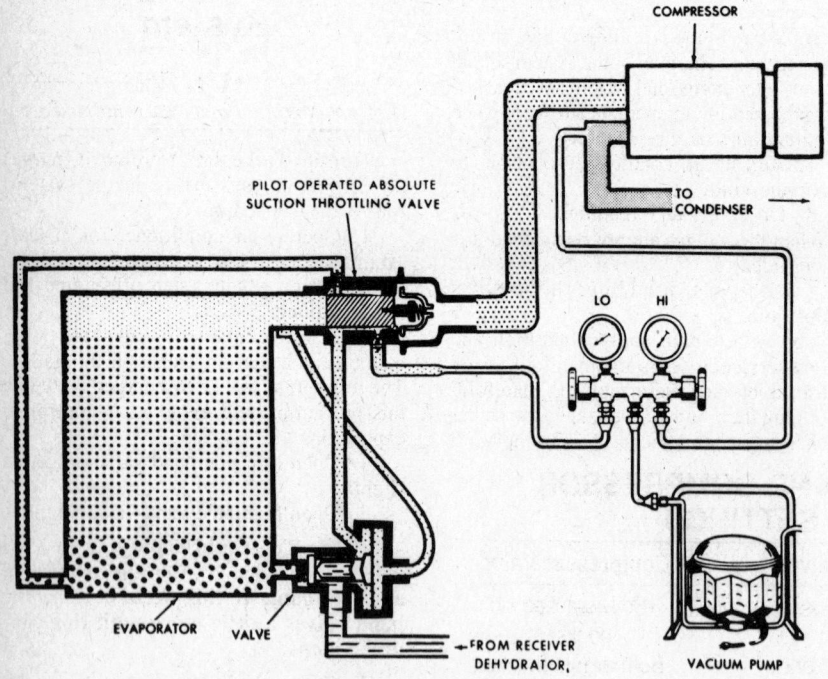

Schematic for evacuating the system

Use this hook-up for the proper evacuation procedure:

1. Connect both service gauge hoses to the high and low service outlets.

2. Open high and low side hand valves on gauge manifold.

3. Open both service valves a slight amount (from back seated position), allow refrigerant to discharge from system.

4. Install center charging hose of gauge set to vacuum pump.

5. Operate vacuum pump for at least one hour. (If the system has been subjected to open conditions for a prolonged period of time it may be necessary to "pump the system down" overnight. Refer to "System Sweep" procedure.)

NOTE: If low pressure gauge does not show at least 28″ hg. within 5 minutes, check the system for a leak or loose gauge connectors.

6. Close hand valves on gauge manifold.

7. Shut off pump.

8. Observe low pressure gauge to determine if vacuum is holding. A vacuum drop may indicate a leak.

System Sweep

An efficient vacuum pump can remove all the air contained in a contaminated air conditioning system very quickly, because of its vapor state. Moisture, however, is far more difficult to remove because the vacuum must force the liquid to evaporate before it will be able to remove it from the system. If a system has become severely contaminated, as, for example, it might become after all the charge was lost in conjunction with vehicle accident damage, moisture removal is extremely time consuming. A vacuum pump could remove all of the moisture only if it were operated for 12 hours or more.

Under these conditions, sweeping the system with refrigerant will speed the process of moisture removal considerably. To sweep, follow the following procedure:

1. Connect vacuum pump to gauges, operate it until vacuum ceases to increase, then continue operation for ten more minutes.

2. Charge system with 50% of its rated refrigerant capacity.

3. Operate system at fast idle for ten minutes.

4. Discharge the system.

5. Repeat twice the process of charging to 50% capacity, running the system for ten minutes, and discharging it, for a total of three sweeps.

6. Replace drier.

7. Pump system down as in step 1.

8. Charge system.

Charging the System

——————— CAUTION ———————

Never attempt to charge the system by opening the high pressure gauge control while the compressor is operating. The compressor accumulating pressure can burst the refrigerant container, causing severe personal injuries.

BASIC SYSTEM

In this procedure the refrigerant enters the suction side of the system as a vapor while the compressor is running. Before proceeding, the system should be in a partial vacuum after adequate evacuation. Both hand valves on the gauge manifold should be closed.

1. Attach both test hoses to their respective service valve ports. Mid-position manually operated service valves, if present.

2. Install dispensing valve (closed position) on the refrigerant container. (Single and multiple refrigerant manifolds are available to accommodate one to four 15 oz. cans.)

3. Attach center charging hose to the refrigerant container valve.

4. Open dispensing valve on the refrigerant can.

5. Loosen the center charging hose coupler where it connects to the gauge manifold to allow the escaping refrigerant to purge the hose of contaminants.

6. Tighten center charging hose connection.

7. Purge the low pressure test hose at the gauge manifold.

8. Start car engine, roll down the car windows and adjust the air conditioner to maximum cooling. The car engine should be at normal operating temperature before proceeding. The heated environment helps the liquid vaporize more efficiently.

9. Crack open the low side hand valve on the manifold. Manipulate the valve so that the refrigerant that enters the system does not cause the low side pressure to exceed 40 psi. Too sudden a surge may permit the entrance of unwanted liquid to the compressor. Since liquids cannot be compressed, the compressor will suffer damage if compelled to attempt it. If the suction side of the system remains in a vacuum the system is blocked. Locate and correct the condition before proceeding any further.

NOTE: Placing the refrigerant can in a container of warm water (no hotter than 125° F) will speed the charging process. Slight agitation of the can is helpful too, but be careful not to turn the can upside down.

Some manufacturers allow for a partial charging of the A/C system in the form of a liquid (can inverted and compressor off) by opening the high side gauge valve only, and putting the high side compressor service valve in the middle position (if so equipped). The remainder of the refrigerant is then added in the form of a gas in the normal manner, through the suction side only.

SYSTEMS WITHOUT SIGHT GLASS, EXCEPT CCOT SYSTEM

The following procedure can be used to quickly determine whether or not an air conditioning system has the proper charge of refrigerant (providing ambient temperature is above 70° F. or 21° C.). This check can be made in a manner of minutes, thus facilitating system diagnosis by pinpointing the problem to the amount of charge in the system or by eliminating this possibility from the overall checkout.

1. Engine must be warm (thermostat open).

2. Hood and body doors open.

3. Selector lever set at NORM.

4. Temperature lever at COLD.

5. Blower on HI.

6. Normal engine idle.

7. Hand-feel temperature of evaporator inlet and outlet pipes with compressor engaged.

a. Both same temperature or some degree cooler than ambient—proper condition: check for other problems.

b. Inlet pipe cooler than outlet pipe—low refrigerant charge.

• Add a slight amount of refrigerant until both pipes feel the same.

• Then add 15 oz. (1 can) additional refrigerant.

c. Inlet pipe has frost accumulation—outlet pipe warmer: proceed as in Step b above.

If during the charging process the head pressure exceeds 200 psi, place an electric fan in front of the car and direct the turbulent air to the condenser. If no fan is available, repeatedly pour cool water over the top of the condenser. These cooling actions may be necessary on an extremely warm day to help dissipate the heat emitted by the engine during idle.

If this fails and pressure on the discharge side continues to rise, the system may be overcharged or the engine might be overheating. *Never* allow head pressure to go beyond 240 psi. during charging. If this condition occurs, stop engine, find and correct the problem.

8. Continue dispensing refrigerant until container is no longer cool to the touch. On a humid day, the outside of the container will frost. When the frost disappears the can is usually empty. To detach dispensing can:

a. close low pressure test gauge hand valve.

b. crack open low pressure test hose at manifold until remaining pressure escapes.

c. tighten hose coupler.

d. loosen hose coupler connected to refrigerant can.

e. discard empty can and repeat steps 2 to 8.

9. Continue to add refrigerant to the required capacity of the system. (Usually marked on the compressor).

CAUTION
DO NOT OVERCHARGE. This condition is usually indicated by an abnormally high side pressure reading and a noisy compressor resulting in ineffective cooling and damage to the system.

SYSTEMS WITH A SIGHT GLASS

The air conditioning systems that use a sight glass as a means to check the refrigerant level, should be carefully checked to avoid under or over charging. The gauge set should be attached to the system for verification of pressures.

To check the system with the sight glass,

Check item \ Amount of refrigerant	Almost no refrigerant	Insufficient	Suitable	Too much refrigerant
Temperature of high pressure and low pressure lines.	Almost no difference between high pressure and low pressure side temperature.	High pressure side is warm and low pressure side is fairly cold.	High pressure side is hot and low pressure side is cold.	High pressure side is abnormally hot.
State in sight glass.	Bubbles flow continuously. **Bubbles will disappear and something like mist will flow when refrigerant is nearly gone.**	The bubbles are seen at intervals of 1 - 2 seconds.	Almost transparent. Bubbles may appear when engine speed is raised and lowered. **No clear difference exists between these two conditions.**	No bubbles can be seen.
Pressure of system.	High pressure side is abnormally low.	Both pressure on high and low pressure sides are slightly low.	Both pressures on high and low pressure sides are normal.	Both pressures on high and low pressure sides are abnormally high.
Repair.	**Stop compressor immediately** and conduct an overall check.	Check for gas leakage, repair as required, replenish and charge system.		Discharge refrigerant from service valve of low pressure side.

Using a sight glass to determine the relative refrigerant charge

clean the glass and start the vehicle engine. Operate the air conditioning controls on maximum for approximately five minutes to stabilize the system. The room temperature should be above 70 degrees. Check the sight glass for one of the following conditions:

1. If the sight glass is clear, the compressor clutch is engaged, the compressor discharge line is warm and the compressor inlet line is cool, the system has a full charge of refrigerant.

2. If the sight glass is clear, the compressor clutch is engaged and there is no significant temperature difference between the compressor inlet and discharge lines, the system is empty or nearly empty. By having the gauge set attached to the system, a measurement can be taken. If the gauge reads less than 25 psi, the low pressure cut-off protection switch has failed.

3. If the sight glass is clear and the compressor clutch is disengaged, the clutch is defective, or the clutch circuit is open, or the system is out of refrigerant. By-pass the low pressure cut-off switch momentarily to determine the cause.

4. If the sight glass shows foam or bubbles, the system can be low on refrigerant. Occasional foam or bubbles is normal when the room temperature is above 110 degrees or below 70 degrees. To verify, increase the engine speed to approximately 1500 rpm and block the airflow through the condenser to increase the compressor discharge pressure to between 225 to 250 psi. If the sight glass still shows bubbles or foam, the refrigerant level is low.

—— CAUTION ——

Do not operate the vehicle engine any longer than necessary with the condenser airflow blocked. This blocking action also blocks the cooling system radiator and will cause the system to overheat rapidly.

When the system is low on refrigerant, a leak is present or the system was not properly charged. Use a leak detector and locate the problem area and repair. If no leakage is found, charge the system to its capacity. (Refer to the refrigerant capacity chart at the end of this section).

—— CAUTION ——

It is not advisable to add refrigerant to a system utilizing the suction throttling valve and a sight glass, because the amount of refrigerant required to remove the foam or bubbles will result in an overcharge and potentially damaged system components.

CCOT SYSTEM

When charging the CCOT system, attach only the low pressure line to the low pressure gauge port, located on the accumulator. Do not attach the high pressure line to any service port or allow it to remain attached to the vacuum pump after evacuation. Be sure both the high and the low pressure control valves are closed on the gauge set. To complete the charging of the system, follow the outline supplied.

1. Start the engine and allow to run at idle, with the cooling system at normal operating temperature.

2. Attach the center gauge hose to a single or multi-can dispenser.

3. With the multi-can dispenser inverted, allow one pound or the contents of one or two 14 oz. cans to enter the system through the low pressure side by opening the gauge low pressure control valve.

4. Close the low pressure gauge control valve and turn the A/C system on to engage the compressor. Place the blower motor in its high mode.

5. Open the low pressure gauge control valve and draw the remaining charge into the system. Refer to the capacity chart at the end of this section for the individual vehicle or system capacity.

6. Close the low pressure gauge control valve and the refrigerant source valve, on the multi-can dispenser. Remove the low pressure hose from the accumulator quickly to avoid loss of refrigerant through the Schrader valve.

7. Install the protective cap on the gauge port and check the system for leakage.

8. Test the system for proper operation.

Leak Testing the System

There are several methods of detecting leaks in an air conditioning system; among them, the two most popular are (1) halide leak-detection or the "open flame method," and (2) electronic leak-detection.

The halide leak detection is a torch like device which produces a yellow-green color when refrigerant is introduced into the flame at the burner. A purple or violet color indicates the presence of large amounts of refrigerant at the burner.

An electronic leak detector is a small portable electronic device with an extended probe. With the unit activated the probe is passed along those components of the system which contain refrigerant. If a leak is detected, the unit will sound an alarm signal or activate a display signal depending on the manufacturer's design. It is advisable to follow the manufacturer's instructions as the design and function of the detection may vary significantly.

—— CAUTION ——

Caution should be taken to operate either type of detector in well ventilated areas, so as to reduce the chance of personal injury, which may result from coming in contact with poisonous gases produced when R-12 is exposed to flame or electric spark.

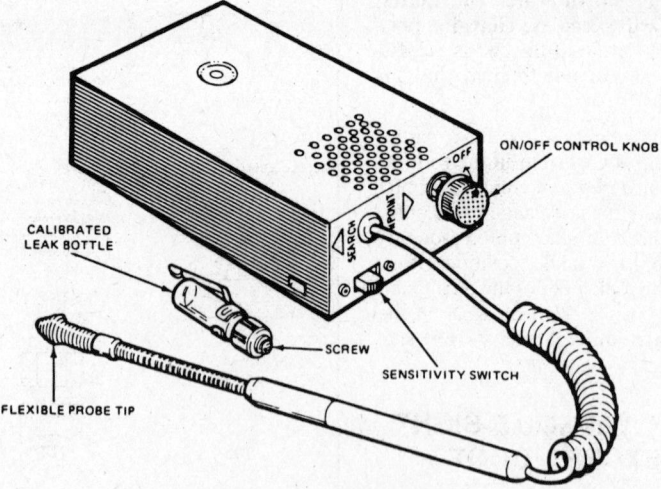

Electronic leak detector

REFRIGERANT CAPACITIES CHART

Auto Manufacturer	1977 Models	Recharge Capacities (lbs.)	1978–79 Models	Recharge Capacities (lbs.)	1980 Models	Recharge Capacities (lbs.)	1981 Models	Recharge Capacities (lbs.)	1982–84 Models	Recharge Capacities (lbs.)
AMERICAN MOTORS CORP. 14250 Plymouth Road Detroit, Michigan 48232	Pacer Gremlin, Hornet Matador	2⅛ 2 3	Pacer Gremlin, Concord, Amx Matador	2⅛ 2 3	Concord Pacer Spirit Eagle	2 2⅛ 2 2	Concord Spirit Eagle	2 2 2	All	2.00
BUICK MOTOR DIVISION General Motors Corporation Flint, Michigan 48550	Skyhawk All others	2¾ 3¾	Skyhawk Skylark All others	2½ 3½ 3¾	Skyhawk Skylark Electra, LeSabre Century, Regal, Riviera	2½ 2¾ 3¾ 3½	Skyhawk Skylark Electra, LeSabre Century, Regal, Riviera	2½ 2¾ 3¾ 3½	Electra, LeSabre Regal, Century, Skylark Riviera Skyhawk	3.50 2.75 3.25 2.50
CADILLAC MOTOR CAR DIVISION General Motors Corporation Detroit, Michigan 48232	All	3¾	Seville All others	3½ 3¾	Seville, Eldorado All others	3½ 3¾	Seville, Eldorado All others	3½ 3¾	Cimarron Seville All others	2.50 2.75 3.50
CHEVROLET MOTOR DIVISION General Motors Corporation General Motors Bldg. Detroit, Michigan 48202	Vega, Monza, Chevette All others	2¾ 3¾	Monza Chevette Camaro Nova Corvette Malibu, Impala, Caprice	2¾ 2¼ 3¼ 3½ 3 3¾	Monza, Nova Chevette Camaro Corvette Citation Malibu, Impala, Caprice	3½ 2¼ 3¼ 3 2¾ 3¾	Monza, Nova Chevette Camaro Corvette Citation Malibu, Impala, Caprice	3½ 2¼ 3¼ 3 2¾ 3¾	Corvette, Camaro Caprice, Impala Monte Carlo Malibu, Celebrity, Citation Chevette	3.00 3.50 3.25 2.75 2.25
CHRYSLER CORPORATION P.O. Box 2119 Detroit, Michigan 48231	Chrysler, Monaco, Fury All others	2¾ 2⅝	Chrysler Omni & Horizon All others	2¾ 2 2⅝	All, except below Omni, Horizon	2⅝ 2⅛	All, except below Omni, Horizon, Aries, Reliant	2⅝ 2⅛	Diplomat, Gran Fury, New Yorker, Mirada, Cordoba, Imperial Aries, Reliant, LeBaron, E-Class, 400, 600 Omni, Horizon	2.62 3.40 3.12
FORD DIVISION Ford Motor Company Rotunda Drive at Southfield Rd. P.O. Box 598 Dearborn, Michigan 48121	Granada LTD Maverick Mustang Pinto LTD II Thunderbird	4 4½ 1⅞ 3¼ 2¼ 4¼ 4¼	Granada LTD Fairmont Mustang Pinto LTD II Thunderbird	4 4½ 3½ 3¼ 2¼ 4½ 4½ 3½	Pinto All others②	2¼ 3½	Escort All others②	2½ 3½	Thunderbird, Fairmont, Granada, Mustang, Escort LTD, Crown Victoria	2.50 3.25
LINCOLN-MERCURY DIVISION Ford Motor Company 3000 Schaefer Road Dearborn, Michigan 48121	Monarch Marquis Comet Bobcat Lincoln Mark V Cougar	4 4½ 1⅞ 2¼ 4¼ 4¼ 4¼	Monarch Marquis Zephyr Bobcat Cougar Lincoln Versailles Mark V Capri	4 4½ 3½ 2¼ 4½ 4½ 4 4½ 3½	Bobcat All others②	2¼ 3½	Lynx All others②	2½ 3½	Lincoln Continental, XR-7, Zephyr, Cougar, Capri, Lynx Lincoln, Mark VI Marquis, Grand Marquis	2.50 3.00 3.25
OLDSMOBILE DIVISION General Motors Corporation Lansing, Michigan	Starfire Omega All others	2½ 3½ 3¾	Starfire Omega, Toronado All others	2½ 3½ 3¾	Cutlass, 88, 98 Toronado Starfire Omega	3¾ 3½ 2½ 2¾	Cutlass, 88, 98 Toronado Starfire Omega	3¾ 3½ 2½ 2¾	88, 98 Cutlass, Cutlass Ciera, Omega Toronado Firenza	3.50 2.75 3.25 2.50
PONTIAC MOTOR DIVISION General Motors Corporation Pontiac, Michigan 48053	Astre, Sunbird Firebird All others	2⅖ 3¼ 3¾	Catalina & Bonneville Firebird Sunbird All others	3¾ 3¼ 2½ 3½	Catalina, Bonneville Firebird Sunbird Phoenix	3½ 3¼ 2½ 2¾	Catalina, Bonneville Lemans, Gran Am, Firebird Sunbird Phoenix	3½ 3¼ 2½ 2¾	Firebird Bonneville Grand Prix 6000, Phoenix J-2000 T-1000	3.00 3.50 3.25 2.75 2.50 2.25

① All refrigerant charges listed are approximate and represent a nmiinal reserve with moderate head pressures. Check label on or near compressor for correct charge.

② Ford, Mercury and Lincoln vehicles using Frigidaire 6 cylinder compressor–4¼ lbs.

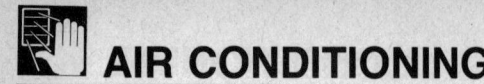

AFTERMARKET UNITS
PASSENGER CARS

ALLSTATE Sears Roebuck & Company	All Sears Models	2½-3
A.R.A. A.R.A. Manufacturing Company P.O. Box 1327 Arlington, Texas 76010	Jupiter II Gladiator Champion Charger II President (Trunk) Custom Units	2¼ 2¼ 2¼ 2½ 3½ 2
CLARDY Clardy Mfg. Co. 1728 Layton Ave. Fort Worth, Texas 76117	Customatic Jet Star	2¼ 2¼
CLIMATIC AIR Climatic Air Sales, Inc. 615 North Good-Latimer Expw. P.O. Box 805 Dallas, Texas 75221	Under Dash Models Trunk Custom Units Compact Models	2½ 3 2¼-2½ 1¾-2
DPD DPD Manufacturing Co., Inc. 2011 Sable Lane San Antonio, Texas 78217	DPD 1 & DPD III DPD 113 DPD II DPD IV DPD KG Porsche Audi 100	1½ 2 2½ 1¾ 1½ 2
EATON Eaton, Yale & Towne, Inc. Eaton Heater Div. East 65th & Central Ave. Cleveland, Ohio 44104	All Eaton Models	2½-3
FLEET AIR Fleet Air Corp. 3737 N.W. 37th Street P.O. Box 12507 Oklahoma City, Oklahoma 73112	Custom Series Models 1-26	2
FOREMOST J. C. Penney Company	Foremost (All Models)	2

FRIGIQUIP
Frigiquip Corporation
405 N. Meridian
P.O. Box 12279
Oklahoma City, Oklahoma
73112
	Under Dash Units
	Custom
	  Imported Cars
	  American Cars
	Standard
	Trunk Unit
		
		1.7
		2
		2
		3

FRIGIKING Frigiking Company Div. Cummins Engine Co., Inc. 10858 Harry Hines Blvd. P.O. Box 20738 Dallas, Texas 75220	Under Dash Models Norseman, Voyager, Sportster, Explorer Custom Units Coldmaster Intermediate Special Slimline Custom, I.S. Custom Trunk Unit	 2-2¼ 2-2¼ 3-3½
MITCHELL MARK IV John E. Mitchell Co., Inc. P.O. Box 1811 3800 Commerce Street Dallas, Texas 75221	Under Dash Unit	2
NORDIC Nordic International Co. 190 N. East 75th Street Miami, Florida 33138	Under Dash Models T-Bird Custom Corvair Custom Roof Top	2 2 2½-3 2
THERMO KING Thermo King Corp. 314 West 90th St. Minneapolis, Minn. 55420	AAC-170 Mercedes- Benz AAC-176 Mercedes- Benz AAC-177 Mercedes- Benz All other Thermo King & Mobilaire Units	 45 oz. 30 oz. 30 oz. 36 oz.
VORNADO Division of Automatic Radio Mfg. Co. 2 Main Street Melrose, Mass. 02176	B-88A Melrose B-90A Pacemaker B-80 Consolaire B-92A Custom Air B-72 Custom Trunk B-79 Airmaster B-97 Volkswagen	2¾ 2½ 3 2½ 3½ 2½ 1.6

Charging and Starting

TESTING THE BATTERY

Selection of Battery

The modern car battery is a 12-volt lead-acid unit having a particular ampere hours capacity, depending upon the required work load (radio, air conditioning, electric windows, tailgate, etc.).

Batteries come in different sizes and shapes as specified by the car manufacturer and are matched to the car's electrical needs.

The prime purpose of the battery is to supply a source of energy for cranking the car engine. It also provides the necessary power for the ignition system. A battery can, for a limited time, supply adequate current to satisfy electrical demands during periods when requirements exceed alternator output.

Replacing a Battery

Before deciding on a particular battery, consider some of the essentials that may put the replacement battery in a different category from the unit originally supplied with the vehicle. When the original battery wears out, resistance in the wiring circuits is probably much increased, and the starter may be less efficient, along with the ignition system. There is also the likelihood that electrical accessories have been added.

All of the above reasons are justification for choosing a battery of greater capacity than the one supplied by the manufacturer.

Preparation

If a dry "charged" battery is selected as a replacement, place the new battery on a bench or work table. Never activate a bat-

tery installed in the car. Remove vent caps from all the cells.

Fill each cell carefully, using sulfuric acid and distilled water (electrolyte) at a strength of 1.250–1.265 specific gravity to about ⅜ in. above the top of the separators, or to indicated level mark.

CAUTION
Because electrolyte is extremely corrosive to metals and many other materials, do not pour into sinks or drains. If battery acid is spilled on battery during filling or charging, or on bench or clothing, immediately flush it off with generous amounts of water and baking soda or ammonia.

Place a battery type thermometer in one of the center cells. Check specific gravity of the electrolyte with a battery hydrometer. The battery temperature must be above 80°F. and specific gravity must be above 1.250 prior to installing the battery.

In charging 12 volt batteries, set charging rate at 35 amperes until electrolyte has reached 80°F. and electrolyte gravity is 1.250 or higher. Lower charging rates also may be used to obtain 80°F. and 1.250 specific gravity. When charging, do not allow electrolyte temperature to exceed 125°F. Normally, 10–15 minutes charging will be sufficient: however, in colder climates a little longer is O.K.

When the battery is removed from the charger, top up with electrolyte, if necessary, and replace the vent plugs.

Many replacement batteries are off the "maintenance free" design, they are pre-filled and may require charging before installation. Refer to the card supplied with the battery, or the label attached to the top for preinstallation charging instructions.

When installing, make sure that both ends of the battery cables are clean and securely tightened, observing correct polarity.

CAUTION
Be careful not to install the battery with cables reversed. Reversed polarity can destroy an alternator and regulator in a very short time.

Start engine and make sure that the alternator is charging with lights and all accessories on.

Battery Troubles—Causes

1. Battery too small for the job (accessories, etc.).
2. Tired battery (worn out).
3. Corroded battery connections.
4. Alternator not charging.
5. Alternator charging rate too low.
6. Regulator defective.
7. Regulator out of adjustment.
8. Regulator has poor ground.
9. Alternator inoperative.
10. Loose alternator drive belt.
11. Constant drain of current due to short circuit.

Battery Troubles—Corrections

1. Battery capacity may be less than requirements demand. Additional accessories, too frequent use of starter, low operational speeds, require a greater source of electrical supply. Install a larger capacity battery.

2. Either age or abuse is the usual cause of a tired battery. No amount of charging will offer more than temporary relief. Install a new battery of proper capacity if plates are sulfated.

3. Corroded battery posts or side terminal cable retaining bolts and connections result from the chemical reaction between dissimilar metals and battery electrolyte. Excessive corrosion at a battery post (or connection) is usually an indication of the

failure of a seal between the post and the battery cover.

— CAUTION —

Always disconnect the negative battery terminal first.

Remove the cable and seal the post-to-battery cover with rubber cement or silicone sealer. Clean the post and cable clamp, install the cable on the post, tighten the clamp, and apply a thin coat of grease to retard corrosion. Felt washers impregnated with an anti-corrosion substance are available; these are slipped over the post prior to cable installation. In the case of a side terminal battery, wire brush the bolt, battery connector plate and cable connector. Install and tighten connector bolt, apply a thin coat of grease to the cable end.

4. Alternator not charging can be caused by a defective alternator or other system component. Check entire charging system and correct the fault.

5. Low charging rate may be caused by a loose drive belt, loose or poor battery post connections, high resistance in charging circuit or a poor or improperly adjusted regulator.

6. Regulator may be defective because of burned points in the regulator or any open circuit in the control system.

7. Regulator out of adjustment.

8. Regulator has poor ground.

9. The alternator may be inoperative because of damaged diodes, poor internal connections, open, grounded, or shorted field circuit, grounded or shorted stator windings.

10. A loose drive belt will cause low, or partial charging. Correct by adjusting drive belt.

11. A constant drain of current from the battery may be caused by frayed insulation on any live wire in the electrical system. This can cause a short circuit. There is also the possibility of a light (in the trunk, glove box, under the hood, etc.) or other electric

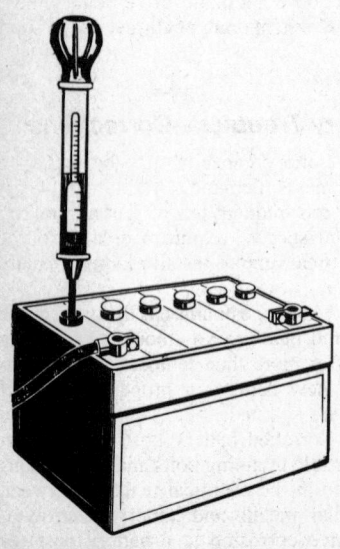

Testing battery specific gravity

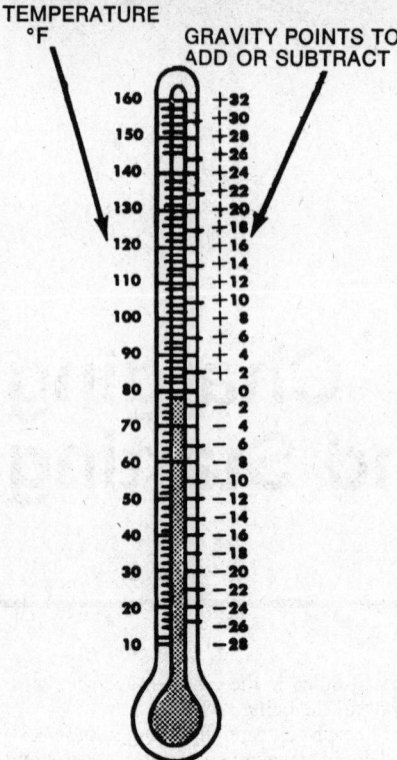

Hydrometer temperature correction chart
(© Chrysler Corp)

accessory remaining on after the ignition is turned off. To correct the situation:

First, with a sensitive ammeter, determine whether or not there is a current drain by opening the circuit at either battery post connection, hooking the ammeter in series, and checking for current drain.

Second, if the meter registers a drain, isolate the leak by reconnecting the battery, then, one by one, check each circuit at the fuse block. This is a tedious but unavoidable procedure and consists of removing each fuse and testing that circuit with the prods of an ammeter (in series). The circuit which activates the meter is the guilty one; identify the trouble spot by elimination. Correct the trouble by correcting the short or replacing the switch or other electrical component.

In the event that the fuse block test does not indicate the trouble, check the circuits which are protected with circuit breakers (headlamps, parking lamps, seat and window controls, etc.).

Specific Gravity Test—Hydrometer

Before attempting any electrical checks, it is important to check the condition of the battery.

While not technically exact, a practical measurement of the chemical condition of the battery is indicated by measuring the specific gravity of the acid (electrolyte) contained in each cell. The electrolyte in a fully charged battery is usually between 1.260 and 1.280 times as heavy as pure

water at the same temperature (80°F.). Variations in the specific gravity readings for a fully charged battery may differ. Therefore, it is most important that all battery cells produce an equal reading.

As a battery discharges, a chemical change takes place within each cell. The sulfate factor of the electrolyte combines chemically with the battery plates, reducing the weight of the electrolyte. A reading of the specific gravity of the acid, or electrolyte, of any partially charged battery, will therefore be less than that taken in a fully charged one.

The hydrometer is the instrument used for determining the specific gravity of liquids. The battery hydrometer is readily available from many sources, including local auto replacement parts stores. The following chart gives an indication of specific gravity value, related to battery charge condition. If, after charging, the specific gravity between any two cells varies more than 50 points (.050), the battery is probably bad.

Specific Gravity Reading	Charged Condition
1.260–1.280	Fully charged
1.230–1.250	three-quarter charged
1.200–1.220	One-half charged
1.170–1.190	One-quarter charged
1.140–1.160	Just about flat
1.110–1.130	All the way down

Testing Battery Polarity

Battery polarity is very important. Permanent damage to the diodes of alternators will result from reversing polarity.

To determine battery polarity, turn the voltmeter selector to the high reading scale. Connect voltmeter leads to the battery posts. If the gauge needle moves in the correct direction, the positive lead of the meter is on the positive (+) post of the battery. If the gauge needle moves in the wrong direction, polarity is reversed.

Testing the "Sealed Top" Battery

Cars equipped with a "sealed top" or "maintenance free" battery do not require the usual maintenance. Because the battery has a greater amount of electrolyte and a reduced need for water, the top of the battery has no filler caps and is sealed. A small vent is provided at one edge of the battery top.

There are two types of sealed batteries used: one has a charge indicator eye and the other does not. Both types may be tested in the following manner:

1. Check the condition of the battery case. If the case is damaged so that loss of electrolyte is possible, the battery must be replaced.

DARKENED INDICATOR
WITH GREEN DOT
—FULL CHARGE

DARKENED INDICATOR
NO GREEN DOT
—NEEDS CHARGING

LIGHTENED INDICATOR
—REPLACE BATTERY

**Delco sealed battery indicator conditions
(© G.M. Corp.)**

2. If the battery has a charge indicator eye, check the following:

a. If the eye is dark, the battery has enough electrolyte. If the eye is light, the electrolyte level is too low and the battery must be replaced.

b. If a green dot appears in the middle of the eye, the battery is sufficiently charged; go on to Step 4. If there is no green dot visible, charge the battery as in Step 3.

3. Charge the battery if there is no green dot visible in the eye, or if it is the type without an eye, at the following rates:

Amps	Time
75	40 min
50	1 hr
25	2 hr
10	5 hr

——— CAUTION ———

If the green dot appears or electrolyte squirts out of the vent, stop the charge and go on with Step 4.

4. Either disconnect the high-tension coil wire or the engine harness (electronic ignition) and crank the starter motor for 15 seconds, to remove the surface charge.

5. Connect a voltmeter and a 230 amp load across the battery terminals.

6. Take a voltmeter reading after the load has been connected for 15 seconds, then disconnect the load.

7. Consult the following chart. If the battery voltage is that specified (or more) for the given ambient temperature, the battery is good. If the voltage falls below that specified, then the battery is bad and must be replaced.

Ambient Temperature (°F)	Minimum Voltage
70 (or above)	9.6
60	9.5
50	9.4
40	9.3
30	9.1
20	8.9
10	8.7
0	8.5

Know Your Instruments
OHMMETER

An ohmmeter is used to measure electrical resistance in a unit or circuit. The ohmmeter has a self-contained power supply. In use, it is connected across (or in parallel with) the terminals of the unit being tested.

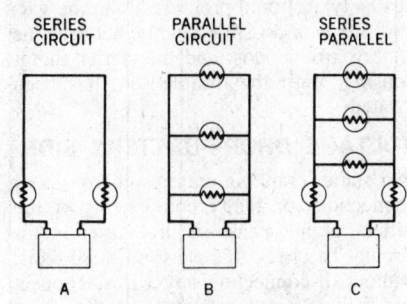

Basic electrical circuits

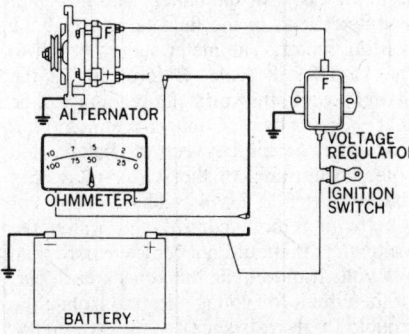

Ohmmeter connected to test wire resistance—typical (ohmmeter has self-contained power supply)

AMMETER

An ammeter is used to measure current (amount of electricity) flowing through a unit, or circuit. Ammeters are always connected in the line (in series) with the unit or circuit being tested.

VOLTMETER

A voltmeter is used to measure voltage (electrical pressure) pushing the current through a unit, or circuit. The meter is connected across the terminals of the unit being tested. The meter reading will be the difference in pressure (voltage drop) between the two sides of the unit.

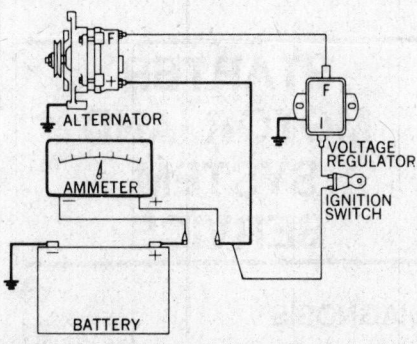

Ammeter connected in series circuits

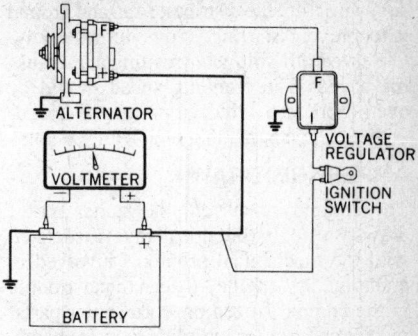

Voltmeter connected in parallel circuits

TESTING THE STARTER MOTOR

Testing the Starter Circuit

The starter circuit should be divided and tested in four separate phases:

1. Cranking voltage check.
2. Amperage draw.
3. Voltage drop—grounded side.
4. Voltage drop—battery side.

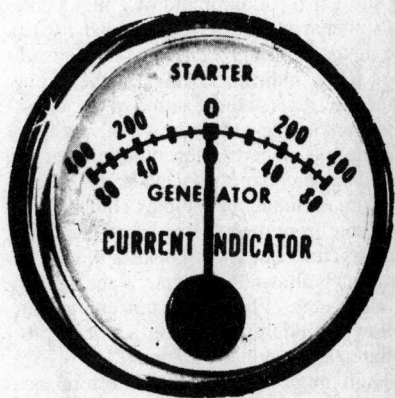

Current indicator

NOTE: The battery must be in good condition for this test to have significance. To accurately check battery condition, use equipment designed to measure its capacity under a load. Instructions accompanying the equipment should be followed.

NOTE: Disconnect the vacuum line to the air pump bypass valve before performing any cranking tests. After tests are completed, run the engine for at least 3 minutes before reconnecting the vacuum line.

CRANKING VOLTAGE

Turn voltmeter selector to the 16–20 volt scale.

Connect voltmeter leads to the battery posts (observe polarity and reverse meter leads if necessary). Remove the high tension wire from the distributor cap and ground it to prevent starting. Now, turn the key. Observe both voltmeter reading and cranking speed. The cranking speed should be even, and at a satisfactory rate of speed, with a voltmeter reading of at least 9.6 volts.

AMPERAGE DRAW

The amount of current the starter motor draws is usually (but not always) associated with the mechanical problems involved in cranking the engine. (Mechanical trouble in the engine, frozen or worn starter parts, misaligned starter or starter components, etc.) Because starter motor amperage draw is directly influenced by anything restricting the free turning of the engine, or starter, it is important that the engine and all components be at operating temperatures.

When measuring starter current draw, remove the high tension wire from the center of the distributor cap and ground it.

NOTE: On cars with electronic ignition, disconnect the control box from the distributor (harness).

A very simple and inexpensive starter current indicator is available at auto parts stores. This indicator is an induction-type gauge and shows, without disconnecting any wires, starter current draw.

Place the yoke of the meter directly over the insulated starter supply cable (cable must be straight for a minimum of 2 in.). Close the starter switch for about 20 seconds, watch the meter dial and record the average reading. If the indicator swings in the wrong direction, reverse the position of the meter. The cranking amperage draw can vary from 150 to 400 amperes, depending on engine size, engine compression and starter design.

More accurate but complex equipment is available from many name brand manufacturers. This equipment consists of a combination voltmeter, ammeter, and carbon pile rheostat. When using this equipment, follow the equipment manufacturer's procedures and recommendations.

High amperage and lazy performance would suggest an excessively tight engine, friction in the starter or starter drive, grounded starter field or armature.

Normal amperage and lazy performance suggest high resistance, or possibly poor connections somewhere in the starter circuit.

Low amperage and lazy or no performance suggest battery condition poor, bad cables or connections along the line.

VOLTAGE DROP—GROUNDED SIDE

With a voltmeter on the 3 volt scale, without disconnecting any wires, connect negative test lead of the voltmeter to a prod secured in the grounded battery post. The positive test lead is connected to a cleaned, bare metal portion of the starter motor housing. Close the starter switch and note the voltmeter reading. If the reading is the same as battery reading, the ground circuit is open somewhere between the battery and the starter. In many cases the reading will be

very small. The reading shown will indicate voltage drop (loss) between battery ground post and starter housing. The drop should not exceed 0.2 volt. If the voltage drop is above the specified amount, the next step is to isolate and correct the cause. It can be a bad cable or connection anywhere in the battery-to-starter ground circuit. A check of this type should progress along the various points of possible trouble, between the battery ground post and the starter motor housing, until the trouble spot has been located.

VOLTAGE DROP—BATTERY SIDE

Bad starter cranking may result from poor connections or faulty components of the battery or hot phase of the starter motor circuit. To check this phase of the circuit, without disconnecting any wires, connect one lead of a voltmeter to a prod secured in the hot post of the battery and the other voltmeter lead to the field terminal of the starting motor. The meter should be set to the 16–20 volt scale. Before closing the starter switch, the voltmeter reading will be that of the battery. Connect a remote control starter switch between the battery and solenoid terminal of the starter relay. Set the voltmeter to 3 volt scale. Crank engine with remote control and watch the voltmeter. It should not register more than 0.5 volt. If more than this, check each part of the circuit for voltage drop to isolate the trouble (high resistance).

Without disturbing the voltmeter-to-battery hook-up, move the free voltmeter lead to the battery terminal of the relay (solenoid), and crank the engine. The voltmeter should show not more than 0.1 volt.

If this reading is correct, move the same voltmeter lead to the starting motor terminal of the relay (solenoid). While the engine is being cranked, the voltmeter should show no more than 0.3 volt. If it does, the trouble lies in the relay.

If the reading is correct, the trouble is in the cable or connections between the relay and the starting motor.

NOTE: Due to the design of the Chrysler reduction gear starter, testing is limited to measuring voltage drop to starter cable connection.

STARTER MOTOR AND SYSTEM SERVICE

DIAGNOSIS

Starter Won't Crank the Engine

1. Dead battery.

2. Open starter circuit, such as:
   a. Broken or loose battery cables.
   b. Inoperative starter motor solenoid.
   c. Broken or loose wire from ignition switch to solenoid.
   d. Poor solenoid or starter ground.
   e. Bad ignition switch.
3. Defective starter internal circuit, such as:
   a. Dirty or burnt commutator.
   b. Stuck, worn or broken brushes.
   c. Open or shorted armature.
   d. Open or grounded fields.
4. Starter motor mechanical faults, such as:
   a. Jammed armature end bearings.
   b. Bad bearing, allowing armature to rub fields.
   c. Bent shaft.
   d. Broken starter housing.
   e. Bad starter drive mechanism.
   f. Bad starter drive or flywheel-driven gear.
5. Engine hard or impossible to crank, such as:
   a. Hydrostatic lock, water in combustion chamber.
   b. Crankshaft seizing in bearings.
   c. Piston or ring seizing.
   d. Bent or broken connecting rod.
   e. Seizing of connecting rod bearings.
   f. Flywheel jammed or broken.

Starter Spins Free, Won't Engage

1. Sticking or broken drive mechanism.
2. Damaged ring gear.

Solenoid and Neutral Safety Switch

IDENTIFICATION

Solenoids Without Relays

This type of starter solenoid is always mounted on the starter. It makes electrical contact for the starter and pulls the starter and drive clutch into mesh with flywheel. The Chrysler reduction gear starter has this solenoid embodied in the starter housing, however an internal relay is integral to the brush plate.

The ignition by-pass terminal is usually marked R or IGN, if it is used.

Solenoids With Separate Relays

The solenoid itself is always mounted on the starter. In addition to making contact for the starter, it also pulls the starter drive clutch gear into mesh with flywheel. A single control terminal is used on the solenoid itself. The relay is usually found mounted to the inner fender panel or on the firewall.

Solenoids With Built-in Relays

These units are always mounted on the starter and are connected, through linkage, to the starter drive clutch. The relay portion is built into and integral with the solenoid assembly.

Neutral Safety Switches

The purpose of the neutral safety switch is to prevent the starter from cranking the engine except when the transmission is in Neutral or Park.

On some cars, the neutral safety switch is located on the transmission. It serves to ground the solenoid or magnetic switch, whichever is used.

On other cars the neutral safety switch is located either at the bottom of the steering column, where it contacts the shift mechanism, on the steering column, underneath the dash, or on the shift linkage (console).

Some manual transmission models have a clutch linkage safety switch to prevent starter operation unless the clutch pedal is depressed.

On most cars, the neutral safety switch and the back-up light switch are combined into a single switch mechanism.

TROUBLESHOOTING NEUTRAL SAFETY SWITCHES—QUICK TEST

If the starter fails to function and the neutral safety switch is to be checked, a jumper can be placed across its terminals. If the starter then functions the safety switch is defective.

In the case of neutral safety switches with one wire, this wire must be grounded for testing purposes. If the starter works with the wire grounded, the switch is defective.

NEUTRAL SAFETY SWITCH— BACK-UP LIGHT SWITCH

When the neutral safety switch is built in combination with the back-up light switch, the easiest way to tell which terminals are for the back-up lights is to take a jumper and cross every pair of wires. The pair of wires which light the back-up lamps should be ignored when testing the neutral safety switch. Once the back-up light wires have been located, jump the other pair of wires to test the neutral safety switch. If the starter functions only when the jumper is placed across these two wires, the neutral safety switch is defective or requires adjustment.

Reduction-Gear Starter Motor

CHRYSLER CORPORATION

NOTE: Refer to following separate sections for Nippondenso and Mitsubishi reduction gear type starter repair procedures.

Disassembly

1. Support assembly in a vise equipped with soft jaws. Do not clamp. Care must

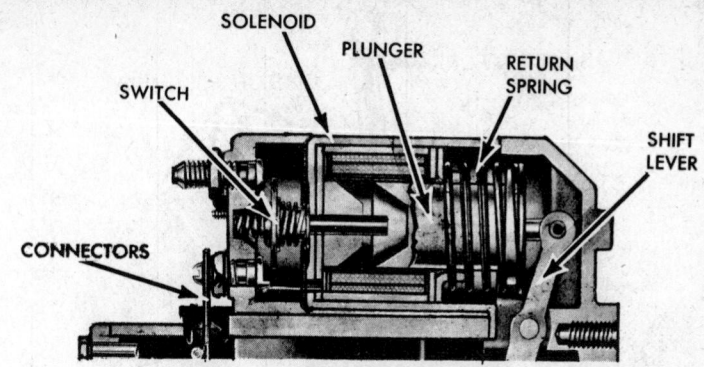

Starter solenoid mounted on starter motor

be used not to distort or damage the die cast aluminum.

2. Remove the thru-bolts and the end housing.

3. Carefully pull the armature up and out of the gear housing, and the starter frame and field assembly. Remove the steel and fiber thrust washer.

NOTE: On eight cylinder engines the starting motors have the wire of the shunt field coil soldered to the brush terminal. Six cylinder engines have the four coils in series and do not have a wire soldered to the brush terminal. One pair of brushes is connected to this terminal. The other pair of brushes is attached to the series field coils by means of a terminal screw. Carefully pull the frame and field assembly up just enough to expose the terminal screw and the solder connection of the

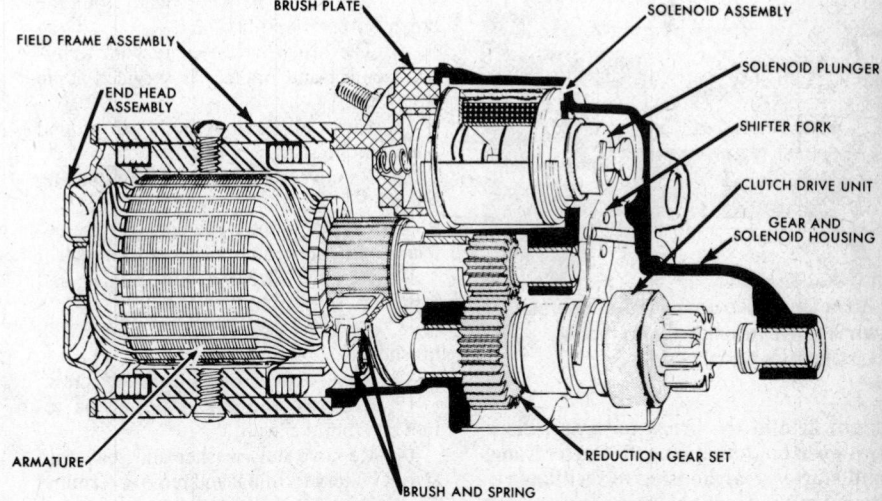

Rear wheel drive reduction gear starter (© Chrysler Corp)

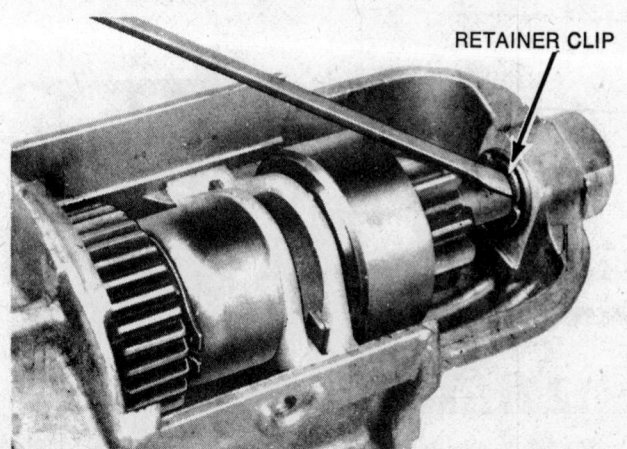

Removing retainer ring—rear wheel drive reduction gear motor (© Chrysler Corp)

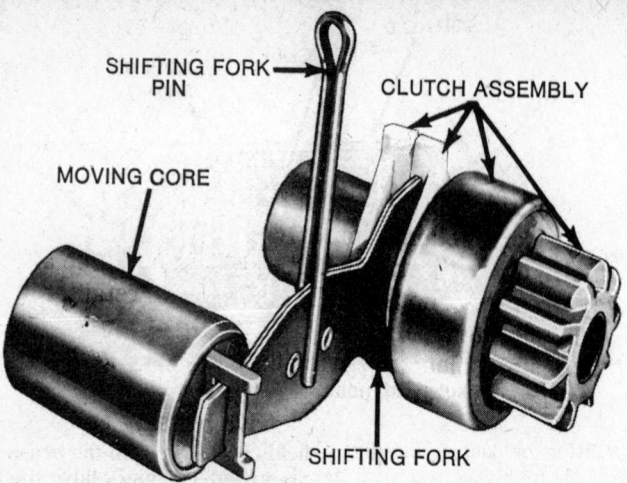

SHIFTING FORK PIN

CLUTCH ASSEMBLY

MOVING CORE

SHIFTING FORK

Shift fork and clutch arrangement—rear wheel drive reduction gear motor (© Chrysler Corp)

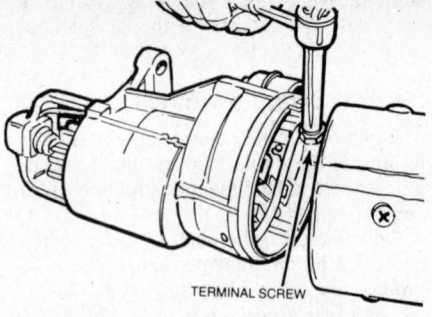

TERMINAL SCREW

Removing terminal screw—rear wheel drive reduction gear starter

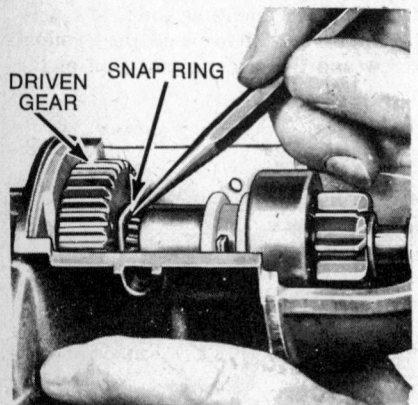

DRIVEN GEAR

SNAP RING

Removing drive gear snap-ring—rear wheel drive reduction gear motor (© Chrysler Corp)

shunt field at the brush terminal. Place two wood blocks between the starter frame and starter gear housing to facilitate removal of the terminal screw and unsoldering of the shunt field wire at the brush terminal.

4. Support the brush terminal with a finger behind terminal and remove screw.

5. On eight cylinder engine starters unsolder the shunt field coil lead from the brush terminal and housing.

6. The brush holder plate with terminal, contact and brushes is serviced as an assembly.

7. Clean all older sealer from around plate and housing.

8. Remove the brush holder attaching screw.

9. On the shunt type, unsolder the solenoid winding from the brush terminal.

10. Remove 11/32 in. nut, washer and insulator from solenoid terminal.

11. Remove brush holder plate with brushes as an assembly.

12. Remove gear housing ground screw.

13. The solenoid assembly can be removed from the well.

14. Remove nut, washer and seal from starter battery terminal and remove terminal from plate.

15. Remove solenoid contact and plunger from solenoid and remove the coil sleeve.

16. Remove the solenoid return spring, coil retaining washer, retainer and the dust cover from the gear housing.

17. Release the snap-ring that locates the driven gear pinion shaft.

18. Release front retaining ring.

19. Push pinion shaft toward the rear and remove snap-ring, thrust washers, clutch and pinion, and two shift fork nylon actuators.

20. Remove driven gear and friction washer.

21. Pull shifting fork forward and remove moving core.

22. Remove fork retainer pin and shifting fork assembly. The gear housing with bushings is serviced as an assembly.

Replacement of Brushes

1. Brushes that are worn more than one-half the length of new brushes or are oil-soaked, should be replaced.

2. When resoldering the shunt field and solenoid lead, make a strong low-resistance connection using a high-temperature solder and resin flux. Do not use acid or acid-core solder. Do not break the shunt field wire units when removing and installing the brushes.

Starter Clutch and Pinion Gear Inspection

1. Do not immerse the starter clutch unit in a cleaning solvent. The outside of the clutch and pinion must be cleaned with a cloth so as not to wash the lubricant from the inside of the clutch.

2. Rotate the pinion. The pinion gear should rotate smoothly and in one direction only. If the starter clutch unit does not function properly, or if the pinion is worn, chipped, or burred, replace the starter clutch unit.

Commutator Inspection

1. Inspect the commutator and the surface contacted by the brushes when the starter is assembled, for flat spots, out-of-roundness, or excessive wear.

2. Reface the commutator if necessary, removing only a sufficient amount of metal to provide a smooth, even surface.

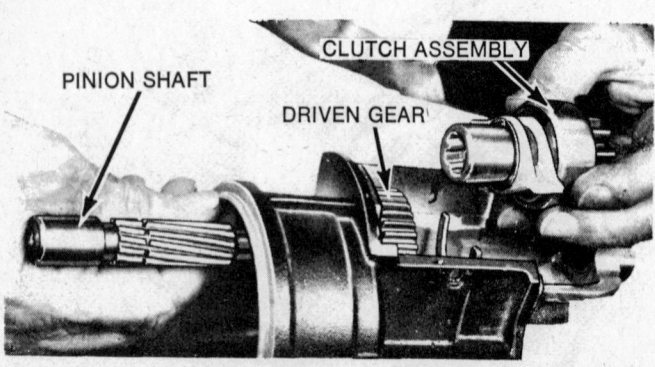

CLUTCH ASSEMBLY

PINION SHAFT

DRIVEN GEAR

Removing clutch assembly—rear wheel drive reduction gear motor (© Chrysler Corp)

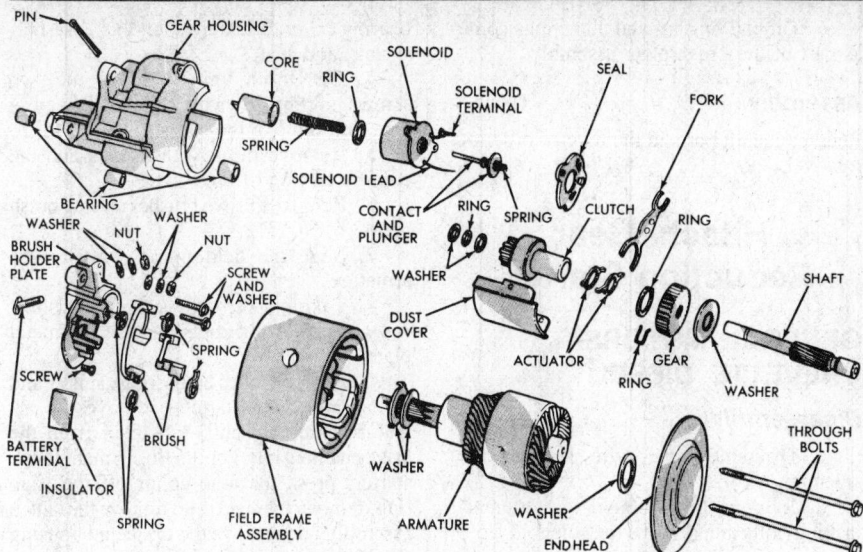

Rear wheel drive reduction gear motor (© Chrysler Corp)

3. Using light pressure, clean the grooves of the face of the commutator with a pointed tool. Neither remove any metal or widen the grooves.

Assembly

1. The shifter fork consists of two spring steel plates held together by two rivets. Before assembling the starter, check the plates for side movement. After lubricating between the plates with a small amount of SAE 10 engine oil, they should have about 1/16 in. side movement to insure proper pinion gear engagement.

2. Position the shift fork in the drive housing and install the shifting fork retainer pin. One tip of the pin should be straight and the other bent at a 15 degree angle away from the housing. The fork and retainer pin should operate freely after bending the tip of the pin.

3. Install the solenoid moving core and engage the shifting fork.

4. Place the pinion shaft into the drive housing and install the friction washer and drive gear.

5. Install the clutch and pinion assembly, thrust washer, and retaining washer.

6. Engage the shifting fork with the clutch actuators.

—————— **CAUTION** ——————
The friction washer must be positioned on the shoulder of the splines of the pinion shaft before the driven gear is positioned.

7. Install the driven gear snap-ring.
8. Install the pinion shaft retaining ring.
9. The starter solenoid return spring can now be inserted in the movable core.
10. Install the solenoid contact plunger assembly into the solenoid and reform the double wires so they can be curved around the contactor. This will allow the terminal stud to enter the brush holder properly.

—————— **CAUTION** ——————
The contactor must not touch these double wires after assembly is complete.

11. Assemble the battery terminal stud in the brush holder.

12. Position the seal on the brush holder plate.

13. Run the solenoid lead wire through the hole in the brush holder and attach the solenoid stud, insulating washer, flat washer, and nut.

14. Wrap the solenoid lead wire tightly around the brush terminal post and solder it.

15. Fix the brush holder to the solenoid attaching screws.

16. Gently lower the solenoid coil and brush plate into the gear housing.

17. Position the brush plate assembly into the starter gear housing, install the nuts, and tighten.

18. Solder the shunt coil lead wire to the starter brush terminal.

19. Install the brush terminal screw.

20. Position the field frame on the gear housing and start the armature into the housing, carefully engaging the splines on the shaft with the reduction gear by rotating the armature.

21. Install the fiber thrust washer and the steel washer on the armature shaft.

22. Replace the starter end housing and starter through-bolts; tighten securely.

NIPPONDENSO/ MITSUBISHI—REDUCTION STARTER

Disassembly

1. Disconnect the wire terminal from the field coil stud and move the rubber shield away from the wire end.

2. Remove the two through bolts from the end frame.

3. Remove the two screws from the end of the frame cap.

4. Remove the upper left solenoid screw and remove the wire retainer.

5. Remove the end shield.

6. Remove the two field frame brushes from the brush plate.

7. Remove the brush plate, slide the armature out of the field frame and remove the field frame.

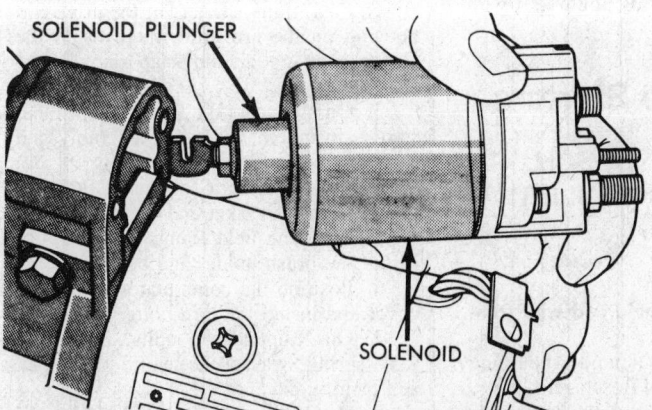

Nippondenso solenoid removal; Bosch similar (© Chrysler Corp.)

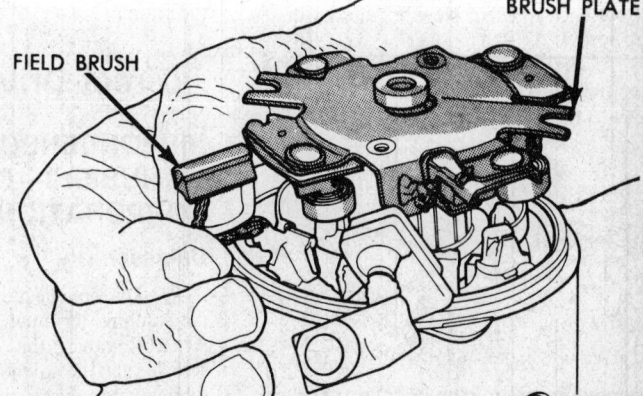

Field brush removal, Bosch starter; Nippondenso similar (© Chrysler Corp.)

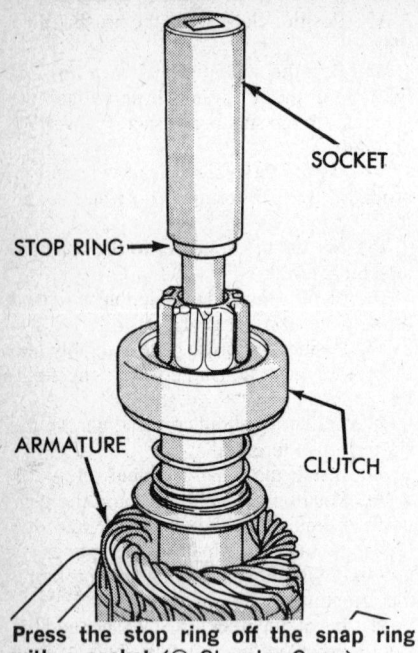

Press the stop ring off the snap ring with a socket (© Chrysler Corp.)

8. Remove the two screws from the gear housing and remove the gear housing from the solenoid.

9. Remove the clutch rollers and retainer. Remove the pinion and clutch.

10. Remove the solenoid steel ball and spring.

11. Remove the solenoid cover screws, remove the solenoid cover and remove the solenoid plunger.

Inspection and Service

1. Do not immerse parts in cleaning solvent. Immersing the field frame and coil assembly and/or armature will damage insulation. Wipe these parts with a cloth only.

2. Do not immerse drive unit in cleaning solvent. Drive clutch is pre-lubricated at the factory and solvent will wash lubrication from clutch.

3. The drive unit may be cleaned with a brush moistened with cleaning solvent and wiped dry with a cloth.

4. Brushes that are worn more than ½ the length of a new brush or are oil soaked should be replaced. New brushes are 11/16 in. long.

5. Field brushes are serviced as part of the field and frame assembly.

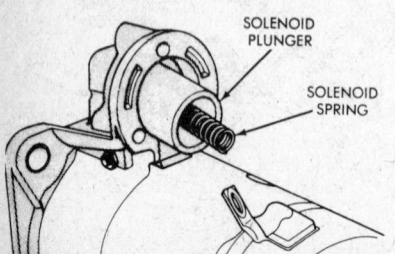

Removing solenoid plunger and spring on Bosch starter used on automatic transmission models (© Chrysler Corp)

6. Ground brushes and all springs come as part of the brush plate assembly.

Assembly

Reassemble all parts in the reverse order of removal.

Hitachi Gear Reduction Starter

GENERAL MOTORS— CHEVETTE DIESEL

Disassembly

1. Disconnect the wire lead at the solenoid.

2. Remove the solenoid to starter attaching bolts and remove the solenoid from the shift lever.

3. Remove the torsion spring from the solenoid.

4. Remove the starter through bolts and the rear cover.

5. Remove the four brushes from the brush holder.

6. Remove the frame, armature and brush holder as a unit from the gear case.

7. Remove the brushes and commutator carefully, do not allow them to contact adjacent parts.

8. Remove the brush holder and pull the armature assembly from the frame.

9. Remove the bearing retainer and the pinion from the gear case.

10. Remove the retaining clip with appropriate tool and then disassemble the pinion assembly.

Inspection and Repair

1. Inspect all component parts, replace any that are damaged or worn.

Assembly

1. Assemble in the reverse order of removal. Apply lubricant to the pinion assembly before installation. Install the brushes in position after armature has been installed by raising the end off the brush springs. Install the brush holder by aligning it with the frame.

Direct Drive Starters

NIPPONDENSO, BOSCH, MITSUBISHI—CHRYSLER CORPORATION

Disassembly

1. Disconnect the field coil wire from the solenoid terminal.

2. Remove the solenoid mounting screws (and the solenoid Bosch auto. trans. models) and work the solenoid (plunger Bosch auto. trans. models) off the shift fork.

3. On Nippondenso units, remove the

bearing cover, armature shaft lock, washer, spring, and seal.

4. On Bosch units, remove the two screws holding down the end shield bearing cap, and remove the cap and washers.

5. Remove the two thru-bolts and the commutator end frame cover.

6. Remove the two brushes and the brush plate.

7. Slide the field frame off over the armature.

8. Take out the shift lever pivot bolt.

9. Take off the rubber gasket and metal plate.

10. For the Bosch auto. trans. starter and all Nippondenso starters, remove the armature assembly and shift lever from the drive end housing. For the Bosch man. trans. starter, press the stop collar off the snap ring, remove the snap ring, remove the clutch assembly and remove the drive end housing from the armature.

11. For all except the Bosch man. trans. starter, press the stop collar off the snap ring, then remove the snap ring, stop collar and clutch.

Inspection and Service

1. Brushes that are worn more than one-half the length of new brushes, or are oil-soaked, should be replaced. New brushes are 11/16 in. long.

2. Do not immerse the starter clutch unit in cleaning solvent. Solvent will wash the lubricant from the clutch.

3. Place the drive unit on the armature shaft and, while holding the armature, rotate the pinion. The drive pinion should rotate smoothly in one direction only. The pinion may not rotate easily but as long as it rotates smoothly it is in good condition. If the clutch unit does not function properly, or if the pinion is worn, chipped, or burred, replace the unit.

Assembly

1. Lubricate the armature shaft and splines with SAE 10 or 30 W oil.

2. On all except the Bosch man. trans. starter, install the clutch, stop collar, lock ring and shift fork on the armature. On the Bosch man. trans. starter, fit the drive end housing on the armature, then install the clutch, stop collar and snap ring on the armature.

3. On all except the Bosch man. trans. starter, install the armature assembly and shift fork in the drive end housing.

4. Install the shift fork pivot bolt. Install the rubber gasket and metal plate.

5. Slide the field frame into position. Install the brush holder and brushes.

6. Position the commutator end frame cover and install the thru-bolts.

7. On Nippondenso units, install the seal, spring, washer, armature shaft lock and bearing cover.

8. On Bosch units, install the shim and armature shaft lock. Check the end play (0.002–0.012 in.). Install the bearing cover.

9. Assemble the solenoid (or plunger—Bosch auto. trans. models) to the shift fork and install the solenoid with its mounting bolts. Connect the field wire to the solenoid.

Autolite/Motorcraft Positive Engagement Starter Motor

FORD MOTOR CO. AND AMERICAN MOTORS

This starting motor is a series-parallel wound, four pole, four brush unit. It is equipped with an overrunning clutch drive pinion, which is engaged with the flywheel ring gear by an actuating lever, operated by a movable pole piece. This pole piece is hinged to the starter frame and can drop into position through an opening in the frame.

Three conventional field coils are located at three pole piece positions. The fourth field coil is designed to serve also as an engaging coil and a hold-in coil for the operation of the drive pinion.

When the ignition switch is turned to the start position, the starter relay is energized and current flows from the battery to the starter motor terminal. This prime surge of

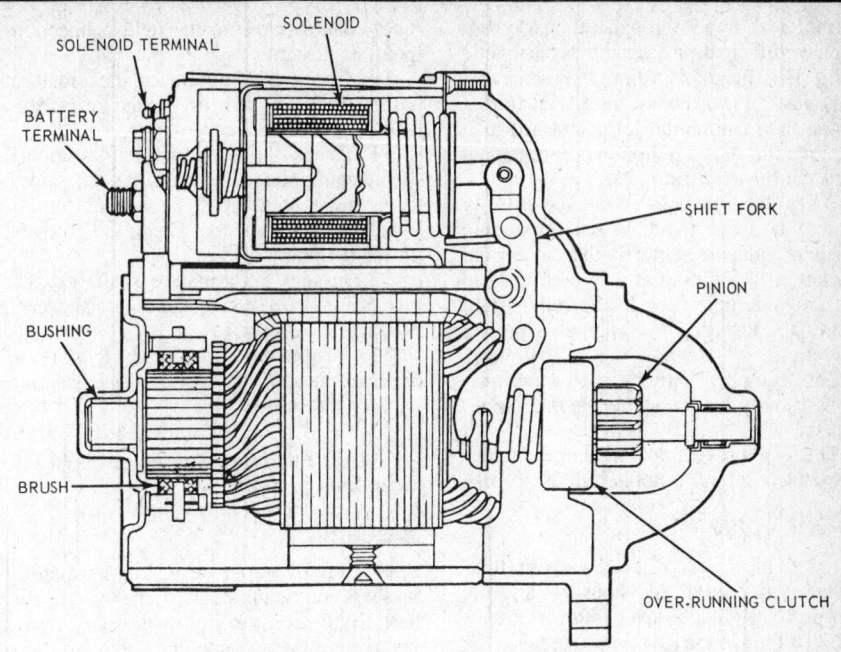

Ford solenoid actuated starter motor (© Ford Motor Co)

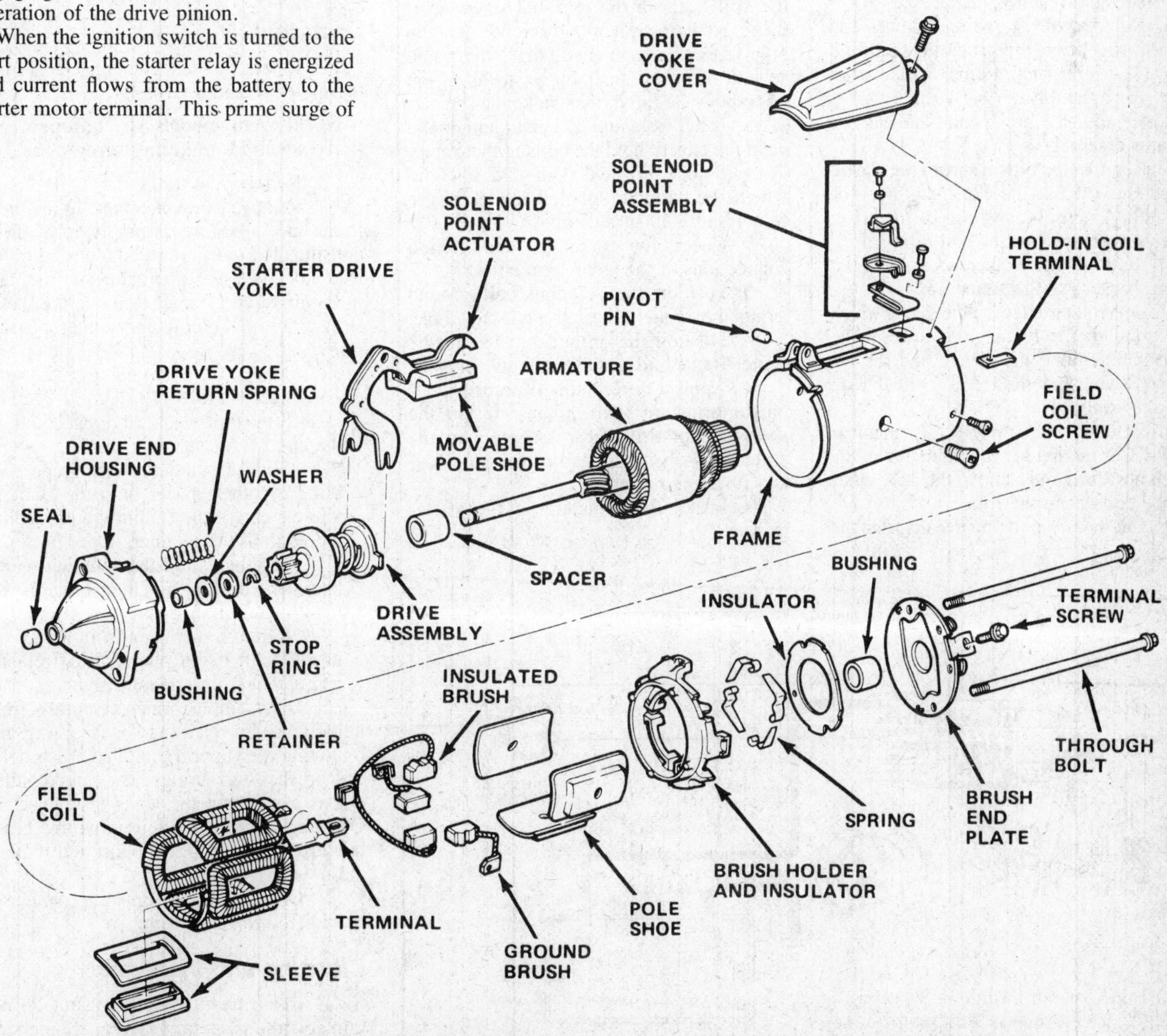

Exploded view of Ford positive engagement starter motor, typical of all later models (© AMC)

U47

current first flows through the starter engaging coil, creating a very strong magnetic field. This magnetism draws the movable pole piece down toward the starter frame, which then causes the lever attached to it to move the starter pinion into engagement with the flywheel ring gear.

When the movable pole shoe is fully seated, it opens the field coil grounding contacts, and the starter is then in normal operation. A holding coil is used to hold the movable pole shoe in the fully seated position during the engine cranking operation.

Cars equipped with automatic transmissions usually have a starter neutral circuit control.

This is to prevent operation of the starter if the selector lever is not in Neutral or Park.

Disassembly

1. Remove the cover screw, cover, thru-bolts, starter drive end housing, and the starter drive plunger lever return spring.
2. Remove the pivot pin that holds the starter gear plunger lever and remove the lever and the armature.
3. Remove the stop ring retainer and the stop ring from the armature shaft and discard the stop ring. Remove the starter drive gear assembly.
4. Remove the brush end plate and the insulator assembly.
5. Remove the brushes from the plastic holder and lift out the brush holder. For reassembly, note the position of the brush holder with respect to the end terminal.
6. Remove the two screws holding the ground brushes to the frame.
7. Bend up the edges of the sleeve which is inserted in the rectangular hole in the frame and remove the sleeve and the retainer. Detach the field coil ground wire from the copper tab.
8. Remove the three coil retaining screws. Cut the field coil connection at the switch post lead and remove the pole shoes and the coils from the frame.
9. Cut the positive brush leads from the

field coils as close to the field connection point as possible.
10. Check the armature and the armature windings for broken or burned insulation and open circuits and grounds.
11. Check the commutator for runout. If the commutator is rough, has flat spots, or is more than 0.005 in. out of round, reface the commutator. Clean the grooves in the commutator face.
12. Inspect the armature shaft and the two bearings for scoring and excessive wear. Replace if necessary.
13. Inspect the starter drive. If the gear teeth are pitted, broken, or excessively worn, replace the starter drive.

NOTE: Factory brush length is ½ in; wear limit is ¼ in.

Assembly

1. Install starter terminal, insulator, washers and retaining nut in the frame. (Be sure to position the slot in the screw perpendicular to the frame end surface.)
2. Position coils and pole pieces, with the coil leads in the terminal screw slot, then install the retaining screws. As the pole screws are tightened, strike the frame several sharp hammer blows to align the pole shoes. Tighten, then stake the screws.
3. Install solenoid coil and retainer and bend the tabs to hold the coils to the frame.
4. Solder the field coils and solenoid wire to the starter terminal, using resin-core solder and a 300 watt iron.
5. Check for continuity and ground connections in the assembled coils.
6. Position the solenoid coil ground terminal over the nearest ground screw hole.
7. Position the ground brushes to the starter frame and install retaining screws.
8. Apply a thin coating of Lubriplate® on the armature shaft splines. Install the starter motor drive gear assembly to the armature shaft and install a new stop ring and stop ring retainer.
9. Install the armature in the starter frame.

10. Position the starter drive gear plunger lever to the frame and the starter drive assembly. Install the pivot pin. Place some grease into the end housing bore. Fill it about ¼ full. Position the drive end housing to the frame.
11. Install the brush holder and install the brush springs. Positive brush leads should be positioned in their respective slots in the brush holder to prevent any grounding problems.
12. Install the brush end plate being certain that the end plate insulator is in the proper position on the end plate.
13. Install the two thru-bolts to the starter frame and torque them to 55–75 inch lbs.
14. Install the starter drive plunger lever cover and tighten the retaining screw.

Delco-Remy Starter Motor

GENERAL MOTORS CORP. AND AMERICAN MOTORS

Disassembly

1. Detach the field coil connectors from the motor solenoid terminal.

NOTE: On models so equipped, remove solenoid mounting screws.

2. Remove the thru-bolts.
3. Remove commutator end frame, field frame and armature assembly from drive housing. The diesel starter has an end frame insulator. The diesel armature will remain in the drive end frame. Remove the diesel shift lever pivot bolt and center bearing screws.
4. Remove the overrunning clutch from the armature shaft as follows:
   a. Slide the two-piece thrust collar off the end of the armature shaft.
   b. Slide a standard ½ in. pipe coupling or other spacer onto the shaft so that the end of the coupling butts against the edge of the retainer.
   c. Tap the end of the coupling with a hammer, driving retainer towards armature end of snap-ring.
   d. Remove snap-ring from its groove in the shaft using pliers. Slide retainer and clutch from armature shaft.
5. Disassemble brush assembly from field frame by releasing the V-spring and removing the support pin. The brush holders, brushes and springs now can be pulled out as a unit and the leads disconnected. On integral frame units, remove the brush holder from the brush support and remove the brush screw.
6. On models so equipped, separate solenoid from lever housing.

Cleaning and Inspection

1. Clean parts with a rag, but do not immerse the parts in a solvent. Immersion in a solvent will dissolve the grease that is

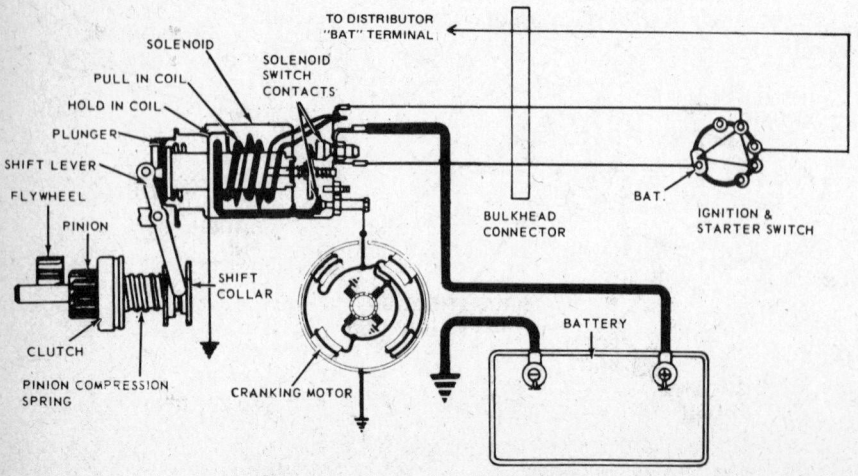

G.M. starter circuit (© G.M. Corp)

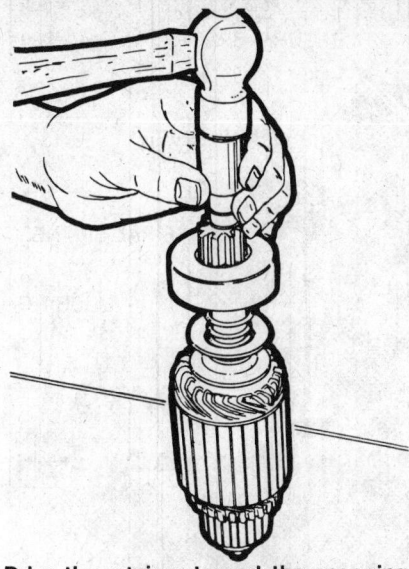

Drive the retainer toward the snap-ring —Delco-Remy starter

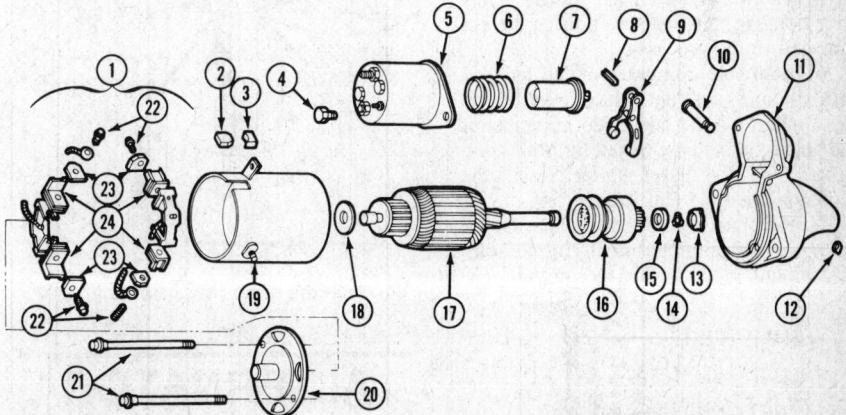

General Motors 350 V8 diesel starter exploded view (© Oldsmobile Div., G.M. Corp.)

packed in the clutch mechanism and damage the armature and field coil insulation.

2. Test overrunning clutch action. The pinion should turn freely in the overrunning direction and must not slip in the cranking direction. Check pinion teeth to see that they have not been chipped, cracked, or excessively worn. Replace the unit if necessary.

3. Inspect the armature commutator. If the commutator is rough or out of round, it should be turned down and undercut.

NOTE: Undercut the insulation between the commutator bars by ¹⁄₃₂ in.

This undercut must be the full width of the insulation and flat at the bottom; a triangular groove will not be satisfactory. Most later starter motor models use a molded armature commutator design and no attempt to undercut the insulation should be made or serious damage may result to the commutator.

Assembly

1. Install brushes into holders. Install solenoid, if so equipped.

2. Assemble insulated and grounded brush holder together using the V-spring and position the assembled unit on the support pin. Push holders and spring to bottom of support and rotate spring to engage the slot in support. Attach ground wire to grounded brush and field lead wire to insulated brush, then repeat for other brush sets.

3. Assemble overrunning clutch to armature shaft as follows:

a. Lubricate drive end of shaft with silicone lubricant.

b. Slide clutch assembly onto shaft with pinion outward. On diesel starter, install center bearing and fiber washer first.

c. Slide retainer onto shaft with cupped surface facing away from pinion.

d. Stand armature up on a wood surface, commutator downwards. Position snap-ring on upper end of shaft and drive it onto shaft with a small block of wood and a hammer. Slide snap-ring into groove.

e. Install thrust collar onto shaft with shoulder next to snap-ring.

f. With retainer on one side of snap-ring and thrust collar on the other side, squeeze together with two sets of pliers until ring seats in retainer. On models without thrust collar use a washer. Remember to remove washer before continuing.

4. Lubricate drive end bushing with silicone lubricant, then slide armature and

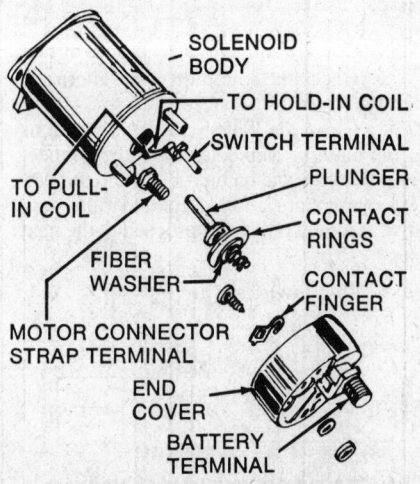

Delco-Remy starter solenoid

1 Brush and holder set
2 Grommet
3 Grommet
4 Screw
5 Solenoid
6 Plunger return spring
7 Plunger
8 Plunger pin
9 Shift fork
10 Shift fork shaft
11 Drive end housing
12 Shift fork shaft retaining ring
13 Thrust collar
14 Pinion stop retainer ring
15 Pinion stop collar
16 Clutch and drive assembly
17 Armature
18 Washer
19 Frame and field assembly
20 Commutator end frame
21 Through bolts
22 Screw
23 Brush
24 Brush holder

Exploded view of the Delco-Remy 5 MT starter, typical of all later models © AMC

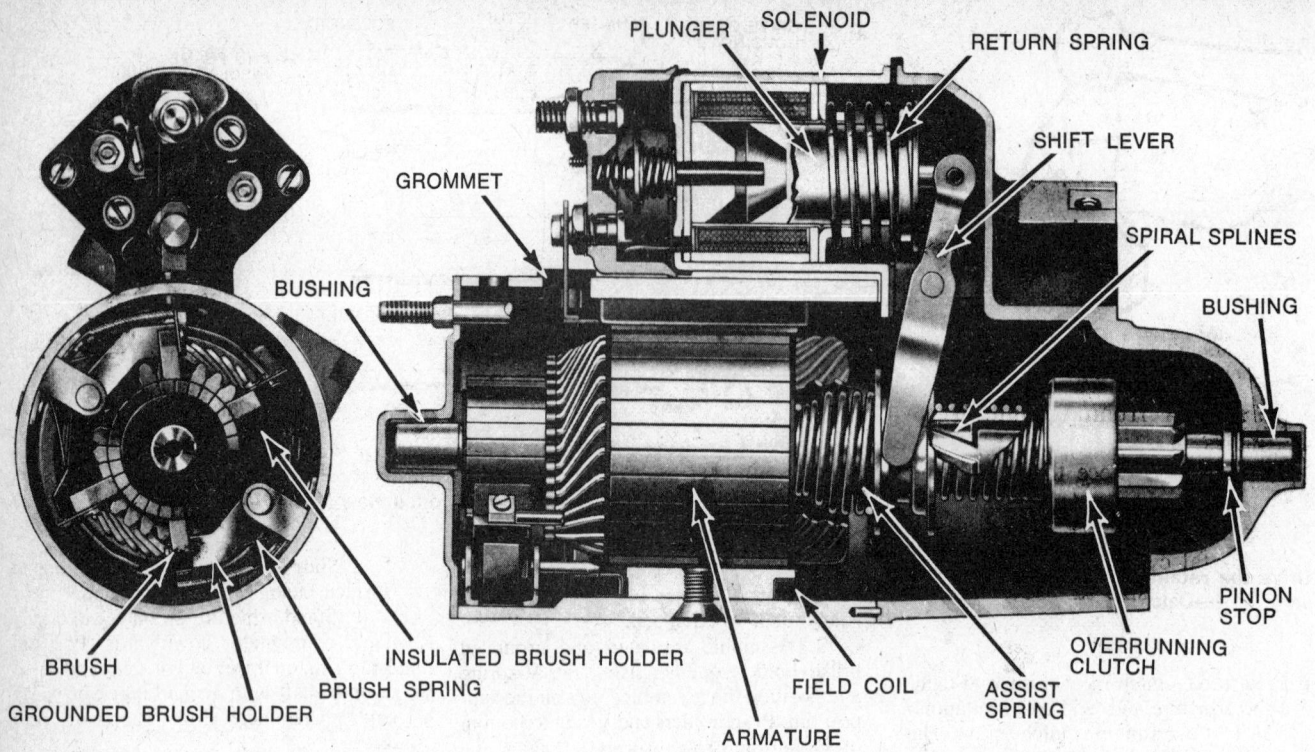

PLUNGER · SOLENOID · RETURN SPRING · SHIFT LEVER · SPIRAL SPLINES · BUSHING · GROMMET · BUSHING · PINION STOP · OVERRUNNING CLUTCH · ASSIST SPRING · FIELD COIL · ARMATURE · INSULATED BRUSH HOLDER · BRUSH SPRING · GROUNDED BRUSH HOLDER · BRUSH

Typical Delco-Remy starter motor using an assist spring—light duty Chevrolet illustrated
(© Chevrolet Div., G.M. Corp)

clutch assembly into place, at the same time engaging shift lever with clutch. On non-integral starters, the shift lever may be installed in the drive gear housing first. Install the center bearing screws and shift lever pivot bolt on the diesel starter.

5. Position field frame over armature and apply sealer (silicone) between frame and solenoid case. Position frame against drive housing, making sure brushes are not damaged in the process.

6. Lubricate commutator end bushing with silicone lubricant, place a washer on the armature shaft and slide commutator end frame onto shaft. Install thru-bolts and tighten. On the diesel starter, install the insulator, then the end frame.

7. Reconnect field coil connectors to the solenoid motor terminal. Install solenoid mounting screws, if so equipped.

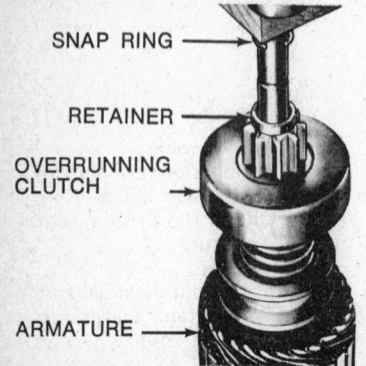

SNAP RING · RETAINER · OVERRUNNING CLUTCH · ARMATURE

Forcing snap ring over armature shaft—Delco-Remy motor
(© Chevrolet Div., G.M. Corp)

8. Check pinion clearance; it should be 0.010–0.140 in. with the pinion in cranking position on all models.

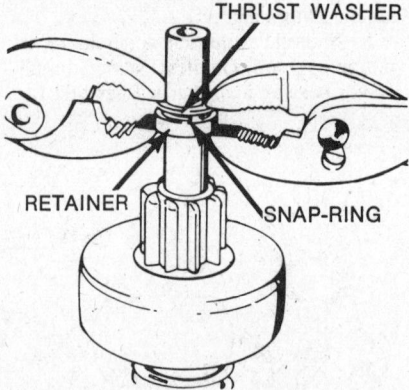

THRUST WASHER · RETAINER · SNAP-RING

Squeeze the snap-ring into its groove

ALTERNATOR SYSTEM SERVICE

PRELIMINARY CHARGING SYSTEM INSPECTION

NOTE: Before performing any tests on the charging system, these precautions should be taken to ensure the accuracy of the tests in this section.

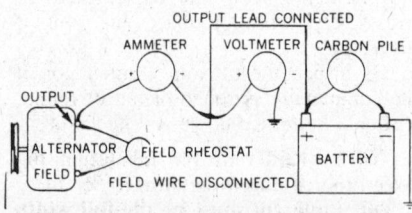

OUTPUT LEAD CONNECTED · AMMETER · VOLTMETER · CARBON PILE · OUTPUT · ALTERNATOR · FIELD · FIELD RHEOSTAT · BATTERY · FIELD WIRE DISCONNECTED

Checking charging system resistance—typical

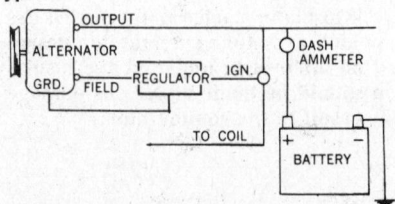

OUTPUT · ALTERNATOR · GRD. · FIELD · REGULATOR · IGN. · DASH AMMETER · TO COIL · BATTERY

Alternator system with ammeter in circuit

1. Check the condition of the alternator belt and tighten it if necessary.

2. Clean the battery cable connections at the battery. Make sure that the connections between the battery wires and the battery clamps are good. Reconnect the negative terminal only, and proceed to the next step.

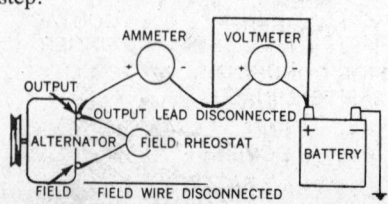

AMMETER · VOLTMETER · OUTPUT · OUTPUT LEAD DISCONNECTED · ALTERNATOR · FIELD RHEOSTAT · BATTERY · FIELD · FIELD WIRE DISCONNECTED

Checking current output of charging system—typical

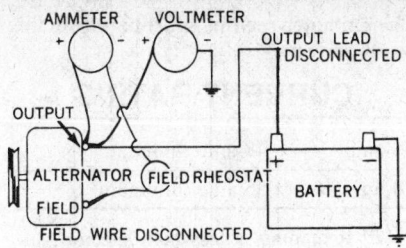

Checking current field draw—typical

3. With the key off, insert a test light between the positive terminal on the battery and the disconnected positive battery terminal clamp. If the test light comes on, there is a short in the electrical system of the car. The short has to be repaired before proceeding. If the light fails to glow, reconnect the clamp and proceed to the next step.

NOTE: **Alternators with transistor-ized regulators sometimes draw a slight current even when the key is turned off. To properly check these systems for a short, the regulator must be disconnected. Also, on cars equipped with an electric clock, disconnect the lead wire from the clock.**

4. Check the charging system wiring for breaks or shorts.

5. Check the battery to make sure that is fully charged and in good condition.

CHRYSLER ISOLATED FIELD ALTERNATOR (ELECTRONIC REGULATOR)

The Chrysler isolated field alternator derives its name from its construction. Both of the brushes are insulated from ground and there is no heat sink connection, thereby isolating the internal field.

Troubleshooting

NOTE: **See the "Preliminary Charging System Inspection" section before proceeding further. Make sure that the continuous running ventilation blower, if equipped, is disconnected. This blower will run with the key turned on even if the blower controls are off unless disconnected.**

Fusible Links

Chrysler Corporation cars have fusible links connected between the starter relay and junction block. Failure of this link will cause all electrical systems to stop functioning.

Charging Circuit Resistance Test

NOTE: **The following test requires the use of a carbon pile rheostat, a voltmeter, and an ammeter.**

1. Disconnect battery ground cable.
2. Disconnect the lead from the alternator output (BAT) terminal.

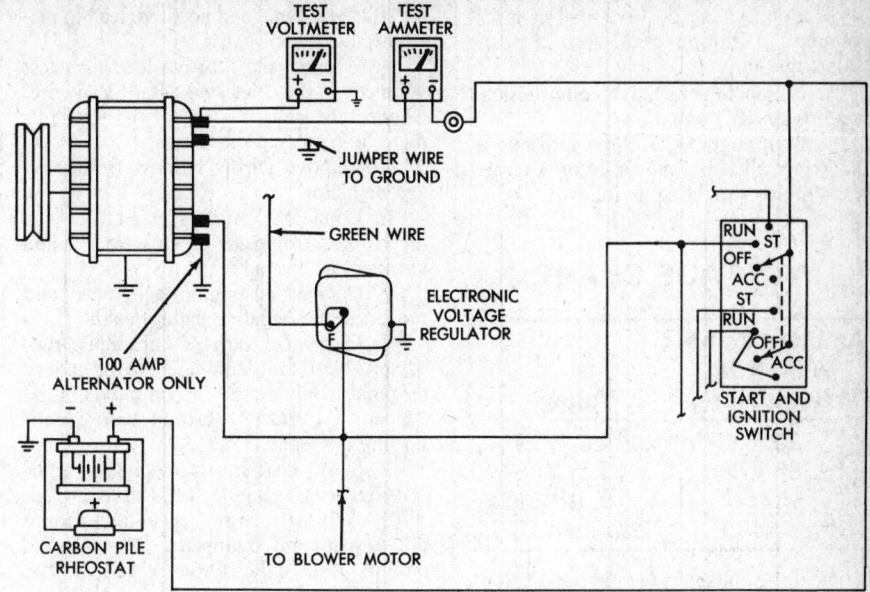

Current output test hookup (© Chrysler Corp.)

3. Hook up an ammeter as follows:
   a. Connect the positive lead to the alternator output terminal.
   b. Connect the negative lead to the lead just disconnected from the alternator output terminal.
4. Hook up voltmeter as follows:
   a. Connect the positive voltmeter lead to the lead just disconnected from the alternator output terminal.
   b. Connect the negative voltmeter lead to the positive battery post.
5. Disconnect the green lead wire from the alternator field (FLD) terminal.
6. Connect a jumper wire between alternator field terminal and ground.
7. Hook up a tachometer to the engine.
8. Connect the battery ground cable, then connect a carbon pile rheostat to the battery terminals.

── CAUTION ──

Be sure the carbon pile is in the "OPEN" or "OFF" position before connecting the leads to the battery terminals.

9. Start the engine and allow to idle.
10. Slowly adjust the engine speed and carbon pile until the ammeter registers 20 amps.
11. The voltmeter reading will now show the voltage drop in the charging circuit. There should not be more than 0.7 volt drop.
12. If the voltage drop exceeds 0.7 volt, stop the engine, clean and tighten all circuit connections, then repeat the test.

Current Output Test

NOTE: **This test requires the use of a carbon pile rheostat, a voltmeter, and an ammeter.**

1. Disconnect the negative battery cable.
2. Disconnect the BAT lead wire at the alternator output terminal. Connect an am-

meter in series between the alternator BAT terminal and the disconnected BAT lead wire.

3. Connect the positive lead of a voltmeter to the BAT terminal of the alternator. Connect the negative voltmeter lead to a ground.

4. Disconnect the green field wire at the alternator. Connect a jumper wire from the field terminal on the alternator to a ground. Connect a tachometer to the engine and reconnect the negative battery cable.

5. Connect a carbon pile rheostat between the battery terminals. Be sure the carbon pile is off before connecting the leads.

6. Start the engine and adjust speed to 1250 rpm; 900 rpm for the 100 or 117 amp alternator.

── CAUTION ──

Reduce the engine speed to idle immediately after starting the engine. Adjust the carbon pile and engine speed incrementally until the specified speed is reached. Do not allow the voltage reading to go above 16 volts.

Note voltmeter and ammeter readings. Maintain a 15 volt reading (13 volts for the 100 and 117 amp alternator) by adjusting the carbon pile control.

7. The current output must be no more than 3 amps below the alternator current rating.

NOTE: **If measured at the battery, current output will be approximately 5 amps lower than specified.**

8. If below specifications, internal trouble is indicated. Remove the alternator for further testing.

Electronic Voltage Regulator Test

1. Make sure battery terminals are clean and battery is charged.

2. Connect the positive lead of a test voltmeter to ignition terminal No. 1 of the ballast resistor.

3. Connect the negative voltmeter lead to a good *body* ground.

4. Start engine and allow it to idle at 1250 rpm, all lights and accessories turned off. Voltage should be as follows:

VOLTAGE CHART

Ambient Temp. ¼ in. from Regulator	Voltage
20°F.	14.9–15.9
80°F.	13.9–14.6
140°F.	13.3–13.9
over 140°F.	less than 13.6

5. If the voltage is *below* specifications or fluctuates, check the following:

a. Voltage regulator ground—check voltage drop between regulator cover and ground.

b. Harness wiring—disconnect regulator plug (ign. switch off), then turn on ign. switch and check for battery voltage at the terminal having the blue and green leads. *Wiring harness must be disconnected from the regulator when checking individuals leads.* If no voltage is present in either lead, the problem is in the car wiring or alternator field.

6. If Step 5 tests showed no malfunctions, install a new regulator and repeat Step 4.

7. If voltage is *above* specifications (Step 4), or fluctuates, check the following:

a. Ground between regulator and body, and between body and engine.

b. Ignition switch circuit between switch and regulator.

8. If voltage is still more than ½ volt above specifications, install a new regulator and repeat Step 4.

Chrysler Alternator and Electronic Voltage Regulator

Charging Circuit Resistance Test

The charging circuit resistance test will show the amount of "Voltage Drop" between the alternator output "Bat" terminal wire and battery.

1. Disconnect negative battery cable.

2. Disconnect "Bat" lead at alternator output terminal.

3. Connect a 0-100 ampere scale D.C. ammeter in series between the alternator "Bat" terminal and the disconnected "Bat" lead wire. Connect ammeter positive lead

to "Bat" terminal and negative lead to disconnected "Bat" lead.

4. Connect the positive lead of a test voltmeter to the connected "Bat" lead wire. Connect the negative lead of the test voltmeter to battery positive post.

5. Remove wiring harness from voltage regulator.

6. Connect a "Jumper" lead from wiring harness connector green wire (outside terminal) to ground.

7. Connect an engine tachometer and reconnect the negative battery cable.

8. Connect a variable carbonpile rheostat (C3950) or its equivalent to the battery terminals. Be sure the carbon pile is in the "Open" or "Off" position before connecting the leads.

9. Start engine. Immediately after starting, reduce engine speed to idle.

10. Adjust the engine speed and carbon pile to maintain 20 amperes flowing in the circuit. Observe the voltmeter reading. The voltmeter reading should not exceed .7 volts.

If a higher voltage drop is indicated, inspect, clean and tighten all connections in the charging circuit. A voltage drop test may be performed at each connection to locate the connection with excessive resistance. If the charging circuit resistance tested satisfactorily, reduce engine speed, turn off carbon pile and turn off ignition switch.

Current Output Test

The current output test determines whether or not the alternator is capable of delivering ts rated current output.

1. Disconnect negative battery cable.

2. Disconnect the "Bat" lead wire at the alternator output terminal.

3. Connect an ammeter (range 0-100 amps minimum) in series between the alternator "Bat" terminal and the disconnected "Bat" lead wire. Connect positive lead to disconnected "Bat" lead.

4. Connect the positive lead of a voltmeter (range 0-15 volts minimum) to the "Bat" terminal of the alternator.

5. Connect the negative lead of the voltmeter to a good ground.

6. Remove wiring harness connector from voltage regulator.

7. Connect a "Jumper Wire" from wiring harness connector green wire (outside terminal) to ground.

8. Connect an engine tachometer and reconnect negative battery cable.

9. Connect a variable carbon pile rheostat between the battery terminals. (Be sure the carbon pile is in the "Open" or "Off" position before connecting leads.)

10. Start engine. Immediately after starting reduce engine speed to idle.

11. Adjust carbon pile and engine speed in increments until a speed of 1250 RPM and voltmeter reading of 15 volts is obtained.

——————— **CAUTION** ———————
Do not allow voltage meter to read above 16 volts.

The ammeter reading must be within the limits shown.

CURRENT RATING

60 amp	— 47 amp minimum
78 amp	— 56 amp minimum

12. If reading is less than specified alternator should be removed from vehicle and "bench tested."

13. After current ouput test is completed reduce engine speed, turn off carbon pile and turn off ignition switch.

14. Disconnect negative battery cable. Remove test ammeter, voltmeter, tachometer and carbon pile.

15. Remove "Jumper Wire" between Voltage Regulator connector and ground. Connect wiring connector to Voltage Regulator.

16. Connect "Bat" lead to alternator "Bat" post. Reconnect negative battery cable.

Voltage Regulator Test

1. Clean the battery terminals and check the specific gravity. It should be above 1.220 to allow a properly regulated voltage check.

If the specific gravity is below 1.220, charge or use another battery and do not leave the uncharged battery in the circuit.

2. Connect positive lead of voltmeter to positive post on battery.

3. Connect the negative lead from the voltmeter to a good vehicle body ground.

4. Connect a tachometer to engine.

5. Start and operate engine at 1250 rpm with all lights and accessories turned off. Check voltmeter, the regulator is working properly if the voltage readings are in accordance with the voltage chart.

VOLTAGE CHART

Ambient Temperature Near Voltage Regulator		Voltage Range
−30°C	−20°F	14.39 to 15.9
27°C	80°F	13.9 to 14.6
60°C	140°F	13.3 to 13.9
Above 60°C	Above 140°F	Less than 13.60

It is normal for the car ammeter to show an immediate charge and then gradually return to normal position. The duration the ammeter hand remains to the right will be dependent on the length of cranking time.

6. If the voltage is below limits or is fluctuating, proceed as follows:

a. Check for a good voltage regulator ground. Voltage regulator ground is obtained through regulator case, to mounting screws and to sheet metal of vehicle. This is ground circuit that is to be checked for opens.

b. Turn off ignition switch and disconnect voltage regulator connector. Be sure terminals of connector have not spread open to cause an open or intermittant connection.

c. Do not start engine or distort terminals with voltmeter probe: turn on ignition switch, check for battery voltage at the wiring harness terminal. Both blue and green leads should read battery voltage. Turn off ignition switch.

d. If previous steps 6a through 6c tested satisfactory, then replace regulator and repeat test.

7. If the voltage is above the limits shown on the chart, proceed as follows:

a. Turn off the ignition switch and disconnect voltage regulator connector. Be sure terminals on the connector have not spread open.

b. Do not start engine or distort terminals with voltmeter probe: turn on ignition switch, check for battery voltage at the wiring harness terminal. Both blue and green leads should read battery voltage. Turn off ignition switch.

c. If previous steps 7a and 7b tested satisfactory, then replace regulator and repeat test.

Mitsubishi Alternator and Electronic Voltage Regulator

CHRYSLER CORP.

Troubleshooting

NOTE: See the "Preliminary Charging System Inspection" section before proceeding further. Make sure that the continuous running blower, if equipped, is disconnected. This blower will run with the key on even with the blower control off, unless disconnected.

Voltage Regulator Test

1. With the ign. switch off, disconnect the positive battery cable and connect an ammeter between the cable and the battery's positive terminal.

2. Connect a voltmeter between terminal "L" of the alternator and ground. The voltmeter reading should be zero. If voltage is present, suspect a defective alternator.

3. Turn the ign. switch on (not start). The voltmeter reading should be considerably lower than the battery voltage. If it is close to battery voltage, suspect a defective alternator.

4. Short circuit the ammeter terminals and start the engine. Make sure that when the engine is started, no starting current is applied to the ammeter.

5. Remove the short circuit from across

the ammeter terminals and increase engine speed immediately to 2,500 rpm and record the ammeter reading.

6. If the ammeter reading is 5A or less, take the voltmeter reading without changing the engine speed (2,500 rpm). The reading will be the charging voltage (14.4 ± 0.3V at 68°F).

7. If the ammeter reading is more than 5A, continue to charge the battery until the reading falls to less than 5A or replace the battery with a fully charged one.

Current Output Test

The current output test determines whether or not the alternator is able to deliver its rated output.

1. Turn off the ignition switch. Disconnect the battery ground (negative) cable.

2. Disconnect the "B" (battery) lead wire from the terminal on the rear of the alternator. Connect an ammeter between the "B" terminal of the alternator and the disconnected lead wire.

3. Connect the positive lead of a voltmeter (range 0–15 volts minimum) to the "B" terminal of the alternator. Connect the negative lead to a good ground.

4. Connect a tachometer to the engine. Reconnect the negative battery cable.

5. Connect a variable carbon pile rheostat between the battery terminals. Be sure the control switch is in the OFF position.

6. Start the engine and allow it to run at idle.

7. Adjust the carbon pile and run the engine at the rpms listed in the chart below. The current output should be close to the specifications.

    17-25A at 13.5 V and   500 rpm
    63-70A at 13.5 V and 1000 rpm
    74A at 13.5 V and 2000 rpm

8. If the readings are below specifications internal trouble is indicated. Remove the alternator for further testing.

Delcotron SI Series

GENERAL MOTORS CORP. AND AMERICAN MOTORS

This system is an integrated AC generating system containing a built-in voltage regulator.

The regulator is mounted inside the slip ring end frame. All regulator components are enclosed in an epoxy molding making the regulator nonadjustable. The rotor bearings contain a sufficient supply of lubricant to eliminate the need for periodic lubrication. No periodic maintenance, except belt adjustment, is necessary.

Troubleshooting

NOTE: See the "Preliminary Charging System Inspection" section before proceeding further. Make sure that the continuous running blower, if equipped, is disconnected. This blower will run with the key on even if the blower control is off, unless disconnected.

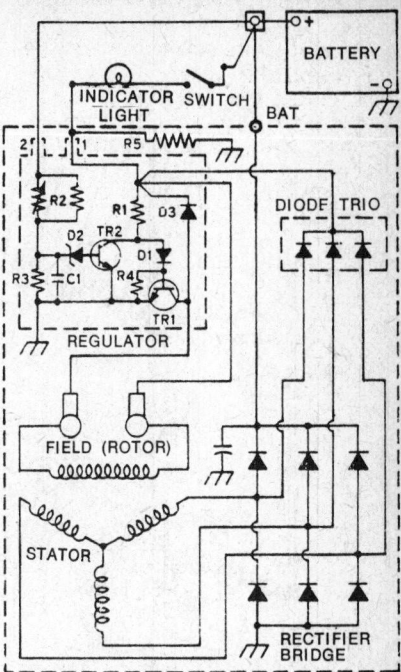

Typical 10-SI charging system circuitry
(© Chevrolet Div., G.M. Corp.)

Fusible Links

All GM cars are equipped with fusible links. The links are made of a piece of wire, several gauges smaller than the supply wire that they are connected to. Their function is similar to that of a fuse, protecting the wiring in the event of an overload or a short circuit. They will usually melt before the wiring is damaged elsewhere in the circuit.

These links must be inspected before continuing with troubleshooting procedures.

Charging System Operation

1. With the engine running and all electrical systems turned off, place a current indicator over the positive battery cable.

2. If a charge of about 5 amps is recorded, the charging system is working. If a draw of about 5 amps is recorded, the system is not working. The needle moves toward the battery when a charge condition is indicated, and away from the battery when a draw condition is indicated. If a draw is indicated, proceed with further testing. If an excessive charge (10–15 amps) is indicated, check for an over charge, caused by a faulty regulator.

Indicator Light Circuit Check:

Check the indicator light for normal operation:

Ignition Switch Condition	Light Condition	Engine Condition
Off	Off	Stopped
On	On	Stopped
On	Off	Running

If the alternator light is operating properly, proceed to the next section. If one of the following conditions exists, proceed as directed:

A. *Ignition switch off, light stays on:* Disconnect leads from Nos. 1 and 2 terminals. If the light remains on, there is a short between these two leads. If the lamp goes out, replace the rectifier bridge.

B. *Ignition switch on, light off, engine not running:* This condition can be caused by the defects listed in A., by reversal of Nos. 1 and 2 leads at the alternator, or by an open circuit. If the circuit is open proceed as follows:

1. Connect a voltmeter from No. 2 alternator terminal to ground. If a reading is obtained, proceed to the next step. If a zero reading is obtained, repair the circuit between No. 2 terminal and the battery. If the light comes on, no further testing is necessary.

2. With the ignition switch on and with No. 1 and 2 terminals disconnected at the alternator, momentarily ground No. 1 terminal lead.

CAUTION
Do not ground No. 2 Lead.

If the light still doesn't light, check for a blown fuse or fusible link, burned out bulb, defective bulb socket, or an open No. 1 lead circuit between generator and ignition switch.

3. If the lamp lights, remove the ground at No. 1 terminal, and with No. 1 and 2 terminals connected to the alternator, insert a screwdriver into the test hole at the back of the alternator to ground the winding.

4. If the light does not come on, check the connection between the wiring harness and No. 1 terminal of the alternator. If the connection is all right, disassemble the alternator and check the brushes, slip rings, and field winding.

5. If a light now comes on, and a reading was obtained in Step 1, check the resistor in line (circuit board), if the resistor checks out alright, replace the regulator.

C. *Switch on, Light on, Engine Running.* The causes for this condition are covered in Charging System Test.

Charging System Test

1. After battery condition, drive belt tension, and wiring terminals and connections have been checked, charge the battery fully and perform the following test:

2. Connect a test voltmeter between the alternator BAT terminal and ground, ignition switch on. Connect the voltmeter in turn to alternator terminals No. 1 and No. 2 the other voltmeter lead being grounded as before. A zero reading indicates an open circuit between the battery and each connection at the alternator. If this test discloses no faults in the wiring, proceed to Step 3.

3. Connect the test voltmeter to the alternator BAT terminals, the other test lead

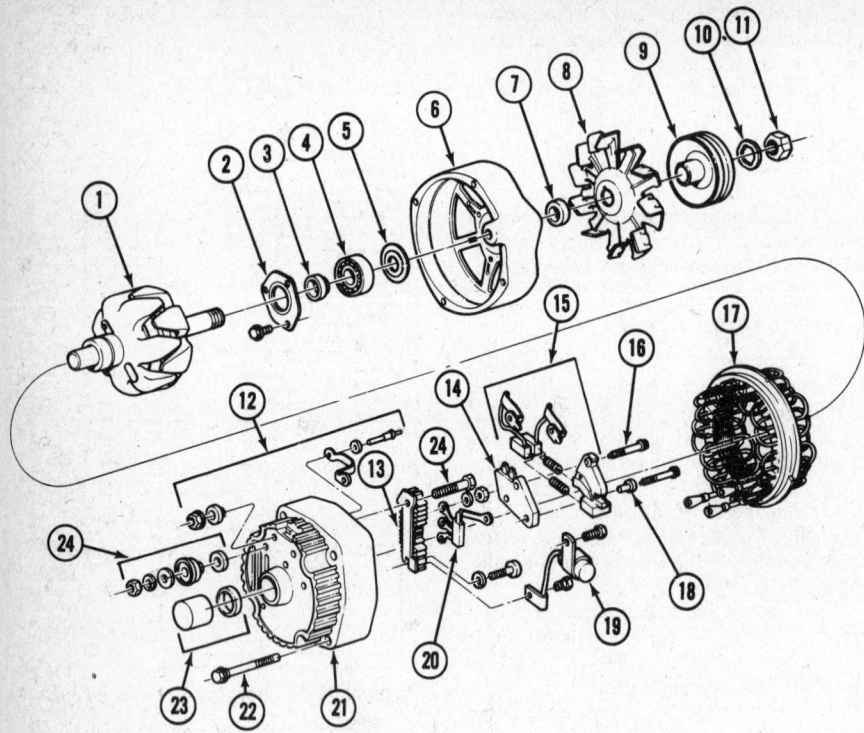

1	Rotor	9	Pulley	17	Stator
2	Front bearing retainer	10	Lockwasher	18	Insulating washer
3	Inner collar	11	Pulley nut	19	Capacitor
4	Bearing	12	Terminal assembly	20	Diode trio
5	Washer	13	Rectifier bridge	21	Rear housing
6	Front housing	14	Regulator	22	Through bolt
7	Outer collar	15	Brush assembly	23	Bearing and seal assembly
8	Fan	16	Screw	24	Terminal assembly

Delcotron 10SI alternator—exploded view (© American Motors Corp.)

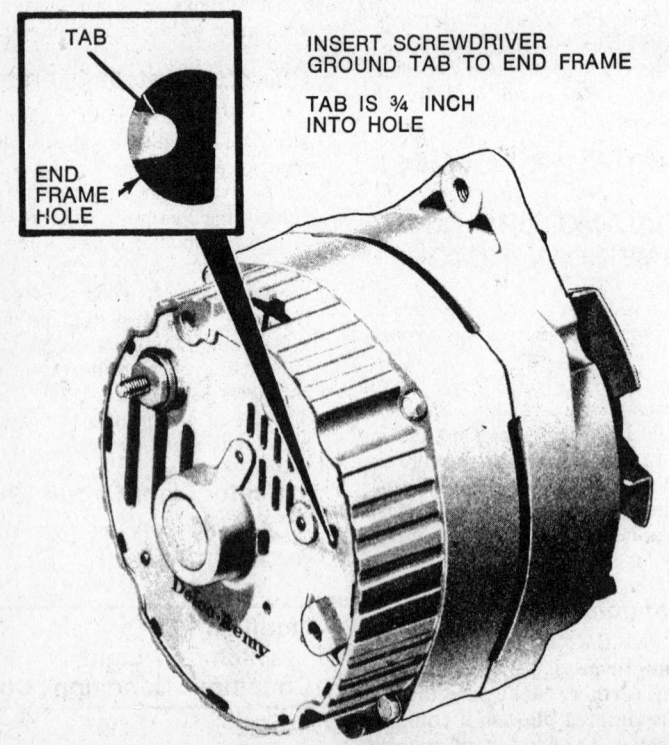

TAB

INSERT SCREWDRIVER
GROUND TAB TO END FRAME

TAB IS ¾ INCH
INTO HOLE

END FRAME HOLE

10-SI Delcotron end view
(© Chevrolet Div., G.M. Corp)

to a ground. Start the engine and run it at 1,500–2,000 rpm with the headlights on high beam and all of the electrical accessories on high. If the voltmeter reads 12.8 volts or greater, the alternator is good and no further checks need be made. If the voltmeter reads less than 12.8 volts, ground the field winding by inserting a screwdriver into the test hole in the end frame.

— CAUTION —
Do not force tab more than ¾ in. into end frame.

a. If the voltage increases to 13 volts or more, the regulator unit is defective.

b. If the voltage does not increase significantly, alternator is defective.

Autolite/Motorcraft Alternator with External Regulator

FORD MOTOR CO. AND AMERICAN MOTORS

Troubleshooting

NOTE: See the "Preliminary Charging System Inspection" section before proceeding further.

Fusible Links

1. Check the fusible link located between the starter relay and the alternator. Replace the link if it is burned or open.

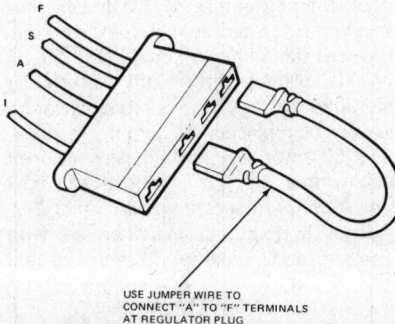

Connecting a jumper wire from the "A" to "F" terminals of the regulator plug (© Ford Motor Co.)

Charging System Operation

NOTE: If the current indicator is to give an accurage reading, the battery cables must be of the same gauge and length as the original equipment.

1. With the engine running, and all electrical systems turned off, place a current indicator over the positive battery cable.

2. If a charge of about 5 amps is recorded, the charging system is not working. If a draw of about 5 amps is recorded, the system is not working. The needle moves

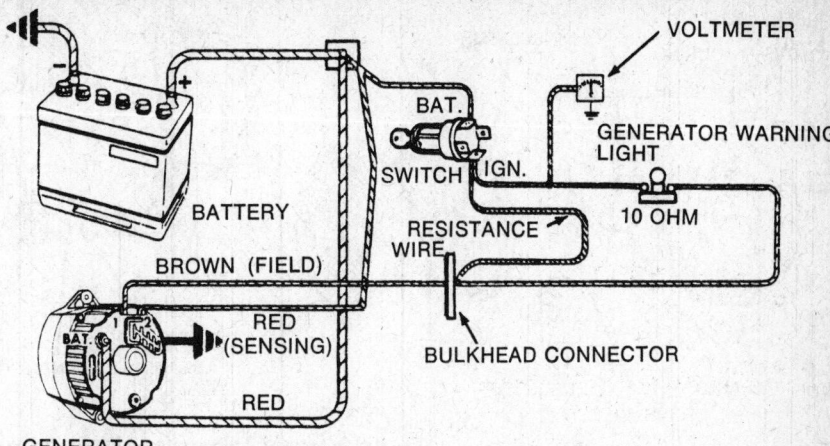

Typical 10-SI alternator charging circuit (© Chevrolet Div., G.M. Corp.)

toward the battery when a charge condition is indicated. If a draw is indicated, continue to the next testing procedure. If an overcharge of 10–15 amps is indicated, check for a faulty regulator or a bad ground at the regulator or the alternator.

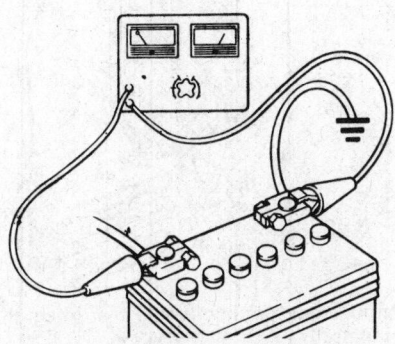

Voltmeter connections isolation test and ignition circuit test (© Ford Motor Co.)

Testing the Ignition Switch to Regulator Circuit

1. Disconnect the regulator wiring harness from the regulator.

2. Turn on the key. Using a test light or voltmeter, check for voltage between the I wire and ground. Check for voltage between the A wire and ground. If voltage is present at this part of the system, the circuit is OK. If there is no voltage at the I wire, check for a burned-out charge indicator bulb, a burned-out resistor, or a break or short in the wiring. If there is no voltage present at the A wire, check for a bad connection at the starter relay or a break or short in the wire.

Isolation Test

This test determines whether the regulator or the alternator is faulty, after the rest of the circuit is found to be in good working order.

1. Disconnect the regulator wiring harness from the regulator.

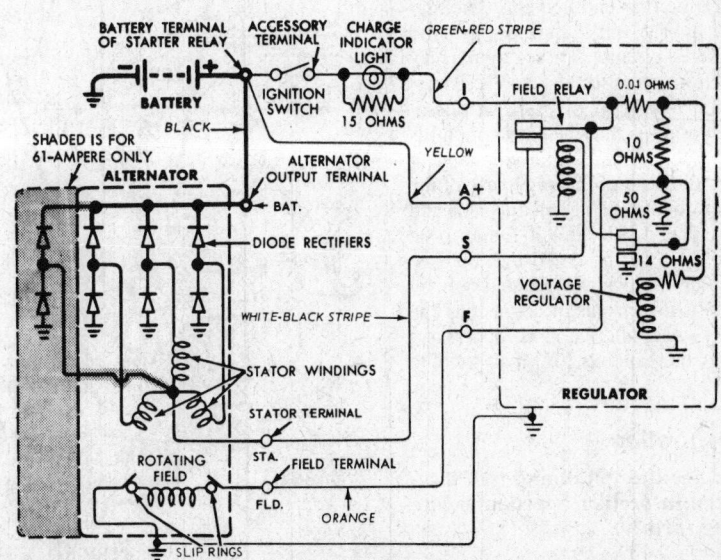

Charging system schematic with electro-mechanical regulator and charging light (© Ford Motor Co)

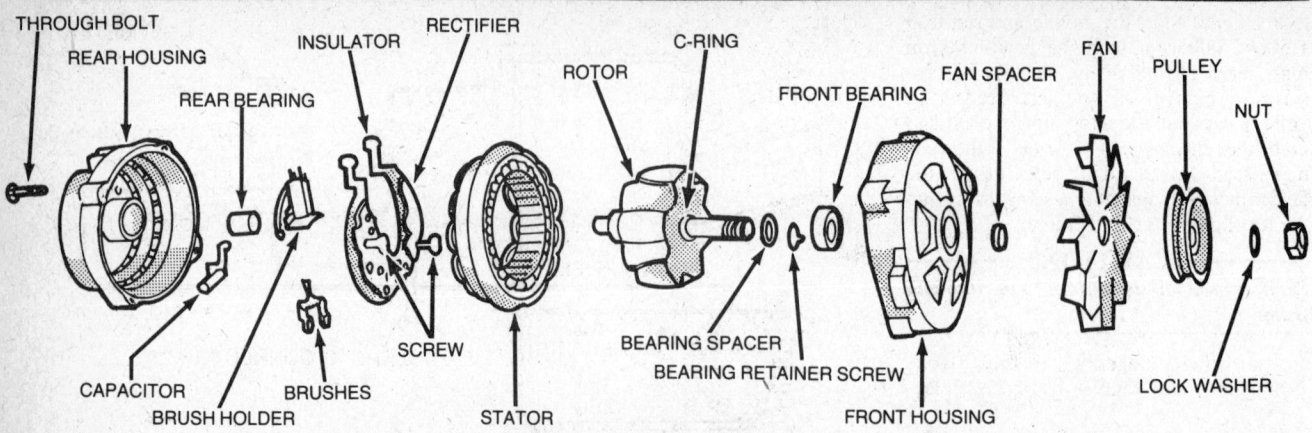

THROUGH BOLT · REAR HOUSING · REAR BEARING · INSULATOR · RECTIFIER · ROTOR · C-RING · FRONT BEARING · FAN SPACER · FAN · PULLEY · NUT · CAPACITOR · BRUSH HOLDER · BRUSHES · SCREW · STATOR · BEARING SPACER · BEARING RETAINER SCREW · FRONT HOUSING · LOCK WASHER

Ford side terminal alternator—exploded view

2. Connect a jumper wire from the A wire to the F wire in the wiring harness plug.

3. Connect a voltmeter to the battery. The positive voltmeter lead goes to the positive terminal and the negative lead to the negative terminal. Record the reading on the voltmeter.

4. Turn off all of the electrical systems and start the engine. Do not race the engine.

5. Gradually increase engine speed to 1500–2000 rpm. The voltmeter reading should increase above the previously recorded battery voltage reading by at least one to two volts. If there is no increase, the alternator is not working correctly. If there is an increase, the voltage regulator needs to be replaced.

Ford/Autolite/ Motorcraft Alternators—with Internal Regulator

Some vehicles are equipped with an Autolite alternator having an integral regulator mounted to the rear end housing. The regulator is a hybrid unit feature use of solid state integrated circuits. These circuits may consist of transistors, diodes and resistors. The unusual feature of this type of micro-electronic circuit is that the entire circuit is within a silicone crystal approximately ⅛ in. square. Because of the small size of the circuit, it is not repairable or adjustable and must be replaced as a unit if found to be defective. It should be noted that the size of the regulator housing is dictated only by the fact that some means of connecting the regulator to the alternator is necessary. Overhaul is the same as for other Autolite alternators.

Troubleshooting

NOTE: See the "Preliminary Charging System Inspection" section before proceeding further.

Fusible Links

1. Check the fusible link located be-

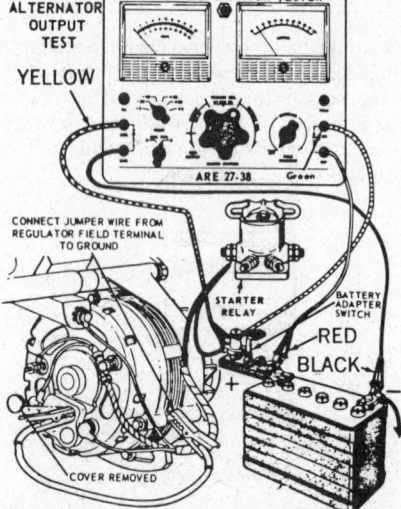

Output test connection—Ford integral regulator

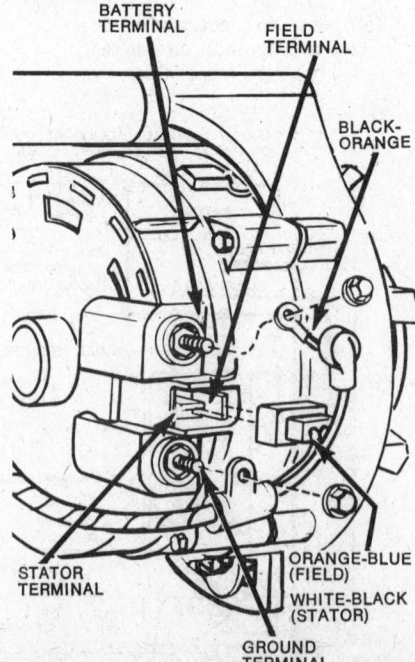

Wiring connections—Ford side terminal alternator (© Ford Motor Co)

tween the starter relay and the alternator. Replace the link if it is burned or open.

Output Test

1. Place transmission in Neutral or Park.

2. Remove the positive battery cable and install a battery adapter switch in the line.

3. Attach one lead of a test voltmeter to the negative battery post and the other test lead to the circuit side of the adapter switch.

4. Connect a test ammeter to each side of the adapter switch, so that charging current will go through the ammeter when the switch is opened.

5. Connect a jumper wire between the alternator frame and the integral regulator field terminal (cover plug removed).

6. Close adapter switch, start engine and open adapter switch.

7. Running engine at 2,000 rpm, observe voltmeter and ammeter. At 15 volts indicated, the ammeter should read 50–57 amps. If so, and there is still a no-charge condition, the regulator is probably faulty and must be replaced. An output 2–8 amps. below 50 amps. usually indicates an open diode rectifier, while an output 10–15 amps. below minimum specifications usually indicates a shorted diode. An alternator with a shorted diode usually will whine at idle speed.

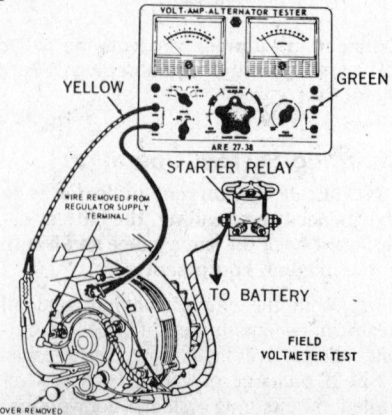

Voltmeter connection for field test—Ford integral regulator

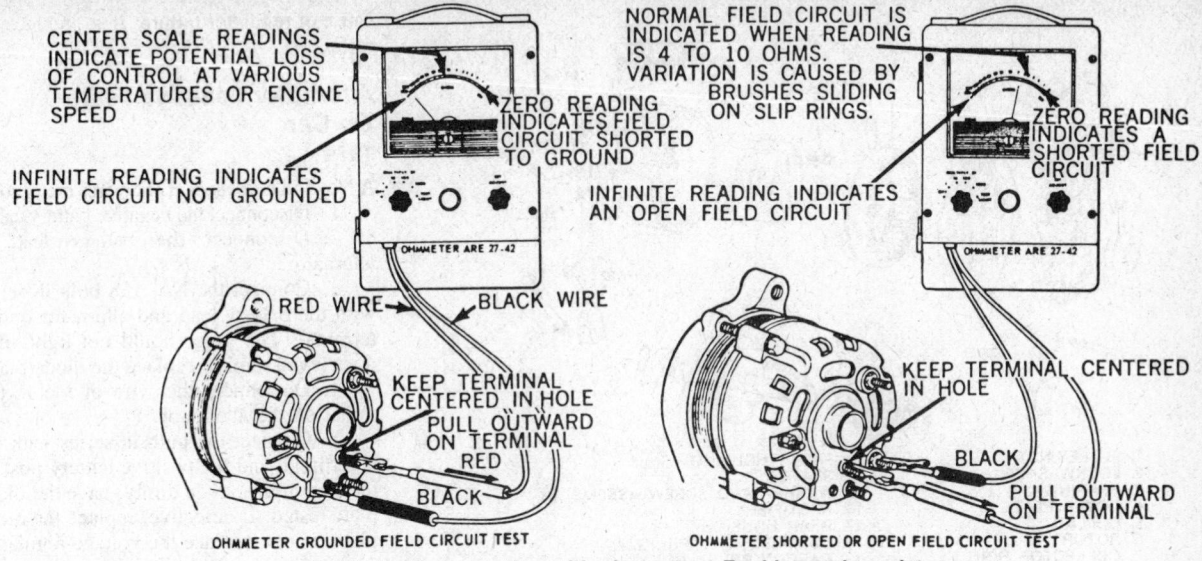

Field circuit connection with ohmmeter—Ford integral regulator

Field Test (Voltmeter)

1. Turn ignition switch to OFF position.
2. Remove wire from regulator supply terminal.
3. Remove cover plug from regulator field terminal and connect one test voltmeter lead to this terminal. A ¼ ohm resistor should be in the circuit.
4. Connect the other test voltmeter lead to a good engine ground.
5. The voltmeter should read 12 volts. If *no* voltage is present, the field circuit is open or grounded.
6. If voltmeter reads more than I volt, but still less than battery voltage, there is probably a partial ground in the alternator field circuit and the circuit should be checked with an ohmmeter.

Field Test (Ohmmeter)

1. Disconnect battery ground cable; remove alternator from car.
2. Remove the regulator from the alternator (covered later).
3. Make the ohmmeter tests as illustrated. If any of the tests indicates a field circuit problem, disassemble the alternator to further isolate the trouble.
   a. Contact each ohmmeter probe to a slip ring. Resistance should be 4–5 ohms. A higher reading indicates a damaged slip ring soldered connection or a broken wire. A lower reading indicates a shorted wire or slip ring assembly.
   b. Contact one ohmmeter probe to a slip ring and the other probe to the rotor shaft. Any reading other than infinite ohms indicates a short to ground. If neither of these tests (A and B) isolates the trouble, the brushes or brush assembly are the probable cause.

Voltage Limiter Test

1. Check the battery specific gravity. If it is not at least 1.230, charge the battery or install a charged battery for the test.
2. Make sure all lights and accessories

are turned off, including such items as dome lights.
3. Make the test connections as illustrated.
4. Place transmission in Neutral or Park, close battery adapter switch and start the engine.
5. Open the battery adapter switch and operate engine at 2,000 rpm for 5 minutes. The voltmeter should read 13.3–15.3 volts.
6. If voltage does not rise above 12 volts, perform a regulator supply voltage test to determine whether or not the regulator is getting voltage from the battery. Before replacing a regulator, check the wiring of the entire charging system for shorts, opens, or high resistance connections.

Regulator Supply Voltage Test

The regulator is "turned on" by the application of battery voltage through a 10 ohm resistor wire. If the supply circuit is defective, the regulator will not function and the alternator will not put out current.

1. Connect a 12-volt test light or voltmeter between the regulator supply lead and ground.
2. Turn on the ignition switch. The test light should glow or the voltmeter indicate. If not, the supply circuit should be checked back to the battery, especially the resistance wire.

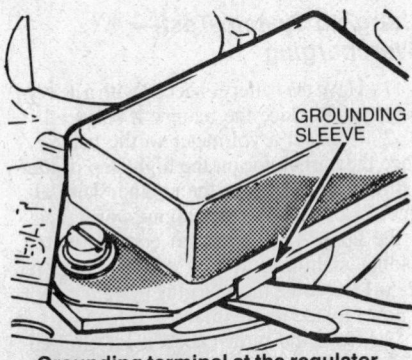

GROUNDING SLEEVE

Grounding terminal at the regulator

Bosch Integral Regulator Alternator

AMERICAN MOTORS

The Bosch charging system is a conventional 12 volt, negative ground unit, consisting of the alternator, regulator, and the battery.

The alternator rotor is supported by ball bearings which are permanently lubricated and require no periodic service. The stator windings are wrapped on a laminated core which forms part of the alternator frame. Six diodes are used to convert the AC voltage to DC, supplied to the output terminal. Alternator field current is supplied through a diode trio, which is also connected to the stator windings. A capacitor mounted on the end housing is used to protect the diode plate assembly from high voltages; it also provides radio noise suppression. It requires no periodic maintenance.

The voltage regulator is a solid state unit mounted on the end plate; it also retains the brushes in an integral holder. The unit is attached to the end frame with two screws, and can be replaced without disturbing the alternator. The regulator is non-adjustable, and must be replaced as a unit if defective.

Troubleshooting

NOTE: See the "Preliminary Charging System Inspection" section before proceeding further.

Indicator Lamp Test

The indicator lamp will only come on when there is a no-charge condition at the alternator (it also lights during starting, as a bulb check). To diagnose:
1. Check the alternator belt tension.
2. Start the engine, then measure and record battery voltage at the battery.
3. Raise the engine speed to fast idle.
4. There is a grounding sleeve on the

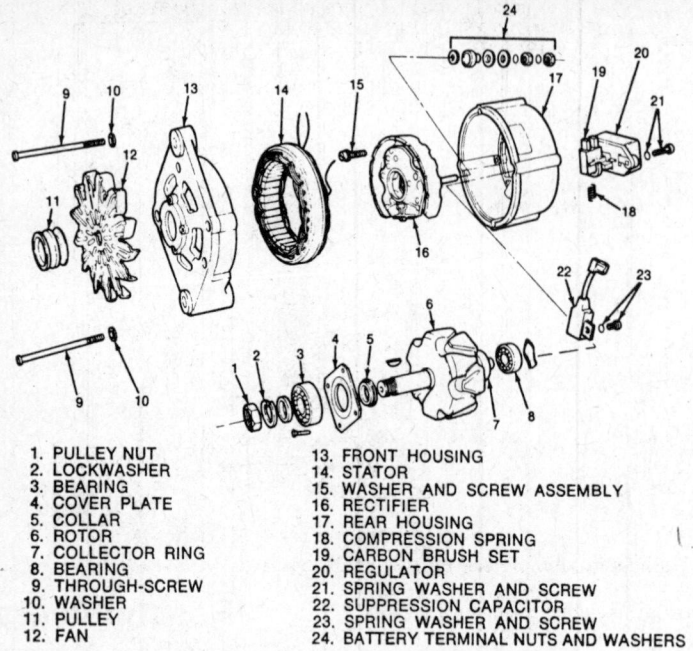

1. PULLEY NUT
2. LOCKWASHER
3. BEARING
4. COVER PLATE
5. COLLAR
6. ROTOR
7. COLLECTOR RING
8. BEARING
9. THROUGH-SCREW
10. WASHER
11. PULLEY
12. FAN
13. FRONT HOUSING
14. STATOR
15. WASHER AND SCREW ASSEMBLY
16. RECTIFIER
17. REAR HOUSING
18. COMPRESSION SPRING
19. CARBON BRUSH SET
20. REGULATOR
21. SPRING WASHER AND SCREW
22. SUPPRESSION CAPACITOR
23. SPRING WASHER AND SCREW
24. BATTERY TERMINAL NUTS AND WASHERS

Exploded view of the Bosch alternator (© AMC)

voltage regulator; it is a metal tab on the upper outside edge. Use a screwdriver to ground the sleeve to the alternator housing. Check the voltage reading at the battery. If the voltage is clearly higher than that recorded earlier, the regulator is defective and must be replaced.

If the voltage is lower or stays the same, the alternator is defective.

Charging System Test— Undercharging

1. Check and adjust the alternator drive belt tension.

2. Make sure that all lights, accessories, underhood light, etc, are off. Disconnect the negative battery cable and connect a test light between the negative post and the disconnected cable. If the light is on, go to Step 3. If off, go to Step 4.

3. If the light was on, the battery is being drained by an electrical component or short. The electrical system will have to be traced to find the source of continuous drain. Correct the cause and retest as in Step 2. If the light is off, the problem should be solved. If the light is on, go to the next step.

4. Reconnect the battery negative cable. Connect a jumper wire between the negative coil terminal and a chassis or engine ground. Connect a voltmeter, positive terminal to the alternator output, negative to ground. Crank the engine and obtain a stabilized voltage reading. Do not crank the engine more than fifteen seconds at a time to avoid starter damage. If the reading is above 9 volts, go to Step 6. If below 9 volts, go to the next step.

5. Check the battery voltage while cranking the engine. If within 0.5 volts of the alternator reading, have the battery tested using a full load procedure. If the battery

is good, go to Step 6. If not, replace the battery, then go to Step 6. If the battery voltage is not within 0.5 volts of alternator voltage, check and correct the battery-to-alternator circuit resistance.

6. Disconnect the jumper wire at the coil. Connect a voltmeter to the battery and record the reading. Place the carburetor on the high step of the fast idle cam, start the engine, turn on all accessories (headlights on high beam, a/c on high, radio and blower on) and check the voltage reading. If lower, go to Step 8. If higher, go to the next step.

7. Turn off the accessories, let the engine warm up (heat in the upper radiator hose), and allow the voltmeter reading to stabilize. If under 12.5 volts, go to the next step. If over 15.5 volts, replace the regulator. If between 12.5 and 15.5 volts, the system is OK; undercharging has been caused by idling, a loose drive belt, or short trip driving.

8. With the engine running as in Step 7, ground the alternator (see Step 4 of the Indicator Lamp Test) and check the voltage reading. If higher than in Step 6, replace the regulator. If lower, the alternator is defective.

Charging System Test— Overcharging

1. Have the battery checked with a heavy load test. Replace the battery if required.

2. Connect a voltmeter to the battery, place the carburetor on the high step of the fast idle cam and start the engine. Turn all accessories off. With the engine warm (heat in the upper radiator hose) and voltmeter reading stabilized, check the reading. If 12.5–15.0 volts, the charging system is ok. If not, replace the regulator.

3. Have the rotor checked for shorted field windings to determine if they were the

cause of regulator failure. If so, replace the rotor.

Alternator Leakage Test— On Car
1979

A No. 158 bulb, socket and wires are needed.

1. Disconnect the negative battery cable.

2. Disconnect the battery lead to alternator.

3. Connect the No. 158 bulb in series with the battery lead and alternator output terminal. The bulb should not light. If it does (even dimly), replace the diode plate.

4. Disconnect the wire at the R terminal on the alternator.

5. Connect the bulb in series with the R terminal and the positive battery post. If the bulb lights, even dimly, have the diode plate tested. If defective, replace the diode plate. If not, replace the voltage regulator.

1980 AND LATER

A No. 158 bulb, socket and wires are needed for this test.

1. Disconnect the negative battery cable.

2. Disconnect the alternator output wire at the starter solenoid junction terminal.

3. Connect the bulb's wires in series with the positive battery cable. Connect the negative battery cable. The bulb should not light. If it does, even dimly, the diode plate assembly must be replaced.

4. Disconnect the bulb. Disconnect the negative battery cable.

5. Unplug the connector from the R terminal at the alternator.

6. Connect the bulb in series with the R terminal and the positive battery cable. Connect the negative battery cable. The bulb should not light. If it does, even dimly, the diode plate or the regulator may be defective. Test and replace as necessary.

Regulator Replacement

1. Remove the regulator/brush holder retaining screws and washers.

2. Tip the assembly and lift it from the rear housing.

3. Installation is the reverse.

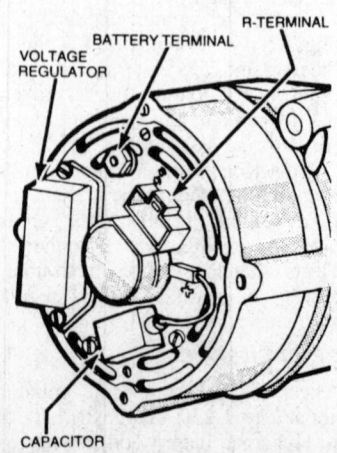

Rear view of Bosch alternator

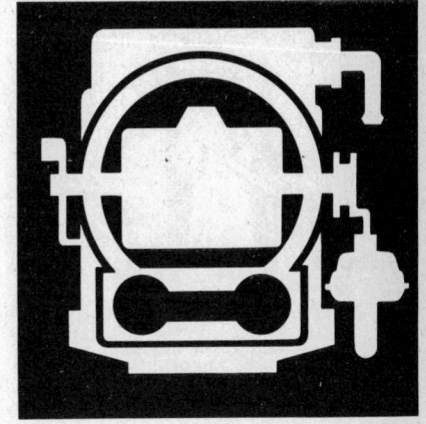

Carburetors

FUNCTIONS

Gasoline is the source of fuel for power in the automobile engine and the carburetor is the mechanism which automatically mixes liquid fuel with air in the correct proportions to provide the desired power output from the engine. The carburetor performs this function by metering, atomizing, and mixing fuel with air flowing through the engine.

A carburetor also regulates the volume of air-to-fuel mixture which enters the engine. It is the carburetor's regulation of the mixture flow which gives the operator control of the engine speed.

Metering

The automotive internal combustion engine operates efficiently within a relatively small range of air-to-fuel ratios. It is the function of the carburetor to meter the fuel in exact proportions to the air flowing into the engine, so that the optimum ratio of air-to-fuel is maintained under all operating conditions. Regulations governing exhaust gas emissions have made the proper metering of fuel by the carburetor an increasingly important factor. Too rich a mixture will result in poor economy and increased emissions, while too lean a mixture will result in loss of power and generally poor performance.

Carburetors are matched to engines so that metering can be accomplished by using carefully calibrated metering jets which allow fuel to enter the engine at a rate proportional to the engine's ability to draw air.

Atomization

The liquid fuel must be broken up into small particles so that it will more readily mix with air and vaporize. The more contact the fuel has with the air, the better the vaporization. Atomization can be accomplished in two ways: air may be drawn into a stream of fuel which will cause a turbulence and break the solid stream of fuel into smaller particles;

or a nozzle can be positioned at the point of highest air velocity in the carburetor and the fuel will be torn into a fine spray as it enters the air stream.

Distribution

The carburetor is the primary device involved in the distribution of fuel to the engine. The more efficiently fuel and air are combined in the carburetor, the smoother the flow of vaporized mixture through the intake manifold to each combustion chamber. Hence, the importance of the carburetor in fuel distribution.

Principles
VACUUM

All carburetors operate on the basic principle of pressure difference. Any pressure less than atmospheric pressure is considered vacuum or a low pressure area. In the engine, as the piston moves down on the intake stroke with the intake valve open, a partial vacuum is created in the intake manifold. The farther the piston travels downward, the greater the vacuum created in the manifold. As vacuum increases in the manifold, a difference in pressure occurs between the carburetor and cylinder. The carburetor is positioned in such a way that the high pressure above it, and the vacuum or low pressure beneath it, causes air to be drawn through it. Fuel and air always move from high to low pressure areas.

Venturi Principle

To obtain greater pressure drop at the tip of the fuel nozzle so that fuel will flow, the principle of increasing the air velocity to create a low pressure area is used. The device used to increase the velocity of the air flowing through the carburetor is called a venturi. A venturi is a specially designed restriction placed in the air flow. In order for the air to pass through the restriction, it must accel-

erate causing a pressure drop or vacuum as it passes.

CARBURETOR CIRCUITS
Float Circuit

The float circuit includes the float, float bowl, and a needle valve and seat. This circuit controls the amount of gas allowed to flow into the carburetor.

As the fuel level rises, it causes the float to rise which pushes the needle valve into its seat. As soon as the valve and seat make contact, the flow of gas is cut off from the fuel inlet. When the level of fuel drops, the float sinks and releases the needle valve from its seat which allows the gas to flow in. In actual operation, the fuel is maintained at practically a constant level. The float tends to hold the needle valve partly closed so that the incoming fuel just balances the fuel being withdrawn.

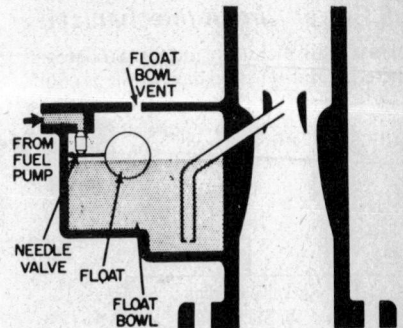

Float circuit
(© United Delco Div., G.M. Corp)

Idle and Low Speed Circuit

When the throttle is closed or only slightly opened, the air speed is low and practically no vacuum develops in the venturi. This means that the fuel nozzle will not feed. Thus, the carburetor must have another circuit to supply fuel during operation with a closed or slightly opened throttle.

This circuit is called the idle and low speed circuit. It consists of passages in which air and gas can flow beneath the throttle plate.

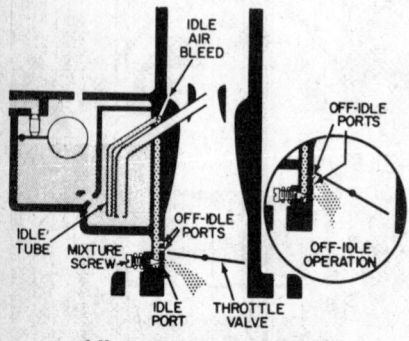

Idle and low speed circuit
(© United Delco Div., G.M. Corp)

With the throttle plate closed, there is high vacuum from the intake manifold. Atmospheric pressure pushes the air/fuel mixture through the passages of the idle and low speed circuit and past the tapered point of the idle adjustment screw, which regulates engine idle mixture volume.

High Speed Partial Load Circuit

When the throttle plate is opened sufficiently, there is little difference in vacuum between the upper and lower part of the air horn. Thus, little air/fuel mixture will discharge from the low speed and idle circuit. However, under this condition enough air is moving through the air horn to produce vacuum in the venturi to cause the main nozzle or high speed nozzle to discharge fuel. The circuit from the float bowl to the main nozzle is called the high speed partial load circuit. A nearly constant air/fuel ratio is maintained by this circuit from part to full-throttle.

High Speed Full Power Circuit

For high-speed, full-power, wide open throttle operation, the air/fuel mixture must be enriched; this is done either mechanically or by intake manifold vacuum.

Full Power Circuit (Mechanical)

This circuit includes a metering rod jet and a metering rod. The rod has two steps of different diameters and is attached to the throttle linkage.

When the throttle is wide open, the metering rod is lifted bringing the smaller diameter of the rod into the jet. When the throttle is partly closed, the larger diameter of the metering rod is in the jet. This restricts fuel flow to the main nozzle but adequate amounts of fuel do flow for part-throttle operation.

Full Power Circuit (Vacuum)

This circuit is operated by intake manifold vacuum. It includes a vacuum diaphragm or piston linked to a valve.

When the throttle is opened so that intake manifold vacuum is reduced, the spring raises the diaphragm or piston. This allows more fuel to flow in, either by lifting a metering rod or by opening a power valve.

Accelerator Pump Circuit

For acceleration, the carburetor must deliver additional fuel. A sudden inrush of air is caused by rapid acceleration or applying full throttle.

When the throttle is opened, the pump lever pushes the plunger down and this forces fuel to flow through the accelerator pump circuit and out the pump jet. This fuel enters the air passage through the carburetor to supply additional fuel demands.

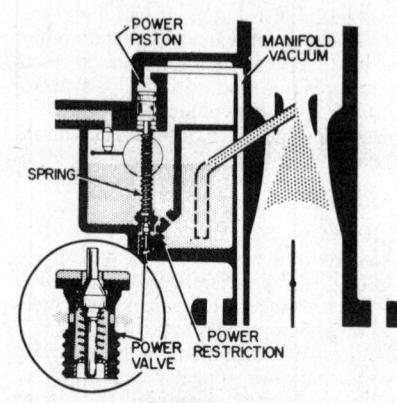

Power circuit
(© United Delco Div., G.M. Corp)

Choke

When starting an engine, it is necessary to increase the amount of fuel delivered to the intake manifold. This increase is controlled by the choke.

The choke consists of a valve in the top of the air horn controlled mechanically by an

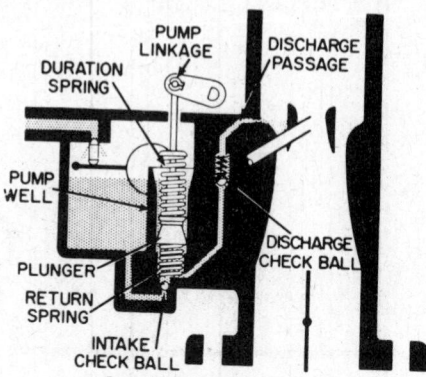

Accelerator pump circuit
(© United Delco Div., G.M. Corp)

automatic device. When the choke valve is closed, only a small amount of air can get past it. When the engine is cranked, a fairly high vacuum develops in the air horn. This vacuum causes the main nozzle to discharge a heavy stream of fuel. The quantity delivered is sufficient to produce the correct air/fuel mixture needed for starting the engine. The choke is released either manually or by heat from the engine.

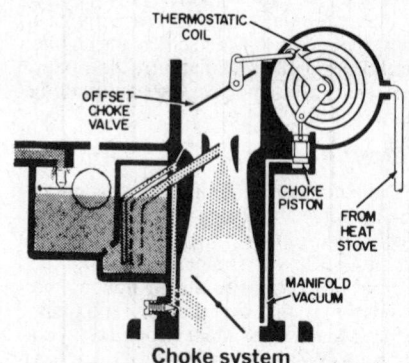

Choke system
(© United Delco Div., G.M. Corp)

 # TROUBLE SHOOTING

ENGINE HESITATES ON ACCELERATION

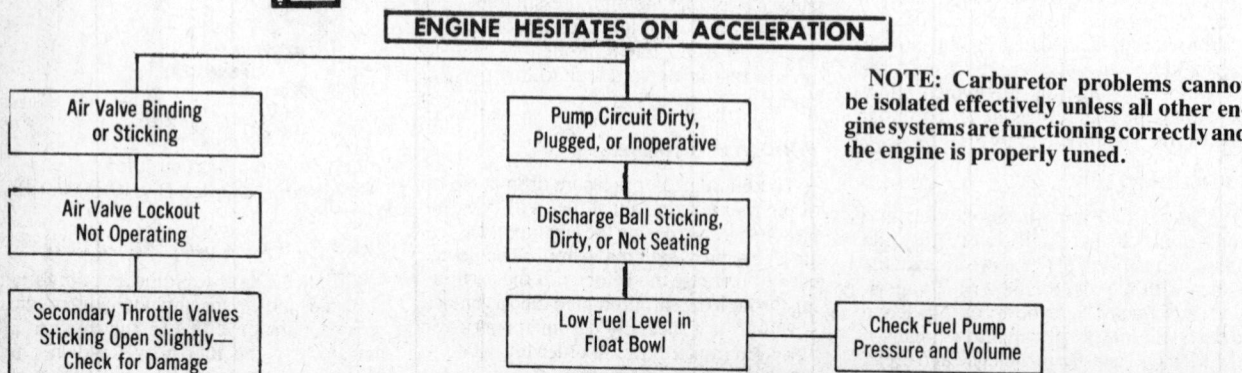

NOTE: Carburetor problems cannot be isolated effectively unless all other engine systems are functioning correctly and the engine is properly tuned.

ENGINE FEELS SLUGGISH OR FLAT ON ACCELERATION

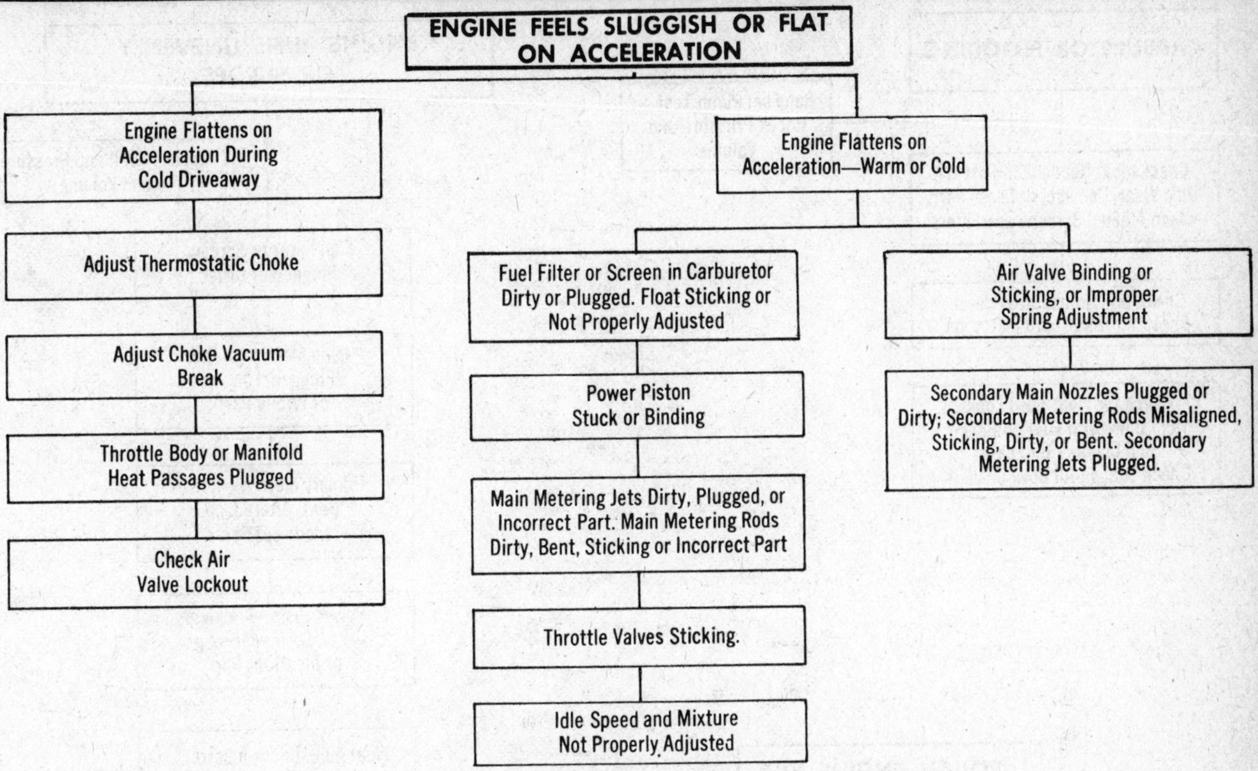

Engine Flattens on Acceleration During Cold Driveaway

Adjust Thermostatic Choke

Adjust Choke Vacuum Break

Throttle Body or Manifold Heat Passages Plugged

Check Air Valve Lockout

Engine Flattens on Acceleration—Warm or Cold

Fuel Filter or Screen in Carburetor Dirty or Plugged. Float Sticking or Not Properly Adjusted

Power Piston Stuck or Binding

Main Metering Jets Dirty, Plugged, or Incorrect Part. Main Metering Rods Dirty, Bent, Sticking or Incorrect Part

Throttle Valves Sticking.

Idle Speed and Mixture Not Properly Adjusted

Air Valve Binding or Sticking, or Improper Spring Adjustment

Secondary Main Nozzles Plugged or Dirty; Secondary Metering Rods Misaligned, Sticking, Dirty, or Bent. Secondary Metering Jets Plugged.

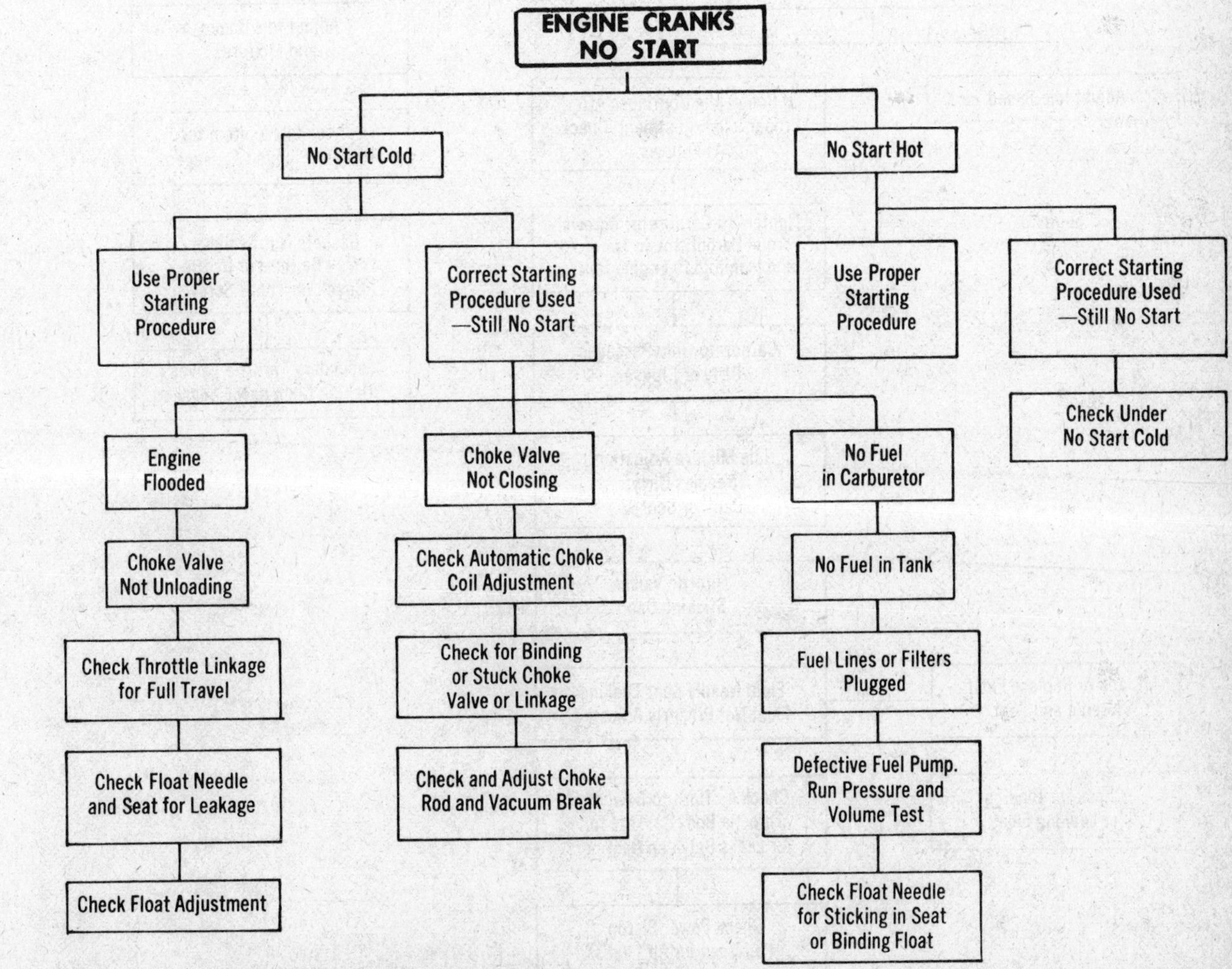

ENGINE CRANKS NO START

No Start Cold

Use Proper Starting Procedure

Correct Starting Procedure Used —Still No Start

Engine Flooded

Choke Valve Not Unloading

Check Throttle Linkage for Full Travel

Check Float Needle and Seat for Leakage

Check Float Adjustment

Choke Valve Not Closing

Check Automatic Choke Coil Adjustment

Check for Binding or Stuck Choke Valve or Linkage

Check and Adjust Choke Rod and Vacuum Break

No Start Hot

Use Proper Starting Procedure

Correct Starting Procedure Used —Still No Start

Check Under No Start Cold

No Fuel in Carburetor

No Fuel in Tank

Fuel Lines or Filters Plugged

Defective Fuel Pump. Run Pressure and Volume Test

Check Float Needle for Sticking in Seat or Binding Float

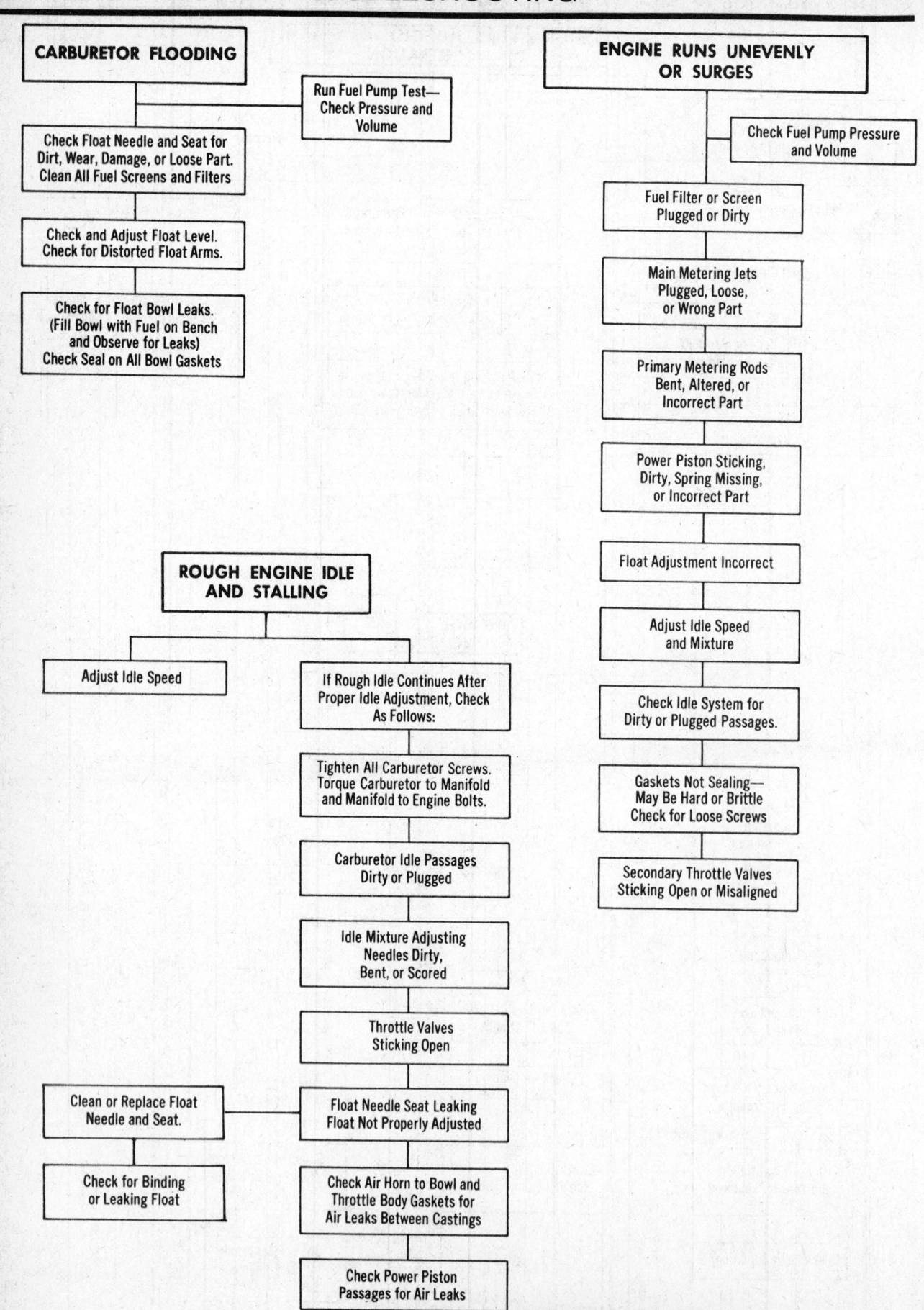

CARBURETOR FLOODING

Run Fuel Pump Test—
Check Pressure and
Volume

Check Float Needle and Seat for
Dirt, Wear, Damage, or Loose Part.
Clean All Fuel Screens and Filters

Check and Adjust Float Level.
Check for Distorted Float Arms.

Check for Float Bowl Leaks.
(Fill Bowl with Fuel on Bench
and Observe for Leaks)
Check Seal on All Bowl Gaskets

**ENGINE RUNS UNEVENLY
OR SURGES**

Check Fuel Pump Pressure
and Volume

Fuel Filter or Screen
Plugged or Dirty

Main Metering Jets
Plugged, Loose,
or Wrong Part

Primary Metering Rods
Bent, Altered, or
Incorrect Part

Power Piston Sticking,
Dirty, Spring Missing,
or Incorrect Part

Float Adjustment Incorrect

Adjust Idle Speed
and Mixture

Check Idle System for
Dirty or Plugged Passages.

Gaskets Not Sealing—
May Be Hard or Brittle
Check for Loose Screws

Secondary Throttle Valves
Sticking Open or Misaligned

**ROUGH ENGINE IDLE
AND STALLING**

Adjust Idle Speed

If Rough Idle Continues After
Proper Idle Adjustment, Check
As Follows:

Tighten All Carburetor Screws.
Torque Carburetor to Manifold
and Manifold to Engine Bolts.

Carburetor Idle Passages
Dirty or Plugged

Idle Mixture Adjusting
Needles Dirty,
Bent, or Scored

Throttle Valves
Sticking Open

Clean or Replace Float
Needle and Seat.

Float Needle Seat Leaking
Float Not Properly Adjusted

Check for Binding
or Leaking Float

Check Air Horn to Bowl and
Throttle Body Gaskets for
Air Leaks Between Castings

Check Power Piston
Passages for Air Leaks

POOR ECONOMY

Run Mileage Test
Check Driver Habits

If Mileage Is Poor, Proceed to Check the Following:

Check Choke Valve and Linkage for Binding or Sticking

Check Power Piston Spring for Distortion

Check Power Piston for Sticking or Being Bent

Check Power Piston Vacuum Passages for Leaks or Being Plugged

Check Metering Rods for Being Bent or Wrong Part

Check Main Metering Jets for Being Plugged, Loose, or Incorrect Part

Make Sure Gaskets Seal Properly on All Vacuum Passages

Carburetor Flooding

Adjust Float

Check Float Needle Seat for Leakage from Dirt, Wear, Damage, Looseness.

Check and Adjust Idle Speed

Float Bent, Loaded, Sticking, or Misaligned

Pump Discharge Ball Not Seating—Check for Dirt, Defective Seat or Discharge Spring

LACK OF HIGH SPEED PERFORMANCE OR POWER

Check for Full Throttle Opening at Carburetor. Adjust Throttle Linkage As Necessary

Air Valve Binding, Sticking or Wrong Tension.

Power Piston Stuck or Binding— Check for Distorted Spring

Air Valve Not Unlocking.

Float Setting Incorrect

Float Sticking Misaligned or Leaking

Secondary Metering Rods Bent or Incorrect Part, or Not Adjusted Properly

Main Metering Jets Plugged, Dirty, or Incorrect Part

Metering Rods Altered, Bent, or Incorrect Part

Gaskets Not Sealing. May Be Hard or Brittle. Check for Loose Screws

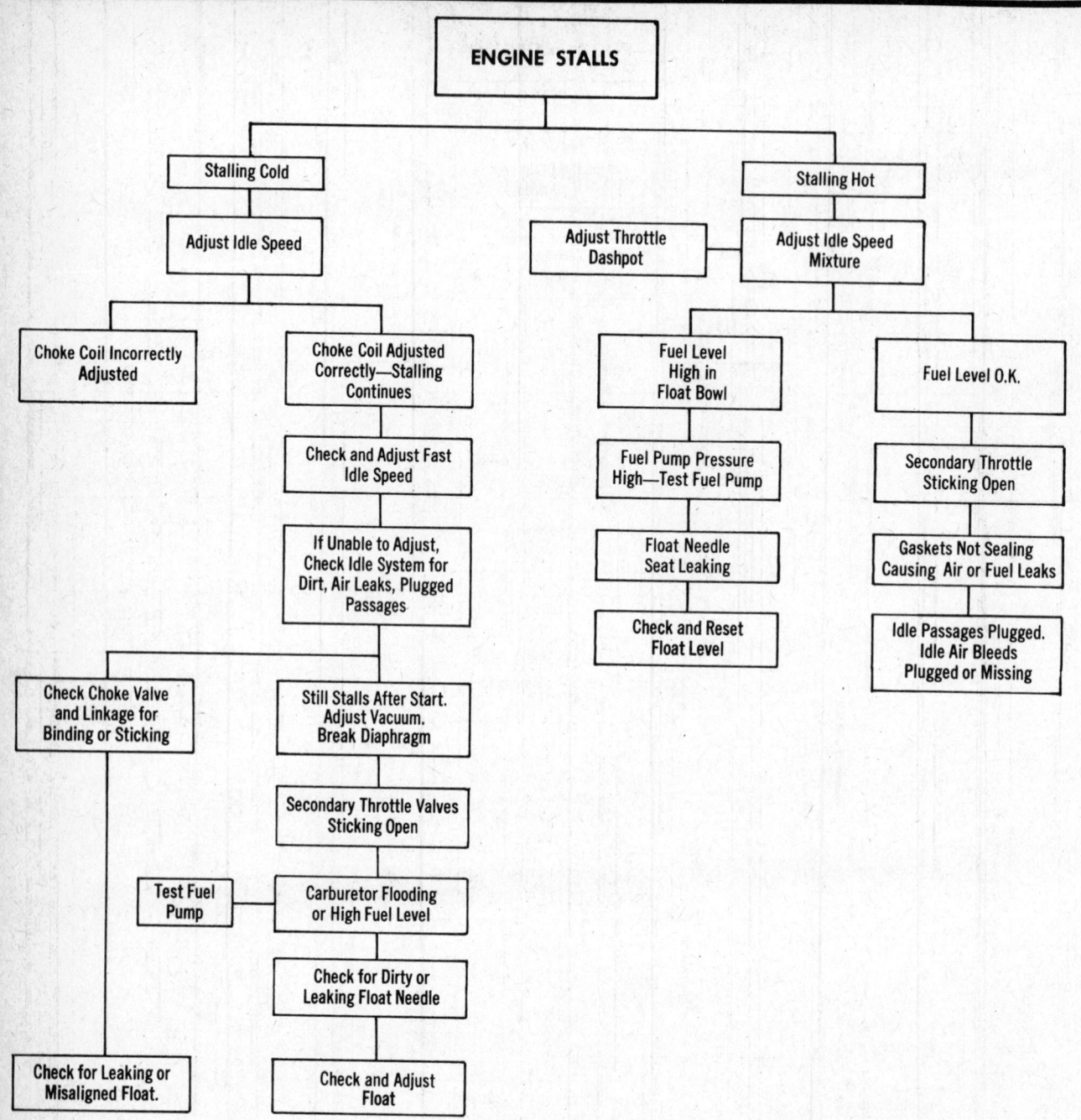

ENGINE STALLS

Stalling Cold
- Adjust Idle Speed
  - Choke Coil Incorrectly Adjusted
  - Choke Coil Adjusted Correctly—Stalling Continues
    - Check and Adjust Fast Idle Speed
    - If Unable to Adjust, Check Idle System for Dirt, Air Leaks, Plugged Passages
      - Check Choke Valve and Linkage for Binding or Sticking
        - Check for Leaking or Misaligned Float.
      - Still Stalls After Start. Adjust Vacuum. Break Diaphragm
        - Secondary Throttle Valves Sticking Open
        - Test Fuel Pump — Carburetor Flooding or High Fuel Level
        - Check for Dirty or Leaking Float Needle
        - Check and Adjust Float

Stalling Hot
- Adjust Throttle Dashpot — Adjust Idle Speed Mixture
  - Fuel Level High in Float Bowl
    - Fuel Pump Pressure High—Test Fuel Pump
    - Float Needle Seat Leaking
    - Check and Reset Float Level
  - Fuel Level O.K.
    - Secondary Throttle Sticking Open
    - Gaskets Not Sealing Causing Air or Fuel Leaks
    - Idle Passages Plugged. Idle Air Bleeds Plugged or Missing

CARBURETOR APPLICATION CHART AND INDEX

The carburetor manufacturer and model and also the carburetor identification numbers which are listed in the specifications charts, appear either on a tag on the carburetor or stamped on the carburetor body.

NOTE: New model year carburetor part numbers and specifications are not released by the manufacturers until well after the press date for this manual. These will be included in the next edition. New model carburetor part numbers are obtained from the most current factory sources, however, carburetors which are new or redesigned by the manufacturer during the production year and designated with new part numbers may not appear.

Car Manufacturer	Year	Carburetor Manufacturer	Carburetor Model	Page Numbers	
				Adjustments	Specifications
American Motors	'78–'84	Carter	BBD	U66	U69
	'78–'79	Carter	YF, YFA	U71	U73
	'78–'79	Ford, Autolite, Motorcraft	2100, 2150	U83	U86
	'78–'79	Holley	5210C	U120	U122
	'80–'84	Rochester	2SE, E2SE	U143	U151
Chrysler Corp.	'78–'83	Carter	BBD	U66	U69
	'78–'84	Carter	TQ	U74	U78
	'78–'82	Holley	1945	U104	U106
	'78–'79	Holley	2245	U113	U115
	'78–'79	Holley	2280	U115	U117
	'78–'84	Holley	5220	U124	U125
	'81–'83	Holley	6145	U128	U129
	'81–'84	Holley	6520	U124	U126
	'82–'84	Mikuni	NA	U180	U180
Ford Motor Co.	'78–'83	Carter	YF, YFA	U71	U73
	'78–'84	Ford, Autolite, Motorcraft	2100, 2150, 2150A	U83	U86
	'78	Ford, Autolite, Motorcraft	4300, 4350	U99	U102
	'78–'82	Ford, Autolite, Motorcraft	5200	U96	U98
	'81–'84	Motorcraft	740	U79	U81
	'78–'81	Motorcraft	2700 VV	U91	U95
	'79–'84	Motorcraft	7200	U102	U103
	'78–'83	Holley	1946	U106	U108
	'84	Holley	1949	U109	U113
	'83–'84	Holley	4180C	U117	U120
	'84	Holley	6149	U109	U113
	'78–'82	Holley	6500	U130	U132

Car Manufacturer	Year	Carburetor Manufacturer	Carburetor Model	Page Numbers	
				Adjustments	Specifications
General Motors	'78	Holley	5210C	U120	U122
	'78–'84	Holley	6510C	U130	U132
	'78–'79	Rochester	1ME	U135	U137
	'78	Rochester	2GC, 2GV, 2GE	U137	U140
	'79–'84	Rochester	2SE, E2SE	U143	U151
	'78–'84	Rochester	2MC, M2MC, M2ME, E2ME, E2MC	U156	U160
	'78–'84	Rochester	Quadrajet	U162	U169

NA—Not Available

CARTER CARBURETORS

Model BBD

The BBD carburetor is a two barrel unit. It is equipped with a dashpot on some applications.

VACUUM STEP-UP PISTON ADJUSTMENT

1. Remove the dust cover.
2. Be sure not to disturb the adjusting screw on top of the piston. If it is disturbed, reset the gap at the top of the piston to 0.035–0.040 in.
3. Back off the curb idle adjustment until the throttle valves are completely closed. Count the number of turns so that the screw can later be returned to the original position. Then turn the idle screw in one full turn on AMC products only.

4. Fully depress the step-up piston while holding moderate pressure on the rod lifter tab and loosen and tighten the rod lifter lockscrew.
5. Release the piston and rod lifter; return the curb idle screw to its original position.
6. Replace the dust cover, unless the accelerator pump is to be adjusted.

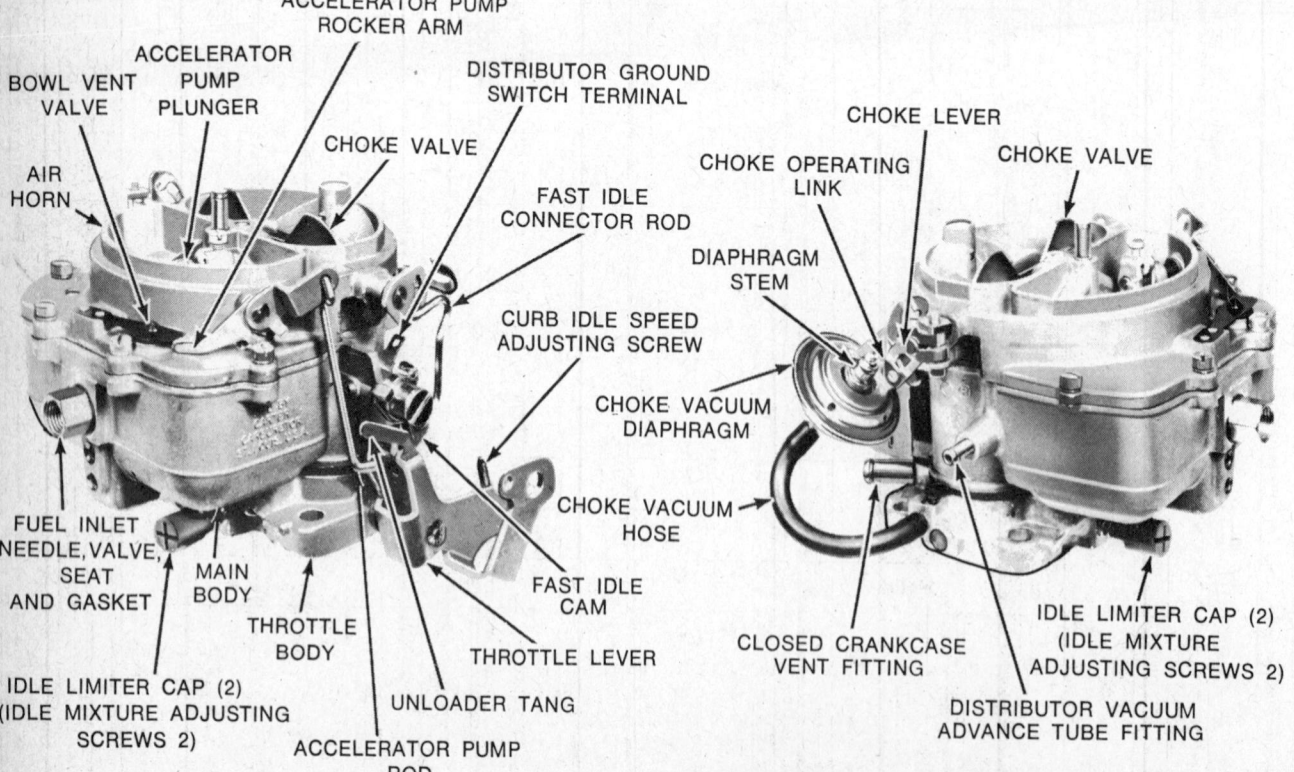

BBD carburetor assembly—typical

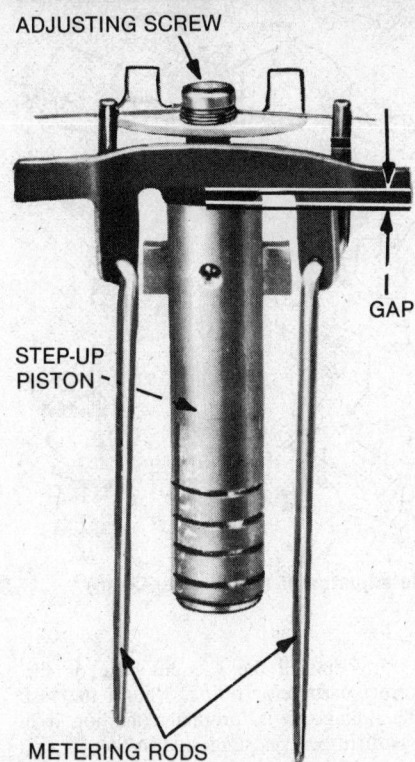

BBD vacuum step-up piston and meter ing rod assembly (© AMC)

ACCELERATOR PUMP STROKE ADJUSTMENT

1. Back off the idle adjusting screw. Open the choke valve so that the fast idle cam allows the throttle valves to close. Be sure that the accelerator pump "S" link is in the outer hole of the pump arm if there are two holes.

2. Turn the idle adjusting screw in two complete turns after it contacts the stop.

3. Remove the dust cover. With the throttle valves closed tightly, measure the distance between the top of the air horn and the top of the pump plunger shaft. If the dimension is not as specified, loosen the pump arm adjusting lockscrew (near the plunger shaft) and rotate the sleve to obtain the correct dimension.

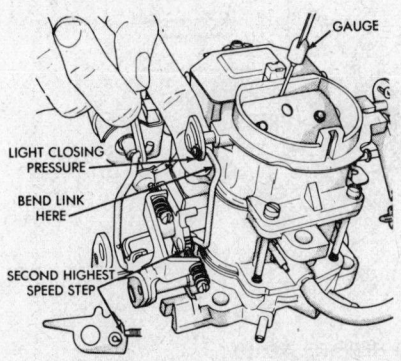

BBD fast idle cam position adjustment (© Chrysler Corp.)

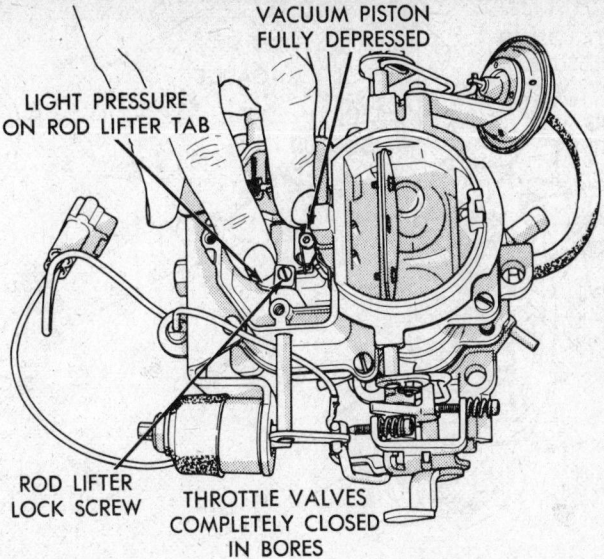

BBD vacuum step-up piston adjustment (© Chrysler Corp.)

FAST IDLE CAM POSITION ADJUSTMENT

1. With the fast idle speed adjusting screw contacting the second highest speed step on the fast idle cam, move the choke valve toward the closed position with light pressure on the choke shaft lever. On AMC, loosen the choke cover and turn ¼ turn rich.

2. Insert the specified drill (refer to Specifications), between the top of the choke valve and the wall of the air horn. An adjustment will be necessary if a slight drag is not obtained as the drill is being removed.

3. If an adjustment is required, bend the fast idle connector rod at the angle.

4. Reset the choke cover to specification.

ACCELERATOR PUMP & BOWL VENT

1978 and later Chrysler

1. The accelerator pump stroke adjustment and the curb idle speed must be adjusted first.

2. Remove the air cleaner, step-up piston cover, and the gasket.

3. Insert the specified gauge (0.080 in.) between the top of the bowl vent valve and the seat.

4. If adjustment is needed, bend the bowl vent lever tab. Support the vent lever before bending the tab.

5. Install the gasket and step-up piston cover, and install the air cleaner.

1978 and later AMC

1. Remove the rollover check valve from the air horn for access to the metering rod.

2. Place the throttle on the high step of the fast idle cam. The bowl vent should be closed.

3. Move the fast idle cam until the

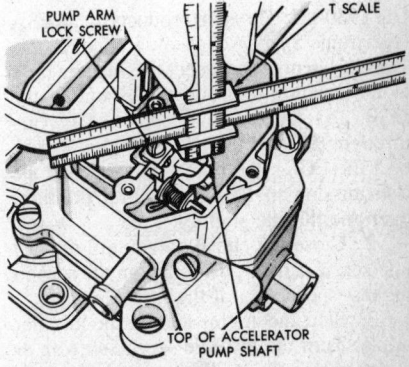

BBD accelerator pump stroke adjustment

throttle screw drops to the second step. The vent should just start to open.

4. If the vent is not closed on the high, fourth and third steps of the cam, and beginning to open on the second step, bend the tab until the adjustment is correct.

CHOKE UNLOADER (WIDE OPEN KICK)

1. Hold the throttle valves in the wide open position. Insert the specified drill (see Specifications) between the upper edge of the choke valve and the inner wall of the air horn.

2. With a finger lightly pressing against the control lever, a slight drag should be felt as the drill is being withdrawn. If an adjustment is necessary, bend the unloader tang on the throttle lever until the correct opening has been obtained.

FAST IDLE SPEED (ON VEHICLE)

1. On Chrysler products, disconnect and plug the connections for the heated air control, EGR, and OSAC valve or distributor.

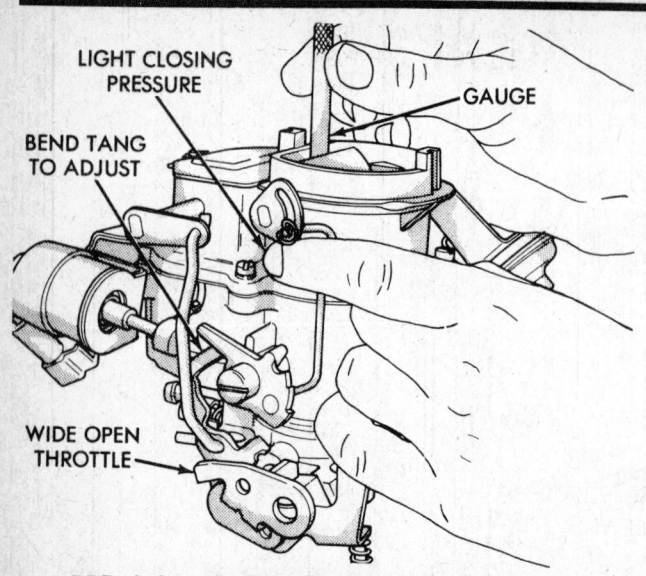

BBD choke unloader (wide open kick) adjustment
(© Chrysler Corp.)

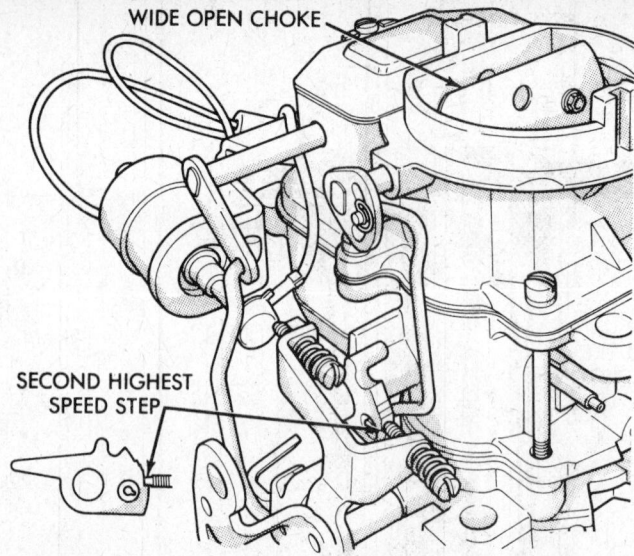

BBD on-car fast idle adjustment (© Chrysler Corp.)

On 1980–81 Chrysler products with ESA (Electronic Spark Advance), ground the idle switch. Do not disconnect the vacuum hose to the vacuum transducer. Disconnect the EGR and TCS solenoid on AMC cars through 1980. On 1981–84 AMC disconnect the EGR. With the engine off and the transmission in Park or Neutral position, open the throttle slightly.

2. Close the choke valve until the fast idle screw can be positioned on the second highest speed step of the fast idle cam.

3. Start the engine and let the idle stabilize. Turn the fast idle speed screw in or out to obtain the specified speed.

4. Stopping the engine between adjustments is not necessary. However, reposition the fast idle speed screw on the cam after each speed adjustment to provide the correct throttle closing torque.

VACUUM KICK (INITIAL CHOKE VALVE CLEARANCE) ADJUSTMENT

Chrysler Products

1. If the adjustment is to be made with the engine running, disconnect the fast idle linkage to allow the choke to close to the kick position with engine at curb idle. If an auxiliary vacuum source is to be used, as recommended, open the throttle valves (engine not running) and move the choke to the closed position. Release the throttle first, then release the choke.

2. When using an auxiliary vacuum source, disconnect the vacuum hose from the carburetor and connect it to the hose from the vacuum supply with a small length of tube to act as a fitting. Removel of the hose from the diaphragm may require sufficient force to damage the system. Apply a vacuum of 15 or more in. of mercury.

3. Insert the specified drill (refer to

Specifications) between the top of the choke valve and the wall of the air horn. Apply sufficient closing pressure on the lever to which the choke rod attaches to provide a minimum choke valve opening without distortion of the diaphragm link. Note that the cylindrical stem of the diaphragm will extend as the internal spring is compressed. This spring must be fully compressed for proper measurement of the vacuum kick adjustment.

4. An adjustment will be necessary if a slight drag is not obtained as the drill is being removed. Shorten or lengthen the diaphragm link to obtain the correct choke opening. Length changes should be made carefully by bending (opening or closing) the U-bend provided in the diaphragm link.

— CAUTION —
Do not apply twisting or bending force to the diaphragm.

5. Reinstall the vacuum hose on the correct carburetor fitting. Return the fast idle linkage to its original condition if it was disturbed, as suggested in Step 1.

6. Make the following check: With no vacuum applied to the diaphragm, the choke valve should move freely between the open and closed positions. If its movement is not free, examine the linkage for misalignment or interference caused by the bending operation. Repeat the adjustment if necessary to provide proper link operations.

AMC Products

This adjustment is called Initial Choke Valve Clearance Adjustment on AMC products.

1. Loosen the choke cover, turn ¼ turn rich, and tighten one cover screw.

2. Apply a vacuum of at least 19 inches of mercury to pull the diaphragm in against the stop.

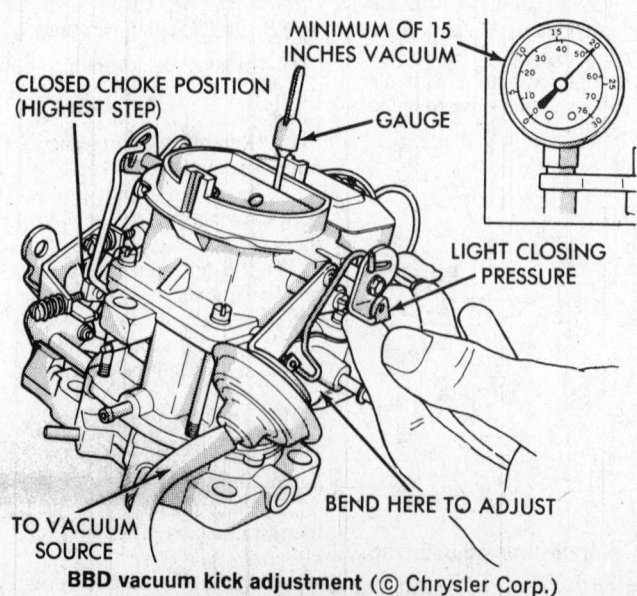

BBD vacuum kick adjustment (© Chrysler Corp.)

3. Open the throttle valve slightly to place the fast idle screw on the high step of the cam.

4. Measure the clearance between the choke plate upper edge and the air horn wall.

5. Adjust the clearance by bending the diaphragm connector link at the angle. Reset the choke or replace the cover.

FLOAT LEVEL

Chrysler Products

1. Invert the carburetor so that the weight of the floats is the only force on the needle and seat.

2. Use a T-scale to check the float level. Measure from the surface of the fuel bowl to the crown of each float at center.

3. To adjust, hold the floats on the bottom of the bowl and bend the float lip to give the specified dimension.

American Motors Products

1. Remove the air horn.
2. Hold the float lip gently against the needle to raise the float.
3. Place a straightedge across the float bowl to measure the float level at the top of the float.
4. To adjust, bend the float lip, being careful not to exert pressure on the synthetic needle tip.

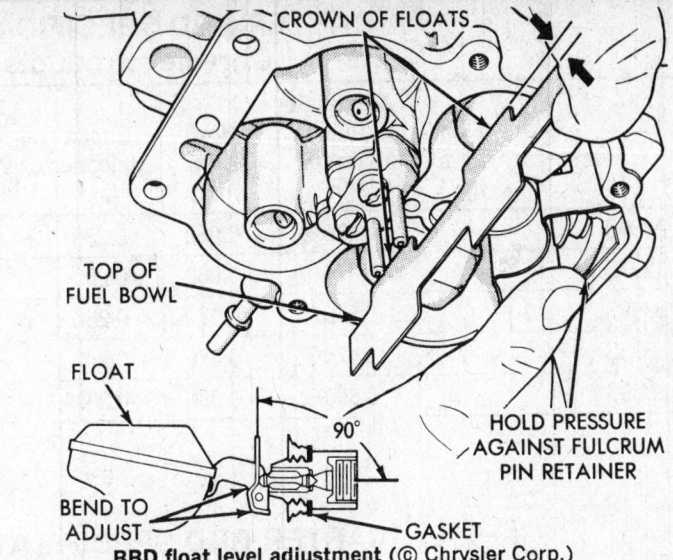

BBD float level adjustment (© Chrysler Corp.)

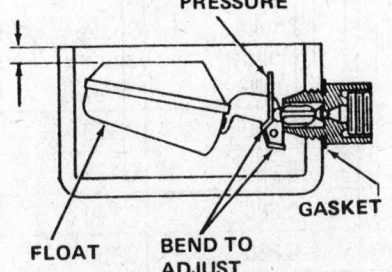

BBD float level adjustment for AMC products (© AMC)

DASHPOT ADJUSTMENT

Chrysler Products

The dashpot is used on manual transmission models only.

1. Make sure that the curb idle speed is correctly adjusted.

2. Start the engine. Position the throttle lever so that the actuating tab is just contacting the dashpot plunger stem. Let the engine speed stabilize for 30 seconds.

3. The speed should be 2500 rpm.

4. Adjust the setting by loosening the locknut and moving the dashpot.

CARTER BBD SPECIFICATIONS
Chrysler Products

Year	Model ②	Float Level (in.)	Accelerator Pump Travel (in.)	Bowl Vent (in.)	Choke Unloader (in.)	Choke Vacuum Kick	Fast Idle Cam Position	Fast Idle Speed (rpm)	Automatic Choke Adjustment
'78	8136S	¼	0.500①	0.080	0.280	0.110	0.070	1500	Fixed
	8137S	¼	0.500①	0.080	0.280	0.100	0.070	1600	Fixed
	8177S	¼	0.500①	0.080	0.280	0.100	0.070	1600	Fixed
	8175S	¼	0.500①	0.080	0.280	0.160	0.070	1400	Fixed
	8143S	¼	0.500①	0.080	0.280	0.150	0.070	1500	Fixed
'79	8198S	¼	0.500①	0.080	0.280	0.100	0.070	1600	Fixed
	8199S	¼	0.500①	0.080	0.280	0.100	0.070	1600	Fixed
'80	8233S	¼	0.500①	0.080	0.280	0.130	0.070	1500	Fixed
	8235S	¼	0.500①	0.080	0.280	0.130	0.070	1700	Fixed
	8237S	¼	0.500①	0.080	0.280	0.110	0.070	1500	Fixed
	8239S	¼	0.500①	0.080	0.280	0.110	0.070	1500	Fixed
	8286S	¼	0.500①	0.080	0.280	0.100	0.070	1400	Fixed
'81-'82	8290S	¼	0.500①	0.080	0.280	0.100	0.070	1600	Fixed
	8291S	¼	0.500①	0.080	0.280	0.130	0.070	1400	Fixed
	8292S	¼	0.500①	0.080	0.280	0.130	0.070	1600③	Fixed

CARTER BBD SPECIFICATIONS
Chrysler Products

Year	Model ②	Float Level (in.)	Accelerator Pump Travel (in.)	Bowl Vent (in.)	Choke Unloader (in.)	Choke Vacuum Kick	Fast Idle Cam Position	Fast Idle Speed (rpm)	Automatic Choke Adjustment
'83	8290S	¼	0.470①	0.080	0.280	0.100	0.070	1600	Fixed
	8291S	¼	0.470①	0.080	0.280	0.130	0.070	1400	Fixed
	8369S	¼	0.500①	0.080	0.280	0.130	0.070	1500	Fixed
'84	8385S	¼	0.470①	0.080	0.280	0.130	0.070	1400	Fixed
	8369S	¼	0.500	0.080	0.280	0.130	0.070	1500	Fixed

CARTER BBD SPECIFICATIONS
American Motors

Year	Model ①	Float Level (in.)	Accelerator Pump Travel (in.)	Choke Unloader (in.)	Choke Vacuum Kick	Fast Idle Cam Position	Fast Idle Speed (rpm)	Automatic Choke Adjustment
'78	8128	¼	0.496	0.280	0.150	0.110	1600	Index
	8129	¼	0.520	0.280	0.128	0.095	1500	1 Rich
'79	8185	¼	0.470	0.280	0.140	0.110	1600	1 Rich
	8186	¼	0.520	0.280	0.150	0.110	1500	1 Rich
	8187	¼	0.470	0.280	0.140	0.110	1600	1 Rich
	8221	¼	0.530	0.280	0.150	0.110	1600	1 Rich
'80	8216	¼	0.520	0.280	0.140	0.090	1850	2 Rich
	8246	¼	0.520	0.280	0.140	0.095	1850	2 Rich
	8247	¼	0.520	0.280	0.150	0.095	1700	1 Rich
	8248	¼	0.520	0.280	0.150	0.095	1700	1 Rich
	8253	¼	0.470	0.280	0.128	0.095	1850	2 Rich
	8256	¼	0.470	0.280	0.128	0.093	1850	2 Rich
	8278	¼	0.542	0.280	0.140	0.093	1850	Index
'81	8310	¼	0.525	0.280	0.140	0.095	1850	Index
	8302	¼	0.500	0.280	0.128	0.095	1850	1 Rich
	8303	¼	0.500	0.280	0.128	0.090	1700	1 Rich
	8306	¼	0.500	0.280	0.128	0.090	1700	1 Rich
	8307	¼	0.500	0.280	0.128	0.095	1850	1 Rich
	8308	¼	0.500	0.280	0.128	0.095	1850	2 Rich
	8309	¼	0.520	0.280	0.128	0.093	1700	2 Rich
'82	8338	¼	0.520	0.280	0.140	0.095	1850	1 Rich
	8339	¼	0.520	0.280	0.140	0.095	1850	1 Rich
'83	8360	¼	0.520	0.280	0.140	0.095	1850	Fixed
	8364	¼	0.520	0.280	0.140	0.095	1700	Fixed
	8367	¼	0.520	0.280	0.140	0.095	1700	Fixed
	8362	¼	0.520	0.280	0.140	0.095	1850	Fixed

CARTER BBD SPECIFICATIONS
American Motors

Year	Model ①	Float Level (in.)	Accelerator Pump Travel (in.)	Choke Unloader (in.)	Choke Vacuum Kick	Fast Idle Cam Position	Fast Idle Speed (rpm)	Automatic Choke Adjustment
'84	8383	¼	0.520	0.280	0.140	0.095	1850	½–1½ Rich
	8384	¼	0.520	0.280	0.140	0.095	1700	½–1½ Rich

① Model numbers located on the tag or casting

Model YF, YFA

The YF carburetor is a single barrel down-draft carburetor with a diaphragm type accelerator pump and diaphragm operated metering rods.

FLOAT ADJUSTMENT

1. Invert the air horn assembly and check the clearance from the top of the float to the surface of the air horn with a T-scale. The air horn should be held at eye level when gauging and the float arm should be resting on the needle pin.

2. Do not exert pressure on the needle valve when measuring or adjusting the float. Bend the float arm as necessary to adjust the float level.

——— CAUTION ———

Do not bend the tab at the end of the float arm as it prevents the float from striking the bottom of the fuel bowl when empty and keeps the needle in place.

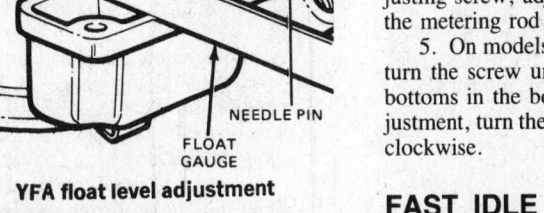

FLOAT — TAB (LOW FUEL LEVEL) — FLOAT ARM — NEEDLE PIN — FLOAT GAUGE

YFA float level adjustment

METERING ROD ADJUSTMENT

1. Remove the air horn. Back out the idle speed adjusting screw until the throttle plate is seated fully in its bore.

2. Press down on the upper end of the diaphragm shaft until the diaphragm bottoms in the vacuum chamber.

3. The metering rod should contact the bottom of the metering rod well. The lifter link at the outer end nearest the springs and at the supporting link should be bottomed.

4. On models not equipped with an adjusting screw, adjust by bending the lip of the metering rod is attached.

5. On models with an adjusting screw, turn the screw until the metering rod just bottoms in the body casting. For final adjustment, turn the screw one additional turn clockwise.

FAST IDLE CAM ADJUSTMENT

1. Put the fast idle screw on the second highest step of the fast idle cam against the shoulder of the high step.

2. Adjust by bending the choke plate

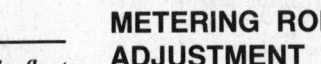

INTERNAL FUEL BOWL VENT — CHOKE COLD AIR PICK-UP CONNECTION — AUTOMATIC CHOKE — ELECTRIC ASSIST — TSP "OFF" IDLE SPEED ADJUSTING SCREW — FAST IDLE SPEED ADJUSTMENT SCREW — THROTTLE LEVER — THROTTLE SOLENOID POSITIONER (TSP) SOME MODELS — CHOKE PLATE — FUEL INLET — CHOKE HOT AIR INLET ADAPTER — VENTURI VACUUM CONNECTION — MECHANICAL FUEL BOWL VENT — FUEL BOWL — ANTI-STALL DASH POT (SOME MODELS)

Carter YFA carburetor—typical

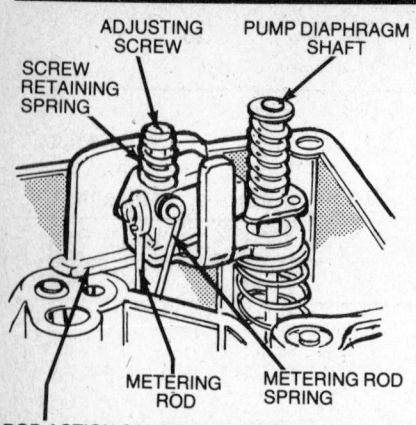

SCREW RETAINING SPRING — ADJUSTING SCREW — PUMP DIAPHRAGM SHAFT — METERING ROD — METERING ROD SPRING

ROD ACTION CAUSED BY SCREW ACTING AS PIVOT POINT FOR LEVER
YFA metering rod adjustment

connecting rod to obtain the specified clearance between the lower edge of the choke plate and the air horn wall.

CHOKE UNLOADER ADJUSTMENT

1. With the throttle valve held wide open and the choke valve held in the closed position, bend the unloader tang on the throttle lever to obtain the specified clearance between the lower edge of the choke valve and the air horn wall.

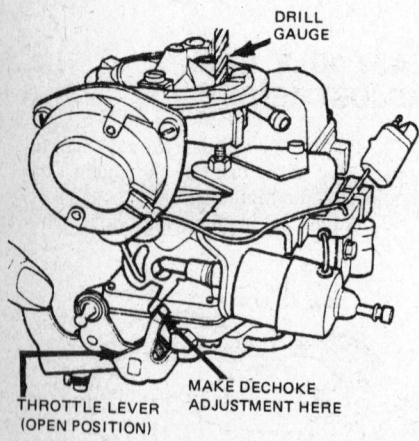

DRILL GAUGE

THROTTLE LEVER (OPEN POSITION) — MAKE DECHOKE ADJUSTMENT HERE
YFA choke unloader adjustment

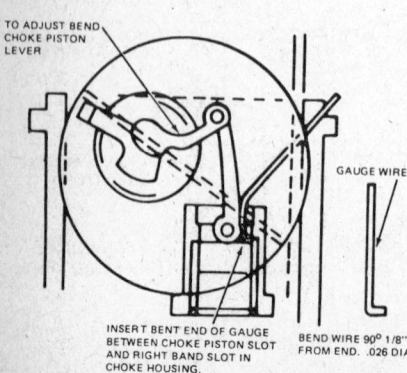

TO ADJUST BEND CHOKE PISTON LEVER

GAUGE WIRE

INSERT BENT END OF GAUGE BETWEEN CHOKE PISTON SLOT AND RIGHT BAND SLOT IN CHOKE HOUSING.
BEND WIRE 90° 1/8" FROM END. .026 DIA

Choke plate pulldown—piston type choke—YFA

AUTOMATIC CHOKE ADJUSTMENT

1. Loosen the choke cover retaining screws.
2. Turn the choke cover so that the index mark on the cover lines up with the specified mark on the choke housing.

CHOKE PLATE PULLDOWN ADJUSTMENT—1983–84

Piston Type Choke

NOTE: This adjustment requires that the thermostatic spring housing and gasket (choke cap) are removed. Refer to the "Choke Cap" removal procedure below.

1. Remove the air cleaner assembly, then the choke cap.
2. Bend a 0.026 in. diameter wire gauge at a 90 degree angle approximately 1/8 in. from one end. Insert the bent end of the gauge between the choke piston slot and the right hand slot in the choke housing. Rotate the choke piston lever counterclockwise until the gauge is shut in the piston slot.
3. Apply light pressure on the choke piston lever to hold the gauge in place. Then measure the clearance between the lower edge of the choke plate and the carburetor bore using a drill with the diameter equal to the specified pulldown clearance.
4. Bend the choke piston lever to obtain the proper clearance.
5. Install the choke cap.

Diaphragm Type Choke

1. Activate the pulldown motor by applying an external vacuum source.
2. Close the choke plate as far as possible without forcing it.
3. Using a drill of the specified size, measure the clearance between the lower edge of the choke plate and the air horn wall.
4. If adjustment is necessary, bend the choke diaphragm link as required.

CHOKE CAP REMOVAL

1983–84

NOTE: The automatic choke has two rivets and a screw, retaining the choke cap in place. There is a locking and indexing plate to prevent misadjustment.

1. Remove the air cleaner assembly from the carburetor.
2. Check choke cap retaining ring rivets to determine if mandrel is well below the rivet head. If mandrel appears to be at or within the rivet head thickness, drive it down or out with a 1/16 inch diameter punch.
3. Use a 1/8 inch diameter of No. 32 drill (.128 inch diameter) for drilling the rivet heads. Drill into the rivet head until

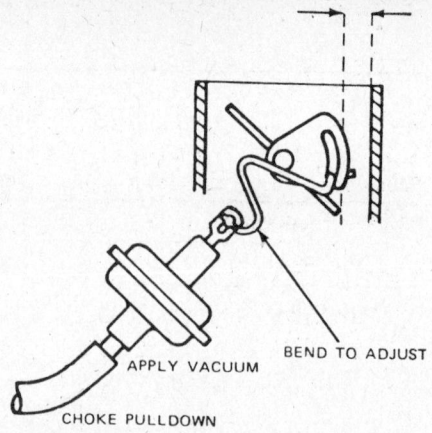

APPLY VACUUM — BEND TO ADJUST — CHOKE PULLDOWN
Choke plate pulldown—diaphragm type choke—YFA

the rivet head comes loose from the rivet body.
4. After the rivet head is removed, drive the remaining portion of the rivet out of the hole with a 1/8 inch diameter punch.

NOTE: This procedure must be followed to retain the hole size.

5. Repeat Steps 1–4 for the remaining rivet.
6. Remove the screw in the conventional manner.

CHOKE CAP INSTALLATION

1. Install choke cap gasket.
2. Install the locking and indexing plate.
3. Install the notched gasket.
4. Install choke cap, making certain that bimetal loop is positioned around choke lever tang.
5. While holding cap in place, actuate choke plate to make certain bimetal loop is properly engaged with lever tang. Set retaining clamp over choke cap and orient clamp to match holes in casting (holes are not equally spaced). Make sure retaining clamp is not upside down.
6. Place rivet in rivet gun and trigger lightly to retain rivet (1/8 inch diameter × 1/2 inch long × 1/4 inch diameter head).
7. Press rivet fully into casting after passing through retaining clamp and pop rivet (mandrel breaks off).
8. Repeat this step for the remaining rivet.
9. Install screw in conventional manner. Tighten to (17-20 lb-in.)

CHOKE PLATE CLEARANCE (DECHOKE) ADJUSTMENT

1. Remove the air cleaner assembly.
2. Hold the throttle plate fully open and close the choke plate as far as possible without forcing it. Use a drill of the proper diameter to check the clearance between the choke plate and air horn.
3. If the clearance is not within spec-

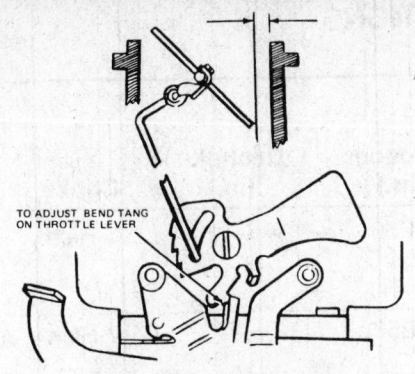

TO ADJUST BEND TANG
ON THROTTLE LEVER

Dechoke adjustment—YFA

MECHANICAL FUEL BOWL VENT ADJUSTMENT

1. Start the engine and wait until it has reached normal operating temperature before proceeding.

2. Check engine idle rpm and set to specifications.

3. Check DC motor operation by opening throttle off idle. The DC motor should extend. Release the throttle, and the DC motor should retract when in contact with the throttle lever.

4. Disconnect the idle speed motor in the idle position.

5. Turn engine Off.

6. Open the throttle lever so that the throttle lever actuating lever does not touch the fuel bowl vent rod.

7. Close the throttle lever to the idle set position and measure the travel of the fuel bowl vent rod at point A. The distance measured represents the travel of the vent rod from where there is no contact with the

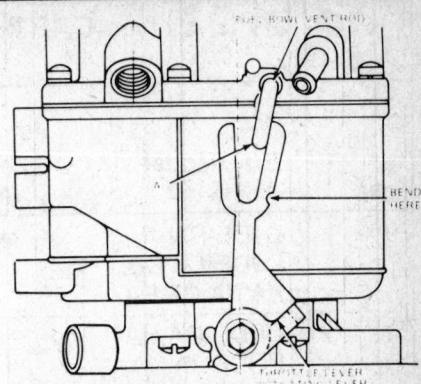

Mechanical fuel bowl vent adjustment— YFA

actuating lever to where the actuating lever moves the vent rod to the idle set position. The travel of the vent rod at point A should be 0.100–0.150 in. (2.54–3.81 mm).

8. If adjustment is required, bend the throttle actuating lever at notch shown.

9. Reconnect the idle speed control motor.

ification, adjust by bending the arm on the choke lever of the throttle lever. Bending the arm downward will decrease the clearance, and bending it upward will increase the clearance. **Always recheck the clearance after making any adjustment.**

CARTER YF, YFA SPECIFICATIONS
American Motors

Year	Model ①	Float Level (in.)	Fast Idle Cam (in.)	Unloader (in.)	Choke
'78-'79	7201	0.476	0.195	0.275	Index
	7228	0.476	0.195	0.275	1 Rich
	7229	0.476	0.195	0.275	1 Rich
	7235	0.476	0.195	0.275	Index
	7267	0.476	0.195	0.275	1 Rich
	7232	0.476	0.201	0.275	2 Rich
	7233	0.476	0.201	0.275	1 Rich
'83–'84	7700	0.600	0.175	0.370	Fixed
	7701	0.600	0.175	0.370	Fixed
	7702	0.600	0.175	0.370	Fixed
	7703	0.600	0.175	0.370	Fixed

① Model numbers located on the tag or casting

CARTER YF, YFA, YFA-FB SPECIFICATIONS
Ford Motor Co.

Year	Model ①	Float Level (in.)	Fast Idle Cam (in.)	Choke Plate Pulldown (in.)	Unloader (in.)	Dechoke (in.)	Choke
'78	D7BE-AA,AB,BA	25/32	0.140	—	0.250	—	Index
	D7BE-FA,HB, GB,GC	25/32	0.140	—	0.250	—	2 Rich
	D7BE-NA,DA	25/32	0.140	—	0.250	—	1 Rich

CARTER YF, YFA, YFA-FB SPECIFICATIONS
Ford Motor Co.

Year	Model ①	Float Level (in.)	Fast Idle Cam (in.)	Choke Plate Pulldown (in.)	Unloader (in.)	Dechoke (in.)	Choke
'79	D9BE-RA D9DE-CB, DB, AA, BA, CA, EA	25/32	0.140	—	0.250	—	1 Rich
'80	DEDE-GA, HA EODE-JA, NA, LA, MA	25/32	0.140	—	0.250	—	2 Rich
'83	E3ZE-LA	0.650	0.140	0.260	—	0.220	—
	E3ZE-MA	0.650	0.140	0.260	—	0.220	—
	E3ZE-TB	0.650	0.140	0.240	—	0.220	—
	E3ZE-UA	0.650	0.140	0.240	—	0.220	—
	E3ZE-VA	0.650	0.140	0.260	—	0.220	—
	E3ZE-YA	0.650	0.140	0.260	—	0.220	—
	E3ZE-NB	0.650	0.160	0.260	—	0.220	—
	E3ZE-PB	0.650	0.160	0.260	—	0.220	—
	E3ZE-ASA	0.650	0.160	0.260	—	0.220	—
	E3ZE-APA	0.650	0.140	0.240	—	0.220	—
	E3ZE-ARA	0.650	0.140	0.240	—	0.220	—
	E3ZE-ADA	0.650	0.140	0.260	—	0.220	—
	E3ZE-AEA	0.650	0.140	0.260	—	0.220	—
	E3ZE-ACA	0.650	0.140	0.260	—	0.220	—
	E3ZE-ATA	0.650	0.160	0.260	—	0.220	—
	E3ZE-ABA	0.650	0.140	0.260	—	0.220	—
	E3ZE-UB	0.650	0.140	0.240	—	0.220	—
	E3ZE-TC	0.650	0.140	0.240	—	0.220	—
'84	E4ZE-HC, DB	0.650	0.140	0.260	—	0.270	—
	E4ZE-MA, NA	0.650	0.140	0.240	—	0.270	—
	E4ZE-PA, RA	0.650	0.140	0.260	—	0.270	—

① Model number located on the tag or casting

Model TQ

The TQ (Thermo-Quad) has a fuel bowl made of phenolic resin. This acts as a heat insulator. Fuel is kept 20 degrees cooler than in metal carburetors. It also has a suspended design metering system which aids in cooling. All the calibration points are in the upper aluminum casting or air horn and are in effect suspended in the cavities in the main body.

FLOAT ADJUSTMENT

1. With the bowl cover inverted, the gasket installed, and the floats resting on the seated needle, the dimension of each float from the bottom side of the float to the cover gasket should be as shown in the specifications chart.
2. To adjust, bend the float lever. Do not allow the float lever lip to be pressed against the needle during adjustment.

SECONDARY THROTTLE LINKAGE

1. Block the choke valve in the wide open position and invert the carburetor.
2. Slowly open the primary throttle

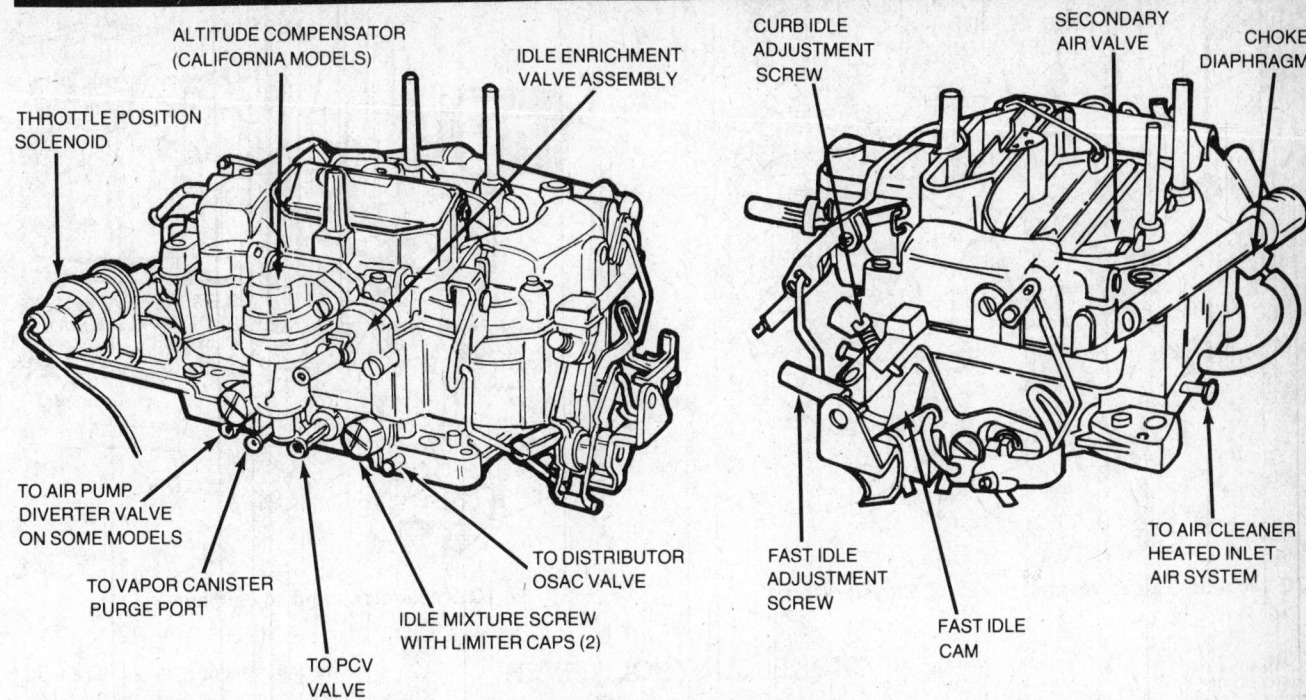

THROTTLE POSITION
SOLENOID

ALTITUDE COMPENSATOR
(CALIFORNIA MODELS)

IDLE ENRICHMENT
VALVE ASSEMBLY

CURB IDLE
ADJUSTMENT
SCREW

SECONDARY
AIR VALVE

CHOKE
DIAPHRAGM

TO AIR PUMP
DIVERTER VALVE
ON SOME MODELS

TO VAPOR CANISTER
PURGE PORT

TO PCV
VALVE

IDLE MIXTURE SCREW
WITH LIMITER CAPS (2)

TO DISTRIBUTOR
OSAC VALVE

FAST IDLE
ADJUSTMENT
SCREW

FAST IDLE
CAM

TO AIR CLEANER
HEATED INLET
AIR SYSTEM

TQ carburetor assembly—typical

valves until the secondary valves start to open. Measure between the lower edge of the primary valve and its bore. Open the throttle to the wide open position. The primary and secondary levers should contact the stops at the same time.

3. If it is necessary to adjust, bend the secondary throttle operating rod at the lower angle until the correct dimension is obtained.

SECONDARY AIR VALVE OPENING

1. With the air valve in the closed position, the opening along the air valve at its long side must be at its maximum and parallel with the air horn gasket surface.

2. With the air valve wide open, the opening of the air valve at the short side

and the air horn must match the dimensions in the Specifications Charts. The corner of the air valve is notched for adjustment. Bend the corner with a pair of pliers to give proper opening.

ACCELERATOR PUMP STOKE ADJUSTMENT

1. Make sure the throttle connector rod is in the correct hole of the pump arm.

2. Measure the height of the accelerator pump plunger at curb idle. The ignition switch must be on if there is an idle stop solenoid.

3. Adjust plunger height by bending the throttle connector rod.

NOTE: Carburetors with staged pump systems require a second height mea-

surement at the throttle position related to a secondary throttle lockout.

First Stage

1. Make sure the throttle connector rod is in the correct pump arm slot.

2. Use a scale to measure the height of the accelerator pump plunger stem at curb idle.

3. Adjust the pump plunger height by bending the throttle connector rod.

Second Stage

1. Open the choke then open the throttle until the secondary lockout is just applied. The plunger downward travel stops at that point.

2. Use a scale to measure the accelerator pump plunger height.

3. Adjust by bending the tang.

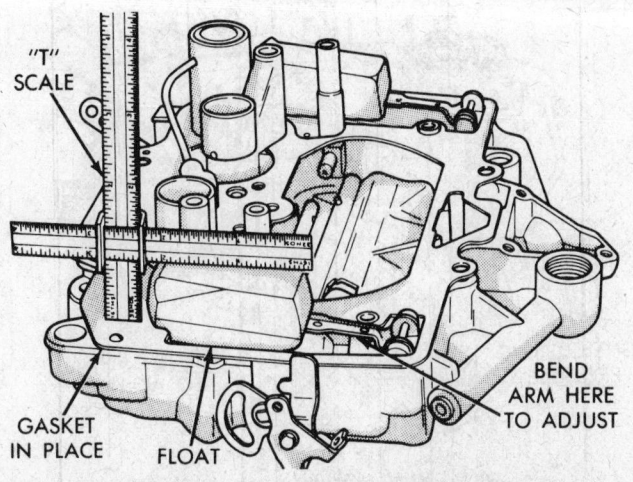

"T" SCALE

GASKET IN PLACE

FLOAT

BEND ARM HERE TO ADJUST

TQ float adjustment (© Chrysler Corp.)

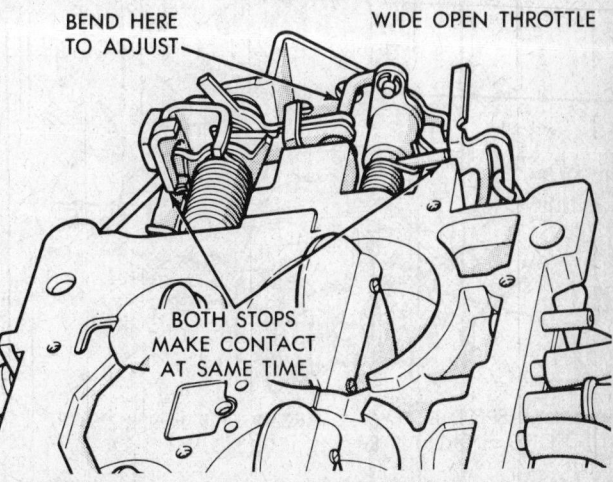

BEND HERE TO ADJUST

WIDE OPEN THROTTLE

BOTH STOPS MAKE CONTACT AT SAME TIME

TQ secondary throttle adjustment (© Chrysler Corp.)

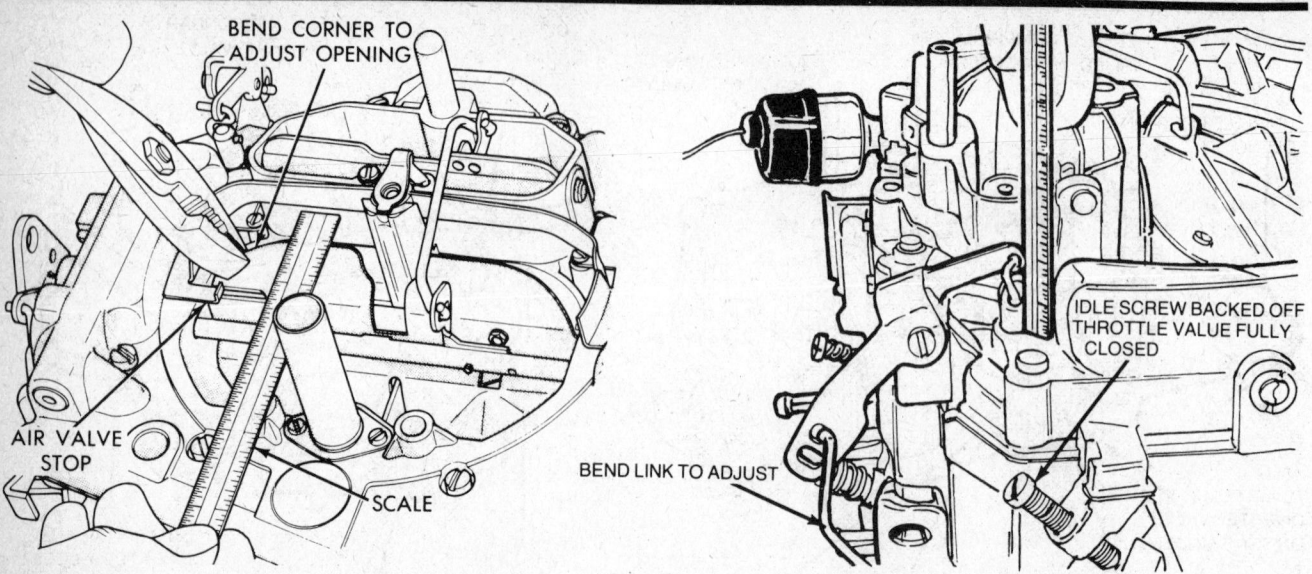

TQ secondary air valve adjustment (© Chrysler Corp.)

TQ accelerator pump adjustment

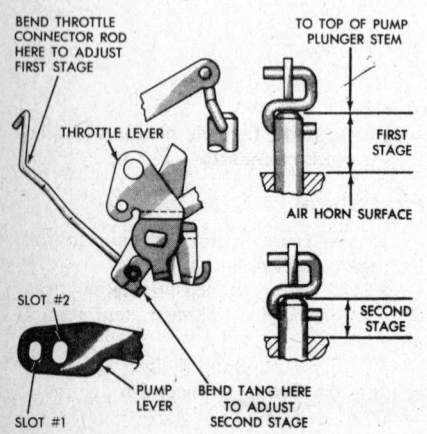

TQ accelerator pump stroke adjustment

CHOKE CONTROL LEVER

1. Disconnect the diaphragm rod.
2. Close the choke by pushing on the choke lever with the throttle partly open.
3. Measure the vertical distance from the top of the rod hole in the control lever down to the carburetor base. The dimension should be as shown in the Specifications Chart.
4. To adjust, bend the link which connects the two choke shafts. If an adjustment is needed, the vacuum kick, fast idle cam, and choke unloader must be readjusted.

CHOKE VACUUM KICK ADJUSTMENT

NOTE: The test can be made on or off the vehicle.

1. If the adjustment is to be made with the engine running, back off the fast idle speed screw until the choke can be closed to the kick position with the engine at curb idle. (Note the number of screw turns required so that the fast idle can be returned to the original adjustment.)
2. If an auxiliary vacuum source is to be used, open the throttle valve (engine not running) and move the choke to the closed position. Release the throttle first, then release the choke.

When using an auxiliary vacuum source, disconnect the vacuum hose from the carburetor and connect it to the hose from the vacuum supply with a small length of tube to act as a fitting. Removal of the hose from the diaphragm may require sufficient force to bend the bracket. Apply a vacuum of 15 or more in. of mercury.
3. Insert the specified drill between the

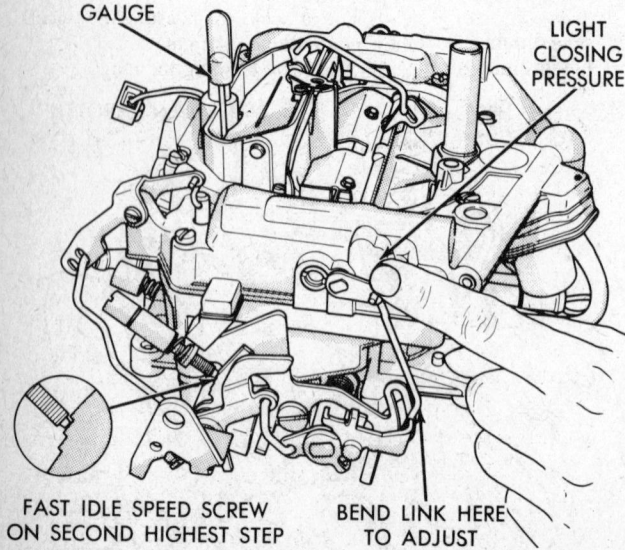

TQ fast idle cam linkage adjustment (© Chrysler Corp.)

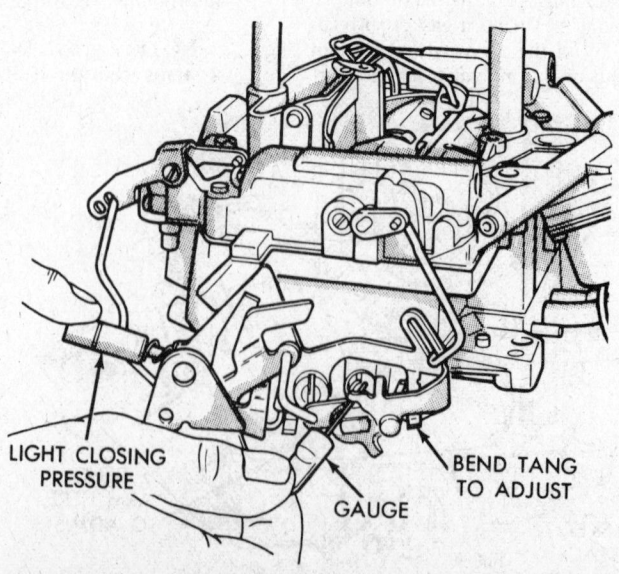

TQ secondary throttle lockout adjustment (© Chrysler Corp.)

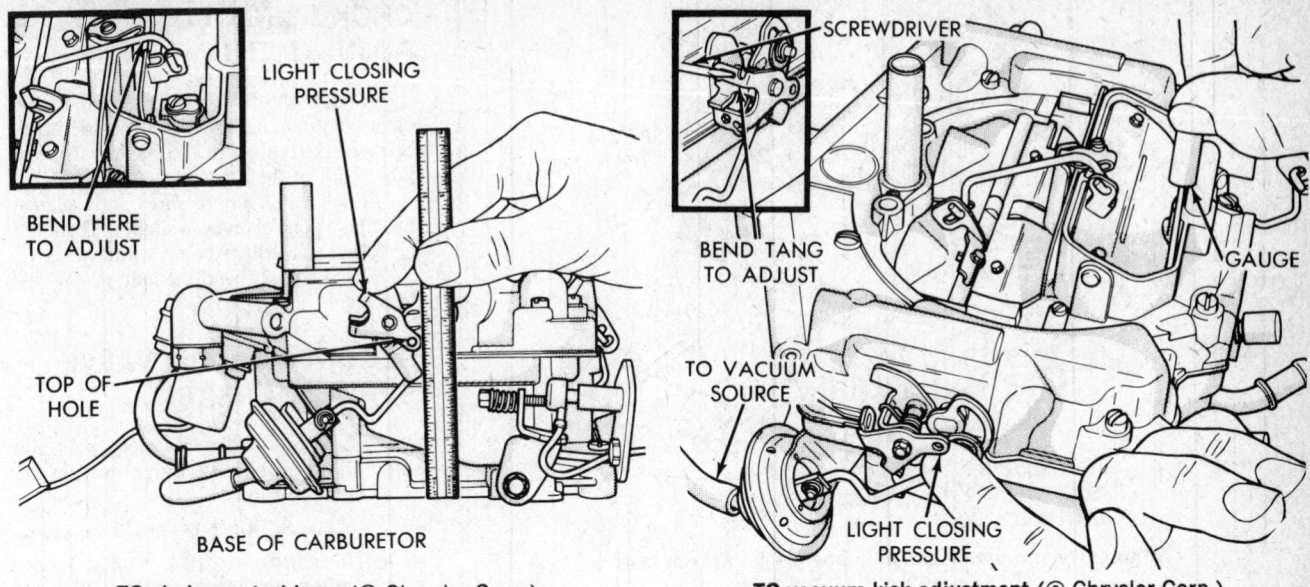

BEND HERE
TO ADJUST

LIGHT CLOSING
PRESSURE

TOP OF
HOLE

BASE OF CARBURETOR

TQ choke control lever (©️ Chrysler Corp.)

SCREWDRIVER

BEND TANG
TO ADJUST

TO VACUUM
SOURCE

GAUGE

LIGHT CLOSING
PRESSURE

TQ vacuum kick adjustment (©️ Chrysler Corp.)

long side, lower edge, of the choke valve and the air horn wall.

4. Apply sufficient pressure on the choke control lever to provide a minimum choke valve opening. The spring connecting the control lever to the adjustment lever must be fully extended for proper adjustment.

5. Bend the tang to change contact with the end of the diaphragm rod. Do not adjust the diaphragm rod. A slight drag should be felt as the drill is being removed.

FAST IDLE CAM LINKAGE

1. With the fast screw on the second fastest step of the cam against the shoulder of the first step, there should be 0.100 in. between the air horn wall and edge of the choke valve.

2. To adjust, bend the fast idle connector rod at the lower angle.

SECONDARY THROTTLE LOCKOUT

1. Move the choke control lever to the open choke position.

2. Measure the clearance between the lockout lever and the stop.

3. Bend the tang on the fast idle control lever to provide the proper clearance. Clearance should be 0.060–0.090 in.

BOWL VENT VALVE ADJUSTMENT

1978

1. Remove the bowl vent valve checking hole plug in the bowl cover.

2. With the throttle valve in the idle position insert a narrow ruler down through the hole.

3. Allow the ruler to rest lightly on the top of the valve. Measure from the top of

the valve to the top of the bowl cover at the opening. The correct dimension should be 3/16 in.

4. Bend the bowl vent operating lever at the notch to adjust.

5. Install a new plug.

1979 and later

1. Remove the air cleaner. Disconnect the hose to the solenoid bowl vent diaphragm.

2. Connect an auxiliary vacuum source. With 15 in. Hg. applied, the valve should move down. This can be observed down through the air horn vent tube.

3. Turn the ignition switch on and disconnect the auxiliary vacuum source. The valve should remain down. With the ignition off, the valve should move back up.

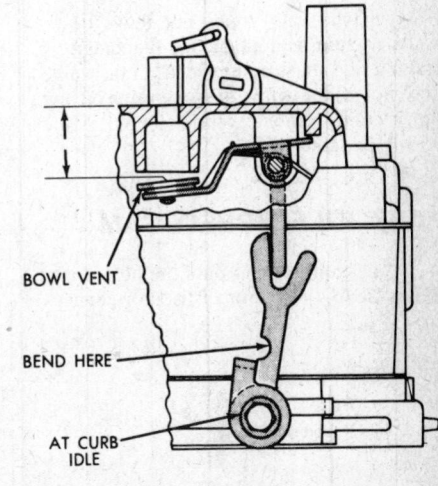

BOWL VENT

BEND HERE

AT CURB
IDLE

TQ bowl vent adjustment

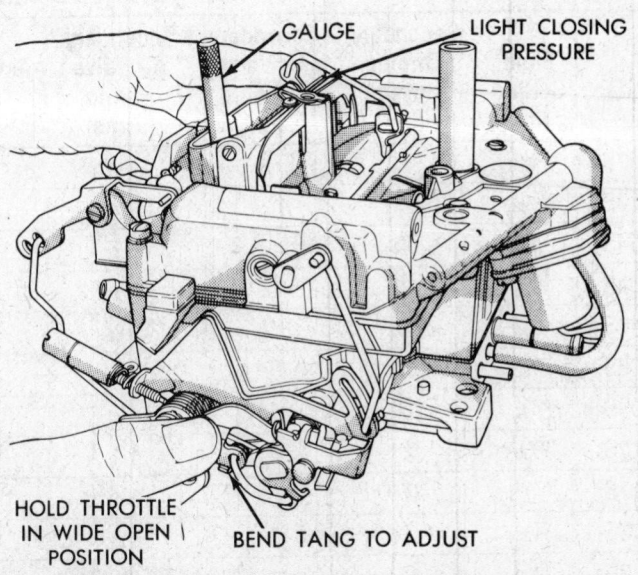

GAUGE

LIGHT CLOSING
PRESSURE

HOLD THROTTLE
IN WIDE OPEN
POSITION

BEND TANG TO ADJUST

TQ choke unloader adjustment (©️ Chrysler Corp.)

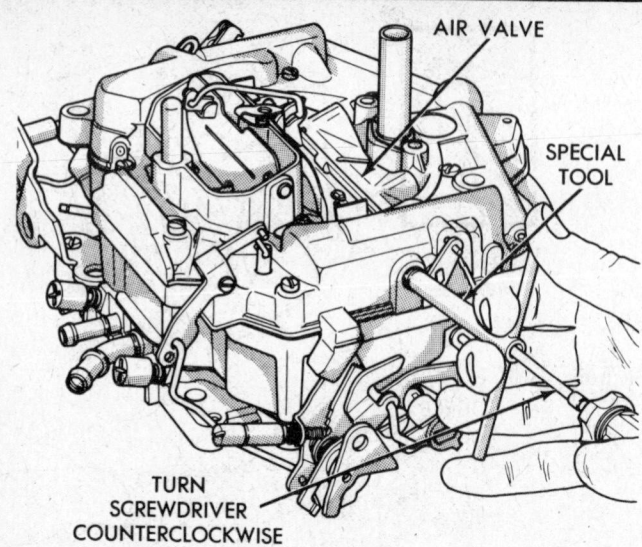

TURN
SCREWDRIVER
COUNTERCLOCKWISE

TQ air valve spring tension adjustment (© Chrysler Corp.)

4. If the valve does not move down when vacuum is applied, the diaphragm is leaking and must be replaced. If the valve does not stay down with the ignition on and the vacuum removed, the solenoid or the wiring is defective.

FAST IDLE SPEED CAM

1. Disconnect and plug the heated air, EGR, OSAC valve, or distributor connec-

tions. With lean burn, do not disconnect the spark control computer hose. Use a jumper wire to ground the carburetor idle stop switch. With the engine off and the transmission in Park or Neutral, open the throttle slightly.

2. Close the choke valve until the fast idle screw can be positioned on the second step of the cam against the shoulder of the first step.

3. Start the engine and adjust the screw to obtain the specified fast idle speed.

CHOKE UNLOADER ADJUSTMENT

1. Hold the throttle valves in the wide open position and insert the specified drill between the bottom of the choke valve and inner wall of the air horn.

2. With a finger pressing lightly against the choke control lever, a slight drag should be felt as the drill is being withdrawn.

3. To adjust, bend the tang on the fast idle lever.

SECONDARY AIR VALVE SPRING TENSION

1. Loosen the air valve lock plug and allow the air valve to position itself in the wide open position.

——————— CAUTION ———————
Hold the adjustment plug with a screwdriver when loosening the lock plug. If you don't, the spring may snap out of position and require carburetor disassembly to retrieve it.

2. With a long screwdriver that will enter the center of tool C-4152 positioned on the air valve adjustment plug, turn the plug counterclockwise until the air valve contacts the stop lightly, then tighten the specified amount.

3. Hold the adjustment plug with the screwdriver and tighten the lock plug with the tool. Make sure the adjustment does not move and that the air valve moves freely.

CARTER TQ SPECIFICATIONS
Chrysler Products

Year	Model ①	Float Setting (in.)	Secondary Throttle Linkage (in.)	Secondary Air Valve Opening (in.)	Secondary Air Valve Spring (turns)	Accelerator Pump (in.)	Choke Control Lever (in.)	Choke Unloader (in.)	Vacuum Kick (in.)	Fast Idle Speed (rpm)
'78	9147S	$^{29}/_{32}$	②	½	1½	$^{31}/_{64}$	3⅜	0.310	0.100	1600
	9137S	$^{29}/_{32}$	②	½	1½	$^{31}/_{64}$	3⅜	0.310	0.100	1600
	9134S	$^{29}/_{32}$	②	½	1½	$^{31}/_{64}$	3⅜	0.310	0.100	1500
	9104S	$^{29}/_{32}$	②	½	1½	$^{31}/_{64}$	3⅜	0.310	0.150	1500
	9140S	$^{29}/_{32}$	②	½	1½	$^{33}/_{64}$	3⅜	0.310	0.150	1500
	9108S	$^{27}/_{32}$	②	½	1½	$^{33}/_{64}$	3⅜	0.310	0.100	1400
	9109S	$^{27}/_{32}$	②	½	1½	$^{33}/_{64}$	3⅜	0.310	0.100	1400
	9110S	$^{27}/_{32}$	②	½	1½	$^{33}/_{64}$	3⅜	0.310	0.100	1600
	9111S	$^{27}/_{32}$	②	½	1½	$^{33}/_{64}$	3⅜	0.310	0.100	1400
	9112S	$^{29}/_{32}$	②	½	1½	$^{33}/_{64}$	3⅜	0.310	0.100	1200
	9148S	$^{29}/_{32}$	②	½	1½	$^{33}/_{64}$	3⅜	0.310	0.100	1600

CARTER TQ SPECIFICATIONS
Chrysler Products

Year	Model ①	Float Setting (in.)	Secondary Throttle Linkage (in.)	Secondary Air Valve Opening (in.)	Secondary Air Valve Spring (turns)	Accelerator Pump (in.)	Choke Control Lever (in.)	Choke Unloader (in.)	Vacuum Kick (in.)	Fast Idle Speed (rpm)
'79	9195S	$^{29}/_{32}$	②	$^{3}/_{8}$	2	$^{33}/_{64}$	$3^{3}/_{8}$	0.310	0.100	1600
	9197S	$^{29}/_{32}$	②	$^{1}/_{2}$	$1^{1}/_{2}$	$^{33}/_{64}$	$3^{3}/_{8}$	0.310	0.100	1600
	9196S, 9198S, 9202S	$^{29}/_{32}$	②	$^{1}/_{2}$	2	$^{33}/_{64}$	$3^{3}/_{8}$	0.310	0.100	1600
'80	9236S	$^{29}/_{32}$	②	$^{1}/_{2}$	3	$^{11}/_{32}$ ③	$3^{3}/_{8}$	0.310	0.100	1600
	9243S	$^{29}/_{32}$	②	$^{1}/_{2}$	$2^{5}/_{8}$	$^{11}/_{32}$ ④	$3^{3}/_{8}$	0.310	0.100	1600
	9244S	$^{29}/_{32}$	②	$^{1}/_{2}$	$2^{1}/_{2}$	$^{11}/_{32}$ ④	$3^{3}/_{8}$	0.310	0.100	1200
'81	9372S	$^{29}/_{32}$	②	$^{13}/_{32}$	$1^{3}/_{4}$	$^{33}/_{64}$ ④	$3^{3}/_{8}$	0.312	0.130	1400
	9373S	$^{29}/_{32}$	②	$^{13}/_{32}$	$1^{3}/_{4}$	$^{33}/_{64}$ ④	$3^{3}/_{8}$	0.312	0.130	1400
	9364S	$^{29}/_{32}$	②	$^{13}/_{32}$	$1^{7}/_{8}$	$^{33}/_{64}$ ③	$3^{3}/_{8}$	0.312	0.100	1500
'82	9372S	$^{29}/_{32}$	②	$^{13}/_{32}$	$1^{3}/_{4}$	$^{33}/_{64}$ ④	$3^{3}/_{8}$	0.310	0.130	1400
'83	9374S	$^{29}/_{32}$	②	$^{13}/_{32}$	$1^{3}/_{4}$	⑤	$3^{3}/_{8}$	0.310	0.130	1400
	9385S	$^{29}/_{32}$	②	$^{13}/_{32}$	$1^{3}/_{4}$	$^{33}/_{64}$ ④	$3^{3}/_{8}$	0.310	0.130	1400
'84	93895	$^{29}/_{32}$	②	$^{13}/_{32}$	$1^{3}/_{4}$	⑤	—	0.310	0.130	1400

NOTE: All choke settings are fixed.
① Model numbers located on the tag or on the casting
② Adjust link so primary and secondary stops both contact at same time
③ Slot #1
④ Slot #2
⑤ First stage—$^{33}/_{64}$
   Second stage—$^{25}/_{64}$

FORD, AUTOLITE, MOTORCRAFT CARBURETORS

Model 740

The model 740 has five basic systems: choke system, idle system, main metering system, acceleration system and power enrichment system. The choke system is used for cold starting and features a bi-metallic spring and an electric heater for faster cold starts and improved warm-up. The idle system is a separate and adjustable system for the correct air/fuel mixture for both idle and low speed performance.

The main metering system provides the correct air/fuel mixture for normal cruising speeds. A main metering system is provided for both primary and secondary stage operation.

The accelerating system is mechanically operated from the primary throttle linkage and provides fuel to the primary stage dur-

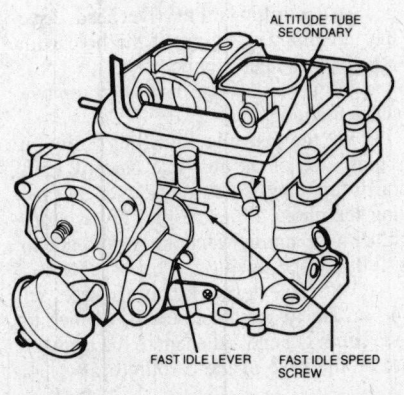

Model 740 carburetor—¾ front view

ing acceleration. Fuel is provided by a diaphragm-type pump. The power enrichment system consists of a vacuum operated power valve and an airflow-regulated pullover system in the secondary. This system is used along with the main metering system to provide satisfactory performance during moderate to heavy acceleration.

Distributor and EGR vacuum ports are located in the primary venturi area of the carburetor.

FAST IDLE CAM

1. Set the fast idle screw on the kickdown step of the cam against the shoulder of the top step.
2. Manually close the primary choke

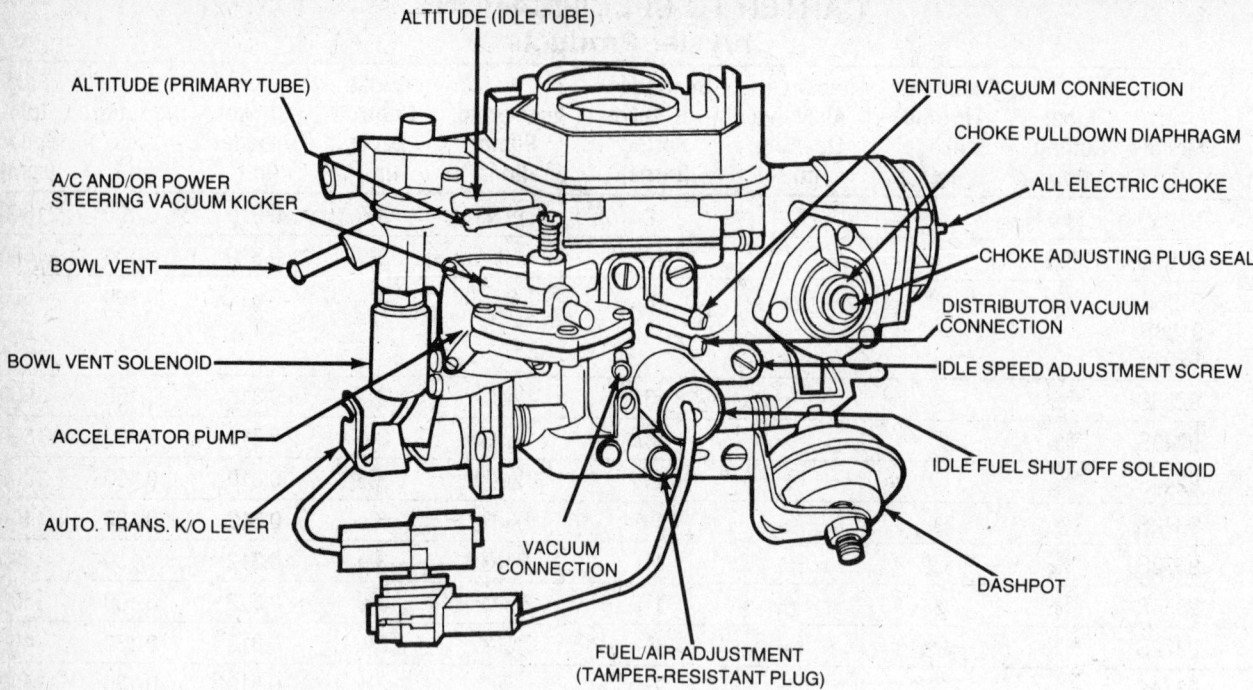

ALTITUDE (IDLE TUBE)

ALTITUDE (PRIMARY TUBE)

A/C AND/OR POWER
STEERING VACUUM KICKER

BOWL VENT

BOWL VENT SOLENOID

ACCELERATOR PUMP

AUTO. TRANS. K/O LEVER

VENTURI VACUUM CONNECTION

CHOKE PULLDOWN DIAPHRAGM

ALL ELECTRIC CHOKE

CHOKE ADJUSTING PLUG SEAL

DISTRIBUTOR VACUUM
CONNECTION

IDLE SPEED ADJUSTMENT SCREW

IDLE FUEL SHUT OFF SOLENOID

DASHPOT

VACUUM
CONNECTION

FUEL/AIR ADJUSTMENT
(TAMPER-RESISTANT PLUG)

Model 740 carburetor—full rear

plate, and measure the distance between the downstream side of the choke plate and the air horn wall.

3. Adjust the right fork of the choke bimetal shaft, which engages the fast idle cam, by bending the fork up and down to obtain the specified clearance.

FAST IDLE

1. Place the transmission in neutral or park.

2. Bring the engine to normal operating temperature.

3. Disconnect and plug the vacuum hose at the EGR and purge valves.

4. Identify the vacuum source to the air by-pass section of the air supply control valve. If a vacuum hose is connected to the carburetor, disconnect the hose and plug the hose at the air supply control valve.

5. Place the fast idle adjustment on the second step of the fast idle cam. Run the engine until the cooling fan comes on.

6. While the cooling fan is on, check the fast idle rpm. If adjustment is necessary, loosen the locknut and adjust to specification on underhood decal.

7. Remove all plugs and reconnect hoses to their original position.

DASHPOT

With the throttle set at the curb idle position, fully depress the dashpot stem and measure the distance between the stem and the throttle lever. Adjust by loosening the locknut and turning the dashpot.

CHOKE PLATE PULLDOWN ADJUSTMENT

NOTE: The following procedure requires the removal of the carburetor and also the choke cap which is retained by two rivets.

1. Remove the carburetor from the engine.

2. Remove the choke cap as follows:

a. Check the rivets to determine if mandrel is well below the rivit head. If mandrel is within the rivit head thickness, drive it down or out with a 1/16 inch diameter tip punch.

b. With a 1/8 inch diameter drill, drill into the rivet head until the rivet head comes loose from the rivet body. Use light pressure on the drill bit or the rivet will just spin in the hole.

c. After drilling off the rivet head, drive the remaining rivet out of the hole with a 1/8 inch diameter punch.

d. Repeat steps (a thru c) to remove the remaining rivet.

3. Set the fast idle adjusting screw on the high step of the fast idle cam by temporarily opening the throttle lever and rotating the choke bimetal shaft lever counterclockwise until the choke plates are in the fully closed position.

4. With an external vacuum source, set to 17 in. Hg.; vacuum should be applied to the vacuum channel adjacent to the primary bore on the base of the carburetor.

NOTE: The modulator spring should not be depressed.

5. Using the drill diameter specified in the carburetor specifications table at the end of this section, measure the clearance between the down-stream side of the choke plate and the air horn wall.

6. If an adjustment is necessary, turn the vacuum diaphragm adjusting screw in or out as required.

DRY FLOAT ADJUSTMENT

1. Place the air horn assembly upside down and at a 45 degree angle (with the air horn gasket in place). The float tang should rest lightly on the inlet needle.

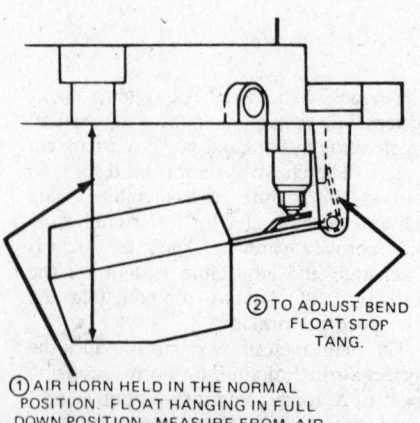

② TO ADJUST BEND
FLOAT STOP
TANG.

① AIR HORN HELD IN THE NORMAL
POSITION. FLOAT HANGING IN FULL
DOWN POSITION. MEASURE FROM AIR
HORN COVER GASKET TO FLOAT,
AS SHOWN.
(43mm ± 8mm SETTING)

Float drop adjustment—Model 740

2. Measure the clearance with a suitable gauge at the extreme end or toe of the float.

3. Remove float and adjust to specification by bending the float level adjusting tang up or down.

NOTE: Care must be taken not to scratch or damage the float tang while adjusting.

FLOAT DROP ADJUSTMENT

1. Suspend air horn assembly in normal position (with air horn gasket in position).

2. The distance from the air horn gasket to the bottom of the float should be 1.69 ± 0.31 in. (43 ± 8mm).

3. Remove float and adjust to specification by bending the float drop tang.

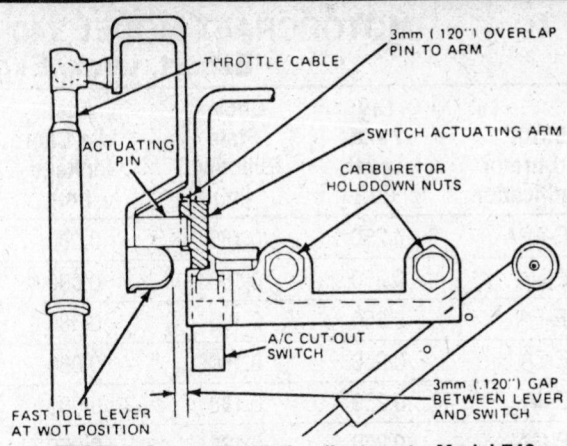

(WOT) A/C cut-off switch adjustment—Model 740

WIDE OPEN THROTTLE (WOT) A/C CUT-OUT SWITCH

A visual inspection is required to ensure adequate pin and actuating arm overlap with the carburetor linkage in the WOT position.

Adjustments to the switch position are made by bending its support bracket outboard. A 0.120 in. (3mm) minimum overlap is desired. Precaution is required to ensure adequate clearance between the tip of the carburetor fast idle lever and switch housing.

MOTORCRAFT MODEL 740 SPECIFICATIONS
Escort, Lynx, Exp, Lynx

Year	(9510)* Carburetor Identification	Dry Float Level (in.)	Choke Plate Pulldown (in.)	Fast Idle Cam Linkage (in.)	Fast Idle (rpm)	Dechoke (in.)	Choke Setting	Dashpot (in.)
'81	E1EE-AAA	0.250	0.120	0.080	①	0.140	Index	0.140
	E1EE-SA	0.250	0.120	0.080	①	0.140	Index	0.140
	E1EE-TA	0.250	0.120	0.080	①	0.140	Index	0.140
	E1EE-AEA	0.250	0.120	0.080	①	0.140	Index	0.140
	E1EE-AFA	0.250	0.120	0.080	①	0.140	Index	0.140
	E1EE-ADA	0.250	0.120	0.080	①	0.140	Index	0.140
	E1EE-LA	0.250	0.120	0.080	①	0.140	Index	0.140
	E1EE-AHA	0.250	0.100	0.080	①	0.140	Index	0.160
	E1EE-ZA	0.250	0.160	0.080	①	0.140	1 Lean	0.160
	E1EE-MA	0.250	0.160	0.080	①	0.140	1 Lean	0.160
	E1EE-NA	0.250	0.160	0.080	①	0.140	1 Lean	0.160
	E1EE-PA	0.250	0.160	0.080	①	0.140	1 Lean	0.160
	E1EE-ACA	0.250	0.160	0.080	①	0.140	1 Lean	0.160
	E1EE-RA	0.250	0.160	0.080	①	0.140	1 Lean	0.160
	E1EE-ARA	0.250	0.118	0.080	①	0.140	Index	0.140
	E1EE-ASA	0.250	0.118	0.080	①	0.140	Index	0.140
	E1EE-AVA	0.250	0.118	0.080	①	0.140	Index	0.140
	E1EE-ATA	0.250	0.118	0.080	①	0.140	Index	0.140
'82	E1GE-CA	0.250	0.120	0.080	2400	0.140	Index	0.140
	E1GE-DA	0.250	0.120	0.080	2400	0.140	Index	0.140
	E1EE-ALA	0.250	0.160	0.080	2400	0.140	1 Lean	0.160
	E1GE-GA	0.250	0.160	0.080	2400	0.140	1 Lean	0.160

MOTORCRAFT MODEL 740 SPECIFICATIONS
Escort, Lynx, Exp, Lynx

Year	(9510)* Carburetor Identification	Dry Float Level (in.)	Choke Plate Pulldown (in.)	Fast Idle Cam Linkage (in.)	Fast Idle (rpm)	Dechoke (in.)	Choke Setting	Dashpot (in.)
	E1EE-APA	0.250	0.160	0.080	2400	0.140	1 Lean	0.160
	E1EE-NA	0.250	0.160	0.080	2400	0.140	1 Lean	0.160
	E1GE-EA	0.250	0.160	0.080	2400	0.140	1 Lean	0.160
	E1EE-ZA	0.250	0.160	0.080	2400	0.140	1 Lean	0.160
	E2EE-JA	0.250	0.138	0.080	2400	0.140	Index	0.060
	E2EE-GA	0.250	0.138	0.080	2200	0.140	Index	0.060
	E2EE-GC	0.250	0.138	0.080	2200	0.140	Index	0.140
	E2EE-EA	0.250	0.138	0.080	2400	0.140	Index	0.160
	E2EE-SA	0.250	0.138	0.080	2400	0.140	Index	0.060
	E2EE-LC	0.250	0.177	0.080	①	0.140	Index	0.160
	E2EE-LA	0.250	0.138	0.080	2400	0.140	Index	0.160
	E2EE-ZA	0.250	0.138	0.080	2400	0.140	2 Rich	0.160
	E2EE-NA	0.250	0.138	0.080	2400	0.140	Index	0.160
	E2EE-AAA	0.250	0.138	0.080	2400	0.140	2 Rich	0.160
	E2EE-PA	0.250	0.138	0.080	2400	0.140	Index	0.160
	E2EE-PC	0.250	0.177	0.080	2200	0.140	Index	0.160
	E2EE-NC	0.250	0.177	0.080	2200	0.140	Index	0.160
	E2EE-VA	0.250	0.138	0.080	2400	0.140	1 Lean	0.160
	E2EE-YA	0.250	0.138	0.080	2400	0.140	1 Lean	0.160
	E2EE-MC	0.250	0.177	0.080	2200	0.140	Index	0.160
	E2EE-MA	0.250	0.138	0.080	2400	0.140	Index	0.160
'83	E3EE-CA	0.300	0.320	0.080	①	0.140	NA	0.140
	E3EE-EA	0.300	0.320	0.080	①	0.140	NA	0.140
	E3EE-DA	0.300	0.340	0.080	①	0.140	NA	0.140
	E3EE-AA	0.300	0.140	0.080	①	0.140	NA	0.140
	E3EE-JA	0.300	0.140	0.080	①	0.140	NA	0.140
	E3EE-BA	0.300	0.140	0.080	①	0.140	NA	0.140
	E3EE-KA	0.300	0.140	0.080	①	0.140	NA	0.140
	E3EE-GB	0.300	0.312	0.080	①	0.140	NA	0.095
	E3EE-NA	0.300	0.140	0.080	①	0.140	NA	—
	E3EE-PA	0.300	0.140	0.080	①	0.140	NA	0.140
	E3GE-DA	0.300	0.170	0.080	①	0.140	NA	0.140
	E3GE-HA	0.300	0.170	0.080	①	0.140	NA	0.140
	E3GE-FA	0.300	0.170	0.080	①	0.140	NA	0.140
	E3GE-JA	0.300	0.170	0.080	①	0.140	NA	0.160
	E3GE-PA	0.300	0.260	0.080	①	0.140	NA	0.140
	E3GE-SA	0.300	0.260	0.080	①	0.140	NA	0.140
	E3GE-RA	0.300	0.260	0.080	①	0.140	NA	0.140

MOTORCRAFT MODEL 740 SPECIFICATIONS
Escort, Lynx, Exp, Lynx

Year	(9510)* Carburetor Identification	Dry Float Level (in.)	Choke Plate Pulldown (in.)	Fast Idle Cam Linkage (in.)	Fast Idle (rpm)	Dechoke (in.)	Choke Setting	Dashpot (in.)
'83	E3GE-MA	0.300	0.280	0.093	①	0.140	NA	0.160
	E3GE-UA	0.300	0.280	0.093	①	0.140	NA	0.160
	E3GE-NA	0.300	0.140	0.093	①	0.140	NA	0.160
	E3GE-KB	0.300	0.300	0.080	①	0.140	NA	0.160
	E3GE-KD	0.300	0.300	0.080	①	0.140	NA	0.160
	E3GE-LA	0.300	0.300	0.080	①	0.140	NA	0.160
	E3GE-LC	0.300	0.300	0.080	①	0.140	NA	0.160
	E3GE-DC	0.300	0.170	0.080	①	0.140	NA	—
	E3GE-FC	0.300	0.170	0.080	①	0.140	NA	—
	E3GE-JC	0.300	0.170	0.080	①	0.140	NA	—
'84	E4EE-YA	0.300	0.320	0.110	①	0.140	NA	0.095
	E4EE-ACA	0.300	0.320	0.080	①	0.140	NA	0.080
	E4EE-ADA	0.300	0.260	0.080	①	0.140	NA	0.140
	E4EE-ABA	0.300	0.320	0.110	①	0.140	NA	0.095
	E4EE-AAA	0.300	0.320	0.095	①	0.140	NA	0.095
	E4EE-AFA	0.300	0.218	0.080	①	0.140	NA	—
	E4GE-LA	0.300	0.300	0.080	①	0.140	NA	0.160
	E4GE-KA	0.300	0.300	0.080	①	0.140	NA	0.160
	E4GE-SA	0.300	0.280	0.100	①	0.140	NA	0.160
	E4GE-MA	0.300	0.300	0.180	①	0.140	NA	0.160
	E4GE-UA	0.300	0.325	0.080	①	0.140	NA	—
	E4GE-TA	0.300	0.300	0.125	①	0.140	NA	—
	E4GE-RA	0.300	0.325	0.130	①	0.140	NA	—
	E4GE-ACA	0.300	0.140	0.080	①	0.140	NA	0.080
	E4GE-ZA	0.300	0.250	0.108	①	0.140	NA	—

*Basic carburetor number for Ford
Carburetors
① See underhood decal.
NA—Not available

Models 2100, 2150

The Model 2100 and 2150 two barrel carburetor are basically the same in construction. Adjustments are performed in the same manner for both carburetors.

FLOAT LEVEL (DRY)

The dry float level measurement is a preliminary check and must be followed by a wet float level measurement with the carburetor mounted on the engine.

1. With the air horn removed gently raise the float to seat the inlet needle by applying light finger pressure at the float tab. Lower the float by reducing finger pressure until a light step is felt.

NOTE: 1983 and later carburetors are equipped with a spring loaded fuel inlet needle and the ball must not be depressed when the fuel level check is being made.
Measure the distance between the main body gasket surface (gasket removed) and the top of the float. This measurement should be taken near the center of the float at a point ⅛ in. from the free end of the float.

2. If necessary, bend the float tab to obtain the correct level.

FLOAT LEVEL (WET)

1. Remove the screws that hold the air horn to the main body and break the seal between the air horn and main body. Leave

the air horn and gasket loosely in place on top of the main body.

2. Start the engine and allow it to idle for at least three minutes.

3. After the engine has idled long enough to stabilize the fuel level, remove the air horn assembly.

4. With the engine idling, use a T-scale to measure the distance from the top of the fuel bowl machined surface to the surface of the fuel. The scale must be held at last ¼ in. away from any vertical surface to ensure proper measurement.

5. If any adjustment is required, stop the engine to avoid a fire from fuel spraying on the engine.

6. Bend the float tab upward to raise the level and downward to lower the level.

--- CAUTION ---

Be sure to hold the fuel inlet needle off its seat when bending the float tab so as not to damage the Viton® tip.

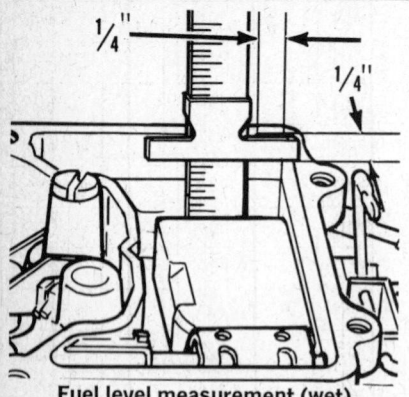

Fuel level measurement (wet)
(© Ford Motor Co)

7. Each time the float level is changed, the air horn must be temporarily positioned and the engine started to stabilize the fuel level before again checking it.

CHOKE PLATE PULLDOWN

Ford Model 2100

1. Loosen the screws on the choke cover and rotate the cover ¼ turn counterclockwise (rich), then tighten the screws.

2. Operate the throttle to allow full closing the choke plate.

3. Press down on the choke modulator arm until the choke modulator diaphragm is bottomed and then measure the distance from the lower edge of the choke plate to the inside air horn wall.

4. Adjustment is achieved by turning the diaphragm stop screw on the underside of the air horn.

5. Turn the screw clockwise to decrease clearance and counterclockwise to increase clearance.

NOTE: Do not reset the choke cover until the fast idle cam adjustment is made.

AMC Model 2100

1. Loosen the choke cover screws and rotate the cover ¼ turn counterclockwise (rich).

2. Disconnect the choke heat inlet tube. Set the fast idle speed screw on the second step of the fast idle cam.

3. Start the engine without moving the throttle linkage. Turn the fast idle cam lever adjusting screw out three turns.

4. Check the clearance between the

lower edge of the choke valve and the air horn wall.

5. Adjust by twisting the modulator arm. Be very careful not to damage the nylon modulator piston rod.

6. Stop the engine and connect the heat tube.

7. Make the fast idle cam adjustment before resetting the choke cover.

Model 2150

1. Remove the air cleaner assembly.

2. Set the throttle on the top step of the fast idle cam.

3. Noting the position of the choke housing cap, loosen the retaining screws and rotate the cap 90 degrees in the rich (closing) direction.

4. Activate the pull-down motor by manually forcing the pull-down control diaphragm link in the direction of applied vacuum or by applying vacuum to the external vacuum tube.

5. Using a drill gauge of the specified diameter, measure the clearance between the choke plate and the center of the air horn wall nearest the fuel bowl.

6. To adjust, reset the diaphragm stop on the end of the choke pull-down diaphragm.

NOTE: Loctite® was applied to the adjusting screw during manufacture and this will have to be loosened before the adjustment can be made. Heat the area around the screw with an electric soldering gun until the Loctite® softens enough to permit the screw to turn freely.

7. After adjusting, check and adjust the fast idle cam. Check and reset fast idle speed, if necessary. Install the air cleaner.

FAST IDLE CAM

1. The choke setting should still be 90° rich, as in Step 1 of the "Pulldown" procedure. Press and release the throttle to set the fast idle cam.

2. Activate the choke pulldown mechanism as in step 4 of the pulldown procedure.

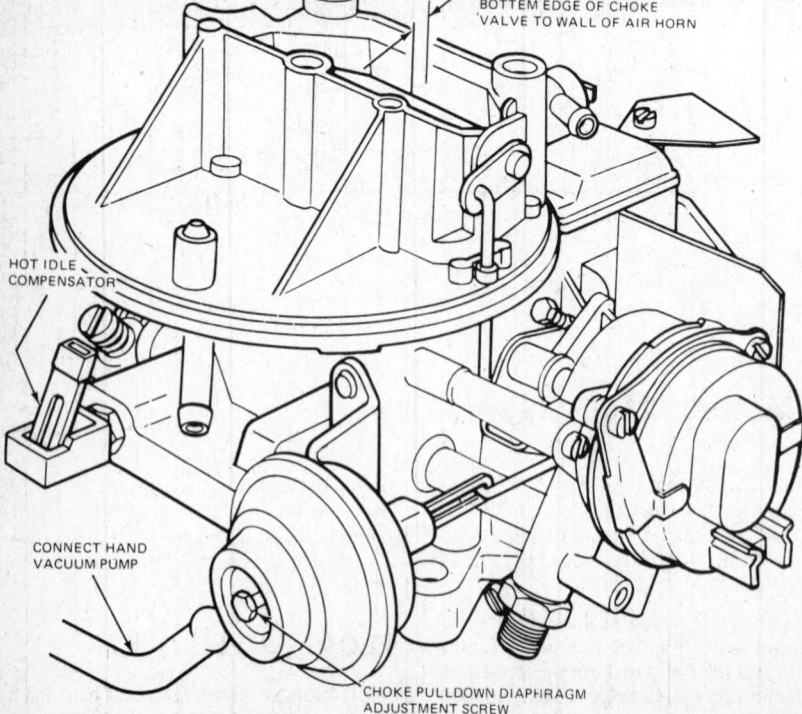

HOT IDLE COMPENSATOR

MEASURE CLEARANCE BOTTOM EDGE OF CHOKE VALVE TO WALL OF AIR HORN

CONNECT HAND VACUUM PUMP

CHOKE PULLDOWN DIAPHRAGM ADJUSTMENT SCREW

Adjusting choke plate pulldown (© Ford Motor Co.)

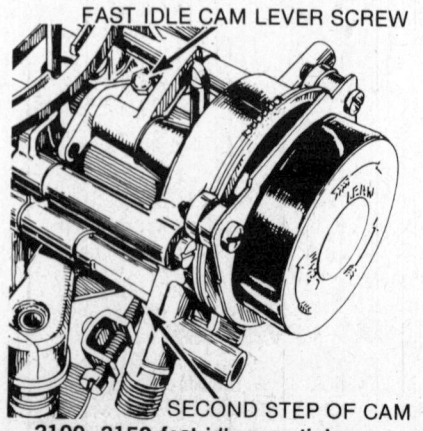

FAST IDLE CAM LEVER SCREW

SECOND STEP OF CAM

2100, 2150 fast idle cam linkage adjustment

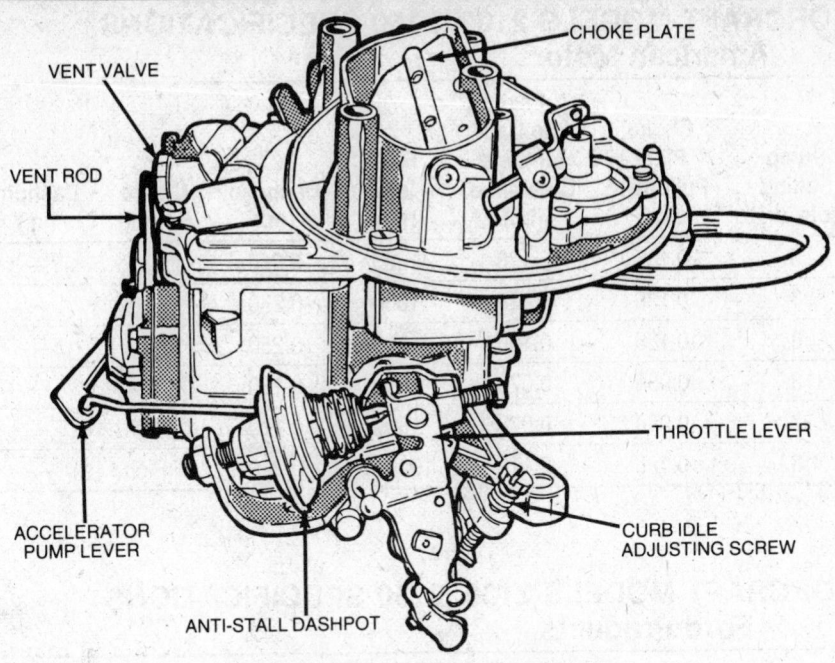

Model 2100 two barrel carburetor

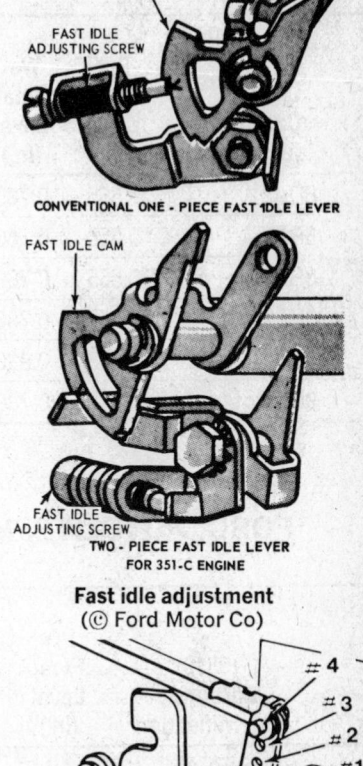

CONVENTIONAL ONE - PIECE FAST IDLE LEVER

**TWO - PIECE FAST IDLE LEVER
FOR 351-C ENGINE**

Fast idle adjustment
(© Ford Motor Co)

Accelerator pump stroke adjustment
(© Ford Motor Co)

3. Press and release the throttle to set the fast idle cam. It should drop to the kick-down step, and the fast idle speed screw should be opposite the V notch in the cam.

4. To adjust, turn the hex head screw on the plastic fast idle cam lever. After adjustment, allow the choke plate to close and check that it closes tightly. Reset the choke cover and connect the vacuum hose if removed.

CHOKE UNLOADER (DECHOKE)

1. With the throttle held completely open, move the choke plate to the closed position.

2. Measure the distance between the lower edge of the choke plate and the air horn wall.

3. Adjust by bending the tang on the fast idle speed lever which is located on the throttle shaft.

NOTE: Final unloader adjustment must be performed on the car and the throttle should be opened by using the accelerator pedal of the car. This is to be sure that full throttle operation is achieved.

ACCELERATOR PUMP

The accelerator pump operating rod must be positioned in the proper holes of the accelerator pump lever and the throttle over-travel lever to assure correct pump travel. If adjusting is required, additional holes are provided in the throttle over-travel lever.

DASHPOT ADJUSTMENT

With the throttle set at the curb idle position, fully depress the dashpot stem and measure the distance between the stem and the throttle lever. Adjust by loosening the locknut and turning the dashpot.

FAST IDLE

Adjust the fast idle with the engine at normal operating temperature. On AMC cars, plug the spark port on the carburetor, and remove the EGR vacuum line at the valve and plug it. On Ford cars, if the engine is equipped with a spark delay valve, remove it and reroute the partial throttle vacuum signal line directly to the advance side of the distributor. If the distributor is a dual diaphragm type, leave the manifold vac-

uum line connected to the retard side of the distributor, and remove and plug the line to the advance side. If an EGR/PVS valve or cold weather modulator is located in the vacuum hose routing, disconnect and plug the hose at the EGR valve. If the engine does not have a cold weather modulator or an EGR/PVS valve, leave the EGR hose attached. On 1979 and later models, trace the thermactor (air pump) dump valve vacuum hose from the dump valve to the carburetor; disconnect the dump valve vacuum hose nearest the carburetor, and plus the original vacuum source and connect the dump valve directly to manifold vacuum. The fast idle screw should be resting against the second step of the fast idle cam on all models except Fords with the 302 engine, which have the screw set on the high step of the cam. Adjust the fast idle speed by turning the fast idle screw.

FORD, AUTOLITE, MOTORCRAFT MODELS 2100, 2150 SPECIFICATIONS
American Motors

Year	(9510)* Carburetor Identification	Dry Float Level (in.)	Wet Float Level (in.)	Pump Setting Hole #①	Choke Plate Pulldown (in.)	Fast Idle Cam Linkage Clearance (in.)	Fast Idle (rpm)	Dechoke (in.)	Choke Setting	Dashpot (in.)
'78	8DA2	0.555	0.780	3	0.136	0.126	1600	0.250	Index	—
	8RA2	0.555	0.780	3	0.136	0.126	1600	0.250	1 Rich	—
	8RA2C	0.555	0.780	3	0.136	0.120	1800	0.250	1 Rich	—
	8RA2A	0.555	0.780	3	0.089	0.078	1800	0.170	2 Rich	—
	8DA2A	0.555	0.930	3	0.089	0.078	1600	0.170	2 Rich	—
'79	9DA2	0.313	0.780	3	0.125	0.113	1600⑦	0.300	1 Rich	—

FORD, AUTOLITE, MOTORCRAFT MODELS 2100, 2150 SPECIFICATIONS
Ford Products

Year	(9510)* Carburetor Identification	Dry Float Level (in.)	Wet Float Level (in.)	Pump Setting Hole #①	Choke Plate Pulldown (in.)	Fast Idle Cam Linkage Clearance (in.)	Fast Idle (rpm)	Dechoke (in)	Choke Setting
'78	D84E-EA	7/16	13/16	2	0.110	⑧	⑨	—	3 Rich
	D8AE-JA	3/8	3/4	3	0.167	⑧	⑨	—	3 Rich
	D8BE-ACA	7/16	3/4	4	0.155	⑧	⑨	—	2 Rich
	D8BE-ADA	7/16	13/16	2	0.110	⑧	⑨	—	3 Rich
	D8BE-AEA	7/16	13/16	2	0.110	⑧	⑨	—	4 Rich
	D8BE-AFA	7/16	13/16	2	0.110	⑧	⑨	—	4 Rich
	D8BE-MB	3/8	13/16	3	0.122	⑧	⑨	—	Index
	D8DE-HA	19/32	13/16	3	0.157	⑧	⑨	—	Index
	D8KE-EA	19/32	13/16	2	0.135	⑧	⑨	—	3 Rich
	D8OE-BA	3/8	3/4	3	0.167	⑧	⑨	—	3 Rich
	D8OE-EA	19/32	13/16	2	0.136	⑧	⑨	—	Index
	D8OE-HA	7/16	13/16	3	0.180	⑧	⑨	—	2 Rich
	D8SE-CA	19/32	13/16	3	0.150	⑧	⑨	—	2 Rich
	D8ZE-TA	3/8	3/4	4	0.135	⑧	⑨	—	Index
	D8ZE-UA	3/8	3/4	4	0.135	⑧	⑨	—	Index
	D8WE-DA	7/16	13/16	4	0.143	⑧	⑨	—	1 Rich
	D8YE-AB	3/8	13/16	3	0.122	⑧	⑨	—	Index
	D8SE-DA, EA	7/16	13/16	3	0.147	⑧	⑨	—	3 Rich
	D8SE-FA, GA	3/8	13/16	3	0.147	⑧	⑨	—	3 Rich
'79	D9AE-AHA	7/16	13/16	3	0.147	⑧	⑨	0.250	3 Rich
	D9AE-AJA	7/16	13/16	3	0.147	⑧	⑨	0.250	3 Rich
	D9AE-ANB	7/16	13/16	3	0.129	⑧	⑨	—	1 Rich
	D9AE-APB	7/16	13/16	3	0.129	⑧	⑨	—	1 Rich
	D9AE-AVB	7/16	13/16	3	0.129	⑧	⑨	—	1 Rich

FORD, AUTOLITE, MOTORCRAFT MODELS 2100, 2150 SPECIFICATIONS
Ford Products

Year	(9510)* Carburetor Identification	Dry Float Level (in.)	Wet Float Level (in.)	Pump Setting Hole # ①	Choke Plate Pulldown (in.)	Fast Idle Cam Linkage Clearance (in.)	Fast Idle (rpm)	Dechoke (in)	Choke Setting
'79	D9AE-AYA	7/16	13/16	3	0.129	⑧	⑨	—	1 Rich
	D9AE-AYB	7/16	13/16	3	0.129	⑧	⑨	—	1 Rich
	D9AE-TB	7/16	13/16	3	0.129	⑧	⑨	—	2 Rich
	D9AE-UB	7/16	13/16	3	0.129	⑧	⑨	—	2 Rich
	D9BE-VB	7/16	13/16	3	0.153	⑧	⑨	0.250	2 Rich
	D9BE-YB	7/16	13/16	3	0.153	⑧	⑨	—	2 Rich
	D9DE-NB	7/16	13/16	3	0.153	⑧	⑨	0.250	2 Rich
	D9DE-RA	7/16	13/16	2	0.125	⑧	⑨	0.115	3 Rich
	D9DE-RB	7/16	13/16	2	0.125	⑧	⑨	0.115	3 Rich
	D9DE-RD	7/16	13/16	2	0.125	⑧	⑨	—	3 Rich
	D9DE-SA	7/16	13/16	2	0.125	⑧	⑨	0.250	3 Rich
	D9DE-SC	7/16	13/16	2	0.125	⑧	⑨	—	3 Rich
	D9ME-BA	7/16	13/16	2	0.136	⑧	⑨	0.115	Index
	D9ME-CA	7/16	13/16	2	0.136	⑧	⑨	0.115	Index
	D9OE-CB	7/16	13/16	3	0.132	⑧	⑨	0.115	3 Rich
	D9OE-DB	7/16	13/16	3	0.132	⑧	⑨	—	3 Rich
	D9OE-EA	7/16	13/16	3	0.132	⑧	⑨	0.115	2 Rich
	D9OE-FA	7/16	13/16	3	0.132	⑧	⑨	0.115	2 Rich
	D9SE-GA	7/16	13/16	3	0.150	⑧	⑨	0.250	2 Rich
	D9VE-LC	7/16	13/16	3	0.145	⑧	⑨	0.250	3 Rich
	D9VE-SA	7/16	13/16	3	0.147	⑧	⑨	—	3 Rich
	D9VE-UB	7/16	13/16	3	0.155	⑧	⑨	0.250	3 Rich
	D9VE-VA	3/8	3/4	3	0.145	⑧	⑨	—	3 Rich
	D9VE-YB	3/8	3/4	2	0.145	⑧	⑨	0.250	3 Rich
	D9WE-CB	7/16	13/16	3	0.132	⑧	⑨	—	3 Rich
	D9WE-DB	7/16	13/16	3	0.132	⑧	⑨	—	3 Rich
	D9WE-EB	7/16	13/16	3	0.132	⑧	⑨	—	2 Rich
	D9WE-FB	7/16	13/16	3	0.132	⑧	⑨	—	2 Rich
	D9WE-JA	7/16	13/16	3	0.150	⑧	⑨	0.250	2 Rich
	D9WE-MB	7/16	13/16	3	0.132	⑧	⑨	—	1 Rich
	D9WE-NB	7/16	13/16	3	0.132	⑧	⑨	—	1 Rich
	D9YE-EA	7/16	13/16	3	0.118	⑧	⑨	0.115	1 Rich
	D9YE-FA	7/16	13/16	3	0.118	⑧	⑨	0.115	1 Rich
	D9YE-AB	7/16	13/16	3	0.118	⑧	⑨	0.115	Index
	D9YE-BB	7/16	13/16	3	0.118	⑧	⑨	0.115	Index
	D9YE-CA	7/16	13/16	2	0.118	⑧	⑨	0.115	Index
	D9YE-DA	7/16	13/16	2	0.118	⑧	⑨	0.115	Index
	D9ZE-AYA	7/16	13/16	3	0.138	⑧	⑨	0.115	Index

FORD, AUTOLITE, MOTORCRAFT MODELS 2100, 2150 SPECIFICATIONS
Ford Products

Year	(9510)* Carburetor Identification	Dry Float Level (in.)	Wet Float Level (in.)	Pump Setting Hole # ①	Choke Plate Pulldown (in.)	Fast Idle Cam Linkage Clearance (in.)	Fast Idle (rpm)	Dechoke (in)	Choke Setting
'79	D9ZE-BFB	7/16	13/16	2	0.125	⑧	⑨	—	3 Rich
	D9ZE-BGB	7/16	13/16	2	0.125	⑧	⑨	—	3 Rich
	D9ZE-BHB	7/16	13/16	2	0.125	⑧	⑨	0.250	3 Rich
	D9ZE-BJB	7/16	13/16	2	0.125	⑧	⑨	—	3 Rich
'80	EO4E-PA, RA	—	13/16	2	0.104	⑧	⑨	¼	⑨
	EOBE-AUA	—	13/16	3	0.116	⑧	⑨	¼	⑨
	EODE-SA, TA	—	13/16	2	0.104	⑧	⑨	¼	⑨
	EOKE-CA, DA	—	13/16	3	0.116	⑧	⑨	¼	⑨
	EOKE-GA, HA	—	13/16	3	0.116	⑧	⑨	¼	⑨
	EOKE-JA, KA	—	13/16	3	0.116	⑧	⑨	¼	⑨
	D84E-TA, UA	—	13/16	2	0.125	⑧	⑨	¼	⑨
	EO4E-ADA, AEA	—	13/16	2	0.104	⑧	⑨	¼	⑨
	EO4E-CA	—	13/16	2	0.104	⑧	⑨	¼	⑨
	EO4E-EA, FA	—	13/16	2	0.104	⑧	⑨	¼	⑨
	EO4E-JA, KA	—	13/16	2	0.137	⑧	⑨	¼	⑨
	EO4E-SA, TA	—	13/16	2	0.104	⑧	⑨	¼	⑨
	EO4E-VA, YA	—	13/16	2	0.104	⑧	⑨	¼	⑨
	EODE-TA, VA	—	13/16	2	0.104	⑧	⑨	¼	⑨
	EOSE-GA, HA	—	13/16	2	0.104	⑧	⑨	¼	⑨
	EOSE-LA, MA	—	13/16	2	0.104	⑧	⑨	¼	⑨
	EOSE-NA	—	13/16	2	0.104	⑧	⑨	¼	⑨
	EOSE-PA	—	13/16	2	0.137	⑧	⑨	¼	⑨
	EOVE-FA	—	13/16	2	0.104	⑧	⑨	¼	⑨
	EOWE-BA, CA	—	13/16	2	0.137	⑧	⑨	¼	⑨
	D9AE-ANA, APA	—	13/16	3	0.129	⑧	⑨	¼	⑨
	D9AE-AVA, AYA	—	13/16	3	0.129	⑧	⑨	¼	⑨
	EOAE-AGA	—	13/16	3	0.159	⑧	⑨	¼	⑨
'81	EIKE-CA	7/16	0.810	3	0.124	⑧	⑨	0.250	⑪
	EIKE-EA	7/16	0.810	3	0.124	⑧	⑨	0.250	⑪
	EIKE-DA	7/16	0.810	3	0.124	⑧	⑨	0.250	⑪
	EIKE-FA	7/16	0.810	3	0.124	⑧	⑨	0.250	⑪
	EIKE-GA	7/16	0.810	3	0.124	⑧	⑨	0.250	⑪
	EIKE-SA	7/16	0.810	3	0.124	⑧	⑨	0.250	⑪
	EIKE-RA	7/16	0.810	3	0.120	⑧	⑨	0.250	⑪
	EIKE-HA	7/16	0.810	3	0.120	⑧	⑨	0.250	⑪
	EIWE-FA	7/16	0.810	2	0.120	⑧	⑨	0.250	⑪
	EIWE-EA	7/16	0.810	2	0.120	⑧	⑨	0.250	⑪

FORD, AUTOLITE, MOTORCRAFT MODELS 2100, 2150 SPECIFICATIONS
Ford Products

Year	(9510)* Carburetor Identification	Dry Float Level (in.)	Wet Float Level (in.)	Pump Setting Hole #①	Choke Plate Pulldown (in.)	Fast Idle Cam Linkage Clearance (in.)	Fast Idle (rpm)	Dechoke (in)	Choke Setting
'81	EIWE-CA	7/16	0.810	2	0.120	⑧	⑨	0.250	⑪
	EIWE-DA	7/16	0.810	2	0.120	⑧	⑨	0.250	⑨
	EIAE-AKA	7/16	0.810	3	0.124	⑧	⑨	0.250	⑪
	EIAE-AJA	7/16	0.810	3	0.124	⑧	⑨	0.250	⑪
	EIAE-YA	7/16	0.810	3	0.124	⑧	⑨	0.250	⑪
	EIAE-ZA	7/16	0.810	3	0.124	⑧	⑨	0.250	⑪
	EIAE-ADA	7/16	0.810	3	0.124	⑧	⑨	0.250	⑪
	EIAE-AEA	7/16	0.810	3	0.124	⑧	⑨	0.250	⑪
	EIAE-TA	—	0.810	2	0.104	⑧	⑨	0.250	⑪
	EIAE-UA	—	0.810	2	0.104	⑧	⑨	0.250	⑪
	EIDE-LA	7/16	0.810	2	0.120	⑧	⑨	0.250	⑪
	EIDE-KA	7/16	0.810	2	0.120	⑧	⑨	0.250	⑪
	EIDE-JA	7/16	0.810	2	0.120	⑧	⑨	0.250	⑪
	EIDE-HA	7/16	0.810	2	0.120	⑧	⑨	0.250	⑪
'82	E2BE-UA	7/16	0.810	2	0.110	⑧	2200	0.250	⑪
	E2BE-AAA	7/16	0.810	2	0.110	⑧	2200	0.250	⑪
	E2BE-VA	7/16	0.810	2	0.113	⑧	2200	0.250	⑪
	E2BE-ABA	7/16	0.810	2	0.113	⑧	2200	0.250	⑪
	E2BE-AGA	7/16	0.810	2	0.113⑩	⑧	2200	0.250	⑪
	E2BE-AHA	7/16	0.810	2	0.113	⑧	2200	0.250	⑪
	E2VE-CA	7/16	0.810	2	0.113	⑧	2200	0.250	⑪
	E24E-CA	7/16	0.810	2	0.110	⑧	1200	0.250	⑪
	E24E-DA	7/16	0.810	2	0.110	⑧	1200	0.250	⑪
	E24E-AA	7/16	0.810	2	0.110	⑧	2100	0.250	⑪
	E24E-BA	7/16	0.810	2	0.110	⑧	2100	0.250	⑪
	E24E-EA	7/16	0.810	2	0.110	⑧	⑨	0.250	⑪
	E24E-FA	7/16	0.810	2	0.110	⑧	⑨	0.250	⑪
	E2KE-AA	7/16	0.810	2	0.140	⑧	1500	0.250	⑪
	E2KE-BA	7/16	0.810	2	0.140	⑧	1500	0.250	⑪
	E2WE-EA	7/16	0.810	2	0.137	⑧	1500	0.250	⑪
	E2WE-FA	7/16	0.810	2	0.137	⑧	1500	0.250	⑪
	E2DE-JA	7/16	0.810	2	0.137	⑧	1600	0.250	⑪
	E2DE-KA	7/16	0.810	2	0.137	⑧	1600	0.250	⑪
	E2DE-LA	7/16	0.810	2	0.137	⑧	1700	0.250	⑪
	E2DE-MA	7/16	0.810	2	0.137	⑧	1700	0.250	⑪
	E25E-DA	7/16	0.810	2	0.144	⑧	1500	0.250	⑪
	E2AE-SA	7/16	0.810	2	0.172	⑧	1550	0.250	⑪
	E25E-CA	7/16	0.810	2	0.137	⑧	1700	0.250	⑪

FORD, AUTOLITE, MOTORCRAFT MODELS 2100, 2150 SPECIFICATIONS
Ford Products

Year	(9510)* Carburetor Identification	Dry Float Level (in.)	Wet Float Level (in.)	Pump Setting Hole # ①	Choke Plate Pulldown (in.)	Fast Idle Cam Linkage Clearance (in.)	Fast Idle (rpm)	Dechoke (in)	Choke Setting
'82	E2ZE-BAA	13/32	0.780	2	0.172⑩	⑧	1400	0.250	⑪
	E2ZE-BBA	13/32	0.780	2	0.172⑩	⑧	1400	0.250	⑪
	E3CE-LA	7/16	0.810	3	0.103	⑧	2200	0.250	⑪
	E3CE-MA	7/16	0.810	3	0.103	⑧	2200	0.250	⑪
	E3CE-JA	7/16	0.810	3	0.103	⑧	2200	0.250	⑪
	E3CE-KA	7/16	0.810	3	0.103	⑧	2200	0.250	⑪
	E3CE-NA	7/16	0.810	3	0.120	⑧	2100	0.250	⑪
	E3CE-PA	7/16	0.810	3	0.120	⑧	2100	0.250	⑪
'83	E3CE-AA	7/16	0.810	3	0.103	⑧	2200	0.250	⑪
	E3CE-BA	7/16	0.810	3	0.103	⑧	2200	0.250	⑪
	E3CE-GA	7/16	0.810	3	0.103	⑧	2200	0.250	⑪
	E3CE-HA	7/16	0.810	3	0.103	⑧	2200	0.250	⑪
	E3CE-EA	7/16	0.810	3	0.113	⑧	2100	0.250	⑪
	E3CE-FA	7/16	0.810	3	0.113	⑧	2100	0.250	⑪
	E3SE-ATA	7/16	0.810	3	0.113	⑧	2200	0.250	⑪
	E3SE-AUA	7/16	0.810	3	0.113	⑧	2200	0.250	⑪
	E3SE-ALA	7/16	0.810	3	0.107	⑧	2200	0.250	⑪
	E3SE-AMA	7/16	0.810	3	0.107	⑧	2200	0.250	⑪
	E3SE-BDA	7/16	0.810	3	0.107	⑧	2200	0.250	⑪
	E3SE-BEA	7/16	0.810	3	0.107	⑧	2200	0.250	⑪
	E3SE-ANA	7/16	0.810	3	0.101	⑧	2200	0.250	⑪
	E3SE-APA	7/16	0.810	3	0.101	⑧	2200	0.250	⑪
	E3SE-AJA								
	E3SE-BFA	7/16	0.810	3	0.107	⑧	2200	0.250	⑪
	E3SE-BGA	7/16	0.810	3	0.107	⑧	2200	0.250	⑪
	E3SE-EA	7/16	0.810	3	0.113	⑧	2200	0.250	⑪
	E3SE-FA	7/16	0.810	3	0.113	⑧	2200	0.250	⑪
	E3SE-LA	7/16	0.810	3	0.107	⑧	2200	0.250	⑪
	E3SE-MA	7/16	0.810	3	0.107	⑧	2200	0.250	⑪
	E3SE-JA	7/16	0.810	3	0.101	⑧	2200	0.250	⑪
	E3SE-KA	7/16	0.810	3	0.101	⑧	2200	0.250	⑪
	E3SE-NA	7/16	0.810	3	0.107	⑧	2200	0.250	⑪
	E3SE-PA	7/16	0.810	3	0.107	⑧	2200	0.250	⑪
	E3SE-GA	7/16	0.810	3	0.120	⑧	2100	0.250	⑪
	E3SE-HA	7/16	0.810	3	0.120	⑧	2100	0.250	⑪
	E3AE-TA	7/16	0.810	3	0.103	⑧	2200	0.250	⑪
	E3AE-ADA	7/16	0.810	3	0.103	⑧	2200	0.250	⑪
	E3AE-UA	7/16	0.810	3	0.103	⑧	2200	0.250	⑪

FORD, AUTOLITE, MOTORCRAFT MODELS 2100, 2150 SPECIFICATIONS
Ford Products

Year	(9510)* Carburetor Identification	Dry Float Level (in.)	Wet Float Level (in.)	Pump Setting Hole # ①	Choke Plate Pulldown (in.)	Fast Idle Cam Linkage Clearance (in.)	Fast Idle (rpm)	Dechoke (in)	Choke Setting
'83	E3AE-AEA	7/16	0.810	3	0.103	⑧	2200	0.250	⑪
	E3AE-TA	7/16	0.810	3	0.103	⑧	2200	0.250	⑪
	E3AE-UA	7/16	0.810	3	0.103	⑧	2200	0.250	⑪
	E3AE-RA	7/16	0.810	3	0.103	⑧	2200	0.250	⑪
	E3AE-SA	7/16	0.810	3	0.103	⑧	2200	0.250	⑪
	E3AE-EA	7/16	0.810	2	—	⑧	1550	0.250	⑪
'84	E3EA-EA	7/16	0.810	2	—	⑧	1550	0.250	⑪
	E4CE-AA	7/16	0.810	3	0.103	⑧	2200	0.250	2NR
	E4CE-BA	7/16	0.810	3	0.103	⑧	2200	0.250	2NR
	E4SE-CA	7/16	0.810	3	0.103	⑧	2200	0.250	⑪
	E4SE-DA	7/16	0.810	3	0.103	⑧	2200	0.250	⑪

* Basic carburetor number for Ford products
① With link in inboard hole of pump lever
② Electric choke; see pulldown procedure in text
③ Figure given is for manual transmission; for automatics add 100 RPM.
④ Figure given is for 49 states Granada and Monarch; for Calif. Granada and Monarch and all Torino, Montego and Cougar models, figure is 1400 RPM.
⑤ Figure given is for 49 states model; Calif. specification is 1150 RPM.
⑥ 1600 with 360V8
⑦ 1500 with manual transmission
⑧ Opposite "V" notch; see text
⑨ See underhood decal
⑩ ± .010"
⑪ V-notch

Model 2700 VV

Since the design of the 2700 VV (variable venturi) carburetor differs considerably from the other carburetors in the Ford lineup, an explanation in the theory and operation is presented here.

In exterior appearance, the variable venturi carburetor is similar to conventional carburetors and, like a conventional carburetor, it uses a normal float and fuel bowl system. However, the similarity ends there. In place of a normal choke plate and fixed area venturis, the 2700VV carburetor has a pair of small oblong castings in the top of the upper carburetor body where you would normally expect to see the choke plate. These castings slide back and forth across the top of the carburetor in response to fuel-air demands. Their movement is controlled by a spring-loaded diaphragm valve regulated by a vacuum signal taken below the venturis in the throttle bores. As the throttle is opened, the strength of the

vacuum signal increases, opening the venturis and allowing more air to enter the carburetor.

Fuel is admitted into the venturi area by means of tapered metering rods that fit into the main jets. These rods are attached to the venturis, and, as the venturis open or close in response to air demand, the fuel needed to maintain the proper mixture increases or decreases as the metering rods slide in the jets. In comparison to a conventional carburetor with fixed venturis and a variable air supply, this system provides much more precise control of the fuel-air supply during all modes of operation. Because of the variable venturi principle, there are fewer fuel metering systems and fuel passages. The only auxiliary fuel metering systems required are an idle trim, accelerator pump (similar to a conventional carburetor), starting enrichment, and cold running enrichment.

NOTE: Adjustment, assembly and disassembly of this carburetor require special tools for some of the operations. These tools are available (see the Tools and Equipment Section). Do not attempt any operations on this carburetor without first checking to see if you need the special tools for that particular operation. The adjustment and repair procedures given here mention when and if you will need the special tools.

NOTE: Some 1978–81 models equipped with the 2700 VV carburetor experienced engine stalling, stumbling and poor performance. According to a Ford Motor Company service bulletin No. 81-9-10 issued in May of 1981, this condition may be caused by fluids trapped in the venturi valve diaphragm cavity which eventually deteriorate the diaphragm, resulting in a leak.

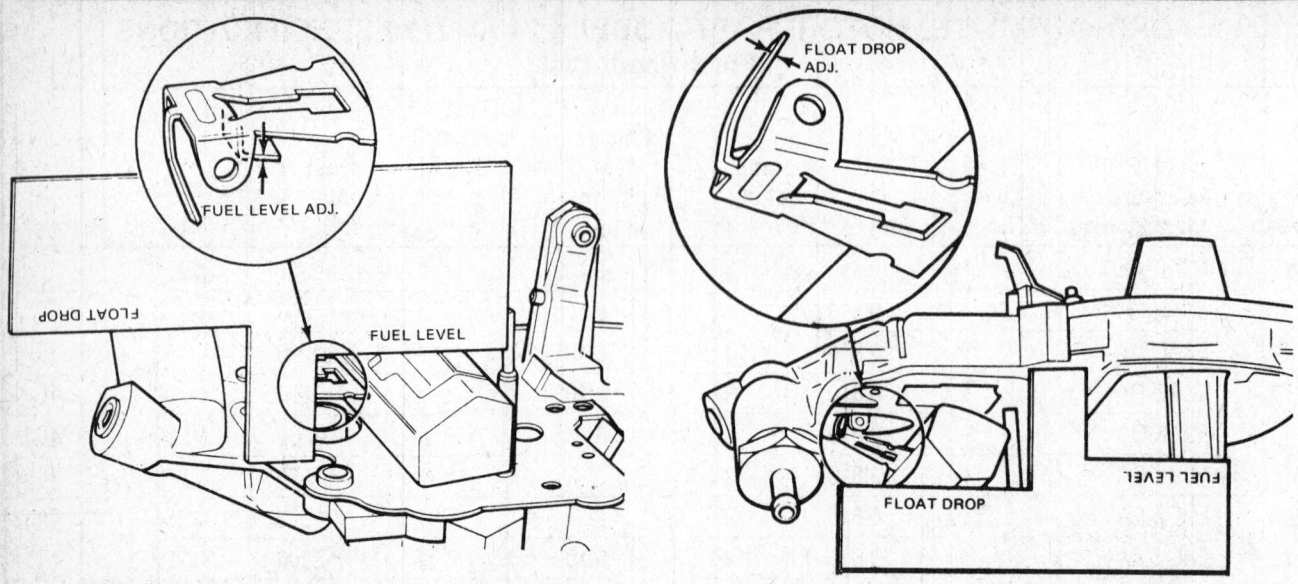

2700 VV float level adjustment (© Ford Motor Co.)   **2700 VV float drop adjustment** (© Ford Motor Co.)

A quick check to verify if the above condition exists is to visually observe the venturi valve action while running the engine. Throttle movement from idle to just above idle should show a corresponding movement of the venturi valves. If no venturi valve action is observed and the valves are not sticking, there may be a leak in the diaphragm (stalls may be encountered while performing this check).

If the above condition is suspected, it is advised that the car be serviced at a Ford or Mercury dealer using the procedure stated in the service bulletin.

FLOAT LEVEL ADJUSTMENT

1. Remove and invert the upper part of the carburetor, with the gasket in place.
2. Measure the vertical distance between the carburetor body, outside the gasket, and the bottom of the float.

3. To adjust, bend the float operating lever that contacts the needle valve. Make sure that the float remains parallel to the gasket surface.

FLOAT DROP ADJUSTMENT

1. Remove and hold upright the upper part of the carburetor.
2. Measure the vertical distance between the carburetor body, outside the gasket, and the bottom of the float.
3. Adjust by bending the stop tab on the float lever that contacts the hinge pin.

FAST IDLE SPEED ADJUSTMENT

1. With the engine warmed up and idling, place the fast idle lever on the step of the fast idle cam specified on the engine compartment sticker or in the specifications chart. Disconnect and plug the EGR vacuum line.

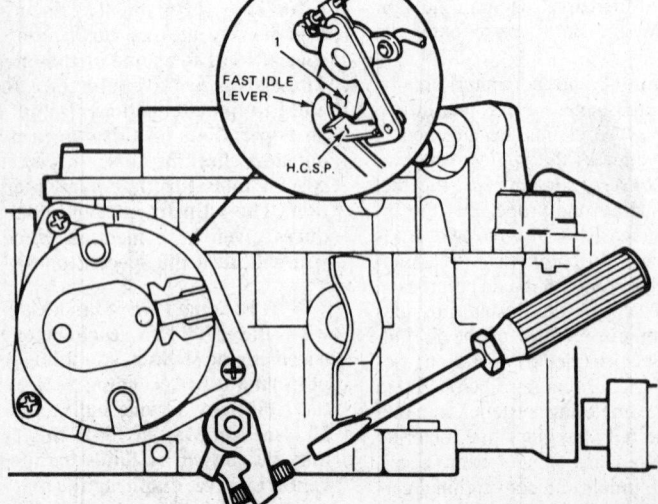

2700 VV fast idle speed adjustment (© Ford Motor Co.)

2. Make sure the high speed cam positioner lever is disengaged.
3. Turn the fast idle speed screw to adjust to the specified speed.

FAST IDLE CAM ADJUSTMENT

You will need a special tool for this job; Ford calls it a stator cap (#T77L-9848-A). It fits over the choke thermostatic lever when the choke cap is removed.

1. Remove the choke coil cap. On 1980 California model and all 1981 and later models, the choke cap is riveted in place. The top rivets will have to be drilled out; the bottom rivet will have to be driven out from the rear. New rivets must be used upon installation.
2. Place the fast idle lever in the corner of the specified step of the fast idle cam (the highest step is first) with the high speed cam positioner retracted.
3. If the adjustment is being made with the carburetor removed, hold the throttle lightly closed with a rubber band.
4. Turn the stator cap clockwise until the lever contacts the fast idle cam adjusting screw.
5. Turn the fast idle cam adjusting screw until the index mark on the cap lines up with the specified mark on the casting.
6. Remove the stator cap. Install the choke coil cap and set to the specified housing mark.

COLD ENRICHMENT METERING ROD ADJUSTMENT

A dial indicator and the stator cap are required for this adjustment.
1. Remove the choke coil cap. See Step 1 of the ''Fast Idle Cam Adjustment.''

2. Attach a weight to the choke coil mechanism to seat the cold enrichment rod.

3. Install and zero a dial indicator with the tip on top of the enrichment rod. Raise and release the weight to verify zero on the dial indicator.

4. With the stator cap at the index position, the dial indicator should read the specified dimension. Turn the adjusting nut to correct.

5. Install the choke cap at the correct setting.

CONTROL VACUUM ADJUSTMENT

1980–82 Only

This adjustment is necessary only on non-feedback systems.

1. Remove the carburetor. Remove the venturi valve diaphragm plug with a centerpunch.

2. If the carburetor has a venturi valve bypass plug, remove it by removing the two cover retaining screws; invert and remove the by-pass screw plug from the cover with a drift. Install the cover.

3. Install the carburetor. Start the engine and allow it to reach normal operating temperature. Connect a vacuum gauge to the venturi valve cover. Set the idle speed to 500 rpm with the transmission in Drive.

4. Push and hold the venturi valve closed. Adjust the bypass screw to obtain a reading of 8 in. H_2O on the vacuum gauge. Make sure the idle speed remains constant. Open and close the throttle and check the idle speed.

5. With the engine idling, adjust the venturi valve diaphragm screw to obtain a reading of 6 in. H_2O. Set the curb idle to specification. Install new venturi valve by-pass and diaphragm plugs.

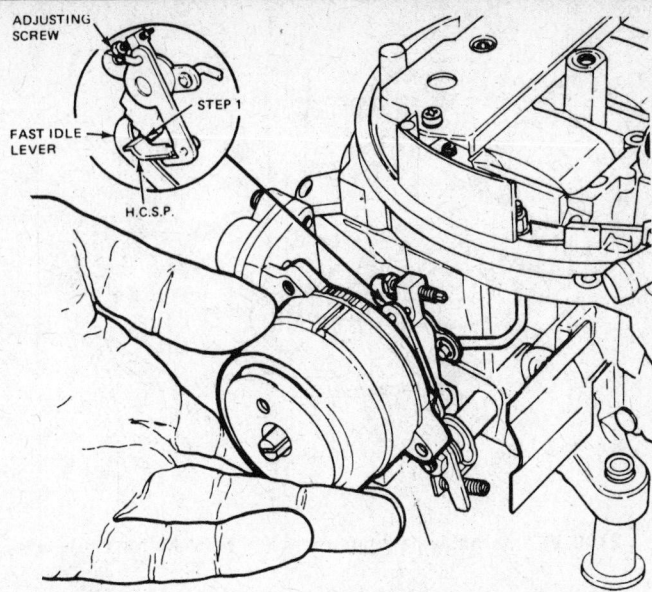

2700 VV fast idle cam adjustment (© Ford Motor Co.)

INTERNAL VENT ADJUSTMENT

1978 Only

This adjustment is required whenever the idle speed adjustment is changed.

1. Make sure the idle speed is correct.

2. Place a 0.010 in. feeler gauge between the accelerator pump stem and the operating link.

3. Turn the nylon adjusting nut until there is a slight drag on the gauge.

VENTURI VALVE LIMITER ADJUSTMENT

1. Remove the carburetor. Take off the venturi valve cover and the two rollers.

2. Use a center punch to loosen the expansion plug at the rear of the carburetor main body on the throttle side. Remove it.

3. Use an Allen wrench to remove the venturi valve wide open stop screw.

4. Hold the throttle wide open.

5. Apply a light closing pressure on the venturi valve and check the gap between the valve and the air horn wall. To adjust, move the venturi valve to the wide open position and insert an Allen wrench into the stop screw hole. Turn clockwise to increase the gap. Remove the wrench and check the gap again.

6. Replace the wide open stop screw and turn it clockwise until it contacts the valve.

7. Push the venturi valve wide open and check the gap. Turn the stop screw to bring the gap to specifications.

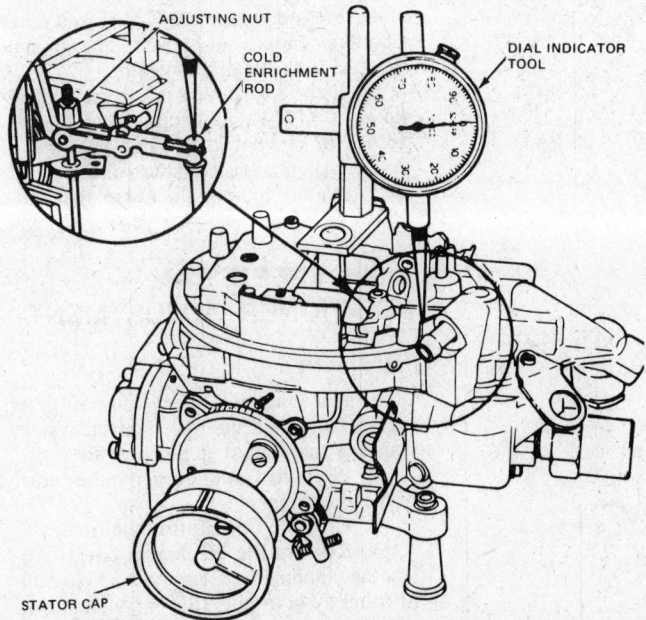

2700 VV cold enrichment metering rod adjustment
(© Ford Motor Co.)

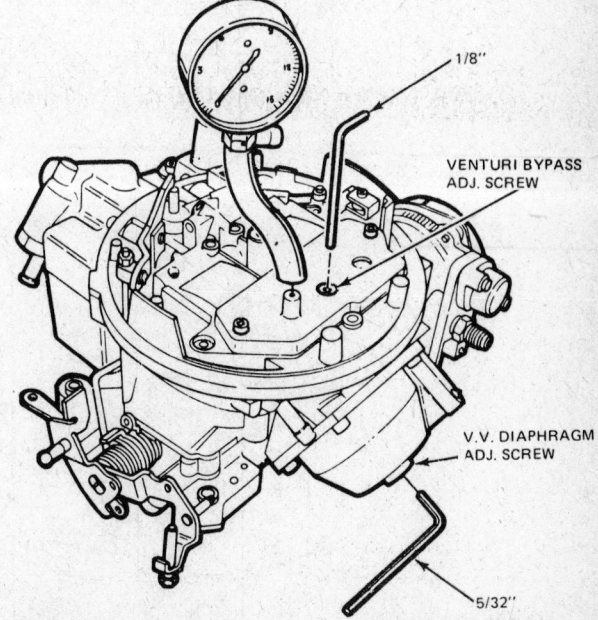

2700 VV control vacuum adjustment (© Ford Motor Co.)

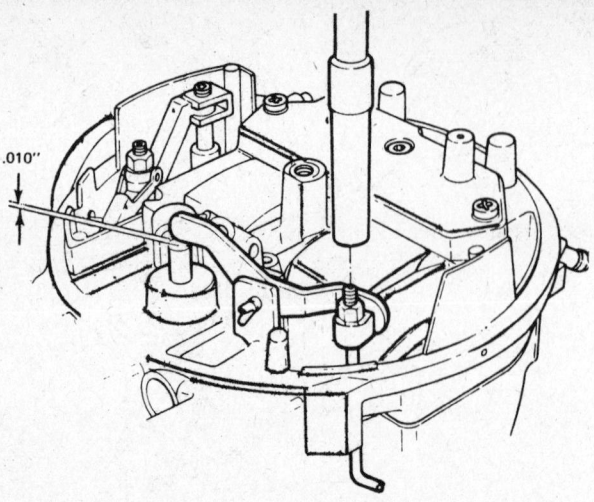

2700 VV internal vent adjustment (© Ford Motor Co.)

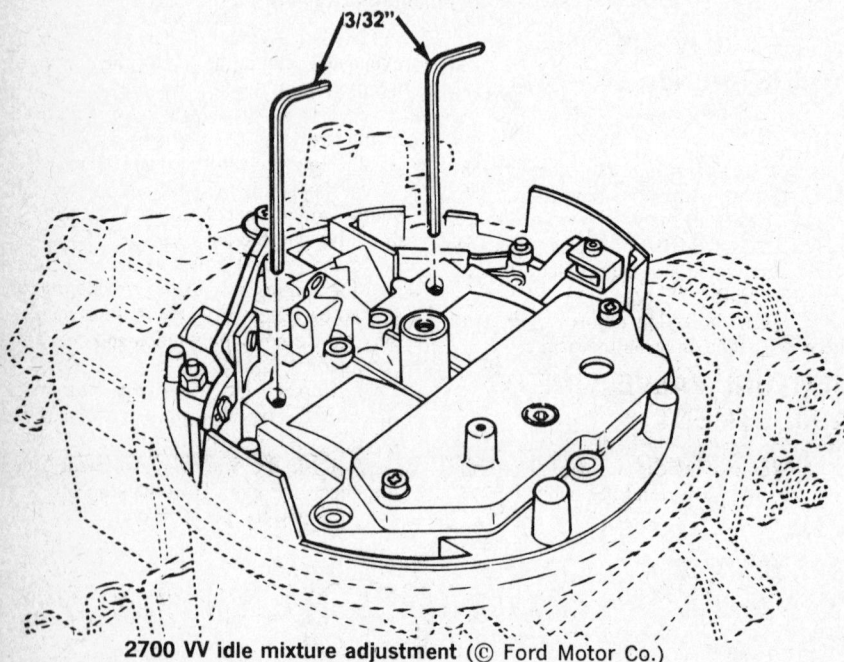

2700 VV idle mixture adjustment (© Ford Motor Co.)

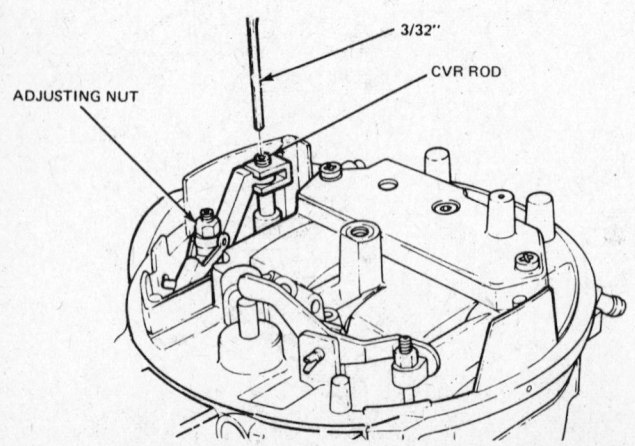

2700 VV control vacuum regulator adjustment (© Ford Motor Co.)

8. Reassemble the carburetor with a new expansion plug.

CONTROL VACUUM REGULATOR ADJUSTMENT

There are two systems used. The earlier system's C.V.R. rod threads directly through the arm. The revised system, introduced in late 1977, has a ⅜ in. nylon hex adjusting nut on the C.V.R. rod and a flange on the rod.

Early System

1. Make sure that the cold enrichment metering rod adjustment is correct.
2. Rotate the choke coil cap half a turn clockwise from the index mark. Work the throttle to set the fast idle cam.
3. Press down lightly on the regulator rod. If there is no down travel, turn the adjusting screw counter-clockwise until some travel is felt.
4. Turn the regulator rod clockwise with an Allen wrench until the adjusting nut just begins to rise.
5. Press lightly on the regulator rod. If there is any down travel, turn the adjusting screw clockwise in ¼ turn increments until it is eliminated.
6. Return the choke coil cap to the specified setting.

Revised System

The cold enrichment metering rod adjustment must be checked and set before making this adjustment.

1. After adjusting the cold enrichment metering rod, leave the dial indicator in place but remove the stator cap. Do not re-zero the dial indicator.
2. Press down on the C.V.R. rod until it bottoms on its seat. Measure this amount of travel with the dial indicator.
3. If the adjustment is incorrect, hold the ⅜ in. C.V.R. adjusting nut with a box wrench to prevent it from turning. Use a ³⁄₃₂ in. Allen wrench to turn the C.V.R. rod; turning counter-clockwise will increase the travel, and vice versa.

HIGH SPEED CAM POSITIONER ADJUSTMENT

1979 Only

1. Place the high speed cam positioner in the corner of the specified cam step, counting the highest step as the first.
2. Place the fast idle lever in the corner of the positioner.
3. Hold the throttle firmly closed.
4. Remove the diaphragm cover. Adjust the diaphragm assembly clockwise until it lightly bottoms. Turn it counterclockwise ½ to 1½ turns until the vacuum port and diaphragm hole line up.
5. Replace the cover.

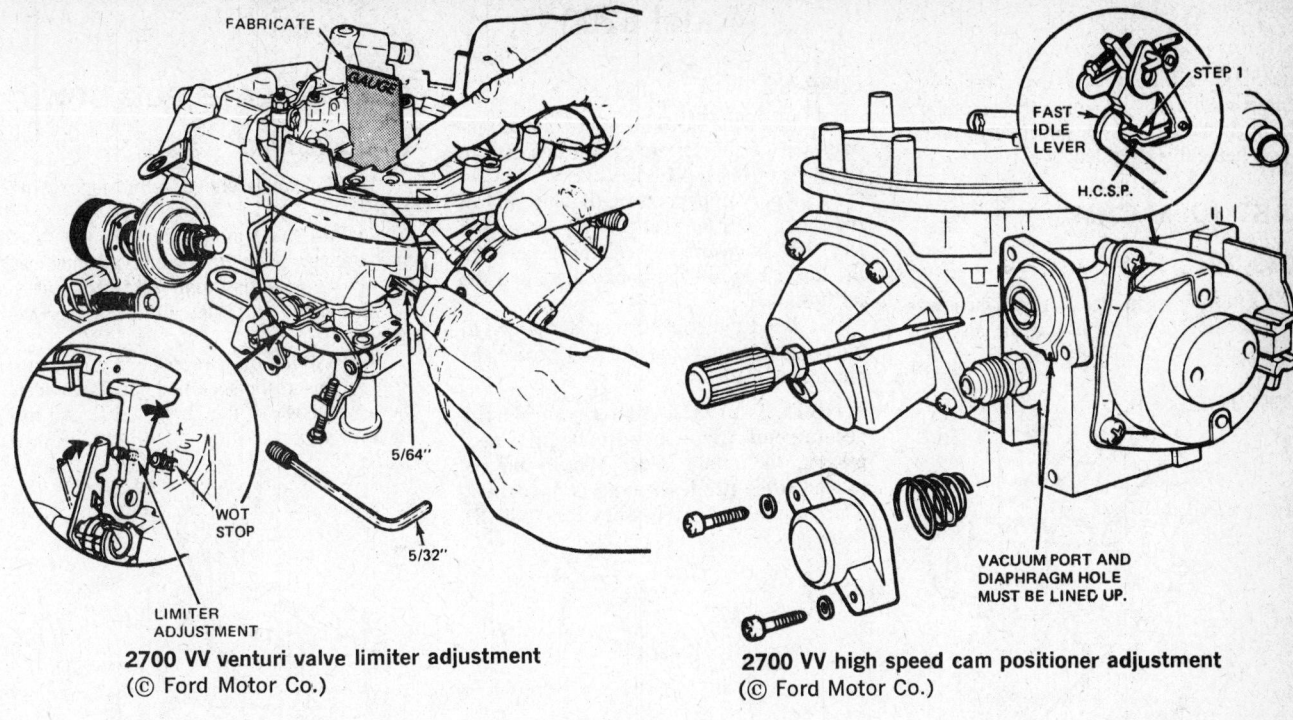

2700 VV venturi valve limiter adjustment
(© Ford Motor Co.)

2700 VV high speed cam positioner adjustment
(© Ford Motor Co.)

MOTORCRAFT MODEL 2700 VV SPECIFICATIONS
Ford Products

Year	Model	Float Level (in.)	Float Drop (in.)	Fast Idle Cam Setting (notches)	Cold Enrichment Metering Rod (in.)	Control Vacuum (in. H₂O)	Venturi Valve Limiter (in.)	Choke Cap Setting (notches)	Control Vacuum Regulator Setting (in.)
'78	Pinto, Bobcat	1³⁄₆₄	1¹⁵⁄₃₂	4 Rich/2nd step	.125	5.0	¹³⁄₃₂	Index	—
	All other	1³⁄₆₄	1¹⁵⁄₃₂	1 Rich/3rd step	.125	5.0	⁶¹⁄₆₄	Index	—
'79	D9ZE-LB	1³⁄₆₄	1¹⁵⁄₃₂	1 Rich/2nd step	.125	①	②	Index	.230
	D84E-KA	1³⁄₆₄	1¹⁵⁄₃₂	1 Rich/3rd step	.125	5.5	⁶¹⁄₆₄	Index	—
'80	All	1³⁄₆₄	1¹⁵⁄₃₂	1 Rich/4th step	.125	③	④	⑤	.075
'81	EIAE-AAA	1.010-1.070	1.430-1.490	1 Rich/4th step	⑥	③	④	Index	—
	D9AE-AZA	1.015-1.065	1.435-1.485	1 Rich/4th step	.125	③	④	Index	—

① Venturi Air Bypass 6.8-7.3
  Venturi Valve Diaphragm 4.6-5.1
② Limiter Setting .38-.42
  Limiter Stop Setting .73-.77
③ See text
④ Opening gap: 0.99-1.01
  Closing gap: 0.94-0.98
⑤ See underhood decal
⑥ 0°F—0.490 @ starting position
  75°F—0.475 @ starting position

Model 5200

The 5200 carburetor is a two-stage, two-venturi carburetor in which the secondary venturi is the larger. The secondary system is mechanically operated.

FAST IDLE CAM

1978–79

1. Insert a 5/32 in. drill between the lower edge of the choke plate and the air horn wall.

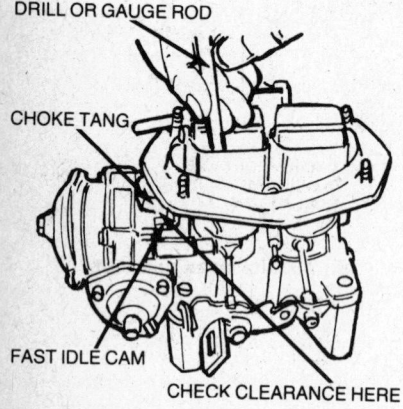

Fast idle cam adjustment—1978–79

2. With the fast idle screw held on the second step of the fast idle cam, measure the clearance between the tang of the choke lever and the arm on the fast idle cam.

3. Bend the choke lever tang to adjust it if it is not up to specification.

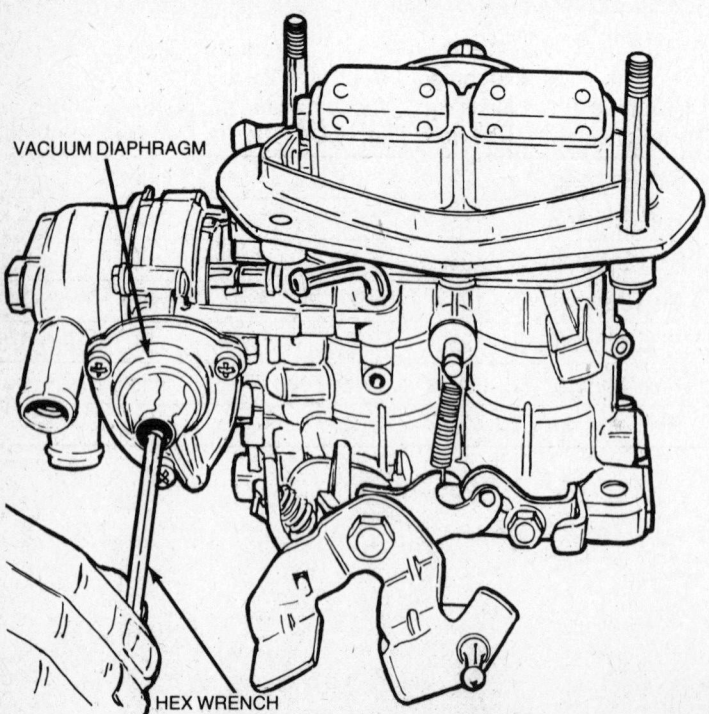

HEX WRENCH
Choke plate pulldown adjustment

1980–82

1. Place the fast idle screw on the second step of the fast idle cam against the shoulder of the top step.

2. Apply light pressure (downward) on the choke lever tang, and, using the proper size drill, measure the clearance between the lower edge of the choke plate and the air horn wall.

3. Bend the choke lever tang down to increase clearance and up to decrease the clearance.

NOTE: On 1982 and later models Ford recommends that if an adjustment is necessary, the choke lever should be replaced since the lever tang is hardened. This may also be necessary for 1980–81 models.

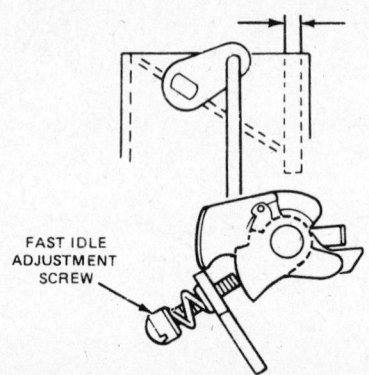

1980 and later fast idle cam adjustment—measure the clearance between the lower edge of the choke plate and the air horn wall

CHOKE PLATE PULLDOWN

Through 1980

1. Remove the choke thermostatic spring cover.

2. Pull the water cover and the thermostatic spring cover assembly or the electric choke assist assembly out of the way.

3. Set the fast idle cam on the second step.

4. Push the diaphragm stem against its stop and insert the specified gauge between the lower edge of the choke valve and the air horn wall.

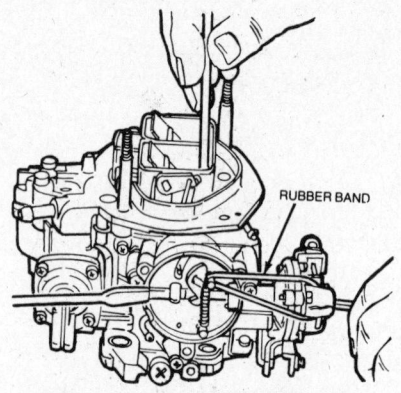

Choke plate pulldown adjustment

5. Apply sufficient pressure to the upper edge of the choke valve to take up any slack in the choke linkage.

6. Turn the adjusting screw in or out to adjust the choke plate-to-air horn clearance.

1981–82

NOTE: The following procedure requires the removal of the carburetor and also the choke cap which is retained by two rivets.

1. Remove the carburetor from the engine.

2. Remove the choke cap as follows:

a. Check the rivets to determine if mandrel is well below the rivit head. If mandrel is within the rivit head thickness, drive it down or out with a 1/16 inch diameter tip punch.

b. With a 1/8 inch diameter drill, drill into the rivet head until the rivet head comes loose from the rivet body. Use light pressure on the drill bit or the rivet will just spin in the hole.

c. After drilling off the rivet head, drive the remaining rivet out of the hole with a 1/8 inch diameter punch.

d. Repeat steps (a thru c) to remove the remaining rivet.

3. Remove the plastic dust cover.

4. Place the fast idle adjusting screw on the high step of the fast idle cam.

5. Attach a rubber band to remove the

slack from the choke linkage. Push the diaphragm stem back against the stop screw.

6. Using the specified diameter drill check the clearance between the lower edge of the choke plate and the air horn wall.

7. If adjustment is necesssary, obtain a replacement kit containing a new choke pulldown diaphragm cover, adjusting screw and cup plug.

8. After installing the adjusting screw in the cover, adjust the pulldown by turning the screw clockwise to decrease and counterclockwise to increase the setting.

9. After making the adjustment, install a new plug in the choke pulldown adjustment access opening.

10. Remove the rubber band and reinstall the choke cap using rivets (⅛ inch diameter × ½ inch long with a ¼ inch diameter head).

DECHOKE (UNLOADER) ADJUSTMENT

Dechoke clearance adjustment is controlled by the fast idle cam adjustment. The figures in the specification chart refer to choke plate clearance between the plate and the air horn wall. Clearance can be measured as follows:

1. Hold the throttle wide open. Remove any slack from the choke linkage by applying pressure to the upper edge of the choke valve.

2. Measure the distance between the lower edge of the choke plate and the air horn wall.

3. Adjust by bending the tab on the fast idle lever where it touches the cam.

FAST IDLE SPEED

Set the fast idle speed with the fast idle screw positioned on the second step of the fast idle cam and with the engine at operating temperature.

Remove the EGR line at the valve and plug it. If the car is equipped with a spark

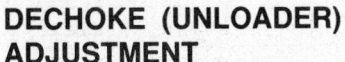
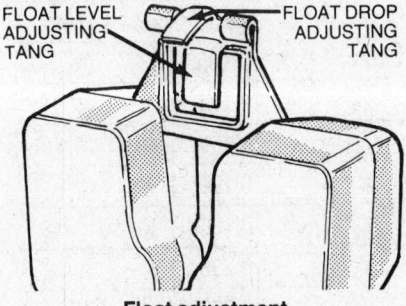

Float adjustment

FLOAT LEVEL ADJUSTING TANG / FLOAT DROP ADJUSTING TANG

delay valve, remove the valve and route the distributor advance vacuum signal directly to the distributor advance diaphragm. On all manual transmission models, remove and plug the vacuum line to the distributor. If the distributor also has a retard diaphragm, leave the hose connected to it alone. If the engine has a deceleration valve, remove this hose at the carburetor and plug it. Finally, if the car has air conditioning it must be off before adjusting the fast idle.

FLOAT LEVEL ADJUSTMENT

With the bowl cover held upside down and the float tang resting lightly on the spring

loaded fuel inlet needle, measure the clearance between the edge of the float and the bowl cover. To adjust the level, bend the float tang up or down as required. Adjust both floats equally.

SECONDARY THROTTLE STOP SCREW

1. Turn the secondary throttle stop screw counterclockwise until the secondary throttle plate seats in its bore.

2. Turn the screw clockwise until it touches the tab on the secondary throttle lever.

3. Add ¼ turn clockwise for four-cylinder engines.

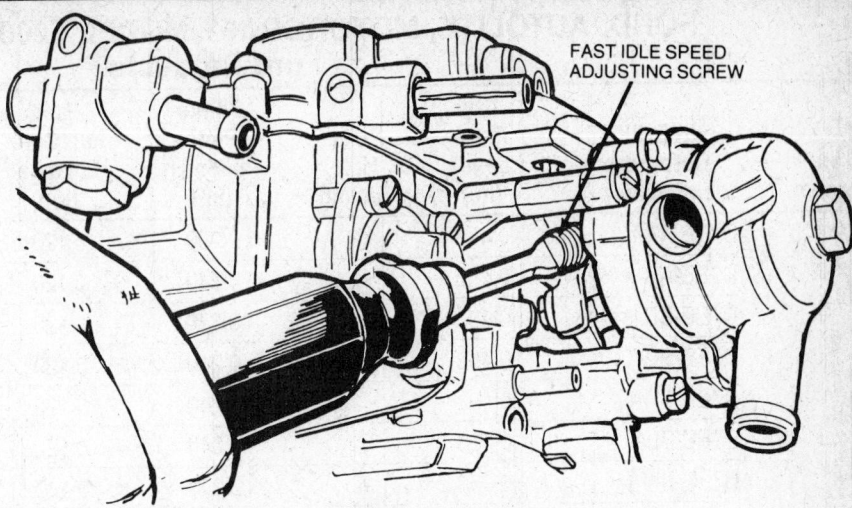

Fast idle adjustment

FAST IDLE SPEED ADJUSTING SCREW

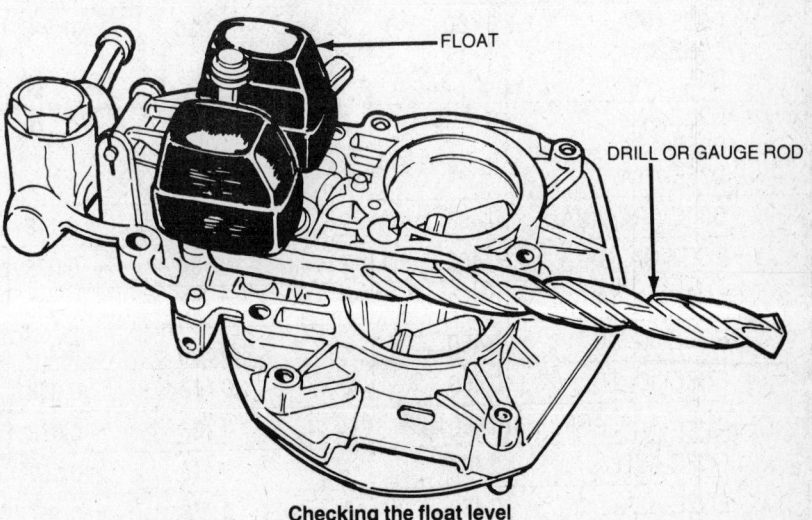

Checking the float level

FLOAT / DRILL OR GAUGE ROD

FORD, AUTOLITE, MOTORCRAFT MODEL 5200 SPECIFICATIONS
Ford Products

Year	(9510)* Carburetor Identification ①	Dry Float Level (in.)	Pump Hole Setting	Choke Plate Pulldown (in.)	Fast Idle Cam Linkage (in.)	Fast Idle (rpm)	Dechoke (in.)	Choke Setting
'78	D7EE-AAA	0.453	2	0.200	0.120	2000	0.180	Index
	D7EE-AB	0.453	2	0.240	0.120	1800	0.240	2 Rich
	D7EE-BDA	0.453	2	0.280	0.120	1500	0.240	2 Rich
	D7EE-BGA	0.453	2	0.240	0.120	1500	0.240	Index
	D7EE-BHA	0.453	2	0.240	0.120	1500	0.240	Index
	D7EE-BLA	0.453	2	0.240	0.120	2000	0.240	Index
	D7EE-BMA	0.453	2	0.240	0.120	2000	0.240	Index
	D7EE-DA	0.453	2	0.240	0.120	1500	0.240	2 Rich
	D7EE-EA	0.453	2	0.240	0.120	2000	0.240	Index
	D7EE-FA	0.453	2	0.240	0.120	1800	0.240	Index
	D7EE-GA	0.453	2	0.200	0.120	2000	0.200	Index
	D7EE-HA	0.453	2	0.240	0.120	1500	0.240	2 Rich
	D7EE-JA	0.453	2	0.240	0.120	1800	0.240	Index
	D7EE-KB	0.453	2	0.240	0.120	1800	0.240	2 Rich
	D7EE-LA	0.453	2	0.240	0.120	1800	0.240	Index
	D7EE-SA	0.453	2	0.240	0.120	1800	0.240	2 Rich
	D7EE-TA	0.453	2	0.240	0.120	1800	0.240	2 Rich
	D7EE-UA	0.453	2	0.240	0.120	1800	0.240	Index
	D7EE-VA	0.453	2	0.240	0.120	1800	0.240	Index
'79	D9ZE-ND	0.460	3	0.236	0.118	1800	0.236	2 Rich
	D9BE-AAA, D9BE-ABA, D9EE-AMA	0.460	2	0.236	0.118	1800	0.236	2 Rich
	D9EE-ANA, D9EE-ASA, D9EE-AYA	0.460	2	0.236	0.118	1800	0.236	1 Rich
'80	D9EE-APA, ANA	0.460	2	0.236	0.118	②	0.236	1 Rich
	EOEE-GA, RA	0.460	2	0.196	0.078	②	0.196	②
	EOEE-JA, TA	0.460	2	0.196	0.078	②	0.196	②
	EOEE-JC, TC	0.460	—	0.196	0.078	②	0.196	②
	EOEE-JD, TD	0.460	2	0.177	0.078	②	0.196	②
	EOEE-AEA, AFA	0.460	2	0.196	0.078	②	0.196	②em
	EOZE-ACB	0.460	—	0.275	0.157	②	0.236	②
	EOZE-AZA	0.460	2	0.275	0.157	②	0.393	②
	EOZE-AAA	0.460	3	0.275	0.157	②	0.236	②
	EOZE-ACA	0.460	2	0.275	0.157	②	0.236	②
	EOZE-ATA	0.460	2	0.275	0.118	②	0.236	②

FORD, AUTOLITE, MOTORCRAFT MODEL 5200 SPECIFICATIONS
Ford Products

Year	(9510)* Carburetor Identification ①	Dry Float Level (in.)	Pump Hole Setting	Choke Plate Pulldown (in.)	Fast Idle Cam Linkage (in.)	Fast Idle (rpm)	Dechoke (in.)	Choke Setting
'81	EIZE-YA	.41-.51	2	0.200	.080	②	0.200	②
	EOEE-RB	.41-.51	2	0.200	.080	②	0.200	②
	EIZE-VA	.41-.51	2	0.200	.080	②	0.200	②
	D9EE-ANA	.41-.51	2	0.240	0.720	②	0.200	②
	D9EE-APA	.41-.51	2	0.240	0.120	②	0.200	②
'82	E1ZE-ADB	.41-.51	3	0.275	0.240	1600	0.393	—
	E1ZE-ACA	.41-.51	2	0.200	.080	1800	0.196	—
	E1BE-RA, GA	.41-.51	2	0.200	.080	1800	0.196	—
	E1ZE-YA	.41-.51	2	0.200	.080	2000	0.196	—
	E1ZE-VA	.41-.51	2	0.200	.080	2000	0.196	—
	E2ZE-AFA	.41-.51	2	0.236	0.118	1800	0.236	—
	E2ZE-AHA	.41-.51	2	0.236	0.118	2000	0.236	—
	E2ZE-ABA	.41-.51	2	0.236	0.118	2000	0.236	—
	E2ZE-AGA	.41-.51	2	0.236	0.118	2000	0.236	—
	E2ZE-AAA	.41-.51	2	0.236	0.118	2000	0.236	—

* Basic carburetor number
① Figure given is for all manual transmissions; for automatic trans. the figures are: (49 states) 2000 RPM; (Calif.) 1800 RPM.
② See underhood decal

Model 4300, 4350

The model 4300 and 4350 4 barrel carburetor is composed of three main assemblies: the air horn, the main body, and the throttle body. The air horn assembly serves as the fuel bowl cover as well as the housing for the choke valve and shaft. It contains the accelerator pump linkage, fuel inlet seat, float and lever, booster venturi, and internal fuel bowl vents.

The main body houses the fuel metering passages, accelerator pump mechanism, and the power valve.

The throttle body contains the primary and secondary throttle valves and shafts, the curb idle adjusting screw, the fast idle adjusting screw, the idle mixture adjusting screws, and the automatic choke assembly. This carburetor is last used in 1978.

FLOAT ADJUSTMENT

1. Adjustments to the fuel lever are best made with the carburetor removed from the engine and the carburetor cleaned upon disassembly.
2. Invert the air horn assembly and remove the gasket from the surface.

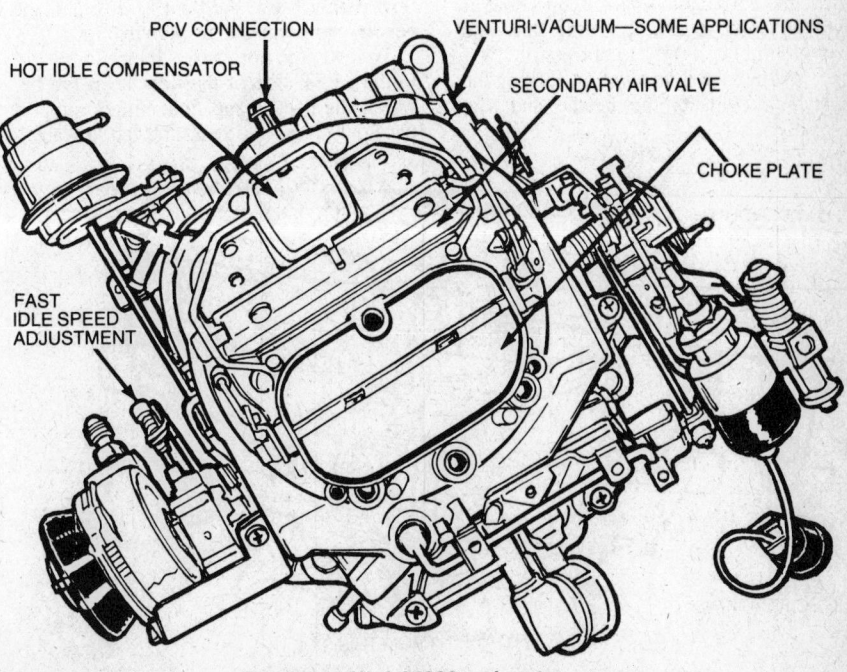

Top view—Model 4300 carburetor

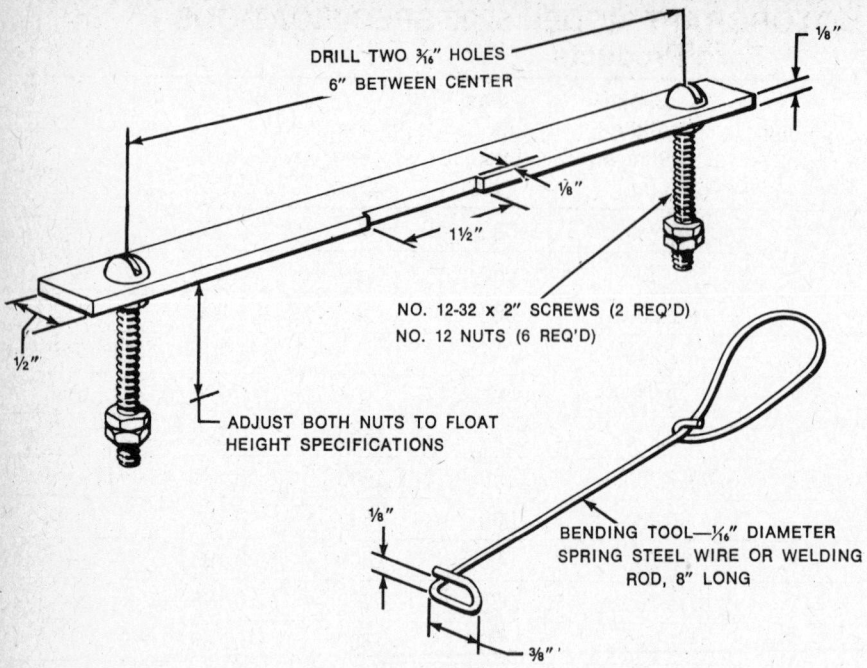

Construction of float level gauge and float arm bending tool
(© Ford Motor Co)

3. Use a T-scale to measure the distance from the floats to the air horn casting. Position the scale horizontally over the flat surface of both floats at the free ends and parallel to the air horn casting. Hold the lower end of the vertical scale in full contact with the smooth surface of the air horn.

--- CAUTION ---

The end of the vertical scale must not come into contact with any gasket sealing ridges while measuring the float level.

4. The free end of each float should just touch the horizontal scale; if one float is lower than the other, twist the float and lever assembly slightly to correct.

5. Adjust the float level by bending the tab which contacts the needle and seat assembly.

NOTE: The illustrations in this section show an alternate method of adjusting the floats on the model 4300 carburetor.

The procedure includes the fabrication of a gauge and a bending device. After fabricating the gauge, it is possible to adjust it to the specified dimensions and insert it into the air horn outboard holes. Both pontoons should just touch the gauge.

A float tab bending tool is also shown and may be used in the following manner.

To raise the float: insert the open end of the bending tool to the RIGHT side of the float lever tab and between the needle and float hinge. Raise the float lever off of the needle and bend the tab downward.

To lower the float: insert the bending tool to the LEFT side of the float lever tab between the needle and float hinge, support the float lever, and bend the tab upward.

CHOKE PLATE PULLDOWN

1. Remove the air cleaner and choke thermostatic spring housing.

2. Bend a wire gauge (0.036 in. diameter) at a 90 degree angle about ⅛ in. from one end.

3. Block the throttle open so that the fast idle screw does not contact the fast idle cam.

4. Insert the bent end of the wire gauge between the lower edge of the piston slot and the upper edge of the right hand slot in the choke housing.

5. Pull the choke piston lever counterclockwise until the gauge is snug in the piston slot. Hold the wire in place by exerting light pressure in a rearward direction on the choke piston lever. Check the distance from the lower edge of the choke valve to the air horn wall.

6. Adjustment is done by loosening the hex head screw (left-hand thread) on the choke valve shaft and prying the link away from the shaft. Use a drill gauge 0.010 in. under the specified clearance between the lower edge of the choke valve and the air horn wall. Hold the choke valve against the gauge and maintain a light rearward pressure on the choke lever.

7. With the choke piston snug against the 0.036 in. wire and the choke valve against the drill, tighten the hex screw on the choke valve shaft. The use of a gauge 0.010 in. undersize compensates for tolerance in the linkage.

8. Use the correct size gauge for final measurement.

9. Replace the housing on the thermostatic spring.

DELAYED CHOKE PULLDOWN

The 4350 is also equipped with a vacuum-diaphragm operated delayed choke pulldown that opens the choke to a wider setting after about 6–18 seconds of engine operation.

1. With the throttle set on the fast idle cam, note the position of the index marks on the cap. Loosen the retaining screws and rotate the cap ninety degrees (¼ turn), in the closing (rich) direction.

2. Disconnect the vacuum supply hose from the port on the delayed choke pulldown diaphragm assembly. After removing the filter cap, place a piece of tape over the purge hole, and apply vacuum to the port.

3. Measure the dimension at the lower edge of the choke plate at the center of the air horn. To adjust this figure, turn the stop screw on the delayed choke pulldown diaphragm.

FAST IDLE CAM ADJUSTMENT

1. Loosen the screws on the choke thermostatic spring cover and rotate the

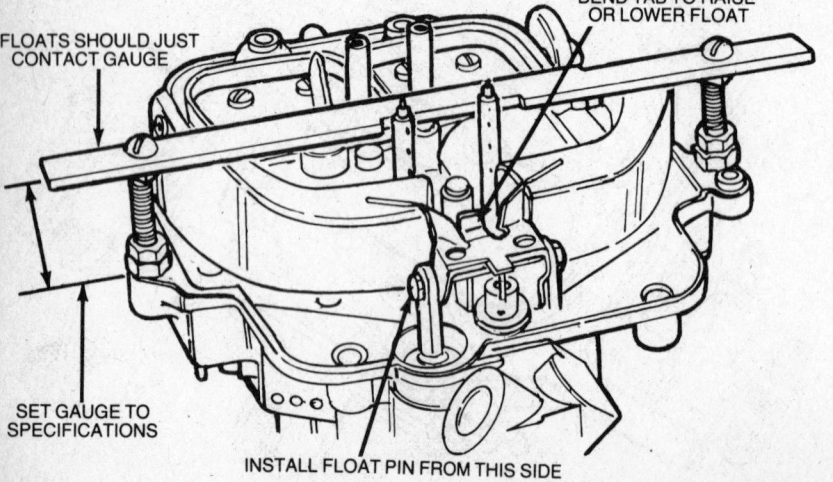

Measuring the float level

housing ¼ turn counter-clockwise. Tighten the screws.

2. Open the throttle and allow the choke valve to close completely.

3. Push down on the fast idle cam counterweight until the fast idle screw is in contact with the second step of the cam and against the high step.

4. Measure the clearance between the lower edge of the choke plate and the air horn wall.

5. Adjust by turning the fast idle cam adjusting screw (inward to increase clearance, outward to decrease clearance).

6. Return the housing on the thermostatic spring to its original position.

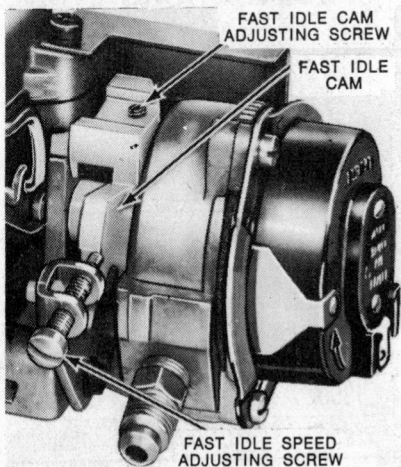

Fast idle adjustment (© Ford Motor Co)

CHOKE UNLOADER (DECHOKE) ADJUSTMENT

1. Open the throttle fully and hold it in this position.

2. Rotate the choke plate toward the closed position until the pawl on the fast idle speed lever contacts the fast idle cam.

3. Check the clearance between the lower edge of the choke plate and the air horn wall.

4. Adjust by bending the pawl on the fast idle speed lever forward to increase the

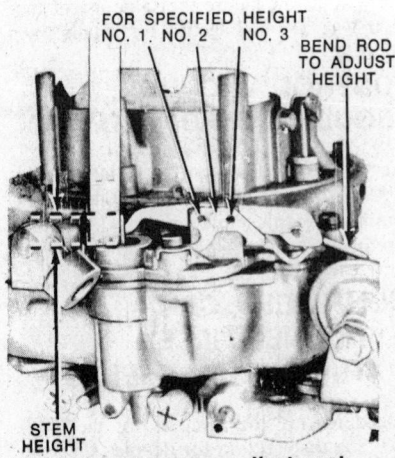

Accelerator pump adjustment
(© Ford Motor Co)

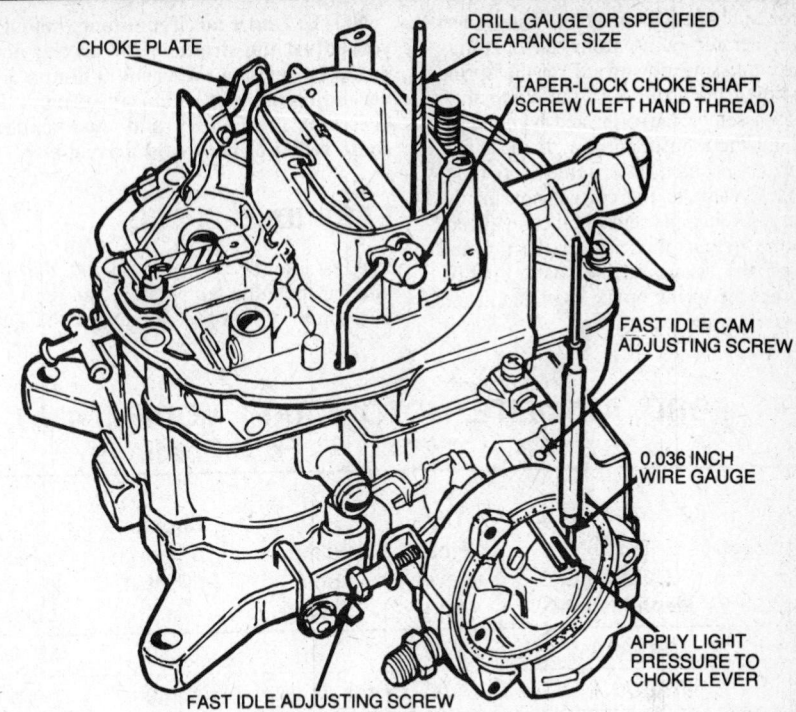

Choke plate pulldown and fast idle cam adjustment

clearance and backward to decrease the clearance.

ACCELERATOR PUMP STROKE ADJUSTMENT

The accelerator pump adjustment is preset at the factory for reduced exhaust emissions. Adjustment is provided only for different engine installations. The adjustment is internal, with three piston-to-shaft pin positions in the pump piston.

To check that the shaft pin is located in the specified piston hole, remove the car-

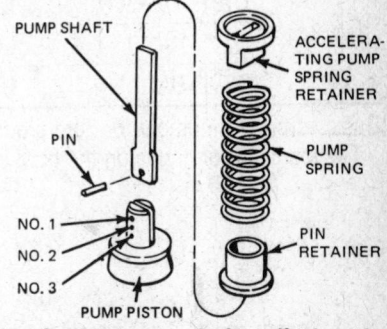

Accelerator pump stroke adjustment—Motorcraft 4350

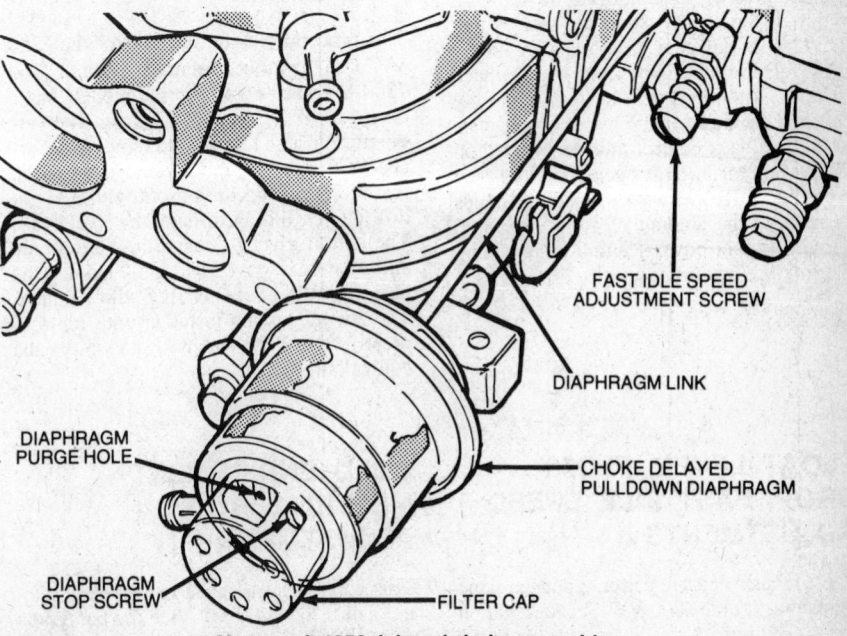

Motorcraft 4350 delayed choke assembly

buretor air horn and invert it. Disconnect the accelerator pump from the operating arm by pressing downward on the spring and sliding the arm out of the pump shaft slot. Disassemble the spring and nylon keeper retaining the adjustment pin. If the pin is not in its specified hole, remove it, reposition the shaft to the correct hole in the piston assembly and reinstall the pin. Then, slide the nylon retainer over the pin and position the spring on the shaft. Finally, compress the spring on the shaft and install the pump on the pump arm.

NOTE: Under no circumstances should you adjust the stroke of the accelerator pump by turning the vacuum limiter lever adjusting nut. This adjustment is preset at the factory and modification could result in poor cold driveability.

FAST IDLE SPEED

The fast idle speed is adjusted with the engine at operating temperature and the fast idle screw on the second step of the fast idle cam. Adjust by turning the fast idle screw in or out as required.

On AMC cars, disconnect and plug the vacuum line at the EGR valve, and remove the electrical connector from the TCS valve. On Ford cars, first remove and plug the distributor vacuum lines. Remove the top and center CSSA system PVS switch hoses (located in the heater elbow) and connect them together. Remove the EGR hose from the carburetor port and plug the port. When the fast idle speed is set, reconnect those hoses removed previously.

FORD, AUTOLITE, MOTORCRAFT MODELS 4300, 4350 SPECIFICATIONS
Ford Products

Year	(9510)* Carburetor Identification①	Dry Float Level (in.)	Pump Hole Setting	Choke Plate Pulldown (in.)	Fast Idle Cam Linkage	Fast Idle (rpm)	Dechoke (in.)	Choke Setting
'78	D7AE-AAA	1.00	2	0.140	0.140	1350	0.300	Index
	D7AE-ANA	1.00	2	0.140	0.140	1350	0.300	Index
	D7AE-ZA	1.00	2	0.140	0.140	1350	0.300	Index
	D7PE-AA	1.00	2	0.140	0.140	1350	0.300	Index
	D7VE-KA	1.00	2	0.140	0.140	1350	0.300	2 Lean
	D7VE-SA	1.00	2	0.140	0.140	1350	0.300	Index

* Basic carburetor number for Ford products.
① The identification tag is on the bowl cover.

Model 7200

The Motorcraft model 7200 variable venturi (VV) carburetor shares most of its design features with the model 2700 VV. The major difference between the two is that the 7200 is designed to work with Ford's EEC (electronic engine control) feedback system. The feedback system precisely controls the air/fuel ratio by varying signals to the feedback control monitor located on the carburetor, which opens or closes the metering valve in response. This expands or reduces the amount of control vacuum above the fuel bowl, leaning or richening the mixture accordingly.

FAST IDLE CAM ADJUSTMENT

This procedure is the same as for the 2700 VV. Use the procedure in that section. The 7200 VV used on California models has a choke cover held on with rivets. The carburetor must be removed to remove the rivets. With the carburetor removed, the top two rivets can be drilled out with a ⅛ in. drill bit. Drill only through the rivet head. The bottom rivet is located in a blind hole and must be removed by lightly tapping the backside of the retainer ring with a punch. The cover must be installed with replacement rivets, Ford part no. 388575, or the equivalent.

FLOAT LEVEL, FLOAT DROP, FAST IDLE SPEED ADJUSTMENTS

These adjustments are performed in the same manner as for the 2700 VV. See that section for procedures.

COLD ENRICHMENT METERING ROD ADJUSTMENT

This adjustment is made in the same manner as for the 2700 VV. See the paragraph under the Fast Idle Cam Adjustment above

concerning the riveted choke cover used on California models.

INTERNAL VENT, VENTURI VALVE LIMITER ADJUSTMENTS

These adjustments are the same as for the 2700 VV. See that section for details.

CONTROL VACUUM REGULATOR ADJUSTMENT

Use the Revised System procedure in the 2700 VV section. Note that the control vacuum is not adjustable on any 7200 carburetor; only the regulator is adjustable.

HIGH SPEED CAM POSITIONER, IDLE MIXTURE ADJUSTMENTS

Procedures are the same as for the 2700 VV. See that section for details. Like the 2700 VV, the 7200 idle trim is preset at the factory and non-adjustable.

MOTORCRAFT MODEL 7200 VV SPECIFICATIONS

Year	Model	Float Level (in.)	Float Drop (in.)	Fast Idle Cam Setting (notches)	Cold Enrichment Metering Rod (in.)	Control Vacuum (in. H₂O)	Venturi Valve Limiter (in.)	Choke Cap Setting (notches)
'79	D9AE-ACA	1³⁄₆₄	1¹⁵⁄₃₂	1 Rich/3rd step	.125	7.5	.73-.77①	Index
	D9ME-AA	1³⁄₆₄	1¹⁵⁄₃₂	1 Rich/3rd step	.125	7.5	.73-.77①	Index
'80	All	1³⁄₆₄	1¹⁵⁄₃₂	1 Rich/3rd step	.125	②	③	④
'81	D9AE-AZA	1.015-1.065	1.435-1.485	1 Rich/3rd step	.125	②	⑤	Index
	EIAE-LA	1.015-1.065	1.435-1.485	0.360/2nd step	⑦	②	⑥	1 Rich
	EIAE-SA	1.015-1.065	1.435-1.485	0.360/2nd step	⑦	②	⑥	1 Rich
	EIAE-KA	1.010-1.070	1.430-1.490	0.360/2nd step	⑩	②	⑭	Index
	EIDE-AA	1.010-1.070	1.430-1.490	0.360/2nd step	⑩	②	⑭	Index
	EIVE-AA	1.015-1.065	1.435-1.485	0.360/2nd step	⑦	②	③	Index
'82	E2AE-LB	1.010-1.070	1.430-1.490	0.360/2nd step	⑧	②	⑨	Index
	E2DE-NA	1.010-1.070	1.430-1.490	0.360/2nd step	⑧	②	⑨	Index
	E2AE-LC	1.010-1.070	1.430-1.490	0.360/2nd step	⑧	②	⑨	Index
	E25E-FA	1.010-1.070	1.430-1.490	0.360/2nd step	⑧	②	⑨	Index
	E25E-GB	1.010-1.070	1.430-1.490	0.360/2nd step	⑧	②	⑨	Index
	E2SE-GA	1.010-1.070	1.430-1.490	0.360/2nd step	⑧	②	⑨	Index
	E2AE-RA	1.010-1.070	1.430-1.490	0.360/2nd step	⑩	②	⑨	Index
	E1AE-ACA	1.010-1.070	1.430-1.490	0.360/2nd step	⑩	②	⑨	Index
	E2SE-DB	1.010-1.070	1.430-1.490	0.360/2nd step	⑪	②	⑨	Index
	E2SE-DA	1.010-1.070	1.430-1.490	0.360/2nd step	⑪	②	⑨	Index
	E1AE-SA	1.010-1.070	1.430-1.490	0.360/2nd step	⑫	②	⑬	1 Rich
	E2AE-MA	1.010-1.070	1.430-1.490	0.360/2nd step	⑫	②	⑬	1 Rich
	E2AE-MB	1.010-1.070	1.430-1.490	0.360/2nd step	⑫	②	⑬	1 Rich
	E2AE-TA	1.010-1.070	1.430-1.490	0.360/2nd step	⑫	②	⑬	Index
	E2AE-TB	1.010-1.070	1.430-1.490	0.360/2nd step	⑫	②	⑬	Index
	E25E-AC	1.010-1.070	1.430-1.490	0.360/2nd step	⑪	②	⑨	Index
	E1AE-AGA	1.010-1.070	1.430-1.490	0.360/2nd step	⑫	②	⑨	Index
	E2AE-NA	1.010-1.070	1.430-1.490	0.360/2nd step	⑫	②	⑨	Index
'83	E2AE-NA	1.010-1.070	1.430-1.490	0.360/2nd step	⑫	②	⑨	Index
	E2AE-AJA	1.010-1.070	1.430-1.490	0.360/2nd step	⑫	②	⑨	Index
	E2AE-APA	1.010-1.070	1.430-1.490	0.360/2nd step	⑫	②	⑨	Index
'84	E2AE-AJA	1.010-1.070	1.430-1.490	0.360/2nd step	⑫	②	⑨	Index
	E2AE-APA	1.010-1.070	1.430-1.490	0.360/2nd step	⑫	②	⑨	Index

① Limiter Stop Setting: .99-1.01
② See text
③ Opening gap: 0.99-1.01
   Closing gap: 0.39-0.41
④ See underhood decal
⑤ Maximum opening: .99/1.01
   Wide open on throttle: .94/.98
⑥ Maximum opening: .99/1.01
   Wide open on throttle: .74/.76
⑦ 0°F—0.490 @ starting position
   75°F—0.475 @ starting position

⑧ 0°F—0.525 @ starting position
   75°F—0.445 @ starting position
⑨ Maximum opening: .99/1.01
   Wide open on throttle: .39/.41
⑩ 0°F—0.490 @ starting position
   75°F—0.445 @ starting position
⑪ 0°F—0.525 @ starting position
   75°F—0.475 @ starting position

⑫ 0°F—0.490 @ starting position
   75°F—0.460 @ starting position
⑬ Maximum opening: .99/1.01
   Wide open on throttle: .74/.76
⑭ Maximum opening: .99/1.01
   Wide open on throttle: .48/.52

HOLLEY CARBURETORS

Model 1945

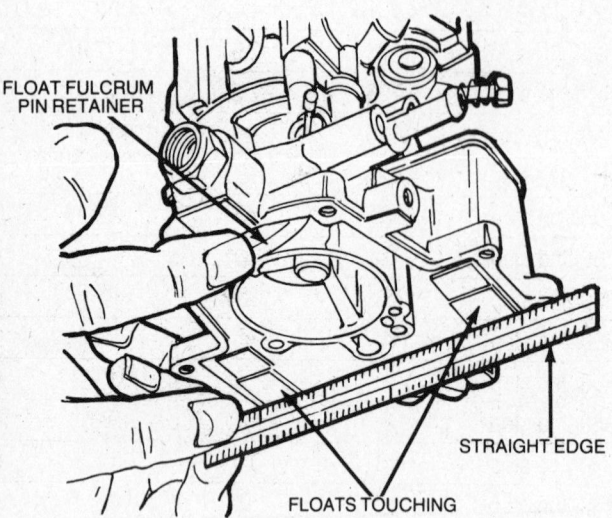

FLOAT FULCRUM
PIN RETAINER

STRAIGHT EDGE

FLOATS TOUCHING

Checking the float adjustment—Holley 1945

The model 1945 carburetor is a concentric downdraft single barrel carburetor with an internal float bowl which completely surrounds the venturi. The unit uses dual nitrophyl floats which permit operation at extreme angles. It is used on Chrysler Corporation six cylinder engines.

FLOAT ADJUSTMENT

1. Remove the float bowl cover and invert the bowl. Hold the retaining spring in place.
2. Place a straight-edge across the surface of the bowl. The gasket should be in place. The straight-edge should just clear the toes of the floats by the specified measurement.
3. If the adjustment is necessary, bend the float tang to obtain the correct adjustment.

FAST IDLE ADJUSTMENT

1. Remove the air cleaner and disconnect the vacuum lines to the heated air control and the OSAC (Orifice Spark Advance Control) valve. If there is no OSAC valve, disconnect the hose to the distributor and the EGR hose. Cap all carburetor vacuum fittings.
2. With the engine off, transmission in Neutral and the parking brake set, open the throttle and close the choke.
3. Close the throttle. This will place the fast idle speed screw on the highest step.
4. Move the fast idle cam until the screw drops to the second highest speed step.
5. Start the engine and stabilize the engine speed. Rotate the fast idle speed screw to obtain the specified setting. See Specifications Chart.

FAST IDLE CAM ADJUSTMENT

1. Place the fast idle speed adjusting screw on the second highest step of the fast idle cam.
2. Place light pressure on the choke shaft lever to move the choke valve towards the close position.
3. Insert the specified gauge between the top of the choke and the air horn wall at the throttle lever side.
4. To adjust bend the fast idle connector rod at angle until the correct valve opening is obtained.

CHOKE UNLOADER ADJUSTMENT

1. Hold the throttle valves wide-open and insert the specified gauge between the upper edge of the choke valve and the inner wall of the air horn.
2. Place slight pressure against the control lever and attempt to remove the gauge. There should be a slight drag as the gauge is being withdrawn. If adjustment is necessary, bend the unloader tang on the throt-

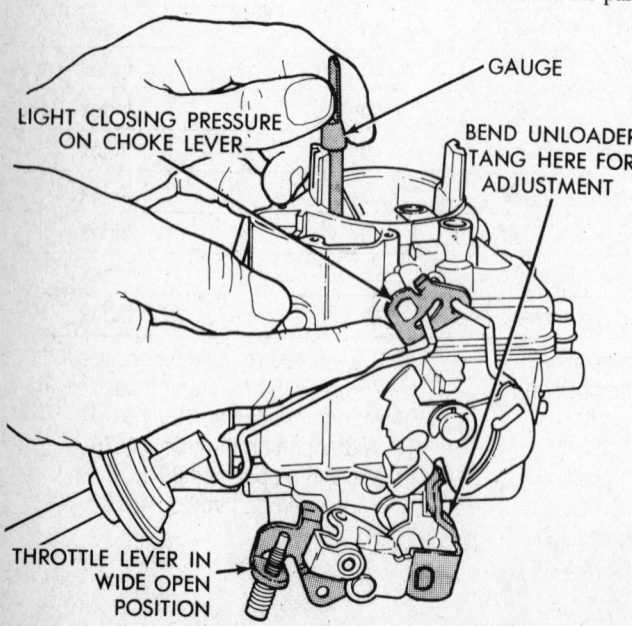

LIGHT CLOSING PRESSURE
ON CHOKE LEVER

GAUGE

BEND UNLOADER
TANG HERE FOR
ADJUSTMENT

THROTTLE LEVER IN
WIDE OPEN
POSITION

Choke unloader adjustment—Holley 1945

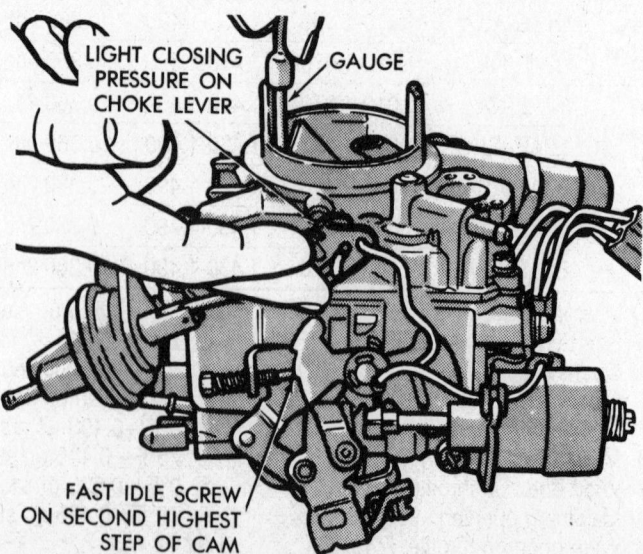

LIGHT CLOSING
PRESSURE ON
CHOKE LEVER

GAUGE

FAST IDLE SCREW
ON SECOND HIGHEST
STEP OF CAM

Fast idle cam adjustment—Holley 1945

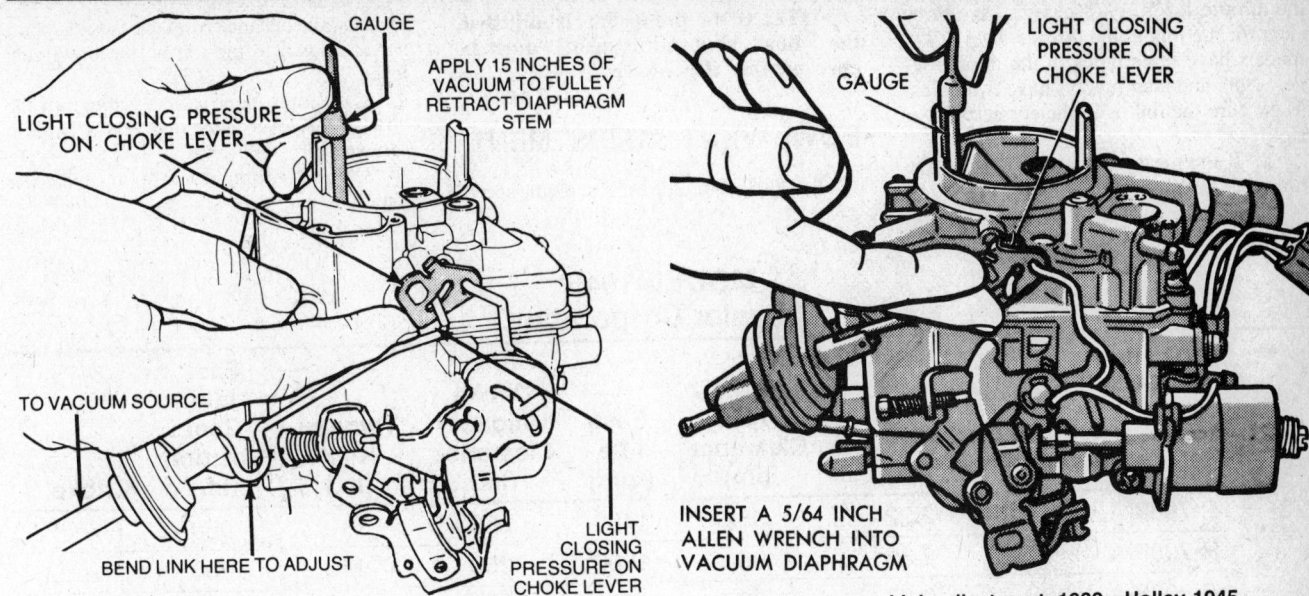

Choke vacuum kick adjustment—Holley 1945

Choke vacuum kick adjustment, 1982—Holley 1945

tle lever until the correct opening has been obtained.

CHOKE VACUUM KICK ADJUSTMENT

1. With the engine not running, open the throttle and move the choke to the closed position. Release the throttle first and then the choke.

2. If an auxiliary vacuum source is used, disconnect the vacuum hose from the carburetor and connect it to the hose from the vacuum supply with an extra length of tube. Apply a vacuum of 15 or more in. of mercury.

3. Insert the correct gauge (see Spec-

ifications chart) between the choke valve upper edge and the wall of the air horn. Close and hold the choke rod lever with light pressure. The cylindrical stem of the diaphragm will extend as the internal spring is compressed. This spring must be fully compressed for proper measurement of the vacuum kick.

4. If adjustment is necessary, shorten or lengthen the diaphragm link to obtain the correct opening on models through 1981. On 1982 and later models insert a 5/64 inch Allen wrench into the vacuum diaphragm and turn to adjust.

——— **CAUTION** ———
Do not twist or bend the diaphragm.

5. Install the vacuum hose on the correct carburetor fitting and connect the fast idle linkage.

6. Check the operation in the following manner. With vacuum applied to the diaphragm, the choke valve should move freely between the open and closed positions. If there is binding, examine the linkage for misalignment or interference caused by bending.

ACCELERATOR PUMP ADJUSTMENT

1. With the throttle in the curb idle position, measure the distance between the pump link pivot and the link connection to

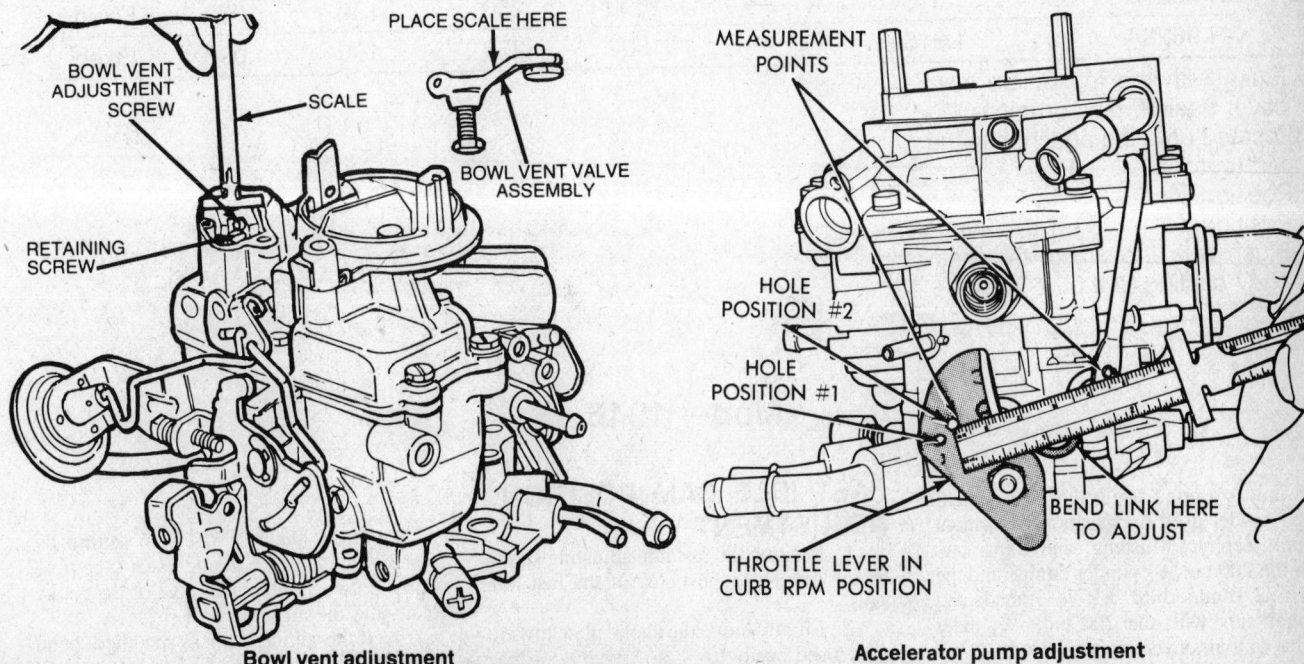

Bowl vent adjustment

Accelerator pump adjustment

the throttle lever. 1978 models have three slots for the link at the throttle lever. 1979 models have three holes in the throttle lever; 1980 and later models have two holes. Make sure the link is in the correct hole or slot.

2. If the measurement is incorrect, the link may be bent at the "U" to adjust.

NOTE: If the pump link is adjusted, the "Bowl Vent Adjustment" must be checked and, if necessary, reset.

BOWL VENT ADJUSTMENT

1. With the throttle set at curb idle speed, measure the distance from the cover support surface down to the flat on the bowl vent lever.

2. If adjustment is necessary, turn the bowl vent lever adjusting screw with a screwdriver.

3. Install the bowl vent spring and cover plate.

MODEL 1945
Chrysler Corporation

Year	Carb. Part No. ②	Float Level (in.)	Accelerator Pump Adjustment (in.)	Bowl Vent Clearance (in.)	Fast Idle (rpm)	Choke Unloader Clearance (in.)	Vacuum Kick (in.)	Fast Idle Cam Position (in.)	Choke
'78	R-7988-A	①	2.22	.062	1400	.250	.110	.080	Fixed
	R-7989-A	①	2.33	.062	1600	.250	.110	.080	Fixed
	R-8008-A	①	2.33	.062	1700	.250	.110	.080	Fixed
	R-8010-A	①	2.33	.062	1500	.250	.130	.080	Fixed
	R-8394-A	①	2.33	.062	1700	.250	.110	.080	Fixed
'79	R-8523-A	①	1.70③	1/16	1400	.250	.110	.080	Fixed
	R-8452-A	①	1.615④	1/16	1600	.250	.110	.080	Fixed
	R-8555-A	①	1.70③	1/16	1400	.250	.110	.080	Fixed
	R-8727-A	①	1.615④	1/16	1600	.250	.110	.080	Fixed
	R-8680-A	①	1.615④	1/16	1500	.250	.130	.080	Fixed
'80	R-8718-A	①	1.70③	1/16	1400	.250	.150	.090	Fixed
	R-8831-A	①	1.615④	1/16	1600	.250	.140	.090	Fixed
	R-8832-A	①	1.70③	1/16	1400	.250	.110	.090	Fixed
	R-8833-A	①	1.615④	1/16	1600	.250	.110	.090	Fixed
'81	R-9253-A	⑤	1.615④	—	1600	.250	.150	.090	Fixed
'82	R-9627A	⑤	1.615④	—	1600	.250	.150	.090	Fixed
	R-9628A	⑤	1.615④	—	1800	.250	.150	.090	Fixed

① Flush with the top of the bowl cover gasket, plus or minus 1/32
② Located on a tag attached to the carburetor.
③ Position #1
④ Position #2
⑤ Flush with the top of the main body casting to 0.050" above

Model 1946

This unit is a one barrel, altitude compensating model used on Fairmont, Fairmont Futura, Zephyr, Mustang, and Capri cars with the 200 cid, 6 cylinder engine and the 1981–82 Thunderbird, XR-7, Granada and Cougar cars with the 200 cid 6 cylinder engine and automatic transmission.

FAST IDLE CAM POSITION ADJUSTMENT

1. Position the fast idle adjusting screw on the second highest step of the fast idle cam.

2. Lightly move the choke plate toward the closed position.

3. Check the fast idle cam setting by placing the correct gauge (see specifications) between the upper edge of the choke plate and the air horn wall.

4. If the setting is not as specified, bend the fast idle cam link.

FAST IDLE ADJUSTMENT

1. Remove the spark delay valve, if so equipped, and route the distributor vacuum hose directly to the advance side of the distributor.

2. Trace the EGR signal vacuum hose from the EGR valve to the carburetor. If an EGR/PVS valve or cold weather modulator is located in the hose, disconnect the EGR hose at the EGR valve and plug the hose. If not equipped with EGR/PVS or a cold weather modulator, do not detach the hose except on 1980 models; disconnect and plug the EGR hose on all 1980 models. On all 1981 and later models disconnect and plug the vacuum hoses at the EGR and purge valves.

3. Run the engine to normal operating temperature. With the choke plate fully open and the transmission in Park, place the fast idle screw on the next to the highest step of the fast idle cam. Allow the engine speed to stabilize and adjust the speed to the fast idle speed specification found on the underhood sticker.

4. Run the engine at 2500 rpm for about 15 seconds and recheck the fast idle speed.

5. When the speed is properly adjusted, turn off the engine and re-route the vacuum lines.

ACCELERATOR PUMP STROKE

The accelerator pump stroke is present at the factory and should not be adjusted to improve driveability.

DECHOKE ADJUSTMENT

1. With the engine off, hold the throttle in the wide open position.

2. Insert the specified gauge between the upper edge of the choke plate and the wall of the air horn.

3. With a slight pressure against the

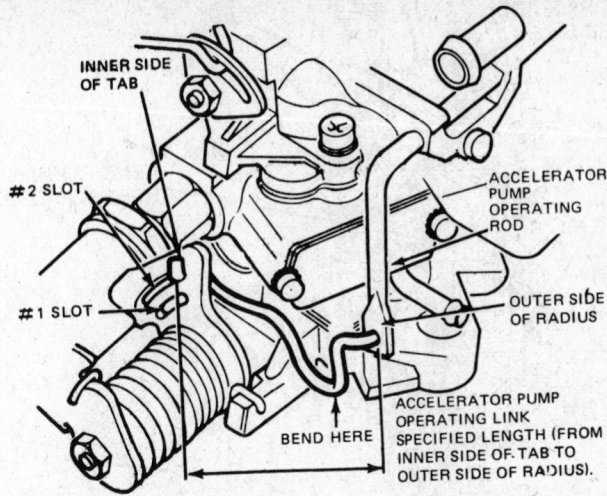

Accelerator pump adjustment (© Ford Motor Co.)

choke shaft a slight drag should be felt when the gauge is withdrawn.

4. To adjust, bend the unloader tab on the throttle lever until the correct opening is obtained.

CHOKE PULLDOWN 1978-80

NOTE: On 1981 and later models this adjustment is preset at the factory and protected by a tamper resistant plug.

1. Set the fast idle screw on the highest step of the fast idle cam.

2. Cool the choke housing until the plate is fully closed.

3. Mark the choke setting for later resetting.

4. On 1980 California models, remove the choke thermostat housing, retaining ring and screws. Temporarily remove the index spacer. Reinstall the housing, retainer, and screws. Then, on all models, loosen the choke housing screws and rotate the choke cap 90° in the rich (closed) direction. Tighten the screws.

5. Activate the pulldown diaphragm by applying vacuum to the external tube.

6. Make sure that the pulldown diaphragm is fully retracted.

7. If the motor does not fully retract with vacuum, test it for leakage. Replace it if it leaks.

8. Insert the specified gauge between the upper edge of the choke plate and the air horn wall.

9. To adjust, bend the pulldown linkage as required.

EXTERNAL FUEL BOWL VENT ADJUSTMENT

1. Disconnect the canister vent hose from the fuel bowl vent.

2. Attach a hand operated vacuum pump to the vent tube using a ⅜ in. adapter.

3. Remove the vent cover and gasket and vent spring.

4. The adjusting screw is located on the nylon arm. Turn it clockwise until no more

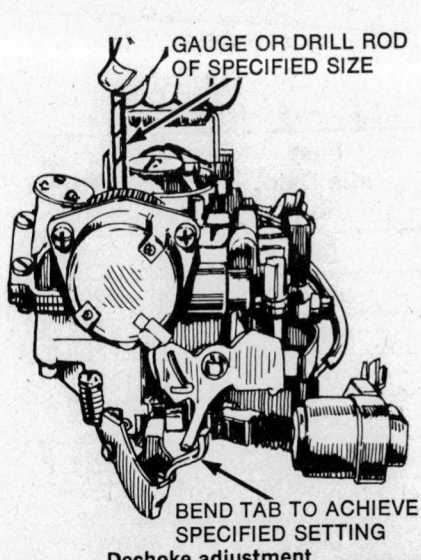

Dechoke adjustment

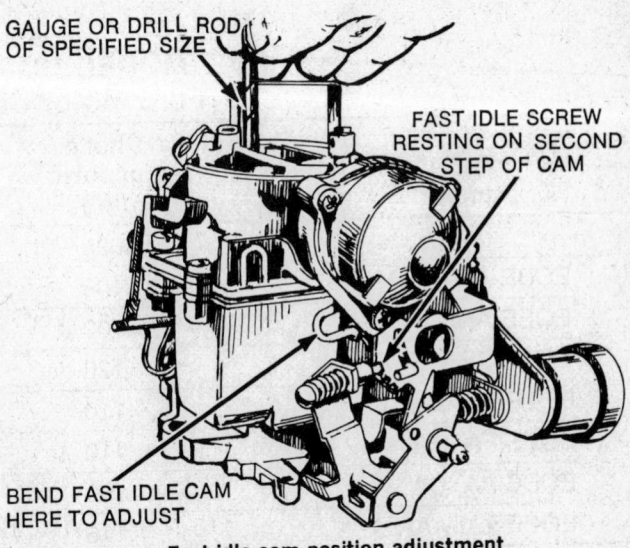

Fast idle cam position adjustment

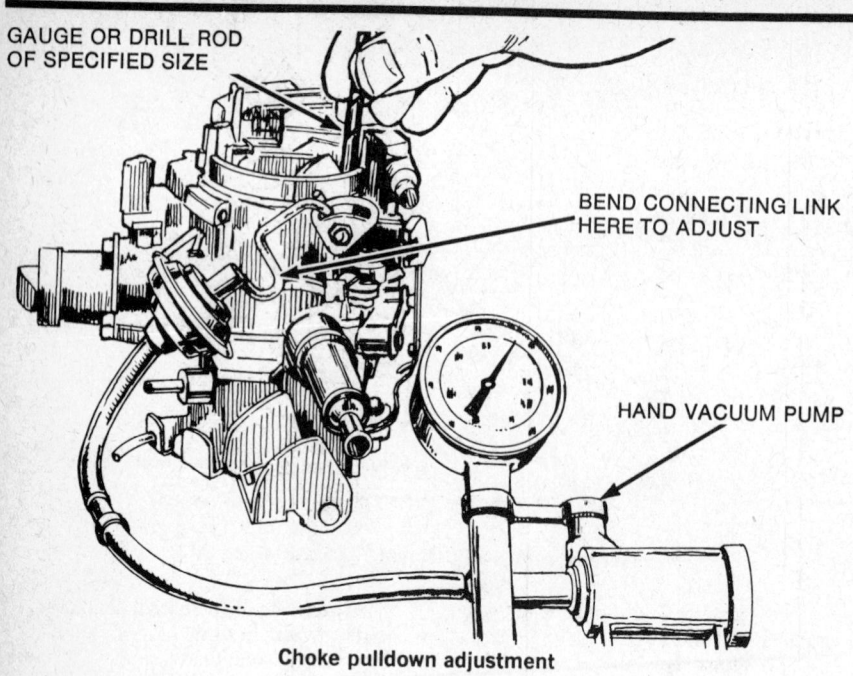

GAUGE OR DRILL ROD
OF SPECIFIED SIZE

BEND CONNECTING LINK
HERE TO ADJUST.

HAND VACUUM PUMP

Choke pulldown adjustment

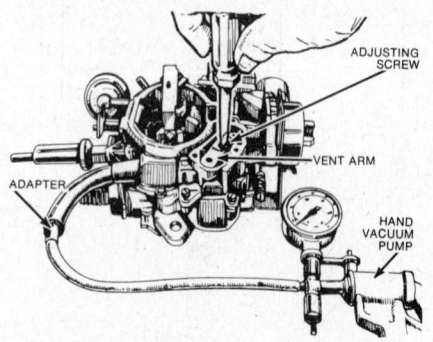

ADJUSTING
SCREW

VENT ARM

ADAPTER

HAND
VACUUM
PUMP

External fuel bowl vent adjustment

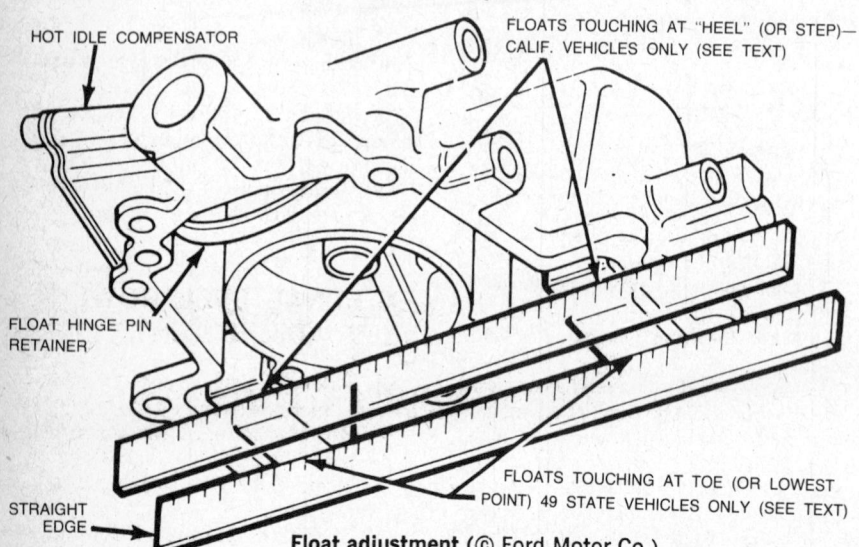

HOT IDLE COMPENSATOR

FLOATS TOUCHING AT "HEEL" (OR STEP)—
CALIF. VEHICLES ONLY (SEE TEXT)

FLOAT HINGE PIN
RETAINER

FLOATS TOUCHING AT TOE (OR LOWEST
POINT) 49 STATE VEHICLES ONLY (SEE TEXT)

STRAIGHT
EDGE

Float adjustment (© Ford Motor Co.)

than ⅛ in. of threads is visible above the vent arm.

5. Operate the hand vacuum pump and turn the screw ⅛ turn at a time counterclockwise, until vacuum is registered on the gauge. Release the vacuum and turn the screw ½ turn clockwise. Disconnect the pump and replace the vent cover.

FLOAT LEVEL

1. Remove the air horn, place a finger over the hinge pin retainer and catch the accelerator pump ball when the main body is inverted.

2. Lay a straight edge across the housing under the floats. The lowest point of the floats should just touch the straight edge for 49 states models through 1981. For California models, through 1981 and all 1982 models the straight edge should just contact the step (or heel) of the float.

3. If necessary, bend the tang on the float arm.

4. Turn the main body back and check the float alignment. No binding should exist through the float movement range.

MODEL 1946
Ford Motor Co.

Year	Part Number	Float Level (in.)	Choke Pulldown (in.)	Dechoke (in.)	Fast Idle Cam (in.)	Accelerator Pump Stroke Slot
'78-'79	All	①	.026	.250	.080	#2
'80	EOBE-ALA, AMA	①	.100	.150	.070	#2
	EOEE-ANA, APA	①	.100	.150	.070	#2
	EOZE-BBA, BAA	①	.120	.150	.086	#2
	EOZE-DA, EA	①	.110	.150	.070	#2
	EOZE-FA, GA	①	.110	.150	.070	#2
	EOBE-AA, CA	①	.100	.150	.070	#2
	EOBE-ZA, AAA	①	.115	.150	.090	#1

MODEL 1946
Ford Motor Co.

Year	Part Number	Float Level (in.)	Choke Pulldown (in.)	Dechoke (in.)	Fast Idle Cam (in.)	Accelerator Pump Stroke Slot
'81	EIBE-AFA	.69	.113	.150	.082	#2
	EIBE-AKA	.69	.113	.150	.082	#2
	EOBE-CA	.69	.100	.150	.070	#2
	EOBE-AA	.69	.100	.150	.070	#2
'82	EIBE-AGA	.69	.120	.150	.086	#2
	E2BE-CA	.69	.110	.150	.078	#2
	E2BE-BA	.69	.110	.150	.078	#2
	E2BE-JA	.69	.110	.150	.078	#2
	E2BE-HA	.69	.110	.150	.078	#2
	E2BE-TA	.69	.110	.150	.078	#2
	E2BE-SA	.69	.110	.150	.078	#2
'83	E2BE-CA	.69	.110	.150	.078	#2
	E2BE-BA	.69	.110	.150	.078	#2
	E2BE-TA	.69	.110	.150	.078	#2
	E2BE-SA	.69	.110	.150	.078	#2
	E3SE-CA	.69	.105	.150	.078	#2
	E3SE-DA	.69	.105	.150	.078	#2
	E3SE-AA	.69	.095	.150	.078	#2
	E3SE-BA	.69	.095	.150	.078	#2

① See text

Model 1949 and 6149

The Holley Models 1949 and 6149 are both single venturi booster style carburetors. The Model 6149 is a feedback carburetor. Both carburetors are used on the 2.3 liter High Swirl Combustion (HSC) engine, in the 1984 and later Tempo and Topaz.

The Model 6149 is used in the U.S.A. and the 1949 in Canada. Both models are used with either manual or automatic transaxles.

The Model 6149 carburetor uses twelve basic systems. The Model 1949 carburetor uses thirteen systems. Ten systems are common to both carburetors.

FLOAT LEVEL ADJUSTMENT—DRY

1. Remove the carburetor air horn.
2. With the air horn assembly removed, place a finger over float hinge pin retainer, and invert the main body. Catch the accelerator pump check ball and weight.
3. Using a straight edge, check the position of the floats. The correct dry float setting is that both pontoons at the extreme outboard edge be flush with the surface of the main body casting (without gasket). If adjustment is required, bend the float tabs to raise or lower the float level.
4. Once adjustment is correct, turn main body right side up, and check the float alignment. The float should move freely throughout its range without contacting the fuel bowl walls. If the float pontoons are misaligned, straighten by bending the float arms. Recheck the float level adjustment.
5. During assembly, insert the check ball first and then the weight.

AUXILIARY MAIN JET/ PULLOVER VALVE (TIMING ADJUSTMENT)

The length of the auxiliary main jet/pullover valve adjustment screw which protrudes through the back side (side opposite the adjustment screw head) of the throttle pick-up lever must be 0.345 ± 0.010 in. (8.76mm). To adjust, turn screw in or out as required.

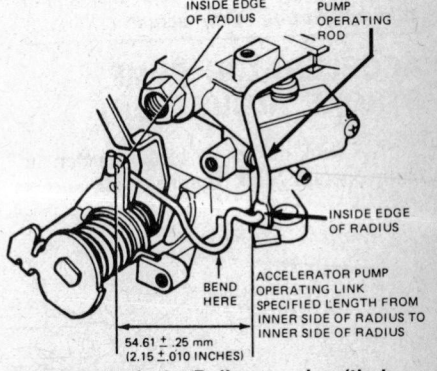

Auxiliary main jet/Pullover valve (timing adjustment)—Models 1949 and 6149

MECHANICAL FUEL BOWL VENT ADJUSTMENT (LEVER CLEARANCE)

Off Vehicle Adjustment

1. Secure the choke plate in the wide-open position.

2. Set the throttle at the TSP Off position.

3. Turn the TSP Off idle adjustment screw counterclockwise until the throttle plate is closed in the throttle bore.

4. Fuel bowl vent clearance: Dimension A, should be within specification: 0.120 ± 0.010 in. (3.05mm).

5. If out of specification, bend the bowl vent actuator lever at the adjustment point to obtain the required clearance.

CAUTION
Do not bend fuel bowl vent arm and/or adjacent portion of the actuator lever.

NOTE: TSP Off rpm must be set after carburetor installation.

On Vehicle Adjustment

NOTE: This adjustment must be performed after curb idle speed has been set to specification.

1. Secure the choke plate in the wide open position.

2. Turn ignition key to the On position to activate the TSP (engine not running). Open throttle so that the TSP plunger extends.

3. Verify that the throttle is in the idle set position (contacting the TSP plunger). Measure the clearance of the fuel bowl vent arm to the bowl vent actuating lever.

4. Fuel bowl vent clearance: Dimension A should be within specification (0.020–0.040 in.).

NOTE: There is a difference in the on vehicle and off vehicle specification.

5. If out of specification, bend the bowl vent actuator lever at the adjustment point to obtain the required clearance.

CAUTION
Do not bend fuel bowl vent arm and/or adjacent portion of the actuating lever.

ACCELERATOR PUMP STROKE ADJUSTMENT

1. Check the length of the accelerator pump operating link from its inside edge at

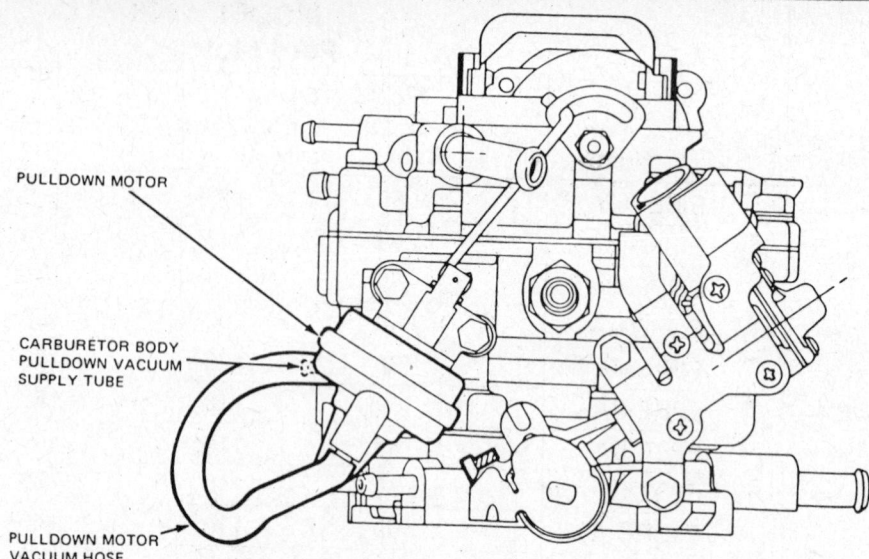

Choke plate pulldown motor—Models 1949 and 6149

the accelerator pump operating rod to its inside edge at the throttle lever hole. The dimension should be 2.15 ± .010 in. (54.61 ± .25mm).

2. Adjust to proper length by bending loop in operating link.

CHOKE PLATE PULLDOWN ADJUSTMENT

NOTE: This adjustment is preset at the factory and protected by a tamper resistant plug.

FAST IDLE CAM INDEX ADJUSTMENT

1. With the engine cool, position the fast idle screw on the high step of the fast idle cam.

2. Activate the pulldown motor by applying an external vacuum source of 15–20 inches Hg.

3. Apply light pressure to the upper edge of the choke plate in the closing direction to remove clearance between the pulldown

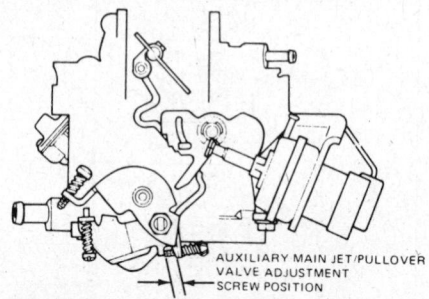

Accelerator pump stroke adjustment— Models 1949 and 6149

motor clevis and the modulator stem.

4. Open the throttle slightly and allow the fast idle cam to drop.

5. Close the throttle and measure the clearance between the top edge of the fast idle rpm adjusting screw and the shoulder of the fast idle cam high step (dimension A is the fast idle cam index shown in the illustration). Refer to the specifications table.

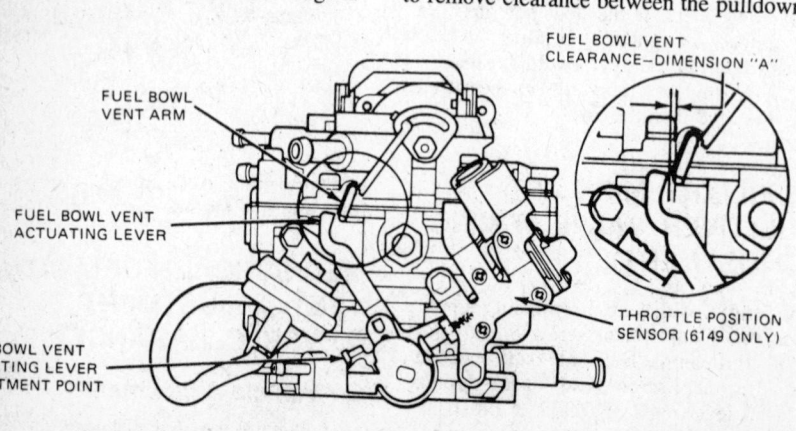

Mechanical fuel bowl vent adjustment—Models 1949 and 6149

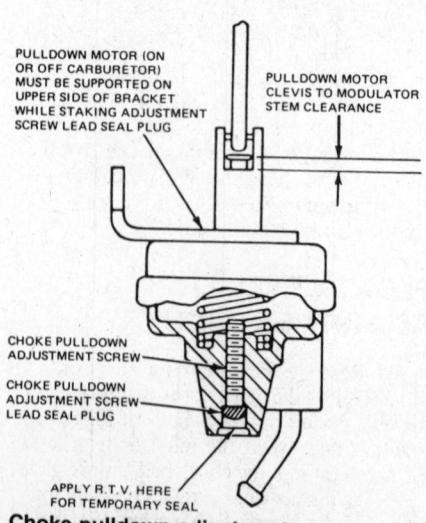

Choke pulldown adjustment— Models 1949 and 6149

6. Remove the light closing pressure from the upper edge of the choke plate.

7. Open the throttle to the wide open position and return slowly.

8. The fast idle adjustment screw must contact the lower end of the fast idle cam kickdown step by at least half of its diameter four carburetors with four step cams or must contact the third step by at least half of its diameter without contacting the second or fourth steps for carburetors with five step cams.

9. If Steps 5 and 8 are okay, the fast idle cam index is within specification. If adjustment is necessary bend the fast idle cam link at the loop to obtain the correct specification at Dimension A (see the specifications table).

DECHOKE ADJUSTMENT

1. With the engine off and cool, hold the throttle in the wide open position.

2. Use a drill of the specified size and measure the clearance between the upper edge of the choke plate and the air horn wall.

3. With slight pressure against the choke shaft, a slight drag should be felt when the gauge is withdrawn.

4. To adjust, bend the tang on the throttle lever as required.

FEEDBACK SYSTEM DIAPHRAGM ADJUSTMENT

Model 6149

1. Remove the main system feedback diaphragm adjustment screw lead sealing disc from the air horn screw boss, by drilling a 3/32 inch diameter hole through the disc. Then, insert a small punch to pry the disc out.

2. Turn the main system feedback adjustment screw as required to position the top of the screw 0.180 ± 0.010 in. (4.57mm) below the top of the air horn adjustment screw boss.

NOTE: For carburetors stamped with an "S" on the top of the air horn adjustment screw boss, adjust screw position to 0.250 ± 0.010 in. (6.35mm).

3. Install a new lead sealing disc and stake with a ¼ inch flat-ended punch.

4. Apply an external vacuum source (hand vacuum pump, 10 in-Hg. maximum) and check for leaks, diaphragm should hold vacuum.

WOT A/C CUT-OFF SWITCH ADJUSTMENT

Model 1949

The WOT A/C cut-off switch is a normally closed switch (allowing current to flow at any throttle position other than wide-open throttle).

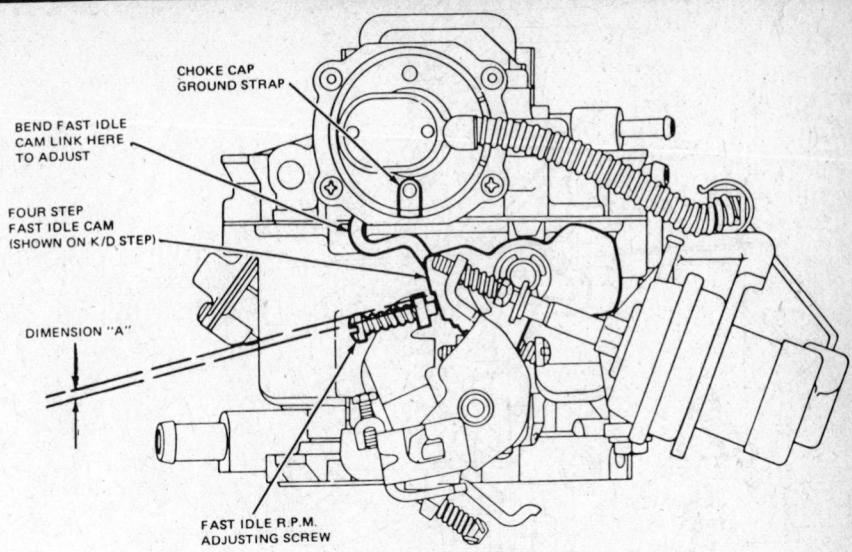

Fast idle cam index adjustment—Models 1949 and 6149

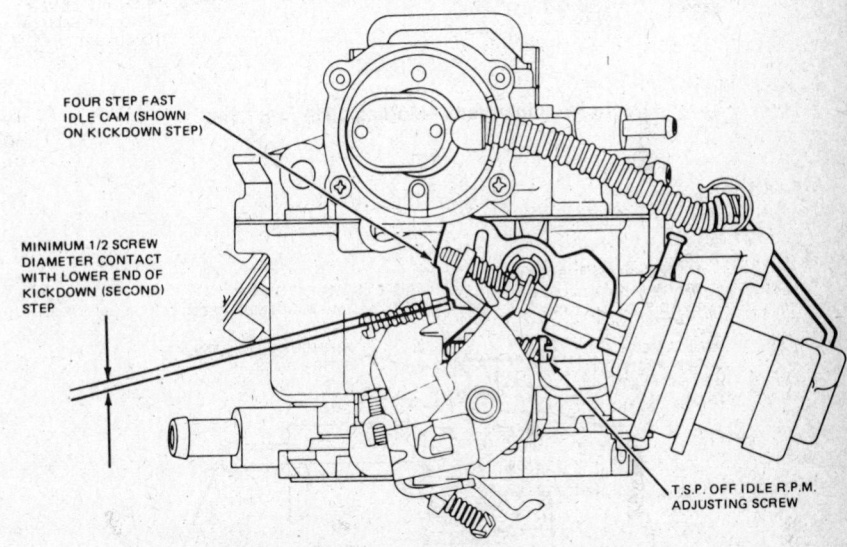

Fast idle cam index (four step idle cams)—Models 1949 and 6149

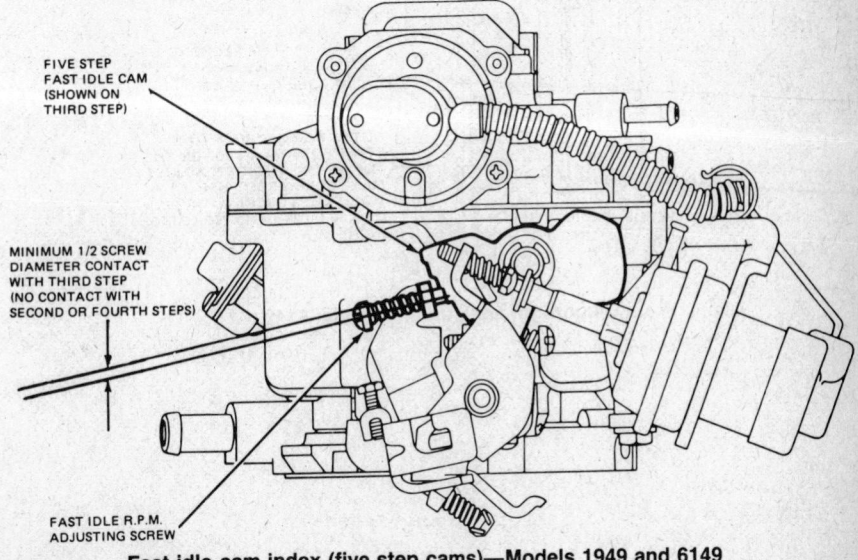

Fast idle cam index (five step cams)—Models 1949 and 6149

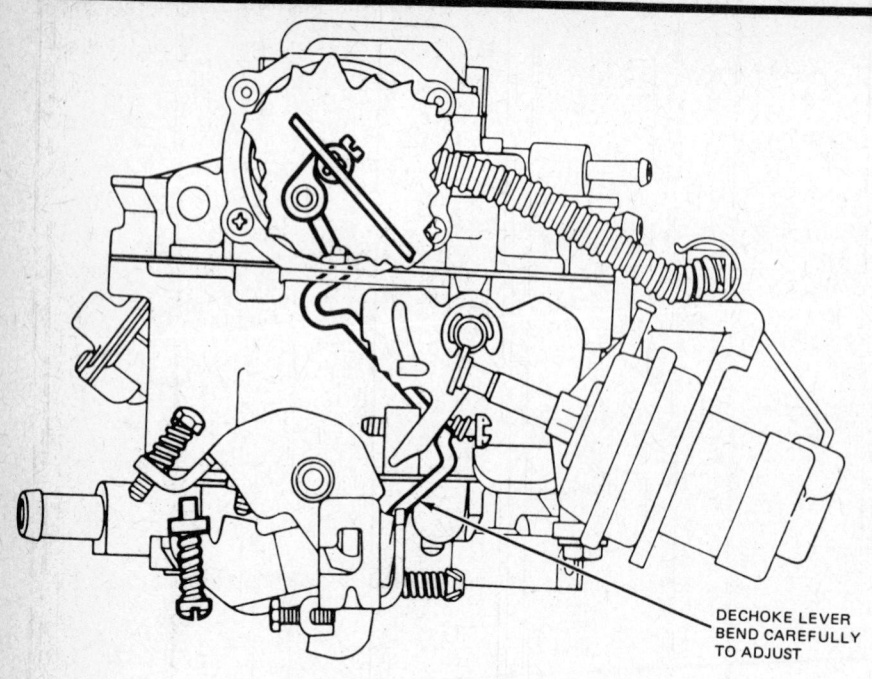

Dechoke adjustment—Models 1949 and 6149

DECHOKE LEVER
BEND CAREFULLY
TO ADJUST

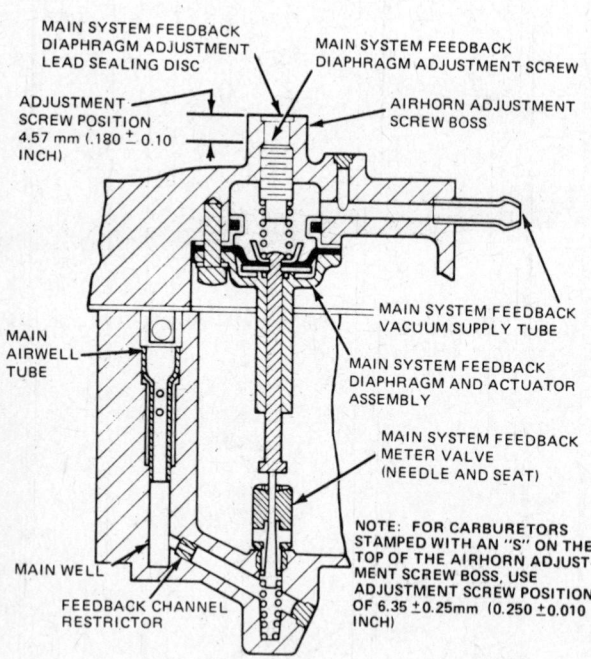

MAIN SYSTEM FEEDBACK
DIAPHRAGM ADJUSTMENT
LEAD SEALING DISC

MAIN SYSTEM FEEDBACK
DIAPHRAGM ADJUSTMENT SCREW

ADJUSTMENT
SCREW POSITION
4.57 mm (.180 ± 0.10
INCH)

AIRHORN ADJUSTMENT
SCREW BOSS

MAIN
AIRWELL
TUBE

MAIN SYSTEM FEEDBACK
VACUUM SUPPLY TUBE

MAIN SYSTEM FEEDBACK
DIAPHRAGM AND ACTUATOR
ASSEMBLY

MAIN SYSTEM FEEDBACK
METER VALVE
(NEEDLE AND SEAT)

MAIN WELL

FEEDBACK CHANNEL
RESTRICTOR

NOTE: FOR CARBURETORS
STAMPED WITH AN "S" ON THE
TOP OF THE AIRHORN ADJUST-
MENT SCREW BOSS, USE
ADJUSTMENT SCREW POSITION
OF 6.35 ± 0.25mm (0.250 ± 0.010
INCH)

Diaphragm adjustment—Model 6149

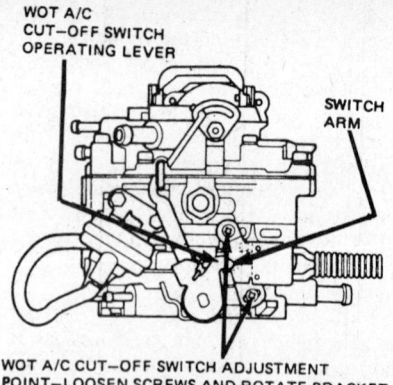

WOT A/C
CUT-OFF SWITCH
OPERATING LEVER

SWITCH
ARM

WOT A/C CUT-OFF SWITCH ADJUSTMENT
POINT—LOOSEN SCREWS AND ROTATE BRACKET

**WOT A/C cut-off switch adjustment
screws—Model 1949**

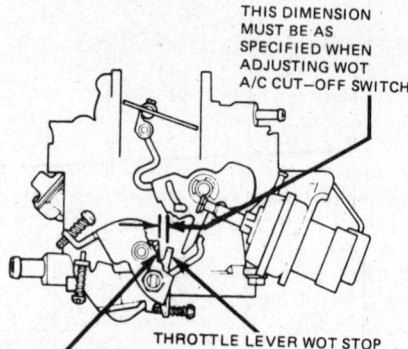

THIS DIMENSION
MUST BE AS
SPECIFIED WHEN
ADJUSTING WOT
A/C CUT—OFF SWITCH

THROTTLE LEVER WOT STOP

MAINBODY CASTING
WOT STOP BOSS

**WOT A/C cut-off switch adjustment
(clearance)—Model 1949**

1. Disconnect the wiring harness at the switch connector.

2. Connect a 12 volt DC power supply and test lamp. With the throttle at curb idle, TSP Off idle or fast idle position, the test light must be On. If the test lamp does not light, replace the switch assembly.

3. Rotate the throttle to the wide-open position. The test lamp must go Off, indicating an open circuit.

4. If the lamp remains On, insert a 0.165 in. drill or gauge between the throttle lever WOT stop and the WOT stop boss on the carburetor main body casting. Hold the throttle open as far as possible against the gauge. Loosen the two switch mounting screws sufficiently to allow the switch to pivot. Rotate the switch assembly so the test lamp just goes out with the throttle held in the above referenced position. If the lamp does not go Off within the allowable adjustment rotation, replace the switch. If the lamp goes out, tighten the two switch bracket-to-carburetor screws to 45 inch lbs. (5 Nm) and remove drill or gauge and repeat Step 3.

MODEL 1949
Ford Motor Co.

Year	Carb. Iden.	Dry Float Level (in.)	Pump Hole Setting	Choke Plate Pulldown (in.)	Fast Idle Cam Linkage (in.)	Dechoke (in.)	Choke Setting
'84	E43E-ADA	①	#2	.080–.120	.020–.030	.180–.220	2 Rich
	E43E-AEA	①	#2	.080–.120	.020–.030	.180–.220	2 Rich
	E43E-ABA	①	#2	.090–.130	.020–.030	.180–.220	1 Rich
	E43E-ABB	①	#2	.090–.130	.020–.030	.180–.220	1 Rich
	E43E-ACA	①	#2	.090–.130	.020–.030	.180–.220	1 Rich
	E43E-ACB	①	#2	.090–.130	.020–.030	.180–.220	1 Rich

①Both float pontoons at outboard edge flush with surface of main body casting (without gasket).

MODEL 6149–FB
Ford Motor Co.

Year	Carb. Iden.	Dry Float Level (in.)	Pump Hole Setting	Choke Plate Pulldown (in.)	Fast Idle Cam Linkage (in.)	Dechoke (in.)	Choke Setting
'84	E43E-VA	①	#2	.095–.135	.020–.030	.180–.220	2 Rich
	E43E-ZA	①	#2	.095–.135	.020–.030	.180–.220	2 Rich

①Both float pontoons at outboard edge flush with surface of main body casting (without gasket).

Model 2245

The model 2245 carburetor is a two barrel unit used on 1978–79 Chrysler products with 360 or 400 cubic inch engines.

FLOAT ADJUSTMENT

1. Invert the air horn so that the weight of the float is forcing the metering needle against its seat.

2. Measure the distance between the top of the float and the float stop. The clearance should be the same as given in the Specifications chart. Make certain that the gauge is level when making the measurement.

3. If adjustment is necessary, bend the float adjusting tab toward or away from the needle until the correct clearance is obtained. A narrow-bladed screwdriver may be used to bend the tab.

4. Check the float drop by holding the air horn upright. The bottom edge of the float should be parallel to the underside of the air horn. If an adjustment is necessary, bend the tang on the float arm.

FAST IDLE CAM POSITION ADJUSTMENT

1. Position the fast idle speed adjusting screw on the second highest notch on the fast idle cam. Move the choke valve toward the closed position by applying light pressure on the choke shaft lever.

2. Insert the correct gauge (see Specifications chart) between the top of the choke valve and the wall of the air horn. An adjustment will be necessary if there is not a

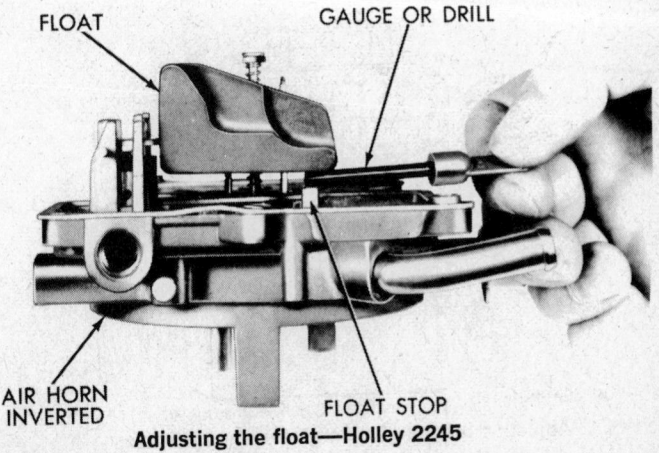

FLOAT   GAUGE OR DRILL

AIR HORN INVERTED   FLOAT STOP

Adjusting the float—Holley 2245

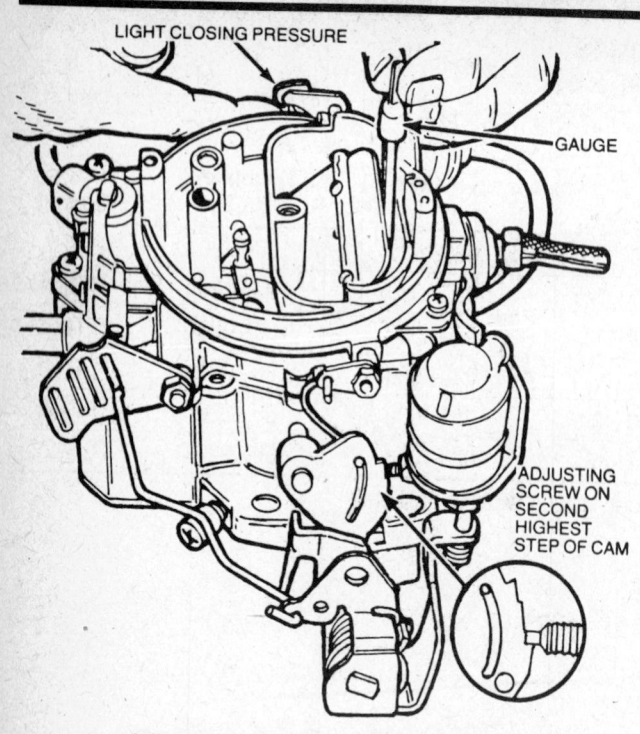

Adjusting the fast idle cam—Holley 2245

Adjusting the choke unloader—Holley 2245

slight drag when the gauge is removed.

3. If an adjustment is necessary, bend the fast idle connector rod at the angle.

VACUUM KICK ADJUSTMENT

1. The adjustment must be made with some type of vacuum source. If the adjustment is made with the engine running, disconnect the fast idle linkage to allow the choke to close to the kick position with the engine at curb idle. If an auxiliary vacuum source is to be used, open the throttle valves and move the choke to the closed position. Release the throttle first and then the choke.

2. If an auxiliary vacuum source is used, disconnect the vacuum hose from the carburetor and connect it to the hose from the vacuum supply with a small length of extra hose. Apply a vacuum of 15 or more in. of mercury.

3. Insert the correct gauge (see Spec-

ifications chart) between the top of the choke valve and the wall of the air horn. Apply pressure to the lever to which the choke rod attaches without distorting the diaphragm link. The cylindrical stem of the diaphragm will extend as the internal spring is compressed. This spring must be fully compressed for proper measurement of the vacuum kick adjustment.

4. If a slight drag is not felt when the gauge is removed, adjustment is necessary. Adjust the diaphragm link to obtain the correct choke valve opening. Adjustments can be made by carefully opening or closing the U-bend in the link.

CAUTION
Do not twist or bend the diaphragm.

5. Connect the vacuum hose to the correct carburetor fitting. Replace the linkage.

6. Make the following check. With vacuum applied to the diaphragm, the choke valve should move freely between open and closed positions. If the movement is not

free, examine the linkage for misalignment or interference caused by the bending operation.

CHOKE UNLOADER (WIDE OPEN KICK) ADJUSTMENT

1. Place the throttle valves in the wide-open position and insert the proper gauge (see Specifications chart) between the upper edge of the choke valve and the inner wall of the air horn.

2. While holding pressure on the choke lever, a slight drag should be felt as the gauge is removed.

3. If an adjustment is necessary, bend the unloader tang on the throttle lever until the correct opening has been obtained.

ACCELERATOR PUMP ADJUSTMENT

1. Make sure that the pump connector rod is in the first slot next to the retaining nut of the pump arm on 360 engines, and in the second slot for the 400.

2. Measure the drop of the pump plunger between curb idle and wide open throttle.

3. Adjust the travel by bending the operating rod.

BOWL VENT VALVE CLEARANCE

1. With the throttle valves set at curb idle, insert the specified gauge between the bowl vent valve plunger stem and the operating rod.

2. If the gauge does not fit, bend the tang on the pump lever until the correct clearance has been obtained.

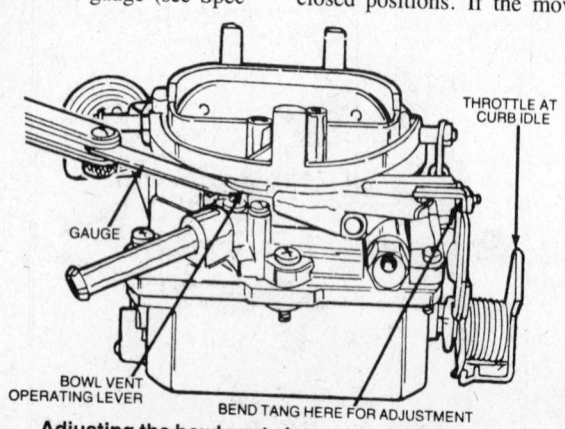

Adjusting the bowl vent clearance—Holley 2245

MODEL 2245
Chrysler Corporation

Year	Carb.★ Part No.	Float Level (in.)	Accelerator Pump Adjustment (in.)	Bowl Vent Clearance (in.)	Fast Idle (rpm)	Choke Unloader Clearance (in.)	Vacuum Kick (in.)	Fast Idle Cam Position (in.)	Choke
'78	R-7991-A	.188	.265	.025	1600	.170	.110	.110	Fixed
	R-8326-A	.188	.265	.025	1600	.170	.110	.110	Fixed
'79	R-8450-A	.188	.266	.025	1600	.170	.110	.110	Fixed
	R-8774-A	.188	.266	.025	1600	.170	.110	.110	Fixed

★ Located on a tag attached to the carburetor.

Model 2280

The model 2280 is a two barrel unit used on 1978–79 Chrysler 318 cid engines with automatic transmission in all states except California.

FLOAT ADJUSTMENT

1. Remove the carburetor air horn.
2. Invert the carburetor body, taking care to catch the pump intake check ball, so that the weight of the floats only is forcing the needle against the seat. Hold a finger against the hinge pin retainer to fully seat the float in the float pin cradle.
3. Lay a straight edge across the float bowl. The toe of each float should be 5/16 in. from the straight-edge. If necessary, bend the float tang to adjust.

ACCELERATOR PUMP STROKE MEASUREMENT

1. Remove the bowl vent cover plate and vent valve lever spring. Take care to avoid loosening the vent valve retainer.
2. Make sure that the accelerator pump connector rod is in the inner hole of pump operating lever and the throttle is at curb idle.
3. Place a straight edge on the bowl vent cover surface of the air horn, over the accelerator pump lever.
4. The lever surface should be flush with the air horn. If not, adjust it by bending the pump connector rod at the 90 degree bend.

NOTE: If this adjustment is changed, both the bowl vent and the mechanical power valve adjustments must be reset.

CHOKE UNLOADER ADJUSTMENT

1. Hold the throttle valves in the wide open position.
2. Lightly press a finger against the control lever to move the choke valve toward the closed position.
3. Insert a 0.310 inch gauge between the top of the choke valve and the air horn wall.
4. Adjust, if necessary, by bending the tang on the accelerator pump lever.

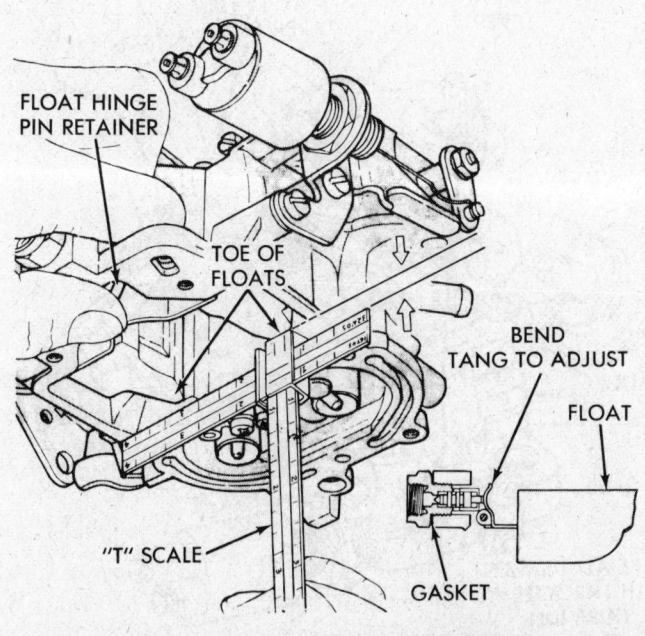

Float adjustment (© Chrysler Corp.)

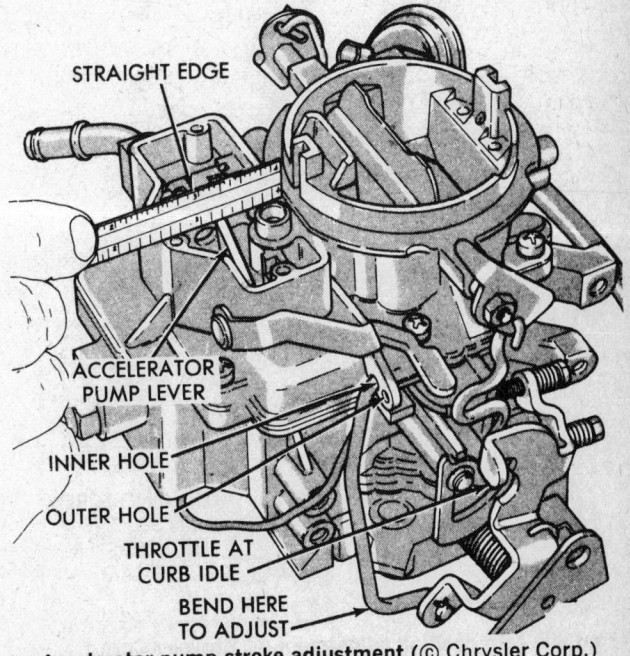

Accelerator pump stroke adjustment (© Chrysler Corp.)

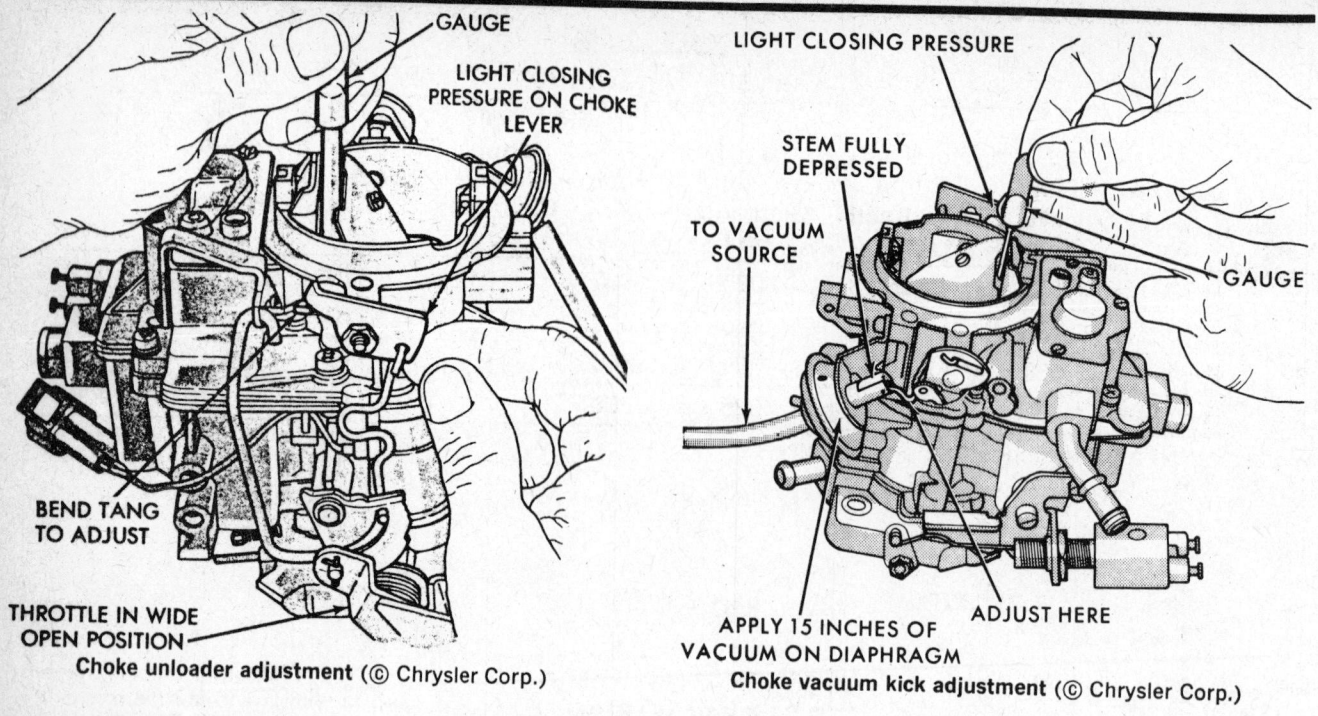

Choke unloader adjustment (© Chrysler Corp.)

Choke vacuum kick adjustment (© Chrysler Corp.)

CHOKE VACUUM KICK ADJUSTMENT

1. Open the throttle, close the choke, then close the throttle to trap the fast idle cam at the closed choke position.
2. Disconnect the vacuum hose from the carburetor and connect it to an auxiliary vacuum source with a length of hose. Apply at least 15 in. Hg.
3. Completely compress the choke lever spring in the diaphragm stem without distorting the linkage.
4. Insert a 0.150 inch gauge between the top of the choke valve and the air horn wall.
5. Adjust by bending the diaphragm link. Check for free movement. Replace the vacuum hose.

FAST IDLE CAM POSITION ADJUSTMENT

1. Position the adjusting screw on the second highest step of the fast idle cam.
2. Move the choke towards the closed position with light finger pressure.

3. Insert a 0.070 inch gauge between the choke valve and the air horn wall.
4. Adjust by opening or closing the U-bend in the fast idle connector link.

BOWL VENT VALVE ADJUSTMENT

1. Remove the bowl vent cover and vent valve lever spring. Take care to avoid disturbing the lever retainer.
2. With the throttle at curb idle, press firmly down on the vent valve lever where the spring seats.

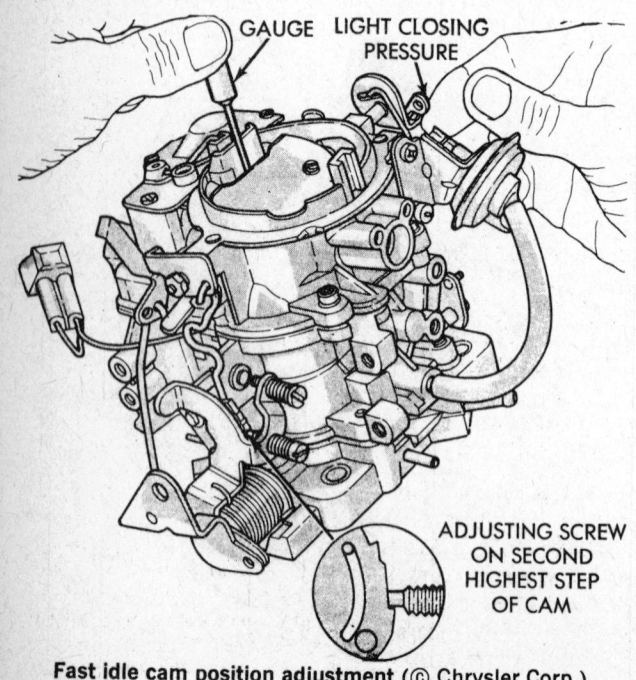

Fast idle cam position adjustment (© Chrysler Corp.)

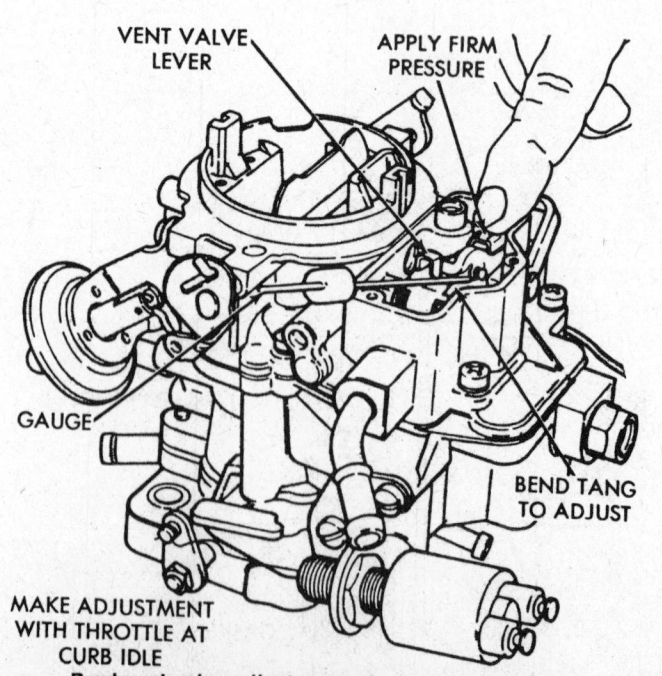

Bowl vent valve adjustment (© Chrysler Corp.)

3. Insert a 0.030 inch gauge between the vent valve tang and the lever.

4. Adjust by bending the end of the vent valve lever up or down.

MECHANICAL POWER VALVE ADJUSTMENT

1. Remove the bowl vent cover plate, vent valve lever, spring and retainer. Remove the lever pivot pin.

2. Hold the throttle in the wide open position.

3. Using a 5/64 in. Allen wrench, press the mechanical power valve adjustment screw down, and release it to determine if clearance exists. Turn the screw clockwise until clear is zero.

4. Adjust by turning the screw one turn counterclockwise.

5. Install all parts.

THROTTLE POSITION TRANSDUCER ADJUSTMENT

1. Disconnect the wire from the unit.

2. Loosen the locknut.

3. Insert an 11/16 in. gauge between the outer portion of the transducer and the transducer mounting bracket.

4. Adjust the transducer by turning it.

5. Tighten the locknut.

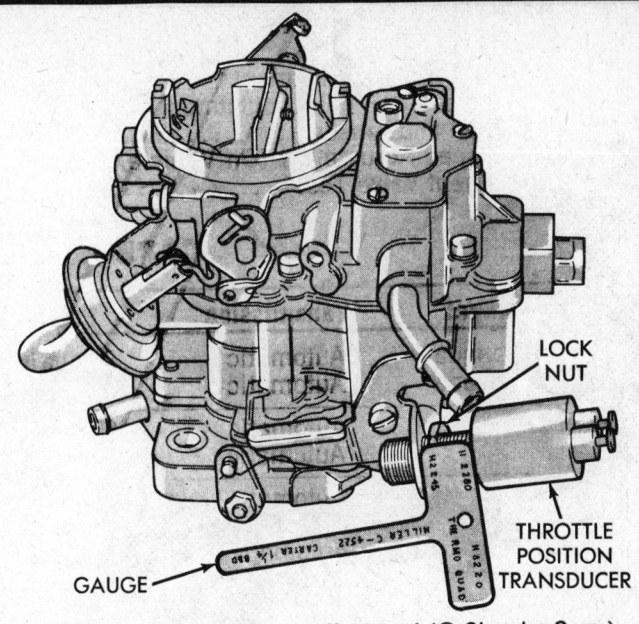

Throttle position transducer adjustment (© Chrysler Corp.)

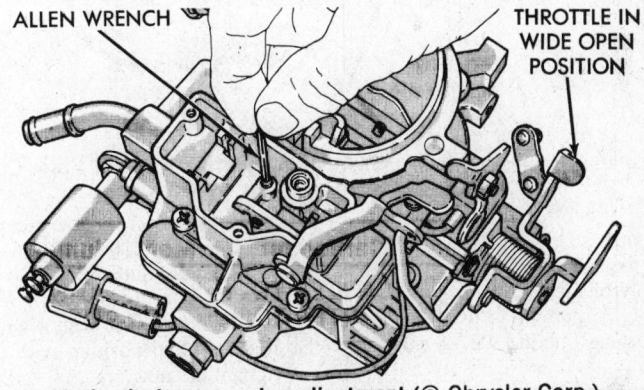

Mechanical power valve adjustment (© Chrysler Corp.)

MODEL 2280
Chrysler Corporation

Year	Carb. Part No.	Float Level (in.)	Accelerator Pump Adjustment (in.)	Bowl Vent Clearance (in.)	Fast Idle (rpm)	Choke Unloader Clearance (in.)	Vacuum Kick (in.)	Fast Idle Cam Position (in.)	Choke
'78	R-7990-A	.313	Flush	.030	1600	.310	.150	.070	Fixed
'79	R-8448-A	.313	Flush	.030	1600	.310	.150	.070	Fixed

Model 4180–C

The Holley 4180–C 4–V carburetor is a downdraft, two-stage carburetor. It can be considered as two dual carburetors; one supplying a fuel/air mixture throughout the entire range of engine operation (primary stage), and the other functioning only when a greater quantity of fuel/air mixture is required (secondary stage).

The **primary stage** (front section of the carburetor contains a fuel bowl, metering block, and an accelerating pump assembly. The primary barrels each contain a primary and booster venturi, main fuel discharge nozzle, throttle plate, and idle fuel passage. The Model 4180–C uses an electric choke with hot air assist.

The **secondary stage**, (rear section) of the carburetor contains a fuel bowl, metering body, and secondary throttle operating diaphragm assembly. Each secondary barrel contains a primary and booster venturi, idle fuel passages, main secondary fuel discharge nozzle, throttle plate, and a transfer system fuel passage from the primary fuel bowl.

U117

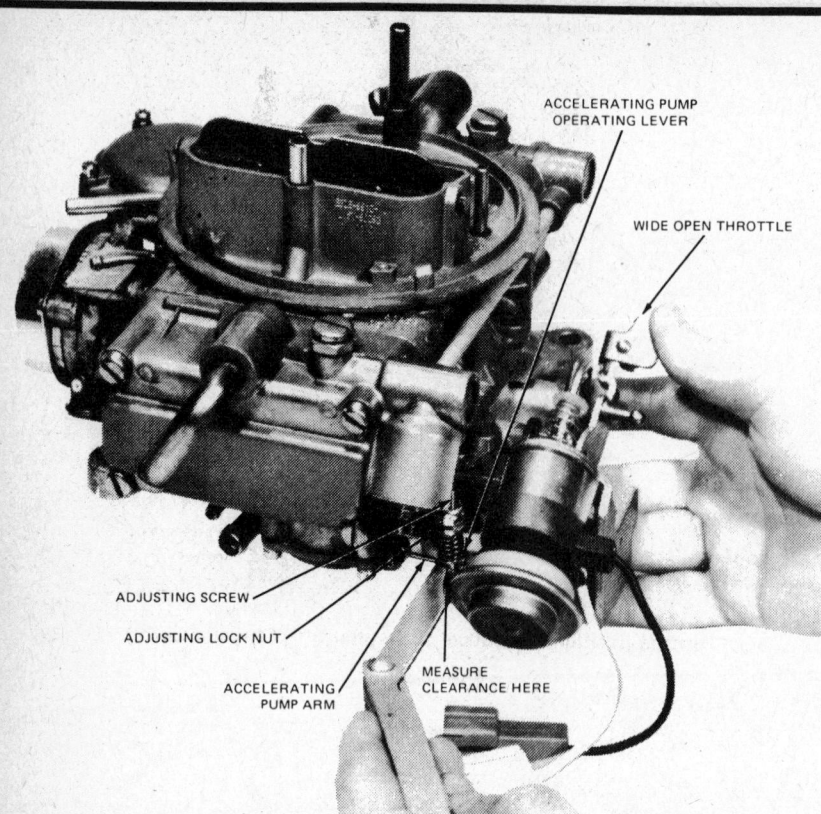

Accelerator pump lever adjustment—Holley 4180C (© Ford Motor Co.)

A fuel inlet system for both the primary and the secondary stages for the carburetor provides the fuel metering systems with a constant supply of fuel.

The 4180–C carburetor is used on the 1983 Ford Mustang with the 302 V8 engine.

ACCELERATING PUMP LEVER ADJUSTMENT

1. Using a feeler gauge and with the throttle plates (primary throttle plates) in the wide open position, there should be the specified clearance between the accelerating pump operating lever adjustment screw head and the pump arm when the pump arm is depressed manually.

2. If adjustment is required, loosen and then hold the lock screw and turn the ad-

justing nut in to increase the clearance and out to decrease the clearance. One half turn of the adjusting nut is equal to approximately 0.015 in. (0.381mm). When the proper adjustment has been obtained hold the adjustment in position with a wrench and tighten the nut.

FUEL LEVEL FLOAT ADJUSTMENT—DRY

The dry float adjustment is a preliminary fuel level adjustment only. The final adjustment ("Fuel Level Adjustment—Wet") must be performed after the carburetor is installed on the engine.

With the fuel bowls and float assemblies removed, adjust the floats so that the floats

are parallel to the fuel bowls, with the top of the fuel bowls inverted.

FUEL LEVEL ADJUSTMENT—WET

The fuel pump pressure and volume must be to specifications prior to performing the following adjustments.

1. Operate the engine to normalize engine temperatures and place the vehicle on a flat surface, as near level as possible. Remove the air cleaner, if it was not previously removed.

2. Run engine at 1000 rpm for about 30 seconds to stabilize fuel level.

3. Stop engine and remove sight plug on side of primary carburetor bowl.

4. Check fuel level. It should be at bottom of sight plug hole. If fuel spills out when sight plug is removed, lower fuel level. If fuel level is below sight plug hole, raise fuel level.

—— CAUTION ——
Do not loosen lock screw or nut or attempt to adjust fuel level with sight plug removed or engine running because fuel may spray out creating a fire hazard.

5. Adjust the front level as necessary by loosening the lock screw, and turning the adjusting nut clockwise to **lower** fuel level or counterclockwise to **raise** fuel level. (⅙ turn adjusting nut will change fuel level approximately 1/32 inch). Tighten lock screw and install sight plug, using old gasket. Start engine and run at 1000 rpm for about 30 seconds to stabilize fuel level.

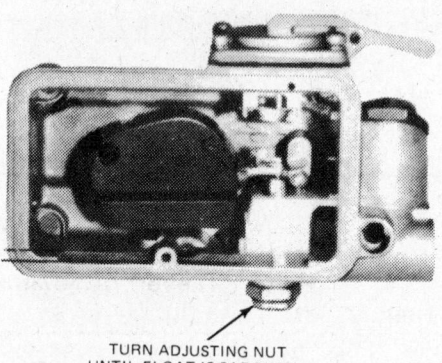

TURN ADJUSTING NUT
UNTIL FLOAT IS PARALLEL
WITH TOP OF BOWL
(HOLDING BOWL UPSIDE DOWN)

Dry float adjustment—Holley 4180C (© Ford Motor Co.)

6. Stop engine, remove sight plug and check fuel level. Repeat Step 5 until fuel level is at bottom of sight plug hole. When fuel level is at bottom of sight plug hole, install sight plug using new adjusting plug gasket.

7. Repeat Steps 3–6 for secondary fuel bowl.

NOTE: The secondary throttle must be used to stabilize the fuel level in the secondary fuel bowl.

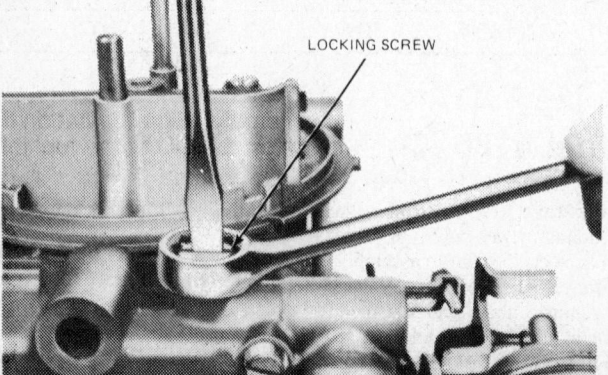

Fuel level adjustment—wet—Holley 4180C (© Ford Motor Co.)

SECONDARY THROTTLE PLATE ADJUSTMENT

1. With carburetor off the engine, hold the secondary throttle plates closed.

2. Turn the secondary throttle shaft lever adjusting screw (stop screw) out (counterclockwise) until the secondary throttle plates seat in the throttle bores.

3. Turn the screw in clockwise until the screw JUST contacts the secondary lever, then turn screw in (clockwise) ¼ turn.

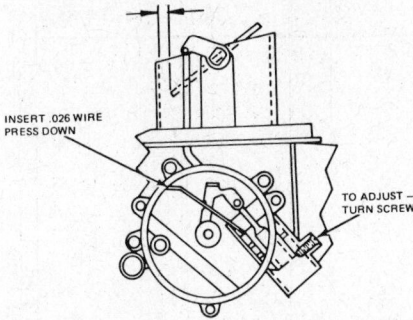

Choke pulldown adjustment—Holley 4180C (© Ford Motor Co.)

CHOKE PULLDOWN ADJUSTMENT

1. Remove the choke thermostat housing, gasket and retainer. See the choke cap removal and installation procedure below.

2. Insert a piece of wire into the choke piston bore to move the piston down against the stop screw. Maintain light closing pressure on the choke plate and measure the gap between the lower edge of the choke plate and the air horn wall.

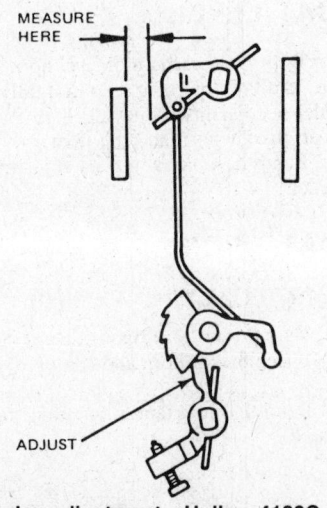

Dechoke adjustment—Holley 4180C (© Ford Motor Co.)

3. To adjust, remove the putty covering the adjustment screw and turn the screw clockwise to decrease or counter-clockwise to increase the gap setting. Take care to close the choke plate during screw adjustment. Screw may be turned into side of piston, resulting in damage to piston.

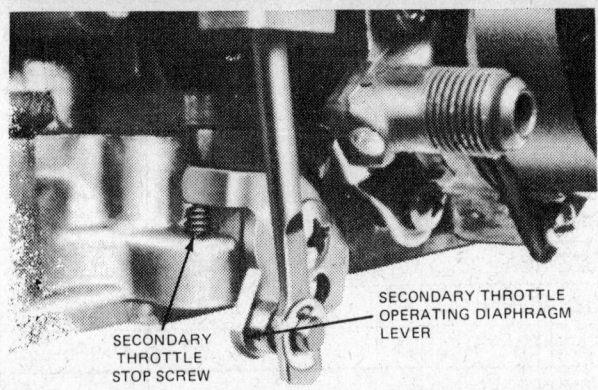

Secondary throttle plate adjustment—Holley 4180C (© Ford Motor Co.)

4. Reinstall the choke thermostatic housing, gasket, and retainer.

DECHOKE ADJUSTMENT

1. Hold the throttle in the wide open position.

2. Apply light closing pressure to the choke plate and measure the gap between the lower edge of the choke plate and the air horn wall.

3. To adjust, bend the pawl on the fast idle lever.

CHOKE THERMOSTATIC SPRING HOUSING— (CHOKE CAP)

Removal

1. Remove the carburetor from vehicle.

2. Using a hacksaw carefully cut a slot in the head of the breakaway screw. Using a proper sized straight blade screw driver, remove the breakaway screw in the conventional manner.

3. Repeat Step 2 for the remaining breakaway screw.

4. Remove the remaining standard screw. Remove the retaining ring, choke cap and gasket

Installation

1. Install the choke cap gasket. Install the choke cap by engaging the bimetal loop on the choke thermostatic lever.

2. Install the retaining ring. Loosely install two new breakaway screws and one standard screw.

3. Align the choke cap to the proper index mark.

4. Tighten the breakaway screws until the heads break off. Tighten the remaining screw to 16–18 inch lbs. (1.8–2.0 Nm).

5. Install carburetor on the vehicle.

FAST IDLE CAM SET

1. Rotate the choke cap 45-degrees counterclockwise (rich) to close the choke plate. Tighten the attaching screw at the time.

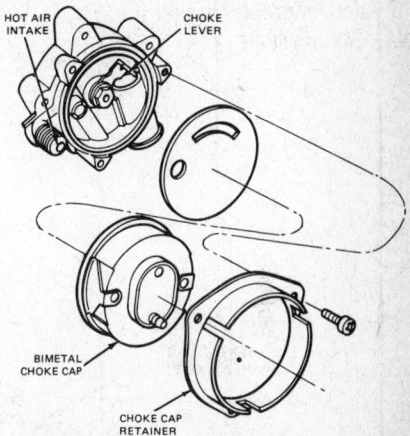

Automatic choke—Holley 4180C (© Ford Motor Co.)

2. Open and close the throttle to place the fast idle screw on the top step of the cam.

3. Place a pulldown gauge between the lower edge of the choke plate and the air horn wall, then open and close the throttle to allow the fast idle cam to drop.

4. Press upward on the fast idle cam. There should be little or no movement indicating that the fast idle screw is on the kickdown (2nd) step of the cam, against the first step.

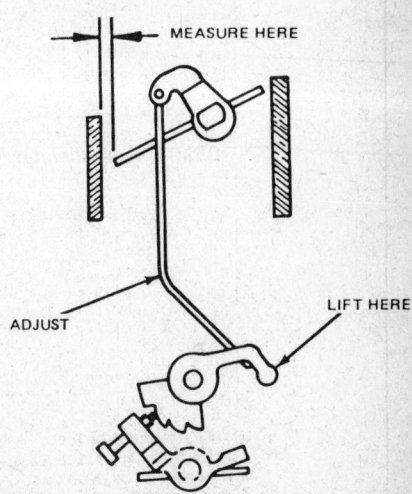

Fast idle cam set—Holley 4180C (© Ford Motor Co.)

MODEL 4180C
Ford Motor Company

Year	(9510)* Carburetor Identification	Dry Float Level (in.)	Wet Float Level (in.)	Pump Setting Hole	Choke Plate Pulldown (in.)	Fast Idle Cam Linkage Clearance (in.)	Fast Idle (rpm)	Dechoke (in)	Choke Setting
'83	E3ZE-AUA	②	①	#1	.195–.215	NA	③	.300	3 Rich
	E3ZE-BGA	②	①	#1	.195–.215	NA	③	.300	3 Rich
'84	E4ZE-SA	②	①	#1	.195–.215	NA	③	.300	1 Lean

① Bottom of sight plug
② See text
③ See Underhood sticker
NA—not available

Model 5210-C

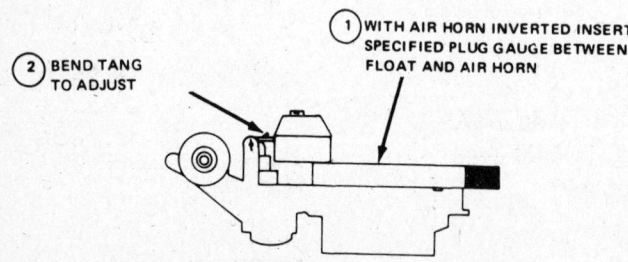

5210-C Float level adjustment (© G.M. Corp.)

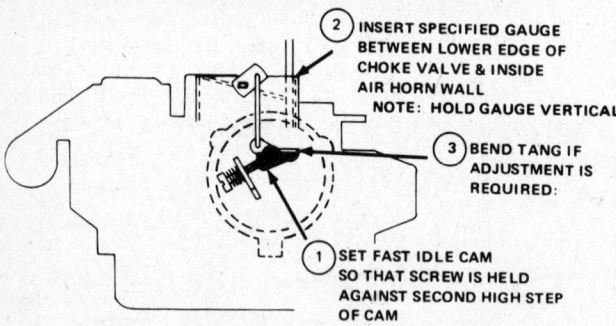

5210-C Fast idle cam adjustment (© G.M. Corp.)

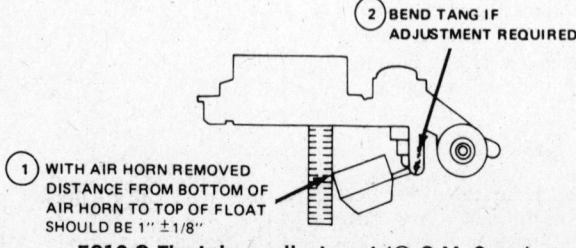

5210-C Float drop adjustment (© G.M. Corp.)

The Holley 5210-C is a progressive two barrel carburetor with an automatic choke system which is activated by a water heated thermostatic coil. An electrically heated choke is used on most later models. It also has an exhaust gas recirculation system with the valve located in the intake manifold. It is used on 1978 General Motors four cylinder engines, 1979–80 Chevettes (U.S.A.), 1979–83 Chevettes (Canada) and 1978–79 AMC four cylinder engines.

FLOAT LEVEL

1. With the carburetor air horn inverted, and the float tang resting lightly on the inlet needle, insert the specified gauge between the air horn and the float.
2. Bend the float tang if an adjustment is needed.

FLOAT DROP

GM (1978 ONLY)

1. With the air horn right side up, measure between the air horn and the top of the float.
2. Bend the float tang if an adjustment is needed.

FAST IDLE CAM ADJUSTMENT

1. Place the fast idle screw on the second step of the fast idle cam and against the shoulder of the high step.
2. Place the specified drill or gauge on the down side of the choke plate.
3. To adjust, bend the choke lever tang.

CHOKE PLATE PULLDOWN (VACUUM BREAK) ADJUSTMENT

Through 1979

1. Remove the three hex headed screws and ring which retain the choke cover.

———— **CAUTION** ————

Do not remove the choke water housing screw if adjusting on the car. Pull the choke water housing and bimetal cover assembly back out of the way.

2. Push the diaphragm shaft against the stop. Push the coil lever clockwise.
3. Insert the specified size gauge on the down side of the primary choke plate.
4. Take the slack out of the linkage and turn the adjusting screw with a 5/22 in. Allen wrench.

1980–83

1. Attach a hand vacuum pump to the vacuum break diaphragm; apply vacuum and seat the diaphragm.
2. Push the fast idle cam lever down to close the choke plate.
3. Take any slack out of the linkage in the open choke position.
4. Insert the specified gauge between the lower edge of the choke plate and the air horn wall.
5. If the clearance is incorrect, turn the vacuum break adjusting screw, located in the break housing, to adjust.

SECONDARY VACUUM BREAK ADJUSTMENT

GM (1978 ONLY)

1. Remove the three screws and the choke coil assembly.
2. Place the cam follower on the highest step of the fast idle cam.
3. Seat the diaphragm by applying an outside source of vacuum.
4. Push the inside choke coil lever clockwise to close the choke valve.
5. Place a gauge of the size specified in the chart between the lower edge of choke valve and the air horn wall.
6. Bend the vacuum break rod to adjust.
7. Replace and adjust the choke.

CHOKE UNLOADER ADJUSTMENT

1. Position the throttle lever at the wide open position.
2. Insert a gauge of the size specified in the chart between the lower edge of the choke valve and the air horn wall.
3. Bend the unloader tang for adjustment.

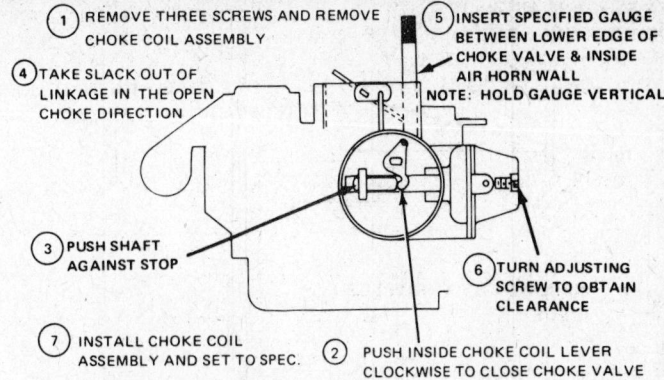

① REMOVE THREE SCREWS AND REMOVE CHOKE COIL ASSEMBLY

④ TAKE SLACK OUT OF LINKAGE IN THE OPEN CHOKE DIRECTION

③ PUSH SHAFT AGAINST STOP

⑦ INSTALL CHOKE COIL ASSEMBLY AND SET TO SPEC.

⑤ INSERT SPECIFIED GAUGE BETWEEN LOWER EDGE OF CHOKE VALVE & INSIDE AIR HORN WALL NOTE: HOLD GAUGE VERTICAL

⑥ TURN ADJUSTING SCREW TO OBTAIN CLEARANCE

② PUSH INSIDE CHOKE COIL LEVER CLOCKWISE TO CLOSE CHOKE VALVE

5210-C Vacuum break (choke plate pulldown) adjustment

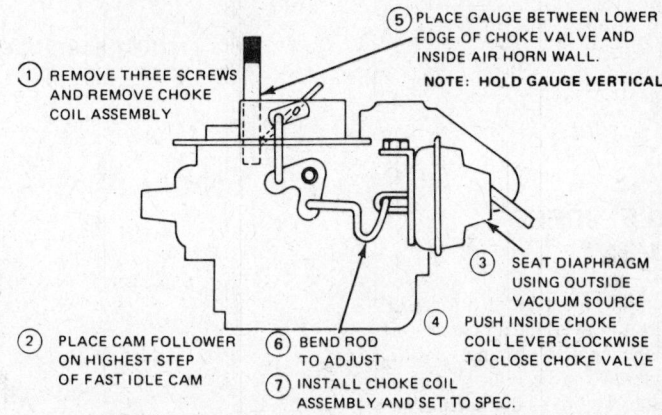

⑤ PLACE GAUGE BETWEEN LOWER EDGE OF CHOKE VALVE AND INSIDE AIR HORN WALL. NOTE: HOLD GAUGE VERTICAL

① REMOVE THREE SCREWS AND REMOVE CHOKE COIL ASSEMBLY

③ SEAT DIAPHRAGM USING OUTSIDE VACUUM SOURCE

④ PUSH INSIDE CHOKE COIL LEVER CLOCKWISE TO CLOSE CHOKE VALVE

② PLACE CAM FOLLOWER ON HIGHEST STEP OF FAST IDLE CAM

⑥ BEND ROD TO ADJUST

⑦ INSTALL CHOKE COIL ASSEMBLY AND SET TO SPEC.

5210-C Secondary vacuum break adjustment (© G.M. Corp.)

SECONDARY THROTTLE STOP SCREW ADJUSTMENT

1. Back off the screw until it doesn't touch the throttle lever.
2. Turn the screw in until it touches the secondary throttle lever. Turn it in ¼ turn more.

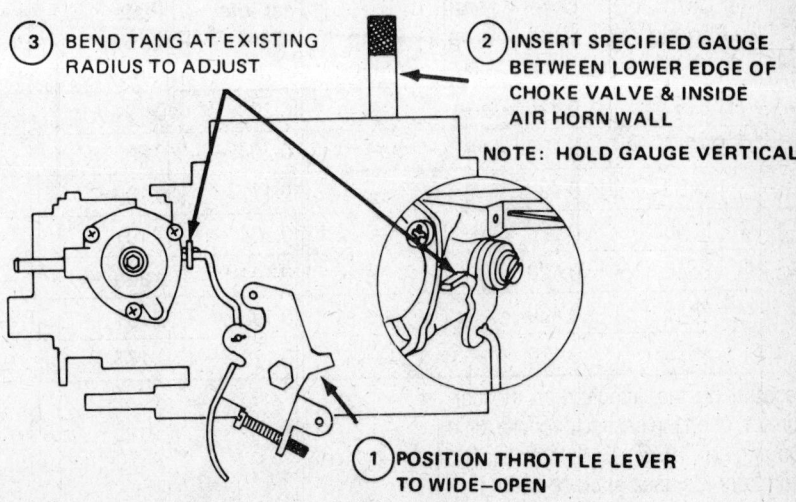

③ BEND TANG AT EXISTING RADIUS TO ADJUST

② INSERT SPECIFIED GAUGE BETWEEN LOWER EDGE OF CHOKE VALVE & INSIDE AIR HORN WALL NOTE: HOLD GAUGE VERTICAL

① POSITION THROTTLE LEVER TO WIDE–OPEN

5210-C Choke unloader adjustment (© G.M. Corp.)

② TURN SCREW IN UNTIL IT TOUCHES SECONDARY THROTTLE LEVER & THEN TURN SCREW AN ADDITIONAL 1/4 TURN

① BACK OFF SCREW UNTIL IT DOES NOT TOUCH THROTTLE LEVER

SECONDARY THROTTLE LEVER

5210-C Secondary throttle stop screw adjustment (© G.M. Corp.)

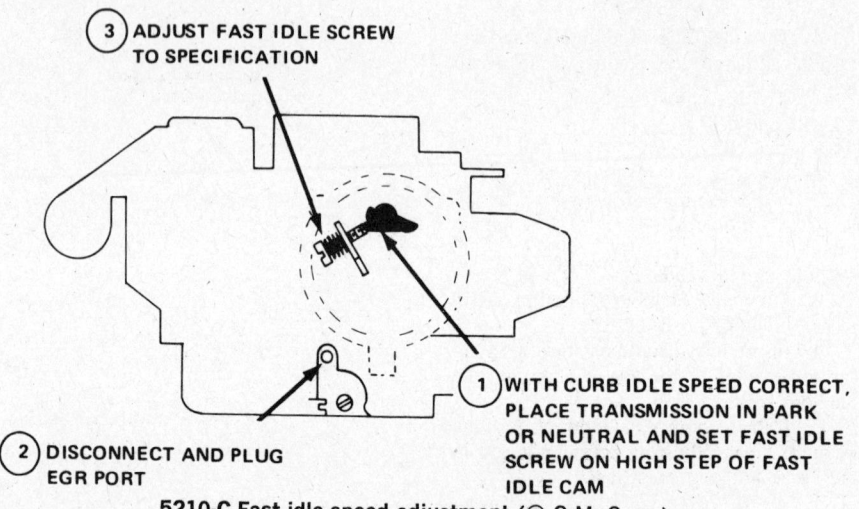

③ ADJUST FAST IDLE SCREW TO SPECIFICATION

FAST IDLE SPEED ADJUSTMENT

1. The engine must be at normal operating temperature with the air cleaner off.

2. With the engine running, position the fast idle screw on the high step of the cam for GM cars, or on the second step against the shoulder of the high step for AMC cars. Plug the EGR Port on the carburetor.

3. Adjust the speed by turning the fast idle screw.

② DISCONNECT AND PLUG EGR PORT

① WITH CURB IDLE SPEED CORRECT, PLACE TRANSMISSION IN PARK OR NEUTRAL AND SET FAST IDLE SCREW ON HIGH STEP OF FAST IDLE CAM

5210-C Fast idle speed adjustment (© G.M. Corp.)

MODEL 5210-C
AMC OHC 4 Cylinder

Year	Carb. Part No. ① ②	Float Level (Dry) (in.)	Float Drop (in.)	Pump Position	Fast Idle Cam (in.)	Choke Plate Pulldown* (in.)	Secondary Vacuum Break (in.)	Fast Idle Setting (rpm)	Choke Unloader (in.)	Choke Setting
'78	8163	0.420	—	—	0.193	0.191	—	1800	0.300	1 NR
	8164	0.420	—	—	0.204	0.202	—	1800	0.300	1 NR
	8165	0.420	—	—	0.177	0.180	—	1800	0.300	Index
'79	8548	0.420	—	—	0.204	0.191	—	1800	0.300	1 Rich
	8549	0.420	—	—	0.191	0.266	—	1800	0.300	1 Rich
	7846	0.420	—	—	0.193	0.191	—	1800	0.300	1 Rich
	8675	0.420	—	—	0.173	0.177	—	1800	0.300	Index

① Located on tag attached to the carburetor, or on the casting or choke plate

② Beginning 1976, GM identification numbers are used in place of the Holley numbers

MODEL 5210-C
Chevrolet Monza, Oldsmobile Starfire, Pontiac Sunbird

Year	Carb. Part No. ①	Float Level (Dry) (in.)	Float Drop (in.)	Pump Position	Fast Idle Cam (in.)	Choke Plate Pulldown* (in.)	Secondary Vacuum Break (in.)	Fast Idle Setting (rpm)	Choke Unloader (in.)	Choke Setting
'77	458102, 458104	0.420	1	③	0.085	0.250	0.400	2500	0.350	3 Rich
	458103, 458105	0.420	1	③	0.120	0.250	0.400	2500	0.350	3 Rich
	458106, 458107, 458108, 458109	0.420	1	③	0.120	0.275	0.400	2500	0.400	3 Rich
	458110, 458112	0.420	1	③	0.120	0.300	0.400	2500	0.400	3 Rich
'78	see notes	0.520	1	—	0.150	②	—	③	0.350	④

① Located on tag attached to the carburetor, or on the casting or choke plate
② Part #10001047, 10001049: .325
   #10004048, 10004049: .300
③ Part #10001047, 10001049: 2200
   #10004048, 10004049: 2400
④ Part #10001047, 10001049: 1 Rich
   #10004048, 10004049: 2 Rich

MODEL 5210-C
Chevrolet Chevette

Year	Carb. Part No. ① ②	Float Level (Dry) (in.)	Fast Idle Cam (in.)	Choke Plate Pulldown* (in.)	Secondary Vacuum Break (in.)	Fast Idle Setting (rpm)	Choke Unloader (in.)	Choke Setting
'79	466361, 466363, 466369, 466371	0.50	0.110	0.245	.245	2500	0.350	2 Rich
	466364, 466362, 466370, 466372	0.50	0.110	0.250	.250	2500	0.350	2 Rich
	466365, 466366, 466367, 466368, 466373, 466374, 466375, 466376	0.50	0.130	0.300	.300	2500	0.350	1 Rich
'80	All	0.50	0.110	—	.120	2500	0.350	Fixed
'81	14032301	0.50	0.110	—	0.120	2500	0.350	Fixed
	14032302	0.50	0.110	—	0.120	2500	0.275	Fixed
'82	14043392	0.50	0.110	—	0.120	2500	0.275	Fixed
	14043393	0.50	0.110	—	0.120	2500	0.350	Fixed

① Located on tag attached to the carburetor, or on the casting or choke plate
② GM identification numbers are used in place of the Holley numbers

U123

Model 5220, 6520

Both these models are staged dual venturi carburetors. The model 6520 has the electronic feedback system. On the 6520 always check the condition of hoses and related wiring before making carburetor adjustments.

FLOAT SETTING AND FLOAT DROP ADJUSTMENT

1. Remove and invert the air horn.
2. Insert a 0.480 inch gauge between the air horn and float.
3. If necessary, bend the tang on the float arm to adjust.
4. Turn the air horn right side up and allow the float to hang freely. Measure the float drop from the bottom of the air horn to the bottom of the float. It should be exactly 1⅞ in. Correct by bending the float tang.

VACUUM KICK ADJUSTMENT

1. Open the throttle, close the choke, then close the throttle to trap the fast idle system at the closed choke position.
2. Disconnect the vacuum hose to the carburetor and connect it to an auxiliary vacuum source.
3. Apply at least 15 inches Hg. vacuum to the unit.
4. Apply sufficient force to close the choke valve without distorting the linkage.
5. Insert a gauge (see Specification Chart) between the top of the choke plate and the air horn wall.
6. Adjust by rotating the Allen screw in the center diaphragm housing.
7. Replace the vacuum hose.

THROTTLE POSITION TRANSDUCER ADJUSTMENT

1978 Only

1. Disconnect the wire from the transducer.

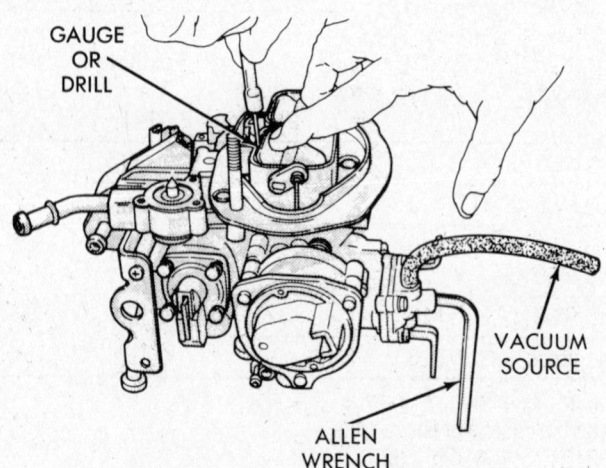

Vacuum kick adjustment

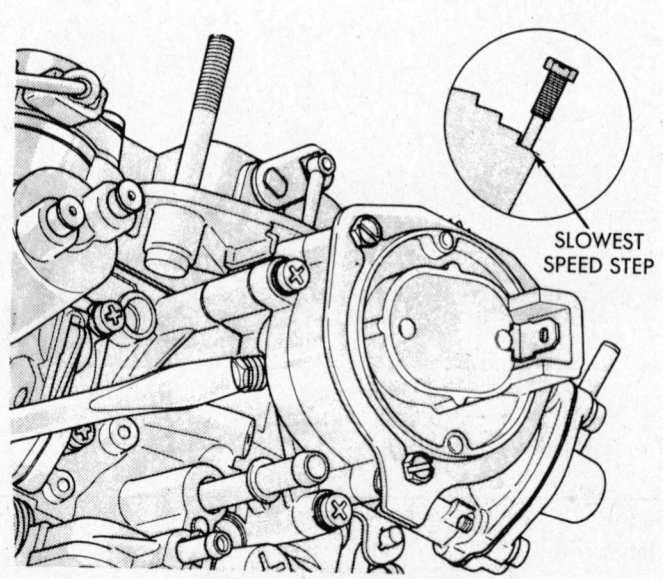

Fast idle speed adjustment

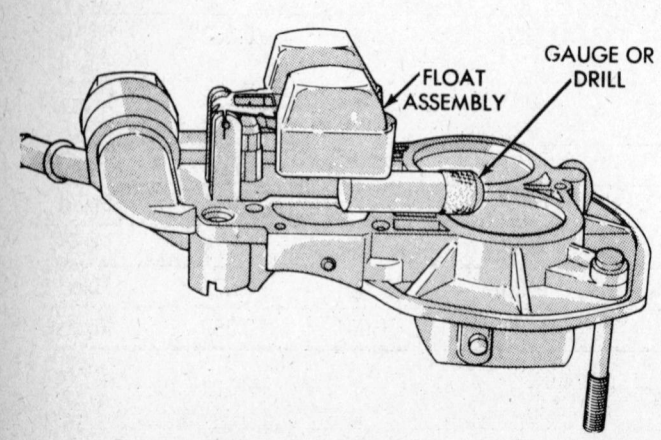

Float setting adjustment

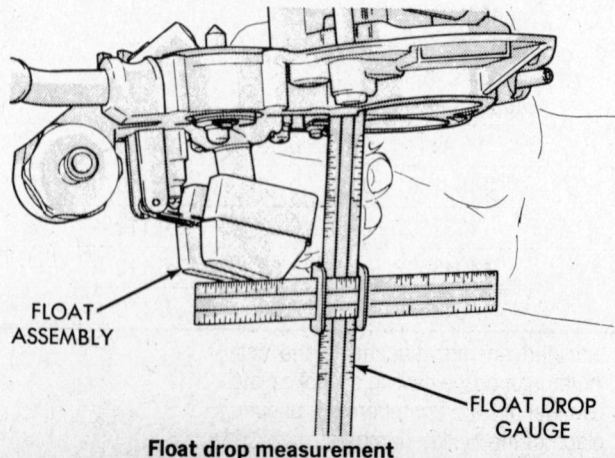

Float drop measurement

2. Loosen the locknut.

3. Place an $^{11}/_{16}$ in. gauge between the outer portion of the transducer and the mounting bracket.

4. To adjust the gap, turn the transducer.

5. Tighten the locknut.

FAST IDLE SPEED ADJUSTMENT

1. Remove the air cleaner, disconnect and plug the EGR line, but do not disconnect the spark control computer vacuum line. Use a jumper wire to ground the idle stop switch (through 1979). Turn the air conditioning off.

2. Disconnect the radiator fan electrical connector and use a jumper wire to complete the circuit at the fan. Do not short to ground, as this will damage the system.

3. With the parking brake set and the transmission in Neutral (engine still off), open the throttle and place the fast idle screw on the slowest step of the cam.

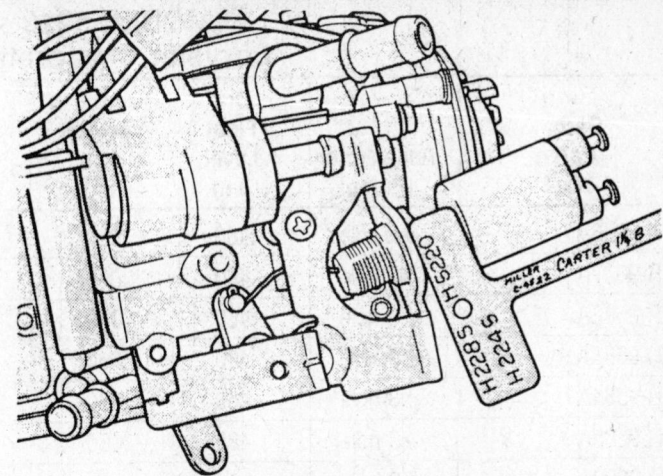

Throttle position transducer adjustment

4. Start the engine and check the idle speed. If it continues to rise slowly, the idle stop switch is not grounded properly.

5. Adjust the fast idle with the screw, moving the screw off the cam each time to adjust. Allow the screw to fall back against the cam and the speed to stabilize between each adjustment.

MODEL 5220
Chrysler Corporation

Year	Carb. Part No.	Accelerator Pump	Dry Float Level (in.)	Vacuum Kick (in.)	Fast Idle RPM (w/fan)	Throttle Position Transducer (in.)	Throttle Stop Speed RPM	Choke
'78	R-8376A, 8378A,8384A, 8439A,8441A, 8505A,8507A	#2 hole	.480	.070	1100	.547	700	2 Rich
'79	R-8524A, 8526A,8532A, 8534A,8528A, 8530A	#2 hole	.480	.040	1700	—	700	2 Rich
	R-8525A, 8541A,8531A, 8533A,8527A, 8529A	#2 hole	.480	.070	1400	—	700	2 Rich
'80	R8838A, 8839A, 9110A, 9111A, 9325A, 9327A	#2 hole	.480	.040	1700	—	700	Fixed
	R8726A, 8727A, 8837A, 9108A, 9321A, 9323A	#2 hole	.480	.070	1400	—	700	Fixed
	R9109A	#2 hole	.480	.100	1400	—	700	Fixed
'81	R-9056A	#2 hole	.480	.070	1400	—	700	Fixed
	R-9057A	#2 hole	.480	.070	1400	—	—	Fixed
	R-9058A	#2 hole	.480	.040	1400	—	700	Fixed
	R-9059A	#2 hole	.480	.040	1400	—	—	Fixed
	R-9064A	#2 hole	.480	.070	1300	—	—	Fixed
	R-9065A	#2 hole	.480	.070	1300	—	—	Fixed

MODEL 5220
Chrysler Corporation

Year	Carb. Part No.	Accelerator Pump	Dry Float Level (in.)	Vacuum Kick (in.)	Fast Idle RPM (w/fan)	Throttle Position Transducer (in.)	Throttle Stop Speed RPM	Choke
'81	R-9066A	#2 hole	.480	.060	1300	—	700	Fixed
	R-9067A	#2 hole	.480	.060	1300	—	—	Fixed
'82	R-9582A	#3 hole	.480	.060	1200	—	700	Fixed
	R-9583A	#3 hole	.480	.060	1200	—	—	Fixed
	R-9584A	#3 hole	.480	.060	1500	—	700	Fixed
	R-9585A	#3 hole	.480	.060	1500	—	700	Fixed
	R-9820A	#2 hole	.480	.080	1400	—	—	Fixed
	R-9513A	#2 hole	.480	.120	1400	—	—	Fixed
	R-9514A	#2 hole	.480	.120	1400	—	—	Fixed
	R-9499A	#2 hole	.480	.130	1400	—	700	Fixed
	R-9511A	#3 hole	.480	.130	1400	—	700	Fixed
	R-9512A	#2 hole	.480	.130	1400	—	—	Fixed
'83	R-40020A	#3 hole	.480	.055	1500	—	—	Fixed
	R-40022A	#3 hole	.480	.055	1500	—	—	Fixed
	R-40023A	#2 hole	.480	.070	1400	—	700	Fixed
	R-40024A	#2 hole	.480	.070	1400	—	700	Fixed
	R-40025A	#2 hole	.480	.070	1400	—	700	Fixed
	R-40026A	#7 hole	.480	.070	1400	—	700	Fixed
'84	R-400601A	#2 hole	.480	.055	1200	—	—	Fixed
	R-400851A	#2 hole	.480	.040	1500	—	—	Fixed
	R-40170A	#3 hole	.480	.060	1650	—	—	Fixed
	R-40171A	#3 hole	.480	.060	1700	—	—	Fixed
	R-400671A	#3 hole	.480	.070	1500	—	—	Fixed
	R-400681A	#3 hole	.480	.070	1700	—	—	Fixed
	R-400581A	#2 hole	.480	.070	1400	—	—	Fixed
	R-401071A	#2 hole	.480	.070	1600	—	—	Fixed

MODEL 6520
Chrysler Corporation

Year	Carb. Part No. ①	Accelerator Pump	Dry Float Level (in.)	Float Drop (in.)	Vacuum Kick (in.)	Fast Idle RPM
'81	R-9052A	#2 hole	.480	1.875	.070	1400②
	R-9053A	#2 hole	.480	1.875	.070	1400②
	R-9054A	#2 hole	.480	1.875	.040	1400②
	R-9055A	#2 hole	.480	1.875	.040	1400②
	R-9060A	#2 hole	.480	1.875	.030	1100②
	R-9061A	#2 hole	.480	1.875	.030	1100②

MODEL 6520
Chrysler Corporation

Year	Carb. Part No. ①	Accelerator Pump	Dry Float Level (in.)	Float Drop (in.)	Vacuum Kick (in.)	Fast Idle RPM
	R-9602A	#2 hole	.480	1.875	.035	1500②
	R-9603A	#2 hole	.480	1.875	.035	1500②
	R-9125A	#2 hole	.480	1.875	.030	1200②
	R-9126A	#2 hole	.480	1.875	.030	1200②
	R-9604A	#2 hole	.480	1.875	.035	1600②
	R-9605A	#2 hole	.480	1.875	.035	1600②
'82	R-9822A	#2 hole	.480	1.875	.080	1400
	R-9823A	#2 hole	.480	1.875	.080	1400
	R-9824A	#2 hole	.480	1.875	.065	1400
	R-9503A	#3 hole	.480	1.875	.085	1300
	R-9504A	#3 hole	.480	1.875	.085	1300
	R-9505A	#3 hole	.480	1.875	.100	1600
	R-9506A	#3 hole	.480	1.875	.100	1600
	R-9750A	#3 hole	.480	1.875	.085	1300
	R-9751A	#3 hole	.480	1.875	.085	1300
	R-9509A	#3 hole	.480	1.875	.085	1600
	R-9510A	#3 hole	.480	1.875	.085	1600
	R-9752A	#3 hole	.480	1.875	.100	1600
	R-9753A	#3 hole	.480	1.875	.100	1600
	R-9507A	#3 hole	.480	1.875	.085	1300
	R-9508A	#3 hole	.480	1.875	.085	1300
'83	R-40003A	#3 hole	.480	1.875	.070	1400
	R-40004A	#3 hole	.480	1.875	.080	1500
	R-40005A	#3 hole	.480	1.875	.080	1350
	R-40006A	#3 hole	.480	1.875	.080	1275
	R-40007A	#3 hole	.480	1.875	.070	1400
	R-40008A	#3 hole	.480	1.875	.070	1600
	R-40010A	#3 hole	.480	1.875	.080	1500
	R-40012A	#3 hole	.480	1.875	.070	1600
	R-40014A	#3 hole	.480	1.875	.080	1275
	R-40080A	#2 hole	.480	1.875	.045	1400
	R-40081A	#3 hole	.480	1.875	.045	1400
'84	R-400641A	#3 hole	.480	1.875	.080	1500
	R-400651A	#3 hole	.480	1.875	.080	1600
	R-400811A	#2 hole	.480	1.875	.080	1500
	R-400821A	#2 hole	.480	1.875	.080	1600
	R-40071A	#3 hole	.480	1.875	.080	1500
	R-40122A	#2 hole	.480	1.875	.080	1500

① Located on tag attached to the carburetor ② With radiator fan running

Model 6145

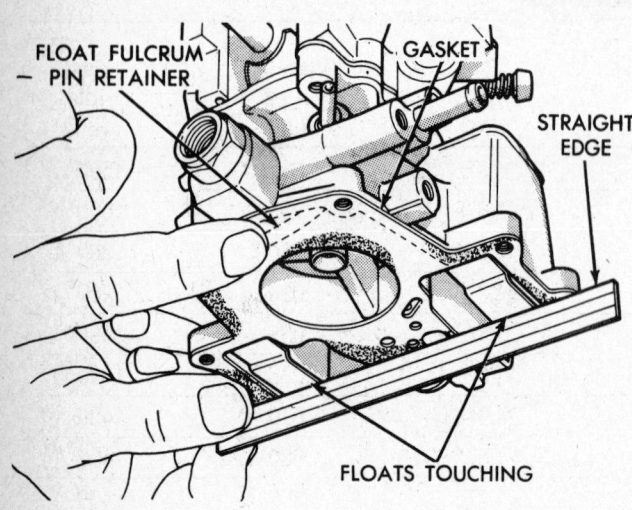

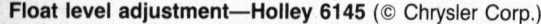

Float level adjustment—Holley 6145 (© Chrysler Corp.)

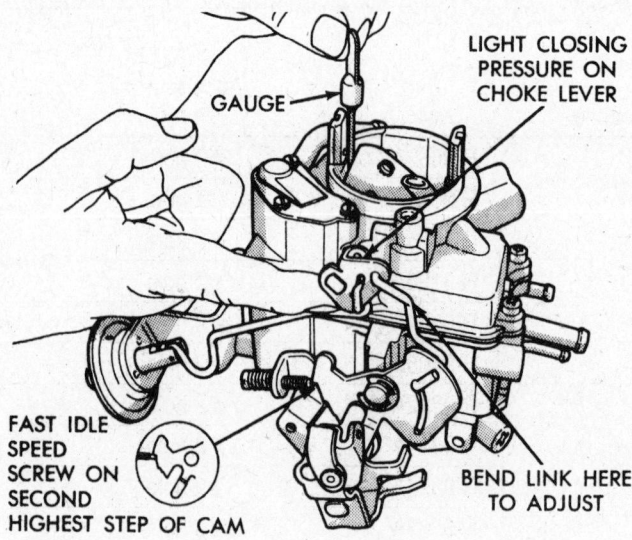

Fast idle cam adjustment, typical—Holley 6145 (© Chrysler Corp.)

FLOAT ADJUSTMENT

1. With the gasket in place invert the bowl and place a straight edge across the gasket surface. The portion of the floats, farthest from the fuel inlet, should just touch the straight edge.

2. If adjustment is necessary, bend the float tang.

CHOKE VACUUM KICK ADJUSTMENT

1. Open the throttle, close choke then close throttle so that the fast idle cam is at the closed position.

2. Disconnect the vacuum hose from the carburetor and connect to a hose of an auxiliary vacuum source with an extra length of tube. Apply a vacuum of 15 or more inches of mercury .

3. Apply light pressure on the choke lever to close the choke and measure the distance between the choke valve and the air horn wall on the throttle lever side with the specified gauge.

4. On 1981 models bend the diaphragm link at the U-bend to adjust on 1982–83 models insert a 5/64 in. allen wrench into the choke diaphragm and turn to adjust the choke vacuum kick.

5. Reconnect the vacuum hose after adjustment.

FAST IDLE CAM ADJUSTMENT

1. Position the fast idle speed adjusting screw on the second highest step of the fast idle cam.

2. Using light pressure on the choke shaft lever, move the choke towards the closed position.

3. Insert the specified gauge between the top of the choke valve and the air horn wall at the throttle lever side.

4. If an adjustment is necessary, bend the fast idle connecting rod at the angle until the correct valve opening is obtained.

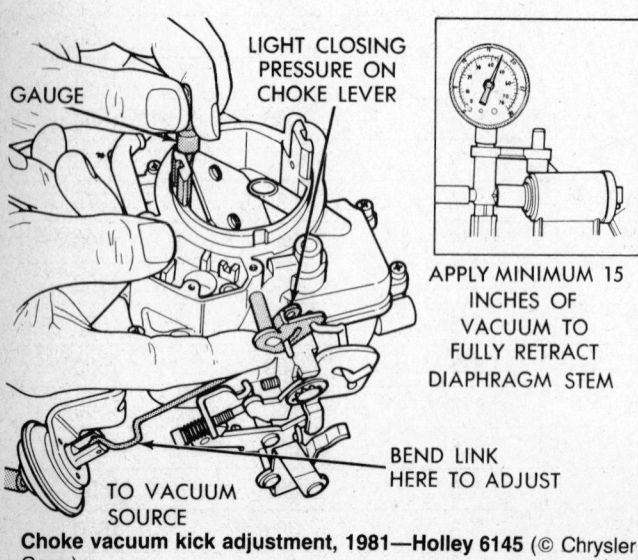

Choke vacuum kick adjustment, 1981—Holley 6145 (© Chrysler Corp.)

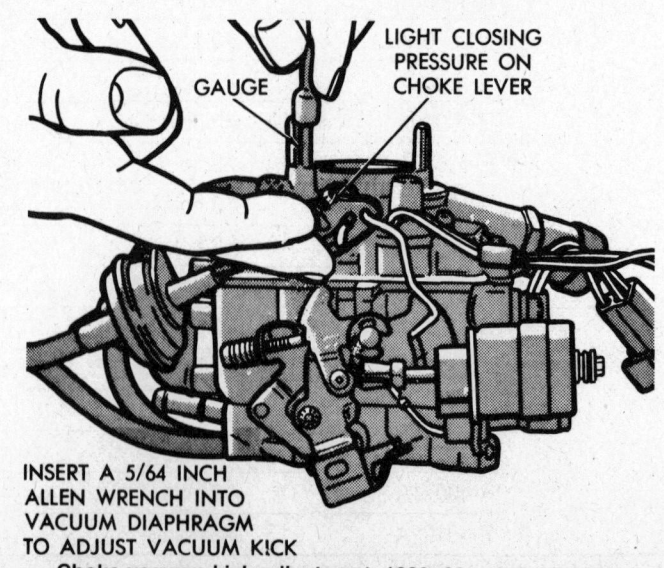

Choke vacuum kick adjustment, 1982–83—Holley 6145

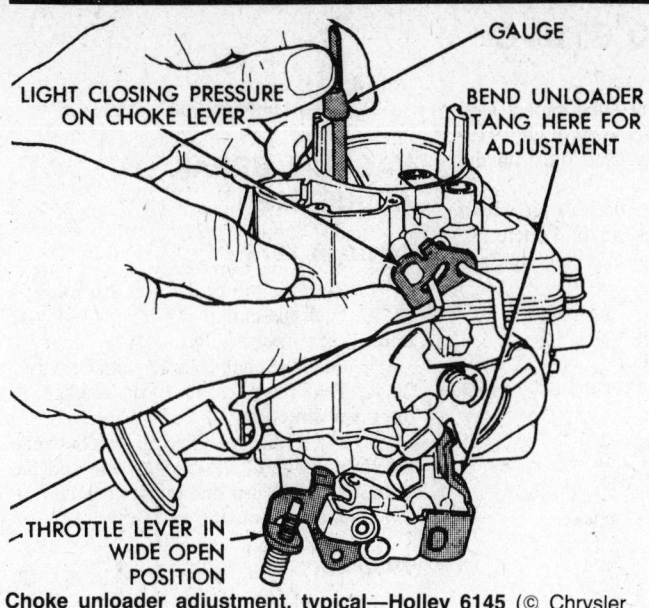

Choke unloader adjustment, typical—Holley 6145 (© Chrysler Corp.)

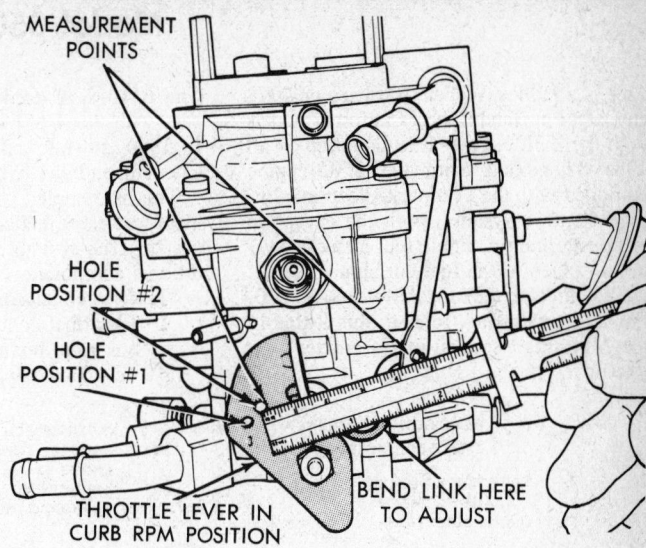

Accelerator pump adjustment, typical—Holley 6145 (© Chrysler Corp.)

CHOKE UNLOADER ADJUSTMENT

1. Hold the throttle valves in the wide open position.
2. Using light pressure on the control lever, move the choke valve towards the closed position.

3. Insert the specified gauge between the top of the choke valve and the air horn wall.
4. To adjust bend the tang on the throttle lever.

ACCELERATOR PUMP ADJUSTMENT

1. Place the throttle in the curb idle position with the accelerator pump operating link in the proper slot in the throttle lever.
2. Measure the pump operating link and bend the link if needed to specifications.

MODEL 6145
Chrysler Corporation

Year	Carb. Part No. ①	Float Level (in.)	Accelerator Pump Adjustment (in.)	Bowl Vent Clearance (in.)	Fast Idle (rpm)	Choke Unloader Clearance (in.)	Vacuum Kick (in.)	Fast Idle Cam Position (in.)	Choke
'81	R-9129A	②	1.615③	④	2000	.250	.150	.090	Fixed
'82	R-9936A	②	1.616③	④	1950	.250	.150	.090	Fixed
	R-9695A	②	1.615③	④	1950⑤	.250	.150	.090	Fixed
'83	R-40042A	②	1.615③	④	2000	.250	.150	.090	Fixed

① Located on a tag attached to the carburetor
② Flush with the top of the main body casting to .050″ above
③ Position #2
④ Not Adjustable
⑤ Cordoba and Mirada—2000 rpm

Model 6500 6510-C

This is a Holley-Weber Unit used on 1978 and later Pinto and Bobcat California models with the 2.3L engine. It is also used on all 1981–82 models with the 2.3L engine equipped with the Feedback Electronic Engine Control System. With the exception of an externally variable fuel metering system in place of the fuel enrichment valve, it is identical to the model Motorcraft 5200. For all adjustments, refer to this listing in the Motorcraft section of Carburetor Unit Repair.

The 6510-C is used on subcompact GM cars with the 4-151 engine through 1979. In 1980 and later, it is used only on the Chevette and T-1000.

This is a staged, two barrel unit which incorporates a feedback air/fuel metering system. The system uses five new and additional components.
1. Oxygen sensor
2. Electrical control unit
3. Vacuum modulator
4. Feedback diaphragm and idle needle
5. Main feedback idle system

VACUUM BREAK ADJUSTMENT

Through 1979

1. Remove the choke coil assembly.
2. Push the choke coil lever clockwise to close the choke valve.
3. Push the choke shaft against its stop.
4. Take the slack out of the linkage, in the open direction.
5. Insert the specified gauge between the lower edge of the choke plate and the air horn wall. Turn the adjusting screw on the diaphragm housing to adjust.

1980-83

1. Attach a hand vacuum pump to the vacuum break diaphragm. Apply vacuum until the diaphragm is seated.
2. Push the fast idle cam lever down to close the choke plate.
3. Take the slack out of the linkage in the open choke position.
4. Insert the specified gauge between the lower edge of the choke plate and the air horn wall.
5. If the clearance is incorrect, turn the screw in the end of the diagphragm to adjust.

FAST IDLE CAM ADJUSTMENT

1. Set the fast idle cam so that the screw is on the second highest step of the fast idle cam.
2. Insert the specified gauge between the lower edge of the choke valve and the air horn wall.
3. Bend the tang on the arm to adjust.

UNLOADER ADJUSTMENT

1. Place the throttle in the wide open position.
2. Insert a 0.350 inch gauge between the lower edge of the choke valve and the air horn wall.
3. Bend the tang on the choke arm to adjust.

CHOKE CAP SETTING

1978-79 Only

1. Loosen the retaining screws.
2. Make sure that the choke coil lever is located inside the coil tang.
3. Turn the cap to the specified setting.
4. Tighten the retaining screws.

FAST IDLE ADJUSTMENT

1. With the curb idle speed correct, place

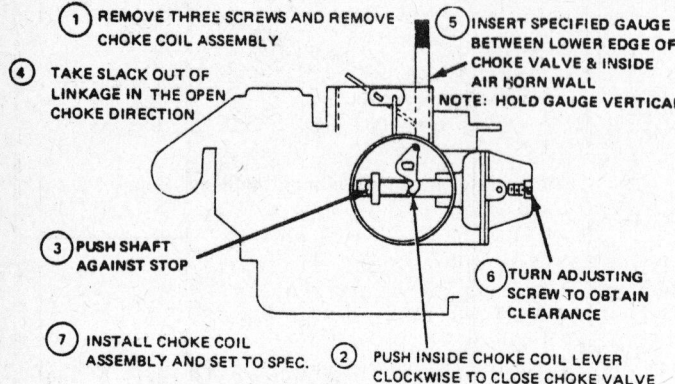

Vacuum break adjustment, thru 1979 (© G.M. Corp.)

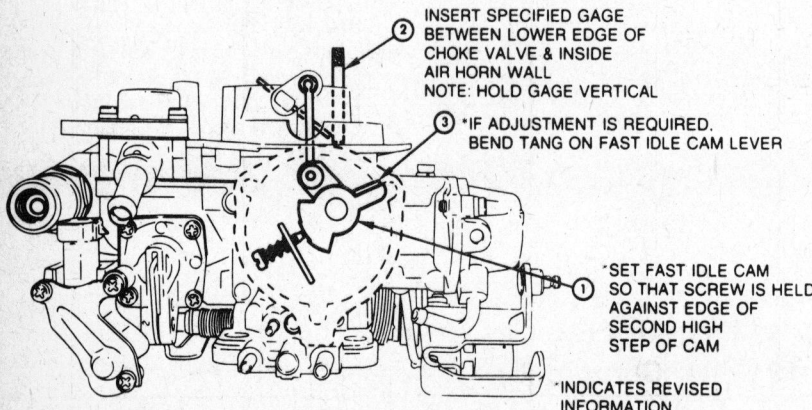

Fast idle cam adjustment—Holley 6510C (© G.M. Corp.)

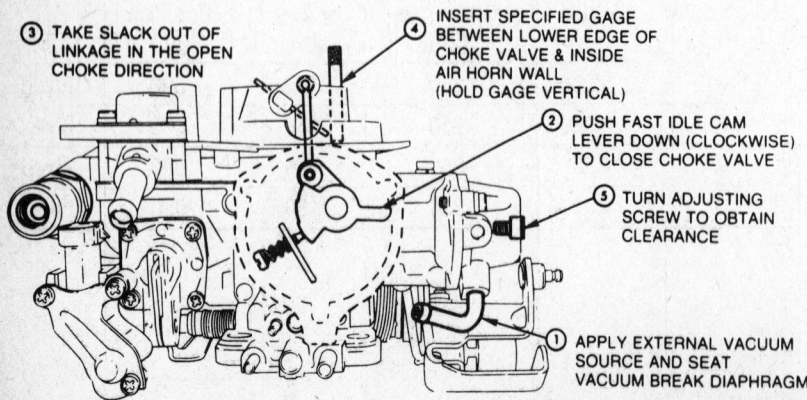

Vacuum break adjustment, 1980 and later—Holley 6510C (© G.M. Corp.)

the fast idle screw on the highest cam step and adjust to the specified rpm.

NOTE: The EGR line must be disconnected and plugged.

FLOAT LEVEL ADJUSTMENT

1. Remove and invert the air horn.
2. Place the specified gauge between the air horn and the float.

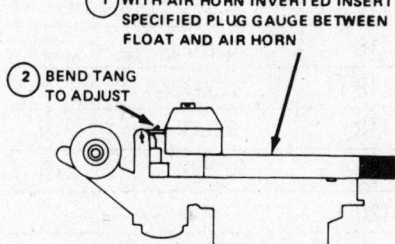

Float level adjustment (© G.M. Corp.)

3. If necessary, bend the float arm tang to adjust.

FLOAT DROP SETTING

Through 1979 Only

1. Hold the air horn right side up. The distance between the bottom of the air horn and the top of the float should be 1 inch.
2. If necessary, bend the tang on the side of the float arm support, to adjust.

SECONDARY THROTTLE STOP SCREW ADJUSTMENT

1. Back off the screw until it does not touch the lever.
2. Turn the screw in until it touches the lever, then turn it an additional ¼ turn.

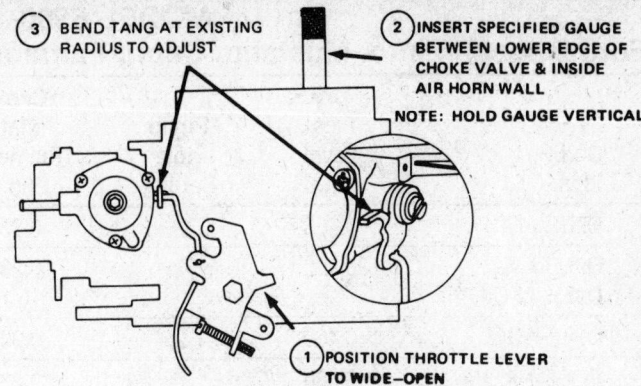

Choke unloader adjustment (© G.M. Corp.)

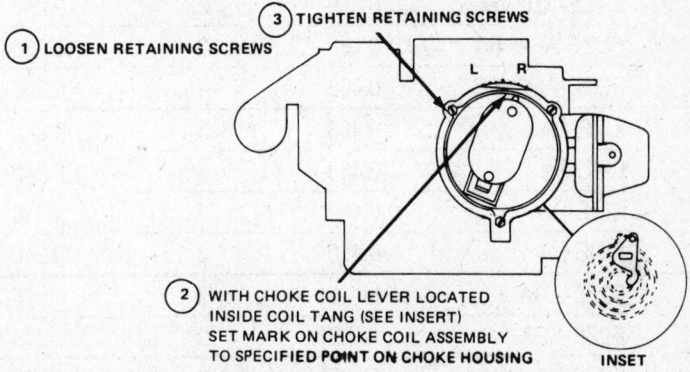

Choke cap setting, thru 1979 (© G.M. Corp.)

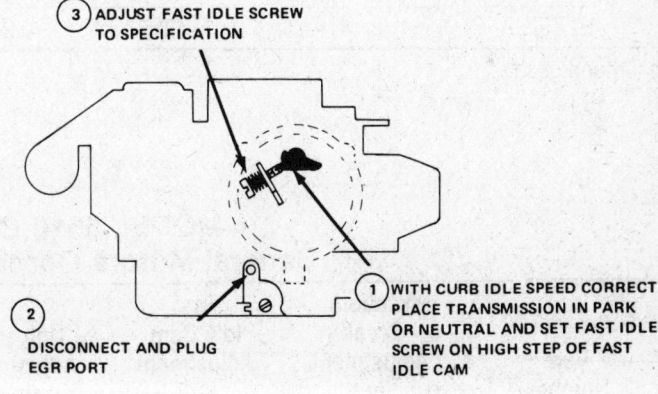

Fast idle speed adjustment (© G.M. Corp.)

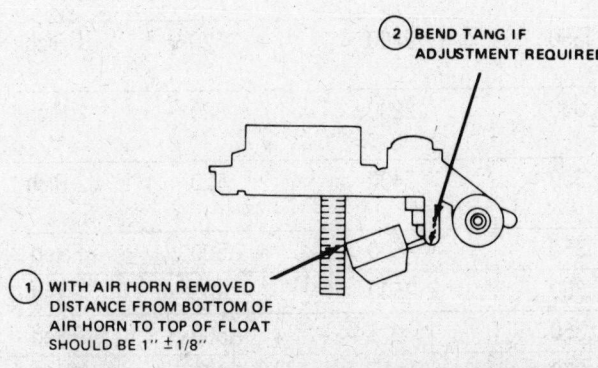

Float drop adjustment, thru 1979 (© G.M. Corp.)

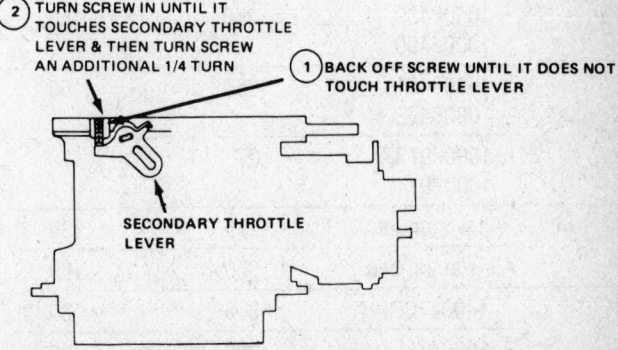

Secondary throttle stop screw adjustment (© G.M. Corp.)

MODEL 6500
Ford Bobcat, Pinto, Mustang, Capri, Fairmont, Zephyr, Granada, Cougar

Year	Carb. Iden.	Dry Float Level (in.)	Pump Hole Setting	Choke Plate Pulldown (in.)	Fast Idle Cam Linkage (in.)	Dechoke (in.)	Choke Setting
'78-'79	D9EE-AFC	0.455	2	0.236	0.118	0.236	2 Rich
	D9EE-AJC, D9EE-AKC	0.460	2	0.236	0.118	0.236	1 Rich
	D9EE-AGC	0.460	2	0.236	0.118	0.236	2 Rich
'80	EOEE-NA, VA	0.460	2	0.236	0.118	0.393	①
	EOEE-NC, NV	0.460	2	0.236	0.118	0.157	①
	EOEE-ND, VD	0.460	2	0.236	0.118	0.393	①
	EOZE-AFA, SA	0.460	2	0.236	0.118	0.393	①
	EOZE-AFC, SC	0.460	—	0.236	0.118	0.393	①
'81	EIZE-RA	0.460	3	0.240	0.120	0.400	—
	EIZE-SA	0.460	3	0.240	0.120	0.400	—
	EIDE-DA	0.460	3	0.240	0.120	0.400	—
	EIDE-EA	0.460	3	0.240	0.120	0.400	—
'82	E2ZE-ARA	.41–.51	2	0.275	0.118	0.393	—
	E2ZE-APA	.41–.51	2	0.275	0.118	0.393	—
	E2ZE-VA	.41–.51	3	0.275	0.118	0.393	—
	E2ZE-ADA	.41–.51	3	0.275	0.118	0.393	—
	E2ZE-ACA	.41–.51	3	0.275	0.118	0.393	—
	E2ZE-UA	.41–.51	3	0.275	0.118	0.393	—

① See underhood decal

MODEL 6510-C
General Motors Corporation

Year	Part Number	Vacuum Break Adjustment (in.)	Fast Idle Cam Adjustment (in.)	Unloader Adjustment (in.)	Fast Idle Adjustment (rpm)	Float Level Adjustment (in.)	Choke Setting
'78	10001056, 10001058	.325	.150	.350	2400	.520	1 Rich
'79	10008489, 10008490	.250	.150	.350	2400	.520	1 Rich
	10008491, 10008492	.250	.150	.350	2200	.520	2 Rich
	10009973, 10009974	.275	.150	.350	2400	.520	2 Rich
'80	All w/manual	.275	.130	.350	2600	.500	Fixed
	All w/automatic	.300	.130	.350	2500	.500	Fixed
'81	14004768	.300	.130	.350	①	.500	Fixed
	14004769	.300	.130	.350	①	.500	Fixed

MODEL 6510-C
General Motors Corporation

Year	Part Number	Vacuum Break Adjustment (in.)	Fast Idle Cam Adjustment (in.)	Unloader Adjustment (in.)	Fast Idle Adjustment (rpm)	Float Level Adjustment (in.)	Choke Setting
'81	14004770	.300	.130	.350	①	.500	Fixed
	14004771	.300	.130	.350	①	.500	Fixed
	14004777	.300	.130	.350	①	.500	Fixed
'82	14032364	.270	.080	.350	①	.500	Fixed
	14032365	.270	.080	.350	①	.500	Fixed
	14032366	.270	.080	.350	①	.500	Fixed
	14032367	.270	.080	.350	①	.500	Fixed
	14032368	.270	.080	.350	①	.500	Fixed
	14032369	.270	.080	.350	①	.500	Fixed
	14032370	.270	.080	.350	①	.500	Fixed
	14032371	.270	.080	.350	①	.500	Fixed
	14033392	.270	.080	.350	①	.500	Fixed
	14033393	.270	.080	.350	①	.500	Fixed
	14047072	.270	.080	.350	①	.500	Fixed
'83	14048827	.270	.080	.350	①	.500	Fixed
	14048828	.300	.080	.350	①	.500	Fixed
	14048829	.270	.080	.350	①	.500	Fixed
'84	14068690	.270	.080	.350	①	.500	Fixed
	14068691	.270	.080	.350	①	.500	Fixed
	14068692	.300	.080	.350	①	.500	Fixed

① See underhood decal

ROCHESTER CARBURETORS

Angle Degree Tool

An angle degree tool is recommended by Rochester Products Division, for use to confirm adjustments to the choke valve and related linkages on their late model two and four barrel carburetors, in place of the plug type gauges.

Decimal and degree conversion charts are provided for use by technicians who have access to an angle gauge and not plug gauges. It must be remembered that the relationship between the decimal and the angle readings are not exact, due to manufacturers tolerances.

To use the angle gauge, rotate the degree scale until zero (0) is opposite the pointer. With the choke valve completely closed, place the gauge magnet squarely on top of the choke valve and rotate the bubble until it is centered. Make the necessary adjustments to have the choke valve at the specified degree angle opening as read from the degree angle tool.

ANGLE DEGREE TO DECIMAL CONVERSION
Model M2MC, M2ME and M4MC Carburetor

Angle Degrees	Decimal Equiv. Top of Valve	Angle Degrees	Decimal Equiv. Top of Valve
5	.023	33	.203
6	.028	34	.211
7	.033	35	.220
8	.038	36	.227
9	.043	37	.234
10	.049	38	.243
11	.054	39	.251
12	.060	40	.260
13	.066	41	.269
14	.071	42	.277
15	.077	43	.287
16	.083	44	.295
17	.090	45	.304
18	.096	46	.314

ANGLE DEGREE TO DECIMAL CONVERSION
Model M2MC, M2ME and M4MC Carburetor

Angle Degrees	Decimal Equiv. Top of Valve	Angle Degrees	Decimal Equiv. Top of Valve
19	.103	47	.322
20	.110	48	.332
21	.117	49	.341
22	.123	50	.350
23	.129	51	.360
24	.136	52	.370
25	.142	53	.379
26	.149	54	.388
27	.157	55	.400
28	.164	56	.408
29	.171	57	.418
30	.179	58	.428
31	.187	59	.439
32	.195	60	.449

ANGLE DEGREE TO DECIMAL CONVERSION
Model 4MV Carburetor

Angle Degrees	Decimal Equiv. Top of Valve	Angle Degrees	Decimal Equiv. Top of Valve
5	.019	33	.158
6	.022	34	.164
7	.026	35	.171
8	.030	36	.178
9	.034	37	.184
10	.038	38	.190
11	.042	39	.197
12	.047	40	.204
13	.051	41	.211
14	.056	42	.217
15	.060	43	.225
16	.065	44	.231
17	.070	45	.239
18	.075	46	.246
19	.080	47	.253
20	.085	48	.260
21	.090	49	.268
22	.095	50	.275
23	.101	51	.283
24	.106	52	.291
25	.112	53	.299
26	.117	54	.306
27	.123	55	.314
28	.128	56	.322
29	.134	57	.329
30	.140	58	.337
31	.146	59	.345
32	.152	60	.353

NOTE: The carburetor may be off the engine for adjustments. Be sure the carburetor is held firmly during the use of the angle gauge.

PLUGGING AIR BLEED HOLES

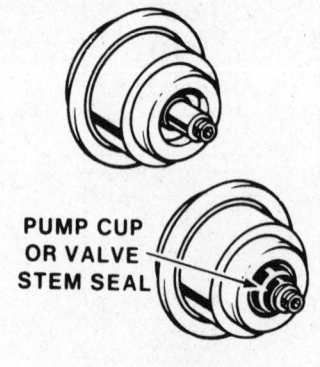

PUMP CUP OR VALVE STEM SEAL

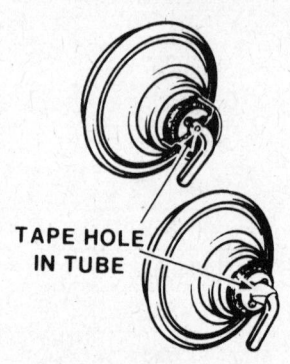

TAPE HOLE IN TUBE

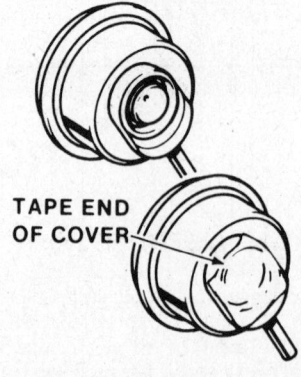

TAPE END OF COVER

Vacuum break information—E2SE

Model Identification

General Motors Rochester carburetors are identified by their model number. The first number indicates the number of barrels, while one of the last letters indicates the type of choke used. These are V for the manifold mounted choke coil, C for the choke coil mounted on the carburetor, and E for electric choke, also mounted on the carburetor. Model numbers ending in A indicate an altitude-compensating carburetor.

Model 1ME

This is a Rochester Monojet carburetor, designed for use on the Chevette and Chevrolet inline sixes. It is a single bore downdraft unit. Some models have a hot idle compensator. The 1ME has an integral automatic choke system with an electrically heated choke coil. The carburetor is last used in 1979.

FLOAT LEVEL ADJUSTMENT

1. Remove the top of the carburetor.
2. Hold the float retaining pin in place and push down on the float arm at the outer end against the top of the float needle valve.
3. Measure the distance from the bump on the top of the float at the end to the bowl gasket surface, without the gasket.
4. To adjust, bend the float arm at the point where it joins the float.

METERING ROD ADJUSTMENT

Chevette

1. Remove the top of the carburetor.
2. Back out the idle stop solenoid and rotate the fast idle cam so that the fast idle screw does not contact the cam.
3. With the throttle valve completely closed, make sure the power piston is all the way up.
4. Insert the specified size gauge between the bowl gasket surface with no gasket and the lower surface of the metering rod holder, next to the metering rod.
5. To adjust, carefully bend the metering rod holder.

Inline Sixes

1. Remove the top of the carburetor and the gasket.
2. Remove the metering rod. Hold the throttle valve wide open. Push down on the metering rod against spring tension, then

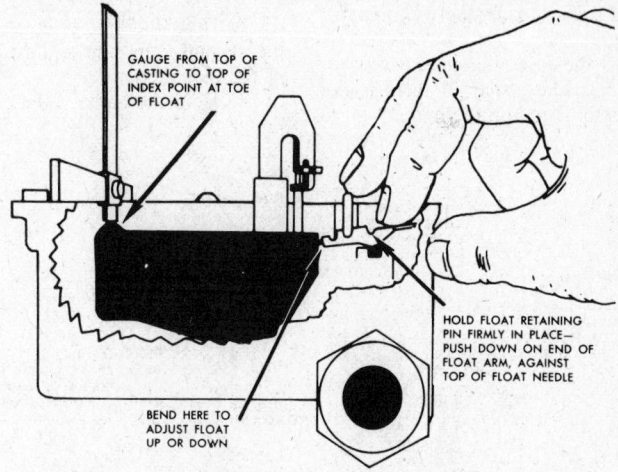

1ME Float level adjustment (© Chevrolet Div., G.M. Corp.)

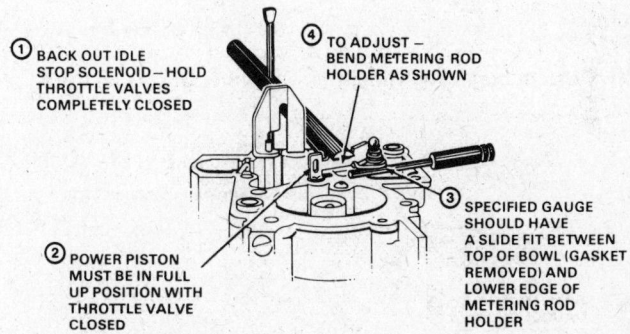

1ME Metering rod adjustment (© Chevrolet Div., G.M. Corp.)

slide the rod out of the slot in the holder and remove it from the main metering jet.
3. Back out the idle stop solenoid and hold the throttle valve completely closed.
4. Hold the power piston down and swing the metering rod holder over the flat surface of the bowl casting next to the carburetor bore. The gauge should be a slide fit between the rod holder and the flat surface.
5. Adjust by carefully bending the metering rod holder.

FAST IDLE SPEED ADJUSTMENT

NOTE: This adjustment is not possible on some California and high altitude carburetors. It should not be done on carburetors with an idle dashpot.

1. The engine should be at normal temperature with the air cleaner in place. Disconnect and plug EGR valve vacuum line.

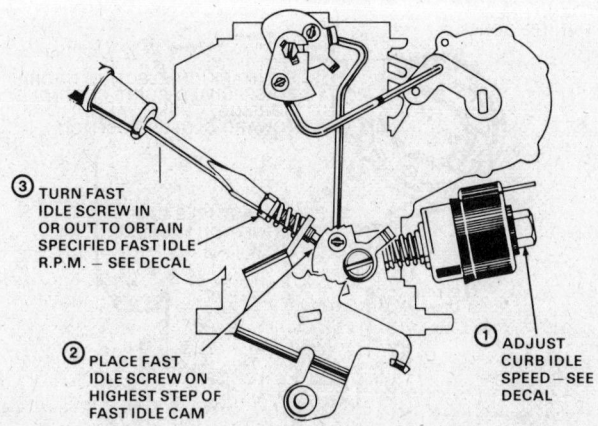

1ME Fast idle speed adjustment (© Chevrolet Div., G.M. Corp.)

1ME Fast idle cam adjustment (© Chevrolet Div., G.M. Corp.)

2. Make sure that the curb idle speed is as specified.

3. Place the fast idle screw or cam follower on the highest cam step with the engine running.

4. Adjust the fast idle speed screw to the correct fast idle speed. If there is no screw, adjust by bending the tang.

FAST IDLE CAM ADJUSTMENT

1. Hold the fast idle speed screw on the second cam step against the shoulder of the high step.

2. Hold the choke valve closed with a finger.

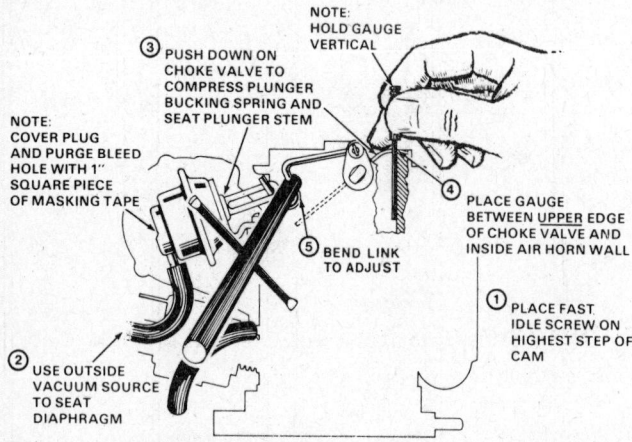

1ME Vacuum break adjustment (© Chevrolet Div., G.M. Corp.)

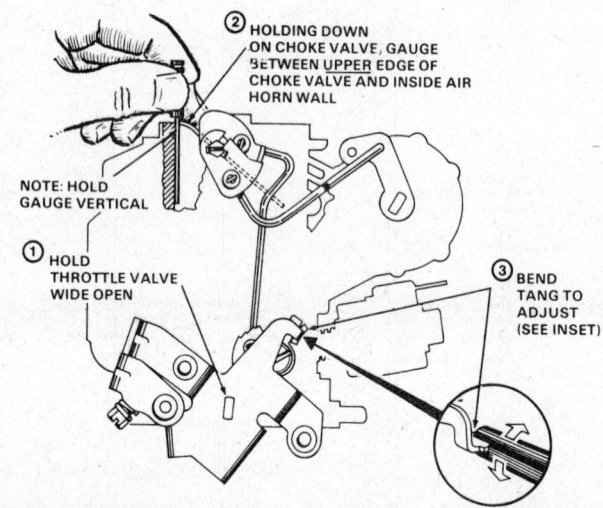

1ME Choke unloader adjustment (© Chevrolet Div., G.M. Corp.)

3. Insert the specified gauge between the center lower edge of the choke valve and the air horn wall.

4. Bend the linkage rod at the upper angle to adjust.

VACUUM BREAK ADJUSTMENT

1. Place the fast idle screw or cam follower on the high step of the cam.

2. Apply vacuum to the vacuum break diaphragm to seat the diaphragm. If the diaphragm has a bleed hole, it must be temporarily taped over.

3. Push down on the choke valve. Compress the plunger bucking spring and seat the plunger stem on models so equipped.

4. Measure between the lower edge of the choke valve and the inside air horn wall.

5. Bend the U-shaped link to adjust.

CHOKE UNLOADER ADJUSTMENT

1. Hold the throttle valve wide open.

2. Hold down the choke valve with a finger and insert the specified gauge between the lower edge of the choke valve and the air horn wall.

3. Bend the linkage tang to adjust.

CHOKE COIL LEVER ADJUSTMENT

1. Place the fast idle speed screw or cam follower on the highest cam step.

2. Hold the choke valve closed.

3. Insert a 0.120 in. gauge through the hole in the arm on the choke housing and into the hole in the casting.

4. Bend the link to adjust.

ELECTRIC CHOKE ADJUSTMENT

1. Place the fast idle cam follower on the high step.

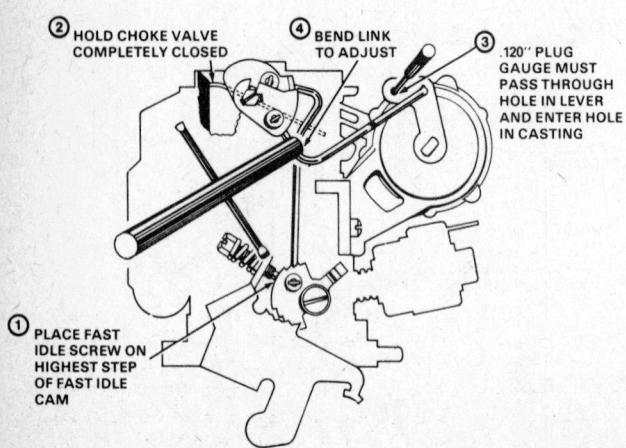

1ME Choke coil lever adjustment (© Chevrolet Div., G.M. Corp.)

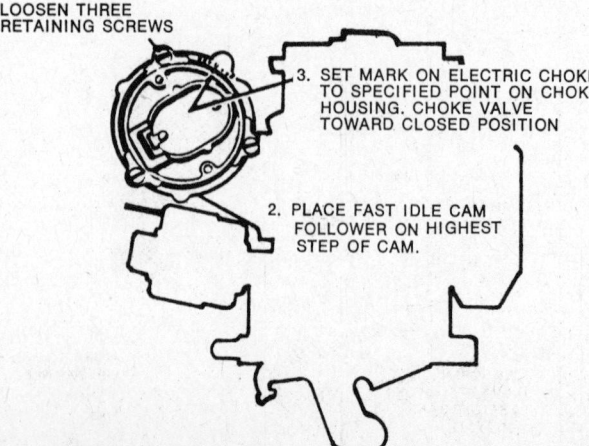

1ME Electric choke adjustment (© Chevrolet Div., G.M. Corp.)

2. Loosen the three retaining screws and rotate the cover counter-clockwise until the choke valve just closes.

3. Align the index mark on the cover with the specified housing mark.
4. Tighten the three screws.

NOTE: Failure of the electric choke heater circuit will cause the oil pressure light to go on.

1ME CARBURETOR SPECIFICATIONS
Chevrolet Products, Chevette

Year	Carburetor Identification① Number	Float Level (in.)	Metering Rod (in.)	Fast Idle Speed (rpm)	Fast Idle Cam (in.)	Vacuum Break (in.)	Choke Unloader (in.)	Choke Setting (notches)
'78	17058013	3/8	0.080	2000	0.180	0.200	0.500	Index
	17058014	5/16	0.100	2100	0.180	0.200	0.500	Index
	17058020	5/16	0.100	2100	0.180	0.200	0.500	Index
	17058314	3/8	0.100	2000	0.190	0.245	0.400	Index
	17058031	5/32	0.080	2400	0.105	0.150	0.500	2 Rich
	17058032	5/32	0.080	2400	0.080	0.130	0.500	3 Rich
	17058033	5/32	0.080	2400	0.080	0.130	0.500	2 Rich
	17058034	5/32	0.080	2400	0.080	0.130	0.500	3 Rich
	17058035	5/32	0.080	2300	0.080	0.130	0.500	3 Rich
	17058036	5/32	0.080	2400	0.080	0.130	0.500	3 Rich
	17058037	5/32	0.080	2400	0.080	0.130	0.500	2 Rich
	17058038	5/32	0.080	2400	0.080	0.130	0.500	3 Rich
	17058042	5/32	0.080	2400	0.080	0.160	0.500	2 Rich
	17058044	5/32	0.080	2400	0.080	0.160	0.500	2 Rich
	17058045	5/32	0.080	2300	0.080	0.160	0.500	2 Rich
	17058332	5/32	0.080	2400	0.080	0.160	0.500	2 Rich
	17058334	5/32	0.080	2400	0.080	0.160	0.500	2 Rich
	17058335	5/32	0.080	2300	0.080	0.160	0.500	2 Rich
'79	17059014	3/8	0.095	2000	0.180	0.200	0.400	Index
	17059020	3/8	0.095	2000	0.180	0.200	0.400	Index
	17059013	3/8	0.095	1800	0.180	0.200	0.400	Index
	17059314	3/8	0.100	2000	0.190	0.245	0.400	Index

① Stamped on float bowl, next to fuel inlet nut

Models 2GC, 2GV and 2GE

This two barrel carburetor is used on General Motors cars through 1978. The newer carburetors use a plastic float and a longer needle and seat to provide better fuel control. See the beginning of the Rochester section for an explanation of the type designations.

FAST IDLE SPEED ADJUSTMENT

1. Except on some Oldsmobile cars, the fast idle is set automatically when the curb idle and mixture is set.
2. Some Oldsmobile 2GC carburetors have a screw to adjust the fast idle.

CHOKE ROD (FAST IDLE CAM)

1. Turn in the idle cam stop screw, if any, until it just contacts the bottom step of the fast idle cam. Then turn the screw one full turn.
2. Place the idle screw on the second step of the fast idle cam against the shoulder of the high step.
3. Hold the choke valve closed and check the clearance between the upper edge of the choke valve and the air horn wall.
4. Adjust the clearance by bending the tang on the choke lever.

2GC, 2GE INTERMEDIATE CHOKE ROD (CHOKE COIL LEVER) ADJUSTMENT

1. Remove the thermostatic cover coil, gasket, and inside baffle plate assembly.
2. Place the idle speed screw on the highest step of the fast idle cam.
3. Close the choke valve by pushing up on the intermediate choke lever.
4. The edge of the coil lever inside the choke housing must line up with the edge of a 0.120 in. drill bit inserted into the hole inside the choke housing.

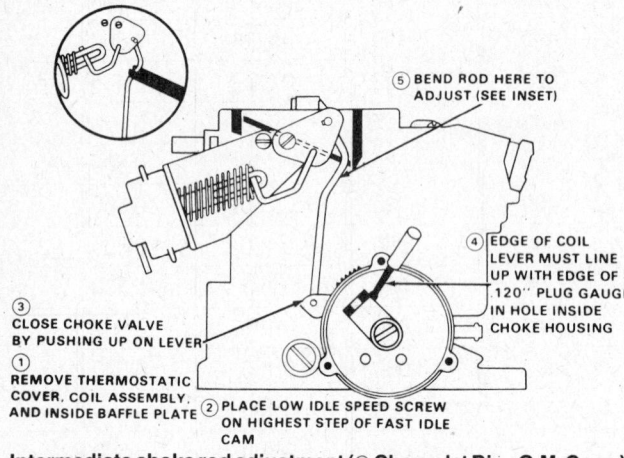

Intermediate choke rod adjustment (© Chevrolet Div., G.M. Corp.)

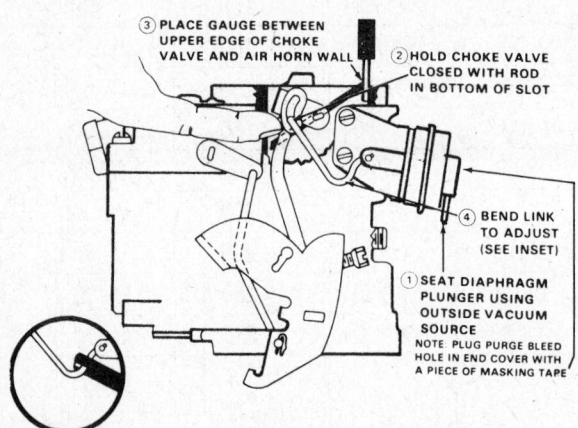

Primary vacuum break adjustment (© Buick Div., G.M. Corp.)

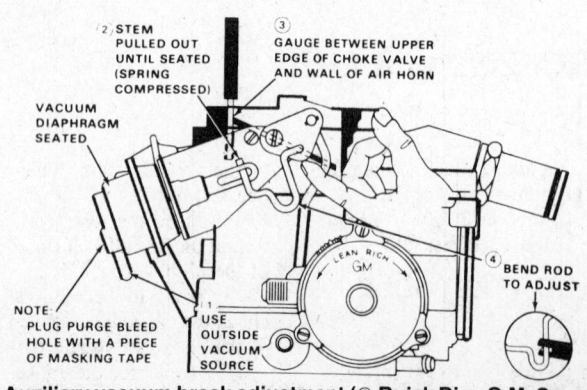

Auxiliary vacuum break adjustment (© Buick Div., G.M. Corp.)

5. Adjust by bending the intermediate choke rod at the first bend from the bottom of the rod.

VACUUM BREAK ADJUSTMENT

1. Remove the air cleaner. Vehicles with a Therm AC air cleaner should have the sensor's vacuum take-off port plugged.
2. Using an external vacuum source, apply vacuum to the vacuum break diaphragm until the plunger is fully seated. If the diaphragm has a bleed hole, tape it over.

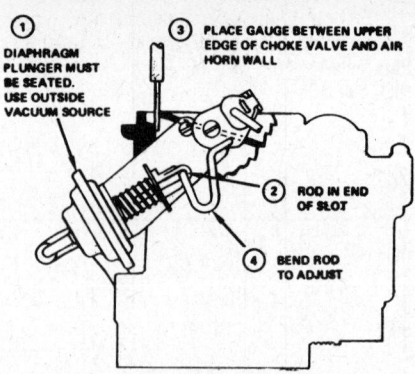

Vacuum Break Adjustment
(© Chevrolet Div., G.M. Corp)

3. When the plunger is seated, push the choke valve toward the closed position.
4. Holding the choke valve in the closed position, place the specified size gauge between the upper edge of the choke valve and the air horn wall.
5. If the measurement is not correct, bend the vacuum break rod.

AUXILIARY VACUUM BREAK

1. Seat the auxiliary vacuum diaphragm by applying an outside source of vacuum. Tape over the vacuum bleed hole so the vacuum will not bleed down.
2. Place the idle speed screw on the high step of the fast idle cam.
3. Hold the choke toward the closed choke position.
4. Measure the distance between the upper edge of the choke valve and the air horn wall.
5. Adjust by bending the auxiliary vacuum break rod at the bottom of the U-shaped bend. Remove the piece of tape from the auxiliary vacuum diaphragm.

CHOKE UNLOADER ADJUSTMENT

1. Hold the throttle valves wide open.

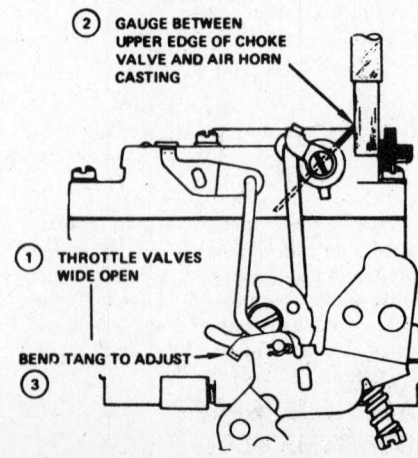

Choke Unloader Adjustment
(© Chevrolet Div., G.M. Corp)

2. Close the choke valve.

3. Bend the unloader tang to obtain the proper clearance between the upper edge of the choke valve and air horn wall.

2GV CHOKE COIL ROD ADJUSTMENT

1. Hold the choke valve completely open.

2. Disconnect the coil rod from the upper lever and push down on the rod to the end of its travel.

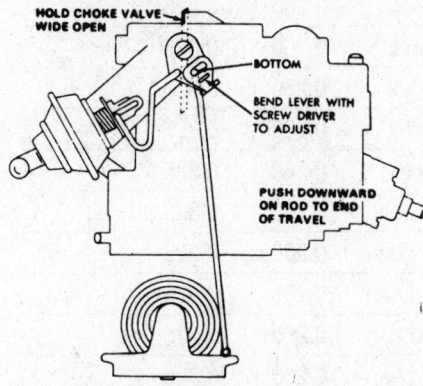

Choke Coil Rod Adjustment
(© Chevrolet Div., G.M. Corp)

3. When the rod is all the way down, the top of the rod should line up with the bottom of the slotted hole on the choke valve linkage.

4. Adjust by bending the lever.

FLOAT LEVEL

With the air horn assembly upside down, measure the distance from the air horn gasket to the lip at the toe of the float. Bend the float arm to adjust to specifications.

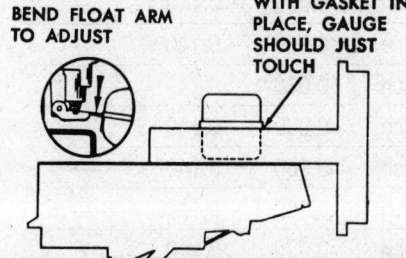

Float Level Measurement, Metal Float

FLOAT DROP

Holding the air horn assembly upright, measure the distance from the gasket to the lip or notch at the toe of the float. If correction is necessary, bend the float tang at the rear, next to the needle and seat.

ACCELERATOR PUMP ROD

1. Back out the idle speed screw and completely close the throttle valves.

2. Place the pump gauge across the air horn ring.

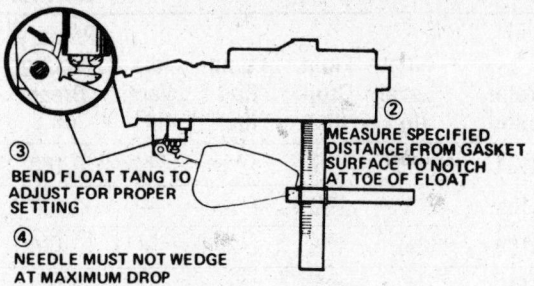

① AIR HORN RIGHT SIDE UP TO ALLOW FLOAT TO HANG FREE (GASKET IN PLACE)

② MEASURE SPECIFIED DISTANCE FROM GASKET SURFACE TO NOTCH AT TOE OF FLOAT

③ BEND FLOAT TANG TO ADJUST FOR PROPER SETTING

④ NEEDLE MUST NOT WEDGE AT MAXIMUM DROP

Float Drop, Plastic Float

3. With the T-scale set to the specified height, the lower leg of the gauge should just touch the top of the accelerator pump rod.

4. Bend the pump rod to adjust.

BOWL VENT VALVE ADJUSTMENT

NOTE: Check and adjust, if necessary, the pump rod clearance and curb idle speed before adjusting the bowl vent valve.

1. Remove the two bowl vent valve cover attaching screws in the top of the air horn and remove the cover and gasket. Remove the bowl vent valve spring.

2. Place the idle speed screw on the second step of the fast idle cam next to the highest step. In this position, the bowl vent valve should just be closed.

3. If the vent valve is just closed with the idle the fast idle cam, rotate the fast idle cam so that the idle speed screw is on the next lower step. In this position, the vent valve should just begin to open.

4. If it is necessary to adjust the bowl vent valve, turn the adjustment screw in the top f of the valve, to obtain the conditions mentioned in Steps 2 and 3.

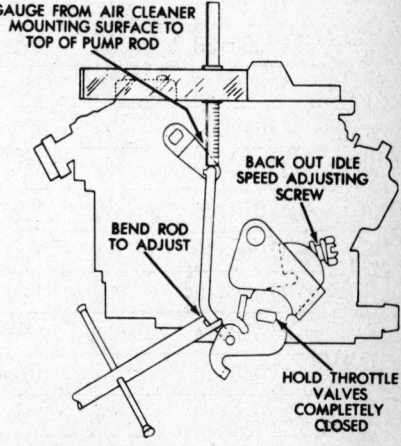

GAUGE FROM AIR CLEANER MOUNTING SURFACE TO TOP OF PUMP ROD

BACK OUT IDLE SPEED ADJUSTING SCREW

BEND ROD TO ADJUST

HOLD THROTTLE VALVES COMPLETELY CLOSED

Accelerator pump rod (© G.M. Corp.)

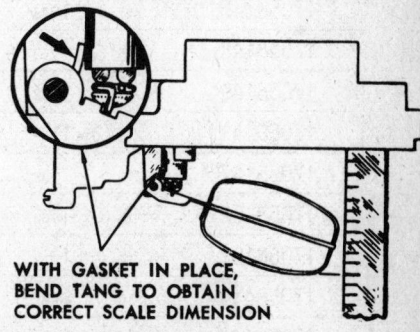

WITH GASKET IN PLACE, BEND TANG TO OBTAIN CORRECT SCALE DIMENSION

Float Drop, Metal Float

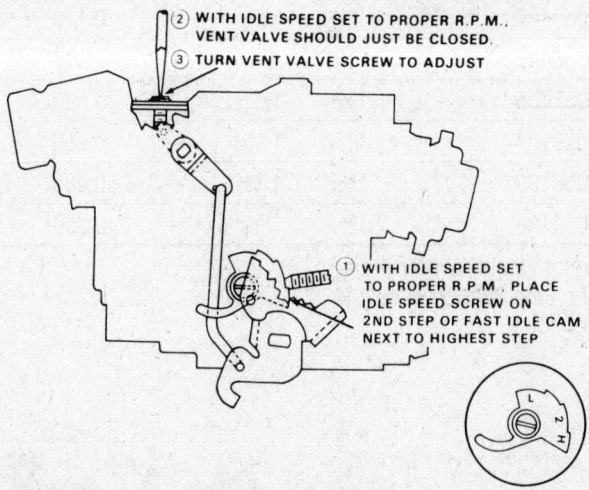

② WITH IDLE SPEED SET TO PROPER R.P.M. VENT VALVE SHOULD JUST BE CLOSED.

③ TURN VENT VALVE SCREW TO ADJUST

① WITH IDLE SPEED SET TO PROPER R.P.M. PLACE IDLE SPEED SCREW ON 2ND STEP OF FAST IDLE CAM NEXT TO HIGHEST STEP

Bowl vent valve adjustment (© Buick Div., G.M. Corp.)

2GC, 2GV, 2GE CARBURETOR SPECIFICATIONS
Buick

Year	Carburetor Identification ①	Float Level (in.)	Float Drop (in.)	Pump Rod (in.)	Idle Vent (in.)	Primary Vacuum Break (in.)	Secondary Vacuum Break (in.)	Automatic Choke (notches)	Choke Rod (in.)	Choke Unloader (in.)	Fast Idle Speed (rpm)
'78	17058104	15/32	1 9/32	1 21/32	—	0.160	—	Index	0.260	0.325	—
	17058105	15/32	1 9/32	1 21/32	—	0.160	—	Index	0.260	0.325	—
	17058108	19/32	1 9/32	1 21/32	—	0.160	—	Index	0.260	0.325	—
	17058110	19/32	1 9/32	1 21/32	—	0.160	—	Index	0.260	0.325	—
	17058112	19/32	1 9/32	1 21/32	—	0.160	—	Index	0.260	0.325	—
	17058114	19/32	1 9/32	1 21/32	—	0.160	—	Index	0.260	0.325	—
	17058126	19/32	1 9/32	1 17/32	—	0.150	—	Index	0.260	0.325	—
	17058128	19/32	1 9/32	1 17/32	—	0.150	—	Index	0.260	0.325	—
	17058404	1/2	1 9/32	1 21/32	—	0.160	—	1/2 Lean	0.260	0.325	—
	17058405	1/2	1 9/32	1 21/32	—	0.160	—	1/2 Lean	0.260	0.325	—
	17058408	21/32	1 9/32	1 21/32	—	0.160	—	1/2 Lean	0.260	0.325	—
	17058410	21/32	1 9/32	1 21/32	—	0.160	—	1/2 Lean	0.260	0.325	—
	17058412	21/32	1 9/32	1 21/32	—	0.160	—	1/2 Lean	0.260	0.325	—
	17058414	21/32	1 9/32	1 21/32	—	0.160	—	1/2 Lean	0.260	0.325	—
	17058140	7/16	1 5/32	1 19/32	—	0.070	0.110	1 Rich	0.080	0.140	—
	17058143	7/16	1 5/32	1 9/16	—	0.080	0.110	1 Rich	0.080	0.140	—
	17058144	7/16	1 5/32	1 5/8	—	0.060	0.110	1 Rich	0.080	0.140	—
	17058145	7/16	1 5/32	1 19/32	—	0.060	0.110	1 Rich	0.080	0.160	—
	17058148	7/16	1 5/32	1 19/32	—	0.080	0.110	1 Rich	0.080	0.150	—
	17058149	7/16	1 5/32	1 19/32	—	0.080	0.110	1 Rich	0.080	0.150	—
	17058141	7/16	1 5/32	1 19/32	—	0.100	0.140	1 Rich	0.080	0.140	—
	17058147	7/16	1 5/32	1 19/32	—	0.100	0.140	1 Rich	0.080	0.140	—
	17058182	7/16	1 5/32	1 19/32	—	0.080	0.110	1 Rich	0.080	0.140	—
	17058183	7/16	1 5/32	1 19/32	—	0.080	0.110	1 Rich	0.080	0.140	—
	17058444	7/16	1 5/32	1 19/32	—	0.100	0.140	1 Rich	0.080	0.140	—
	17058446	7/16	1 5/32	1 19/32	—	0.110	0.130	1 Rich	0.080	0.140	—
	17058447	7/16	1 5/32	1 19/32	—	0.110	0.150	1 Rich	0.080	0.140	—
	17058448	7/16	1 5/32	1 9/16	—	0.100	0.140	1 Rich	0.080	0.140	—
	17058185	7/16	1 5/32	1 19/32	—	0.050	0.110	1 Rich	0.080	0.140	—
	17058187	7/16	1 5/32	1 19/32	—	0.050	0.110	1 Rich	0.080	0.140	—
	17058189	7/16	1 5/32	1 19/32	—	0.080	0.110	1 Rich	0.080	0.140	—
	17058188	7/16	1 5/32	1 5/8	—	0.050	0.120	1 Rich	0.080	0.140	—

① The carburetor identification number is stamped on the float bowl, next to the fuel inlet nut.

2GC, 2GV, 2GE CARBURETOR SPECIFICATIONS
Chevrolet

Year	Carburetor Identification①	Float Level (in.)	Float Drop (in.)	Pump Rod (in.)	Idle Vent (in.)	Primary Vacuum Break (in.)	Secondary Vacuum Break (in.)	Automatic Choke (notches)	Choke Rod (in.)	Choke Unloader (in.)	Fast Idle Speed (rpm)
'78	17058102	$^{15}/_{32}$	$1^9/_{32}$	$1^{17}/_{32}$	—	0.150	—	Index	0.260	0.325	—
	17058103	$^{15}/_{32}$	$1^9/_{32}$	$1^{17}/_{32}$	—	0.150	—	Index	0.260	0.325	—
	17058104	$^{15}/_{32}$	$1^9/_{32}$	$1^{21}/_{32}$	—	0.160	—	Index	0.260	0.325	—
	17058107	$^{15}/_{32}$	$1^9/_{32}$	$1^{17}/_{32}$	—	0.160	—	Index	0.260	0.325	—
	17058109	$^{15}/_{32}$	$1^9/_{32}$	$1^{17}/_{32}$	—	0.160	—	Index	0.260	0.325	—
	17058404	$^1/_2$	$1^9/_{32}$	$1^{21}/_{32}$	—	0.160	—	½ Lean	0.260	0.325	—
	17058405	$^1/_2$	$1^9/_{32}$	$1^{21}/_{32}$	—	0.160	—	Index	0.260	0.325	—
	17058447	$^7/_{16}$	$1^5/_{32}$	$1^5/_8$	—	0.110	0.150	1 Rich	0.080	0.140	—
	17058143	$^7/_{16}$	$1^5/_{32}$	$1^5/_8$	—	0.040	0.110	1 Rich	0.080	0.140	—
	17058147	$^7/_{16}$	$1^5/_{32}$	$1^5/_8$	—	0.100	0.140	1 Rich	0.080	0.140	—
	17058144	$^7/_{16}$	$1^5/_{32}$	$1^5/_8$	—	0.060	0.110	1 Rich	0.080	0.140	—

① The carburetor identification number is stamped on the float bowl, next to the fuel inlet nut.

2GC, 2GV, 2GE, CARBURETOR SPECIFICATIONS
Chevrolet Vega, Monza

Year	Carburetor Identification①	Float Level (in.)	Float Drop (in.)	Pump Rod (in.)	Idle Vent (in.)	Primary Vacuum Break (in.)	Secondary Vacuum Break (in.)	Automatic Choke (notches)	Choke Rod (in.)	Choke Unloader (in.)	Fast Idle Speed (rpm)
'78	17058102	$^{15}/_{32}$	$1^9/_{32}$	$1^{17}/_{32}$	—	0.150	—	Index	0.260	0.325	—
	17058103	$^{15}/_{32}$	$1^9/_{32}$	$1^{17}/_{32}$	—	0.150	—	Index	0.260	0.325	—
	17058104	$^{15}/_{32}$	$1^9/_{32}$	$1^{21}/_{32}$	—	0.160	—	Index	0.260	0.325	—
	17058107	$^{15}/_{32}$	$1^9/_{32}$	$1^{17}/_{32}$	—	0.160	—	Index	0.260	0.325	—
	17058109	$^{15}/_{32}$	$1^9/_{32}$	$1^{17}/_{32}$	—	0.160	—	Index	0.260	0.325	—
	17058404	$^1/_2$	$1^9/_{32}$	$1^{21}/_{32}$	—	0.160	—	½ Lean	0.260	0.325	—
	17058405	$^1/_2$	$1^9/_{32}$	$1^{21}/_{32}$	—	0.160	—	Index	0.260	0.325	—
	17058447	$^7/_{16}$	$1^5/_{32}$	$1^5/_8$	—	0.110	0.150	1Rich	0.080	0.140	—
	17058143	$^7/_{16}$	$1^5/_{32}$	$1^5/_8$	—	0.040	0.110	1Rich	0.080	0.140	—
	17058147	$^7/_{16}$	$1^5/_{32}$	$1^5/_8$	—	0.100	0.140	1Rich	0.080	0.140	—
	17058144	$^7/_{16}$	$1^5/_{32}$	$1^5/_8$	—	0.060	0.110	1 Rich	0.080	0.140	—

① The carburetor identification number is stamped on the float bowl, next to the fuel inlet nut.

2GC, 2GV, 2GE CARBURETOR SPECIFICATIONS
Oldsmobile

Year	Carburetor Identification①	Float Level (in.)	Float Drop (in.)	Pump Rod (in.)	Idle Vent (in.)	Primary Vacuum Break (in.)	Secondary Vacuum Break (in.)	Automatic Choke (notches)	Choke Rod (in.)	Choke Unloader (in.)	Fast Idle Speed (rpm)
'78	17058102	$^{15}/_{32}$	$1^9/_{32}$	$1^{17}/_{32}$	—	0.130	—	Index	0.260	0.325	—
	17058103	$^{15}/_{32}$	$1^9/_{32}$	$1^{17}/_{32}$	—	0.130	—	Index	0.260	0.325	—
	17058104	$^{15}/_{32}$	$1^9/_{32}$	$1^{21}/_{32}$	—	0.130	—	Index	0.260	0.325	—
	17058105	$^{15}/_{32}$	$1^9/_{32}$	$1^{21}/_{32}$	—	0.130	—	Index	0.260	0.325	—
	17058107	$^{15}/_{32}$	$1^9/_{32}$	$1^{17}/_{32}$	—	0.130	—	Index	0.260	0.325	—
	17058108	$^{19}/_{32}$	$1^9/_{32}$	$1^{21}/_{32}$	—	0.130	—	Index	0.260	0.325	—
	17058109	$^{15}/_{32}$	$1^9/_{32}$	$1^{17}/_{32}$	—	0.130	—	Index	0.260	0.325	—
	17058110	$^{19}/_{32}$	$1^9/_{32}$	$1^{21}/_{32}$	—	0.130	—	Index	0.260	0.325	—
	17058111	$^{19}/_{32}$	$1^9/_{32}$	$1^{17}/_{32}$	—	0.130	—	Index	0.260	0.325	—
	17058113	$^{19}/_{32}$	$1^9/_{32}$	$1^{17}/_{32}$	—	0.130	—	Index	0.260	0.325	—
	17058121	$^{19}/_{32}$	$1^9/_{32}$	$1^{17}/_{32}$	—	0.130	—	Index	0.260	0.325	—
	17058123	$^{19}/_{32}$	$1^9/_{32}$	$1^{17}/_{32}$	—	0.130	—	Index	0.260	0.325	—
	17058126	$^{19}/_{32}$	$1^9/_{32}$	$1^{17}/_{32}$	—	0.130	—	Index	0.260	0.325	—
	17058128	$^{19}/_{32}$	$1^9/_{32}$	$1^{17}/_{32}$	—	0.130	—	Index	0.260	0.325	—
	17058140	$^7/_{16}$	$1^5/_{32}$	$1^{19}/_{32}$	—	0.070	0.110	1 Rich	0.080	0.140	—
	17058145	$^7/_{16}$	$1^5/_{32}$	$1^{19}/_{32}$	—	0.060	0.110	1 Rich	0.080	0.160	—
	17058147	$^7/_{16}$	$1^5/_{32}$	$1^{19}/_{32}$	—	0.100	0.140	1 Rich	0.080	0.140	—
	17058182	$^7/_{16}$	$1^5/_{32}$	$1^{19}/_{32}$	—	0.080	0.110	1 Rich	0.080	0.140	—
	17058183	$^7/_{16}$	$1^5/_{32}$	$1^{19}/_{32}$	—	0.080	0.110	1 Rich	0.080	0.140	—
	17058185	$^7/_{16}$	$1^5/_{32}$	$1^{19}/_{32}$	—	0.050	0.110	1 Rich	0.080	0.140	—
	17058187	$^7/_{16}$	$1^5/_{32}$	$1^{19}/_{32}$	—	0.080	0.110	1 Rich	0.080	0.140	—
	17058189	$^7/_{16}$	$1^5/_{32}$	$1^{19}/_{32}$	—	0.080	0.110	1 Rich	0.080	0.140	—
	17058404	$^1/_2$	$1^9/_{32}$	$1^{21}/_{32}$	—	0.140	—	½ Lean	0.260	0.325	—
	17058405	$^1/_2$	$1^9/_{32}$	$1^{21}/_{32}$	—	0.140	—	½ Lean	0.260	0.325	—
	17058408	$^{21}/_{32}$	$1^9/_{32}$	$1^{21}/_{32}$	—	0.140	—	½ Lean	0.260	0.325	—
	17058410	$^{21}/_{32}$	$1^9/_{32}$	$1^{21}/_{32}$	—	0.140	—	½ Lean	0.260	0.325	—
	17058444	$^7/_{16}$	$1^5/_{32}$	$1^{19}/_{32}$	—	0.100	0.140	1 Rich	0.080	0.140	—
	17058446	$^7/_{16}$	$1^5/_{32}$	$1^{19}/_{32}$	—	0.110	0.130	1 Rich	0.080	0.140	—
	17058447	$^7/_{16}$	$1^5/_{32}$	$1^{19}/_{32}$	—	0.110	0.150	1 Rich	0.080	0.140	—
	17058448	$^7/_{16}$	$1^5/_{32}$	$1^9/_{16}$	—	0.100	0.140	1 Rich	0.080	0.140	—

① The carburetor identification is stamped on the float bowl, next to the fuel inlet nut.

2GC, 2GV, 2GE CARBURETOR SPECIFICATIONS
Pontiac

Year	Carburetor Identification①	Float Level (in.)	Float Drop (in.)	Pump Rod (in.)	Idle Vent (in.)	Primary Vacuum Break (in.)	Secondary Vacuum Break (in.)	Automatic Choke (notches)	Choke Rod (in.)	Choke Unloader (in.)	Fast Idle Speed (rpm)
'78	17058102	$^{19}/_{32}$	$1^9/_{32}$	$1^{17}/_{32}$	—	0.130	—	Index	0.260	0.325	—
	17058103	$^{19}/_{32}$	$1^9/_{32}$	$1^{17}/_{32}$	—	0.130	—	Index	0.260	0.325	—

2GC, 2GV, 2GE CARBURETOR SPECIFICATIONS
Pontiac

Year	Carburetor Identification ①	Float Level (in.)	Float Drop (in.)	Pump Rod (in.)	Idle Vent (in.)	Primary Vacuum Break (in.)	Secondary Vacuum Break (in.)	Automatic Choke (notches)	Choke Rod (in.)	Choke Unloader (in.)	Fast Idle Speed (rpm)
'78	17058108	19/32	19/32	1 21/32	—	0.130	—	Index	0.260	0.325	—
	17058110	19/32	19/32	1 21/32	—	0.130	—	Index	0.260	0.325	—
	17058111	19/32	19/32	1 5/8	—	0.130	—	Index	0.260	0.325	—
	17058112	19/32	19/32	1 21/32	—	0.130	—	Index	0.260	0.325	—
	17058113	19/32	19/32	1 5/8	—	0.130	—	Index	0.260	0.325	—
	17058114	19/32	19/32	1 21/32	—	0.130	—	Index	0.260	0.325	—
	17058121	19/32	19/32	1 5/8	—	0.130	—	Index	0.260	0.325	—
	17058123	19/32	19/32	1 5/8	—	0.130	—	Index	0.260	0.325	—
	17058126	19/32	19/32	1 17/32	—	0.130	—	Index	0.260	0.325	—
	17058128	19/32	19/32	1 17/32	—	0.130	—	Index	0.260	0.325	—
	17058145	7/16	1 5/32	1 5/8	—	0.110	0.110	1 Lean	0.080	0.160	—
	17058147	7/16	1 5/32	1 5/8	—	0.140	0.140	1 Rich	0.080	0.140	—
	17058182	7/16	1 5/32	1 5/8	—	0.110	0.110	1 Rich	0.080	0.140	—
	17058183	7/16	1 5/32	1 5/8	—	0.110	0.110	1 Rich	0.080	0.140	—
	17058185	7/16	1 5/32	1 19/32	—	0.110	0.110	1 Rich	0.080	0.140	—
	17058187	7/16	1 5/32	1 19/32	—	0.110	0.110	1 Rich	0.080	0.140	—
	17058189	7/16	1 5/32	1 19/32	—	0.110	0.110	1 Rich	0.080	0.140	—
	17058408	21/32	19/32	1 21/32	—	0.140	0.140	½ Lean	0.260	0.325	—
	17058410	21/32	19/32	1 21/32	—	0.140	0.140	½ Lean	0.260	0.325	—
	17058412	21/32	19/32	1 21/32	—	0.140	0.140	½ Lean	0.260	0.325	—
	17058414	21/32	19/32	1 21/32	—	0.140	0.140	½ Lean	0.260	0.325	—
	17058444	7/16	1 5/32	1 5/8	—	0.140	0.140	1 Rich	0.080	0.140	—
	17058446	7/16	1 5/32	1 5/8	—	0.140	0.140	1 Rich	0.080	0.140	—
	17058447	7/16	1 5/32	1 5/8	—	0.150	0.150	1 Rich	0.080	0.140	—
	17058448	7/16	1 5/32	1 5/8	—	0.140	0.140	1 Rich	0.080	0.140	—

① The carburetor identification number is stamped on the float bowl, next to the fuel inlet nut.

Models 2SE and E2SE

The Rochester 2SE and E2SE Varajet II carburetors are two barrel, two stage downdraft units. Most carburetor components are aluminum, although a zinc choke housing is used on four cylinder engines installed in 1980 models. The E2SE is used both in conventional installations and in the Computer Controlled Catalytic Converter System. In that installation the E2SE is equipped with an electrically operated mixture control solenoid, controlled by the Electronic Control Module. The 2SE and E2SE are also used on the AMC four cylinder in 1980–83.

FLOAT ADJUSTMENT

1. Remove the air horn from the throttle body.
2. Use your fingers to hold the retainer in place, and to push the float down into light contact with the needle.
3. Measure the distance from the toe of the float (furthest from the hinge) to the top of the carburetor (gasket removed).
4. To adjust, remove the float and gently bend the arm to specification. After adjustment, check the float alignment in the chamber.

NOTE: Some models have a float stabilizer spring. If used, remove the spring with float. Use care when removing.

PUMP ADJUSTMENT

1. With the throttle closed and the fast idle screw off the steps of the fast idle cam, measure the distance from the air horn casting to the top of the pump stem.
2. To adjust, remove the retaining screw and washer and remove the pump lever. Bend the end of the lever to correct the

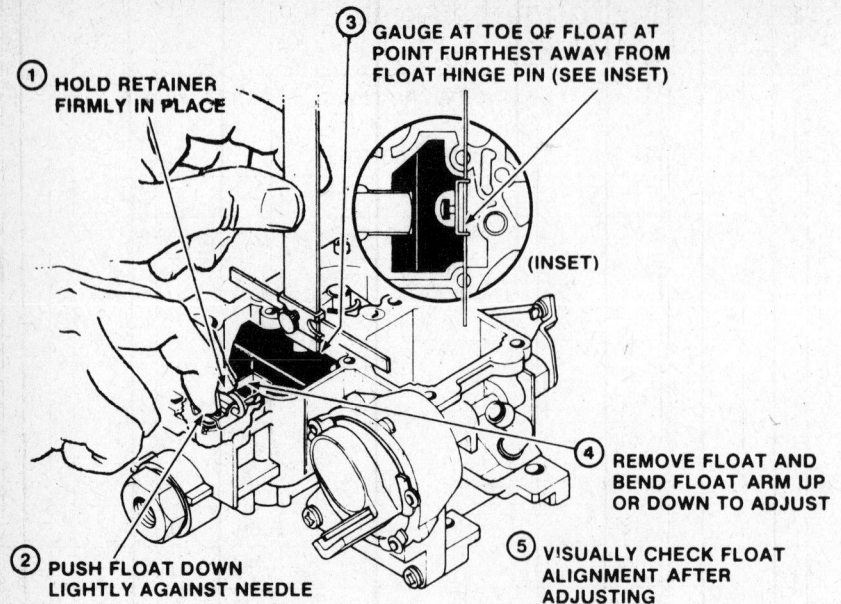

① HOLD RETAINER FIRMLY IN PLACE

③ GAUGE AT TOE OF FLOAT AT POINT FURTHEST AWAY FROM FLOAT HINGE PIN (SEE INSET)

(INSET)

④ REMOVE FLOAT AND BEND FLOAT ARM UP OR DOWN TO ADJUST

② PUSH FLOAT DOWN LIGHTLY AGAINST NEEDLE

⑤ VISUALLY CHECK FLOAT ALIGNMENT AFTER ADJUSTING

2SE, E2SE float adjustment (© G.M. Corp.)

stem height. Do not twist the lever or bend it sideways.

3. Install the lever, washer and screw and check the adjustment. When correct, open and close the throttle a few times to check the linkage movement and alignment.

NOTE: No pump adjustment is required on 1981 and later models.

NOTE: ON MODELS USING A CLIP TO RETAIN PUMP ROD IN PUMP LEVER, NO PUMP ADJUSTMENT IS REQUIRED. ON MODELS USING THE "CLIPLESS" PUMP ROD, THE PUMP ADJUSTMENT SHOULD NOT BE CHANGED FROM ORIGINAL FACTORY SETTING UNLESS GAUGING SHOWS OUT OF SPECIFICATION. THE PUMP LEVER IS MADE FROM HEAVY DUTY, HARDENED STEEL MAKING BENDING DIFFICULT. DO NOT REMOVE PUMP LEVER FOR BENDING UNLESS ABSOLUTELY NECESSARY.

① THROTTLE VALVES COMPLETELY CLOSED. MAKE SURE FAST IDLE SCREW IS OFF STEPS OF FAST IDLE CAM.

③ IF NECESSARY TO ADJUST, REMOVE PUMP LEVER RETAINING SCREW AND WASHER AND REMOVE PUMP LEVER BY ROTATING LEVER TO REMOVE FROM PUMP ROD. PLACE LEVER IN A VISE, PROTECTING LEVER FROM DAMAGE, AND BEND END OF LEVER (NEAREST NECKED DOWN SECTION).

NOTE: DO NOT BEND LEVER IN A SIDEWAYS OR TWISTING MOTION.

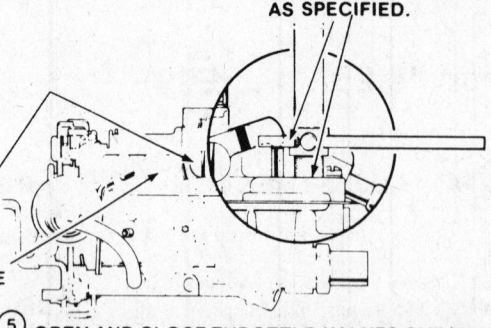

② GAUGE FROM AIR HORN CASTING SURFACE TO TOP OF PUMP STEM. DIMENSION SHOULD BE AS SPECIFIED.

⑤ OPEN AND CLOSE THROTTLE VALVES CHECKING LINKAGE FOR FREEDOM OF MOVEMENT AND OBSERVING PUMP LEVER ALIGNMENT.

④ REINSTALL PUMP LEVER, WASHER AND RETAINING SCREW. RECHECK PUMP ADJUSTMENT ① AND ②. TIGHTEN RETAINING SCREW SECURELY AFTER THE PUMP ADJUSTMENT IS CORRECT.

2SE, E2SE pump adjustment (© G.M. Corp.)

FAST IDLE ADJUSTMENT

1. Set the ignition timing and curb idle speed, and disconnect and plug hoses as directed on the emission control decal.
2. Place the fast idle screw on the highest step of the cam.
3. Start the engine and adjust the engine speed to specification with the fast idle screw.

CHOKE COIL LEVER ADJUSTMENT

1. Remove the three retaining screws and remove the choke cover and coil. On models with a riveted choke cover, drill out the three rivets and remove the cover and choke coil.

NOTE: A choke stat cover retainer kit is required for reassembly.

2. Place the fast idle screw on the high step of the cam.
3. Close the choke by pushing in on the intermediate choke lever. On front wheel drive models, the intermediate choke lever is behind the choke vacuum diaphragm.
4. Insert a drill or gauge of the specified size into the hole in the choke housing. The choke lever in the housing should be up against the side of the gauge.
5. If the lever does not just touch the gauge, bend the intermediate choke rod to adjust.

FAST IDLE CAM (CHOKE ROD) ADJUSTMENT

1980–82

NOTE: A special angle gauge should be used.

1. Adjust the choke coil lever and fast idle first.
2. Rotate the degree scale until it is zeroed.
3. Close the choke and install the degree scale onto the choke plate. Center the leveling bubble.
4. Rotate the scale so that the specified degree is opposite the scale pointer.
5. Place the fast idle screw on the second step of the cam (against the high step). Close the choke by pushing in the intermediate lever.
6. Push on the vacuum break lever in the direction of opening choke until the lever is against the rear tang on the choke lever.
7. Bend the fast idle cam rod at the U to adjust angle to specifications.

1983–84

Refer to the illustration for the adjustment procedure on these models.

AIR VALVE ROD ADJUSTMENT

1980

1. Seat the vacuum diaphragm with an outside vacuum source. Tape over the purge bleed hole if present.
2. Close the air valve.
3. Insert the specified gauge between the rod and the end of the slot in the plunger on fours, or between the rod and the end of the slot in the air valve on V6s.
4. Bend the rod to adjust the clearance.

1981–82

1. Align the zero degree mark with the pointer on an angle gauge.

2. Close the air valve and place a magnet on top of it.

3. Rotate the bubble until it is centered.

4. Rotate the degree scale until the specified degree mark is aligned with the pointer.

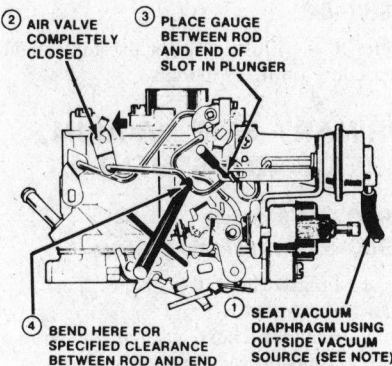

② AIR VALVE COMPLETELY CLOSED

③ PLACE GAUGE BETWEEN ROD AND END OF SLOT IN PLUNGER

④ BEND HERE FOR SPECIFIED CLEARANCE BETWEEN ROD AND END OF SLOT IN PLUNGER.

① SEAT VACUUM DIAPHRAGM USING OUTSIDE VACUUM SOURCE (SEE NOTE)

NOTE: PLUG END COVER WITH TAPE IF PURGE BLEED HOLE IS USED. REMOVE TAPE AFTER ADJUSTMENT.

2SE and E2SE air valve rod adjustment—1980 G.M. models, 1980–82 American Motors (© G.M. Corp.)

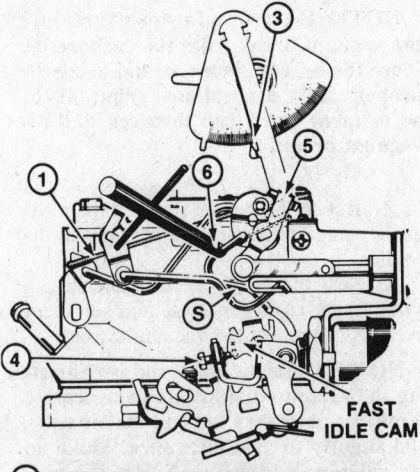

① ATTACH RUBBER BAND TO INTERMEDIATE CHOKE LEVER.

② OPEN THROTTLE TO ALLOW CHOKE VALVE TO CLOSE.

③ SET UP ANGLE GAGE AND SET ANGLE TO SPECIFICATIONS.

④ PLACE FAST IDLE SCREW ON SECOND STEP OF CAM AGAINST RISE OF HIGH STEP.

⑤ PUSH ON CHOKE SHAFT LEVER TO OPEN CHOKE VALVE AND TO MAKE CONTACT WITH BLACK CLOSING TANG.

⑥ SUPPORT AT "S" AND ADJUST BY BENDING FAST IDLE CAM ROD UNTIL BUBBLE IS CENTERED.

E2SE fast idle cam (choke rod) adjustment—1983 and later

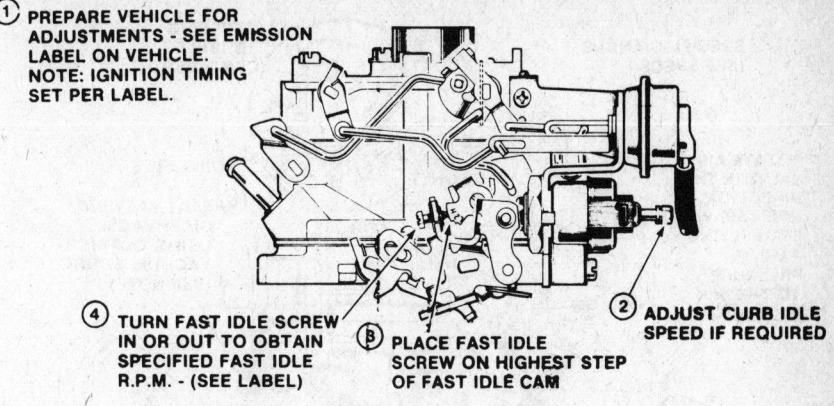

① PREPARE VEHICLE FOR ADJUSTMENTS - SEE EMISSION LABEL ON VEHICLE. NOTE: IGNITION TIMING SET PER LABEL.

④ TURN FAST IDLE SCREW IN OR OUT TO OBTAIN SPECIFIED FAST IDLE R.P.M. - (SEE LABEL)

③ PLACE FAST IDLE SCREW ON HIGHEST STEP OF FAST IDLE CAM

② ADJUST CURB IDLE SPEED IF REQUIRED

2SE, E2SE fast idle adjustment (© G.M. Corp.)

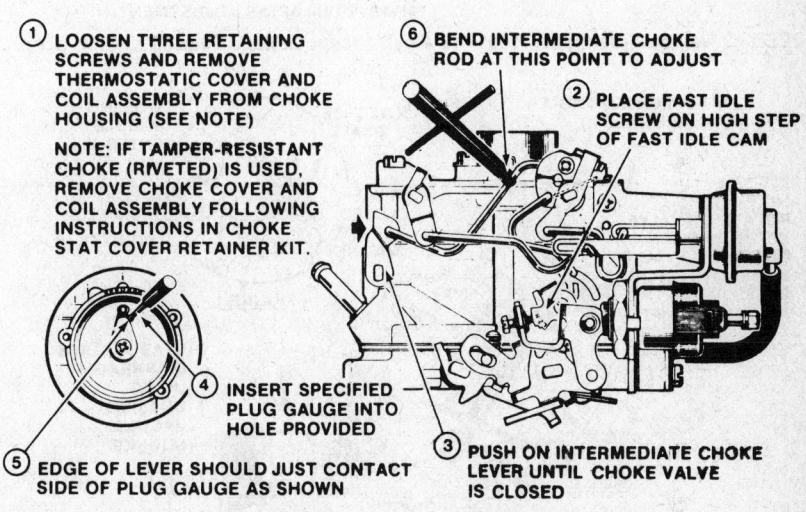

① LOOSEN THREE RETAINING SCREWS AND REMOVE THERMOSTATIC COVER AND COIL ASSEMBLY FROM CHOKE HOUSING (SEE NOTE)

NOTE: IF TAMPER-RESISTANT CHOKE (RIVETED) IS USED, REMOVE CHOKE COVER AND COIL ASSEMBLY FOLLOWING INSTRUCTIONS IN CHOKE STAT COVER RETAINER KIT.

④ INSERT SPECIFIED PLUG GAUGE INTO HOLE PROVIDED

⑤ EDGE OF LEVER SHOULD JUST CONTACT SIDE OF PLUG GAUGE AS SHOWN

⑥ BEND INTERMEDIATE CHOKE ROD AT THIS POINT TO ADJUST

② PLACE FAST IDLE SCREW ON HIGH STEP OF FAST IDLE CAM

③ PUSH ON INTERMEDIATE CHOKE LEVER UNTIL CHOKE VALVE IS CLOSED

2SE, E2SE choke coil lever adjustment (© G.M. Corp.)

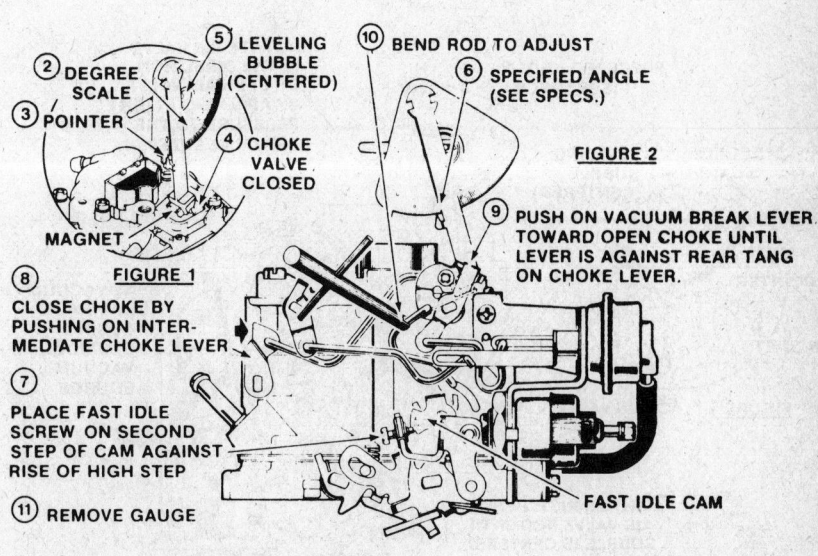

② DEGREE SCALE

③ POINTER

⑤ LEVELING BUBBLE (CENTERED)

④ CHOKE VALVE CLOSED

MAGNET

⑧ **FIGURE 1**

CLOSE CHOKE BY PUSHING ON INTERMEDIATE CHOKE LEVER.

⑦ PLACE FAST IDLE SCREW ON SECOND STEP OF CAM AGAINST RISE OF HIGH STEP

⑪ REMOVE GAUGE

⑩ BEND ROD TO ADJUST

⑥ SPECIFIED ANGLE (SEE SPECS.)

FIGURE 2

⑨ PUSH ON VACUUM BREAK LEVER TOWARD OPEN CHOKE UNTIL LEVER IS AGAINST REAR TANG ON CHOKE LEVER.

FAST IDLE CAM

2SE, E2SE fast idle cam adjustment—models through 1982 © G.M. Corp.

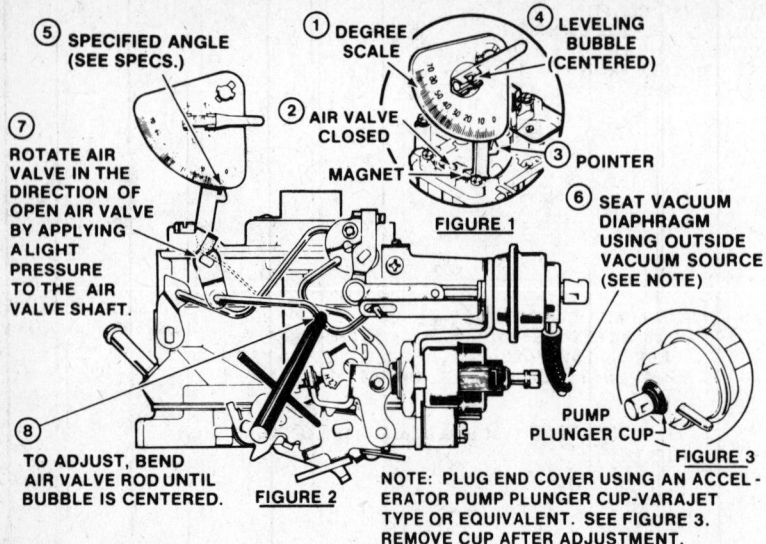

E2SE air valve adjustment—1981–82 4 cyl. except G.M. "J" series © G.M. Corp.

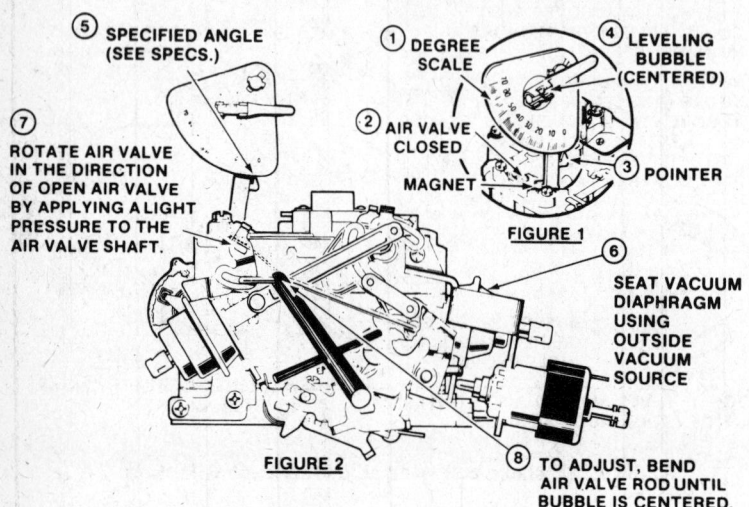

E2SE air valve adjustment—1981–82 V6 engine © G.M. Corp.

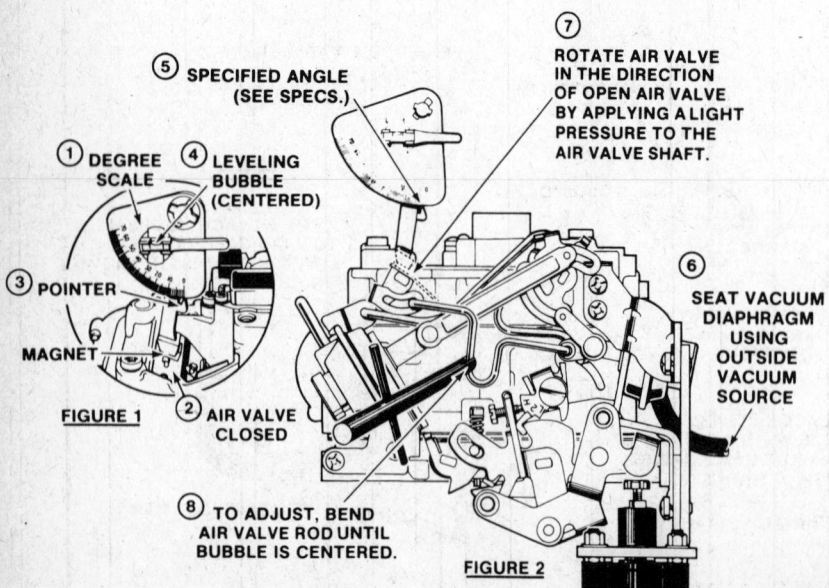

E2SE air valve adjustment—1982 G.M. J series (© G.M. Corp.)

5. Seat the vacuum diaphragm using an external vacuum source.

6. On four cylinder models plug the end cover. Unplug after adjustment.

7. Apply light pressure to the air valve shaft in the direction to open the air valve until all the slack is removed between the air link and plunger slot.

8. Bend the air valve link until the bubble is centered.

1983–84

Refer to the illustration for the adjustment procedure on these models.

PRIMARY SIDE VACUUM BREAK ADJUSTMENT

1980 GM Models
1980–83 American Motors

1. Follow Steps 1–4 of the "Fast Idle Cam Adjustment".

2. Seat the choke vacuum diaphragm with an outside vacuum source.

3. Push in on the intermediate choke lever to close the choke valve, and hold closed during adjustment.

4. Adjust by bending the vacuum break rod until the bubble is centered.

1981–82 GM Models

NOTE: Prior to adjustment, remove the vacuum break from the carburetor. Place the bracket in a vise and using the proper safety precautions, grind off the adjustment screw cap then reinstall the vacuum break.

1. Rotate the degree scale on the measuring gauge until the zero is opposite the pointer.

2. Seat the choke vacuum diaphragm by applying an external vacuum source of over 5" vacuum to the vacuum break.

NOTE: If the air valve rod is restricting the vacuum diaphragm from seating it may be necessary to bend the air valve rod slightly to gain clearance. Make an air valve rod adjustment after the vacuum break adjustment.

3. Read the angle gauge while lightly pushing on the intermediate choke lever so that the choke valve is toward the close position.

4. Use a 1/8 in. hex wrench and turn the screw in the rear cover until the bubble is centered. Apply a silicone sealant over the screw head to seal the setting.

1983–84 GM Models

Refer to the illustration for the adjustment procedure on these models.

ELECTRIC CHOKE SETTING

This procedure is only for those carburetors with choke covers retained by screws. Riv-

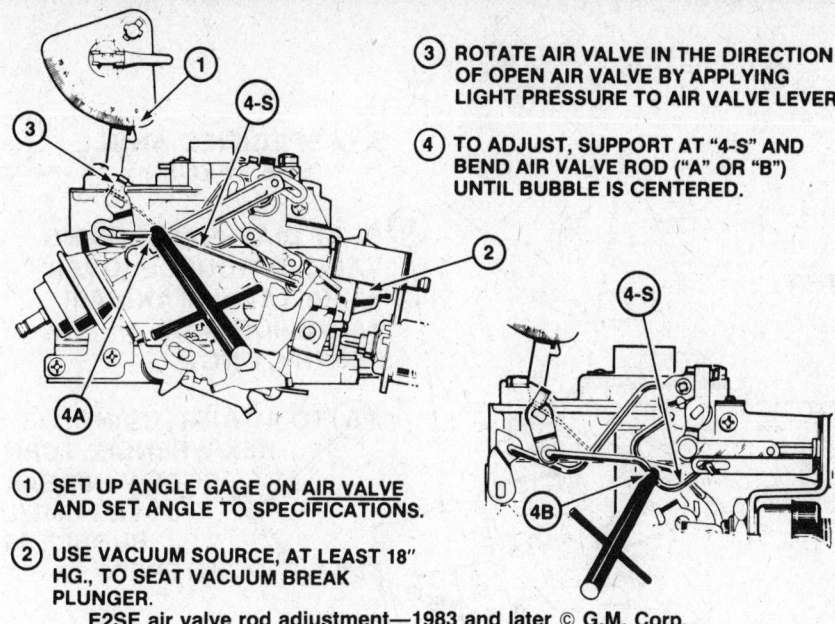

③ ROTATE AIR VALVE IN THE DIRECTION OF OPEN AIR VALVE BY APPLYING LIGHT PRESSURE TO AIR VALVE LEVER.

④ TO ADJUST, SUPPORT AT "4-S" AND BEND AIR VALVE ROD ("A" OR "B") UNTIL BUBBLE IS CENTERED.

① SET UP ANGLE GAGE ON AIR VALVE AND SET ANGLE TO SPECIFICATIONS.

② USE VACUUM SOURCE, AT LEAST 18" HG., TO SEAT VACUUM BREAK PLUNGER.

E2SE air valve rod adjustment—1983 and later © G.M. Corp.

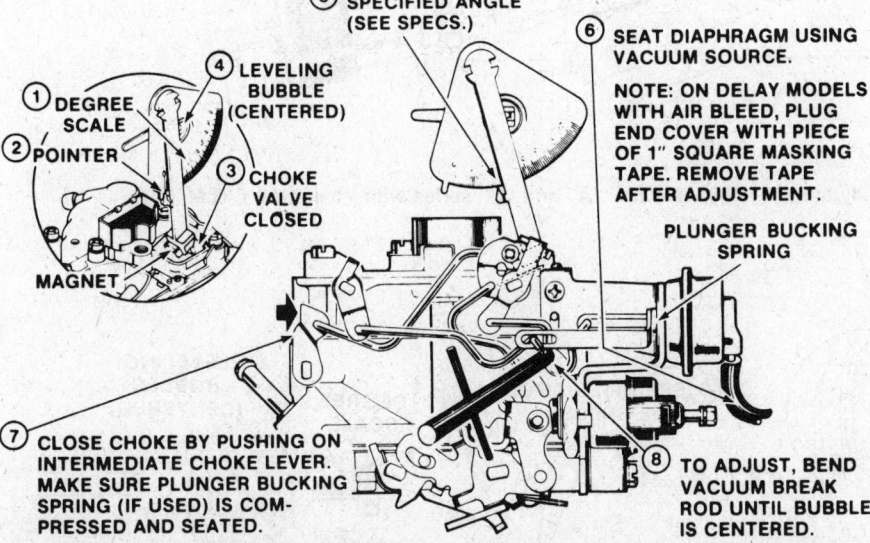

⑤ SPECIFIED ANGLE (SEE SPECS.)

⑥ SEAT DIAPHRAGM USING VACUUM SOURCE.

NOTE: ON DELAY MODELS WITH AIR BLEED, PLUG END COVER WITH PIECE OF 1" SQUARE MASKING TAPE. REMOVE TAPE AFTER ADJUSTMENT.

① DEGREE SCALE
② POINTER
④ LEVELING BUBBLE (CENTERED)
③ CHOKE VALVE CLOSED
MAGNET
PLUNGER BUCKING SPRING

⑦ CLOSE CHOKE BY PUSHING ON INTERMEDIATE CHOKE LEVER. MAKE SURE PLUNGER BUCKING SPRING (IF USED) IS COMPRESSED AND SEATED.

⑧ TO ADJUST, BEND VACUUM BREAK ROD UNTIL BUBBLE IS CENTERED.

2SE, E2SE primary vacuum break adjustment—1980 G.M. and 1980–83 American Motors with 4 cyl. engines © G.M. Corp.

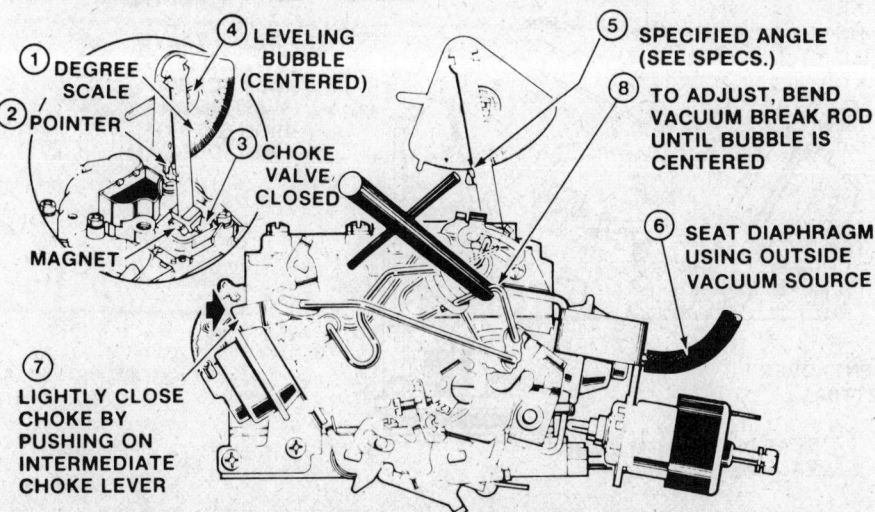

① DEGREE SCALE
② POINTER
④ LEVELING BUBBLE (CENTERED)
③ CHOKE VALVE CLOSED
MAGNET

⑤ SPECIFIED ANGLE (SEE SPECS.)
⑧ TO ADJUST, BEND VACUUM BREAK ROD UNTIL BUBBLE IS CENTERED
⑥ SEAT DIAPHRAGM USING OUTSIDE VACUUM SOURCE

⑦ LIGHTLY CLOSE CHOKE BY PUSHING ON INTERMEDIATE CHOKE LEVER

V6 2SE and E2SE primary vacuum break adjustment—1980 (© G.M. Corp.)

eted choke covers are preset and nonadjustable.

1. Loosen the three retaining screws.
2. Place the fast idle screw on the high step of the cam.
3. Rotate the choke cover to align the cover mark with the specified housing mark.

NOTE: The specification "index" which appears in the specification table refers to the mark between "1 notch lean" and "1 notch rich".

SECONDARY VACUUM BREAK ADJUSTMENT

1980

This procedure is for V6 installations in front wheel drive models only.

1. Follow Steps 1–4 of the "Fast Idle Cam Adjustment".
2. Seat the choke vacuum diaphragm with an outside vacuum source.
3. Push in on the intermediate choke lever to close the choke valve, and hold closed during adjustment. Make sure the plunger spring is compressed and seated, if present.
4. Bend the vacuum break rod at the U next to the diaphragm until the bubble is centered.

1981–82 GM Models

NOTE: Prior to adjustment, remove the vacuum break from the carburetor. Place the bracket in the vise and using the proper safety precautions, grind off the adjustment screw cap then reinstall the vacuum break.

NOTE: Plug the end cover using an accelerator pump plunger cup or equivalent. Remove the cup after the adjustment (A and X series only).

1. Rotate the degree scale on the measuring gauge until the zero is opposite the pointer.
2. Seat the choke vacuum diaphragm by applying an external vacuum source of over 5 in. vacuum to the vacuum break.

NOTE: If the air valve rod is restricting the vacuum diaphragm from seating it may be necessary to bend the air valve rod slightly to gain clearance. Make an air valve rod adjustment after the vacuum break adjustment.

3. Read the angle gauge while lightly pushing on the intermediate choke lever so that the choke valve is toward the close position.
4. Use a 1/8 in. hex wrench and turn the screw in the rear cover until the bubble is centered. Apply a silicone sealant over the screw head to seal the setting.

1983–84 GM Models

Refer to the illustration for the adjustment procedure on these models.

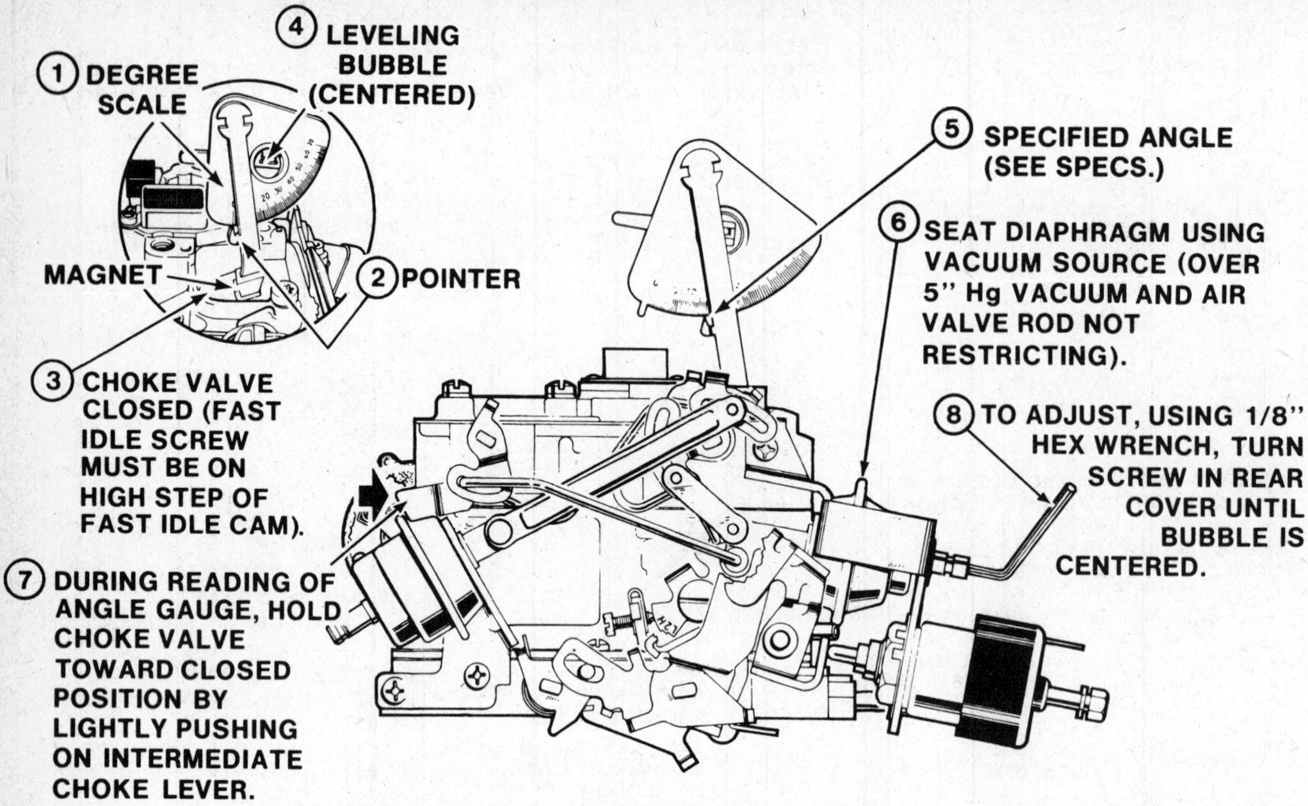

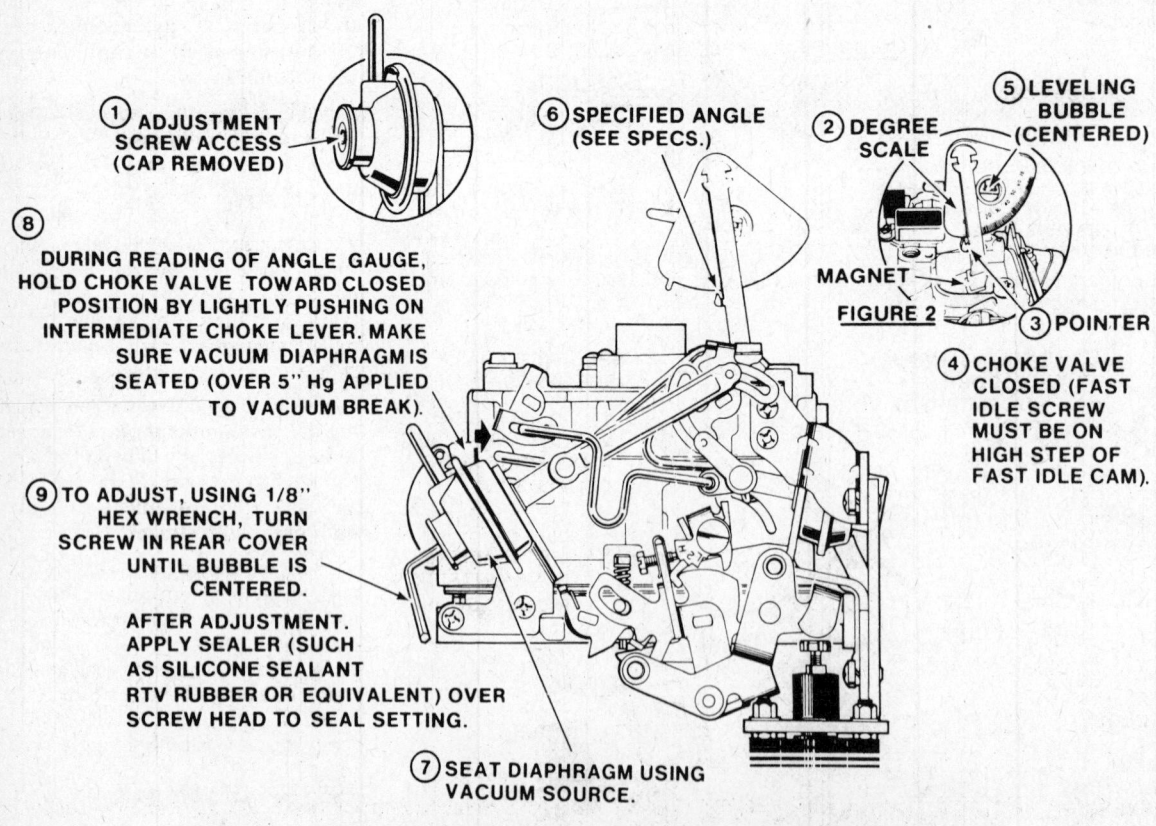

① **DEGREE SCALE**

④ **LEVELING BUBBLE (CENTERED)**

MAGNET

② **POINTER**

③ **CHOKE VALVE CLOSED (FAST IDLE SCREW MUST BE ON HIGH STEP OF FAST IDLE CAM).**

⑦ **DURING READING OF ANGLE GAUGE, HOLD CHOKE VALVE TOWARD CLOSED POSITION BY LIGHTLY PUSHING ON INTERMEDIATE CHOKE LEVER.**

⑤ **SPECIFIED ANGLE (SEE SPECS.)**

⑥ **SEAT DIAPHRAGM USING VACUUM SOURCE (OVER 5" Hg VACUUM AND AIR VALVE ROD NOT RESTRICTING).**

⑧ **TO ADJUST, USING 1/8" HEX WRENCH, TURN SCREW IN REAR COVER UNTIL BUBBLE IS CENTERED.**

E2SE primary vacuum break adjustment—1981–82 G.M. "A" and "X" series with V6 engine © G.M. Corp.

① **ADJUSTMENT SCREW ACCESS (CAP REMOVED)**

⑧ **DURING READING OF ANGLE GAUGE, HOLD CHOKE VALVE TOWARD CLOSED POSITION BY LIGHTLY PUSHING ON INTERMEDIATE CHOKE LEVER. MAKE SURE VACUUM DIAPHRAGM IS SEATED (OVER 5" Hg APPLIED TO VACUUM BREAK).**

⑨ **TO ADJUST, USING 1/8" HEX WRENCH, TURN SCREW IN REAR COVER UNTIL BUBBLE IS CENTERED.**

AFTER ADJUSTMENT, APPLY SEALER (SUCH AS SILICONE SEALANT RTV RUBBER OR EQUIVALENT) OVER SCREW HEAD TO SEAL SETTING.

⑥ **SPECIFIED ANGLE (SEE SPECS.)**

⑤ **LEVELING BUBBLE (CENTERED)**

② **DEGREE SCALE**

MAGNET

FIGURE 2

③ **POINTER**

④ **CHOKE VALVE CLOSED (FAST IDLE SCREW MUST BE ON HIGH STEP OF FAST IDLE CAM).**

⑦ **SEAT DIAPHRAGM USING VACUUM SOURCE.**

E2SE secondary vacuum break adjustment—1982 G.M. J series (© G.M. Corp.)

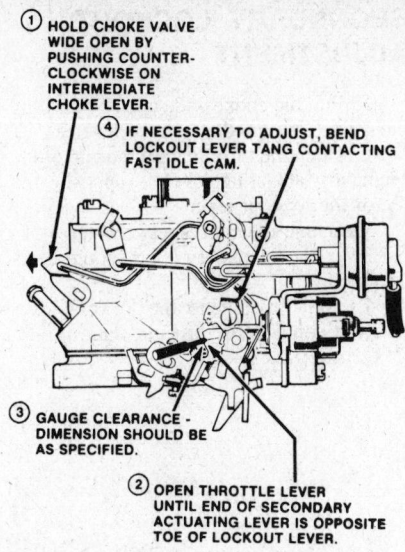

① HOLD CHOKE VALVE WIDE OPEN BY PUSHING COUNTER-CLOCKWISE ON INTERMEDIATE CHOKE LEVER.

④ IF NECESSARY TO ADJUST, BEND LOCKOUT LEVER TANG CONTACTING FAST IDLE CAM.

③ GAUGE CLEARANCE - DIMENSION SHOULD BE AS SPECIFIED.

② OPEN THROTTLE LEVER UNTIL END OF SECONDARY ACTUATING LEVER IS OPPOSITE TOE OF LOCKOUT LEVER.

2SE and E2SE secondary lockout adjustment—typical (© G.M. Corp.)

CHOKE UNLOADER ADJUSTMENT

Through 1982

1. Follow Steps 1–4 of the ''Fast Idle Cam Adjustment''.
2. Install the choke cover and coil, if removed, aligning the marks on the housing and cover as specified.
3. Hold the primary throttle wide open.
4. If the engine is warm, close the choke valve by pushing in on the intermediate choke lever.
5. Bend the unloader tang until the bubble is centered.

1983–84

Refer to the illustration for the adjustment procedure on these models.

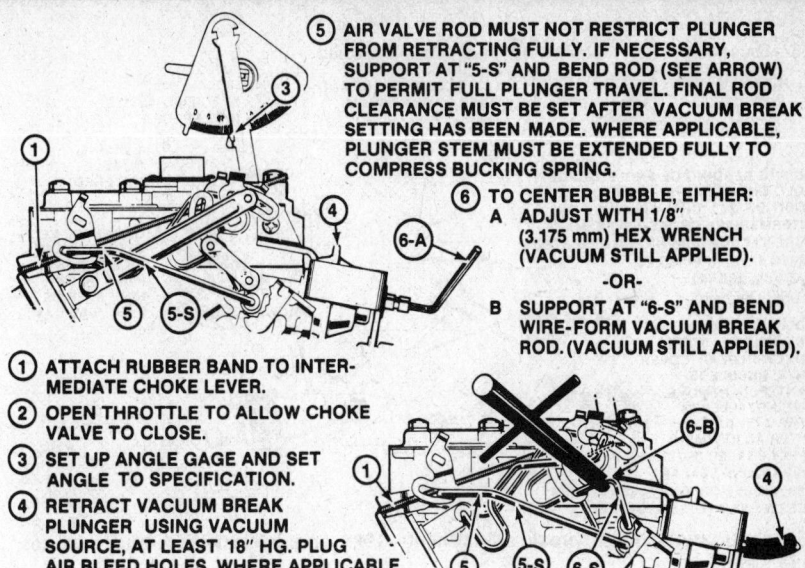

⑤ AIR VALVE ROD MUST NOT RESTRICT PLUNGER FROM RETRACTING FULLY. IF NECESSARY, SUPPORT AT "5-S" AND BEND ROD (SEE ARROW) TO PERMIT FULL PLUNGER TRAVEL. FINAL ROD CLEARANCE MUST BE SET AFTER VACUUM BREAK SETTING HAS BEEN MADE. WHERE APPLICABLE, PLUNGER STEM MUST BE EXTENDED FULLY TO COMPRESS BUCKING SPRING.

⑥ TO CENTER BUBBLE, EITHER:
A ADJUST WITH 1/8" (3.175 mm) HEX WRENCH (VACUUM STILL APPLIED).
-OR-
B SUPPORT AT "6-S" AND BEND WIRE-FORM VACUUM BREAK ROD. (VACUUM STILL APPLIED).

① ATTACH RUBBER BAND TO INTERMEDIATE CHOKE LEVER.
② OPEN THROTTLE TO ALLOW CHOKE VALVE TO CLOSE.
③ SET UP ANGLE GAGE AND SET ANGLE TO SPECIFICATION.
④ RETRACT VACUUM BREAK PLUNGER USING VACUUM SOURCE, AT LEAST 18" HG. PLUG AIR BLEED HOLES WHERE APPLICABLE.

E2SE primary vacuum break adjustment—1983 and later © G.M. Corp.

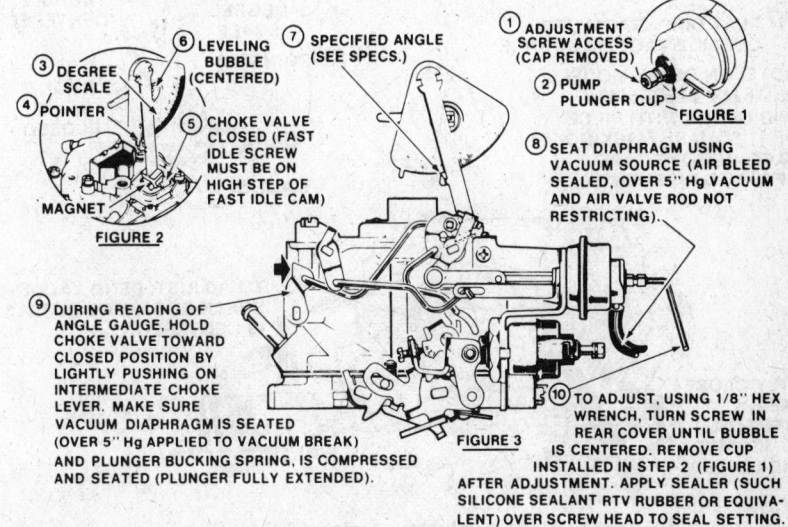

③ DEGREE SCALE
④ POINTER
⑥ LEVELING BUBBLE (CENTERED)
⑦ SPECIFIED ANGLE (SEE SPECS.)
⑤ CHOKE VALVE CLOSED (FAST IDLE SCREW MUST BE ON HIGH STEP OF FAST IDLE CAM)

MAGNET
FIGURE 2

① ADJUSTMENT SCREW ACCESS (CAP REMOVED)
② PUMP PLUNGER CUP
FIGURE 1

⑧ SEAT DIAPHRAGM USING VACUUM SOURCE (AIR BLEED SEALED, OVER 5" Hg VACUUM AND AIR VALVE ROD NOT RESTRICTING).

⑨ DURING READING OF ANGLE GAUGE, HOLD CHOKE VALVE TOWARD CLOSED POSITION BY LIGHTLY PUSHING ON INTERMEDIATE CHOKE LEVER. MAKE SURE VACUUM DIAPHRAGM IS SEATED (OVER 5" Hg APPLIED TO VACUUM BREAK) AND PLUNGER BUCKING SPRING, IS COMPRESSED AND SEATED (PLUNGER FULLY EXTENDED).

FIGURE 3

⑩ TO ADJUST, USING 1/8" HEX WRENCH, TURN SCREW IN REAR COVER UNTIL BUBBLE IS CENTERED. REMOVE CUP INSTALLED IN STEP 2 (FIGURE 1) AFTER ADJUSTMENT. APPLY SEALER (SUCH SILICONE SEALANT RTV RUBBER OR EQUIVALENT) OVER SCREW HEAD TO SEAL SETTING.

E2SE primary vacuum break adjustment—1981–82 G.M. "A" and "X" series with 4 cyl engine © G.M. Corp.

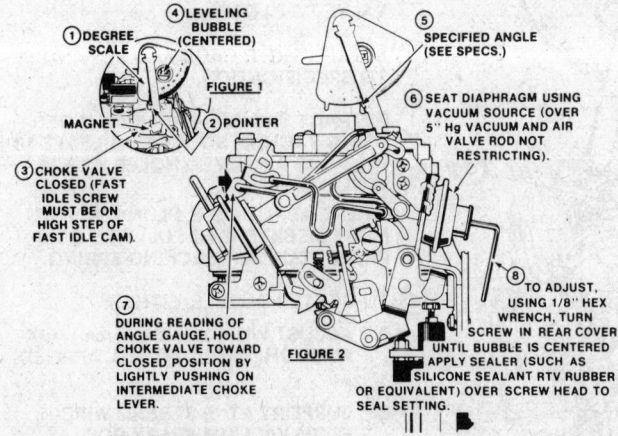

① DEGREE SCALE
④ LEVELING BUBBLE (CENTERED)
FIGURE 1
② POINTER
⑤ SPECIFIED ANGLE (SEE SPECS.)
③ CHOKE VALVE CLOSED (FAST IDLE SCREW MUST BE ON HIGH STEP OF FAST IDLE CAM).

MAGNET

⑥ SEAT DIAPHRAGM USING VACUUM SOURCE (OVER 5" Hg VACUUM AND AIR VALVE ROD NOT RESTRICTING).

⑦ DURING READING OF ANGLE GAUGE, HOLD CHOKE VALVE TOWARD CLOSED POSITION BY LIGHTLY PUSHING ON INTERMEDIATE CHOKE LEVER.
FIGURE 2

⑧ TO ADJUST, USING 1/8" HEX WRENCH, TURN SCREW IN REAR COVER UNTIL BUBBLE IS CENTERED. APPLY SEALER (SUCH AS SILICONE SEALANT RTV RUBBER OR EQUIVALENT) OVER SCREW HEAD TO SEAL SETTING.

E2SE primary vacuum break adjustment—4 cyl.—1982 G.M. J series (© G.M. Corp.)

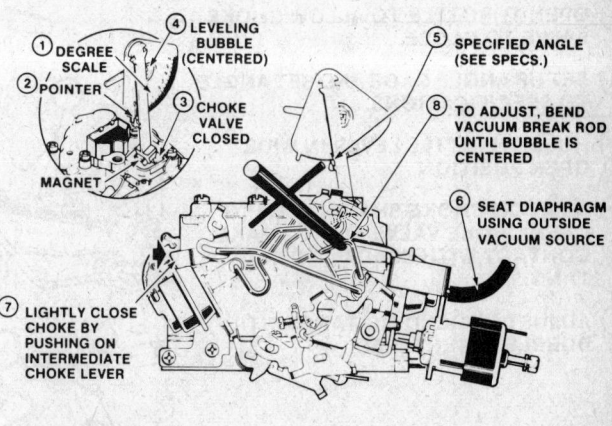

① DEGREE SCALE
② POINTER
④ LEVELING BUBBLE (CENTERED)
③ CHOKE VALVE CLOSED
⑤ SPECIFIED ANGLE (SEE SPECS.)
⑧ TO ADJUST, BEND VACUUM BREAK ROD UNTIL BUBBLE IS CENTERED

MAGNET

⑥ SEAT DIAPHRAGM USING OUTSIDE VACUUM SOURCE

⑦ LIGHTLY CLOSE CHOKE BY PUSHING ON INTERMEDIATE CHOKE LEVER

E2SE secondary vacuum break adjustment—1980 models (© G.M. Corp.)

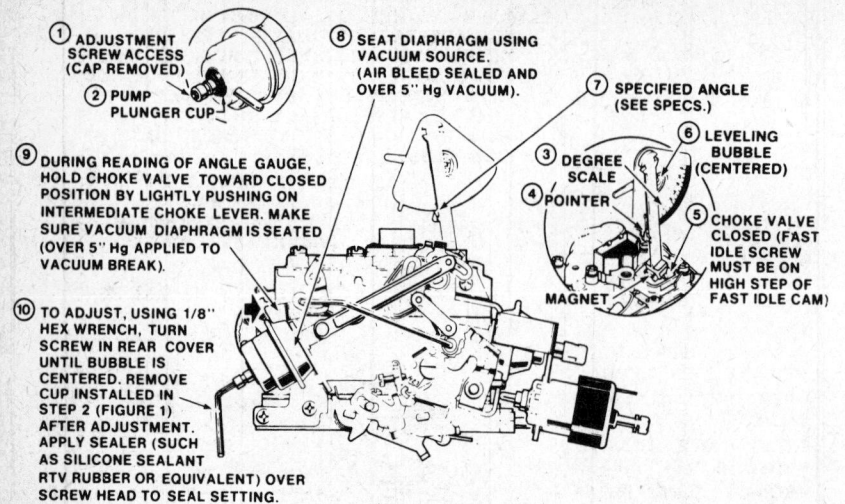

① ADJUSTMENT SCREW ACCESS (CAP REMOVED)

② PUMP PLUNGER CUP

⑧ SEAT DIAPHRAGM USING VACUUM SOURCE. (AIR BLEED SEALED AND OVER 5" Hg VACUUM).

⑦ SPECIFIED ANGLE (SEE SPECS.)

⑥ LEVELING BUBBLE (CENTERED)

③ DEGREE SCALE

④ POINTER

⑤ CHOKE VALVE CLOSED (FAST IDLE SCREW MUST BE ON HIGH STEP OF FAST IDLE CAM)

MAGNET

⑨ DURING READING OF ANGLE GAUGE, HOLD CHOKE VALVE TOWARD CLOSED POSITION BY LIGHTLY PUSHING ON INTERMEDIATE CHOKE LEVER. MAKE SURE VACUUM DIAPHRAGM IS SEATED (OVER 5" Hg APPLIED TO VACUUM BREAK).

⑩ TO ADJUST, USING 1/8" HEX WRENCH, TURN SCREW IN REAR COVER UNTIL BUBBLE IS CENTERED. REMOVE CUP INSTALLED IN STEP 2 (FIGURE 1) AFTER ADJUSTMENT. APPLY SEALER (SUCH AS SILICONE SEALANT RTV RUBBER OR EQUIVALENT) OVER SCREW HEAD TO SEAL SETTING.

E2SE secondary vacuum break adjustment—1981 and later G.M. A and X series (© G.M. Corp.)

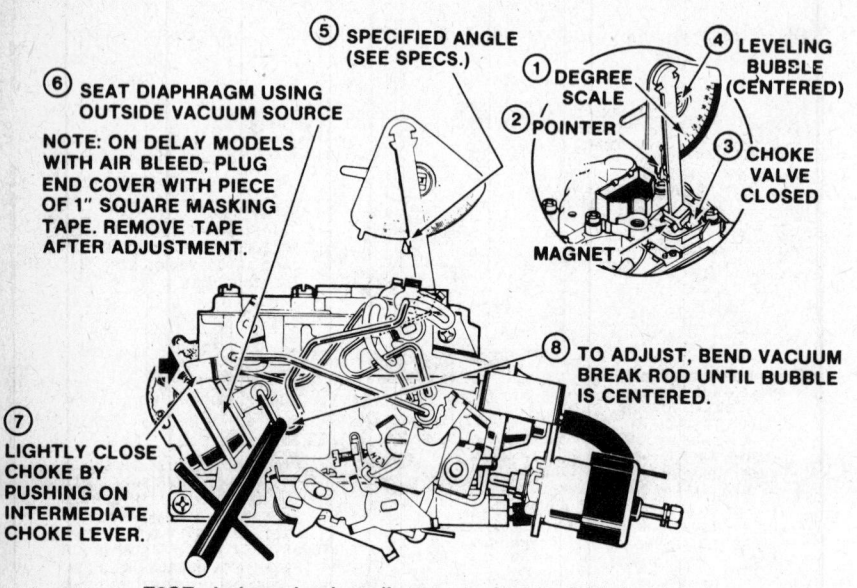

⑤ SPECIFIED ANGLE (SEE SPECS.)

⑥ SEAT DIAPHRAGM USING OUTSIDE VACUUM SOURCE

NOTE: ON DELAY MODELS WITH AIR BLEED, PLUG END COVER WITH PIECE OF 1" SQUARE MASKING TAPE. REMOVE TAPE AFTER ADJUSTMENT.

① DEGREE SCALE

② POINTER

④ LEVELING BUBBLE (CENTERED)

③ CHOKE VALVE CLOSED

MAGNET

⑧ TO ADJUST, BEND VACUUM BREAK ROD UNTIL BUBBLE IS CENTERED.

⑦ LIGHTLY CLOSE CHOKE BY PUSHING ON INTERMEDIATE CHOKE LEVER.

E2SE choke unloader adjuster—typical (© G.M. Corp.)

① ATTACH RUBBER BAND TO INTERMEDIATE CHOKE LEVER.

② OPEN THROTTLE TO ALLOW CHOKE VALVE TO CLOSE.

③ SET UP ANGLE GAGE AND SET ANGLE TO SPECIFICATIONS.

④ HOLD THROTTLE LEVER IN WIDE OPEN POSITION.

⑤ PUSH ON CHOKE SHAFT LEVER TO OPEN CHOKE VALVE AND TO MAKE CONTACT WITH BLACK CLOSING TANG.

⑥ ADJUST BY BENDING TANG UNTIL BUBBLE IS CENTERED.

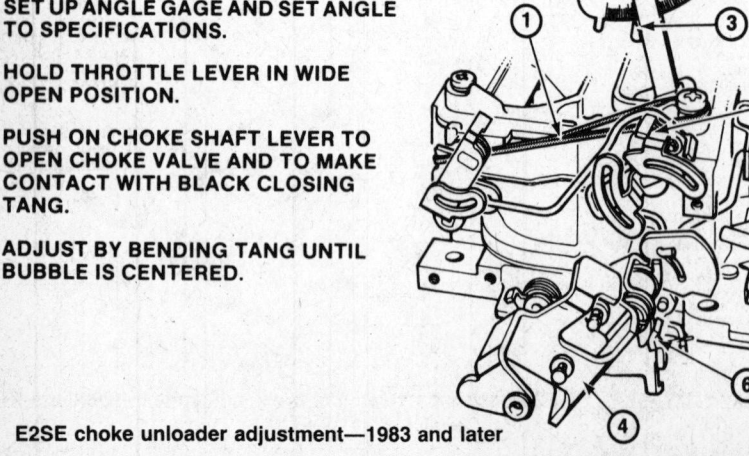

E2SE choke unloader adjustment—1983 and later

SECONDARY LOCKOUT ADJUSTMENT

1. Pull the choke wide open by pushing out on the intermediate choke lever.
2. Open the throttle until the end of the secondary actuating lever is opposite the toe of the lockout lever.
3. Gauge clearance between the lockout lever and secondary lever should be as specified.
4. To adjust, bend the lockout lever where it contacts the fast idle cam.

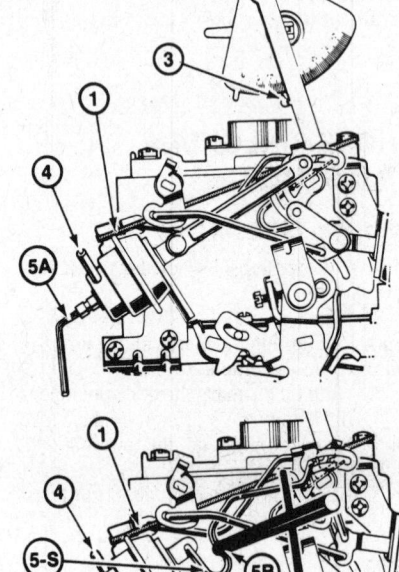

① ATTACH RUBBER BAND TO INTERMEDIATE CHOKE LEVER.

② OPEN THROTTLE TO ALLOW CHOKE VALVE TO CLOSE.

③ SET UP ANGLE GAGE AND SET ANGLE TO SPECIFICATION.

④ RETRACT VACUUM BREAK PLUNGER USING VACUUM SOURCE, AT LEAST 18" HG. PLUG AIR BLEED HOLES WHERE APPLICABLE.

WHERE APPLICABLE, PLUNGER STEM MUST BE EXTENDED FULLY TO COMPRESS PLUNGER BUCKING SPRING.

⑤ TO CENTER BUBBLE, EITHER:

A. ADJUST WITH 1/8" (3.175 mm) HEX WRENCH (VACUUM STILL APPLIED)

-OR

B. SUPPORT AT "5-S", BEND WIREFORM VACUUM BREAK ROD (VACUUM STILL APPLIED)

E2SE secondary vacuum break adjustment—1983 and later

2SE, E2SE CARBURETOR SPECIFICATIONS
American Motors

Year	Carburetor Identification	Float Level (in.)	Pump Rod (in.)	Fast Idle (rpm)	Choke Coil Lever (in.)	Fast Idle Cam (deg./in.)	Air Valve Rod (in.)	Primary Vacuum Break (deg./in.)	Choke Setting (notches)	Choke Unloader (deg./in.)	Secondary Lockout (in.)
'80	17080681	3/16	17/32	2400	.142	18/0.096	.018	20/.110	Fixed	32/.195	N.A.
	17080683	3/16	1/2	2400	.142	18/0.096	.018	20/.110	Fixed	32/.195	N.A.
	17080686	3/16	1/2	2600	.142	18/0.096	.018	20/.110	Fixed	32/.195	N.A.
	17080688	3/16	1/2	2600	.142	18/0.096	.018	20/.110	Fixed	32/.195	N.A.
'81	17081790	0.256	0.128	2600	0.085	25/0.142	.011	19/.103	Fixed	32/.195	0.065
	17081791	0.256	0.128	2400	0.085	25/0.142	.011	19/.103	Fixed	32/.195	0.065
	17081792	0.256	0.128	2400	0.085	25/0.142	.011	19/.103	Fixed	32/.195	0.065
	17081794	0.256	0.128	2600	0.085	25/0.142	.011	19/.103	Fixed	32/.195	0.065
	17081795	0.256	0.128	2600	0.085	25/0.142	.011	19/.103	Fixed	32/.195	0.065
	17081796	0.208	0.128	2400	0.065	25/0.142	.011	19/.103	Fixed	32/.195	0.065
	17081797	0.208	0.128	2600	0.085	25/0.142	.011	19/.103	Fixed	32/.195	0.085
	17081793	0.256	0.128	2400	0.085	25/0.142	.011	19/.103	Fixed	32/.195	0.065
'82	17082385	0.256	0.128	2400	0.085	18/.096	2①	21/.117	Fixed	34/.211	0.065
	17082383	0.256	0.128	2400	0.085	18/.096	2①	21/.117	Fixed	34/.211	0.065
	17082380	0.216	0.128	2400	0.085	18/.096	2①	21/.117	Fixed	34/.211	0.065
	17082386	0.125	0.128	2400	0.065	18/.096	2①	19/.103	Fixed	34/.211	0.065
	17082387	0.125	0.128	2600	0.085	18/.096	2①	19/.103	Fixed	34/.211	0.065
	17082388	0.125	0.128	2500	0.085	18/.096	2①	19/.103	Fixed	34/.211	0.065
	17082389	0.125	0.128	2500	0.085	18/.096	2①	19/.103	Fixed	34/.211	0.065
'83–'84	1982380	0.216②	0.128	2500③	0.085	18/.096	2①	21/.117	Fixed	34/.211	0.065
	1983384	0.138	0.128	2700	0.085	18/.096	2①	19/.103	Fixed	34/.211	0.065
	1983385	0.138	0.128	2500	0.085	18/.096	②①	19/.103	Fixed	34/.211	0.065

N.A.: Not Available
① Degrees—see procedure
② Auto. trans.—.138
③ Auto. trans.—2700

2SE, E2SE CARBURETOR SPECIFICATIONS
General Motors—U.S.A.

Year	Carburetor Identification	Float Level (in.)	Pump Rod (in.)	Fast Idle (rpm)	Choke Coil Lever (in.)	Fast Idle Cam (deg./in.)	Air Valve Rod (in.)	Primary Vacuum Break (deg./in.)	Choke Setting (notches)	Secondary Vacuum Break (deg./in.)	Choke Unloader (deg./in.)	Secondary Lockout (in.)
'79	17059674	13/64	1/2	2400	.120	18/0.096	.025	19/.103	2 Rich	—	32/.195	.030
	17059675	13/64	17/32	2200	.120	18/0.096	.025	21/.117	1 Rich	—	32/.195	.030
	17059676	13/64	1/2	2400	.120	18/0.096	.025	19/.103	2 Rich	—	32/.195	.030
	17059677	13/64	17/32	2200	.120	18/0.096	.025	21/.117	1 Rich	—	32/.195	.030
'80	17059614	3/16	1/2	2600	.085	18/.096	.025	17/.090	Fixed	—	36/.227	.120
	17059615	3/16	5/32	2600	.085	18/.096	.025	19/.103	Fixed	—	36/.227	.120
	17059616	3/16	1/2	2600	.085	18/.096	.025	17/.090	Fixed	—	36/.227	.120

2SE, E2SE CARBURETOR SPECIFICATIONS
General Motors—U.S.A.

Year	Carburetor Identification	Float Level (in.)	Pump Rod (in.)	Fast Idle (rpm)	Choke Coil Lever (in.)	Fast Idle Cam (deg./in.)	Air Valve Rod (in.)	Primary Vacuum Break (deg./in.)	Choke Setting (notches)	Secondary Vacuum Break (deg./in.)	Choke Unloader (deg./in.)	Secondary Lockout (in.)
'80	17059617	3/16	5/32	2600	.085	18/.096	.025	19/.103	Fixed	—	36/.227	.120
	17059618	3/16	1/2	2600	.085	18/.096	.025	17/.090	Fixed	—	36/.227	.120
	17059619	3/16	5/32	2600	.085	18/.096	.025	19/.103	Fixed	—	36/.227	.120
	17059620	3/16	1/2	2600	.085	18/.096	.025	17/.090	Fixed	—	36/.227	.120
	17059621	3/16	5/32	2600	.085	18/.096	.025	19/.103	Fixed	—	36/.227	.120
	17059650	3/16	3/32	2600	.085	27/.157	.025	30/.179	Fixed	38/.243	30/.179	.120
	17059651	3/16	3/32	1900	.085	27/.157	.025	22/.123	Fixed	23/.120	30/.179	.120
	17059652	3/16	3/32	2000	.085	27/.157	.025	30/.179	Fixed	38/.243	30/.179	.120
	17059653	3/16	3/32	1900	.085	27/.157	.025	22/.123	Fixed	23/.120	30/.179	.120
	17059714	11/16	5/32	2600	.085	18/.096	.025	23/.129	Fixed	—	32/.195	.120
	17059715	11/16	3/32	2200	.085	18/.096	.025	25/.142	Fixed	—	32/.195	.120
	17059716	11/16	5/32	2600	.085	18/.096	.025	23/.129	Fixed	—	32/.195	.120
	17059717	11/16	3/32	2200	.085	18/.096	.025	25/.142	Fixed	—	32/.195	.120
	17059760	1/8	5/64	2000	.085	17.5/.093	.025	20/.110	Fixed	33/.203	35/.220	.120
	17059762	1/8	5/64	2000	.085	17.5/.093	.025	20/.110	Fixed	33/.203	35/.220	.120
	17059763	1/8	5/64	2000	.085	17.5/.093	.025	20/.110	Fixed	33/.203	35/.220	.120
	17059774	5/32	1/2	①	.085	18/0.096	.018	19/.103	Fixed	—	32/.195	.012
	17059775	5/32	17/32	①	.085	18/0.096	.018	21/.117	Fixed	—	32/.195	.012
	17059776	5/32	1/2	①	.085	18/0.096	.018	19/.103	Fixed	—	32/.195	.012
	17059777	5/32	17/32	①	.085	18/0.096	.018	21/.117	Fixed	—	32/.195	.012
	17080674	3/16	1/2	①	.085	18/0.096	.018	19/.103	Fixed	—	32/.195	.012
	17080675	3/16	1/2	①	.085	18/0.096	.018	21/.117	Fixed	—	32/.195	.012
	17080676	3/16	1/2	①	.085	18/0.096	.018	19/.103	Fixed	—	32/.195	.012
	17080677	3/16	1/2	①	.085	18/0.096	.018	21/.117	Fixed	—	32/.195	.012
'81	17081650	1/4	Fixed	2600	.085	17/.090	1②	25/.142	Fixed	34/.211	35/.220	.012
	17081651	1/4	Fixed	2400	.085	17/.090	1②	29/.171	Fixed	35/.220	35/.220	.012
	17081652	1/4	Fixed	2600	.085	17/.090	1②	25/.142	Fixed	34/.211	35/.220	.012
	17081653	1/4	Fixed	2600	.085	17/.090	1②	29/.171	Fixed	35/.220	35/.220	.012
	17081670	5/32	Fixed	2600	.085	18/.096	1②	19/.103	Fixed	—	32/.195	.012
	17081671	5/32	Fixed	2600	.085	33.5/.207	1②	21/.117	Fixed	—	32/.195	.012
	17081672	5/32	Fixed	2600	.085	18/.096	1②	19/.103	Fixed	—	32/.195	.012
	17081673	5/32	Fixed	2600	.085	33.4/.207	1②	21/.117	Fixed	—	32/.195	.012
	17081740	1/4	Fixed	2400	.085	17/.090	1②	25/.142	Fixed	35/.220	35/.220	.012
	17081742	1/4	Fixed	2400	.085	17/.090	1②	25/.142	Fixed	35/.220	35/.220	.012
'82	17081600	5/16	Fixed	①	③	24/.136	1②	20/.110	Fixed	27/.157	35/.220	③
	17081601	5/16	Fixed	①	③	24/1.36	1②	20/.110	Fixed	27/.157	35/.220	③
	17081607	5/16	Fixed	①	③	24/.136	1②	20/.110	Fixed	27/.157	35/.220	③
	17081700	5/16	Fixed	①	③	24/.136	1②	20/.110	Fixed	27/.157	35/.220	③

2SE, E2SE CARBURETOR SPECIFICATIONS
General Motors—U.S.A.

Year	Carburetor Identification	Float Level (in.)	Pump Rod (in.)	Fast Idle (rpm)	Choke Coil Lever (in.)	Fast Idle Cam (deg./in.)	Air Valve Rod (in.)	Primary Vacuum Break (deg./in.)	Choke Setting (notches)	Secondary Vacuum Break (deg./in.)	Choke Unloader (deg./in.)	Secondary Lockout (in.)
'82	17081701	5/16	Fixed	①	③	24/.136	1②	20/.110	Fixed	27/.157	35/.220	③
	17082196	5/16	Fixed	①	.085	18/.096	1②	21/.117	Fixed	19/.103	27/157	③
	17082316	1/4	Fixed	2600	.085	17/.090	1②	30/.179	Fixed	34/.211	45/.304	③
	17082317	1/4	Fixed	260	.085	17/.090	1②	30/.179	Fixed	35/.220	45/.304	③
	17082320	1/4	Fixed	2800	.085	25/.142	1②	30/.179	Fixed	35/.220	45/.304	③
	17082321	1/4	Fixed	2600	.085	25/.142	1②	30/.179	Fixed	35/.220	45/.304	③
	17082390	13/32	Fixed	2500	.085	17/.090	1②	26/.149	Fixed	34/.211	35/.220	.011–.040
	17082391	13/32	Fixed	2600	.085	25/.142	1②	29/.171	Fixed	35/.220	35/.220	.011–.040
	17082490	13/32	Fixed	2500	.085	17/.090	1②	26/.149	Fixed	34/.211	35/.220	.011–.040
	17082491	13/32	Fixed	2600	.085	25/.142	1②	29/.171	Fixed	35/.220	35/.220	.011–.040
	17082640	1/4	Fixed	2600	.085	17/.090	1②	30/.179	Fixed	34/.211	45/.304	③
	17082641	1/4	Fixed	2400	.085	17/.090	1②	30/.179	Fixed	35/.220	45/.304	③
	17082642	1/4	Fixed	2800	.085	25/.142	1②	30/.179	Fixed	35/.220	45/.304	③
'83	17083356	13/32	Fixed	①	.085	22/.123	1②	25/.142	Fixed	35/.220	30/.179	.025
	17083357	13/32	Fixed	①	.085	22/.123	1②	25/.142	Fixed	35/.220	30/.179	.025
	17083358	13/32	Fixed	①	.085	22/.123	1②	25/.142	Fixed	35/.220	30/.179	.025
	17083359	13/32	Fixed	①	.085	22/.123	1②	25/.142	Fixed	35/.220	30/.179	.025
	17083368	13/32	Fixed	①	.085	22/.123	1②	25/.142	Fixed	35/.220	30/.179	.025
	17083369	13/32	Fixed	①	.085	22/.123	1②	25/.142	Fixed	35/.220	30/.179	.025
	17083370	13/32	Fixed	①	.085	22/.123	1②	25/.142	Fixed	35/.220	30/.179	.025
	17083391	13/32	Fixed	①	.085	28/.164	1②	30/.179	Fixed	35/.220	38/.243	.025
	17083392	13/32	Fixed	①	.085	28/.164	1②	30/.179	Fixed	35/.220	38/.243	.025
	17083393	13/32	Fixed	①	.085	28/.164	1②	30/.179	Fixed	35/.220	38/.243	.025
	17083394	13/32	Fixed	①	.085	28/.164	1②	30/.179	Fixed	35/.220	38/.243	.025
	17083395	13/32	Fixed	①	.085	28/.164	1②	30/.179	Fixed	35/.220	38/.243	.025
	17083396	13/32	Fixed	①	.085	28/.164	1②	30/.179	Fixed	35/.220	38/.243	.025
	17083397	13/32	Fixed	①	.085	28/.164	1②	30/.179	Fixed	35/.220	38/.243	.025
	17083450	1/4	Fixed	①	.085	28/.164	1②	27/.157	Fixed	35/.220	45/.304	.025
	17083451	1/4	Fixed	①	.085	28/.164	1②	27/.157	Fixed	35/.220	45/.304	.025
	17083452	1/4	Fixed	①	.085	28/.164	1②	27/.157	Fixed	35/.220	45/.304	.025
	17083453	1/4	Fixed	①	.085	28/.164	1②	27/.157	Fixed	35/.220	45/.304	.025
	17083454	1/4	Fixed	①	.085	28/.164	1②	27/.157	Fixed	35/.220	45/.304	.025
	17083455	1/4	Fixed	①	.085	28/.164	1②	27/.157	Fixed	35/.220	45/.304	.025
	17083456	1/4	Fixed	①	.085	28/.164	1②	27/.157	Fixed	35/.220	45/.304	.025
	17083630	1/4	Fixed	①	.085	28/.164	1②	27/.157	Fixed	35/.220	45/.304	.025
	17083631	1/4	Fixed	①	.085	28/.164	1②	27/.157	Fixed	35/.220	45/.304	.025
	17083632	1/4	Fixed	①	.085	28/.164	1②	27/.157	Fixed	35/.220	45/.304	.025
	17083633	1/4	Fixed	①	.085	28/.164	1②	27/.157	Fixed	35/.220	45/.304	.025

2SE, E2SE CARBURETOR SPECIFICATIONS
General Motors—U.S.A.

Year	Carburetor Identification	Float Level (in.)	Pump Rod (in.)	Fast Idle (rpm)	Choke Coil Lever (in.)	Fast Idle Cam (deg./in.)	Air Valve Rod (in.)	Primary Vacuum Break (deg./in.)	Choke Setting (notches)	Choke Unloader (deg./in.)	Secondary Lockout (in.)
'83	17083634	¼	Fixed	①	.085	28/.164	1②	27/.157	Fixed	35/.220	45/.304	.025
	17083635	¼	Fixed	①	.085	28/.164	1②	27/.157	Fixed	35/.220	45/.304	.025
	17083636	¼	Fixed	①	.085	28/.164	1②	27/.157	Fixed	35/.220	45/.304	.025
'84	17072683	9/32	Fixed	①	.085	28/.164	1②	25/.142	Fixed	35/.220	45/.304	.025
	17074812	9/32	Fixed	①	.085	28/.164	1②	25/.142	Fixed	35/.220	45/.304	.025
	17084356	9/32	Fixed	①	.085	22/.123	1②	25/.142	Fixed	30/.179	30/.179	.025
	17084357	9/32	Fixed	①	.085	22/.123	1②	25/.142	Fixed	30/.179	30/.179	.025
	17084358	9/32	Fixed	①	.085	22/.123	1②	25/.142	Fixed	30/.179	30/.179	.025
	17084359	9/32	Fixed	①	.085	22/.123	1②	25/.142	Fixed	30/.179	30/.179	.025
	17084368	⅛	Fixed	①	.085	22/.123	1②	25/.142	Fixed	30/.179	30/.179	.025
	17084370	⅛	Fixed	①	.085	22/.123	1②	25/.142	Fixed	30/.179	30/.179	.025
	17084430	11/32	Fixed	①	.085	15/.077	1②	26/.149	Fixed	30/.179	30/.179	.025
	17084431	11/32	Fixed	①	.085	15/.077	1②	26/.149	Fixed	38/.243	42/.277	.025
	17084434	11/32	Fixed	①	.085	15/.077	1②	26/.149	Fixed	38/.243	42/.277	.025
	17084435	11/32	Fixed	①	.085	15/.077	1②	26/.149	Fixed	38/.243	42/.277	.025
	17084452	5/32	Fixed	①	.085	28/.164	1②	25/.142	Fixed	38/.243	42/.277	.025
	17084453	5/32	Fixed	①	.085	28/.164	1②	25/.142	Fixed	35/.220	45/.304	.025
	17084455	5/32	Fixed	①	.085	28/.164	1②	25/.142	Fixed	35/.220	45/.304	.025
	17084456	5/32	Fixed	①	.085	28/.164	1②	25/.142	Fixed	35/.220	45/.304	.025
	17084458	5/32	Fixed	①	.085	28/.164	1②	25/.142	Fixed	35/.220	45/.304	.025
	17084532	5/32	Fixed	①	.085	28/.164	1②	25/.142	Fixed	35/.220	45/.304	.025
	17084534	5/32	Fixed	①	.085	28/.164	1②	25/.142	Fixed	35/.220	45/.304	.025
	17084535	5/32	Fixed	①	.085	28/.164	1②	25/.142	Fixed	35/.220	45/.304	.025
	17084537	5/32	Fixed	①	.085	28/.164	1②	25/.142	Fixed	35/.220	45/.304	.025
	17084538	5/32	Fixed	①	.085	28/.164	1②	25/.142	Fixed	35/.220	45/.304	.025
	17084540	5/32	Fixed	①	.085	28/.164	1②	25/.142	Fixed	35/.220	45/.304	.025
	17084542	⅛	Fixed	①	.085	28/.164	1②	25/.142	Fixed	35/.220	45/.304	.025
	17084632	9/32	Fixed	①	.085	28/.164	1②	25/.142	Fixed	35/.220	45/.304	.025
	17084633	9/32	Fixed	①	.085	28/.164	1②	25/.142	Fixed	35/.220	45/.304	.025
	17084635	9/32	Fixed	①	.085	28/.164	1②	25/.142	Fixed	35/.220	45/.304	.025
	17084636	9/32	Fixed	①	.085	28/.164	1②	25/.142	Fixed	35/.220	45/.304	.025

① See underhood decal
② Measurement in degrees
③ Not available

2SE, E2SE CARBURETOR SPECIFICATIONS
General Motors—Canada

Year	Carburetor Identification	Float Level (In.)	Pump Rod (in.)	Fast Idle (rpm)	Choke Coil Lever (in.)	Fast Idle Cam (deg./in.)	Air Valve Rod (deg.)	Primary Vacuum Break (deg./in.)	Choke Setting (notches)	Secondary Vacuum Break (deg./in.)	Choke Unloader (deg./in.)	Secondary Lockout (in.)
'81	17059660	¼	¹⁷/₃₂	①	.085	24/.136	1	30/.179	Fixed	32/.195	30/.179	②
	17059662	¼	¹⁷/₃₂	①	.085	24/.136	1	30/.179	Fixed	37/.195	30/.179	②
	17059651	¼	¹⁷/₃₂	①	.085	24/.136	1	30/.179	Fixed	32/.195	30/.179	②
	17059666	¼	¹⁷/₃₂	①	.085	24/.136	1	26/.149	Fixed	32/.195	30/.179	②
	17059667	¼	¹⁷/₃₂	①	.085	24/.136	1	26/.149	Fixed	32/.195	30/.179	②
	17059622	⁵/₃₂	¹⁷/₃₂	①	.085	18/.096	1	17/.090	Fixed	—	36/.227	②
	17059623	⁵/₃₂	¹⁷/₃₂	①	.085	18/.096	1	19/.103	Fixed	—	36/.227	②
	17059624	⁵/₃₂	¹⁷/₃₂	①	.085	18/.096	1	17/.090	Fixed	—	36/.227	②
'82	17082440	¼	¹⁹/₃₂	①	.085	24/.136	1	30/.179	Fixed	32/.195	45/.304	②
	17082441	¼	¹⁹/₃₂	①	.085	24/.136	1	30/.179	Fixed	32/.195	45/.304	②
	17082443	¼	¹⁹/₃₂	①	.085	24/.136	1	30/.179	Fixed	32/.195	45/.304	②
	17082460	¼	¹⁹/₃₂	①	.085	18/.096	1	21/.117	Fixed	—	36/.227	②
	17082461	¼	¹⁹/₃₂	①	.085	18/.096	1	21/.117	Fixed	—	36/.227	②
	17082462	¼	¹⁹/₃₂	①	.085	18/.096	1	21/.117	Fixed	—	36/.227	②
	17082464	⅛	¹⁹/₃₂	①	.085	18/.096	1	21/.117	Fixed	—	36/.227	②
	17082465	⅛	¹⁹/₃₂	①	.085	18/.096	1	21/.117	Fixed	—	36/.227	②
	17082466	⅛	¹⁹/₃₂	①	.085	18/.096	1	21/.117	Fixed	—	36/.227	②
	17082620	⁷/₁₆	¹⁹/₃₂	①	.085	24/.136	1	30/.179	Fixed	32/.195	45/.304	②
	17082621	⁷/₁₆	¹⁹/₃₂	①	.085	24/.136	1	30/.179	Fixed	32/.195	45/.304	②
	17082622	⁷/₁₆	¹⁹/₃₂	①	.085	24/.136	1	30/.179	Fixed	32/.195	45/.304	②
	17082623	⁷/₁₆	¹⁹/₃₂	①	.085	24/.136	1	30/.179	Fixed	32/.195	45/.304	②
'83	17083311	⁵/₁₆	Fixed	①	.085	24/.136	1	18/.096	Fixed	20/.110	35/.220	.025
	17083401	⁵/₁₆	Fixed	①	.085	24/.136	1	18/.096	Fixed	20/.110	35/.220	.025
	17083440	¼	¹⁹/₃₂	①	.085	24/.136	1	28/.164	Fixed	32/.195	40/.260	.025
	17083441	¼	¹⁹/₃₂	①	.085	24/.136	1	28/.164	Fixed	32/.195	40/.260	.025
	17083442	¼	¹⁹/₃₂	①	.085	24/.136	1	28/.164	Fixed	32/.195	40/.260	.025
	17083443	¼	¹⁹/₃₂	①	.085	24/.136	1	28/.164	Fixed	32/.195	40/.260	.025
	17083444	¼	¹⁹/₃₂	①	.085	24/.136	1	28/.164	Fixed	32/.195	40/.260	.025
	17083445	¼	¹⁹/₃₂	①	.085	24/.136	1	28/.164	Fixed	32/.195	40/.260	.025
	17083460	¼	¹⁹/₃₂	①	.085	18/.096	1	19/.103	Fixed	—	36/.227	.025
	17083461	¼	¹⁹/₃₂	①	.085	18/.096	1	18/.096	Fixed	—	36/.227	.025
	17083462	¼	¹⁹/₃₂	①	.085	18/.096	1	19/.103	Fixed	—	36/.227	.025
	17083464	⅛	¹⁹/₃₂	①	.085	18/.096	1	19/.103	Fixed	—	36/.227	.025
	17083465	⅛	¹⁹/₃₂	①	.085	18/.096	1	20/.110	Fixed	—	36/.227	.025
	17083466	⅛	¹⁹/₃₂	①	.085	18/.096	1	19/.103	Fixed	—	36/.227	.025
	17083620	⁷/₁₆	¹⁹/₃₂	①	.085	24/.136	1	28/.164	Fixed	32/.195	40/.260	.025
	17083621	⁷/₁₆	¹⁹/₃₂	①	.085	24/.136	1	28/.164	Fixed	32/.195	40/.260	.025
	17083622	⁷/₁₆	¹⁹/₃₂	①	.085	24/.136	1	28/.164	Fixed	34/.195	40/.260	.025
	17083623	⁷/₁₆	¹⁹/₃₂	①	.085	24/.136	1	28/.164	Fixed	32/.195	40/.260	.025

2SE, E2SE CARBURETOR SPECIFICATIONS
General Motors—Canada

Year	Carburetor Identification	Float Level (In.)	Pump Rod (in.)	Fast Idle (rpm)	Choke Coil Lever (in.)	Fast Idle Cam (deg./in.)	Air Valve Rod (deg.)	Primary Vacuum Break (deg./in.)	Choke Setting (notches)	Secondary Vacuum Break (deg./in.)	Choke Unloader (deg./in.)	Secondary Lockout (in.)
'84	17084312	5/16	Fixed	①	.085	24/.136	1	18/.096	Fixed	20/.110	35/.220	.025
	17084314	5/16	Fixed	①	.085	29/.171	1	16/.083	Fixed	20/.110	30/.179	.025
	17084480	1/4	Fixed	①	.085	24/.136	1	28/.164	Fixed	32/.195	45/.304	.025
	17084481	1/4	Fixed	①	.085	24/.136	1	28/.164	Fixed	32/.195	45/.304	.025
	17084482	1/4	Fixed	①	.085	24/.136	1	28/.164	Fixed	32/.195	45/.304	.025
	17084483	1/4	Fixed	①	.085	24/.136	1	28/.164	Fixed	32/.195	45/.304	.025
	17084484	1/4	Fixed	①	.085	24/.136	1	28/.164	Fixed	32/.195	45/.304	.025
	17084485	1/4	Fixed	①	.085	24/.136	1	28/.164	Fixed	32/.195	45/.304	.025
	17084486	1/4	Fixed	①	.085	24/.136	1	28/.164	Fixed	32/.195	45/.304	.025
	17084487	1/4	Fixed	①	.085	24/.136	1	28/.164	Fixed	32/.195	45/.304	.025
	17084620	7/16	Fixed	①	.085	24/.136	1	26/.149	Fixed	32/.195	45/.304	.025
	17084621	7/16	Fixed	①	.085	24/.136	1	26/.149	Fixed	32/.195	45/.304	.025
	17084622	7/16	Fixed	①	.085	24/.136	1	26/.149	Fixed	32/.195	45/.304	.025
	17084623	7/16	Fixed	①	.085	24/.136	1	26/.149	Fixed	32/.195	45/.304	.025

① See underhood decal
② Not available

Models 2MC, M2MC, M2ME and E2ME

The Rochester model 2MC carburetor is a two-barrel single stage carburetor which incorporates the design features of the primary side of the Rochester Quadrajet four-barrel carburetor. It is used on small displacement V8s. The M2MC version with front and rear vacuum break diaphragms, was introduced in 1977 on the 301 V8.

The Dualjet E2ME Model 210 is a variation of the M2ME, modified for use with the Electronic Fuel Control System (also called the Computer Controlled Catalytic Converter, or C-4, System). An electrically operated mixture control solenoid is mounted in the float bowl. Mixture is thus controlled by the Electronic Control Module, in response to signals from the oxygen sensor mounted in the exhaust system upstream of the catalytic converter.

FLOAT LEVEL ADJUSTMENT

See the illustration for float level adjustment for all carburetors. The E2ME procedure is the same except for adjustment (step 4 in the figure). For the E2ME only, if the float level is too high, hold the retainer firmly in place and push down on the center of the float to adjust.

If the float level is too low on the E2ME, lift out the metering rods. Remove the solenoid connector screws. Turn the lean mixture solenoid screw in clockwise, counting the exact number of turns until the screw is lightly bottomed in the bowl. Then turn the screw out counterclockwise and remove it. Lift out the solenoid and connector. Remove the float and bend the arm up to adjust. Install the parts, installing the mixture solenoid screw in until it is lightly bottomed, then turning it out the exact number of turns counted earlier.

FAST IDLE SPEED

1. Place the fast idle lever on the high step of the fast idle cam.
2. Turn the fast idle screw out until the throttle valves are closed.
3. Turn the screw in to contact the lever, then turn it in the number of turns listed in the specifications. Check this preliminary setting against the sticker figure.

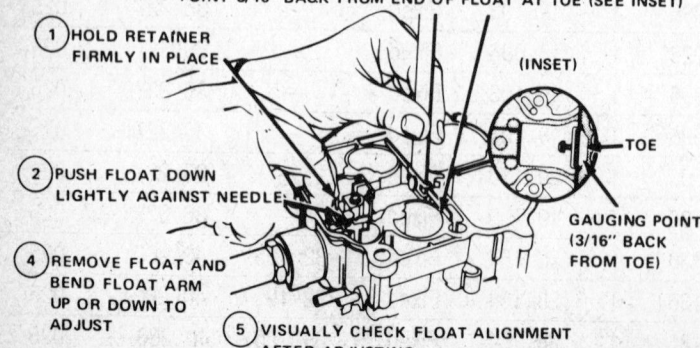

③ GAUGE FROM TOP OF CASTING TO TOP OF FLOAT – GAUGING POINT 3/16" BACK FROM END OF FLOAT AT TOE (SEE INSET)

① HOLD RETAINER FIRMLY IN PLACE

(INSET)

② PUSH FLOAT DOWN LIGHTLY AGAINST NEEDLE

— TOE

GAUGING POINT (3/16" BACK FROM TOE)

④ REMOVE FLOAT AND BEND FLOAT ARM UP OR DOWN TO ADJUST

⑤ VISUALLY CHECK FLOAT ALIGNMENT AFTER ADJUSTING

2MC, M2MC, M2ME, E2ME float level adjustment—typical (© G.M. Corp.)

FAST IDLE CAM (CHOKE ROD) ADJUSTMENT

1. Adjust the fast idle speed.

2. Place the cam follower lever on the second step of the fast idle cam, holding it firmly against the rise of the high step.

3. Close the choke valve by pushing upward on the choke coil lever inside the choke housing, or by pushing up on the vacuum break lever tang.

4. Gauge between the upper edge of the choke valve and the inside of the air horn wall.

5. Bend the tang on the fast idle cam to adjust.

PUMP ADJUSTMENT

This adjustment is not required on E2ME carburetors used in conjunction with the computer controlled systems.

1. With the fast idle cam follower off the steps of the fast idle cam, back out the idle speed screw until the throttle valves are completely closed.

2. Place the pump rod in the proper hole of the lever.

3. Measure from the top of the choke valve wall, next to the vent stack, to the top of the pump stem.

4. Bend the pump lever to adjust.

CHOKE COIL LEVER ADJUSTMENT

1. Remove the choke cover and thermostatic coil from the choke housing. On models with a fixed choke cover, drill out the rivets and remove the cover. A stat cover kit will be required for assembly.

2. Push up on the coil tang (counterclockwise) until the choke valve is closed. The top of the choke rod should be at the bottom of the slot in the choke valve lever. Place the fast idle cam follower on the high step of the cam.

3. Insert a 0.120 in. plug gauge in the hole in the choke housing.

4. The lower edge of the choke coil lever should just contact the side of the plug gauge.

5. Bend the choke rod to adjust.

2MC LEAN/RICH VACUUM BREAK ADJUSTMENT

1. Place the cam follower on the highest step of the fast idle cam.

2. Seat the vacuum break diaphragm by using an outside vacuum source. Tape over the bleed hole, if any, under the rubber cover on the diaphragm.

3. Remove the choke cover and thermostatic coil and push up on the coil lever inside the choke housing until the tang on the vacuum break lever contacts the tang on the vacuum break plunger stem. Do not compress the bucking spring for lean ad-

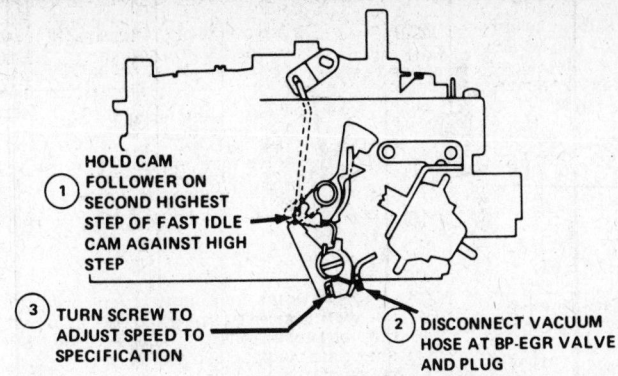

M2MC and E2ME fast idle speed adjustment—typical (© G.M. Corp.)

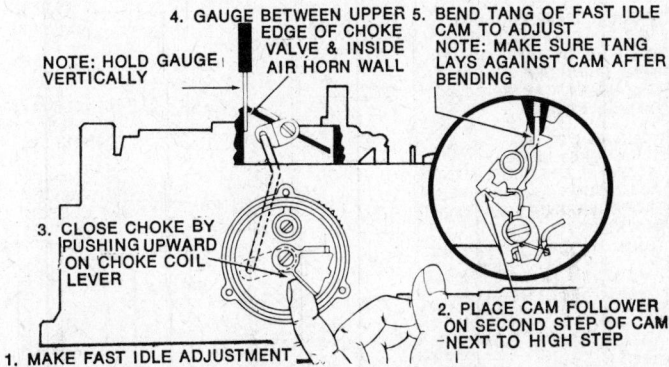

2MC, M2MC, M2ME, E2ME fast idle cam (choke rod) adjustment—typical (© G.M. Corp.)

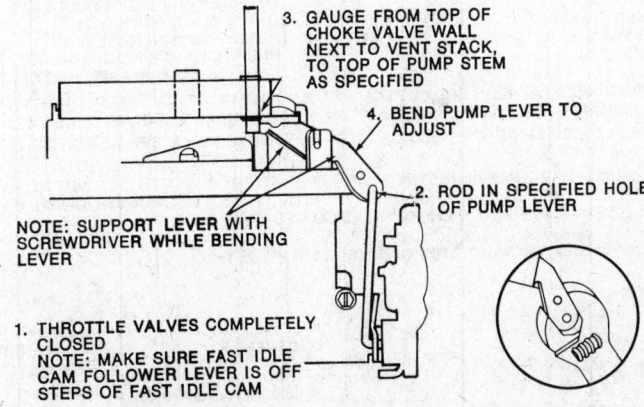

Pump adjustment (© Buick Div., G.M. Corp.)

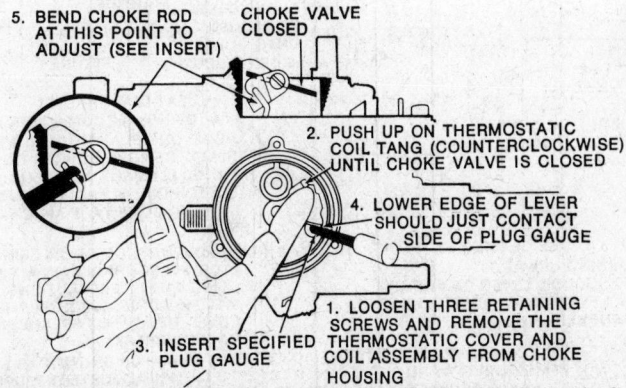

2MC, M2MC, M2ME, E2MC choke coil lever adjustment—typical (© G.M. Corp.)

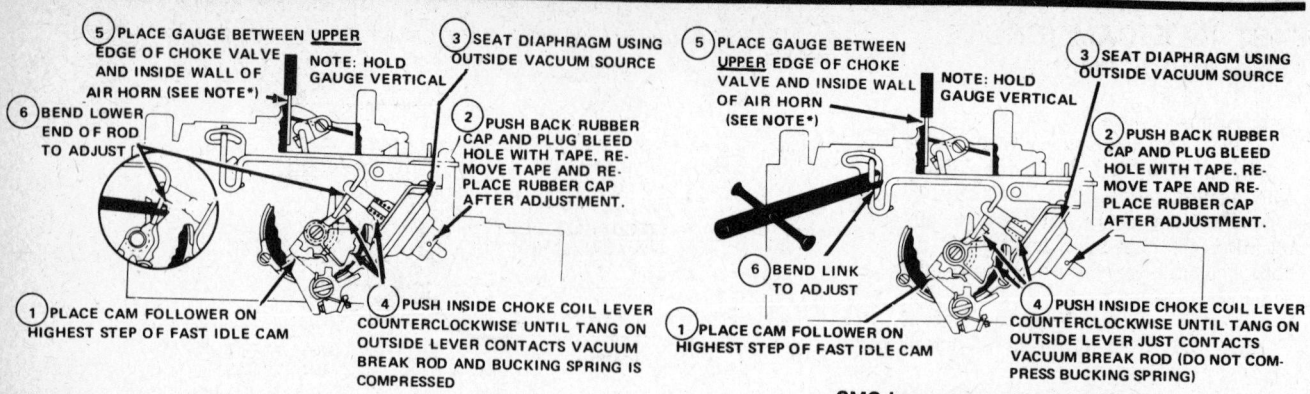

① PLACE CAM FOLLOWER ON HIGHEST STEP OF FAST IDLE CAM

② PUSH BACK RUBBER CAP AND PLUG BLEED HOLE WITH TAPE. REMOVE TAPE AND REPLACE RUBBER CAP AFTER ADJUSTMENT.

③ SEAT DIAPHRAGM USING OUTSIDE VACUUM SOURCE

④ PUSH INSIDE CHOKE COIL LEVER COUNTERCLOCKWISE UNTIL TANG ON OUTSIDE LEVER CONTACTS VACUUM BREAK ROD AND BUCKING SPRING IS COMPRESSED

⑤ PLACE GAUGE BETWEEN UPPER EDGE OF CHOKE VALVE AND INSIDE WALL OF AIR HORN (SEE NOTE*)

⑥ BEND LOWER END OF ROD TO ADJUST

NOTE: HOLD GAUGE VERTICAL

2MC rich vacuum break setting (© Oldsmobile Div., G.M. Corp.)

① PLACE CAM FOLLOWER ON HIGHEST STEP OF FAST IDLE CAM

② PUSH BACK RUBBER CAP AND PLUG BLEED HOLE WITH TAPE. REMOVE TAPE AND REPLACE RUBBER CAP AFTER ADJUSTMENT.

③ SEAT DIAPHRAGM USING OUTSIDE VACUUM SOURCE

④ PUSH INSIDE CHOKE COIL LEVER COUNTERCLOCKWISE UNTIL TANG ON OUTSIDE LEVER JUST CONTACTS VACUUM BREAK ROD (DO NOT COMPRESS BUCKING SPRING)

⑤ PLACE GAUGE BETWEEN UPPER EDGE OF CHOKE VALVE AND INSIDE WALL OF AIR HORN (SEE NOTE*)

⑥ BEND LINK TO ADJUST

NOTE: HOLD GAUGE VERTICAL

2MC lean vacuum break setting (© Oldsmobile Div., G.M. Corp.)

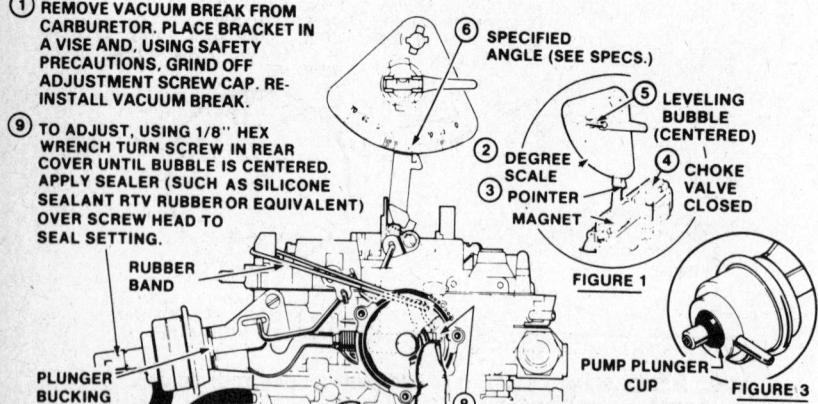

① REMOVE VACUUM BREAK FROM CARBURETOR. PLACE BRACKET IN A VISE AND, USING SAFETY PRECAUTIONS, GRIND OFF ADJUSTMENT SCREW CAP. REINSTALL VACUUM BREAK.

⑨ TO ADJUST, USING 1/8" HEX WRENCH TURN SCREW IN REAR COVER UNTIL BUBBLE IS CENTERED. APPLY SEALER (SUCH AS SILICONE SEALANT RTV RUBBER OR EQUIVALENT) OVER SCREW HEAD TO SEAL SETTING.

RUBBER BAND

PLUNGER BUCKING SPRING

FIGURE 2

⑦ SEAT DIAPHRAGM USING VACUUM SOURCE (SEE NOTE 2)

⑥ SPECIFIED ANGLE (SEE SPECS.)

② DEGREE SCALE

③ POINTER MAGNET

⑤ LEVELING BUBBLE (CENTERED)

④ CHOKE VALVE CLOSED

FIGURE 1

PUMP PLUNGER CUP

FIGURE 3

⑧ LIGHTLY CLOSE CHOKE BY PUSHING UPWARD ON CHOKE COIL LEVER OR VACUUM BREAK LEVER TANG (HOLD IN POSITION WITH RUBBER BAND). MAKE SURE PLUNGER BUCKING SPRING (IF USED) IS COMPRESSED AND SEATED.

NOTE 2: ON DELAY MODELS, PLUG END COVER USING AN ACCELERATOR PUMP PLUNGER CUP - 2G TYPE (FIGURE 3) OR EQUIVALENT. SEAT VACUUM DIAPHRAGM MAKING SURE VACUUM IS ABOVE 5" Hg WHEN READING GAUGE (STEP 9). REMOVE CUP AFTER ADJUSTMENT.

NOTE 1: MAKE CHOKE COIL LEVER ADJUSTMENT AND FAST IDLE ADJUSTMENT. DO NOT REMOVE RIVETS AND CHOKE COVER TO PERFORM THIS ADJUSTMENT. USE RUBBER BAND ON VACUUM BREAK LEVER TANG TO HOLD CHOKE VALVE CLOSED (STEP 8).

E2ME rear vacuum break adjustment—1981-82 (© G.M. Corp.)

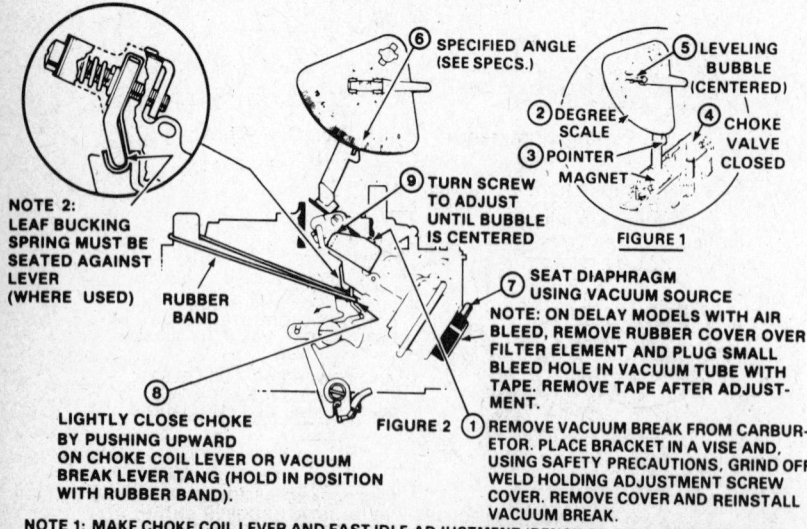

NOTE 2: LEAF BUCKING SPRING MUST BE SEATED AGAINST LEVER (WHERE USED)

RUBBER BAND

⑥ SPECIFIED ANGLE (SEE SPECS.)

② DEGREE SCALE

③ POINTER MAGNET

⑤ LEVELING BUBBLE (CENTERED)

④ CHOKE VALVE CLOSED

FIGURE 1

⑨ TURN SCREW TO ADJUST UNTIL BUBBLE IS CENTERED

⑦ SEAT DIAPHRAGM USING VACUUM SOURCE

NOTE: ON DELAY MODELS WITH AIR BLEED, REMOVE RUBBER COVER OVER FILTER ELEMENT AND PLUG SMALL BLEED HOLE IN VACUUM TUBE WITH TAPE. REMOVE TAPE AFTER ADJUSTMENT.

⑧ LIGHTLY CLOSE CHOKE BY PUSHING UPWARD ON CHOKE COIL LEVER OR VACUUM BREAK LEVER TANG (HOLD IN POSITION WITH RUBBER BAND).

FIGURE 2

① REMOVE VACUUM BREAK FROM CARBURETOR. PLACE BRACKET IN A VISE AND, USING SAFETY PRECAUTIONS, GRIND OFF WELD HOLDING ADJUSTMENT SCREW COVER. REMOVE COVER AND REINSTALL VACUUM BREAK.

NOTE 1: MAKE CHOKE COIL LEVER AND FAST IDLE ADJUSTMENT (BENCH OR ON-THE-CAR SETTING). DO NOT REMOVE RIVETS AND CHOKE COVER TO PERFORM THIS ADJUSTMENT. USE RUBBER BAND ON VACUUM BREAK LEVER TANG TO HOLD CHOKE VALVE CLOSED (STEP 8).

E2ME front vacuum break adjustment—1981-82 (© G.M. Corp.)

justment. Compress the bucking spring for rich adjustment.

4. With the choke rod in the bottom of the slot in the choke lever, gauge between the upper edge of the choke valve and the inside wall of the air horn.

5. Bend the link rod at the vacuum break plunger stem to adjust the rich setting. Bend the link rod at the opposite end from the diaphragm to adjust the lean setting.

FRONT/REAR VACUUM BREAK ADJUSTMENT

M2MC, M2ME and E2ME (1978-80)

1. Seat the front diaphragm, using an outside vacuum source. If there is an air bleed hole on the diaphragm, tape it over.

2. Remove the choke cover and coil. Rotate the inside coil lever counter-clockwise. On models with a fixed choke cover (riveted), push up on the vacuum break lever tang and hold it in position with a rubber band.

3. Check that the specified gap is present between the top of the choke valve and the air horn wall.

4. Turn the front vacuum break adjusting screw to adjust.

5. To adjust the rear vacuum break diaphragm, perform Steps 1-3 on the rear diaphragm, but make sure that the plunger bucking spring is compressed and seated in Step 2. Adjust by bending the link at the bend nearest the diaphragm.

1981-84

On these models a choke valve measuring gauge J-26701 or equivalent is used to measure angle (degrees instead of inches). See illustration for procedure.

UNLOADER ADJUSTMENT

1. With the choke valve completely closed, hold the throttle valves wide open.

2. Measure between the upper edge of the choke valve and air horn wall.

3. Bend the tang on the fast idle lever to obtain the proper measurement.

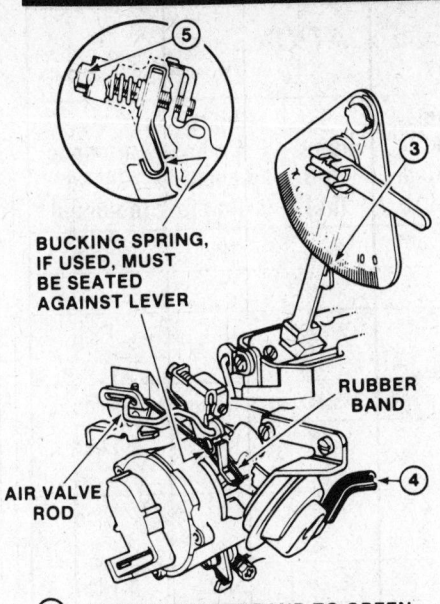

BUCKING SPRING,
IF USED, MUST
BE SEATED
AGAINST LEVER

RUBBER
BAND

AIR VALVE
ROD

① ATTACH RUBBER BAND TO GREEN
TANG OF INTERMEDIATE CHOKE
SHAFT

② OPEN THROTTLE TO ALLOW CHOKE
VALVE TO CLOSE

③ SET UP ANGLE GAGE AND SET TO
SPECIFICATION

④ RETRACT VACUUM BREAK PLUNGER
USING VACUUM SOURCE, AT LEAST
18" HG. PLUG AIR BLEED HOLES
WHERE APPLICABLE
ON QUADRAJETS, AIR VALVE ROD
MUST NOT RESTRICT PLUNGER
FROM RETRACTING FULLY. IF
NECESSARY, BEND ROD (SEE
ARROW) TO PERMIT FULL PLUNGER
TRAVEL. FINAL ROD CLEARANCE
MUST BE SET AFTER VACUUM
BREAK SETTING HAS BEEN MADE.

⑤ WITH AT LEAST 18" HG STILL
APPLIED, ADJUST SCREW TO
CENTER BUBBLE

**E2ME front vacuum break adjstment—1983
and later**

① ATTACH RUBBER BAND TO GREEN TANG OF INTERMEDIATE CHOKE SHAFT.

② OPEN THROTTLE TO ALLOW CHOKE VALVE TO CLOSE.

③ SET UP ANGLE GAGE AND SET ANGLE TO SPECIFICATION.

④ RETRACT VACUUM BREAK PLUNGER, USING VACUUM
SOURCE, AT LEAST 18" HG. PLUG AIR BLEED HOLES
WHERE APPLICABLE.

④A ON QUADRAJETS, AIR VALVE ROD MUST NOT RESTRICT
PLUNGER FROM RETRACTING FULLY. IF NECESSARY. BEND
ROD HERE TO PERMIT FULL PLUNGER TRAVEL.
WHERE APPLICABLE, PLUNGER STEM MUST
BE EXTENDED FULLY TO COMPRESS
PLUNGER BUCKING SPRING.

⑤ TO CENTER BUBBLE,
EITHER:
A. ADJUST WITH
1/8" HEX WRENCH
(VACUUM STILL
APPLIED)

-OR-

B. SUPPORT AT "S"
AND BEND
VACUUM BREAK
ROD (VACUUM
STILL APPLIED)

E2ME rear vacuum break adjustment— 1983 and later

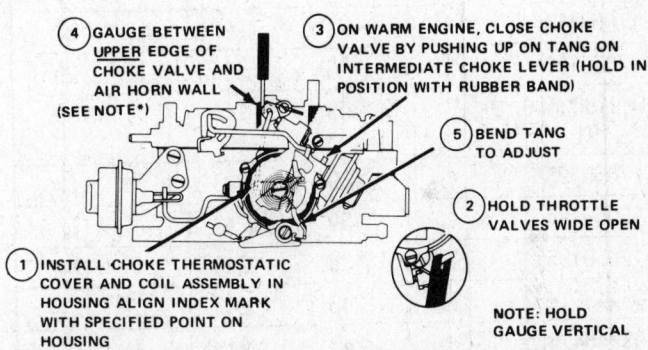

④ GAUGE BETWEEN UPPER EDGE OF CHOKE VALVE AND AIR HORN WALL (SEE NOTE*)

③ ON WARM ENGINE, CLOSE CHOKE VALVE BY PUSHING UP ON TANG ON INTERMEDIATE CHOKE LEVER (HOLD IN POSITION WITH RUBBER BAND)

⑤ BEND TANG TO ADJUST

② HOLD THROTTLE VALVES WIDE OPEN

① INSTALL CHOKE THERMOSTATIC COVER AND COIL ASSEMBLY IN HOUSING ALIGN INDEX MARK WITH SPECIFIED POINT ON HOUSING

NOTE: HOLD GAUGE VERTICAL

2MC, M2MC, M2ME, E2ME unloader adjustment—typical
(© G.M. Corp.)

AIR CONDITIONING IDLE SPEED-UP SOLENOID ADJUSTMENT

1. With the engine at normal operating
temperature and the air conditioning turned
on but the compressor clutch lead disconnected, the solenoid should be electrically
energized (plunger stem extended). Open
the throttle slightly to allow the solenoid
plunger to fully extend.

2. Adjust the plunger screw to obtain
the specified idle speed.

3. Turn off the air conditioner. The solenoid plunger should move away from the
tang on the throttle lever.

4. Adjust the curb idle speed with the
idle speed screw, if necessary.

**NOTE: Do not adjust if carburetor is
computer controlled.**

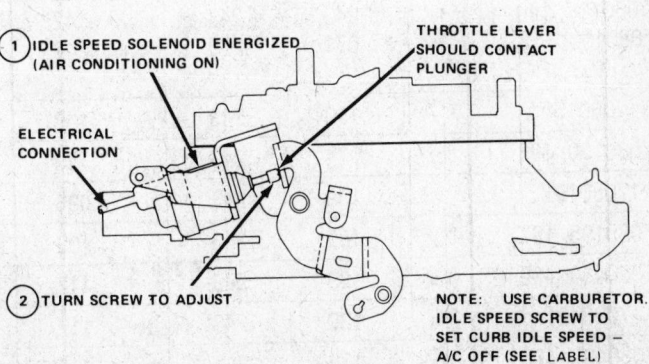

① IDLE SPEED SOLENOID ENERGIZED (AIR CONDITIONING ON)

THROTTLE LEVER SHOULD CONTACT PLUNGER

ELECTRICAL CONNECTION

② TURN SCREW TO ADJUST

NOTE: USE CARBURETOR IDLE SPEED SCREW TO SET CURB IDLE SPEED – A/C OFF (SEE LABEL)

2MC, M2MC air conditioning idle speed-up solenoid adjustment
(© Oldsmobile Div., G.M. Corp.)

2MC, M2MC, M2ME, E2ME CARBURETOR SPECIFICATIONS
General Motors—U.S.A.

Year	Carburetor Identification ①	Flat Level (in.)	Choke Rod (in.)	Choke Unloader (in.)	Vacuum Break Lean or Front (deg./in.)	Vacuum Break Rich or Rear (deg./in.)	Pump Rod (in.)	Choke Coil Lever (in.)	Automatic Choke (notches)
'78	All Chev.	1/4	.314	.314	.136	—	9/32 ②	.120	Index
	17058150, 152	3/8	.065	.203	.203	.133	1/4 ②	.120	2 Rich
	17058151, 156, 158	3/8	.065	.203	.229	.133	11/32 ③	.120	2 Rich
	17058154, 155	3/8	.071	.220	.157	.260	11/32 ③	.120	2 Rich
	17058160 Buick	11/32	.133	.220	.149	.227	1/4 ②	.120	2 Lean
	17058160 Pontiac	11/32	.126	.203	.142	.195	1/4 ②	.120	2 Rich
	17058192	1/4	.074	.350	.117	.103	9/32 ②	.120	1 Rich
	17058450	3/8	.065	.203	.146	.289	11/32 ③	.120	2 Rich
	17058496	1/4	.077	.243	.136	.211	3/8 ③	.120	1 Rich
'79	17059134, 135, 136, 137	11/32	.243	.243	.157	—	9/32 ②	.120	1 Lean
	17059150, 152	3/8	.065	.203	.203	.133	1/4 ②	.120	2 Rich
	17059151	3/8	.071	.220	.243	.142	11/32 ③	.120	2 Rich
	17059154	3/8	.071	.220	.157	.260	11/32 ③	.120	2 Rich
	17059160	11/32	.110	.195	.129	.187	1/4 ②	.120	2 Rich
	17059180, 190, 191	11/32	.039	.243	.103	.090	1/4 ②	.120	2 Rich
	17059193	5/16	.139	.243	.117	.187	Fixed	.120	Fixed
	17059194	5/16	.139	.243	.117	.179	Fixed	.120	Fixed
	17059196	5/16	.139	.243	.164	.136	Fixed	.120	Fixed
	17059430, 432	9/32	.243	.243	.157	—	1/4 ②	.120	1 Lean
	17059434, 436	13/32	.243	.243	.171	—	1/4 ②	.120	1 Lean
	17059492, 493	11/32	.139	.277	.129	.117	9/32 ②	.120	1 Rich
'80	17080108, 110 17080130, 131	3/8	.243	.243	.142	—	5/16 ②	.120	Fixed
	17080132, 133, 147, 148, 149	5/16	.243	.243	.142	—	5/16 ②	.120	Fixed
	17080138, 140	3/8	.243	.243	.142	—	5/16 ②	.120	Fixed
	17080150, 152, 153	3/8	.071	.220	.243	.157	11/32 ③	.120	Fixed
	17080160	5/16	.110	.243	.168	.207	1/4 ②	.120	Fixed
	17080190, 192	9/32	.074	.243	.123	.110	1/4 ②	.120	Fixed
	17080191	11/32	.139	.243	.096	.096	1/4 ②	.120	Fixed
	17080195, 197	9/32	.139	.243	.103	.071	1/4 ②	.120	Fixed
	17080490, 492	5/16	.139	.243	.117	.203	1/4 ②	.120	Fixed
	17080491	5/16	.139	.243	.117	.220	1/4 ②	.120	Fixed
	17080493, 495	5/16	.139	.243	.117	.179	3/8	.120	Fixed

2MC, M2MC, M2ME, E2ME CARBURETOR SPECIFICATIONS
General Motors—U.S.A.

Year	Carburetor Identification ①	Flat Level (in.)	Choke Rod (in.)	Choke Unloader (in.)	Vacuum Break Lean or Front (deg./in.)	Vacuum Break Rich or Rear (deg./in.)	Pump Rod (in.)	Choke Coil Lever (in.)	Automatic Choke (notches)
'80	17080494	5/16	.139	.243	.117	.179	1/4 ②	.120	Fixed
	17080496, 498	5/16	.139	.243	.117	.203	Fixed	.120	Fixed
'81	17080185, 187	9/32	.139	.243	19/.103	14/.071	1/4 ②	.120	Fixed
	17080191	11/32	.139	.243	18/.096	18/.096	1/4 ②	.120	Fixed
	17081130, 131, 132, 133	11/32	.110	.243	25/.142	—	Fixed	.120	Fixed
	17081138, 140	11/32	.110	.260	25/.142	—	Fixed	.120	Fixed
	17081150, 152	13/32	.071	.220	24/.136	36/.227	Fixed	.120	Fixed
	17081160	11/32	.074	.220	24/.136	37/.234	④	.120	Fixed
	17081196	5/16	.139	.243	28/.164	24/.136	④	.120	Fixed
	17081190, 193	5/16	.139	.243	21/.117	31/.187	Fixed	.120	Fixed
	17081191, 194	5/16	.139	.243	28/.164	24/.136	④	.120	Fixed
	17081198	3/8	.139	.243	28/.164	24/.136	④	.120	Fixed
	17081192, 197	5/16	.139	.243	21/.117	30/.179	④	.120	Fixed
	17081199	3/8	.096	.243	18/.096	24/.136	Fixed	.120	Fixed
'82	17082130, 132, 138, 140	3/8	.110	.164	27/.157	—	④	④	Fixed
	17082150	13/32	.071	.220	24/.136	38/.243 ⑤	④	④	Fixed
	17082182, 184	5/16	.096	.195	28/.164	24/.136	④	④	Fixed
	17082192, 194	5/16	.096	.195	28/.164	24/.136	④	④	Fixed
	17082196	5/16	.096	.157	21/.117	19/.103	④	④	Fixed
	17082497	5/16	.113	.195	28/.164	24/.136	④	.120	Fixed
'83	17082130, 132	3/8	.110	.243	27/.157	—	④	.120	Fixed
	17083190, 192	5/16	.096	.195	28/.164	24/.136	④	.120	Fixed
	17083193	5/16	.090	.157	23/.129	28/.164	④	.120	Fixed
	17083194	5/16	.090	.220	27/.157	25/.142	④	.120	Fixed
'84	17082130	3/8	.110	.243	27/.157	None	④	.120	Fixed
	17082132	3/8	.110	.243	27/.157	None	④	.120	Fixed
	17084191	5/16	.096	.195	28/.164	24/.136	④	.120	Fixed
	17084193	5/16	.090	.220	27/.157	25/.142	④	.120	Fixed
	17084194	5/16	.090	.220	27/.157	25/.142	④	.120	Fixed
	17084195	5/16	.090	.220	27/.157	25/.142	④	.120	Fixed

① The carburetor identification number is stamped on the float bowl, next to the fuel inlet nut.
② Inner hole
③ Outer hole
④ Not Adjustable
⑤ High altitude—0.206

2MC, M2MC, M2ME, E2ME CARBURETOR SPECIFICATIONS
General Motors—Canada

Year	Carburetor Identification ①	Float Level (in.)	Choke Rod (in.)	Choke Unloader (in.)	Vacuum Break Lean or Front (deg./in.)	Vacuum Break Rich or Rear (deg./in.)	Pump Rod (in.)	Choke Coil Lever (in.)	Automatic Choke (notches)
'81	17080191	11/32	.139	.243	18/.096	18/.096	1/4 ②	.120	Fixed
	17081492	9/32	.139	.243	17/.090	19/.103	1/4 ②	.120	Fixed
	17081493	9/32	.139	.243	17/.090	19/.103	1/4 ②	.120	Fixed
	17081170	13/32	.110	.243	25/.142	—	1/4 ②	.120	Fixed
	17081171	13/32	.110	.243	25/.142	—	1/4 ②	.120	Fixed
	17081174	9/32	.110	.243	25/.142	—	1/4 ②	.120	Fixed
	17081175	9/32	.110	.243	25/.142	—	1/4 ②	.120	Fixed
'82	17082174	9/32	.110	.243	25/.142	—	5/16 ②	.120	Fixed
	17082175	9/32	.110	.243	25/.142	—	5/16 ②	.120	Fixed
	17082492	9/32	.139	.243	17/.090	19/.103	1/4 ②	.120	Fixed
	17082172	9/32	.110	.243	25/.142	—	5/16 ②	.120	Fixed
	17082173	9/32	.110	.243	25/.142	—	5/16 ②	.120	Fixed
'83–'84	17083172	9/32	.139	.243	17/.090	19/.103	1/4 ②	.120	Fixed

① The carburetor identification number is stamped on the float bowl, next to the fuel inlet nut.
② Inner hole

Quadrajet

The Rochester Quadrajet carburetor is a two stage, four-barrel downdraft carburetor. It has been built in many variations designated as 4MC, 4MV, M4MC, M4MCA, M4ME, M4MEA, E4MC, and E4ME. See the beginning of the Rochester section for an explanation of these designations.

The primary side of the carburetor is equipped with two primary bores and a triple venturi with plain tube nozzles. During off idle and part throttle operation, the fuel is metered through specially designed jets positioned by a manifold vacuum responsive piston.

The secondary side of the carburetor contains two secondary bores. An air valve is used on the secondary side for metering control and supplements the primary bore.

The secondary air valve operates tapered metering rods which regulate the fuel in constant proportion to the air being supplied.

FAST IDLE SPEED

1. Position the fast idle lever on the high step of the fast idle cam.
2. Be sure that the choke is wide open and the engine warm. Plug the EGR vacuum hose. Disconnect the vacuum hose to the front vacuum break unit, if there are two.
3. Make a preliminary adjustment by turning the fast idle screw out until the throttle valves are closed, then screwing it in the specified number of turns after it contacts the lever (see the carburetor specifications).
4. Use the fast idle screw to adjust the fast idle to the speed, and under the conditions, specified on the engine compartment sticker or in the specifications chart.

CHOKE ROD (FAST IDLE CAM)

1. Adjust the fast idle and place the cam follower on the second step of the fast idle cam against the shoulder of the high step.
2. Close the choke valve by exerting counter-clockwise pressure on the external choke lever. Remove the coil assembly from

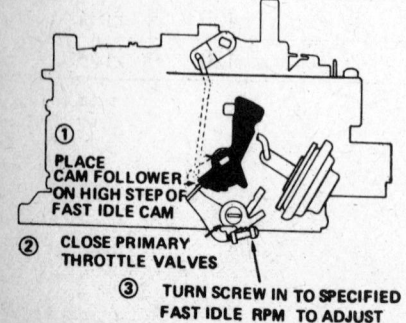

Quadrajet fast idle adjustment (© G.M. Corp.)

① PLACE CAM FOLLOWER ON HIGH STEP OF FAST IDLE CAM
② CLOSE PRIMARY THROTTLE VALVES
③ TURN SCREW IN TO SPECIFIED FAST IDLE RPM TO ADJUST

④ GAUGE BETWEEN UPPER EDGE OF CHOKE VALVE & INSIDE AIR HORN WALL
NOTE: HOLD GAUGE VERTICAL
③ CLOSE CHOKE BY PUSHING UPWARD ON CHOKE COIL LEVER
① MAKE FAST IDLE ADJUSTMENT
⑤ BEND TANG ON FAST IDLE CAM TO ADJUST
FAST IDLE CAM
② PLACE CAM FOLLOWER ON SECOND STEP OF CAM NEXT TO HIGH STEP

Quadrajet choke rod (fast idle cam) adjustment—typical (© G.M. Corp.)

the choke housing and push upon the choke coil lever. On models with a fixed (riveted) choke cover, push up on the vacuum break lever tang and hold in position with a rubber band.

3. Insert a gauge of the proper size between the upper edge of the choke valve and the inside air horn wall.

4. To adjust, bend the tang on the fast idle cam. Be sure that the tang rests against the cam after bending.

PRIMARY (FRONT) VACUUM BREAK ADJUSTMENT

1978–81

1. Loosen the three retaining screws and remove the thermostatic cover and coil assembly from the choke housing through 1979.

2. Seat the front vacuum diaphragm using an outside vacuum source. If there is a diaphragm unit bleed hole, tape it over.

3. Push up on the inside choke coil lever until the tang on the vacuum break lever contacts the tang on the vacuum break plunger. On models with a fixed choke coil cover, push up on the vacuum break lever tang.

4. Place the proper size gauge between the upper edge of the choke valve and the inside of the air horn wall.

5. To adjust, turn the adjustment screw on the vacuum break plunger lever.

6. Install the vacuum hose to the vacuum break unit.

1982—84

On these models a choke valve measuring gauge J-26701 or equivalent is used to measure angle (degrees instead of inches). See illustration for procedure.

SECONDARY (REAR) VACUUM BREAK ADJUSTMENT

1978–80

1. Remove the thermostatic cover and coil assembly from the choke housing through 1979.

2. Tape over the bleed hole in the rear vacuum break diaphragm and seat the diaphragm using an outside vacuum source. Make sure the diaphragm plunger bucking spring, if any, is compressed. On delay models (1980), plug the end cover with a pump plunger cup or equivalent and remove after adjustment.

3. Close the choke by pushing up on the choke coil lever inside the choke housing. On models with a fixed choke coil cover, push up on the vacuum break lever tang and use a rubber band to hold in place.

4. With the choke rod in the bottom of the slot in the choke lever, measure be-

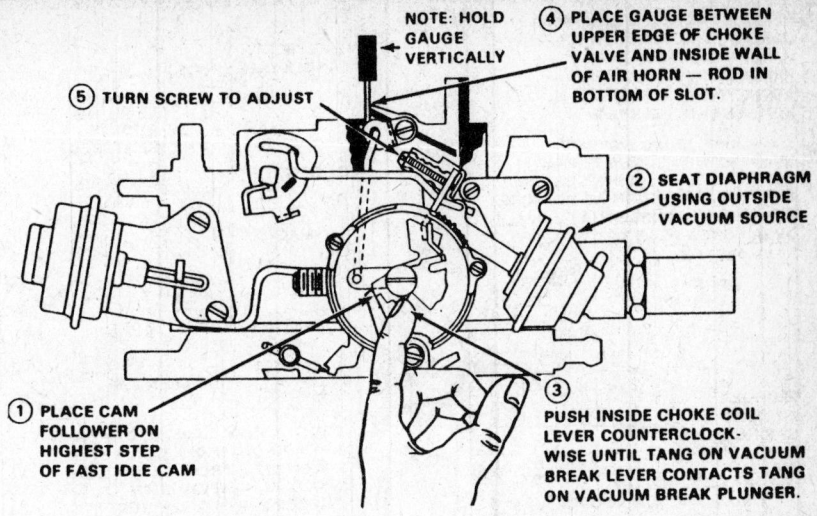

④ PLACE GAUGE BETWEEN UPPER EDGE OF CHOKE VALVE AND INSIDE WALL OF AIR HORN — ROD IN BOTTOM OF SLOT.

NOTE: HOLD GAUGE VERTICALLY

⑤ TURN SCREW TO ADJUST

② SEAT DIAPHRAGM USING OUTSIDE VACUUM SOURCE

① PLACE CAM FOLLOWER ON HIGHEST STEP OF FAST IDLE CAM

③ PUSH INSIDE CHOKE COIL LEVER COUNTERCLOCKWISE UNTIL TANG ON VACUUM BREAK LEVER CONTACTS TANG ON VACUUM BREAK PLUNGER.

Quadrajet front vacuum break adjustment—typical through 1981

① ATTACH RUBBER BAND TO GREEN TANG OF INTERMEDIATE CHOKE SHAFT

② OPEN THROTTLE TO ALLOW CHOKE VALVE TO CLOSE

③ SET UP ANGLE GAGE AND SET TO SPECIFICATION

④ RETRACT VACUUM BREAK PLUNGER USING VACUUM SOURCE, AT LEAST 18″ HG. PLUG AIR BLEED HOLES WHERE APPLICABLE

ON QUADRAJETS, AIR VALVE ROD MUST NOT RESTRICT PLUNGER FROM RETRACTING FULLY. IF NECESSARY, BEND ROD (SEE ARROW) TO PERMIT FULL PLUNGER TRAVEL. FINAL ROD CLEARANCE MUST BE SET AFTER VACUUM BREAK SETTING HAS BEEN MADE.

⑤ WITH AT LEAST 18″ HG STILL APPLIED, ADJUST SCREW TO CENTER BUBBLE

BUCKING SPRING, IF USED, MUST BE SEATED AGAINST LEVER

RUBBER BAND

AIR VALVE ROD

Quadrajet front vacuum break adjustment—1982 and later © G.M. Corp.

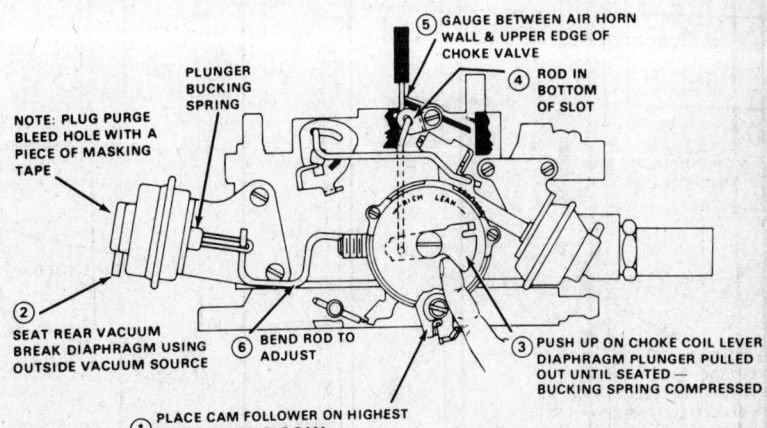

⑤ GAUGE BETWEEN AIR HORN WALL & UPPER EDGE OF CHOKE VALVE

ROD IN BOTTOM OF SLOT

PLUNGER BUCKING SPRING

NOTE: PLUG PURGE BLEED HOLE WITH A PIECE OF MASKING TAPE

② SEAT REAR VACUUM BREAK DIAPHRAGM USING OUTSIDE VACUUM SOURCE

① PLACE CAM FOLLOWER ON HIGHEST STEP OF FAST IDLE CAM

⑥ BEND ROD TO ADJUST

③ PUSH UP ON CHOKE COIL LEVER DIAPHRAGM PLUNGER PULLED OUT UNTIL SEATED — BUCKING SPRING COMPRESSED

Quadrajet rear vacuum break adjustment (without adjusting screw)—through 1980 (© G.M. Corp.)

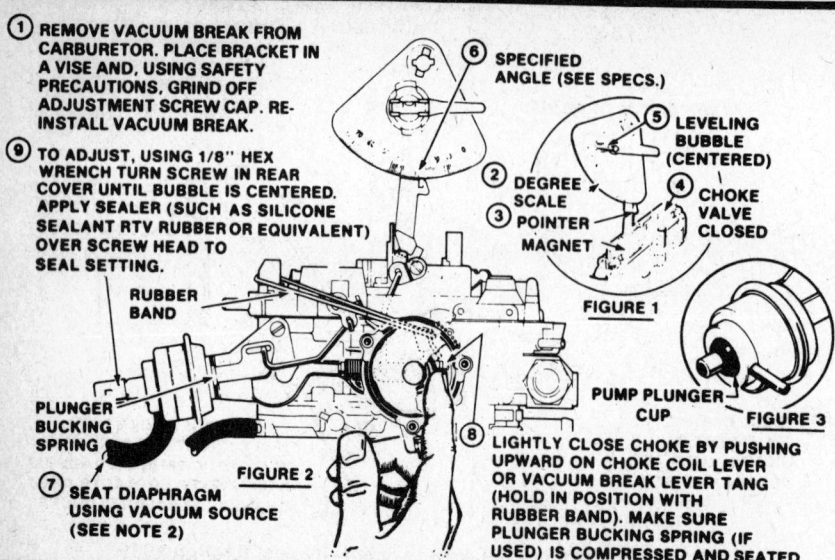

① REMOVE VACUUM BREAK FROM CARBURETOR. PLACE BRACKET IN A VISE AND, USING SAFETY PRECAUTIONS, GRIND OFF ADJUSTMENT SCREW CAP. RE-INSTALL VACUUM BREAK.

⑨ TO ADJUST, USING 1/8" HEX WRENCH TURN SCREW IN REAR COVER UNTIL BUBBLE IS CENTERED. APPLY SEALER (SUCH AS SILICONE SEALANT RTV RUBBER OR EQUIVALENT) OVER SCREW HEAD TO SEAL SETTING.

RUBBER BAND

PLUNGER BUCKING SPRING

⑦ SEAT DIAPHRAGM USING VACUUM SOURCE (SEE NOTE 2)

FIGURE 2

⑥ SPECIFIED ANGLE (SEE SPECS.)

⑤ LEVELING BUBBLE (CENTERED)

② DEGREE SCALE

③ POINTER MAGNET

④ CHOKE VALVE CLOSED

FIGURE 1

PUMP PLUNGER CUP

FIGURE 3

⑧ LIGHTLY CLOSE CHOKE BY PUSHING UPWARD ON CHOKE COIL LEVER OR VACUUM BREAK LEVER TANG (HOLD IN POSITION WITH RUBBER BAND). MAKE SURE PLUNGER BUCKING SPRING (IF USED) IS COMPRESSED AND SEATED.

NOTE 2: ON DELAY MODELS, PLUG END COVER USING AN ACCELERATOR PUMP PLUNGER CUP - 2G TYPE (FIGURE 3) OR EQUIVALENT. SEAT VACUUM DIAPHRAGM MAKING SURE VACUUM IS ABOVE 5" Hg WHEN READING GAUGE (STEP 9). REMOVE CUP AFTER ADJUSTMENT.

NOTE 1: MAKE CHOKE COIL LEVER ADJUSTMENT AND FAST IDLE ADJUSTMENT. DO NOT REMOVE RIVETS AND CHOKE COVER TO PERFORM THIS ADJUSTMENT. USE RUBBER BAND ON VACUUM BREAK LEVER TANG TO HOLD CHOKE VALVE CLOSED (STEP 8).

Quadrajet rear vacuum break adjustment—1981–82 (© G.M. Corp.)

① ATTACH RUBBER BAND TO GREEN TANG OF INTERMEDIATE CHOKE SHAFT.

② OPEN THROTTLE TO ALLOW CHOKE VALVE TO CLOSE.

③ SET UP ANGLE GAGE AND SET ANGLE TO SPECIFICATION.

④ RETRACT VACUUM BREAK PLUNGER, USING VACUUM SOURCE, AT LEAST 18" HG. PLUG AIR BLEED HOLES WHERE APPLICABLE.

④A ON QUADRAJETS, AIR VALVE ROD MUST NOT RESTRICT PLUNGER FROM RETRACTING FULLY. IF NECESSARY. BEND ROD HERE TO PERMIT FULL PLUNGER TRAVEL. WHERE APPLICABLE, PLUNGER STEM MUST BE EXTENDED FULLY TO COMPRESS PLUNGER BUCKING SPRING.

⑤ TO CENTER BUBBLE, EITHER:
A. ADJUST WITH 1/8" HEX WRENCH (VACUUM STILL APPLIED)
-OR-
B. SUPPORT AT "S" AND BEND VACUUM BREAK ROD (VACUUM STILL APPLIED)

Quadrajet rear vacuum break adjustment—typical 1983 and later

tween the upper edge of the choke valve and the air horn wall with a wire type gauge.

5. To adjust, bend the vacuum break rod at the first bend near the diaphragm except on 1980 models with a screw at the rear of the diaphragm; on those models, turn the screw to adjust.

6. Remove the tape covering the bleed hole of the diaphragm and connect the vacuum hose.

1981–84

On these models a choke valve measuring gauge J-26701 or equivalent is used to measure angle (degrees instead of inches). See illustration for procedure.

CHOKE UNLOADER

1. Push up on the vacuum break lever to close the choke valve, and fully open the throttle valves.
2. Measure the distance from the upper edge of the choke valve to the air horn wall.
3. To adjust, bend the tang on the fast idle lever.

4MV CHOKE COIL ROD

1. Close the choke valve by rotating the choke coil lever counter-clockwise.
2. Disconnect the thermostatic coil rod from the upper lever.
3. Push down on the rod until it contacts the bracket of the coil.
4. The rod must fit in the notch of the upper lever.
5. If it does not, it must be bent on the curved portion just below the upper lever.

MC, ME CHOKE COIL LEVER ADJUSTMENT

1. Remove the choke cover and thermostatic coil from the choke housing. On models with a fixed (riveted) choke cover, the rivets must be drilled out. A choke stat kit is necessary for assembly. Place the fast idle cam follower on the high step.
2. Push up on the coil tang (counterclockwise) until the choke valve is closed.

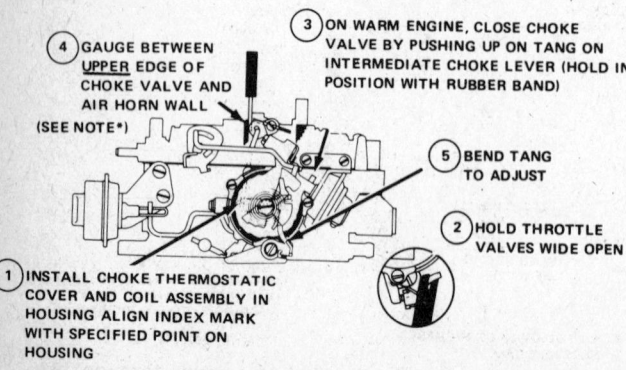

④ GAUGE BETWEEN UPPER EDGE OF CHOKE VALVE AND AIR HORN WALL (SEE NOTE*)

③ ON WARM ENGINE, CLOSE CHOKE VALVE BY PUSHING UP ON TANG ON INTERMEDIATE CHOKE LEVER (HOLD IN POSITION WITH RUBBER BAND)

⑤ BEND TANG TO ADJUST

② HOLD THROTTLE VALVES WIDE OPEN

① INSTALL CHOKE THERMOSTATIC COVER AND COIL ASSEMBLY IN HOUSING ALIGN INDEX MARK WITH SPECIFIED POINT ON HOUSING

Quadrajet unloader adjustment—typical (© G.M. Corp.)

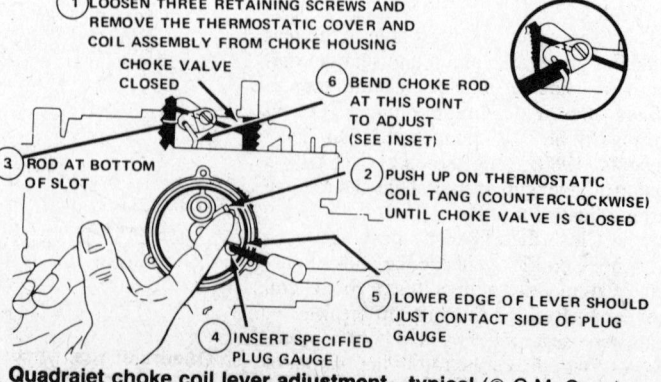

① LOOSEN THREE RETAINING SCREWS AND REMOVE THE THERMOSTATIC COVER AND COIL ASSEMBLY FROM CHOKE HOUSING

CHOKE VALVE CLOSED

⑥ BEND CHOKE ROD AT THIS POINT TO ADJUST (SEE INSET)

③ ROD AT BOTTOM OF SLOT

② PUSH UP ON THERMOSTATIC COIL TANG (COUNTERCLOCKWISE) UNTIL CHOKE VALVE IS CLOSED

④ INSERT SPECIFIED PLUG GAUGE

⑤ LOWER EDGE OF LEVER SHOULD JUST CONTACT SIDE OF PLUG GAUGE

Quadrajet choke coil lever adjustment—typical (© G.M. Corp.)

The top of the choke rod should be at the bottom of the slot in the choke valve lever.

3. Insert a 0.120 in. drill bit in the hole in the choke housing.

4. The lower edge of the choke coil lever should just contact the side of the plug gauge.

5. Bend the choke rod at the top angle to adjust.

SECONDARY CLOSING ADJUSTMENT

This adjustment assures proper closing of the secondary throttle plates.

1. Set the slow idle as per instructions in the appropriate car section. Make sure that the fast idle cam follower is not resting on the fast idle cam and the choke valve is wide open.

2. There should be 0.020 in. clearance between the secondary throttle actuating rod and the front of the slot on the secondary throttle lever with the closing tang on the throttle lever resting against the actuating lever.

3. Bend the secondary closing tang on the primary throttle actuating rod or lever to adjust.

SECONDARY OPENING ADJUSTMENT

1. Open the primary throttle valves until the actuating link contacts the upper tang on the secondary lever.

2. With two point linkage, the bottom of the link should be in the center of the secondary lever slot.

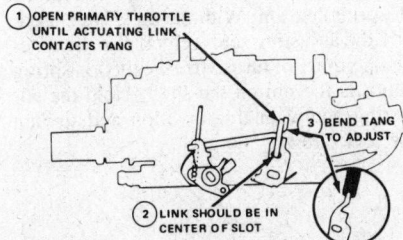

Quadrajet secondary opening adjustment, two point linkage (© G.M. Corp.)

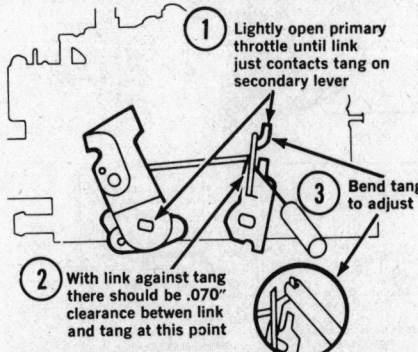

Secondary opening adjustment—three point linkage (© G.M. Corp.)

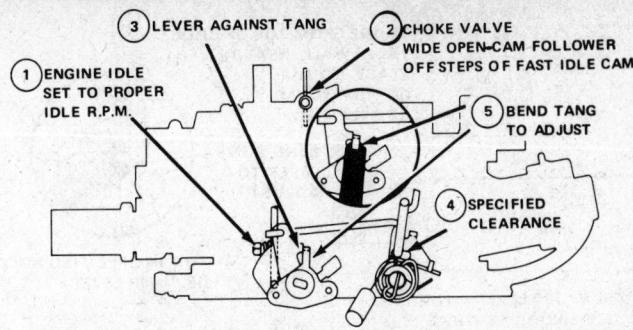

Quadrajet Secondary Closing Adjustment (© G.M. Corp.)

3. With three point linkage, there should be 0.070 in. clearance between the link and the middle tang.

4. Bend the upper tang on the secondary lever to adjust as necessary.

FLOAT LEVEL

With the air horn assembly removed, measure the distance from the air horn gasket surface (gasket removed) to the top of the float at the toe (3/16 in. back from the toe).

NOTE: Make sure the retaining pin is firmly held in place and that the tang of the float is lightly held against the needle and seat assembly.

Remove the float and bend the float arm to adjust except on carburetors used with the computer controlled systems (E4MC and E4ME). For those carburetors, if the float level is too high, hold the retainer firmly in place and push down on the center of the float to adjust. If the float level is too low on models with the computer controlled

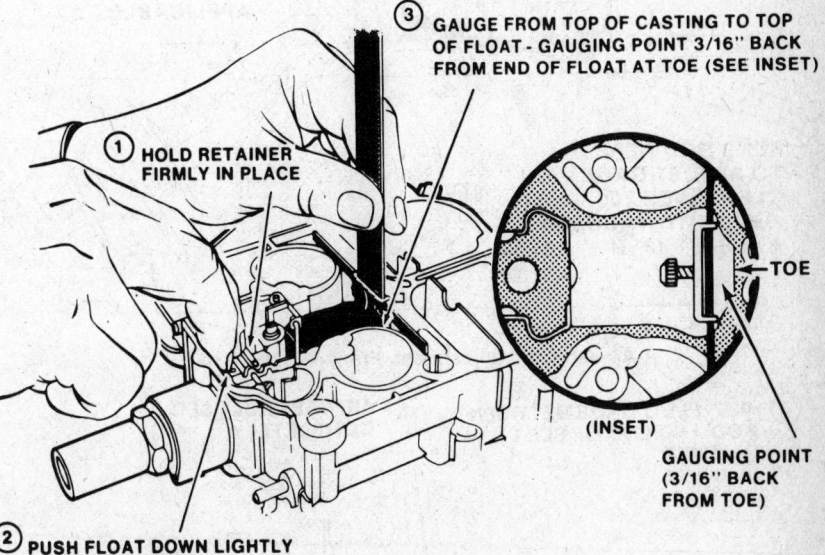

Quadrajet float level adjustment—typical (© G.M. Corp.)

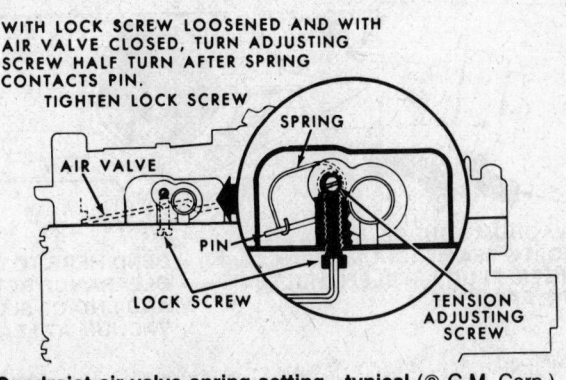

Quadrajet air valve spring setting—typical (© G.M. Corp.)

U165

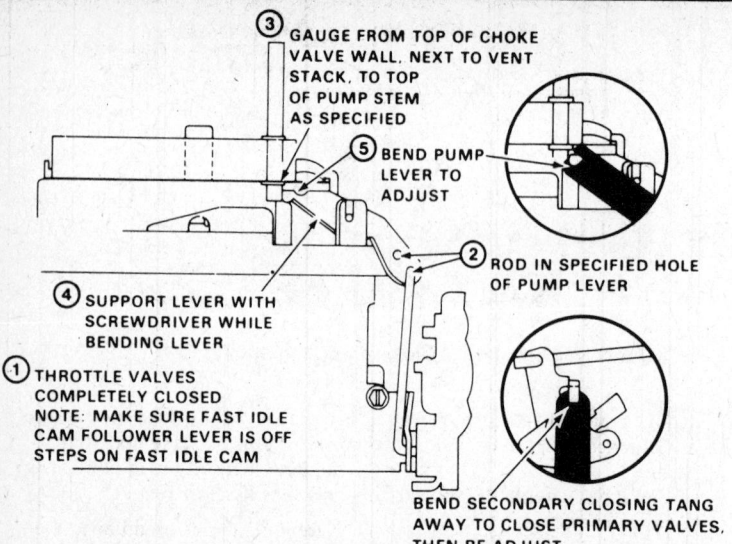

③ GAUGE FROM TOP OF CHOKE VALVE WALL, NEXT TO VENT STACK, TO TOP OF PUMP STEM AS SPECIFIED

⑤ BEND PUMP LEVER TO ADJUST

② ROD IN SPECIFIED HOLE OF PUMP LEVER

④ SUPPORT LEVER WITH SCREWDRIVER WHILE BENDING LEVER

① THROTTLE VALVES COMPLETELY CLOSED NOTE: MAKE SURE FAST IDLE CAM FOLLOWER LEVER IS OFF STEPS ON FAST IDLE CAM

BEND SECONDARY CLOSING TANG AWAY TO CLOSE PRIMARY VALVES. THEN RE-ADJUST

Quadrajet accelerator pump rod adjustment (© G.M. Corp.)

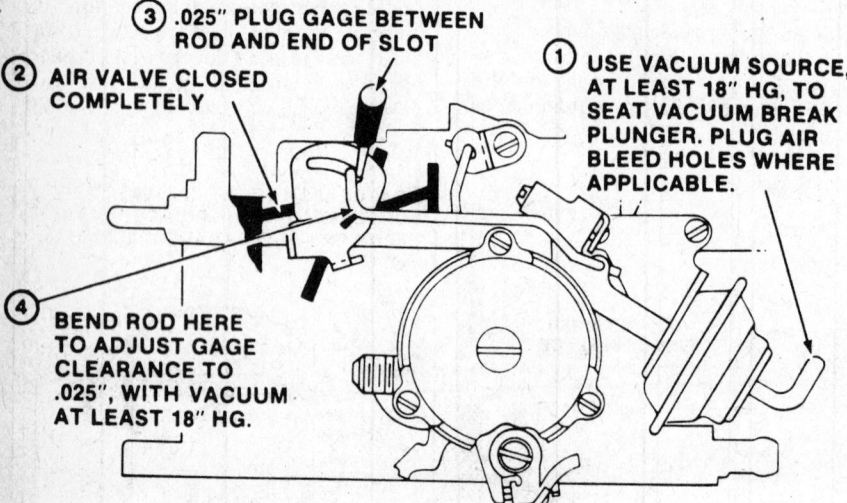

③ .025" PLUG GAGE BETWEEN ROD AND END OF SLOT

② AIR VALVE CLOSED COMPLETELY

① USE VACUUM SOURCE, AT LEAST 18" HG, TO SEAT VACUUM BREAK PLUNGER. PLUG AIR BLEED HOLES WHERE APPLICABLE.

④ BEND ROD HERE TO ADJUST GAGE CLEARANCE TO .025", WITH VACUUM AT LEAST 18" HG.

Air valve rod adjustment, Front—E4ME, E4MC

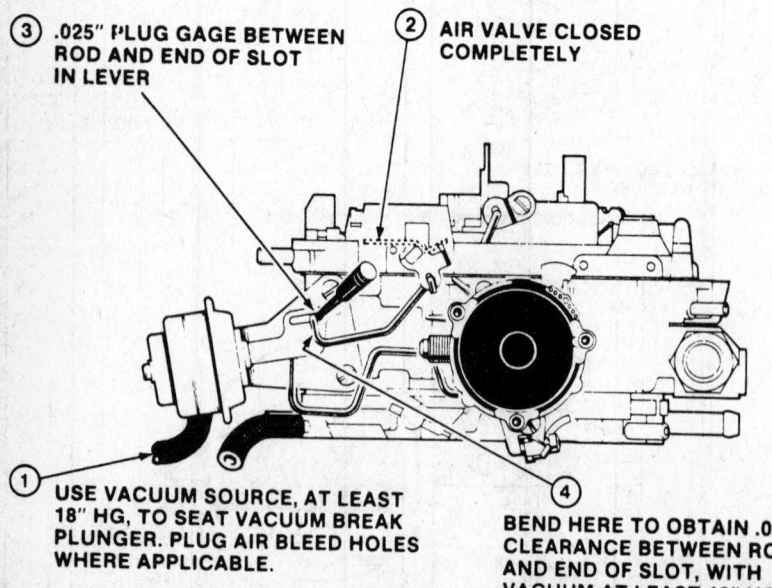

③ .025" PLUG GAGE BETWEEN ROD AND END OF SLOT IN LEVER

② AIR VALVE CLOSED COMPLETELY

① USE VACUUM SOURCE, AT LEAST 18" HG, TO SEAT VACUUM BREAK PLUNGER. PLUG AIR BLEED HOLES WHERE APPLICABLE.

④ BEND HERE TO OBTAIN .025" CLEARANCE BETWEEN ROD AND END OF SLOT, WITH VACUUM AT LEAST 18" HG.

Air valve rod adjustment, Rear—E4ME, E4MC

system, lift out the metering rods. Remove the solenoid connector screw. Turn the lean mixture solenoid screw in clockwise, counting and recording the exact number of turns until the screw is lightly bottomed in the bowl. Then turn the screw out clockwise and remove. Lift out the solenoid and connector. Remove the float and bend the arm up to adjust. Install the parts, turning the mixture solenoid screw in until it is lightly bottomed, then unscrewing it the exact number of turns counted earlier.

ACCELERATOR PUMP

The accelerator pump is not adjustable on computer controlled carburetors (E4MC and E4ME).

1. Close the primary throttle valves by backing out the slow idle screw and making sure that the fast idle cam follower is off the steps of the fast idle cam.

2. Bend the secondary throttle closing tang away from the primary throttle lever, if necessary, to insure that the primary throttle valves are fully closed.

3. With the pump in the appropriate hole in the pump lever, measure from the top of the choke valve wall to the top of the pump stem.

4. To adjust, bend the pump lever.

5. After adjusting, readjust the secondary throttle tang and the slow idle screw.

AIR VALVE SPRING ADJUSTMENT

To adjust the air valve spring windup, loosen the Allen head lockscrew and turn the adjusting screw counter-clockwise to remove all spring tension. With the air valve closed, turn the adjusting screw clockwise the specified number of turns after the torsion spring contacts the pin on the shaft. Hold the adjusting screw in this position and tighten the lockscrew.

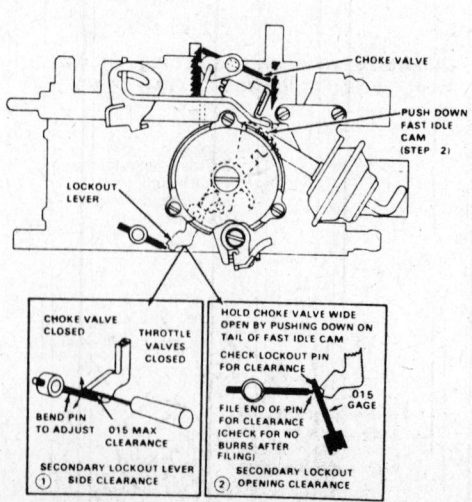

CHOKE VALVE

PUSH DOWN FAST IDLE CAM (STEP 2)

LOCKOUT LEVER

CHOKE VALVE CLOSED

THROTTLE VALVES CLOSED

BEND PIN TO ADJUST   .015 MAX CLEARANCE

SECONDARY LOCKOUT LEVER ① SIDE CLEARANCE

HOLD CHOKE VALVE WIDE OPEN BY PUSHING DOWN ON TAIL OF FAST IDLE CAM

CHECK LOCKOUT PIN FOR CLEARANCE

FILE END OF PIN FOR CLEARANCE (CHECK FOR NO BURRS AFTER FILING)

.015 GAGE

SECONDARY LOCKOUT ② OPENING CLEARANCE

Secondary lockout adjustment— E4ME, E4MC

QUADRAJET CARBURETOR SPECIFICATIONS
Cadillac

Year	Carburetor Identification①	Float Level (in.)	Air Valve Spring (turn)	Pump Rod (in.)	Primary Vacuum Break (in./deg.)	Secondary Vacuum Break (in./deg.)	Secondary Opening (in.)	Choke Rod (in.)	Choke Unloader (in.)	Fast Idle Speed (rpm)
'78	17058230	13/32	1/2	3/8	0.150	0.165	③	0.080	0.230	1500
	All others	13/32	1/2	3/8	0.140	0.250	③	0.080	0.230	1400
'79	17059230	13/32	1/2	9/32②	0.142	0.234	0.015	0.083	0.142	1000
	17059232	13/32	1/2	9/32②	0.142	0.234	0.015	0.083	0.142	1500
	17059530	13/32	1/2	9/32②	0.149	0.164	0.015	0.083	0.142	1500
	17059532	13/32	1/2	9/32②	0.149	0.164	0.015	0.083	0.142	1500
'80	17080230	7/16	1/2	9/32②	0.149	0.136	③	0.083	0.220	1450
	17080530	17/32	1/2	Fixed	0.142	0.400	③	0.083	0.260	1350
'81	17081248	3/8	5/8	Fixed	0.164	0.136	③	0.139	0.243	④
	17081289	13/32	5/8	Fixed	0.164	0.136	③	0.139	0.243	④
'82	17082246	3/8	5/8	Fixed	0.149/26	0.149/26	③	0.139	0.195	④
	17082247	13/32	5/8	Fixed	0.164/28	0.136/24	③	0.139	0.243	④
'83	17082266	3/8	5/8	Fixed	0.149/26	0.149/26	③	0.071	0.195	④
	17082267	3/8	5/8	Fixed	0.149/26	0.149/26	③	0.071	0.195	④

① The carburetor identification number is stamped on the float bowl, near the secondary throttle lever.
② Inner hole
③ No measurement necessary on two point linkage; see text.
④ See underhood decal.

QUADRAJET CARBURETOR SPECIFICATIONS
Buick

Year	Carburetor Identification①	Float Level (in.)	Air Valve Spring (turn)	Pump Rod (in.)	Primary Vacuum Break (in./deg.)	Secondary Vacuum Break (in./deg.)	Secondary Opening (in.)	Choke Rod (in.)	Choke Unloader (in.)	Fast Idle Speed④ (rpm)
'78	17058240	7/32	3/4	9/32	0.117	0.117	②	0.074	0.243	⑤
	17058241	5/16	3/4	3/8	0.120	0.103	②	0.096	0.243	⑤
	17058250	13/32	1/2	9/32	0.129	0.183	②	0.096	0.220	⑤
	17058253	13/32	1/2	9/32	0.129	0.183	②	0.096	0.220	⑤
	17058254	15/32	1/2	9/32	0.136	—	②	0.103	0.220	⑤
	17058257	13/32	1/2	9/32	0.136	0.231	②	0.103	0.220	⑤
	17058258	13/32	1/2	9/32	0.136	0.231	②	0.103	0.220	⑤
	17058259	13/32	1/2	9/32	0.136	0.231	②	0.103	0.220	⑤
	17058582	15/32	7/8	9/32	0.179	—	②	0.314	0.277	⑤
	17058584	15/32	7/8	9/32	0.179	—	②	0.314	0.277	⑤
	17058282	15/32	7/8	9/32	0.157	—	②	0.314	0.277	⑤
	17058284	15/32	7/8	9/32	0.157	—	②	0.314	0.277	⑤

CARBURETORS ROCHESTER

QUADRAJET CARBURETOR SPECIFICATIONS
Buick

Year	Carburetor Identification ①	Float Level (in.)	Air Valve Spring (turn)	Pump Rod (in.)	Primary Vacuum Break (in./deg.)	Secondary Vacuum Break (in./deg.)	Secondary Opening (in.)	Choke Rod (in.)	Choke Unloader (in.)	Fast Idle Speed ④ (rpm)
'78	17058228	15/32	1	9/32	0.179	—	②	0.314	0.277	⑤
	17058502	15/32	7/8	9/32	0.164	—	②	0.314	0.277	⑤
	17058504	15/32	7/8	9/32	0.164	—	②	0.314	0.277	⑤
	17058202	15/32	7/8	9/32	0.157	—	②	0.314	0.277	⑤
	17058204	15/32	7/8	9/32	0.157	—	②	0.314	0.277	⑤
	17058540	7/32	3/4	9/32	0.117	0.117	②	0.074	0.243	⑤
	17058550	13/32	1/2	9/32	0.136	0.231	②	0.103	0.220	⑤
	17058553	15/32	1/2	9/32	0.129	0.231	②	0.096	0.220	⑤
	17058559	15/32	1/2	9/32	0.136	—	②	0.096	0.231	⑤
'79	17059240	7/32	3/4	9/32	0.117	0.117	②	0.074	0.179	⑥
	17059243	7/32	3/4	9/32	0.117	0.117	②	0.074	0.179	⑥
	17059540	7/32	3/4	9/32	0.117	0.129	②	0.074	0.243	⑥
	17059543	7/32	3/4	9/32	0.117	0.129	②	0.074	0.243	⑥
	17059242	7/32	3/4	9/32	0.066	0.066	②	0.074	0.179	⑥
	17059553	13/32	1/2	9/32	0.136	0.230	②	0.103	0.220	⑥
	17059555	13/32	1/2	9/32	0.149	0.230	②	0.103	0.220	⑥
	17059250	13/32	1/2	9/32	0.129	0.182	②	0.096	0.220	⑥
	17059253	13/32	1/2	9/32	0.129	0.182	②	0.096	0.220	⑥
	17059208	15/32	7/8	9/32	—	0.129	②	0.314	0.277	⑥
	17059209	15/32	7/8	9/32	—	0.129	②	0.314	0.277	⑥
	17059210	15/32	1	9/32	0.157	—	②	0.243	0.243	⑥
	17059211	15/32	1	9/32	0.157	—	②	0.243	0.243	⑥
	17059228	15/32	1	9/32	0.157	—	②	0.243	0.243	⑥
	17059241	5/16	3/4	3/8	0.120	0.113	②	0.096	0.243	⑥
	17059247	5/16	3/4	3/8	0.110	0.103	②	0.096	0.243	⑥
	17059272	15/32	5/8	3/8	0.136	0.195	②	0.074	0.220	⑥
'80	17080240	3/16	9/16	9/32③	0.083	0.083	②	0.074	0.179	⑥
	17080241	7/16	3/4	9/32③	0.129	0.114	②	0.096	0.243	⑥
	17080242	13/32	9/16	9/32③	0.077	0.096	②	0.074	0.220	⑥
	17080243	3/16	9/16	9/32③	0.083	0.083	②	0.074	0.179	⑥
	17080244	5/16	5/8	9/32③	0.096	0.071	②	0.139	0.243	⑥
	17080249	7/16	3/4	9/32③	0.129	0.114	②	0.096	0.243	⑥
	17080253	13/32	1/2	9/32③	0.149	0.211	②	0.090	0.220	⑥
	17080259	13/32	1/2	9/32③	0.149	0.211	②	0.090	0.220	⑥
	17080270	15/32	5/8	3/8⑦	0.149	0.211	②	0.074	0.220	⑥
	17080271	15/32	5/8	3/8⑦	0.142	0.211	②	0.110	0.203	⑥
	17080272	15/32	5/8	3/8⑦	0.129	0.175	②	0.074	0.203	⑥
	17080502	1/2	7/8	Fixed	0.136	0.179	②	0.110	0.243	⑥

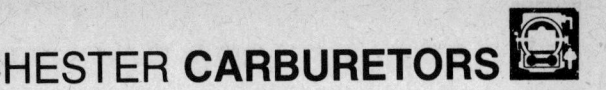

QUADRAJET CARBURETOR SPECIFICATIONS
Buick

Year	Carburetor Identification①	Float Level (in.)	Air Valve Spring (turn)	Pump Rod (in.)	Primary Vacuum Break (in./deg.)	Secondary Vacuum Break (in./deg.)	Secondary Opening (in.)	Choke Rod (in.)	Choke Unloader (in.)	Fast Idle Speed④ (rpm)
'80	17080504	½	⅞	Fixed	0.136	0.179	②	0.110	0.243	⑥
	17080540	⅜	9/16	Fixed	0.103	0.129	②	0.074	0.243	⑥
	17080542	⅜	9/16	Fixed	0.103	0.066	②	0.074	0.243	⑥
	17080543	⅜	9/16	Fixed	0.103	0.129	②	0.074	0.243	⑥
	17080553	15/32	½	Fixed	0.142	0.220	②	0.090	0.220	⑥
	17080554	15/32	½	Fixed	0.142	0.211	②	0.090	0.220	⑥
81	17081202 204	11/32	⅞	Fixed	0.157⑧	—	②	0.110	0.243	⑩
	17081203 207	11/32	⅞	Fixed	0.157⑧	—	②	0.110	0.243	⑩
	17081216 218	11/32	⅞	Fixed	0.157⑧	—	②	0.110	0.243	⑩
	17081242	⅜	9/16	Fixed	0.090⑧	0.077⑨	②	0.139	0.243	⑩
	17081243	5/16	9/16	Fixed	0.103⑧	0.090⑨	②	0.139	0.243	⑩
	17081245	⅜	⅝	Fixed	0.164⑧	0.136⑨	②	0.139	0.243	⑩
	17081247	⅜	⅝	Fixed	0.164⑧	0.136⑨	②	0.139	0.243	⑩
	17081248 249	⅜	⅝	Fixed	0.164⑧	0.136⑨	②	0.139	0.243	⑩
	17081253 254	15/32	½	Fixed	0.142⑧	0.227⑨	②	0.071	0.220	⑩
	17081270	7/16	⅝	Fixed	0.136⑧	0.211⑨	②	0.074	0.220	⑩
	17081272	⅝	⅝	Fixed	0.136⑧	0.260⑨	②	0.074	0.220	⑩
	17081274	⅝	⅝	Fixed	0.136⑧	0.220⑨	②	0.083	0.220	⑩
	17081289	⅝	⅝	Fixed	0.164⑧	0.136⑨	②	0.139	0.243	⑩
'82	17082202	11/32	⅞	Fixed	0.110/20	—	②	0.110	0.243	⑤
	17082204	11/32	⅜	Fixed	0.110/20	—	②	0.110	0.243	⑤
	17082244	7/16	9/16	Fixed	0.117/21	0.083/16	②	0.139	0.195	⑤
	17082245	⅜	⅝	Fixed	0.149/26	0.149/26	②	0.139	0.195	⑤
	17082246	⅜	⅝	Fixed	0.149/26	0.149/26	②	0.139	0.195	⑤
	17082247	13/32	⅝	Fixed	0.164/28	0.136/24	②	0.139	0.243	⑤
	17082248	13/32	⅝	Fixed	0.164/28	0.136/24	②	0.139	0.243	⑤
	17082251	15/32	½	Fixed	0.142/25	0.304/45	②	0.071	0.220	⑤
	17082253	15/32	½	Fixed	0.142/25	0.227/36	②	0.071	0.220	⑤
	17082264	7/16	9/16	Fixed	0.117/20	0.083/16	②	0.139	0.195	⑤
	17082265	⅜	⅝	Fixed	0.149/26	0.149/26	②	0.139	0.195	⑤
	17082266	⅜	⅝	Fixed	0.149/26	0.149/26	②	0.139	0.195	⑤
	17082267	⅜	⅝	Fixed	0.164/28	0.136/24	②	0.139	0.243	⑤
	17082268	13/32	⅝	Fixed	0.164/28	0.136/24	②	0.139	0.243	⑤

CARBURETORS ROCHESTER

QUADRAJET CARBURETOR SPECIFICATIONS
Buick

Year	Carburetor Identification ①	Float Level (in.)	Air Valve Spring (turn)	Pump Rod (in.)	Primary Vacuum Break (in./deg.)	Secondary Vacuum Break (in./deg.)	Secondary Opening (in.)	Choke Rod (in.)	Choke Unloader (in.)	Fast Idle Speed ④ (rpm)
'83	17082265	⅜	⅝	Fixed	0.149/26	0.149/26	②	0.139	0.195	⑪
	17082266	⅜	⅝	Fixed	0.149/26	0.149/26	②	0.139	0.195	⑪
	17082267	⅜	⅝	Fixed	0.149/26	0.149/26	②	0.096	0.195	⑪
	17082268	⅜	⅝	Fixed	0.149/26	0.149/26	②	0.096	0.195	⑪
	17083242	9/32	9/16	Fixed	0.110/20	—	②	0.139	0.243	⑪
	17083244	¼	9/16	Fixed	0.117/21	0.083/16	②	0.139	0.195	⑪
	17083248	⅜	⅝	Fixed	0.149/26	0.149/26	②	0.139	0.195	⑪
	17083250	7/16	½	Fixed	0.157/27	0.271/42	②	0.071	0.220	⑪
	17083253	7/16	½	Fixed	0.151/27	0.269/41	②	0.071	0.220	⑪
	17083553	7/16	½	Fixed	0.157/27	0.269/41	②	0.071	0.220	⑪
'84	17084201	11/32	⅞	Fixed	0.157/27	—	②	0.110	0.243	⑪
	17084205	11/32	⅞	Fixed	0.157/27	—	②	0.243	0.243	⑪
	17084208	11/32	⅞	Fixed	0.157/27	—	②	0.110	0.243	⑪
	17084209	11/32	⅞	Fixed	0.157/27	—	②	0.243	0.243	⑪
	17084210	11/32	⅞	Fixed	0.157/27	—	②	0.110	0.243	⑪
	17084240	5/16	1	Fixed	0.136/24	—	②	—	0.195	⑪
	17084244	5/16	1	Fixed	0.136/24	—	②	—	0.195	⑪
	17084246	5/16	1	Fixed	0.123/22	0.136/24	②	—	0.195	⑪
	17084248	5/16	1	Fixed	0.136/24	—	②	—	0.195	⑪
	17084252	7/16	½	Fixed	0.157/27	0.269/41	②	—	0.220	⑪
	17084254	7/16	½	Fixed	0.157/27	0.269/41	②	—	0.220	⑪

① The carburetor identification number is stamped on the float bowl, near the secondary throttle lever.
② No measurement necessary on two point linkage; see text
③ Inner hole
④ On high step of cam, automatic in Park
⑤ 3 turns after contacting lever for preliminary setting
⑥ 2 turns after contacting lever for preliminary setting
⑦ Outer hole
⑧ Front
⑨ Rear
⑩ 4½ turns after contacting lever for preliminary setting
⑪ See underhood decal

QUADRAJET CARBURETOR SPECIFICATIONS
Chevrolet

Year	Carburetor Identification ①	Float Level (in.)	Air Valve Spring (turn)	Pump Rod (in.)	Primary Vacuum (deg./in.)	Secondary Vacuum (deg./in.)	Secondary Opening (in.)	Choke Rod (in.)	Choke Unloader (in.)	Fast Idle Speed ④ (rpm)
'78	17058202	15/32	7/8	9/32	0.179	—	⑤	0.314	0.277	⑥
	17058203	15/32	7/8	9/32	0.179	—	⑤	0.314	0.277	⑥
	17058204	15/32	7/8	9/32	0.179	—	⑤	0.314	0.277	⑥
	17058210	15/32	1/2	9/32	0.203	—	⑤	0.314	0.277	⑥
	17058211	15/32	1/2	9/32	0.203	—	⑤	0.314	0.277	⑥
	17058228	15/32	7/8	9/32	0.203	—	⑤	0.314	0.277	⑥
	17058502	15/32	7/8	9/32	0.187	—	⑤	0.314	0.277	⑥
	17058504	15/32	7/8	9/32	0.187	—	⑤	0.314	0.277	⑥
	17058582	15/32	7/8	9/32	0.203	—	⑤	0.314	0.277	⑥
	17058584	15/32	7/8	9/32	0.203	—	⑤	0.314	0.277	⑥
'79	17059203	15/32	7/8	1/4	0.157	—	⑤	0.243	0.243	⑦
	17059207	15/32	7/8	1/4	0.157	—	⑤	0.243	0.243	⑦
	17059216	15/32	7/8	1/4	0.157	—	⑤	0.243	0.243	⑦
	17059217	15/32	7/8	1/4	0.157	—	⑤	0.243	0.243	⑦
	17059218	15/32	7/8	1/4	0.164	—	⑤	0.243	0.243	⑦
	17059222	15/32	7/8	1/4	0.164	—	⑤	0.243	0.243	⑦
	17059502	15/32	7/8	1/4	0.164	—	⑤	0.243	0.243	⑦
	17059504	15/32	7/8	1/4	0.164	—	⑤	0.243	0.243	⑦
	17059582	15/32	7/8	11/32	0.203	—	⑤	0.243	0.314	⑦
	17059584	15/32	7/8	11/32	0.203	—	⑤	0.243	0.314	⑦
	17059210	15/32	1	9/32	0.157	—	⑤	0.243	0.243	⑦
	17059211	15/32	1	9/32	0.157	—	⑤	0.243	0.243	⑦
	17029228	15/32	1	9/32	0.157	—	⑤	0.243	0.243	⑦
'80	17080202	7/16	7/8	1/4 ⑧	0.157	—	⑤	0.110	0.243	⑩
	17080204	7/16	7/8	1/4 ⑧	0.157	—	⑤	0.110	0.243	⑩
	17080207	7/16	7/8	1/4 ⑧	0.157	—	⑤	0.110	0.243	⑩
	17080228	7/16	7/8	9/32 ⑧	0.179	—	⑤	0.110	0.243	⑩
	17080243	3/16	9/16	9/32 ⑧	0.016	0.083	⑤	0.074	0.179	⑩
	17080274	15/32	5/8	5/16 ⑨	0.110	0.164	⑤	0.083	0.203	⑩
	17080282	7/16	7/8	11/32 ⑨	0.142	—	⑤	0.110	0.243	⑩
	17080284	7/16	7/8	11/32 ⑨	0.142	—	⑤	0.110	0.243	⑩
	17080502	1/2	7/8	Fixed	0.136	0.179	⑤	0.110	0.243	⑩
	17080504	1/2	7/8	Fixed	0.136	0.179	⑤	0.110	0.243	⑩
	17080542	3/8	9/16	Fixed	0.103	0.066	⑤	0.074	0.243	⑩
	17080543	3/8	9/16	Fixed	0.103	0.129	⑤	0.074	0.243	⑩
'81	17081202	11/32	7/8	Fixed	0.149	—	⑤	0.110	0.243	⑪
	17081203	11/32	7/8	Fixed	0.149	—	⑤	0.110	0.243	⑪
	17081204	11/32	7/8	Fixed	0.149	—	⑤	0.110	0.243	⑪

QUADRAJET CARBURETOR SPECIFICATIONS
Chevrolet

Year	Carburetor Identification ①	Float Level (in.)	Air Valve Spring (turn)	Pump Rod (in.)	Primary Vacuum (deg./in.)	Secondary Vacuum (deg./in.)	Secondary Opening (in.)	Choke Rod (in.)	Choke Unloader (in.) ·	Fast Idle Speed ④ (rpm)
'81	17081207	11/32	7/8	Fixed	0.149	—	⑤	0.110	0.243	⑪
	17081216	11/32	7/8	Fixed	0.149	—	⑤	0.110	0.243	⑪
	17081217	11/32	7/8	Fixed	0.149	—	⑤	0.110	0.243	⑪
	17081218	11/32	7/8	Fixed	0.149	—	⑤	0.110	0.243	⑪
	17081242	5/16	9/16	Fixed	0.090	0.077	⑤	0.139	0.243	⑪
	17081243	1/4	9/16	Fixed	0.103	0.090	⑤	0.139	0.243	⑪
'82	17082202	11/32	7/8	Fixed	0.157	—	⑤	0.110	0.243	⑫
	17082204	11/32	7/8	Fixed	0.157	—	⑤	0.110	0.243	⑫
	17082203	11/32	7/8	Fixed	0.157	—	⑤	0.243	0.243	⑫
	17082207	11/32	7/8	Fixed	0.157	—	⑤	0.243	0.243	⑫
'83	17083202	11/32	7/8	Fixed	—	27/.157	⑤	0.110	0.243	⑬
	17083203	11/32	7/8	Fixed	—	27/.157	⑤	0.243	0.243	⑬
	17083204	11/32	7/8	Fixed	—	27/.157	⑤	0.110	0.243	⑬
	17083207	11/32	7/8	Fixed	—	27/157	⑤	0.243	0.243	⑬
	17083216	11/32	7/8	Fixed	—	27/.157	⑤	0.110	0.243	⑬
	17083218	11/32	7/8	Fixed	—	27/.157	⑤	0.110	0.243	⑬
	17083236	11/32	7/8	Fixed	—	27/.157	⑤	0.110	0.243	⑬
	17083506	7/16	7/8	Fixed	27/.157	36/.227	⑤	0.110	0.227	⑬
	17083508	7/16	7/8	Fixed	27/.157	36/.227	⑤	0.110	0.227	⑬
	17083524	7/16	7/8	Fixed	25/.142	36/.227	⑤	0.110	0.227	⑬
	17083526	7/16	7/8	Fixed	25/.142	36/.227	⑤	0.110	0.227	⑬
'84	17084201	11/32	7/8	Fixed	.157/27	—	⑤	0.110	0.243	⑬
	17084205	11/32	7/8	Fixed	.157/27	—	⑤	0.243	0.243	⑬
	17084208	11/32	7/8	Fixed	.157/27	—	⑤	0.110	0.243	⑬
	17084209	11/32	7/8	Fixed	.157/27	—	⑤	0.243	0.243	⑬
	17084210	11/32	7/8	Fixed	.157/27	—	⑤	0.110	0.243	⑬
	17084507	7/16	1	Fixed	.157/27	.227/36	⑤	0.110	0.227	⑬
	17084509	7/16	1	Fixed	.157/27	.227/36	⑤	0.110	0.227	⑬
	17084525	7/16	1	Fixed	.142/25	.227/36	⑤	0.110	0.227	⑬
	17084527	7/16	1	Fixed	.142/25	.227/36	⑤	0.110	0.227	⑬

① The carburetor identification number is stamped on the float bowl, near the secondary throttle lever.
② Without vacuum advance.
③ With automatic transmission; vacuum advance connected and EGR disconnected and the throttle positioned on the high step of cam.
④ With manual transmission; without vacuum advance and the throttle positioned on the high step of cam.

⑤ No measurement necessary on two point linkage; see text.
⑥ 3 turns after contacting lever for preliminary setting.
⑦ 2 turns after contacting lever for preliminary setting.
⑧ Inner hole
⑨ Outer hole

⑩ 4 turns after contacting lever for preliminary setting.
⑪ 4½ turns after contacting lever for preliminary setting
⑫ 3⅛ turns after contacting lever for preliminary setting
⑬ See underhood sticker

QUADRAJET CARBURETOR SPECIFICATIONS
Oldsmobile

Year	Carburetor Identification ①	Float Level (in.)	Air Valve Spring (turn)	Pump Rod (in.)	Primary Vacuum Break (in./deg.)	Secondary Vacuum Break (in./deg.)	Secondary Opening (in.)	Choke Rod (in.)	Choke Unloader (in.)	Fast Idle Speed ④ (rpm)
'78	17058202	15/32	7/8	9/32	0.157	—	④	0.314	0.277	⑤
	17058204	15/32	7/8	9/32	0.157	—	④	0.314	0.277	⑤
	17058250	13/32	1/2	9/32	0.129	0.183	④	0.096	0.220	⑤
	17058253	13/32	1/2	9/32	0.129	0.183	④	0.096	0.220	⑤
	17058257	13/32	1/2	9/32	0.136	0.230	④	0.103	0.220	⑤
	17058258	13/32	1/2	9/32	0.136	0.230	④	0.103	0.220	⑤
	17058259	13/32	1/2	9/32	0.136	0.183	④	0.103	0.220	⑤
	17058502	15/32	7/8	9/32	0.164	—	④	0.314	0.277	⑤
	17058504	15/32	7/8	9/32	0.164	—	④	0.314	0.277	⑤
	17058553	13/32	1/2	9/32	0.136	0.230	④	0.103	0.220	⑤
	17058555	13/32	1/2	9/32	0.136	0.230	④	0.103	0.220	⑤
	17058582	15/32	7/8	9/32	0.179	—	④	0.314	0.277	⑤
	17058584	15/32	7/8	9/32	0.179	—	④	0.314	0.277	⑤
'79	17059202	1/2	7/8	1/4	0.164	—	④	0.314	0.243	⑥
	17059207	15/32	7/8	1/4	0.157	—	④	0.243	0.243	⑥
	17059216	15/32	7/8	1/4	0.157	—	④	0.243	0.243	⑥
	17059217	15/32	7/8	1/4	0.157	—	④	0.243	0.243	⑥
	17059218	15/32	7/8	9/32	0.164	—	④	0.243	0.243	⑥
	17059222	15/32	7/8	9/32	0.164	—	④	0.243	0.243	⑥
	17059250	13/32	1/2	9/32	0.129	0.183	④	0.096	0.220	⑥
	17059251	13/32	1/2	9/32	0.129	0.183	④	0.096	0.220	⑥
	17059253	13/32	1/2	9/32	0.129	0.183	④	0.096	0.220	⑥
	17059256	13/32	1/2	9/32	0.136	0.195	④	0.103	0.220	⑥
	17059258	13/32	1/2	9/32	0.136	0.195	④	0.103	0.220	⑥
	17059502	15/32	7/8	1/4	0.164	—	④	0.243	0.243	⑥
	17059504	15/32	7/8	1/4	0.164	—	④	0.243	0.243	⑥
	17059553	13/32	1/2	9/32	0.136	0.230	④	0.103	0.220	⑥
	17059554	13/32	1/2	9/32	0.136	0.230	④	0.103	0.220	⑥
	17059582	15/32	7/8	11/32	0.203	—	④	0.243	0.314	⑥
	17059584	15/32	7/8	11/32	0.203	—	④	0.243	0.314	⑥
'80	17080202	7/16	7/8	1/4 ⑦	0.157	—	④	0.110	0.243	⑤
	17080204	7/16	7/8	1/4 ⑦	0.157	—	④	0.110	0.243	⑤
	17080250	13/32	1/2	9/32 ⑦	0.149	0.211	④	0.090	0.220	⑤
	17080251	13/32	1/2	9/32 ⑦	0.149	0.211	④	0.090	0.220	⑤
	17080252	13/32	1/2	9/32 ⑦	0.149	0.211	④	0.090	0.220	⑤
	17080253	13/32	1/2	9/32 ⑦	0.149	0.211	④	0.090	0.220	⑤
	17080259	13/32	1/2	9/32 ⑦	0.149	0.211	④	0.090	0.220	⑤
	17080260	13/32	1/2	9/32 ⑦	0.149	0.211	④	0.090	0.220	⑤

QUADRAJET CARBURETOR SPECIFICATIONS (Cont'd)
Oldsmobile

Year	Carburetor Identification ①	Float Level (in.)	Air Valve Spring (turn)	Pump Rod (in.)	Primary Vacuum Break (in./deg.)	Secondary Vacuum Break (in./deg.)	Secondary Opening (in.)	Choke Rod (in.)	Choke Unloader (in.)	Fast Idle Speed ④ (rpm)
'80	17080504	½	⅞	⑧	0.136	0.179	④	0.110	0.243	⑤
	17080553	15/32	½	⑧	0.142	0.220	④	0.090	0.220	⑤
	17080554	15/32	½	⑧	0.142	0.211	④	0.090	0.220	⑤
'81	17081250	13/32	½	9/32 ⑦	0.149 ⑨	0.211 ⑩	④	0.090	0.220	⑤
	17081253	15/32	½	⑧	0.142 ⑨	0.227 ⑩	④	0.071	0.220	⑤
	17081254	15/32	½	⑧	0.142 ⑨	0.227 ⑩	④	0.071	0.220	⑤
	17081248	⅜	—	⑧	0.164 ⑨	0.136 ⑩	④	0.139	0.243	⑤
	17081289	13/32	—	⑧	0.164 ⑨	0.136 ⑩	④	0.139	0.243	⑤
'82	17082202	11/32	⅞	Fixed	0.110/20	—	④	0.110	0.243	⑤
	17082204	11/32	⅜	Fixed	0.110/20	—	④	0.110	0.243	⑤
	17082244	7/16	9/16	Fixed	0.117/21	0.083/16	④	0.139	0.195	⑤
	17082245	⅜	⅝	Fixed	0.149/26	0.149/26	④	0.139	0.195	⑤
	17082246	⅜	⅝	Fixed	0.149/26	0.149/26	④	0.139	0.195	⑤
	17082247	13/32	⅝	Fixed	0.164/28	0.136/24	④	0.139	0.243	⑤
	17082248	13/32	⅝	Fixed	0.164/28	0.136/24	④	0.139	0.243	⑤
	17082251	15/32	½	Fixed	0.142/25	0.304/45	④	0.071	0.220	⑤
	17082253	15/32	½	Fixed	0.142/25	0.227/36	④	0.071	0.220	⑤
	17082264	7/16	9/16	Fixed	0.117/20	0.083/16	④	0.139	0.195	⑤
	17082265	⅜	⅝	Fixed	0.149/26	0.149/26	④	0.139	0.195	⑤
	17082266	⅜	⅝	Fixed	0.149/26	0.149/26	④	0.139	0.195	⑤
	17082267	⅜	⅝	Fixed	0.164/28	0.136/24	④	0.139	0.243	⑤
	17082268	13/32	⅝	Fixed	0.164/28	0.136/24	④	0.139	0.243	⑤
'83	17082265	⅜	⅝	Fixed	0.149/26	0.149/26	②	0.139	0.195	⑪
	17082266	⅜	⅝	Fixed	0.149/26	0.149/26	②	0.139	0.195	⑪
	17082267	⅜	⅝	Fixed	0.149/26	0.149/26	②	0.096	0.195	⑪
	17082268	⅜	⅝	Fixed	0.149/26	0.149/26	②	0.096	0.195	⑪
	17083242	9/32	9/16	Fixed	0.110/20	—	②	0.139	0.243	⑪
	17083244	¼	9/16	Fixed	0.117/21	0.083/16	②	0.139	0.195	⑪
	17083248	⅜	⅝	Fixed	0.149/26	0.149/26	②	0.139	0.195	⑪
	17083250	7/16	½	Fixed	0.157/27	0.271/42	②	0.071	0.220	⑪
	17083253	7/16	½	Fixed	0.157/27	0.269/41	②	0.071	0.220	⑪
	17083553	7/16	½	Fixed	0.157/27	0.269/41	②	0.071	0.220	⑪
'84	17084201	11/32	⅞	Fixed	0.157/27	—	②	0.110	0.243	⑪
	17084205	11/32	⅞	Fixed	0.157/27	—	②	0.243	0.243	⑪
	17084208	11/32	⅞	Fixed	0.157/27	—	②	0.110	0.243	⑪
	17084209	11/32	⅞	Fixed	0.157/27	—	②	0.243	0.243	⑪
	17084210	11/32	⅞	Fixed	0.157/27	—	②	0.110	0.243	⑪
	17084240	5/16	1	Fixed	0.136/24	—	②	—	0.195	⑪

QUADRAJET CARBURETOR SPECIFICATIONS
Oldsmobile

Year	Carburetor Identification①	Float Level (in.)	Air Valve Spring (turn)	Pump Rod (in.)	Primary Vacuum Break (in./deg.)	Secondary Vacuum Break (in./deg.)	Secondary Opening (in.)	Choke Rod (in.)	Choke Unloader (in.)	Fast Idle Speed ④ (rpm)
'84	17084244	5/16	1	Fixed	0.136/24	—	②	—	0.195	⑪
	17084246	5/16	1	Fixed	0.123/22	0.136/24	②	—	0.195	⑪
	17084248	5/16	1	Fixed	0.136/24	—	②	—	0.195	⑪
	17084252	7/16	½	Fixed	0.157/27	0.269/41	②	—	0.220	⑪
	17084254	7/16	½	Fixed	0.157/27	0.269/41	②	—	0.220	⑪

① The carburetor identification number is stamped on the float bowl, next to the secondary throttle lever.
② 1800 rpm on Omega and 400 cu. in. engines with the cam follower on the highest step of the fast idle cam; 900 rpm on all others with the fast idle cam follower on the lowest step of the fast idle cam.
④ No measurement necessary on two point linkage; see text.

⑤ 3 turns after contacting lever for preliminary setting.
⑥ 2 turns after contacting lever for preliminary setting.
⑦ Inner hole
⑧ Not Adjustable
⑨ Front
⑩ Rear
⑪ See underhood sticker

QUADRAJET CARBURETOR SPECIFICATIONS
Pontiac

Year	Carburetor Identification①	Float Level (in.)	Air Valve Spring (turn)	Pump Rod (in.)	Primary Vacuum Break (in./deg.)	Secondary Vacuum Break (in./deg.)	Secondary Opening (in.)	Choke Rod (in.)	Choke Unloader (in.)	Fast Idle Speed ② (rpm)
'78	17058202	15/32	—	9/32	0.157	—	④	0.314	0.277	③
	17058204	15/32	—	9/32	0.157	—	④	0.314	0.277	③
	17058241	5/16	¾	3/8	0.117	0.103	④	0.096	0.243	③
	17058250	13/32	½	9/32	0.119	0.167	④	0.088	0.203	③
	17058253	13/32	½	9/32	0.119	0.167	④	0.088	0.203	③
	17058258	13/32	½	9/32	0.126	0.212	④	0.092	0.203	③
	17058263	17/32	5/8	3/8	0.164	0.260	④	0.129	0.220	③
	17058264	17/32	½	3/8	0.149	0.260	④	0.129	0.220	③
	17058266	17/32	½	3/8	0.149	0.260	④	0.129	0.220	③
	17058272	15/32	5/8	3/8	0.126	0.195	④	0.071	0.222	③
	17058274	17/32	½	3/8	0.149	0.260	④	0.129	0.220	③
	17058276	17/32	½	3/8	0.149	0.260	④	0.129	0.220	③
	17058278	17/32	½	3/8	0.149	0.260	④	0.129	0.220	③
	17058502	15/32	—	9/32	0.164	—	④	0.314	0.277	③
	17058504	15/32	—	9/32	0.164	—	④	0.314	0.277	③
	17058553	13/32	½	9/32	0.126	0.212	④	0.092	0.203	③
	17058582	15/32	7/8	9/32	0.179	—	④	0.314	0.277	③
	17058584	15/32	7/8	9/32	0.179	—	④	0.314	0.277	③

QUADRAJET CARBURETOR SPECIFICATIONS
Pontiac

Year	Carburetor Identification ①	Float Level (in.)	Air Valve Spring (turn)	Pump Rod (in.)	Primary Vacuum Break (in./deg.)	Secondary Vacuum Break (in./deg.)	Secondary Opening (in.)	Choke Rod (in.)	Choke Unloader (in.)	Fast Idle Speed ② (rpm)
'79	17058263	17/32	5/8	3/8	0.164	0.243	④	0.129	0.220	⑤
	17059250,253	13/32	1/2	9/35	0.129	0.183	④	0.096	0.220	⑤
	17059241	5/16	3/4	3/8	0.120	0.113	④	0.096	0.243	⑤
	17059271	9/16	5/8	3/8	0.142	0.227	④	0.010	0.203	⑤
	17059272	15/32	5/8	3/8	0.136	0.195	④	0.074	0.220	⑤
	17059502,504	15/32	7/8	1/4	0.164	—	④	0.243	0.243	⑤
	17059553	13/32	1/2	9/32	0.136	0.230	④	0.103	0.220	⑤
	17059582,584	15/32	7/8	11/32	0.203	—	④	0.243	0.314	⑤
'80	17080249	7/16	3/4	9/32 ⑥	0.129	0.114	④	0.096	0.243	③
	17080270	15/32	5/8	3/8 ⑦	0.149	0.211	④	0.074	0.220	③
	17080272	15/32	5/8	3/8 ⑦	0.129	0.175	④	0.074	0.203	③
	17080274	15/32	5/8	5/16 ⑥	0.110	0.164	④	0.083	0.203	③
	17080502	1/2	7/8	⑧	0.136	0.179	④	0.110	0.243	③
	17080504	1/2	7/8	⑧	0.136	0.179	④	0.110	0.243	③
	17080553	15/32	1/2	⑧	0.142	0.220	④	0.090	0.220	③
'81	17081202,204	11/32	7/8	⑧	0.157 ⑩	—	④	0.110	0.243	⑨
	17081203,207	11/32	7/8	⑧	0.157 ⑩	—	④	0.110	0.243	⑨
	17081216, 17,218	11/32	7/8	⑧	0.157 ⑩	—	④	0.110	0.243	⑨
	17081242	3/8	9/16	⑧	0.090 ⑩	0.077 ⑪	④	0.139	0.243	⑨
	17081243	5/16	9/16	⑧	0.103 ⑩	0.090 ⑪	④	0.139	0.243	⑨
	17081245	3/8	5/8	⑧	0.164 ⑩	0.136 ⑪	④	0.139	0.243	⑨
	17081247	3/8	5/8	⑧	0.164 ⑩	0.136 ⑪	④	0.139	0.243	⑨
	17081248,249	3/8	5/8	⑧	0.164 ⑩	0.136 ⑪	④	0.139	0.243	⑨
	17081253,254	15/32	1/2	⑧	0.142 ⑩	0.227 ⑪	④	0.071	0.220	⑨
	17081270	7/16	5/8	⑧	0.136 ⑩	0.211 ⑪	④	0.074	0.220	⑨
	17081272	7/16	5/8	⑧	0.136 ⑩	0.260 ⑪	④	0.074	0.220	⑨
	17081274	7/16	5/8	⑧	0.136 ⑩	0.220 ⑪	④	0.083	0.220	⑨
	17081289	13/36	5/8	⑧	0.164 ⑩	0.136 ⑪	④	0.139	0.243	⑨
'82	17082202	11/32	7/8	Fixed	0.110/20 ⑭	—	④	0.110	0.243	⑫ ⑮
	17082204	11/32	3/8 ⑬	Fixed	0.110/20 ⑭	—	④	0.110	0.243	⑫ ⑮
	17082203	11/32	7/8	Fixed	0.157/27	—	④	0.243	0.243	⑮
	17082207	11/32	7/8	Fixed	0.157/27	—	④	0.243	0.243	⑮
	17082244	7/16	9/16	Fixed	0.117/21	0.083/16	④	0.139	0.195	⑫
	17082245	3/8	5/8	Fixed	0.149/26	0.149/26	④	0.139	0.195	⑫
	17082246	3/8	5/8	Fixed	0.149/26	0.149/26	④	0.139	0.195	⑫
	17082247	13/32	5/8	Fixed	0.164/28	0.136/24	④	0.139	0.243	⑫
	17082248	13/32	5/8	Fixed	0.164/28	0.136/24	④	0.139	0.243	⑫
	17082251	15/32	1/2	Fixed	0.142/25	0.304/45	④	0.071	0.220	⑫

QUADRAJET CARBURETOR SPECIFICATIONS
Pontiac

Year	Carburetor Identification ①	Float Level (in.)	Air Valve Spring (turn)	Pump Rod (in.)	Primary Vacuum Break (in./deg.)	Secondary Vacuum Break (in./deg.)	Secondary Opening (in.)	Choke Rod (in.)	Choke Unloader (in.)	Fast Idle Speed ② (rpm)
'83	17082253	15/32	1/2	Fixed	0.142/25	0.227/36	④	0.071	0.220	⑫
	17082264	7/16	9/16	Fixed	0.117/20	0.083/16	④	0.139	0.195	⑫
	17082265	3/8	5/8	Fixed	0.149/26	0.149/26	④	0.139	0.195	⑫
	17082266	3/8	5/8	Fixed	0.149/26	0.149/26	④	0.139	0.195	⑫
	17082267	3/8	5/8	Fixed	0.164/28	0.136/24	④	0.139	0.243	⑫
	17082268	13/32	5/8	Fixed	0.164/28	0.136/24	④	0.139	0.243	⑫
'83	17082265	3/8	5/8	Fixed	0.149/26	0.149/26	②	0.139	0.195	⑯
	17082266	3/8	5/8	Fixed	0.149/26	0.149.26	②	0.139	0.195	⑯
	17082267	3/8	5/8	Fixed	0.149/26	0.149/26	②	0.096	0.195	⑯
	17082268	3/8	5/8	Fixed	0.149/26	0.149/26	②	0.096	0.195	⑯
	17083242	9/32	9/16	Fixed	0.110/20	—	②	0.139	0.243	⑯
	17083244	1/4	9/16	Fixed	0.117/21	0.083/16	②	0.139	0.195	⑯
	17083248	3/8	5/8	Fixed	0.149/26	0.149/26	②	0.139	0.195	⑯
	17083250	7/16	1/2	Fixed	0.157/27	0.271/42	②	0.071	0.220	⑯
	17083253	7/16	1/2	Fixed	0.157/27	0.269/41	②	0.071	0.220	⑯
	17083553	7/16	1/2	Fixed	0.157/27	0.269/41	②	0.071	0.220	⑯
'84	17084201	11/32	7/8	Fixed	0.157/27	—	②	0.110	0.243	⑪
	17084205	11/32	7/8	Fixed	0.157/27	—	②	0.243	0.243	⑪
	17084208	11/32	7/8	Fixed	0.157/27	—	②	0.110	0.243	⑪
	17084209	11/32	7/8	Fixed	0.157/27	—	②	0.243	0.243	⑪
	17084210	11/32	7/8	Fixed	0.157/27	—	②	0.110	0.243	⑪
	17084240	5/16	1	Fixed	0.136/24	—	②	—	0.195	⑪
	17084244	5/16	1	Fixed	0.136/24	—	②	—	0.195	⑪
	170804246	5/16	1	Fixed	0.123/22	.136/24	②	—	0.195	⑪
	17084248	5/16	1	Fixed	0.136/24	—	②	—	0.195	⑪
	17084252	7/16	1/2	Fixed	0.157/27	.269/41	②	—	0.220	⑪
	17084254	7/16	1/2	Fixed	0.157/27	.269/41	②	—	0.220	⑪

① The carburetor identification number is stamped on the float bowl, near the secondary throttle lever.
② On highest step.
③ 1½ turns after contacting lever for preliminary setting
④ No measurement necessary on two point linkage; see text.
⑤ 2 turns after contacting lever for preliminary setting.
⑥ Inner hole
⑦ Outer hole
⑧ Not adjustable
⑨ 4½ turns after contacting lever for preliminary setting

⑩ Front
⑪ Rear
⑫ 3 turns after contacting lever for preliminary setting
⑬ Firebird—7/8
⑭ Firebird—0.157 in./27°
⑮ Firebird—3⅛ turns after contacting lever for preliminary setting
⑯ See underhood sticker

CARBURETORS ROCHESTER

QUADRAJET CARBURETOR SPECIFICATIONS
All Canadian Models

Year	Carburetor Identi-fication①	Float Level (in.)	Air Valve Spring (turn)	Pump Rod (in.)	Primary Vacuum Break (deg./in.)	Secondary Vacuum Break (deg./in.)	Secondary Opening (in.)	Choke Rod (in.)	Choke Unloader (in.)	Fast Idle Speed② (rpm)
'81	17080201	15/32	7/8	9/32②	—	23/0.129	④	0.314	0.277	⑤
	17080205	15/32	7/8	9/32②	—	23/0.129	④	0.314	0.277	⑤
	17080206	15/32	7/8	9/32②	—	23/0.129	④	0.314	0.277	⑤
	17080290	15/32	7/8	9/32②	—	26/0.149	④	0.314	0.277	⑤
	17080291	15/32	7/8	9/32②	—	26/0.149	④	0.314	0.277	⑤
	17080292	15/32	7/8	9/32②	—	26/0.149	④	0.314	0.277	⑤
	17080213	3/8	1	9/32②	23/0.129	30/0.179	④	0.234	0.260	⑤
	17080215	3/8	1	9/32②	23/0.129	30/0.179	④	0.234	0.260	⑤
	17080298	3/8	1	9/32②	23/0.129	30/0.179	④	0.234	0.260	⑤
	17080507	3/8	1	9/32②	23/0.129	30/0.179	④	0.234	0.260	⑤
	17080513	3/8	1	9/32②	23/0.129	30/0.179	④	0.234	0.260	⑤
	17081250	13/32	1/2	9/32②	26/0.149	34/0.211	④	0.090	0.220	⑤
	17080260	13/32	1/2	9/32②	26/0.149	34/0.211	④	0.090	0.220	⑤
	17081276	15/32	5/8	5/16②	20/0.110	28/0.164	④	0.083	0.203	⑤
	17081286	13/32	1/2	9/32②	18/0.096	34/0.211	④	0.077	0.220	⑤
	17081287	13/32	1/2	9/32②	18/0.096	34/0.211	④	0.077	0.220	⑤
	17081282	3/8	5/8	9/32②	20/0.110	—	④	0.110	0.243	⑤
	17081283	3/8	7/8	9/32②	20/0.110	—	④	0.110	0.243	⑤
	17081284	1/2	7/8	9/32③	20/0.110	—	④	0.110	0.243	⑤
	17081285	1/2	7/8	9/32③	20/0.110	—	④	0.110	0.243	⑤
	17080243	3/16	9/16	9/32②	14.5/0.075	16/0.083	④	0.075	0.179	⑤
	17081295	13/32	9/16	9/32②	14.5/0.075	13/0.066	④	0.075	0.220	⑤
	17081294	5/16	5/8	9/32②	24.5/0.139	14/0.071	④	0.139	0.243	⑤
	17081290	13/32	7/8	9/32②	46/0.314	24/0.136	④	0.314	0.277	⑤
	17081291	13/32	7/8	9/32②	46/0.314	24/0.136	④	0.314	0.277	⑤
	17081292	13/32	7/8	9/32②	46/0.314	24/0.136	④	0.314	0.277	⑤
	17081506	13/32	7/8	9/32②	46/0.314	36/0.227	④	0.314	0.227	⑤
	17081508	13/32	7/8	9/32②	46/0.314	36/0.227	④	0.314	0.227	⑤
	17080202	7/16	7/8	1/4②	20/0.110	—	④	0.110	0.243	⑤
	17080204	7/16	7/8	1/4②	20/0.110	—	④	0.110	0.243	⑤
	17080207	7/16	7/8	1/4②	20/0.110	—	④	0.110	0.243	⑤

QUADRAJET CARBURETOR SPECIFICATIONS
All Canadian Models

Year	Carburetor Identification[1]	Float Level (in.)	Air Valve Spring (turn)	Pump Rod (in.)	Primary Vacuum Break (deg./in.)	Secondary Vacuum Break (deg./in.)	Secondary Opening (in.)	Choke Rod (in.)	Choke Unloader (in.)	Fast Idle Speed[2] (rpm)
'82	17082280	3/8	7/8	9/32[2]	25/0.142	—	[4]	0.110	0.243	[5]
	17082281	3/8	7/8	9/32[2]	25/0.142	—	[4]	0.110	0.243	[5]
	17082282	3/8	7/8	9/32[2]	25/0.142	—	[4]	0.110	0.243	[5]
	17082283	3/8	7/8	9/32[2]	25/0.142	—	[4]	0.110	0.243	[5]
	17082286	13/32	1/2	9/32[2]	22/0.123	34/0.211	[4]	0.077	0.243	[5]
	17082287	13/32	1/2	9/32[2]	22/0.123	34/0.211	[4]	0.077	0.243	[5]
	17082288	3/8	7/8	9/32[2]	25/0.142	—	[4]	0.110	0.243	[5]
	17082289	3/8	7/8	9/32[2]	25/0.142	—	[4]	0.110	0.243	[5]
	17082296	1/2	7/8	9/32[2]	25/0.142	—	[4]	0.110	0.243	[5]
	17082297	1/2	7/8	9/32[2]	25/0.142	—	[4]	0.110	0.243	[5]
'83	17080213	3/8	1	9/32	23/.129	30/.179	[4]	0.234	0.260	[5]
	17082213	9/32	1	9/32	23/.129	30/.179	[4]	0.234	0.260	[5]
	17082282	3/8	7/8	9/32	25/.142	—	[4]	0.110	0.243	[5]
	17082283	3/8	7/8	9/32	25/.142	—	[4]	0.110	0.243	[5]
	17082286	13/32	1/2	9/32	23/.129	34/.211	[4]	0.107	0.220	[5]
	17082287	13/32	1/2	9/32	23/.129	34/.211	[4]	0.107	0.220	[5]
	17082296	1/2	7/8	9/32	25/.142	—	[4]	0.110	0.243	[5]
	17082297	1/2	7/8	9/32	25/.142	—	[4]	0.110	0.243	[5]
	17083280	3/8	7/8	9/32	25/.142	—	[4]	0.110	0.243	[5]
	17083281	3/8	7/8	9/32	25/.142	—	[4]	0.110	0.243	[5]
	17083282	3/8	7/8	9/32	25/.142	—	[4]	0.110	0.243	[5]
	17083283	3/8	7/8	9/32	25/.142	—	[4]	0.110	0.243	[5]
	17083290	13/32	7/8	9/32	—	24/.136	[4]	0.314	0.251	[5]
	17083292	13/32	7/8	9/32	—	24/.136	[4]	0.314	0.251	[5]
	17083298	3/8	1	9/32	23/.129	30/.179	[4]	0.234	0.260	[5]
'84	17084280	3/8	7/8	9/32[2]	23/.129	—	[4]	0.110	0.243	[5]
	17084281	3/8	7/8	9/32[2]	23/.129	—	[4]	0.110	0.243	[5]
	17084282	3/8	7/8	9/32[2]	23/.129	—	[4]	0.110	0.243	[5]
	17084283	3/8	7/8	9/32[2]	23/.129	—	[4]	0.110	0.243	[5]
	17084284	3/8	7/8	9/32[2]	23/.129	—	[4]	0.110	0.243	[5]
	17084285	3/8	7/8	9/32[2]	23/.129	—	[4]	0.110	0.243	[5]

QUADRAJET CARBURETOR SPECIFICATIONS
All Canadian Models

Year	Carburetor Identi- fication①	Float Level (in.)	Air Valve Spring (turn)	Pump Rod (in.)	Primary Vacuum Break (deg./in.)	Secondary Vacuum Break (deg./in.)	Secondary Opening (in.)	Choke Rod (in.)	Choke Unloader (in.)	Fast Idle Speed② (rpm)
'84	17084286	13/32	1/2	9/32②	23/.129	34/.211	④	0.107	0.220	⑤
	17084287	13/32	1/2	9/32②	23/.129	34/.211	④	0.107	0.220	⑤
	17084288	3/8	7/8	9/32②	23/.129	—	④	0.110	0.243	⑤
	17084289	3/8	7/8	9/32②	23/.129	—	④	0.110	0.243	⑤
	17084296	1/2	7/8	9/32②	23/.129	—	④	0.110	0.243	⑤
	17084297	1/2	7/8	9/32②	23/.129	—	④	0.110	0.243	⑤

① The carburetor identification number is stamped on the float bowl, near the secondary throttle lever.
② Inner hole
③ Outer hole
④ No measurement necessary on two point linkage; see text.
⑤ See underhood decal

MIKUNI CARBURETORS

All front wheel drive models (U.S.A.) with the 2.6 liter (156 cubic inch) Mitsubishi engine are equipped with a conventional downdraft two barrel compound type carburetor. The automatic choke is a thermowax type which is controlled by engine coolant temperature. The main body is a black resin compound.

This carburetor also features a diaphragm type accelerator pump, bowl vent, fuel cut-off solenoid, air switching valve (ASV), sub EGR valve, coasting air valve (CAV), jet air control valve (JACV) and a high altitude compensation system (HAC) (California only).

DRY FLOAT ADJUSTMENT

1. Invert the air horn assembly without a gasket.
2. With a gauge, measure the distance from the bottom of the float to the surface of the air horn. The distance should be 0.0787-0.779 in. (17.8-20.8mm).

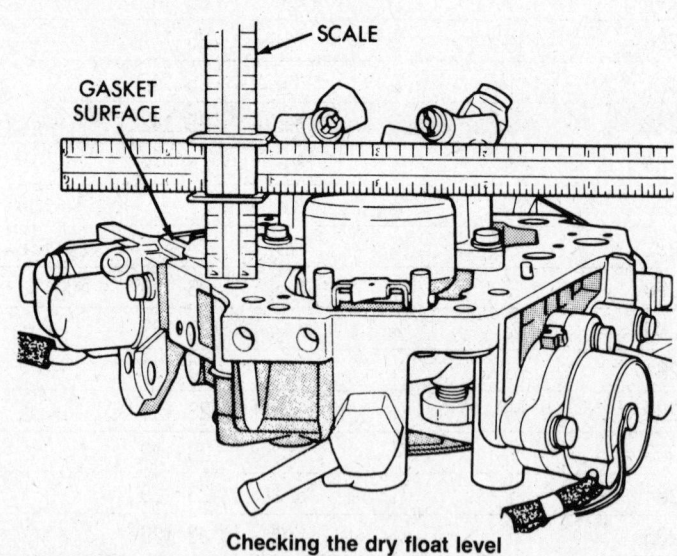

Checking the dry float level

3. If the reading is not within this range the shim under the needle seat must be changed. Shim kits are available which have three shims: 0.0118 in. (0.3mm), 0.0157 in. (0.4mm), 0.0196 in. (0.5mm). Adding or removing a shim will change the float level by three times the thickness of the shim.

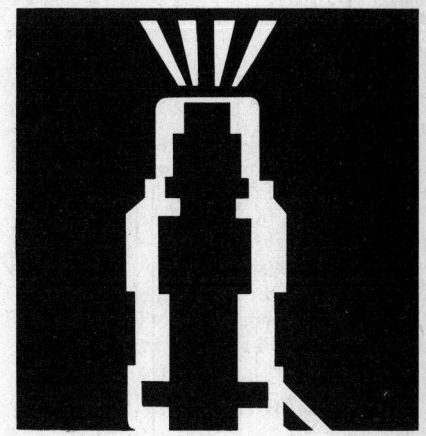

Fuel Injection

INTRODUCTION

The introduction of fuel injection systems on many late model cars is due in part to the stringent emission control standards U.S. automakers face. Fuel injection allows a more precise control of the air/fuel mixture than carburetion does. Fuel injectors can be controlled electrically or through fuel pressure to inject exact amounts of fuel, whereas carburetors in most cases supply fuel in a constant stream. Under certain operating conditions (deceleration, etc.), a percentage of carbureted fuel is blown, unburned, out the exhaust pipe—lowering engine efficiency while raising poisonous hydrocarbon emissions into the atmosphere— one reason carbureted engines usually require more emission control equipment than fuel injected engines.

FUEL INJECTION SYSTEMS

There are two basic gasoline fuel injection systems; port and throttle body injection.

On port injection systems, the fuel mixes with the air drawn into the combustion chamber by the action of the piston moving down in its cylinder. The air and fuel are mixed in the cylinder head rather than in the intake manifold.

On throttle body injection systems, the injectors are mounted in a common throttle body (which resembles a carburetor in appearance) and spray fuel into the intake manifold. On this system, each cylinder does not require its own fuel injector, as direct and indirect injection cylinders do. All cylinders are fed by a few (usually two) centrally mounted injectors. The fuel mixes with the incoming air in the throttle body and the mixture is drawn into the cylinders.

By comparison, port injection systems allow quicker and more controlled air/fuel mixture adjustments than do throttle body injection systems. However, the port fuel injection systems are much more costly than the throttle body system.

CADILLAC SYSTEMS

Cadillac has used two different types of fuel injection systems: Electronic Fuel Injection (EFI) and Digital Fuel Injection (DFI).

The EFI system is a port fuel injection system, on which each cylinder has its own fuel injector mounted behind the intake valve. The EFI system was used on 1978-79 Sevilles as standard equipment and on 1978-79 full size Cadillacs as an option.

The DFI system is a throttle body fuel injection system, on which two solenoid actuated fuel injectors are mounted in the throttle body and inject fuel down into the intake manifold. The DFI system, introduced on 1980 Seville, is used on 1980 6.0 liter (368 cu in.) engines and all 1981 and later Cadillacs except the 252 cu. in. V6.

Both systems control the air/fuel mixture for combustion by monitoring selected engine operating conditions and electronically metering fuel requirements to meet those conditions.

The EFI system consists of four basic subsystems: the fuel delivery system, the air induction system, the network of sensors, and the Electronic Control Unit (ECU). The DFI system includes the same subsystems as the EFI, use a more detailed Electronic Control Module (ECM) and adds several more subsystems. These include the electronic spark timing system (EST), idles speed control system (ISC), EGR (all) and charcoal canister (1981 and later) control

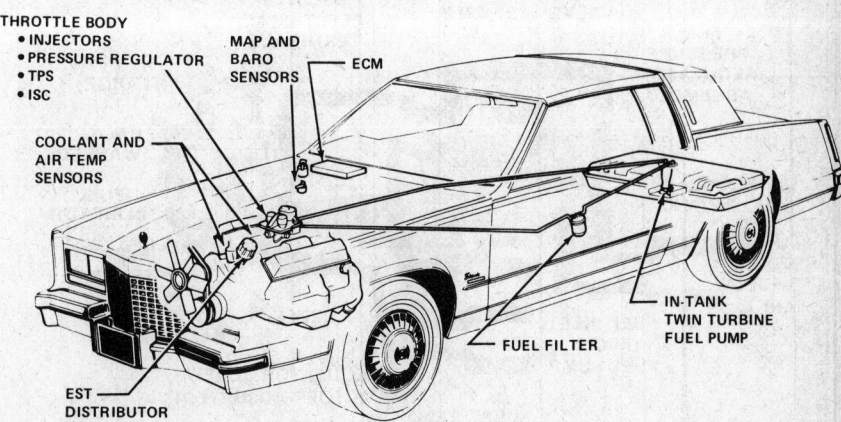

THROTTLE BODY
- INJECTORS
- PRESSURE REGULATOR
- TPS
- ISC

MAP AND BARO SENSORS

ECM

COOLANT AND AIR TEMP SENSORS

IN-TANK TWIN TURBINE FUEL PUMP

FUEL FILTER

EST DISTRIBUTOR

Cadillac DFI system: all cylinders are fed by two fuel injectors located in the throttle body.

systems, modulated cylinder displacement (on cars so equipped), closed loop/open loop oxygen sensor system (1981 and later), and the failure operation circuit and diagnostics readout system.

Fuel Delivery System

The EFI fuel delivery subsystem is made up of an in-tank fuel pump, a chassis mounted fuel pump, fuel filter, fuel pressure regulator, fuel rails, and an injector for each cylinder.

The DFI fuel delivery subsystem consists of an in-tank fuel pump, fuel filter, fuel feed and return lines, a throttle body with dual injectors and a pressure regulator.

FUEL PUMPS

The electric fuel pump(s) are connected in parallel to the ECU/ECM and are activated by the ECU/ECM when the ignition is turned on and the engine is cranking or operating. If the engine stalls or if the starter is not engaged, the fuel pumps will stop in about one second. The fuel is pumped from the fuel tank, through the supply line and filter, through the pressure regulator, fuel rails (EFI) and to the injectors, with excess fuel being returned to the fuel tank.

The fuel tank pump supplies fuel to the chassis mounted fuel pump or to the throttle body pressure regulator.

The chassis mounted fuel pump (EFI) is a constant-displacement, roller-vane pump with a check valve to prevent fuel from flowing back into the tank. This pump has a flow rate of 33 gallons per hour and maintains a minimum pressure of 39 psi. An internal relief valve opens at 55-95 psi to protect the system from excessive pressure. The pump is mounted under the vehicle, forward of the left rear wheel on all vehicles except the Eldorado, where it is mounted in front of the right rear wheel.

FUEL FILTER

The fuel filter is located on a bracket on the lower left front of the engine or on the frame near the right rear wheel. The filter consists of a casing with an internal throwaway type paper filter element.

FUEL PRESSURE REGULATOR

The EFI fuel pressure regulator, located on the fuel rail at the front of the engine, maintains a constant 39 psi pressure across the fuel injectors. The DFI fuel pressure regulator is integral with the throttle body and cannot be serviced separately. The regulator contains an air chamber and fuel chamber separated by a spring-loaded diaphragm. The air chamber, on EFI systems, is connected by a hose to the throttle body assembly. The pressure in the air chamber of the regulator is identical to the pressure in the intake manifold. The changing manifold pressure and the spring control the action of the diaphragm valve, opening or closing an orifice in the fuel chamber of the regulator. At this point excess fuel is routed out of the regulator and back to the fuel tank.

FUEL INJECTOR

The fuel injector, on EFI systems, is a solenoid operated pintle valve that meters fuel to each cylinder. The injectors are controlled by an electronic pulse signal from the ECU. When energized, the valve opens for precisely the proper amount of time to spray the exact amount of fuel droplets required by the engine. When the injector is de-energized, it prevents any further fuel flow to the engine.

The eight injectors are divided into two groups of four each. Cylinders 1, 2, 7, and 8 form group 1 and the remaining injectors form group 2. All four injectors in each group are opened and closed simultaneously; the two groups operate alternately

The injectors are located on the intake manifold above the intake valve of each cylinder.

The DFI system uses two fuel injectors located in the throttle body. They are controlled by the electronic control module (ECM) and meter the atomized fuel into the throttle bore. Each injector contains a spring loaded ball valve controlled by a solenoid. When the ball valve is lifted from its seat by the solenoid plunger, fuel is fed through the atomizer/spray injector nozzle.

Air Induction System

The air induction system is made up of the throttle body assembly, idle speed control, and the intake manifold.

THROTTLE BODY

Air for combustion enters the throttle body and is controlled by the throttle valves which are connected to the accelerator pedal linkage, much like a conventional carburetor. The throttle body consists of a housing with two bores and two shaft mounted throttle valves. The throttle valves are pre-set slightly

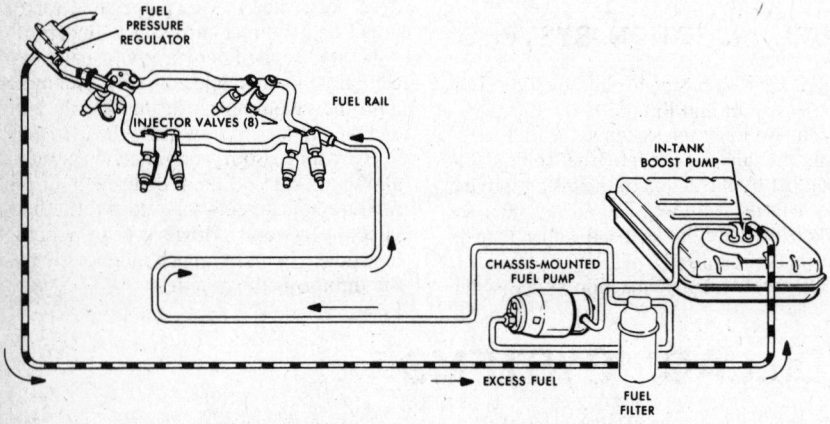

Cadillac EFI system: each cylinder has its own fuel injector

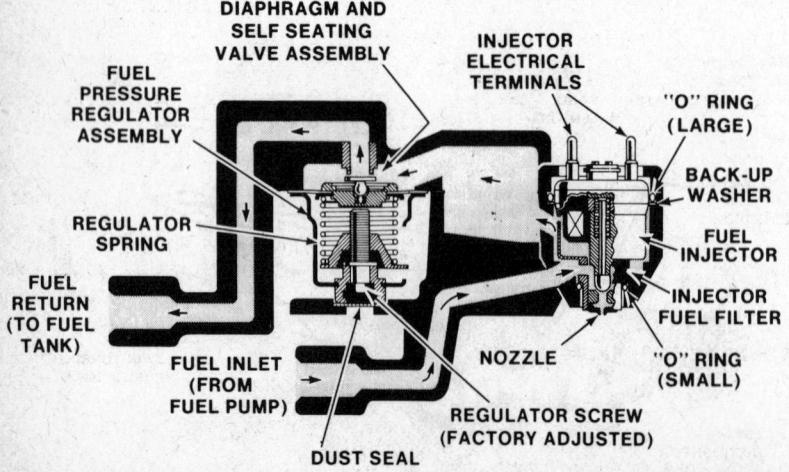

Cadillac DFI pressure regulator and fuel injector system. Both are contained in the throttle body

open when the throttle lever is resting against the idle stop position. *The adjustment is not to be tampered with.* An adjustable set screw on the front of the throttle body adjusts an idle by-pass air passage incorporated within the throttle body and allows a regulated amount of air to by-pass the throttle valves, adjusting warm engine idle speed.

A large port on top of the EFI throttle body contains the fast idle valve.

On the EFI equipped Seville, a solenoid operated idle air compensator is added to provide more air to the engine when the air conditioner clutch is engaged at idle.

FAST IDLE VALVE

The EFI system fast idle valve, installed on the top of the throttle body, consists of a plastic body that houses an electric heater, a spring and plunger, and a temperature sensitive unit.

The fast idle valve is connected electrically to the fuel pump circuit through the ECU. When the engine is started cold, the open valve allows extra air to bypass the throttle valves.

The heater warms the thermal element which expands and forces the spring and plunger toward the air orifice, restricting the flow of extra air and gradually reducing the engine speed to the normal idle rpm. The fast idle valve has no effect after the thermal element reaches about 140°F. The rate at which the valve closes is a function of time and temperature. The warmer the air, the faster the valve closes. At 68°F the valve will close in about 90 seconds and at −20°F the valve will require about 5 minutes to close.

IDLE SPEED CONTROL

The DFI system idle speed control subsystem is controlled by the ECM. The system acts to control the engine idle speed using a small electric motor which, when used in conjunction with the throttle switch, adjusts idle speed by opening or closing the throttle valves. When the engine is cold, the idle speed motor opens the throttle valve to provide faster warmup time, and as such acts as a fast idle device.

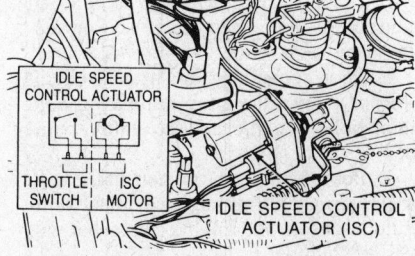

Idle Speed Control actuator (ISC)

INTAKE MANIFOLD

The intake manifold is basically the same as those installed on carbureted engines.

There are, however, a few minor differences: On EFI systems only air travels through the intake manifold. There is a hole above each cylinder for injector installation. A port is made available for the installation of the air temperature sensor. There is no exhaust heat cross-over passage. The exhaust passage from the right cylinder head is for EGR only.

On the DFI system, both air and fuel travel through the intake manifold, much in the same manner as on a carbureted engine.

Engine Sensors

All the engine sensors are electrically connected to the Electronic Control Unit (ECU) or the Electronic Control Module (ECM). Each of the sensors operates independently, monitors a specific engine operating condition, and transmits this information via electronic signal to the ECU/ECM. The sensors continuously send information signals to the ECU/ECM while the ignition switch is in the On or Start position.

MANIFOLD ABSOLUTE PRESSURE SENSOR (MAP)

The manifold absolute pressure (MAP) sensor monitors pressure changes within the intake manifold which are the direct result of engine load, speed, and barometric pressure. As pressure in the intake manifold increases, additional fuel is required. The MAP sensor sends this information to the ECU/ECM so that the length of time the injectors are energized is increased or decreased accordingly.

The sensor is mounted within the electronic control unit. A manifold pressure line is routed with the engine harness and is connected to the front of the throttle body at one end to the MAP sensor at the other end.

THROTTLE POSITION SWITCH (TPS)

The throttle position switch (TPS) is mounted to the throttle body, connnected to the throttle valve shaft, and monitors the opening or closing of the throttle valves. The switch senses the shaft movement and position and transmits electrical signals to the ECU/ECM. The ECU/ECM processes these signals to determine the fuel requirement for the engine.

MANIFOLD AIR TEMPERATURE SENSOR (MAT)

The MAT sensor is used on the DFI system and is installed in the intake manifold in front of the throttle body. This sensor measures the temperature of the air/fuel mixture

in the intake manifold and provides this information to the ECM.

COOLANT TEMPERATURE SENSOR

This coolant temperature sensor is used on the DFI system and is installed in the right front corner of the engine directly below the thermostat. The sensor provides data to the ECM for fuel enrichment during cold operation, for idle speed control, ignition timing and EGR operation.

SPEED SENSOR

On EFI systems the speed sensor is incorporated within the ignition distributor, and consists of two components. The first is a plastic housing containing two reed switches. The second is a rotor with two magnets attached to it and rotating with the distributor shaft.

The rotation of the magnets past the reed switches causes them to open and close, providing two signals: one for synchronization of the ECU and the proper injector group with the intake valve timing; and the engine rpm for fuel scheduling.

On DFI systems the engine speed signal pulses are picked up by an electronic module in the distributor. The pulses are sent to the ECM where they are used to calculate engine speed and spark advance.

OXYGEN SENSOR SYSTEM

The oxygen sensor system used on 1981 and later cars controls fuel injection quantity by monitoring the amount of oxygen present in the exhaust gases and sending this information to the ECM, which adjusts the amount of fuel injected to provide the ideal air/fuel mixture ratio (14.7:1). The oxygen sensor is attached to the exhaust system ahead of the catalytic converter. When the oxygen sensor system is controlling the air/fuel mixture, the DFI system is said to be in closed loop operation. When the oxygen sensor is not controlling the air/fuel mixture (engine cold, etc.) the DFI system is said to be in open loop operation.

BAROMETRIC PRESSURE SENSOR (BARO)

This unit senses ambient or barometric pressure and provides information to the ECM or ambient pressure changes due to altitude and/or weather. This sensor is used only on the DFI system and is mounted under the instrument panel near the right-hand A/C outlet. The sensor's atmospheric opening is covered by a foam filter.

ELECTRONIC CONTROL UNIT

The electronic control unit/module (ECU/

ECM) located under the instrument panel or in the glove box is a pre-programmed computer. The ECU/ECM is electrically connected to the vehicle's power supply, all of the EFI/DFI system electrical components, plus the EGR activation solenoid and other emission controls by a harness routed through the firewall.

When the ECU/ECM is energized by the ignition switch being turned to the On or Crank position, it continuously receives information from all of the engine sensors, and activates the fuel pump(s), fast idle valve, fuel injectors, and emission control components.

The commands for proper air/fuel ratios for various driving and atmospheric conditions are designed into the ECU/ECM. As the electronic signals are received from the sensors, the ECU/ECM analyzes the signals and computes the exact fuel requirement for the engine. The ECU/ECM then causes the fuel injectors to open for a specific amount of time. The duration of time the injectors are open varies as the engine operating conditions change.

The electronic control units are calibrated differently depending on where the car is sold (California or 49 states) and in which vehicle the unit is installed. Each ECU/ECM is labeled for its intended use. The proper unit must be used for each application.

Electronic Fuel Injection (EFI) Troubleshooting

NOTE: Because a special electronic tester is necessary to diagnose problems in the ECU, this section will deal with troubleshooting only mechanical and basic electrical problems of the EFI system. If the ECU is diagnosed as being the possible cause of a problem, the unit should be checked with an appropriate tester, available through manufacturer or aftermarket sources.

DFI system troubleshooting is not given here due to the involved diagnostic techniques.

—————— CAUTION ——————

Before disconnecting any part of the fuel delivery system on EFI equipped vehicles, the pressure within the fuel lines must be bled off. Refer to steps 1-4 of the Chassis-Mounted Fuel Pump Removal in the Car Section for the proper procedure.

PROBLEM: Engine cranks but will not start.
POSSIBLE CAUSE:

NOTE: The following possible causes assume that the rest of the vehicle electrical system is functioning properly.

1. Blown 10 amp in-line fuel pump fuse (located under the instrument panel near the ECU wiring harness connectors) or, depending on year, a 20 amp fuse located in the fuse panel. To check, listen for the whine of the chassis-mounted fuel pump when the ignition key is turned to the On position. The fuel pump should only operate for one second before shutting off. Do not turn the ignition key to the Start position.
2. Poor connection of the green wire at the fuel pump wiring harness near the ECU harness below the instrument panel. Check the operation of the fuel pump in the same manner as in POSSIBLE CAUSE 1 above.
3. Malfunction in the chassis-mounted pump.
4. Open circuit in the purple wire between the starter solenoid and the ECU.
5. Open circuit in the green wire between the alternator BAT terminal and the ECU.
6. Poor connection at the engine coolant sensor or an open circuit in the wiring or the sensor, with the engine cold only. To check, connect an ohmmeter to the temperature sensor connector terminals. If the resistance in the sensor is greater than 1600 ohms, replace the sensor.
7. Poor connection of the ECU wiring harness.

8. Poor connection at the speed sensor on the distributor.
9. The speed sensor trigger is stuck closed.
10. The wide-open-throttle section of the throttle position switch is shorted. To check, disconnect the switch; the engine should start.
11. A restriction in the fuel delivery system.
PROBLEM: Hard starting
POSSIBLE CAUSE:
1. Open circuit in the engine coolant temperature sensor. This should occur only when the engine is cold or partially warm. The engine should start satisfactorily when hot.
2. The wide-open-throttle section of the throttle position switch is shorted. To check, disconnect the switch; the engine should start.
3. The fuel pressure regulator is malfunctioning.
4. The chassis-mounted fuel pump is malfunctioning.
PROBLEM: Poor fuel economy
POSSIBLE CAUSE:
1. The manifold absolute air pressure sensor is disconnected or leaking.
2. The vacuum hose at the fuel pressure regulator or throttle body is disconnected.
3. The air temperature or coolant temperature sensors are malfunctioning. Check the coolant temperature sensor as outlined under Engine cranks but will not start, number 6. Check the air temperature sensor by connecting an ohmmeter to the sensor connector terminals; if the sensor resistance is less than 700 ohms. replace the sensor.
PROBLEM: Engine stalls after being started
POSSIBLE CAUSE:
1. A poor connection or open circuits in the black and yellow ignition signal wire between the fuse block and the ECU.
2. A poor connection or open circuit in the wiring or body of the engine coolant temperature sensor; cold or warm engine only. Check as outlined under Engine cranks but will not start, number 6.
3. On 1978 and later Seville, a malfunctioning idle air compensator solenoid will cause stalling at idle.
PROBLEM: Rough idle
POSSIBLE CAUSE:
1. Disconnected, leaking, or pinched manifold absolute air pressure sensor vacuum hose.
2. Poor connection or an open circuit in the air temperature sensor or wiring; cold engine only. See Poor fuel economy, number 3.
3. Poor connection or short in the sensor or wiring of the engine coolant temperature sensor. See Engine cranks but will not start, number 6.
4. Poor connection at the injectors.
PROBLEM: Fast idle condition is prolonged.
POSSIBLE CAUSE:
1. Throttle position switch needs adjusting.

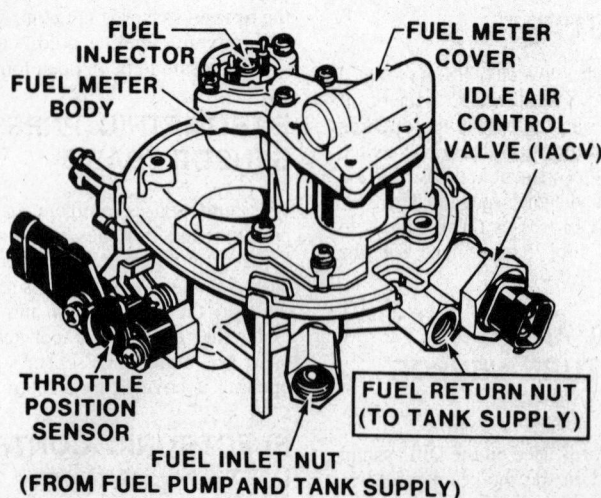

FUEL INJECTOR
FUEL METER BODY
FUEL METER COVER
IDLE AIR CONTROL VALVE (IACV)
THROTTLE POSITION SENSOR
FUEL RETURN NUT (TO TANK SUPPLY)
FUEL INLET NUT (FROM FUEL PUMP AND TANK SUPPLY)
GM single bore throttle body fuel injection unit

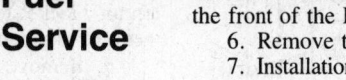
2. Poor connection at the fast idle valve or an open circuit in the heating element.

3. A vacuum leak in or around the throttle body.

PROBLEM: Hesitation of the engine under acceleration
POSSIBLE CAUSE:

1. Leaking, restricted, or disconnected manifold absolute air pressure sensor vacuum hose.

2. Throttle position switch needs adjusting or is malfunctioning.

3 Poor connection of the ECU wiring harness at the ECU.

4. Poor connection at the EGR valve solenoid or solenoid stuck open; cold engine only.

5. Intermittent malfunction of the speed sensor trigger at the distributor.

PROBLEM: High speed performance is poor
POSSIBLE CAUSE:

1. The wide-open-throttle section of the throttle position switch needs adjusting or the switch is malfunctioning.

2. The fuel filter is blocked or restricted.

3. The chassis-mounted fuel pump is malfunctioning.

4. Intermittent malfunction of the speed sensor trigger.

5. An open circuit in the purple wire between the starter solenoid and the ECU.

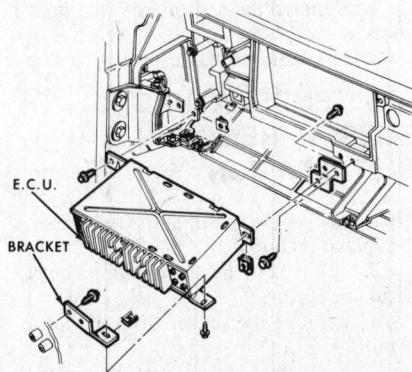

ECU mounting

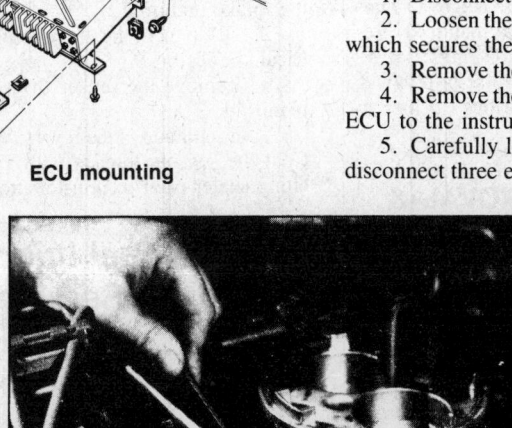

Adjusting idle speed

Electronic Fuel Injection (EFI)Service

IDLE SPEED ADJUSTMENT

NOTE: Before low idle speed adjustment is made distributor vacuum advance hose(s) must be disconnected at the distributor and plugged. The hose must be disconnected at this location to include any calibrated leakage in balance of the system. Reset timing before making idle speed adjustment.

1. Disconnect parking brake hose at vacuum release cylinder and plug the hose. Set the parking brake and block and wheels. Disconnect the air leveling compressor hose at air cleaner and plug the hose.

2. Connect a tachometer, start and warm-up the engine to operating temperature.

3. Place the transmission in drive and turn the air conditioner off.

4. Loosen the lock nut on the idle by-pass adjusting screw on the front of the throttle body.

5. Adjust the idle by-pass adjusting screw to give 650 rpm.

6. Tighten the lock nut.

7. Turn off the engine and remove the tachometer.

8. Reconnect all hoses.

ELECTRONIC CONTROL UNIT REMOVAL & INSTALLATION

Seville

1. Disconnect the negative battery cable.

2. Loosen the right hand forward screw which secures the ECU cover to the ECU.

3. Remove the three remaining screws.

4. Remove the screws which secure the ECU to the instrument panel supports.

5. Carefully lower the ECU enough to disconnect three electrical connectors from

the left hand side and the MAP hose from the front of the ECU.

6. Remove the ECU.

7. Installation is the reverse of removal.

Except Eldorado and Seville

1. Disconnect the negative battery cable.

2. Remove the glove box liner.

3. Remove the ECU mounting screws and remove the ECU.

4. Disconnect the three electrical connectors (red, black and blue) and the MAP sensor hose.

5. Installation is the reverse of removal.

Eldorado

1. Disconnect the negative battery cable.

2. Remove the three climate control outlet grilles right, left and center.

3. Working through the outlet openings, remove the three fasters securing the pad to the instrument panel support.

4. Remove the screws securing the pad to the instrument panel horizontal support.

5. Pull the pad outward and disconnect the electrical connector from the windshield wiper switch.

6. Remove the pad.

NOTE: To facilitate removal and/or installation place the shift lever in low range. Vehicles equipped with tilt wheel, place the wheel in the lowest position.

7. Remove the MAP sensor hose.

8. Remove the mounting screws and then the ECU.

9. Remove the electrical connectors.

10. Installation is the reverse of removal.

THROTTLE BODY ASSEMBLY REMOVAL & INSTALLATION

1. Remove the air cleaner.

2. Disconnect the throttle return springs from the throttle lever.

3. Remove the retainer and remove the cruise control chain from the throttle lever on cars so equipped.

4. Remove the "hairpin" clip and disconnect the throttle cable.

5. Remove the rear throttle body mounting screws and position the throttle linkage out of the way.

6. Disconnect the throttle position switch electrical connector and fast idle valve electrical connector. Slide the fast idle valve wiring out of the notch in the throttle body.

7. Remove the vacuum hoses from the nipples on the throttle body. Use a backup wrench when removing the power brake vacuum line.

8. Remove the remaining throttle body mounting screws and remove the throttle body.

9. Remove the gasket material from the intake manifold and bottom of the throttle body.

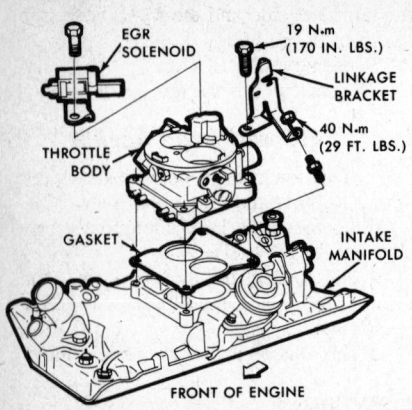

EGR SOLENOID

19 N·m (170 IN. LBS.)

LINKAGE BRACKET

40 N·m (29 FT. LBS.)

THROTTLE BODY

GASKET

INTAKE MANIFOLD

FRONT OF ENGINE

Throttle body mounting

10. The following parts are not included in a new throttle body assembly and should be removed as needed. Throttle position switch, fast idle valve seat, fast idle valve spring, fast idle valve, fast idle valve heater assembly, power brake vacuum fitting.

11. Installation is the reverse of removal.

FAST IDLE VALVE REMOVAL & INSTALLATION

1. Remove the air cleaner and disconnect the electrical connector from the fast idle valve heater.

2. Remove the air cleaner stud.

3. Remove the fast idle valve heater by pushing down and twisting 90° counter clockwise.

4. Remove the fast idle valve, spring and seat from the throttle body.

5. Installation is the reverse of removal.

FUEL RAIL REMOVAL & INSTALLATION

Except Seville

1. Remove and discard the hose clamp securing the pressure regulator hose to the front fuel rail.

2. Using a back-up wrench at the side rail fitting, remove the flare nut from each end of the fuel rail.

3. Disengage the front rail from the pressure regulator hose and remove it from the vehicle.

4. Installation is the reverse of removal.

INJECTION VALVE REMOVAL & INSTALLATION

Seville Only

1. Disconnect the electrical leads from all injectors on the fuel rail being removed and position the harness out of the way.

2. Remove the fuel inlet line from the fuel rail using a back-up wrench.

3. Remove the return hose and vacuum hose from the pressure regulator.

4. Disconnect the fuel rail from the fuel regulator.

5. Remove the screw holding each injector bracket to the intake manifold, and remove the brackets and grommets.

6. Remove the fuel rail and injectors from the engine as a complete unit.

NOTE: Some injectors may stick in the fuel rail while others may remain in the manifold.

7. Remove the injectors from the fuel rail and from the intake as required.

8. Injection valves are sealed by O-rings at the fuel rail and intake manifold. Remove and discard all used O-rings.

9. Installation is the reverse of removal.

NOTE: A conical shaped metal gasket should be used when servicing EFI fuel rail fittings. The gasket Part #1608786 or its equal is not required during production, but is needed during service procedures. This gasket should be inserted in the fuel rail inverted flare fitting each time a fitting is separated and reconnected in the field. These gaskets can not be re-used.

All Others

1. Remove the front and rear fuel rails.

2. Remove the electrical conduit from the injector brackets (4 places on each side).

3. Disconnect the electrical leads from all injectors on the fuel rail being removed.

4. Remove the two screws holding each injector bracket to the intake manifold and remove the brackets and grommets.

5. Remove the fuel rail and injector from the engine as a unit. Some injectors may stick in the fuel rail while others may remain in the manifold.

6. Remove the injectors from the fuel rail and from the intake manifold as required.

7. Injection valves are sealed by O-rings at both fuel rail and intake manifold. Remove and discard all used O-rings.

8. Installation is the reverse of removal. Lubricate the new O-rings prior to installation.

FUEL PRESSURE REGULATOR REMOVAL & INSTALLATION

1. Remove the vacuum hose from the nipple on top of the pressure regulator.

2. Remove and discard clamps securing the flexible fuel hose connecting the regulator to the fuel rail. Remove the return line.

3. Remove one nut securing the pressure regulator to the bracket.

NOTE: This nut has metric threads.

4. Work the regulator off the flexible fuel hose and out of the bracket.

5. Installation is the reverse of removal.

THROTTLE POSITION SWITCH REMOVAL & INSTALLATION

1. Remove the electrical connections from the switch.

2. Remove the two mounting screws and remove the switch from the throttle body.

3. Installation is the reverse of removal. Adjust the switch as necessary.

ADJUSTMENT

1. Loosen two throttle position switch mounting screws to permit rotation of the switch.

2. Hold the throttle valves in the idle position while performing step 3 and 4.

3. Turn the throttle position switch carefully counterclockwise until the end-stop has been reached.

4. Tighten throttle position switch mounting screws to 11 in./lbs.

5. Check to insure that throttle valves close to the throttle stop. If not, repeat steps 2, 3 and 4.

COOLANT TEMPERATURE SENSOR REMOVAL & INSTALLATION

1. Drain the radiator.

2. Locate the water temperature sensor in the heater hose outlet at the rear of the right hand cylinder head.

3. Disconnect the electrical connector from the sensor.

4. Remove the sensor from the heater hose.

5. Installation is the reverse of removal.

AIR TEMPERATURE SENSOR REMOVAL & INSTALLATION

1. Locate the sensor at the right rear of the intake manifold.

2. Disconnect the sensor from its electrical connector.

3. Remove the sensor from the intake manifold.

4. Installation is the reverse of removal. Coat the sensors threads with a non-hardening sealer prior to reinstallation.

Digital Fuel Injection (DFI) Service

THROTTLE BODY REMOVAL & INSTALLATION

1. Remove the air cleaner.

2. Disconnect the following electrical connectors and position them out of the way. ISC-Idle speed control, TPS-Throttle position sensor, and both injectors.

3. Remove both throttle return springs, cruise control and throttle linkage and downshift cable.

4. Disconnect the following hoses and lines from the rear of the throttle body.

NOTE: Use flare nut wrench on all fuel lines.

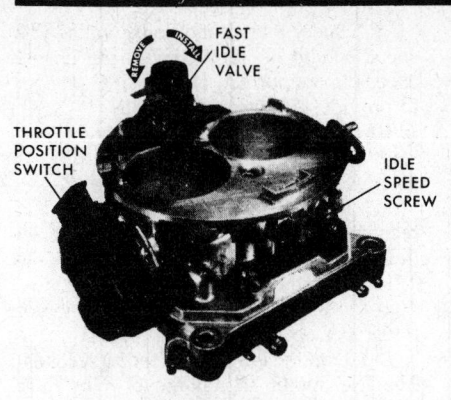

Throttle body

Fuel inlet and return line, brake booster line, MAP hose and the AIR hose.

5. Remove the PCV, EVAP, and EGR hoses from the front of the throttle body.

6. Remove the three throttle body mounting screws and remove the throttle body and gasket.

7. Installation is the reverse of removal. Check the adjustment of the TPS and ISC after reinstallation.

MAP SENSOR REMOVAL & INSTALLATION

1. Remove the instrument panel lower cover.

2. Working under the extreme right hand side of the instrument panel, disconnect the MAP hose from the sensor.

3. Disconnect MAP sensor electrical connector, being careful not to damage small gauge wires on the sensor side.

NOTE: THE MAP sensor has a female connector on the sensor side and a male connector on the harness. The BARO connector is reversed.

4. Remove the one screw securing MAP sensor to the bracket and remove the sensor.

5. Installation is the reverse of removal.

BARO SENSOR REMOVAL & INSTALLATION

1. Remove the instrument panel lower cover.

2. Remove the glove box liner.

3. Disconnect the BARO sensor electrical connector. Be careful not to damage the small gauge wires on the sensor side.

4. Working through the glove box opening, remove one screw securing MAP/BARO bracket to the instrument panel.

5. Remove one screw securing the BARO sensor and ground strap to the bracket.

6. Installation is the reverse of removal.

COOLANT SENSOR REMOVAL & INSTALLATION

1. Drain the radiator coolant until the level is below the level of the sensor.

2. Remove the alternator if necessary.

3. Disconnect the electrical pigtail and remove the sensor.

4. Installation is the reverse of removal.

Coat the sensor threads with a non-hardening sealer during reinstallation.

THROTTLE POSITION SENSOR REMOVAL & INSTALLATION

1. Remove the electrical connector from the TPS sensor.

2. Remove the throttle body assembly from the intake manifold to gain access to the spot welds on the bottom side that hold the TPS attaching screws. Invert the throttle body. Support it to prevent damage to the injector electrical connections. Using a 5/16 in. drill bit, drill completely through the TPS screw access holes (2) in the base of the throttle body.

3. Remove the two TPS attaching screws, lockwashers, and retainers. Then remove the TPS sensor from the throttle body, noting the location of the TPS lever in relation to the tang on the lever on the throttle shaft. Discard the TPS screws. New screws are supplied in service kits.

4. Installation is the reverse of removal. Adjust the TPS as necessary.

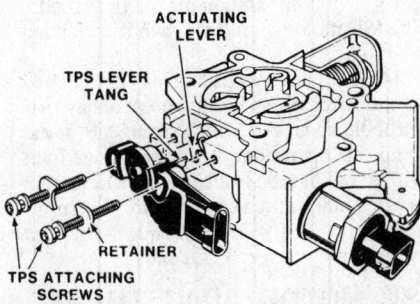

Throttle position switch (TPS) attaching screws

INJECTOR REMOVAL AND INSTALLATION

1. Remove the air cleaner.

2. Remove the electrical connectors from the injectors.

3. Remove the eight screws securing the pressure regulator assembly and remove the regulator.

4. Using a pair of small pliers, gently grasp the center collar of the injector (between the electrical connections). Carefully remove the injector with a lifting/twisting motion.

5. Discard the upper and lower O-rings. Note the presence of the backup basher under the upper O-ring.

6. Installation is the reverse of removal.

Lubricate the new O-rings with transmission fluid. (Dexron® II) prior to installation.

PRESSURE REGULATOR REMOVAL & INSTALLATION

1. Remove the air cleaner.

2. Remove the electrical connection on the injectors.

3. Remove the eight screws securing the pressure regulator assembly to the throttle body and remove the regulator.

4. Installation is the reverse of removal. Lubricate the new O-ring with Dexron® II transmission fluid and install a new gasket.

FUEL METER BODY REMOVAL & INSTALLATION

1. Remove the fuel inlet and outlet nuts and gaskets from the fuel meter body.

2. Remove the three screws and lockwashers. Remove the fuel meter body from the throttle body assembly.

3. Remove the fuel meter body insulator gasket.

TPS spot weld removal

NOTE: Do not remove the center screw and staking at each end, holding the fuel distribution skirt in the throttle body. The skirt is an integral part of the throttle body and not serviced separately.

4. Installation is the reverse of removal.

IDLE SPEED CONTROL MOTOR (ISC) REMOVAL & INSTALLATION

1. Disconnect the electrical connector.
2. Remove the two ISC mounting screws.
3. Remove the ISC control.
4. Installation is the reverse of removal. Adjust the ISC motor if necessary.

NOTE: The idle speed control is specially calibrated at the factory and no attempt should be made to disassemble the unit. Do not immerse it in any type of cleaner. It must be removed before servicing or cleaning the throttle body. It is replaced only as an assembly.

ENGINE IDLE SPEED AND DIAGNOSTIC CHECK

1. Remove the air cleaner, start the engine, and warm the engine up to normal operating temperature (upper radiator hose hot). Turn A/C off.
2. Connect a tachometer to the engine and connect the digital voltmeter as follows:

A. (+) lead to the TPS harness test point which connects to pin A, (0.8 blue-dark wire),

B. (−) lead to the TPS harness test point which connects to pin B, (0.8 black/white wire), circuit #476.

C. Select the 2V DC scale.
3. Open the set timing connect.
4. Retract the ISC motor by pressing the plunger (switch activated) in while the throttle is opened to approximately 1500 RPM. When the ISC motor fully retracts, disconnect the ISC connector, before releasing the throttle.
5. Jumper the ISC harness connector pins A and B together.
6. Under these conditions, the ISC plunger should not be touching the throttle lever. If contact is noted, adjust the ICS plunger (turn in) with pliers or suitable available special tool so that it is not touching the throttle lever.
7. The idle speed should now be 375 ± 25 rpm all except non-Calif. Eldorado/Seville cars (Calif. Eldorado/Seville—400 RPM). Adjust throttle stop screw to proper RPM, if necessary. If the engine speed is not correct check that the throttle is not held off the minimum stop because of linkage pre-load. If necessary, adjust the throttle stop as described in the "Minimum Air Rate Adjustment" to obtain 375 rpm, all except non-Calif. Eldor-

ado/Seville cars (Calif. Eldorado/Seville—400 rpm).
8. Digital voltmeter should indicate .50 ± .05 volts. If necessary, adjust Throttle Position Sensor as described in steps 9 thru 11. If voltmeter reading is correct, proceed with step 12, below.
9. Remove throttle body assembly from the intake manifold to gain access to the spot welds on the bottom side holding the TPS attaching screws in place. Invert throttle body assembly and support the assembly to prevent damage to the injector electrical connections. Using a 5/16 in. drill bit, drill completely through TPS screw access holes in base of throttle body to be sure of removing the spot welds holding screws in place. Then loosen the screws just enough to permit rotation of the sensor.
10. With the engine idling at 375 rpm, all except non-Calif. Eldorado/Seville cars (Calif. Eldorado/Seville cars—400 rpm) loosen the TPS mounting screws and position the TPS lever so that the voltmeter reads .50 ± .05 volts.
11. Tighten the TPS mounting screws with the sensor in this position. Recheck the voltmeter reading when the screws are tight to make sure that the adjustment has not changed.
12. Disconnect the test equipment and reconnect all connections including the set timing connector.
13. Turn the ignition off for 10 seconds. The ISC motor should move to its extended position.
14. The above procedure may have turned on the check engine light and may have set a trouble code. After the system is restored to normal operation, the check engine light will go out but the trouble code will remain as an "intermittent" problem. Enter diagnostics, clear the stored codes, and turn the ignition off for 10 seconds.

ISC MOTOR ADJUSTMENT

Adjustment of the ISC motor is necessary to establish the initial position of the motor after it has been replaced. ISC motor adjustment may also be necessary if the throttle pedal ratchets when the ignition is turned off or on.

1. Remove the air cleaner, start the engine, and warm the engine up to normal operating temperature (upper radiator hose hot). Turn the A/C off.
2. Connect a tachometer to the engine.
3. Check the TPS adjustment as described in steps 2 through 7 in the "TPS Adjustment" section.
4. Open the set timing connector.
5. Disconnect the TPS connector.
6. Turn the ignition off for 10 seconds and observe the ISC plunger movement. It should fully extend.
7. When the ISC plunger is fully extended, disconnect the ISC connector. Jumper the ISC harness pins A and B together.
8. Reconnect the TPS and start the engine.

9. Under these conditions, engine idle speed should be 1500 rpm. If the engine speeds is not correct, turn the ISC plunger to provide 1500 rpm.
10. Reconnect the ISC motor and repeat steps 5 through 8. If the engine speed is too low, adjust the TPS as needed.
11. Disconnect the test equipment and reconnect all connections including the set timing connector.
12. Turn the ignition off for 10 seconds. Start the engine and check the ISC motor for proper operation.
13. Turn the ignition off for 10 seconds. The ISC motor should move to its fully extended position.
14. The above procedure may have turned on the check engine light and may have set a trouble code. After the system is restored to its normal operation, the check engine light will go out but the trouble code will remain as an "intermittent" problem. Enter diagnostics, clear the stored codes, and turn the ignition off for 10 seconds.

MINIMUM AIR RATE ADJUSTMENT

This adjustment should be performed only when the throttle body parts have been replaced or when required to do so by the TPS adjustment.

1. Remove the air cleaner, start the engine, and warm it up to normal operating temperature. Turn the A/C off.
2. Connect a tachometer to the engine.
3. Open the set timing connector.
4. Retract the ISC motor by pressing holding the plunger (switch-activated) in while the throttle is opened to approximately 1500 rpm. When the ISC motor fully retracts, disconnect the ISC connector before releasing the throttle.
5. Jumper the ISC harness connector pins A and B together.
6. Under these conditions, the ISC plunger should not be touching the throttle lever. If contact is noted, adjust the ISC motor as described under that heading.
7. The idle speed should now be 375 ± 25 rpm all except non-Calif. Eldorado/Seville cars (Calif. Eldorado/Seville—400 rpm). Adjust throttle stop screw to proper rpm, if necessary. If the engine speed is not correct check that the throttle is not held off the minimum stop because of linkage pre-load. If necessary, adjust the throttle stop as described in the "Minimum Air Rate Adjustment" to obtain 375 rpm—all except non-Calif. Eldorado/Seville cars (Calif. Eldorado/Seville—400 rpm).
8. Check the TPS adjustment as described under that heading.
9. Disconnect the test equipment and reconnect all connections including the set timing connector.
10. Turn ignition off for 10 seconds. The ISC motor should move to its extended position.

11. The above procedure may have turned on the check engine light and may have set a trouble code. After the system is restored to normal operation, the check engine light will go out but the trouble code will remain as an "intermittent" problem. Enter diagnostics, clear the stored codes, and turn the ignition off for 10 seconds.

GM THROTTLE BODY INJECTION

All 1982 and later USA cars equipped with the Pontiac 4-151, the 1.8L OHC or the 2.0L OHU engine use a single bore, throttle body fuel injection unit. All Canadian 4-151s retain the 2 bbl carburetors. The 1982 and later Corvette equipped with the V8 350 and the 1982 and later Camaro and Firebird equipped with the V8 305 engine use a pair of single bore throttle body injection units.

In this throttle body system, a single fuel injector mounted at the top of the throttle body sprays fuel down through the throttle valve and into the intake manifold. The throttle body resembles a carburetor in appearance but does away with much of the carburetor's complexity (choke system and linkage, power valves, accelerator pump, jets, fuel circuits, etc.), replacing these with the electrically operated fuel injector.

The injector is actually a solenoid which when activated lifts a pintle valve off its seat, allowing the pressurized (10 psi) fuel behind the valve to spray out. The nozzle of the injector is designed to atomize the fuel for complete air/fuel mixture.

The activating signal for the injector originates with the Electronic Control Module (ECM), which monitors engine temperature, throttle position, vehicle speed and several other engine-related conditions then continuously updates injector opening times in relation to the information given by these sensors.

The throttle body is also equipped with an idle air control motor. The idle air control motor operates a pintle valve at the side of the throttle body. When the valve opens it allows air to bypass the throttle, which provides the additional air required to idle at elevated speeds when the engine is cold. The idle air control motor also compensates for accessory loads and changing engine friction during break-in. The idle speed control motor is controlled by the ECM.

Fuel pressure for the system is provided by an in-tank fuel pump. The pump is a two-stage turbine designed powered by a DC motor. It is designed for smooth, quiet operation, high flow and fast priming. The design of the fuel inlet reduces the possibility of vapor lock under hot fuel conditions. The pump sends fuel forward through the fuel line to a stainless steel high-flow fuel filter mounted on the engine. From the filter the fuel moves to the throttle body. The fuel pump inlet is located in a reservoir in the fuel tank which insures a constant supply of fuel to the pump during hard cornering and on steep inclines. The fuel pump is controlled by a fuel pump relay, which in turn recieves its signal from the ECM. A fuel pressure regulator inside the throttle body maintains fuel pressure at 10 psi and

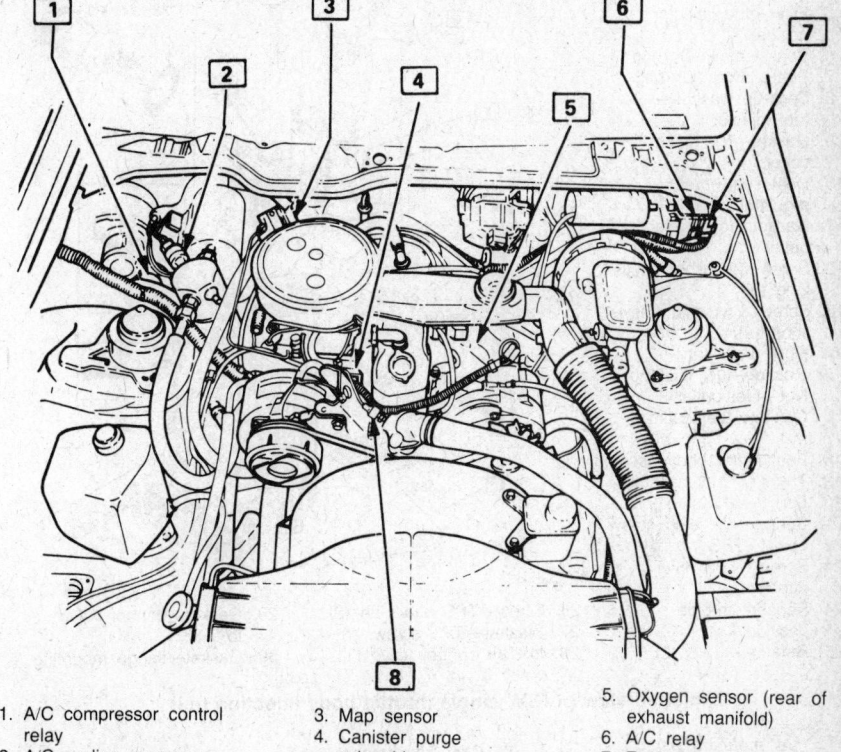

1. A/C compressor control relay
2. A/C cycling pressure switch
3. Map sensor
4. Canister purge solenoid
5. Oxygen sensor (rear of exhaust manifold)
6. A/C relay
7. Fuel pump relay
8. Coolant sensor

Engine component locations—G.M. 4 cyl. 151 cu. in. engine with electronic fuel injection

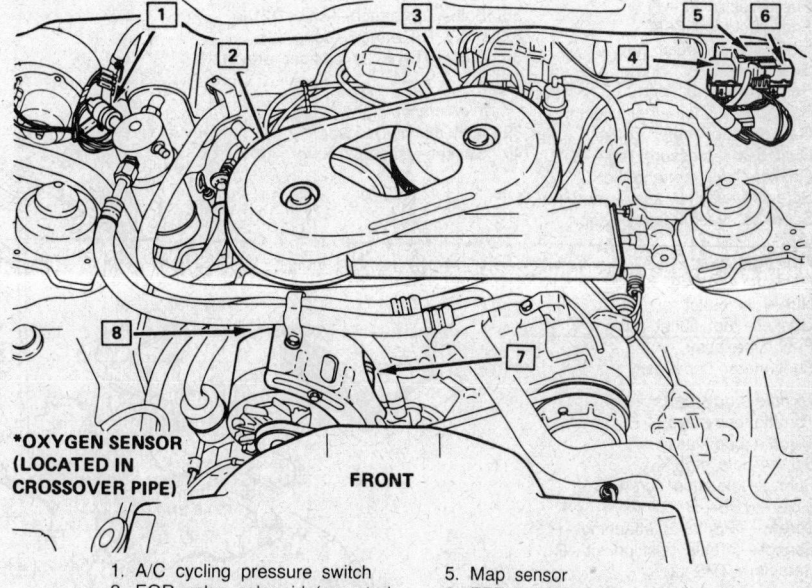

1. A/C cycling pressure switch
2. EGR valve solenoid (mounted on valve cover)
3. Oil pressure switch (rear of intake manifold)
4. Hood scoop relay
5. Map sensor
6. EFE & EGR valve relay
7. Coolant sensor
8. ESC sensor (next to motor mount)

*OXYGEN SENSOR (LOCATED IN CROSSOVER PIPE) FRONT

Engine component locations—G.M. 8 cyl. 305 cu. in. engine with electronic fuel injection—Camaro and Firebird shown Corvette similar (© G.M. Corp.)

routes unused fuel back to the fuel tank through a fuel return line. On the dual throttle body system, a fuel pressure compensator is used on the second throttle body assembly to compensate for a momentary fuel pressure drop between the two units. This constant circulation of fuel through the throttle body prevents component overheating and vapor lock.

The electronic control module (ECM), also called a micro-computer, is the brain of the fuel injection system. After receiving inputs from various sensing elements in the system, The ECM commands the fuel injector, idle air control motor, EST distributor, torque converter clutch and other engine actuators to operate in a preprogrammed manner to improve driveability and fuel economy while controlling emissions. The sensing elements update the computor every tenth of a second for general information and every 12.5 milli-seconds for critical emissions and driveability information.

The ECM has limited system diagnostic capability. If certain system malfunctions occur, the diagnostic "check engine" light in the instrument panel will light, alerting the driver to the need for service.

Since both idle speed and mixture are controlled by the ECM on this system, no adjustments are possible or necessary.

TOOLS

The system does not require special tools for diagnosis. A tachometer, test light, ohmmeter, digital voltmeter with 10 megohms impedance, vacuum pump, vacuum

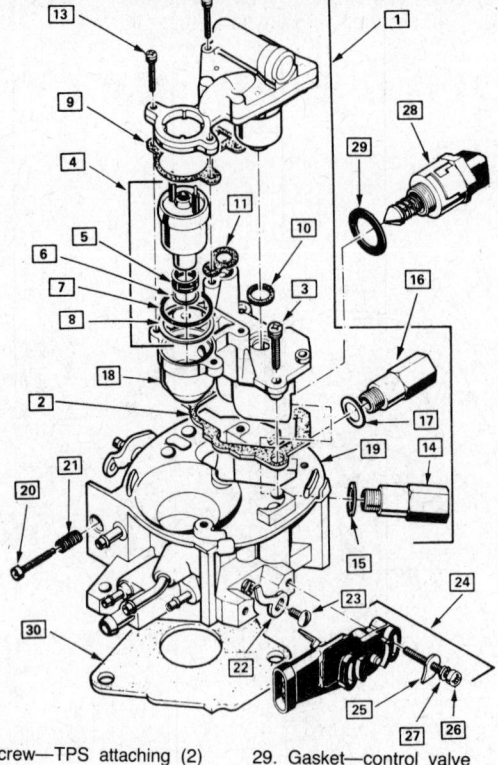

1. Fuel meter assembly
2. Gasket—fuel meter body
3. Screw & washer assy—attach. (3)
4. Fuel injector kit
5. Filter—fuel injector nozzle
6. Seal—small "O" ring
7. Seal—large "O" ring
8. Back-up washer—fuel injector
9. Gasket—fuel meter cover
10. Dust seal—press, regulator
11. Gasket—fuel meter outlet
12. Screw & washer assy—long (3)
13. Screw & washer assy—short (2)
14. Nut—fuel inlet
15. Gasket—fuel inlet nut
16. Nut—fuel outlet
17. Gasket—fuel outlet nut
18. Fuel meter body assembly
19. Throttle body assembly
20. Screw—idle stop
21. Spring—idle stop screw
22. Lever—TPS
23. Screw—TPS lever attaching
24. Sensor—throttle position kit
25. Retainer—TPS (2)

26. Screw—TPS attaching (2)
27. Washer—TPS screw (2)
28. Idle air control valve

29. Gasket—control valve to T.B.
30. Gasket—flange mounting

Exploded view of G.M. single throttle body injection unit

Fuel metering parts
1. Fuel meter assy—F
   Fuel meter assy—R
2. Gasket—fuel meter body
3. Screw & washer assy—attach. (3)
4. Fuel injector kit—F
   Fuel injector kit—R
5. Filter—fuel injector nozzle
6. Seal—small "O" ring
7. Seal—large "O" ring
8. Back-up washer—fuel injector
9. Gasket—fuel meter cover
10. Dust seal—pressure reg.—R
11. Gasket—fuel meter cover
12. Screw & washer assy—long (3)
13. Screw & washer assy—short (2)
14. Nut—fuel inlet
15. Gasket—fuel inlet nut
16. Nut—fuel outlet
17. Gasket—fuel outlet nut
18. Fuel tube assy
19. Fuel meter body assy

Throttle body parts
20. Throttle body assy—F
    Throttle body assy—R
21. Screw—idle stop
22. Spring—idle stop screw
23. Lever—TPS—R
24. Screw—TPS lever attaching—R
25. Sensor—throttle position kit—R
26. Retainer—TPS (2)
27. Screw—TPS attaching (2)
28. Washer—TPS screw (2)
29. Idle air control valve
30. Gasket—control valve to T.B.
31. Screw—idle balance

32. Clip—idle balance screw (service only)
33. Throttle rod & bearing assembly
34. Clip—throttle rod (2)
35. Gasket—TBI mounting
36. Bolt—TBI attach.—short (2)
37. Bolt—TBI attach.—long (2)
38. Stud—TBI & air cleaner attach. (2)

Inlet manifold parts
39. Inlet manifold cover
40. Gasket—manifold cover

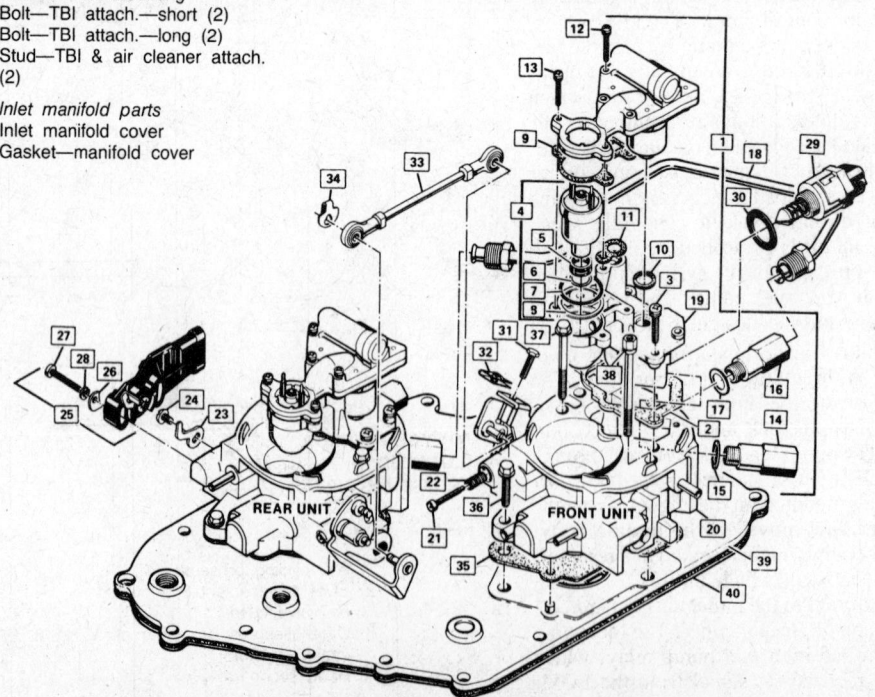

Exploded view of G.M. dual throttle body injection unit—all parts common between units except those marked F (front) or R (rear)

gauge and jumper wires are required for diagnosis. A test light or voltmeter must be used when specified in the procedures.

Throttle Body Injection Service

FUEL SYSTEM PRESSURE TEST

——— CAUTION ———
To reduce the risk of fire and personal injury, it is necessary to relieve the fuel system pressure before servicing fuel system components.

1. Remove the fuel pump fuse from the fuse block.
2. Crank the engine. The engine will run until it runs out of fuel. Crank the engine again for 3 seconds making sure it is out of fuel.
3. Turn the ignition off and replace the fuse.
4. Remove the air cleaner. Plug the thermal vacuum port on the throttle body.
5. Remove the fuel line between the throttle body and filter.
6. Install a fuel pressure gauge between the throttle body and fuel filter. The gauge should be able to register at least 15 psi.
7. Start the car. Observe the fuel pressure reading. It should be 9-13 psi.

NOTE: Before removing the fuel pressure gauge the fuel system must be depressurized.

8. Reinstall the parts in the reverse order of removal.

IDLE AIR CONTROL ASSEMBLY REMOVAL & INSTALLATION

1. Remove the air cleaner.
2. Disconnect the electrical connection from the idle air control assembly.
3. Using a 1¼ in. wrench, remove the idle air control assembly from the throttle body.

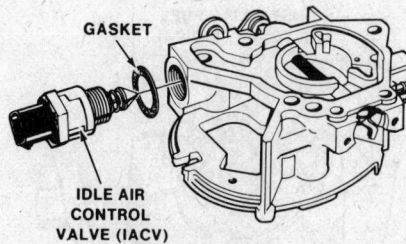

Idle air control

NOTE: Before installing a new assembly, measure the distance that the conical valve is extended. This measurement should be made from motor housing to

end of cone. It should be greater than 1.259 in. If the cone is extended too far damage to the motor may result.

On cars with manual transmissions, idle speed will be controlled when operating temperature is reached. For automatic transmission cars, engage the transmission in drive after operating temperature is reached. This will allow the ECM to control idle speed.

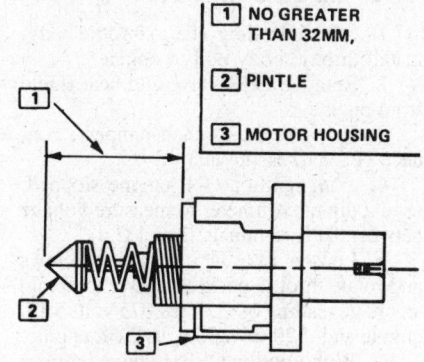

Idle air control installation check

FUEL PRESSURE REGULATOR/ COMPENSATOR REMOVAL & INSTALLATION

1. Remove air cleaner.
2. Disconnect electrical connector to injector by squeezing on two tabs and pulling straight up.
3. Remove five screws securing fuel meter cover to fuel meter body. Notice location of two short screws during removal.

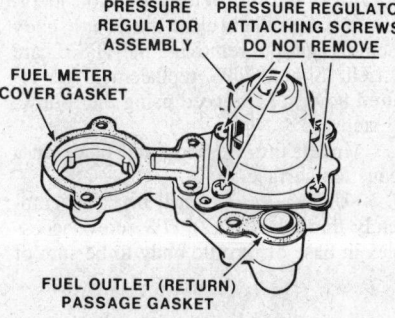

Fuel pressure regulator

——— CAUTION ———
Do not remove the four screws securing the pressure regulator to the fuel meter cover. The fuel pressure regulator includes a large spring under heavy tension which, if accidentally released, could cause personal injury. The fuel meter cover is only serviced as a complete assembly and includes the fuel pressure regulator preset and plugged at the factory.

NOTE: DO NOT immerse the fuel meter cover (with pressure regulator) in any

type of cleaner. Immersion in cleaner will damage the internal fuel pressure regulator diaphragms and gaskets.

4. Installation is the reverse of removal.

MINIMUM AIR RATE ADJUSTMENT

2.5L Engine

This adjustment should be performed only when the throttle body parts have been replaced or required to do so by the T.P.S. adjustment. Engine should be at normal operating temperature before making adjustment.

1. Remove air cleaner and air cleaner to TBI gasket. Plug vacuum port on TBI unit for THERMAC.

NOTE: On vehicles equipped with a tamper resistant plug covering the minimum air adjustment screw, the throttle body unit must be removed from the engine to remove the plug.

2. Remove T.V. cable from throttle control bracket to allow access to minimum air adjustment screw.
3. Connect a tachometer to engine.
4. Start engine, transmission in Park (Neutral on manual transmission) and allow engine RPM to stabilize.
5. Install tool J-33047, or equivalent, and idle air passage of throttle body. Be certain that tool seats fully in passage and no air leaks exist.
6. Using appropriate screwdriver, turn minimum air screw until engine rpm is 500 ± 25 in neutral with automatic transaxle, and 775 ± 25 in neutral with manual transaxle.
7. Stop engine and remove tool J-33047 from throttle body.
8. Reinstall T.V. cable into throttle control bracket.
9. Use silicone sealant or equivalent to cover minimum air adjustment screw.
10. Install air cleaner gasket and air cleaner to engine.

CURB IDLE AIR RATE (5.0L CROSSFIRE INJECTION SYSTEM)

The throttle position of each throttle body must be balanced so that the throttle plates are synchronized to open simultaneously. This is a checking and adjustment procedure adjustment should be performed only when a throttle body has been replaced or when checking procedure indicates an adjustment is required.

1. Remove air cleaner and air cleaner to TBI unit for THERMAC.
2. Start engine and allow engine rpm to stabilize.
3. Plug idle air passages of each throttle body with plugs J-33047, or their equal. Be certain plugs are fully seated in passages and no air leaks exist. Engine rpm should

decrease to curb idle air rate. If engine rpm does not decrease, check for vacuum leak.

4. Remove cap from ported tube on rear TBI unit and connect the vacuum gauge.

5. Observe the gauge, reading should be approximately .45 in. Hg. If adjustment is required proceed as follows:

a. Remove tamper resistant screw covering the minimum air adjustment screw if required.

b. Adjust minimum air adjustment screw to obtain approximately .45 in. Hg

c. After adjustment, proceed to front TBI unit.

6. Remove gauge from rear TBI unit and re-install cap on ported tube.

7. Remove cap from ported tube on front TBI unit and connect vacuum gauge. Reading should also be approximately .45 in. Hg. if adjustment is required proceed as follows:

a. Locate split lever screw on throttle linkage. If screw is welded for tamper resistance, break weld and install new screw with thread locking compound applied.

b. Adjust split lever screw to obtain approximately .45 in. Hg.

8. Remove gauge from front TBI unit and re-install cap on ported tube.

9. If both readings are approximately .45 in. Hg., no adjustment is required; throttle plates are synchronized.

10. Stop engine and remove idle air passage plugs.

11. Check T.P.S. voltage and adjust if required.

12. Install air cleaner gaskets, connect vacuum line to TBI unit and install air cleaner.

THROTTLE POSITION SENSOR CHECK

Throttle position sensor adjustment should be checked after minimum air adjustment is completed.

1. Remove air cleaner.

2. Disconnect T.P.S. harness from T.P.S.

3. Using three jumper wires connect T.P.S. harness to T.P.S.

4. With ignition ON, engine stopped, used a digital voltmeter to measure voltage between terminals B and C.

5. Voltage should read .525 ± .075 volts on the 5.0L engine and .820 + .250 volts 2.5L engine.

6. Adjust T.P.S. if required.

7. With ignition OFF, remove jumpers and connect T.P.S. harness to T.P.S.

8. Install air cleaner.

TPS ADJUSTMENT

1. After installing TPS to throttle body, install throttle body unit to engine.

2. Remove EGR valve and heat shield from engine.

3. Using three six inch jumpers, connect TPS harness to TPS

4. With ignition ON, engine stopped, used a digital voltmeter to measure voltage between TPS terminals B and C.

5. Loosen two TPS attaching screws and rotate throttle position sensor to obtain a voltage reading of .525 ± .075 volts 5.0L engine and .820 ± .250 volts 2.5L engine.

6. With ignition OFF, remove jumpers and reconnect TPS harness to TPS

7. Install EGR valve and heat shield to engine, using new gasket as necessary.

8. Install air cleaner gasket and air cleaner to throttle body unit.

THROTTLE POSITION SENSOR REMOVAL & INSTALLATION

The Throttle Postion Sensor (TPS) is an electricl unit and must not be immersed in any type of liquid solvent or cleaner. The TPS is factory adjusted and the retaining screws are spot welded in place to retain the critical setting. With these considerations, it is possible to clean the throttle body assembly without removing the TPS if care is used. Should TPS replacement be required however, proceed using the following steps:

1. Invert throttle body and place on a clean, flat surface.

2. Using a ⁵⁄₁₆ in. drill bit, drill completely through two (2) TPS screw access holes in base of throttle body to be sure of removing the spot welds holding TPS screws in place.

3. Remove the two TPS attaching screws, lockwashers, and retainers. Then, remove TPS sensor from throttle body. DISCARD SCREWS. New screws are supplied in service kits.

4. If necessary, remove screw holding Throttle Position Sensor actuator lever to end of throttle shaft.

5. Remove the Idle Air Control assembly and gasket from the throttle body.

NOTE: DO NOT immerse the Idle Air Control motor in any type of cleaner and it should always be removed before throttle body cleaning. Immersion in cleaner will damage the IAC assembly. It is replaced only as a complete assembly.

Further disassembly of the throttle body is not required for cleaning purposes. The throttle valve screws are permanently staked in place and should not be removed. The throttle body is serviced as a complete assembly.

Assembly

1. Place throttle body assembly on holding fixture to avoid damaging throttle valve.

2. Using a new sealing gasket, install Idle Air Control motor in throttle body. Tighten motor securely.

NOTE: DO NOT overtighten to prevent damage to valve.

3. If removed, install Throttle Position Sensor actuator lever by aligning flats on lever with flats on end of shaft. Install retaining screw and tighten securely.

NOTE: Install Throttle Position Sensor after completion of assembly of the throttle body unit. Use thread locking compound supplied in service kit on attaching screws.

FUEL INJECTOR REMOVAL & INSTALLATION

1. Remove the air cleaner.

2. Disconnect injector electrical connector by squeezing two tabs together and pulling straight up.

NOTE: Use care in removing to pre-

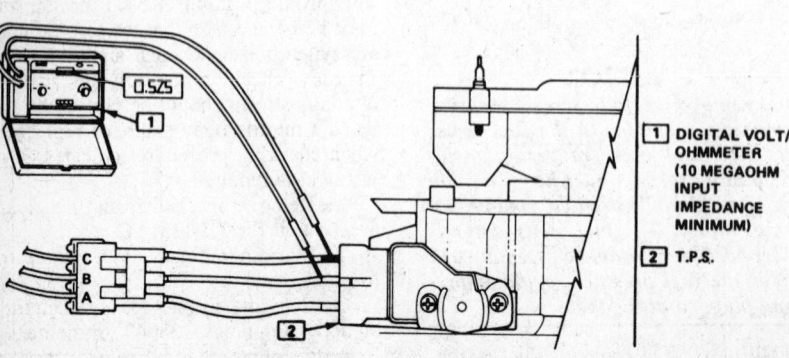

Throttle position sensor adjustment

1 DIGITAL VOLT/ OHMMETER (10 MEGAOHM INPUT IMPEDANCE MINIMUM)

2 T.P.S.

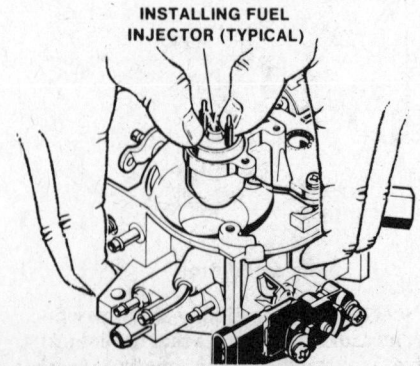

INSTALLING FUEL INJECTOR (TYPICAL)

Injector installation

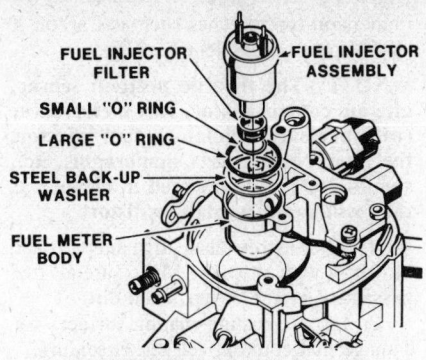

Injector components

vent damage to the electrical connector pins on top of the injector, injector fuel filter and nozzle. The fuel injector is only serviced as a complete assembly. Do not immerse it in any type of cleaner.

3. Remove the fuel meter cover.

4. Using a small awl, gently pry up on the injector evenly and carefully remove it.

5. Installation is the reverse of removal, with the following recommendations.

Use Dexron II® transmission fluid to lubricate all O-rings. Install the steel backup washer in the recess of the fuel meter body. Then, install the O-ring directly above backup washer, pressing the O-ring into the recess.

NOTE: Do not attempt to reverse this procedure and install backup washer and O-ring after injector is located in the cavity. To do so will prevent seating of the O-ring in the recess.

FUEL METER COVER REMOVAL & INSTALLATION

1. Remove the five fuel meter cover screws and lockwashers holding the cover on the fuel meter body.

2. Lift off fuel meter cover (with fuel pressure regulator assembly).

3. Remove the fuel meter cover gaskets.

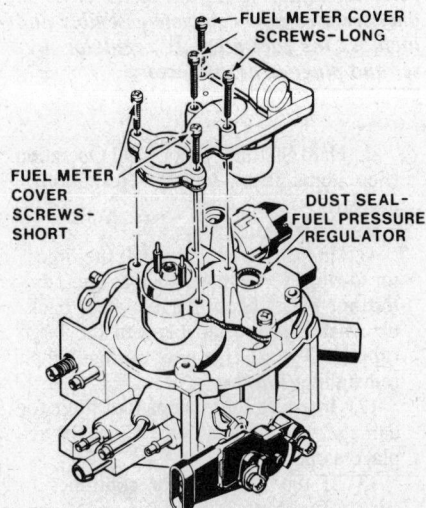

Fuel meter cover removal

CAUTION

Do not remove the four screws securing the pressure regulator to the fuel meter cover. The fuel pressure regulator includes a large spring under heavy tension which, if accidentally released, could cause personal injury. The fuel meter cover is only serviced as a complete assembly and includes the fuel pressure regulator preset and plugged at the factory.

NOTE: Do not immerse the fuel meter cover (with pressure regulator) in any type of cleaner. Immersion in cleaner will damage the internal fuel pressure regulator diaphragms and gaskets.

4. Remove the sealing ring (dust seal from the fuel meter body).

5. Installation is the reverse of removal.

FUEL METER BODY REMOVAL & INSTALLATION

1. Remove the fuel inlet and outlet nuts and gaskets from fuel meter body.

2. Remove three screws and lockwashers. Remove fuel meter body from throttle body assembly.

NOTE: The air cleaner stud must have been removed previously.

3. Remove fuel meter body insulator gasket.

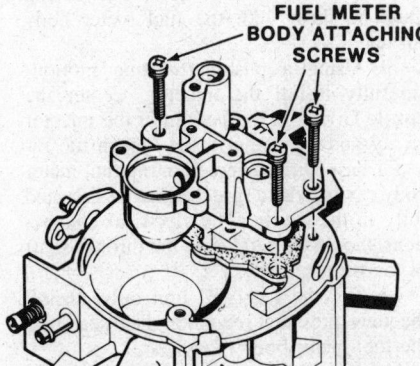

Removing fuel meter body assembly

4. Installation is the reverse of removal.

THROTTLE BODY REMOVAL & INSTALLATION

Single Unit—Four Cylinder Engine

NOTE: Refer to the "Rear Unit-V8 Engine" procedure which follows. Disregard steps 6 and 7 of that procedure, instead, just disconnect the fuel feed and return lines.

Front Unit—V8 Engine

1. Disconnect the battery cables at the battery.

2. Remove the air cleaner assembly, noting the connection points of the vacuum lines.

---

3. Disconnect the electrical connectors at the injector and the idle air control motor.

4. Disconnect the vacuum line from the TBI unit, noting the connection points. During installation, refer to the underhood emission control information decal for vacuum line routing information.

5. Disconnect the transmission detent cable from the TBI unit.

6. Disconnect the fuel inlet (feed) and fuel balance line connections at the front TBI unit.

7. Disconnect the throttle control rod between the two TBI units.

8. Unbolt and remove the TBI unit.

9. Installation is the reverse of the previous steps. Torque the TBI bolts to 120–168 inch lbs. during installation.

Rear Unit—V8 Engine

1. Disconnect the battery cables at the battery.

2. Remove the air cleaner assembly, noting the connection points of the vacuum lines.

3. Disconnect the electrical connectors at the injector, idle air control motor, and throttle position sensor.

4. Disconnect the vacuum lines from the TBI unit, noting the connection points. During installation, refer to the underhood emission control information decal for vacuum line routing information.

5. Disconnect the throttle and cruise control (if so equipped) cables at the TBI unit.

6. Disconnect the fuel return and balance line connections from the rear TBI unit.

7. Disconnect the throttle control rod between the two units.

8. Unbolt and remove the TBI unit.

9. Installation is the reverse of the previous steps. Torque the TBI bolts to 120–168 inch lbs. during installation.

THROTTLE BODY DISASSEMBLY

When servicing the single TBI unit on four cylinder engines, follow all steps except those specified "front unit." "Rear Unit" steps DO apply.

CAUTION

Use extreme care when handling the TBI unit to avoid damage to the swirl plates located beneath the throttle valve.

NOTE: If both TBI units are to be disassembled, DO NOT mix parts between either unit.

1. Remove the fuel meter cover assembly (five screws). Remove the gaskets after the cover has been removed. The fuel meter cover assembly is serviced only as a unit. If necessary, the entire unit must be replaced.

CAUTION

DO NOT remove the four screws which

retain the pressure regulator (rear unit) or pressure compensator (front unit). There is a spring beneath the cover which is under great pressure. If the cover is accidentally released, personal injury could result. Do not immerse the fuel meter cover in any type of cleaning solvent.

2. Remove the foam dust seal from the meter body of the rear unit.

3. Remove the fuel injector using a pair of small pliers as follows:

a. Grasp the injector collar, between the electrical terminals.

b. Carefully pull the injector upward, in a twisting motion.

c. If the injectors are to be removed from both TBI units, mark them so that

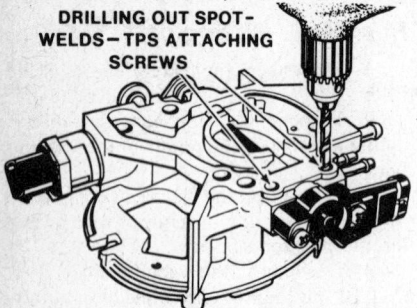

DRILLING OUT SPOT-WELDS—TPS ATTACHING SCREWS

Spot weld removal

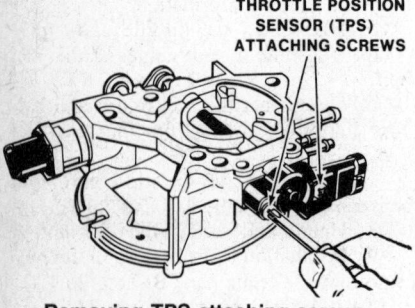

THROTTLE POSITION SENSOR (TPS) ATTACHING SCREWS

Removing TPS attaching screws

they may be installed in their original units.

4. Remove the filter from the base of the injector by rotating it back and forth.

5. Remove the O-ring and the steel washer from the top of the fuel meter body, then remove the small O-ring from the bottom of the injector cavity.

6. Remove the fuel inlet and outlet nuts (and gaskets) from the fuel meter body.

7. Remove the fuel meter body assembly and gasket from the throttle body assembly (three screws).

8. For the rear TBI unit only: Remove the throttle position sensor (TPS) from the throttle body (two screws). If necessary, remove the screw which holds the TPS actuator lever to the end of the throttle shaft.

9. Remove the idle air control motor from the throttle body.

— **CAUTION** —

Because the TPS and idle air control motors are electrical units, they must not be immersed in any type of cleaning solvent.

ASSEMBLY

NOTE: During assembly, replace the gaskets, injector washer, O-rings, and pressure regulator dust seal with new parts.

1. Install the idle air control motor in the throttle body, using a new gasket. Torque the retaining screws to 13 ft. lbs.

NOTE: DO NOT overtighten the screws.

2. For the rear TBI unit only: If removed, install the TPS actuator lever by aligning the flats of the lever and the shaft. Install and tighten the retaining screw.

3. Install the fuel meter body on the throttle body, using a new gasket. Also, apply thread locking compound to the three fuel meter body screws according to the chemical manufacturers instructions. Torque the screws to 35 inch lbs.

4. Install the fuel inlet and outlet nuts, using new gaskets. Torque the nuts to 260 inch lbs.

5. Carefully twist the fuel filter onto the injector base.

6. Lubricate the new O-rings with Dexron II® transmission fluid.

7. Install the small O-ring onto the injector, pressing it up against the fuel filter.

8. Install the steel washer into the injector cavity recess of the fuel meter body. Install the large O-ring above the steel washer, in the cavity recess. The O-ring must be flush with the fuel meter body surface.

9. Using a pushing/twisting motion, carefully install the injector. Center the nozzle O-ring in the bottom of the injector cavity and align the raised lug on the injector base with the notch in the fuel meter body cavity. Make sure the injector is seated fully in the cavity. The electrical connections should be parallel to the throttle shaft of the throttle body.

10. For the rear TBI unit only: Install the new pressure regulator dust seal into the fuel meter body recess.

11. Install the new fuel meter cover and fuel outlet passage gaskets on the fuel meter cover.

12. Install the fuel meter cover assembly, using thread locking compound on the five retaining screws. Torque the screws to 28 inch lbs. Note that the two short screws must be installed alongside the fuel injector (one screw each side).

13. For the rear TBI unit only: With the throttle valve in the closed (idle) position, install the TPS but do not tighten the attaching screws. The TPS lever must be located ABOVE the tang on the throttle actuator lever.

14. Install the TBI unit(s) as previously outlined and adjust the throttle position sensor.

CLEANING AND INSPECTION

The throttle body injection parts, except as noted below, should be cleaned in a cold

immersion-type cleaner such as Carbon X (X-55) or its equivalent.

NOTE: The throttle position sensor, idle air control motor, fuel meter cover (with pressure regulator), fuel injector, fuel filter, rubber parts, diaphragms, etc., should NOT be immersed in cleaner as they will swell, harden or distort.

1. Thoroughly clean all metal parts and blow dry with shop air. Make sure all fuel passages are free of burrs and dirt.

2. Inspect casting mating surfaces for damage that could affect gasket sealing.

3. Check, repair or replace parts as required, if the following problems are encountered:

a. Flooding

(1) Inspect large and small fuel injector O-rings for damage such as cuts, distortion, etc. Check that the steel back-up washer is located beneath the large (upper) O-ring. Use new O-rings when reinstalling injector.

(2) Inspect fuel injector fuel filter for damage, cleanliness, etc. Clean or replace as necessary.

(3) If the fuel injector continues to supply fuel with injector electrical connections removed, replace injector as required.

b. Hesitation

(1) Inspect fuel injector fuel filter for being plugged, dirty, etc. Clean or replace as necessary.

(2) If improper fuel inlet and outlet pressure readings, are noted check for restricted passages or inoperative fuel pressure regulator. Repair or replace as required.

— **CAUTION** —

DO NOT remove the four screws securing the fuel pressure regulator to the fuel meter cover. The fuel pressure regulator includes a large spring under heavy tension, which if accidentally released, could cause personal injury. The fuel meter cover is only serviced as a complete assembly and includes the fuel pressure regulator preset and plugged at the factory.

c. Hard Starting - Poor Cold Operation (See items listed under "Hesitation," above.)

d. Rough Idle

(1) Inspect large and small fuel injector O-rings for damage such as cuts, distortion, etc. Check that the steel back-up washer is located beneath the large (upper) O-ring. Use new O-rings when reinstalling injector.

(2) Inspect fuel injector fuel filter for damage, cleanliness, etc. Clean or replace as necessary.

(3) If the fuel injector continues to supply fuel with injector electrical connections removed, replace injector as required.

GM MULTI-PORT FUEL INJECTION SYSTEM

On 1984 and later models, a new multiport fuel injection (MFI) sytem is available. The MFI system is controlled by an electronic control module (ECM) which monitors engine operations and generates output signals to provide the correct air/fuel mixture, ignition timing and engine idle speed control. Input to the control unit is provided

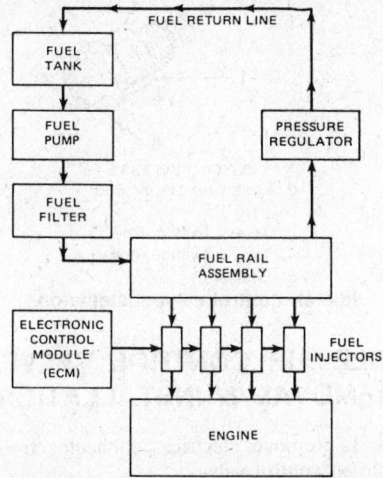

Schematic of multiport fuel injection system

by an oxygen sensor, coolant temperature sensor, detonation sensor, hot film air mass sensor and throttle position sensor. The ECM also receives information concerning engine rpm, road speed, transmission gear position, power steering and air conditioning.

The MFI system uses Bosch injectors, one at each intake port, rather than the single injector found on the earlier throttle body

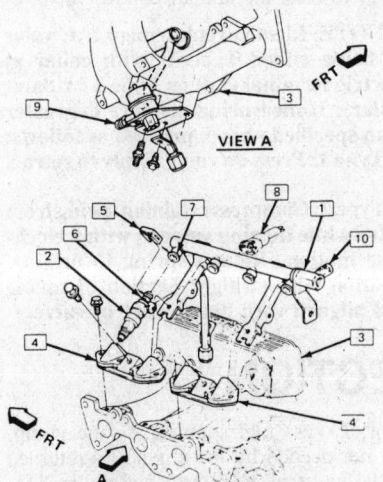

1. Fuel rail assembly
2. Injector
3. Intake manifold
4. Injector housing assembly
5. Injector retaining clip
6. Injector retaining groove
7. Injector cup flange
8. Injector control harness
9. Pressure regulator
10. Fuel pressure test point

Exploded view of fuel rail and injector assembly

system. The injectors are mounted on a fuel rail and are activated simultaneously, once each engine revolution, on a signal from the electronic control module. For each combustion cycle, two fuel charges at the cylinder are mixed with the incoming air. The injector is a solenoid-operated valve which remains open depending on the width of the electronic pulses from the ECM; the longer the open time, the more fuel is injected. In this manner, the air/fuel mixture can be precisely controlled for maximum performance with minimum emissions.

Fuel is pumped from the tank by a high pressure fuel pump, located inside the fuel tank. It is a positive displacement roller vane pump. The impeller serves as a vapor separator and pre-charges the high pressure assembly. A pressure regulator maintains 28–36 psi in the fuel line to the injectors and the excess fuel is fed back to the tank. A fuel accumulator is used to dampen the hydraulic line hammer in the system created when all injectors open simultaneously.

The Mass Air Flow Sensor is used to measure the mass of air that is drawn into the engine cylinders. It is located just ahead of the air throttle in the intake system and consists of a heated film which measures the mass of air, rather than just the volume.

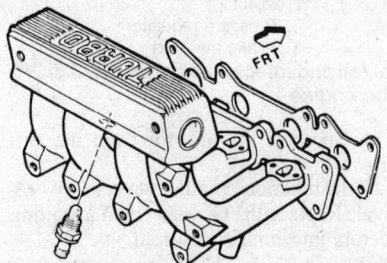

Intake manifold (1) showing manifold air temperature (MAT) sensor (2) location

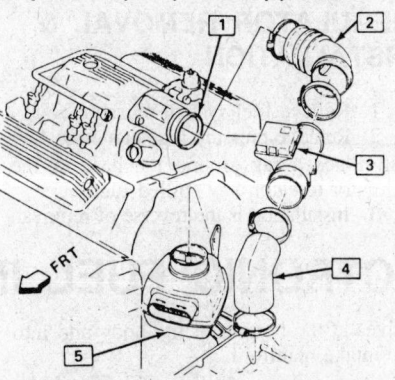

1. Throttle body assembly
2. Rear air intake duct
3. Mass air flow sensor
4. Intake air duct
5. Air cleaner assembly

Mass air flow (MAF) sensor assembly—V6 engine shown

A resistor is used to measure the temperature of the incoming air and the air mass sensor maintains the temperature of the film at 75 degrees above ambient temperature. As the ambient (outside) air temperature

rises, more energy is required to maintain the heated film at the higher temperature and the control unit uses this difference in required energy to calculate the mass of the incoming air. The control unit uses this information to determine the duration of fuel injection pulse, timing and EGR.

The throttle body incorporates an idle air control (IAC) that provides for a bypass channel through which air can flow. It consists of an orifice and pintle which is controlled by the ECM through a stepper motor. The IAC provides air flow for idle and allows additional air during cold start until the engine reaches operating temperature. As the engine temperature rises, the opening through which air passes is slowly closed.

The throttle position sensor (TPS) provides the control unit with information on throttle position, in order to determine in-

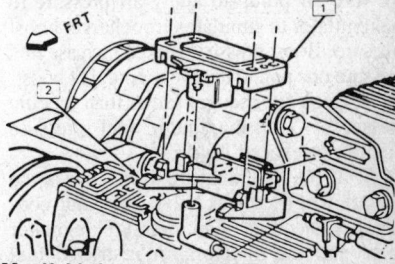

Manifold air pressure (MAP) sensor (1) and mounting bracket (2)—1.8L engine

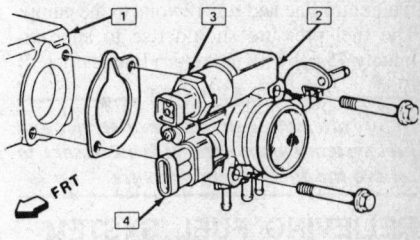

1. Intake manifold
2. Throttle body assembly
3. Idle air control valve
4. Idle position sensor

Throttle body assembly showing component location—1.8L engine shown

jector pulse width and hence correct mixture. A small amount of engine coolant is routed through the throttle assembly to prevent freezing inside the throttle bore during cold operation.

Multi-Port Service

FUEL SYSTEM PRESSURE TEST

When the ignition switch is turned ON, the in-tank fuel pump is energized for as long as the engine is cranking or running and the control unit is receiving signals from the HEI distributor. If there are no reference pulses, the control unit will shut off the fuel pump within two seconds. The pump will deliver fuel to the fuel rail and injectors, then the pressure regulator where the system pressure is controlled to maintain 26–46 psi.

1. Connect pressure gauge J-34370-1, or equivalent, to fuel pressure test point on the fuel rail. Wrap a rag around the pressure tap to absorb any leakage that may occur when installing the gauge.

2. Turn the ignition ON and check that pump pressure is 34–40 psi. This pressure is controlled by spring pressure within the regulator assembly.

3. Start the engine and allow it to idle. The fuel pressure should drop to 28–32 psi due to the lower manifold pressure.

NOTE: The idle pressure will vary somewhat depending on barometric pressure. Check for a drop in pressure indicating regulator control, rather than specific values.

4. On turbocharged models, use a low pressure air pump to apply air pressure to the regulator to simulate turbocharger boost pressure. Boost pressure should increase fuel pressure one pound for every pound of boost. Again, look for changes rather than specific pressures. The maximum fuel pressure should not exceed 46 psi.

5. If the fuel pressure drops, check the operation of the check valve, the pump coupling connection, fuel pressure regulator valve and the injectors. A restricted fuel line or filter may also cause a pressure drop. To check the fuel pump output, restrict the fuel return line and run 12 volts to the pump. The fuel pressure should rise to approximately 75 psi with the return line restricted.

--- CAUTION ---
Before attempting to remove or service any fuel system component, it is necessary to relieve the fuel system pressure.

RELIEVING FUEL SYSTEM PRESSURE

1. Remove the fuel pump fuse from the fuse block.

2. Start the engine. It should run and then stall when the fuel in the lines is exhausted. When the engine stops, crank the starter for about three seconds to make sure all pressure in the fuel lines is released.

3. Replace the fuel pump fuse.

FUEL INJECTOR REMOVAL & INSTALLATION

Use care in removing the fuel injectors to prevent damage to the electrical connector pins on the injector and the nozzle. The fuel injector is serviced as a complete assembly only and should not be immersed in any kind of cleaner.

1. Relieve fuel system pressure.

2. Remove the injector electrical connections.

3. Remove the fuel rail.

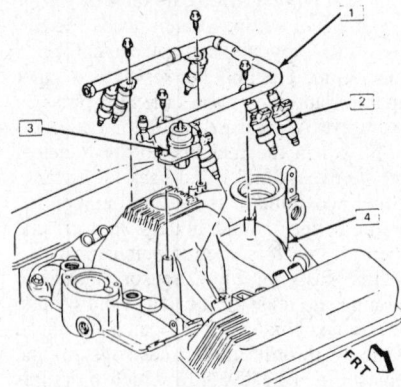

1. Fuel rail assembly
2. Injector
3. Pressure regulator
4. Intake manifold

Fuel rail and injector assembly on 3.8L V6 turbo engine

4. Separate the injector from the fuel rail.

5. Installation is the reverse of removal. Replace the O-rings when installing injectors into intake manifold.

FUEL PRESSURE REGULATOR REMOVAL & INSTALLATION

1. Relieve fuel system pressure.

2. Remove pressure regulator from fuel rail. Place a rag around the base of the regulator to catch any spilled fuel.

3. Installation is the reverse of removal.

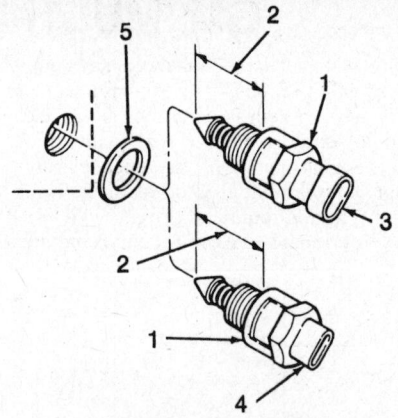

1. Idle air control valve
2. Less than 1⅛ inch (28 mm)
3. Type 1 (with collar)
4. Type 2 (without collar)
5. Gasket

Idle air control valve installation

IDLE AIR CONTROL VALVE REMOVAL & INSTALLATION

1. Remove electrical connector from idle air control valve.

2. Remove the idle air control valve using a suitable wrench.

3. Installation is the reverse of removal. Before installing the idle air control valve, measure the distance that the valve is extended. Measurement should be made from the motor housing to the end of the cone. The distance should not exceed 1⅛ inches, or damage to the valve may occur when installed. Use a new gasket and turn the ignition on then off again to allow the ECM to reset the idle air control valve.

NOTE: Identify replacement IAC valve as being either Type 1 (with collar at electric terminal end) or Type 2 (without collar). If measuring distance is greater than specified above, proceed as follows:

Type 1: Press on valve firmly to retract it.

Type 2: Compress retaining spring from valve while turning valve in with a clockwise motion. Return spring to original position with straight portion of spring end aligned with flat surface of valve.

FORD ELECTRONIC FUEL INJECTION

Rear Wheel Drive Models

The Ford electronic fuel injection system is used on the 1981 Ford/Mercury, the 1980 and later Lincoln Continental/Continental Mark VI, the 1982 and later Lincoln Town Car/Continental Mark VI, Grand Marquis and Crown Victoria. It is a throttle body injection system in which two fuel injectors are mounted in a common throttle body, spraying fuel down through the throttle

valves at the bottom of the body and into the intake manifold.

OPERATION

Fuel is supplied from the fuel tank by a high pressure, in-tank fuel pump. The fuel passes through a filter and is sent to the throttle body where a regulator keeps the fuel delivery pressure at a constant 39 psi. The two fuel injectors are mounted vertically above the throttle plates and are connected in line with the fuel pressure regulator. Excess fuel supplied by the pump, but not needed by the engine, is returned to the fuel tank by a steel fuel return line.

The fuel injection system is linked with and controlled by the Electronic Engine Control III (EEC III) system, a description of which is contained in the Emission Control Unit Repair Section.

COMPONENT DESCRIPTION

Air and Fuel Control

The throttle body assembly is comprised of

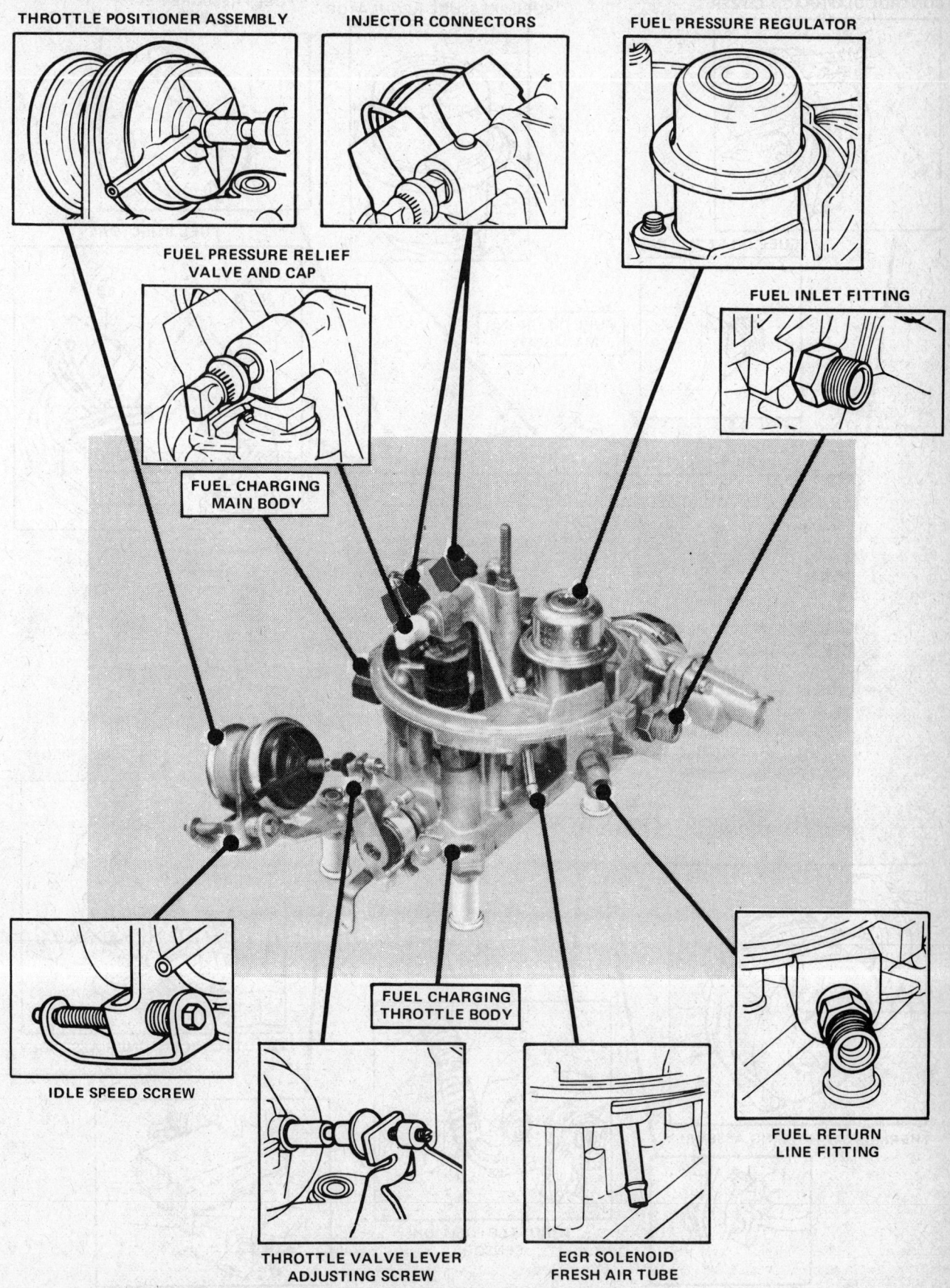

THROTTLE POSITIONER ASSEMBLY

INJECTOR CONNECTORS

FUEL PRESSURE REGULATOR

FUEL PRESSURE RELIEF VALVE AND CAP

FUEL INLET FITTING

FUEL CHARGING MAIN BODY

IDLE SPEED SCREW

FUEL CHARGING THROTTLE BODY

THROTTLE VALVE LEVER ADJUSTING SCREW

EGR SOLENOID FRESH AIR TUBE

FUEL RETURN LINE FITTING

Electronic Fuel Injection (EFI) (2 pictures)

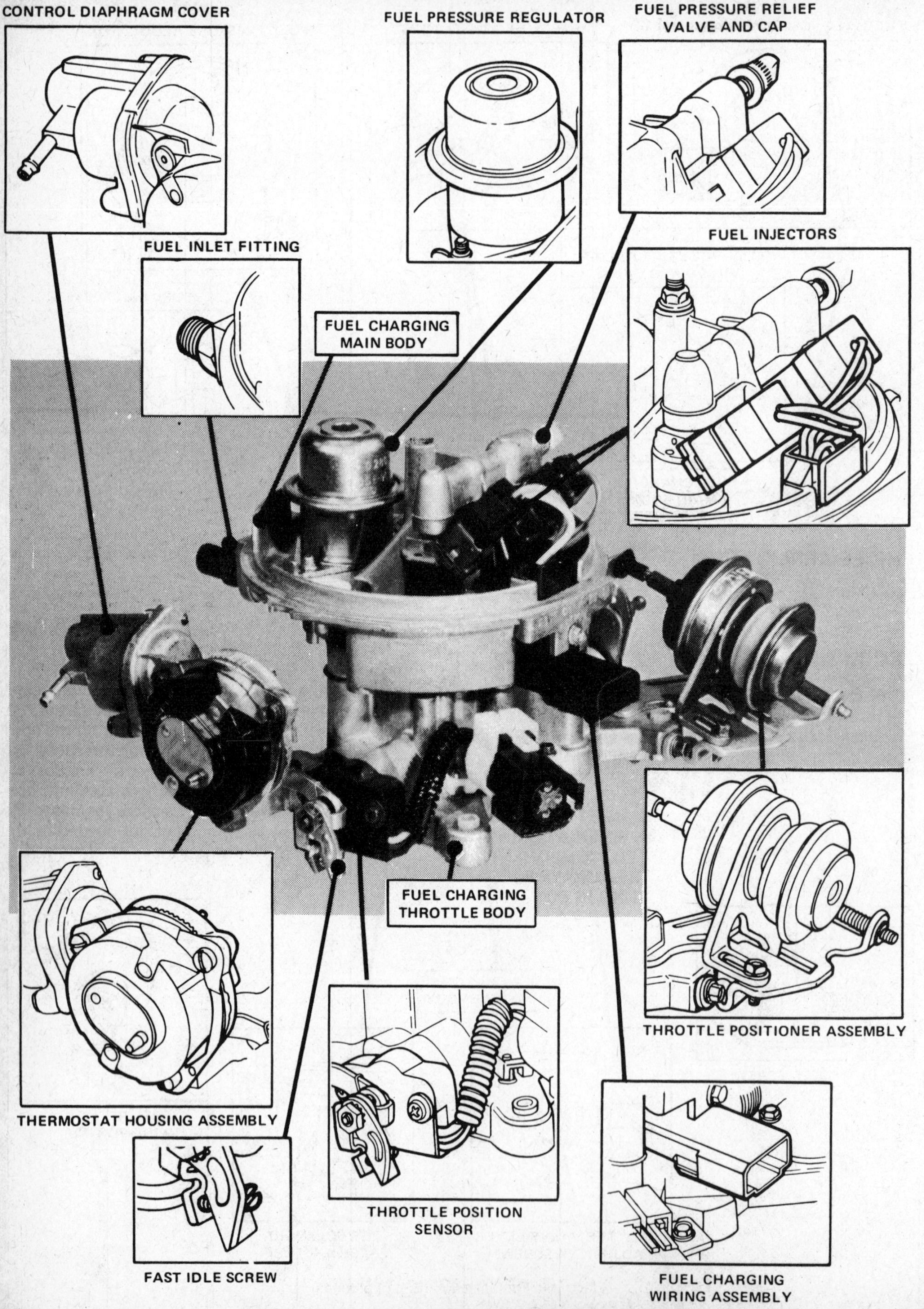

CONTROL DIAPHRAGM COVER

FUEL PRESSURE REGULATOR

FUEL PRESSURE RELIEF
VALVE AND CAP

FUEL INLET FITTING

FUEL INJECTORS

FUEL CHARGING
MAIN BODY

FUEL CHARGING
THROTTLE BODY

THROTTLE POSITIONER ASSEMBLY

THERMOSTAT HOUSING ASSEMBLY

THROTTLE POSITION
SENSOR

FAST IDLE SCREW

FUEL CHARGING
WIRING ASSEMBLY

six individual components which perform the job of mixing the air and fuel to the ideal ratio for controlling exhaust emissions and providing performance and economy. The six components are: air control, fuel injector nozzles, fuel pressure regulator, fuel pressure diagnostic valve, cold engine speed control, and throttle position sensor.

Air Control

Air flow to the engine is controlled by two butterfly valves mounted in a two piece, die-cast aluminum housing called the throttle body. The butterfly valves, or throttle valves, are identical in design to the throttle plates of a conventional carburetor and are

actuated by a similar linkage and pedal cable arrangement.

Fuel Injector Nozzles

The fuel injector nozzles are mounted in the throttle body and are electro-mechanical devices which meter and atomize the fuel

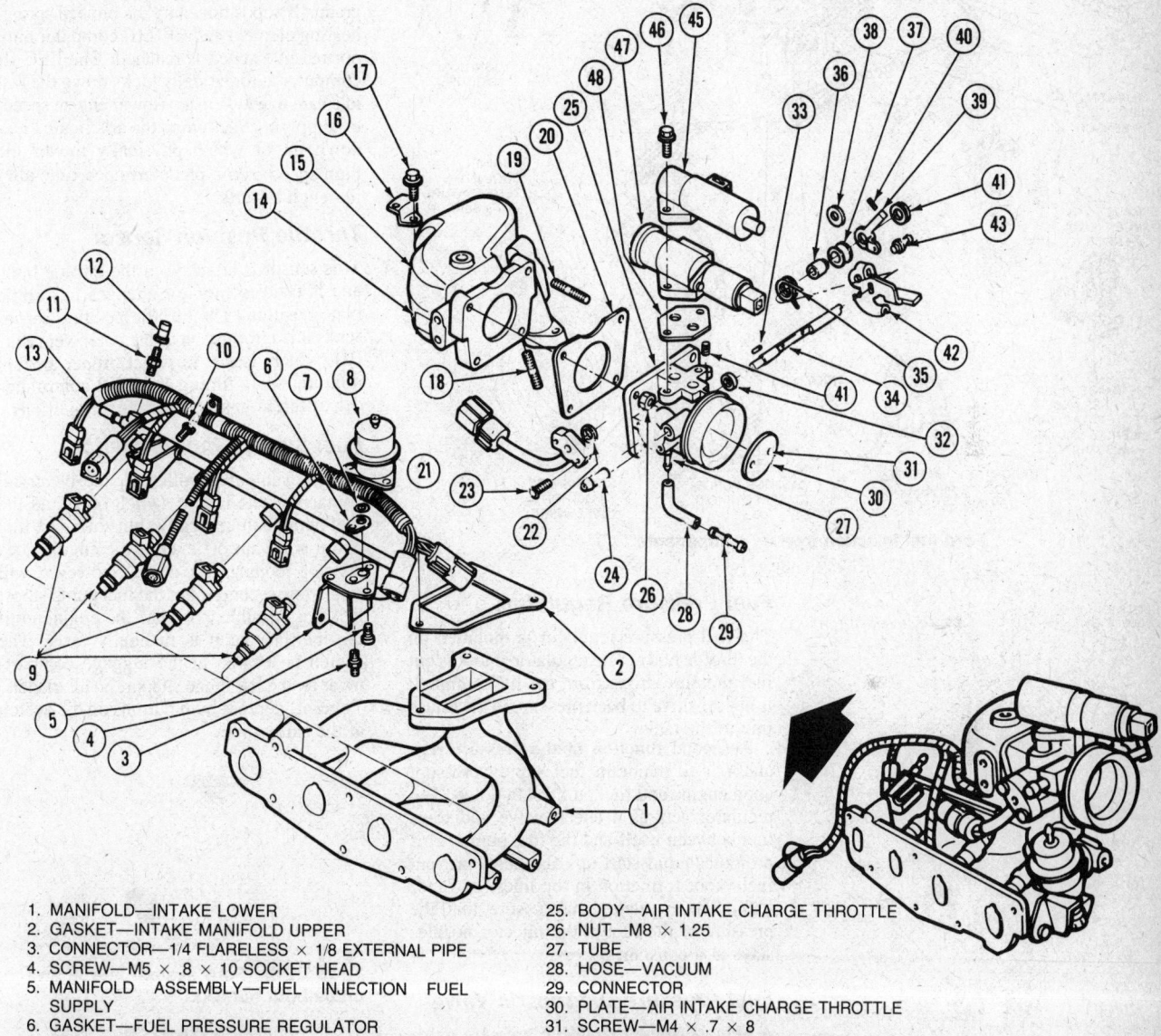

1. MANIFOLD—INTAKE LOWER
2. GASKET—INTAKE MANIFOLD UPPER
3. CONNECTOR—1/4 FLARELESS × 1/8 EXTERNAL PIPE
4. SCREW—M5 × .8 × 10 SOCKET HEAD
5. MANIFOLD ASSEMBLY—FUEL INJECTION FUEL SUPPLY
6. GASKET—FUEL PRESSURE REGULATOR
7. SEAL—5/16 × .070 "O" RING
8. REGULATOR ASSEMBLY—FUEL PRESSURE
9. INJECTOR ASSEMBLY—FUEL
10. BOLT—M8 × 1.25 × 20 HEX FLANGE HEAD
11. VALVE ASSEMBLY—FUEL PRESSURE RELIEF
12. CAP—FUEL PRESSURE RELIEF
13. WIRING HARNESS—FUEL CHARGING
14. DECAL—CARBURETOR IDENTIFICATION
15. MANIFOLD—INTAKE UPPER
16. RETAINER—WIRING HARNESS
17. BOLT—M8 × 1.25 × 30 HEX FLANGE HEAD
18. STUD—M6 × 1.0 × 1.0 × 40
19. STUD—M8 × 1.25 × 1.25 × 47.5
20. GASKET—AIR INTAKE CHARGE TO INTAKE MANIFOLD
21. POTENTIOMETER—THROTTLE POSITION
22. BUSHING—CARBURETOR THROTTLE SHAFT
23. SCREW AND WASHER ASSEMBLY M4 × 22
24. TUBE—EMISSION INLET

25. BODY—AIR INTAKE CHARGE THROTTLE
26. NUT—M8 × 1.25
27. TUBE
28. HOSE—VACUUM
29. CONNECTOR
30. PLATE—AIR INTAKE CHARGE THROTTLE
31. SCREW—M4 × .7 × 8
32. SEAL—THROTTLE CONTROL SHAFT
33. PIN—SPRING COILED 1/16 × .42
34. SHAFT
35. SPRING—THROTTLE RETURN
36. BUSHING—ACCELERATOR PUMP OVERTRAVEL SPRING
37. BEARING—THROTTLE CONTROL LINKAGE
38. SPACER—THROTTLE CONTROL TORSION SPRING (MTX ONLY)
39. LEVER—CARBURETOR TRANSMISSION LINKAGE
40. SCREW—M5 × .8 × 16.25 SLOT HEAD
41. SPACER—CARBURETOR THROTTLE SHAFT
42. LEVER—CARBURETOR THROTTLE
43. BALL—CARBURETOR THROTTLE LEVER
44. VALVE ASSEMBLY—THROTTLE AIR BYPASS (ALT)
45. BOLT—M6 × 1.0 × 20 HEX FLANGE HEAD
46. VALVE ASSEMBLY—THROTTLE AIR BYPASS
47. GASKET—AIR BYPASS VALVE

Electronic Fuel Injection—exploded view

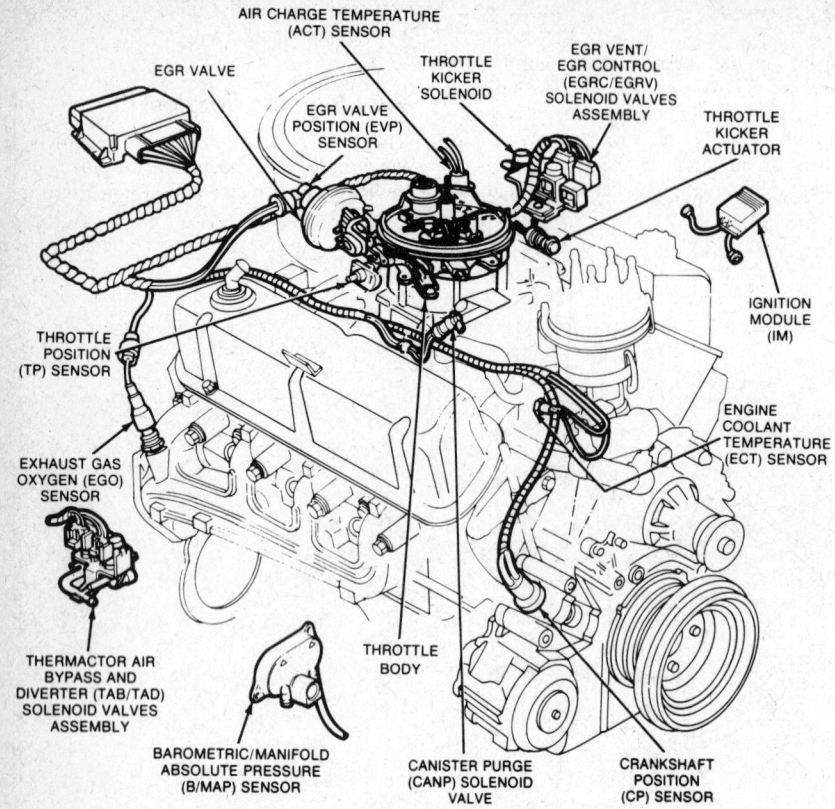

Ford fuel injection system components

AIR CHARGE TEMPERATURE (ACT) SENSOR
EGR VALVE
THROTTLE KICKER SOLENOID
EGR VALVE POSITION (EVP) SENSOR
EGR VENT/ EGR CONTROL (EGRC/EGRV) SOLENOID VALVES ASSEMBLY
THROTTLE KICKER ACTUATOR
IGNITION MODULE (IM)
THROTTLE POSITION (TP) SENSOR
ENGINE COOLANT TEMPERATURE (ECT) SENSOR
EXHAUST GAS OXYGEN (EGO) SENSOR
THERMACTOR AIR BYPASS AND DIVERTER (TAB/TAD) SOLENOID VALVES ASSEMBLY
THROTTLE BODY
BAROMETRIC/MANIFOLD ABSOLUTE PRESSURE (B/MAP) SENSOR
CANISTER PURGE (CANP) SOLENOID VALVE
CRANKSHAFT POSITION (CP) SENSOR

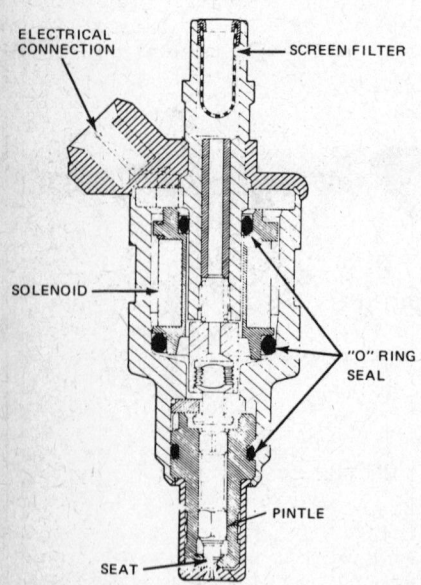

ELECTRICAL CONNECTION
SCREEN FILTER
SOLENOID
"O" RING SEAL
PINTLE
SEAT

Cross section of Ford electrically operated fuel injector

delivered to the engine. The injector valve bodies consist of a solenoid actuated pintle and needle valve assembly. An electrical control signal from the EEC III electronic processor activates the solenoid causing the pintle to move inward off its seat and allowing fuel to flow. The fuel flow through the injector is controlled by the amount of time the injector solenoid holds the pintle off its seat.

Fuel Pressure Regulator

The fuel pressure regulator is mounted on the throttle body. The regulator smooths out fuel pressure drops from the fuel pump. It is not sensitive to back pressure in the return line to the tank.

A second function of the pressure regulator is to maintain fuel supply pressure upon engine and fuel pump shut down. The regulator acts as a check valve and traps fuel between itself and the fuel pump. This promotes rapid start ups and helps prevent fuel vapor formation in the lines, or vapor lock. The regulator makes sure that the pressure of the fuel at the injector nozzles stays at a constant 39 psi.

Fuel Pressure Diagnostic Valve

A Schrader-type diagnostic pressure valve is located at the top of the throttle body. This valve can be used by service personnel to monitor fuel pressure, bleed down the system pressure prior to maintenance and to bleed out air which may have been introduced during assembly or filter servicing. A special Ford tool (T80L-9974-A) is used to accomplish these procedures.

─────── CAUTION ───────
Under no circumstances should compressed air be forced into the fuel system using the diagnostic valve.

Cold Engine Speed Control

The cold engine speed control serves the

same purpose as the fast idle speed device on a carbureted engine, which is to raise engine speed during cold engine idle. A throttle stop cam positioner is used. The cam is positioned by a bimetal spring and an electric heating element. The cold engine speed control is attached to the throttle body. As the engine heats up, the fast idle cam on the cold engine speed control is gradually repositioned by the bimetal spring, heating element and EEC III computer until normal idle speed is reached. The EEC III computer automatically kicks down the fast idle cam to a lower step (lower engine speed) by supplying vacuum to the automatic kickdown motor which physically moves the high speed cam a predetermined time after the engine starts.

Throttle Position Sensor

This sensor is attached to the throttle body and is used to monitor changes in throttle plate position. The throttle position sensor sends this information to the computer (EEC III), which uses it to select proper air/fuel mixture, spark timing and EGR control under different engine operating conditions.

Fuel System Inertia Switch

In the event of a collision, the electrical contacts in the inertia switch open and the fuel pump automatically shuts off. The fuel pump will shut off even if the engine does not stop running. The engine, however, will stop a few seconds after the fuel pump stops. It is not possible to restart the engine until the inertia switch is manually reset. The switch is located in the luggage compartment on the left hinge support on all models. To reset, depress both buttons on the switch at the same time.

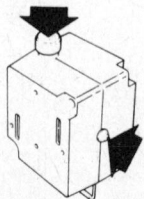

To reset the Ford system inertia switch, press both buttons

─────── CAUTION ───────
Do not reset the inertia switch until the complete fuel system has been inspected for leaks.

Ford EFI Service (Rear Wheel Drive)

FUEL CHARGING ASSEMBLY REMOVAL & INSTALLATION

1. Remove the air cleaner.
2. Release the pressure from the fuel

system at the diagnostic valve using Tool T80L-9974-A or its equivalent.

3. Disconnect the throttle cable and transmission throttle valve lever.

4. Disconnect the fuel, vacuum and electrical connections. Use care to prevent combustion of spilled fuel.

5. Remove the fuel charging assembly retaining nuts then remove the fuel charging assembly.

6. Remove the mounting gasket from the intake manifold.

7. Installation is the reverse of removal. Tighten the fuel charging assembly nuts to 120 inch lb.

THROTTLE BODY DISASSEMBLY/ASSEMBLY

1. Remove the air cleaner mounting stud in order to separate the upper body from the throttle body.

2. Turn the fuel charging assembly (Throttle Body) over and remove the four screws from the bottom of the throttle body.

3. Separate the throttle body (lower half) from the main body (upper half).

4. Remove the old gasket. If stuck and scraping is necessary, use only a plastic or dull scraper. Take care not to damage gasket surfaces.

5. Remove the three pressure regulator mounting screws. Remove the pressure regulator.

6. Disconnect the electrical connectors at each injector by pulling outward on the connector and not on the wire. Loosen but do not remove the wiring harness retaining screw. Push in on the harness tabs to remove from the upper body.

7. Remove the fuel injector retaining screw. Remove the injector retainer.

8. Pull the injectors, one at a time, from the upper body. Mark the injectors for identification, they must be reinstalled in the same position (choke or throttle side). Each injector is equipped with a small O-ring. If the O-ring does not come out with the injector, carefully pick out of body.

9. Remove the fuel diagnostic valve assembly.

10. Remove the choke cover by drilling the retaining rivets. A 1/8 in. or No. 30 drill is required. A choke mounting kit for reinstallation is available from Ford.

11. Remove the choke cap retaining ring, choke cap and gasket. Remove the thermostat lever screw and lever. Remove the fast idle cam assembly and control rod positioner.

12. Hold the control diaphragm cover in position and remove the two mounting screws. Carefully remove the cover, spring and pull down diaphragm.

13. Remove the fast idle retaining nut, fast idle cam adjuster lever, fast idle lever and E-clip.

14. Remove the potentionmeter (sensor) connector bracket retaining screw. Mark the throttle body and throttle position sensor for correct reinstallation position. Remove

the throttle sensor retaining screws and slide the sensor off of the throttle shaft. Remove the throttle positioner retaining screw and remove the throttle positioner.

15. Perform any necessary cleaning or repair.

16. Assemble the upper body by first installing the fuel diagnostic fuel pressure valve assembly.

17. Lubricate the new injector O-rings with a light grade oil. Install the O-rings on each injector. Install the injectors in their appropriate choke or throttle side position. Use a light, twisting, pushing motion to install the injectors.

18. Install the injector retainer and tighten the retaining screw to 30-60 inch lbs.

19. Install the injector wiring harness and snap into position. Tighten the harness retaining screw to 8-10 inch lbs.

20. Snap the electrical connectors into position on the injectors. Lubricate the fuel pressure regulator O-ring with light oil. Install the O-ring and new gasket on the regulator, install the regulator and tighten retaining screws to 27-40 inch lbs.

21. Install the throttle positioner onto the throttle body. Tighten the retaining screw to 32-44 inch lbs.

22. Hold the throttle sensor (potentiometer) with the location identification mark (see step 14) in the 12 o'clock position. The two rotary tangs should be at 3 o'clock and 9 o'clock positions.

23. Slide the sensor onto the throttle shaft with the identification mark still in the 12 o'clock position. Hold the sensor firmly against the throttle body.

24. Rotate the sensor until the identification marks on the sensor and body are aligned. Install the retaining screws and tighten to 13-18 inch lbs.

25. Install the sensor wiring harness bracket retaining screw, tighten to 18-22 inch lbs. Install the E-clip, fast idle lever, fast idle adjustment lever and fast idle retaining nut. Tighten the retaining nut to 16-20 inch lbs.

26. Install the pull down diaphragm, spring and cover. Hold the cover in position and tighten the retaining screws to 13-19 inch lbs.

27. Install the fast idle control rod positioner, fast idle cam and the thermostat lever. Tighten the retaining screw to 13-19 inch lbs.

28. Install the choke cap gasket, bi-metal spring, cap and retaining ring. Install new rivets and snug them with the rivet gun. Do not break rivets, loosely install so choke cover can rotate. Index choke and break rivets to tighten.

29. Install the gasket between the main body and the throttle body. Place the throttle body in position. Install the four retaining screws loosely. Install the air cleaner stud and tighten to 70-95 inch lbs. Tighten the four retaining screws.

30. The rest of the assembly is in the reverse order of disassembly.

Front Wheel Drive Models

The Electronic Fuel Injector System (EFI) is classified as a multi-point, pulse time, mass air flow fuel injection system. Fuel is metered into the intake air steam in accordance with engine demand through four injectors mounted on a tuned intake manifold.

An on board vehicle electronic engine control (EEC) computer accepts inputs from various engine sensors to compute the required fuel flow rate necessary to maintain a prescribed air/fuel ration throughout the entire engine operational range. The computer then outputs a command to the fuel injectors to meter the approximate quantity of fuel.

OPERATION

The fuel delivery sub-system consists of a high pressure, chassis mounted, electric fuel pump delivering fuel from the fuel tank through a 20 micron fuel filter to a fuel charging manifold assembly.

The fuel charging manifold assembly incorporates electrically actuated fuel injectors directly above each of the engine's four intake ports. The injectors, when energized, spray a metered quantity of fuel into the intake air stream.

A constant fuel pressure drop is maintained across the injector nozzles by a pressure regulator. The regulator is connected in series with the fuel injectors and positioned down stream from them. Excess fuel supplied by the pump, but not required by the engine, passes through the regulator and returns to the fuel tank through a fuel return line.

All injectors are energized simultaneously, once every crankshaft revolution. The period of time that the injectors are energized (injector "on time" or the pulse width) is controlled by the vehicles' Engine Electronic Control (EEC) computer. Air entering the engine is measured by a vane air flow meter located between the air cleaner and the fuel charging manifold assembly. This air flow information and input from various other engine sensors is used to compute the required fuel flow rate necessary to maintain a prescribed air/fuel ratio for the given engine operation. The computer determines the needed injector pulse width and outputs a command to the injector to meter the exact quantity of fuel.

COMPONENT DESCRIPTION

Fuel Injectors

The four fuel injector nozzles are electromechanical devices which both meter and atomize fuel delivered to the engine. The injectors are mounted in the lower intake manifold and are positioned so that their tips are directing fuel just ahead of the engine intake valves. The injector bodies consist of a solenoid actuated pintle and needle valve assembly. An electrical control signal from the Electronic Engine Control unit activates the injector solenoid causing the pintle to move inward off the seat, allowing fuel to flow. Since the injector flow orifice is fixed and the fuel pressure drop across the injector tip is constant, fuel flow to the engine is regulated by how long the solenoid is energized. Atomization is obtained by contouring the pintle at the point where the fuel separates.

Fuel Pressure Regulator

The fuel pressure regulator is attached to the fuel supply manifold assembly downstream of the fuel injectors. It regulates the fuel pressure supplied to the injectors. The regulator is a diaphragm operated relief valve in which one side of the diaphragm senses fuel pressure and the other side is subjected to intake manifold pressure. The nominal fuel pressure is established by a spring preload applied to the diaphragm. Balancing one side of the diaphragm with manifold pressure maintains a constant fuel pressure drop across the injectors. Fuel, in excess of that used by the engine, is bypassed through the regulator and returns to the fuel tank.

Air Vane Meter Assembly

The air vane meter assembly is located between the air cleaner and the throttle body and is mounted on a bracket near the LH shock tower. The vane air meter contains two sensors which furnish input to the Electronic Control Assembly—a vane airflow sensor and a vane air temperature. The air vane meter measures the mass of air flow to the engine. Air flow through the body moves a vane mounted on a pivot pin. This vane is connected to a variable resistor (potentiometer) which in turn is connected to a 5 volt reference voltage. The output of this potentiometer varies depending on the volume of air flowing through the sensor. The temperature sensor in the air vane meter measures the incoming air temperature. These two inputs, air volume and temperature, are used by the Electronic Control Assembly to compute the mass air flow. This valve is then used to compute the fuel flow necessary for the optimum air/fuel ratio which is fed to the injectors.

Air Throttle Body Assembly

The throttle body assembly controls air flow to the engine through a single butterfly-type valve. The throttle position is controlled by conventional cable/cam throttle linkage. The body is a single piece die casting made of aluminum. It has a single bore with an air bypass channel around the throttle plate. This bypass channel controls both cold and warm engine idle airflow control as regulated by an air bypass valve assembly mounted directly to the throttle body. The valve assembly is an electromechanical device controlled by the EEC computer. It

incorporates a linear actuator which positions a variable area metering valve.

Other features of the air throttle body assembly include:

- An adjustment screw to set the throttle plate at a minimum idle airflow position.
- A preset stop to locate the WOT position.
- A throttle body mounted throttle position sensor.
- A PCV fresh air source located upstream of the throttle plate.
- Individual ported vacuum taps (as required) for PCV and EVAP control signals.

Fuel Supply Manifold Assembly

The fuel supply manifold assembly is the component that delivers high pressure fuel from the vehicle fuel supply line to the four fuel injectors. The assembly consists of a single preformed tube or stamping with four injector connectors, a mounting flange for the fuel pressure regulator, a pressure relief valve for diagnositic testing or field service fuel system pressure bleed down and mounting attachments which locate the fuel manifold assembly and providde fuel injector retention.

Air Intake Manifold

The air intake manifold is a two piece (upper and lower intake manifold) aluminum casting. Runner lengths are tuned to optimize engine torque and power output. The manifold provides mounting flanges for the air throttle body assembly, fuel supply manifold and accelerator control bracketry and the EGR valve and supply tube. Vacuum taps are provided to support various engine accessories. Pockets for the fuel injectors are machined to prevent both air and fuel leakage. The pockets, in which the injectors are mounted, are placed to direct the injector fuel spray immediately in front of each engine intake valve.

Ford EFI Service (Front Wheel Drive)

FUEL CHARGING ASSEMBLY

NOTE: If any of the sub-assemblies are to be serviced and/or removed, with the fuel charging assembly mounted to the engine, the following steps must be taken.

1. Make sure the ignition key is in the off position.
2. Drain the coolant from the radiator.
3. Disconnect the negative battery cable.
4. Remove the fuel cap to relieve fuel tank pressure.
5. Relieve the pressure from the fuel system at the pressure relief valve. Special tool T80L-9974-A or its equal is needed for this procedure.
6. Disconnect the fuel supply line.
7. Identify and disconnect the fuel re-

turn lines and vacuum connections.
8. Disconnect the injector wiring harness by disconnecting the ECT sensor in the heater supply tube, under the lower intake manifold.
9. Disconnect the air by-pass connector from EEC harness.

NOTE: Not all assemblies may be serviceable while on the engine. In some cases, removal of the fuel charging assembly may facilitate service of the various sub-assemblies. To remove the entire fuel charging assembly, the following should be observed.

REMOVAL & INSTALLATION

1. Remove the engine air cleaner outlet tube between the vane air meter and air throttle body by loosening two clamps.
2. Disconnect and remove the accelerator and speed control cables (if so equipped) from the accelerator mounting bracket and throttle lever.
3. Disconnect the top manifold vacuum fitting connections by disconnecting:
    a. Rear vacuum line to the dash panel vacuum tree.
    b. Front vacuum line to the air cleaner and fuel pressure regulator.
4. Disconnect the PCV system by removing the following:
    a. Two large forward facing connectors on the throttle body and intake manifold.
    b. Throttle body port hose at the straight plastic connector.
    c. Canister purge line at the straight plastic connector.
    d. PCV hose at the valve cover.
    e. Unbolt the PCV separator support bracket from cylinder head and remove PCV system.
5. Disconnect the EGR vacuum line at the EGR valve.
6. Disconnect the EGR tube from the upper intake manifold by removing the two flange nuts.
7. Remove the dipstick and its tube.
8. Remove the fuel return line.
9. Remove six manifold mounting nuts.
10. Remove the manifold with wiring harness and gasket.
11. Installation is the reverse of removal. Tighten the manifold bolts 12-15 ft. lbs.

FUEL PRESSURE REGULATOR REMOVAL & INSTALLATION

NOTE: Before attempting this procedure depressurize the fuel system.

1. Remove the vacuum line at the pressure regulator.
2. Remove the three Allen retaining screws from the regulator housing.
3. Remove the pressure regulator, gasket and O-ring. Discard gasket and inspect O-ring for deterioration.

NOTE: If scraping is necessary be careful not to damage the gasket surface.

4. Installation is the reverse of removal. Lubricate the O-ring with light oil prior to installation. Tighten the three screws 27-40 inch lbs.

FUEL INJECTOR MANIFOLD ASSEMBLY REMOVAL & INSTALLATION

1. Remove the fuel tank cap. Release the pressure from the fuel system.
2. Disconnect the fuel supply and return lines.
3. Disconnect the wiring harness from the injectors.
4. Disconnect the vacuum line from the fuel pressure regulator valve.
5. Remove the two fuel injector manifold retaining bolts.
6. Carefully disengage the manifold from the fuel injectors. Remove the manifold.
7. Installation is the reverse of removal. Torque the fuel manifold bolts 15-22 ft. lbs.

PRESSURE RELIEF VALVE REMOVAL & INSTALLATION

1. If the fuel charging assembly is mounted to engine, the fuel system must be depressurized.
2. Using an open end wrench or suitable deep well socket, remove the pressure relief valve from the injection manifold.
3. Installation is the reverse of removal. Torque the valve 48-84 inch lbs.

THROTTLE POSITION SENSOR REMOVAL & INSTALLATION

1. Disconnect the throttle position sensor from the wiring harness.
2. Remove the two retaining screws.
3. Remove the throttle position sensor.
4. Installation is the reverse of removal. Torque the sensor screws 11-16 inch lbs.

NOTE: This throttle position sensor is not adjustable.

AIR BYPASS VALVE ASSEMBLY REMOVAL & INSTALLATION

1. Disconnect the air bypass valve assembly connector from the wiring harness.
2. Remove the two air bypass valve retaining screws.
3. Remove the air bypass valve and gasket.

NOTE: If necessary to remove the gasket by scraping, be careful not to damage the gasket surface.

4. Installation is the reverse of removal. Torque the air bypass valve assembly 71-102 inch lbs.

AIR INTAKE THROTTLE BODY REMOVAL & INSTALLATION

1. Remove four throttle body nuts. Make sure that the throttle position sensor connector and air by-pass valve connector have been disconnected from the harness. Disconnect air cleaner outlet tube.
2. Identify and disconnect vacuum hoses.
3. Remove throttle bracket.
4. Carefully separate the throttle body from the upper intake manifold.
5. Remove and discard the gasket between the throttle body and the upper intake manifold.

NOTE: If scraping is necessary be careful not to damage gasket surfaces, or allow any material to drop into the manifold.

6. Installation is the reverse of removal. Tighten the throttle body to upper intake manifold nuts 12-15 ft. lbs.

UPPER INTAKE MANIFOLD REMOVAL & INSTALLATION

1. Disconnect the air cleaner outlet tube from the air intake throttle body.
2. Unplug the throttle position sensor from the wiring harness.
3. Unplug the air by-pass valve connector.
4. Remove three upper manifold retaining bolts.
5. Remove upper manifold assembly.
6. Remove and discard the gasket from the lower manifold assembly.

NOTE: If scraping is necessary be careful not to damage gasket surfaces, or allow any material to drop into the lower manifold.

7. Installation is the reverse of removal. Tighten the upper intake manifold bolts 15-22 ft. lbs. Use a new gasket between the manifolds.

FUEL INJECTOR REMOVAL & INSTALLATION

NOTE: The fuel system must be depressurized prior to starting this procedure.

1. Disconnect the fuel supply and return lines.
2. Remove the vacuum line from the fuel pressure regulator.
3. Disconnect the wiring harness.
4. Remove the fuel injector manifold assembly.
5. Carefully remove the connectors from the individual injectors.
6. Grasping the injectors body, pull up while gently rocking the injector from side to side.
7. Inspect the injector O-rings (two per injector) for signs of deterioration. Replace as needed.
8. Inspect the injector ''plastic hat'' (covering the injector pintle) and washer for signs of deterioration. Replace as needed. If a hat is missing, look for it in the intake manifold.
9. Installation is the reverse of removal. Lubricate all O-rings with a light oil. Carefully seat the fuel injector manifold assembly on the four injectors and secure the manifold with the attaching bolts. Torque the bolts 15-22 ft. lbs.

VANE AIR METER REMOVAL & INSTALLATION

1. Loosen the hose clamp which secures engine air cleaner outlet hose to the vane meter assembly.
2. Remove air intake and outlet tube from the air cleaner.
3. Disengage four spring clamps and remove air cleaner front cover and air cleaner filter panel.
4. Remove the two screw and washer assemblies which secure the air meter to its bracket. Remove the vane air meter assembly.
5. Installation is the reverse of removal.

FORD ELECTRONIC FUEL INJECTION TROUBLESHOOTING

Symptom	Possible Problem Areas
Surging, backfire, misfire, runs rough	1. EEC distributor rotor registry① 2. EGR solenoid(s) defective 3. Distributor, cap, body, rotor, ignition wires, plugs, coil defective 4. Pulse ring behind vibration damper misaligned or damaged 5. Spark plug fouling
Stalls on deceleration	1. EGR solenoid(s) or valve defective 2. EEC distributor rotor registry①

FORD ELECTRONIC FUEL INJECTION TROUBLESHOOTING

Symptom	Possible Problem Areas
Stalls at idle	1. Idle speed wrong 2. Throttle kicker not working
Hesitates on acceleration	1. Acceleration enrichment system defective 2. Fuel pump ballast bypass relay not working
Fuel pump noisy	1. Fuel pump ballast bypass relay not working
Engine won't start	1. Fuel pump power relay defective, no spark, EGR system defective, no or low fuel pressure 2. Crankshaft position sensor not seated, clearance wrong, defective 3. Pulse ring behind vibration damper misaligned, sensor tabs damaged 4. Power and ground wires open or shorted, poor electrical connections 5. Inertia switch tripped
Engine starts and stalls or runs rough	1. Fuel pump ballast wire defective 2. Manifold absolute pressure (MAP) sensor circuit not working 3. Low fuel pressure 4. EGR system problem 5. Microprocessor and calibration assembly faulty
Starts hard when cold	1. Cranking signal circuit faulty

① See Ford Electronic Engine Control (EEC) in the Emission Control Unit Repair Section for adjustment procedures.

CHRYSLER ELECTRONIC FUEL INJECTION

1981-83 Imperial

The Chrysler Electronic Fuel Injection (EFI) system is used on the 1981-83 Imperial exclusively. The system is broken down into three parts; the Fuel Hydraulic System, the Air Induction System, and the Fuel, Air and Ignition Command System.

FUEL HYDRAULIC SYSTEM

The fuel hydraulic system includes all parts of the EFI system which are in physical contact with the fuel. Together they form the fuel flow path from the fuel tank to the fuel injection assembly and back again. The fuel hydraulic system is divided into two subsystems; the fuel supply subsystem and

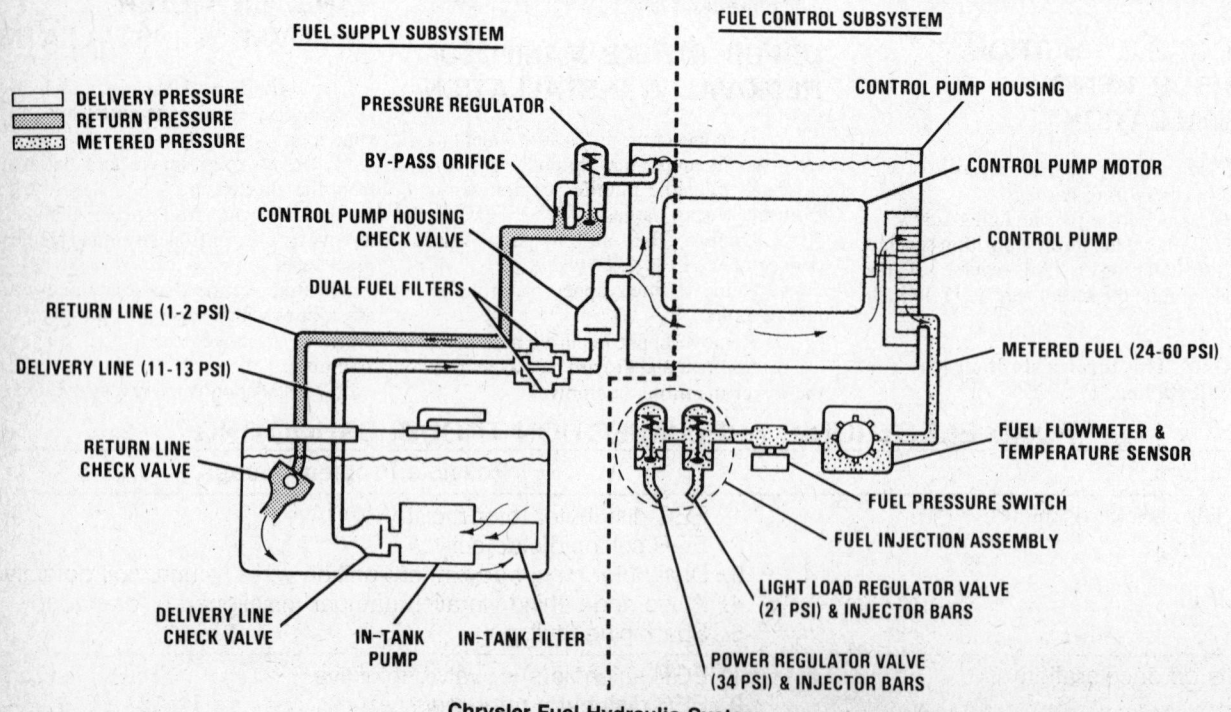

Chrysler Fuel Hydraulic System

the fuel control subsystem.

Fuel Supply Subsystem

This system is composed of the in-tank fuel pump, the fuel delivery and return lines, a pair of parallel fuel filters, the control pump housing, the pressure regulator and bypass orifice and a pair of check valves.

In operation, the in-tank fuel pump picks up fuel from the fuel tank and delivers it forward through the fuel delivery line and pair of fuel filters until it reaches the control pump housing. The control pump housing serves as a connecting link between the fuel delivery and return lines. It also serves as a fuel reservoir for the control pump and ensures that the pump is always primed with fuel. A check valve in the control housing prevents the fuel from draining back into the lines when the engine is off (in-tank fuel pump not running).

The pressure regulator maintains the desired fuel pressure within the control pump housing by releasing excess fuel into the fuel return line, which carries it back to the fuel tank. The pressure regulator is equipped with a bypass orifice which purges fuel vapors from the control pump housing when the system is shut down. The fuel return line has a check valve which prevents fuel from running backwards out the return line in the event of an accident in which the vehicle rolls over.

Fuel Control Subsystem

The fuel control subsystem consists of the control pump, located in the control pump housing, the fuel flowmeter and temperature sensor, the fuel pressure switch and the fuel injection assembly.

The control pump is a positive displacement pump driven by a variable-speed electric motor. The control pump delivers fuel at high pressure (24-60 psi) through the fuel flowmeter, temperature sensor and fuel pressure switch to the fuel injection assembly.

The fuel flowmeter consists of a cylindrical cavity containing a free-turning vaned wheel. The fuel flowing through the flowmeter causes the wheel to spin at a rate proportionate to fuel flow. As the wheel spins, the vanes interrupt the light path between a light-emitting diode (LED) and a phototransistor. The frequency of the interruptions (pulses) is interpreted as flow rate by the fuel flowmeter module. A temperature sensor is used in conjunction with the fuel flowmeter to monitor fuel temperature. Together, these two sensors relay part of the information needed for precise control of the control pump motor speed.

A fuel pressure switch is located between the fuel flowmeter and the fuel injection assembly which opens when there is sufficient fuel pressure to start or run the engine, and closes when pressure is insufficient. When closed, the fuel pressure switch completes a by-pass circuit which drives the control pump at full speed (with the ignition key in the start position). This pressurizes the fuel control circuit and insures quick starts. It also prevents vapor locks in the control pump. This entire pressurization process is completed within the time it takes the engine to revolve once.

Metered fuel entering the fuel injection assembly is directed to two pressure-regulating valves. Each valve feeds into its own U-shaped fuel injection bar, located over the throttle body assembly. The light load regulator valve opens when fuel pressure reaches or exceeds 21 psi and delivers fuel to the light load injector bar. Four tiny holes in the lower surface of the injector bar spray fuel onto crescent-shaped ridges at the edges of the throttle plates, where the actual fuel-air mixing occurs. Airfoil-shaped nozzles around the injector holes help refine fuel spray patterns and promote fuel atomization. The light load circuit supplies all engine fuel when fuel pressure is between 21 and 34 psi, and some of the requirements beyond these pressures. At pressures above 34 psi (heavy engine loads, starting, etc.) the power regulator valve opens and allows the power fuel injection bar to add its spray pattern to the air/fuel mixing process.

AIR INDUCTION SYSTEM

This system is broken down into two subsystems, the air supply subsystem and the air control subsystem.

Air Supply Subsystem

The air supply subsystem is comprised of the fresh/heated air mixing unit, which provides heated intake air during engine warm-up, the air cleaner assembly and the airflow sensor assembly. The airflow sensor assembly is located inside the inlet duct on the air cleaner and measures engine intake airflow volume. This information is compared with fuel flowmeter information electronically and insures precise air/fuel mixture control.

Air Control Subsystem

The air control subsystem is contained in the throttle body assembly. Major parts include the throttle plate and blade subassembly, a throttle position potentiometer, a closed throttle switch and an automatic idle speed motor.

The throttle plates are similar to those used on a carburetor with the exception of a crescent-shaped ridge on the leading edge of each plate which promotes uniform air/fuel mixing.

The throttle position potentiometer senses the angle of throttle blade opening and sends this information to the combustion

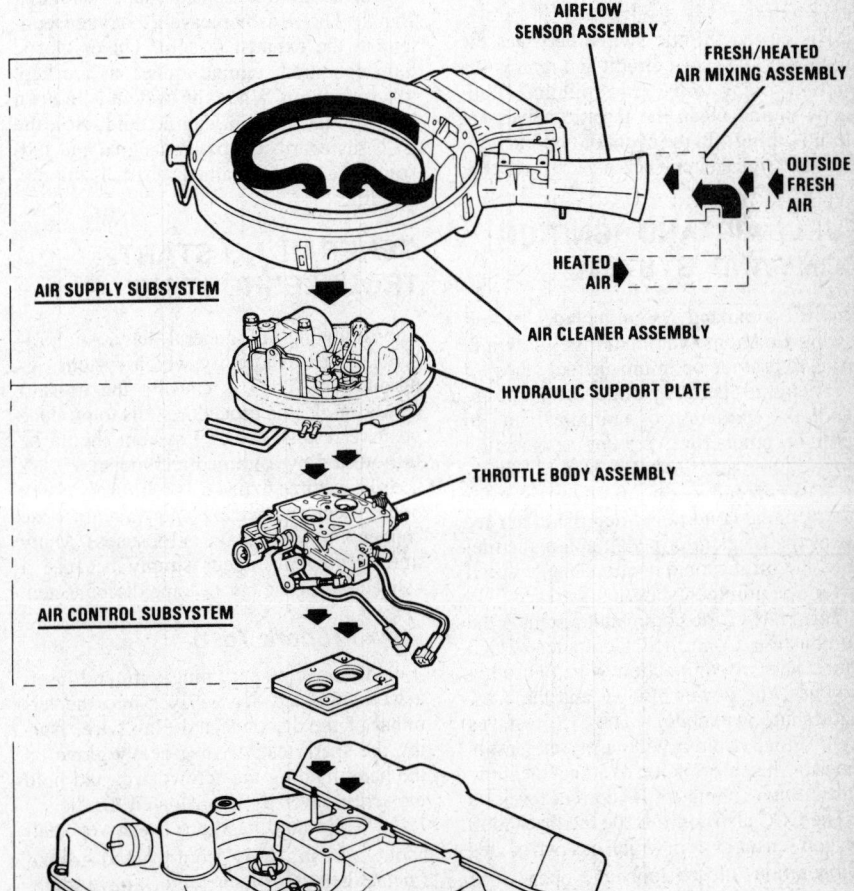

Chrysler Air Induction System

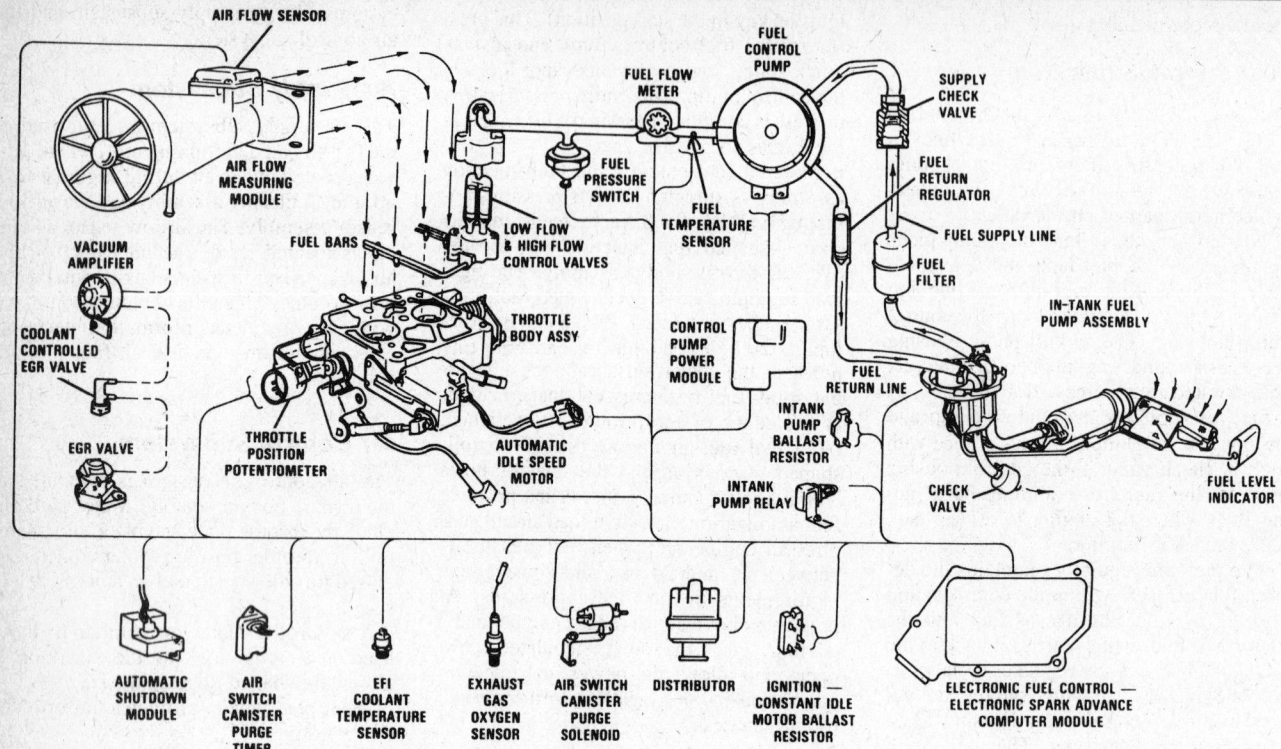

Chrysler Fuel, Air and Ignition Command System

control computer which then adjusts the air/fuel mixture.

The closed throttle switch activates the automatic idle speed circuit and returns the ignition timing to its basic (minimum) advance timing when the throttle valves are closed (idling). In the event of malfunction, the brake signal circuit acts a back-up circuit.

FUEL, AIR AND IGNITION COMMAND SYSTEM

The EFI command system includes the following functions: automatic fuel flow metering to provide optimum air/fuel ratios for every engine operating mode; automatic advance or retardation of ignition timing to optimum points for every engine operating mode; automatic throttle opening adjustment to maintain optimum idling speed for every engine condition when the driver releases the accelerator pedal; automatic fuel flow shut off if certain ignition, engine speed or time requirements are not satisfied.

The heart of the command system is the Combustion Controlled Computer (CCC) which acts in conjunction with two other modules, the power module and the automatic shutdown module. The CCC receives input signals from a wide array of sensors and uses this information to adjust fuel flow and ignition timing to the correct levels.

The CCC also controls the feedback loop oxygen sensor system which has two modes of operation, closed loop and open loop. Under closed loop operation, the CCC receives signals from the oxygen sensor (located in the exhaust gas stream) and adjusts

the air/fuel mixture in accordance with that signal. The sensor measures oxygen content in the exhaust system. Under closed loop operation, engine emissions are kept to a minimum. When the system is in open loop (initial start-up, engine cold, etc), the CCC disregards the oxygen signal and substitutes a pre-progamed air/fuel mixture circuit.

GENERAL NO-START TROUBLESHOOTING

The following is a general diagnostic procedure used to identify which system (ignition, fuel, etc.) is causing the no-start condition. If this procedure fails to produce positive results, the EFI system should be fully tested by a trained technician.

Take the time to make a preliminary check of all electrical wiring and vacuum hose connections for damage or looseness. Many times, problems occur simply because a connector or hose has become disconnected.

Step 1 (Spark Test)

1. Remove a spark plug wire and insert a well insulated screwdriver into the terminal of the disconnected plug wire. During the spark test, wear a heavy glove on the hand holding the screwdriver and hold the screwdriver by its insulated handle.

2. While holding the screwdriver shaft about 3/16 in. away from a good ground (metal alternator bracket, etc.), have someone crank the engine. Make sure no clothing, etc., is in the way of moving engine parts.

3. If there is a good spark between the screwdriver and ground, perform Step 2 (Fuel Flow Test). If there is no spark, the problem is in the ignition system, not in the fuel injection system.

Step 2 (Fuel Flow Test)

1. Remove the air cleaner.

2. Remove the secondary coil wire from the distributor cap and *ground this wire*.

3. Have someone crank the engine while observing the fuel flow from the fuel injection nozzles on the hydraulic support plate.

4. If there is an adequate fuel flow from the nozzles, the fuel system is probably OK. Perform Step 3 (Spark Plug Test). If there is little or no flow from the injection nozzles, or if there seems to be too much flow from the nozzles (along with other indications of flooding) the fuel system is faulty and should be tested by a qualified technician.

Step 3 (Spark Plug Test)

1. Remove the spark plugs and check for plug fouling. Clean or replace as necessary.

2. Attempt to start the engine. If the engine still won't start, the fault could be with incorrect ignition timing. Have the timing checked. If it is not 12° ± 2° BTDC, have it reset to 12° BTDC and attempt to restart.

Chrysler Electronic Fuel Injection (2.2L Engines)

The Electronic Fuel Injection System is a

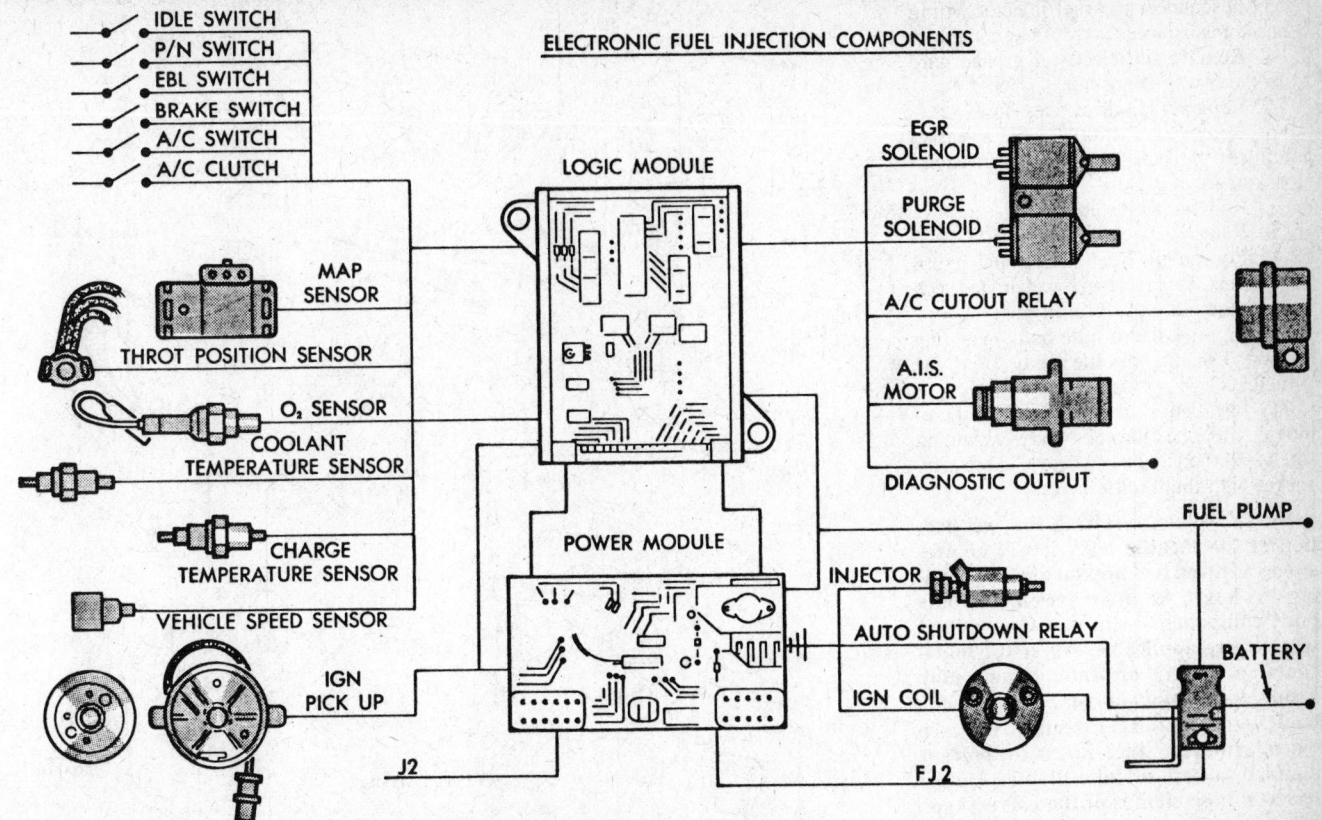

ELECTRONIC FUEL INJECTION COMPONENTS

IDLE SWITCH
P/N SWITCH
EBL SWITCH
BRAKE SWITCH
A/C SWITCH
A/C CLUTCH

LOGIC MODULE

EGR SOLENOID
PURGE SOLENOID
A/C CUTOUT RELAY
A.I.S. MOTOR
DIAGNOSTIC OUTPUT

MAP SENSOR
THROT POSITION SENSOR
O₂ SENSOR
COOLANT TEMPERATURE SENSOR
CHARGE TEMPERATURE SENSOR
VEHICLE SPEED SENSOR
IGN PICK UP

POWER MODULE

INJECTOR
AUTO SHUTDOWN RELAY
IGN COIL

FUEL PUMP
BATTERY

J2
FJ2

Electronic Fuel Injection components

computer regulated single point fuel injection system that provides precise air/fuel ratio for all driving conditions. At the center of this system is a digital pre-programmed computer known as a Logic Module that regulates ignition timing, air/fuel ratio, emission control devices and idle speed. This component has the ability to update and revise its programming to meet changing operating conditions.

Various sensors provide the input necessary for the Logic Module to correctly regulate the fuel flow at the fuel injector. These include the Manifold Absolute Pressure, Throttle Position, Oxygen Feedback, Coolant Temperature, Charge Temperature and Vehicle Speed sensors. In addition to the sensors, various switches also provide important information. These include the Neutral-safety, Heated Back Lite, Air conditioning, Air Conditioning Clutch switches, and an Electronic Idle switch.

All inputs to the Logic Module are converted into signals sent to the Power Module. These signals cause the Power Module to change either the fuel flow at the injector or ignition timing or both.

The Logic Module tests many of its own input and output circuits. If a fault is found in a major system this information is stored in the Logic Module. Information on this fault can be displayed to a technician by means of a flashing light emitting diode (LED) or by connecting a diagnostic read out and reading a numbered display code which directly relates to a specific fault.

POWER MODULE

The Power Module contains the circuits necessary to power the ignition coil and the fuel injector. These are high current devices and their power supply has been isolated to minimize any ''electrical noise'' reaching the Logic Module. The Power Module also energizes the Automatic Shut Down (ASD) Relay which activates the fuel pump, ignition coil, and the Power Module itself. The module also receives a signal from the distributor and sends this signal to the Logic Module. In the event of no distributor signal, the ASD relay is not activated and power is shut off from the fuel pump and ignition coil. The Power Module contains a voltage converter which reduces battery voltage to a regulated 8.0V output. This 8.0V output powers the distributor and also powers the Logic Module.

LOGIC MODULE

The Logic Module is a digital computer containing a microprocessor. The module receives input signals from various switches, sensors, and components. It then computes the fuel injector pulse width, spark advance, ignition coil dwell, Automatic Idle Speed actuation, and purge, and EGR control solenoid cycles.

The Logic Module tests many of its own input and output circuits. If a fault is found in a major system. this information is stored

in the Logic Module. Information on this fault can be displayed to a technician by means of a flashing, light emitting diode (LED) of by connecting a diagnostic read out and reading a numbered display code which directly relates to a specific fault.

Service

FUEL SYSTEM PRESSURE RELEASE

The EFI Fuel system is under a constant pressure of approximately 36 psi. Before servicing the fuel system the pressure must be released.

1. Loosen the gas cap to release tank pressure.
2. Remove the wiring harness connect from an injector.
3. Ground one injector terminal.
4. Connect a jumper wire to the second terminal and touch the battery positive post from no longer than 10 seconds. This releases system pressure.
5. Remove the jumper wires.

THROTTLE BODY REMOVAL & INSTALLATION

1. Release the fuel pressure from the system.
2. Disconnect the negative battery terminal.

3. Disconnect the fuel injector wiring connector and throttle body 6-way connector.

4. Remove the electrical ground wire from the 6-way connector.

5. Remove the air cleaner hose.

6. Remove the throttle cable and if so equipped, the speed control and transmission kickdown cables.

7. Remove the return spring.

8. Remove the vacuum hoses.

9. Loosen the fuel intake and return line clamps. Wrap a shop towel around each hose; twist and pull off each hose.

10. Remove the throttle body mounting screws. Lift the throttle body from the vehicle.

11. Installation is the reverse of removal. Torque throttle body mounting screws 200 inch lbs. Always use a new gasket with the throttle body.

NOTE: When servicing the fuel portion of the throttle body it will be necessary to bleed fuel pressure before opening any hoses. Always reassemble throttle body components with new O-rings and seals where applicable. Never use lubricants on O-rings or seals, damage may result. If assembly of components is difficult use water to aid assembly. Use care when removing fuel hoses to prevent damage to hose or hose nipple. Always use new hose clamps of the correct type when reassembling and torque hose clamps to 10 inch lb. Do not use Aviation style clamps on this system or hose damage may result.

FUEL INJECTOR REMOVAL & INSTALLATION

NOTE: It is not necessary to remove the throttle body from the intake manifold to perform component disassembly. If fuel system hoses are to be replaced, only hoses marked EFI/EFM may be used.

1. Perform fuel system pressure release.

2. Disconnect negative battery cable.

3. Remove 4 Torx® screws holding fuel inlet chamber to throttle body.

4. Remove vacuum tube from pressure regulator to throttle body.

——— CAUTION ———

Place a shop towel around fuel inlet chamber to contain any fuel left in system.

5. Lift fuel inlet chamber and injector off throttle body.

6. Pull injector from fuel inlet chamber.

7. Remove upper and lower O-ring from fuel injector by peeling them off.

8. Remove snap ring that retains seal and washer on injector and remove seal and washer.

9. Installation is the reverse of removal. Torque the four torx head screws to 35 inch lbs.

PRESSURE REGULATOR REMOVAL & INSTALLATION

1. Perform fuel system pressure release.

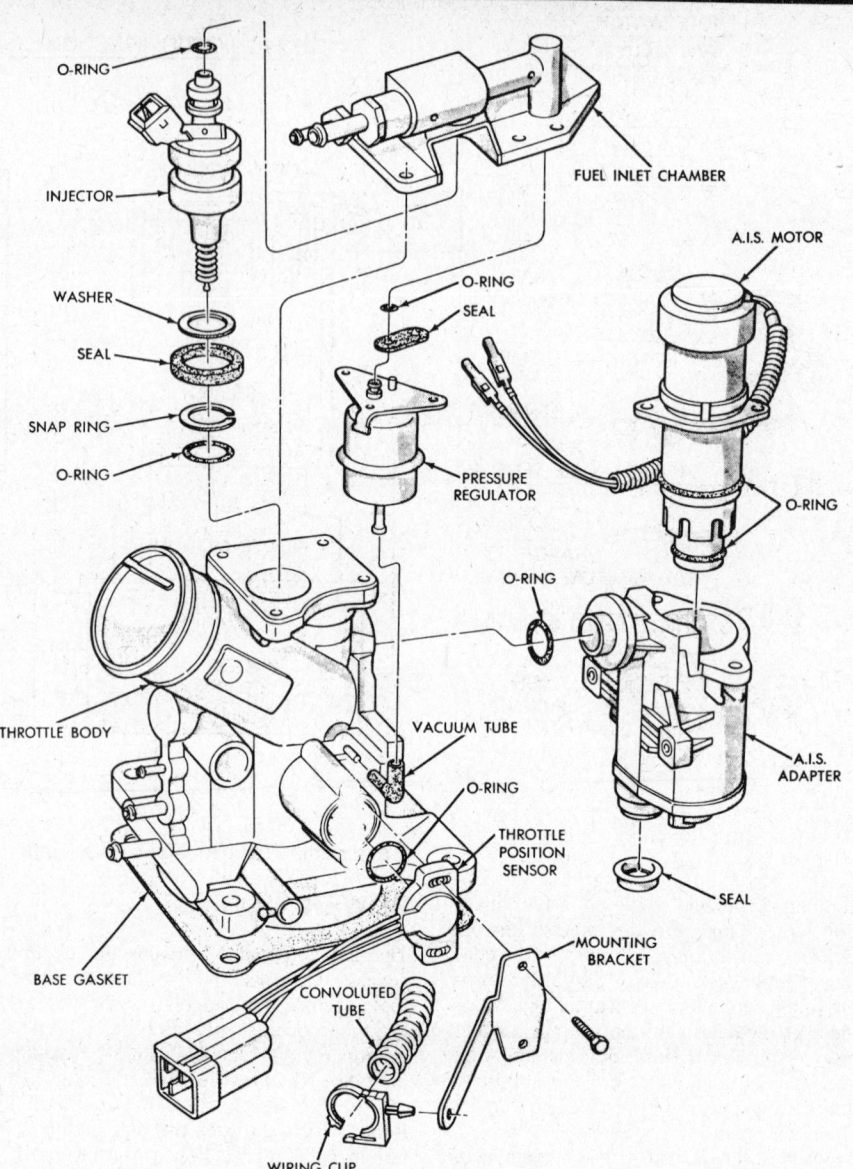

Throttle body exploded view

2. Disconnect negative battery cable.

3. Remove 3 Torx® screws mounting pressure regulator to fuel inlet chamber.

——— CAUTION ———

Place a shop towel around fuel inlet chamber to contain any fuel left in system.

4. Remove vacuum tube from pressure regulator to throttle body.

5. Pull pressure regulator from throttle body.

6. Carefully peel O-ring off pressure regulator and remove flat seal.

7. Installation is the reverse of removal. Torque the pressure regulator screws to 40 inch lbs.

THROTTLE POSITION SENSOR REMOVAL & INSTALLATION

1. Disconnect negative battery cable and

6-way throttle body connector.

2. Remove 2 screws mounting throttle position sensor to throttle body.

3. Unclip wiring clip from convoluted tube and remove mounting bracket.

4. Lift throttle position sensor off throttle shaft and remove O-ring.

5. Pull the 3 wires of the throttle position sensor from the convoluted tubing.

6. Look inside the 6-way throttle body connector and lift a locking tab with a small screwdriver for each T.P.S. wire blade terminal. Remove each blade from connector. (Note wiring position for reassembly.)

7. Installation is the reverse of removal. Torque retaining screws to 20 inch lbs.

IDLE SPEED MOTOR REMOVAL & INSTALLATION

1. Disconnect negative battery cable and

6-way throttle body connector.

2. Remove 2 screws that mount the A.I.S. to its adaptor. (Do not remove the clamp on the A.I.S. or damage will result.)

3. Remove wiring clips and remove the two A.I.S. wires from the 6-way throttle body connector. Lift each locking tab with a small screwdriver and remove each blade terminal. (Note wiring position for reassembly.)

4. Lift A.I.S. from its adaptor.

5. Remove the 2 O-rings on the A.I.S. carefully.

6. Installation is the revserse of removal.

AUTOMATIC IDLE SPEED MOTOR ASSEMBLY REMOVAL & INSTALLATION

1. Disconnect negative battery cable and 6-way throttle body connector.

2. Remove 2 screws on back of throttle body from A.I.S. adaptor.

3. Remove wiring clips and remove the two A.I.S. wires from the 6-way throttle body connector. Lift each locking tab with a small screwdriver and remove each blade terminal. (Note wiring position for reassembly).

4. Carefully pull the assembly from the rear of the throttle body. The O-ring at the top and seal at the bottom may fall off the adaptor.

5. Remove O-ring and seal.

6. Installation is the reverse of removal. Torque the retaining screws to 65 inch lbs.

CHRYSLER MULTI-POINT FUEL INJECTION

General Information

The turbocharged multi-point Electronic Fuel Injection system combines an electronic fuel and spark advance control system with a turbocharged intake system.

At the center of this system is a digital pre-programmed computer known as a Logic Module that regulates ignition timing, air-fuel ratio, emission control devices and idle speed. This component has the ability to update and revise its programming to meet changing operating conditions.

Various sensors provide the input necessary for the Logic Module to correctly regulate fuel flow at the fuel injectors. These include the Manifold Absolute Pressure, Throttle Position, Oxygen Feedback, Coolant Temperature, Charge Temperature, and Vehicle Speed Sensors. In addition to the sensors, various switches also provide important information. These include the Transmission Neutral-Safety, Heated Backlite, Air Conditioning, and the Air Conditioning Clutch Switches.

Inputs to the Logic Module are converted into signals sent to the Power Module. These signals cause the Power Module to change either the fuel flow at the injector or ignition timing or both.

The Logic Module tests many of its own input and output circuits. If a fault is found in a major circuit, this information is stored in the Logic Module. Information on this fault can be displayed to a technician by means of the instrument panel power loss lamp or by connecting a diagnostic readout and observing a numbered display code which directly relates to a general fault.

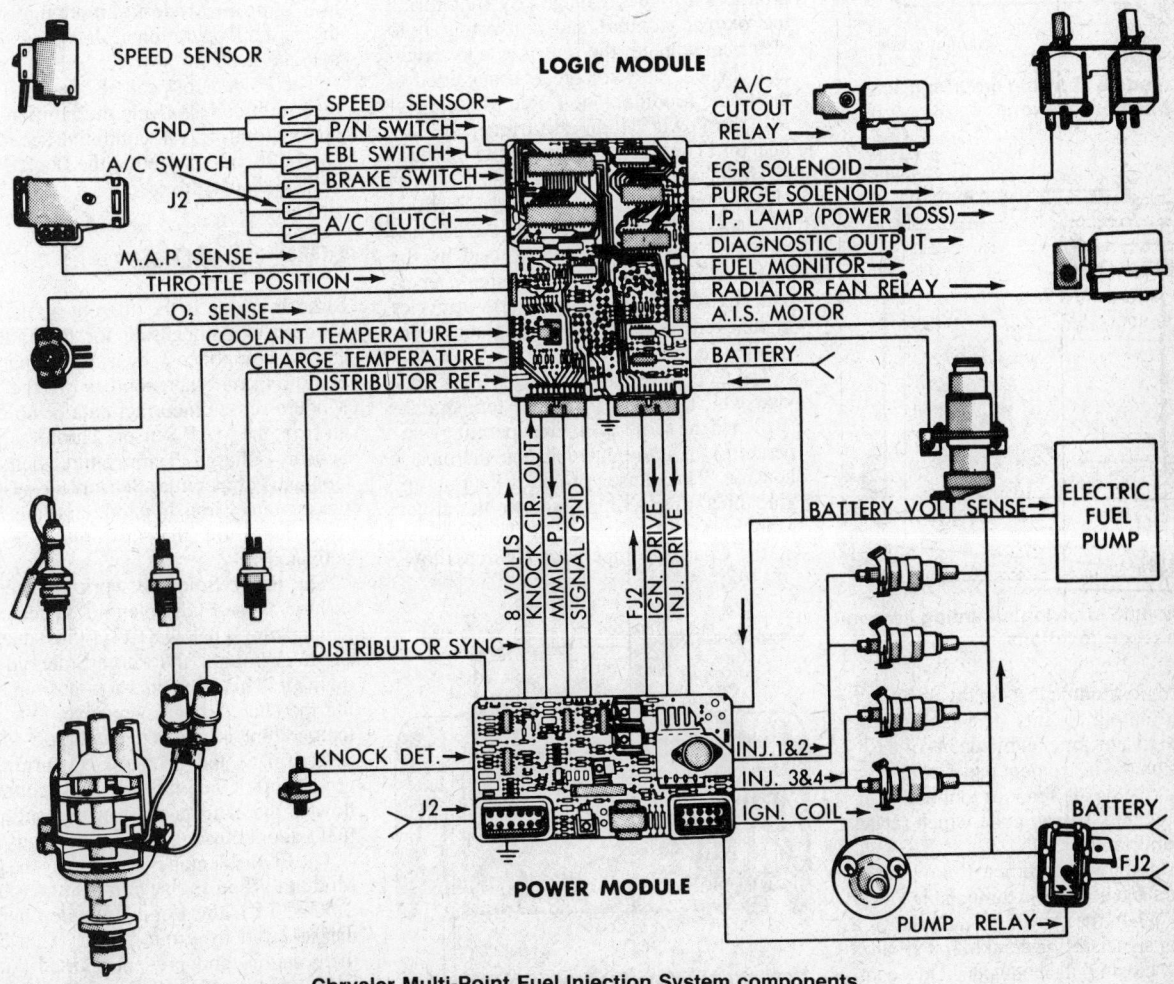

Chrysler Multi-Point Fuel Injection System components

The Power Module contains the circuits necessary to power the ignition coil and the fuel injector. These are high current devices and their power supply has been isolated to minimize any "electrical noise" reaching the Logic Module. The Power Module also energizes the Automatic Shut Down (ASD) Relay which activates the fuel pump, ignition coil, and the Power Module itself. The module also receives a signal from the distributor. In the event of no distributor signal, the ASD relay is not activated and power is shut off from the fuel pump and ignition coil. The Power Module contains a voltage converter which reduces battery voltage to a regulated 8.0V output. This 8.0V output powers the distributor and also powers the Logic Module.

The logic module is a digital computer containing a microprocessor. The module receives input signals from various switches, sensors, and components. It then computes the fuel injector pulse width, spark advance, ignition coil dwell, idle speed, and purge and EGR solenoid cycles from this information.

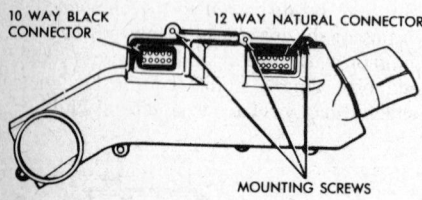

Power module showing mounting screws and connector locations

10 WAY BLACK CONNECTOR
12 WAY NATURAL CONNECTOR
MOUNTING SCREWS

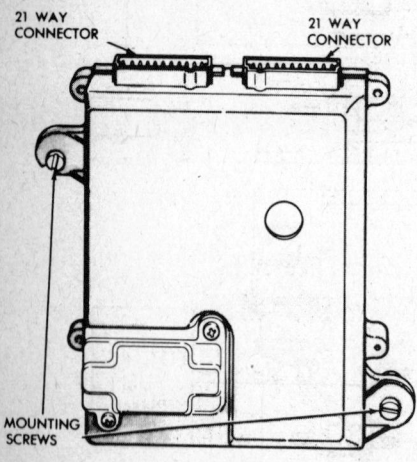

21 WAY CONNECTOR
21 WAY CONNECTOR
MOUNTING SCREWS

Logic module showing mounting screws and connector locations

The Logic Module tests many of its own input and output circuits. If a fault can be displayed to a technician by means of flashing lamp on the instrument panel or by connecting a diagnostic readout tool and reading a numbered display code which relates to a general fault.

The Automatic Shutdown Relay (ASD) is powered and controlled through the Power Module. When the Power Module senses a distributor signal during cranking, it grounds the ASD closing its contacts. This completes the circuit for the electric fuel pump, Power Module, and ignition coil. If the distributor signal is lost for any reason the ASD interrupts this circuit in less than one second preventing fuel, spark, and engine operations.

SYSTEM SENSORS

The Manifold Absolute Pressure (MAP) sensor is a device which monitors manifold vacuum. It is mounted in the right side passenger compartment and is connected to a vacuum nipple on the throttle body and, electrically to the Logic Module. The sensor transmits information on manifold vacuum conditions and barometric pressure to the Logic Module. The MAP sensor data on engine load is used with data from other sensors to determine the correct air-fuel mixture.

The Oxygen Sensor (O2 Sensor) is a device which produces an electrical voltage when exposed to the oxygen present in the exhaust gases. The sensor is mounted in the exhaust manifold and must be heated by the exhaust gases before producing the voltage. When there is a large amount of oxygen present (lean mixture), the sensor produces a low voltage. When there is a lesser amount present (rich mixture) it produces a higher voltage. By monitoring the oxygen content and converting it to electrical voltage, the sensor acts as a rich-lean switch. The voltage is transmitted to the Logic Module. The Logic Module signals the Power Module to trigger the fuel injector. The injector changes the mixture.

The Charge Temperature Sensor is a device mounted in the intake manifold which measures the temperature of the air-fuel mixture. This information is used by the Logic Module to determine engine operating temperature and engine warm-up cycles in the event of a Coolant Temperature Sensor failure.

The Coolant Temperature Sensor is a device which monitors coolant temperature (which is the same as engine operating temperature). It is mounted in the thermostat housing. This sensor provides data on engine operating temperature to the Logic Module. This data along with data provided by the Charge Temperature Switch allows

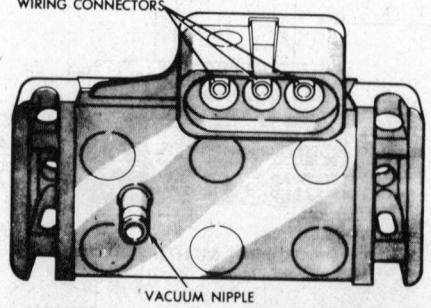

WIRING CONNECTORS
VACUUM NIPPLE

Manifold Absolute Pressure (MAP) sensor

the Logic Module to demand slightly richer air-fuel mixtures and higher idle speed until normal operating temperatures are reached. The sensor is a variable resistor with a range of −60°F to 300°F.

SWITCH INPUT

Various switches provide information to the Logic Module. These include the Neutral Safety, Air Conditioning Clutch, and Brake Light switches. If one or more of these switches is sensed as being in the on position, the Logic Module signals the Automatic Idle Speed Motor to increase idle speed to a scheduled rpm.

With the air conditioning on and the throttle blade above a specific angle, the wide open throttle cut-out relay prevents the air conditioning clutch from engaging until the throttle blade is below this angle.

The Power Loss Lamp comes on each time the ignition key is turned on and stays on for a few seconds as a bulb test.

If the Logic Module receives an incorrect signal or no signal from either the Coolant Temperature Sensor, Manifold Absolute Pressure Sensor, or the Throttle Position Sensor, the Power Loss Lamp on the instrument panel is illuminated. This is a warning that the Logic Module has gone into Limp in Mode in an attempt to keep the system operational. It signals an immediate need for service.

The Power Loss can also be used to display fault codes. Cycle the ignition switch on, off, on, off, on within five seconds and any fault codes stored in the Logic Module will be displayed.

LIMP IN MODE

Limp In Mode is the attempt by the Logic Module to compensate for the failure of certain components by substituting information from other sources. If the Logic Module senses incorrect data or no data at all from the MAP Sensor, Throttle Position Sensor, Charge Temperature Sensor or Coolant Temperature Sensor, the system is placed into Limp In Mode and the Power Loss lamp on the instrument panel is activated.

The Purge Solenoid works in the same fashion as the EGR solenoid. When engine temperature is below 61°C (145°F) the Logic Module grounds the Purge Solenoid energizing it. This prevents vacuum from reaching the charcoal canister valve. When this temperature is reached the Logic Module de-energizes the solenoid by turning the ground off. Once this occurs vacuum will flow to the canister purge valve and purge fuel vapors through the throttle body.

The EGR solenoid is operated by the Logic Module. When engine temperature is below 21°C (70°F), the Logic Module energizes the solenoid by grounding it. This closes the solenoid and prevents ported vacuum from reaching the EGR valve. When the prescribed temperature is reached, the logic module will turn off the ground for the solenoid de-energizing it. Once the solenoid is de-energized, ported vacuum from the throttle body will pass through to the EGR valve. At idle and wide open throttle the solenoid is energized which prevents EGR operation.

The air conditioning cut out relay is electrically in series with the cycling clutch switch and low pressure cut out switch. This relay is in the normally closed (on) position during engine operation. When the Logic Module senses wide open throttle through the Throttle Position Sensor, it will energize the relay, open its contacts, and prevent air conditioning clutch engagement.

FUEL DELIVERY SYSTEM

The throttle body assembly replaces a conventional carburetor air intake system and is connected to both the turbocharger and the intake manifold. The throttle body houses the Throttle Position Sensor and the Automatic Idle Speed Motor. Air flow through the throttle body is controlled by a cable operated throttle blade located in the base of the throttle body.

Fuel is pumped to the fuel rail by an electrical pump which is mounted in the fuel tank. The pump inlet is fitted with a filter to prevent water and other contaminants from entering the fuel supply circuit.

Fuel pressure is controlled to a preset level above intake manifold pressure by a pressure regulator which is mounted near the fuel rail. The regulator uses intake manifold pressure at the vacuum tee as a reference.

The four fuel injectors are retained in the fuel rail by lock rings. The rail and injector

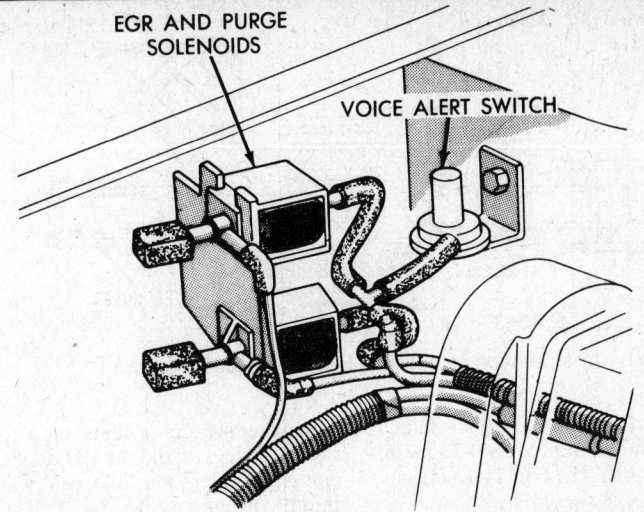

EGR and canister purge solenoids showing location of voice alert switch

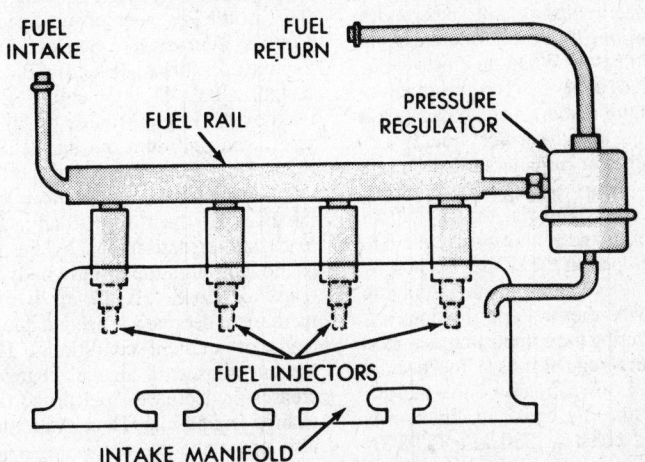

Fuel supply system on multi-point injection

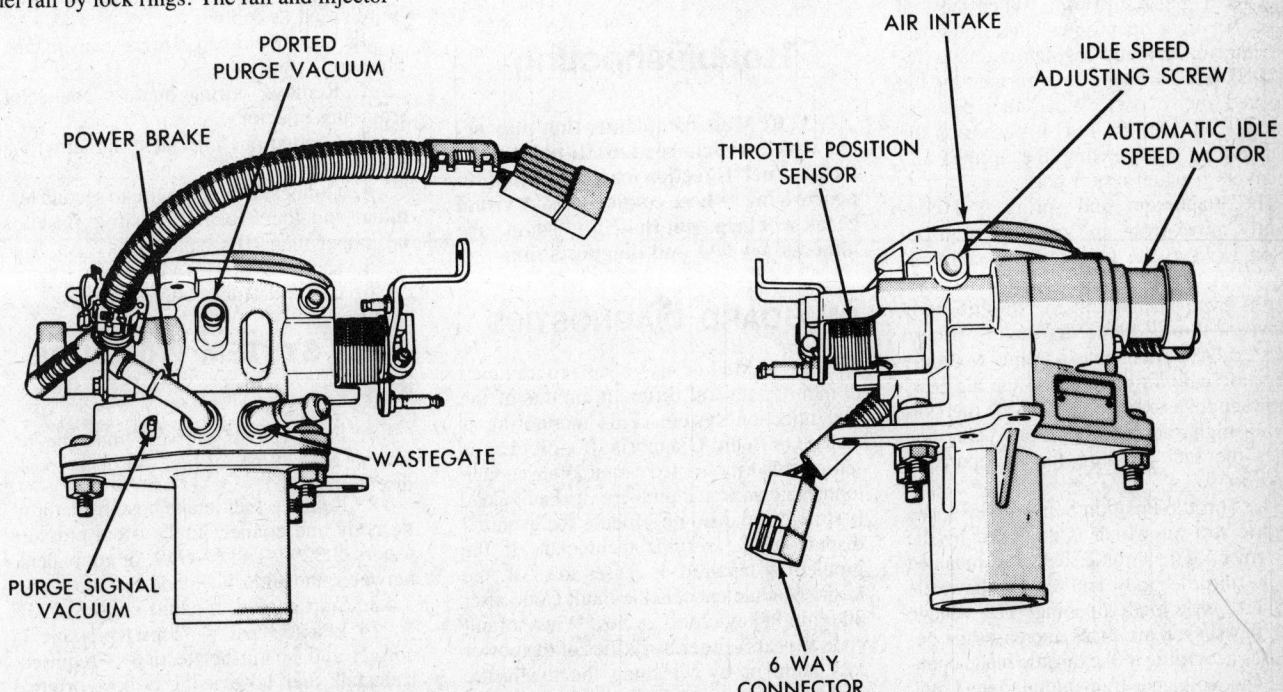

Left and right views of throttle body assembly showing component location

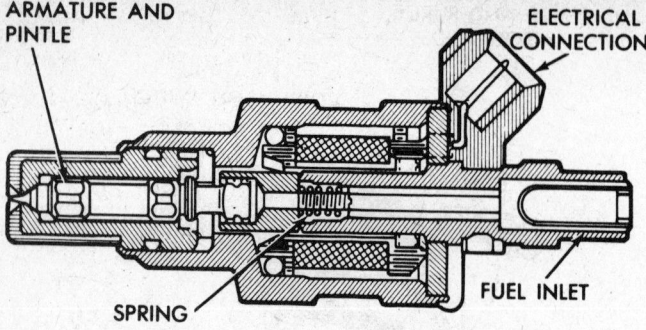

ARMATURE AND PINTLE · ELECTRICAL CONNECTION · SPRING · FUEL INLET

Cross section of typical solenoid-type fuel injector

assembly is then bolted in position with the injectors inserted in the recessed holes in the intake manifold. The Fuel Injector is an electric solenoid powered by the Power Module but, controlled by the Logic Module. The Logic Module, based on ambient, mechanical, and sensor input, determines when and how long the Power Module should operate the injector. When an electric current is supplied to the injector, the armature and pintle move a short distance against a spring, opening a small orifice. Fuel is supplied to the inlet of the injector by the fuel pump, then passes through the injector, around the pintle, and out of the orifice. Since the fuel is under high pressure a fine spray is developed in the shape of a hollow cone. The injector, through this spraying action, atomizes the fuel and distributes it into the air entering the combustion chamber.

The pressure regulator is a mechanical device located downstream of the fuel injector on the throttle body. Its function is to maintain a constant 380 kPa (53 PSI) across the fuel injector tip. The regulator uses a spring loaded rubber diaphragm to uncover a fuel return port. When the fuel pump becomes operational, fuel flows past the injector into the regulator, and is restricted from flowing any further by the blocked return port. When fuel pressure reaches 380 kPa (53 PSI) it pushes on the diaphragm, compressing the spring, and uncovers the fuel return port.

The diaphragm and spring will constantly move from an open to closed position to keep the fuel pressure constant. An assist to the spring loaded diaphragm comes from vacuum in the throttle body above the throttle blade. As venturi vacuum increases less pressure is required to supply the same amount of fuel into the air flow. The vacuum assists in opening the fuel port during high vacuum conditions. This fine tunes the fuel pressure for all operating conditions.

The Throttle Position Sensor (TPS) is an electric resistor which is activated by the movement of the throttle shaft. It is mounted on the throttle body and senses the angle of the throttle blade opening. The voltage that the sensor produces increases or decreases according to the throttle blade opening. This voltage is transmitted to the Logic Module where it is used along with data

from other sensors to adjust the air-fuel ratio to varying conditions and during acceleration, deceleration, idle, and wide open throttle operations.

The Automatic Idle Speed Motor (AIS) is operated by the Logic Module. Data from the Throttle Position Sensor, Speed Sensor, Coolant Temperature Sensor, and various switch operations, (Electric Backlite, Air Conditioning, Safety/Neutral, Brake) are used by the Logic Module to adjust engine idle to an optimum during all idle conditions. The AIS adjusts the air portion of the air-fuel mixture through an air bypass on the back of the throttle body. Basic (no load) idle is determined by the minimum air flow through the throttle body. The AIS opens or closes off the air bypass as an increase or decrease is needed due to engine loads or ambient conditions. The Logic Module senses an air/fuel change and increases or decreases fuel proportionally to change engine idle. Deceleration die out is also prevented by increasing engine idle when the throttle is closed quickly after a driving (speed) condition.

Troubleshooting

NOTE: Most complaints that may occur with turbocharged multi-point Electronic Fuel Injection can be traced to poor wiring or hose connections. A visual check will help spot these faults and save unnecessary test and diagnosis time.

ON BOARD DIAGNOSTICS

The Logic Module has been programmed to monitor several different circuits of the fuel injection system. This monitoring is called On Board Diagnosis. If a problem is sensed with a monitored circuit, often enough to indicate an actual problem, its Fault Code is stored in the Logic Module for eventual display to the service technician. If the problem is repaired or ceases to exist, the Logic Module cancels the Fault Code after 30 ignition key on/off cycles. When a fault code appears (either by flashes of the power loss lamp or by watching the diagnostic readout—Tool C-4805), it indicates that the Logic Module has recognized an abnormal

signal in the system. Fault codes indicate the results of a failure but do not always identify the failed component.

OBTAINING FAULT CODES

1. Connect Diagnostic Readout Box Tool C-4805, to the diagnostic connector located in the engine compartment near the passenger side strut tower.
2. Start the engine if possible, cycle the transmission selector and the A/C switch if applicable. Shut off the engine.
3. Turn the ignition switch on, off, on, off, on. Within 5 seconds record all the diagnostic codes shown on the Diagnostic Readout Box Tool C-4805, observe the power loss lamp on the instrument panel the lamp should light for 2 seconds then go out (bulb check).

SWITCH TEST

After all codes have been shown and has indicated Code 55 end of message, actuate the following component switches. The digital display must change its numbers when the switch is activated and released:
- Brake Pedal
- Gear Shift Selector park, reverse, park.
- A/C Switch (if applicable).
- Electric Backlite Switch (if applicable).

FUEL SYSTEM PRESSURE RELEASE

The E.F.I. fuel system is under a constant pressure of approximately 380 kPa (53 psi). Before servicing the fuel tank, fuel pump, fuel lines, fuel filter, or fuel components of the throttle body the fuel pressure must be released as follows.

1. Loosen gas cap to release any in tank pressure.
2. Remove wiring harness connector from any injector.
3. Ground one injector terminal with a jumper.
4. Connect a jumper wire to second terminal and touch battery positive post for no longer than 10 seconds.
5. Remove jumper wires.
6. Continue fuel system service.

FUEL SYSTEM PRESSURE TEST

1. Fuel system pressure must be released each time a fuel hose is to be disconnected.
2. Remove fuel intake hose from throttle body and connect fuel system pressure testers C-3292, and C-4749, or equivalent, between fuel filter hose and throttle body.
3. Start engine. If gauge reads 380 kPa = 14 kPa (53 psi = 2 psi) pressure is correct and no further testing is required. Reinstall fuel hose using a new original equipment type clamp and torque to 1 N·m (10 in. lbs.).

4. If fuel pressure is **below** specifications, install tester between fuel filter hose and fuel line.

5. Start engine. If pressure is now correct, replace fuel filter. If no change is observed, gently squeeze return hose. If pressure increases, replace pressure regulator. If no change is observed, problem is either a plugged pump filter sock or defective fuel pump.

6. If pressure is **above** specifications, remove fuel return hose from pressure regulator end. Connect a substitute hose and place other end of hose in clean container. Start engine. If pressure is now correct, check for restricted fuel return line. If no change is observed, replace fuel regulator.

NOTE: Mechanical malfunctions are more difficult to diagnose with the EFI system. The Logic Module has been programmed to compensate for some mechanical malfunctions such as incorrect cam timing, vacuum leaks, etc. If engine performance problems are encountered, and no fault codes are displayed, the problem may be mechanical rather than electronic.

Service

When servicing the fuel portion of the throttle body it will be necessary to bleed fuel pressure before opening any hoses. Always reassemble throttle body components with new O-rings and seals where applicable. Never use lubricants on O-rings or seals, damage may result. If assembly of components is difficult use water to aid assembly. Use care when removing fuel hoses to prevent damage to hose or hose nipple. Always use new hose clamps of the correct type when reassembling and torque hose clamps to 10 inch lbs. (1 Nm). Do not use Aviation style clamps on this system or hose damage may result.

NOTE: It is not necessary to remove the throttle body from the intake manifold to perform component disassembly. If fuel system hoses are to be replaced, only hoses marked EFI/EFM may be used.

THROTTLE POSITION SENSOR

Removal

1. Disconnect negative battery cable and 6-way throttle body connector.
2. Remove 2 screws mounting throttle position sensor to throttle body.
3. Unclip wiring clip from convoluted tube and remove mounting bracket.
4. Lift throttle position sensor off throttle shaft and remove O-ring.
5. Pull the 3 wires of the throttle position sensor from the convoluted tubing.
6. Look inside the 6-way throttle body connector and lift a locking tab with a small screwdriver for each T.P.S. wire blade terminal. Remove each blade from connector. (Note wiring position for reassembly.)

Installation

1. Insert each wire blade terminal into throttle body connector. Make sure wires are inserted into correct locations.
2. Insert wires from throttle position sensor into convoluted tube.
3. Install throttle position sensor and new O'ring with mounting bracket to throttle body. Torque screws to 20 inch lbs. (2 Nm).
4. Install wiring clips to convoluted tube.
5. Connect 6 way connector and battery cable.

AUTOMATIC IDLE SPEED MOTOR

Removal

1. Disconnect negative battery cable and 6-way throttle body connector.
2. Remove 2 screws that mount the A.I.S. to its adaptor. (Do not remove the clamp on the A.I.S. or damage will result.)
3. Remove wiring clips and remove the two A.I.S. wires from the 6-way throttle body connector. Lift each locking tab with a small screwdriver and remove each blade terminal. (Note wiring position for reassembly).
4. Lift A.I.S. from its adaptor.
5. Remove the 2 O-rings on the A.I.S. carefully.

Installation

1. Install 2 new O-rings on A.I.S.
2. Carefully work A.I.S. into its adaptor.
3. Install 2 mounting screws and torque to 20 inch lbs. (2 Nm) (20 in. lbs.).
4. Route A.I.S. wiring to 6-way connector and install each wire blade terminal into the connector. Make sure wires are inserted in correct locations.
5. Connect wiring clips, 6-way connector, and battery cable.

AUTOMATIC IDLE SPEED MOTOR ASSEMBLY

Removal

1. Disconnect negative battery cable and 6-way throttle body connector.
2. Remove 2 screws on back of throttle body from A.I.S. adaptor.
3. Remove wiring clips and remove the two A.I.S. wires from the 6-way throttle body connector. Lift each locking tab with a small screwdriver and remove each blade terminal. (Note wiring position for reassembly).
4. Carefully pull the assembly from the rear of the throttle body. The O-ring at the top and seal at the bottom may fall off adaptor.
5. Remove O-ring and seal.

Installation

1. Place a new O-ring and seal on adaptor.
2. Carefully position assembly onto back of throttle body (make sure seals stay in place) insert screws and torque to 65 inch lbs. (7 Nm).
3. Route A.I.S. wiring to 6-way connector and install each wire blade terminal into the connector. Make sure wires are inserted in correct locations.
4. Connect wiring clips, 6-way connector, and battery cable.

THROTTLE BODY

Removal & Installation

1. Disconnect Negative battery cable.
2. Remove air cleaner to throttle body screws, loosen hose clamp and remove air cleaner adaptor.
3. Remove accelerator, speed control, and transmission kickdown cables and return spring.
4. Remove throttle cable bracket from throttle body.
5. Disconnect 6 way connector.
6. Disconnect vacuum hoses from throttle body.
7. Loosen throttle body to turbocharger hose clamp.
8. Remove throttle body to intake manifold screws.
9. Remove throttle body.
10. Reverse the above procedure for installation.

OXYGEN SENSOR

Removal and Installation

Removing the oxygen sensor from the exhaust manifold may be difficult if the sensor was overtorqued during installation. Use Tool C-4589 or equivalent to remove the sensor. The threads in the exhaust manifold must be cleaned with a 18mm × 1.5 × 6E tap. If the same sensor is to be reinstalled, the threads must be coated with an anti-seize compound such as Loctite® 771-64 or equivalent. New sensors are packaged with anti-seize compound on the threads and no additional compound is required. Sensors must be torqued to 20 ft. lbs. (27 Nm).

IDLE SET ADJUSTMENT

Before adjusting the idle on an Electronic Fuel Injected vehicle the following items must be checked:
   a. AIS motor has been checked for operation.
   b. Engine has been checked for vacuum or EGR leaks.
   c. Engine timing has been checked and set to specifications.
   d. Coolant Temperature Sensor has been checked for operation.

1. Install a tachometer.

2. Warm up engine to normal operating temperature (accessories off).

3. Shut engine off and disconnect radiator fan.

4. Disconnect Throttle Body 6-way connector. Remove the brown with white tracer AIS wire from the connector and reconnect connector.

5. Start engine with transaxle selector in park or neutral.

6. Apply 12 volts to AIS brown with white tracer wire. This will drive the AIS fully closed and the idle rpm should drop.

7. Disconnect then reconnect coolant temperature sensor.

8. With transaxle in neutral idle speed should be 775 ± 25 rpm (700 ± 25 green engine).

9. If idle is not to specifications adjust idle air bypass screw.

10. If idle rpm will not adjust down, check for vacuum leaks, AIS motor damage, throttle body damage, or speed control cable adjustment.

11. Shut off engine, reconnect 6 way connector, remove jumper wire, remove tachometer.

IGNITION TIMING PROCEDURE

1. Connect a power timing light to the number one cylinder, or a magnetic timing unit to the engine. (Use a 10 degree offset when required).

2. Connect a tachometer to the engine and turn selector to the proper cylinder position.

3. Start engine and run until operating temperature is reached.

4. Disconnect and reconnect the water temperature sensor connector on the thermostat housing. The loss of power lamp on the dash must come on and stay on. Engine rpm should be within emission label specifications.

5. Aim power timing light at timing hole in bell housing or read the magnetic timing unit.

6. Loosen distributor and adjust timing to emission label specification if necessary.

7. Shut engine off, disconnect and reconnect positive battery quick disconnect. Start vehicle, the loss of power lamp should be off.

Turbocharging

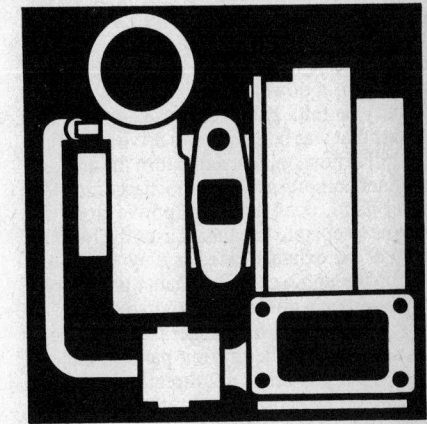

THEORY

The internal combustion engine can be throught of as an air pump. The action of the pistons moving down or up in their cylinders when the intake or exhaust valves are open alternately draws air and fuel into the engine or expells burnt gases into the atmosphere. The amount of air and fuel pulled into the engine (known as an engine's volumetric efficiency) is governed by the drawing efficiency of the piston as it descends in its cylinder, and by the scavenging effect of the exiting exhaust gases, which act to pull additional air/fuel mixture in through the open intake valves during valve overlap periods. The more air and fuel each cylinder pulls in, the more power the engine will produce.

Theoretically, a normally asperated engine should be able to draw in an amount of air and fuel equal to its displacement (e.g. a 350 cu in. engine should draw in 350 cu in. of air and fuel). In practice, however, only about 80% of the displacement capacity is drawn through because of flow restrictions, the slight pressure drop through the carburetor, and the inability of the exhaust stroke to drive out all of the burnt gases.

There are several ways to increase an engine's drawing power (volumetric efficiency). These include increasing valve overlap, increasing engine bore and/or stroke, supercharging the engine, or, the most practical approach, turbocharging.

In effect, the turbocharger crams more air/fuel mixture into the cylinders than they could possibly draw in by themselves. In doing so, the turbocharger increases the engine's volumetric effeciency past its normal 80%, which proportionately increases engine horsepower and torque output.

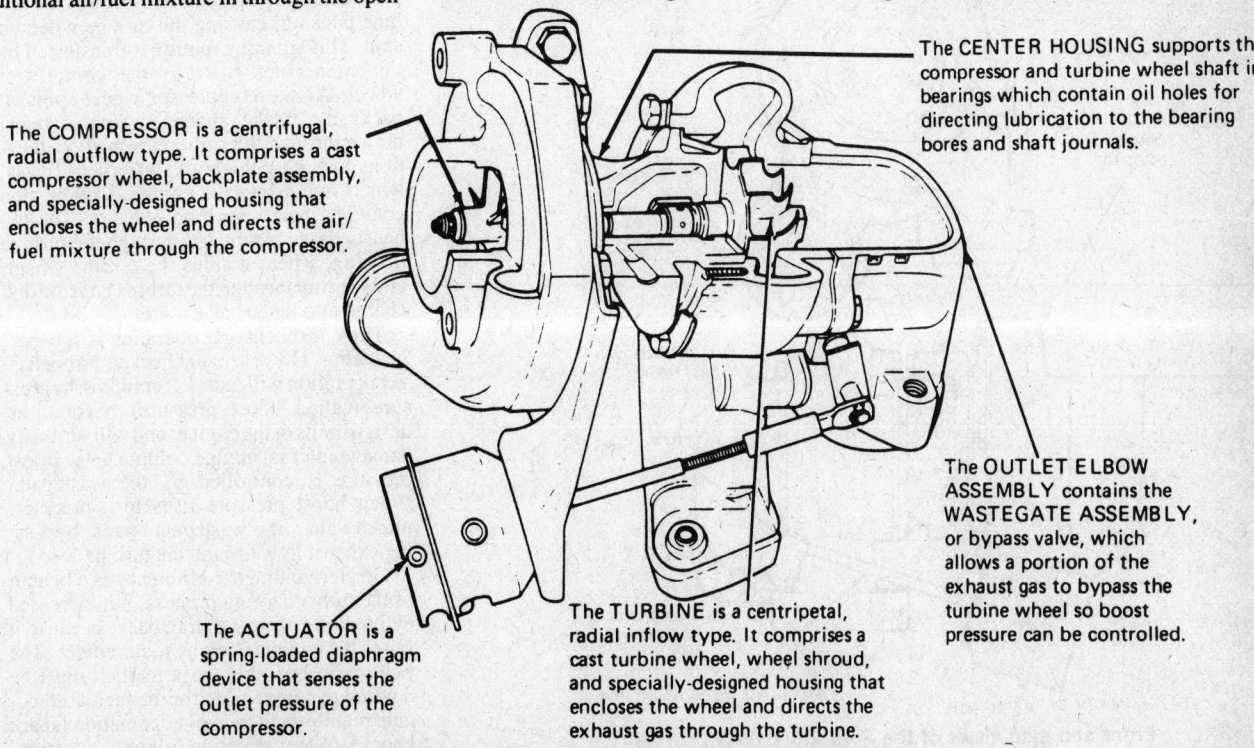

The COMPRESSOR is a centrifugal, radial outflow type. It comprises a cast compressor wheel, backplate assembly, and specially-designed housing that encloses the wheel and directs the air/fuel mixture through the compressor.

The CENTER HOUSING supports the compressor and turbine wheel shaft in bearings which contain oil holes for directing lubrication to the bearing bores and shaft journals.

The ACTUATOR is a spring-loaded diaphragm device that senses the outlet pressure of the compressor.

The TURBINE is a centripetal, radial inflow type. It comprises a cast turbine wheel, wheel shroud, and specially-designed housing that encloses the wheel and directs the exhaust gas through the turbine.

The OUTLET ELBOW ASSEMBLY contains the WASTEGATE ASSEMBLY, or bypass valve, which allows a portion of the exhaust gas to bypass the turbine wheel so boost pressure can be controlled.

Turbocharger components, typical of all models (© Ford Motor Co.)

Perhaps the most advantageous aspect of the turbocharger is that it does not require usable engine horsepower to operate. By comparison, say a car is climbing a steep hill and the driver decides to turn on the air conditioner. The moment the air conditioner is turned on, a power drain on the engine can usually be felt. That's because some of the power that was being used to drive the car up the hill is now being used to turn the air conditioner compressor. A turbocharger, on the other hand, does not drain power from the engine to operate because it uses the free energy of the exhaust gases as they are blown out of the engine. This exhaust gas energy is wasted on a normally aspirated engine.

Because the turbocharger is not mechanically linked to the driving parts of the engine, its operation is not directly dependant on engine rpm alone, but rather on engine rpm *and* engine load: a turbocharger is responsive to throttle position. Say a car is driving at 55 mph on a flat road: the throttle valves are not open a great deal, because the car does not need a great deal of energy to travel at this speed. Soon the car starts to climb a steep hill: to maintain 55 mph the throttle valves must be opened more. This increases the intake charge, which in turn increases the exhaust gas volume as it leaves the engine. This increased volume spins the turbocharger faster, making the turbocharger force more air/fuel mixture into the engine, and so on. After the car climbs the hill and is once again travelling on a flat road, the throttle valves return to their position before the hill, and the turbocharger slows down.

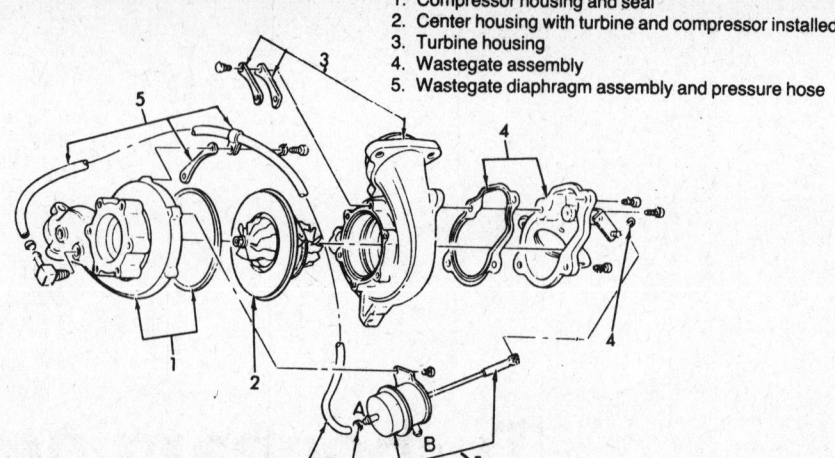

1. Compressor housing and seal
2. Center housing with turbine and compressor installed
3. Turbine housing
4. Wastegate assembly
5. Wastegate diaphragm assembly and pressure hose

Typical GM 3.8L (231 cu in.) engine turbocharger. "A" is pressure side of wastegate diaphragm, "B" is vacuum side (© Buick Div., GM Corp.)

COMPONENTS

The turbocharger unit consists of two vaned wheels (compressor and turbine) connected by a common axle (shaft), and a housing which can be sub-divided into three sections: inlet (or compressor), center, and outlet (or turbine). The inlet housing surrounds the compressor wheel, and connects to the air intake and the intake manifold. The outlet housing surrounds the turbine wheel, and connects to the exhaust system; it also houses the wastegate assembly in many installations. The center housing surrounds and supports the shaft, and connects the inlet and outlet housings.

The wastegate is a bypass valve, which opens at a predetermined pressure. It shunts a portion of the exhaust gas around the turbine wheel, thus controlling boost pressure. Wastegate assemblies in all installations covered in this book are installed in the outlet housing.

OPERATION

Turbocharger operation is remarkably simple. The turbine wheel is installed in the path of the engine's exhaust gas, and the compressor wheel is installed in the intake path. Exhaust gas is directed through the turbine housing, causing the turbine wheel to spin. This spinning motion is transferred by the connecting shaft to the compressor wheel. As the compressor wheel spins, it packs the intake charge (which is being drawn through the carburetor in all installations covered in this book) into a dense mass, which is fed into the engine. Combustion converts the charge into exhaust. The exhaust charge is directed through the turbine housing, where it spins the turbine wheel, and then out through the turbine housing discharge into the exhaust system.

Thus, turbocharger operation is self-perpetuating. However, unchecked turbocharger operation will increase compressor pressure (called boost pressure) beyond the design limits of the engine, and will seriously damage internal engine components. Boost pressure is controlled by the wastegate. When boost pressure rises to a predetermined value, the wastegate opens, bypassing exhaust flow around the turbine.

Greater volumetric efficiency is a benefit of the turbocharging process, but increased cylinder pressure is a drawback, because it raises the engine's octane requirement. The two are inseparable, so a method must be devised to compensate for the increased octane requirement to avoid detonation (spark knock). Water injection, alcohol injection, low boost pressures, charge intercoolers, ig-

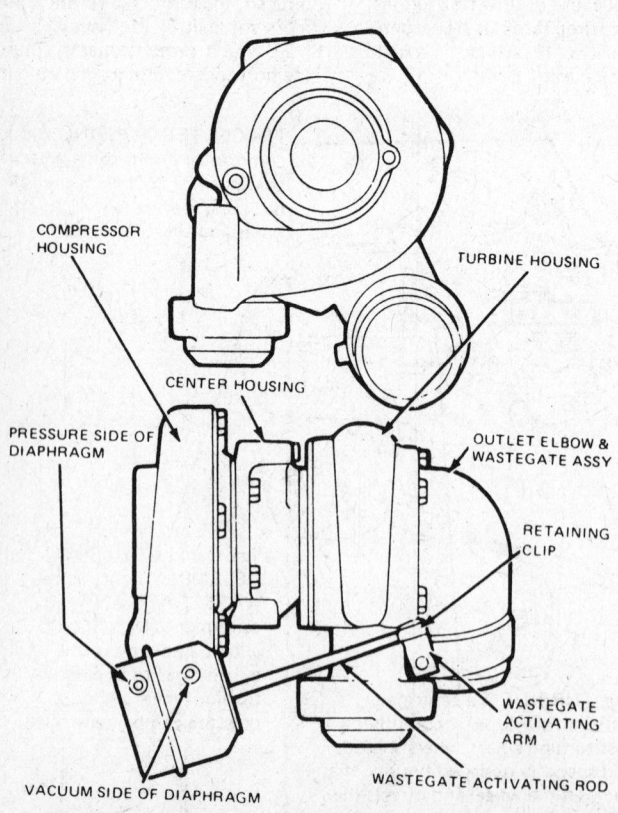

COMPRESSOR HOUSING

TURBINE HOUSING

CENTER HOUSING

PRESSURE SIDE OF DIAPHRAGM

OUTLET ELBOW & WASTEGATE ASSY

RETAINING CLIP

WASTEGATE ACTIVATING ARM

VACUUM SIDE OF DIAPHRAGM

WASTEGATE ACTIVATING ROD

Front and side views of the Ford 2.3 L turbocharger (© Ford Motor Co.)

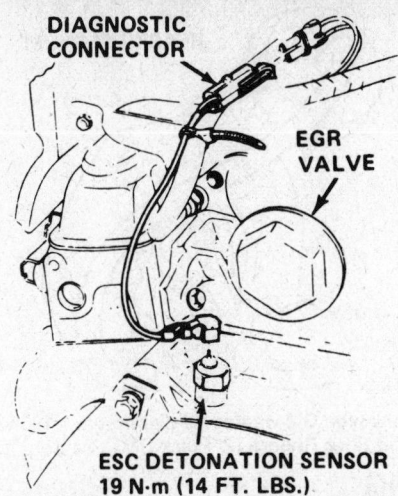

DIAGNOSTIC
CONNECTOR

EGR
VALVE

ESC DETONATION SENSOR
19 N·m (14 FT. LBS.)

Buick 231 V6 (3.8 L) detonation sensor installation (© Buick Div., GM Corp.)

nition spark retardation, and alcohol fuels have all been used to control detonation, with varying degrees of success.

Ford controls detonation by limiting boost and by spark retardation. Wastegate operation begins at five p.s.i., and enough exhaust gas is routed around the turbine to limit boost to a maximum of six p.s.i. The electronic ignition system has been modified in the turbocharged engine to include two spark retardation points. When boost pressure reaches approximately one-half to one p.s.i., a switch in the intake manifold sends a signal to the ignition module, which retards ignition timing six degrees. A second manifold switch sends its signal when boost reaches four p.s.i., resulting in an additional six degrees of retard.

The General Motors system of detonation control is slightly different. Boost is limited to a maximum of six p.s.i. In addition, a detonation sensor is installed in the engine block (V6) or intake manifold (V8). Vibrations caused by detonation are transmitted to the sensor, which sends a signal to the Electronic Spark Control (ESC) module. The module processes this signal, and sends a command signal to the HEI distributor to retard timing. Timing retard ranges up to 22° on V6s, or 15° on V8s.

Testing Wastegate Operation

As noted before, the wastegate is a safety valve for the engine. If the wastegate sticks

shut, boost pressure will build until the air/fuel mixture charge becomes too powerful for the mechanical components (pistons, bearings, etc.) and causes engine damage.

If the wastegate sticks open, little or no boost will be received from the turbocharger, which translates into mediocure engine performance.

The simplest wastegate test is to remove the pressure hose at the wastegate diaphragm unit, connect a pressure pump (such as the type used for cooling system testing) and apply pressure. At the specified opening pressure (7 psi for Ford, 8.5–9.5 for GM), the link between the wastegate and its diaphragm unit will just move (about .015 in.). The movement is not great, but it should be easy to see.

If the wastegate does not move, try to operate the linkage by hand. It should move under moderate hand pressure. If it moves, the problem is probably in the diaphragm unit (broken diaphragm).

To test the diaphragm, remove the vacuum hose from the diaphragm, hook up a manual vacuum pump and apply 25 inches-Hg of vacuum to the diaphragm unit. If the vacuum drops below 18 inches-Hg within one minute, replace the diaphragm unit.

NOTE: Some 1981 and later GM turbos have a new type of diaphragm which opens the wastegate during idle and part throttle, when there's no boost, to reduce engine backpressure and improve fuel economy. To test this type of unit, apply about 20 inches-Hg of vacuum to the diaphram unit: the wastegate link should move slightly. This unit operates solely with plenum vacuum and can be identified by the absence of a boost pressure signal line on the diaphragm unit.

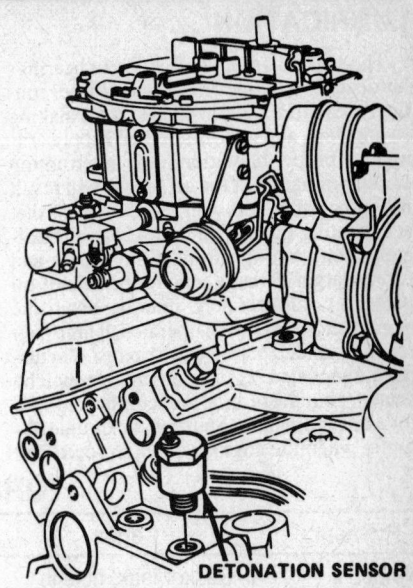

DETONATION SENSOR

Pontiac turbocharged V8 detonation sensor location (© Pontiac Div., GM Corp.)

Testing Operation of GM Detonation Sensor

Connect a tachometer and timing light to the engine, run the engine at 1800-2500 rpm and tap on the intake manifold next to the detonation sensor.

NOTE: Be careful to keep all wires, clothing and tools away from moving engine parts.

Rap continuously, quickly and moderately hard. This should trigger the detonation sensor. When it triggers, engine speed should drop at least 200 rpm and timing should retard at least 4°, probably more.

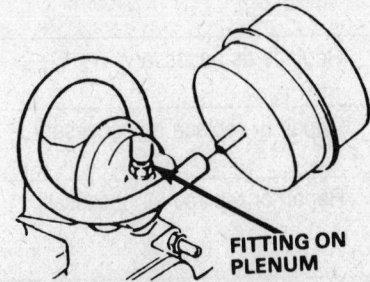

FITTING ON
PLENUM

New type GM wastegate diaphragm uses plenum vacuum only—1981 and later Buick Regal unit shown (© Buick Div., GM Corp.)

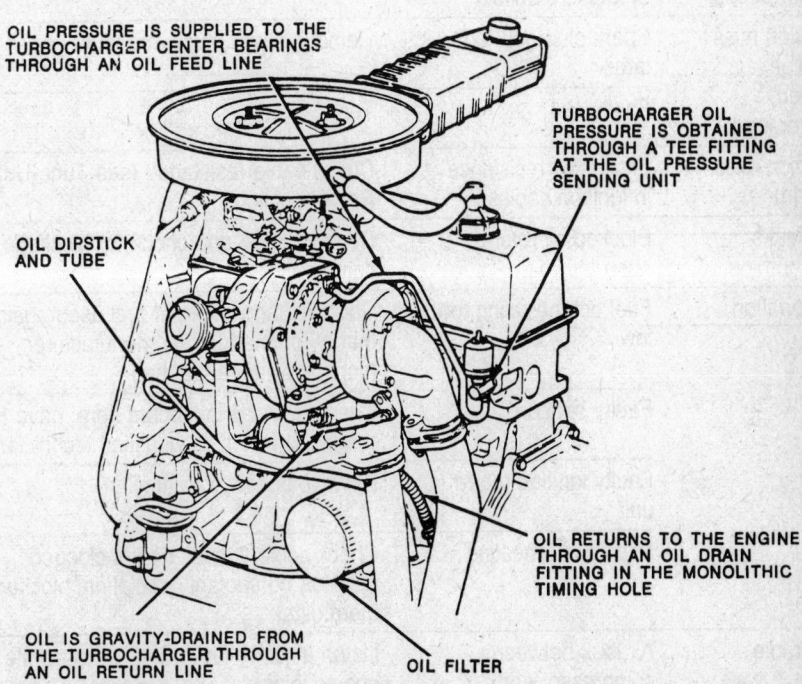

OIL PRESSURE IS SUPPLIED TO THE TURBOCHARGER CENTER BEARINGS THROUGH AN OIL FEED LINE

TURBOCHARGER OIL PRESSURE IS OBTAINED THROUGH A TEE FITTING AT THE OIL PRESSURE SENDING UNIT

OIL DIPSTICK AND TUBE

OIL RETURNS TO THE ENGINE THROUGH AN OIL DRAIN FITTING IN THE MONOLITHIC TIMING HOLE

OIL IS GRAVITY-DRAINED FROM THE TURBOCHARGER THROUGH AN OIL RETURN LINE

OIL FILTER

Ford 2.3 L turbocharger lubrication (© Ford Motor Co.)

LUBRICATION

The turbocharger shaft spins in bearings lubricated by engine oil. Turbine speeds routinely reach 120,000–140,000 rpm, making an adequate and well-filtered oil supply critical for proper operation. Any interruption or contamination of the oil supply will result in engine damage as well. Ford cautions that accelerating the engine to top rpm immediately after starting can result in engine and turbocharger damage (due to the lack of oil pressure). Immediately shutting down the engine after it has been operated at high rpm for an extended period can also result in turbocharger damage, since oil pressure will be shut off, but the turbine will continue to spin for a few moments. (Shutting the throttle abruptly when the engine is at high speed can also cause extensive damage, but for a different reason: sudden closed throttle operation causes the mixture to become very lean, resulting in detonation, high engine temperature, and consequent damage.)

General Motors recommends that following procedure before starting the engine when changing the oil and filter, or performing any operation which results in oil drainage or loss:

1. Disconnect the ignition switch connector (pink wire) from the HEI distributor module.

2. Crank the engine several times until the oil light goes out. Do not crank the engine for more than thirty seconds at a time, to avoid starter damage.

3. Reconnect the pink wire. Start the engine.

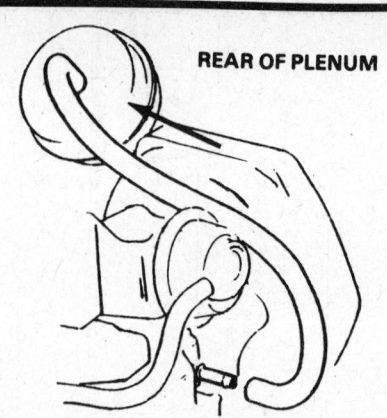

REAR OF PLENUM

New type GM wastegate diaphragm—1981 and later Riviera (© Buick Div., GM Corp.)

TURBOCHARGER TROUBLESHOOTING

Problem	Cause	How To Check	Solution
No boost	Gasket leak, hole in exhaust system	Temporarily block tailpipe with engine running. Any exhaust leaks in the system will be heard.	Repair leaks (usually at gasket surfaces)
	Dirty air filter	Remove air filter and check	Replace or clean filter
	Blocked air intake	Visually inspect for blockage	Clear intake
	Worn valves or rings	Compression test engine	Repair
	Throttle valves not opening completely	Manually operate throttle linkage, check valve movement	Adjust linkage, repair carburetor
	Exhaust blockage	Check catalytic converter for melted and blocked catalyst, check muffler and exhaust pipes for debris	Replace catalytic converter, repair exhaust system
	Wastegate stuck open	Test wastegate operation	Repair or replace wastegate assembly
Fuel odor under boost	Leak at compressor or intake manifold	Look for fuel stains at fittings	Tighten fittings or replace gaskets
Ignition miss at high speed, under load	Spark plug gap too large	Remove spark plugs, measure gap	Reduce gap
	Faulty coil	Test Coil	Replace
Ignition miss (often)	Excessive resistance in ignition cables	Check cable resistance (see Tune-Up Unit Repair section)	Replace cables as necessary
Oil leaks into turbine	Blocked oil return hose	Remove hose and check for blockage or crimps	Repair or replace hose
Detonation	Fuel octane rating too low	Check octane rating of fuel used against that recommended by manufacturer (consult owner's manual)	Switch to higher octane unleaded fuel
	Faulty sensor	Check G.M. as instructed here; have Ford system checked by qualified technician	Replace as necessary
	Faulty ignition retard unit	Refer to qualified technician	Repair or replace as necessary
	Engine overheating	Check coolant level, debris clogged radiator, no coolant circulation, blocked thermostat	Repair or replace as necessary
Poor idle	Air leak between compressor and carburetor	Listen at joints for hissing sound while the engine idles	Repair

Electronic Ignition Systems

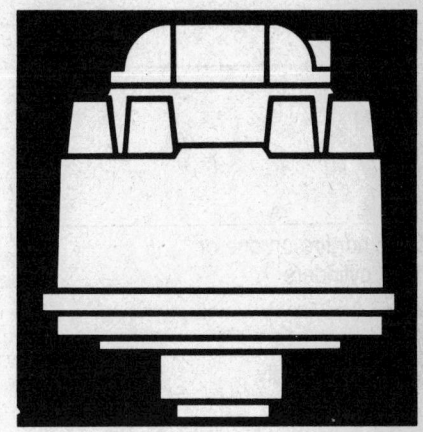

General Information

The solid state electronic ignition system has replaced the breaker point distributor on all current production automotive gasoline engines. By eliminating the breaker points, electronic ignition systems have become almost maintenance-free and performance doesn't deteriorate with mileage. In a typical system, the distributor contains an electronic control unit or module which replaces the breaker plate. Within the distributor body is a permanent magnet and a variable reluctance pick-up (or Hall Effect pick-up and rotating shutter). The electronic control module receives signals from the pick-up coil and in turn charges and fires the secondary ignition coil. A rotor then distributes the high voltage current to the proper spark plug through the distributor cap and wires. The only exception to this general description is the new GM Computer Controlled Coil Ignition (C3I) system which eliminates the distributor altogether.

All solid state ignition systems can be checked for proper operation by performing simple resistance tests, however some computer-based electronic ignition systems can be damaged by the use of incorrect test equipment. Before testing any primary ignition components, a secondary system inspection should be done to eliminate obvious problems such as loose or corroded connections, broken or shorted wires and damaged components.

--------- CAUTION ---------
Due to the dangerously high voltage levels present in any electronic ignition system, DO NOT touch any secondary ignition system components while the engine is running or the starter is being cranked. Use insulated tools to hold coil or spark plug wires when testing.

Intermittent problems can be caused by extremely high or low temperature operating conditions and any damage to the trigger wheel or Hall Effect pick-up (cracks, chips, etc.) will degrade ignition system performance. Service of solid state ignition systems involves testing and fault diagnosis of electronic components and circuits, using a voltohmmeter or digital multimeter. The control units, magnetic pick-ups and other solid state components are replaced as a unit so accurate troubleshooting is essential to avoid the needless replacement of expensive parts.

General Service Precautions

- Always turn the ignition switch OFF when disconnecting or connecting any electrical connectors or components.

- Never reverse the battery polarity or disconnect the battery with the engine running.

- Do not pierce spark plug or wiring harness wires with test probes for any reason. Due to their more pliable construction, it is important to route spark plug wires properly to avoid chafing or cutting.

- Disconnect the ignition switch feed wire at the distributor when making compression tests to avoid arcing that may damage components, especially on computer-based ignition systems.

- Do not remove grease or dielectric compound from components or connectors when installing. Some manufacturers use grease to prevent corrosion and dielectric compound to dissipate heat generated during normal module operation.

- Check all replacement part numbers carefully. Installing the wrong component for a specific application can damage the system.

- All manufacturers instructions included with any testing equipment must be read carefully to insure proper capability and test results. Inaccurate readings and/or damage to ignition system components may result due to the use of improper test equipment.

ELECTRONIC IGNITION QUICK CHECK CHART
(Non-computer controlled systems only)

Condition	Possible Cause	Correction
Abrupt backfire	Control unit or ignition module malfunction. Incorrect timing. Bad cap or rotor	Check ignition timing. Replace control unit or module. Replace cap or rotor

ELECTRONIC IGNITION QUICK CHECK CHART
(Non-computer controlled systems only)

Condition	Possible Cause	Correction
Intermittent running	Magnetic pick-up or stator malfunction. Bad trigger wheel, reluctor or armature. Control unit or ignition module failure	Replace defective components after testing as described under appropriate system in this unit repair section
Does not fire on one or more cylinders	Defective pick-up, stator, trigger wheel, reluctor or armature. Bad spark plugs or ignition wires	Replace components as necessary
Cuts off suddenly	Malfunction in control unit of module. Damaged pick-up or stator	Check operation of pick-up and stator. Replace control unit or module
Won't start	Control unit or module failure. Defective cap, rotor, pick-up or stator ①	Replace control unit or module after testing. Replace distributor components as necessary
Poor performance, no power under load	Defective pick-up, stator, or ignition coil. Worn or fouled spark plugs. Bad plug wires	Check distributor components for signs of wear or damage. Replace spark plugs and wires
Arcing or excessive burning on rotor or distributor cap	Worn or fouled spark plugs. Bad plug wires	Replace spark plugs and wires

NOTE: This chart assumes the described conditions are problems in the electronic ignition system and not the result of another malfunction. Always perform basic checks for fuel, spark and compression first. See the individual system sections for all test procedures
① Check ballast resistor on Chrysler models

AMC Solid State Ignition (SSI) System

GENERAL INFORMATION

AMC Solid State Ignition (SSI) is standard equipment on all 1978 and later six and eight cylinder engines. 1980 and later four cylinder engines use the Delco HEI system, covered later in this section.

The system consists of a sensor and toothed trigger wheel inside the distributor, and a permanently sealed electronic control unit which determines dwell, in addition to the coil, ignition wires, and spark plugs.

The trigger wheel rotates on the distributor shaft. As one of its teeth nears the sensor magnet, the magnetic field shifts toward the tooth. When the tooth and sensor are aligned, the magnetic field is shifted to its maximum, signaling the electronic control unit to switch off the coil primary cur-

rent. This starts an electronic timer inside the control unit, which allows the primary current to remain off only long enough for the spark plug to fire. The timer adjusts the amount of time primary current is off according to conditions, thus automatically adjusting dwell. There is also a special circuit within the control unit to detect and ignore spurious signals. Spark timing is adjusted by both mechanical (centrifugal) and vacuum advance.

A wire of 1.35 ohms resistance is spliced

SOLID STATE IGNITION: AMC

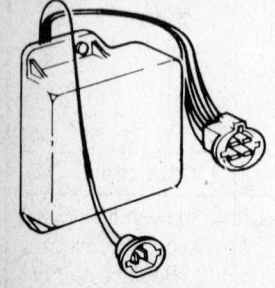

CONTROL UNIT

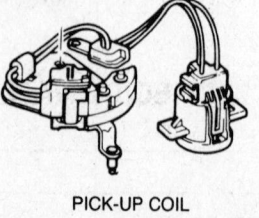

PICK-UP COIL

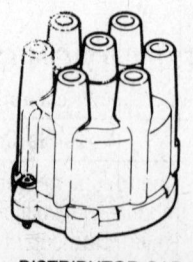

DISTRIBUTOR CAP

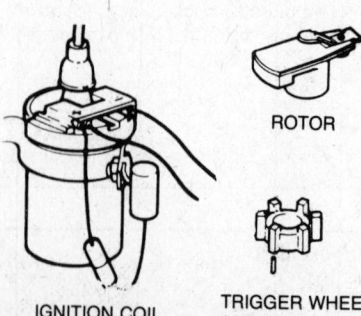

IGNITION COIL

ROTOR

TRIGGER WHEEL AND PIN

into the ignition feed to reduce voltage to the coil during running conditions. The resistance wire is by-passed when the engine is being started so that full battery voltage may be supplied to the coil. Bypass is accomplished by the I-terminal on the solenoid.

SECONDARY CIRCUIT TEST

1. Disconnect the coil wire from the center of the distributor cap.

NOTE: Twist the rubber boot slightly in either direction, then grasp the boot and pull straight up. Do not pull on the wire, and do not use pliers.

Hold the wire ½ in. from a ground with a pair of insulated pliers and a heavy glove. As the engine is cranked, watch for a spark.

2. If a spark appears, reconnect the coil wire. Remove the wire from one spark plug, and test for a spark as above.

—— CAUTION ——
Do not remove the spark plug wires from cylinders 3 or 5 (1978–79) or 1 or 5 (1980 and later) on a 6 cylinder engine, or cylinders 3 or 4 of a V8 when performing this test, as sensor damage could occur.

If a spark occurs, the problem is in the fuel system or ignition timing. If no spark occurs, check for a defective rotor, cap, or spark plug wires.

3. If no spark occurs from the coil wire in Step 2, test the coil wire resistance with an ohmmeter. It must not exceed 10,000 ohms.

COIL PRIMARY CIRCUIT TEST

1. Turn the ignition On. Connect a voltmeter to the coil positive (+) terminal and a ground. If the voltage is 5.5–6.5 volts, go to Step 2. If above 7 volts, go to Step 4. If below 5.5 volts, disconnect the condenser lead and measure. If the voltage is now 5.5–65. volts, replace the condenser. If not, go to Step 6.

2. With the voltmeter connected as in Step 1, read the voltage with the engine cranking. If battery voltage is indicated, the circuit is okay. If not, go to Step 3.

3. Check for a short or open in the starter solenoid I-terminal wire. Check the solenoid for proper operation.

4. Disconnect the wire from the starter solenoid I-terminal, with the ignition On and the voltmeter connected as in Step 1. If the voltage drops to 5.5–6.5 volts, replace the solenoid. If not, connect a jumper between the coil negative (−) terminal and a ground. If the voltage drops to 5.5–6.5 volts, go to Step 5. If not, repair the resistance wire.

5. Check for continuity between the coil (−) terminal and D4, and D1 to ground. If the continuity is okay, replace the control unit. If not, check for an open wire and go back to Step 2.

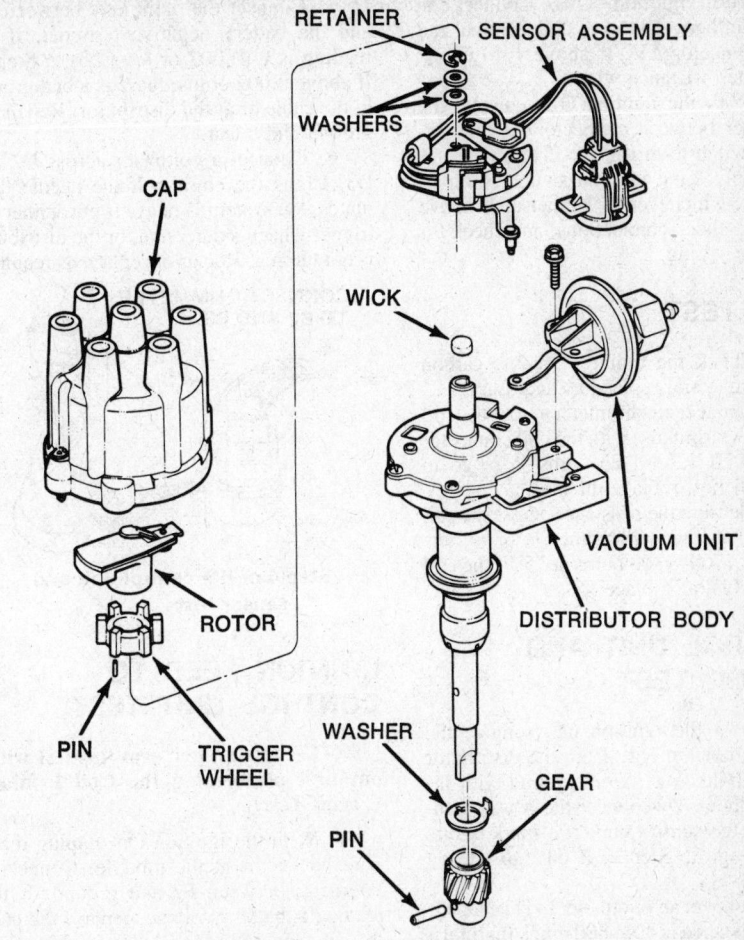

Six cylinder SSI distributor—V8 similar

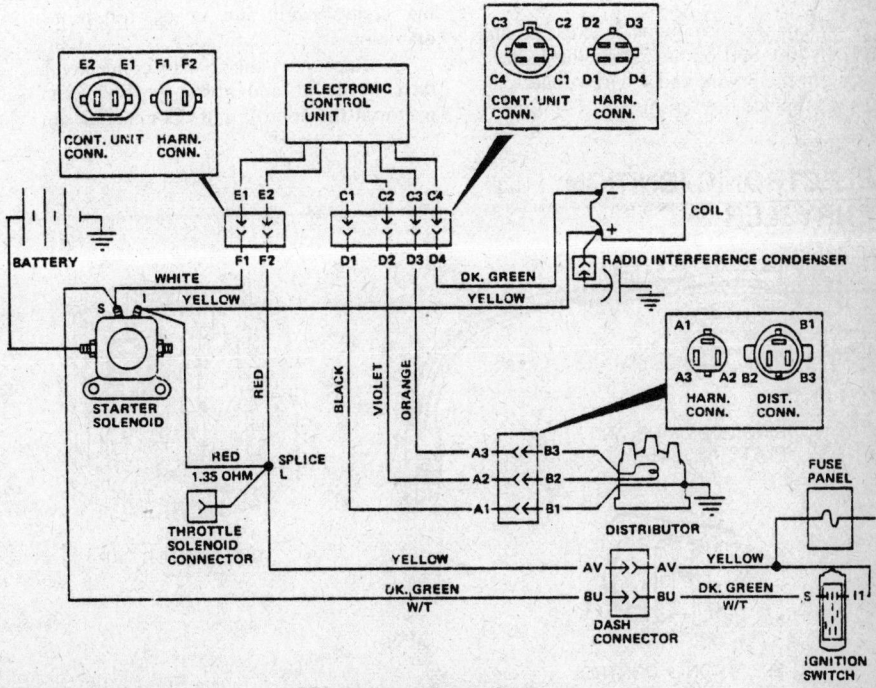

SSI system schematic

6. Turn ignition Off. Connect an ohmmeter between the + coil terminal and dash connector AV. If above 1.40 ohms, repair the resistance wire.

7. With the ignition Off, connect the ohmmeter between connector AV and ignition switch terminal 11. If less than 0.1 ohm, replace the ignition switch or repair the wire, whichever is the cause. If above 0.1 ohm, check connections, and check for defective wiring.

COIL TEST

1. Check the coil for cracks, carbon tracks, etc., and replace as necessary.

2. Connect an ohmmeter across the coil + and − terminals, with the coil connector removed. If 1.13–1.23 ohms/75°F, go to Step 3. If not, replace the coil.

3. Measure the resistance across the coil center tower and either the + or − terminal. If 7700–9300 ohms at 75°F, the coil is okay. If not, replace.

CONTROL UNIT AND SENSOR TEST

1. With the ignition On, remove the coil high tension wire from the distributor cap and hold ½ in. from ground with insulated pliers. Disconnect the 4 wire connector at the control unit. If a spark occurs (normal), go to Step 2. If not, go to Step 5.

2. Connect an ohmmeter to D2 and D3. If the resistance is 400–800 ohms (normal), go to Step 6. If not, go to Step 3.

3. Disconnect and reconnect the 3 wire connector at distributor. If the reading is now 400–800 ohms, go to Step 6. If not, disconnect the 3 wire connector and go to Step 4.

4. Connect the ohmmeter across B2 and B3. If 400–800 ohms, repair the harness between the 3 wire and 4 wire connectors. If not, replace the sensor.

5. Connect the ohmmeter between D1 and the battery negative terminal. If the reading is 0 (0.002 or less), go to Step 2. If above 0.002 ohms, there is a bad ground in the cable or at the distributor. Repair the ground and retest.

6. Connect a voltmeter across D2 and D3. Crank the engine. If the needle fluctuates, the system is okay. If not, either the trigger wheel is defective, or the distributor is not turning. Repair or replace as required.

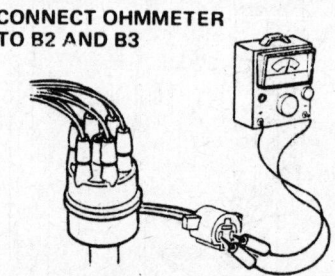

CONNECT OHMMETER TO B2 AND B3

Step 4 of the control unit and sensor test

IGNITION FEED TO CONTROL UNIT TEST

NOTE: Do not perform this test without first performing the Coil Primary Circuit Test.

1. With the ignition On, unplug the 2 wire connector at the module. Connect a voltmeter between F2 and ground. If the reading is battery voltage, replace the control unit and go to Step 3. If not, go to Step 2.

2. Repair the cause of the voltage reduction: either the ignition switch or a corroded dash connector. Check for a spark at the coil wire. If okay, stop. If not, replace the control unit and check for proper operation.

3. Reconnect the 2 wire connector at the control unit, and unplug the 4 wire connector at the control unit. Connect an am-

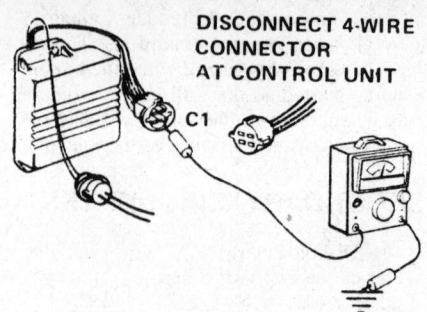

DISCONNECT 4-WIRE CONNECTOR AT CONTROL UNIT

Step 3 of the ignition feed to control unit test

meter between C1 and ground. If it reads 0.9–1.1 amps, the system is okay. If not, replace the module.

Chrysler Electronic Ignition System

NOTE: This section applies to all Chrysler products except the Omni, Horizon, Aries and Reliant, which are covered in the following sections.

GENERAL INFORMATION

This system consists of a special pulse-sending distributor, an electronic control unit, a two-element ballast resistor, and a special ignition coil.

The distributor does not contain breaker points or a condenser, these parts being replaced by a distributor reluctor and a pick-up unit.

For better timing control and fuel economy, some 1981–84 models use a dual pickup system. Vehicles with this system use a "start" pick-up, a "run" pick-up, and a dual pick-up start-run delay. In the "run" mode, the operation of the dual pick-up system is the same as that of the single pick-up system. During cranking, the dual pick-up start-run relay is energized (through

ELECTRONIC IGNITION: CHRYSLER

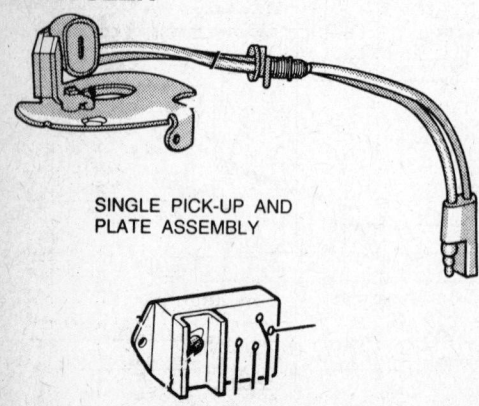

SINGLE PICK-UP AND PLATE ASSEMBLY

ELECTRONIC CONTROL UNIT (ECU)

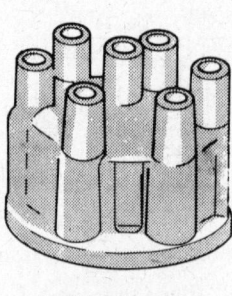

DISTRIBUTOR CAP

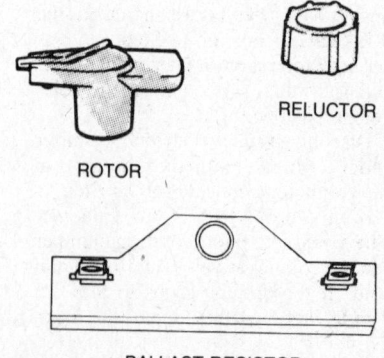

ROTOR

RELUCTOR

BALLAST RESISTOR

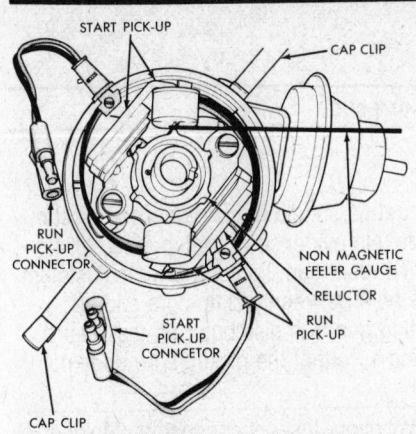

View of a dual pick-up Chrysler electronic ignition distributor

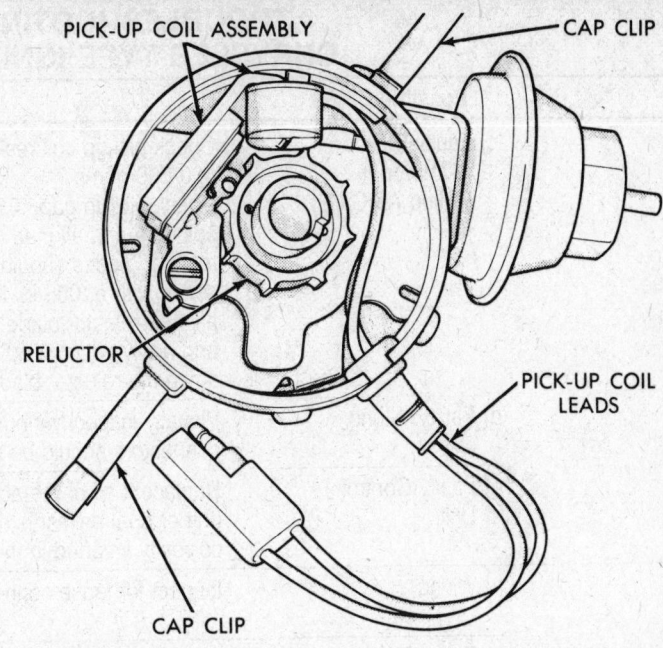

View of a single pick-up Chrysler electronic ignition distributor—eight cylinder version shown, six cylinder similar

the starter solenoid circuit), which allows the start pick-up to adjust the timing for starting purposes only. As soon as the starter solenoid is de-energized, the start-run relay switches the sensing function back to the ''run'' pick-up.

NOTE: Prior to the 1981 model year, the dual pick-up system was used only with the Lean Burn/Electronic Spark Control systems.

OPERATION

The ignition primary circuit is connected from the battery, through the ignition switch, through the primary side of the ignition coil, to the control unit where it is grounded. The secondary circuit is the same as in conventional ignition systems: the secondary side of the coil, the coil wire to the distributor, the rotor, the spark plug wires, and the spark plugs.

The magnetic pulse distributor is also connected to the control unit. As the distributor shaft rotates, the distributor reluctor turns past the pick-up unit. As the reluctor turns past the pick-up unit, each of the eight (or six) teeth on the reluctor pass near the pickup unit once during each distributor revolution (two crankshaft revolutions since the distributor runs at one-half crankshaft speed). As the reluctor teeth move close to the pick-up unit, the magnetic rotating reluctor induces voltage into the magnetic pick-up unit. This voltage pulse is sent to the ignition control unit from the magnetic pick-up unit. When the pulse enters the control unit, it signals the control unit to interrupt the ignition primary circuit. This causes the primary circuit to collapse and begins the induction of the magnetic lines of force from the primary side of the coil into the secondary side of the coil. This induction provides the required voltage to fire the spark plugs.

The advantages of this system are that the transistors in the control unit can make and break the primary ignition circuit much faster than conventional ignition points can, and higher primary voltage can be utilized, since this system can be made to handle higher voltage without adverse effects, whereas ignition breaker points cannot. The quicker switching time of this system allows longer coil primary circuit saturation time and longer induction time when the primary circuit collapses. This increased time allows the primary circuit to build up more current and the secondary circuit to discharge more current.

TROUBLESHOOTING
CHRYSLER TYPE IGNITION

Condition	Possible Cause	Correction
ENGINE WILL NOT START (Fuel and Carburetion Known to be OK)	a) Dual Ballast	Check resistance of each section: Compensating resistance: .50-.60 ohms @ 70°-80°F Auxiliary Ballast: 4.75-5.75 ohms Replace if faulty. Check wire positions.
	b) Faulty Ignition Coil	Check for carbonized tower. Check primary and secondary resistances: Primary: 1.41-1.79 ohms @ 70°-80°F Secondary: 9,200—11,700 ohms @ 70°—80°F Check in coil tester.

TROUBLESHOOTING
CHRYSLER TYPE IGNITION

Condition	Possible Cause	Correction
ENGINE WILL NOT START (Fuel and Carburetion Known to be OK)	c) Faulty Pickup or Improper Pickup Air Gap	Check pickup coil resistance: 400-600 ohms. Check pickup gap. .010 in. feeler gauge should not slip between pickup coil core and aligned reluctor blade. No evidence of pickup core striking reluctor blades should be visible. To reset gap, tighten pickup adjustment screw with a .008 in. feeler gauge held between pickup core and an aligned reluctor blade. After resetting gap, run distributor on test stand and apply vacuum advance, making sure that the pickup core does not strike the reluctor blades.
	d) Faulty Wiring	Visually inspect wiring for brittle insulation. Inspect connectors. Molded connectors should be inspected for rubber inside female terminals.
	e) Faulty Control Unit	Replace if all of the above checks are negative. Whenever the control unit or dual ballast is replaced, make sure the dual ballast wires are correctly inserted in the keyed molded connector.
ENGINE SURGES SEVERELY (Not Lean) Carburetor	a) Wiring	Inspect for loose connection and/or broken conductors in harness
	b) Faulty Pickup Leads	Disconnect vacuum advance. If surging stops, replace pickup.
	c) Ignition Coil	Check for intermittent primary.
ENGINE MISSES (Carburetion OK)	a) Spark Plugs	Check plugs. Clean and regap if necessary.
	b) Secondary Cable	Check cables with an ohmmeter, or observe secondary circuit performance with an oscilloscope.
	c) Ignition Coil	Check for cabonized tower. Check in coil tester.
	d) Wiring	Check for loose or dirty connections.
	e) Faulty Pickup Lead	Disconnect vacuum advance. If miss stops, replace pickup.
	f) Control Unit	Replace if the above checks are negative.

SYSTEM TEST

Single Pick-Up Systems

A voltmeter with a 20,000 ohm/volt rating and a 1½ volt battery powered ohmmeter are required. Car battery voltage must be at least 12 volts.

1. Remove the wiring plug from the control unit.

— CAUTION —

Make sure the ignition switch is off when removing or replacing the control unit connector.

2. Turn the ignition switch ON.
3. Ground the negative voltmeter lead.
4. Connect the voltmeter positive lead to the harness connector cavity No. 1 (shown on the schematic). Voltage should be within 1 volt of battery voltage with all accessories off. If not, check the circuit through to the battery.
5. Connect the voltmeter positive lead to cavity No. 2. Voltage should be within 1 volt of battery voltage with all accessories off. If not, check the circuit through to the battery.
6. This test is for models through 1979 only. Connect the voltmeter positive lead

to cavity No. 3. Voltage should be within 1 volt of battery voltage with all accessories off. If not, check the circuit through to the battery.

7. Turn the ignition switch off.
8. Connect the ohmmeter leads to cavities No. 4 and 5. The resistance should be 150–900 ohms. If it isn't, detach the dual lead connector from the distributor. Check the resistance at the dual lead connector. If it still isn't within the range, replace the distributor pick-up coil.

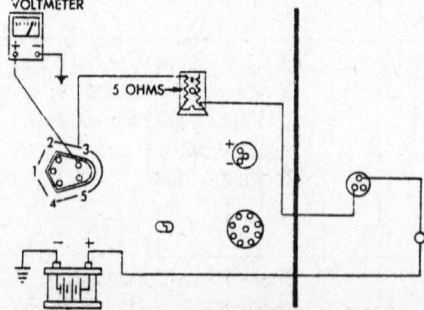

Single pick-up Chrysler system— circuit to be checked if the voltage at ECU connector cavity No. 3 is not within battery voltage

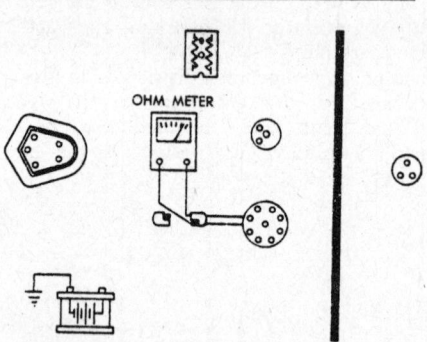

Single pick-up Chrysler system—checking the resistance at the pick-up coil connector

9. Connect one ohmmeter lead to a ground and the other to either distributor connector. If the ohmmeter shows a reading, replace the distributor pick-up coil.
10. Connect one ohmmeter lead to a ground and the other to the control unit pin No. 5. The ohmmeter should show continuity. If not, remove and remount the control unit and check again. Replace the control unit if no continuity can be established.
11. Make sure the ignition switch is off and replace the control unit connector plug and the distributor plug.

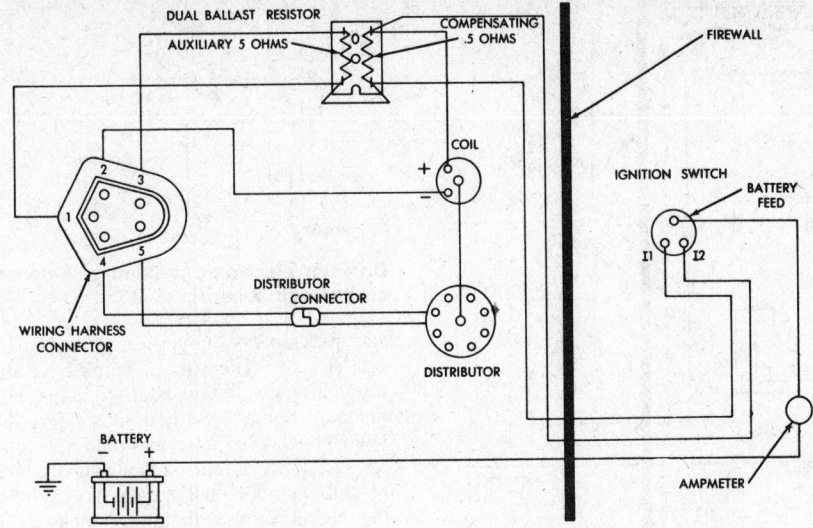

Single pick-up Chrysler electronic ignition system schematic

12. Check the air gap adjustment, as shown later.

13. Remove the center wire from the distributor cap. Very cautiously, using insulated pliers and a very heavy glove, hold the cable about ³/₁₆ in. from the engine block and have the starter operated. If there is no spark, replace the control unit. Try the test again. If there is still no spark, replace the coil.

Dual Pick-Up Systems
— CAUTION —
The ignition must be OFF before connecting or disconnecting the ECU wiring.

A voltmeter with a 20,000 ohm/volt rating, and a self-powered (by a 9V battery) ohmmeter are needed for this testing procedure. Check and note the battery voltage, and make sure the specific gravity of the battery is at least 1.220 (temperature corrected). The battery must be fully charged to properly test the system.

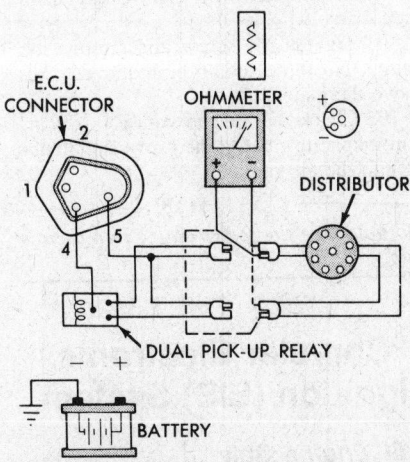

Dual pick-up Chrysler system—testing the resistance of both pick-up coils

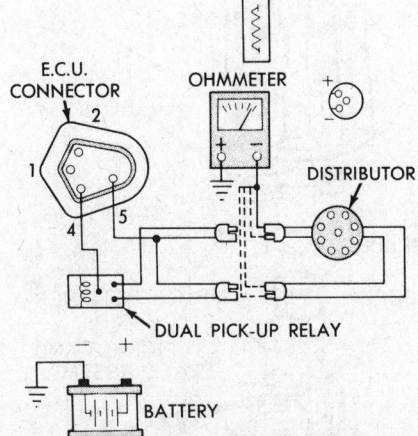

Dual pick-up Chrysler system—testing for shorts at each pick-up coil terminal

1. Disconnect the high voltage (secondary) coil wire from the distributor cap.

2. Turn the ignition switch ON. Using insulated pliers, hold the exposed coil wire terminal about ¼ in. away from a good engine ground and momentarily ground the negative (−) coil terminal, using a jumper wire. A spark should jump from the coil wire terminal to ground. If spark is evident, proceed to Step 8.

3. If no spark was noted:

a. Turn the ignition OFF.

b. Disconnect the four-terminal connector from the electronic control unit (ECU).

c. Repeat Step 2.

d. If spark was noted, replace the ECU.

4. If no spark was noted during step 3c:

a. Turn the ignition ON and measure the voltage at the postive (+) coil terminal; it should be within 1 volt of battery voltage. If the voltage is correct, proceed to Step 6.

5. If the voltage at the positive (+) coil

terminal was not within 1 volt of battery voltage:

a. Replace the starter relay and check all wiring between the battery and the positive (+) coil terminal. Correct any wiring fault(s) as required.

b. If the circuit between the battery and the positive (+) coil terminal is not continuous, replace the ignition resistor and repeat Step 4a.

6. With the ignition ON, check the voltage at the coil negative (−) terminal; it should be within 1 volt of battery voltage. If battery voltage is not obtained at the negative (−) coil terminal, turn the ignition OFF, and disconnect the ECU harness connector from the ECU. Using an ohmmeter, check for continuity between the negative (−) coil terminal and cavity 2 of the harness connector. Repair the wiring as necessary.

7. If battery voltage was available during Step 6, but no spark was produced during Step 2, replace the ignition coil.

8. If spark was obtained during Step 2, but the engine won't start, turn the ignition OFF and disconnect the wiring from the ECU. Turn the ignition ON and check the voltage at cavity 2 of the ECU harness connector; it should be within 1 volt of battery voltage. If the proper voltage is obtained:

a. Turn the ignition OFF. Using an ohmmeter, check the resistance between cavities 4 and 5 of the ECU wiring harness connector. Resistance should be 150–190 ohms: if it is, proceed to Step 8c; if not, proceed to Step 8b.

b. Disconnect the pick-up leads and measure the resistance as shown. If the resistance is not 150–900 ohms, replace the pick-up coil(s) and proceed to Steps 9a and 9b.

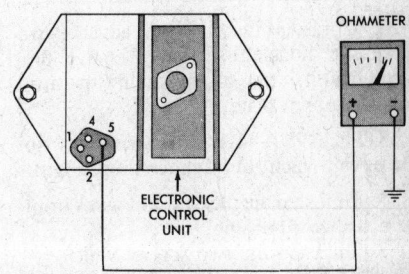

Dual pick-up Chrysler system—testing pin 5 of the ECU for ground

c. If the resistance is okay, either the wires between cavities 4 and 5 are opened or shorted, or the dual pick-up start-run relay is defective. Repair the wires or replace the relay as necessary.

9. Check for shorts at each pick-up lead with an ohmmeter (ignition OFF). To do this, ground one ohmmeter lead and touch the other ohmmeter lead to each of the pick-up wires. If a reading is noted, the pick-up is shorted. If either pick-up is shorted, replace it.

a. If there is no short, check pin 5 of the ECU to make sure that it is properly

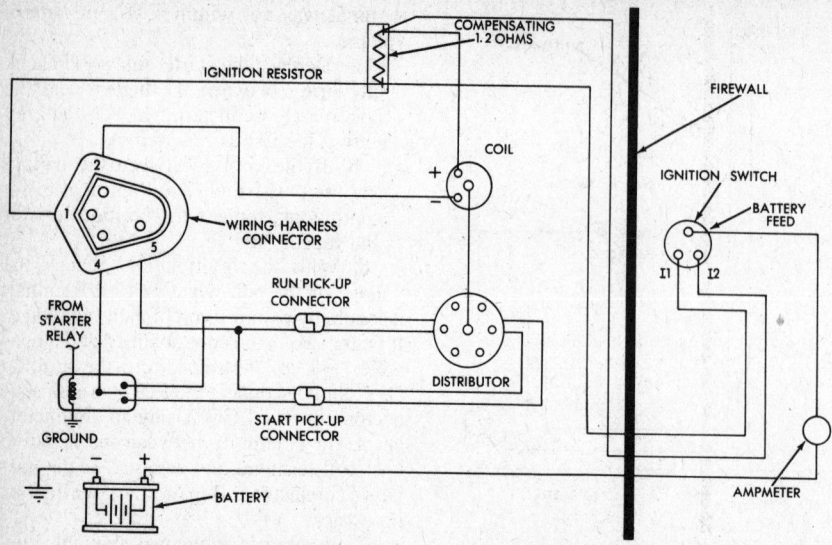

Dual pick-up Chrysler electronic ignition system schematic

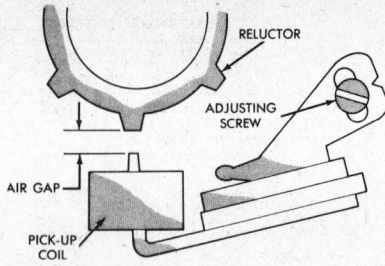

Chrysler electronic ignition pick-up coil air gap adjustment

grounded. If the ohmmeter registers an open circuit between pin 5 and ground, check the ECU for bad connections and/or loose mounting screws.

b. If the ECU ground is okay, reinstall all connectors and again check for spark. If no spark is obtained, replace the ECU.

PICK-UP COIL REPLACEMENT

1. Remove the distributor from the engine as outlined in the appropriate car section.

2. Using two small pry-bars (maximum ⁷⁄₁₆ in. wide), pry the reluctor off the shaft from the bottom.

— CAUTION —
Do not damage the teeth on the reluctor.

3. Unfasten the vacuum advance-to-distributor housing screws. Remove the vacuum unit, after disconnecting the arm from the upper plate.

NOTE: 1980–84 ESA distributors do not have a vacuum advance diaphragm.

4. Unfasten the pick-up coil wires from the distributor housing.

5. Unfasten the two screws which secure the lower plate to the distributor housing. Lift out the lower plate together with the upper plate and pick-up coil(s).

6. Separate the upper and lower plates by depressing the retaining clip on the underside of the plate and slide it away from the stud. The pick-up coil(s) will come off with the upper plate; they cannot be separated; they must be serviced as an assembly.

Installation is the reverse of removal. Place a small amount of distributor grease on the support pins on the lower plate.

AIR GAP ADJUSTMENT

Lean Burn engines through 1977 (first generation system) have two pick-up coils. The

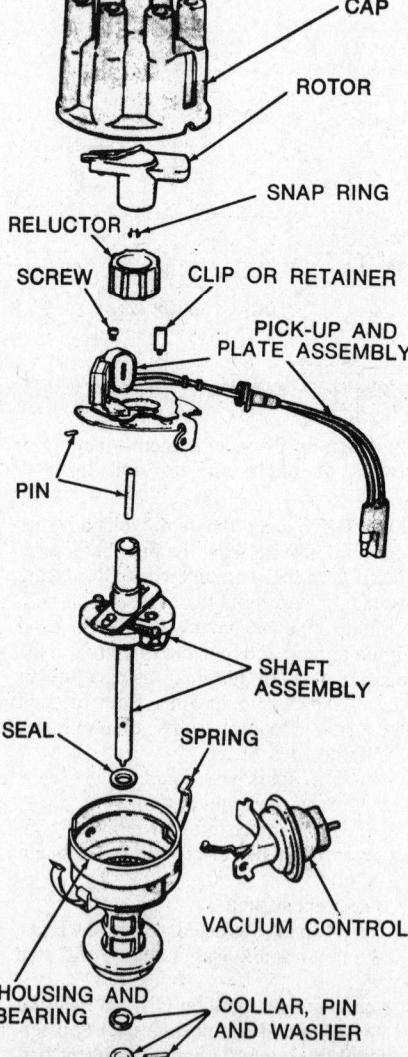

Disassembled view of a typical single pick-up Chrysler electronic ignition distributor

start pick-up has a larger connector than the run pick-up. The two pick-ups have different air gaps, but are adjusted in the same manner. Some 1980 and most 1981 and later models also have two pick-ups.

1. Align one reluctor tooth with the pick-up coil tooth. On dual pick-up models, align the reluctor tooth with the start pick-up coil tooth.

2. Loosen the pick-up coil hold-down screw.

3. Insert a non-magnetic feeler gauge between the reluctor tooth and the pick-up coil tooth. The gauge should be 0.006 in. 1978 and later.

4. Adjust the air gap so that contact is made between the reluctor tooth, the feeler gauge, and the pick-up coil tooth.

5. Tighten the pick-up coil screw.

6. Remove the feeler gauge.

NOTE: No force should be required to remove the gauge.

7. Check the air gap with a non-magnetic feeler gauge: 0.008 in. for 1977 and later. The gauge should not fit into the air gap.

— CAUTION —
Do not force the feeler gauge into the air gap.

8. On dual pick-up models, align one reluctor tooth with the run pick-up coil. Loosen the pick-up coil screw. Insert a 0.012 in. non-magnetic feeler gauge between the reluctor and pick-up coil, and move the pick-up coil against the feeler gauge, as in Step 4.

9. Tighten the screw and remove the gauge. No force should be required to remove the gauge.

10. Check the air gap with a 0.014 in. non-magnetic gauge. The gauge should not fit into the air gap.

— CAUTION —
Do not force the feeler gauge into the air gap.

Chrysler Electronic Ignition (EIS) System

2.6L Engine Only

This system consists of the battery, ignition switch, ignition coil, IC igniter (electronic control unit) which is built into the distributor, spark plugs and primary and secondary wiring. Primary current to the coil is switched on and off by the IC igniter in response to timing signals produced by a distributor magnetic pick-up.

TROUBLESHOOTING

1. Remove the coil wire from the center of the distributor cap.

2. Using heavy gloves and insulated pilers, hold the end of the wire 3/16–3/8 in. away from a good engine ground and crank the engine.

NOTE: Make sure there are no fuel leaks before performing this test.

3. If there is a spark at the coil wire, it must be bright blue in color and fire consistently. If it is, continue to crank the engine while slowly moving the coil wire away from ground. Look for arcing at the coil tower. If arcing occurs, replace coil. If there is no spark, or spark is weak or not consistent, proceed to the next step.

If a good spark is present, check the condition of the distributor cap, rotor, plug wires and spark plugs. If these check out, the ignition system is working: check the fuel system and engine mechanical systems.

4. With the ignition on, measure the voltage at the negative coil terminal. It should be the same as battery voltage. If it is 3V or less, the IC distributor is defective. If there is no voltage, check for an open circuit in the coil or wiring.

5. With the ignition on, hold the coil wire as instructed in Step 2 and, using a jumper wire, momentarily connect the negative coil terminal to ground. There should be a spark at the coil wire.

6. If there is no spark, check for voltage at the positive coil terminal with the key on. Voltage should be at least 9V. If proper voltage is obtained, the coil is defective and should be replaced. If proper voltage is not obtained, check the wiring and connections.

Chrysler Corporation Hall Effect Electronic Ignition

Except 2.6L Engine

The Hall Effect electronic ignition is used in conjunction with the Chrysler Lean Burn/Electronic Spark Control System (covered in the Emission Controls Unit Repair Section). It consists of a sealed Spark Control Computer, five engine sensors (vacuum transducer, coolant switch, Hall Effect pickup assembly, throttle position transducer, and carburetor switch), coil, spark plugs, ballast resistor, and the various wires needed to connect the components. Only four of the five engine sensors are used on all 1979–80 models and on 1981 and later

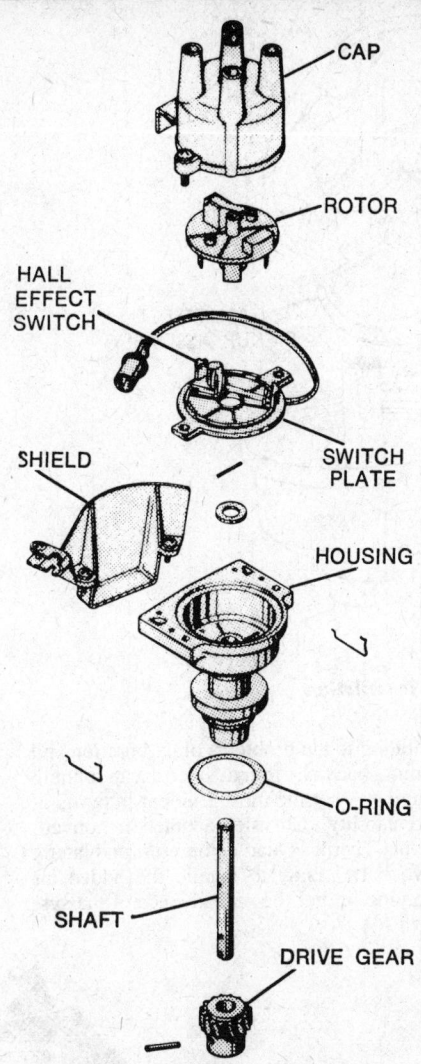

Hall Effect distributor—exploded view

models not equipped with the Feed Back carburetor; the throttle position transducer is no longer used. On 1981 and later models with Feed Back carburetor, an oxygen sensor in the exhaust manifold is included.

The distributor contains the Hall Effect pickup assembly which replaces the breaker points assembly in conventional systems. The pickup assembly supplies the computer with information on engine speed and crankshaft position, and is only one of signals which the computer uses as input to determine ignition timing. The Hall Effect is a shift in magnetic field, caused, in this installation, when one of the rotor blades passes between the two arms of the sensor.

OPERATION

There are essentially two modes of operation of the Spark Control computer: the start mode and the run mode. The start mode is only used during engine cranking. During cranking only the Hall Effect pickup signals the computer. These signals are interpreted to provide a fixed number of degrees of spark advance. The computer shuts off coil

primary current in accordance with the pickup signals. As in conventional ignition systems, primary current shutdown causes secondary field collapse, and the high voltage is sent from the coil to the distributor, which then sends it to the spark plug.

After the engine starts, and during normal engine operation, the computer functions in the run mode. In this mode the Hall Effect pickup serves as only one of the signals to the computer. It is a reference signal of maximum possible spark advance. The computer then determines, from information provided by the other engine sensors, how much of this advance is necessary, and shuts down the primary current accordingly to fire the spark plug at the exact moment when this advance (crankshaft position) is reached.

There is a third mode of operation which only becomes functional when the computer fails. This is the limp-in mode. This mode functions on signals from the pickup only, and results in very poor engine performance. However, it does allow the car to be driven to a repair shop. If a failure occurs in the pickup assembly or the start mode of the computer, the engine will neither start nor run.

SYSTEM TESTS

All system tests are covered under "Chrysler Corporation Lean Burn/Electronic Spark Control System".

The ignition coil can be tested on a conventional coil tester. The ballast resistor, mounted on the firewall, must be included in all tests (through 1980). Primary resistance at 70°F should be 1.60–1.79 ohms for the Chrysler Prestolite coil, and 1.41–1.62 ohms for the Chrysler Essex coil. Secondary resistance should be 9400–11,700 ohms for the Prestolite, 8000–11,200 ohms (through 1980), 9000–12,200 ohms (1981 and later) for the Essex. The ballast resistor should measure 0.50–0.60 ohms resistance at 70°F. through 1979. The ignition resistor used on 1980 models should measure 1.2 ohms resistance at 70°F.

HALL EFFECT PICKUP REPLACEMENT

1. Loosen the distributor cap retaining screws and remove the cap.

2. Pull straight up on the rotor and remove it from the shaft.

3. Disconnect the pickup assembly lead.

4. Remove the pickup lead hold down screw.

5. Remove the pickup assembly lock springs and lift off the pickup.

6. Install the new pickup assembly onto the distributor housing and fasten it into place with the lock springs.

7. Fasten the pickup lead to the housing with the hold down screw.

8. Reconnect the lead to the harness.

9. Press the rotor back into place on

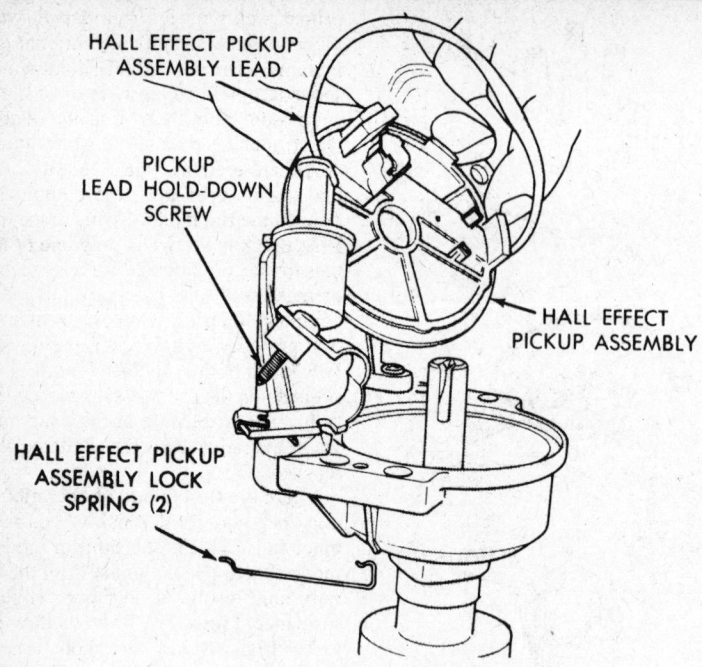

HALL EFFECT PICKUP ASSEMBLY LEAD

PICKUP LEAD HOLD-DOWN SCREW

HALL EFFECT PICKUP ASSEMBLY

HALL EFFECT PICKUP ASSEMBLY LOCK SPRING (2)

Hall Effect pickup installation

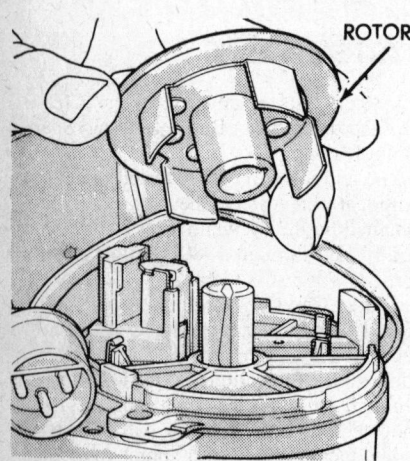

ROTOR

Hall Effect rotor removal

the shaft. Do not wipe off the silicone grease on the metal portion of the rotor.

10. Replace the distributor cap and tighten the retaining screws.

Chrysler Corporation Lean Burn/Electronic Spark Control System

GENERAL INFORMATION

This system was introduced in 1976 as the Lean Burn System; it was renamed Electronic Spark Control in 1979. It is based on the principle that lower NOx emissions would occur if the air/fuel ratio inside the cylinder area was raised from its current point (15.5:1) to a much leaner point (18:1). In order to make the engine workable, a

solution to the problems of carburetion and timing had to be found, since a lean running enging is not the most efficient in terms of driveability. Chrysler adapted a conventional Thermo-Quad carburetor, and later a two barrel unit, to handle the added air coming in, but the real advance of the sys-

tem is the Spark Control Computer. Since a lean burning engine demands precise ignition timing, additional spark control was needed for the distributor. The computer supplies this control by providing an infinitely variable advance curve. Input data is fed instantaneously to the computer by a series of sensors located in the engine compartment which monitor timing, water temperature, air temperature, throttle position, idle/off-idle operation, and intake manifold vacuum. The program schedule module of the Spark Control Computer receives the information from the sensors, processes it, and then directs the ignition control module to advance or retard the timing as necessary. This whole process is going on continuously as the engine is running, taking only a thousandth of a second to complete a circuit from sensor to distributor. The components of the system are as follows: Modified carburetor; Spark Control Computer, consisting of two interacting modules, the Program Schedule Module which is responsible for translating input data, and the Ignition Control Module which transmits data to the distributor to advance or retard the timing.

The start pick-up sensor, located inside the distributor, supplies a signal to the computer providing a fixed timing point that is only used for starting the car. It also has a back-up function of taking over engine timing in case the run pick-up fails. Since the timing in this pick-up is fixed at one point, the car will be able to run but not very well.

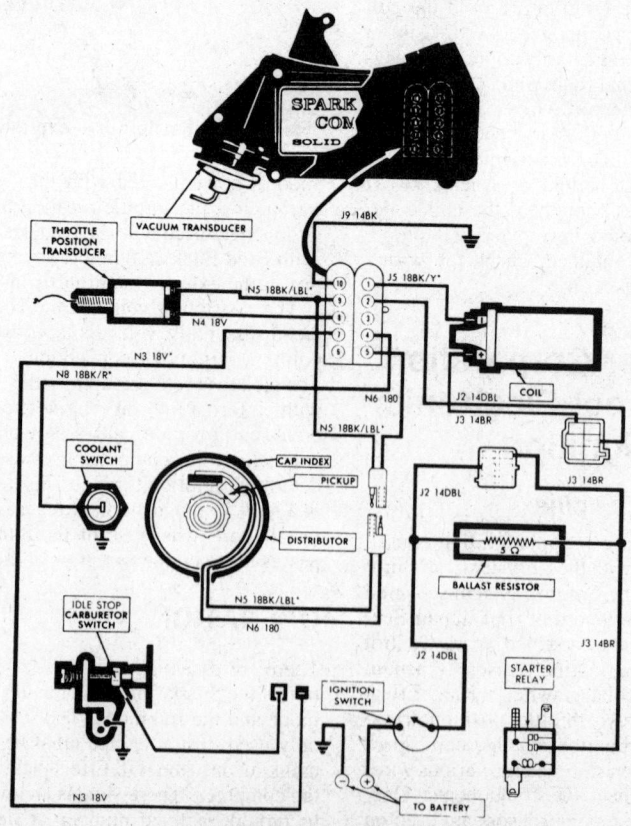

Single pick-up electronic ignition

The run pick-up sensor, also located in the distributor, provides timing data to the computer once the engine is running. It also monitors engine speed, and helps the computer decide when the piston is reaching the top of its compression stroke. Starting 1978, the system is simplified to use only one distributor pick-up. This pick-up provides the basic timing signal to the computer for both the start and the run modes. However, 1980-82 models with Micro-processor Electronic Spark Advance (a digital system, instead of an analog system) use two pick-ups in the distributor, which function in the same manner as the two pick-ups used previously.

NOTE: The two systems will not operate at the same time.

The coolant temperature sensor, located in the thermostat housing (4 cyl.), in the head (6 cyl) or in the intake manifold (V8), informs the computer when the coolant temperature reaches normal oeprating levels.

The throttle position transducer, located on the carburetor, monitors the position and rate of change of the throttle plates. When the throttle plates start to open and as they continue to open toward full throttle, more and more spark advance is called for by the computer. If the throttle plates are opened quickly, even more spark advance is given for about one second. The throttle position transducer is not used on the 1979 Omni and Horizon and is eliminated altogether starting in 1980.

The carburetor switch sensor, located on the end of the idle stop solenoid, tells the computer if the engine is at idle or off-idle.

The vacuum transducer, located on the computer, monitors the amount of intake manifold vacuum; the more vacuum, the more spark advance to the distributor. In order to obtain this spark advance in the distributor, the carburetor switch sensor has to remain open for a specified amount of time, during which time the advance will slowly build up to the amount indicated as necessary by the vacuum transducer. If the carburetor switch should close during that time, the advance to the distributor will be cancelled. From here the computer will start with an advance countdown if the carburetor switch is reopened within a certain amount of time. The advance will continue from a point decided by the computer. If the switch is reopened after the computer has counted down to "no advance," the vacuum advance process must start over again.

Some 1980 and later models have a detonation sensor mounted on the intake manifold. The sensor is tuned to the frequency characteristic of engine knocking. When detonation (knocking) occurs, the sensor sends a low voltage signal to the computer, which retards ignition timing in proportion to the strength and frequency of the signal. The maximum amount of retard is 11°. When the detonation has ceased, the computer advances timing to the original value.

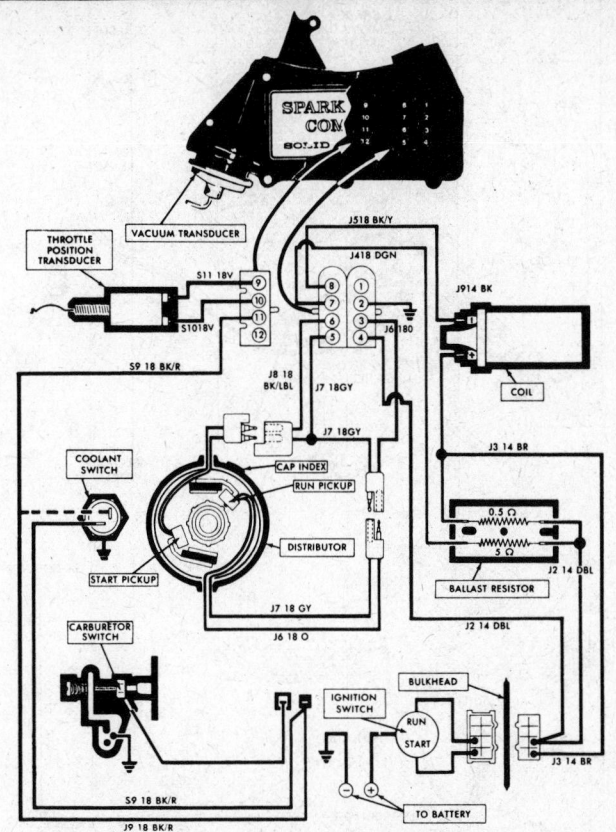

Dual pick-up electronic ignition

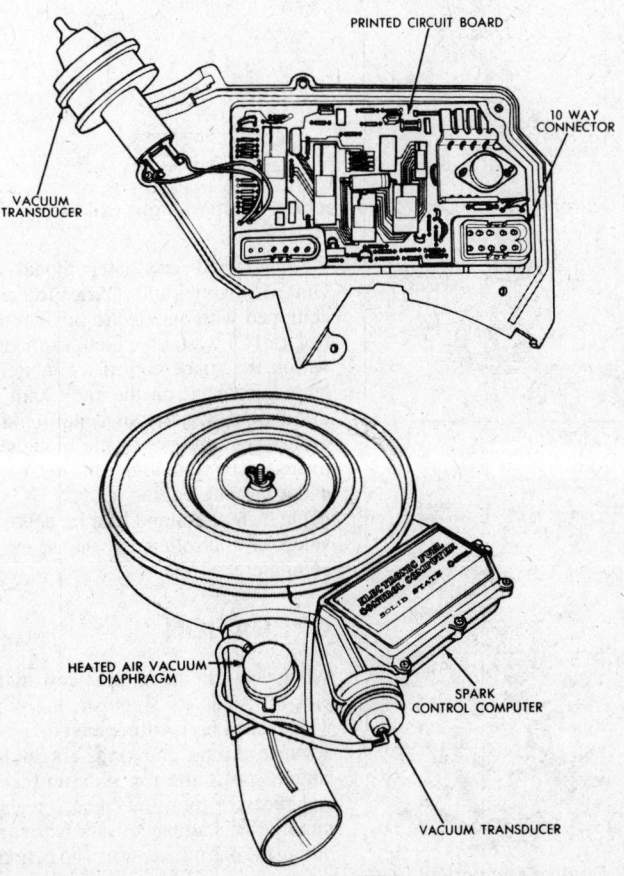

Typical combustion computer assembly

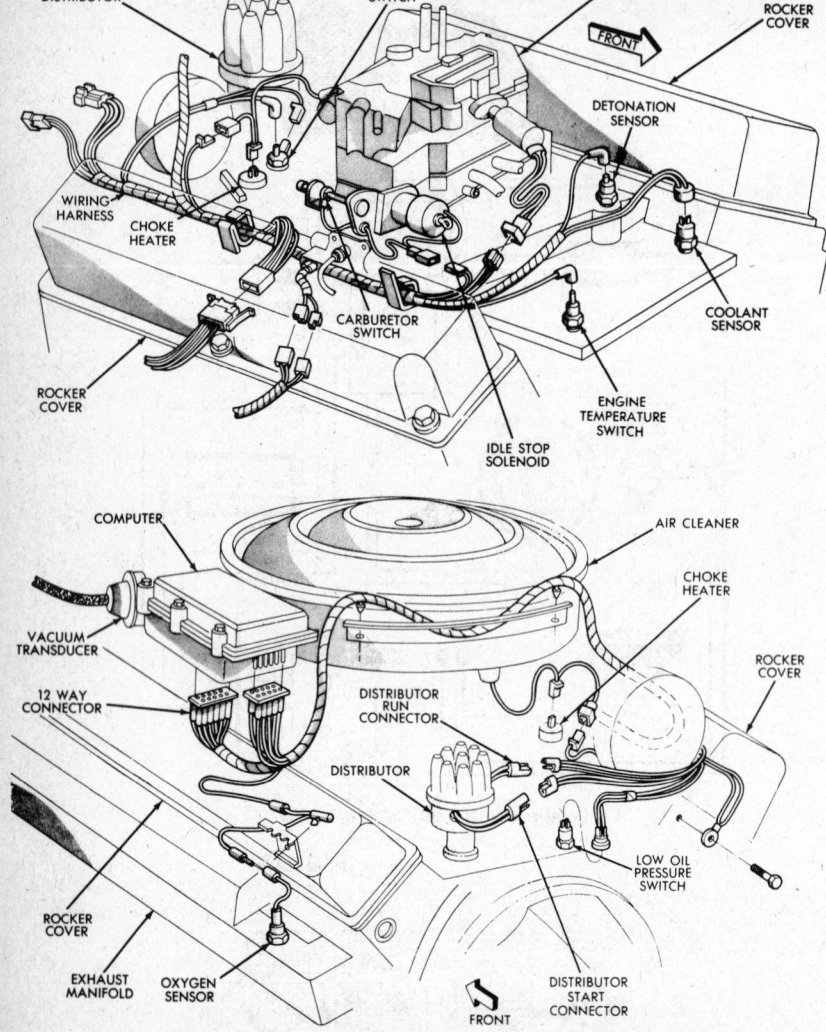

Electronic Spark Control component location-eight cylinder

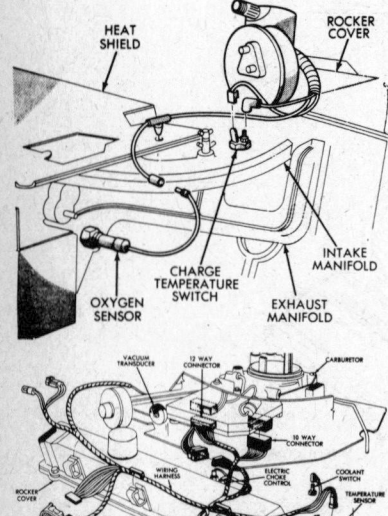

Electronic Spark Control component location-six cylinder

perature sensor), no more advance will be given to the distributor until it reaches normal operation temperature. At this point, normal operation of the system will begin.

In most 1978–1980 models, there is only one pick-up coil. The computer functions on two modes: the start mode and the run mode. These modes are equivalent in function to the two pick-up coils used earlier. 1981 and later 6 and 8 cylinder models are equipped with dual pick-up coils.

In normal operation, the basic timing information is related by the run pick-up to the computer along with input signals from all the other sensors. From this data, the computer determines the maximum allowable advance or retard to be sent to the distributor for any situation.

If either the run pick-up or the computer should fail, the back up system of the start pick-up takes over. This supplies a fixed timing signal to the distributor which allows the car to be driven until it can be repaired. In this mode, very poor fuel economy and performance will be experienced. If the start pick-up or the ignition control module section of the computer should fail, the car will not start or run. Since most 1978–1980 models, including most Omni/Horizon and Aries/Reliant models, have only one pick-up, if that pick-up coil or the start mode of the computer should fail, the engine will not start or run.

NOTE: Some of the procedures in this section refer to an adjustable timing light. This is also known as a spark advance tester, i.e., a device that will measure how much spark advance is present going from one point, a base figure, to another. Since precise timing is very important to the system, do not attempt to perform any of the tests calling for an adjustable timing light without one.

TROUBLESHOOTING

NOTE: Refer to appropriate car sections for specifications.

1. Remove the coil wire from the distributor cap and hold it cautiously about ¼ in. away from an engine ground, then have someone crank the engine while you check for spark.

2. If you have a good spark, slowly

Many 1981 and later models (except Omni/Horizon and Aries/Reliant) are equipped with an Electronic Throttle Control (ETC) system which is incorporated within the spark control computer. A solenoid mounted on the carburetor is energized whenever the air conditioning (A/C) or electronic timers (some models) are activated. The solenoid acts to control idle under varying engine loads.

On many 1981 and later models, the EGR value is controlled by the spark control computer.

OPERATION

When you turn the ignition key on, the start pick-up sends its signal to the computer, which relays back information for more spark advance during cranking. As soon as the engine starts, the run pick-up takes over, and receives more advance for about one minute. This advance is slowly eliminated during the one minute warm up period. While the engine is cold, (coolant temperature below 150° as monitored by the coolant tem-

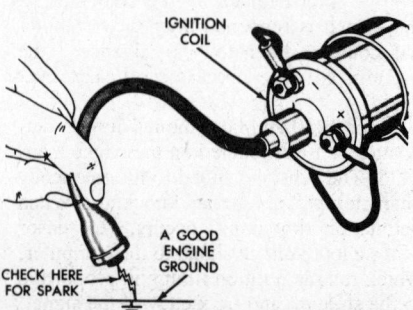

Testing for spark during engine cranking. Use insulated pliers and gloves to handle coil wire

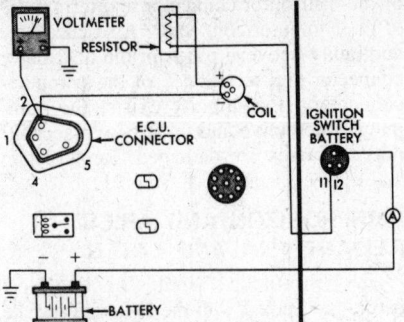

move the coil wire away from the engine and check for arcing at the coil while cranking.

3. If you have good spark and it is not arcing at the coil, check the rest of the parts of the ignition system.

Engine Not Running Will Not Start

ALL EXCEPT OMNI/HORIZON AND ARIES/RELIANT

This test is for the start pick-up in dual pick-up models, and the entire pick-up assembly in all single pick-up models except the Omni/ Horizon and the Aries/Reliant.

1. Check the battery specific gravity; it must be at least 1.220 to deliver the necessary voltage to fire the plugs.

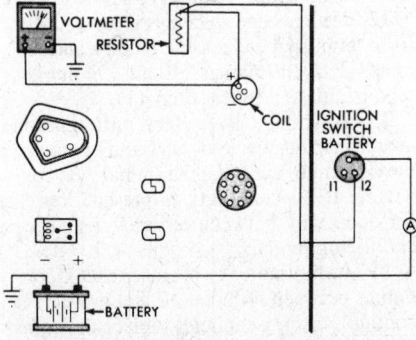

Testing for battery voltage at positive coil terminal

2. Remove the terminal connector from the coolant switch (1978–79), and put a piece of paper or plastic between the curb idle adjusting screw and the carburetor switch (all).

3. Connect the negative lead of a voltmeter to a good engine ground, turn the ignition switch to the "run" position and measure the voltage at the carburetor switch terminal. On 1978–79 models, if a reading of more than 5 but less than 10 volts is received, go on to Step 7. On 1978–79 models, if the voltage is more than 10 volts, check for continuity between terminal 2 and ground or terminal 10 and ground. On 1980 and later models, if voltage is approximately 5 volts, proceed to Step 8.

4. If the voltage was less than 5, turn

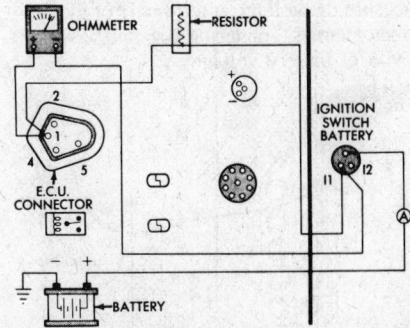

Checking continuity between cavity 1 and the ignition switch

the ignition switch "off" and disconnect the double terminal connector from the bottom of the Spark Control Computer. Turn the ignition switch back to the "run" position and measure the voltage at terminal 2 for 1978 and later models. If the voltage is not within 1 volt of the voltage you received in Step 1, check the wiring between the terminal and the ignition switch. If the voltage is correct, proceed to Step 5.

5. Turn the ignition switch "off" and disconnect the double connector. Using an ohmmeter, check for continuity between terminal 7 and the carburetor switch. There should be continuity. If not, check the wiring.

6. For 1978 and later models, if there is continuity in Step 5, next check for continuity between terminal 10 and a ground. If continuity exists, replace the computer. If not, check the wire for open or poor connections, and only proceed to Step 7 if the engine still won't start.

7. Turn the ignition switch to the "run" position and touch the positive voltmeter lead to terminal 1 and the negative lead to ground. Voltage should be within one volt of battery voltage measured in Step 1. If so, go to Step 8. If not, check the wiring and connections between the connector and the ignition switch.

8. Turn the ignition switch "off" and with an ohmmeter, measure resistance between terminals 5 and 9. On 1980 and later dual pick-up coil models, test between ter-

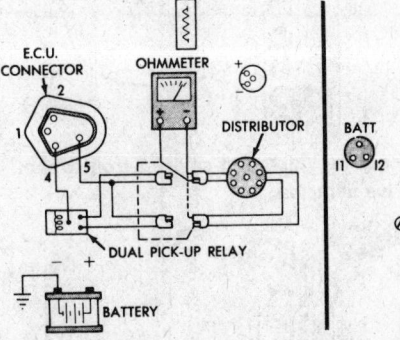

Testing resistance at both pick-up coils

minals 5 and 9 for the run pick-up coil, and between terminals 3 and 9 for the start pick-up coil. If you do not receive a reading of 150–900 ohms disconnect the pick-up leads at the distributor.

9. Connect one lead of an ohmmeter to a good engine ground and with the other lead, check the continuity of both pick-up leads going into the distributor. If there is not continuity, go on to the next step. If you do get a reading, replace the pickup.

10. Remove the distributor cap and check the air gap of the pick-up coil(s). Adjust if necessary and proceed to the next step.

11. Replace the distributor cap, and start the engine. If it still will not start, replace the Spark Control Computer. If the engine still does not work, put the old one back and retrace your steps paying close attention to any wiring which may be shorted.

OMNI/HORIZON THROUGH 1980

1. Before performing this test, be sure the "Troubleshooting" test has been performed. Measure the battery specific gravity; it must be at least 1.220, temperature corrected. Measure the battery voltage and make a note of it.

2. Disconnect the thin wire from the negative coil terminal.

3. Remove the coil high tension lead at the distributor cap.

4. Turn the ignition On. While holding the coil high tension lead ¼ in. from a ground, connect a jumper wire from the negative coil terminal to a ground. A spark should be obtained from the high tension lead.

5. If there is no spark, use a voltmeter to test for at least 9 volts at the positive coil terminal (ignition On). If so, the coil must be replaced. If less than 9 volts is obtained, check the ballast resistor (through 1979),

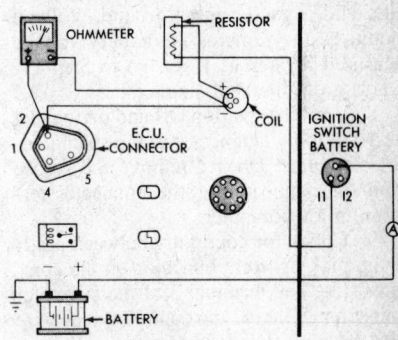

Checking continuity between cavity 2 and the negative coil terminal

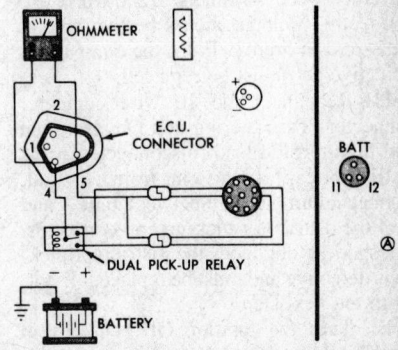

Checking resistance between cavities 4 and 5

Testing for voltage at cavity 2

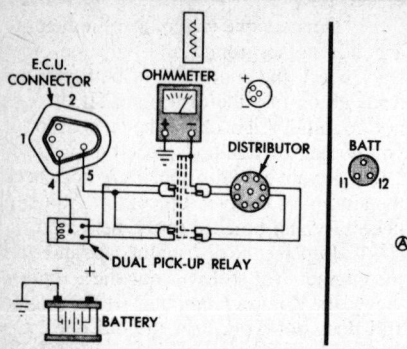

Testing for short circuits at each pick-up coil terminal

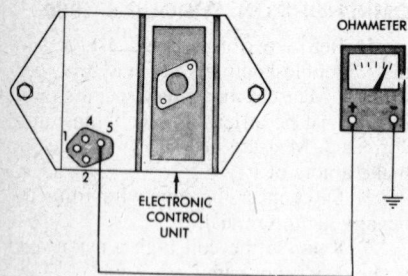

Testing electronic control unit pin 5 for ground

wiring, and connection. If the car still won't start, proceed to Step 6.

6. If there was a spark in Step 4, turn the ignition Off, reconnect the wire to the negative coil terminal, and disconnect the distributor pick-up coil connector.

7. Turn the ignition On, and measure voltage between pin B of the pick-up coil connector on the spark control computer side, and a good engine ground. Voltage should be the same as the battery voltage measured in Step 1. If so, go to Step 11. If not, go to the next step.

8. Turn the ignition Off and disconnect the 10 terminal connector at the spark control computer. Do not remove the grease from the connector or the connector terminal in the computer.

9. Check for continuity between pin B of the pick-up coil connector on the computer side, and terminal 3 of the computer connector. If there is no continuity, the wire must be replaced. If continuity exists, go to the next step.

10. With the ignition On, connect a voltmeter between terminals 2 and 10 of the connector. Voltage should be the same as measured in Step 1. If so, the computer is defective and must be replaced.

11. Reconnect the 10 wire computer connector. Turn the ignition On. Hold the coil high tension lead (disconnected at the distributor cap) about ¼ in. from a ground. Connect a jumper wire between pins A and C of the distributor pick-up coil connector. If a spark is obtained, the distributor pick-up is defective and must be replaced. If not, go to the next step.

12. Turn the ignition Off. Disconnect the 10 wire computer connector.

13. Check for continuity between pin C

of the distributor connector and terminal 9 of the computer connector. Also check for continuity between pin A of the distributor connector and terminal 5 of the computer connector. If continuity exists, the computer is defective and must be replaced. If not, the wires are damaged. Repair them and recheck, starting at Step 11.

OMNI/HORIZON AND ARIES/ RELIANT 1981 AND LATER

1. Perform the "Troubleshooting" test before proceeding with the following. Make sure the battery is fully charged, then measure and record the battery voltage.

2. Remove the coil secondary wire from the distributor cap.

3. With the key on, use the special jumper wire and momentarily connect the negative terminal of the ignition coil to ground while holding the coil secondary wire (using insulated pliers and heavy gloves) about ¼ in. from a good ground. A spark should fire.

4. If spark was obtained, go to Step 9.

5. If no spark was obtained, turn off the ignition and disconnect the 10-wire harness going into the Spark Control Computer. Do not remove the grease from the connector.

6. With the ignition key on, use the special jumper wire and momentarily connect the negative terminal of the ignition coil to ground while holding the coil wire ¼ in. from a good engine ground. A spark should fire.

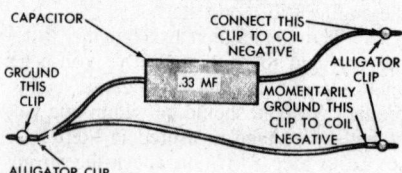

Special jumper wire from coil negative terminal to ground-front wheel drive vehicles

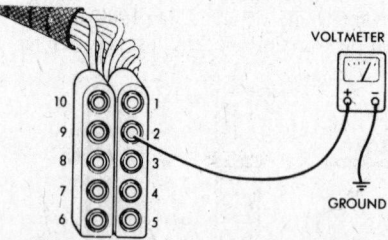

Checking voltage at cavity 2-front wheel drive vehicles

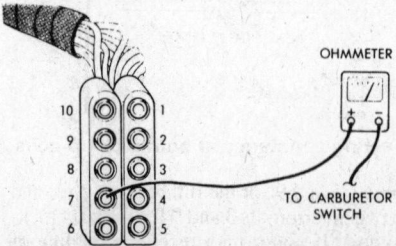

Checking continuity at cavity 7-front wheel drive vehicles

7. If a spark is present, the computer output is shorted; replace the computer.

8. If no spark is obtained, measure the voltage at the coil positive terminal. It should be within 1 volt of battery voltage. If voltage is present but no spark is available when shorting negative terminal, replace the coil. If no voltage is present, replace the coil or check the primary wiring.

9. If voltage was obtained but the engine will not start, hold the carburetor switch open with a thin cardboard insulator and measure the voltage at the switch. It should be at least 5 volts. If voltage is present, go to Step 16.

10. If no voltage is present, turn the ignition switch off and disconnect the 10 wire harness going into the computer.

11. Turn the ignition switch on and measure the voltage at terminal 2 of the harness. It should be within 1 volt of battery voltage.

12. If no battery voltage is present, check for continuity between the battery and terminal 2 of the harness. If no continuity, repair fault and repeat Step 11.

13. If voltage is present turn ignition switch off and check for continuity between the carburetor switch and terminal 7 on connector. If no continuity is present, check for open wire between terminal 7 and the carburetor switch.

14. If continuity is present, check continuity between terminal 10 and ground. If continuity is present here, replace the computer. Repeat Step 9.

15. If no continuity is present, check for an open wire. If wiring is OK, but the engine still won't start, go to next step.

16. Plug the 10 terminal dual connector back into the computer and turn the ignition switch on, hold the secondary coil wire near a good ground and disconnect the distributor harness connector. Using a regular jumper wire (not the special one mentioned earlier), jump terminal 2 to terminal 3 of the connector: a spark should fire at the coil wire.

17. If spark is present at the coil wire but the engine won't start, replace the Hall Effect pick-up and check the rotor for cracks or burning. Replace as necessary.

NOTE: When replacing a pick-up, always make sure rotor blades are grounded using a ohmmeter.

18. If no spark is present at the coil wire, measure the voltage at terminal 1 of the distributor harness connector: it should be within 1 volt of battery voltage.

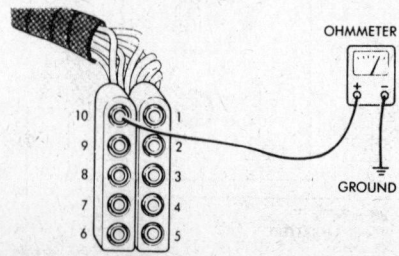

Checking continuity at cavity 10-front wheel drive vehicles

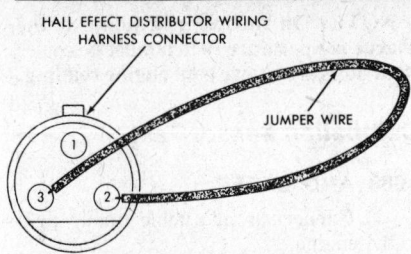

Using jumper wires between terminals 2 and 3-front wheel drive vehicles

19. If correct, disconnect the dual connector from the computer and check for continuity between terminal 2 of distributor harness and terminal 9 of the dual connector. Repeat test on terminal 3 of distributor harness and terminal 5 of dual connector. If no continuity, repair the harness. If continuity is present, replace the computer and repeat Step 16.

20. If no battery voltage is present in Step 18, turn off the ignition switch, disconnect the 10 terminal dual connector for the computer and check for continuity between terminal 1 of distributor harness and terminal 3 of dual connector. If no continuity, repair wire and repeat Step 16.

21. If continuity is present, turn the ignition switch on and check for battery voltage between terminal 2 and terminal 10 of the dual connector. If voltage is present, replace the computer and repeat Step 16. If no battery voltage is present, the computer is not grounded. Check and repair the ground wire and repeat Step 16.

Start Timer Advance Test

1978 AND LATER

1. Connect an adjustable timing light.
2. Connect a jumper wire from the carburetor switch to a ground.
3. Start the engine and immediately adjust the timing light so that the basic timing light is seen on the timing plate of the engine. The meter (on the timing light) should

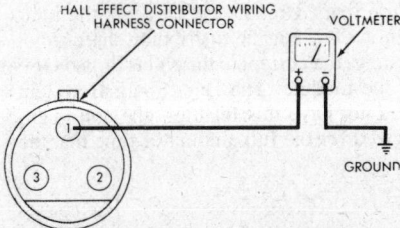

Checking voltage at distributor harness cavity 1-front wheel drive vehicles

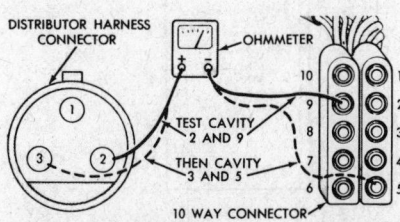

Testing cavities 2 and 9; then 3 and 5 for continuity-front wheel drive vehicles

show an 8° advance on all engines through 1979. For 1980 and later models, refer to the emission control decal in the engine compartment for the proper specification. Continue to observe the mark for 90 seconds, adjusting the light as necessary. The additional advance will slowly decrease to the basic timing signal over a period of about one minute. If not, replace the Spark Control Computer and recheck. If it is ok, go on to the next test.

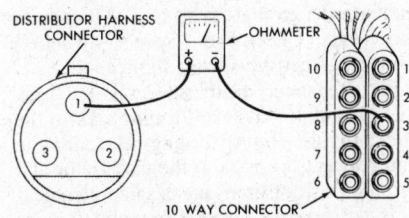

Testing for continuity between cavities 1 and 3-front wheel drive vehicles

Throttle Advance Test

Before performing this test, the throttle position transducer must be adjusted. (This test does not apply to 1978 Omnis and Horizons with automatic transmissions, or to any 1979 and later Omnis or Horizons or any 1980 and later models.) The adjustments are as follows:

1978–79 ALL MODELS

1. Disconnect the throttle position transducer wiring.
2. Loosen the locknut.
3. Place the Chrysler special tool #C-4522 between the outer body of the transducer and its mounting bracket.
4. Adjust the transducer for a clearance fit by rotating the body.
5. Retighten the locknut. Go on to Step 6 of this procedure.
6. Turn the ignition switch off and disconnect the single connector computer.
7. With an ohmmeter, measure the resistance between terminals 8 and 9. The measured resistance should be between 50–90 ohms. If it is, reconnect it and go on to the next step. If not, remove the connector from the throttle position transducer and measure the resistance at the transducer terminals. If you now get a reading of 50–90 ohms, check the wiring between the connector terminals and the transducer terminals. If you do not get the 50–90 reading, replace the transducer and proceed to the next step.

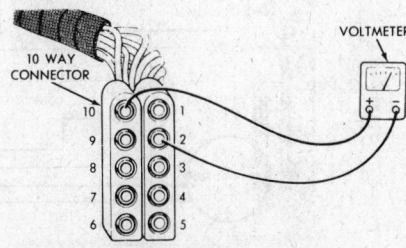

Testing for voltage between cavities 2 and 10-front wheel drive vehicles

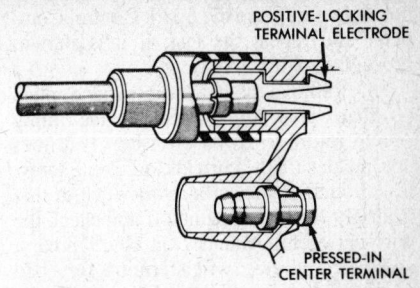

Positive locking secondary ignition wire terminal. To remove, press lock together and push wire out of distributor cap-front wheel drive vehicles

8. Position the throttle linkage on the fast idle cam and ground the carb switch with a jumper wire. Disconnect the wiring connector from the transducer and connect it to a transducer that you know is good.

9. Move the core of the transducer all the way in, start the engine, wait about 90 seconds and then move the core out about an inch.

10. Adjust the timing light so that it registers the basic timing. The timing light meter should show the additional amount of advance as given on the tune-up sticker in the engine compartment. If it is within the specifications, move the core back into the transducer, and the timing should go back to the original position. If it did not advance and/or return, replace the Spark Control Computer and try this test over again. If it still fails, replace the transducer.

11. Remove the test transducer (from Step 9) and reconnect all wiring.

Vacuum Advance Test (Vacuum Transducer)

1978

1. Hook up an adjustable timing light.
2. Start the engine and let it warm up; make sure the transmisison is in Neutral and the parking brake is on.
3. Place a small piece of plastic or paper between the carburetor switch and the curb idle adjusting screw (on the Omni/Horizon, between the carburetor switch and throttle lever); if the screw is not touching the switch make sure the fast idle cam is not on or binding; the linkage is not binding, or the throttle stop screw is not overadjusted. Adjust the timing light for the basic timing figure.

On all 1978 models, let the engine run for at least 9 minutes, and check for at least 16 in. Hg. vacuum at the transducer. After this period, the meter on the light should show the additional advance indicated on the tune-up sticker in the engine compartment. If not, replace the Spark Control Computer. On the Omni/Horizon, stop here. On all other 1978 models, go on to Step 5.

4. After the 9 minute waiting period, adjust the timing light so that it registers the basic timing figure. The timing light meter should now register 32–35° of additional engine advance. If the advance is

not shown, replace the Spark Control Computer and repeat the test; if it is shown, proceed to Step 5.

5. Remove the insulator (paper or plastic) that was installed in Step 3; the timing should return to its base setting. If it does not, make sure the curb idle adjusting screw is not touching the carburetor switch. If that is alright, turn the engine off and check the wire between terminal 7 on all 1978 cars, and the carburetor switch terminal for a bad connection. If it turns out alright, and the timing still will not return to its base setting, replace the Spark Control Computer.

1979–80

A number of different computer programs are used on 1979 and later cars. Refer to the emission control sticker in the engine compartment for the correct timing settings; no timing figures will be given in the following procedure.

1. Connect an adjustable timing light and a tachometer to the engine.

2. Start the engine and allow it to reach normal operating temperature. If the engine is already hot, allow it to idle for at least one minute before beginning tests. The transmission should be in Neutral; apply the parking brake.

3. Check the basic timing (see the emission sticker for the correct figure); adjust if necessary.

4. Disconnect and plug the vacuum line at the vacuum transducer; be careful not to split the hose. The vacuum transducer is located on the Spark Control Computer.

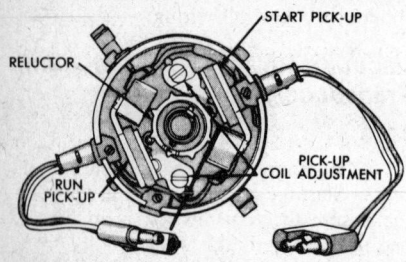

Air gap adjustment locations, dual pick-up shown

5. Ground the carburetor switch on 1979 models. On 1980 models, remove the carburetor ground switch. If the engine has a throttle position transducer, remove its electrical connector.

6. Increase the engine speed to 1,100 rpm.

7. Check the "Speed Advance Timing" against the figure given on the emission sticker.

8. On the Omni/Horizon raise the engine speed to 2,000 rpm; leave it at 1,100 rpm on all other cars. On all 1979 models, remove the carburetor switch ground and connect the vacuum hose to the transducer. On 1980 models, connect the vacuum hose to the transducer.

9. Check the "Zero Time Offset" against the timing figure given on the emission sticker (1979 models only).

10. Allow the engine to run for 8 minutes; this allows the accumulator in the computer to "clock up." After the time has elapsed, check the "Vacuum Advance" timing against the sticker figure. The engine should be running at 1,100 rpm (2,000 rpm Omni/Horizon) on all models when checking this figure.

11. Disconnect and plug the vacuum hose at the vacuum transducer again. Increase the engine speed to 1,500 rpm (2,500 rpm, 1980) on all cars except the Omni/Horizon, increase the engine speed to 3,000 rpm on those cars. Check the "Speed Advance" timing against the sticker figure.

12. Reconnect the transducer hose. Check the "Vacuum Advance" timing against the sticker figure. Return the engine to curb idle and connect the wire to the carburetor and throttle position transducer as applicable.

If the Spark Control Computer fails to meet the specified settings, it must be replaced.

1981 AND LATER

1. Run the engine to normal operating temperature. Disconnect or unground the carburetor switch. The temperature sensor should remain connected.

2. Remove the plug vacuum hose at the vacuum transducer on the spark control computer.

3. Connect an auxiliary vacuum supply to the vacuum transducer and apply 16 in. of vacuum.

4. Raise the engine speed to 2,000 rpm, wait one minute and (or specified accumulator clock-up time) and check the specifications (see underhood sticker). Advance specifications are in addition to basic advance specifications.

If the spark control computer fails to obtain specified settings, replace the computer.

Coolant Switch Test

1. Connect one lead of the ohmmeter to a good engine ground, the other to the center terminal of the coolant switch.

2. If the engine is cold (below 150°) there should be continuity in the switch. With the thermostat open, and the engine warmed up, there should be no continuity. If either of the conditions in this step are not met, replace the switch.

NOTE: On models so equipped, the charge temperature switch must be cooler than 60°F to achieve cold engine reading.

Detonation Sensor Test

1980 AND LATER

1. Connect an adjustable timing light to the engine.

2. Place the fast idle screw on the second highest step of the fast idle cam. Start the engine and allow it to idle. The engine should be running at 1,200 rpm or more.

3. Use an open end wrench or the like to tap lightly on the intake manifold next to the detonation sensor. As you do this, watch the timing marks; a decrease in timing advance should be seen. The amount of decrease should be directly proportional to the strength and frequency of tapping. Maximum retard is 11°.

4. If the sensor is not working correctly, install a new sensor and retest.

Ford Motor Company Electronic Ignition Systems

GENERAL INFORMATION

Basically, four electronic ignition systems have been used in Ford Motor Company vehicles from 1978–85:

1. Dura Spark I
2. Dura Spark II
3. Dura Spark III
4. TFI (Thick Film Integrated)

In 1977, the Dura Spark systems, were introduced. Dura Spark I and Dura Spark II systems are nearly identical in operation, and virtually identical in appearance. The Dura Spark I uses a special control module which senses current flow through the ignition coil and adjust the dwell, or coil "on" time for maximum spark intensity. If the Dura Spark I module senses that the ignition is ON, but the distributor shaft is not turning, the current to the coil is turned OFF by the module. The Dura Spark II system does not have this feature—the coil is energized for the full amount of time that the

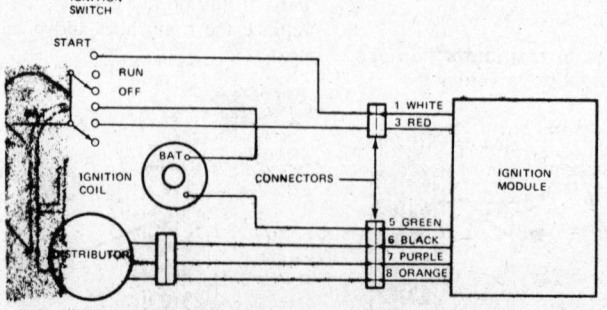

Electronic module schematic—Dura Spark I

HAS SPARK BUT ENGINE WON'T START

STEP 1: TURN IGNITION SWITCH "OFF," PULL E.C.U. HARNESS CONNECTOR AND TURN IGNITION SWITCH ON

CHECK FOR BATTERY VOLTAGE AT CAVITY 2 OF E.C.U. HARNESS IT SHOULD BE WITHIN 1 VOLT OF BATTERY VOLTAGE

IF VOLTAGE IS OK CHECK VOLTAGE AT CAVITY 1 OF ECU CONNECTOR. IT SHOULD BE WITHIN 1 VOLT OF BATTERY VOLTAGE

IF VOLTAGE IS NOT OK CHECK FOR CONTINUITY BETWEEN CAVITY 2 AND COIL NEGATIVE. FIND FAULT AND REPAIR. REPEAT STEP 1

IF VOLTAGE IS ON GO TO STEP 2

IF VOLTAGE IS NOT OK, CHECK FOR CONTINUITY BETWEEN CAVITY 1 AND IGNITION SWITCH, FIND FAULT AND REPAIR

STEP 2: TURN IGNITION SWITCH "OFF" AND CHECK RESISTANCE BETWEEN CAVITIES 4 AND 5 OF E.C.U. CONNECTOR. IT SHOULD BE 150 TO 900 OHMS

IF IT IS, GO TO STEP 3

IF IT IS NOT, TURN IGNITION SWITCH "OFF", DISCONNECT DUAL PICK-UP LEADS AND CHECK RESISTANCE. IT SHOULD BE 150 TO 900 OHMS

IF IT IS, PICK-UPS ARE OK BUT WIRE BETWEEN CAVITIES 4 AND 5 AND DUAL CONNECTOR IS OPEN OR SHORTED— REPAIR CIRCUIT

IF IT IS NOT, REPLACE PICK-UP COIL AND GO TO STEP 3

STEP 4: CHECK FOR GROUND AT PIN 5 OF E.C.U.

SHOWS GROUND, GO TO STEP 5

NO GROUND, CHECK THAT E.C.U. UNIT CONNECTIONS ARE CLEAN AND MOUNTING SCREWS ARE TIGHT REPEAT STEP 4

STEP 5: REINSTALL ALL CONNECTORS AND CHECK FOR A SPARK

HAS SPARK, SYSTEM OK

HAS NO SPARK, REPLACE E.C.U.

MEASURE AND RECORD BATTERY VOLTAGE WITH VOLTMETER MEASURE SPECIFIC GRAVITY IT SHOULD BE AT LEAST 12.20 IF NOT, CHARGE BATTERY TO SPECIFICATION

TURN IGNITION SWITCH TO ON POSITION

HOLD COIL SECONDARY WIRE NEAR GROUND

INTERMITTENTLY SHORT COIL NEGATIVE TO GROUND

STEP A: MEASURE VOLTAGE AT COIL POSITIVE. IT SHOULD BE WITHIN 1 VOLT OF BATTERY VOLTAGE

IF VOLTAGE IS OK, CHECK VOLTAGE AT COIL NEGATIVE. IT SHOULD BE WITHIN 1 VOLT OF BATTERY VOLTAGE.

IF YOU GET BATTERY VOLTAGE BUT NO SPARK WHEN SHORTING NEGATIVE TERMINAL, REPLACE COIL

STEP 3: CHECK FOR A GROUND OR SHORT AT EACH LEAD OF PICK-UP COILS WITH AN OHMMETER, GROUND ONE SIDE OF OHMMETER

IF THERE IS NO SHORT GO TO STEP 4

IF SHORTED, REPLACE PICK-UP COILS AND SET AIR GAP TO .006 WITH A NON-MAGNETIC FEELER GAUGE. A .008 GAUGE SHOULD NOT GO THROUGH GAP REPEAT STEP 3

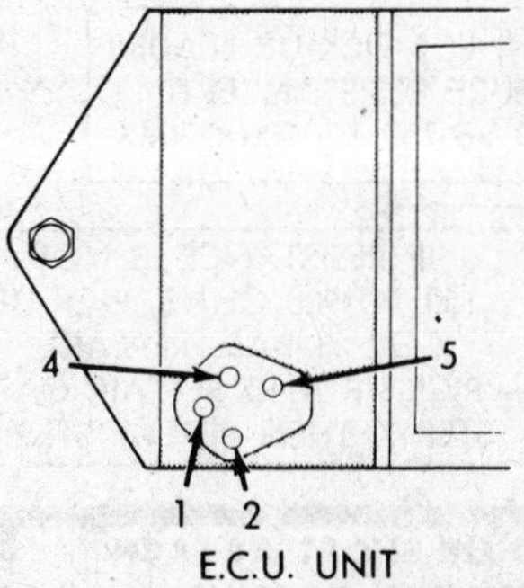

HAS NO SPARK UNPLUG E.C.U.

INTERMITTENTLY SHORT COIL NEGATIVE TO GROUND

STILL HAS NO SPARK

NOW HAS SPARK REPLACE E.C.U. CONTROL UNIT

REPLACE STARTER RELAY AND CHECK WIRING BETWEEN BATTERY AND COIL POSITIVE

CIRCUIT NOT CONTINUOUS BETWEEN BATTERY AND COIL POSITIVE, REPLACE IGNITION RESISTOR AND REPEAT STEP A

E.C.U. UNIT

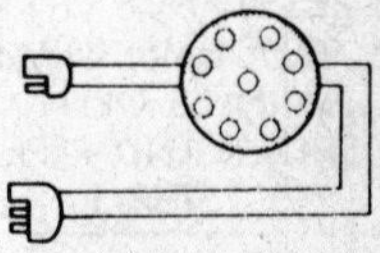

DUAL PICK-UP LEADS

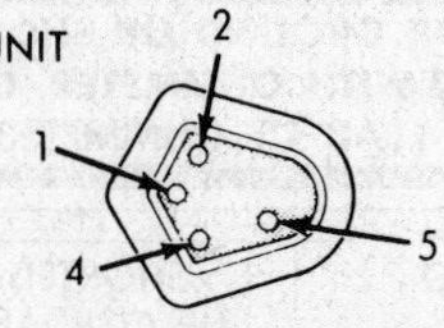

E.C.U. CONNECTOR

Electronic ignition system diagnosis

ELECTRONIC IGNITION SYSTEMS

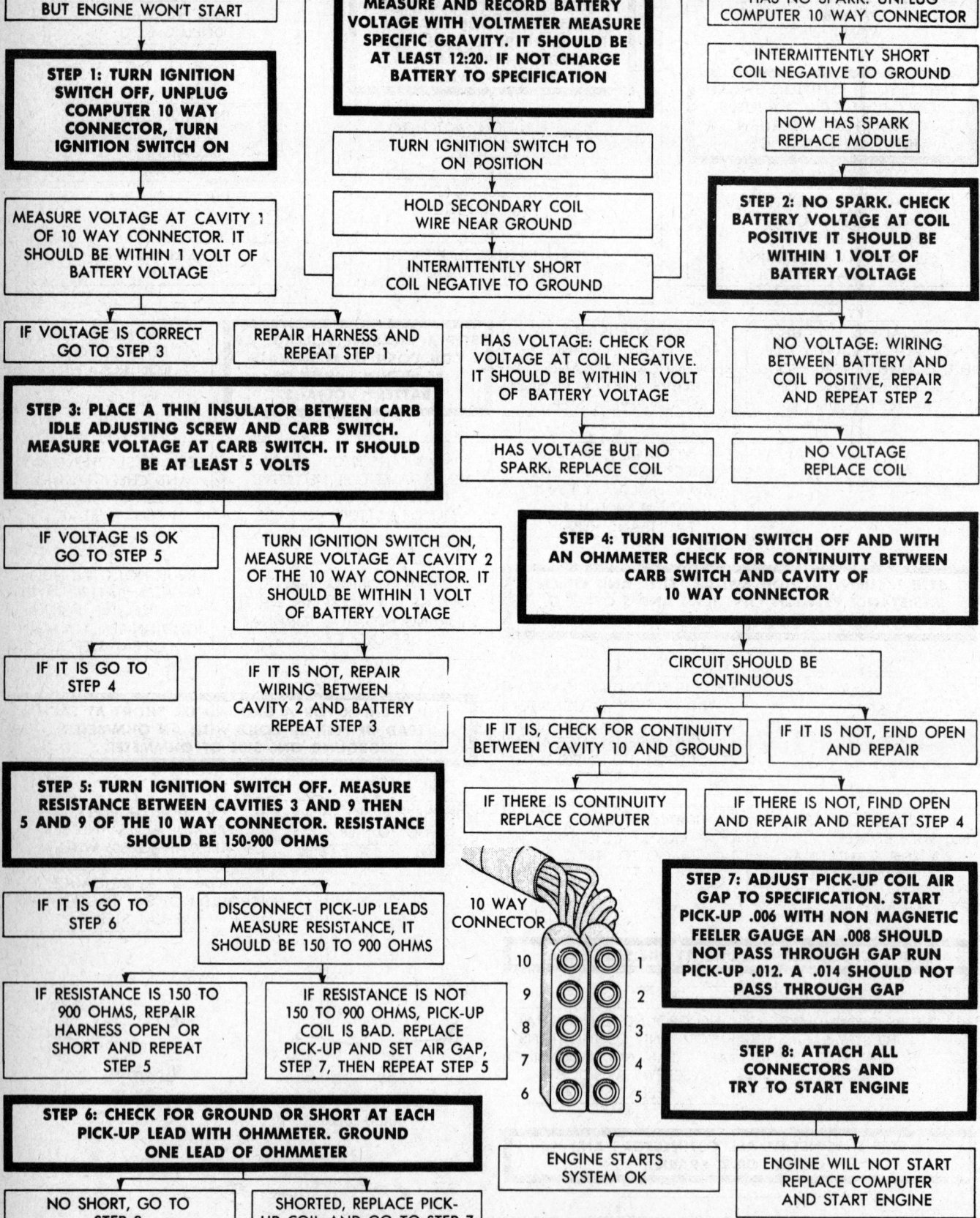

HAS SPARK BUT ENGINE WON'T START

STEP 1: TURN IGNITION SWITCH OFF, UNPLUG COMPUTER 10 WAY CONNECTOR, TURN IGNITION SWITCH ON

MEASURE VOLTAGE AT CAVITY 1 OF 10 WAY CONNECTOR. IT SHOULD BE WITHIN 1 VOLT OF BATTERY VOLTAGE

IF VOLTAGE IS CORRECT GO TO STEP 3

REPAIR HARNESS AND REPEAT STEP 1

STEP 3: PLACE A THIN INSULATOR BETWEEN CARB IDLE ADJUSTING SCREW AND CARB SWITCH. MEASURE VOLTAGE AT CARB SWITCH. IT SHOULD BE AT LEAST 5 VOLTS

IF VOLTAGE IS OK GO TO STEP 5

TURN IGNITION SWITCH ON, MEASURE VOLTAGE AT CAVITY 2 OF THE 10 WAY CONNECTOR. IT SHOULD BE WITHIN 1 VOLT OF BATTERY VOLTAGE

IF IT IS GO TO STEP 4

IF IT IS NOT, REPAIR WIRING BETWEEN CAVITY 2 AND BATTERY REPEAT STEP 3

STEP 5: TURN IGNITION SWITCH OFF. MEASURE RESISTANCE BETWEEN CAVITIES 3 AND 9 THEN 5 AND 9 OF THE 10 WAY CONNECTOR. RESISTANCE SHOULD BE 150-900 OHMS

IF IT IS GO TO STEP 6

DISCONNECT PICK-UP LEADS MEASURE RESISTANCE, IT SHOULD BE 150 TO 900 OHMS

IF RESISTANCE IS 150 TO 900 OHMS, REPAIR HARNESS OPEN OR SHORT AND REPEAT STEP 5

IF RESISTANCE IS NOT 150 TO 900 OHMS, PICK-UP COIL IS BAD. REPLACE PICK-UP AND SET AIR GAP, STEP 7, THEN REPEAT STEP 5

STEP 6: CHECK FOR GROUND OR SHORT AT EACH PICK-UP LEAD WITH OHMMETER. GROUND ONE LEAD OF OHMMETER

NO SHORT, GO TO STEP 8

SHORTED, REPLACE PICK-UP COIL AND GO TO STEP 7

MEASURE AND RECORD BATTERY VOLTAGE WITH VOLTMETER MEASURE SPECIFIC GRAVITY. IT SHOULD BE AT LEAST 12:20. IF NOT CHARGE BATTERY TO SPECIFICATION

TURN IGNITION SWITCH TO ON POSITION

HOLD SECONDARY COIL WIRE NEAR GROUND

INTERMITTENTLY SHORT COIL NEGATIVE TO GROUND

HAS VOLTAGE: CHECK FOR VOLTAGE AT COIL NEGATIVE. IT SHOULD BE WITHIN 1 VOLT OF BATTERY VOLTAGE

HAS VOLTAGE BUT NO SPARK. REPLACE COIL

HAS NO SPARK. UNPLUG COMPUTER 10 WAY CONNECTOR

INTERMITTENTLY SHORT COIL NEGATIVE TO GROUND

NOW HAS SPARK REPLACE MODULE

STEP 2: NO SPARK. CHECK BATTERY VOLTAGE AT COIL POSITIVE IT SHOULD BE WITHIN 1 VOLT OF BATTERY VOLTAGE

NO VOLTAGE: WIRING BETWEEN BATTERY AND COIL POSITIVE, REPAIR AND REPEAT STEP 2

NO VOLTAGE REPLACE COIL

STEP 4: TURN IGNITION SWITCH OFF AND WITH AN OHMMETER CHECK FOR CONTINUITY BETWEEN CARB SWITCH AND CAVITY OF 10 WAY CONNECTOR

CIRCUIT SHOULD BE CONTINUOUS

IF IT IS, CHECK FOR CONTINUITY BETWEEN CAVITY 10 AND GROUND

IF IT IS NOT, FIND OPEN AND REPAIR

IF THERE IS CONTINUITY REPLACE COMPUTER

IF THERE IS NOT, FIND OPEN AND REPAIR AND REPEAT STEP 4

10 WAY CONNECTOR

STEP 7: ADJUST PICK-UP COIL AIR GAP TO SPECIFICATION. START PICK-UP .006 WITH NON MAGNETIC FEELER GAUGE AN .008 SHOULD NOT PASS THROUGH GAP RUN PICK-UP .012. A .014 SHOULD NOT PASS THROUGH GAP

STEP 8: ATTACH ALL CONNECTORS AND TRY TO START ENGINE

ENGINE STARTS SYSTEM OK

ENGINE WILL NOT START REPLACE COMPUTER AND START ENGINE

Electronic Spark Control System diagnosis

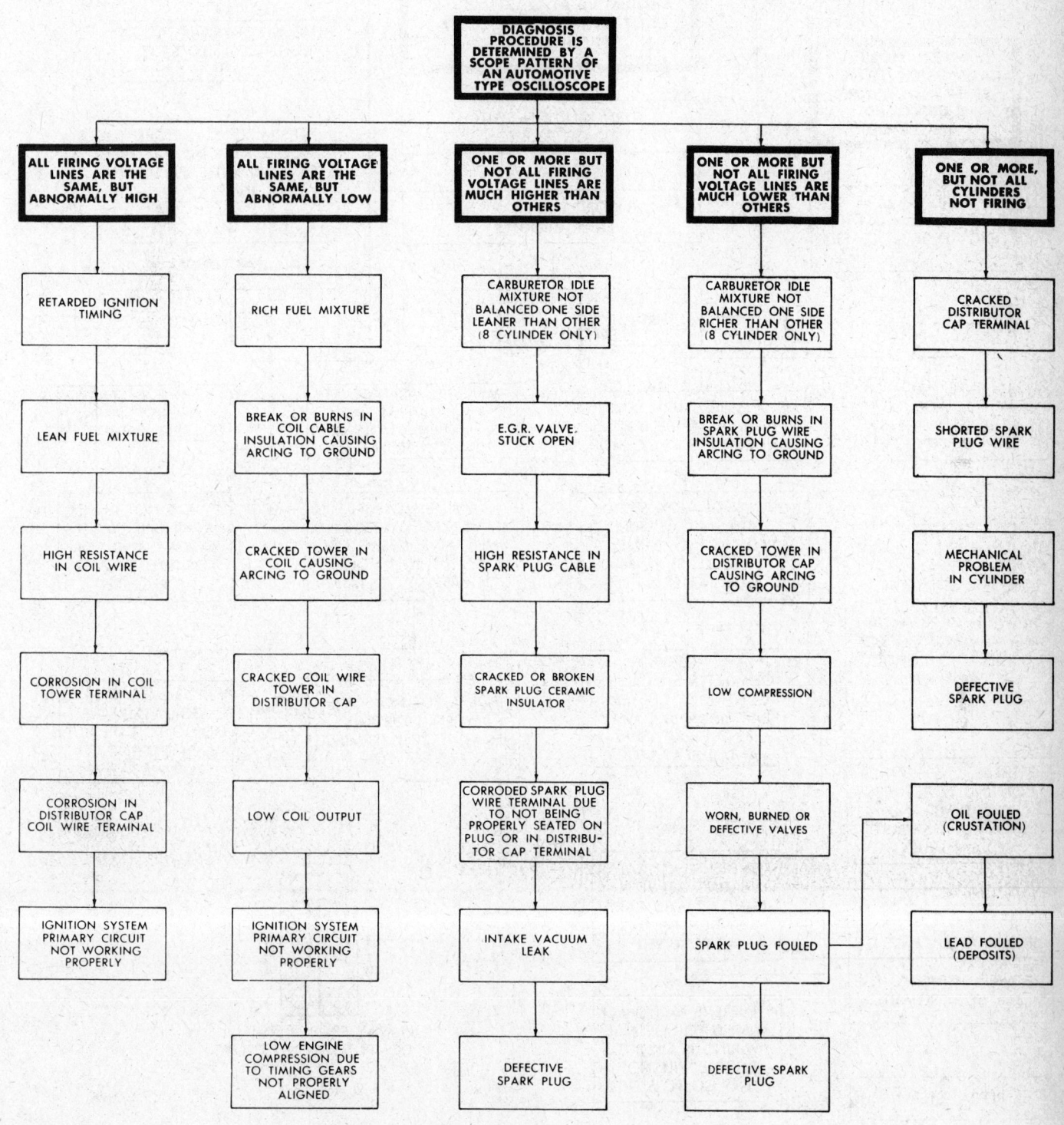

Electronic ignition system secondary circuit diagnosis

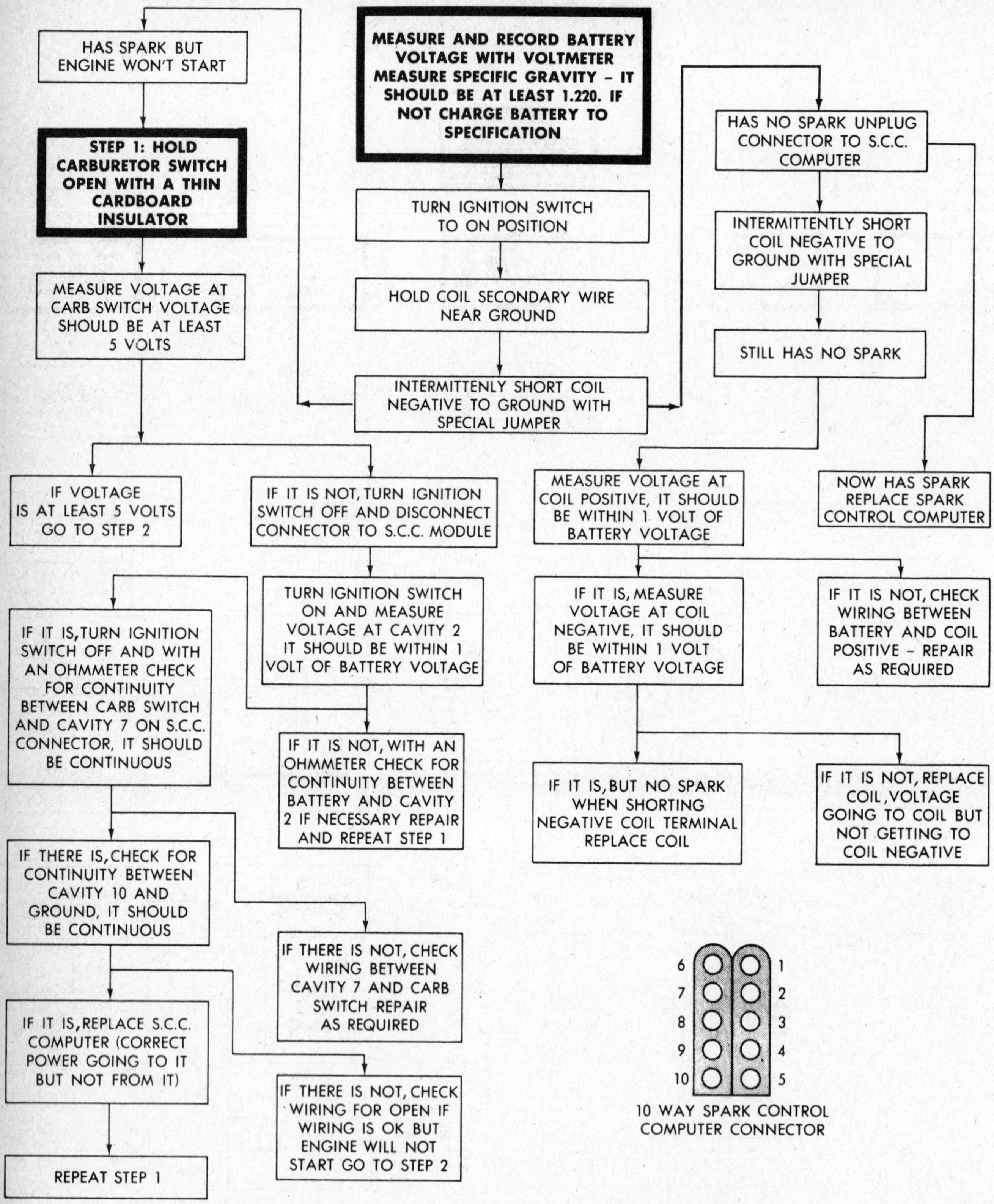

HAS SPARK BUT ENGINE WON'T START

MEASURE AND RECORD BATTERY VOLTAGE WITH VOLTMETER MEASURE SPECIFIC GRAVITY – IT SHOULD BE AT LEAST 1.220. IF NOT CHARGE BATTERY TO SPECIFICATION

HAS NO SPARK UNPLUG CONNECTOR TO S.C.C. COMPUTER

STEP 1: HOLD CARBURETOR SWITCH OPEN WITH A THIN CARDBOARD INSULATOR

TURN IGNITION SWITCH TO ON POSITION

INTERMITTENTLY SHORT COIL NEGATIVE TO GROUND WITH SPECIAL JUMPER

MEASURE VOLTAGE AT CARB SWITCH VOLTAGE SHOULD BE AT LEAST 5 VOLTS

HOLD COIL SECONDARY WIRE NEAR GROUND

STILL HAS NO SPARK

INTERMITTENLY SHORT COIL NEGATIVE TO GROUND WITH SPECIAL JUMPER

IF VOLTAGE IS AT LEAST 5 VOLTS GO TO STEP 2

IF IT IS NOT, TURN IGNITION SWITCH OFF AND DISCONNECT CONNECTOR TO S.C.C. MODULE

MEASURE VOLTAGE AT COIL POSITIVE, IT SHOULD BE WITHIN 1 VOLT OF BATTERY VOLTAGE

NOW HAS SPARK REPLACE SPARK CONTROL COMPUTER

IF IT IS, TURN IGNITION SWITCH OFF AND WITH AN OHMMETER CHECK FOR CONTINUITY BETWEEN CARB SWITCH AND CAVITY 7 ON S.C.C. CONNECTOR, IT SHOULD BE CONTINUOUS

TURN IGNITION SWITCH ON AND MEASURE VOLTAGE AT CAVITY 2 IT SHOULD BE WITHIN 1 VOLT OF BATTERY VOLTAGE

IF IT IS, MEASURE VOLTAGE AT COIL NEGATIVE, IT SHOULD BE WITHIN 1 VOLT OF BATTERY VOLTAGE

IF IT IS NOT, CHECK WIRING BETWEEN BATTERY AND COIL POSITIVE – REPAIR AS REQUIRED

IF IT IS NOT, WITH AN OHMMETER CHECK FOR CONTINUITY BETWEEN BATTERY AND CAVITY 2 IF NECESSARY REPAIR AND REPEAT STEP 1

IF THERE IS, CHECK FOR CONTINUITY BETWEEN CAVITY 10 AND GROUND, IT SHOULD BE CONTINUOUS

IF IT IS, BUT NO SPARK WHEN SHORTING NEGATIVE COIL TERMINAL REPLACE COIL

IF IT IS NOT, REPLACE COIL, VOLTAGE GOING TO COIL BUT NOT GETTING TO COIL NEGATIVE

IF THERE IS NOT, CHECK WIRING BETWEEN CAVITY 7 AND CARB SWITCH REPAIR AS REQUIRED

IF IT IS, REPLACE S.C.C. COMPUTER (CORRECT POWER GOING TO IT BUT NOT FROM IT)

IF THERE IS NOT, CHECK WIRING FOR OPEN IF WIRING IS OK BUT ENGINE WILL NOT START GO TO STEP 2

REPEAT STEP 1

```
6  ◯ ◯  1
7  ◯ ◯  2
8  ◯ ◯  3
9  ◯ ◯  4
10 ◯ ◯  5
```

10 WAY SPARK CONTROL COMPUTER CONNECTOR

Hall-Effect electronic spark advance system diagnosis

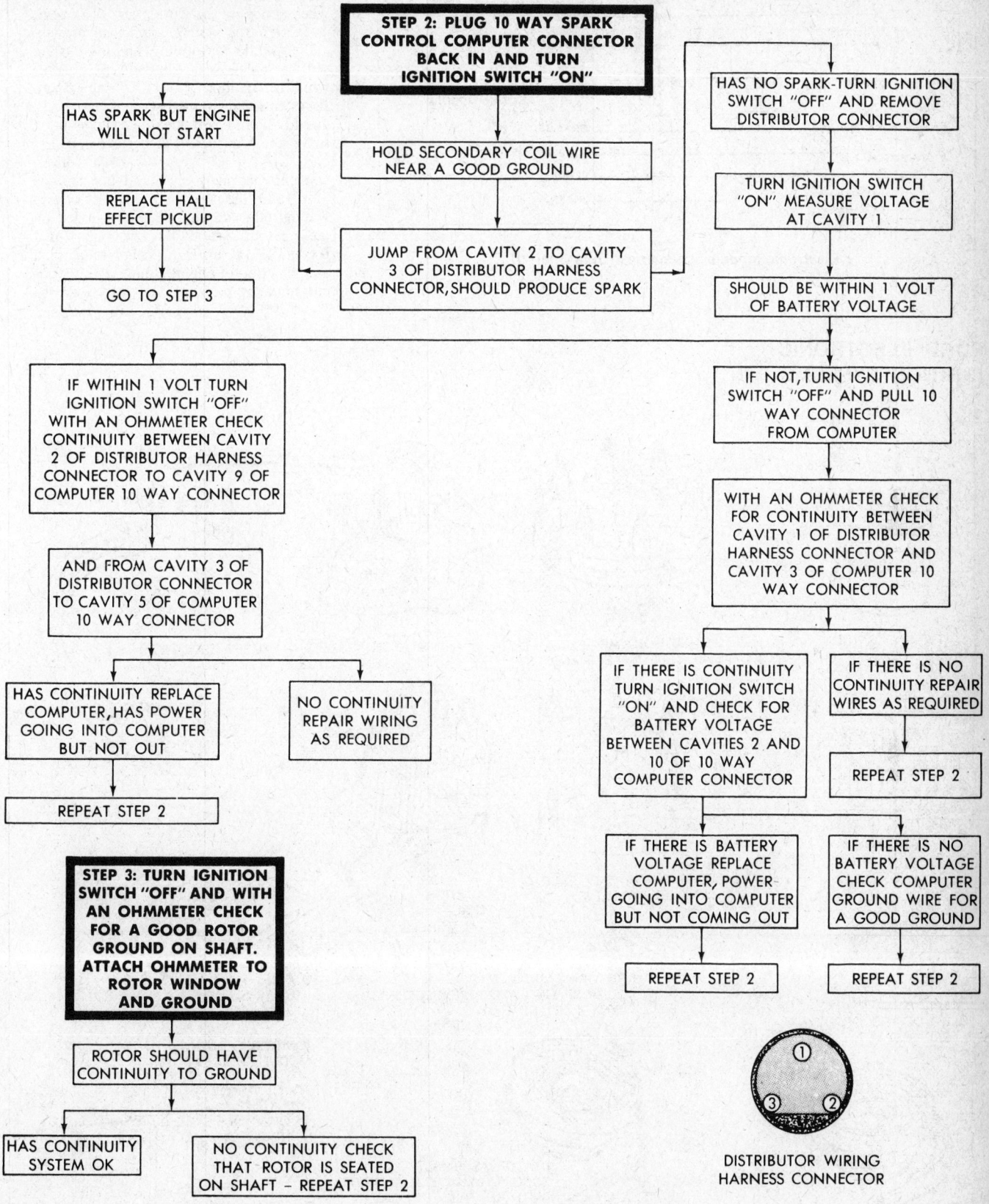

STEP 2: PLUG 10 WAY SPARK CONTROL COMPUTER CONNECTOR BACK IN AND TURN IGNITION SWITCH "ON"

HAS SPARK BUT ENGINE WILL NOT START

REPLACE HALL EFFECT PICKUP

GO TO STEP 3

HOLD SECONDARY COIL WIRE NEAR A GOOD GROUND

JUMP FROM CAVITY 2 TO CAVITY 3 OF DISTRIBUTOR HARNESS CONNECTOR, SHOULD PRODUCE SPARK

HAS NO SPARK-TURN IGNITION SWITCH "OFF" AND REMOVE DISTRIBUTOR CONNECTOR

TURN IGNITION SWITCH "ON" MEASURE VOLTAGE AT CAVITY 1

SHOULD BE WITHIN 1 VOLT OF BATTERY VOLTAGE

IF WITHIN 1 VOLT TURN IGNITION SWITCH "OFF" WITH AN OHMMETER CHECK CONTINUITY BETWEEN CAVITY 2 OF DISTRIBUTOR HARNESS CONNECTOR TO CAVITY 9 OF COMPUTER 10 WAY CONNECTOR

AND FROM CAVITY 3 OF DISTRIBUTOR CONNECTOR TO CAVITY 5 OF COMPUTER 10 WAY CONNECTOR

HAS CONTINUITY REPLACE COMPUTER, HAS POWER GOING INTO COMPUTER BUT NOT OUT

NO CONTINUITY REPAIR WIRING AS REQUIRED

REPEAT STEP 2

STEP 3: TURN IGNITION SWITCH "OFF" AND WITH AN OHMMETER CHECK FOR A GOOD ROTOR GROUND ON SHAFT. ATTACH OHMMETER TO ROTOR WINDOW AND GROUND

ROTOR SHOULD HAVE CONTINUITY TO GROUND

HAS CONTINUITY SYSTEM OK

NO CONTINUITY CHECK THAT ROTOR IS SEATED ON SHAFT – REPEAT STEP 2

IF NOT, TURN IGNITION SWITCH "OFF" AND PULL 10 WAY CONNECTOR FROM COMPUTER

WITH AN OHMMETER CHECK FOR CONTINUITY BETWEEN CAVITY 1 OF DISTRIBUTOR HARNESS CONNECTOR AND CAVITY 3 OF COMPUTER 10 WAY CONNECTOR

IF THERE IS CONTINUITY TURN IGNITION SWITCH "ON" AND CHECK FOR BATTERY VOLTAGE BETWEEN CAVITIES 2 AND 10 OF 10 WAY COMPUTER CONNECTOR

IF THERE IS NO CONTINUITY REPAIR WIRES AS REQUIRED

REPEAT STEP 2

IF THERE IS BATTERY VOLTAGE REPLACE COMPUTER, POWER GOING INTO COMPUTER BUT NOT COMING OUT

IF THERE IS NO BATTERY VOLTAGE CHECK COMPUTER GROUND WIRE FOR A GOOD GROUND

REPEAT STEP 2

REPEAT STEP 2

DISTRIBUTOR WIRING HARNESS CONNECTOR

Hall-Effect electronic spark advance system diagnosis

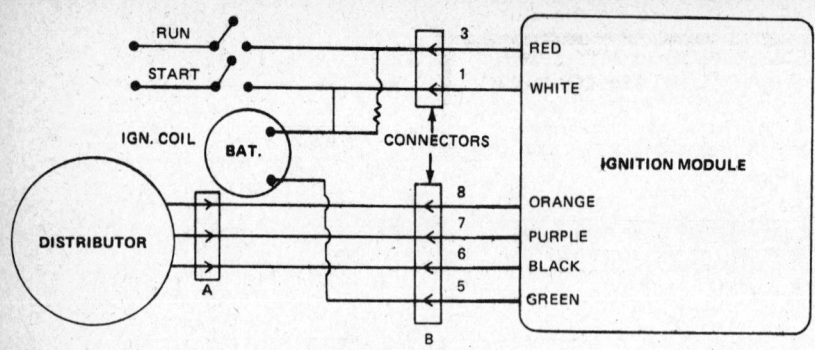

Electronic module schematic—Dura Spark II

ignition switch is ON. Keep this in mind when servicing the Dura Spark II system, as the ignition system could inadvertently "fire" while performing ignition system services (such as distributor cap removal) while the ignition is ON. All Dura Spark II systems (except the Escort, Lynx, EXP, and LN7) are easily identified by having a two-piece, flat topped distributor cap. Escort, Lynx, EXP, and LN7 models use a conventional one-piece distributor cap.

In 1980, the new Dura Spark III system was introduced. This version is based on the previous systems, but the input signal is controlled by the EEC system, rather than as a function of engine timing and distributor armature position. The distributor, ro-

FORD ELECTRONIC IGNITION SYSTEMS

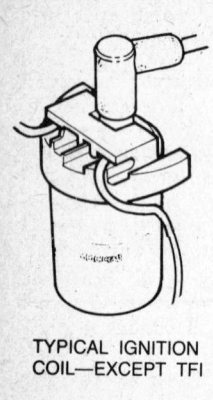

TYPICAL IGNITION COIL—EXCEPT TFI

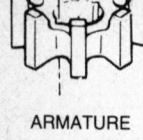

ARMATURE

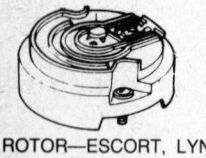

ROTOR—ESCORT, LYNX, EXP AND LN7

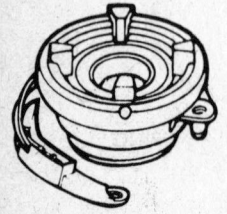

STATOR ASSEMBLY— ESCORT, LYNX, EXP AND LN7 (WITH TFI)

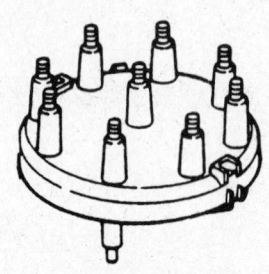

DISTRIBUTOR CAP—EXCEPT ESCORT, LYNX, EXP AND LN7

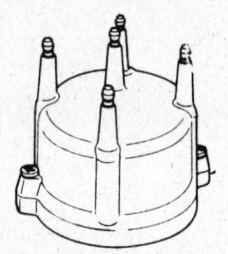

DISTRIBUTOR CAP—ESCORT, LYNX, EXP AND LN7

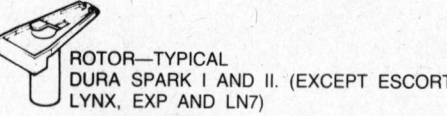

ROTOR—TYPICAL DURA SPARK I AND II. (EXCEPT ESCORT, LYNX, EXP AND LN7)

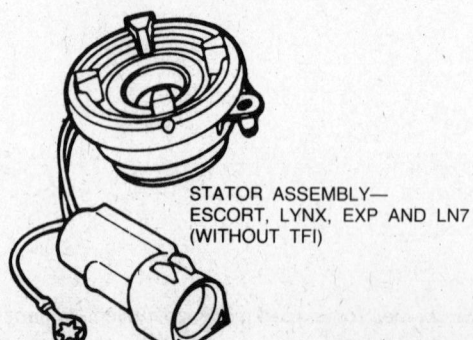

STATOR ASSEMBLY— ESCORT, LYNX, EXP AND LN7 (WITHOUT TFI)

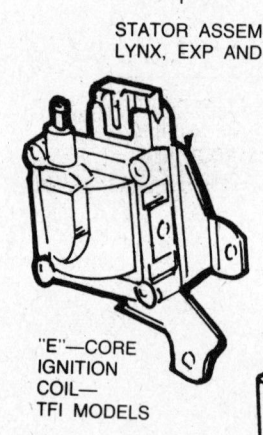

"E"—CORE IGNITION COIL— TFI MODELS

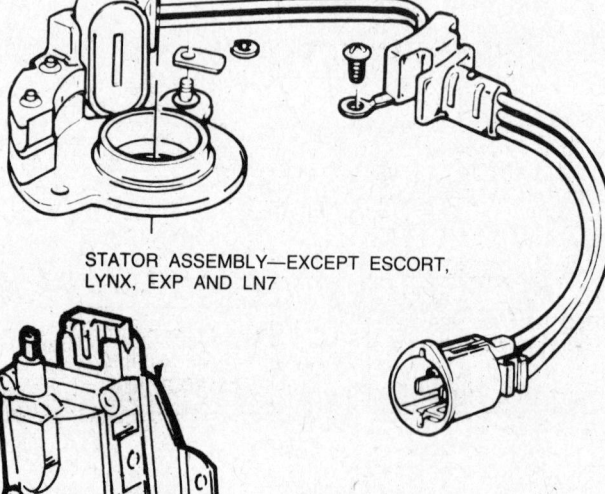

STATOR ASSEMBLY—EXCEPT ESCORT, LYNX, EXP AND LN7

IGNITION CONTROL MODULE—EXCEPT TFI

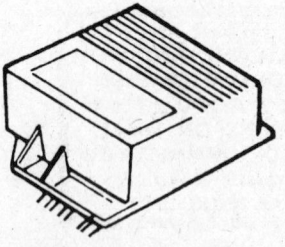

TFI IGNITION MODULE

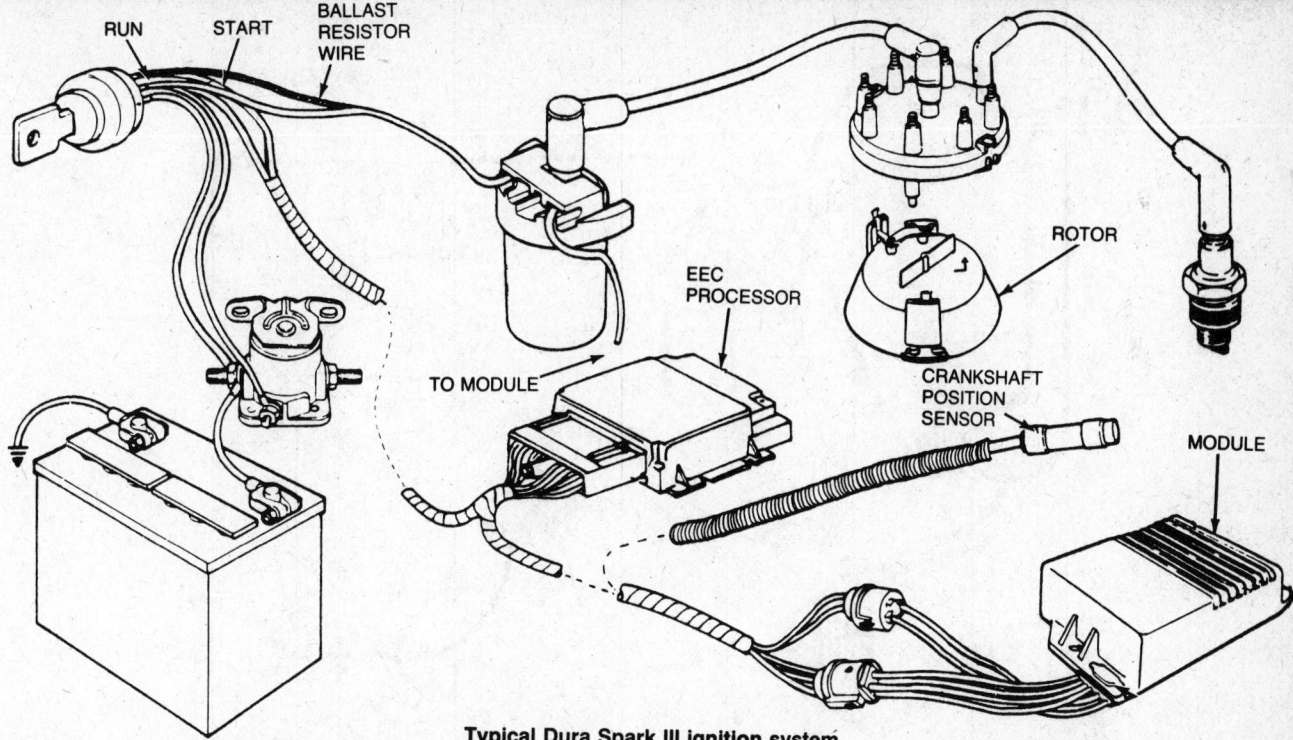

Typical Dura Spark III ignition system

tor, cap, and control module are unique to this system; the spark plugs and plug wires are the same as those used with the Dura Spark II system. Although the Dura Spark II and III control modules are similar in appearance, they cannot be interchanged between systems.

The TFI (Thick Film Integrated) ignition system is used on 1982–84 Escort, Lynx, EXP, and LN7 models with automatic

transaxles. Previous models, and those with manual transaxles, use the Dura Spark II system. The main difference between Dura Spark II and TFI is not in operation, but in component usage. The TFI system uses a new distributor base-mounted, TFI ignition module, which is contained in a moulded thermo-plastic. Also, this system uses an E-Core ignition coil in lieu of the Dura Spark coil.

Special Control Modules

The 1978–79 Versailles with the modified Dura Spark II system, uses a special control module designed to function with the vehicles EEC system.

Some 1978 and later engines use a special Dura Spark Dual Mode ignition control module. The module is equipped with an altitude sensor, an economy modulator, or

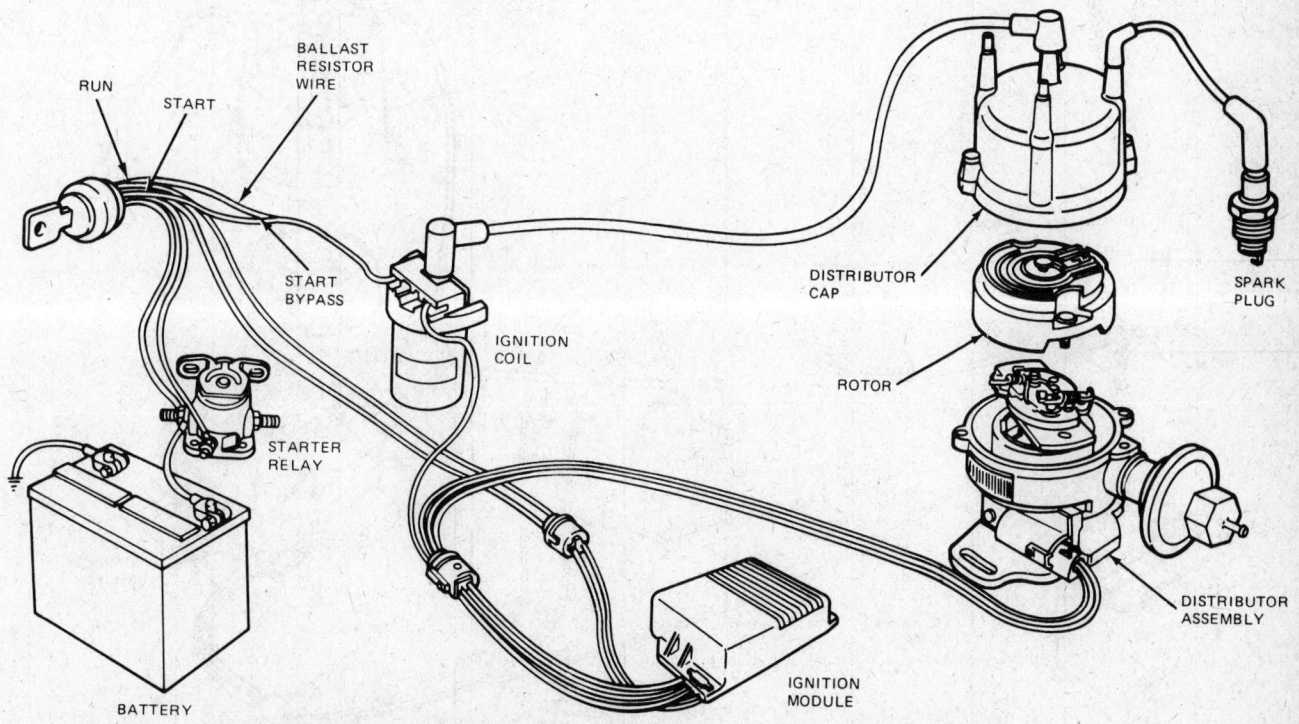

Escort, EXP, Lynx and LN7 ignition system—Dura Spark II (© Ford Motor Co.)

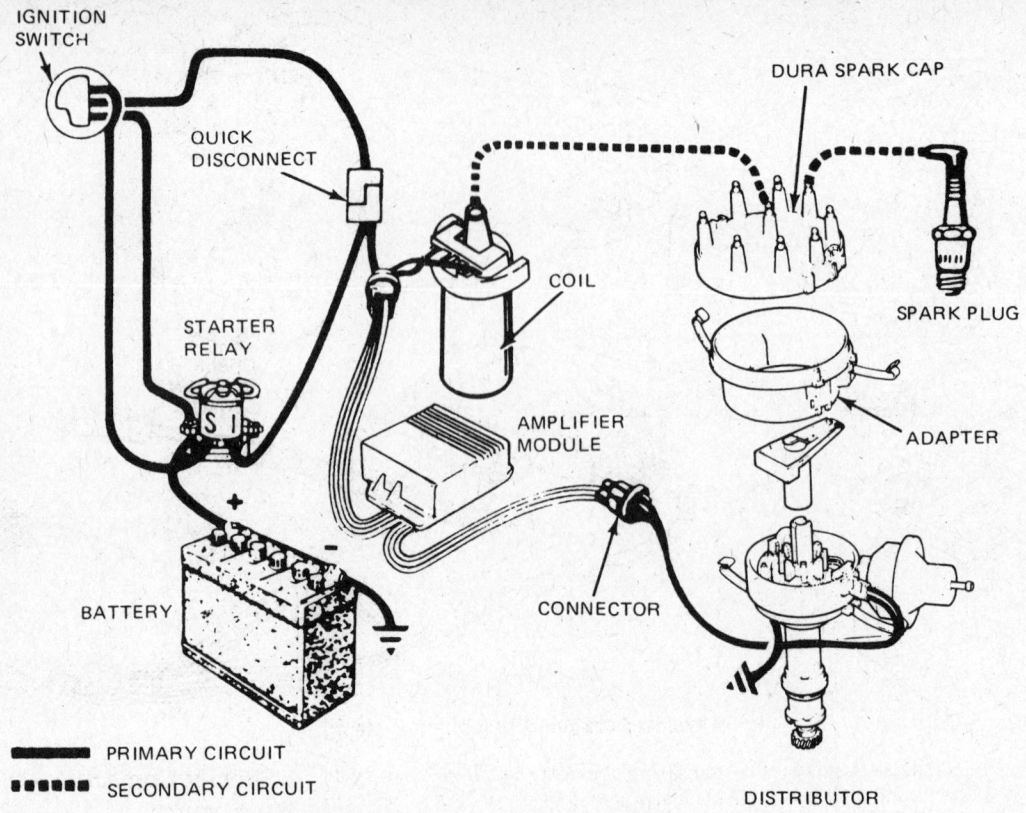

Dura Spark I and II ignition system—basic wiring; except Escort, Lynx, EXP and LN7

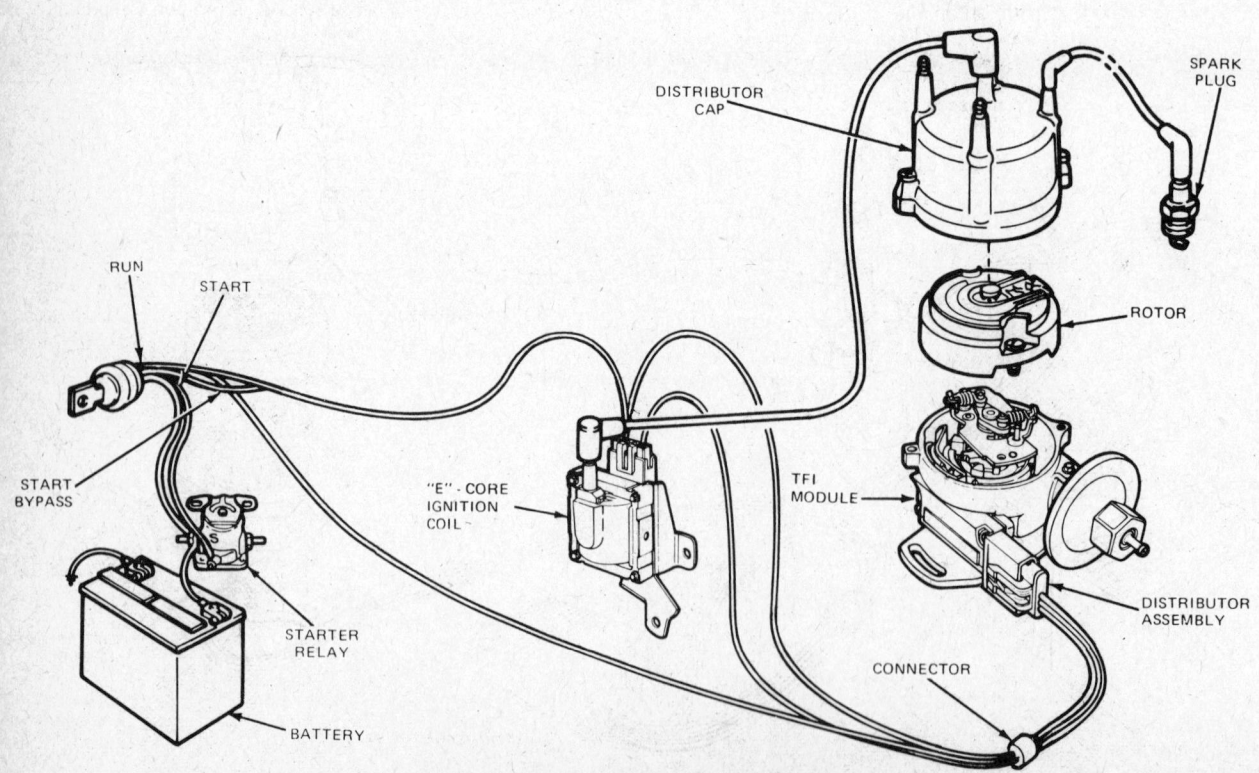

Thick Film Integrated (TFI) ignition system—basic wiring

pressure switches (turbocharged engines only). This module, when combined with the additional switches and sensor, varies the base engine timing according to altitude and engine load conditions. Dura Spark Dual Mode ignition control modules have three wiring harness from the module.

1980–81 49-state and 1982 Canadian 2.3 liter engines with automatic transmissions have a Dual Mode Crank Retard ignition module, which has the same function as the Dura Spark II module plus an ignition timing retard function which is operational during engine cranking. The spark timing retard feature eases engine starting, but allows normal timing advance as soon as the engine is running. This module can be identified by the presence of a white connector shell on the four-pin connector at the module.

Some 1981 and later Dura Spark II systems used with some 255 and 302 cu. in. engines are equipped with a Universal Ignition Module (UIM) which includes a run-retard function. The operation of the module is basically the same as the Dura Spark Dual Mode module.

NOTE: When replacing the ignition control module, always use the old module as a reference to identify the wiring, connectors, and type of the new module.

OPERATION

NOTE: For a description of the EEC systems, refer to the Unit Repair section under "Ford Electronic Engine Control Systems."

With the ignition switch "on," the primary circuit is on and the ignition coil is energized. When the armature "spokes" approach the magnetic pickup coil assem-

FORD MOTOR COMPANY ELECTRONIC IGNITION APPLICATION CHART

Dura Spark I	
1978-79	All California 302 cu. in. engines, except the Versailles
Dura Spark II	
1978-79	All Versailles, and all engines except the California 302 cu. in. engine
1980-81	All models without EEC
1982-84	All models except: Lincoln and Mark VI and VII with the 302 cu. in. engine
	Police models with the 351 cu. in.
	Escort, Lynx, EXP, and LN7 with automatic transaxles
Dura Spark III	
1980-81	All models with EEC
1982-84	Lincoln and Mark VI and VII with 302 cu. in. engine
	Police models with 351 cu. in. engine
TFI	
1982-84	Escort, Lynx, EXP, and LN7 with automatic transaxles

bly, they induce a voltage which tells the amplifier to turn the coil primary current off. A timing circuit in the amplifier module will turn the current on again after the coil field has collapsed. When the current is "on," it flows from the battery through the ignition switch, the primary windings of the ignition coil, and through the amplifier module circuits to ground. When the current is off, the magnetic field built up in the ignition coil is allowed to collapse, inducing a high voltage into the secondary windings of the coil. High voltage is produced each time the field is thus built up and collapsed. When Dura Spark is used in conjunction with EEC, the EEC com-

puter tells the Dura Spark module when to turn the coil primary current off or on. In this case, the armature position is only a reference signal of engine timing, used by the EEC computer in combination with other reference signals to determine optimum ignition spark timing.

The high voltage flows through the coil high tension lead to the distributor cap where the rotor distributes it to one of the spark plug terminals in the distributor cap. This process is repeated for every power stroke of the engine.

Ignition system troubles are caused by a failure in the primary and/or the secondary circuit; incorrect ignition timing; or incor-

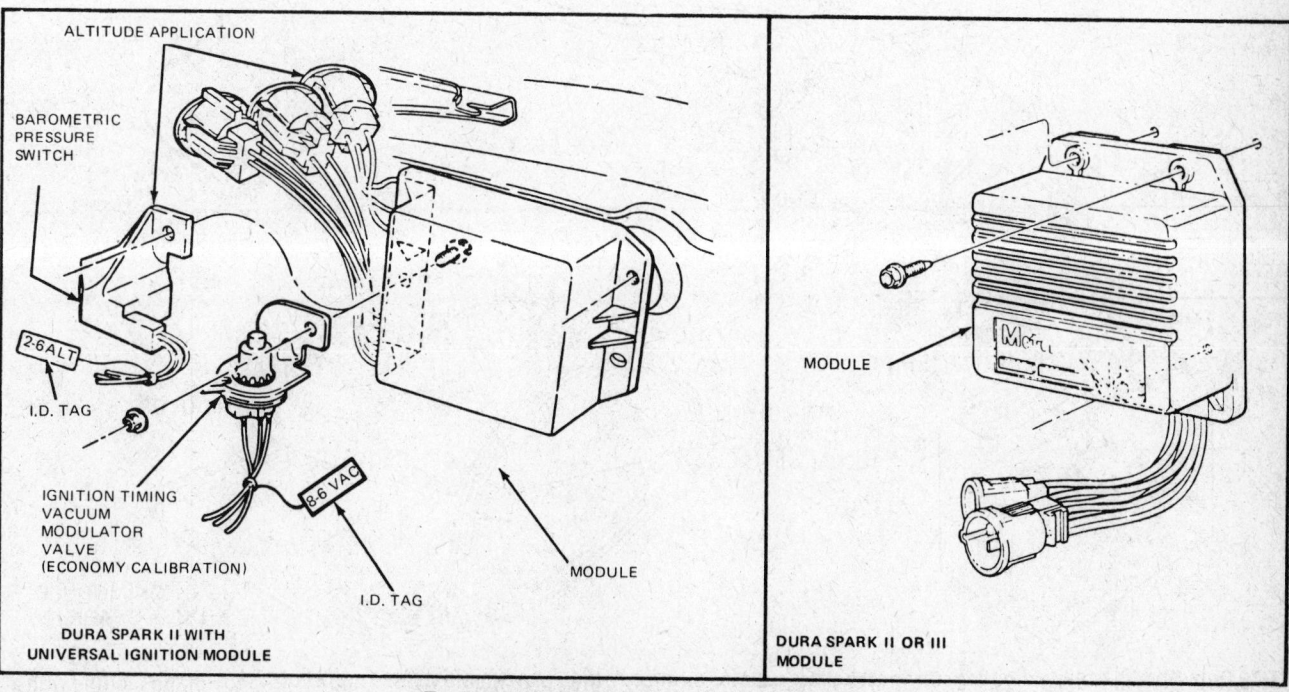

Typical Dura Spark ignition control modules

rect distributor advance. Circuit failures may be caused by shorts, corroded or dirty terminals, loose connections, defective wire insulation, cracked distributor cap or rotor, defective pick-up coil assembly or amplifier module, defective distributor points or fouled spark plugs.

If an engine starting or operating trouble is attributed to the ignition system, start the engine and verify the complaint. On engines that will not start, be sure that there is gasoline in the fuel tank and that fuel is reaching the carburetor. Then locate the ignition system problem using the following procedures.

TROUBLESHOOTING DURA SPARK I

The following Dura Spark II troubleshooting procedures may be used on Dura Spark I systems with a few variations. The Dura Spark I module has internal connections which shut off the primary circuit in the run mode when the engine stalls. To perform the above troubleshooting procedures, it is necessary to by-pass these connections. However, with these connections by-passed, the current flow in the primary becomes so great that it will damage both the ignition coil and module unless a ballast resistor is installed in series with the primary circuit at the BAT terminal of the ignition coil. Such a resistor is available from Ford (Motorcraft part number DY-36). A 1.3 ohm,

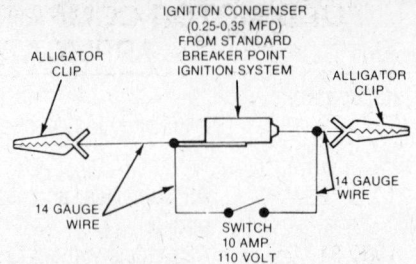

Test jumper switch used for trouble-shooting the Dura Spark II ignition system;

100 watt wire-wound power resistor can also be used.

To install the resistor, proceed as follows.

NOTE: The resistor will become very hot during testing.

1. Release the BAT terminal lead from the coil by inserting a paper clip through the hole in the rear of the horseshoe coil connector and manipulating it against the locking tab in the connector until the lead comes free.

2. Insert a paper clip in the BAT terminal of the connector on the coil. Using jumper leads, connect the ballast resistor as shown.

3. Using a straight pin, pierce both the red and white leads of the module to short these two together. This will by-pass the internal connections of the module which turn off the ignition circuit when the engine is not running.

4. With the ballast resistor and by-pass in place, proceed with the Dura Spark II troubleshooting procedures.

TROUBLESHOOTING DURA SPARK II

NOTE: Troubleshooting procedures for the EEC systems are given in the "Engine Controls" Unit Repair Section.

The following procedures can be used to determine whether the ignition system is working or not. If these procedures fail to correct the problem, a full troubleshooting procedure should be performed.

Preliminary Checks

1. Check the battery's state of charge and connections.

2. Inspect all wires and connections for breaks, cuts, abrasions, or burn spots. Repair as necessary.

3. Unplug all connectors one at a time and inspect for corroded or burned contacts. Repair and plug connectors back together. DO NOT remove the Lubriplate® compound in the connectors.

4. Check for loose or damaged spark plug or coil wires. A wire resistance check

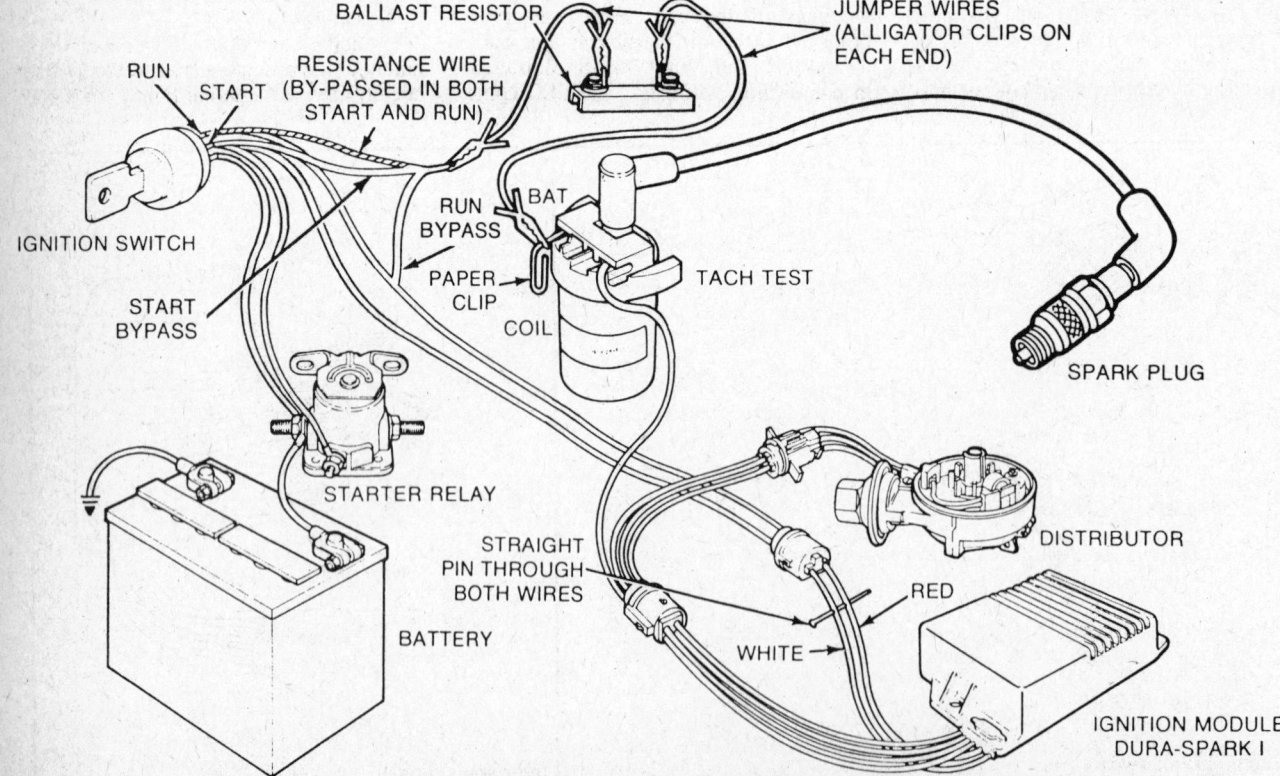

1977-79 Dura Spark I troubleshooting: Connect ballast resistor as shown, *then* **pierce both the red and white leads of the module with a straight pin**

is given at the end of this section. If the boots or nipples are removed on 8mm ignition wires, reline the inside of each with new silicone di-electric compound (Motorcraft WA 10).

Special Tools

To perform the following tests, two special tools are needed; the ignition test jumper shown in the illustration and a modified spark plug. Use the illustration to assemble the ignition test jumper. The test jumper must be used when performing the following tests. The modified spark plug is basically a spark plug with the side electrode removed. Ford makes a special tool called a Spark Tester for this purpose, which besides not having a side electrode is equipped with a spring clip so that it can be grounded to engine metal. It is recommended that the Spark Tester be used as there is less chance of being shocked.

Run Mode Spark Test

NOTE: The wire colors given here are the main colors of the wires, not the dots or hashmarks.

STEP 1

1. Remove the distributor cap and rotor from the distributor.
2. With the ignition off, turn the engine over by hand until one of the teeth on the distributor armature aligns with the magnet in the pick-up coil.
3. Remove the coil wire from the distributor cap. On 1978 and later models, install the modified spark plug (see Special Tools, above) in the coil wire terminal and using heavy gloves and insulated pliers, hold the spark plug shell against the engine block.
4. Turn the ignition to RUN (not START) and tap the distributor body with a screwdriver handle. There should be a spark at the modified spark plug or at the coil wire terminal.
5. If a good spark is evident, the primary circuit is OK: perform Start Mode Spark Test. If there is no spark, proceed to Step 2.

STEP 2

1. Unplug the module connector(s) which contain(s) the green and black module leads.
2. In the harness side of the connector(s), connect the special test jumper (see Special Tools, above) between the leads which connect to the green and black leads of the module pig tails. Use paper clips on connector socket holes to make contact. Do not allow clips to ground.
3. Turn the ignition switch to RUN (not START) and close the test jumper switch. Leave closed for about 1 second, then open. Repeat several times. There should be a spark each time the switch is opened. On Dura Spark I systems, close the test switch for 10 seconds on the first cycle. After that, 1 second is adequate.

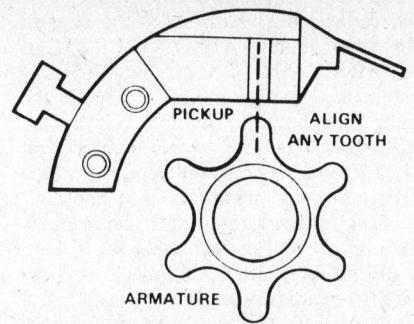

Align any tooth of the distributor armature with the magnet in the pick-up coil

4. If there is no spark, the problem is probably in the primary circuit through the ignition switch, the coil, the green lead or the black lead, or the ground connection in the distributor: perform Step 3. If there is a spark, the primary circuit wiring and coil are probably OK. The problem is probably in the distributor pick-up, the module red wire, or the module: perform Step 6.

STEP 3

1. Disconnect the test jumper lead from the black lead and connect it to a good ground. Turn the test jumper switch on and off several times as in Step 2.
2. If there is no spark, the problem is probably in the green lead, the coil, or the coil feed circuit: perform Step 5.
3. If there is spark, the problem is probably in the black lead or the distributor ground connection: perform Step 4.

STEP 4

1. Connect an ohmmeter between the black lead and ground. With the meter on its lowest scale, there should be no measureable resistance in the circuit. If there is resistance, check the distributor ground connection and the black lead from the module. Repair as necessary, remove the ohmmeter, plug in all connections and repeat step 1.

If there is no resistance, the primary ground wiring is OK: perform Step 6.

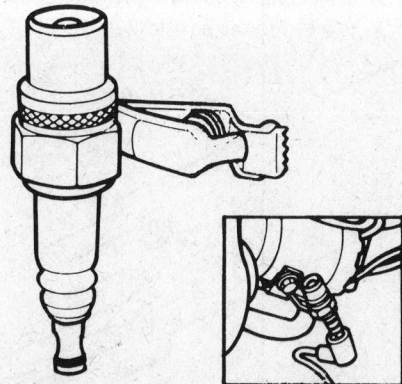

Ford Spark Tester: actually a modified spark plug (side electrode removed) with a spring clip for ground

STEP 5

1. Disconnect the test jumper from the green lead and ground and connect it between the TACH-TEST terminal of the coil and a good ground on the engine.
2. With the ignition switch in the RUN position, turn the jumper switch on. Hold it on for about 1 second then turn it off as in Step 2. Repeat several times. There should be a spark each time the switch is turned off. If there is no spark, the problem is probably in the primary circuit running through the ignition switch to the coil BAT terminal, or in the coil itself. Check coil resistance (test given later in this section), and check the coil for internal shorts or opens. Check the coil feed circuit for opens, shorts or high resistance. Repair as necessary, reconnect all connectors and repeat Step 1. If there is spark, the coil and its feed circuit are OK. The problem could be in the green lead between the coil and the module. Check for open or short, repair as necessary, reconnect all connectors and repeat Step 1.

STEP 6

To perform this step, a voltmeter which is not combined with a dwell meter is needed. The slight needle oscillations (½ V) you'll be looking for may not be detectable on the combined voltmeter/dwell meter unit.

1. Connect a voltmeter between the orange and purple leads on the harness side of the module connectors.

CAUTION

On catalytic converter equipped cars, disconnect the air supply line between the Thermactor by-pass valve and the manifold before cranking the engine with the ignition off. This will prevent damage to the catalytic converter. After testing, run the engine for at least 3 minutes before reconnecting the by-pass valve, to clear excess fuel from the exhaust system.

2. Set the voltmeter on its lowest scale and crank the engine. The meter needle should oscillate slightly (about ½ volt). If the meter does not oscillate, check the circuit through the magnetic pick-up in the distributor for open, shorts, shorts to ground and resistance. Resistance between the orange and purple leads should be 400–1000 ohms, and between each lead and ground should be more than 70,000 ohms. Repair as necessary, reconnect all connectors and repeat Step 1.

If the meter oscillates, the problem is probably in the power feed to the module (red wire) or in the module itself: proceed to Step 7.

STEP 7

1. Remove all meters and jumpers and plug in all connectors.
2. Turn the ignition switch to the RUN position and measure voltage between the battery positive terminal and engine ground. It should be 12 volts.

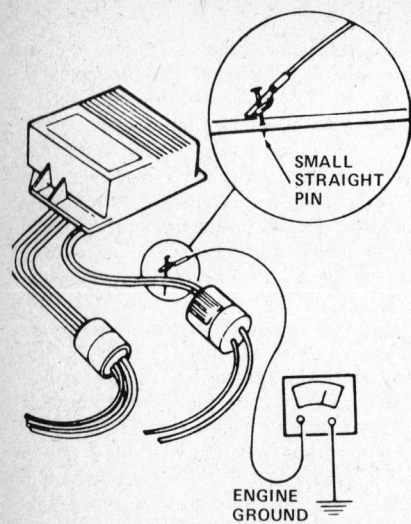

Use a small straight pin to pierce wires in order to measure voltage. Do not allow the pin to ground itself

3. Next, measure voltage between the red lead of the module and engine ground. To make this measurement, it will be necessary to pierce the red wire with a straight pin and connect the voltmeter to the straight pin and to ground. DO NOT ALLOW THE STRAIGHT PIN TO GROUND ITSELF.

4. The two readings should be within one volt of each other. If not within one volt, the problem is in the power feed to the red lead. Check for shorts, open, or high resistance and correct as necessary. After repairs, repeat Step 1.

If the readings are within one volt, the problem is probably in the module. Replace with a good module and repeat Step 1. If this corrects the problem, reconnect the old module and repeat Step 1. If problem returns, permanently install the new module.

Start Mode Spark Test

NOTE: The wire colors given here are the main colors of the wires, not the dots or hashmarks.

1. Remove the coil wire from the distributor cap. On 1978 and later models, install the modified spark plug mentioned under "Special Tools", above, in the coil wire and ground it to engine metal either by its spring clip (Spark Tester) or by holding the spark plug shell against the engine block with insulated pliers.

NOTE: See "CAUTION" under Step 6 of "Run Mode Spark Test", above.

2. Have an assistant crank the engine using the ignition switch and check for spark. If there is good spark, the problem is probably in the distributor cap, rotor, ignition cables or spark plugs. If there is no spark, proceed to Step 3.

3. Measure the battery voltage. Next, measure the voltage at the white wire of the module while cranking the engine. To make this measurement, it will be necessary to pierce the white wire with a straight pin

and connect the voltmeter to the straight pin and to ground. DO NOT ALLOW THE STRAIGHT PIN TO GROUND ITSELF. The battery voltage and the voltage at the white wire should be within 1 volt of each other. If the readings are not within 1 volt of each other, check and repair the feed through the ignition switch to the white wire. Recheck for spark (Step 1). If the readings are within 1 volt of each other, or if there is still no spark after power feed to white wire is repaired, proceed to Step 4.

4. Measure the coil BAT terminal voltage while cranking the engine. The reading should be within 1 volt of battery voltage. If the readings are not within 1 volt of each other, check and repair the feed through the ignition switch to the coil. If the readings are within 1 volt of each other, the problem is probably in the ignition module. Substitute another module and repeat test for spark (Step 1).

TFI SYSTEM TESTING

NOTE: After performing any test which requires piercing a wire with a straight pin, remove the straight pin and seal the holes in the wire with silicone sealer.

Ignition Coil Secondary Voltage

1. Disconnect the secondary (high voltage) coil wire from the distributor cap and install a spark tester (see Special Tools, located with the Dura Spark Troubleshooting) between the coil wire and ground.

2. Crank the engine—a good, strong spark should be noted at the spark tester. If spark is noted, but the engine will not start, check the spark plugs, spark plug wiring, and fuel system. If there is no spark at the tester:

 a. Check the ignition coil secondary wire resistance; it should be no more than 5000 ohms per inch.

 b. Inspect the ignition coil for damage and/or carbon tracking.

 c. With the distributor cap removed, verify that the distributor shaft turns with the engine; if it does not, repair the engine as required.

 d. If the fault was not found in a, b, or c, proceed to the next test.

Ignition Coil Primary Circuit Switching

1. Insert a small straight pin in the wire which runs from the coil negative (−) terminal to the TFI module, about one inch from the module.

----- **CAUTION** -----
The pin must not touch ground.

2. Connect a 12VDC test lamp between the straight pin and an engine ground.

3. Crank the engine, noting the operation of the test lamp. If the test lamp flashes, proceed to the next test. If the test lamp lights but does not flash, proceed to the Wiring Harness test. If the test lamp does not light at all, proceed to the Primary Circuit Continuity test.

Ignition Coil Resistance

Refer to the General Testing for an explanation of the resistance tests. Replace the ignition coil if the resistance is out of the specification range.

Wiring Harness

1. Disconnect the wiring harness connector from the TFI module; the connector tabs must be PUSHED to disengage the connector. Inspect the connector for damage, dirt, and corrosion.

2. Attach the negative lead of a voltmeter to the base of the distributor. Attach the other voltmeter lead to a small straight pin.

 a. With the ignition switch in the RUN position, insert the straight pin into the No. 1 terminal of the TFI module connector. Note the voltage reading and proceed to b.

 b. With the ignition switch in the RUN position, move the straight pin to the No. 2 connector terminal. Again, note the voltage reading, then proceed to c.

 c. Move the straight pin to the No. 3 connector terminal, then turn the ignition switch to the START position. Note the voltage reading then turn the ignition OFF.

3. The voltage readings from a, b, and c should all be at least 90% of the available battery voltage. If the readings are okay,

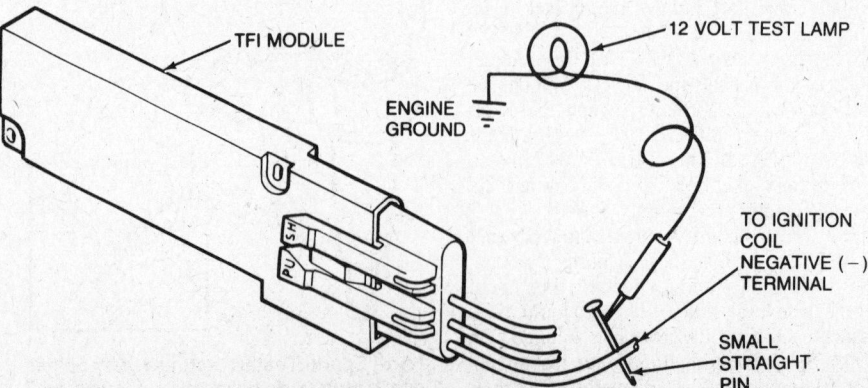

TFI ignition system—ignition coil primary circuit switching test arrangement

proceed to the Stator Assembly and Module test. If any reading is less than 90% of the battery voltage, inspect the wiring, connectors, and/or ignition switch for defects. If the voltage is low only at the No. 1 terminal, proceed to the ignition coil primary voltage test.

Stator Assembly and Module

1. Remove the distributor from the engine according to the procedure listed in the appropriate car section.

2. Remove the TFI module from the distributor as outlined under Component Replacement in this section.

3. Inspect the distributor terminals, ground screw, and stator wiring for damage. Repair as necessary.

4. Measure the resistance of the stator assembly, using an ohmmeter. If the ohmmeter reading is 800–975 ohms; the stator is okay, but the TFI module must be replaced. If the ohmmeter reading is less than 800 ohms or more than 975 ohms; the TFI module is okay, but the stator assembly must be replaced.

5. Reinstall the TFI module and the distributor according to the appropriate sections.

Primary Circuit Continuity

This test is performed in the same manner as the previous Wiring Harness test, but only the No. 1 terminal conductor is tested (ignition switch in RUN position). If the voltage is less than 90% of the available battery voltage, proceed to the next test.

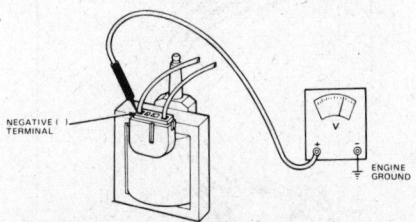

TFI ignition system—coil primary voltage test arrangement

Ignition Coil Primary Voltage

1. Attach the negative lead of a voltmeter to the distributor base.

2. Turn the ignition switch ON and connect the positive voltmeter lead to the negative (−) ignition coil terminal. Note the voltage reading and turn the ignition OFF. If the voltmeter reading is less than 90% of the available battery voltage, inspect the wiring between the ignition module and the negative (−) coil terminal, then proceed to the last test, which follows.

Ignition Coil Supply Voltage

1. Attach the negative lead of a voltmeter to the distributor base.

2. Turn the ignition switch ON and connect the positive voltmeter lead to the positive (+) ignition coil terminal. Note

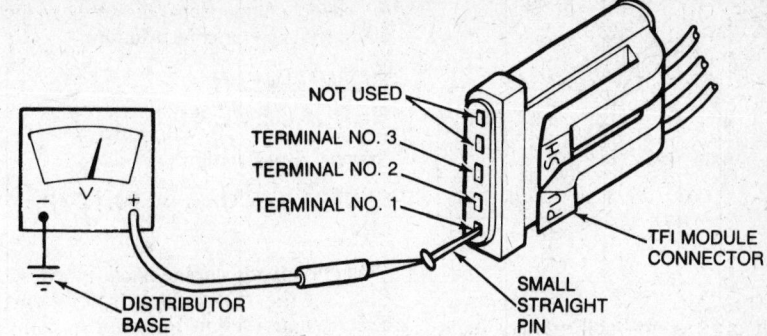

TFI ignition system—wiring harness test arrangement

the voltage reading then turn the ignition OFF.

a. If the voltage reading is at least 90% of the battery voltage, yet the engine will still not run: first, check the ignition coil connector and terminals for corrosion, dirt, and/or damage; second, replace the ignition switch if the connectors and terminals are okay.

3. Connect any remaining wiring.

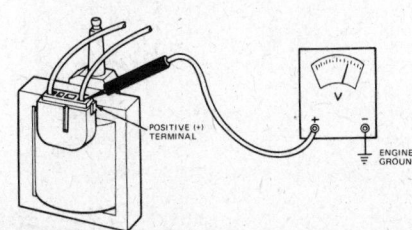

TFI ignition system—coil supply voltage test arrangement

GENERAL TESTING—ALL SYSTEMS

Ignition Coil Test

The ignition coil must be diagnosed separately from the rest of the ignition system.

1. Primary resistance is measured between the two primary (low voltage) coil terminals, with the coil connector disconnected and the ignition switch off. Primary

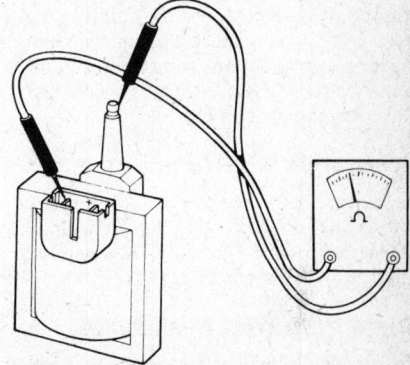

TFI ignition system—coil secondary resistance test arrangement

resistance must be 0.71–0.77 ohms for Dura Spark I. For Dura Spark II, it must be 1.13–1.23 ohms. For TFI systems, the primary resistance should be 0.3–1.0 ohms.

2. On Dura Spark ignitions, the secondary resistance is measured between the BATT and high voltage (secondary) terminals of the ignition coil with the ignition off, and the wiring from the coil disconnected. On TFI systems, refer to the accompanying illustration. Secondary resistance must be 7350–8250 ohms on Dura Spark I systems. Dura Spark II figure is 7700–9300 ohms. For TFI systems, the primary resistance should be 8000–11,500 ohms.

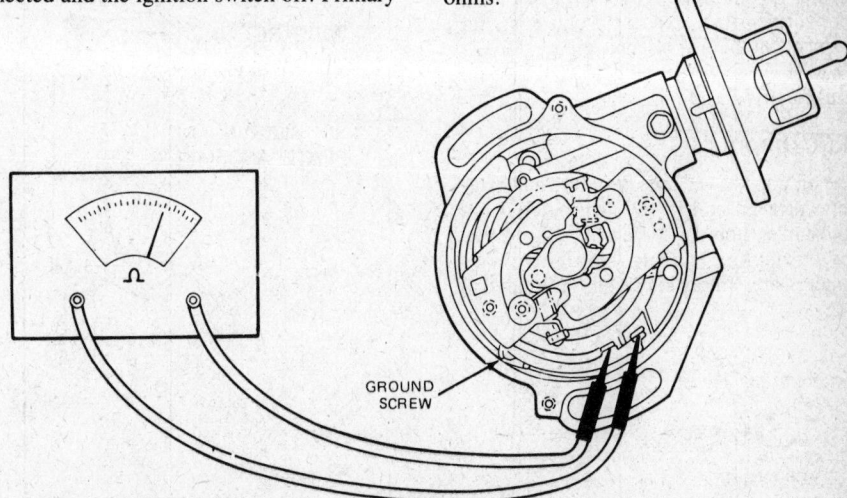

TFI ignition system—stator assembly and module test arrangement

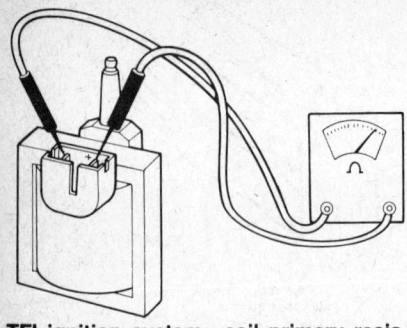

TFI ignition system—coil primary resistance test arrangement

3. If resistance tests are alright, but the coil is still suspected, test the coil on a coil tester by following the test equipment manufacturer's instructions for a standard coil. If the reading differs from the original test, check for a defective harness.

Resistance Wire Test

Replace the resistance wire if it doesn't show a resistance of 1.05–1.15 for Dura Spark II. The resistance wire isn't used on Dura Spark I or TFI systems.

Spark Plug Wire Resistance

Resistance on these wires must not exceed 5,000 ohms per inch. To properly measure this, remove the wires from the plugs, and remove the distributor cap. Measure the resistance through the distributor cap at that end. Do not pierce any ignition wire for any reason. Measure only from the two ends.

NOTE: Silicone grease must be reapplied to the spark plug wires whenever they are removed:

When removing the wires from the spark plugs, a special tool such as the one pictured should be used. Do not pull on the wires. Grasp and twist the boot to remove the wire.

Whenever the high tension wires are removed from the plugs, coil, or distributor, silicone grease must be applied to the boot before reconnection. Use a clean small screwdriver blade to coat the entire interior surface with Ford silicone grease D7AZ-19A331-A, Dow Corning #111, or General Electric G-627.

Adjustments

The air gap between the armature and magnetic pick-up coil in the distributor is not adjustable, nor are there any adjustments for the amplifier module. Inoperative components are simply replaced. Any attempt

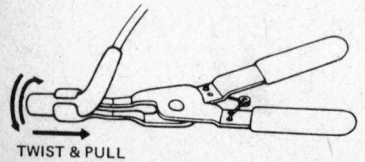

TWIST & PULL

Special tool for removing spark plug wires

to connect components outside the vehicle may result in component failure.

COMPONENT REPLACEMENT

Stator Assembly

EXCEPT ESCORT, LYNX, EXP, LN7

NOTE: If the engine is equipped with EEC, see the "Engine Control Systems" Unit Repair section for information on rotor alignment and identification.

1. Remove the distributor cap and rotor and disconnect the distributor harness plug.

NOTE: To remove the two-piece Dura Spark distributor cap, take off the top portion, then the rotor, then the bottom adaptor.

2. Using a small gear puller or two awls, lift or pry the armature from the advance plate sleeve. Remove the roll pin.

3. Remove the large wire retaining clip from the base plate annular groove.

For 1978–81 models:

4. Remove the snap-ring which secures the vacuum advance link to the pick-up assembly.

5. Remove the magnetic pick-up assembly ground screw and lift the assembly from the distributor.

6. Lift the vacuum advance arm off the post on the pick-up assembly and move it out against the distributor housing.

For 1982-84 models:

7. Remove the ground screw which retains the ground strap.

8. Pull upward on the lead wires to remove the rubber grommet from the distributor base.

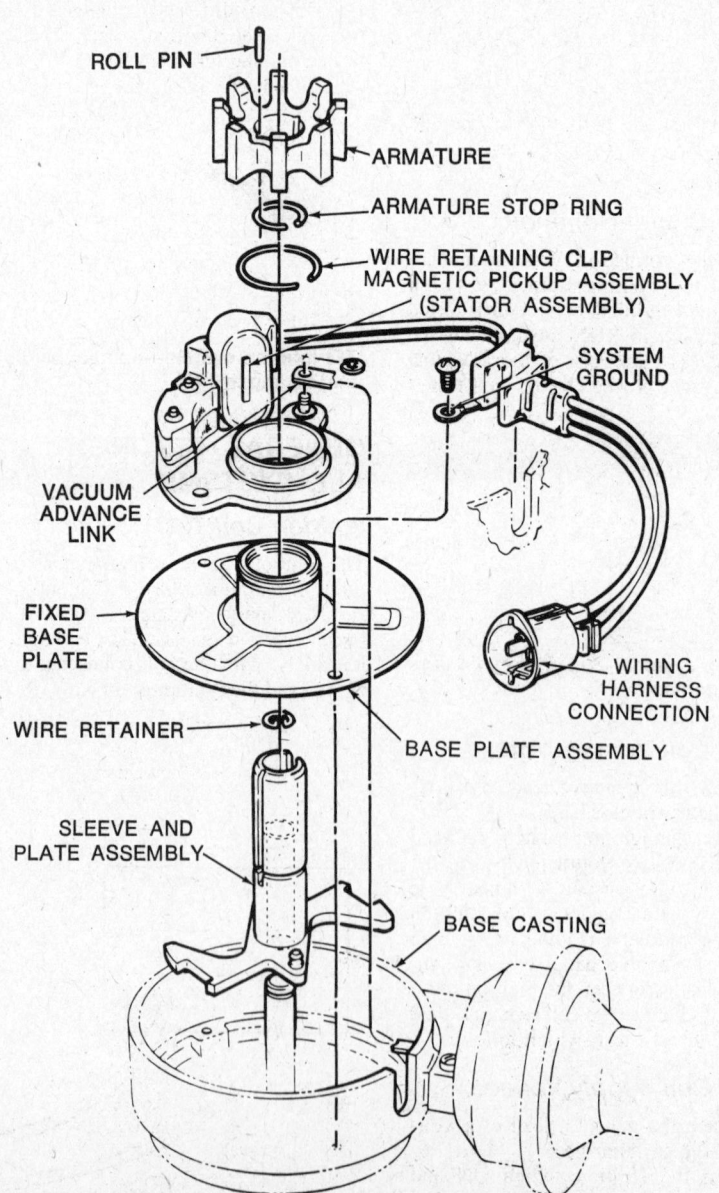

Partially disassembled view of a typical Solid State or Dura Spark ignition system

9. Remove the E-clip which retains the vacuum advance pull rod to the stator assembly.

10. Lift the pull rod off of the stator post and move the rod out against the distributor housing.

11. Remove the stator assembly.

Installation—all models:

12. Place the new pick-up assembly in position over the fixed base plate and slide the wiring in position through the slot in the side of the distributor housing.

13. Install the wire snap-ring securing the pick-up assembly to the fixed base plate.

14. Position the vacuum advance arm over the post on the pick-up assembly and install the snap-ring.

15. Install the grounding screw through the tab on the wiring harness and into the fixed base plate.

16. Install the armature on the advance plate sleeve making sure that the roll pin is engaged in the matching slots.

17. Install the distributor rotor cap.

18. Connect the distributor wiring plug to the vehicle harness.

ESCORT, LYNX, EXP, AND LN7

1. Remove the distributor cap from the distributor, and set it aside (spark plug wires intact).

2. Remove the distributor as outlined in the appropriate car section.

3. Remove the rotor from the distributor.

4. Carefully remove the drive coupling spring, using a small screwdriver.

5. Blow the dirt and oil from the drive end of the distributor with compressed air.

6. Paint matchmarks on the drive coupling and the shaft to indicate their relationship for reassembly. Align the drive pin with the slot in the base.

7. Carefully support the distributor and drive out the roll pin using a 1/8 in. drift punch and a hammer.

8. Remove the distributor drive coupling.

9. Check the end of the distributor shaft for burrs. If any are present, smooth them with emery paper and wipe the shaft clean. Withdraw the shaft assembly from the distributor.

10. Remove the two screws which retain the stator connector to the distributor bowl.

11. On TFI systems, remove the connector from the top of the TFI module.

12. Remove the three screws which retain the stator assembly to the distributor base. Carefully lift the stator assembly from the distributor base.

NOTE: While the distributor is disassembled, inspect all parts for damage, wear, and freedom of operation.

To install the stator assembly:

13. Assemble the stator retainer to the stator assembly by sliding the stator bumper into the groove in the bottom of the stator, with the horseshoe opening at the diaphragm rod pivot pin.

14. On TFI systems, place the connector on top of the module (with pins aligned).

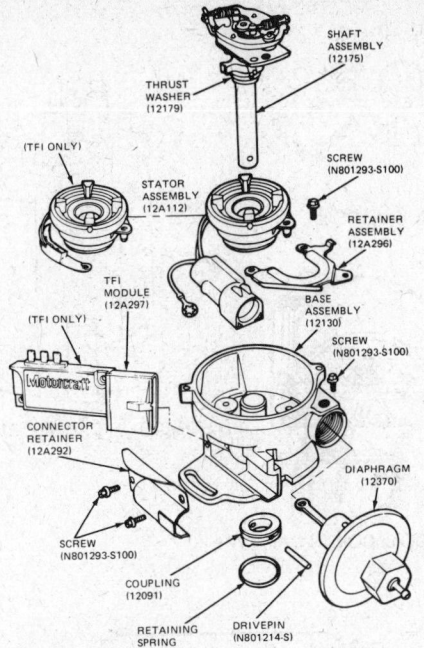

Exploded view of the Escort, Lynx, EXP and LN7 distributor

Press down on the connector to properly seat it.

15. Place the stator assembly over the distributor base bushing, with the diaphragm pivot pin positioned in front of the diaphragm mounting hole.

16. Align the holes in the stator retaining plate with the holes in the distributor base. Install the three stator retaining screws and torque the screws to 1.8–3.0 ft. lbs. Check the stator for free rotation.

17. Install the two screws which secure the connector to the base and torque the screws to 1.8–3.0 ft. lbs.

18. Place the two stator wires behind the wire guard of the connector. The wires must not be tangled or twisted.

19. Install the diaphragm assembly.

20. Apply a SMALL amount of Ford M2C162A (or its equivalent) lubricant to the distributor shaft below the armature.

21. Install the distributor shaft and the drive coupling, lining up the marks made during Step 6.

22. Support the distributor securely and drive the roll pin into place. The end of the pin should be flush with the step in the drive coupling. Check for free movement of the drive coupling and the distributor shaft.

23. Install the drive coupling retaining spring.

24. Install the distributor assembly, following the procedure listed in the appropriate car section.

25. Install the distributor cap and the rotor.

TFI Module

1. Remove the distributor cap from the distributor, and set it aside (spark plug wires intact).

2. Disconnect the TFI harness connector.

3. Remove the distributor as outlined in the appropriate car section.

4. Remove the two TFI module retaining screws.

5. To disengage the module terminals from the distributor base connector, pull the right side of the module down the distributor mounting flange and then back up. Carefully pull the module toward the flange and away from the distributor.

—— CAUTION ——

Step 5 must be followed EXACTLY; failure to do so will result in damage to the distributor/module connector pins.

To install the TFI module

6. Coat the TFI module baseplate with a 1/32 in. layer of silicone grease (Ford #D7AZ-19A331-A or its equivalent).

7. Place the TFI module on the distributor base mounting flange. Position the module assembly toward the distributor bowl and carefully engage the distributor connector pins. Install and torque the two TFI module retaining screws to 9–16 in. lbs.

8. Install the distributor assembly.

9. Install the distributor cap and check the engine timing.

NOTE: It is recommended to use a new roll pin in the armature groove positioned 180° away from the original groove.

Delco-Remy High Energy Ignition (HEI) System

NOTE: For details on the Oldsmobile Toronado Electronic Spark Timing Control System, see the Electronic Engine Controls Unit Repair Section.

GENERAL INFORMATION

The Delco-Remy High Energy Ignition (HEI) System is a breakerless, pulse triggered, transistor controlled, inductive discharge ignition system used on all GM passenger car engines as standard equipment.

The ignition coil is located in the top of the distributor cap on all V6 and V8 engines and some 4 cylinder engines. 1978 and later inline 4 cylinder engines mount the coil externally on the engine block. 1978 and later inline 6 cylinder engines mount the coil in the distributor cap.

NOTE: Some distributors are equipped with a Hall effect switch, located inside the distributor cap.

OPERATION

The magnetic pick-up assembly located inside the distributor contains a permanent magnet, a pole piece with internal teeth,

◪ ELECTRONIC IGNITION SYSTEMS

HIGH ENERGY IGNITION (H.E.I.): GM, AMC

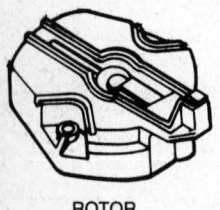

ROTOR

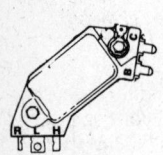

CONTROL MODULE

PICK-UP COIL

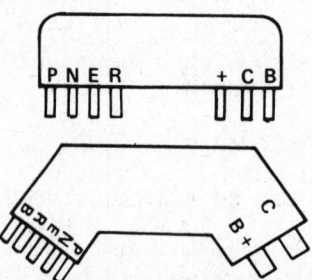

IGNITION COIL: COIL IN CAP TYPE

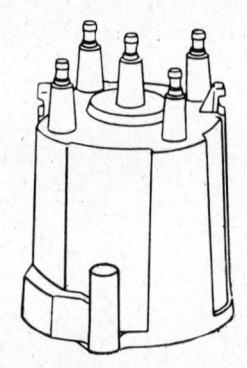

DISTRIBUTOR CAP: EXTERNAL COIL TYPE

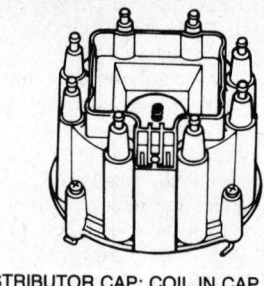

DISTRIBUTOR CAP: COIL IN CAP TYPE

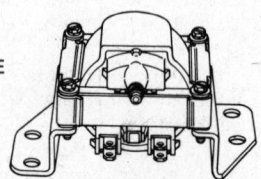

IGNITION COIL: EXTERNAL COIL TYPE

and a pick-up coil. When the teeth of the rotating timer core and pole piece align, an induced voltage in the pick-up coil signals the electronic module to open the coil primary circuit. As the primary current decreases, a high voltage is induced in the secondary windings of the ignition coil, directing a spark through the rotor and high voltage leads to fire the spark plugs. The dwell period is automatically controlled by the electronic module and is increased with increasing engine rpm. The HEI System features a longer spark duration which is instrumental in firing lean and EGR (Exhaust Gas Recirculation) diluted fuel/air mixtures. The condenser (capacitor) located within the HEI distributor is provided for noise (static) suppression purposes only and is not a regularly replaced ignition system component.

Beginning in 1980, three different modules are used. The original four terminal module is continued in use for most applications in 1980. Some 1980 models and most 1981 and later models are equipped with an Electronic Spark Timing (EST) distributor, which is part of the C-4 or CCC System (see the Emission Control Systems section). On these, the ignition timing is determined by the C-4 or CCC Electronic Control Module (ECM). The EST module has seven terminals. The EST distributor

EST distributor module connector identification. The upper module is used in the 4-cylinder engine, the lower is used in all others

can be quickly identified: it has no vacuum advance diaphragm. The EST distributor can be equipped with an additional spark control, the Electronic Spark Control (ESC) system. This is a closed loop system that controls engine detonation by retarding the spark timing. The ESC is usually used on turbocharged engines. Some models are equipped with Electronic Module Retard (EMR). This system uses a five terminal module which retards ignition timing a calibrated number of crankshaft degrees. Distributors with this system are equipped with vacuum advance. When replacing modules on these three systems, be certain to obtain the correct part: the modules are not interchangeable.

ON-CAR SERVICE PROCEDURES (DISTRIBUTOR IN ENGINE)

Internal Ignition Coil Replacement

1. Disconnect the feed and module wire terminal connectors from the distributor cap.
2. Remove the ignition wire set retainer.
3. Remove the 4 coil cover-to-distributor cap screws and the coil cover.

4. Remove the 4 coil-to-distributor cap screws.
5. Using a blunt drift, press the coil wire spade terminals up out of distributor cap.
6. Lift the coil up out of the distributor cap.
7. Remove and clean the coil spring, rubber seal washer and coil cavity of the distributor cap.
8. Reverse the above procedures to install.

External Ignition Coil Replacement

1. Remove the ignition switch-to-coil lead from the coil.
2. Unfasten the distributor leads from the coil.
3. Remove the screws which secure the coil to the engine and lift it off.
Installation is the reverse of removal.

Distributor Cap Replacement, All Engines

1. Remove the feed and module wire terminal connectors from the distributor cap.
2. Remove the retainer and spark plug wires from the cap.
3. Depress and release the 4 distributor cap-to-housing retainers and lift off the cap assembly.
4. If the cap has an internal coil, remove the coil from the old cap and install into the new cap.
5. Using a new distributor cap, reverse the above procedures to assemble.

Rotor Replacement, All Engines

1. Disconnect the feed and module wire connectors from the distributor.
2. Depress and release the 4 distributor cap to housing retainers and lift off the cap assembly.
3. Remove the two rotor attaching screws and rotor.

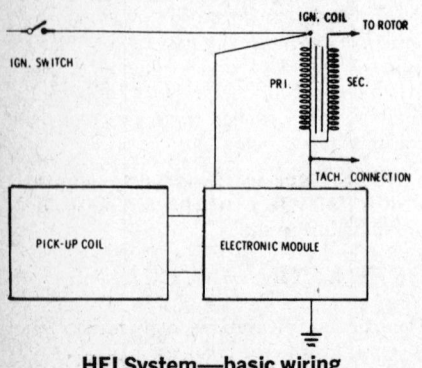

HEI System—basic wiring

4. Reverse the above procedure to install.

Vacuum Advance Unit Replacement, All Engines So Equipped

1. Remove the distributor cap and rotor as previously described.

2. Disconnect the vacuum hose from the vacuum advance unit. Remove the module.

3. Remove the two vacuum advance retaining screws, pull the advance unit outward, rotate and disengage the operating rod from its tang.

4. Reverse the above procedure to install.

Module Replacement, All Engines

1. Remove the distributor cap and rotor as previously described.

2. Disconnect the harness connector and pick-up coil spade connectors from the module (note their positions).

3. Remove the two screws and module from the distributor housing.

4. Coat the bottom of the new module with silicone dielectric compound.

NOTE: The compound is required for proper module cooling.

Reverse the above procedure to install. Be sure that the leads are installed correctly.

NOTE: If a five terminal or seven terminal module is replaced, the ignition timing must be checked and reset as necessary.

Distributor Removal And Installation

Distributor removal and installation procedures are given in the appropriate car section.

SERVICE PROCEDURES (DISTRIBUTOR REMOVED)

Driven Gear Replacement, All Engines

1. Mark the distributor shaft and gear so they can be reassembled in the same position. With the distributor removed, use a ⅛ in. pin punch and tap out the driven gear roll pin.

2. Hold the rotor end of shaft and rotate the driven gear to shear any burrs in the roll pin hole.

3. Remove the driven gear from the shaft.

4. Reverse the above procedure to install.

Mainshaft Replacement, All Engines

1. With the driven gear and rotor re-

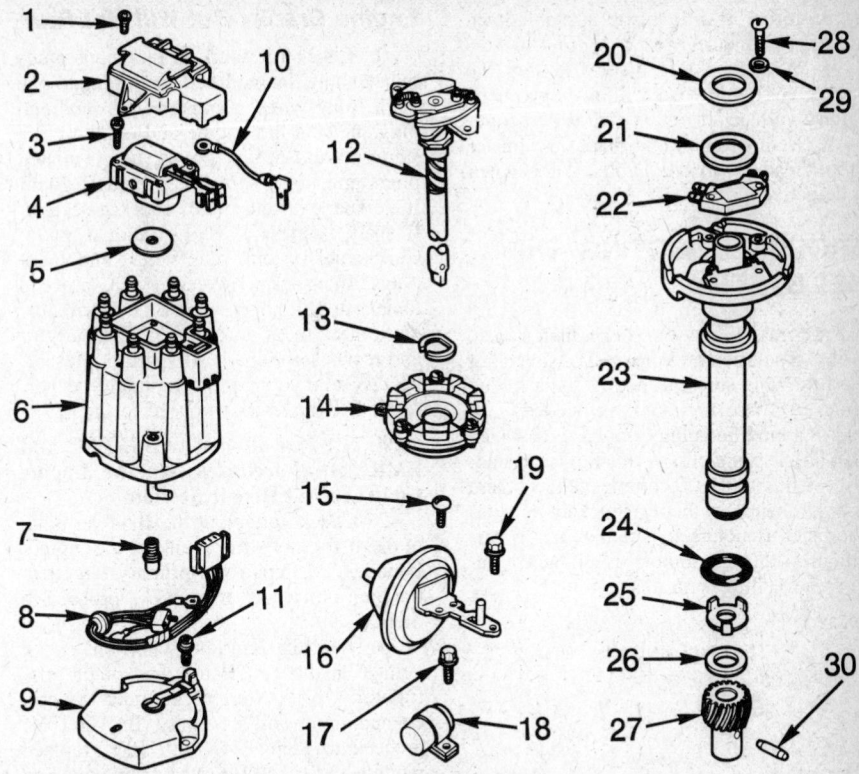

1. Cap cover attaching screw
2. Distributor cap cover
3. Coil attaching screw
4. Distributor coil
5. Coil to distributor cap seal
6. Distributor cap
7. Resistor brush
8. Module coil harness
9. Distributor rotor
10. Distributor ground lead
11. Rotor screw
12. Distributor mainshaft
13. Pole piece and plate retainer
14. Distributor pole piece and plate
15. Vacuum control attaching screw
16. Distributor vacuum control
17, 18. Capacitor and attaching screw
19. Vacuum control attaching screw
20. Felt washer
21. Distributor housing seal
22. Module
23. Distributor housing
24. Housing stem washer
25. Shaft spacer washer
26. Shaft thrust washer
27. Distributor drive gear
28. Module attaching screw
29. Washer
30. Gear attaching pin

HEI integral coil electronic ignition distributor

moved, gently pull the mainshaft out of the housing.

2. Remove the advance springs, weights and slide the weight base plate off the mainshaft.

3. Reverse the above procedure to install.

Pole Piece, Magnet Or Pick-Up Coil Replacement, All Engines

The pole piece, magnet, and pickup coil are serviced as an assembly.

1. With the mainshaft out of its housing, remove the three screws and the magnetic shield (1981–84), remove the thin "C" washer on top of the pickup coil assembly, remove the pickup coil leads from the module, and remove the pickup coil as an assembly. Do not remove the three screws and attempt to service the parts individually on models through 1980. They are aligned at the factory.

NOTE: Remove the Hall effect switch during this procedure, if so equipped.

2. Reverse the removal procedure to install. Note the alignment marks when the drive gear is reinstalled.

HALL EFFECT SWITCH TEST

1. Remove the Hall effect switch from the distributor.

2. Connect a 12 volt battery and voltmeter to the switch. Carefully note the polarity markings.

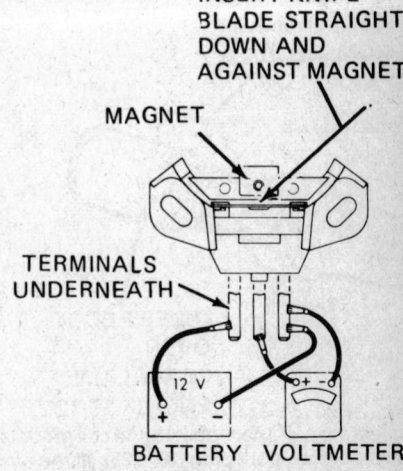

INSERT KNIFE BLADE STRAIGHT DOWN AND AGAINST MAGNET

MAGNET

TERMINALS UNDERNEATH

12 V

BATTERY   VOLTMETER

Testing the Hall Effect Switch

3. Insert a knife blade straight down against the magnet.

4. With the knife blade inserted, the voltmeter should read within 0.5 volts of battery voltage. If not, switch is defective.

5. Remove the knife blade. Voltmeter should read less than 0.5 volts. If not switch is defective.

TROUBLESHOOTING THE HEI SYSTEM

An accurate diagnosis is the first step to problem solution and repair. For several of the following steps, a modified spark plug (side electrode removed) is needed. GM makes a modified plug (tool ST 125) which also has a spring clip to attach it to ground. Use of this tool is recommended, as there is less chance of being shocked. If a tachometer is connected to the TACH terminal on the distributor, disconnect it before proceeding with this test.

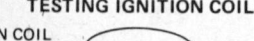

TESTING IGNITION COIL

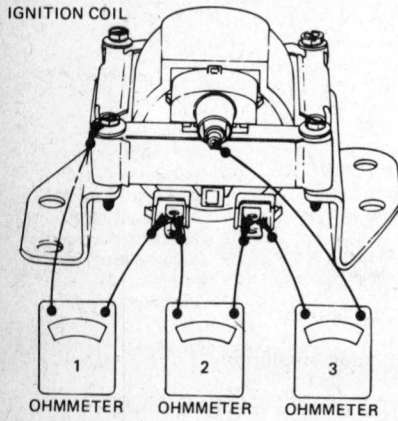

IGNITION COIL

OHMMETER   OHMMETER   OHMMETER

1   2   3

To test HEI ignition coil on external coil models, attach an ohmmeter as shown: Test 1, use high scale. Reading should be very high or infinite. Test 2, use low scale. Reading should be very low or zero. Test 3, use high scale. Reading should not be infinite. If any test proves otherwise, replace coil.

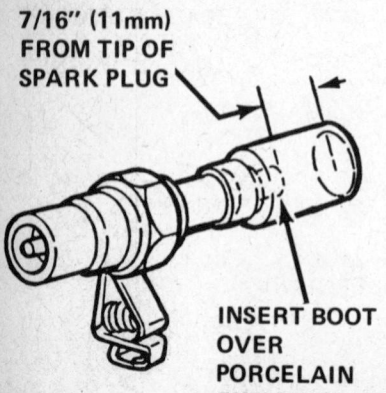

7/16" (11mm) FROM TIP OF SPARK PLUG

INSERT BOOT OVER PORCELAIN END OF ST-125

To test for coil spark on integral coil models, cut a plug boot so that it fits as shown over the modified spark plug (ST-125), fit the modified plug on the center terminal of the distributor cap and connect the plug to ground with a jumper wire

Engine Cranks But Will Not Run

1. Check for spark at the spark plugs by attaching the modified spark plug to one of the plug wires, grounding the modified plug shell on the engine and cranking the starter. Wear heavy gloves, use insulated pliers and make sure the ground is good. If no spark on one wire, check a second. If spark is present, HEI system is good. Check fuel system, plug wires, and spark plugs. If no spark (except EST), proceed to next step. If no spark on EST distributor, disconnect the 4 terminal EST connector and recheck for spark. If spark is present, EST system service check should be performed. If no spark, proceed to Step 2.

NOTE: For all EST, ESS, ESC and EMR test procedures, see the Engine Controls Unit Repair Section.

2. Check voltage at the BAT terminal of the distributor while cranking the engine. If under 7V, repair the primary circuit to the ignition switch. If over 7V, proceed to Step 3.

3. With the ignition switch on, check voltage at the TACH terminal of the distributor or coil (external). If under 1V, coil connection or coil are faulty. If over 10V, proceed to Step 4. If 1 to 10V, replace module and check for spark from coil. See Step 4.

4. On external coil models, disconnect coil wire from distributor and connect to grounded modified spark plug. On integral coils, remove distributor cap from distributor without removing its electrical connectors, remove the rotor, then modify a plug boot so that the modified plug can be connected directly to the center terminal of the distributor cap. Ground the shell of the modified plug to the engine block with a jumper wire. Make sure no wires, clothing, etc., are in the way of moving parts and crank the engine. On external coils, if no spark, check secondary coil wire continuity and repair. On both external and integral coils, if spark is present, inspect distributor cap for moisture, cracks, etc. If cap is OK, install new rotor. If no spark, proceed to Step 5.

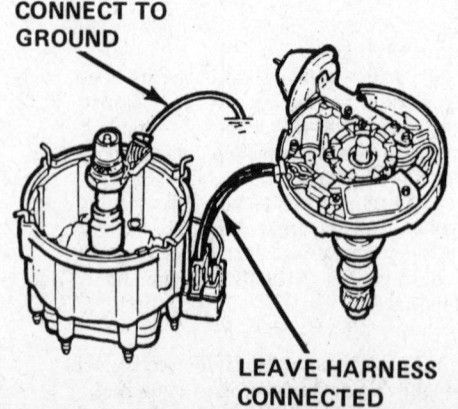

CONNECT TO GROUND

LEAVE HARNESS CONNECTED

TESTING PICKUP COIL

OHMMETER   OHMMETER

1   2

PICKUP COIL LEADS DISCONNECTED FROM MODULE

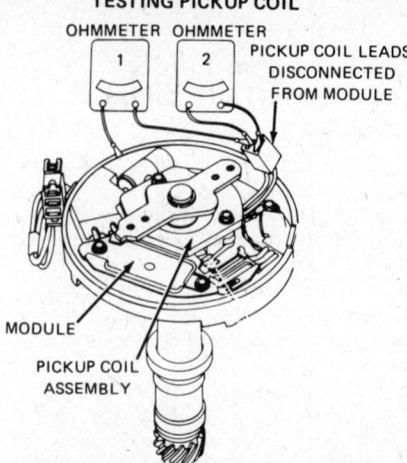

MODULE

PICKUP COIL ASSEMBLY

Testing HEI pick-up coil: Ohmmeter in test 1 should read infinite at all times; ohmmeter in test 2 should read 500-1500 ohm range. On vacuum advance equipped models, attach an external vacuum and run the vacuum advance unit through its range while making tests: Reading should not change. Ohmmeter may deflect if vacuum unit causes teeth to align. This is not a defect

5. Remove the pick-up coil leads from the module and check TACH terminal voltage with the ignition on. Watch the voltmeter and momentarily (not more than 5 seconds) connect a test light from the positive battery terminal to the appropriate module terminal: 4 terminal module, terminal "G" (small terminal); 5 terminal module (ESS or ESC), terminal "D"; 5 terminal module (EMR) terminal "H"; 7 terminal module, terminal "P". If no drop in voltage, test the module, check module

TESTING IGNITION COIL

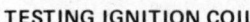

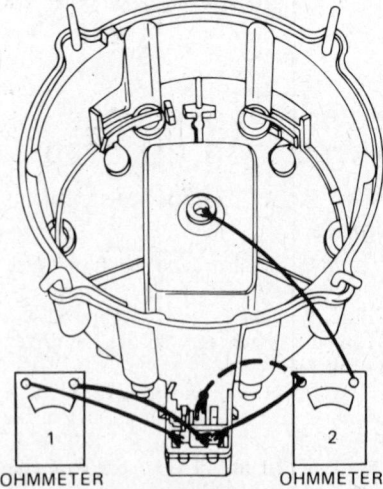

1   2

OHMMETER   OHMMETER

To test HEI ignition coil on coil in cap models, connect the ohmmeter as shown in test 1: Reading should be zero or nearly zero. Next connect ohmmeter both ways as indicated in test 2: With the meter set on high scale, replace the coil only if both readings are infinite.

ground, and check for open in wires from cap to distributor. If OK, replace module. If voltage drops, proceed to next step.

NOTE: 4 terminal modules may be tested with simple tools, according to the Module Test procedure which follows.

6. Reconnect modified plug to ignition coil as instructed in Step 4, and check for spark as the test light is removed from the appropriate module terminal (see Step 5 for appropriate terminal). Do not connect test light for more than 5 seconds. If spark is present, problem is with pick-up coil or connections. Pick-up coil resistance should be 500–1500 ohms and not grounded. If no spark, proceed to next step.

7. On integral coil distributors, check the coil ground by attaching a test light from the BAT terminal of the cap to the coil ground wire. If the light lights when the ignition is on, replace the ignition coil and repeat Step 6. If the light does not light, repair the ground. On external coil models, replace the ignition coil and repeat Step 6. On both the integral and external coil distributors, if no spark is present, replace the module and reinstall the original coil. Repeat Step 6 again. If no spark is present, replace the original ignition coil with a good one.

MODULE TESTING

NOTE: This procedure applies only to 4 terminal HEI modules.

1. Remove the module from the distributor as previously outlined. Connect a 12VDC test lamp between the B and C module terminals.
2. Connect a jumper wire from a 12VDC source to the B module terminal.
3. Connect the module ground terminal to a good ground. If the test lamp lights, the module is defective and must be replaced.
4. Connect a jumper wire between the B and G module terminals. The test lamp will light if the module is okay.

Chrysler Electronic Ignition System

NOTE: For details on the Chrysler Lean Burn/Electronic Spark Control system, refer to the Emission Control Systems Section.
This section applies to all Chrysler products except the Omni, Horizon, Aries and Reliant, which are covered in the following sections.

COMPONENTS

This system consists of a special pulse-sending distributor, an electronic control unit, a two-element ballast resistor, and a special ignition coil.

The distributor does not contain breaker points or a condenser, these parts being

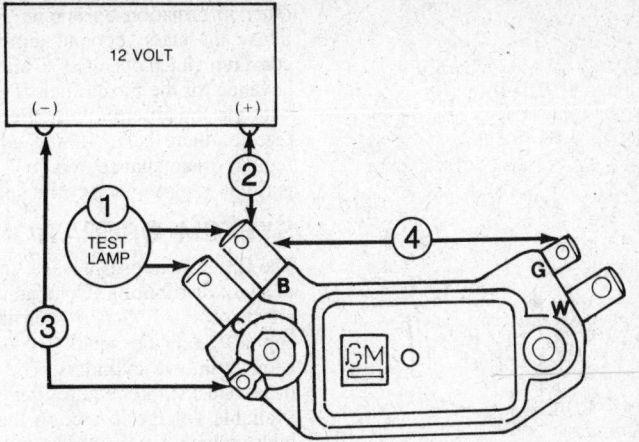

Testing the 4-terminal HEI module. Note that the numbers illustrated correspond with the steps of the testing procedure.

replaced by a distributor reluctor and a pick-up unit.

For better timing control and fuel economy, some 1981–84 models use a dual pick-up system. Vehicles with this system use a "start" pick-up, a "run" pick-up, and a dual pick-up start-run delay. In the "run" mode, the operation of the dual pick-up system is the same as that of the single pick-up system. During cranking, the dual pick-up start-run relay is energized (through the starter solenoid circuit), which allows the start pick-up to adjust the timing for starting purposes only. As soon as the starter solenoid is de-energized, the start-run relay switches the sensing function back to the "run" pick-up.

NOTE: Prior to the 1981 model year, the dual pick-up system was used only with the Lean Burn/Electronic Spark Control systems.

OPERATION

The ignition primary circuit is connected from the battery, through the ignition switch, through the primary side of the ignition coil, to the control unit where it is grounded. The secondary circuit is the same as in conventional ignition systems: the secondary side of the coil, the coil wire to the distributor, the rotor, the spark plug wires, and the spark plugs.

The magnetic pulse distributor is also connected to the control unit. As the distributor shaft rotates, the distributor reluctor turns past the pick-up unit. As the reluctor turns past the pick-up unit, each of the eight (or six) teeth on the reluctor pass near the pickup unit once during each distributor revolution (two crankshaft revolutions since the distributor runs at one-half crankshaft speed). As the reluctor teeth move close to the pick-up unit, the magnetic rotating reluctor induces voltage into the magnetic pick-up unit. This voltage pulse is sent to the ignition control unit from the magnetic pick-up unit. When the pulse enters the control unit, it signals the control unit to interrupt the ignition primary circuit.

This causes the primary circuit to collapse and begins the induction of the magnetic lines of force from the primary side of the coil into the secondary side of the coil. This induction provides the required voltage to fire the spark plugs.

The advantages of this system are that the transistors in the control unit can make and break the primary ignition circuit much faster than conventional ignition points can, and higher primary voltage can be utilized, since this system can be made to handle higher voltage without adverse effects, whereas ignition breaker points cannot. The quicker switching time of this system allows longer coil primary circuit saturation time and longer induction time when the primary circuit collapses. This increased time allows the primary circuit to build up more current and the secondary circuit to discharge more current.

GM Computer Controlled Coil Ignition (C3I) System

GENERAL INFORMATION

The C3I system eliminates the need for a distributor to control the flow of current between the battery and spark plugs. In its place, an electromagnetic sensor consisting of a Hall effect switch, magnet and interruptor ring. The gear on the shaft of this sensor is connected directly to the camshaft gear. At the heart of this system is an electronic coil module that replaces the distributor and coil used on previous electronic ignition systems. A microprocessor within the module receives and processes signals from the crankshaft and camshaft and, by way of three interconnecting coils, distributes high voltage current to the spark plugs.

Electromagnetic sensors take position readings from the crankshaft and camshaft, then transmit these readings to the electronics package. Using the information relayed from the electronic control module,

1 C³ IGNITION MODULE AND COIL ASSEMBLY
2 CAM SENSOR
3 CRANKSHAFT SENSOR

Computer Controlled Coil Ignition (C3I) System components-V6 shown

the microprocessor then selects and sequentially triggers each of the three interconnecting coils to fire the spark plugs at the proper crankshaft position. An electronic spark control (ESC) is incorporated into the system to adjust the spark timing according to engine load and operating conditions. This closed loop system includes a piezoelectric sensor which transforms engine detonation vibrations into an electrical signal which is then fed to the electronic control module. The ECM uses this and

other information on engine speed (rpm), intake air mass, coolant temperature and converter clutch operation to adjust the spark advance for the most efficient performance with the lowest emissions. Because of this feature, there is no timing adjustment or regular maintenance required aside from periodic replacement of the spark plugs.

SYSTEM OPERATION

The C3I system uses a waste spark method of spark distribution. Companion cylinders are paired (1-4, 5-2, 3-6 on the 3.8L V6 engine) and the spark occurs simultaneously in both cylinders. The cylinder on the exhaust stroke requires very little of the available voltage to arc, so the remaining high voltage is used by the cylinder in the firing position (TDC/compression). This same process is repeated when the companion cylinders reverse roles. There are three separate coils combined in the sealed coil/module assembly on the V6 engine. Spark distribution is synchronized by a signal from the crankshaft sensor which the ignition module uses to trigger each coil at the proper time.

NOTE: The signal from the camshaft sensor is also used by the fuel injection electronic control module to trigger the fuel injectors, so a failed sensor can affect both the fuel and ignition system. A 7.5 amp ECM fuse is used to provide a low current source for the voltage to the sensors and internal circuitry; a 10 amp fuse provides voltage for the ignition coils.

This system also incorporates an electronic spark timing (EST) system similar to other Delco distributor ignition systems. All connectors are lettered to make circuit identification easier. Terminal C (crankshaft sensor) provides the ECM with engine speed (rpm) and crankshaft position information by passing a signal to the ignition module and then to ECM terminal B5. A plate with three vanes is mounted to the harmonic balancer and the vanes pass through slots in the crankshaft sensor. As the vanes pass through the slots, the Hall effect switch triggers and sends a voltage signal to the ECM. The signal from the Hall effect switch is either high or low and is used to trigger the ignition module for proper engine timing. Both the camshaft and crankshaft signal must be received by the ignition module in order for the ECM to take over spark timing control from the ignition module. An open or grounded circuit (terminal B) will set a trouble code 42 in the ECM memory and the engine will run in the bypass of "limp home" mode with the timing fixed at 10 degrees BTDC. The EST terminal A circuit triggers the HEI module by passing a reference signal which the ECM uses to advance or retard the timing according to the input from the crankshaft sensor. Cam terminal E is used by the ECM to determine when the No. 1 cylinder is on the compression stroke by a signal from the Hall effect camshaft position sensor. A loss of the cam signal will store a trouble code 41 if the engine is running and a loss of sensor signal

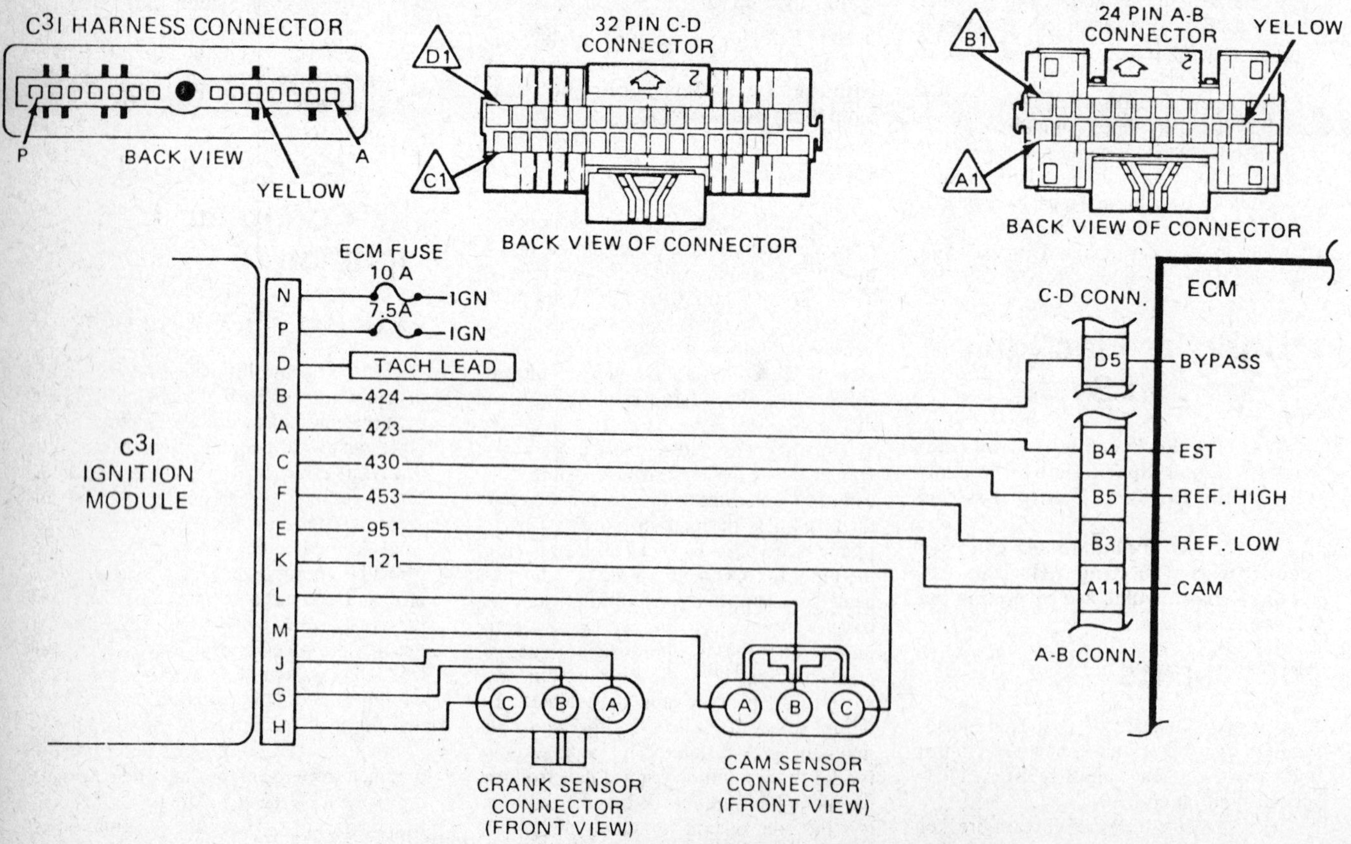

C³I HARNESS CONNECTOR

BACK VIEW

P   A

YELLOW

32 PIN C-D CONNECTOR

D1
C1

BACK VIEW OF CONNECTOR

24 PIN A-B CONNECTOR   YELLOW

B1
A1

BACK VIEW OF CONNECTOR

ECM FUSE

C3I IGNITION MODULE		
N	10 A	IGN
P	7.5A	IGN
D	TACH LEAD	
B	424	
A	423	
C	430	
F	453	
E	951	
K	121	
L		
M		
J		
G		
H		

C-D CONN.   ECM

D5 — BYPASS
B4 — EST
B5 — REF. HIGH
B3 — REF. LOW
A11 — CAM

A-B CONN.

CRANK SENSOR CONNECTOR (FRONT VIEW)   C B A

CAM SENSOR CONNECTOR (FRONT VIEW)   A B C

C3I System wiring-V6 shown

during cranking will prevent the engine form starting.

The electronic control module uses information from the coolant sensor and mass air flow sensor in addition to engine speed to calculate the spark advance to allow more spark advance when the engine is cold or under minimum load. The ECM will retard the timing when the engine is hot or under a heavy load. When the system is running on the HEI module, it grounds the electronic spark timing signal. If the ECM detects voltage in the bypass circuit through a loss of ground for the EST signal, it sets a trouble code 42 and will not switch into the EST mode. When the engine reaches 400 rpm, the ECM applies 5 volts to the bypass circuit and the EST voltage will vary. If the bypass circuit is open, the ECM will store a trouble code 42.

TROUBLE DIAGNOSIS

Component Replacement

IGNITION COIL

Removal and Installation

1. Disconnect the negative battery cable.
2. Remove the spark plug wires.
3. Remove the Torx screws holding the coil to the ignition module.
4. Tilt the coil assembly to the rear and remove the coil to module connectors.
5. Remove the coil assembly.
6. Installation is the reverse of removal.

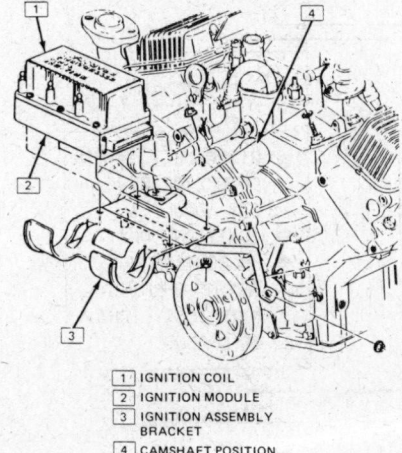

1. IGNITION COIL
2. IGNITION MODULE
3. IGNITION ASSEMBLY BRACKET
4. CAMSHAFT POSITION SENSOR

C3I System ignition coil assembly-V6 shown

IGNITION MODULE

Removal and Installation

1. Disconnect the negative battery cable.
2. Disconnect the 14-pin connector at the ignition module.
3. Remove the spark plug wires at the coil assembly.

4. Remove the nuts and washers securing the ignition module assembly to the mounting bracket.
5. Remove the Torx screws securing the ignition module to the coil.
6. Tilt the coil and disconnect the coil to module connectors.
7. Separate the coil and module.
8. Installation is the reverse of removal.

CRANKSHAFT SENSOR

Removal and Installation

NOTE: It is not necessary to remove the sensor bracket.

1. Disconnect the negative battery cable.
2. Disconnect the sensor 3-way connector.
3. Raise the vehicle and support it safely.
4. Rotate the harmonic balancer so the slot in the disc is aligned with the sensor.
5. Loosen the sensor retaining bolt.
6. Slide the sensor outboard and remove through the notch in the sensor housing.
7. Install the new sensor in the housing and rotate the harmonic balancer so that the disc is positioned in the sensor.
8. Adjust the sensor so that there is an equal distance on each side of the disc. There should be approximately 0.030 in. (0.76mm) clearance between the disc and the sensor.
9. Tighten the retaining bolt and recheck the clearance.
10. Install remaining components in the reverse order of removal.

CAMSHAFT POSITION SENSOR

Removal and Installation

NOTE: If only the camshaft sensor is being replaced, it is not necessary to remove the entire assembly. The sensor is replaceable separately.

1. Disconnect the negative battery cable.

2. Disconnect the ignition module 14-pin connector.
3. Remove the spark plug wires at the coil assembly.
4. Remove the ignition module bracket assembly.
5. Disconnect the sensor 3-way connector.
6. Remove the sensor mounting screws, then remove the sensor.
7. Installation is the reverse of removal.

CAMSHAFT POSITION SENSOR DRIVE ASSEMBLY

Removal and Installation

1. Follow Steps 1–6 of the cam sensor removal procedure. Note the position of the slot in the rotating vane.
2. Remove the bolt securing the drive assembly to the engine.
3. Remove the drive assembly.
4. Install the drive assembly with the slot in the vane. Install mounting bolt.
5. Install the camshaft sensor.
6. Rotate the engine to set the No. 1 cylinder at TDC/compression.
7. Mark the harmonic balancer and rotate the engine to 25 degrees ATDC.
8. Remove the plug wires from the coil assembly.
9. Using weatherpack removal tool J-28742-A, or equivalent, remove terminal B of the sensor 3-way connector on the module side.
10. Probe terminal B by installing a jumper and reconnecting the wire removed to the jumper wire.
11. Connect a voltmeter between the jumper wire and ground.
12. With the key ON and the engine stopped, rotate the camshaft sensor counterclockwise until the sensor switch just closes. This is indicated by the voltage reading going from a high 5-12 volts to a low 0-2 volts. The low voltage indicates the switch is closed.
13. Tighten the retaining bolt and reinstall the wire into terminal B.
14. Install remaining components.

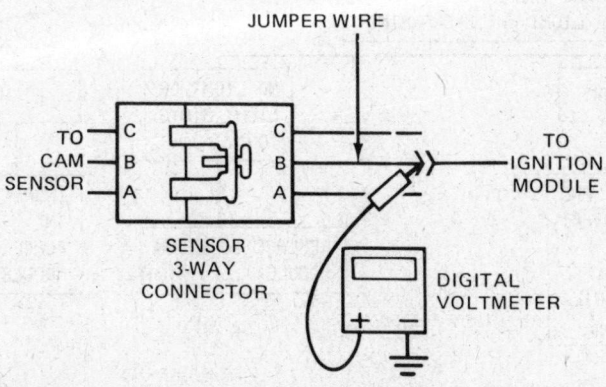

C3I camshaft sensor adjustment-typical

1984
CHART C-4A
PORT FUEL INJECTION – 3.8L TURBO
IGNITION SYSTEM CHECK (1 OF 2)

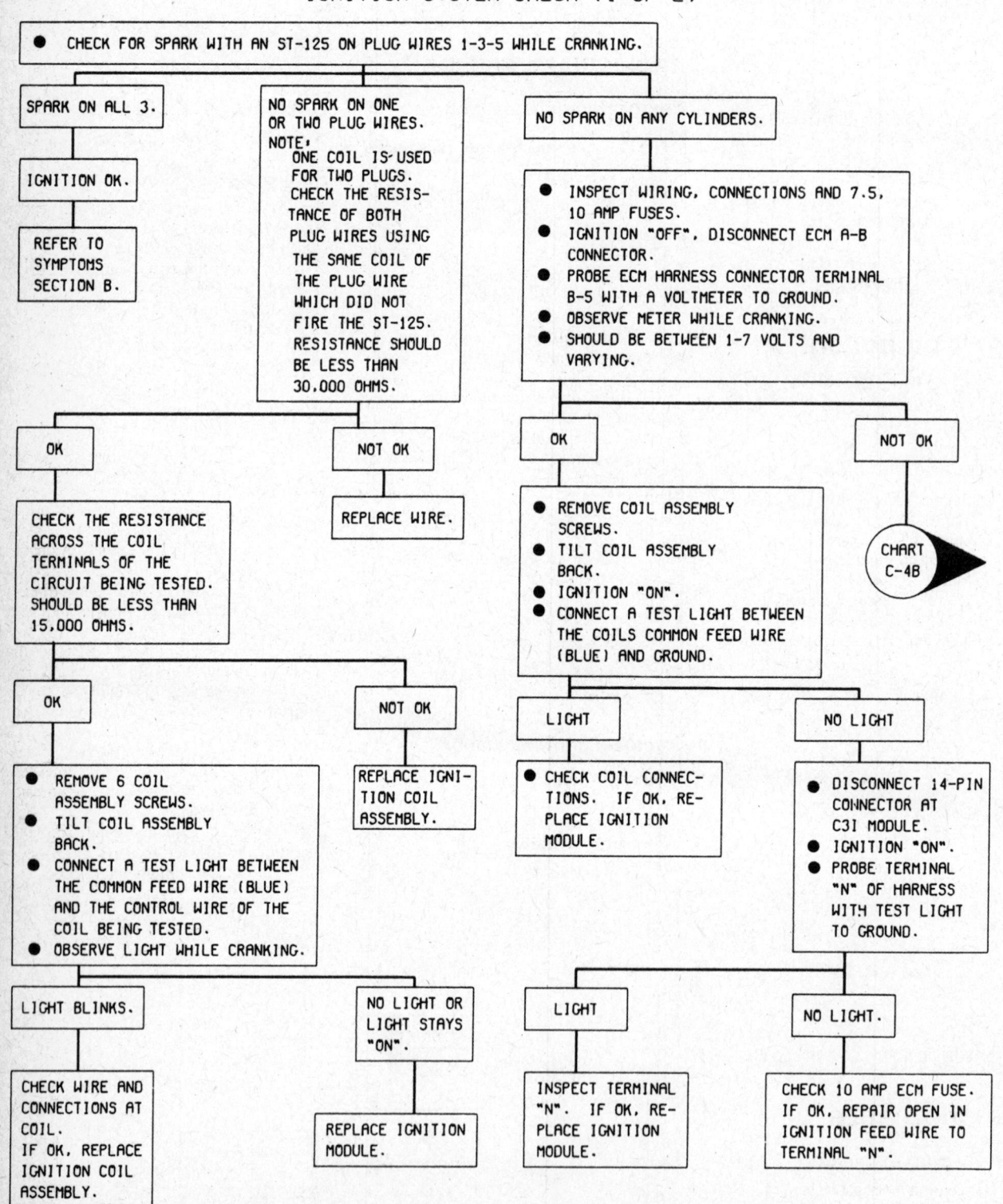

Computer Controlled Coil Ignition (C3I) diagnosis-3.8L turbo engine

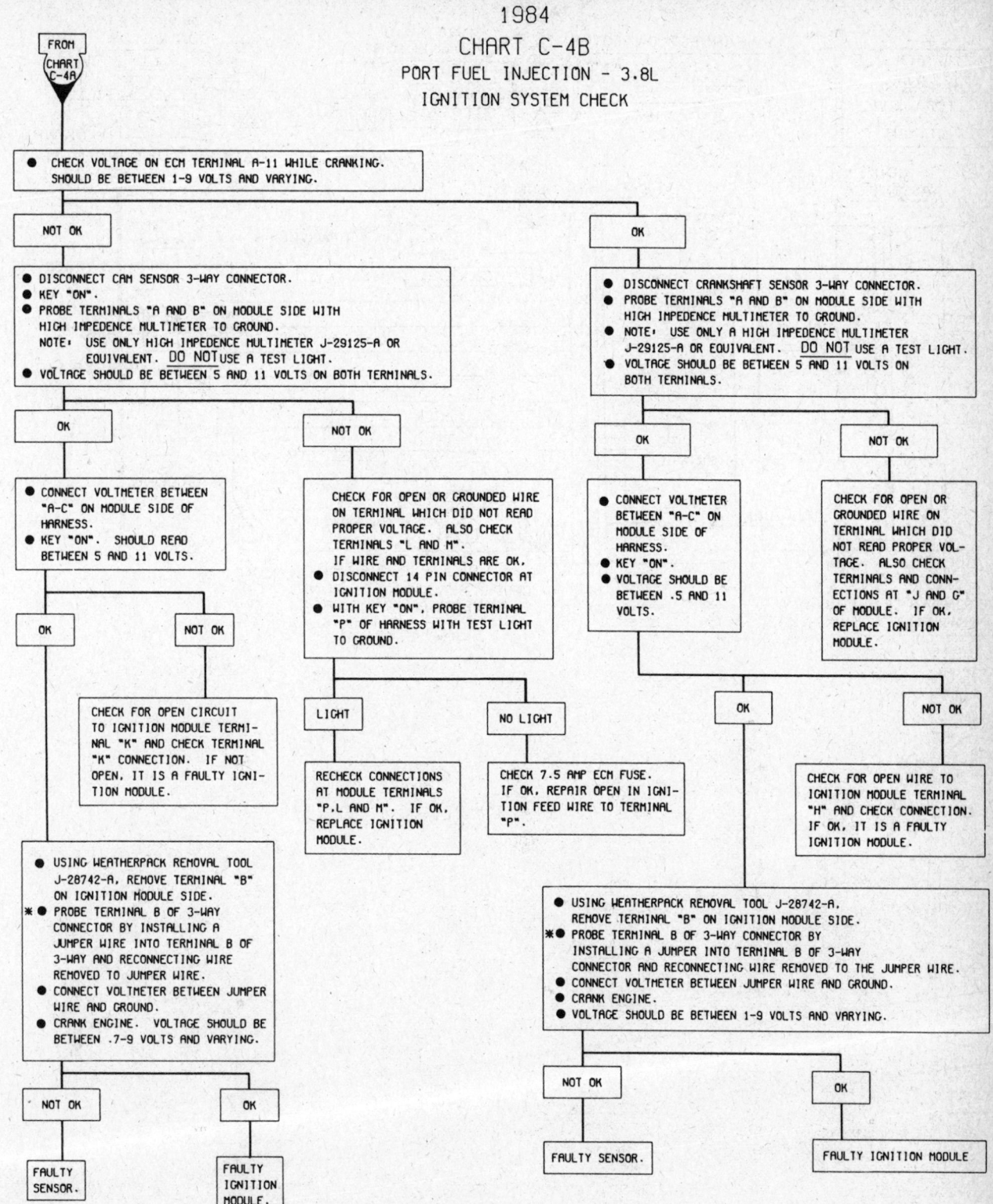

1984
CHART C-4B
PORT FUEL INJECTION - 3.8L
IGNITION SYSTEM CHECK

FROM
CHART
C-4A

- CHECK VOLTAGE ON ECM TERMINAL A-11 WHILE CRANKING. SHOULD BE BETWEEN 1-9 VOLTS AND VARYING.

NOT OK

- DISCONNECT CAM SENSOR 3-WAY CONNECTOR.
- KEY "ON".
- PROBE TERMINALS "A AND B" ON MODULE SIDE WITH HIGH IMPEDENCE MULTIMETER TO GROUND.
  NOTE: USE ONLY HIGH IMPEDENCE MULTIMETER J-29125-A OR EQUIVALENT. DO NOT USE A TEST LIGHT.
- VOLTAGE SHOULD BE BETWEEN 5 AND 11 VOLTS ON BOTH TERMINALS.

OK

- CONNECT VOLTMETER BETWEEN "A-C" ON MODULE SIDE OF HARNESS.
- KEY "ON". SHOULD READ BETWEEN 5 AND 11 VOLTS.

OK / **NOT OK**

CHECK FOR OPEN CIRCUIT TO IGNITION MODULE TERMINAL "K" AND CHECK TERMINAL "K" CONNECTION. IF NOT OPEN, IT IS A FAULTY IGNITION MODULE.

NOT OK

CHECK FOR OPEN OR GROUNDED WIRE ON TERMINAL WHICH DID NOT READ PROPER VOLTAGE. ALSO CHECK TERMINALS "L AND M".
IF WIRE AND TERMINALS ARE OK,
- DISCONNECT 14 PIN CONNECTOR AT IGNITION MODULE.
- WITH KEY "ON", PROBE TERMINAL "P" OF HARNESS WITH TEST LIGHT TO GROUND.

LIGHT / **NO LIGHT**

RECHECK CONNECTIONS AT MODULE TERMINALS "P,L AND M". IF OK, REPLACE IGNITION MODULE.

CHECK 7.5 AMP ECM FUSE. IF OK, REPAIR OPEN IN IGNITION FEED WIRE TO TERMINAL "P".

OK

- DISCONNECT CRANKSHAFT SENSOR 3-WAY CONNECTOR.
- PROBE TERMINALS "A AND B" ON MODULE SIDE WITH HIGH IMPEDENCE MULTIMETER TO GROUND.
- NOTE: USE ONLY A HIGH IMPEDENCE MULTIMETER J-29125-A OR EQUIVALENT. DO NOT USE A TEST LIGHT.
- VOLTAGE SHOULD BE BETWEEN 5 AND 11 VOLTS ON BOTH TERMINALS.

OK / **NOT OK**

- CONNECT VOLTMETER BETWEEN "A-C" ON MODULE SIDE OF HARNESS.
- KEY "ON".
- VOLTAGE SHOULD BE BETWEEN .5 AND 11 VOLTS.

CHECK FOR OPEN OR GROUNDED WIRE ON TERMINAL WHICH DID NOT READ PROPER VOLTAGE. ALSO CHECK TERMINALS AND CONNECTIONS AT "J AND G" OF MODULE. IF OK, REPLACE IGNITION MODULE.

OK / **NOT OK**

CHECK FOR OPEN WIRE TO IGNITION MODULE TERMINAL "H" AND CHECK CONNECTION. IF OK, IT IS A FAULTY IGNITION MODULE.

- USING WEATHERPACK REMOVAL TOOL J-28742-A, REMOVE TERMINAL "B" ON IGNITION MODULE SIDE.
✱ ● PROBE TERMINAL B OF 3-WAY CONNECTOR BY INSTALLING A JUMPER WIRE INTO TERMINAL B OF 3-WAY AND RECONNECTING WIRE REMOVED TO JUMPER WIRE.
- CONNECT VOLTMETER BETWEEN JUMPER WIRE AND GROUND.
- CRANK ENGINE. VOLTAGE SHOULD BE BETWEEN .7-9 VOLTS AND VARYING.

NOT OK / **OK**

FAULTY SENSOR.

FAULTY IGNITION MODULE.

- USING WEATHERPACK REMOVAL TOOL J-28742-A, REMOVE TERMINAL "B" ON IGNITION MODULE SIDE.
✱ ● PROBE TERMINAL B OF 3-WAY CONNECTOR BY INSTALLING A JUMPER INTO TERMINAL B OF 3-WAY CONNECTOR AND RECONNECTING WIRE REMOVED TO THE JUMPER WIRE.
- CONNECT VOLTMETER BETWEEN JUMPER WIRE AND GROUND.
- CRANK ENGINE.
- VOLTAGE SHOULD BE BETWEEN 1-9 VOLTS AND VARYING.

NOT OK / **OK**

FAULTY SENSOR.

FAULTY IGNITION MODULE

✱ REQUIRES JUMPER WIRE USING TERMINALS "10214836 AND 12014837".

CLEAR CODES AND CONFIRM "CLOSED LOOP" OPERATION AND NO "CHECK ENGINE" LIGHT.

Computer Controlled Coil Ignition (C3I) diagnosis-3.8L turbo engine

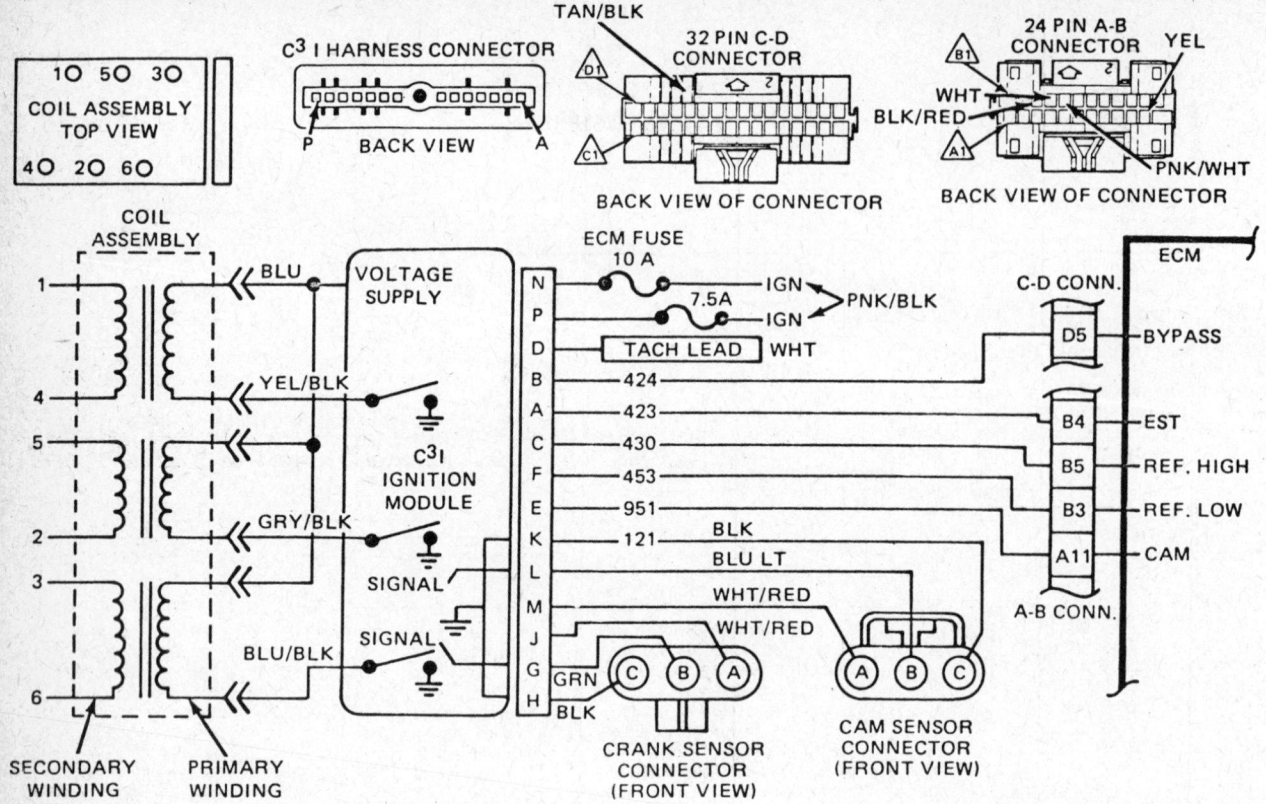

Emission Controls

General Information

Emission control devices are designed to eliminate the chemical compounds that escape from the engine crankcase, from the exhaust, and from evaporation of fuel out of the tank and carburetor. Emission controls consist of changes in engine design, calibration, or add-on devices (like an air pump) that either reduce or eliminate the amount of harmful emissions formed as a byproduct of combustion.

Changes in engine design on domestic cars consist mostly of refinements in combustion chamber shape or variations in bore and stroke to produce ideal surface-to-volume ratios. If the amount of surface in the combustion chamber is kept to a minimum, the emissions will be reduced because there is less chance for gasoline to cling to the surface without burning. The unburned gasoline is swept out the exhaust and causes high hydrocarbon emissions from the tailpipe. Reducing compression ratios is another design change that lowers the heat of the burning mixture and cuts down on NOx (oxides of nitrogen) emissions. With the growing use of on-board computers, it has become possible for car manufacturers to meet strict Federal emission standards by using electronic engine controls to monitor operating conditions and adjust engine calibrations for the best possible performance and economy with minimum emissions.

Engine calibration has a big effect on emissions out the tailpipe. The calibration consists of spark timing, fuel mixture, choke setting, idle speed, and spark plug gap. Calibrations are not a service problem as long as the engine is adjusted to the factory specifications, which are found on a sticker in the engine compartment. Engines must be adjusted to these factory specifications, or emissions will be high. Additionally, emission control systems have become such an integral part of the overall engine design that best engine performance is dependent on best emission control system performance. This is especially true for computer-controlled systems.

NOTE: Any attempt to disconnect or bypass any OEM emission device is a violation of federal law.

The biggest problems in servicing are the add-on devices for emission control. They are classified as Crankcase controls, Evaporation controls, or Exhaust controls. Crankcase and evaporation controls are simple in design, with few variations. But exhaust controls include air cleaner devices, exhaust gas recirculation, air injection systems, carburetor devices, and a tremendous number of spark advance devices. The latest emission control systems use electronic instead of vacuum devices and are much more sensitive to malfunctions in any component. Following is a description of each group of controls and how they work to reduce emissions.

NOTE: On many later model computer controlled emissions systems, ultimate control of individual components (EGR valve, evaporative controls, etc.) rests with the computer assembly. See the individual systems for details.

Emission Service Indicators

RESET PROCEDURES

Indicator lights or flags will periodically appear on or near the instrument cluster to alert the driver that various emission control components need to be serviced or replaced. Most of the reminder lights are triggered at preset mileages programmed into either mechanical or electronic counter or odometer switches. The mechanical counter switches are normally operated by the speedometer cable, while the electronic counter switches are pulsed by a speed sensor usually located in the speedometer assembly. After servicing the indicated emission system (EGR valve, Oxygen sensor, etc.), the service indicator device will have to be reset to eliminate the light or flag. Follow the appropriate procedure outlined below for each year and model listed.

American Motors
1980 AND LATER MODELS

The reset switch is located under the hood on the left side of the firewall, between the upper and lower speedometer cables. There is a reset screw on the unit that must be turned one-quarter turn to the detent position.

Chrysler Corporation
1979–80 MODELS

Chrysler models use either electronic or mechanical service counters. The electronic switch is located under the instrument panel somewhere near the lower left instrument cluster. It is usually covered with a green plastic case.

To reset the mechanical switch, remove it from the mounting bracket and then remove the plastic case. Insert a small screwdriver or rod into the hole in the switch body to close the contacts and turn off the indicator light. To reset the mechanical switch, first locate the unit between the upper and lower speedometer cables. Turn the screw on the upper side of the siwtch to reset.

General Motors
1979–80 CADILLAC

To reset the switch, remove the lower steering column cover and locate the reset cable at the lower left side of the speedometer cluster. Pull the cable lightly to reset the switch, then replace the column cover. Do not pull hard on the cable or damage to the cable and switch will occur.

1980 AND LATER MODELS

An emission indicator flag will appear in the odometer window when service is necessary on some 1980 and later GM models. The flags are marked SENSOR, EMISSIONS, or CATALYST, depending on the device that is scheduled for regular maintenance. To reset the flag, first remove the instrument panel trim plate and instrument cluster cover lens. There are reset notches on the driver's side of the indicator flag.

Insert a long, pointed probe diagonally into the detents on the upper left side and rotate the flag downward until an alignment mark becomes visible in the left side of the odometer window. Once the flag has been lowered, replace the cluster lens and trim plate.

CRANKCASE CONTROLS

PCV System

GENERAL INFORMATION

The first emission control device was the positive crankcase ventilation (PCV) system, which appeared on new domestic cars in the early 1960s. Ventilation of a crankcase is necessary because of the compression blow-by past the piston rings. This blow-by is mostly unburned gasoline. If allowed to stay in the crankcase, it dilutes the oil and increases engine wear. Before PCV systems, the crankcase was vented through a road draft tube. The suction of airflow past the end of the tube drew out the crankcase fumes and fresh air entered through the oil breather cap. When the car was moving, there was a continuous flow of fresh air through the crankcase.

The PCV system accomplishes the same thing, but it uses engine vacuum instead of the road draft to draw out the crankcase fumes. The crankcase or the rocker arm cover is connected by a hose to engine vacuum at the intake manifold or carburetor. When the engine is running, the crankcase fumes are drawn into the engine and burned in the combustion chamber. Fresh air enters the crankcase through the oil filler cap on the open system. When the oil filler cap is connected to the air cleaner, it is known as a closed system.

At wide open throttle, there is little vacuum in the engine, so the PCV system doesn't pull any fumes out of the crankcase.

FLAG WINDOW IN SPEEDOMETER FACE

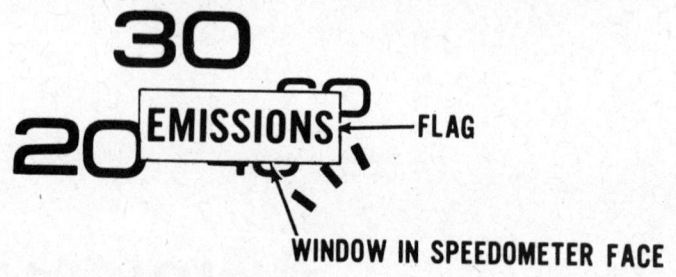

RESETTING FLAG WITH DOWNWARD MOVEMENT

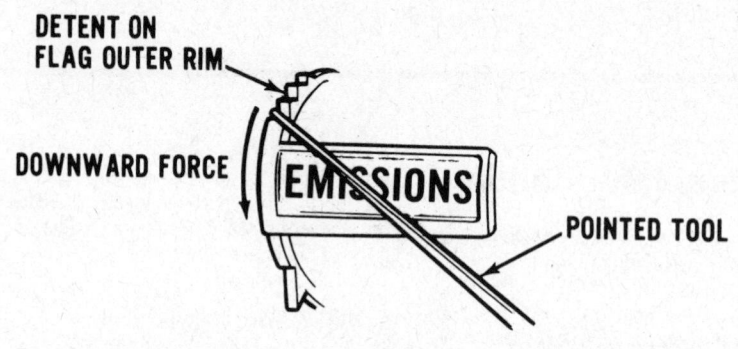

FLAG IN RESET POSITION

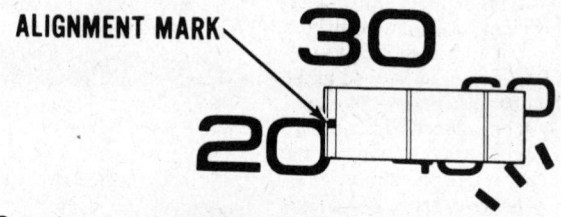

Resetting Emissions flag on 1980 GM models—typical

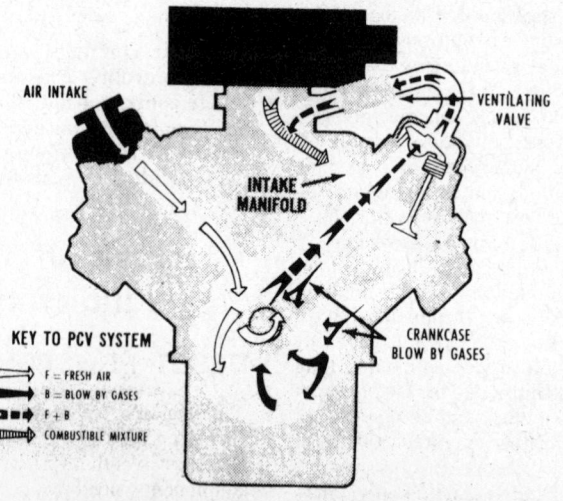

Typical open crankcase ventilation system

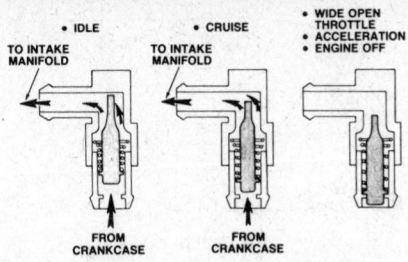

PCV valve operation

On the open system the fumes go out through the oil filler cap into the atmosphere. On the closed system the fumes go into the air cleaner, where they are drawn into the engine by the rush of air through the cleaner.

Because the hose connection from the crankcase to the intake manifold acts like a vacuum leak, there has to be some kind of control to limit the air flow. The PCV valve is the control. It can be an actual valve, with an internal plunger, or a simple orifice without any moving parts. In the plunger types, a spring moves the plunger against engine vacuum, allowing less flow at high vacuum and more flow at low vacuum. In the event of a backfire, the plunger moves to close the PCV valve and prevent a possible crankcase explosion.

Originally, all PCV systems used a simple hose from the rocker cover to the intake manifold or carburetor, with the PCV valve mounted at one end of the hose. Fresh air always entered through the oil filler cap, whether it connected to the air cleaner or not. On later models, the plumbing is not as simple, but the principle is still the same. Fresh air enters the air cleaner and goes through a hose to the crankcase or rocker cover. The fumes exit the crankcase and enter the intake manifold, either through a hose or some other type of connection, usually with a PCV valve controlling the flow.

Most systems use some kind of PCV filter, usually mounted at the end of the hose in the air cleaner. The filter keeps dust from entering the crankcase, and also prevents oil fumes from ruining the air cleaner element.

G.M. diesel V8 engines are equipped with one of two different crankcase ventilation systems. The first system uses a crankcase depression regulator valve to meter the flow of crankcase gases back into the engine. The regulator limits crankcase vacuum as the gases are drawn from the valve covers through the regulator, and into the air crossover. This system is used on 1981 and later non-California models. Other models use a crankcase flow control valve to meter the blow-by gases back into the engine. On these models, a ventilation hose runs from each valve cover and connects at the flow control valve, which is screwed into the back of the air crossover.

TESTING PCV SYSTEMS

NOTE: Do not attempt to test the crankcase controls on G.M. V8 diesels.

Instead, clean the valve cover filter assemblies and vent pipes and check rubber fittings every 15,000 miles, and replace or clean the breather cap assembly and ventilation regulator valve (if equipped) every 30,000 miles.

Checking crankcase vacuum is the most effective way to test any PCV system. If there is a vacuum in the crankcase, then the major part of the system has to be working.

Inspect the system to find out where the fresh air enters the engine. This is usually through a hose attached to the air cleaner, but it may be through the oil filler cap on some models. If the fresh air entry is separate from the oil filler cap, remove the hose and plug it so fresh air cannot enter the crankcase. If the fresh air entry is through the oil filler cap, simply remove the cap.

On all models, use a piece of paper or a PCV tester to measure the crankcase vacuum at the oil filler cap, with the cap removed and the engine idling in Park or Neutral. It may take a few seconds for the vacuum to build up enough to suck the piece of paper against the oil filler hole. If the vacuum does not build up, check to be sure you have plugged the fresh air entry. An alternate method on some cars is to use the piece of paper or PCV tester on the end of the fresh air entry hose. When you do it that way, the oil filler cap must be the solid type and you must leave it in place.

If there is no crankcase vacuum, pull the PCV valve from the crankcase and hold your finger over the end of it. You should feel full manifold vacuum with the engine idling. If not, the valve is plugged or there is an obstruction in a hose or passageway. On some designs the valve may be screwed into its mounting, with a hose leading to the rocker cover or crankcase. If the valve has good suction, but there is no crankcase vacuum, check the hose to be sure it is open. PCV valves that are restricted or plugged must be replaced, unless they are the type that will come apart for cleaning. Lack of crankcase vacuum can also be caused by vacuum leaks at rocker cover, oil pan, or other engine gaskets. Usually, tightening the bolts will stop the leak.

In some extreme cases, usually on high mileage engines, the PCV system is in good shape, but the blow-by past the rings is so

much that the system can't handle it, and the engine will blow smoke out the oil filler hole. Switching to a PCV valve with a higher flow may temporarily correct the problem, but the only good solution is to overhaul the engine. If the motor oil is contaminated with gasoline, the PCV system will pick up the unburned vapors, add them to the intake mixture and cause the engine to run excessively rich.

After checking crankcase vacuum, always check the condition of the fresh air filter and hose, to be sure they are clean and not clogged.

NOTE: The PCV system operation is not computer controlled, but if inoperative it will directly affect the operation of any computerized emission system. If poor performance is a problem, check the PCV system first.

FUEL EVAPORATION CONTROLS

Charcoal Vapor System

Most fuel evaporation losses come from the fuel tank. On an uncontrolled car the vapors go out through the tank vent, which may be in several places at the top of the tank or in the cap. There are also some losses through the bowl vent on the carburetor, but these are minor compared to the tank.

Evaporation controls are made up of hoses which allow the tank and carburetor vapors to go to a canister filled with charcoal. When the engine is running, a hose to the intake manifold or carburetor base allows engine vacuum to pull fresh air through the canister, drawing the vapors into the engine where they are burned. Fresh air enters the canister through a filter, which keeps the charcoal clean.

When the engine is running, air must enter the tank to replace the fuel that is used up and prevent a vacuum. On all makes of canister storage models, air enters the tank through the filter in the canister, but air can

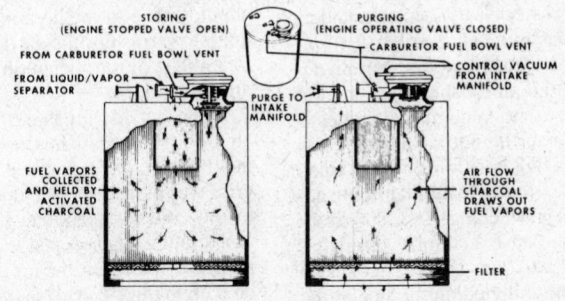

Vapor storage canister operation—typical

also enter the tank through the pressure-vacuum tank cap.

All evaporation control systems use some sort of vapor separator at the fuel tank to prevent liquid fuel from traveling along the vent line to the canister. The early models had very elaborate separators mounted separately from the tank, but now they are simpler and usually attached to the top of the tank. The only periodic servicing required on evaporation controls is replacement of the canister filter on those models on which it is replaceable.

NOTE: If the vent lines become blocked, it is possible for some evaporation control systems to pull liquid fuel from the the tank into the charcoal canister. If any charcoal canister is found to be fuel-soaked it should be replaced and all hoses checked for obstructions.

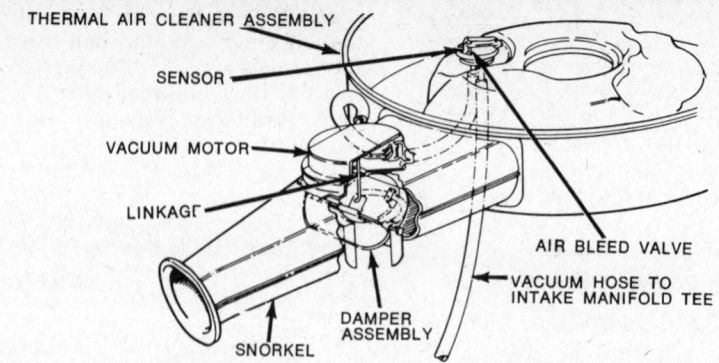

Vacuum controlled thermostatic air cleaner.

EXHAUST CONTROLS

Exhaust controls vary considerably in design. There are almost 60 different systems or devices used on the domestic makes to control exhaust emissions. Following are basic descriptions of the common systems.

Thermostatic Air Cleaner

GENERAL INFORMATION

Fresh air supplied to the air cleaner comes either from the normal snorkle, or from a tube connected to an exhaust manifold stove. A door in the snorkle regulates the source of incoming air so that a warm engine always takes in warm air, approximately 100°F. The snorkle door may be controlled in any number of ways, but most late models are vacuum operated. The vacuum operated designs use a thermostatic bimetal switch inside the air cleaner that bleeds off vacuum as the engine warms up, and regulates the position of the air door. On all late model cars, the snorkle is connected to a long tube so it takes in cooler air from outside the engine compartment. In hot climates the cool air tube is necessary because underhood air can easily reach 200°F.

Vacuum operated air doors are all designed so that the air cleaner takes in cold air when there is no vacuum. This means that an air door in the hot air position will switch to the cold position at wide open throttle because of the loss of manifold vacuum. The sudden switching of the door from hot to cold may cause a stumble or misfire in the engine, so some designs include a modulator valve mounted on the side of the air cleaner to block the vacuum and hold

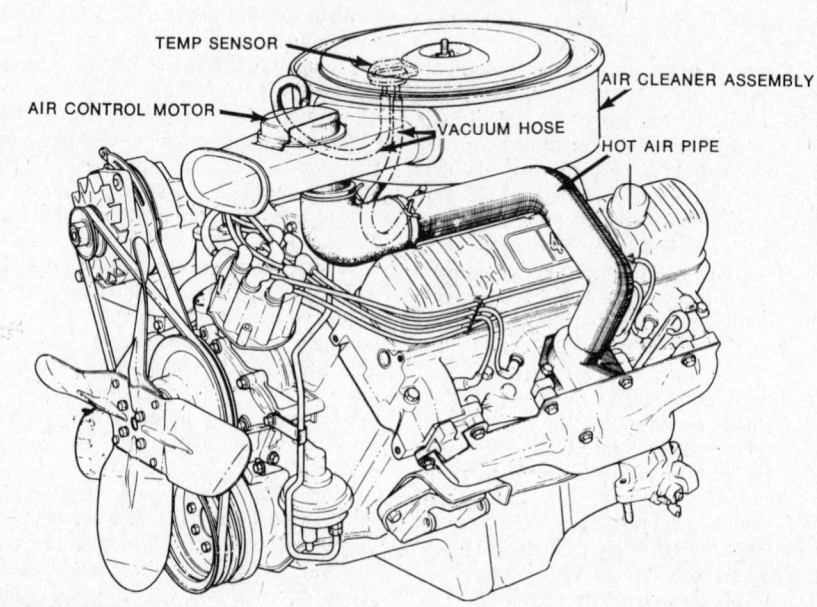

A typical heated air cleaner system, with the hot air pipe connected to the left exhaust manifold

the door in the hot air position. A small thermostat inside the modulator opens it when the underhood temperatures reach normal. Other designs use a delay valve that allows the air door to move to the cold position slowly, to prevent stumble.

TESTING TAC OPERATION

To test the vacuum type of heated air cleaner, inspect the air door with the engine off. It should be in the cold air position. Start the engine. If the engine is cold, the air door should move to the hot air position. As the engine warms up, the air door should move to a mid position, depending on the outside air temperature.

If the outside air is extremely cold, the air door may stay in the hot air position indefinitely. On a warm day, after the engine warms up, the air door should move to the cold air position. If it doesn't, the temperature sensor inside the air cleaner might be faulty, or the air door itself might be hanging up. Check the air door (a small mirror can be helpful here) by using a hand

vacuum pump, or by running a hose from manifold vacuum to the vacuum motor. Connect and disconnect the hose to see if the air door moves freely. If the air door is free, check out the hoses for leaks or blockage. If the hoses are okay, the trouble must be in the temperature sensor, and it should be replaced.

Both General Motors and Ford use a modulator in the air cleaner vacuum line on some engines. The modulator mounts on the side of the air cleaner and has two hose connections, one to the air cleaner temperature sensor, and the other to the vacuum motor. Below 50–80°F. the modulator is a one-way check valve, which allows vacuum to move the air door to the hot air position, but traps the vacuum so the door will not jump back to the cold air position during acceleration. This prevents a stumble.

After the modulator warms up, the check valve unseats so that the vacuum can pass freely in either direction, and the air door then operates normally. The connections for the modulator are important. The connection in the center (usually the larger diameter) goes to the vacuum motor, and the connection on the edge goes to the vacuum source, which is the temperature sensor.

To test the modulator on a cold engine, apply enough vacuum to the edge port to move the air door to the hot position. Then remove the hose from the port, and the air door should stay in the hot position. Make the same test when the engine is warmed up, and the air door should move to the cold position when you pull off the hose.

Exhaust Gas Recirculation

GENERAL INFORMATION

Gasoline Engines

NOx (oxides of nitrogen) is a tailpipe emission caused by the oxidation of nitrogen in the combustion chamber. When the peak combustion temperatures go over 2500°F., NOx is formed in excessive amounts. To keep the combustion temperatures down, exhaust gas is recirculated on most cars. Recirculation is accomplished by allowing intake manifold vacuum to draw exhaust gas into the intake manifold. The lower combustion temperatures also help control spark knock (ping).

An EGR valve is used to control the flow of exhaust gas into the intake manifold. All EGR valves look alike, and are operated by vacuum. When the vacuum is off, the valve is closed. Several different types of controls are used to turn the vacuum to the EGR valve on and off. Most of them have to do with engine temperature, as described later. On computerized control systems, EGR operation is regulated by the electronic control unit.

NOTE: All EGR systems are designed to cut off exhaust recirculation when the engine is cold, at idle, or under hard acceleration. If the EGR valve is stuck open, the engine won't idle.

Ported vacuum EGR systems are the simplest. When the EGR valve hose is connected to the base of the carburetor, without a separate amplifier, the system is operated by ported vacuum. The hose may not run directly from the EGR valve to the carburetor, but may go through a temperature control valve of some sort. In a ported vacuum system, the vacuum to operate the EGR valve is taken from a port that is above the throttle plate at idle, and thus not subject to vacuum. Because there is no vacuum, the spring in the EGR valve closes it, and the exhaust gas does not recirculate. As the throttle is opened, the port is exposed to vacuum, and the EGR valve opens.

Venturi vacuum systems, with an amplifier, are the most complicated, because of the number of hoses. Manifold vacuum is connected to the amplifier by a hose, and then connects to the EGR valve. The am-

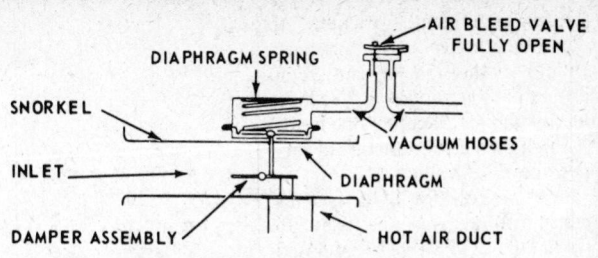

Underhood air delivery position

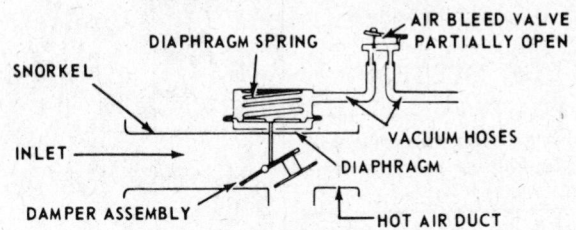

Regulating position

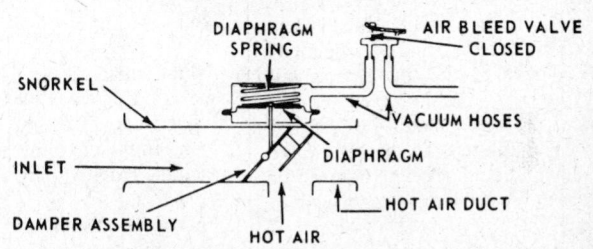

Hot air delivery position

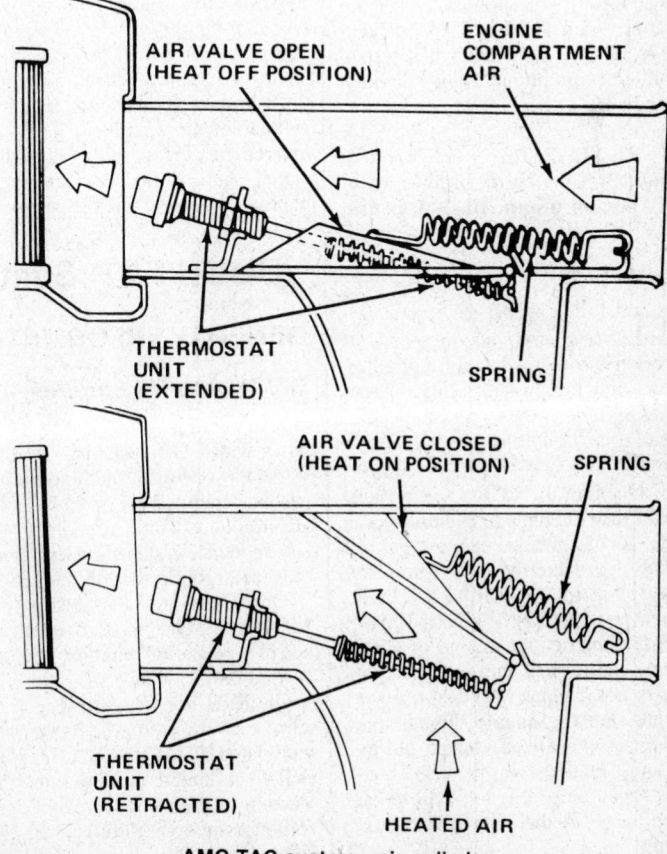

AMC TAC system—six cylinder

plifier also connects to venturi vacuum. At idle there is no venturi vacuum, but above idle the air moves through the carburetor venturi fast enough to create a vacuum. This slight amount of vacuum opens the amplifier, which then allows manifold vacuum to open the EGR valve.

Temperature controls for EGR systems come in many different designs. They are all made so that the EGR valve stays closed when the engine is cold. After the engine warms up, the temperature control allows the EGR valve to operate normally.

TESTING EGR SYSTEM

CAUTION

The EGR valve gets hot during normal operation. Take normal precautions to avoid accidental burns.

Testing of EGR systems should verify that when the engine is at normal operating temperature, the EGR valve is closed at idle, open above idle, and that the exhaust gas is actually recirculating. If the EGR valve sticks open at idle, the engine will run very rough, or may not even start. If this happens the valve should be removed and cleaned, or replaced. To check for valve opening above idle, check with a mirror or your fingers to see if the diaphragm or stem moves when the engine is at a fast idle in Park or Neutral. If the diaphragm does not move when the throttle is opened, there is either a problem with vacuum, or the valve is stuck closed. With a vacuum gauge hooked up to the EGR port, you should see vacuum on the gauge when the throttle is opened. EGR valves should not leak when tested with a hand vacuum pump. If they do they must be replaced.

NOTE: The EGR valve should open when about 3–5 in. Hg is applied with the hand vacuum pump. Back pressure operated EGR valves cannot be vacuum tested.

To find out if the exhaust gas is actually recirculating, use a hand vacuum pump or mouth suction through a hose to open the EGR valve with the engine idling. If the engine runs rough or dies, you know the exhaust gas is recirculating. If the engine does not run rough, make a second test at 2500 rpm. Opening the EGR valve at that rpm should cause a change in engine speed. If it does, you know the exhaust gas is recirculating. To make the 2500 rpm test, remove and plug the hose from the EGR port. Attach your suction hose to the EGR valve before running the engine at 2500 rpm. Simply pulling off the EGR hose at 2500 rpm is not a valid test, because the extra air entering the engine through the hose could cause a speed change all by itself. On most engines you won't have to go this far, because opening the EGR valve at idle will prove that the exhaust is recirculating.

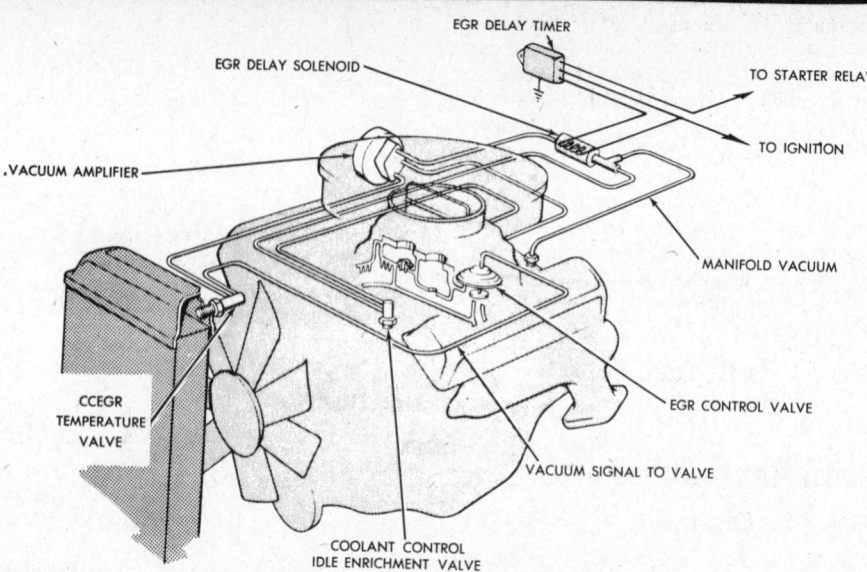

Venturi vacuum exhaust gas recirculation

If the exhaust is not recirculating, it means that a passageway or the valve itself is clogged up. The only way to fix it is to clean out the clogging as best you can, replace the clogged part, or replace the EGR valve.

Many 1978 and later EGR valves have a back pressure sensor built into the valve. This sensor is a pressure operated bleed that disables the EGR valve and keeps it closed when there is no exhaust pressure. This type of valve cannot be tested with a hand vacuum pump with the engine off because the bleed is open. The only practical way to test these new valves is by substitution of a known good valve. If a valve is not available, the suspected valve can be removed, and the mounting holes temporarily taped shut. If this corrects the problem, then a new valve should be installed.

Diesel EGR Systems

GENERAL INFORMATION

GM V6 and V8 Engines

GM has equipped its V8 and V6 diesel engines with EGR systems. The diesel EGR systems work in the same basic manner as gasoline engine EGR systems: exhaust gases are introduced into the combustion chambers to reduce combustion temperatures, and thus lower the formation of nitrogen oxides (NO_x). There are two systems used on the V8 diesels. One is used on the B (large body)-type station wagons, and one system is used on all other cars.

On the B-body station wagon EGR system, vacuum from the vacuum pump is modulated by the Vacuum Regulator Valve (VRV) mounted on the injection pump. Vacuum is highest at idle and decreases to zero at wide open throttle. The EGR valve is therefore fully open at idle and closed at

wide open throttle. A Response Vacuum Reducer Valve is used between the VRV and the EGR valve to allow the EGR valve to change position quickly as throttle position is changed.

On all other V8 diesel engines, the EGR system is the same as used on the "B" wagon, except a solenoid is added to the system that shuts off vacuum to the EGR valve when the Torque Converter Clutch is engaged. This solenoid is fed 12V from the TCC switch portion of the VRV and is grounded through the transmission's governor pressure switch.

On all V6 diesel EGR systems, the vacuum from the vacuum pump is modulated by the Vacuum Regulator Valve (VRV) mounted on the injection pump, as it is on the V8 diesels. The amount of EGR valve opening is further modulated by a Vacuum Modulator Valve (VMV). The VMV allows for an increase in vacuum to the EGR valve as the throttle is closed, up to the switching point of the VMV. The system also employs an RVR valve in the same manner as the V8 diesel system.

TESTING DIESEL EGR SYSTEM

Vacuum Regulator Valve (VRV)

The VRV is attached to the side of the injection pump and regulates vacuum in proportion to throttle angle. Vacuum from the vacuum pump is supplied to port A and vacuum at port B (see illustration) is reduced as the throttle is opened. At closed throttle the vacuum is 15 in. Hg; at half throttle, 6 in. Hg; at wide open throttle there should be zero vacuum.

Exhaust Gas Recirculation (EGR) VALVE

Apply vacuum to the vacuum port. On V8

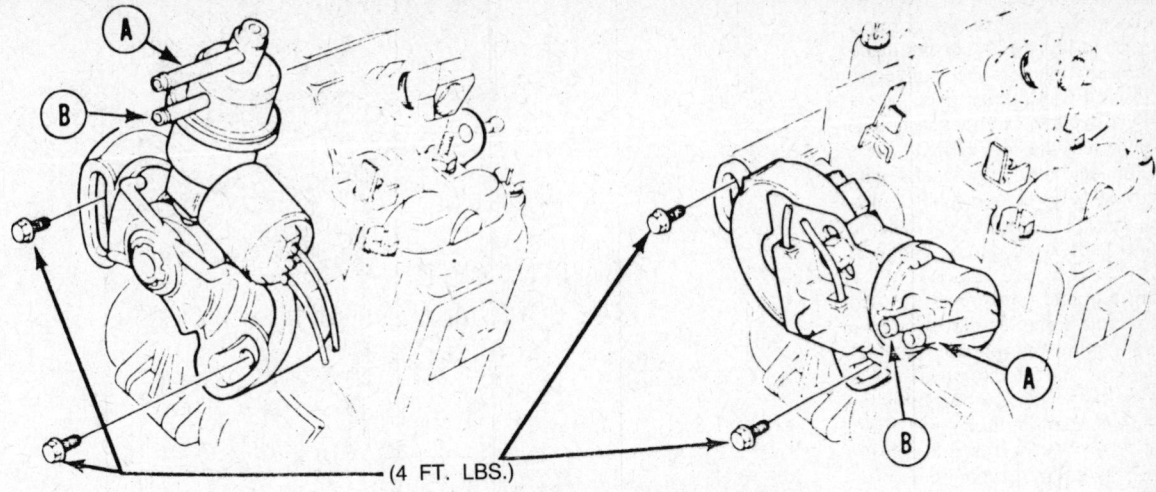

(4 FT. LBS.)

Vacuum Regulator Valve (VRV)—GM diesel

engines, the valve should be fully open at 10.5 in. Hg and closed below 6 in. Hg. On V6 engines, the valve should be fully open at 12 in. Hg and closed below 6 in. Hg.

Response Vacuum Reducer (RVR)

Connect a vacuum gauge to the port marked "To EGR valve or TCC solenoid". Connect a hand operated vacuum pump to the VRV port. Draw 15 in. of vacuum on the pump and the reading on the vacuum gauge should be .75 in. Hg. lower than the vacuum pump reading on all except High Altitude V8 engines. On High Altitude V8 engines ONLY, the reading should be 2.5 in. Hg. lower.

Exhaust Pressure Regulator Valve (V6 Diesels)

Apply vacuum to the vacuum port of the valve. The valve should be fully closed at 12 in. Hg and open below 6 in. Hg.

Vacuum Modulator Valve (VMV)

To test the VMV, block the drive wheels, and apply the parking brake. With the shift lever in Park, start the engine and run at a slow idle. Connect a vacuum gauge to the hose that connects to the port marked "MAN". There should be at least 14 in. Hg of vacuum. If not, check the vacuum pump, VRV, RVR, solenoid, and all connecting hoses. Reconnect the hose to the "MAN" port. Connect a vacuum gauge to the "DIST" port on the VMV. The vacuum reading should be 12 in. Hg except on High Altitude cars, which should be 9 in. Hg.

Catalytic Converters

GENERAL INFORMATION

The catalytic converters are mounted in the engine exhaust stream and works as a gas reactor in which its major function is to

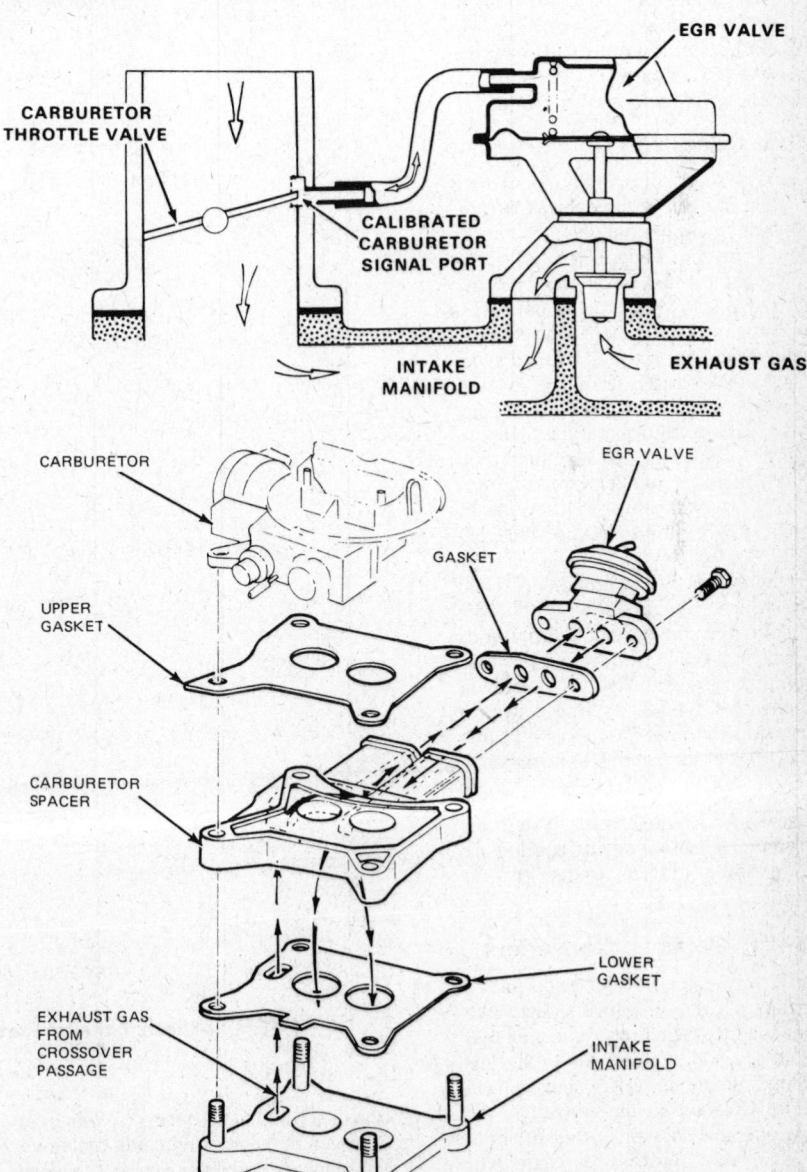

Most cars use an EGR system with a valve and a ported vacuum signal, as shown here. Some cars use the venturi vacuum with a separate amplifier to operate the valve.

speed up the heat-producing chemical reaction between the exhaust gas components, in order to reduce the air pollutants in the engine exhaust. The converters produce CO_2 and water when operating.

The catalyst material is either a ceramic substrate or pellets that are coated with a base of alumina and then impregnated with catalytically active, precious (noble) metals. It is the surface of the catalyst material that controls the heat producing chemical reaction.

Two main types of converters are used on today's vehicles, one, an oxidation type converter containing two precious (noble) metals, platinum and palladium to effectively catalyze the oxidation of the hydrocarbons (HC) and carbon monoxide (CO). The second type converter used is considered a three-way catalyst, containing platinum and rhodium in the front part of the converter to reduce the oxides of nitrogin (NOx), while platinum and palladium are used in the rear section to oxidize the hydrocarbons (HC) and carbon monoxide (CO), as was done in the two-way converters.

Oxidizing Catalytic Converters

The converters do not operate unless there is sufficient oxygen in the exhaust stream. It is extremely important that the proper amount of oxygen is supplied at all times. This is accomplished by a secondary air source, provided by either an air pump system or a pulse air type system. The catalytic converter system is protected by several devices that block out the secondary air supply when the engine is laboring under any abnormal hot or cold operating situation, preventing converter overheating and burnout. Converter temperatures are normally between 900 and 1500 degrees F. with peak temperatures around 1800 degrees F., so we can understand that the converters must be hot to properly perform their functions. Should the converters be supplied too rich a mixture of hydrocarbons (HC), such as would result from a misfiring spark plug or stuck choke valve, along with an oversupply of fresh air, the converter temperature would increase sharply, causing a burnout of the catalyst material.

NOTE: Some computer controlled systems use an air management valve to increase converter efficiency by routing air to the exhaust system under certain conditions.

Three-Way Catalytic Converters

The three-way catalytic converters use a combination of catalysts which produce two different chemical reactions, oxidation and reduction. By adding fresh air to the unburned hydrocarbons (HC) and carbon monoxide (CO) within the converter, the oxidizing or combustion process takes place.

Just the reverse process is required to lower the oxides of nitrogen (NOx) emissions. The oxides of nitrogen (NOx) already contains excessive oxygen and the

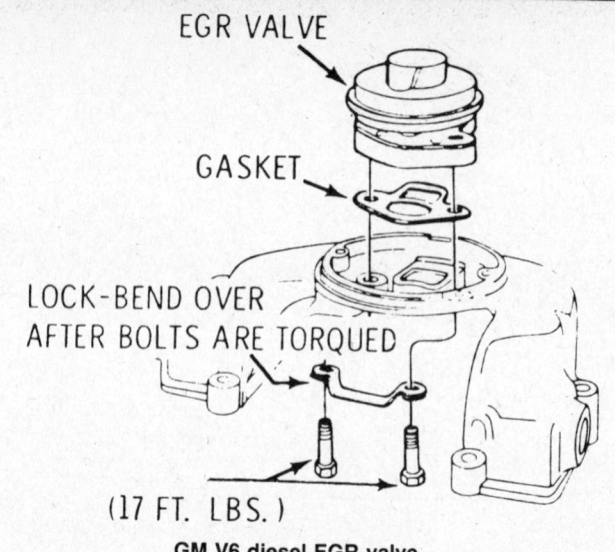

GM V6 diesel EGR valve

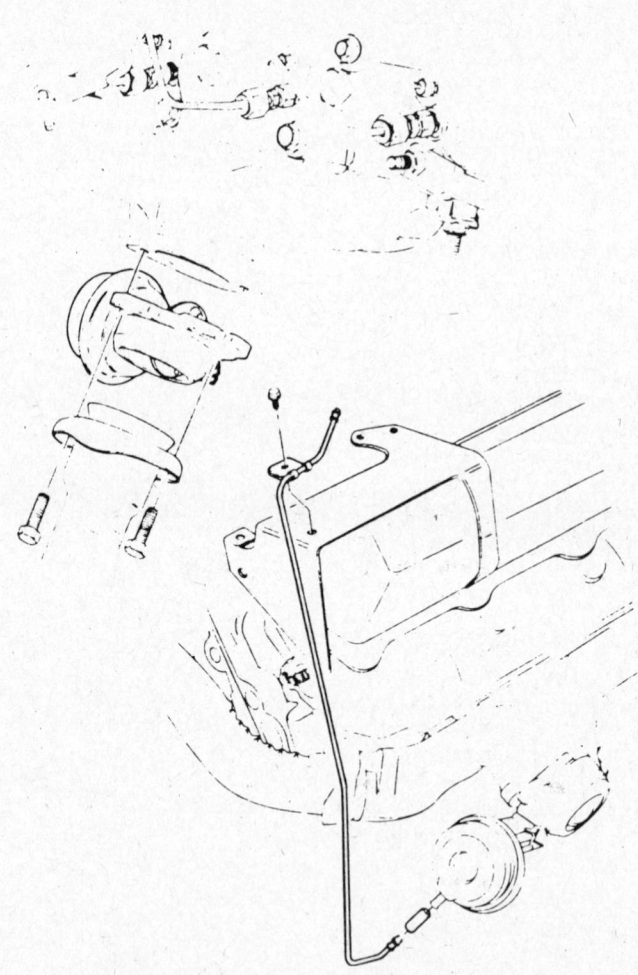

GM V6 diesel Exhaust Pressure Regulator Valve (EPR)

process of separating the excess oxygen from the nitrogen is called a reducing reaction.

This reducing or reduction process is done in the front section of the converter while the oxidizing process is accomplished in the rear section. A fresh air connector is located on the center of the converter shell, to add fresh air from the air system as required.

To enable the three-way converter to operate properly, the engine's air/fuel ratio must be held within a tight range, called a "Stoichiometric" range. This is accomplished with the use of the closed loop, feedback fuel management systems incorporating the latest electronic controls.

Different controls are used by the vehicle manufacturers to prevent converter damage and/or burnout. Unleaded fuels must be used in the vehicles when equipped with the catalytic converters to prevent contamination failure. Refer to the individual system sections for specific information.

The catalyst inside the converter is made in two forms. Some General Motors and American Motors converters use the pellet form, in which loose pellets are packed into the converter and can be emptied out and changed, if necessary. Ford and Chrysler use the honeycomb catalyst, which is built into the converter shell and is not replaceable. On Ford and Chrysler products the entire converter must be replaced if it goes bad. Later G.M. and AMC models also use small honeycomb catalysts in both one and two-converter applications.

TESTING

There is no way to test a converter in the field to see if it is actually working. Tailpipe readings may be used to set carburetor idle mixtures, when the car maker requires it, but taking a tailpipe reading to determine if the converter is working is not possible.

The one field check that is recommended in all cases is to inspect for mechanical damage. If a converter gets overheated, the catalyst can melt and block the exhaust. Pellets or pieces of the catalyst may even come flying out the tailpipe while the engine is running. If this happens, the pellets or the entire converter must be changed.

Checking for a melted converter that restricts the exhaust can be done with a vacuum gauge connected to the engine. Run the engine at about 2500 rpm in Park or Neutral. If the vacuum reading is steady, the exhaust is okay. If the vacuum reading slowly drops, it indicates a buildup of pressure in the exhaust.

The use of leaded fuel will slowly destroy the efficiency of the catalyst. If used long enough, leaded fuel can even cause catalyst plugging to the point where the engine will not run. If you know that a car has been run on several tanks of leaded fuel, then you can be sure that the catalyst is ruined. The only thing you can do is change the catalyst or install a new converter.

NOTE: Do not change the catalyst if the car has been run on only one tank or less of leaded fuel. Switching back to unleaded will allow the catalyst to recover and be almost as efficient as it was.

CONVERTER OVERHEAT PROTECTION

Some cars have overheat protection systems for the converter. Ford Motor Co.

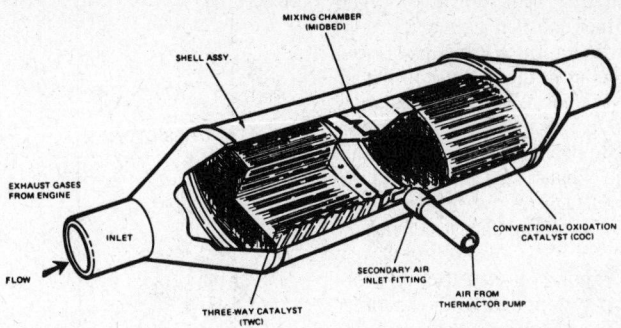

Sectional view of three-way catalytic converter

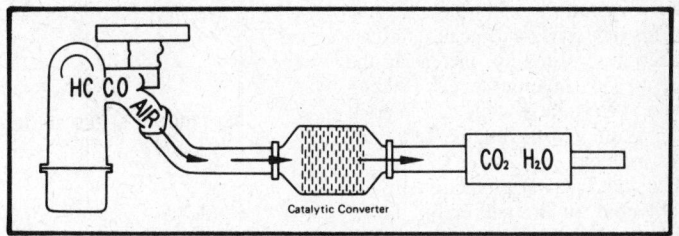

Typical catalytic converter installation

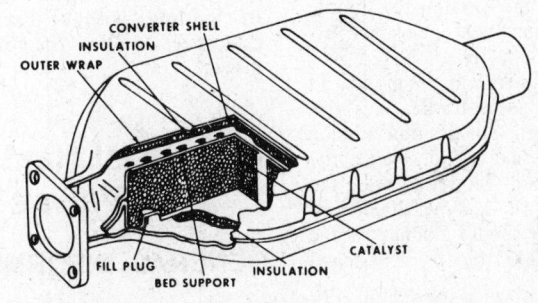

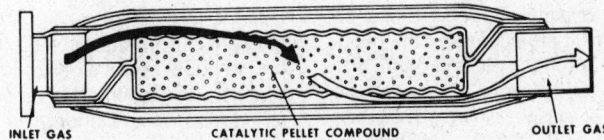

Pellet type catalytic converter

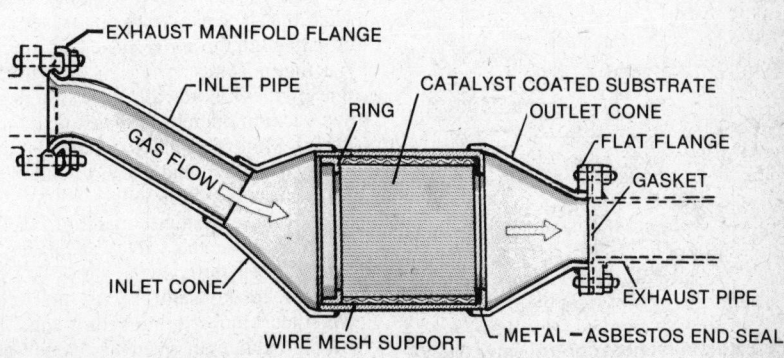

Cross section of typical catalytic converter

sometimes uses a heat sensitive switch mounted in the floorpan above the converter. The switch turns a vacuum solenoid on and off to control the vacuum to the air pump bypass valve. When the vacuum is shut off the bypass valve dumps the pump air into the atmosphere, diverting the air away from the exhaust system. Without the air in the exhaust, the converter's catalytic heat reaction slows and the system cools down.

Chrysler Corporation cars use an overheat protection system that holds the throttle open to prevent high speed closed throttle deceleration. Any engine decelerating on closed throttle is usually running rich, because the high vacuum pulls so much fuel out of the carburetor bowl through the idle circuit. This rich mixture can cause the catalytic reaction to speed up, increasing the heat generated to dangerous levels. Holding the throttle open slightly while decelerating allows more air into the engine and eliminates the problem.

The Chrysler catalyst protection system uses a solenoid on the carburetor that is identical to an anti-dieseling solenoid. The solenoid is controlled by an electronic speed switch and only comes on when the engine speed is above 2000 rpm. When the solenoid is on, its stem extends to the equivalent of a 1500 rpm fast idle setting. If the driver takes his foot off the throttle, the throttle does not close, but rests against the extended solenoid stem. The solenoid goes off below 2000 rpm so that the engine doesn't run away with the car in traffic.

To test the system put the transmission in Park or Neutral and operate the throttle from under the hood. Slowly increase the engine speed until it is above 2000 rpm. The solenoid stem should extend. As the speed drops below 2000 rpm, the stem should retract.

To determine if the car is equipped with the system, look for the speed switch on the right fender panel. Some cars may not have the overheat protection system, but do have an anti-dieseling solenoid on the carburetor. The anti-dieseling solenoid is easily identified because it is energized whenever the ignition switch is on. Check for 12 volts at the switch connector with a test light or voltmeter with the key ON.

VACUUM TAP ON INTAKE MANIFOLD

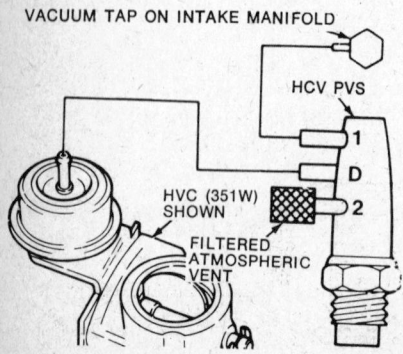

Vacuum exhaust heat control valve (HCV) system

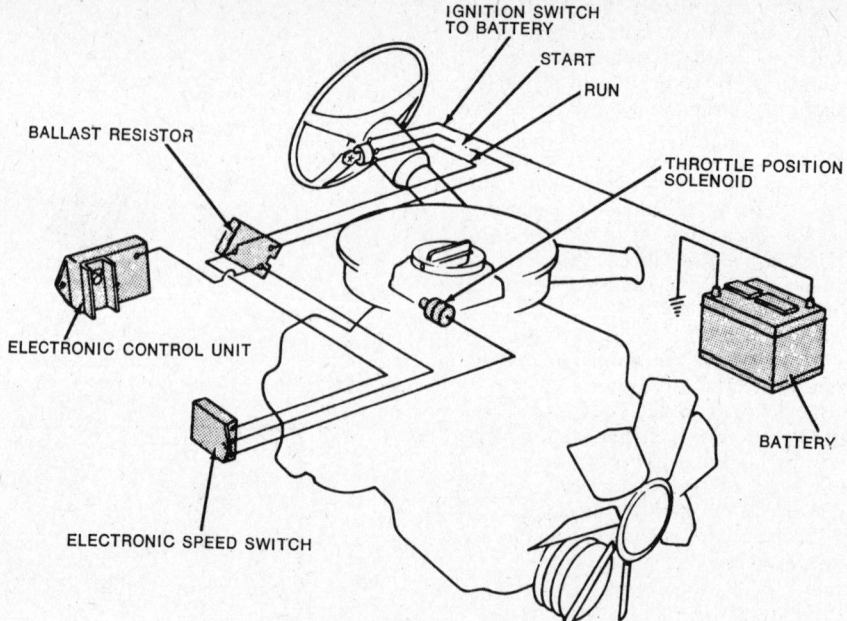

Catalyst overheat protection system

NOTE: Because the catlytic converter operating temperature increases with the engine idling, DO NOT allow any catalyst-equipped vehicle to idle for more than five minutes without increasing the engine speed to allow the converter to cool down.

Exhaust Heat Riser Valves

GENERAL INFORMATION

Exhaust heat riser valves have been used for many years to force part of the engine exhaust through a passageway under the intake manifold and preheat the fuel mixture to allow better atomization of the fuel droplets. The heat valve was spring loaded into the closed position, but heat would make the spring relax so that during high speed operation or after warmup the exhaust would push it open.

Now, many engines use vacuum operated heat valves, controlled by a vacuum switch that is sensitive to engine temperature (although the above system, controlled by a thermostatic spring, is still used in some engines). Ford calls their system simply a vacuum operated exhaust heat valve. General Motors refers to theirs as Early Fuel Evaporation, and Chrysler calls theirs a Power Heat Control Valve.

On all these systems, manifold vacuum is used to close the valve, and force the exhaust gases through the crossover passage in the intake manifold. All the systems have some kind of temperature valve that shuts the vacuum off when the engine warms up.

Both Chrysler and Ford products use a simple coolant temperature-sensitive vacuum switch mounted on the intake manifold coolant passage. The Chrysler switch has two hose connections. It actually does triple duty because it also controls the vacuum supply to the idle enrichment system and the air switching valve. Ford's vacuum switch has three hose connections, but one of them is a vent with a filter to keep the dirt out.

General Motors cars use either a coolant vacuum switch, or a vacuum solenoid connected to an oil temperature switch. The coolant vacuum switch has two hose connections and a vent when it controls the heat valve only. When it is tied into other emission control systems, it can have as many as five hose connections, and a vent. Many General Motors cars also have a check valve in the hose so that vacuum will be trapped in the heat valve actuator when the engine is accelerated. This keeps the heat valve in the closed position and prevents a rattle.

TESTING

VACUUM OPERATED VALVES

Testing the vacuum operated heat riser valve is a matter of making sure it closes and opens freely. You can move it by hand to see if it works, on a warm engine. On a cold engine, the valve should be closed, and disconnecting the hose should allow it to open (engine idling). On a cold engine, there should be vacuum at the vacuum actuator, and on a warm engine the vacuum should be shut off.

Spring Operated Valves

Operation of the manifold heat control valve

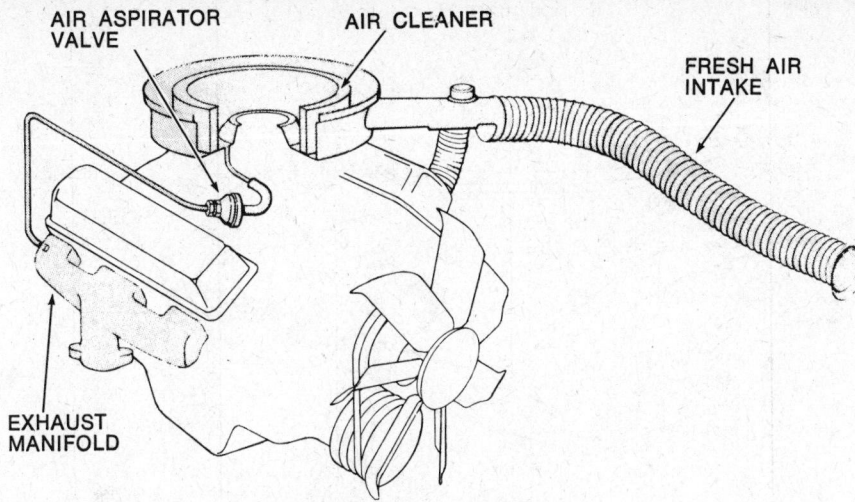

Chrysler Air Aspirator system

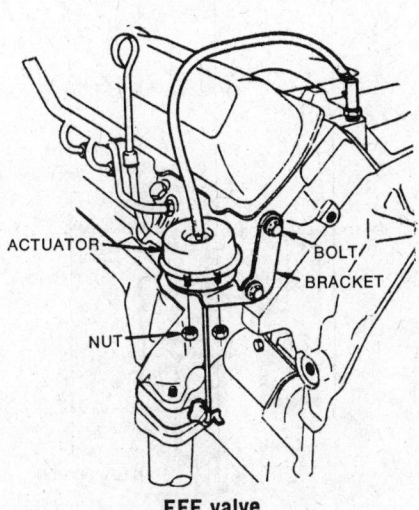

EFE valve

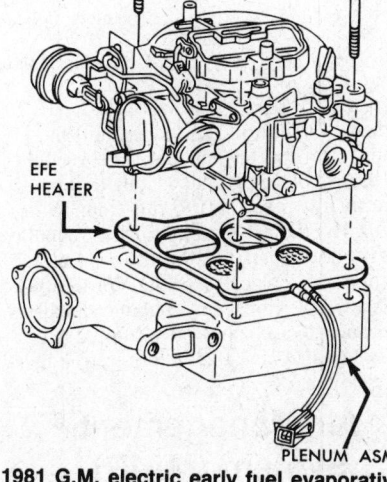

1981 G.M. electric early fuel evaporative heater

should be inspected periodically. Warm up the engine and let it idle. Briefly accelerate the engine; the counter-weight should respond by moving roughly ½ inch in its normal direction of rotation. If little or no movement is noticed, the valve shaft is stuck due to the accumulation of deposits, or the thermostatic spring is broken or weak.

Applying a suitable heat control valve solvent, available in spray cans, at every oil change to the ends of the valve shaft (at the bushings) will keep the valve working freely. The solvent should be sprayed on when the manifold is cool and allowed to soak a few minutes to dissolve deposits. Work the valve back and forth by hand until it turns freely.

— CAUTION —
Valve may be hot. Allow it to cool for a few minutes if the engine is warm.

If the thermostatic spring is broken or weak it will have to be replaced. Position the valve plate, and grind off the spot welds

from the valve plate and shaft. Remove the counterweight and shaft assembly, and the valve plate. Remove the thermostatic spring, after pressing off the counterweight from the end of the shaft. Position the new spring on the shaft so the center end or tab is pointing left and the hook or outer end points down. Install the thermostatic spring on the counterweight. Press the counterweight on the shaft so it is flush with the end of the shaft. Install the shaft assembly to the manifold, and have the valve plate arc welded to the shaft with a stainless steel rod. Test the valve for free operation.

NOTE: Wear eye protection when grinding off spot welds.

GM Early Fuel Evaporation (EFE) System

The electrically operated EFE system used

on some 1981 and later GM engines performs the same function as the vacuum operated heat riser on other engines, which is to preheat the engine induction system during cold driveaway. Rapid heating is desirable because it provides quick fuel evaporation and more uniform fuel distribution to aid cold driveability.

The electrically heated EFE system has a ceramic heater grid located underneath the primary bore(s) of the carburetor which is part of the carburetor insulator. When the ignition is turned on and engine coolant temperature is low, voltage is applied to the EFE relay, which in turn transfers the voltage to the EFE heater in the ceramic grid. When temperature increases, a thermal valve switch de-energizes the relay and the heater is turned off.

TESTING EFE HEATER

To check the resistance of the heater, turn the ignition off, disconnect the heater electrical connector, and using an ohmmeter, measure the resistance across the two terminals of the heater connector. If resistance is under 2 ohms, the heater is good. If not, replace the heater.

Air Aspirator System (AAS)

1978 and later Chrysler Corporation cars (all states except California) which use this system have done away with the air pump. The complete air aspirator system consists of a hose from the clean side of the air cleaner, the aspirator valve mounted on top of the engine, and a tube connecting the valve with the exhaust manifold. The suction in the exhaust draws in air through the air cleaner and this extra air helps the catalytic converter burn up the pollutants. The aspirator valve is similar to the check valve used with all air pump systems. It keeps the exhaust from flowing back into the air cleaner, but allows clean air to go into the exhaust.

TESTING AAS VALVE

Testing the air aspirator valve is done by disconnecting the hose from the air cleaner and checking for slight suction at idle with a piece of paper over the end of the valve. Speeding the engine up slightly will show if the valve is leaking. Exhaust should not come out of the valve. Vibration of the valve diaphragm is normal, due to exhaust impulses.

Chrysler Pulse Air Feeder (PAF) System

This system is used on 1981 and later Aries, Reliants and 1982 and later LeBarons and

U269

Dodge 400s equipped with the optional 2.6L engine. The PAF system supplies secondary air into the exhaust system between the front and rear catalytic converters, which promotes oxidation of exhaust emissions in the rear catalytic converter. The system consists of a pulse air feeder, which contains two reed valve assemblies, a hose which links the pulse air feeder to the air cleaner, and a tube which runs from the feeder to the exhaust system. At the bottom of the feeder there are two tubes, one which runs into the oil sump and one which connects to No. 3 cylinder crankcase above the oil level. The main reed valve is actuated by a diaphragm in the feeder which, in turn, is activated by the pressure pulsation generated by the reciprocating motion of No. 3 piston. This pressure pulsation is fed to the diaphragm by a seal cover in the crankcase, which acts much like the human body's diaphragm when a person is breathing.

TESTING PAF SYSTEM

With the engine running, remove the hose at the air cleaner which runs to the feeder and check for vacuum. If no vacuum is present, check the hoses for leaks and evidence of oil leaks. Periodic maintenance service for the system is not required.

GM Pulse Air Injection System

This system is used on 1978 and later Chevette and T1000 1600cc 4-cylinder engines, and on Vega, Astre, Sunbird, Monza 140 cu. in. 4 cylinder engines. It is not used on the 151 cu. in. engine in the 1978–79 models, but is used on some 1980 models. It is also used on the 1980 173 V6. The system is similar to Chrysler's Air Aspirator. A hose from the clean side of the air cleaner connects to the pulse air valve. Tubes connect the pulse air valve to each cylinder's exhaust port. Suction in the exhaust draws fresh air from the air cleaner into the exhaust, and the air helps the catalytic converter burn up the pollutants. The pulse air valve consists of four or six check valves built into a housing. It allows each exhaust port to suck in fresh air independently of the other ports. The check valves only open when there is suction in the exhaust. If there is any back pressure, the check valves close to prevent exhaust flow back into the air cleaner. On some applications the pulse air valve is connected to only three of the four exhaust ports on a 4-cylinder engine.

TESTING PULSE AIR INJECTION SYSTEM

To test the pulse air valve, remove the rubber hose from the valve and run the engine at idle. You should notice a slight pulsation of the valves, drawing air into the exhaust.

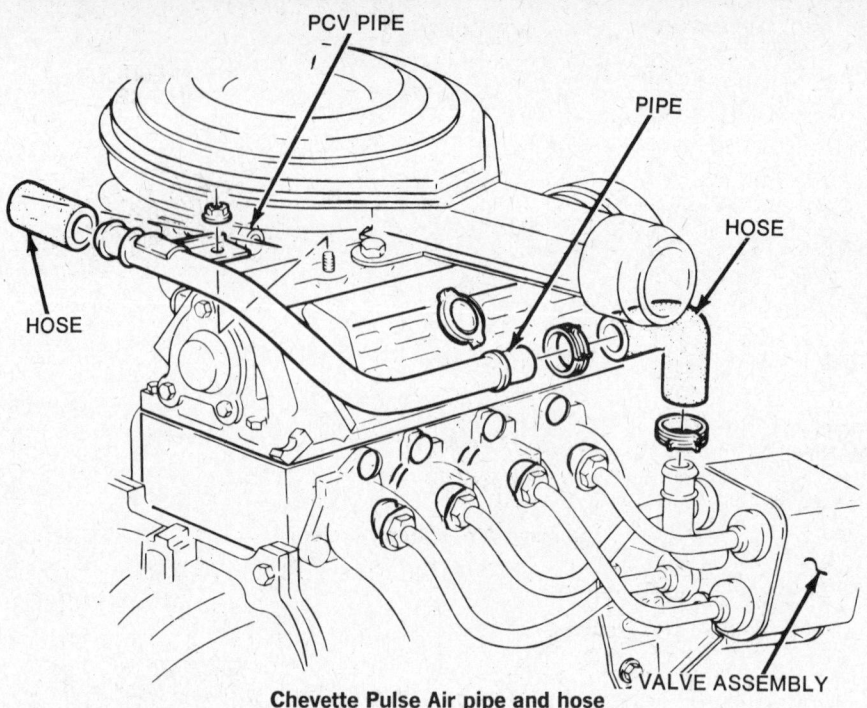

Chevette Pulse Air pipe and hose

With the engine off, use a vacuum pump to apply 15 in. Hg. vacuum. The vacuum will slowly bleed off, but as long as it takes more than two seconds to fall from 15 in. to 5 in. Hg. the valve is okay. If the vacuum falls off faster than that, the valve is leaking and must be replaced. On the V6, the two pulse air valves must be tested individually. Disconnect the solenoid valve (if used) from the front pulse air valve before testing that valve on the V6.

Air Management System (MAIR)

The Air Management System is found on 1981 and later GM gasoline engines. The system helps reduce HC and CO emissions in the same basic manner of a typical air pump-type air injection system, except that the MAIR system is controlled by signals from the electronic control module (ECM).

When the engine is cold, the ECM energizes an Air Control Solenoid. This allows air to flow to an Air Switching Valve, which is energized to direct air to the exhaust ports.

On a warm engine or when in "Closed Loop" operation, the ECM de-energizes the Air Switching Valve, directing air between the beds of the catalytic converter. This provides additional oxygen for the oxidizing catalyst to decrease the HC and CO levels. If the Air Control Valve detects a rapid increase in manifold vacuum (deceleration, etc.), certain operating modes (wide open throttle, etc.), or the ECM self-diagnostic system detects any problem in the MAIR system as a whole, air is diverted (divert mode) to the air cleaner or directly into the atmosphere.

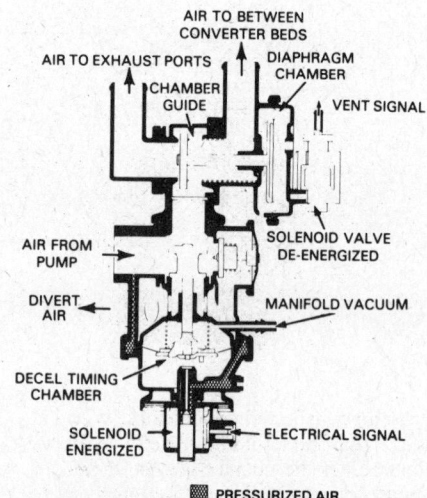

AIR SWITCHING VALVE CROSS SECTION (AIR TO CONVERTER OPERATION)

Typical GM air switching valve (ASV) assembly

A primary purpose of the divert mode is to prevent backfiring in the exhaust system. Throttle closure at the beginning of deceleration will temporarily create fuel-air mixtures which are too rich to burn completely. These mixtures become burnable when they reach the exhaust, when combined with injection air. The next firing of the engine ignites this mixture causing an exhaust backfire. Momentary diverting of the injection air from the exhaust prevents the backfiring.

The air-flow and control hoses transmit pressurized air to the catalytic converter or to the exhaust ports through internal (intake manifold) passages or external piping. The check valves prevent backflow of exhaust gas into the air distribution system. The valve prevents backflow when the air pump "bypasses" at high speed and loads, or in case the air pump malfunctions.

NOTE: For electronic testing and diagnosis procedures on the GM Air Management System, see the appropriate C4 or CCC System later in this section.

Ford Pulse Air (Thermactor II) System

Some 1978 and later Ford engines are equipped with an air injection system which does not use an air pump. Instead, natural pulses present in the exhaust system are used to pull the air into the system through the pulse air valves. The pulse valve is connected to the exhaust manifold by a tube and to the air cleaner or silencer with a hose. Make sure air can flow freely through the air cleaner or silencer to the check valve.

Air Injection Systems

GENERAL INFORMATION

A belt-driven air pump supplies air to small tubes positioned in the exhaust port near each exhaust valve. The air mixes with any unburned hydrocarbons in the exhaust and the hydrocarbons actually burn up in the exhaust system. On late model engines, air may not be pumped to every exhaust port, and some engines have only a single air injection fitting on the exhaust pipe near its connection to the exhaust manifold. Air injection systems are frequently used on engines with catalytic converters, and nearly all California cars, so that the converter gets enough air to keep the reaction going.

Plumbing on air injection systems varies considerably. At first, all the plumbing was external, with individual tubes inserted into each exhaust port either through the cylinder head or the exhaust manifold. Now many engines have internal passageways to duct the air to the exhaust port.

A check valve is used between the pump and the exhaust port nozzle to keep hot exhaust gases from traveling up the plumbing and destroying the pump. Some V8 and V6 engines use two check valves.

An anti-backfire valve, also called a bypass valve or diverter valve, is used between the pump and the check valve. Usually, the diverter valve is mounted on the pump or near it. A small sensing hose connects the diverter valve to intake manifold vacuum. When the vacuum rises during deceleration, the diverter valve opens, and sends the pump air into the atmosphere. This prevents the over-rich deceleration mixture in the exhaust system from exploding or backfiring out the tailpipe.

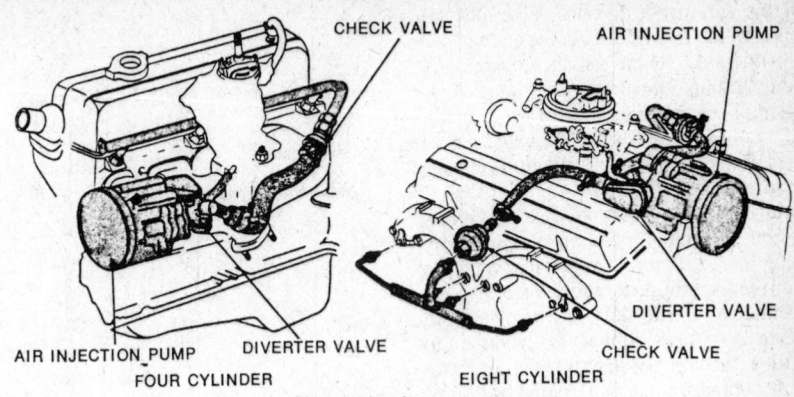

Chevrolet air pump system

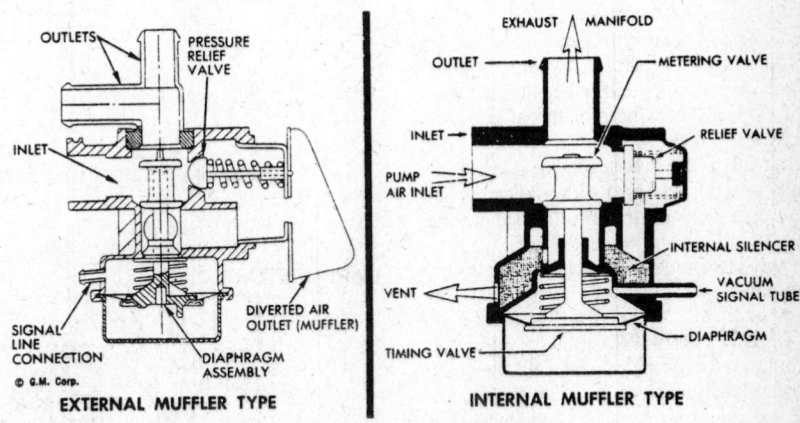

General Motors Diverter Valves

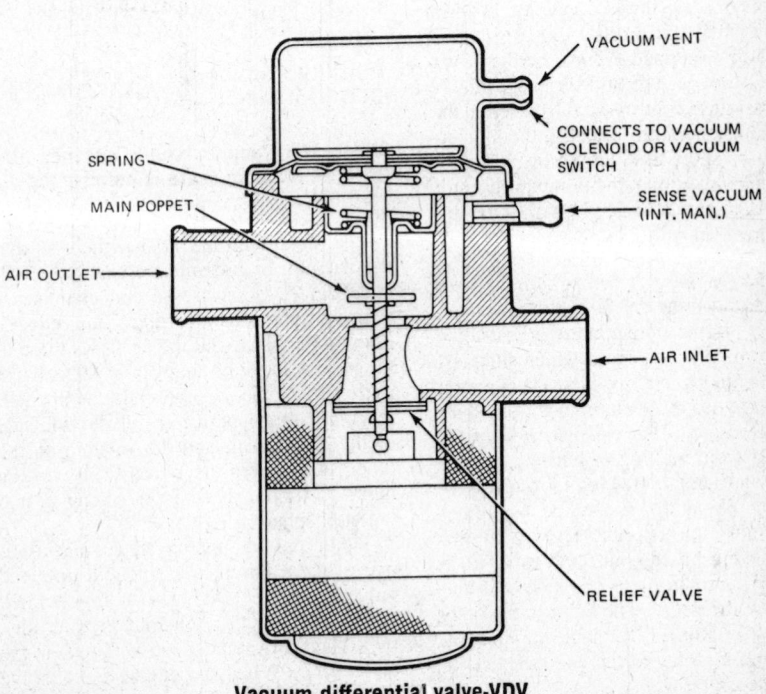

Vacuum differential valve-VDV

Some cars use a diverter valve that has a small hose cconnection on the end instead of on the side. These valves are normally in the "dump" position. They must have the small sensing line hooked up to manifold vacuum, which pulls the valve mechanism from the "dump" position into the normal running position.

Unfortunately, this type of valve will not go into the dump position automatically during deceleration. To get the valve to dump, a vacuum differential valve (VDV) is connected in the sensing line. Manifold vacuum goes through the VDV and then to the diverter valve. When the manifold vacuum increases during deceleration, the VDV closes the sensing line. This shuts off the vacuum to the diverter valve, and the valve goes into the dump position.

A further refinement of this design is to connect the sensing line to ported (above the throttle plates) vacuum instead of manifold vacuum, and eliminate the VDV. In this situation, the diverter valve only receives vacuum above idle, because the vacuum port in the carburetor throat is above the throttle plate at idle. So whenever the engine idles, the diverter valve goes to the dump position. It also dumps during deceleration, because the throttle at that time is in the idle position.

Some late model Ford engines use a Differential Valve Delay Valve (DVDV) in series with the VDV. The installation of the DVDV with the VDV delays operation during sudden drops in manifold vacuum, such as hard acceleration. During sudden deceleration, however, the sudden rise in intake manifold vacuum opens the check in the delay valve, passing the signal along instantly.

Some systems have a delay valve, similar to a spark delay valve, in the sensing hose. This delays for a few seconds the drop in vacuum when the throttle closes, so that the air is not dumped every time the driver takes his foot off the throttle in traffic.

Temperature controls are also used in the sensing hose hookup. Usually, the temperature valve shuts the vacuum off when the engine is cold, so that the pump air doesn't go to the engine exhaust ports until the engine warms up.

Some cars have a temperature sensor mounted under the car above the catalytic converter. If the converter overheats, the sensor turns off a solenoid which shuts off the air to the diverter valve. The diverter valve then goes to the dump position, shutting off the air to the exhaust to keep the converter from melting or burning up.

1978 and later Ford Motor Company 4-cylinder, V6, and some inline 6 engines use a unique air bypass valve, with two small sensing hoses connected to it. Each of the hoses connects to one side of a diaphragm in the valve. The hose on the body of the valve connects to manifold vacuum, and the hose closer to the end connects to a separate on-off valve.

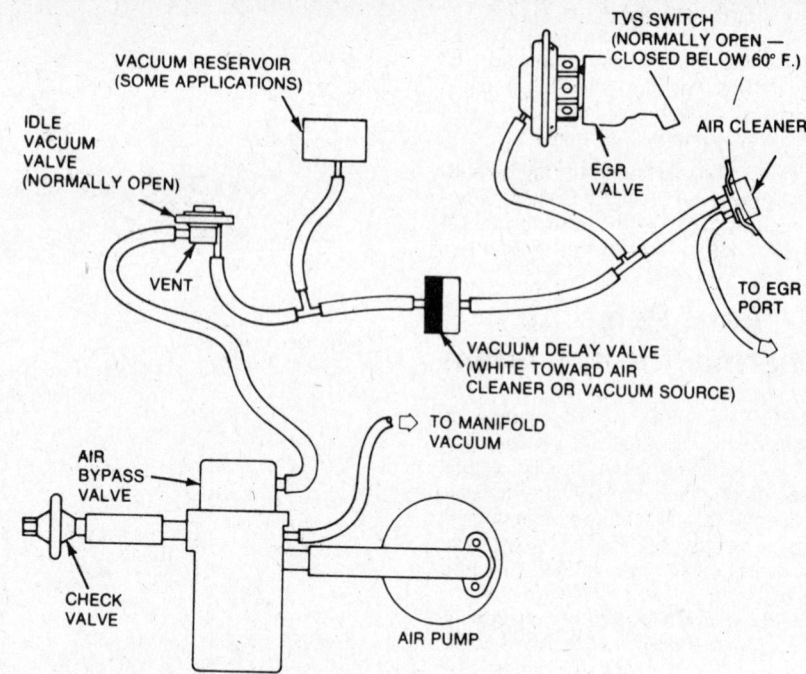

Air pump system using a timed air by-pass valve vacuum vent

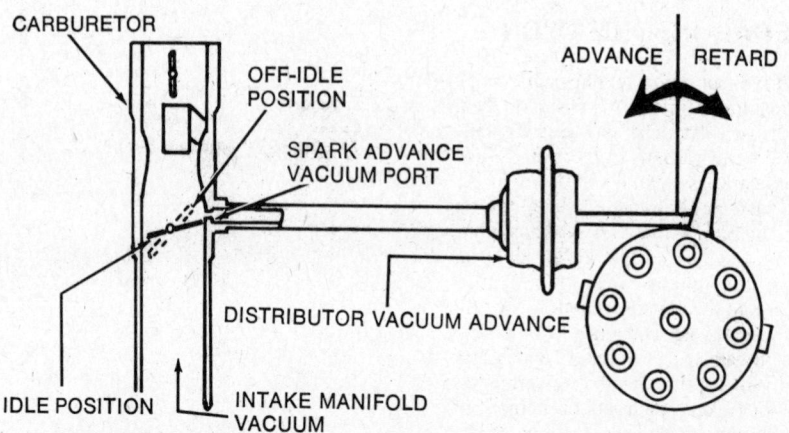

When the vacuum spark advance is "ported" it means the port is above the throttle plate so there is no advance at idle

The diaphragm has a small hole so that the vacuum or pressure on each side will equalize. As long as the end chamber is sealed by the separate valve being closed, nothing happens, and the air flows through the bypass valve on the way to the exhaust ports. But if the separate valve is opened, it admits atmospheric pressure to one side of the diaphragm, and the vacuum on the other side moves the bypass valve to the dump position, exhausting the pump air into the atmosphere.

Two types of separate valves are used, one of them an electric solenoid operated valve, and the other a vacuum-operated valve. The electric solenoid is controlled by a Thermo Actuated Valve (TAV) in the air cleaner. When the engine is cold, the TAV closes, which energizes the solenoid.

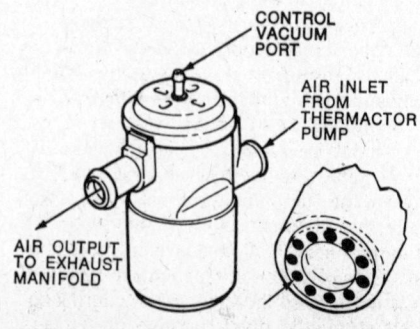

Catalyst cars use a different air bypass valve, with small hose connecting to the end.

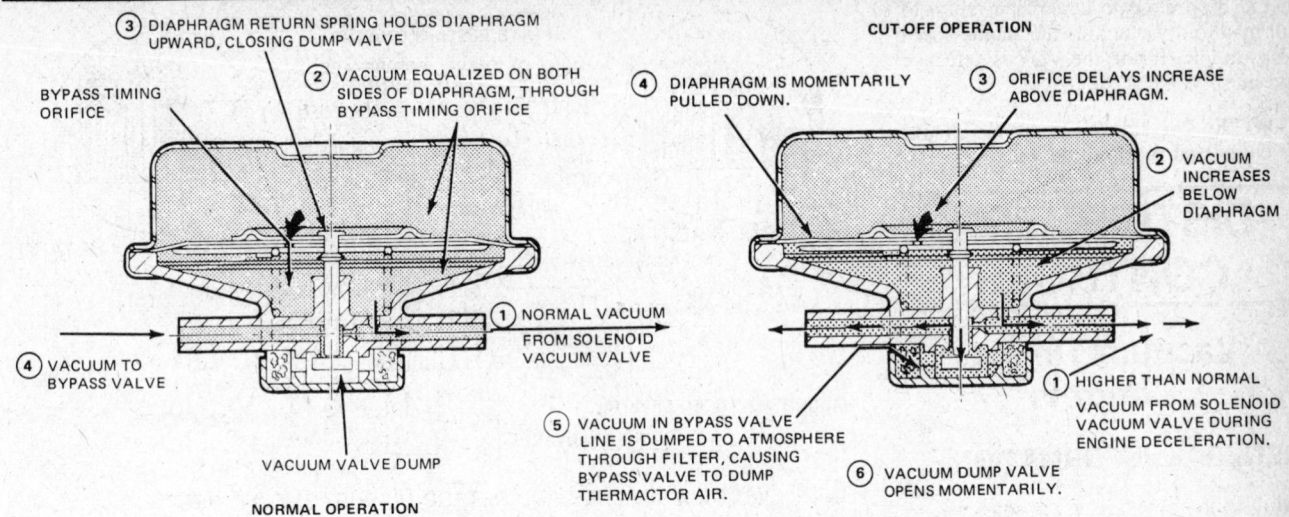

Timed air bypass valve with integral vacuum differential function

Atmospheric pressure then enters the upper chamber on the bypass valve and it goes to the dump position. When the engine warms up, the TAV opens, shuts off the solenoid, and the bypass valve goes into the normal running position.

On some California engines the solenoid is connected so that manifold vacuum passes through the solenoid to get to the bypass valve. A small filter-vent is placed over the end of the nozzle on the end cap of the bypass valve. With the same electrical hookup, this setup has the same action as that described earlier.

The vacuum operated valve, which takes the place of the solenoid on V6 and some inline 6 engines, is connected to ported (above the throttle plates) carburetor vacuum. It is called the Idle Vacuum Valve. At idle, there is no ported vacuum, and the idle vacuum valve opens, which causes the bypass valve to go to the dump position. Above idle, the idle vacuum valve closes, and the bypass valve goes into the running position. A temperature control, a delay valve, and a vacuum reservoir all control the ported vacuum supply to the idle vacuum valve.

AIR PUMP TESTS

CAUTION

Do not hammer on, pry or bend the pump housing while tightening the drive belt or testing the pump.

Before proceeding with the tests, check the pump drive belt tension.

If the belt squeals when the engine is running, the pump may be dragging or seized. Remove the belt and turn the pump by hand to check for seizure. Disregard any chirping, squealing, or rolling sounds from inside the pump when turning it by hand, as these are normal.

Check the hoses and connections for leaks. Hissing or a blast of air is indicative of a leak. Soapy water, applied lightly around the area in question, is a good method for detecting leaks.

To test air output, disconnect the air hose from the pump wherever it is convenient. If you disconnect it from one check valve on a V8 or V6, the other hose should also be disconnected and plugged for the test. Run the engine at idle and feel the blast of air from the hose with your hand. Increase the engine speed to 1500 rpm and feel the blast of air again. If the blast increases, and is steady, the pump is okay.

Pump Noise Diagnosis

The air pump is normally noisy; as engine speed increases, the noise of the pump will rise in pitch. The rolling sound the pump bearings make is normal. However, if this sound becomes objectionable at certain speeds, the pump is defective and will have to be replaced.

A continual hissing sound from the air pump pressure relief valve at idle indicates a defective valve. Replace the relief valve.

If the pump rear bearing fails, a continual knocking sound will be heard. Since the rear bearing is not separately replaceable, the pump will have to be replaced as an assembly.

DIVERTER (ANTI-BACKFIRE) VALVE TEST

Detach the hose, which runs from the bypass valve to the check valve.

Connect a tachometer to the engine. With the engine running at normal idle speed, check to see that air is flowing from the bypass valve hose connection.

Speed the engine up, so that it is running at 1500–2000 rpm. Allow the throttle to snap shut. The flow of air from the bypass valve at the check valve hose connection should stop momentarily and air should then flow from the exhaust port on the valve body or the silencer assembly.

Let the throttle snap shut several times. If the flow of air is not diverted into the atmosphere from the valve exhaust port or if it fails to stop flowing from the hose connection, check the vacuum lines and connections. If these are tight, either the bypass valve or one of the accessory valves in the small sensing hose is defective and must be replaced.

A leaking diaphragm will cause the air to flow out both the hose connection and the exhaust port at the same time. If this happens, replace the valve.

NOTE: Late model systems should stop flowing at idle, as described earlier. If not, the bypass valve or accessory valve is defective.

CHECK VALVE TEST

Remove the hose from the check valve. With the engine running at 1500 rpm in Park or Neutral, hold the back of your hand near the check valve to test for exhaust gas leakage. If the valve leaks, it must be replaced.

NOTE: Vibration and flutter of the valve at idle is a normal condition caused by exhaust pulsations. It does not mean that the valve is defective.

VACUUM DIFFERENTIAL VALVE TEST

Disconnect the small sensing hose at the bypass valve and connect a vacuum gauge to the hose. With the engine idling in Park or Neutral, the gauge should read full manifold vacuum.

Run the engine at a steady 2500 rpm in Park or Neutral, and release the throttle. As the engine decelerates, the vacuum gauge should drop close to zero, then return to full manifold vacuum as the engine speed drops to idle. If not, the VDV is defective and must be replaced.

NOTE: The small hose nozzle should be connected to manifold vacuum.

DISTRIBUTOR CONTROLS

Vacuum Timing Controls

GENERAL INFORMATION

All distributor controls act in some way to change or eliminate vacuum advance during certain operating conditions. Usually, the control cuts down on the amount of vacuum advance, in effect retarding the spark, so that the exhaust will get hotter and burn up hydrocarbon and carbon monoxide emissions before they go out the tailpipe.

The distributor vacuum advance unit might be connected, according to factory design, to either manifold vacuum or ported (above the throttle plates) carburetor vacuum. Either way, the vacuum spark advance curve is approximately the same for all running conditions above idle. At idle, however, the manifold vacuum hookup results in full advance, while the ported hookup gives zero advance. If the hoses are hooked up the wrong way, the addition or lack of advance will affect idle speed, requiring a readjustment of the throttle position to bring the idle speed back to specifications. When this is done, emissions will usually be high, so it is important to keep the hoses hooked up correctly.

NOTE: When in doubt, connect a timing light and check advance while switching hoses at idle.

Dual Diaphragm Distributors

These distributors have two hose connections, one in the normal position, and the other closer to the distributor body. The hose fitting next to the body is for the retard diaphragm, and is connected to manifold vacuum. The retard diaphragm affects the spark only at idle, when there is no vacuum on the advance diaphragm. In effect, the retard diaphragm provides a movable resting place for the advance diaphragm. When ported vacuum is not acting on the advance diaphragm, it returns to the neutral or no-advance position against the retard diaphragm. At idle, manifold vacuum pulls the retard diaphragm to the retard position, and the advance diaphragm follows along to retard the spark.

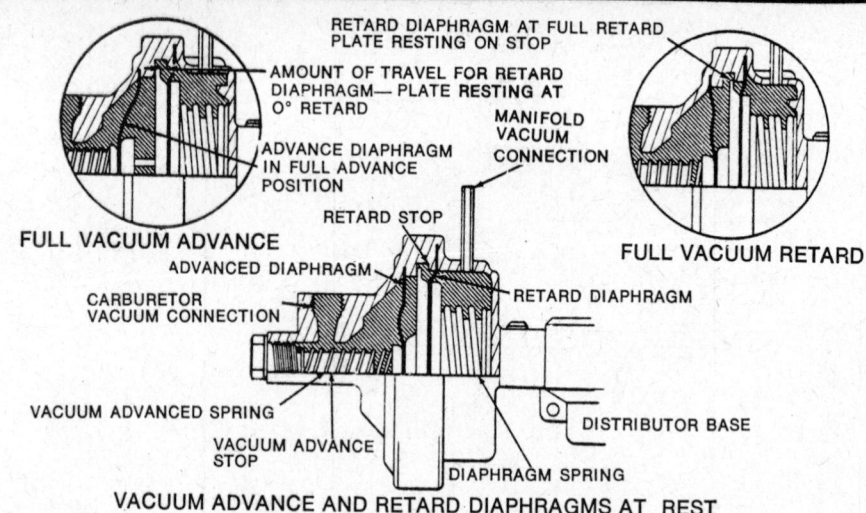

Operation of the dual diaphragm-type vacuum advance. All makes similar

TESTING

To test a dual diaphragm distributor, connect a timing light to the engine. Remove the retard hose from the distributor and plug the hose. With the engine running, increase the speed to a fast idle and watch the timing marks. The timing should advance. If not, either the vacuum unit is faulty, the vacuum port is plugged, or there is a temperature control device that is shutting off the vacuum. Apply hand pump or mouth suction vacuum to the advance diaphragm and the timing should advance. If not, the distributor must be disassembled and repaired. Failure to advance could be caused by a faulty diaphragm or a sticking advance plate.

Remove the advance hose from the vacuum unit and read the timing at normal idle speed. Remove the plug that was inserted in the retard hose, and check for full manifold vacuum at the end of it. If there is no vacuum, temperature controls may be shutting it off. Connect the hose to the retard diaphragm, or apply vacuum from another source. The timing should immediately retard several degrees. If not, the diaphragm is not working, and the unit must be replaced. Reconnect all hoses as they were originally.

Distributor Vacuum Deceleration Valve

First used on Chrysler Corporation engines as part of the original Clean Air Package, this valve was later used on AMC, Ford, and Pontiac engines. It was commonly known as a spark valve. Its purpose is to advance the spark during deceleration, by sending full manifold vacuum to the vacuum advance unit. At all other times the vacuum advance unit receives ported (above the throttle plates) carburetor vacuum.

Three checks should be made on the valve: the amount of vacuum at the distributor, any valve leaks, and the adjustment. To check the amount of vacuum at the distributor, use a T-fitting and a short length of vacuum hose to connect a vacuum gauge into the distributor vacuum line near the distributor. At idle, with the engine fully warmed up, the vacuum on the gauge should be less than 1 in. Hg. If the gauge shows more than 1 in. Hg, the idle speed is too fast or the valve is leaking. To check for a leak, remove the large manifold vacuum hose on the side of the valve. If the vacuum drops the valve is leaking and must be replaced. If the vacuum stays high, reduce the engine idle speed so that the port in the carburetor is covered.

ADJUSTMENT

To check the valve adjustment, connect the manifold vacuum hose and run the engine at 2000 rpm for 5 seconds. Then release the throttle. The distributor vacuum should go over 16 in. Hg. and stay there for about one second. Within about three seconds after you release the throttle, the distributor vacuum should drop to below 6 in. Hg. If the carburetor is equipped with a dashpot to make the throttle close slowly, the time may be about one second longer. If the time is too long, remove the cover on the valve and turn the screw clockwise to reduce the time. To increase the time, turn the screw counterclockwise. If the valve will not adjust properly, it must be replaced, and the new valve adjusted to specifications.

Spark Delay Valve

This small valve is connected between the carburetor and the distributor vacuum advance, so that the ported (above the throttle plates) vacuum to the distributor must pass through the valve. A restriction in the valve delays the vacuum applied to the vacuum advance unit so that the advance comes in slowly. When there is no vacuum at the carburetor port, as during idle or wide open throttle, a check valve inside the spark delay valve opens and dumps the vacuum so that the vacuum advance unit returns to the no-advance position without any delay.

Ford Products use spark delay valves with one side black and the other colored. The colored side indicates the amount of delay, which can be from one to 28 seconds. The valve should always be installed with the black side toward the source of vacuum, and the colored side toward the distributor.

General Motors spark delay valves are a different shape than Ford, and are marked on both sides with the names of the components they connect to. Usually, they are marked CARB on one side, and either TVS or DIST on the other. Of course, the CARB side must be connected to the carburetor port.

TESTING

Spark delay valves can be tested for correct operation and leaks with a source of vacuum such as a hand vacuum pump or a running engine, and a vacuum gauge. Connect the vacuum gauge to the distributor side of the valve, and the vacuum source to the other side. The gauge should rise slowly until it reads the amount of vacuum available. The time to rise to the maximum reading should be from one to 28 seconds. If the vacuum gauge does not read anything, the valve is plugged. If the vacuum reads instantly, without any delay, the valve is open. In either case, the spark delay valve must be replaced. To test the check valve part of the spark delay valve, remove the vacuum source—the vacuum gauge should drop instantly to zero without any delay. If there is any delay, the spark delay valve is defective and must be replaced.

Distributor Vacuum Vent Valve

Some 1978 and later Ford engines have a distributor vacuum vent valve to prevent fuel from flowing to the distributor through the vacuum line, and to act as a delay valve. Vacuum spark advance is delayed during acceleration by this valve. It also eliminates vacuum advance during heavy acceleration, deceleration, and idle by venting the spark port vacuum to the atmosphere.

The valve can be tested with an external vacuum source, a length of vacuum hose, and a vacuum gauge. Apply 10 in. Hg. of vacuum to the ''VAC'' side of the valve. This is the side with the code number. Connect a 24 in. length of hose to the gauge; connect the other end to the other side of

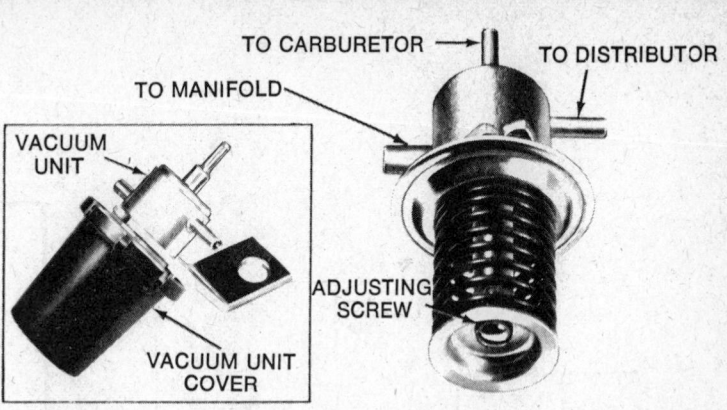

Distributor vacuum control valve, sometimes called a spark valve

the vent valve. Observe the time in seconds for the gauge to register 8 in. Hg., while applying a constant 10 in. Hg. If the code number on the valve is 20, it should take 16–36 seconds. If the code number is 40, it should take 28–67 seconds. Be careful when making this test not to allow oil or dirt to enter the valve. No repairs are possible to the valve. It must be replaced if found defective.

Thermal Check and Delay Valve

This is a spark delay valve with a built-in temperature control. Below 50°F. the valve is open and the distributor receives ported (above the throttle plates) carburetor vacuum without any delay. Above 50°F. the valve closes to a small orifice so that it takes about 40 seconds at part throttle before the distributor gets all of the ported vacuum.

To test the valve, connect a hand vacuum pump to the CARB nozzle and a vacuum gauge to the TVS nozzle. Be sure the valve is at room temperature (68°F.). Work the pump rapidly to create a vacuum of about 20 in. Hg. on the pump gauge. The vacuum gauge should lag behind. When you stop pumping, the pump gauge should drop slightly, and in a few seconds should read the same as the vacuum gauge. If not, the valve is defective and must be replaced. When the valve is cold, it is open, and vacuum should pass freely through so that both gauges register the same with no lag.

Transmission Controlled Spark

AMERICAN MOTORS

Manual transmission models use a solenoid control switch on the transmission and a solenoid vacuum valve to eliminate vacuum advance in the lower gears.

The vacuum supply to the distributor vacuum advance unit is controlled by a solenoid vacuum valve mounted on the top of the engine. This valve receives current whenever the ignition switch is on, and is grounded to complete the circuit through a solenoid control switch on the transmission. The solenoid vacuum valve is normally open, but is held closed in the lower gears by the completed circuit through the transmission switch, which is normally closed. When the transmission is shifted into high gear, the shifter shaft opens the transmission switch, which breaks the circuit and allows the solenoid vacuum valve to open for normal vacuum advance.

Automatic transmission models use a solenoid control switch and a solenoid vacuum valve to eliminate vacuum advance below a certain speed.

The same solenoid vacuum valve is used as on the manual transmission models, but it is connected to a solenoid control switch mounted on top of the engine which is sensitive to governor hydraulic pressure. A hydraulic line from the transmission conducts governor pressure to the switch. In the top center of the switch is a small Allen screw that is used to adjust the switching point to 36 mph.

TESTING

To test the system, connect a vacuum gauge to the distributor vacuum hose, using enough additional hose to come out from under the hood and through the side window into the car, so that the vacuum gauge can be seen while driving. Then drive the car to test the system. On a manual transmission car, you should see vacuum on the gauge in high gear only. On an automatic, you should see vacuum above approximately 34 mph only. Because the distributor runs on ported vacuum, you must have the throttle open a little to get vacuum. Also, you must slow down to approximately 25 mph before the solenoid vacuum valve will close. This means that once you have gone above 34 mph, you will continue

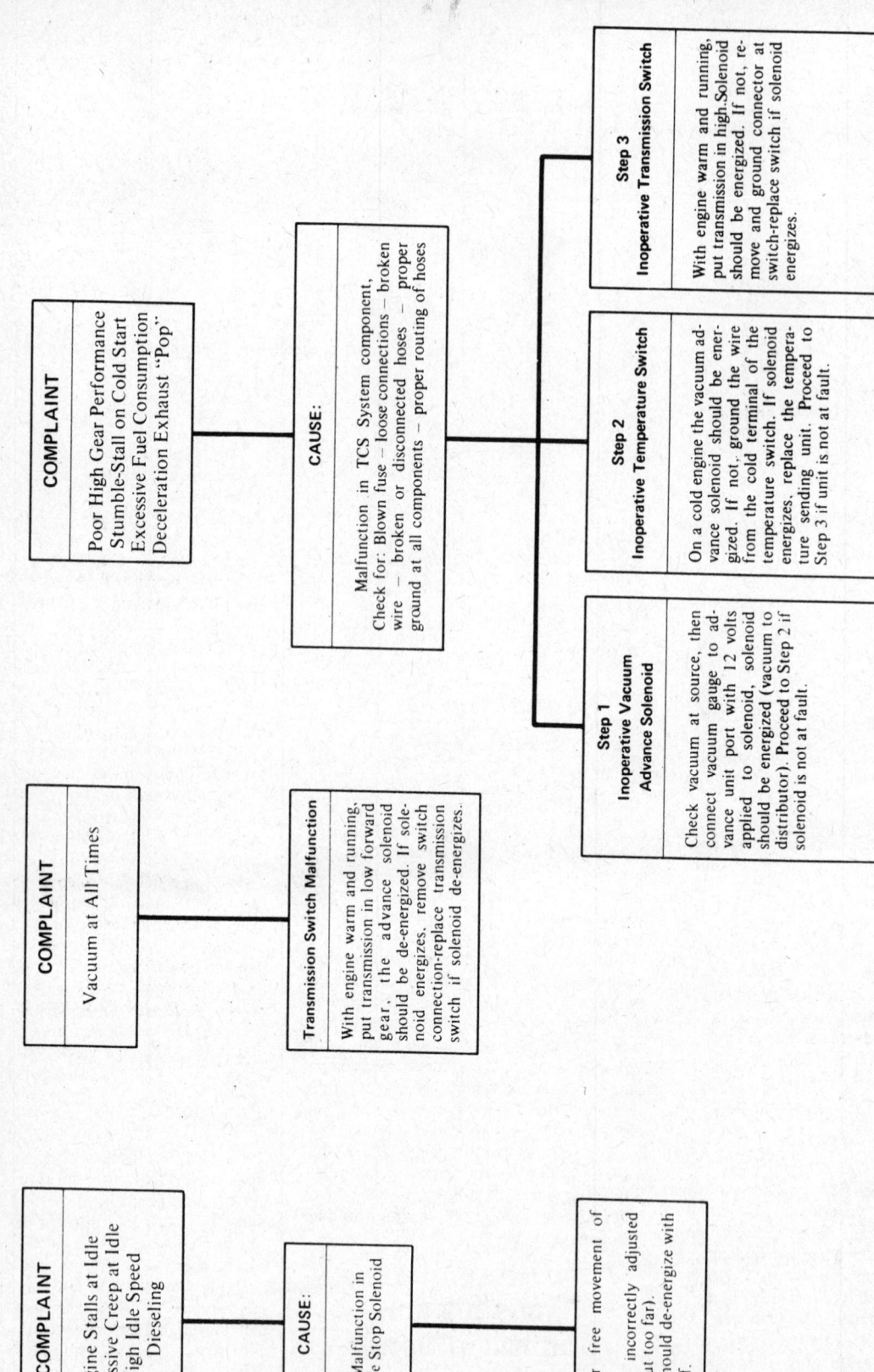

COMPLAINT

Engine Stalls at Idle
Excessive Creep at Idle
High Idle Speed
Dieseling

CAUSE:

Malfunction in
Idle Stop Solenoid

Check for free movement of plunger.
Check for incorrectly adjusted plunger (out too far).
Solenoid should de-energize with ignition off.

COMPLAINT

Vacuum at All Times

Transmission Switch Malfunction

With engine warm and running, put transmission in low forward gear, the advance solenoid should be de-energized. If solenoid energizes, remove switch connection-replace transmission switch if solenoid de-energizes.

COMPLAINT

Poor High Gear Performance
Stumble-Stall on Cold Start
Excessive Fuel Consumption
Deceleration Exhaust "Pop"

CAUSE:

Malfunction in TCS System component, Check for: Blown fuse – loose connections – broken wire – broken or disconnected hoses – proper ground at all components – proper routing of hoses

Step 1
Inoperative Vacuum Advance Solenoid

Check vacuum at source, then connect vacuum gauge to advance unit port with 12 volts applied to solenoid, solenoid should be energized (vacuum to distributor). Proceed to Step 2 if solenoid is not at fault.

Step 2
Inoperative Temperature Switch

On a cold engine the vacuum advance solenoid should be energized. If not, ground the wire from the cold terminal of the temperature switch. If solenoid energizes, replace the temperature sending unit. Proceed to Step 3 if unit is not at fault.

Step 3
Inoperative Transmission Switch

With engine warm and running, put transmission in high. Solenoid should be energized. If not, remove and ground connector at switch-replace switch if solenoid energizes.

TCS System trouble shooting

to see vacuum on the gauge when the throttle is open, as long as the car does not go below the speed that closes the solenoid. If the system does not work correctly, check out the individual units or the hose connections.

Chrysler Orifice Spark Advance Control (OSAC)

GENERAL INFORMATION

This system is used on several years and models (found mainly on the 225 Slant Six). In effect, it is simply a mechanism that delays the application of vacuum to the distributor vacuum advance unit. When the throttle is opened, the carburetor port is exposed to vacuum. This vacuum goes through a hose to the OSAC valve, and then to the distributor vacuum advance. The OSAC valve is sometimes mounted on the firewall, and sometimes on the air cleaner. Inside the OSAC valve is a calibrated orifice that delays the vacuum as much as 27 seconds, depending on the calibration of the valve.

Some OSAC valves have temperature control that senses the temperature inside the air cleaner or inside the plenum chamber behind the firewall, depending on where the valve is mounted. If the valve contains temperature control, it will be wide open below 60°F bypassing the orifice and allowing vacuum advance without any delay. Above 60°F the bypass closes and the delay takes over.

TESTING

To test the valve, just connect a vacuum gauge to the DIST connection on the valve. With the engine idling, you should have no reading on the gauge. If there is a reading,

the engine is idling too fast. With the engine idling, open the throttle to a fast idle, and hold it steady. The vacuum on the gauge will rise slowly until it reaches a maximum reading. If not, there is something wrong with the system, and you should check out the hoses and the carburetor port, or replace the valve if necessary.

Vacuum Reducer Valve

Inserted between the manifold vacuum source and the distributor, this valve reduces the vacuum acting on the advance diaphragm by about 3 in. Hg. This valve is always used on a system that includes a distributor thermal vacuum switch. The vacuum advance unit operates on ported (above the throttle plates) vacuum, except when the engine overheats above 225°F. This opens the thermal vacuum switch and sends full manifold vacuum through the vacuum reducer valve to the advance unit. Thus, the vacuum reducer valve is only operating when the engine is overheated.

To test the valve, connect a vacuum gauge to the TVS nozzle, and a hand vacuum pump to the MAN nozzle. When you pump up 15 in. Hg. vacuum on the hand pump, the vacuum on the separate gauge should be 3–4 in. Hg. lower. Both gauges should hold the vacuum without leakdown. If not, the valve is defective and must be replaced.

Retard Delay Valve

When the throttle is suddenly opened, engine vacuum drops immediately, and this causes the vacuum advance to move quickly from the advance position to the neutral or no-advance position. A retard delay valve is a restriction with a one-way check valve. It allows the vacuum to act on the vacuum advance unit normally, but when the vacuum drops, the delay valve traps the vacuum in the advance unit and lets it out slowly. It takes several seconds for the advance unit to return to the neutral position.

Some cars have the retard delay valve hooked up so that it only operates when the engine is cold. At normal operating temperature the delay is bypassed.

Testing of the delay valve can be done with a hand vacuum pump. Connect the pump to the MAN side of the valve, or the side that connects to the vacuum source on the engine. Connect a separate vacuum gauge to the other side of the valve. When the hand pump is operated, the vacuum will rise on both the pump gauge and the separate gauge equally. When the release is pulled, the pump gauge will drop to zero immediately, but the separate gauge will take several seconds to drop to zero. If it doesn't work that way, the delay valve is defective, and must be replaced.

Cold Start Spark Advance

Ford uses this system on most 1978 and later models. A coolant sensitive vacuum switch (PVS) is combined with a delay valve (Distributor Retard Control Valve) to provide retard delay when the engine coolant is below 128°F. This hose routing is set up so that the vacuum advance unit operates on manifold vacuum through the retard delay valve when the engine is cold, and on ported vacuum through a spark delay valve when the engine is warm. The system also has an overheat PVS that switches the vacuum advance over to manifold vacuum (through the spark delay valve) when the engine coolant gets over 235°F.

Testing the spark delay valve is covered in this section under Spark Delay Valve. Testing for the Distributor Retard Control Valve is the same as for the Retard Delay Valve in this section.

When the 128° PVS is cold, connection No. 2 is blocked and D and 1 are connected. When it is over 128°F., No. 1 is blocked and D and 2 are connected.

Cold Start Spark Hold

Ford uses this system on some models beginning in 1978. The system provides momentary spark advance hold during acceleration when the engine is cold to prevent stumble. When the engine coolant temperature is below 128°F, the CSSH PVS (ported vacuum switch) is closed, so that distributor vacuum must travel through a restrictor.

When the engine is started (cold engine), high vacuum acts on the distributor diaphragm, giving maximum advance. When the engine is then accelerated, the high vacuum already in the diaphragm is slowly bled down through the restrictor, which results in a greater amount of distributor advance when the engine is cold than when warm.

The system can be tested easily. When the engine is cold, vacuum should bleed

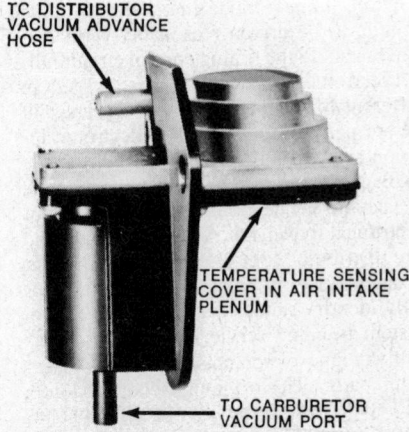

Chrysler orifice spark advance control (OSAC) valve

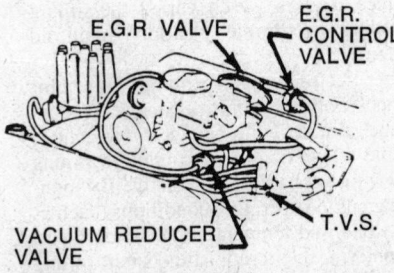

Vacuum reducer valve. The valve has one port on the manifold side and two ports on the DTVS side of the valve; the center port is open to vent at the carburetor air horn, the outboard port to the "MT" port of the DTVS (distributor thermal vacuum switch).

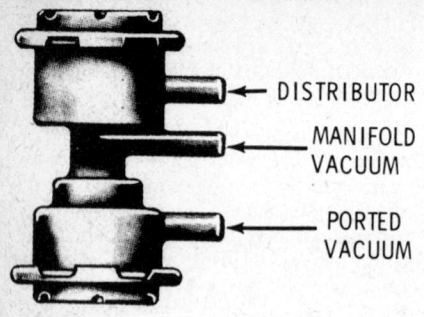

Oldsmobile spark advance vacuum modulator

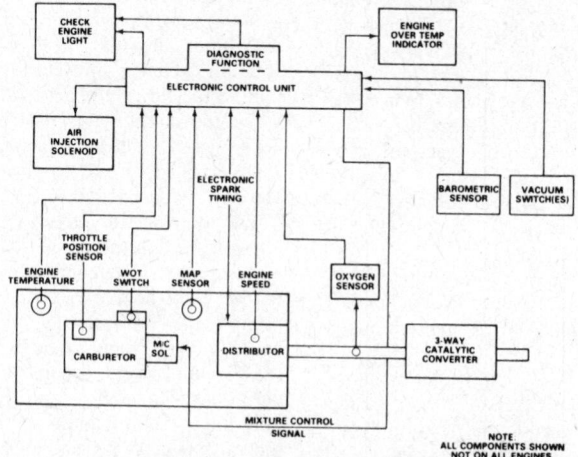

Ford cold start spark advance (CSSA) system

slowly through the restrictor. When the engine is hot, vacuum should flow through the PVS easily; it should not flow through the restrictor at all.

Spark Advance Vacuum Modulator

The three hoses in this double-headed valve are connected to the vacuum advance unit, manifold vacuum, and ported vacuum. The SAVM switches back and forth between manifold vacuum and ported (above the throttle plates) vacuum so that the vacuum advance unit gets either ported vacuum or manifold vacuum reduced to 7 in. Hg. As long as the ported vacuum is over 7 in. Hg. that is what the vacuum advance receives. But if the ported vacuum drops below 7 in. Hg. as at wide open throttle or idle, then the valve switches and provides manifold vacuum up to 7 in. Hg.

To test the SAVM, connect a vacuum gauge to the "distributor" connection, and a hand vacuum pump to the "intake manifold" connection. Slowly pump up the vacuum. The reading on the separate gauge should equal the pump vacuum up to 7 in. Hg. As the pump goes on up to 15 in. Hg. or more, the gauge should stay at 7 in. Hg.

For the second test, switch the hand pump to the connection marked "carburetor" but leave the separate gauge on "distributor," and plug the manifold vacuum connection. Slowly pump up vacuum. The separate gauge should stay at zero until the pump output reaches 7 in. Hg. At that point the separate gauge should show the same vacuum as the pump, and it should continue to show the same vacuum as the pump output rises to 15 in. Hg. and beyond.

For the third test, switch the hoses so the vacuum pump is connected to "distributor" and the separate gauge connected to "carburetor," with the manifold vacuum connection plugged. Pump up several inches of vacuum. The separate gauge should stay at zero. If not, the SAVM is leaking, and must be replaced.

The SAVM must pass all three tests. If it fails any one, it must be replaced.

Typical schematic of electronic control system

Electronic Timing Controls

GENERAL INFORMATION

Before the development of computerized engine control systems, ignition timing advance has been regulated by mechanical weights which centrifugally varied the timing with engine speed (rpm), or vacuum advance devices which varied the timing according to throttle position (manifold vacuum).

The electronic spark timing distributor replaces both the centrifugal and vacuum advance devices with an electronic control module which controls the ignition timing much more reliably and exactly. By monitoring engine operating conditions (such as rpm, load and temperature), the on-board computer is able to adjust the spark timing once each crankshaft revolution to the programmed setting for those instantaneous values and insure that the engine operates with peak efficiency at all times.

Under normal operating conditions, the on-board computer will control the spark advance. However, under certain operating conditions such as cranking or setting base timing, the distributor will operate in a by-pass mode and timing will be maintained at a fixed, preset value programmed into the distributor module to aid engine starting. Some systems are programmed to advance or retard the spark timing according to engine temperature to meet different emission requirements for cold operation and some on-board computers incorporate a "limp home" mode that will allow the vehicle to be driven reasonably short distances should the timing control circuit fail.

Electronic spark timing has existed in different forms for a number of years, but all are part of some form of electronic ignition system. Distributors with electronic spark controls can be identified by their lack of vacuum connections and the absence of centrifugal flyweights. Since some early and late distributor control modules are similar in appearance, it is very important to carefully identify exactly which engine control system is being serviced in order to correctly diagnose problems and order replacement parts. The original General Motors HEI spark control module, for example has a four terminal connector, while the later distributor modules have five or seven terminals. In addition to different calibrations, some spark control systems incorporate different functions and capabilities than earlier models, such as detonation sensors to retard the spark advance during periods of engine operation when detonation occurs. This is particularly critical for turbocharged engines where detonation under boost can cause serious engine damage.

Oldsmobile Electronic Spark Timing (EST) System

The 1978 EST system eliminates the crankshaft sensor and disc used on earlier models. Timing inputs are received from the distributor which contains the HEI rotor, terminal and pole piece, and a special pick-up coil and harness. The distributor has no vacuum or centrifugal advance equipment. Timing in this system is adjusted conventionally by turning the distributor.

The controller receives electronic inputs from the distributor on engine speed and crankshaft position and from a coolant temperature sensor which varies in resistance with temperature. It also receives direct inputs from engine vacuum and atmospheric (underhood) pressure. An instrument panel "Check Ignition" light warns of controller failure. The light will also come on whenever the reference timing connector is grounded, or under low system voltage. Electronic Spark Timing is not used on 1979 and later models.

TIMING ADJUSTMENT—1978 ONLY

1. Ground the reference timing connector (purple wire) with a jumper wire.

2. Connect a timing light and a tachometer, and start the engine. The "Check Ignition" light should be on. If not, check the connector ground.

3. Timing should be 20°/1100 rpm for 49 States cars, and 22°/1100 rpm for California cars. Check underhood emission label to verify timing specifications.

4. To adjust the timing, loosen the distributor clamp bolt and turn it clockwise to advance, counterclockwise to retard. After adjustment, tighten the clamp bolt and recheck the timing. Remove the jumper wire.

Troubleshooting—1978 Only

1. Carefully check for a spark at one of the plugs. If the spark is ok, the trouble is not in the ignition. Check the spark plugs, and fuel system.

— CAUTION —
Dangerously high voltages are produced by all HEI ignition systems. When checking for spark, hold the wire with insulated pliers or a heavy rubber glove.

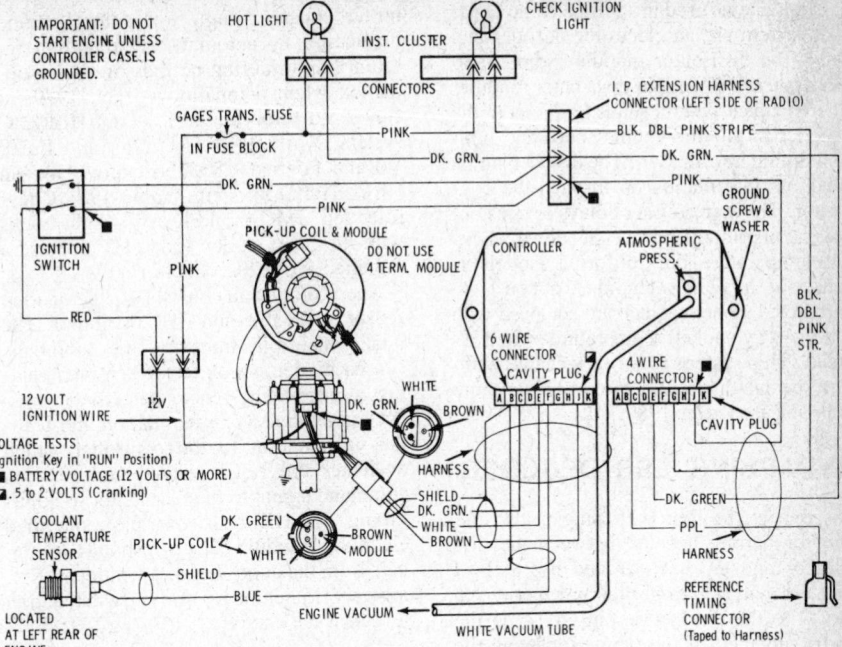

Oldsmobile Electronic Spark Timing schematic, 1978 only G.M. Corp.)

2. Check for battery voltage and cranking voltage at the points indicated in the schematic.

3. If the voltages are ok, check the distributor cap and rotor, ignition coil and module. Also check the controller-to-distributor wiring for continuity.

4. If the Step 2 voltages are not ok, turn the ignition OFF. Ground one lead of an ohmmeter and touch the other probe to each terminal in the distributor half of the distributor-to-controller harness connector. All readings must exceed 1000 ohms.

5. If the resistance readings are not as specified, check the wires into the distributor for shorts. If the module (brown) reading was bad and the wire is ok, test the module. Replace the pick-up coil and harness if the module test indicates normal operation.

6. If the Step 4 readings are correct, connect the ohmmeter across the two pick-up coil terminals (white and dark green). If the reading is not 500–1500 ohms, replace the pick-up coil and harness assembly.

7. If the Step 6 reading is ok, remove the distributor cap. Remove the single wire terminal from the module. Connect an ohmmeter across this wire and the brown module terminal in the distributor-to-controller connector. The reading should be zero ohms. If not, replace the pick-up coil and harness.

8. If the Step 7 reading is normal, use a jumper wire to ground the module wire removed in Step 7. Reconnect the distributor harness connector. Remove the 6 wire connector from the controller. Connect an ohmmeter across terminals E (white) and C (dark green) in the harness connector. Resistance should be 500–1500 ohms. If

not, replace the harness. Connect one ohmmeter lead to a ground, and the other to terminal J (brown); zero resistance should be measured. If not, replace the harness.

9. If all Step 8 readings are ok, check to make sure the controller is grounded. If so, be sure the ignition is off, and replace the controller. Do not turn on the ignition again until the controller is properly grounded, or it will be destroyed.

NOTE: The controllers used on California models have a different advance specification.

Cadillac Electronic Spark Selection (ESS) System

Electronic Spark Selection is used on 1978 Cadillac Sevilles, all 1979 Seville, Eldorado, Limousine, Commercial Chassis and carbureted standard Cadillac models, and all 1980 Seville and Eldorado EFI models, and all other Cadillac models through 1980 except diesels. The system advances or retards ignition timing according to conditions. Timing is retarded during starting to reduce the load on the starter. By delaying ignition until the piston is nearly at TDC, the piston is not forced downward prematurely. Timing is also retarded on California cars when coolant temperature is below 130°F. This reduces catalyst warm-up time. Spark timing is advanced during high engine vacuum/high engine rpm conditions (highway cruise) to increase efficiency and fuel economy.

Components used in addition to the G.M. HEI system are an electronic decoder and a five-pin distributor module. Some 1980 models use a seven-pin distributor module. The HEI pick-up coil sends its signal to the decoder to provide engine speed and ignition timing information. The decoder signal sends its information on through the connector. The signal either delays or does not delay coil primary current shut down. Coolant temperature on California models is sensed at the EGR solenoid except on 1980 carbureted models, which are equipped with a three-way coolant temperature switch instead. This system is not serviceable without special diagnostic tools. This system was not used after 1980.

BYPASSING ESS DECODER

Disconnect the four wire plug in the distributor harness located between the distributor and the decoder and use a short piece of wire to jumper the green wire pin No. 2 to the black wire pin No. 4 on the distributor half of the plug. Bypassing the decoder allows the engine to operate without influence from the ESS system. The engine timing will be six degrees higher than normal engine timing when the decoder is bypassed in this manner.

NOTE: For all ignition timing procedures, see the individual car sections.

GM Electronic Module Retard (EMR) System

This system is used on 1980 Oldsmobile (engine code F, Y and R) and 1981 Chevrolet (engine code K) models. EMR is a spark control system which uses an HEI module with five terminals. The ignition timing is electronically retarded when the HEI module is grounded through the EMR vacuum switch on all except California models. On California engines, the EMR module is controlled by the C4 system electronic control module (ECM). EMR retards the timing about 10 degrees during engine warm-up (coolant below 120 degrees F), but operates like a standard HEI module the rest of the time. On California models, the timing is retarded only when the coolant is between 66-130 degrees F, with the throttle open position below 45% and the engine speed above 400 rpm. When the retard circuit is open, there is no delay and the distributor fires the spark plugs as controlled by engine speed and vacuum. If the EMR-HEI module is removed and/or replaced for any reason, the ignition timing must be checked and set to specifications.

GM Electronic Spark Control (ESC) System

This modified spark control system is used

on turbocharged engines to control engine detonation by automatically retarding ignition timing during periods of engine operation when detonation occurs. 1979–80 Buick V6 turbo engines use an HEI/ESC system, while 1981 Chevrolet and Buick V6 and Pontiac V8 turbo engines use an HEI/EST/ESC system. Some 1981 Chevrolet and GMC C and K series light trucks with the 5.0L engine (code H) also use a modified HEI/ESC system.

The ESC system consists of a detonation sensor, controller and HEI distributor. The intake manifold transmits the vibrations caused by detonation to the sensor mounting location. The sensor detects the presence and intensity of detonation and feeds this information to the controller which evaluates the sensor signal and sends a command signal to the distributor to adjust timing. The HEI distributor has a modified electronic module which responds to signals from the controller and will retard timing up to 15 degrees to minimize detonation levels, if necessary.

NOTE: A slight amount of engine knock is normal on vehicles equipped with this system.

GM Electronic Spark Timing (EST) System

Electronic spark timing is used on engines equipped with Computer Command Control (CCC) systems. The electronic control module (ECM) is used to advance or retard the ignition timing in place of the mechanical and vacuum advance units in the distributor. The system uses a seven pin HEI module which converts the pick-up coil signal into a crankshaft position signal that the ECM modifies to advance or retard the spark timing. Early Computer Control Command engines and 1982 CCC minimum function systems do not use EST. For all testing and diagnosis procedures, or for more information, see the Computer Command Control section.

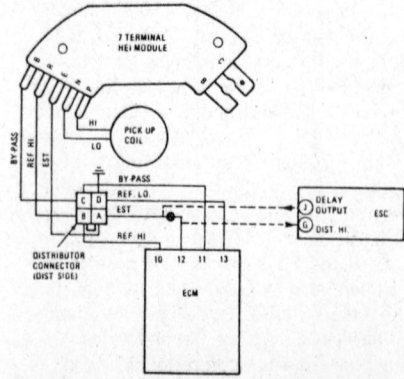

Electronic spark timing (EST) control circuit-7 pin type shown

Ford Electronic Engine Control (EEC)

GENERAL INFORMATION

EEC I System

Ford's EEC I system was introduced in 1978 on the Lincoln Versailles. Designed to precisely control ignition timing, EGR and Thermactor (air pump) flow, the system consists of an Electronic Control Assembly (ECA), seven monitoring sensors, a Dura Spark II ignition module and coil, a special distributor assembly, and an EGR system designed to operate on air pressure.

The ECA is a solid state micro computer, consisting of a processor assembly and a calibration assembly. The processor continuously receives inputs from the seven sensors, which it converts to usable information for the calculating section of the computer. The computer performs ignition timing, Thermactor and EGR flow calculations, processes the information and sends out signals to the ignition module and control solenoids to adjust the timing and flow of the systems accordingly. The calibration assembly contains the memory and programming for the processor. The EEC system makes all adjustments and calculations according to a set of preprogrammed instructions contained within the calibration assembly.

Processor inputs come from sensors monitoring manifold pressure, barometric pressure, engine coolant temperature, inlet air temperature, crankshaft position, throttle position, and EGR valve position.

The manifold absolute pressure sensor determines changes in intake manifold pressure (barometric pressure minus manifold vacuum) which result from changes in engine load and speed, or in atmospheric pressure. Its signal is used by the ECA to set part throttle spark advance and EGR flow rate.

Barometric pressure is monitored by a sensor mounted on the firewall. Measurements taken are converted into a useable (digital) electrical signal. The ECA uses this reference signal to adjust the EGR flow rate according to the altitude at which the engine is operating.

Engine coolant temperature is measured at the rear of the intake manifold by a sensor consisting of a brass housing containing a thermistor (resistance decreases as temperature rises). When the processor applies a reference voltage (about 9 volts) to the sensor, the resistance can be measured by the resulting voltage drop. Resistance is then interpreted as coolant temperature by the ECA. This sensor replaces the ported vacuum switches (PVS) used in conventional systems. EGR flow is cut off by the ECA when a predetermined temperature value is reached. The ECA will also advance initial ignition timing to increase idle speed if the coolant overheats due to prolonged idle. A faster idle speed increases coolant and radiator air flow, thereby lowering the temperature.

Inlet air temperature is measured by a sensor mounted in the air cleaner, which functions in the same way as the coolant sensor. The ECA uses its signal for proper spark advance and Thermactor flow. At high inlet temperatures (above 90°F) the ECA modifies timing advance to prevent spark knock.

The crankshaft is fitted with a four-lobed powdered metal pulse ring, positioned 10° BTDC. Its position is constantly monitored by the crankshaft position sensor. Signals are sent to the ECA describing both the position of the crankshaft at any given moment, and the frequency of the pulses (engine rpm). These signals are used to determine optimum ignition timing advance. If either the sensor or wiring is broken, the ECA will not receive a signal, and thus be unable to send any signal to the ignition module. This will prevent the engine from starting.

NOTE: Check the wiring and connectors for damage or corroded contacts before performing any other diagnosis testing to correct a no-start problem.

The throttle position sensor is a rheostat connected to the throttle plate shaft. Changes in throttle plate angle change the resistance value of the reference voltage supplied by the processor. Signals are interpreted in one of three ways by the ECA:
- Closed throttle (idle or deceleration)
- Part throttle (cruise)
- Full throttle (maximum acceleration)

A position sensor is also built into the EGR valve. The ECA uses its signal to determine EGR valve position. The valve and position sensor are replaced as a unit, should either fail.

Because of the complicated nature of this system, special diagnostic tools are necessary for troubleshooting. Any troubleshooting without these tools must be limited to mechanical checks of connectors and wiring. Aftermarket testers are available (albeit expensive) to aid in troubleshooting.

The distributor is locked in place during engine manufacture; no rotational adjustment is possible for initial ignition timing, since all timing is controlled by the ECA. There are no mechanical advance mechanisms or adjustments under the rotor, thus there is no need to remove it except for replacement.

--- **CAUTION** ---

Before attempting to connect or use ANY test equipment, make sure it is compatible with the EEC System. Consult the manufacturers instructions supplied with the test equipment to avoid accidentally damaging the on-board computer or other EEC components.

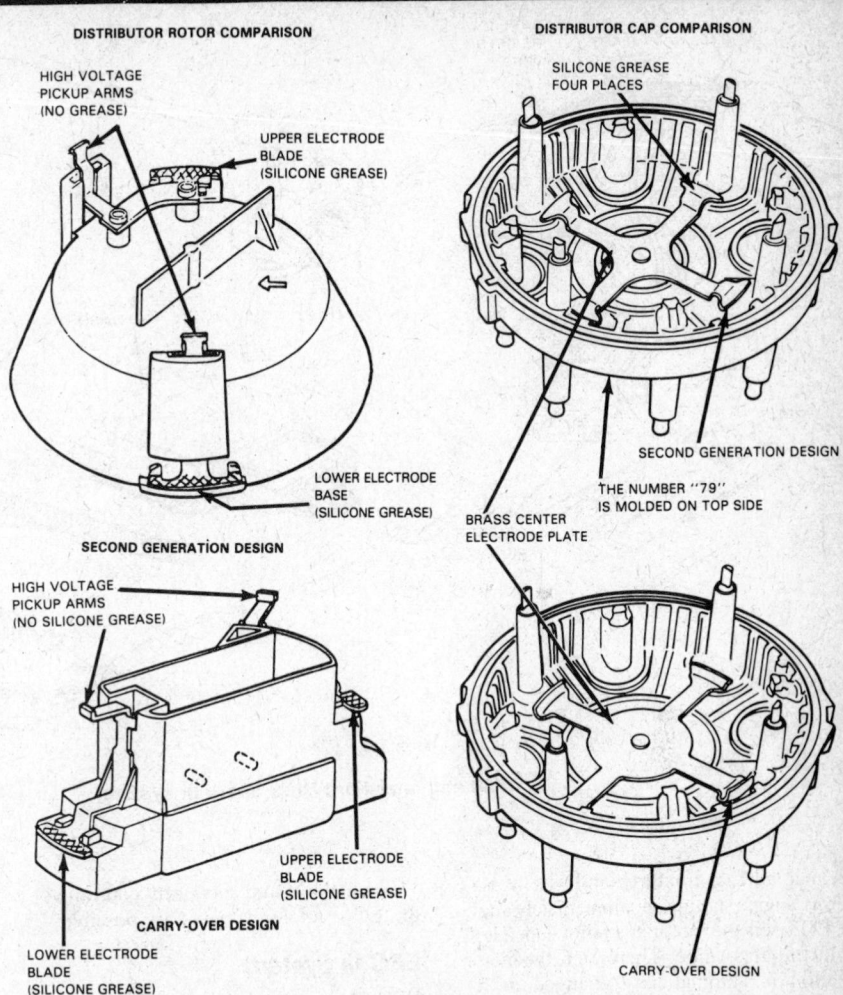

DISTRIBUTOR ROTOR COMPARISON

HIGH VOLTAGE PICKUP ARMS (NO GREASE)

UPPER ELECTRODE BLADE (SILICONE GREASE)

LOWER ELECTRODE BASE (SILICONE GREASE)

SECOND GENERATION DESIGN

HIGH VOLTAGE PICKUP ARMS (NO SILICONE GREASE)

UPPER ELECTRODE BLADE (SILICONE GREASE)

CARRY-OVER DESIGN

LOWER ELECTRODE BLADE (SILICONE GREASE)

DISTRIBUTOR CAP COMPARISON

SILICONE GREASE FOUR PLACES

SECOND GENERATION DESIGN

THE NUMBER "79" IS MOLDED ON TOP SIDE

BRASS CENTER ELECTRODE PLATE

CARRY-OVER DESIGN

Comparison of first and second generation EEC distributor caps

EEC II System

The second generation EEC II system was introduced in 1979 on full size Fords and Mercurys. It is based on the EEC I system used on the Versailles, but some changes have been made to reduce complexity and cost, increase the number of controlled functions, and improve reliability and performance.

In general, the EEC II system operates in the same manner as EEC I. An Electronic Control Assembly (ECA) monitors reports from six sensors, and adjusts the EGR flow, ignition timing, Thermactor (air pump) air flow, and carburetor air/fuel mixture in response to the incoming signals. Although there are only six sensors, seven conditions are monitored: (1) Engine Coolant Temperature, (2) Throttle Position, (3) Crankshaft Position, (4) Exhaust Gas Oxygen, (5) Barometric and Manifold Absolute Pressure, and (6) EGR Valve Position. These sensors function in the same manner as the EEC I sensors, and are described in the EEC I section. Note that inlet air temperature is not monitored in the EEC II system, and that the baromatric and manifold pressure sensors have been combined into one

unit. One more change from the previous system is in the location of the crankshaft sensor: it is mounted on the front of the engine, behind the vibration damper and crankshaft pulley.

NOTE: Due to the similar appearance of the EEC systems, it is important to correctly identify which system is being serviced. Components that look identical may be calibrated very differently. Check all ID and part numbers carefully.

The biggest difference between EEC I and EEC II is that the newer system is capable of continually monitoring and adjusting the carburetor air/fuel ratio. Monitoring is performed by the oxygen sensor installed in the right exhaust manifold; adjustment is made via an electric stepper motor installed on the model 7200 VV carburetor.

The stepper motor has four separate armature windings, which can be sequentially energized by the ECA. As the motor varies the position of the carburetor metering valve, it changes the amount of control vacuum exposed to the fuel bowl. Increased vacuum reduces pressure in the fuel bowl, causing

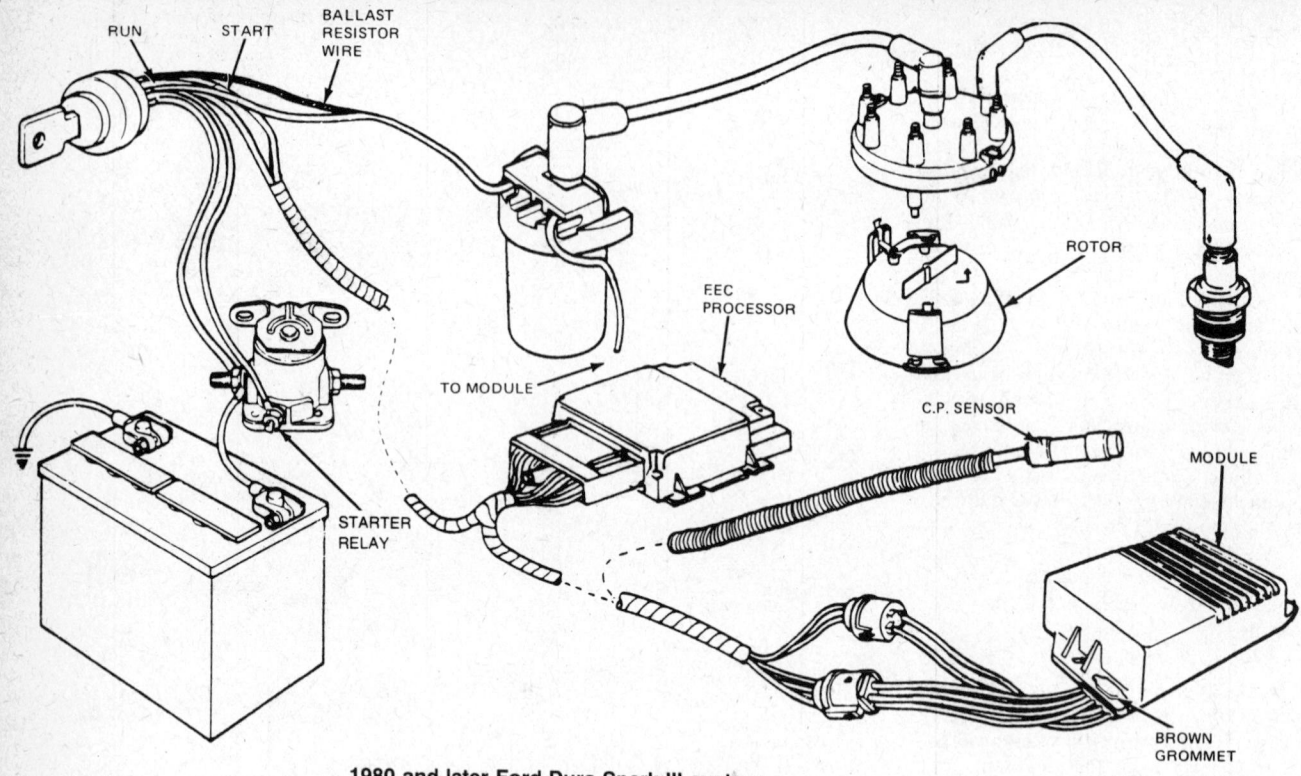

RUN START BALLAST RESISTOR WIRE

TO MODULE

E.E.C. PROCESSOR

ROTOR

C.P. SENSOR

MODULE

STARTER RELAY

BROWN GROMMET

1980 and later Ford Dura Spark III system

a leaner air/fuel mixture, and vise versa. During engine starting and immediately after, the ECA sets the motor at a point dependent on its initial position. Thereafter, the motor position is automatically changed in response to the ECA calculations of the six input signals.

EEC II is also capable of controlling the purging of vapors from the evaporative emission control storage canister. A canister purge solenoid, a combination solenoid and valve, is located in the line between the intake manifold purge fitting and the carbon canister. It controls the flow of vapors from the canister to the intake manifold, opening and closing in response to signals from the ECA.

As is the case with EEC I, diagnosis and repair of the system requires special tools and equipment. Troubleshooting must not be performed unless both an EEC II diagnostic tester and a digital volt/ohmmeter are available. The EEC II tester (Ford part Rotunda T79L-50-EEC II) is also used to test the EEC III system; no modifications are necessary. Instructions for diagnosis and troubleshooting are included with the equipment; thus, no separate procedures are included here.

The distributor is locked in place during engine manufacture; no rotational adjustment is possible for initial ignition timing, since all timing is controlled by the ECA. There are no mechanical advance mechanisms or adjustments under the ignition rotor, and thus there is no need to remove it except for replacement.

Air/fuel mixture is entirely controlled by the ECA; no adjustments are possible.

EEC III System

EEC III was introduced in 1980. It is a third generation system developed entirely from EEC II and used on 1980 and later feedback carburetor and fuel injection equipped models. (Dura Spark II systems are continued in other models). The only real differences between EEC II and III are contained within the Electronic Control Assembly (ECA) and the Dura-Spark ignition module. The EEC III system uses a separate program module which plugs into the main ECA module. This change allows various programming calibrations for specific applications to be made to the program module, while allowing the main ECA module to be standardized. Additionally, EEC III uses a Dura-Spark III ignition module, which contains fewer electronic functions than the Dura-Spark II module; the functions have been incorporated into the main ECA module.

NOTE: Dura-Spark II and III modules are NOT interchangeable.

Rotor

REMOVAL & INSTALLATION

First Generation Design

A special rotor alignment tool is essential

for this job. Don't remove the rotor unless the alignment tool is available to install it.

1. Remove the distributor cap by releasing the two spring clips. If any spark plug wires must be removed, number each wire with tape and note that their order on the cap is not the same as the engine firing order. The inner ring of numbers on the cap is for the Versailles. It reads 1-2-7-5-6-8-4-3. The engine firing order is 1-5-4-2-6-3-7-8. The outer ring of numbers is for use on the Ford and Mercury 351 W V8. It reads 1-2-4-3-6-8-7-5. The 351 W firing order is 1-3-7-2-6-5-4-8.

NOTE: Do not remove any of the silicone grease from the distributor cap electrodes. It turns brown with age but this does not affect its performance.

2. Rotate the crankshaft to align the distributor rotor upper blade, which is slotted, with the slot in the distributor adapter, which is an integral part of the distributor. Use the rotor alignment tool to ensure that the rotor is properly positioned before diassembly.

3. If the rotor or adapter is damaged so that alignment with the tool is impossible, position the crankshaft with the No. 1 piston at compression TDC. This is done by aligning the zero mark on the crankshaft damper with the front cover timing pointer. Make sure No. 1 cylinder is on the compression stroke.

4. Remove the rotor alignment tool. Use a magnetic screwdriver to remove the two screws securing the rotor. Remove the rotor.

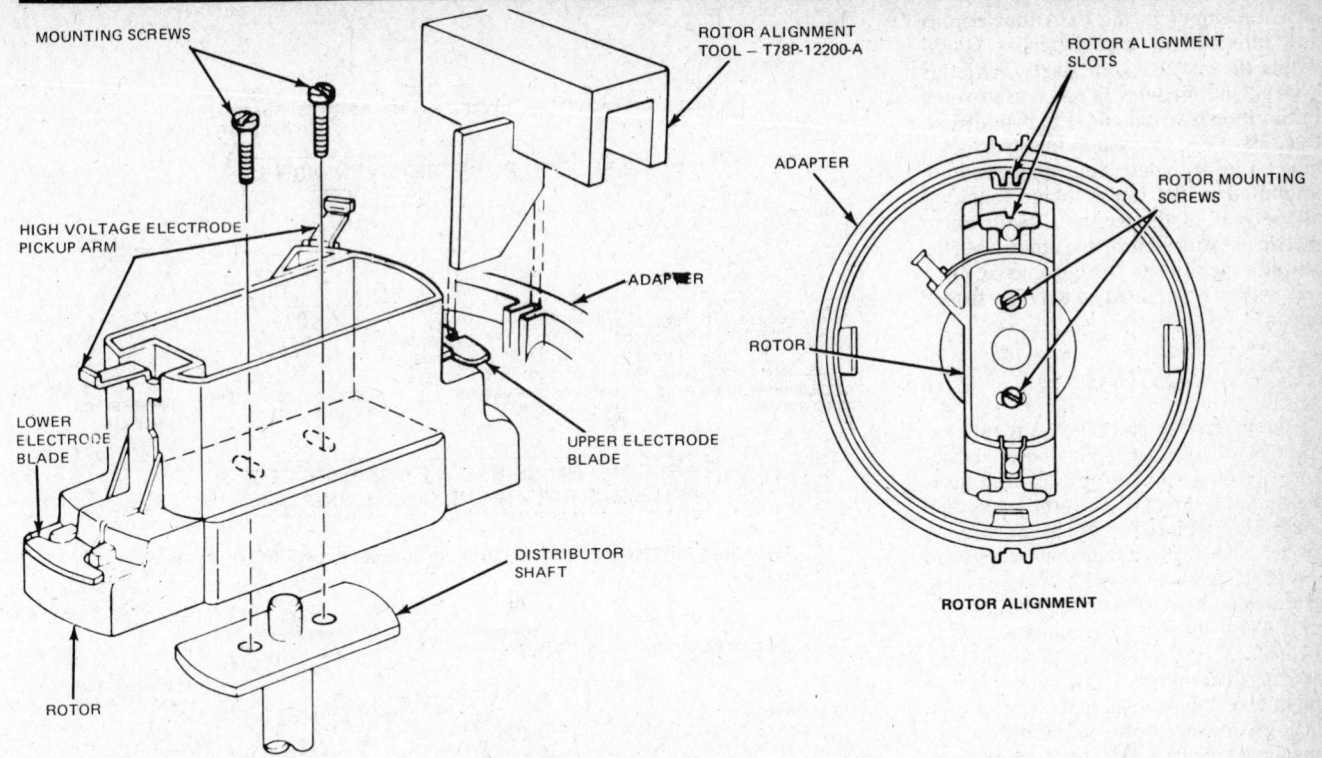

EEC rotor alignment through mid-1979

———— CAUTION ————
Do not rotate the crankshaft with the rotor removed.

5. Before installing the new rotor, the lower electrode blades must be coated with silicone grease (Ford part no. D7AZ-19A331-A, Dow 111, G.E. G-627 or equivalent). The coating should be 1/32 in. thick on all sides outboard of the plastic.

6. Place the new rotor on the distributor shaft with the upper blade slot pointing to the slot in the distributor adapter. Install the two retaining screws, but do not tighten them.

7. Position the rotor alignment tool in place. Be sure its blade engages both the rotor and the adapter notches.

8. Tighten the rotor retaining screws. Remove the alignment tool and reinstall the distributor cap. If any wires were removed from the cap, their ends should be coated with the special grease mentioned in Step 5 before installation.

Second Generation Design

A second generation EEC distributor was introduced midway through the 1979 model year. It is used on most new EEC applications, although the first generation design is still used in some cases. The two distributors are interchangeable as complete assemblies, but parts are *not* interchangeable between them.

The new design allows removal and installation of the ignition rotor without the

need for realignment upon installation. However, if the distributor adapter is replaced, it must be aligned. To replace the rotor:

1. Remove the distributor cap by levering off the two clips.

2. Pull straight up on the rotor to remove.

3. To install, align the arrow on the rotor with the large keyway in the distributor sleeve. Press the rotor down onto the sleeve until the retention spring snaps into the slot. Be certain the rotor is properly seated, or it will break.

4. Coat the lower electrode blades approximately 1/32 in. thick on all sides outboard of the plastic with silicone grease. (Ford part no. D7AZ-19A331-A, Dow III, G.E. G-627 or equivalent).

5. Install the distributor cap.

EEC IV System

EEC IV is used on the 1.6L and 2.3L engines in the 1983 and later Escort/Lynx and EXP/LN7. All 1984 engines use the EEC IV system.

The heart of the EEC-IV system is a microprocessor called an electronic control assembly (ECA). The ECA receives data from a number of sensors and other electronic components (switches, relays, etc.). Based on information received and information programmed in the ECA's memory, it generates output signals to control various relays, solenoids and other actuators. The ECA in the EEC-IV system has calibration mod-

ules located inside the assembly that contain calibration specifications for optimizing emissions, fuel economy and drive ability. The calibration module is called a PROM.

A potentiometer senses the position of the vane airflow meter in the engine's air induction system and generates a voltage signal that varies with the amount of air drawn into the engine. A sensor in the area of the vane airflow meter measures the temperature of the incoming air and transmits a corresponding electrical signal. Another temperature sensor inserted in the engine coolant tells if the engine is cold or warmed up. And a switch that senses throttle plate position produces electrical signals that tell the control unit when the throttle is closed or wide open.

A special probe (oxygen sensor) in the exhaust manifold measures the amount of oxygen in the exhaust gas, which is an indication of combustion efficiency, and sends a signal to the control unit. The sixth signal, Crankshaft position information, is transmitted by a sensor intergral with the new-design distributor.

The EEC IV microcomputer circuit process the input signals and produces output control signals to the fuel injectors to regulate fuel discharged to the injectors. It also adjusts ignition spark timing to provide the best balance between driveability and economy.

NOTE: The 2.3L system is similar to the 1.6L, with the addition of a "keep

alive" memory in the ECA that retains any intermittent trouble codes stored within the last 20 engine starts. With this system, the memory is not erased when the ignition is switched OFF. In addition, the 2.3L EEC IV system incorporates a knock sensor to detect engine detonation (mounted in the lower intake manifold at the rear of the engine), and a barometric pressure sensor to compensate for altitude variations. The barometric pressure sensor is mounted on the right fender apron.

EEC IV TESTING

As in any service procedure, a routine inspection of the system for loose connections, broken wires or obvious damage is the best way to start. Perform the system Quick Test outlined below before going any further. Check all vacuum connections and secondary ignition wiring before assuming that the problem lies with the EEC IV system. A self-diagnosis capability is built in to the EEC IV system to aid in troubleshooting. The primary tool necessary to read the trouble codes stored in the system is an analog voltmeter or special Self Test Automatic Readout (STAR) tester (Motorcraft No. 007-0M004, or equivalent). While the self-test is not conclusive by itself, when activated it checks the EEC IV system by testing its memory integrity and processing capability.

The self-test also verifies that all sensors and actuators are connected and working properly.

When a service code is displayed on an analog voltmeter, each code number is represented by pulses or sweeps of the meter needle. A code 3, for example, will be read as three needle pulses followed by a six-second delay. If a two digit code is stored, there will be a two second delay between the pulses for each digit of the number. Code 23, for example, will be displayed as two needle pulses, a two second pause, then three more pulses followed by a four second pause. All testing is complete when the codes have been repeated once. The pulse format is ½ second ON-time for each digit, 2 seconds OFF-time between digits, 4 seconds OFF-time between codes and either 6 seconds (1.6L) or 10 seconds (2.3L) OFF-time before and after the half-second separator pulse.

NOTE: If using the STAR tester, or equivalent, consult the manufacturers instructions included with the unit for correct hookup and trouble code interpretation.

In addition to the service codes, two other types of coded information are outputted during the self-test; engine identification and fast codes. Engine ID codes are one digit numbers equal to one-half the number of engine cylinders (e.g. 4 cylinder is code 2, 8 cylinder is code 4, etc.). Fast codes are

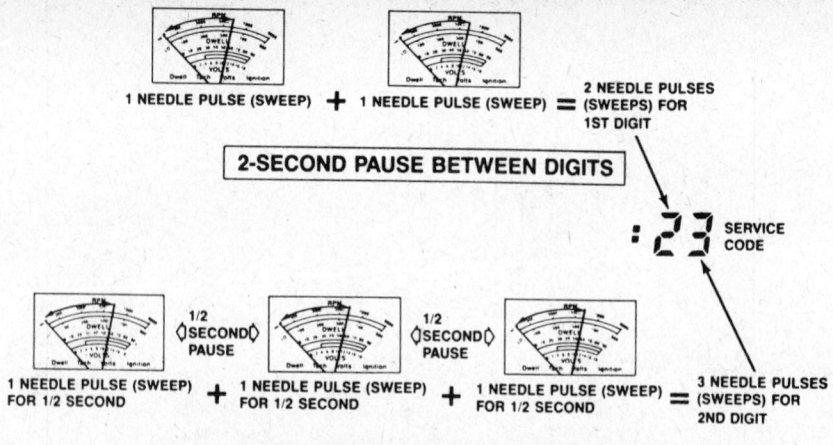

Reading service codes with analog voltmeter on EEC IV system

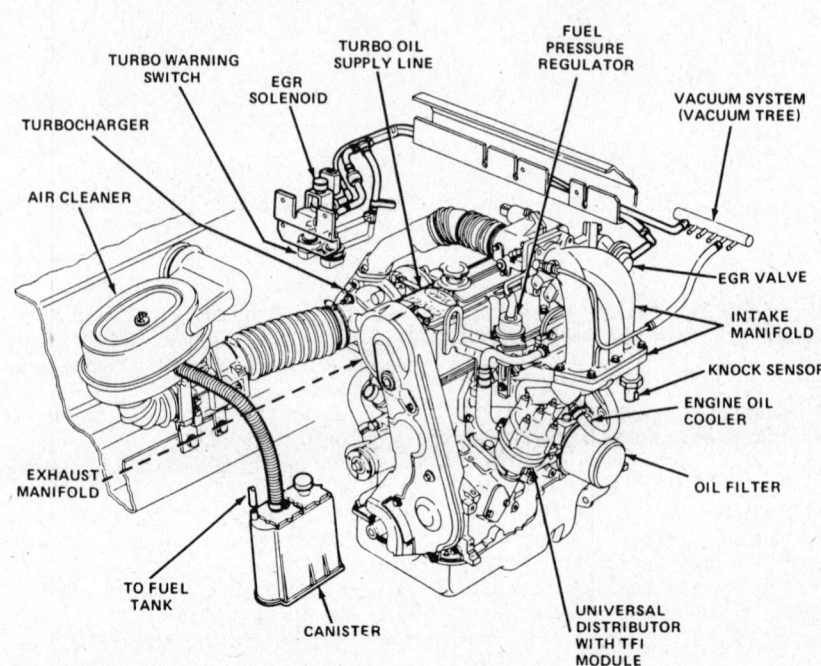

Ford EEC IV system component locations on 2.3L turbocharged engine

simply the service codes transmitted at 100 times the normal rate in a short burst of information. Some meters may detect these codes and register a slight meter deflection just before the trouble codes are flashed. Both the ID and fast codes serve no purpose in the field and this meter deflection should be ignored.

Activating Self-Test Mode on EEC IV

Turn the ignition key OFF. On the 2.3L engine, connect a jumper wire from the self-test input (STI) to pin 2 (signal return) on the self-test connector. On the 1.6L engine, connect a jumper wire from pin 5 self-test input to pin 2 (signal return) on the self-test connector.

Set the analog voltmeter on a DC voltage range to read from 0–15 volts, then connect the voltmeter from the battery positive (+) terminal to pin 4 self-test output in the self-test connector. Turn the ignition switch ON (engine off) and read the trouble codes on the meter needle as previously described. A code 11 means that the EEC IV system is operating properly and no faults are detected by the computer.

NOTE: This test will only detect "hard" failures that are present when the self-test is activated. For intermittent problems, remove the voltmeter clip from the self-test trigger terminal and wiggle the wiring harness. With the voltmeter still attached to the self-test output, watch for a needle deflection that signals an inter-

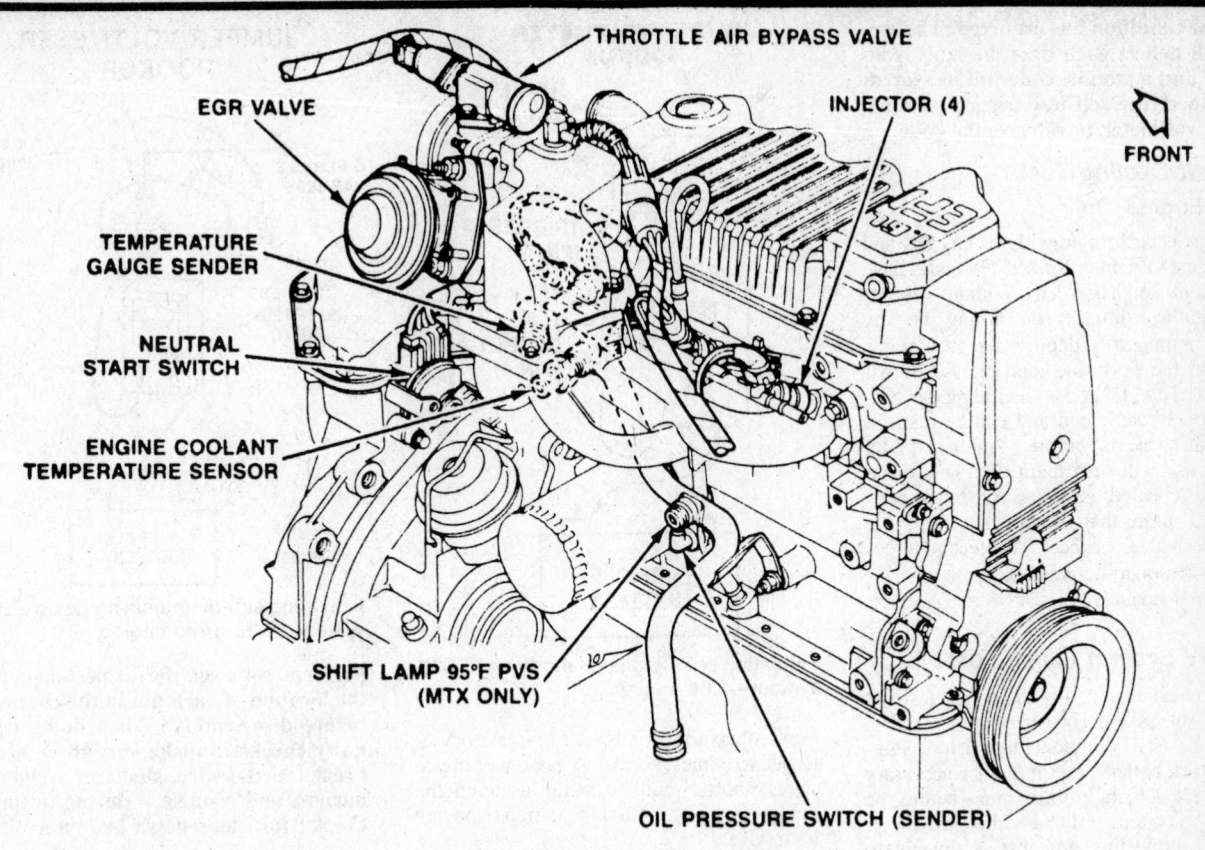

THROTTLE AIR BYPASS VALVE

EGR VALVE

INJECTOR (4)

FRONT

TEMPERATURE
GAUGE SENDER

NEUTRAL
START SWITCH

ENGINE COOLANT
TEMPERATURE SENSOR

SHIFT LAMP 95°F PVS
(MTX ONLY)

OIL PRESSURE SWITCH (SENDER)

Ford EEC IV system component locations on 1.6L engine—rear view

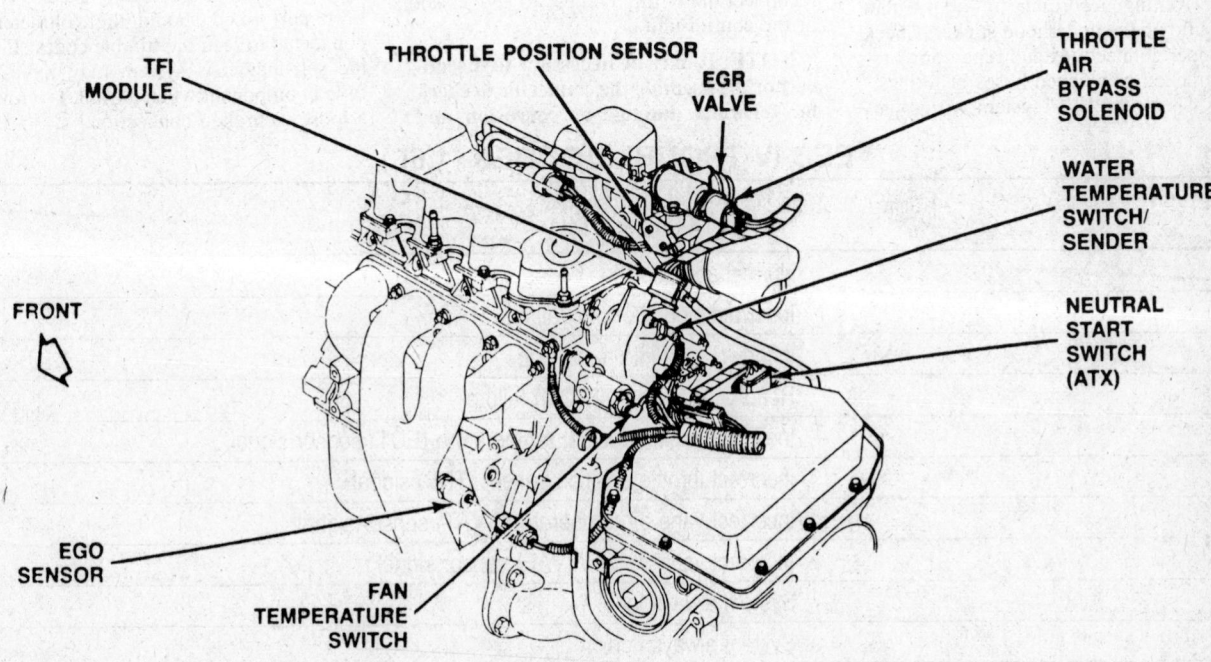

TFI
MODULE

THROTTLE POSITION SENSOR

EGR
VALVE

THROTTLE
AIR
BYPASS
SOLENOID

WATER
TEMPERATURE
SWITCH/
SENDER

NEUTRAL
START
SWITCH
(ATX)

FRONT

EGO
SENSOR

FAN
TEMPERATURE
SWITCH

Ford EEC IV system component locations on 1.6L engine—front view mittent condition has occurred. The meter will deflect each time the fault is induced and a trouble code will be stored. Reconnect the self-test trigger terminal to the voltmeter to retrieve the code.

Output Cycling Test

2.3L Engine Only

This test is performed with the key ON and the engine OFF after the self-test codes have been sent and recorded. Without disconnecting the voltmeter or turning the key OFF, momentarily depress the accelerator pedal to the floor and then release it. All auxiliary EEC IV codes (including the self-test) will be activated and can be read on the voltmeter as before. Another pedal depression will turn them off. This cycle may be repeated as necessary, but if activated for more than 10 minutes, the cycle will automatically cancel. This feature forces the processor to activate these outputs for additional diagnosis.

EEC IV System Quick Test

Correct test results for the quick test are dependent on the correct operation of related non-EEC components, such as ignition wires, battery, etc. It may be necessary to correct defects in these areas before the EEC IV system will pass the quick test. Before connecting any test equipment to check the EEC system, make the following checks:

1. Check the air cleaner and intake ducts for leaks or restrictions. Replace the air cleaner if excessive amounts of dust or dirt are found.

2. Check all engine vacuum hoses for proper routing according to the vacuum schematic on the underhood sticker. Check for proper connections and repair any broken, cracked or pinched hoses or fittings.

3. Check the EEC system wiring harness connectors for tight fit, loose or detached terminals, corrosion, broken or frayed wires, short circuits to metal in the engine compartment or melted insulation exposing bare wire.

4. Check the control module, sensors and actuators for obvious physical damage.

5. Turn off all electrical loads when testing and make sure the doors are closed whenever readings are made. DO NOT disconnect any electrical connector with the key ON. Turn the key off to disconnect or reconnect the wiring harness to any sensor or the control unit.

NOTE: It may be necessary to disconnect or disassemble the connector to check for terminal damage or corrosion and

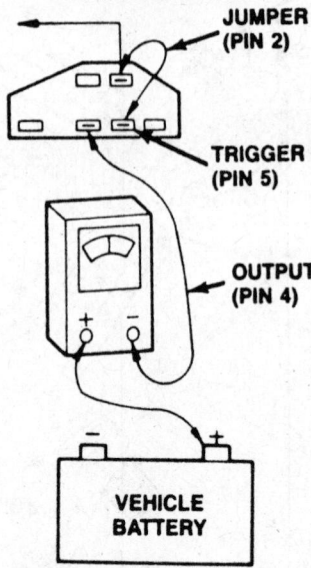

Activating self-diagnosis mode on EEC IV system—1.6L engine

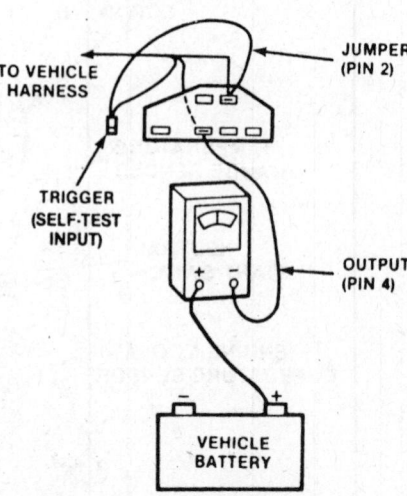

Activating self-diagnosis mode on EEC IV system—2.3L turbo engine

perform some of the inspections. Note the location of each pin in the connector before disassembly. When doing continuity checks to make sure there are no breaks in the wire, shake or wiggle the harness and connector during testing to check for looseness or intermittent contact.

6. Make sure the engine coolant and oil are at the proper level.

7. Check for leaks around the exhaust manifold, oxygen sensor and vacuum hoses connections with the engine idling at normal operating temperature.

8. Only after all the above checks have been performed should the voltmeter be connected to read the trouble codes. If not, the self-diagnosis system may indicate a failed component when all that is wrong is a loose or broken connection.

EEC IV TROUBLE CODES (1.6L)

Code	Diagnosis
11	Normal operation (no codes stored)
12	Incorrect high idle rpm value
13	Incorrect curb idle rpm value
15	Read Only Memory (ROM) failure
21	Incorrect engine coolant temperature (ECT) sensor signal
23	Incorrect throttle position sensor (TPS) signal
24	Incorrect vane air temperature (VAT) sensor signal
26	Incorrect vane air flow (VAF) sensor signal
41	System always lean
42	System always rich
67	Neutral/Drive switch in Neutral

NOTE: Incorrect rpm values could be high or low and an incorrect sensor signal could be caused by a defective sensor or a wiring harness problem. Use the trouble codes to isolate the circuit, then continue diagnosis to determine the exact cause of the problem

EEC IV TROUBLE CODES (2.3L)

Code	Diagnosis
11	Normal operation (no codes stored)
12	Incorrect high idle rpm value
13	Incorrect curb idle rpm value
14	Erratic Profile Ignition Pickup (PIP) signal
15	Read Only Memory (ROM) failure
21	Incorrect engine coolant temperature (ECT) sensor signal
22	Incorrect barometric pressure (BAP) sensor signal
23	Incorrect throttle position sensor (TPS) signal
24	Incorrect vane air temperature (VAT) sensor signal
26	Incorrect vane air flow (VAF) sensor signal
41	System always lean
42	System always rich
51	Engine coolant temperature (ECT) sensor signal too high
53	Throttle position sensor (TPS) signal too high
54	Vane air temperature (VAT) sensor signal too high
56	Vane air flow (VAF) sensor signal too high
61	Engine coolant temperature (ECT) signal too low
63	Throttle position sensor (TPS) signal too low
64	Vane air temperature (VAT) signal too low
66	Vane air flow (VAF) sensor signal too low
67	A/C compressor clutch ON
73	No vane air temperature (VAT) signal change when engine speed is increased
76	No vane air flow (VAF) signal change when engine speed is increased
77	Engine speed not increased to check VAT and VAF signal change

NOTE: Incorrect sensor signals could be out of range or not being received by the control unit. Perform wiring harness and sensor checks to determine the cause, or check for additional codes to indicate high or low reading

CARBURETOR CONTROLS

NOTE: For all carburetor test and adjustments, see the "Carburetor Unit Repair Section."

Electric Choke

GENERAL INFORMATION

A non-electric choke uses a "stove" on the exhaust manifold or a well on the intake manifold to provide heat. When the well is used, the choke coil is surrounded by the warm intake manifold, heated by the exhaust crossover passage. When the stove is used, the choke housing is connected to engine vacuum, and a long tube pulls the heated air from the stove into the choke housing to heat up the choke coil and cause the choke to open as the engine warms up. When an electric choke is used, it can be in addition to all the above, or it can be the only source of choke heat, depending on the design.

The electric choke has a small heater next to the choke coil. This heater receives its current from different sources, depending on the car maker.

Ford and AMC Models

Ford Motor Company and American Motors electric chokes are powered from the alternator "center tap," which produces about 7 volts. As the alternator is only putting out voltage when the engine is running, the electric choke is automatically shut off when the engine is off. It is important that the choke is connected only to the special "center tap" provided on the alternator. The description "center tap" refers to the construction of the alternator wiring, and not to the location of the connection.

Inside the Ford choke cover is a thermostatic switch that turns on the heating element at approximately 80°F. Above that, the element stays on as long as the engine is running. The 80°F. figure was selected because the engine is warm enough at that temperature to keep running without the choke. When the heater comes on, the choke opens very quickly. When the engine is shut off and cools down, the choke switch may stay on to as low at 65°F. at the choke housing. On a warm restart, where the choke switch was still on, the heating element would heat up the choke and open it shortly after the engine started.

It isn't necessary to check the exact switching temperature of the choke housing. Just be sure that the switch is open when the engine is cold, and closed when it is warm. The switch can be tested with a penlight-powdered test light, between the choke terminal and ground, with the wire from the alternator disconnected.

Some Ford 4-cylinder engines use a similar choke without the bimetal switch. The heating element is on whenever the engine is running.

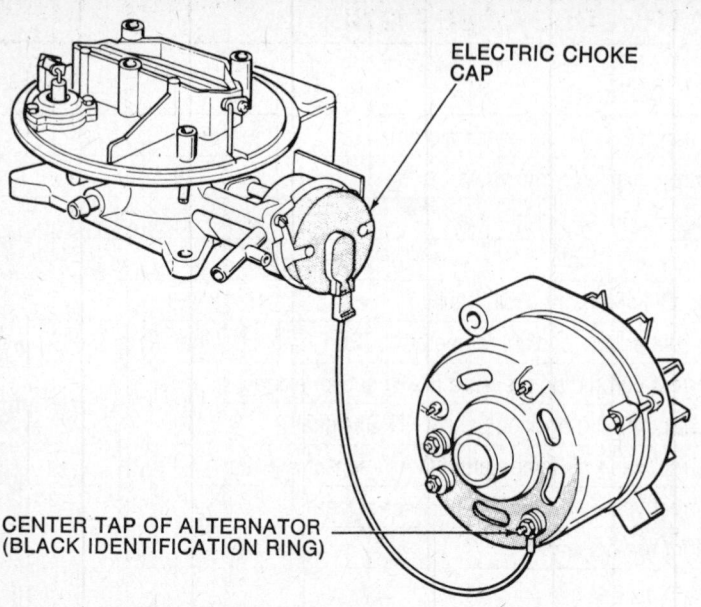

ELECTRIC CHOKE CAP

CENTER TAP OF ALTERNATOR (BLACK IDENTIFICATION RING)

Ford electric choke system

Chrysler Models

Many Chrysler Corporation vehicles with an electric choke use a well type choke, which receives heat both from the intake manifold and the electric choke heater. A separate choke control unit is mounted on top of the intake manifold and connected to the heater with a wire. This wire disconnects at the choke control unit only, not at the heater.

Choke control units may be single and double stage. The double stage is recognized by the external resistor alongside the unit. The single stage unit turns on the choke heat at approximately 60°F. and off at 80°F. The double stage unit keeps the heater on below 60°F. but the current runs through the resistor. At approximately 60°F. the resistor is taken out of the circuit and the heater gets full current. At 80°F. control unit turns the heater off.

Testing can be done by connecting a non-powered test light in series with the choke terminal (lead wire) and a ground, to find out if the heater is on or off. The ignition switch must be on. If the light glows, you know the control unit is on. On two-stage units, the light will glow dimly when the resistor is in the circuit, and brightly when the resistor is out. The current to the control unit comes from the ignition switch, and there is no fuse.

Chrysler Omni, Horizon, Aries, Reliant and 1982 and later LeBaron and Dodge 400 models with the 1.7L or 2.2L engines have electric chokes which require constant electricity to keep the choke open when the engine is running. Electrical current is supplied from the oil pressure sending unit. A switch inside the choke is calibrated for summer or winter operation and automatically adjusts choke opening times.

The choke heater can be tested by disconnecting its lead and connecting a jumper wire directly from the positive battery terminal to the heater. The choke valve should open within five minutes.

All models equipped with the Mitsubishi 2.6L engine have thermo-wax pellet type automatic choke systems. The choke valve is operated by a sealed wax element which senses engine coolant temperature.

GM Models

Cadillac, Chevrolet, Chevette and T1000 use an electric choke that is mounted on the carburetor. The choke has a dual ele-

ment behind the coil spring. Whenever the engine is running, the choke heater is in operation. Below 50–70°F. a bimetal snap disc in the choke cover turns off the large section of the heating element so that only the small section gives off heat. Above 50–70°F. the disc switches on the large heating element for faster choke opening.

Current to the choke is controlled by a three-terminal oil pressure switch. One of the terminals is a ground for the red oil pressure light on the instrument panel. The other two terminals are a switch in series between the ignition switch and the choke heater. Oil pressure operates the switch so that the choke gets current only when the engine is running. The circuit is fused through the backup light or transmission fuse in the fuse block.

NOTE: Failure of the choke heater circuit will cause the oil pressure light to go on.

Delayed Choke Pulldown

1978 and later Ford-Motorcraft 4300 series 4-bbl. carburetors use a delayed pulldown system. When the engine starts, a vacuum piston inside the choke housing opens the choke partway. About 6 to 18 seconds later, the delayed pulldown located on the carburetor in front of the choke housing pulls the choke open further, and also pulls the fast idle cam to a lower step. This gives more precise choking, and slows the engine down to prevent damage to the catalytic converter from overly long fast idle.

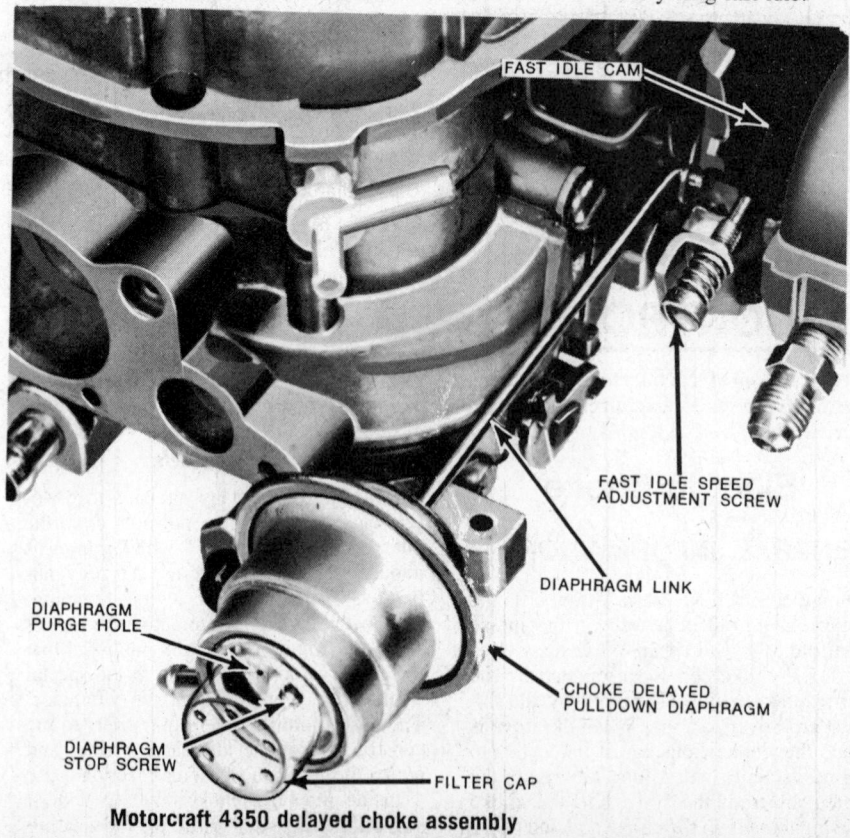

FAST IDLE CAM

FAST IDLE SPEED ADJUSTMENT SCREW

DIAPHRAGM LINK

CHOKE DELAYED PULLDOWN DIAPHRAGM

FILTER CAP

DIAPHRAGM PURGE HOLE

DIAPHRAGM STOP SCREW

Motorcraft 4350 delayed choke assembly

Auxiliary vacuum break unit used with temperature controlled choke vacuum break system on six cylinder engines.

Auxiliary vacuum break unit used with temperature controlled choke vacuum break system on four cylinder one-barrel engines

The pulldown diaphragm housing has an internal restriction in the vacuum passage. It receives full manifold vacuum when the engine starts, but the restriction delays the stroke of the pull rod, giving the engine a few seconds to warm up before it opens the choke and slows down the fast idle.

The action of the pulldown diaphragm can be checked on a running engine by disconnecting the hose, waiting until the pull rod extends, and then connecting the hose again. The pull rod should take several seconds to stroke back into the housing. If not, the unit should be replaced.

Temperature Controlled Choke Vacuum Break

GENERAL INFORMATION

1978 and later General Motors (Buick, Chevrolet, Oldsmobile, Pontiac) passenger cars use this system on 6-cylinder inline and 140 cubic inch OHC 4-cylinder engines. The system uses an extra vacuum break diaphragm or electric solenoid to open the choke as the engine warms up. There are three different carburetors used on these two engines, and each carburetor uses a slightly different system.

6-Cylinder Engines

The normal vacuum break unit is on the choke coil side of the carburetor. It opens the choke partway as soon as the engine starts. The temperature controlled vacuum break is on the throttle lever side of the carburetor. It opens the choke to an almost wide open position whenever the engine is running, and the coolant temperature is above 80°F. Manifold vacuum comes through a hose from a thermal vacuum switch on the right front of the cylinder head. Above the switch is a manifold vacuum fitting screwed

into the intake manifold part of the head. (This system is used only on the engine with the integral head and manifold.) Below 80°F coolant temperature, the thermal vacuum switch is closed. Above 80°F it is open, and supplies vacuum to the vacuum break unit at all times during engine operation.

Testing of the vacuum break unit can be done by applying vacuum to see that it moves through a full stroke, and does not leak. The thermal vacuum switch can be tested by blowing through it to see that it is open above approximately 80°F.

4-Cylinder OHC 140 Cubic Inch Engines

The 140 4-cylinder engine has either a 1-bbl. or 2-bbl. carburetor. The 1-bbl. carburetor uses a normal vacuum break unit on the choke-coil side of the carburetor, and a temperature controlled vacuum break on the throttle lever side. It opens the choke to a nearly wide open position when the coolant temperature is above 93°F on automatic transmission, or 120°F on manual transmission.

The manifold vacuum supply to the break unit is controlled by a vacuum solenoid, operated by a relay and temperature switch. Current goes to the relay whenever the ignition switch is on. The ground circuit from the relay grounds at the same sending unit that turns on the red HOT light. The sending unit has two terminals, one for the relay and another for the HOT light. The relay also connects to the vacuum solenoid, supplying current to operate the solenoid.

The relay points are normally closed. When the temperature switch is cold, it closes and provides a ground for the relay. This completed circuit causes the relay points to open, blocking any current flow to the vacuum solenoid, which stays closed so no vacuum can pass.

When the temperature switch warms up, it opens, breaking the ground circuit from the relay, and allowing the spring inside

the relay to close the points. With the points closed, current flows to the vacuum solenoid, which then opens and allows the vacuum to operate the vacuum break unit and open the choke.

TESTING

Testing the 1-bbl. system is done by removing the air cleaner, opening the throttle, and closing the choke by hand. Then start the engine and the choke should open immediately on a warm engine. You can also check it by disconnecting and reconnecting the hose on a running engine, to see if the vacuum break unit makes a full stroke. Each unit can also be tested to see if it gets vacuum or electric current according to the description above.

The 2-bbl. carburetor uses a system that is much simpler because no vacuum is used. We continue to call it a vacuum break, but actually the whole system is electric. An electric solenoid is mounted on the carburetor near the cam cover. The solenoid receives current through a relay on the firewall, controlled by the engine temperature switch. When the temperature switch is cold its points are closed, completing the ground circuit and energizing the relay, which opens the relay points. This blocks current to the solenoid.

As the coolant temperature goes over 93°F on automatic transmission, or 120°F on manual, the temperature switch opens, de-energizing the relay and allowing the relay points to close. Current then flows up the solenoid, which opens the choke.

Testing the electric 2-bbl. system should be done by closing the choke and then starting the engine to see if the solenoid opens it. The solenoid itself can be tested with a hot wire from the battery. When energized, the solenoid stem should stay in when you push it in, and you should not be able to pull it out with your fingers. When de-energized, you should be able to move the stem in and out.

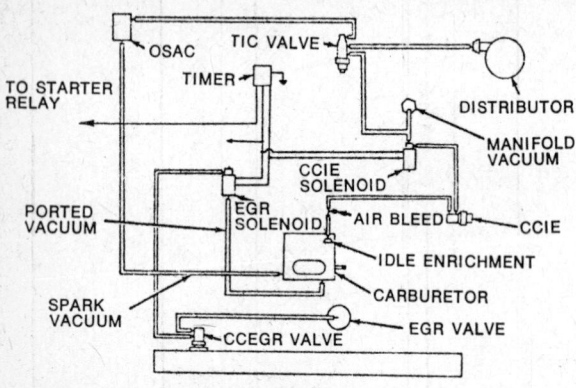

Idle enrichment system (Federal)

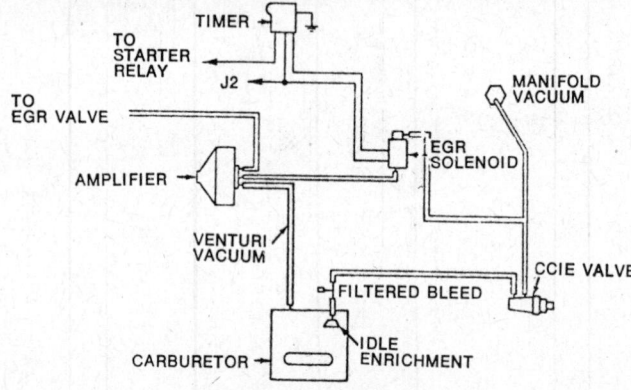

Idle enrichment system (California)

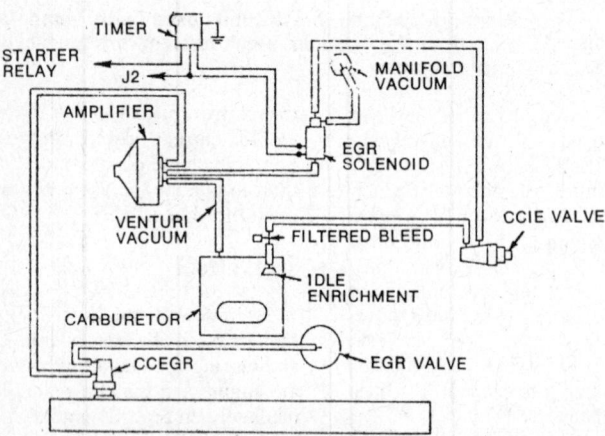

Idle enrichment system (Federal)

Idle Enrichment System

GENERAL INFORMATION

Some Chrysler Corporation automatic transmission cars, 1978 and later, have an idle enrichment valve built into the carburetor. The valve opens or closes a passageway that admits extra air to the idle system. When the valve is open, the idle mixture is lean from the excess air. When the valve is closed, the idle mixture is rich, because the air is shut off. The valve is turned on and off by manifold vacuum, connected by a hose.

All cars have a coolant temperature control valve called a Coolant Control Idle Enrichment valve. This is a mechanical valve, mounted on a coolant passage and connected by hoses between the manifold vacuum source and the idle enrichment valve. When the engine is cold, the valve is open, allowing vacuum to operate the idle enrichment valve and richen the idle. When the engine warms up, the valve closes, and stops the idle enrichment.

Some engines also have a vacuum solenoid connected to the same timer that provides EGR delay. On most engines the so-lenoid has three hose connections, one to manifold vacuum, one to the idle enrichment valve, and the third to the EGR amplifier. When the solenoid is not energized, it allows vacuum to go to the EGR valve, but blocks the vacuum to the idle enrichment valve. When energized, the vacuum to the EGR amplifier is blocked, but the vacuum passes to the idle enrichment valve. The timer energizes the solenoid during the first 35 or 60 seconds, depending on the car model. This means that when the engine is cold, the idle is enriched during the first 35 or 60 seconds of engine operation.

One engine, the 49-State 318 V8 with catalytic converter, uses two separate so-lenoids, one for EGR and one for Idle enrichment, but the working of the system is the same.

Next to the idle enrichment valve, inserted in the hose, is a small air bleed. It lets a constant small supply of air into the hose to keep it purged of fuel vapor.

TESTING

Testing the system can be done on a cold engine by disconnecting the hose at the carburetor and connecting a vacuum gauge to the hose. Start the engine and note the length of time that vacuum appears on the gauge. At the end of the timed period, the gauge should drop to zero. Allow the engine to warm up to operating temperature and make the test again. This time you should not see any vacuum on the gauge, because the CCIE valve should be closed. If your car does not have a timer, you will see vacuum for several minutes after a cold start, until the engine warms up.

To check the effect of the idle enrichment, use a hand vacuum pump on the idle enrichment valve on the carburetor. With vacuum applied, the valve will be closed, richening the idle, and changing the idle speed. Release the vacuum and the speed should go back where it was. If there is no speed change, either the valve is not working, or a carburetor passage is blocked with dirt. The valve should also hold vacuum without leaking down.

Altitude Compensation System

GENERAL INFORMATION

Air at high altitude is much thinner than at sea level, so engines run rich. To keep the mixture correct, and prevent rich running that causes high emissions, many 1978 and later 4-bbl. carburetors have an altitude compensation system.

The heart of an altitude compensation system is a sealed bellows chamber, called an aneroid. The aneroid is sealed at sea level, and expands at high altitude. This expansion is used to open or close a passageway and lean out the mixture. The Carter Thermo-Quad, used on some Chrysler Corporation products, and the Ford-Motorcraft 4300 series 4-bbl. use an aneroid that opens an air passage to lean the mixture. The Thermo-Quad bleeds this air into the main metering system, while the Ford 4300s bleed the air into the main venturi.

The General Motors Rochester 4-bbl. uses an aneroid that works with the fuel metering adjustable part throttle feature. The adjustable part throttle fuel feed is adjusted at the factory to give the right fuel mixture at sea level. When the aneroid expands at high altitude, it shuts off the adjustable fuel passage to lean the mixture.

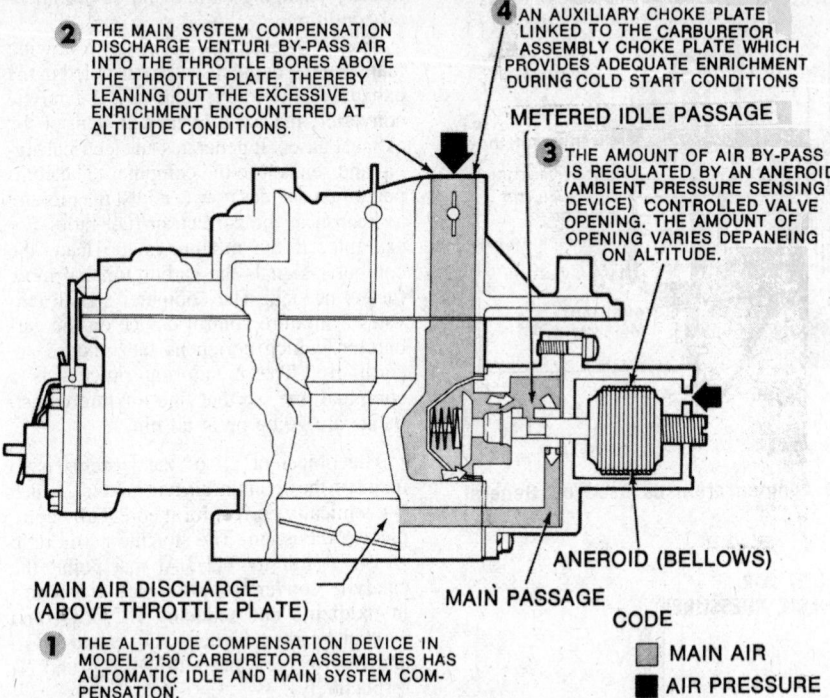

② THE MAIN SYSTEM COMPENSATION DISCHARGE VENTURI BY-PASS AIR INTO THE THROTTLE BORES ABOVE THE THROTTLE PLATE, THEREBY LEANING OUT THE EXCESSIVE ENRICHMENT ENCOUNTERED AT ALTITUDE CONDITIONS.

④ AN AUXILIARY CHOKE PLATE LINKED TO THE CARBURETOR ASSEMBLY CHOKE PLATE WHICH PROVIDES ADEQUATE ENRICHMENT DURING COLD START CONDITIONS

METERED IDLE PASSAGE

③ THE AMOUNT OF AIR BY-PASS IS REGULATED BY AN ANEROID (AMBIENT PRESSURE SENSING DEVICE) CONTROLLED VALVE OPENING. THE AMOUNT OF OPENING VARIES DEPANEING ON ALTITUDE.

MAIN AIR DISCHARGE (ABOVE THROTTLE PLATE)

MAIN PASSAGE

ANEROID (BELLOWS)

CODE
- ▨ MAIN AIR
- ■ AIR PRESSURE

① THE ALTITUDE COMPENSATION DEVICE IN MODEL 2150 CARBURETOR ASSEMBLIES HAS AUTOMATIC IDLE AND MAIN SYSTEM COMPENSATION.

Motorcraft two-barrel and four-barrel altitude compensation device.

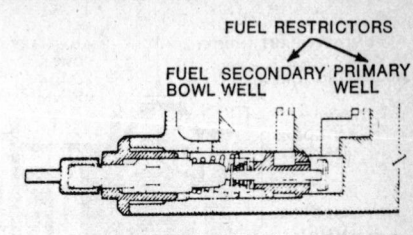

FUEL RESTRICTORS

FUEL SECONDARY PRIMARY
BOWL WELL WELL

VALVE OPEN (SEA LEVEL POSITION)

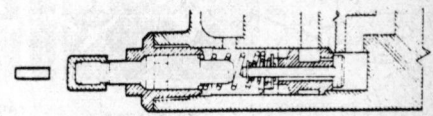

VALVE CLOSED (ALTITUDE POSITION)
Motorcraft 2300 four cylinder manual altitude control

NOTE: Since the aneroid device is sealed and sensitive to barometric pressure alone, no testing is possible. If the vehicle is found to run excessively rich in high altitude areas, replace the aneroid unit and recheck HC and CO tailpipe emissions with a suitable analyzer.

Choke Air Modulator

GENERAL INFORMATION

Some 1978 and later Buick-built engines (sometimes used in other GM division cars) have a choke coil that is mounted on the carburetor. The coil housing receives heated air from a stove on the exhaust crossover passage in the intake manifold. Fresh air enters the stove through a hose attached to the clean side of the air cleaner.

To slow down the heating of the coil when the engine is cold, the hose at the air cleaner is connected to a small thermostatic valve. This valve restricts the flow of air when the temperature inside the air cleaner is below normal operating temperature. Once the air cleaner gets warmed up, the modulator opens and there is normal air flow through the choke hose.

Use a hand vacuum pump or air pressure to check the air flow through the modulator with the engine warm. If air flows freely, allow the engine to cool completely or cool the modulator with dry ice, then check for restricted air flow. Air volume should be restricted, not stopped. Replace the modulator valve if no change is noted during test.

Idle Speedup Solenoid

Many 1978 and later cars use an idle speed-up solenoid on air conditioned models. The solenoid looks just like the old anti-dieseling or idle stop solenoid. The difference is that the idle speedup solenoid is connected to the air conditioning system and only comes on when the air conditioning is turned on. Its only purpose is to speed up the idle so the engine won't die.

On carburetors equipped with the solenoid, curb idle speed adjustments are made with the throttle screw, not the solenoid screw. There is a specification for the engine speed with the solenoid energized, but it is higher than the normal curb idle. See the Carburetor Unit Repair Section for adjustments.

Automatic Idle Speed Diaphragm

1978 and later Chrysler Corporation 6-cylinder engines with a 1-bbl. carburetor use a special diaphragm or dashpot on some models. The stem of the dashpot touches the throttle lever. The dashpot is connected to manifold vacuum, which compresses a spring inside the dashpot housing. If the load on the engine is changed by turning the air conditioner on or shifting into DRIVE, the vacuum will drop, and the dashpot spring will open the throttle to bring the speed back up to what it was. Theoretically, whatever load is put on the engine will be balanced by the dashpot, and the idle speed will remain constant. The dashpot has a threaded housing and locknut.

To adjust the dashpot, start the engine in Neutral and position the throttle lever so the actuating tab on the lever is touching the stem of the dashpot, but not depressing

HOT AIR CHOKE SYSTEM

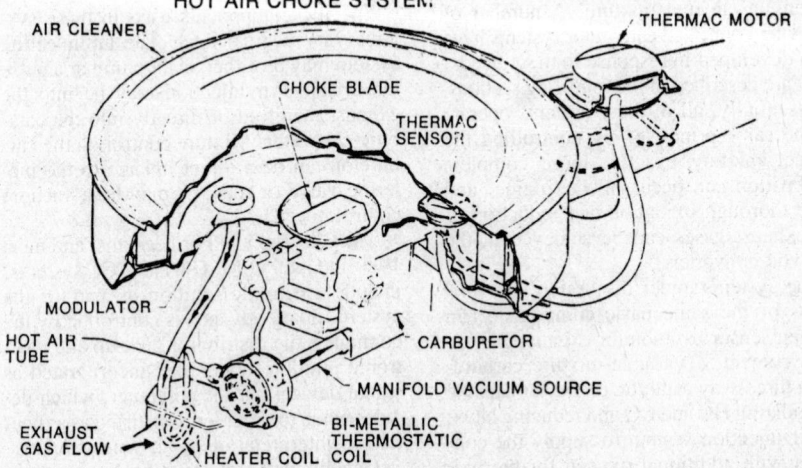

AIR CLEANER

CHOKE BLADE

THERMAC SENSOR

THERMAC MOTOR

MODULATOR

HOT AIR TUBE

CARBURETOR

MANIFOLD VACUUM SOURCE

EXHAUST GAS FLOW

HEATER COIL

BI-METALLIC THERMOSTATIC COIL

G.M. choke hot air modulator system

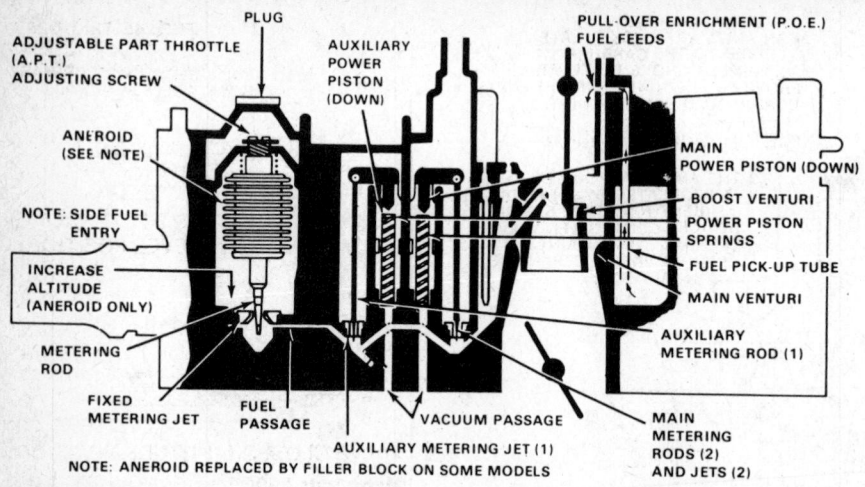

Rochester four barrel carburetor with altitude compensation as used on General Motors cars.

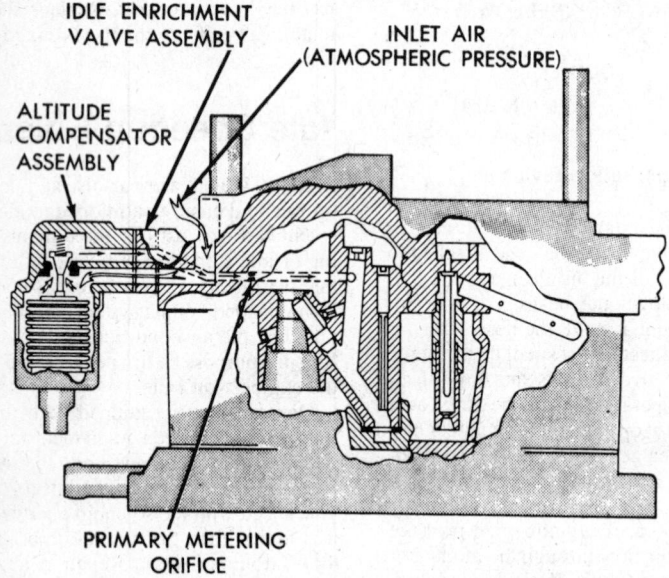

Carter Thermo-Quad four-barrel carburetor with altitude compensation, as used on Chrysler Corporation cars.

it. Wait 30 seconds to allow the engine to settle down, but keep the throttle so it is just touching the stem. In that position, the engine speed should be 2500 rpm (through 1979), or 2300 rpm (1980 and later). If not, move the throttle so the speed is as specified, and adjust the dashpot by loosening the locknut and turning the housing so the stem just touches the throttle lever.

COMPUTER CONTROLLED CARBURETORS

General Information

The need for better fuel economy combined with increasingly strict emission control regulations dictate a more exact control of the engine air/fuel mixture. A number of computer controlled carburetor systems have been developed in response to these needs. They are described in the following sections.

Essentially, all of these systems operate on the same principle. By controlling the air/fuel mixture exactly, more complete combustion can occur in the engine, and more thorough oxidation and reduction of the exhaust gases can be achieved in the catalytic converter.

The systems under discussion use variations of the same basic components: an oxygen sensor, to monitor exhaust gas oxygen content; a variable-mixture carburetor; a three-way catalytic converter capable of oxidizing HC and CO and reducing NOx; an air injection system to supply the converter with additional oxygen for the oxidation reaction; and a computer to monitor the process and adjust it according to con-

tinually changing engine and environmental conditions.

These systems operate in the following manner: The oxygen sensor, installed in the exhaust manifold upstream of the catalytic converter, reads the oxygen content of the exhaust gases. It generates an electrical signal and sends it to the computer. The computer then decides how to adjust the mixture to keep it at the correct air/fuel ratio. For example, if the mixture is too lean, the computer signals the carburetor that more fuel is needed. The computer signal activates a mixture control device on the carburetor, which enrichens the mixture accordingly. The monitoring process is a continual one, so that fine mixture adjustments are going on at all times.

The object of all of the systems is to maintain the optimum air/fuel mixture, which is chemically correct for theoretically complete combustion. The stoichiometric ratio is 14.7:1 (air to fuel). At that point, the catalytic converter's efficiency is greatest in oxidizing and reducing HC, CO, and NOx into carbon dioxide (CO_2), water H_2O), and free oxygen and nitrogen (O_2 and N_2 respectively).

Most of the systems have two modes of operation: closed loop and loop. Closed loop operation occurs when the converter and oxygen sensor have warmed to efficient levels. All sensors become interdependent in this mode: the oxygen sensor sends signals to the computer, which signals the carburetor, which adjusts the mixture, which changes the oxygen sensor's readings, which go back to the computer, and so on. A continual and ongoing feedback of information and adjustment is achieved. Open loop operation generally takes place when the engine is still cold. In this mode, the computer simply provides a predetermined and invariable signal; the signal may affect only the carburetor air/fuel ratio, although in most installations it also provides a fixed spark advance signal to the electronic ignition module as well. In open loop operation, no signals are accepted by the computer.

Specific components used in these systems vary a great deal. The air injection system may be either an air pump or a pulse air design. Air injection may be into the exhaust manifold or directly into the catalytic converter. Mixture control on the carburetor can be a direct linkage to the metering valve or rods, or may be a vacuum control.

The Chrysler and Ford designs, and most 1980 and later G.M. C-4 and CCC systems, include electronic ignition as part of the system. Spark advance is controlled by the computer; the distributor pick-up and electronic ignition module are incorporated as signal devices for the computer, which decides when to order ignition firing as a function of interpretation of all sensor inputs.

One thing all of the systems have in common is a certain amount of nonadjustability. Mixture is always nonadjustable in these installations. If a mixture screw is provided on the carburetor, it is concealed under a staked-in plug, or locked in place. In many cases, ignition timing is also non-adjustable; idle speed, choke setting and fast idle rpm may also be either fixed during manufacture or under the control of the computer, and therefore not adjustable.

Unfortunately, most of the systems do not respond favorably to conventional troubleshooting techniques. Problems with these devices almost invariably must be diagnosed with sophisticated and expensive test equipment.

Ford Feedback Carburetor (FBC) Engine Control System

GENERAL INFORMATION

This system, first used on 1978 Pinto and Bobcat models sold in California with the 2.3 liter four cylinder engine, actually consists of three subsystems: a two part catalytic converter, a Thermactor (air pump) system, and an electronically controlled feedback carburetor.

The converter consists of two catalytic converters in one shell. The front section is designed to control all three engine emissions (NOx, HC, and CO). The rear section acts only on HC and CO. There is a space between the two sections which serves as a mixing chamber. Air is pumped into this area by the Thermactor system to assist in the oxidation of HC and CO.

The Thermactor system is the same as that found on conventional Ford models, with the addition of a second air control valve and a second exhaust check valve.

An electronically controlled feedback carburetor (Motorcraft model 6500 or 7200/2700) is used to precisely calibrate fuel metering. The air/fuel ratio is externally controlled and variable. It is adjusted according to conditions by the Electronic Control Unit (ECU), 1978–79, or the Microprocessor Control Unit (MCU), 1980 and later. There are two modes of operation: closed loop control and open loop control. Under closed

loop operation, each component in the chain is sensitive to the signals sent by the other components. This means that the carburetor mixture is being controlled by the vacuum regulator/solenoid, which is adjusted by the control unit, which is receiving signals from the oxygen sensor in the exhaust manifold, which is measuring a mixture determined by the carburetor, and so on. In this case, the feedback loop is complete. Under open loop operation, the carburetor air/fuel mixture is controlled directly by the control unit according to a predetermined setting. Open loop operation takes place when the coolant temperature is below 125°F, or when the throttle is closed, during idle or deceleration.

The control unit receives signals from the exhaust gas oxygen sensor, the throttle angle vacuum switch, and the cold temperature vacuum switch, analyzes them, and sends out commands to the vacuum solenoid/regulator, which in turn adjusts, by means of vacuum, the height of the carburetor fuel metering rod. In this way, the fuel mixture is adjusted according to conditions. The control unit also varies the transition time from rich to lean (and vice versa) according to engine rpm. The rpm

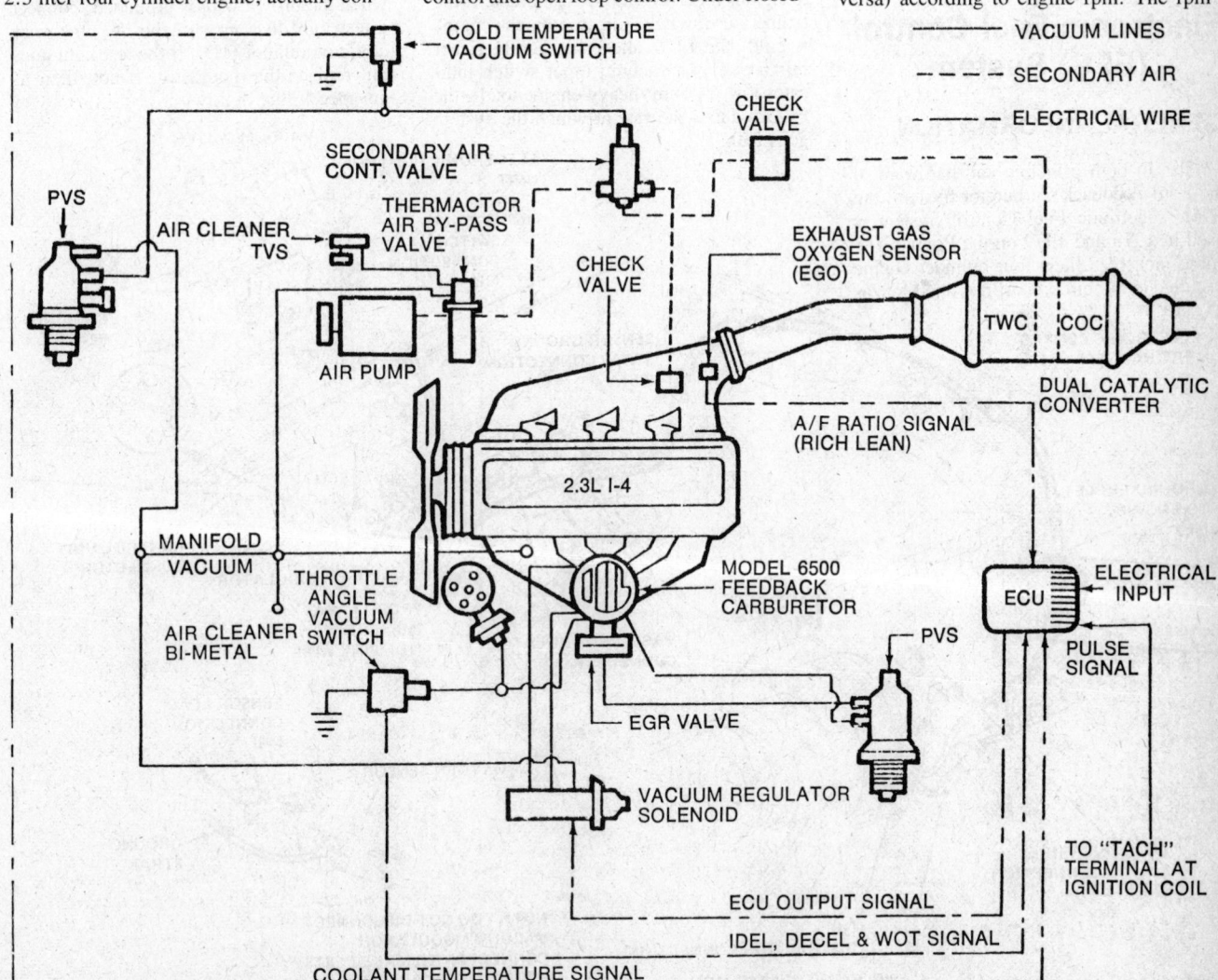

Ford Feedback Carburetor Electronic Engine Control schematic

signal is taken from the coil connector TACH terminal.

There are two differences between the ECU, used in 1978 and 1979, and the MCU, used in 1980 and later models. The MCU is programmable, enabling it to be used with many different engine calibrations. Additionally, the MCU controls the Thermactor solenoid valves, thus directing the air flow to the exhaust manifold, the catalytic converter mixing chamber, or the atmosphere when air flow is not needed or wanted.

Because of the complicated nature of the Ford system, special diagnostic tools are necessary for troubleshooting and repair. No attempt at testing or repair should be made unless both the Feedback Control Tester (Ford part no. T78L-50-FBC-1) and a digital volt/ohmmeter (Ford part no. T78L-50-DVOM) are available. A tachometer, vacuum gauge, hand vacuum pump and gauge, and a special throttle rpm tool are also required for diagnosis. No troubleshooting procedures will be given here, since they are supplied with the testing equipment.

General Motors Electronic Fuel Control (EFC) System

GENERAL INFORMATION

Similar in both principle and hardware to the Ford Feedback Carburetor System, the G.M. Electronic Fuel Control System is used in 1978 and 1979 on the Pontiac 151 cubic inch (2.5 liter) four cylinder engine installed in Sunbirds, Starfires, and Monzas

sold in California. It is designed to closely regulate the air/fuel ratio through electronic monitoring. A two part catalytic converter oxidizes all three pollutants, but does not have either the mixing chamber or air injection used in the Ford system. Other components in this system include an oxygen sensor which monitors the oxygen content in the exhaust, an Electronic Control Unit (ECU) which receives signals from the oxygen sensor, engine temperature switch, and vacuum input switch and sends a control signal to the vacuum modulator, the vacuum modulator which adjusts the carburetor air/fuel mixture, and a carburetor equipped with feedback diaphragms.

The ECU monitors the voltage output of the oxygen sensor. Lean mixtures reduce voltage, rich mixtures increase voltage. Adjustments of the signal sent to the vacuum modulator are made by the ECU according to the oxygen sensor output. Unlike the Ford system, there is no open loop or closed loop operation. The oxygen sensor input is a constant function. However, the ECU may limit the amount of leanness applied by the vacuum modulator according to signals received from two sources. If the temperature switch indicates that the engine is cold, the ECU allows a slightly richer mixture. If the vacuum input switch indicates low vacuum (heavy engine load), the ECU reduces the rate at which the system goes lean.

TROUBLESHOOTING

1. Before any tests are made, check the vacuum hoses for leaks, breaks, kinks, or improper connections. Inspect the wiring for breaks, shorts, or fraying. Be sure the electrical connector at the ECU is tight. Disconnect the wire from the vacuum switch (3B), and connect a test light between it and the positive battery terminal. Run the engine at 1500 rpm, with the transmission in Neutral. The test light should go on and off as the vacuum hose is removed and replaced at the switch. If not, replace the switch.

2. Turn the ignition switch ON.

3. The vacuum modulator should emit a steady clicking sound. If so, go to Step 4. If not, ground one end of a jumper wire to a ground, the other to the brown wire in the modulator connector (5B). If the modulator clicks once, check the ECU connector for tightness. If it's ok, remove the ECU connector and touch 5A with the jumper wire. If there's no click, there is an open in the brown wire. If it clicks once, replace the ECU. If the modulator does not click when the brown wire is grounded, connect a test light to a ground and the pink wire at the modulator (1D). If the test light goes on, replace the modulator. If not, there is an open in the pink wire.

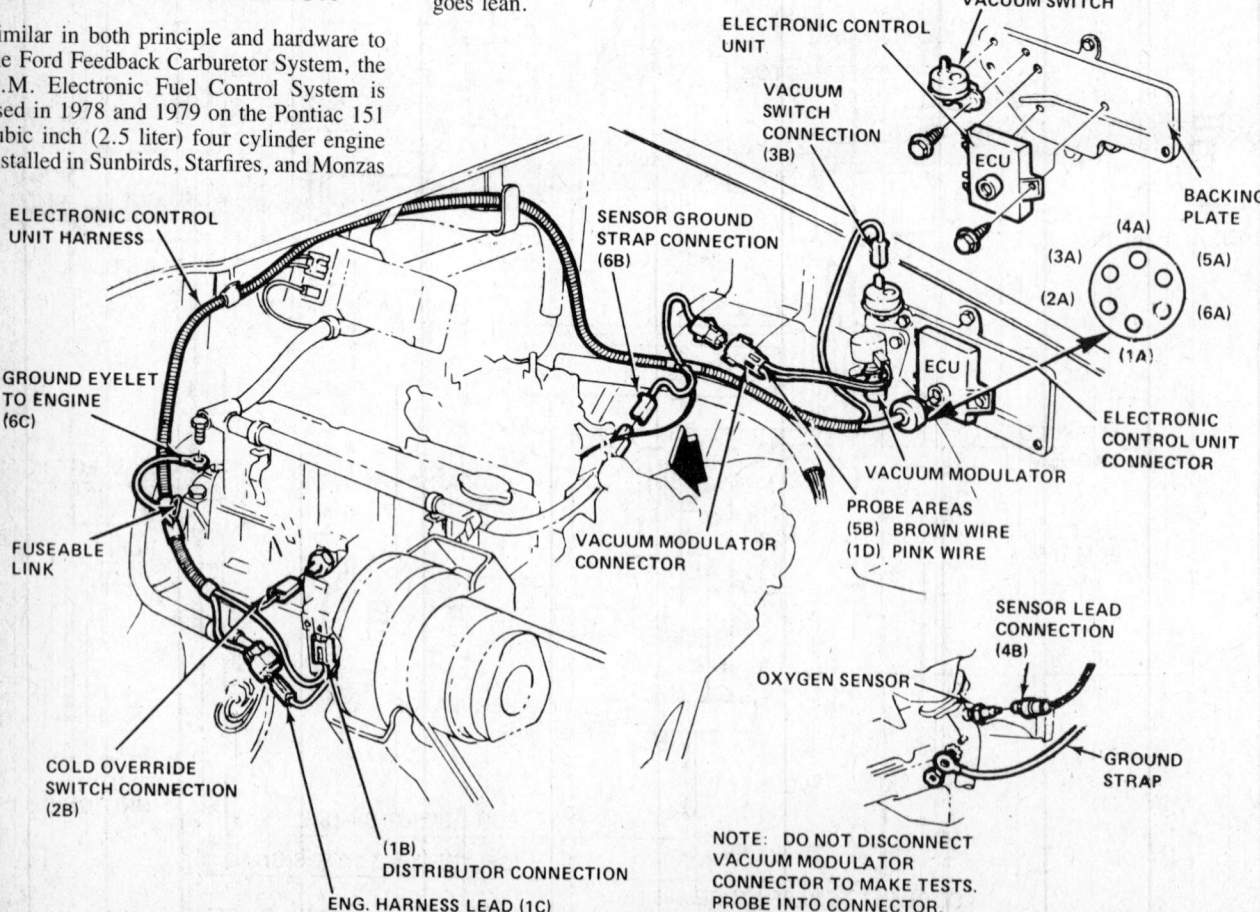

Electronic Fuel Control system components and test connections

4. If a clicking sound is heard, use a T-fitting to attach a vacuum gauge between the center port of the vacuum modulator and the carburetor. Start the engine, allow it to reach operating temperature, and let the engine idle. Automatic transmission should be in Drive (front wheels blocked, parking brake on), manual in Neutral. If the gauge reads above 7 in. Hg., replace the vacuum modulator. If the gauge reads 2–4 in. Hg., shift the transmission to Neutral or Park, with an automatic, and increase the engine speed to 3500 rpm. If the reading is still 2–4 in., the system is ok; either the ignition or fuel supply is faulty. If it reads below 2–4 in., the carburetor is faulty. If the gauge reads below 2–4 in., shift to Neutral or Park, with automatic transmission, and increase the engine speed to 3500 rpm. If it now reads 2–4 in., adjust the idle speed to read 2–4 in. at normal

ECU WIRE HARNESS CONTINUITY CHECK

Test Light		Probe	Test Result	Correction
Clip Lead				
Ground		1A	Light	OK
			No Light	Check and repair wiring or fusible link
Positive (+) battery terminal		2A	Light	OK
			No Light	Disconnect connector wire at cold override switch and ground connector wire. If the light comes on, replace the switch. No light-open circuit
Positive (+) battery terminal		3A	Light	OK
			No Light	Disconnect wire connector at vacuum switch and ground connector wire. If the light comes on, replace the switch. If not, open circuit in wire
Positive (+) battery terminal ①		4A	Light	OK
			No Light	Check and repair wire
Positive (+) battery terminal		5A	Light	OK
			No Light	If test 1A was OK, open circuit or defective vacuum modulator. If 1A was not OK, repair wire problem and retest 5A
Positive (+) battery terminal		6A	Light	OK
			No Light	Check wiring and eyelet ground at engine block

NOTE: All tests performed with the main wire connector at the ECU disconnected, the engine at normal operating temperature, ignition ON/engine off. Disconnect ECU harness with the key OFF
① Before testing terminal 4A, remove the wire connector at the oxygen sensor and ground the wire connector. Applying 12 volts to the sensor may damage it

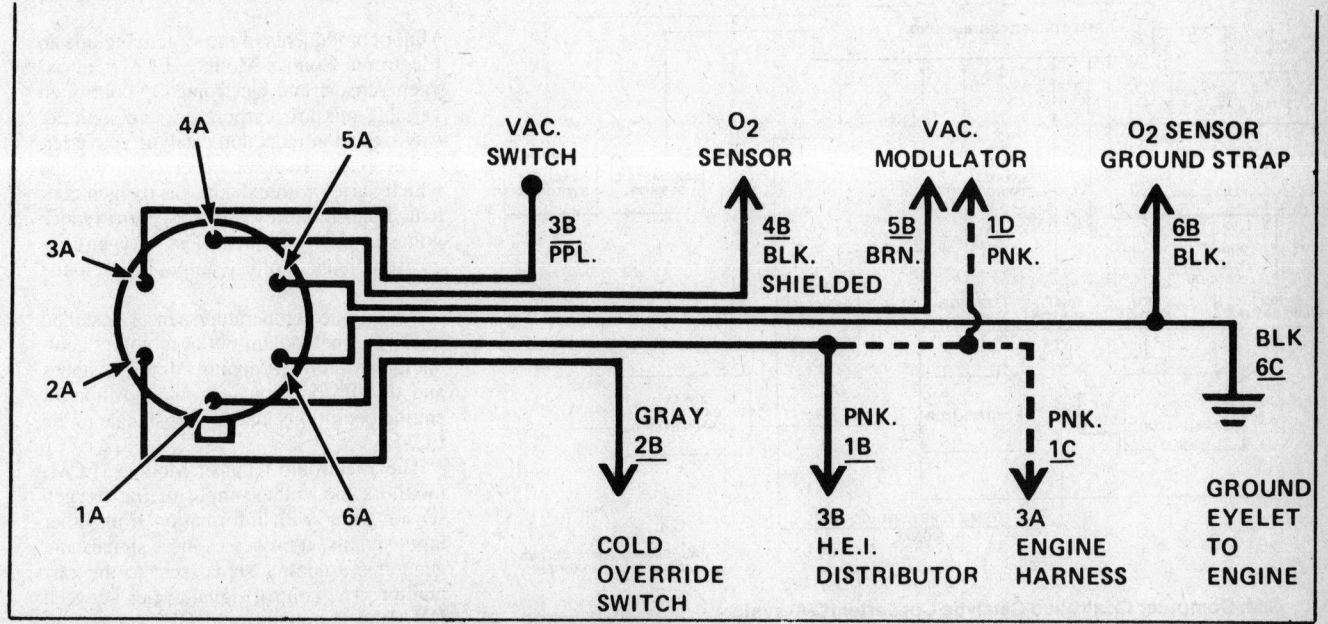

idle, according to the emission sticker in the engine compartment. If the reading is still below that figure, go to the next Step.

5. Remove the oxygen sensor wire (4B). If the vacuum gauge reads above 1 in. Hg., disconnect the modulator connector. If the vacuum falls below 1 in., replace the ECU. If it stays above 1 in., replace the vacuum modulator. If it reads below 1 in., connect a jumper wire from the positive battery terminal to the oxygen sensor terminal (4B). Go to the next Step.

6. If the gauge reads below 4 in., go to Step 7. If it reads 4–7 in., leave the jumper connected, and disconnect the vacuum hose at the center port of the modulator. Set the fast idle screw on the high step of the cam and note the engine rpm. Reconnect the hose and note the rpm. If the engine speed drops 50 rpm or more when the hose is reconnected, replace the oxygen sensor. If it drops less than 50 rpm, the problem is in the carburetor.

7. If after Step 5b the gauge still reads below 4 in., remove the jumper wire and reconnect the oxygen sensor wire. Ground the jumper wire and connect the other end to the brown wire at the modulator connector (5B). If the gauge reads 4–7 in., go to the next Step. If the gauge reads below 4 in., remove and plug the modulator vacuum hose from the carburetor. If the reading is still below 4 in., replace the modulator. If it is above 4 in., the problem is in the carburetor.

8. If the gauge reads 4–7 in. in Step 7, remove the jumper wire at the modulator, and ground the engine temperature switch wire (2B). If the vacuum gauge reads 4–7 in., replace the temperature switch. If it reads under 4 in., go to the ECU Wiring

Harness Continuity Check (diagram). If after the check the reading is still below 4 in., repair the ECU harness. If not, replace the ECU.

GENERAL MOTORS COMPUTER CONTROLLED CATALYTIC CONVERTER (C–4) SYSTEM, AND COMPUTER COMMAND CONTROL (CCC) SYSTEM

General Information

The GM designed Computer Controlled Catalytic Converter System (C–4 System), introduced in 1979 and used on GM cars through 1980, is a revised version of the 1978–79 Electronic Fuel Control System (although parts are not interchangeable between the systems). The C–4 System primarily maintains the ideal air/fuel ratio at which the catalytic converter is most effective. Some versions of the system also control ignition timing of the distributor.

The Computer Command Control System (CCC System), introduced on some 1980 California models and used on all 1981 and later carbureted car lines, is an expansion of the C–4 System. The CCC System monitors up to fifteen engine/vehicle operating conditions which it uses to control up to nine engine and emission control systems. In addition to maintaining the ideal air/fuel ratio for the catalytic converter and adjusting ignition timing, the CCC System also controls the Air Management System so that the catalytic converter can operate at the highest efficiency possible. The system also controls the lockup on the transmission torque converter clutch (certain automatic transmission models only), adjusts idle speed over a wide range of conditions, purges the evaporative emissions charcoal canister, controls the EGR valve operation and operates the early fuel evaporative (EFE) system. Not all engines use all of the above sub-systems.

There are two operation modes for both the C–4 System and the CCC System: closed loop and open loop fuel control. Closed loop fuel control means the oxygen sensor is controlling the carburetor's air/fuel mixture ratio. Under open loop fuel control operating conditions (wide open throttle, engine and/or oxygen sensor cold), the oxygen sensor has no effect on the air/fuel mixture.

NOTE: On some engines, the oxygen sensor will cool off while the engine is idling, putting the system into open loop operation. To restore closed loop operation, run the engine at part throttle and accelerate from idle to part throttle a few times.

C4 System Operation

Major components of the system include an Electronic Control Module (ECM), an oxygen sensor, and electronically controlled variable-mixture carburetor, and a three-way oxidation-reduction catalytic converter.

The oxygen sensor generates a voltage which varies with exhaust gas oxygen content. Lean mixtures (more oxygen) reduce voltage; rich mixtures (less oxygen) increase voltage. Voltage output is sent to the ECM.

An engine temperature sensor installed in the engine coolant outlet monitors coolant temperatures. Vacuum control switches and throttle position sensors also monitor engine conditions and supply signals to the ECM.

The Electronic Control Module (ECM) monitors the voltage input of the oxygen sensor along with information from other input signals. It processes these signals and generates a control signal sent to the carburetor. The control signal cycles between ON (lean command) and OFF (rich com-

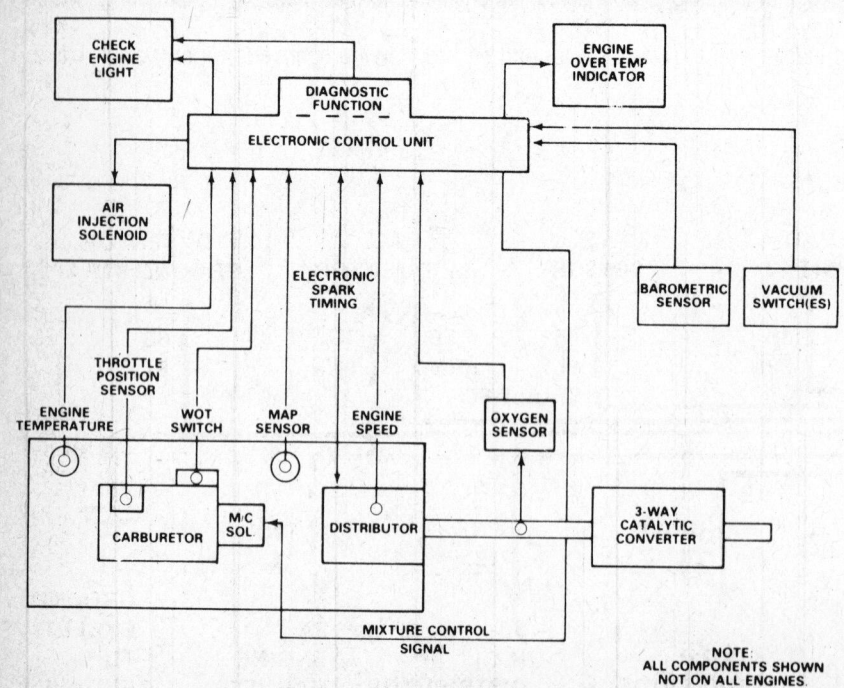

G.M. Computer Controlled Catalytic Converter (C-4) system

mand). The amount of ON and OFF time is a function of the input voltage sent to the ECM by the oxygen sensor. The ECM has a calibration unit called a PROM (Programable Read Only Memory) which contains the specific instructions for a given engine application. In other words, the PROM unit is specifically programed or ''tailor made'' for the system in which it is installed. The PROM assembly is a replacable component which plugs into a socket on the ECM and requires a special tool for removal and installation.

SERVICE PRECAUTIONS

To prevent ECM damage on 1980 and later Cadillac C-4, CCC, DFI and DEFI-equipped vehicles, the power supply feeding the ECM must not be interrupted with the ignition switch in the run, start or ACC position. The ignition switch must be placed in the *off* position when performing the following service operations:

- Disconnecting or connecting either battery cable.
- Removing or replacing the fuse providing continuous battery power to the ECM.
- Disconnecting or connecting any ECM connectors.
- Disconnecting (unless the engine is running) or connecting jumper cables (the jumper polarity must be correct, as even a momentary reversal of cable polarity may cause ECM damage).
- Disconnecting or connecting a battery charger (it is recommended that the battery be charged with both battery cables disconnected using the battery side terminal adapter, AC Delco ST-1201 or equivalent).

On some 231 cu in. V6 engines, the ECM controls the Electronic Spark Timing System (EST), AIR control system, and on the Turbo-charged 231 cu in. C–4 System it controls the early fuel evaporative system (EFE) and the EGR valve control (on some models). On some 350 V8 engines, the ECM controls the electronic module retard (EMR) system, which retards the engine timing 10 degrees during certain engine operations to reduce the exhaust emissions.

NOTE: Electronic Spark Timing (EST) allows continuous spark timing adjustments to be made by the ECM. Engines with EST can easily be identified by the absence of vacuum and mechanical spark advance mechanisms on the distributor. Engines with EMR systems may be recognized by the presence of five connectors, instead of the HEI module's usual four.

To maintain good idle and driveability under all conditions, other input signals are used to modify the ECM output signal. Besides the sensors and switches already mentioned, these input signals include the manifold absolute pressure (MAP) or vacuum sensors and the barometric pressure (BARO) sensor. The MAP or vacuum sensors sense changes in manifold vacuum, while the

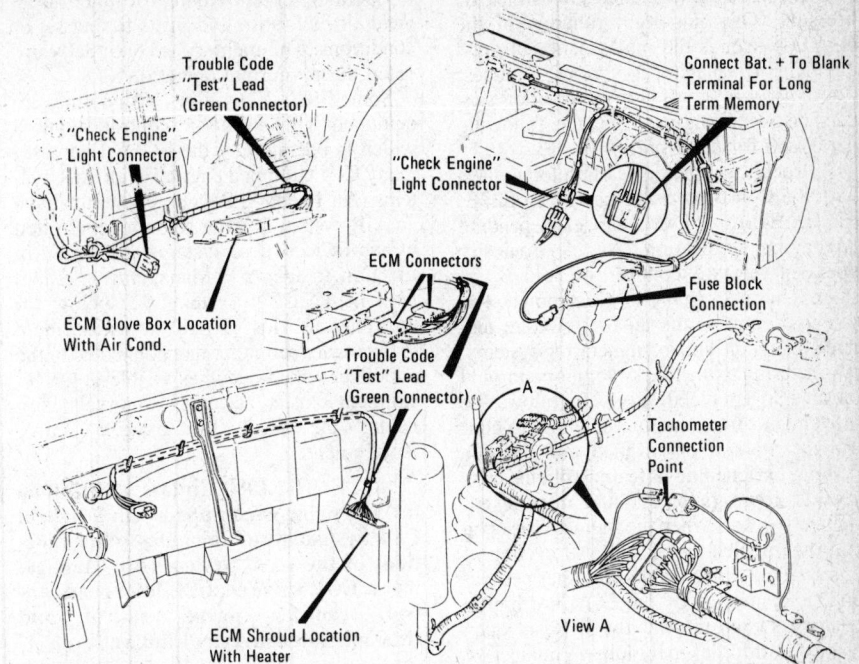

Typical 1979 C-4 system harness layout. Ground trouble code test lead to get diagnostic readout

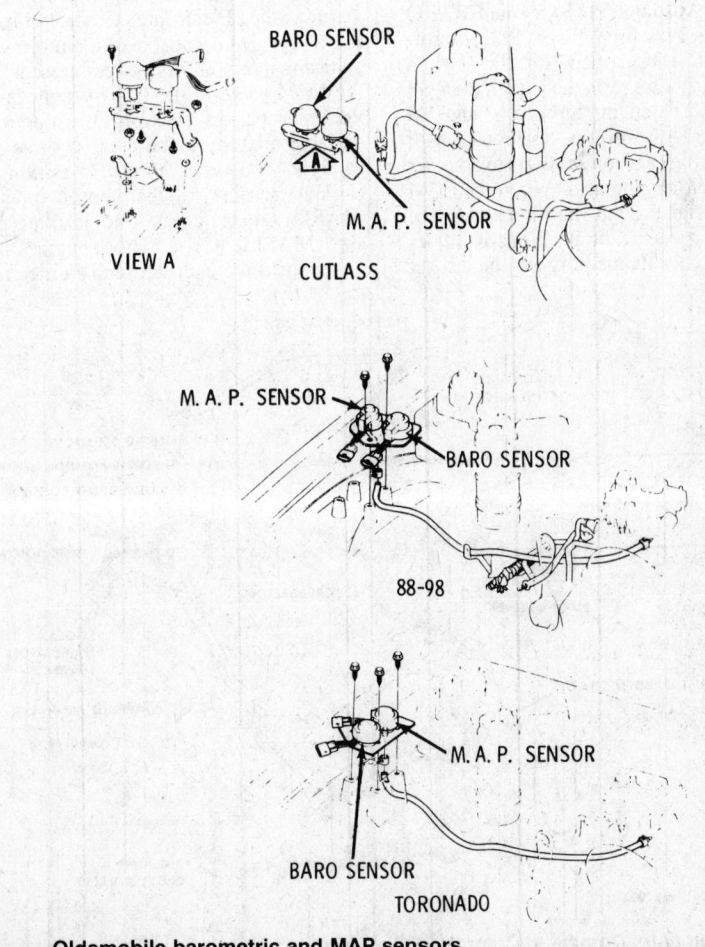

Oldsmobile barometric and MAP sensors

BARO sensor senses changes in barometric pressure. One important function of the BARO sensor is the maintenance of good engine performance at various altitudes. These sensors act as throttle position sensors on some engines. See the following paragraph for description.

A Rochester Dualjet carburetor is used with the C–4 System. It may be an E2SE, E2ME, E4MC or E4ME model, depending on engine application. An electronically operated mixture control solenoid is installed in the carburetor float bowl. The solenoid controls the air/fuel mixture metered to the idle and main metering systems. Air metering to the idle system is controlled by an idle air bleed valve. It follows the movement of the mixture solenoid to control the amount of air bled into the idle system, enriching or leaning out the mixture as appropriate. Air/fuel mixture enrichment occurs when the fuel valve is open and the air bleed is closed. All cycling of this system, which occurs ten times per second, is controlled by the ECM. A throttle position switch informs the ECM of open or closed throttle operation. A number of different switches are used, varying with application. The four cylinder engine (151 cu. in.) uses two vacuum switches to sense open throttle and closed throttle operation. The V6 engines (except the 231 cu. in. turbo V6) use two pressure sensors—MAP (Manifold Absolute Pressure) and BARO (Barometric Pressure)—as well as a throttle-actuated wide open throttle switch mounted in a bracket on the side of the float bowl. The 231 cu in. turbo V6, and V8 engines, use a throttle position sensor mounted in the carburetor bowl cover under the accelerator pump arm. When the ECM receives a signal from the throttle switch, indicating a change of position, it immediately searches its memory for the last set of operating conditions that resulted in an ideal air/fuel ratio, and shifts to that set of conditions. The memory is continually updated during normal operation.

Some 1980 173 cu in. V6 engines are equipped with a Pulsair control solenoid which is operated by the ECM. Likewise, many C–4 equipped engines with AIR systems (Air Injection Reaction systems) have an AIR system diverter solenoid controlled by the ECM. These systems are similar in function to the AIR Management system used in the CCC System. See below for information. Most C–4 Systems include a maintenance reminder flag connected to the odometer which becomes visible in the instrument cluster at regular intervals, signaling the need for oxygen sensor replacement.

NOTE: The 1980 Cutlass with 260 cu in. V8 engine is equipped with a hybrid C–4 System which includes some functions of the CCC System (Air Management, EGR valve control, Idle speed control, canister purge control and transmission converter clutch).

CCC System Operation

The CCC has many components in common with the C-4 system (although they should not be interchanged between systems). These include the Electronic Control Module (ECM), which is capable of monitoring and adjusting more sensors and components than the ECM used on the C-4 System, an oxygen sensor, an electronically controlled variable-mixture carburetor, a three way catalytic converter, throttle position and coolant sensors, a barometric pressure (BARO) sensor, a manifold absolute pressure (MAP) sensor, a "check engine" light on the instrument cluster, and an Electronic Spark Timing (EST) distributor, which on some engines (turbcharged) is equipped with an Electronic Spark Control (ESC) which retards ignition spark under some conditions (detonation, etc.).

Components used almost exclusively by the CCC System include the Air Injection Reaction (AIR) Management System, charcoal canister purge solenoid, EGR valve control, vehicle speed sensor (located in the instrument cluster), transmission torque converter clutch solenoid (automatic transmission models only), idle speed control, and early fuel evaporative (EFE) system.

NOTE: See the operation descriptions under C-4 System for those components (except the ECM) the CCC System shares with the C-4 System.

The CCC System ECM, in addition to monitoring sensors and sending a control signal to the carburetor, also control the following components or sub-systems: charcoal canister purge, AIR Management System, idle speed control, automatic transmission converter lockup, distributor ignition timing, EGR valve control, EFE control, and the air conditioner compressor clutch operation. The CCC ECM is equipped with a PROM assembly similiar to the one used in the C-4 ECM. See above for description.

SERVICE PRECAUTIONS

To prevent ECM damage on 1980 and later Cadillac C-4, CCC, DFI and DEFI-equipped vehicles, the power supply feeding the ECM must not be interrupted with the ignition switch in the run, start or ACC position. The ignition switch must be placed in the *off* position when performing the following service operations:

• Disconnecting or connecting either battery cable.

• Removing or replacing the fuse provided continuous battery power to the ECM.

• Disconnecting or connecting any ECM connectors.

• Disconnecting (unless the engine is running) or connecting jumper cables (the jumper polarity must be correct, as even a momentary reversal of cable polarity may cause ECM damage).

• Disconnecting or connecting a battery charger (it is recommended that the battery be charged with both battery cables disconnected using the battery side terminal adapter, AC Delco ST-1201 or equivalent).

The AIR Management System is an emission control which provides additional oxygen either to the catalyst or the cylinder head ports (in some cases exhaust manifold). An AIR Management System, composed of an air switching valve and/or an air control valve, controls the air pump flow and is itself controlled by the ECM. A complete description of the AIR system is given towards the front of this unit repair section. The major difference between the CCC AIR System and the systems used on other cars

CHECK ENGINE LIGHT
SPEED SENSOR
DIAGNOSTIC CONNECTOR
ELECTRONIC CONTROL MODULE
DISTRIBUTOR
TO TRANSMISSION
FUEL METERING SOLENOID
THROTTLE POSITION SENSOR
IDLE SPEED CONTROL
DASH GROMMET
EGR SOLENOID
CARBURETOR
MANIFOLD DIFFERENTIAL PRESSURE SENSOR
COOLANT TEMPERATURE SENSOR
EXHAUST OXYGEN SENSOR
TO L.H. MANIFOLD AIR VALVE
TO A/C COMPRESSOR
CATALYTIC CONVERTER
ELECTRIC AIR SWITCHING VALVE
AIR PUMP & DIVERTER VALVE
R.H. MANIFOLD AIR VALVE
CONVERTER AIR VALVE

G.M. Computer Command Control (CCC) system

is that the flow of air from the air pump is controlled electrically by the ECM, rather than by vacuum signal.

The charcoal canister purge control is an electrically operated solenoid valve controlled by the ECM. When energized, the purge control solenoid blocks vacuum from reaching the canister purge valve. When the ECM de-energizes the purge control solenoid, vacuum is allowed to reach the canister and operate the purge valve. This releases the fuel vapors collected in the canister into the induction system.

The EGR valve control solenoid is activated by the ECM in similar fashion to the canister purge solenoid. When the engine is cold, the ECM energizes the solenoid, which blocks the vacuum signal to the EGR valve. When the engine is warm, the ECM de-energizes the solenoid and the vacuum signal is allowed to reach and activate the EGR valve.

The Transmission Converter Clutch (TCC) lock is controlled by the ECM through an electrical solenoid in the automatic transmission. When the vehicle speed sensor in the instrument panel signals the ECM that the vehicle has reached the correct speed, the ECM energizes the solenoid which allows the torque converter to mechanically couple the engine to the transmission. When the brake pedal is pushed or during deceleration, passing, etc., the ECM returns the transmission to fluid drive.

The idle speed control adjusts the idle speed to load conditions, and will lower the idle speed under no-load or low-load conditions to conserve gasoline.

The Early Fuel Evaporative (EFE) system is used on some engines to provide rapid heat to the engine induction system to promote smooth start-up and operation. There are two types of system: vacuum servo and electrically heated. They use different means to achieve the same end, which is to pre-heat the incoming air/fuel mixture. They are controlled by the ECM.

Diagnosis and Troubleshooting

NOTE: The following explains how to activate the Trouble Code signal light in the instrument cluster and gives an explanation of what each code means. This is not a full C-4 or CCC System troubleshooting and isolation procedure.

Before suspecting the C-4 or CCC System or any of its components as faulty, check the ignition system including distributor, timing, spark plugs and wires. Check the engine compression, air cleaner, and emission control components not controlled by the ECM. Also check the intake manifold, vacuum hoses and hose connectors for leaks and the carburetor bolts for tightness.

The following symptoms could indicate a possible problem with the C-4 or CCC System.

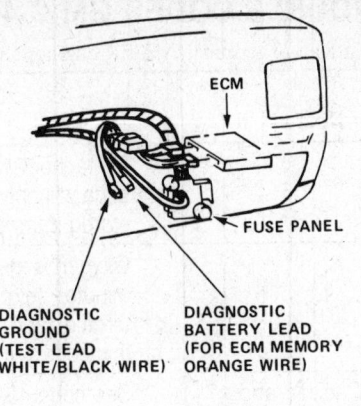
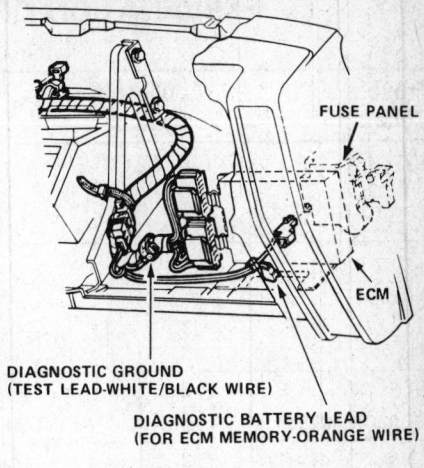

2.8L-V6 **2.5L-L4**

C-4 diagnostic test lead locations for 1980 Citation, Phoenix, Omega and Skylark

1. Detonation
2. Stalls or rough idle—cold
3. Stalls or rough idle—hot
4. Missing
5. Hesitation
6. Surges
7. Poor gasoline mileage
8. Sluggish or spongy performance
9. Hard starting—cold
10. Hard starting—hot
11. Objectionable exhaust odors (that "rotten egg" smell)
12. Cuts out
13. Improper idle speed (CCC System and C-4 equipped 1980 Cutlass with 260 cu. in. engine only)

As a bulb and system check, the "Check Engine" light will come on when the ignition switch is turned to the ON position but the engine is not started.

The "Check Engine" light will also produce the trouble code or codes by a series of flashes which translate as follows. When the diagnostic test lead (C-4) or terminal (CCC) under the dash is grounded, with the ignition in the ON position and the engine not running, the "Check Engine"

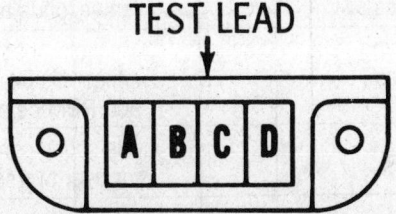

1980 Oldsmobile Cutlass 260 cu in. (4.3L) V8 with C-4 system has test terminal similar to CCC system equipped cars

light will flash once, pause, then flash twice is rapid succession. This is a code 12, which indicates that the diagnostic system is working. After a longer pause, the code 12 will repeat itself two more times. The cycle will then repeat itself until the engine is started or the ignition is turned off.

NOTE: The C-4 equipped 1980 Cutlass with 260 cu in. V8 engine has a test terminal similar to the kind used on the CCC System.

When the engine is started, the "Check Engine" light will remain on for a few seconds, then turn off. If the "Check Engine" light remains on, the self-diagnostic system has detected a problem. If the test lead (C-4) or test terminal (CCC) is then grounded, the trouble code will flash three times. If more than one problem is found, each trouble code will flash three times. Trouble codes will flash in numerical order (lowest code number to highest). The trouble codes series will repeat as long as the test lead or terminal is grounded.

A trouble code indicates a problem with a given circuit. For example, trouble code 14 indicates a problem in the cooling sensor circuit. This includes the coolant sensor, its electrical harness, and the Electronic Control Module (ECM).

Since the self-diagnostic system cannot diagnose every possible fault in the system, the absence of a trouble code does not mean the system is trouble-free. To determine problems within the system which do not activate a trouble code, a system performance check must be made. This job should be left to a qualified technician.

In the case of an intermittant fault in the system, the "Check Engine" light will go out when the fault goes away, but the trouble code will remain in the memory of the ECM. Therefore, if a trouble code can be obtained even though the "Check Engine" light is not on, the trouble code must be evaluated. It must be determined if the fault is intermittant or if the engine must be at certain operating conditions (under load, etc.) before the "Check Engine" light will come on. Some trouble codes will not be recorded in the ECM until the engine has been operated at part throttle for about 5 to 18 minutes.

On the C-4 System, the ECM erases all trouble codes every time the ignition is turned off. In the case of intermittant faults, a long

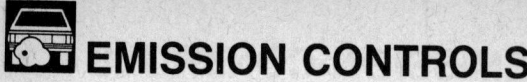

EXPLANATION OF TROUBLE CODES GM C-4 AND CCC SYSTEMS

(Ground test lead or terminal AFTER engine is running.)

Trouble Code	Applicable System	Notes	Possible Problem Area
12	C-4, CCC		No tachometer or reference signal to computer (ECM). This code will only be present while a fault exsists, and will not be stored if the problem is intermittent.
13	C-4, CCC		Oxygen sensor circuit. The engine must run for about five minutes (eighteen on C-4 equipped 231 cu in. V6) at part throttle (and under road load—CCC equipped cars) before this code will show.
13 & 14 (at same time)	C-4	Except Cadillac and 171 cu in. V6	See code 43.
13 & 43 (at same time)	C-4	Cadillac and 171 cu in. V6	See code 43.
14	C-4, CCC		Shorted coolant sensor circuit. The engine has to run 2 minutes before this code will show.
15	C-4, CCC		Open coolant sensor circuit. The engine has to operate for about five minutes (18 minutes for C-4 equipped 231 cu in. V6) at part throttle (some models) before this code will show.
21	C-4		Shorted wide open throttle switch and/or open closed-throttle switch circuit (when used).
	C-4, CCC		Throttle position sensor circuit. The engine must be run up to 10 seconds (25 seconds—CCC System) below 800 rpm before this code will show.
21 & 22 (at same time)	C-4		Grounded wide open throttle switch circuit (231 cu in. V6, 151 cu in. 4 cylinder).
22	C-4		Grounded closed throttle or wide open throttle switch circuit (231 cu in. V6, 151 cu in. 4 cylinder).
23	C-4, CCC		Open or grounded carburetor mixture control (M/C) solenoid circuit.
24	CCC		Vehicle speed sensor (VSS) circuit. The car must operate up to five minutes at road speed before this code will show.
32	C-4, CCC		Barometric pressure sensor (BARO) circuit output low.
32 & 55 (at same time)	C-4		Grounded +8V terminal or V(REF) terminal for barometric pressure sensor (BARO), or faulty ECM computer.
34	C-4	Except 1980 260 cu in. Cutlass	Manifold absolute pressure (MAP) sensor output high (after ten seconds and below 800 rpm).
34	CCC	Including 1980 260 cu in. Cutlass	Manifold absolute pressure (MAP) sensor circuit or vacuum sensor circuit. The engine must run up to five minutes below 800 RPM before this code will set.
35	CCC		Idle speed control (ISC) switch circuit shorted (over ½ throttle for over two seconds).
41	CCC		No distributor reference pulses to the ECM at specified engine vacuum. This code will store in memory.
42	CCC		Electronic spark timing (EST) bypass circuit grounded.

EXPLANATION OF TROUBLE CODES GM C-4 AND CCC SYSTEMS

(Ground test lead or terminal AFTER engine is running.)

Trouble Code	Applicable System	Notes	Possible Problem Area
43	C-4		Throttle position sensor adjustment (on some models, engine must run at part throttle up to ten seconds before this code will set).
44	C-4, CCC		Lean oxygen sensor indication. The engine must run up to five minutes in closed loop (oxygen sensor adjusting carburetor mixture), at part throttle and under road load (drive car) before this code will set.

EXPLANATION OF TROUBLE CODES
GM C-4 AND CCC SYSTEMS

(Ground test lead or terminal AFTER engine is running.)

Trouble Code	Applicable System	Notes	Possible Problem Area
44 & 55 (at same time)	C-4, CCC		Faulty oxygen sensor circuit.
45	C-4, CCC	Restricted air cleaner can cause code 45	Rich oxygen sensor system indication. The engine must run up to five minutes in closed loop (oxygen sensor adjusting carburetor mixture), at part throttle under road load before this code will set.
51	C-4, CCC		Faulty calibration unit (PROM) or improper PROM installation in electronic control module (ECM). It takes up to thirty seconds for this code to set.
52 & 53	C-4		"Check Engine" light off: Intermittent ECM computer problem. "Check Engine" light on: Faulty ECM computer (replace).
52	C-4, CCC		Faulty ECM computer.
53	CCC	Including 1980 260 cu in. Cutlass	Faulty ECM computer.
54	C-4, CCC		Faulty mixture control solenoid circuit and/or faulty ECM computer.
55	C-4	Except 1980 260 cu in. Cutlass	Faulty oxygen sensor, open manifold absolute pressure sensor or faulty ECM computer (231 cu in. V6). Faulty throttle position sensor or ECM computer (except 231 cu in. V6). Faulty ECM computer (151 cu in. 4 cylinder)
55	CCC	Including 1980 260 cu in. Cutlass	Grounded + 8 volt supply (terminal 19 of ECM computer connector), grounded 5 volt reference (terminal 21 of ECM computer connector), faulty oxygen sensor circuit or faulty ECM computer.

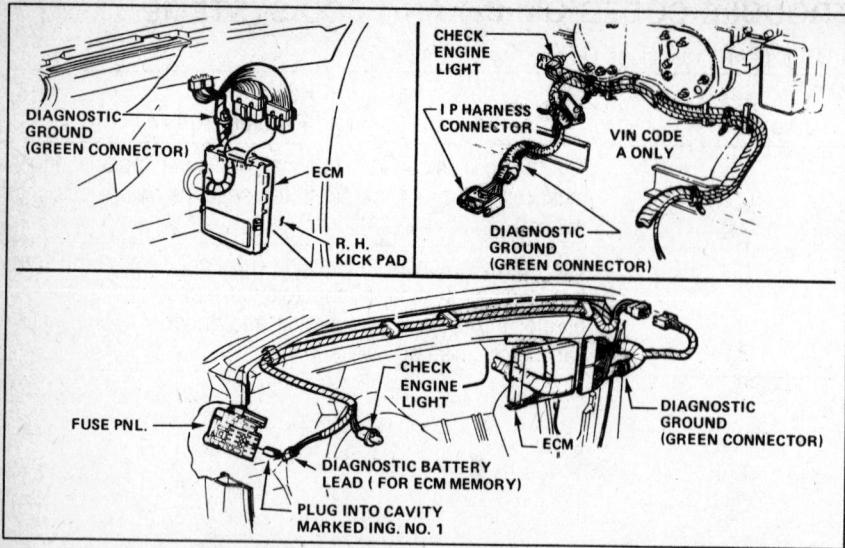

Typical 1980 C-4 system harness layouts. Location of the test lead (diagnostic ground) will depend on position of ECM computer and body style

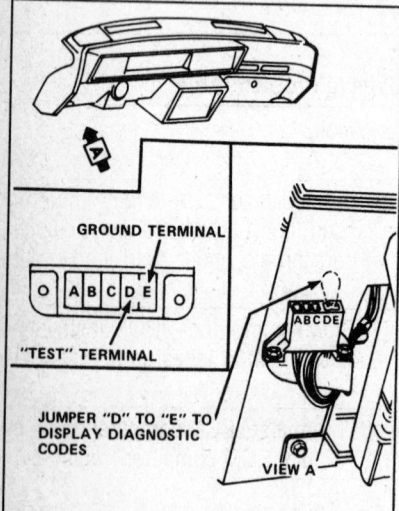

Typical 1981 and later CCC test terminal location. Ground test terminal for code display

term memory is desirable. This can be produced by connecting the orange connector/lead from terminal "S" of the ECM directly to the battery (or to a "hot" fuse panel terminal). This terminal must be disconnected after diagnosis is complete or it will drain the battery.

On the CCC System, a trouble code will be stored until terminal "R" of the ECM has been disconnected from the battery for 10 seconds.

NOTE: On 1980 Cutlass with 260 cu in. V8, the trouble code is stored in the same manner as on the CCC System. In addition, some 1980 Buicks have a long term constant memory similar to that used on the CCC System. In which case terminal S (terminal R on the 3.8 Liter V6) must be disconnected in the same manner as on the CCC System to erase the memory.

An easy way to erase the computer memory on the CCC System is to disconnect the battery terminals from the battery. If this method is used, don't forget to reset clocks and electronic preprogramable radios. Another method is to remove the fuse marked ECM in the fuse panel. Not all models have such a fuse.

CHRYSLER ELECTRONIC FEEDBACK CARBURETOR

General Information

The Chrysler Electronic Feedback Carburetor (EFC) system was introduced in mid-1979 on Volarés and Aspens sold in California with the six cylinder engine. The system is a conventional one, incorporating an oxygen sensor, a three-way catalytic converter, an oxidizing catalytic converter, a feedback carburetor, a solenoid-operated vacuum regulator valve, and a Combustion Computer. Also incorporated into the system are Chrysler's Electronic Spark Control, and a mileage counter which illuminates a light on the instrument panel at 15,000 mile intervals, signaling the need for oxygen sensor replacement.

In Chrysler's system, "Combustion Computer" is a collective term for the Feedback Carburetor Controller and the Electronic Spark Control computer, which are housed together in a case located on the air cleaner. The feedback carburetor controller is the information processing component of the system, monitoring oxygen sensor voltage (low voltage/lean mixture, high voltage/rich mixture), engine coolant temperature, manifold vacuum, engine speed, and engine operating mode (starting or running). The controller examines the incoming information and then sends a signal to the solenoid-operated vacuum regulator valve (also located in the Combustion Computer housing), which then sends the proper rich or lean signal to the carburetor.

The 1 bbl Holley R-8286A carburetor (and 1 bbl Holley 6145 on later models) is equipped with two diaphragms, controlling the idle system and the main metering system. The diaphragms move tapered rods, which vary the size of the orifices in the idle system air bleed and the main metering system fuel flow. A "lean" command from the controller to the vacuum regulator results in increased vacuum to both diaphragms, which simultaneously raise both the idle air bleed rod (increasing idle air bleed) and the main metering rod (reducing fuel flow). A "rich" command reduces vacuum level, causing the spring-loaded rods to move in the other direction, enriching the mixture.

Both closed loop and open loop operation are possible in the EFC system. Open loop operation occurs under any one of the following conditions: coolant temperature under 150°F; oxygen sensor temperature under 660°F; low manifold vacuum (less than 4.5 in. Hg. engine cold, or less than 3.0 in. Hg. engine hot): oxygen sensor failure; or hot engine starting. Closed loop operation begins when engine temperature reaches 150°F.

Air injection is supplied by an air pump. At cold engine temperature, air is injected into the exhaust manifold upstream of both catalytic converters. At operating temperature, an air switching valve diverts air from the exhaust to an injection point downstream from the three-way catalyst, but upstream of the conventional oxidizing catalyst.

In 1980, the system was modified slightly and used on all California models, and on all 318 4-bbl. V8's nationwide. The 1980 and later system is used with Electronic Spark Advance (ESA), not Electronic Spark Control (ESC)—see the Electronic Ignition Systems section in this book for details. Differences lie in the deletion of some components within the combustion computer. The start timer, vacuum transducer count-up clock and memory throttle transducer, and ambient air temperature sensor are not used.

The feedback system for the six cylinder engines is essentially unchanged. The four and eight cylinder systems differ from the six mainly in the method used to control the carburetor mixture. Instead of having vacuum-controlled diaphragms to raise or lower the mixture rods, the carburetors are equipped with an electric solenoid valve, which is part of the carburetor. These later carburetors include the Carter BBD and Carter Thermo-Quad.

Other differences between the systems are minor. On the four cylinder, the ignition sensor is the Hall Effect distributor, but it functions in the same manner as the six cylinder pick-up coil. The eight cylinder uses two pick-up coils (a Start pick-up and a Run pick-up); troubleshooting is included in the ''Lean Burn/Electronic Spark Control'' section. The four and six cylinder engines use a 150°F coolant switch; the eight cylinder uses a 150°F switch with Combustion Computer 4145003, and a 98°F switch with Computer 4145088. The eight cylinder engine has a detonation sensor (see the ''Lean Burn/Electronic Spark Control'' section), and the six and eight cylinder engines have a charge temperature switch to monitor intake charge temperature. Below approximately 60°F, the switch prevents EGR timer function and EGR valve operation; additionally, on eight cylinder engines, air injection is routed upstream of the exhaust manifolds.

Finally, the replacement interval for the oxygen sensor has been doubled, from 15,000 to 30,000 miles. Replacement procedures and odometer resetting are the same as for the 1979 six cylinder system.

Note that two completely different troubleshooting procedures have been included here. Use the 1979 procedure only for 1979 Aspens and Volarés with the six cylinder engine. Use the 1980 and Later procedure as applicable.

Diagnosis and Troubleshooting

1979 SYSTEM TESTING

Troubleshooting requires the use of a few special tools. A 0–5 in. Hg. vacuum gauge accurate within ½ in. Hg.; a 0–30 in. Hg. vacuum gauge; a hand vacuum pump with vacuum gauge; two short lengths of 3/16 in. I.D. vacuum hose; two 3/16 in. vacuum tees; and a jumper wire approximately five feet long.

NOTE: Before performing any tests, check all vacuum hoses for leaks, breaks, kinks, or improper connections, all electrical connections for soundness, and all wires for fraying or breaks. Check for leakage at both the intake and exhaust manifolds.

1. Warm the engine to normal operating temperature. Install a tee into the control vacuum hose which runs to the carburetor. Install the 0–5 in. vacuum gauge on the tee. Start the engine and allow it to idle. The vacuum gauge should read 2.5 in. for approximately 100 seconds, then fall to zero, then gradually rise to between 1.0 and 4.0 in. The reading may oscillate slightly.

2. If the vacuum reading is incorrect, increase the engine speed to 2000 rpm. If vacuum reads between 1.0 and 4.0 in., re-

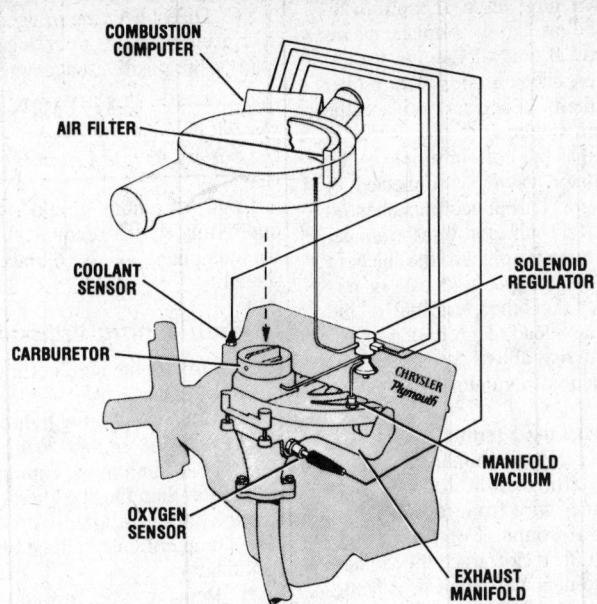

Electronic feedback carburetor control system used on 1979 automatic sixes in California

turn the engine to idle. If the reading is now correct, the system was not warmed up; originally, but is OK.

3. If the gauge is correct at 2000 rpm but not at idle, the carburetor must be replaced.

4. If the vacuum is either above 4.0 in. or below 1.0 in., follow the correct troubleshooting procedure given next. Note that in most cases of system malfunction, control vacuum will be either 0 in. or 5.0 in.

Control Vacuum Above 4.0 In. Hg.

Start the engine, apply the parking brake, place the transmission in Neutral, and place the throttle on the next to lowest step of the fast idle cam.

1. Remove the PCV hose from the PCV valve. Cover the end of the hose with your thumb. Gradually uncover the end of the hose until the engine runs rough. If control vacuum gets lower as the hose is uncovered, the carburetor must be replaced; however, complete Step 2 before replacing it. If control vacuum remains high, continue with the tests.

2. Before replacing the carburetor, examine the heat shield. Interference may exist between the heat shield and the mechanical power enrichment valve lever. If so, the carburetor will be running rich. Correct the problem and repeat Step 1.

NOTE: A new heat shield is used starting in 1979 which has clearance for the enrichment lever. Earlier heat shields should not be used unless modified for clearance.

3. Disconnect the electrical connector at the solenoid regulator valve. Control vacuum should drop to zero. If not, replace the solenoid regulator valve.

4. Disconnect the oxygen sensor wire. Use the jumper wire to connect the *harness* lead to the negative battery terminal.

——— **CAUTION** ———

Do not connect the oxygen sensor wire to ground or to the battery.

Control vacuum should drop to zero in approximately 15 seconds. If not, replace the Combustion Computer. If it does, replace the oxygen sensor. Before replacing either part, check the Computer to sensor wire for continuity.

Control Vacuum Below 1.0 In. Hg.

1. Start the engine and allow it to idle in Neutral. Disconnect the vacuum hose at the computer transducer and connect the hose to the 0–30 in. Hg. vacuum gauge. The gauge should show manifold vacuum (above 12 in.). If not, trace the hose to its source and then connect it properly to a source of manifold vacuum.

The following Steps should be made with the engine warm, parking brake applied, transmission in Neutral, and throttle placed on the next to lowest step of the fast idle cam.

2. Remove the air cleaner cover. Gradually close the choke plate until the engine begins to run roughly. If control vacuum increases to 5.0 in. as the choke is closed, go to Step 3. If control vacuum remains low, go to Step 4.

3. Disconnect the air injection hose from its connection to a metal tube at the rear of the cylinder head. Plug the tube. If control vacuum remains below 1.0 in., replace the carburetor. If control vacuum returns to the proper level, reconnect the air injection hose and disconnect the 3/16 in. vacuum hose

from the air switching valve. If control vacuum remains below 1.0 in., replace the air switching valve. If control vacuum rises to the proper level, check all hoses for proper connections, then, if correct, replace the coolant vacuum switch.

4. Check that the bottom nipple of the solenoid regulator valve is connected to manifold vacuum. Disconnect the solenoid regulator electrical connector. Use the jumper wire to connect one terminal of the solenoid regulator lead to the positive battery terminal. Connect the other terminal of the solenoid regulator lead to ground. Control vacuum should rise above 5.0 in. If not, replace the solenoid regulator. If so, go to the next Step.

5. Disconnect the 5 terminal connector at the computer. The terminals are numbered 1 to 5, starting at the rounded end. Connect a jumper wire from terminal 2 in the harness to a ground. Control vacuum should rise to 5 in. If not, trace the voltage to the battery to discover where it is being lost. If so, go to the next Step.

NOTE: Wiring harness problems are usually in the connectors. Check them for looseness or corrosion.

6. Disconnect the oxygen sensor wire. Use a jumper wire to connect the *harness* lead to the positive battery terminal.

— **CAUTION** —

Do not connect the oxygen sensor wire to the battery or to a ground.

Control vacuum should rise to 5 in. in approximately 15 seconds. If not, replace the computer. If so, replace the oxygen sensor.

Ignition Timing Adjustment

1. Ground the carburetor switch with a jumper wire.
2. Connect a timing light to the engine.
3. Start the engine. Wait one minute.
4. With the engine running at a speed not greater than the specified curb idle rpm (see the emission control sticker in the engine compartment), adjust the timing to specification.
5. Remove the ground wire after adjustment.

Curb Idle Adjustment

Adjust the curb idle only after ignition tim-

ing has been checked and set to specification.

1. Start the engine and run in Neutral on the second step of the fast idle cam until the engine is fully warmed up and the radiator becomes hot. This may take 5 to 10 minutes.
2. Disconnect and plug the EGR hose at the EGR valve.
3. Ground the carburetor switch with a jumper wire.
4. Adjust the idle rpm in Neutral to the curb idle rpm figure given on the emission control sticker in the engine compartment.
5. Reconnect the EGR hose and remove the jumper wire.

Oxygen Sensor Replacement

1. Disconnect the negative battery cable. Remove the air cleaner.
2. Disconnect the sensor electrical lead. Unscrew the sensor using Chrysler special tool C-4589.
3. Installation is the reverse. Before installation, coat the threads of the sensor with a nickel base anti-seize compound. Do not use other type compounds since they may electrically insulate the sensor. Torque the sensor to 35 ft. lbs.

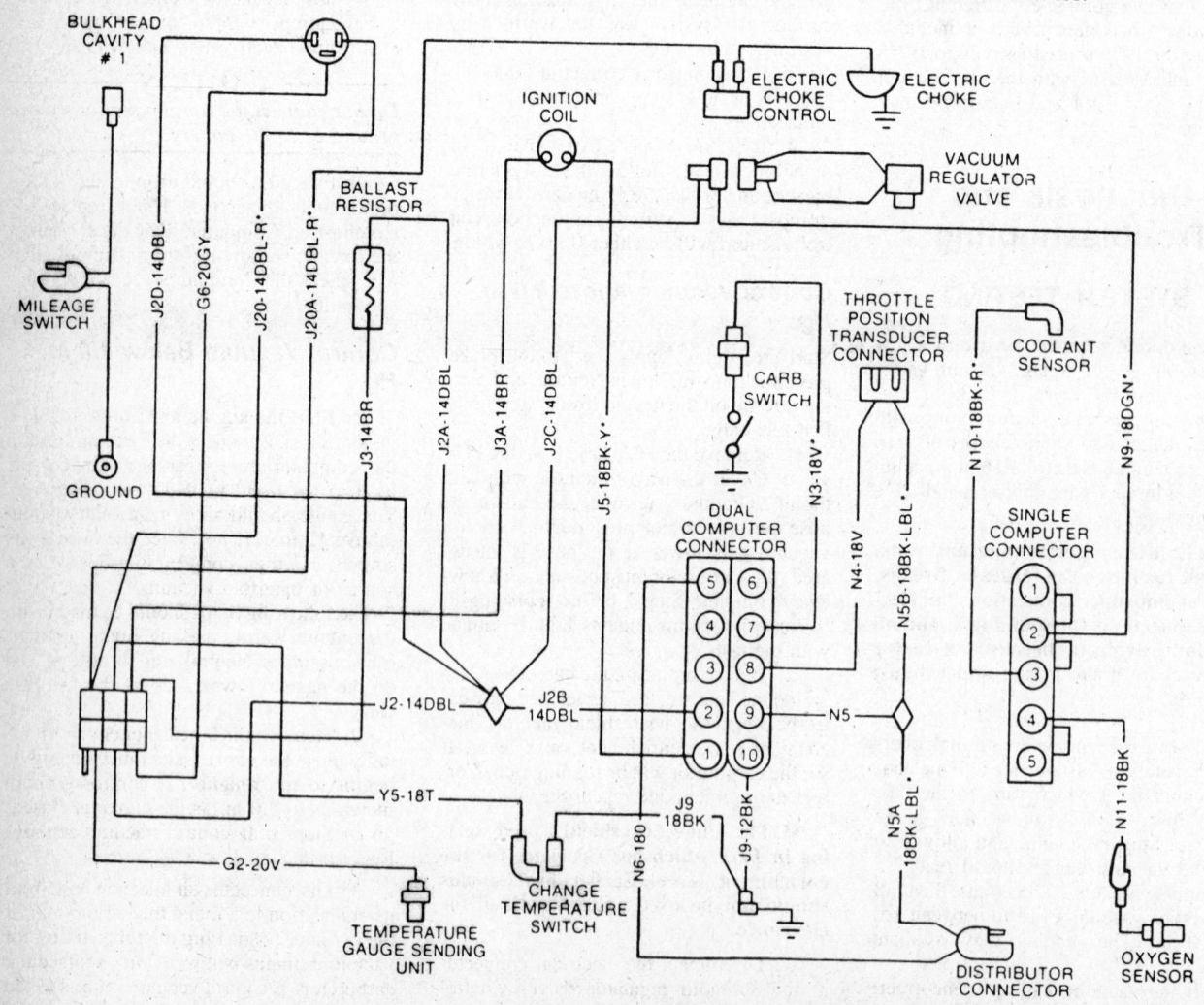

Schematic of the 1979 Chrysler Electronic Feedback Carburetor System

Mileage Counter Reset

The mileage counter will illuminate every 15,000 miles, signaling the need for oxygen sensor replacement. After replacing the oxygen sensor, reset the counter as follows:

1. Locate the mileage counter. It is spliced into the speedometer cable, covered by a rubber boot.

2. Slide the rubber boot up the speedometer cable to expose the top of the mileage counter. Turn the reset screw on top of the counter to reset. Replace the boot.

NOTE: Use the following procedures for diagnosing all 1980 and later C4 or CCC systems.

1980 AND LATER SYSTEM TESTING

ESA Test

1. Connect a timing light to the engine.
2. Disconnect and plug the vacuum hose at the vacuum transducer. Connect a vacuum pump to the transducer fitting and apply 14–16 in. Hg. of vacuum.
3. With the engine at normal operating temperature, raise the speed to 2000 rpm. Wait one minute, then check the timing advance. Specifications are as follows (timing in addition to basic advance):

1980 4 cyl. M/T: 20°–28°
1980 4 cyl. A/T: 31°–39°
1981 1.7 A/T: 31°–39°
1981 1.7 M/T Fed.: 34°–42°, 39°–47°
1981 2.2 M/T Fed.: 24°–32°, 29°–37°
1981 2.2 M/T Cal.: 19°–27°
1981 2.2 A/T: 21°–29°
1980 6 cyl.: 10°–18°
1980 8 cyl.: 15°–23°
1981 6 cyl.: 16°–24°
1981 8 cyl.: 30°–38°
1982 1.7 A/T Fed.: 51°–59°
1982 1.7 M/T: 46°–54°
1982 2.2 A/T: 41°–49°
1982 2.2 M/T: 43°–51°
1982 6 cyl.: 16°–24°
1982 8 cyl.: EFI 19°–27°
1982 8 cyl.: 30°–38°
1983 1.7 M/T: 26°–34°
1983 2.2 Can.: 20°–28°
1983 2.2 Fed.: 24°–32°
1983 2.2 Hi. Alt.: 30°–38°
1983 2.2 Cal. M/T: 30°–38°
1983 2.2 Cal. A/T: 27°–35°
1983 225 Fed.: 10°–18°
1983 225 Calif.: 4°–12°
1983 318-2 USA: 26°–34°
1983 318-2 Can.: 21°–29°
1983 318-4 Can.: 21°–29°
1983 318-4 Fed.: 16°–22°
1983 318 EFI: 16°–24°

AIR SWITCHING SYSTEM TESTS

1. Remove the vacuum hose from the air switching valve; connect a vacuum gauge to the hose.

2. Start the engine. With the engine cold, engine vacuum should be present on the gauge until the engine coolant temperature is as follows:

1980 four cylinder M/T: 98°F
1980 four cylinder A/T: 125°F
1981–83 four cylinder 2.2L California: 125°F
1981–83 four cylinder 2.2L 49 states: 150°F
6 cylinder (all): 150°F
8 cylinder with computer 4145003: 150°F
8 cylinder with computer 4145088: 98°F

On the 8 cylinder models, the charge temperature switch must be open and fuel mixture temperature above 60°F.

3. When the indicated temperatures are reached, vacuum should drop to zero. If no vacuum is present on the gauge before the temperature is reached:

On the four cylinder, check the vacuum supply and the Coolant Controlled Engine Vacuum Switch (CCEVS); on the six and eight cylinder, check the vacuum supply, air switching solenoid, coolant switch (and charge temperature switch on the eight), and the wiring and connections to the computer. If all these systems are OK, it is possible that the computer is faulty, preventing air switching.

4. With the engine warm on the four cylinder, no vacuum should be present; if there is vacuum, check the CCEVS.

5. With the engine warm on the six and eight: on the 1980 six, vacuum should be present for 100 seconds; on the 1981 six for 65 seconds; on the 1980 eight with 4145003 for 25 seconds; on the 1980 eight with 4145088 for 90 seconds; on the 1981 Cal. eight for 20 seconds; on the 1981 Fed. 4 bbl eight for 30 seconds; on the 1981 Fed. 2 bbl eight for 90 seconds after the engine starts. After the period indicated, vacuum should drop to zero. If there is no vacuum, check as follows:

Connect a voltmeter to the light green wire on the air switching solenoid. On the eight cylinder, also disconnect the coolant switch and charge temperature switch. Start the engine; voltage should be less than one volt. Allow the warm-up schedule to finish (time as specified at the beginning of this step). The solenoid should de-energize and the voltmeter should then read charging system voltage. If not, replace the solenoid and repeat the test. If the voltmeter indicates charging system voltage before the warm-up schedule finishes, replace the computer.

6. Test the air switching valve: remove the air supply hose from the valve. Remove the vacuum hose from the valve and connect a vacuum pump to the fitting. Start the engine; air should be discharged from the side port. When vacuum is applied, discharge from the side port should cease, and air should then be discharged from the bottom port.

FEEDBACK CARBURETOR TESTS

Check all vacuum hose connections and the spark advance schedule before performing these tests. Check the resistance of all related wiring, and examine all electrical connections for soundness. On the four cylinder, connect a vacuum pump to the vacuum transducer and apply 10 in. Hg. (16 in. Hg. on 1981 and later) of vacuum. On all engines, start the engine and allow it to reach normal operating temperature.

NOTE: After a hot restart, run the engine at 1200–2000 rpm for at least two minutes before continuing. DO NOT GROUND THE CARBURETOR SWITCH.

1. On the four and eight and 1981 six cylinder engines, disconnect the electrical connector from the regulator solenoid. Engine speed should increase at least 50 rpm. (If not, on the four cylinder only disconnect the four-way tee from the air cleaner temperature sensor and repeat the test. If no response, replace the computer.) Connect the regulator solenoid; engine speed should return to 1200–2000 rpm. Disconnect the six (twelve-1981 reardrive) pin connector from the computer, and connect a ground to the #15 harness connector pin. Engine speed should drop 50 rpm. If not, check for carburetor air leaks, and service the carburetor as necessary.

On 1980 six cylinders, tee a 0–5 in. Hg. vacuum gauge into the vacuum regulator supply line to the carburetor. Disconnect the regulator wiring. With the engine idling and no voltage to the regulator, vacuum should be zero, and engine speed should increase by at least 50 rpm. Using a jumper wire, apply battery voltage to one terminal of the regulator, and ground the other terminal; vacuum should rise to 5 in. Hg., and engine speed should drop at least 50 rpm. If not, replace the regulator and repeat the test; if still faulty, replace the computer.

2. With the engine cold, check the coolant switch. It should have continuity to ground on the four cylinder, or have a resistance of less than 10 ohms on the six and eight. With the engine warm (above 150°F) the switch should be open.

3. With the engine hot, disconnect the coolant temperature switch. *Do not ground the carburetor switch.* Maintain an engine speed of 1200–2000 rpm (use a tachometer). Disconnect the oxygen sensor electrical lead at the sensor and connect a jumper wire to the harness end of the connector. Ground the other end of the jumper wire. The engine speed should increase (at least 50 rpm) for 15 seconds, then return to 1200–2000 rpm. (If not, on the four cylinder *only*, disconnect the four-way tee from the air cleaner temperature sensor, allowing the engine to draw in air. Repeat the test; if no response, replace the computer.) Next, connect the end of the jumper wire to the positive battery terminal; engine speed should

drop. If the computer fails these tests, replace it. Reconnect the wires.

4. To test the oxygen sensor, run the engine at 1200–2000 rpm. Connect a voltmeter to the solenoid output wire which runs to the carburetor (18 DGN). Hold the choke plate closed. Over the next ten seconds, voltage should drop to 3 V. or less. If not, disconnect the air cleaner temperature sensor four-way tee and repeat the test. If no response, replace the computer.

Disconnect the PCV hose and/or the canister purge hose. Over the next ten seconds, voltage should be over 9 V. Voltage should then drop slightly, and remain there until the vacuum hoses are reconnected.

If the oxygen sensor fails these tests, replace it. Reconnect all wires.

NOTE: Oxygen sensor replacement and mileage counter reset procedures are the same as outlined in the 1979 system tests.

AMERICAN MOTORS FEEDBACK SYSTEM

General Information

American Motors introduced feedback systems on all cars (except Eagle) in 1980. Two different, but similar, systems are used. The four cylinder engine uses the G.M. C-4 feedback system, which is covered earlier in this section. Component usage is identical to that of the G.M. 151 cu. in four cylinder engine, including an oxygen sensor, a vacuum switch (which is closed at idle and partial throttle positions), a wide open throttle switch, a coolant temperature sensor (set to open at 150°F), an Electronic Control Module (ECM) equipped with modular Programmable Read Only Memory (PROM), and a mixture control solenoid installed in the air horn on the E2SE carburetor. A "Check Engine" light is included on the instrument panel as a service and diagnostic indicator.

The six cylinder engine is equipped with a Computerized Emission Control (CEC) System.

1980 CEC components include an oxygen sensor; two vacuum switches (one ported and one manifold) to detect three operating conditions: idle, partial throttle, and wide

open throttle; a coolant temperature switch; a Micro Computer Unit (MCU), the control unit for the system which monitors all data and sends an output signal to the carburetor; and a stepper motor installed in the main body of the BBD carburetor, which varies the position of the two metering pins controlling the size of the air bleed orifices in the carburetor. The MCU also interprets signals from the distributor (rpm voltage) to monitor engine rpm.

On 1981 and later models with CEC, the number of sensors has been increased. Three vacuum operated electric switches, two mechanically operated electric switches, one engine coolant switch and an air temperature operated switch are used to detect and send engine operating data to the MCU concerning the following engine operating conditions: cold engine start-up and operation; wide open throttle; idle (closed throttle); and partial and deep throttle.

Both AMC systems are conventional in operation. As in other feedback systems, two modes of operation are possible: open loop and closed loop. Open loop operation occurs during engine starting, cold engine operation, cold oxygen sensor operation, engine idling, wide open throttle operation, and low battery voltage operation. In open loop, a fixed air/fuel mixture signal is provided by the ECM or MCU to the carburetor, and oxygen sensor data is ignored. Closed loop operation occurs at all other times, and in this mode all signals are used by the control unit to determine the optimum air/fuel mixture.

Component Replacement

OXYGEN SENSOR

Removal and Installation

1. Disconnect the two wire plug.
2. Remove the sensor from the exhaust manifold on the four cylinder, or the exhaust pipe on the six.
3. Clean the threads in the manifold or pipe.
4. Coat the threads of the replacement sensor with an electrically-conductive anti-seize compound. Do not use a conventional antiseize compound, which may electrically insulate the sensor.
5. Install the sensor. Installation torque is 25 ft. lbs. for the four cylinder, 31 ft. lbs. for the six cylinder.
6. Connect the sensor lead. Do not push the rubber boot into the sensor body more than ½ inch above the base.
7. If the sensor's pigtail is broken, replace the sensor. The wires cannot be spliced or soldered.

VACUUM SWITCH

Removal and Installation

The vacuum switches are mounted in a bracket bolted to the left inner fender panel in the engine compartment. They are not replaceable individually; the complete unit must be replaced.

1. Tag all the vacuum hoses, then disconnect them from the switches. Disconnect the electrical plugs. The four cylinder has two plugs and the six has one.
2. Remove the switch and bracket assembly from the fender panel.
3. Installation is the reverse.

CONTROL UNIT

Removal and Installation

The control unit, whether ECM or MCU, is mounted in the passenger compartment, beneath the right side of the instrument panel.

1. The ECM is installed in a mounting bracket; remove it from the bracket. The MCU is attached with bolts; remove the bolts and remove the unit.
2. Disconnect the electrical plugs.
3. Installation is the reverse. The four cylinder ECM is electrically insulated from the chassis; *do not ground the ECM bracket!*

MIXTURE CONTROL SOLENOID

Removal and Installation

The E2SE mixture control solenoid is installed in the air horn.

1. Remove the air cleaner case.
2. Disconnect the solenoid electrical plug.
3. Remove the solenoid retaining screws.
4. Remove the solenoid from the air horn.
5. Before installation, coat the rubber seal on the end of the stem with silicone grease or light engine oil. Install the solenoid, accurately aligning the stem with the recess at the bottom of the bowl. Use a new gasket. Connect the electrical plug and install the air cleaner.

STEPPER MOTOR

Removal and Installation

The BBD stepper motor is installed in the side of the main body of the carburetor.

1. Remove the air cleaner case.
2. Disconnect the electrical plug.
3. Remove the retaining screw and remove the motor from the side of the carburetor. Be careful not to drop the metering pins or the spring when removing the motor.
4. Installation is the reverse.

Engine Rebuilding

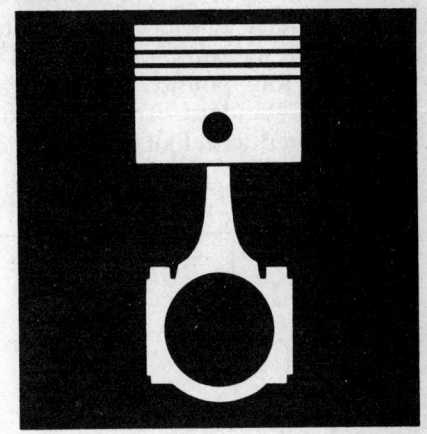

This section describes, in detail, the procedures involved in rebuilding a typical engine. The procedures are basically identical to those used in rebuilding engines of nearly all design and configurations.

The section is divided into two parts. The first, Cylinder Head Reconditioning, assumes that the cylinder head is removed from the engine, all manifolds are removed, and the cylinder head is on a workbench. The camshaft should be removed from overhead cam cylinder heads. The second section, Cylinder Block Reconditioning, covers the block, pistons, connecting rods and crankshaft. It is assumed that the engine is mounted on a work stand, and the cylinder head and all accessories are removed.

Procedures are identified as follows:

Unmarked—Basic procedures that must be performed in order to successfully complete the rebuilding process.

Starred (*)—Procedures that should be performed to ensure maximum performance and engine life.

Double starred (**)—Procedures that may be performed to increase engine performance and reliability.

In many cases, a choice of methods is also provided. Methods are identified in the same manner as procedures. The choice of method for a procedure is at the discretion of the user.

The tools required for the basic rebuilding procedure should, with minor exceptions, be those included in a mechanic's tool kit. An accurate torque wrench, and a dial indicator (reading in thousandths) mounted on a universal base should be available. Special tools, where required, all are readily available from the major tool suppliers. The services of a competent automotive machine shop must also be readily available.

When assembling the engine, any parts that will be in frictional contact must be pre-lubricated, to provide protection on initial start-up. Any product specifically formulated for this purpose may be used. NOTE: *Do not use engine oil*. Where semi-permanent (locked but removable) installation of bolts or nuts is desired, threads should be cleaned and coated with Loctite® or a similar product (non-hardening).

Aluminum has become increasingly popular for use in engines, due to its low weight and excellent heat transfer characteristics. The following precautions must be observed when handling aluminum engine parts:

—Never hot-tank aluminum parts.

—Remove all aluminum parts (identification tags, etc.) from engine parts before hot-tanking (otherwise they will be removed during the process).

—Always coat threads lightly with engine oil or anti-seize compounds before installation, to prevent seizure.

—Never over-torque bolts or spark plugs in aluminum threads. Should stripping occur, threads can be restored using any of a number of thread repair kits available (see next section).

Magnaflux and Zyglo are inspection techniques used to locate material flaws, such as stress cracks. Magnafluxing coats the part with fine magnetic particles, and subjects the part to a magnetic field. Cracks cause breaks in the magnetic field, which are outlined by the particles. Since Magnaflux is a magnetic process, it is applicable only to ferrous materials. The Zyglo process coats the material with a fluorescent dye penetrant, and then subjects it to blacklight inspection, under which cracks glow brightly. Parts made of any material may be tested using Zyglo. While Magnaflux and Zyglo are excellent for general inspection, and locating hidden defects, specific checks of suspected cracks may be made at lower cost and more readily using spot check dye. The dye is sprayed onto the suspected area, wiped off, and the area is then sprayed with a developer. Cracks then will show up brightly. Spot check dyes will only indicate surface cracks; therefore, structural cracks below the surface may escape detection. When questionable, the part should be tested using Magnaflux or Zyglo.

REPAIRING DAMAGED THREADS

Several methods of repairing damaged threads are available. Heli-Coil® (shown here), Keenserts® and Microdot® are among the most widely used. All involve basically the same principle—drilling out stripped threads, tapping the hole and installing a pre-wound insert— making welding, plugging and oversize fasteners unnecessary.

Two types of thread repair inserts are usually supplied—a standard type for most Inch Coarse, Inch Fine, Metric Coarse and Metric Fine thread sizes and a spark plug type to fit most spark plug port sizes. Consult the individual manufacturer's catalog to determine exact applications. Typical thread repair kits will contain a selection of prewound threaded inserts, a tap (corresponding to the outside diameter threads of the insert) and an installation tool. Most manufacturers also supply blister-packed thread repair inserts separately and a master kit with a variety of taps and inserts plus installation tools.

Before effecting a repair to a threaded hole, remove any snapped, broken or damaged bolts or studs. Penetrating oil can be used to free frozen threads; the offending item can be removed with locking pliers or with a screw or stud extractor. After the hole is clear, the thread can be repaired as follows.

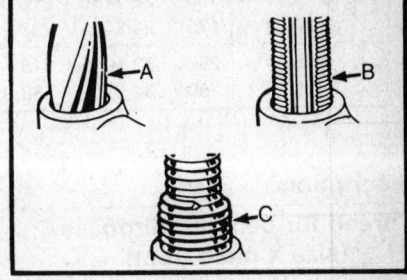

A. Drill out the damaged threads with the specified drill. Drill completely through the hole or to the bottom of a blind hole.

B. With the tap supplied tap the hole to receive the threaded insert. Keep the tap well oiled and back it out frequently to avoid clogging the threads.

C. Screw the threaded insert onto the installation tool until the tang engages the slot. Screw the insert into the tapped hole until it is ¼–½ turn below the top surface. After installation, break the tang off with a hammer and punch.

STANDARD TORQUE SPECIFICATIONS AND CAPSCREW MARKINGS

Newton-Meter has been designated as the world standard for measuring torque and will gradually replace the foot-pound and kilogram-meter torque measuring standard. Torquing tools are still being manufactured with foot-pounds and kilogram-meter scales, along with the new Newton-Meter standard. To assist the repairman, foot-pounds, kilogram-meter and Newton-Meter are listed in the following charts, and should be followed as applicable.

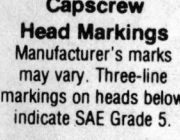

U.S. BOLTS

SAE Grade Number	1 or 2			5			6 or 7			8		
Capscrew Head Markings	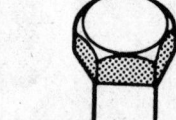											
Usage	Used Frequently			Used Frequently			Used at Times			Used at Times		
Quality of Material	Indeterminate			Minimum Commercial			Medium Commercial			Best Commercial		
Capacity Body Size	Torque			Torque			Torque			Torque		
(inches)–(thread)	Ft-Lb	kgm	Nm	Ft-Lb	kgm	Nm	Ft-Lb	kgm	Nm	Ft-Lb	kgm	Nm
1/4–20	5	0.6915	6.7791	8	1.1064	10.8465	10	1.3630	13.5582	12	1.6596	16.2698
–28	6	0.8298	8.1349	10	1.3830	13.5582				14	1.9362	18.9815
5/16–18	11	1.5213	14.9140	17	2.3511	23.0489	19	2.6277	25.7605	24	3.3192	32.5396
–24	13	1.7979	17.6256	19	2.6277	25.7605				27	3.7341	36.6071
3/8–16	18	2.4894	24.4047	31	4.2873	42.0304	34	4.7022	46.0978	44	6.0852	59.6560
–24	20	2.7660	27.1164	35	4.8405	47.4536				49	6.7767	66.4351
7/16–14	28	3.8132	37.9629	49	6.7767	66.4351	55	7.6065	74.5700	70	9.6810	94.9073
–20	30	4.1490	40.6745	55	7.6065	74.5700				78	10.7874	105.7538
1/2–13	39	5.3937	52.8769	75	10.3725	101.6863	85	11.7555	115.2445	105	14.5215	142.3609
–20	41	5.6703	55.5885	85	11.7555	115.2445				120	16.5860	162.6960
9/16–12	51	7.0533	69.1467	110	15.2130	149.1380	120	16.5960	162.6960	155	21.4365	210.1490
–18	55	7.6065	74.5700	120	16.5960	162.6960				170	23.5110	230.4860
5/8–11	83	11.4789	112.5329	150	20.7450	203.3700	167	23.0961	226.4186	210	29.0430	284.7180
–18	95	13.1385	128.8027	170	23.5110	230.4860				240	33.1920	325.3920
3/4–10	105	14.5215	142.3609	270	37.3410	366.0660	280	38.7240	379.6240	375	51.8625	508.4250
–16	115	15.9045	155.9170	295	40.7985	399.9610				420	58.0860	568.4360
7/8–9	160	22.1280	216.9280	395	54.6285	535.5410	440	60.8520	596.5520	605	83.6715	820.2590
–14	175	24.2025	237.2650	435	60.1605	589.7730				675	93.3525	915.1650
1–8	236	32.5005	318.6130	590	81.5970	799.9220	660	91.2780	894.8280	910	125.8530	1233.7780
–14	250	34.5750	338.9500	660	91.2780	849.8280				990	136.9170	1342.2420

METRIC BOLTS

Description Thread for general purposes (size x pitch (mm))	Torque ft-lbs. (Nm)			
	Head Mark 4		Head Mark 7	
6 x 1.0	2.2 to 2.9	(3.0 to 3.9)	3.6 to 5.8	(4.9 to 7.8)
8 x 1.25	5.8 to 8.7	(7.9 to 12)	9.4 to 14	(13 to 19)
10 x 1.25	12 to 17	(16 to 23)	20 to 29	(27 to 39)
12 x 1.25	21 to 32	(29 to 43)	35 to 53	(47 to 72)
14 x 1.5	35 to 52	(48 to 70)	57 to 85	(77 to 110)
16 x 1.5	51 to 77	(67 to 100)	90 to 120	(130 to 160)
18 x 1.5	74 to 110	(100 to 150)	130 to 170	(180 to 230)
20 x 1.5	110 to 140	(150 to 190)	190 to 240	(160 to 320)
22 x 1.5	150 to 190	(200 to 260)	250 to 320	(340 to 430)
24 x 1.5	190 to 240	(260 to 320)	310 to 410	(420 to 550)

CAUTION: Bolts threaded into aluminum require much less torque

NOTE: This engine rebuilding section is a guide to accepted rebuilding procedures. Typical examples of standard rebuilding procedures are illustrated.

CYLINDER HEAD RECONDITIONING

Procedure	Method
Identify the valves:	Invert the cylinder head, and number the valve faces front to rear, using a permanent felt-tip marker.
Remove the rocker arms (OHV engines only):	Remove the rocker arms with shaft(s) or balls and nuts. Wire the sets of rockers, balls and nuts together, and identify according to the corresponding valve.
Remove the camshaft (OHC engines only):	See the engine service procedures earlier in this book for details concerning specific engines.
Remove the valves and springs:	Using an appropriate valve spring compressor (depending on the configuration of the cylinder head), compress the valve springs. Lift out the keepers with needlenose pliers, release the compressor, and remove the valve, spring, and spring retainer.
Remove glow plugs and fuel injectors (Diesel engines only):	Label and remove all fuel injectors and glow plugs from the head. Glow plugs unscrew. See the appropriate car section for injector removal. Inspect glow plugs for bulges, cracks or signs of melting. Clean injector tips with a steel brush, then inspect for evidence of melting.
**Remove pre-combustion chamber inserts (Diesel engines only): 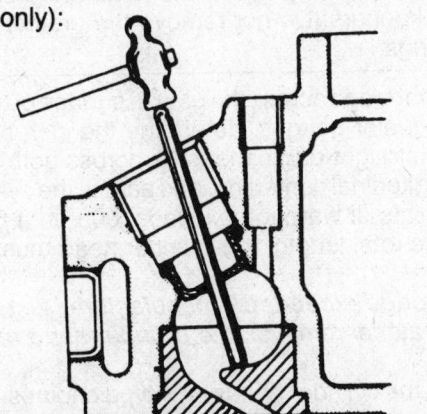 Removing pre-combustion chamber with a drift (© G.M. Corp.)	**Remove the pre-combustion chambers using a hammer and a thin, blunt brass drift, inserted through the injector hole (or glow plug hole, whichever is more convenient). If chamber is to be reused, carefully remove all carbon from it. NOTE: *Remove chamber only if being replaced, if a glow plug tip has broken off and must be removed, or if chamber is obviously damaged or loose.*
Check the valve stem-to-guide clearance: DIAL INDICATOR VALVE STEM Checking the valve stem-to-guide clearance	Clean the valve stem with lacquer thinner or a similar solvent to remove all gum and varnish. Clean the valve guides using solvent and an expanding wire-type valve guide cleaner. Mount a dial indicator so that the stem is at 90° to the valve stem, as close to the valve guide as possible. Move the valve off its seat, and measure the valve guide-to-stem clearance by rocking the stem back and forth to actuate the dial indicator. Measure the valve stems using a micrometer, and compare to specifications, to determine whether stem or guide wear is responsible for excessive clearance.

CYLINDER HEAD RECONDITIONING

Procedure	Method

De-carbon the cylinder head and valves:

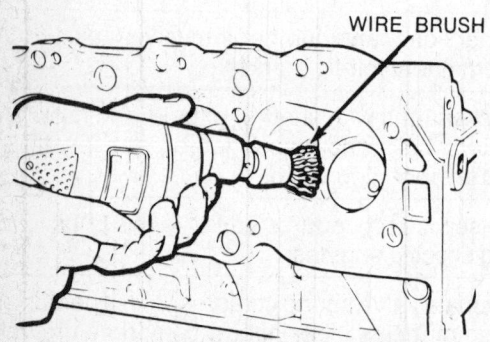

WIRE BRUSH

Removing carbon from the cylinder head

Chip carbon away from the valve heads, combustion chambers, and ports, using a chisel made of hardwood. Remove the remaining deposits with a stiff wire brush.
NOTE: *Ensure that the deposits are actually removed, rather than burnished.*

Hot-tank the cylinder head (cast iron heads only):
CAUTION: *Do not hot-tank aluminum parts.*

Have the cylinder head hot-tanked to remove grease, corrosion, and scale from the water passages.
NOTE: *In the case of overhead cam cylinder heads, consult the operator to determine whether the camshaft bearings will be damaged by the caustic solution.*

Degrease the remaining cylinder head parts:

Using solvent (i.e., Gunk), clean the rockers, rocker shaft(s) (where applicable), rocker balls and nuts, springs, spring retainers, and keepers. Do not remove the protective coating from the springs.

Check the cylinder head for warpage:

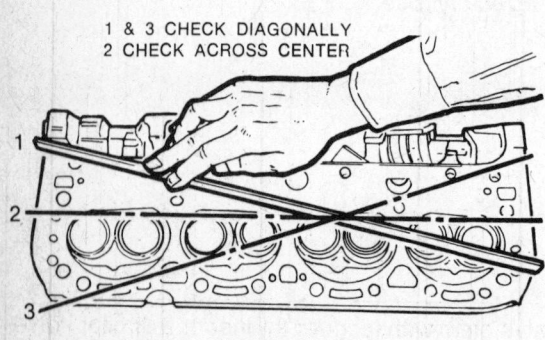

1 & 3 CHECK DIAGONALLY
2 CHECK ACROSS CENTER

Checking cylinder head for warpage

Place a straight-edge across the gasket surface of the cylinder head. Using feeler gauges, determine the clearance at the center of the straight-edge. Measure across both diagonals, along the longitudinal centerline, and across the cylinder head at several points. If warpage exceeds .003' in a 6' span, or .006' over the total length, the cylinder head must be resurfaced.
NOTE: *If warpage exceeds the manufacturer's maximum tolerance for material removal, the cylinder head must be replaced.*
When milling the cylinder heads of V-type engines, the intake manifold mounting position is altered, and must be corrected by milling the manifold flange a proportionate amount.

**Porting and gasket matching:

**Coat the manifold flanges of the cylinder head with Prussian blue dye. Glue intake and exhaust gaskets to the cylinder head in their installed position using rubber cement and scribe the outline of the ports on the manifold flanges. Remove the gaskets. Using a small cutter in a hand-held power tool gradually taper the walls of the port out to the scribed outline of the gasket. Further enlargement of the ports should include the removal of sharp edges and radiusing of sharp corners. Do not alter the valve guides.
NOTE: *The most efficient port configuration is determined only by extensive testing. Therefore, it is best to consult someone experienced with the head in question to determine the optimum alterations.*

CYLINDER HEAD RECONDITIONING

Procedure	Method

*Knurling the valve guides:

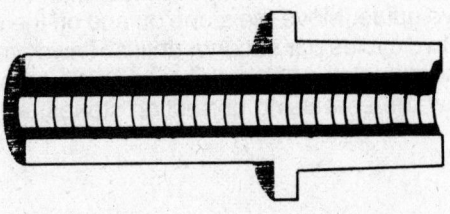

Cut-away view of a knurled valve guide

*Valve guides which are not excessively worn or distorted may, in some cases, be knurled rather than replaced. Knurling is a process in which metal is displaced and raised, thereby reducing clearance. Knurling also provides excellent oil control. The possibility of knurling rather than replacing valve guides should be discussed with a machinist.

Replacing the valve guides:
NOTE: *Valve guides should only be replaced if damaged or if an oversize valve stem is not available.*

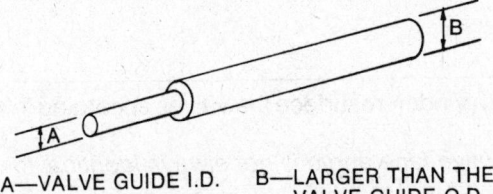

A—VALVE GUIDE I.D.   B—LARGER THAN THE VALVE GUIDE O.D.

Valve guide removal tool

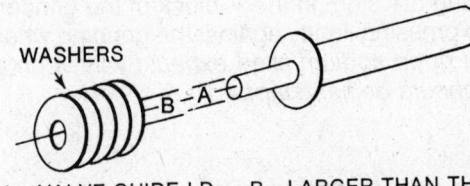

WASHERS

A—VALVE GUIDE I.D.   B—LARGER THAN THE VALVE GUIDE O.D.

Valve guide installation tool (with washers used for installation)

Depending on the type of cylinder head, valve guides may be pressed, hammered, or shrunk in. In cases where the guides are shrunk into the head, replacement should be left to an equipped machine shop. In other cases, the guides are replaced as follows: Press or tap the valve guides out of the head using a stepped drift (see illustration). Determine the height above the boss that the guide must extend, and obtain a stack of washers, their I.D. similar to the guide's O.D., of that height. Place the stack of washers on the guide, and insert the guide into the boss.
NOTE: *Valve guides are often tapered or beveled for installation.*
Using the stepped installation tool (see illustration), press or tap the guides into position. Ream the guides according to the size of the valve stem.

Replacing valve seat inserts:

Replacement of valve seat inserts which are worn beyond resurfacing or broken, if feasible, must be done by a machine shop.

Resurfacing the valve seats using reamers:

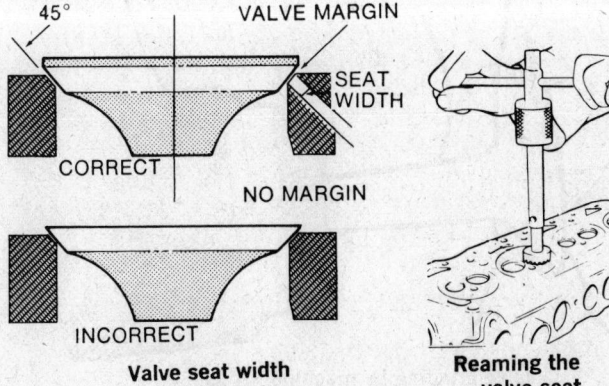

45°   VALVE MARGIN

SEAT WIDTH

CORRECT

NO MARGIN

INCORRECT

Valve seat width and centering

Reaming the valve seat

Select a reamer of the correct seat angle, slightly larger than the diameter of the valve seat, and assemble it with a pilot of the correct size. Install the pilot into the valve guide, and using steady pressure, turn the reamer clockwise.
CAUTION: *Do not turn the reamer counterclockwise.*
Remove only as much material as necessary to clean the seat. Check the concentricity of the seat (see below). If the dye method is not used, coat the valve face with Prussian blue dye, install and rotate it on the valve seat. Using the dye marked area as a centering guide, center and narrow the valve seat to specifications with correction cutters.
NOTE: *When no specifications are available, minimum seat width for exhaust valves should be 5/64", intake valves 1/16".*
After making correction cuts, check the position of the valve seat on the valve face using Prussian blue dye.
NOTE: *Do not cut induction hardened seats; they must be ground.*

CYLINDER HEAD RECONDITIONING

Procedure	Method

*Resurfacing the valve seats using a grinder:

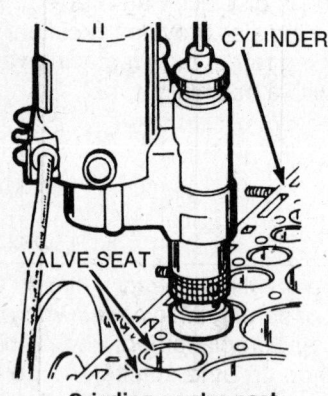

Grinding a valve seat

*Select a pilot of the correct size, and a coarse stone of the correct seat angle. Lubricate the pilot if necessary, and install the tool in the valve guide. Move the stone on and off the seat at approximately two cycles per second, until all flaws are removed from the seat. Install a fine stone, and finish the seat. Center and narrow the seat using correction stones, as described above.

Resurfacing (grinding) the valve face:

Using a valve grinder, resurface the valves according to specifications.

CAUTION: *Valve face angle is not always identical to valve seat angle.*

A minimum margin of 1/32" should remain after grinding the valve. The valve stem top should also be squared and resurfaced, by placing the stem in the V-block of the grinder, and turning it while pressing lightly against the grinding wheel.

NOTE: *Do not grind sodium filled exhaust valves on a machine. These should be hand lapped.*

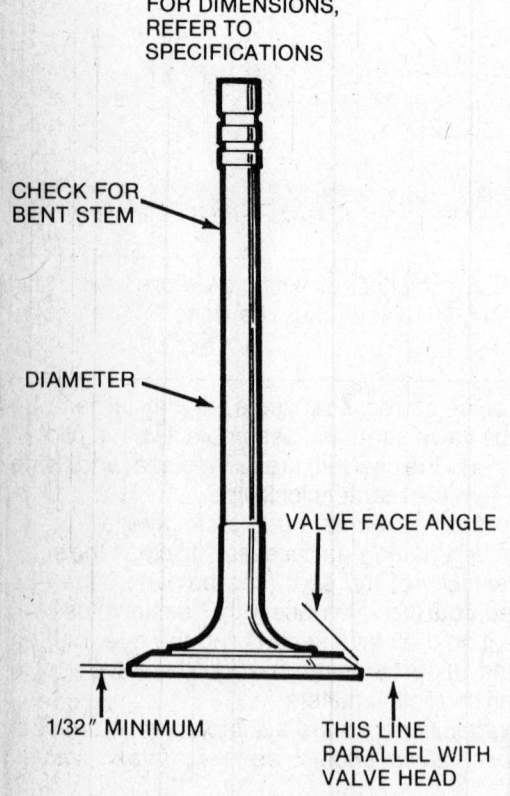

Critical valve dimensions

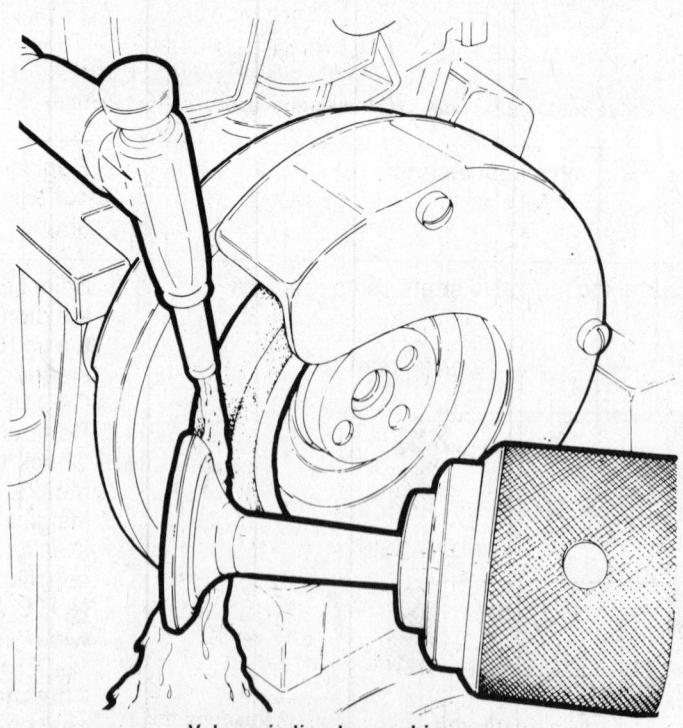

Valve grinding by machine

CYLINDER HEAD RECONDITIONING

| Procedure | Method |

Checking the valve seat concentricity:

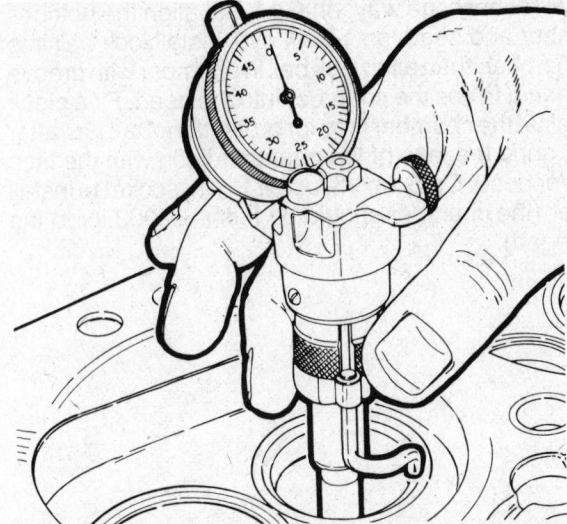

Checking valve seat concentricity using a dial gauge

Coat the valve face with Prussian blue dye, install the valve, and rotate it on the valve seat. If the entire seat becomes coated, and the valve is known to be concentric, the seat is concentric.

*Install the dial gauge pilot into the guide, and rest the arm on the valve seat. Zero the gauge, and rotate the arm around the seat. Run-out should not exceed .002".

*Lapping the valves:
NOTE: *Valve lapping is done to ensure efficient sealing of resurfaced valves and seats.*

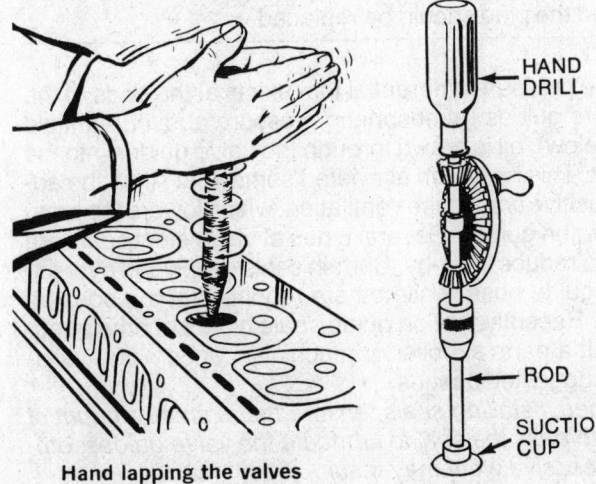

HAND DRILL

ROD

SUCTION CUP

Hand lapping the valves

*Invert the cylinder head, lightly lubricate the valve stems, and install the valves in the head as numbered. Coat valve seats with fine grinding compound, and attach the lapping tool suction cup to a valve head.
NOTE: *Moisten the suction cup.*
Rotate the tool between the palms, changing position and lifting the tool often to prevent grooving. Lap the valve until a smooth, polished seat is evident. Remove the valve and tool, and rinse away all traces of grinding compound.
**Fasten a suction cup to a piece of drill rod, and mount the rod in a hand drill. Proceed as above, using the hand drill as a lapping tool.
CAUTION: *Due to the higher speeds involved when using the hand drill, care must be exercised to avoid grooving the seat.* Lift the tool and change direction of rotation often.

Home made mechanical valve lapping tool

Check the valve springs:

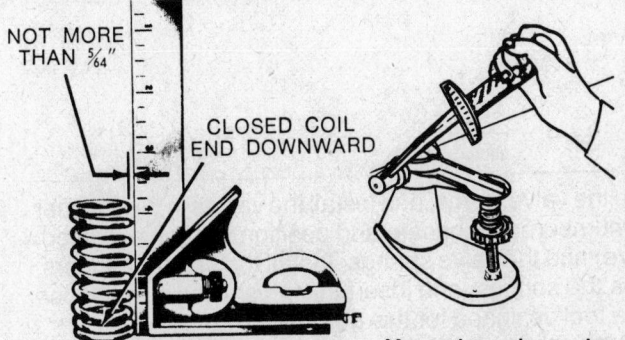

NOT MORE THAN ⁵⁄₆₄"

CLOSED COIL END DOWNWARD

Checking valve spring free length and squareness

Measuring valve spring test pressure

Place the spring on a flat surface next to a square. Measure the height of the spring, and rotate it against the edge of the square to measure distortion. If spring height varies (by comparison) by more than 1/16" or if distortion exceeds 1/16", replace the spring.
**In addition to evaluating the spring as above, test the spring pressure at the installed and compressed (installed height minus valve lift) height using a valve spring tester. Springs used on small displacement engines (up to 3 liters) should be ∓ 1 lb. of all other springs in either position. A tolerance of ∓ 5 lbs. is permissible on larger engines.

CYLINDER HEAD RECONDITIONING

Procedure

Method

Install pre-combustion chambers (Diesel engines only)

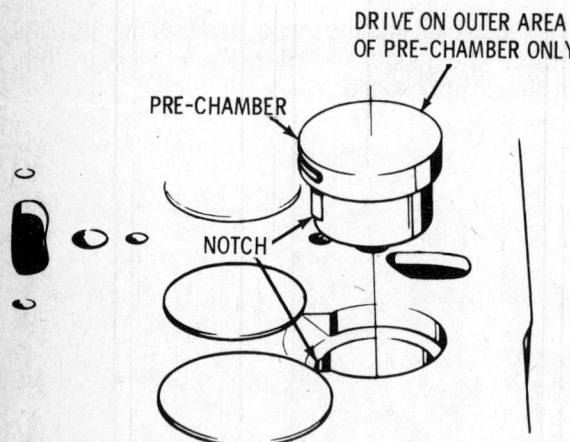

Align the notches to install the pre-combustion chamber
(© G.M. Corp.)

Pre-combustion chambers are press-fit into the head. The chambers will fit only one way: on G.M. V8, align the notches in the chamber and head; on 1.8L 4 cyl., install lock ball into groove in chamber, then align lock ball in chamber with groove in cylinder head. Press the chamber into the head. Fit a piece of metal against the chamber face for protection. On 1.8L, after installation, grind the face of the chamber flush with the face of the cylinder head. On G.M. V8, use a 1¼ in. socket to install the chamber (the chamber should be flush ± .003 in. to the face of the head).

Install fuel injectors and glow plugs (Diesel engines)

Before installing glow plugs, check for continuity across plug terminals and body. If no continuity exists, the heater wire is broken and the plug should be replaced.

*Install valve stem seals:

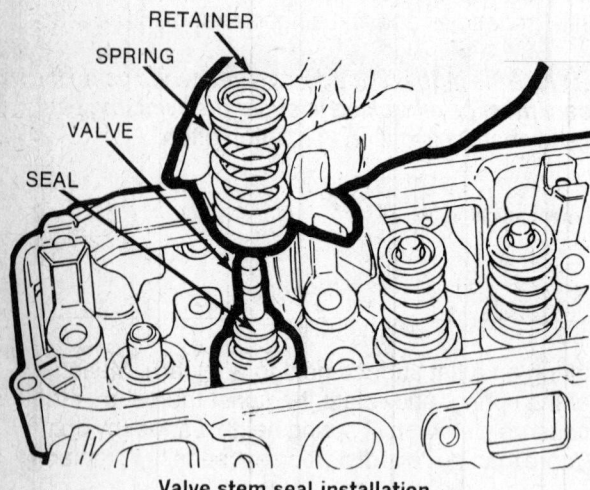

Valve stem seal installation

*Due to the pressure differential that exists at the ends of the intake valve guides (atmospheric pressure above, manifold vacuum below), oil is drawn through the valve guides into the intake port. This has been alleviated somewhat since the addition of positive crankcase ventilation, which lowers the pressure above the guides. Several types of valve stem seals are available to reduce blow-by. Certain seals simply slip over the stem and guide boss, while others require that the boss be machined. Recently, Teflon guide seals have become popular. Consult a parts supplier or machinist concerning availability and suggested usages.
NOTE: *When installing seals, ensure that a small amount of oil is able to pass the seal to lubricate the valve guides; otherwise, excessive wear may result.*

Install the valves:

Lubricate the valve stems, and install the valves in the cylinder head as numbered. Lubricate and position the seals (if used, see above) and the valve springs. Install the spring retainers, compress the springs, and insert the keys using needlenose pliers or a tool designed for this purpose.
NOTE: *Retain the keys with wheel bearing grease during installation.*

CYLINDER HEAD RECONDITIONING

Procedure	Method

Check valve spring installed height:

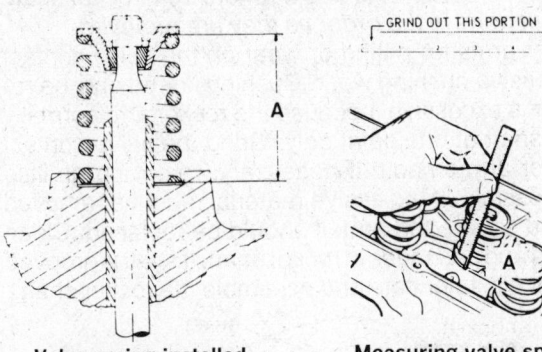

GRIND OUT THIS PORTION

Valve spring installed
height dimension

Measuring valve spring
installed height

Measure the distance between the spring pad and the lower edge of the spring retainer, and compare to specifications. If the installed height is incorrect, add shim washers between the spring pad and the spring.
CAUTION: *Use only washers designed for this purpose.*

Install the camshaft (OHC engines only) and check end play:

See the engine service procedures earlier in this book for details concerning specific engines.

Inspect the rocker arms, balls, studs, and nuts (OHV engines only):

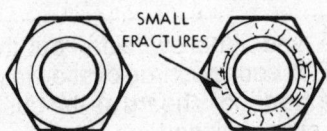

SMALL FRACTURES

Stress cracks in the rocker nuts

Visually inspect the rocker arms, balls, studs, and nuts for cracks, galling, burning, scoring or wear. If all parts are intact, liberally lubricate the rocker arms and balls, and install them on the cylinder head. If wear is noted on a rocker arm at the point of valve contact, grind it smooth and square, removing as little material as possible. Replace the rocker arm if excessively worn. If a rocker stud shows signs of wear, it must be replaced (see below). If a rocker nut shows stress cracks, replace it. If an exhaust ball is galled or burned, substitute the intake ball from the same cylinder (if it is intact), and install a new intake ball.
NOTE: *Avoid using new rocker balls on exhaust valves.*

Replacing rocker studs (OHV engines only):

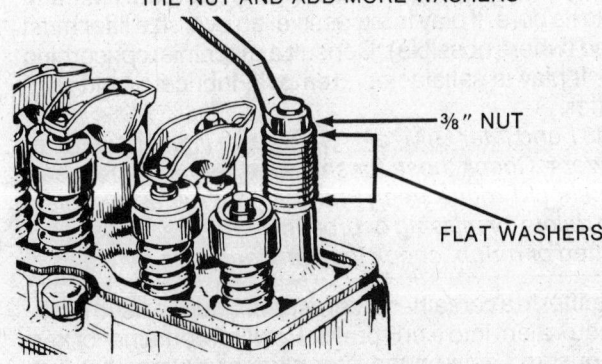

AS STUB BEGINS TO PULL UP,
IT WILL BE NECESSARY TO REMOVE
THE NUT AND ADD MORE WASHERS

⅜" NUT

FLAT WASHERS

Extracting a pressed-in rocker stud

In order to remove a threaded stud, lock two nuts on the stud, and unscrew the stud using the lower nut. Coat the lower threads of the new stud with Loctite®, and install.
Two alternative methods are available for replacing pressed in studs. Remove the damaged stud using a stack of washers and a nut (see illustration). In the first, the boss is reamed .005–.006" oversize, and an oversize stud pressed in. Control the stud extension over the boss using washers, in the same manner as valve guides. Before installing the stud, coat it with white lead and grease. To retain the stud more positively drill a hole through the stud and boss, and install a roll pin. In the second method, the boss is tapped, and a threaded stud installed. Retain the stud using Loctite® Stud and Bearing Mount.

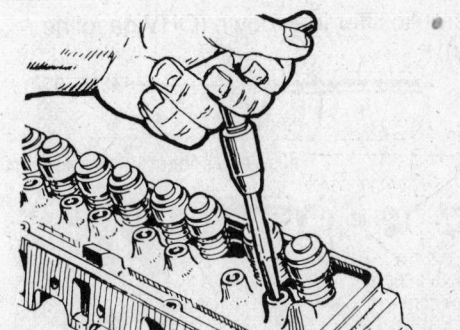

Reaming the stud bore for oversize rocker studs

CYLINDER HEAD RECONDITIONING

Procedure

Method

Inspect the rocker shaft(s) and rocker arms (OHV engines only):

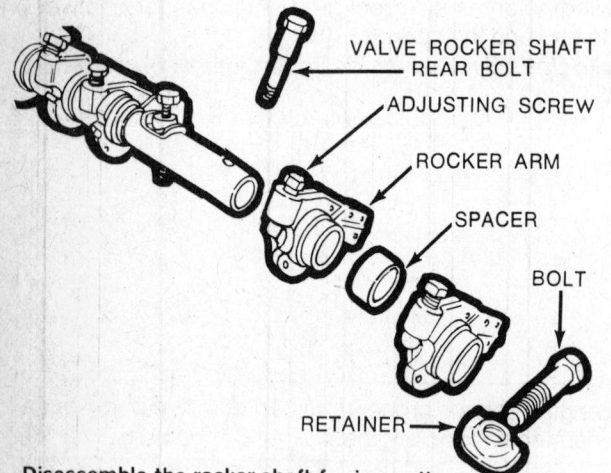

VALVE ROCKER SHAFT REAR BOLT

ADJUSTING SCREW

ROCKER ARM

SPACER

BOLT

RETAINER

Disassemble the rocker shaft for inspection

Remove rocker arms, springs and washers from rocker shaft. NOTE: *Lay out parts in the order as they are removed.* Inspect rocker arms for pitting or wear on the valve contact point, or excessive bushing wear. Bushings need only be replaced if wear is excessive, because the rocker arm normally contacts the shaft at one point only. Grind the valve contact point of rocker arm smooth if necessary, removing as little material as possible. If excessive material must be removed to smooth and square the arm, it should be replaced. Clean out all oil holes and passages in rocker shaft. If shaft is grooved or worn, replace it. Lubricate and assemble the rocker shaft.

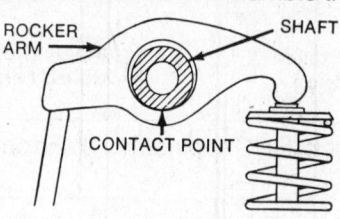

ROCKER ARM

SHAFT

CONTACT POINT

Rocker arm-to-rocker shaft contact area

Inspect the camshaft bushings and the camshaft (OHC engines):

See next section.

Inspect the pushrods (OHV engines only):

Remove the pushrods, and, if hollow, clean out the oil passages using fine wire. Roll each pushrod over a piece of clean glass. If a distinct clicking sound is heard as the pushrod rolls, the rod is bent, and must be replaced.

*The length of all pushrods must be equal. Measure the length of the pushrods, compare to specifications, and replace as necessary.

Inspect the valve lifters (OHV engines only):

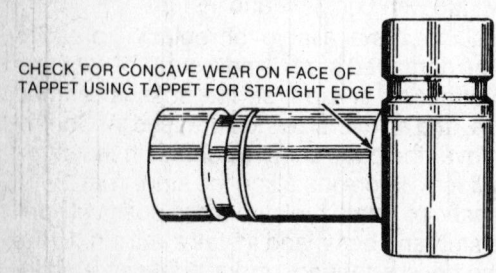

CHECK FOR CONCAVE WEAR ON FACE OF TAPPET USING TAPPET FOR STRAIGHT EDGE

Checking the lifter face

Remove lifters from their bores, and remove gum and varnish, using solvent. Clean walls of lifter bores. Check lifters for concave wear as illustrated. If face is worn concave, replace lifter, and carefully inspect the camshaft. Lightly lubricate lifter and insert it into its bore. If play is excessive, an oversize lifter must be installed (where possible). Consult a machinist concerning feasibility. If play is satisfactory, remove, lubricate, and reinstall the lifter.
NOTE: *1981 and later G.M. diesel V8 valve lifters have roller cam followers. Check these for smooth operation and wear. The roller should rotate freely, but without excessive play. Check the rollers for missing or broken needle bearings. If the roller is pitted or rough, check the camshaft lobe for wear.*

*Testing hydraulic lifter leak down (OHV gasoline engines only):

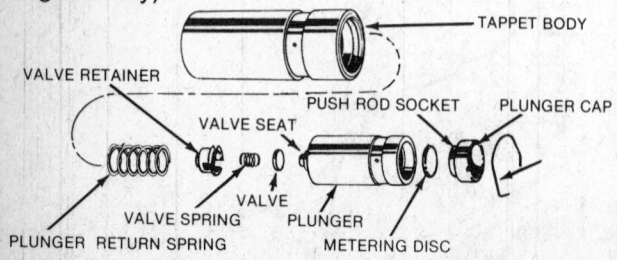

TAPPET BODY

VALVE RETAINER

PUSH ROD SOCKET

PLUNGER CAP

VALVE SEAT

VALVE

PLUNGER

PLUNGER RETURN SPRING

VALVE SPRING

METERING DISC

Typical exploded view of hydraulic valve lifter

Submerge lifter in a container of kerosene. Chuck a used pushrod or its equivalent into a drill press. Position container of kerosene so pushrod acts on the lifter plunger. Pump lifter with the drill press, until resistance increases. Pump several more times to bleed any air out of lifter. Apply very firm, constant pressure to the lifter, and observe rate at which fluid bleeds out of lifter. If the fluid bleeds very quickly (less than 15 seconds), lifter is defective. If the time exceeds 60 seconds, lifter is sticking. In either case, recondition or replace lifter. If lifter is operating properly (leak down time 15–60 seconds), lubricate and install it.

CYLINDER HEAD RECONDITIONING

Procedure	Method
Bleed the hydraulic lifters (diesel engines only):	After the cylinder heads are installed on G.M. V8 diesels, the valve lifters must be bled down before the crankshaft is turned. Failure to bleed down the lifters will cause damage to the valve train. See diesel engine rocker arm replacement procedure in Oldsmobile 88, 98, etc. car section for procedures. NOTE: *When installing new lifters, prime by working the lifter plunger while submerged in clean kerosene or diesel fuel.*

CYLINDER BLOCK RECONDITIONING

Procedure	Method
Checking the main bearing clearance: 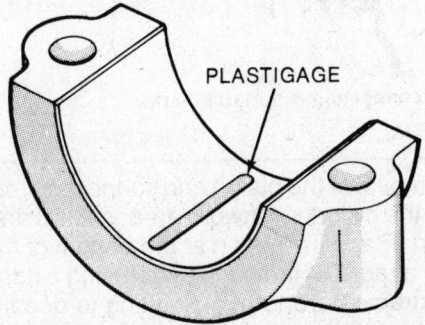 Plastigage® installed on the lower bearing shell 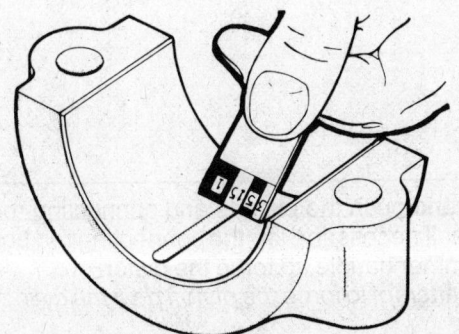 Measuring Plastigage® to determine bearing clearance	Invert engine, and remove cap from the bearing to be checked. Using a clean, dry rag, thoroughly clean all oil from crankshaft journal and bearing insert. NOTE: *Plastigage is soluble in oil; therefore, oil on the journal or bearing could result in erroneous readings.* Place a piece of Plastigage along the full length of journal, reinstall cap, and torque to specifications. Remove bearing cap, and determine bearing clearance by comparing width of Plastigage to the scale on Plastigage envelope. Journal taper is determined by comparing width of the Plastigage strip near its ends. Rotate crankshaft 90° and retest, to determine journal eccentricity. NOTE: *Do not rotate crankshaft with Plastigage installed.* If bearing insert and journal appear intact, and are within tolerances, no further main bearing service is required. If bearing or journal appear defective, cause of failure should be determined before replacement. *Remove crankshaft from block (see below). Measure the main bearing journals at each end twice (90° apart) using a micrometer, to determine diameter, journal taper and eccentricity. If journals are within tolerances, reinstall bearing caps at their specified torque. Using a telescope gauge and micrometer, measure bearing I.D. parallel to piston axis and at 30° on each side of piston axis. Subtract journal O.D. from bearing I.D. to determine oil clearance. If crankshaft journals appear defective, or do no meet tolerances, there is no need to measure bearings; for the crankshaft will require grinding and/or undersize bearings will be required. If bearing appears defective, cause for failure should be determined prior to replacement.
Checking the connecting rod bearing clearance:	Connecting rod bearing clearance is checked in the same manner as main bearing clearance, using Plastigage. Before removing the crankshaft, connecting rod side clearance also should be measured and recorded. *Checking connecting rod bearing clearance, using a micrometer, is identical to checking main bearing clearance. If no other service is required, the piston and rod assemblies need not be removed.

CYLINDER BLOCK RECONDITIONING

Procedure	Method

Removing the crankshaft:

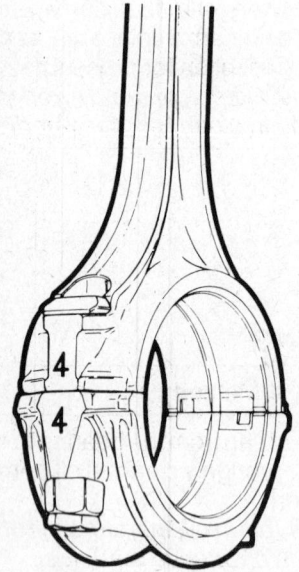

Connecting rod matched to cylinder with a number stamp

Using a punch, mark the corresponding main bearing caps and saddles according to position (i.e., one punch on the front main cap and saddle, two on the second, three on the third, etc.). Using number stamps, identify the corresponding connecting rods and caps, according to cylinder (if no numbers are present). Remove the main and connecting rod caps, and place sleeves of plastic tubing over the connecting rod bolts, to protect the journals as the crankshaft is removed. Lift the crankshaft out of the block.

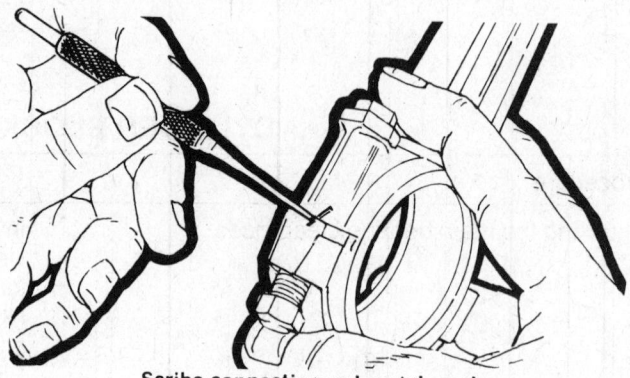

Scribe connecting rod matchmarks

Remove the ridge from the top of the cylinder:

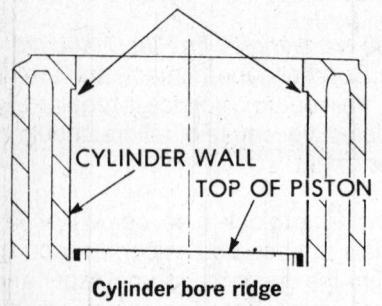

RIDGE CAUSED BY CYLINDER WEAR

CYLINDER WALL

TOP OF PISTON

Cylinder bore ridge

In order to facilitate removal of the piston and connecting rod, the ridge at the top of the cylinder (unworn area; see illustration) must be removed. Place the piston at the bottom of the bore, and cover it with a rag. Cut the ridge away using a ridge reamer, exercising extreme care to avoid cutting to deeply. Remove the rag, and remove cuttings that remain on the piston.

CAUTION: *If the ridge is not removed, and new rings are installed, damage to rings will result.*

Removing the piston and connecting rod:

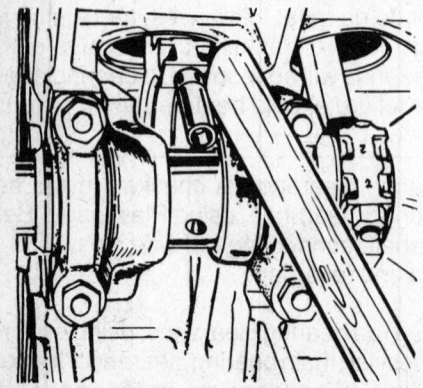

Removing the piston

Invert the engine, and push the pistons and connecting rods out of the cylinders. If necessary, tap the connecting rod boss with a wooden hammer handle, to force the piston out.

CAUTION: *Do not attempt to force the piston past the cylinder ridge (see above).*

CYLINDER BLOCK RECONDITIONING

Procedure	Method
Service the crankshaft:	Ensure that all oil holes and passages in the crankshaft are open and free of sludge. If necessary, have the crankshaft ground to the largest possible undersize.
	**Have the crankshaft Magnafluxed, to locate stress cracks. Consult a machinist concerning additional service procedures, such as surface hardening (e.g., nitriding, Tuftriding) to improve wear characteristics, cross drilling and chamfering the oil holes to improve lubrication, and balancing.
Removing freeze plugs:	Drill a small hole in the middle of the freeze plugs. Thread a large sheet metal screw into the hole and remove the plug with a slide hammer.
Remove the oil gallery plugs:	Threaded plugs should be removed using an appropriate (usually square) wrench. To remove soft, pressed in plugs, drill a hole in the plug, and thread in a sheet metal screw. Pull the plug out by the screw using pliers.
Hot-tank the block: NOTE: *Do not hot-tank aluminum parts.*	Have the block hot-tanked to remove grease, corrosion, and scale from the water jackets. NOTE: *Consult the operator to determine whether the camshaft bearings will be damaged during the hot-tank process.*

Check the block for cracks:	Visually inspect the block for cracks or chips. The most common locations are as follows:
	     Adjacent to freeze plugs.
	     Between the cylinders and water jackets.
	     Adjacent to the main bearing saddles.
	     At the extreme bottom of the cylinders.
	 Check only suspected cracks using spot check dye (see introduction). If a crack is located, consult a machinist concerning possible repairs.
	
	 **Magnaflux the block to locate hidden cracks. If cracks are located, consult a machinist about feasibility of repair.

Install the oil gallery plugs and freeze plugs:	Coat freeze plugs with sealer and tap into position using a piece of pipe, slightly smaller than the plug, as a driver. To ensure retention, stake the edges of the plugs. Coat threaded oil gallery plugs with sealer and install. Drive replacement soft plugs into block using a large drift as a driver. *Rather than reinstalling lead plugs, drill and tap the holes, and install threaded plugs.
*Check the deck height:	*The deck height is the distance from the crankshaft centerline to the block deck. To measure, invert the engine, and install the crankshaft, retaining it with the center main cap. Measure the distance from the crankshaft journal to the block deck, parallel to the cylinder centerline. Measure the diameter of the end (front and rear) main journals, parallel to the centerline of the cylinders, divide the diameter in half, and subtract it from the previous measurement. The results of the front and rear measurements should be identical. If the difference exceeds .005″, the deck height should be corrected. NOTE: *Block deck height and warpage should be corrected at the same time.*

CYLINDER BLOCK RECONDITIONING

Procedure	Method
Check the block deck for warpage:	Using a straightedge and feeler gauges, check the block deck for warpage in the same manner that the cylinder head is checked (see Cylinder Head Reconditioning). If warpage exceeds specifications, have the deck resurfaced. NOTE: *In certain cases a specification for total material removal (Cylinder head and block deck) is provided. This specification must not be exceeded.*
Check the bore diameter and surface:  Measuring the cylinder bore with a dial gauge	Visually inspect the cylinder bores for roughness, scoring, or scuffing. If evident, the cylinder bore must be bored or honed oversize to eliminate imperfections, and the smallest possible oversize piston used. The new pistons should be given to the machinist with the block, so that the cylinders can be bored or honed exactly to the piston size (plus clearance). If no flaws are evident, measure the bore diameter using a telescope gauge and micrometer, or dial guage, parallel and perpendicular to the engine centerline, at the top (below the ridge) and bottom of the bore. Subtract the bottom measurements from the top to determine taper, and the parallel to the centerline measurements from the perpendicular measurements to determine eccentricity. If the measurements are not within specifications, the cylinder must be bored or honed, and an oversize piston installed. If the measurements are within specifications the cylinder may be used as is, with only finish honing (see below). NOTE: *Prior to boring, check the block deck warpage, height and bearing alignment.* CAUTION: *The 4 cyl. 140 G.M. engine cylinder walls are impregnated with silicone. Boring or honing can be done only by a shop with the proper equipment.*

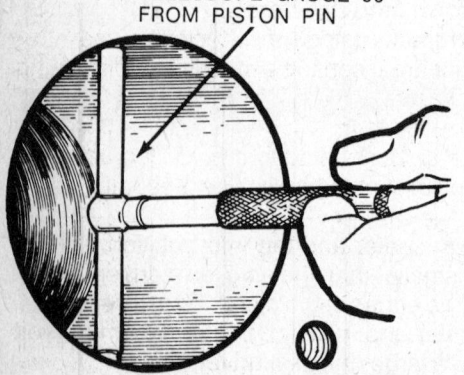

Measuring cylinder bore with a
telescope gauge

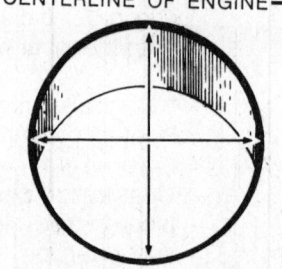

A—AT RIGHT ANGLE TO
CENTERLINE OF ENGINE
B—PARALLEL TO
CENTERLINE OF ENGINE
Cylinder bore measuring points

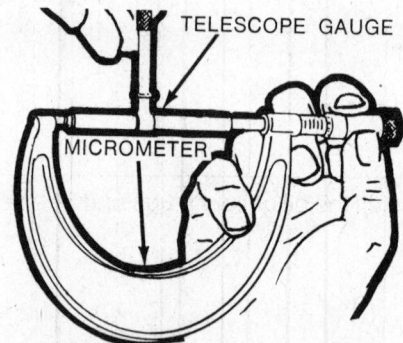

Determining cylinder bore by measuring
telescope gauge with a micrometer

Procedure	Method
Check the cylinder block bearing alignment: 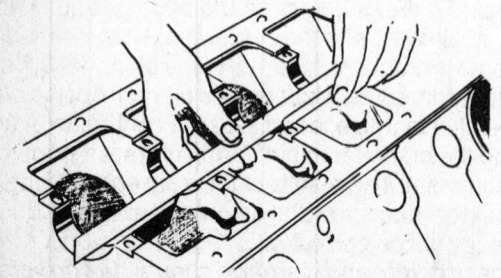 Checking main bearing saddle alignment	Remove the upper bearing inserts. Place a straightedge in the bearing saddles along the centerline of the crankshaft. If clearance exists between the straightedge and the center saddle, the block must be alignbored.

CYLINDER BLOCK RECONDITIONING

Procedure	Method

Clean and inspect the pistons and connecting rods:

Using a ring expander, remove the rings from the piston. Remove the retaining rings (if so equipped) and remove piston pin.

NOTE: *If the piston pin must be pressed out, determine the proper method and use the proper tools; otherwise the piston will distort.*

Clean the ring grooves using an appropriate tool, exercising care to avoid cutting too deeply. Thoroughly clean all carbon and varnish from the piston with solvent.

CAUTION: *Do not use a wire brush or caustic solvent on pistons.*

Inspect the pistons for scuffing, scoring, cracks, pitting, or excessive ring groove wear. If wear is evident, the piston must be replaced. Check the connecting rod length by measuring the rod from the inside of the large end to the inside of the small end using calipers (see illustration). All connecting rods should be equal length. Replace any rod that differs from the others in the engine.

*Have the connecting rod alignment checked in an alignment fixture by a machinist. Replace any twisted or bent rods.

*Magnaflux the connecting rods to locate stress cracks. If cracks are found, replace the connecting rod.

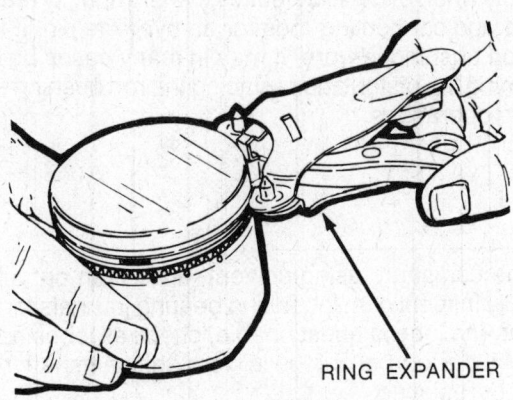

RING EXPANDER

Removing the piston rings

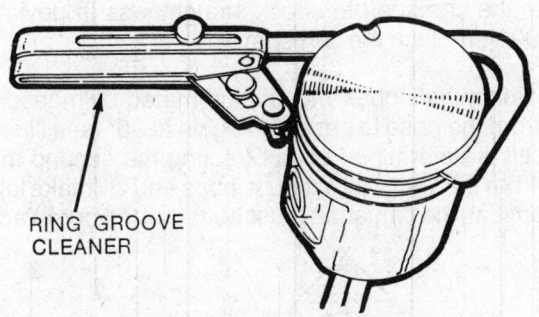

RING GROOVE CLEANER

Cleaning the piston ring grooves

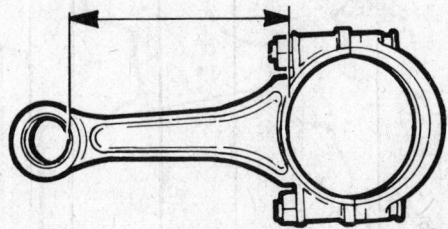

Check the connecting rod length (arrow)

Fit the pistons to the cylinders:

Using a telescope gauge and micrometer, or a dial gauge, measure the cylinder bore diameter perpendicular to the piston pin, 2½° below the deck. Measure the piston perpendicular to its pin on the skirt. The difference between the two measurements is the piston clearance. If the clearance is within specifications or slightly below (after boring or honing), finish honing is all that is required. If the clearance is excessive, try to obtain a slightly larger piston to bring clearance within specifications. Where this is not possible, obtain the first oversize piston, and hone (or if necessary, bore) the cylinder to size.

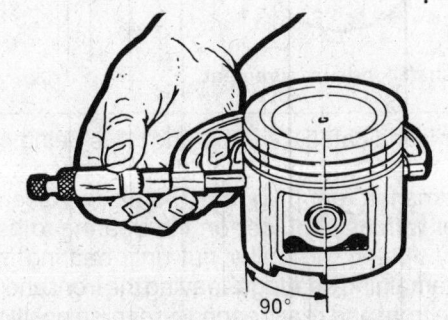

90°

Measuring the piston prior to fitting

Assemble the pistons and connecting rods:

Inspect piston pin, connecting rod small end bushing, and piston bore for galling, scoring, or excessive wear. If evident, replace defective part(s). Measure the I.D. of the piston boss and connecting rod small end, and the O.D. of the piston pin. If within specifications, assemble piston pin and rod.

CAUTION: *If piston pin must be pressed in, determine the proper method and use the proper tools; otherwise the piston will distort.*

CYLINDER BLOCK RECONDITIONING

Procedure

Method

Installing piston pin lock rings

Install the lock rings; ensure that they seat properly. If the parts are not within specifications, determine the service method for the type of engine. In some cases, piston and pin are serviced as an assembly when either is defective. Others specify reaming the piston and connecting rods for an oversize pin. If the connecting rod bushing is worn, it may in many cases be replaced. Reaming the piston and replacing the rod bushing are machine shop operations.

Clean and inspect the camshaft:

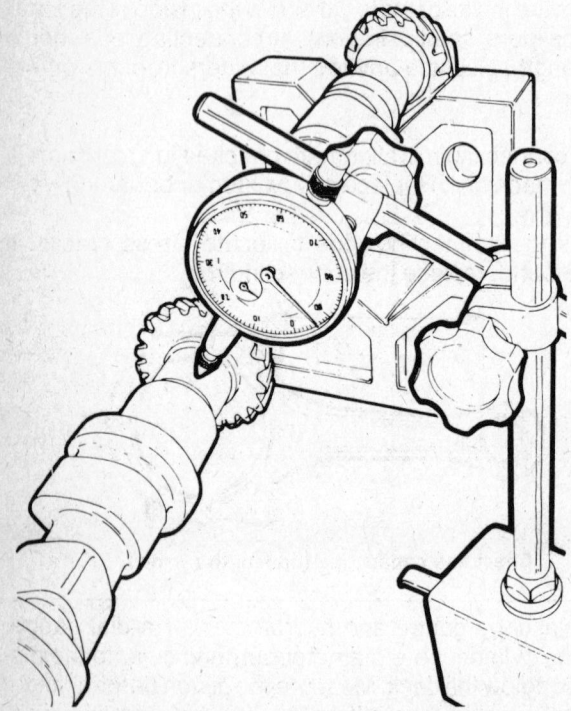

Checking the camshaft for straightness

Degrease the camshaft, using solvent, and clean out all oil holes. Visually inspect cam lobes and bearing journals for excessive wear. If a lobe is questionable, check all lobes as indicated below. If a journal or lobe is worn, the camshaft must be reground or replaced.

NOTE: *If a journal is worn, there is a good chance that the bushings are worn.*

If lobes and journals appear intact, place the front and rear journals in V-blocks, and rest a dial indicator on the center journal. Rotate the camshaft to check straightness. If deviation exceeds .001°, replace the camshaft.

*Check the camshaft lobes with a micrometer, by measuring the lobes from the nose to base and again at 90° (see illustration). The lift is determined by subtracting the second measurement from the first. If all exhaust lobes and all intake lobes are not identical, the camshaft must be reground or replaced.

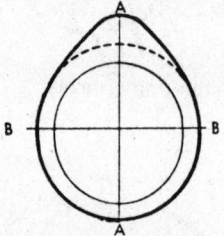

Camshaft lobe measurement

Replace the camshaft bearings (OHV engines only):

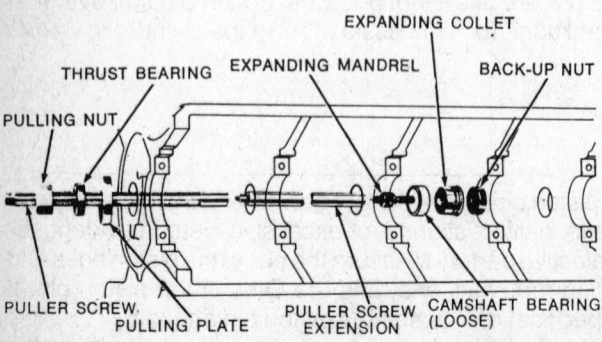

Camshaft removal and installation tool (typical)

If excessive wear is indicated, or if the engine is being completely rebuilt, camshaft bearings should be replaced as follows: Drive the camshaft rear plug from the block. Assemble the removal puller with its shoulder on the bearing to be removed. Gradually tighten the puller nut until bearing is removed. Remove remaining bearings, leaving the front and rear for last. To remove front and rear bearings, reverse position of the tool, so as to pull the bearings in toward the center of the block. Leave the tool in this position, pilot the new front and rear bearings on the installer, and pull them into position: Return the tool to its original position and pull remaining bearings into postion.

NOTE: *Ensure that oil holes align when installing bearings.*

Replace camshaft rear plug, and stake it into position to aid retention.

CYLINDER BLOCK RECONDITIONING

Procedure	Method

Finish hone the cylinders:

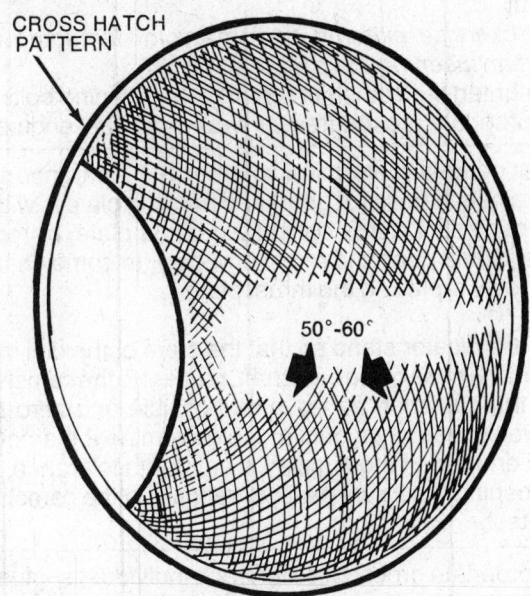

CROSS HATCH PATTERN

50°-60°

Chuck a flexible drive hone into a power drill, and insert it into the cylinder. Start the hone, and move it up and down the cylinder at a rate which will produce approximately a 60° cross-hatch pattern (see illustration).
NOTE: *Do not extend the hone below the cylinder bore.*
After developing the pattern, remove the hone and recheck piston fit. Wash the cylinders with a detergent and water solution to remove abrasive dust, dry, and wipe several times with a rag soaked in engine oil.

Check piston ring end-gap:

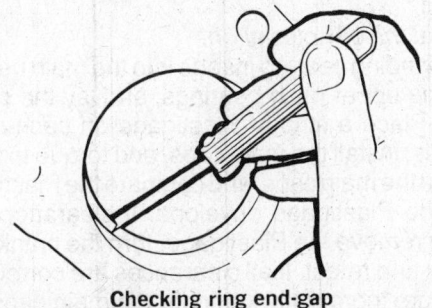

Checking ring end-gap

Compress the piston rings to be used in a cylinder, one at a time, into that cylinder, and press them approximately 1″ below the deck with an inverted piston. Using feeler gauges, measure the ring end-gap, and compare to specifications. Pull the ring out of the cylinder and file the ends with a fine file to obtain proper clearance.
CAUTION: *If inadequate ring end-gap is utilized, ring breakage will result.*

Install the piston rings:

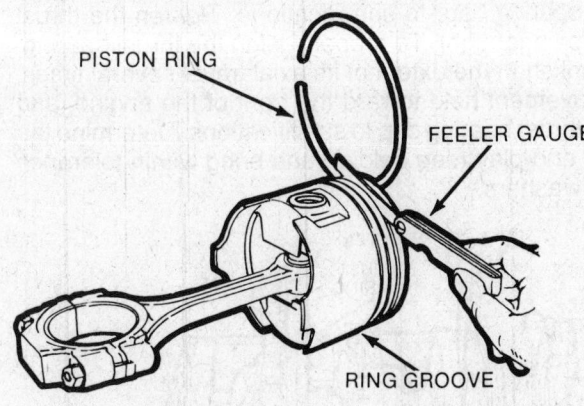

PISTON RING

FEELER GAUGE

RING GROOVE

Checking ring side clearance

Inspect the ring grooves in the piston for excessive wear or taper. If necessary, recut the groove(s) for use with an overwidth ring or a standard ring and spacer. If the groove is worn uniformly, overwidth rings, or standard rings and spacers may be installed without recutting. Roll the outside of the ring around the groove to check for burrs or deposits. If any are found, remove with a fine file. Hold the ring in the groove, and measure side clearance. If necessary, correct as indicated above.
NOTE: *Always install any additional spacers above the piston ring.*
The ring groove must be deep enough to allow the ring to seat below the lands (see illustration). In many cases, a "go-no-go" depth gauge will be provided with the piston rings. Shallow grooves may be corrected by recutting, while deep grooves require some type of filler or expander behind the piston. Consult the piston ring supplier concerning the suggested method. Install the rings on the piston, lowest ring first, using a ring expander.
NOTE: *Position the ring markings as specified by the manufacturer (see car section).*

CYLINDER BLOCK RECONDITIONING

Procedure	Method
Install the camshaft (OHV engines only):	Liberally lubricate the camshaft lobes and journals, and install the camshaft. CAUTION: *Exercise extreme care to avoid damaging the bearings when inserting the camshaft.* Install and tighten the camshaft thrust plate retaining bolts. See the appropriate procedures for each individual engine.

Check camshaft end-play (OHV engines only):

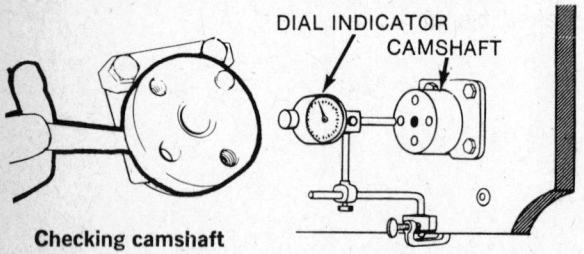

DIAL INDICATOR
CAMSHAFT

Checking camshaft end-play with a feeler gauge

Checking camshaft end-play with a dial indicator

Using feeler gauges, determine whether the clearance between the camshaft boss (or gear) and backing plate is within specifications. Install shims behind the thrust plate, or reposition the camshaft gear and retest end-play. In some cases, adjustment is by replacing the thrust plate.

*Mount a dial indicator stand so that the stem of the dial indicator rests on the nose of the camshaft, parallel to the camshaft axis. Push the camshaft as far in as possible and zero the gauge. Move the camshaft outward to determine the amount of camshaft endplay. If the endplay is not within tolerance, install shims behind the thrust plate, or reposition the camshaft gear and retest.

Install the rear main seal (where applicable):	See the appropriate procedures for each individual engine.

Install the crankshaft:

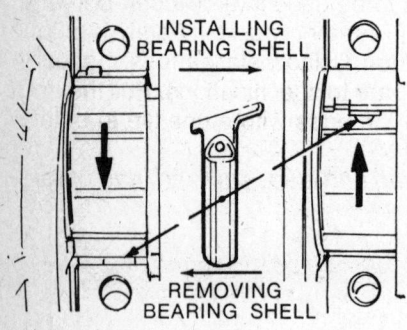

INSTALLING BEARING SHELL

REMOVING BEARING SHELL

Removal and installation of upper bearing insert using a roll-out pin

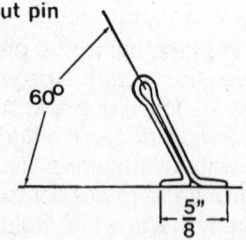

60°

$\frac{5}{8}$"

Home-made bearing roll-out pin

Thoroughly clean the main bearing saddles and caps. Place the upper halves of the bearing inserts on the saddles and press into position.
NOTE: *Ensure that the oil holes align.*
Press the corresponding bearing inserts into the main bearing caps. Lubricate the upper main bearings, and lay the crankshaft in position. Place a strip of Plastigage on each of the crankshaft journals, install the main caps, and torque to specifications. Remove the main caps, and compare the Plastigage to the scale on the Plastigage envelope. If clearances are within tolerances, remove the Plastigage, turn the crankshaft 90°, wipe off all oil and retest. If all clearances are correct, remove all Plastigage, thoroughly lubricate the main caps and bearing journals, and install the main caps. If clearances are not within tolerance, the upper bearing inserts may be removed, without removing the crankshaft, using a bearing roll out pin (see illustration). Roll in a bearing that will provide proper clearance, and retest. Torque all main caps, excluding the thrust bearing cap, to specifications. Tighten the thrust bearing cap finger tight. To properly align the thrust bearing, pry the crankshaft the extent of its axial travel several times, the last movement held toward the front of the engine, and torque the thrust bearing cap to specifications. Determine the crankshaft end-play (see below), and bring within tolerance with thrust washers.

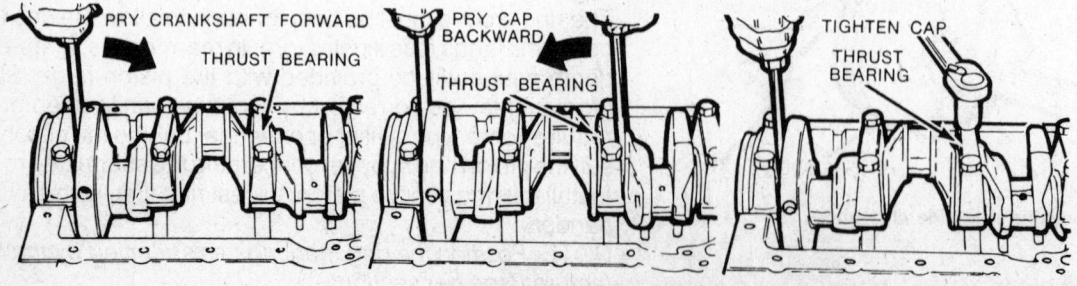

PRY CRANKSHAFT FORWARD
THRUST BEARING

PRY CAP BACKWARD
THRUST BEARING

TIGHTEN CAP
THRUST BEARING

Aligning the thrust bearing

CYLINDER BLOCK RECONDITIONING

Procedure	Method

Measure crankshaft end-play:

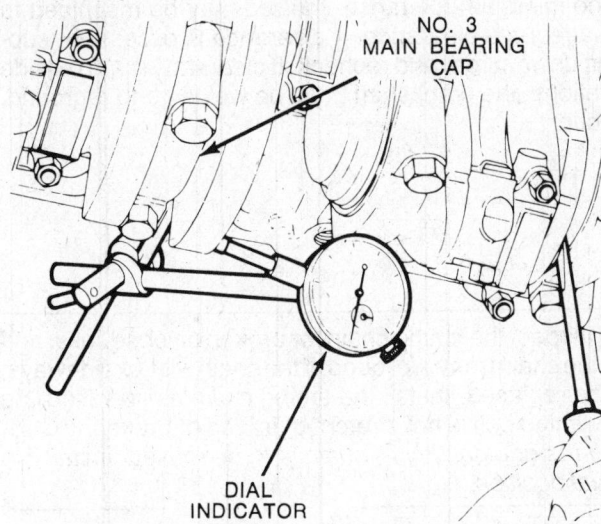

NO. 3 MAIN BEARING CAP

DIAL INDICATOR

Checking crankshaft end-play with a dial indicator

Mount a dial indicator stand on the front of the block, with the dial indicator stem resting on the nose of the crankshaft, parallel to the crankshaft axis. Pry the crankshaft the extent of its travel rearward, and zero the indicator. Pry the crankshaft forward and record crankshaft end-play.
NOTE: *Crankshaft end-play also may be measured at the thrust bearing, using feeler gauges* (see illustration).

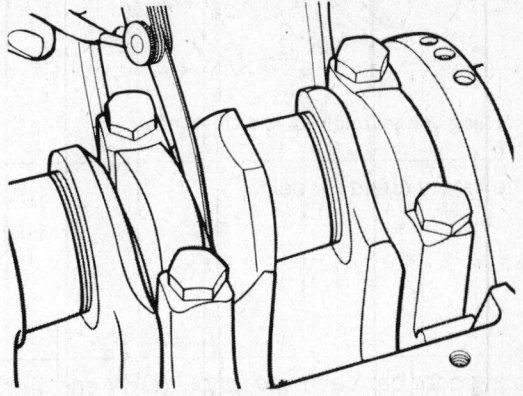

Checking crankshaft end-play with a feeler gauge

Install the pistons:

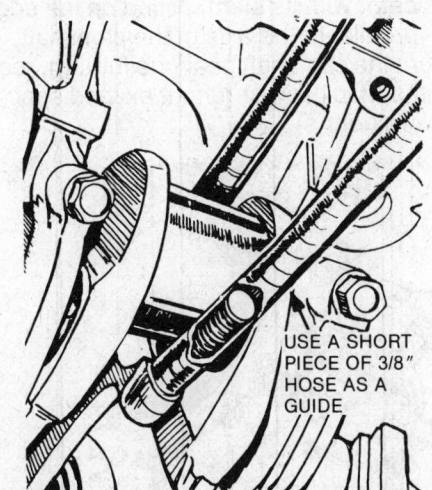

USE A SHORT PIECE OF 3/8" HOSE AS A GUIDE

Tubing used to protect crankshaft journals and cylinder walls during piston installation

Press the upper connecting rod bearing halves into the connecting rods, and the lower halves into the connecting rod caps. Position the piston ring gaps according to specifications (see car section), and lubricate the pistons. Install a ring compressor on a piston, and press two long (8") pieces of plastic tubing over the rod bolts. Using the tubes as a guide, press the pistons into the bores and onto the crankshaft with a wooden hammer handle. After seating the rod on the crankshaft journal, remove the tubes and install the cap finger tight. Install the remaining pistons in the same manner. Invert the engine and check the bearing clearance at two points (90° apart) on each journal with Plastigage.
NOTE: *Do not turn the crankshaft with Plastigage installed.*
If clearance is within tolerances, remove *all* Plastigage, thoroughly lubricate the journals, and torque the rod caps to specifications. If clearance is not within specifications, install different thickness bearing inserts and recheck.
CAUTION: *Never shim or file the connecting rods or caps.*
Always install plastic tube sleeves over the rod bolts when the caps are not installed, to protect the crankshaft journals.

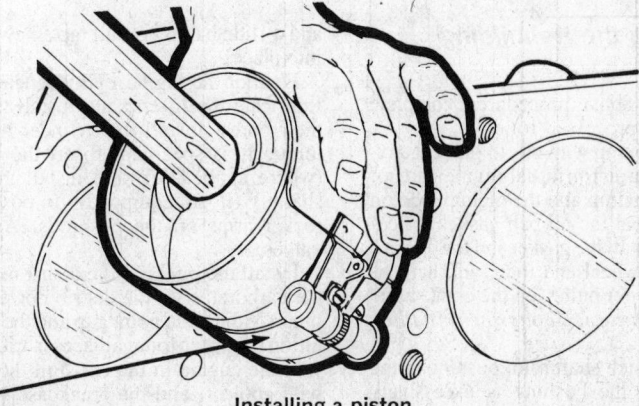

RING COMPRESSOR

Installing a piston

CYLINDER BLOCK RECONDITIONING

Procedure	Method
Check connecting rod side clearance: 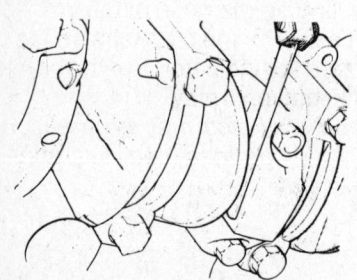 Checking connecting rod side clearance	Determine the clearance between the sides of the connecting rods and the crankshaft, using feeler gauges. If clearance is below the minimum tolerance, the rod may be machined to provide adequate clearance. If clearance is excessive, substitute an unworn rod, and recheck. If clearance is still outside specifications, the crankshaft must be welded and reground, or replaced.
Inspect the timing chain (or belt):	Visually inspect the timing chain for broken or loose links, and replace the chain if any are found. If the chain will flex sideways, it must be replaced. Install the timing chain as specified. Be sure the timing belt is not stretched, frayed or broken. NOTE: *If the original timing chain is to be reused, install it in its original position.*
Check timing gear backlash and runout (OHV engines): 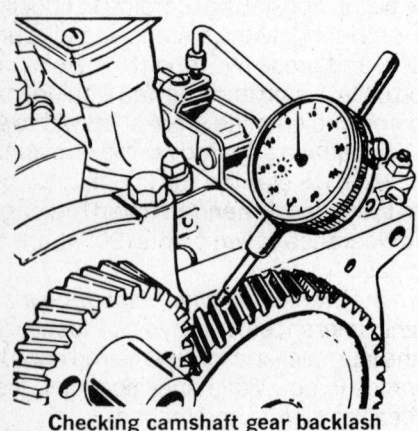 Checking camshaft gear backlash	Mount a dial indicator with its stem resting on a tooth of the camshaft gear (as illustrated). Rotate the gear until all slack is removed, and zero the indicator. Rotate the gear in the opposite direction until slack is removed, and record gear backlash. Mount the indicator with its stem resting on the edge of the camshaft gear, parallel to the axis of the camshaft. Zero the indicator, and turn the camshaft gear one full turn, recording the runout. If either backlash or runout exceed specifications, replace the worn gear(s).  Checking camshaft gear runout

Completing the Rebuilding Process

Following the above procedures, complete the rebuilding process as follows:

Fill the oil pump with oil, to prevent cavitating (sucking air) on initial engine start up. Install the oil pump and the pickup tube on the engine. Coat the oil pan gasket as necessary, and install the gasket and the oil pan. Mount the flywheel and the crankshaft vibration damper or pulley on the crankshaft. NOTE: *Always use new bolts when installing the flywheel.*

Inspect the clutch shaft pilot bushing in the crankshaft. If the bushing is excessively worn, remove it with an expanding puller and a slide hammer, and tap a new bushing into place.

Position the engine, cylinder head side up. Lubricate the lifters, and install them into their bores. Install the cylinder head, and torque it as specified. Insert the pushrods (where applicable), and install the rocker shaft(s) (if so equipped) or position the rocker arms on the pushrods. Adjust the valves.

Install the intake and exhaust manifolds, the carburetor(s), the distributor and spark plugs. Adjust the point gap and the static ignition timing. Mount all accessories and install the engine in the car. Fill the radiator with coolant, and the crankcase with high quality engine oil.

Break-in Procedure

Start the engine, and allow it to run at low speed for a few minutes, while checking for leaks. Stop the engine, check the oil level, and fill as necessary. Restart the engine, and fill the cooling system to capacity. Check the point dwell angle and adjust the ignition timing and the valves. Run the engine at low to medium speed (800–2500 rpm) for approximately ½ hour, and retorque the cylinder head bolts. Road test the car, and check again for leaks.

Follow the manufacturer's recommended engine break-in procedure and maintenance schedule for new engines.

Manual Transmissions

HOW TO IDENTIFY A TRANSMISSION

Refer to the Basic Manual Transmission Application chart to determine if more than one type of transmission could have been used in your vehicle. If only one type is applicable, refer to the page index of the Manual Transmission identification and Page Index chart, which will tell you where the overhaul procedures for your transmission are located.

Should more than one type of transmission be listed under the same basic description (e.g. two different 4 speeds), then refer to the Manual Transmission Identification and Page Index chart. This chart contains identifying characteristics of each transmission which will enable you to make a positive identification. In many cases, it will be necessary to view the transmission from beneath the vehicle to correctly identify your particular transmission.

—————— **CAUTION** ——————
Care must be exercised during the disassembly and assembly of manual transmission due to the usage of metric nuts and bolts. The proper wrenches and sockets should be used to avoid damage to the transmission and fasteners. Do not attempt to interchange metric threaded fasteners with U.S. Fine or Standard fasteners as damage can result.

BASIC MANUAL TRANSMISSION APPLICATIONS

| Model | Year | Transmission Type | | |
		3 Speed	4 Speed	5 Speed
AMERICAN MOTORS				
All	1978-79	4	17	
	1980-81	—	6	—
	1982-85	—	6.21	22
CHRYSLER CORPORATION				
Rear Wheel Drive	1978-83	1, 4	3	—
Front Wheel Drive	1978-85	—	18	—
	1981-85	—	19	19
FORD MOTOR COMPANY				
Rear Wheel Drive				
Except Mustang, Mustang II	1978-85	4	5, 7, 8	9
Mustang II	1978	—	6	—
Mustang	1979-85	—	5, 6	9
Front Wheel Drive	1981-85	—	2	2

BASIC MANUAL TRANSMISSION APPLICATIONS

Model	Year	Transmission Type		
		3 Speed	4 Speed	5 Speed
GENERAL MOTORS				
Rear Wheel Drive Except Astre, Chevette, Monza, Skyhawk, Starfire, Sunbird, Vega, 1984-85 Corvette	1978-85	10	11, 14, 23, 24	16, 22
Astre, Monza, Skyhawk Starfire, Sunbird Vega	1978-81	10	11, 12	16
Corvette	1984-85	—	15	—
Chevette	1978-81	—	12	—
	1982-85 ①	—	12	22
	1982-85 ②	—	—	23
Front Wheel Drive	1980-85	—	20	25

① Gasoline engines only
② Diesel engines only

MANUAL TRANSMISSION IDENTIFICATION

Chilton Type	Transmission Designation				Identifying Characteristics
	AMC	Chrysler	Ford	GM	
1	—	A-230	—	—	A,D,F
2	—	—	MTX	—	E,G,H$_1$
3	—	Overdrive-4	—	—	A,D,G or G$_1$
4	150-T	A-390	3.03	—	B$_2$,D,F
5	—	—	ET	—	B,C,G,I
6	SR4	—	RAD	—	B,C,G,J
7	—	—	4-Speed Overdrive	—	B,D,G$_1$
8	—	—	Single Rail 4-Speed Overdrive (S.R.O.D.)	—	B,C,G$_1$
9	—	—	RAP	—	B,C,H$_1$
10	—	—	—	Saginaw	A,D,F
11	—	—	—	Saginaw	A$_2$,D,G,K
12	—	—	—	70 mm	C,G,I
13	T-14	—	—	—	B$_1$,D,F
14	—	—	—	Warner T-10	A$_1$,D,G,P
15	—	—	—	83 mm	N.A.
16	—	—	—	Warner T-50	C,H
17	HR-1	—	—	—	B,C,G
18	—	A-412	—	—	E,G,R
19	—	A-460/A-465/A-525	—	—	E,G,S,H
20	—	—	—	FWD Transaxle	E,G
21	Warner T-4	—	—	—	B,C,G,N
22	Warner T-5	—	—	77 mm	B,C,H$_1$,N

MANUAL TRANSMISSION IDENTIFICATION

Chilton Type	Transmission Designation				Identifying Characteristics
	AMC	Chrysler	Ford	GM	
23	—	—	—	77.5 mm	C,H_1,O
24	—	—	—	Muncie	A_2,D,G,L,Q
25	—	—	—	FWD Transaxle	E,H

A—Side cover
A_1—6 bolt side cover
A_2—7 bolt side cover
B—Top cover
B_1—6 bolt top cover
B_2—9 bolt top cover
C—Internal shift linkage
D—External shift linkage
E—Transaxle
F—Three-speed
G—Four-speed
G_1—Four-speed overdrive
H—Five-speed
H_1—Five-speed overdrive

I—The bellhousing is bolted to the transmission case from INSIDE the bellhousing—bolts not exposed while installed.
J—Transmission case-to-bellhousing bolts are accessible with the transmission installed. Also, reverse is positioned at the upper left portion of the gearshift pattern.
K—Cast iron case
L—Aluminum case
M—Overdrive unit only
N—Reverse is positioned at the right rear portion of the gearshift pattern.

O—No cover on transmission case; bellhousing integral with transmission case.
P—Side cover has curved bottom.
Q—Side cover has straight bottom.
R—Starter motor located on the radiator side of the engine compartment, near the radiator fan motor.
S—Starter motor located near the firewall side of the engine compartment.
N.A.—Not available

CHILTON TYPE 1

Disassembly

SHIFT HOUSING AND MECHANISM

1. Shift to second gear.
2. Unbolt and remove side cover with shift mechanism.

If shaft O-ring seals need replacement:

3. Pull shaft forks out of shafts.
4. Remove nuts and operating levers from shafts.
5. Deburr shafts. Remove shafts. Remove the O-ring retainers and O-rings.

DRIVE PINION RETAINER AND EXTENSION HOUSING

1. Unbolt pinion bearing retainer from front of transmission case. Remove retainer and gasket. Pry off retainer oil seal.

For clearance:

2. With a brass drift, tap drive pinion as far forward as possible. Rotate cut away part of second gear next to countershaft gear. Shift second-third synchronizer sleeve forward.
3. Remove speedometer pinion adapter retainer. Work adapter and pinion out of extension housing.
4. Unbolt extension housing. Break housing loose with plastic hammer and carefully remove.

IDLER GEAR AND MAINSHAFT

1. Insert dummy shaft in case to push reverse idler shaft and key out of case.
2. Remove dummy shaft and idler gear together to prevent losing rollers.
3. Remove both tanged idler gear thrust washers.
4. Remove mainshaft assembly through rear of case.

COUNTERSHAFT GEAR AND DRIVE PINION

1. Using a mallet and dummy shaft, tap the countershaft rearward enough to remove key. Drive countershaft out of case, maintaining contact between countershaft and dummy shaft so that washers will not drop out.
2. Lower countershaft gear to bottom of case.
3. Remove snap-ring from pinion bearing outer race (outside front of case).
4. Drive pinion shaft into case with plastic hammer. Remove assembly through rear of case.
5. If bearing is to be replaced, remove snap-ring and press off bearing.
6. Lift countershaft gear and dummy shaft out through rear of case.

MAINSHAFT

1. Remove snap-ring from front end of mainshaft along with second gear stop ring. Remove the synchronizer and second gear from mainshaft.

2. Spread snap-ring in mainshaft bearing retainer. Slide retainer back off the bearing race.
3. Remove snap-ring at rear of mainshaft. Support front side of reverse gear. Press bearing off mainshaft. Be careful not to let parts drop when bearing clears shaft.
4. Remove from press. Remove mainshaft bearing and reverse gear from shaft.
5. Remove snap-ring from rear of shaft. Slide first-reverse synchronizer assembly off splines and remove rearward. Remove stop-ring and first gear through the rear.

Assembly

COUNTERSHAFT GEAR

1. Slide dummy shaft into countershaft gear.
2. Slide one roller thrust washer over dummy shaft and into gear, followed by 22 greased rollers.
3. Repeat Step 2, adding one roller thrust washer on end.
4. Repeat Steps 2 and 3 at other end of countershaft gear. There are a total of 88 rollers and 6 thrust washers.
5. Place greased front thrust washer on dummy shaft against gear with tangs forward.
6. Grease rear thrust washer and install it in the case, with tangs rearward. Place countershaft gear assembly in bottom of transmission case until drive pinion is installed.

PINION GEAR

1. Press new bearing on pinion shaft

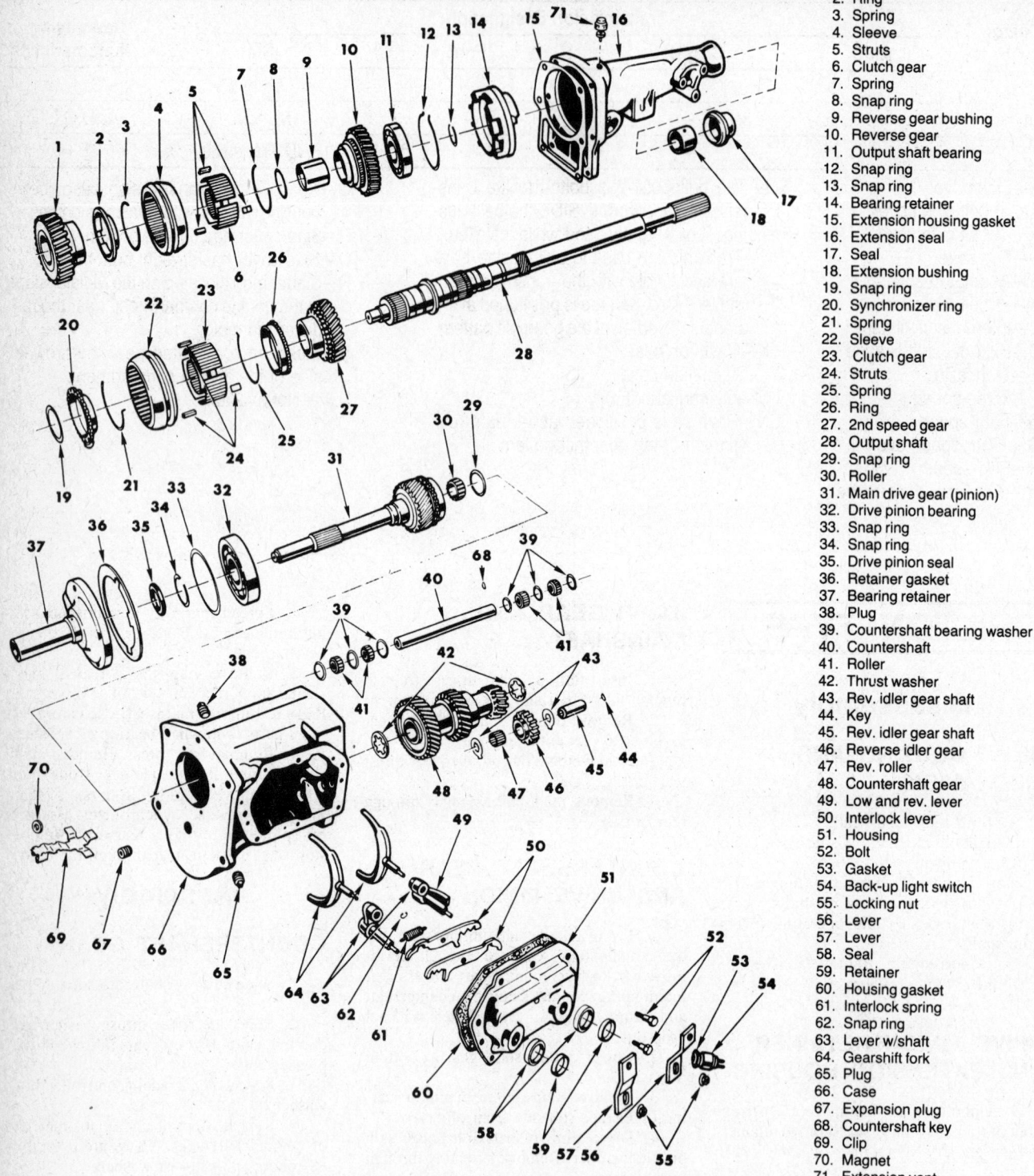

1. 1st speed gear
2. Ring
3. Spring
4. Sleeve
5. Struts
6. Clutch gear
7. Spring
8. Snap ring
9. Reverse gear bushing
10. Reverse gear
11. Output shaft bearing
12. Snap ring
13. Snap ring
14. Bearing retainer
15. Extension housing gasket
16. Extension seal
17. Seal
18. Extension bushing
19. Snap ring
20. Synchronizer ring
21. Spring
22. Sleeve
23. Clutch gear
24. Struts
25. Spring
26. Ring
27. 2nd speed gear
28. Output shaft
29. Snap ring
30. Roller
31. Main drive gear (pinion)
32. Drive pinion bearing
33. Snap ring
34. Snap ring
35. Drive pinion seal
36. Retainer gasket
37. Bearing retainer
38. Plug
39. Countershaft bearing washer
40. Countershaft
41. Roller
42. Thrust washer
43. Rev. idler gear shaft
44. Key
45. Rev. idler gear shaft
46. Reverse idler gear
47. Rev. roller
48. Countershaft gear
49. Low and rev. lever
50. Interlock lever
51. Housing
52. Bolt
53. Gasket
54. Back-up light switch
55. Locking nut
56. Lever
57. Lever
58. Seal
59. Retainer
60. Housing gasket
61. Interlock spring
62. Snap ring
63. Lever w/shaft
64. Gearshift fork
65. Plug
66. Case
67. Expansion plug
68. Countershaft key
69. Clip
70. Magnet
71. Extension vent

Exploded view of the Chrysler A-230 (Chilton Type 1) transmission (© Chrysler Corp.)

with snap-ring groove forward. Install new snap-ring.

2. Install 15 rollers and retaining ring in drive pinion gear.

3. Install drive pinion and bearing assembly into case.

4. Install the countershaft gear assembly by positioning it and thrust washers so countershaft can be tapped into position.

Be careful to keep the countershaft against the dummy shaft to keep parts from falling between them. Install key in countershaft.

5. Tap drive pinion forward for clearance.

MAINSHAFT

1. Place a stop-ring flat on the bench.

Place a clutch gear and a sleeve on top. Drop the struts in their slots and snap in a strut spring placing the tang inside one strut. Turn the assembly over and install second strut spring, tang in a different strut.

2. Slide first gear and stop-ring over rear of mainshaft and against thrust flange between first and second gears on shaft.

3. Slide first-reverse synchronizer assembly over rear of mainshaft, indexing hub slots to first gear stop-ring lugs.

4. Install first-reverse synchronizer clutch gear snap-ring on mainshaft.

5. Slide reverse gear and mainshaft bearing into place. Press bearing on shaft, supporting inner race of bearing. Be sure snap-ring groove on outer race is forward.

6. Install bearing retaining snap-ring on mainshaft. Spread snap-ring in retainer groove and slide it over the bearing. Seat ring in groove. This snap-ring is selected for minimum end play. There are several thicknesses available.

7. Place second gear over front of mainshaft with thrust surface against flange.

8. Install stop-ring and second-third synchronizer assembly against second gear. Install second-third synchronizer clutch gear snap-ring on shaft.

9. Move second-third synchronizer sleeve forward as far as possible. Install front stop-ring, inside the sleeve with lugs indexed to struts. Coat the stop-ring with grease to hold it in position.

10. Rotate cut-out on second gear toward countershaft gear to provide clearance.

11. Insert mainshaft assembly into case. Tilt assembly to clear cluster gears and insert pilot rollers in drive pinion gear. If assembly is correct, the bearing retainer will bottom to the case without force. If not, check for a misplaced strut, pinion roller, or stop-ring.

REVERSE IDLER GEAR

1. Place dummy shaft into idler gear. Insert 22 greased rollers.

2. Position reverse idler thrust washers in case with grease.

3. Position idler gear and dummy shaft in case. Install idler shaft and key.

EXTENSION HOUSING

1. Remove extension housing yoke seal. Drive bushing out from inside housing.

2. Align oil hole in bushing with oil slot in housing. Drive bushing into place. Drive new seal into housing.

3. Install extension housing and gasket to hold mainshaft and bearing retainer in place.

DRIVE PINION BEARING RETAINER

1. Install outer snap-ring on drive pinion bearing. Tap assembly back until snapring contacts case.

2. Install a new seal in retainer bore.

3. Position main drive pinion bearing retainer and gasket on front of case. Coat threads with sealing compound, install bolts, torque to 30 ft. lbs.

GEARSHIFT MECHANISM AND HOUSING

1. If removed, place two interlock levers on pivot pin with spring hangers offset toward each other, so that spring installs in a straight line. Place E-clip on pivot pin.

2. Grease and install new O-ring seals on both shift shafts. Grease housing bores. Push each shaft into its bore.

3. Install spring on interlock lever hangers.

4. Rotate each shift shaft fork bore to vertical position. Install shift forks through bores and under both interlock levers.

5. Position second-third synchronizer sleeve to rear, in second gear position. Position first-reverse synchronizer sleeve to middle of travel, in neutral position. Place shift forks in the same positions.

6. Install gasket and gearshift mechanism. The bolt with the extra long shoulder must be installed at the center rear of the case. Torque bolts to 15 ft. lbs.

7. Install speedometer drive pinion gear and adapter. Range number on adapter, which represents the number of teeth on the gear, should be in 6 o'clock position.

CHILTON TYPE 2

Transmission

DISASSEMBLY

NOTE: If equipped with a 5 speed transaxle, refer to the note following Step 13.

1. Insert a drift into the input shift shaft hole and shift the transaxle into neutral by either pushing or pulling the shaft into the center detent position.

2. Place the transaxle on a bench with the clutch housing face down and drain the transmission fluid.

3. Remove the reverse idler shaft retaining bolt.

4. Remove the detent plunger retaining screw, then using a magnet, remove the detent spring and the detent plunger.

NOTE: Label these parts as they appear similar to the input shift shaft plunger and spring contained in the clutch case.

5. Using a 19mm socket, remove the shift fork interlock sleeve retaining pin.

6. Using a 10mm socket, remove the bolts which attach the clutch housing to the transmission case.

7. Tap the transmission case with a plastic tipped hammer to break the seal between the case halves. Separate the case halves while being careful that the tapered roller bearing cups or shims do not drop from the case housing.

NOTE: Do not insert pry bars or screwdrivers between the case halves.

8. Remove the case magnet.

9. Remove the reverse idler shaft and reverse idler gear by lifting the shaft straight upward.

10. Using a 4mm Allen wrench, remove the set screw from the shift lever assembly.

11. Using a pair of pliers, rotate the shift lever shaft 90 degrees to disengage the reverse inhibitor plunger from the detent notch in the shift lever shaft. Slide the shaft toward the differential (away from the expansion plug in the clutch housing) and remove the shift lever assembly.

NOTE: On models equipped with a 4.05:1 final drive ratio, it may be necessary to tilt the differential assembly slightly for removal of the shift lever assembly.

12. Remove the main shaft assembly, input cluster shaft assembly and the main shift control shaft assembly as one unit.

13. Lift the differential and final drive gear assembly from the clutch housing case.

NOTE: If your vehicle is equipped with a 5 speed transaxle the following procedures are used in conjunction with the previous ones.

1. Remove the C-clip retaining ring from the 5th gear shift relay lever.

2. Remove the 5th gear shift relay lever.

3. Use a punch to drive the roll spring pin from the shift lever shaft.

4. Gently pry the shift shaft lever to remove it from the case.

5. Insert a punch into the hole in the shift shaft lever. Rotate the shaft 90 degrees, disengaging the inhibitor.

6. Hold a rag over the hold in the lever. This will prevent the ball and inhibitor spring from shooting out.

7. Remove the shift shaft.

8. Remove the ball and spring from the inhibitor.

9. Remove the shift lever and 3-4 bias spring as assembly.

10. Remove the 5th gear shaft assembly and 5th gear fork assembly from the case.

Mainshaft

DISASSEMBLY

1. Remove the tapered roller bearing from the pinion end of the main shaft using a puller and an arbor press. Label the bearing for proper installation.

NOTE: This bearing does not have to be removed to disassemble the main shaft, only to replace it if damaged.

2. Remove and label the bearing on the 4th gear end of the shaft.

3. Remove the 4th speed gear and synchronizer blocker ring.

4. Remove the 3rd-4th synchronizer retaining ring.

5. Slide the 3rd–4th gear synchronizer assembly, blocker ring, and 3rd speed gear from the shaft.

6. Remove the 2nd–3rd thrust washer retaining ring and the two-piece 2nd–3rd gear thrust washer.

7. Remove the 2nd speed gear and blocker ring.

8. Remove the 1st–2nd synchronizer retaining ring.

9. Slide the 1st–2nd synchronizer assembly, blocking ring, and 1st speed gear off the shaft.

NOTE: If equipped with a 5 speed, proceed with the following steps:

1. Remove the bearing from the gear end of the shaft.

2. Remove the 5th gear and blocker ring.

3. Remove the synchronizer assembly.

4. Remove the press fit bearing from the pinion end of the shaft.

NOTE: This bearing must be pressed on and off.

ASSEMBLY

1. Clean, inspect and lightly oil all parts with the appropriate transmission fluid.

NOTE: Before assembling the synchronizers note the following points: (1) All index marks must be aligned, (2) Place the tab on the synchronizer spring into the groove of one of the inserts and snap the spring into place. Place the tab of the other spring into the same insert on the other side of the synchronizer assembly and rotate the spring in the opposite direction and snap into place, (3) The sleeve and the hub have extremely close fit and must be held square to prevent jamming. Do not force the sleeve onto the hub.

2. Slide the blocker ring and the 1st speed gear onto the main shaft. Slide the 1st–2nd synchronizer assembly into place, making sure that the shift fork groove on the reversing slide gear faces the 1st speed gear. When installing the synchronizer, align the three grooves in the 1st gear blocker ring with the synchronizer inserts. Install the synchronizer retaining ring.

3. Install the 2nd speed blocker ring and the 2nd speed gear.

4. Install the thrust washer halves and retaining ring.

5. Slide the 3rd speed gear onto the shaft followed by the 3rd speed gear synchronizer blocker ring and the 3rd–4th gear synchronizer assembly. Install the synchronizer retaining ring.

6. Install the 4th gear blocking ring and 4th speed gear.

7. Using a 1 1/16 in. socket and an arbor press install the bearing on the 4th gear end of the shaft. Install the bearing on the pinion

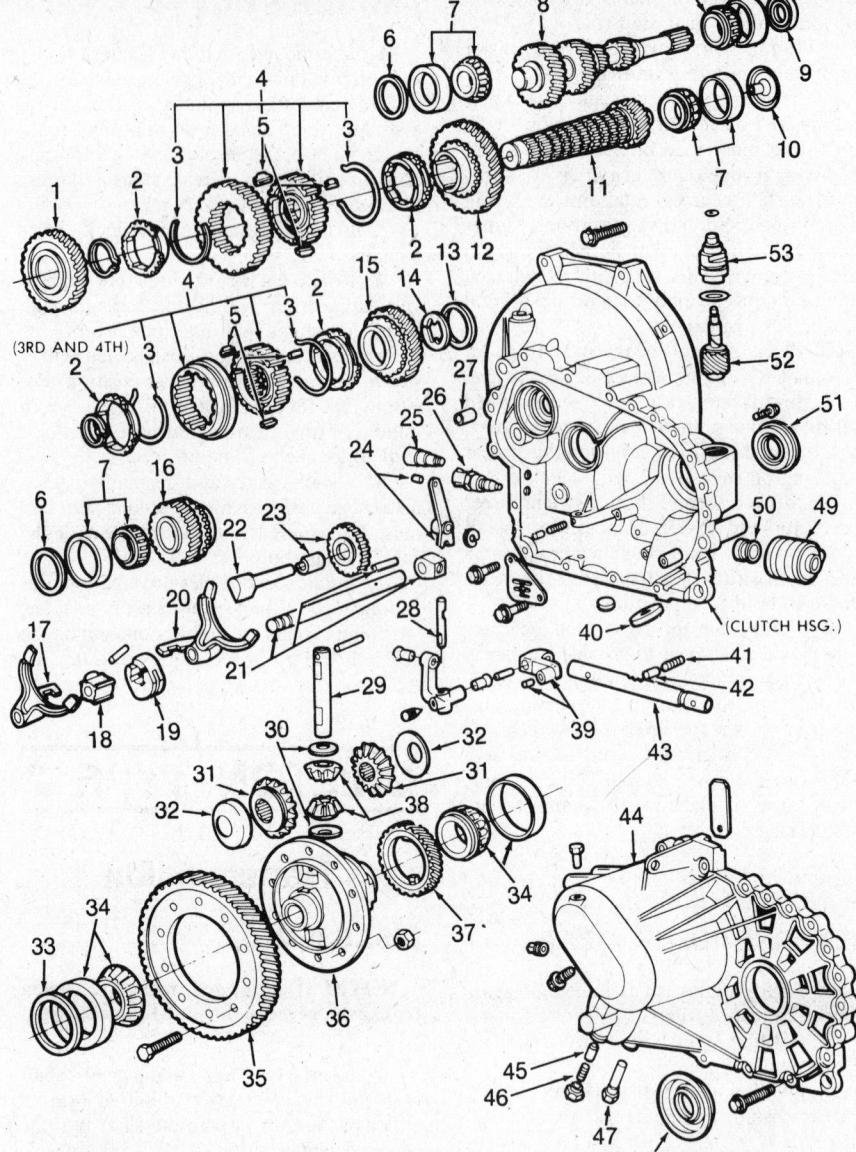

1. 2nd speed gear	16. 4th speed gear	34. Differential bearing assembly
2. Synchronizer blocking ring	17. 3rd/4th fork	35. Final drive output gear
3. Synchronizer spring	18. Fork selector arm	36. Transaxle case assy.
4. 1st and 2nd synchronizer assy.	19. Fork interlock sleeve	37. Speedometer drive gear
5. Synchronizer hub 1st/2nd insert	20. 1st/2nd fork	38. Differential pinion gear
6. Input shaft seal	21. Main shift shaft	39. Input shift shaft selector plate arm
7. Input shaft bearing and cup-front and rear	22. Reverse idler shaft	40. Case magnet
8. Input cluster shaft	23. Reverse idler gear	41. Input detent shift shaft spring
9. Input shaft seal	24. Reverse relay lever	42. Input shift shaft detent plunger
10. Mainshaft funnel	25. Reverse relay lever pivot pin	43. Input shift shaft
11. Main shaft	26. Back-up lamp switch	44. Transaxle case
12. 1st speed gear	27. Dowel	45. Main shift shaft detent plunger
13. 2nd/3rd gear thrust washer retaining ring	28. Shift lever shaft	46. Main shift shaft detent spring
14. 2nd/3rd gear thrust washer	29. Pinion shaft	47. Fork interlock sleeve retaining spring
15. 3rd speed gear	30. Pinion thrust washer	48. Differential seal assembly
	31. Side gear kit	
	32. Side gear thrust washer	
	33. Shim	

MTX 4 speed transaxle—exploded view (Chilton Type 2)

end of the shaft in the same manner.

NOTE: Make sure the bearings are placed on the proper end as labeled during disassembly and that they are seated against the shoulder of the main shaft.

Internal Shift Linkage

DISASSEMBLY

1. Cover the reverse inhibitor plunger

1. INPUT SHAFT SEAL ASSEMBLY
2. ROLLER BEARING CUP
3. INPUT SHAFT FRONT BEARING
4. INPUT CLUSTER SHAFT

23. BEARING PRELOAD SHIM
24. MAINSHAFT FUNNEL
25. ROLLER BEARING CUP
26. MAINSHAFT FRONT BEARING
27. MAIN SHAFT
28. 1ST SPEED GEAR

29. SYNCHRONIZER BLOCKING RING
30. SYNCHRONIZER SPRING
31. 1ST/2ND SYNCHRONIZER HUB
32. SYNCHRONIZER HUB 1ST/2ND INSERT
33. REVERSE SLIDING GEAR
34. SYNCHRONIZER SPRING
35. SYNCHRONIZER BLOCKING RING
36. 1ST/2ND SYNCHRONIZER RETAINING RING
37. 2ND SPEED GEAR
38. 2ND/3RD THRUST WASHER RETAINING RING
39. 2ND/3RD GEAR THRUST WASHER
40. 3RD SPEED GEAR
41. SYNCHRONIZER BLOCKING RING
42. SYNCHRONIZER SPRING
43. 3RD/4TH SYNCHRONIZER HUB
44. SYNCHRONIZER HUB 3RD/4TH INSERT
45. 3RD/4TH SYNCHRONIZER SLEEVE
46. SYNCHRONIZER SPRING
47. SYNCHRONIZER BLOCKING RING
48. 3RD/4TH SYNCHRONIZER RING
49. 4TH SPEED GEAR
50. MAINSHAFT REAR BEARING
51. ROLLER BEARING CUP
52. BEARING PRELOAD SHIM
53. CLUTCH HOUSING CASE
54. SWITCH ASSEMBLY BACK-UP LAMPS
55. REVERSE RELAY LEVER
56. REVERSE RELAY LEVER PIVOT PIN
57. EXTERNAL RETAINING RING
58. REVERSE RELAY LEVER PIN
59. SHIFT LEVER
60. 10.319mm BALL
61. 5TH/REVERSE INHIBITOR SPRING
62. 3RD/4TH SHIFT BIAS SPRING
63. SHIFT LEVER SHAFT
64. SHIFT LEVER PIN
65. SHIFT LEVER SHAFT SEAL
66. SHIFT GATE ATTACHING BOLTS
67. SHIFT GATE PLATE
68. SELECTOR ARM PIN
69. SHIFT GATE SELECTOR PIN
70. SHIFT GATE SELECTOR ARM
71. INPUT SHIFT SHAFT
72. SHIFT SHAFT DETENT PLUNGER
73. SHIFT SHAFT DETENT SPRING
74. ASSEMBLY–SHIFT SHAFT SEAL
75. SHIFT SHAFT BOOT
76. FORK CONTROL SHAFT BLOCK
77. REVERSE RELAY LEVER ACTUATING PIN
78. MAIN SHIFT FORK CONTROL SHAFT
79. 1ST/2ND FORK
80. FORK INTERLOCK SLEEVE
81. SPRING PIN
82. FORK SELECTOR ARM
83. 3RD/4TH FORK
84. 5TH SHIFT RELAY LEVER
85. REVERSE SHIFT RELAY LEVER PIN
86. 5TH RELAY LEVER PIVOT PIN
87. EXTERNAL RETAINING RING
88. 5TH FORK
89. 5TH FORK RETAINING PIN
90. 5TH FORK CONTROL SHAFT
91. REVERSE IDLER GEAR SHAFT
92. REVERSE IDLER GEAR BUSHING
93. REVERSE IDLER GEAR
94. CASE MAGNET
95. TRANSAXLE CASE
96. VENT ASSEMBLY
97. FILL PLUG
98. REVERSE SHAFT RETAINING BOLT
99. DETENT PLUNGER RETAINING SCREW
100. SHIFT SHAFT DETENT PLUNGER
101. SHIFT SHAFT DETENT SPRING
102. FORK INTERLOCK SLEEVE RETAINING PIN
103. TRANSAXLE CASE BOLT
104. SEAL ASSEMBLY (LH) DIFFERENTIAL
105. SHIM DIFFERENTIAL BEARING PRELOAD
106. DIFFERENTIAL BEARING CUP
107. DIFFERENTIAL BEARING ASSEMBLY
108. SIDE GEAR THRUST WASHER
109. SIDE GEAR
110. PINION GEAR
111. PINION GEAR THRUST WASHER
112. PINION GEAR SHAFT
113. PINION GEAR SHAFT RETAINING PIN
114. FINAL DRIVE GEAR
115. DIFFERENTIAL (LH) CASE
116. DIFFERENTIAL (RH) CASE
117. CASE AND DRIVE GEAR ATTACHING RIVET
118. SPEEDO DRIVE GEAR
119. 5.16mm × 1.6 O-RING SEAL
120. SPEEDO GEAR RETAINER
121. SPEEDO RETAINER-TO-CASE SEAL
122. SPEEDO DRIVEN GEAR
123. CASE-TO-CLUTCH HOUSING DOWEL
124. TRANSAXLE NEUTRAL SENSING SWITCH

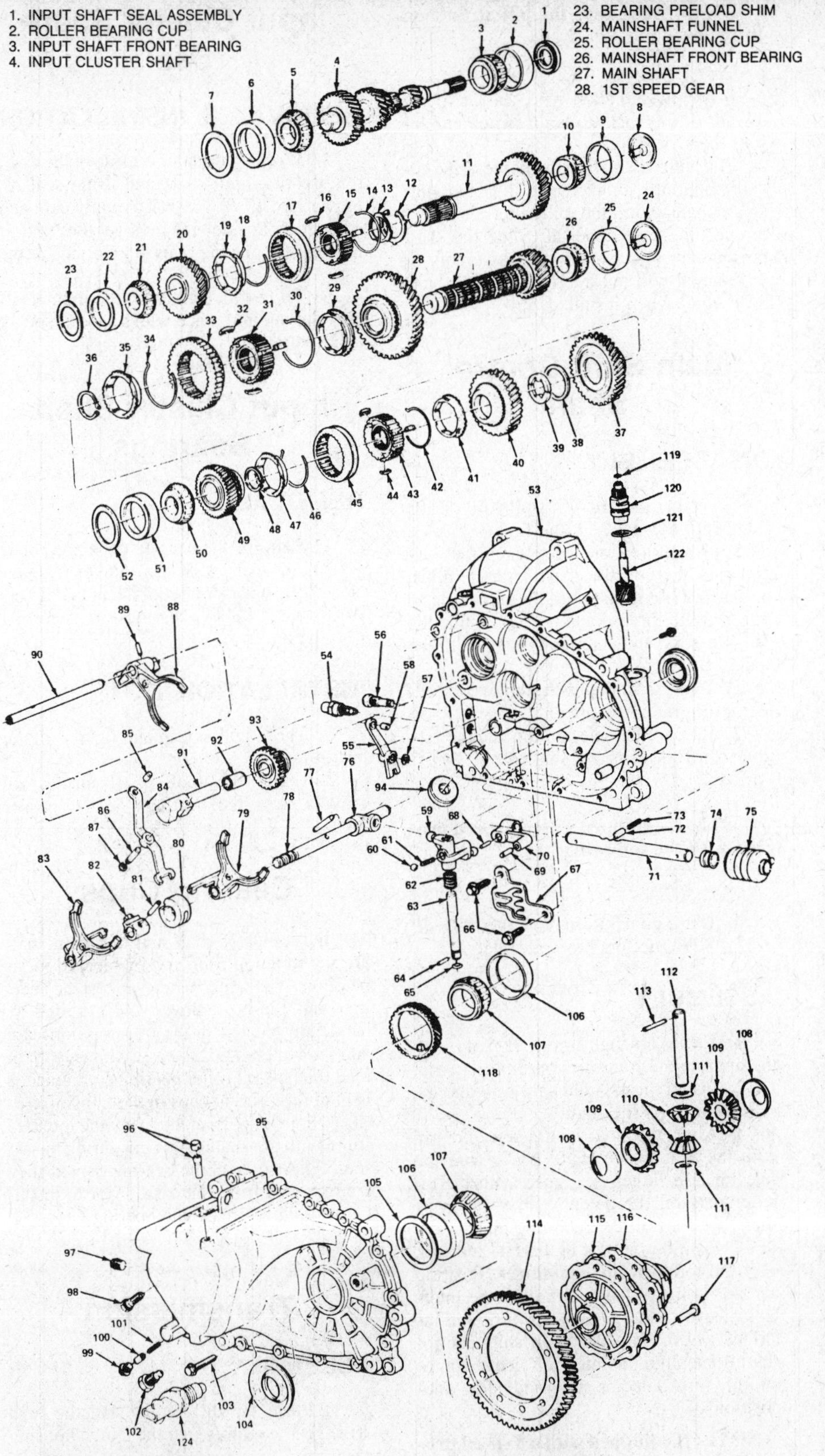

5. INPUT SHAFT REAR BEARING
6. ROLLER BEARING CUP
7. BEARING PRELOAD SHIM
8. 5TH GEAR FUNNEL
9. ROLLER BEARING CUP
10. 5TH GEAR SHAFT–FRONT BEARING
11. 5TH GEAR DRIVESHAFT
12. SYNCHRONIZER INSERT RETAINER
13. SYNCHRONIZER RETAINING SPACER

14. SYNCHRONIZER SPRING
15. 5TH SYNCHRONIZER HUB
16. SYNCHRONIZER HUB 5TH INSERT
17. 5TH SYNCHRONIZER SLEEVE
18. SYNCHRONIZER SPRING
19. SYNCHRONIZER BLOCKING RING
20. 5TH SPEED GEAR
21. 5TH GEAR SHAFT–REAR BEARING
22. ROLLER BEARING CUP

MTX 5 speed transaxle—disassembled

bore, then slide the shift lever shaft completely from its bore.

— CAUTION —

To avoid possible eye injury, make sure that the inhibitor bore area is covered so that the plunger does not spring from the case when removing the shift lever shaft.

2. Using a 30mm deep socket remove the back-up lamp switch.

3. Remove the C-clip then remove the reverse relay lever.

NOTE: It is not necessary to remove the pivot pin.

4. Using a 10mm socket, remove the two control selector plate attaching bolts and remove the plate from the case.

5. With the input shift shaft in the center detent position, drive the spring pin through the selector plate arm assembly and through the input shift shaft into the recess in the clutch housing case.

6. Remove the shift shaft boot. Using a drift, rotate the input shift shaft 90 degrees depressing the detent plunger from the shaft detent notches inside the housing and without damaging the seal pull the input shift shaft out. Remove the input shift shaft selector plate arm assembly and the spring pin.

7. Using a pencil magnet, remove the input shift shaft detent plunger and spring and label for proper installation. Using a seal remover/installer No. T77F-7288-A or equivalent and a Slide Hammer No. T50T-100-A or equivalent and remove the transmission input shift shaft oil seal assembly.

ASSEMBLY

1. Grease the lip of a new shift shaft oil seal and install it using the tools described in disassembly.

2. Using a small drift, force the detent spring and plunger down into its bore while sliding the input shift shaft into its bore and over the plunger.

NOTE: Be careful not to damage the shift shaft oil seal.

3. Install the selector plate arm in its working position and slide the shaft through the selector plate arm. Align the hole in the selector plate arm with the hole in the shaft and install the roll pin. Install the boot. When properly installed the pin on the selector arm will be facing up. Also make sure the notches in the shift shaft face the detent plunger.

4. Install the selector plate and tighten the attaching bolts to 6–8 ft. lbs.

NOTE: The pin in the selector arm must ride in the cut-out of the gate in the selector plate.

5. If removed, apply a Teflon-type sealant to the threads reverse relay lever pivot pin and install. Install the reverse relay lever and secure with the retaining clip.

NOTE: Make sure the pin at the end of the lever faces outward.

6. Apply a Teflon-type sealant to the threads of the back-up lamp switch and install the switch.

7. Using a small drift, depress the reverse inhibitor plunger and slide the shift lever shaft (with the oil relief flat first) through the case pedestal. Slide the shaft far enough so the main shaft assembly or differential will not interfere with the shift lever shaft when installed.

Main Shift Control Shaft

DISASSEMBLY

1. Rotate the 3rd–4th shift fork on the shaft until the notch in the fork is located over the interlock sleeve. Rotate the 1st–2nd shift fork on the shaft until the notch in the fork is located over the selector arm finger. With the forks in position, slide the 3rd–4th fork and interlock sleeve off the shaft.

2. Using a 5mm punch, remove the selector arm retaining pin.

3. Remove the selector arm and the 1st–2nd shift fork from the shaft.

NOTE: If equipped with a 5 speed proceed with the following:

4. Use a punch to remove the roll pin.
5. Slide the fork from the shaft.

ASSEMBLY

1. Clean and lightly oil all parts with the appropriate transmission fluid.

2. Install the 1st–2nd shift fork and the selector arm on the shaft.

3. Align the hole in the selector arm with the hole in the shaft. Make sure the selector arm finger is aligned with the oil relief flats on the detent end of the shift shaft, then install the retaining pin.

4. Position the slot in the 1st–2nd fork over the fork selector arm finger. Position the slot in the 3rd–4th fork over the interlock sleeve. Slide the 3rd–4th fork and interlock sleeve onto the main shift control shaft, then align the interlock sleeve spines on the fork selector arm and slide into position.

NOTE: If equipped with a 5 speed proceed with the following:

5. Hold the shaft with the hole on the left.

6. Install the fork so that the protruding spline is pointing toward the long end of the shaft.

7. Install the roll pin.

Input Cluster Shaft Seal

REMOVAL & INSTALLATION

1. Working from the outside of the case, remove the input shaft seal using seal remover No. T77F-7050-A or equivalent and a hammer. Position the remover tool against the seal by placing it in the slot cut in the case.

2. To install, lightly oil the input shaft seal and tap into place with a 1¼ in. socket and a hammer.

Input Cluster Shaft Bearings

REMOVAL

1. Remove the bearing cone and roller assemblies using a Bearing Puller/Installer No. D79L-4621-A or equivalent and an arbor press. Label bearings for correct installation.

INSTALLATION

1. Thoroughly clean and lightly oil the bearings.

2. Using the tools used during removal, press the bearings on the proper end.

Bearing Cups

The input cluster shaft and the main shaft are supported at each end by tapered roller bearings. The cups, which support the bearings and can be removed and installed by hand, are located in the transmission case and the clutch housing case. Shims, to preload the tapered roller bearings, are located behind the bearing cups in the transmission case. It is important to keep the preload shim with its matching cup during disassembly. Also label the bearing cups if they are removed from the case. Prior to installation, lightly grease the bearing cups.

Transmission

ASSEMBLY

1. Place the differential and the final drive gear assembly into the clutch housing case.

2. Position the main shift control shaft assembly so that the shift forks engage their respective slots in the synchronizer sleeves on the main shaft assembly.

3. Mesh the main shaft assembly with the input cluster shaft assembly. Hold the input cluster shaft assembly, main shaft and

the main shift control shaft in their respective working positions, lower them into their bores in the clutch housing case as one unit.

4. Position the shift lever assembly in its working position, with one shift lever pin located in the socket of the input shift shaft selector plate arm assembly and the other in the socket of the main shift control shaft block. Slide the shift lever shaft through the shift lever and into its bore in the clutch housing. Rotate the shift lever shaft so the reverse inhibitor notch faces the reverse inhibitor plunger.

5. Position the shift lever shaft so the set screw hole on the shaft aligns with the hole in the shift lever.

6. Make sure the selector pin is in the neutral gate of the control selector plate and the finger of the fork selector arm is partially engaged with the 1st–2nd fork and partially with the 3rd–4th fork.

7. Place the reverse idler gear groove in engagement with the pin at the end of the reverse relay lever, and slide the shaft through the gear and into its bore. Align the retaining screw hole in the case. This will allow proper alignment between the reverse idler shaft retaining screw hole in the transmission case when the case is placed over this assembly.

8. Install the magnet in its pocket in the clutch housing case.

9. Apply a 1/16 in. wide bead of sealer to the clean surface of the clutch housing. Carefully lower the transmission case over the clutch housing case and move gently until the shift control shaft, main shaft and the input cluster shaft align with their respective bores in the transmission case. Gently slide the transmission case over the dowels and flush onto the clutch housing case. Make sure the case does not bind on the magnet.

10. Install the 14 transmission case-to-clutch housing bolts and tighten to 13–17 ft. lbs. using a 10mm socket.

11. Align the bore in the reverse idler shaft with the retaining screw hole in the transmission case, using a drift if necessary.

12. Install the reverse idler shaft retaining bolt and tighten to 16–20 ft. lbs.

13. Apply a pipe sealant containing Teflon to the threads of the interlock sleeve retaining pin in a clockwise direction. Align the slot in the interlock sleeve with the hole in the transaxle case, using a drift if necessary, then install the retaining pin and tighten to 12–15 ft. lbs.

14. Apply a pipe sealant containing Teflon to the threads of the detent plunger retaining screw in a clockwise direction. Install the detent plunger and spring and tighten the retaining screw to 9–12 ft. lbs.

15. Place the transaxle in an upright position and insert a drift through the hole in the input shift shaft. Shift the transaxle into and out of all gears to check installation.

CHILTON TYPE 3

Transmission Disassembly

GEARSHIFT HOUSING AND SHIFT MECHANISM

1. If available, mount the transmission in a work stand.

2. Remove the reverse operating lever from the shift lever shaft.

3. Position the operating levers in their Neutral positions. Remove the gearshift housing retaining bolts and remove the housing from the transmission.

NOTE: If either the 1st-2nd or 3rd-4th shift forks stick to their respective synchronizer sleeves, carefully work the forks away from the sleeves, then remove the assembly. Also note that Steps 4, 5, and 6 need to be performed only if oil leakage is noticed around the gearshift lever shafts.

4. Remove the operating lever-to-shift lever attaching nuts (and washers, if so equipped). Disengage the levers from the flats on the shafts and remove the levers.

NOTE: Before performing step 5, the lever shafts must be free of burrs. Housing bore damage and subsequent oil leakage will result if burred shafts are pulled through the housing bores.

5. Remove the shift levers from the housing.

6. Remove the O-ring retainers and the O-rings from the housing.

7. Remove the ring from the interlock pivot pin. Remove the interlock levers and the spring from the housing.

8. Remove the reverse detent spring and ball from the bore of the transmission case.

EXTENSION HOUSING, MAINSHAFT, AND DRIVE PINION

9. Remove the bolt and retainer which secure the speedometer pinion adapter. Carefully remove the adapter and pinion from the extension housing.

10. Remove the extension housing-to-transmission case attaching bolts.

11. Rotate the extension around the mainshaft in order to expose the rear of the countershaft.

NOTE: One of the extension attaching bolts may be installed to hold the extension in this inverted position.

12. Drill or centerpunch a hole in the front countershaft expansion plug.

13. Push the countershaft rearward (through the hole made during Step 12) until the Woodruff key is exposed. Remove the key.

14. Push the countershaft forward against the expansion plug, then tap the shaft with a brass drift and a hammer (in the same direction) in order to drive the expansion plug from the transmission case.

15. Using a countershaft arbor (Chrysler tool #C-3938 or its equivalent), push the countershaft out of the rear of the case.

— CAUTION —
Be careful not to allow the countershaft washers to fall out of position.

16. Lower the cluster gear to the bottom of the transmission case.

17. Move the extension housing back to its original position.

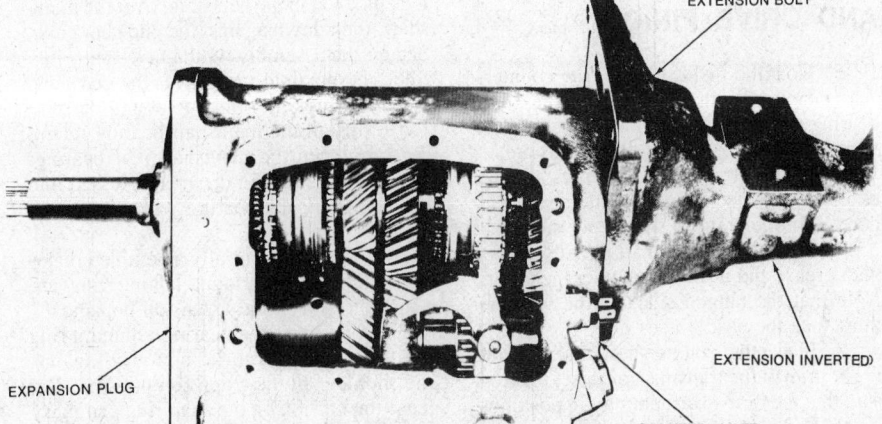

EXTENSION BOLT

EXPANSION PLUG

EXTENSION INVERTED)

COUNTER SHAFT

CASE-UPRIGHT

Rotating the extension housing on an Overdrive-4 (© Chrysler Corp.)

18. Remove the attaching bolts of the drive pinion bearing retainer.

19. Remove the retainer and gasket, then remove the oil seal from the retainer.

——————— CAUTION ———————

Be careful not to damage the seal bore of the retainer; oil leakage could occur.

20. Tap the pinion and bearing assembly forward, using a brass drift and a hammer. Remove the assembly from the front of the transmission case.

21. Slide the 3rd-4th synchronizer sleeve slightly forward, then slide the reverse idler gear to the center of its shaft. Using a soft-faced hammer, tap the extension housing rearward. Remove the housing and the mainshaft from the transmission case as an assembly.

22. Remove the snap-ring which retains the 3rd-4th synchronizer to the mainshaft, then remove the synchronizer assembly.

23. Slide the 4th speed gear and the stop-ring off of the mainshaft.

NOTE: DO NOT separate the synchronizer parts unless replacement of a particular part is required due to damage.

24. Compress the snap-ring which retains the mainshaft ball bearing in the extension housing; hold the snap-ring compressed, then pull the mainshaft assembly and bearing from the extension housing.

25. Remove the snap-ring which retains the mainshaft bearing to the shaft. To separate the mainshaft from the bearing, the shaft should be pressed through the bearing. It may be driven through (carefully), if a press is not available.

26. Remove the following parts from the mainshaft:
 a. Bearing
 b. Bearing retainer ring
 c. 1st speed gear
 d. 1st speed stop-ring

27. Remove the snap-ring which retains the 1st-2nd synchronizer assembly to the mainshaft, then remove the assembly from the mainshaft. Refer to the note which follows Step 23.

DRIVE PINION AND COUNTERSHAFT GEAR

28. Remove the inner snap-ring from the pinion bearing, then press the bearing off of the pinion.

29. Remove the snap-ring and the bearing rollers (16) from the drive pinion cavity.

30. Remove the countershaft gear from the bottom of the transmission case.

31. Remove the arbor, needle bearings (76), thrust washers, and spacers from the center of the countershaft gear.

32. Obtain Chrysler tool #C-3638 or its equivalent, then push a 7/16 in. socket (1/4 or 3/8 in. drive) onto the smaller hex of the tool. Position the tool in the transmission case so that the blunt end of the tool is against the case, and the socket end of the

tool is against the reverse idler gear shaft.

33. Expand the tool so that the tool pushes the reverse idler gear shaft out of the transmission case. It may be necessary to remove the tool and use a socket and an extension to push the shaft completely out of the case. Remove the reverse idler gear.

34. If oil leakage is noted around the reverse idler shift fork bore, perform the following:
 a. Remove any burrs from the lever shaft to prevent bore damage as the shift lever is withdrawn.
 b. Push the lever toward the inside of the transmission case and remove the fork.
 c. Remove the O-ring and the O-ring retainer from the bore of the transmission case.

35. Clean, inspect, and lubricate all transmission parts prior to assembly. Replace any parts which are irreparably damaged.

Transmission Assembly

REVERSE GEAR, LEVER, AND FORK

1. If removed, install the reverse lever, O-ring (lubricated), and the O-ring retainer.

2. Drive the reverse idler gear shaft in just enough for the reverse idler gear to be positioned on the shaft. Install the reverse idler gear (fork slot toward the rear), engaging the slot with the reverse shift fork.

3. Drive the reverse gear shaft into the case until the Woodruff key may be installed. Install the Woodruff key, then drive the shaft inward until it is flush with the end of the case.

4. If removed, install the back-up lamp switch (with a new gasket) and torque to 15 ft. lbs.

COUNTERSHAFT GEAR AND DRIVE PINION

5. Coat the inside ends of the countershaft gear bore with grease. Install the roller bearing spacer and the arbor tool (used previously) into the countershaft gear bore.

6. Install the 38 roller bearings and the two spacer rings into the countershaft gear bore (19 rollers and 1 spacer per side).

7. Coat the countershaft thrust washers with grease and install them over the arbor. Note that the tanged sides of the washers must face the case bosses.

8. Place the countershaft assembly at the bottom of the transmission case, making sure that the thrust washers stay in position.

9. With the outer snap-ring groove of the drive pinion bearing facing forward, press the bearing onto the pinion shaft until the bearing is fully seated against the drive gear shoulder.

10. Install a new snap-ring onto the

bearing, making sure that the snap-ring is fully seated. Note that the snap-ring is selective, in that various thicknesses are available to alter the end-play.

11. Install the 16 bearing rollers (coated with grease) into the cavity of the drive pinion gear. Install the bearing retaining snap-ring.

12. Carefully drive a new oil seal into the pinion bearing retainer.

EXTENSION HOUSING BUSHING REPLACEMENT

13. Remove the extension housing yoke seal, then drive the bushing out of the housing using an appropriate driver (Chrysler tool #C-3974 or its equivalent).

14. Obtain a new bushing and position the bushing on the driver used during step 13. Align the oil hole of the bushing with the oil slot of the extension housing, then drive the bushing into place.

15. Carefully tap a new extension housing oil seal into place.

MAINSHAFT

16. If previously disassembled, partially assemble the synchronizers as follows:
 a. Place a stop-ring on the workbench, followed by the clutch gear and sleeve.
 b. Drop the struts into their slots. Snap in a strut spring, placing the tang inside one of the struts.
 c. Turn the assembly over on the stop-ring, then install the second strut spring, with the tang inside a different strut than the first spring.

17. Install the 2nd speed gear over the mainshaft with the synchronizer cone toward the rear. The gear must be pushed against the shoulder on the mainshaft.

18. Install the 1st-2nd synchronizer assembly (including the stop-ring, with the lugs indexed in the hub slots) over the mainshaft, then down against the 2nd gear cone. Secure the assembly with a new snap-ring. Slide the next stop-ring over the shaft and index the lugs into the hub slots.

19. Install the mainshaft bearing retaining ring, then the mainshaft rear bearing. The bearing must be driven or pressed into place. Secure the bearing with a new (selective) snap-ring.

20. Install the partially assembled mainshaft until the bearing retaining ring engages the slot in the extension housing.

21. Compress the bearing retaining ring until the bearing can be bottomed against the shoulder in the extension housing. Release the tension on the snap-ring and make sure that it fully seats in the snap-ring groove.

22. Slide the 4th speed gear over the mainshaft (with the synchronizer cone toward the front), followed by the 4th speed gear stop-ring.

23. Install the 3rd-4th synchronizer clutch gear assembly onto the mainshaft, with the shift fork slot positioned toward the rear. Be sure to index the rear stop-ring with the clutch gear struts.

24. Install the retaining snap-ring, then position the front stop-ring (greased) over the clutch gear, again indexing the ring lugs with the struts.

25. Coat a new extension housing gasket with grease, then position it on the extension.

26. Slide the reverse idler gear to the center of the reverse idler shaft, then move the 3rd-4th synchronizer sleeve as far forward as possible without dislodging the struts.

27. Carefully insert the mainshaft assembly into the transmission case, tilting it as required to clear the gears.

28. Position the 3rd-4th synchronizer sleeve in the Neutral position.

29. Rotate the extension housing in order to expose the rear of the countershaft, then install a bolt to hold the extension in this position.

30. Install the drive pinion and the bearing into the front of the transmission case, seating the bearing in the case bore. If necessary, tap the assembly into place (lightly) using a soft-faced hammer.

NOTE: The bearing outer snap-ring should bottom against the case face with a minimal amount of effort. If the snap-ring will not seat in this manner, check for a mispositioned strut, pinion roller, or stop-ring.

31. While holding the countershaft gear to prevent damage, turn the transmission assembly upside down. Lower the countershaft gear assembly into place, making sure that the thrust washers stay in position. The thrust washer tangs must be aligned with the corresponding case slots.

32. Install the countershaft gear about half way into the bore (in a forward motion), then install the Woodruff key. Push the countershaft fully forward until the end of the shaft is flush with the rear case face. Remove the arbor tool.

33. Rotate the extension housing to its proper position, then install the extension housing bolts. Tighten the bolts to 30 ft. lbs.

34. Rotate the transmission to an upright position. Install the pinion bearing retainer. Coat the retainer bolts with sealing compound, then install the bolts and torque them to 30 ft. lbs.

35. Install a new countershaft bore expansion plug.

GEARSHIFT HOUSING AND SHIFT MECHANISM

36. Install the interlock levers on the pivot pin and retain them with the E–clip. Install the interlock spring onto the interlock levers using pliers.

37. Grease the shift lever bores of the gearshift housing, then install the shift levers into their respective bores. Install the shift lever shaft O-rings and the O-ring retainers.

38. Install the operating levers onto their respecitve shift lever shafts. Install and tighten the operating lever retaining nuts and tighten them to 18 ft. lbs.

39. Rotate each operating lever until the fork bores of the shift levers are positioned straight up. Install the 3rd-4th shift fork into its bore and under both interlock levers.

40. Position both of the synchronizer sleeves in their neutral positions (centered in their travel). Position the 1st-2nd shift fork into the groove of the 1st-2nd synchronizer sleeve.

41. Slide the reverse idler gear to its Neutral position, then lay the transmission on its right side. Place a new case-to-housing gasket on the transmission case, retaining it with grease.

42. Install the reverse lever detent ball and spring (in that order) into the bore in the side of the case.

43. Lower the gearshift housing into place on the transmission case, guiding the 3rd-4th shift fork into the groove of the 3rd-4th synchronizer, and the shaft of the 1st-2nd shift fork into the 1st-2nd shift lever bore.

NOTE: Hold the reverse interlock link against the 1st-2nd shift lever to provide clearance.

44. Using a screwdriver, raise the interlock lever against its spring tension, which will allow the 1st-2nd shift fork shaft to slip under the levers. Make sure that the reverse detent spring is positioned in the cover bore. The shift housing should now seat against the transmission case.

45. Install the housing retaining bolts and tighten them finger-tight. Shift the transmission through all gears to make sure that it is operating properly, without any binding. Tighten the housing bolts evenly to 15 ft. lbs.

NOTE: Make sure that the housing bolts are installed in their original locations: Eight of the bolts are shoulder bolts, used for locating purposes; one bolt shoulder is longer. This bolt is installed in the center hole along the rearward housing surface. The two standard-style bolts are placed above and below the long-shouldered bolt.

46. Grease the reverse shaft and attach the operating lever with the nut. Torque the nut to 18 ft. lbs.

47. Install the speedometer drive pinion gear and the adapter, making sure that the stamped range number is at the 6 o'clock position.

48. Install the transmission as outlined in the appropriate car section.

CHILTON TYPE 4

NOTE: Versions of this transmission are identified with the name Tremec. It is built in Mexico and purchased for use by several manufacturers. The service procedures are very similar, regardless of application.

Transmission Disassembly

1. Drain the lubricant, then remove the cover bolts and the case cover. Late models are drained by removing the lower extension housing bolt.

2. Remove the five attaching screws, then remove the extension housing from the transmission case. Remove a long spring which retains the detent plug in the case. Remove the detent plug with a small magnet.

3. Remove the four attaching screws, then remove the front bearing retainer from the case.

4. Remove the filler plug. Working through the filler plug hole, drive the roll pin out of the case and countershaft with a small punch.

5. With a dummy shaft, push the countershaft out of the rear of the case until the countershaft cluster gear can be lowered to the bottom of the case. Remove the countershaft from the front of the case.

6. Remove the snap-ring. Lift the input gear and shaft from the front of the case. Press the shaft out of the bearing.

7. Remove the snap-ring that holds the speedometer gear onto the shaft. Slide the speedometer gear off the output shaft. Remove the speedometer gear lockball.

8. Remove the snap-ring that holds the output shaft bearing on the shaft. With a puller, remove the bearing from both the case and shaft.

9. Place both shift levers in the neutral position.

10. Remove the set screw that holds the 1st-reverse shift fork to the shift rail. Slide first and reverse shift rail out through the rear of the case.

11. Rotate the 1st-reverse shift fork upward, then lift it from the case.

12. Remove the set screw that holds the 2nd-3rd shift fork to the shift rail. Rotate the shift rail 90°.

13. With a magnet, lift the interlock plug from the case.

14. Tap on the inner end of the 2nd-3rd shift rail to remove the expansion plug from the front of the case. Remove the shift rail.

15. Rotate the 2nd-3rd shift fork upward, then lift it from the case.

16. Lift the output shaft out through the top of the case.

17. Working through the front bearing opening, drive the reverse idler shaft out through the rear of the case.

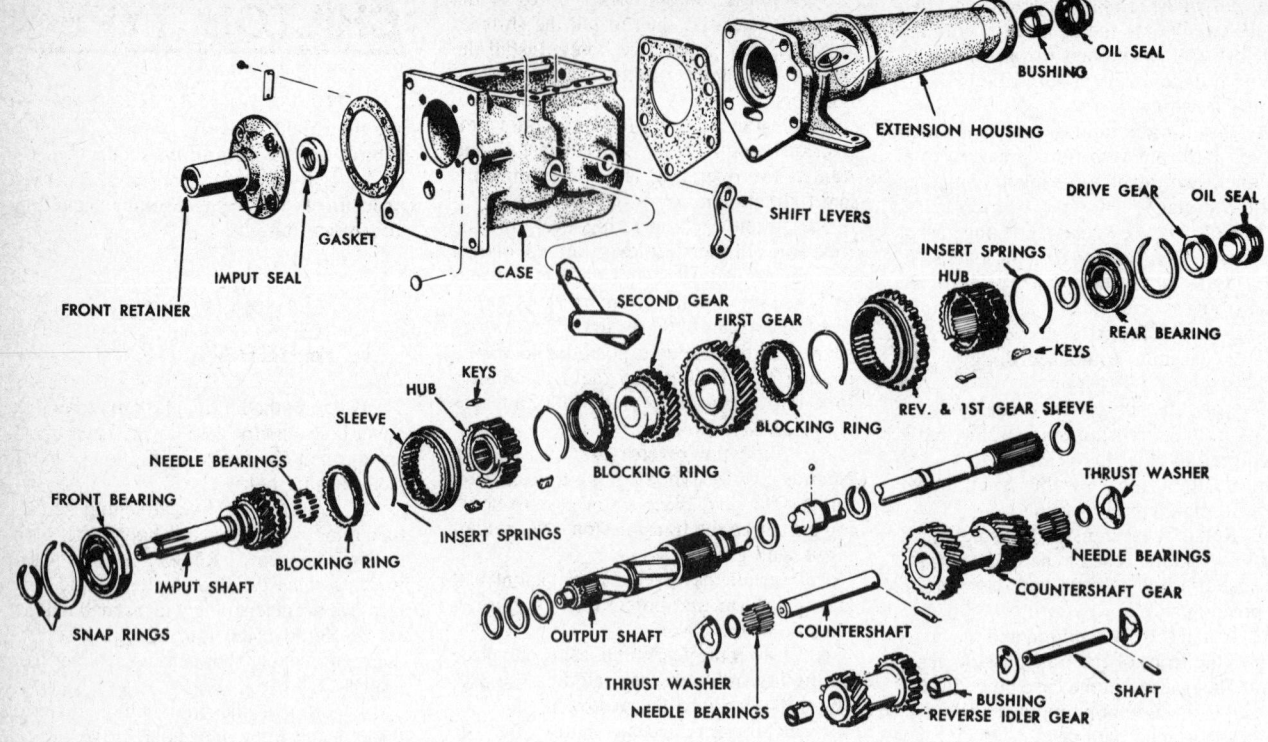

Disassembled view of a Chilton Type 4 transmission—Ford 3.03 version shown (© Ford Motor Co.)

18. Lift the reverse idler gear and two thrust washers from the case.

19. Lift the countershaft gear and thrust washers from the case.

20. Remove the countershaft-to-case retaining pin and any needle bearings which may have fallen into the case.

21. Remove the shift levers and shafts from the case. Discard the O-rings.

22. Remove the snap-ring from the front of the output shaft, then slide the synchronizer and the 2nd speed gear from the shaft.

23. Remove the next snap-ring and thrust washer from the output shaft, then slide the 1st speed gear and blocking ring off the shaft.

24. Remove the next snap-ring from the output shaft, then press off the 1st-reverse synchronizer hub from the shaft.

25. Remove the dummy shaft, 50 bearing rollers and the two retainer washers from the countershaft gear.

26. Disassemble the synchronizers.

Transmission Assembly

1. Coat the bore in each end of the countershaft gear with grease. Hold the dummy shaft in the gear and install 25 bearing rollers and a retainer washer in each end of the gear. Install the countershaft gear, thrust washers and dummy shaft in the case. End-play is controlled with variable thickness thrust washers to 0.004–0.018 in. Let the gear cluster assembly lie in the bottom of the case.

2. Install the reverse idler gear, thrust washers and shaft in the case. Make sure that the thrust washer with the flat side, is at the web end and that the spur gear is toward the rear of the case. Idler gear end-play should be 0.004–0.018 in.

3. Install an insert spring into the groove of the 1st-reverse synchronizer hub. Be sure that the spring covers all insert grooves. Start the hub in the sleeve, being sure the alignment marks are properly indexed. Position the three inserts in the hub and be sure the small end is over the spring and that the shoulder is on the inside of the hub. Slide the sleeve and reverse gear onto the hub until the detent is engaged. Install the other insert spring in the front of the hub to hold the inserts against it.

4. Install one insert spring into a groove of the second-third synchronizer hub. With the alignment marks on the hub and sleeve aligned, start the hub into the sleeve. Place the three inserts on top of the retaining spring and push the assembly together. Install the remaining insert spring, so that the spring ends cover the same slots as do the other spring. Do not stagger the springs. Place a synchronizer blocking ring in each end of the synchronizer sleeve.

5. Lubricate the output shaft splines and machined surfaces with transmission lubricant.

6. Press the 1st-reverse synchronizer hub onto the output shaft, with the teeth end of the gear facing toward the rear end of the shaft. Secure it with the snap-ring.

7. Place the blocking ring on the tapered machined surface of the first gear.

8. Slide the first speed gear onto the output shaft, with the blocking ring toward the rear of the shaft. Rotate the gear to engage the three notches in the blocking ring with the synchronizer inserts. Secure the first speed gear with the thrust washer and snap-ring.

9. Slide the blocking ring onto the tapered, machined surface of the second speed gear. Slide the second speed gear, with blocking ring and the second and third gear synchronizer, onto the mainshaft. The tapered machined surface of the second speed gear must be toward the front of the shaft. Secure the synchronizer with a snap-ring. Check the end-play between the synchronizer and snap-ring with a feeler gauge. It should be 0.004 in.

10. Install new O-rings onto the two shift lever shafts. Lubricate the shafts with transmission fluid and install them into the case. Secure each shift lever onto its shaft.

11. Coat the bore of the input shaft with a light coat of grease. Install the 15 bearing rollers into the bore.

NOTE: The input shaft is installed through the front of the transmission.

12. Position the output shaft assembly in the case.

13. Place the 2nd-3rd speed shift fork in the synchronizer groove. Rotate the fork into position and install the 2nd-3rd speed shift rail. Move the rail inward until the detent plug engages the forward notch (second). Secure the fork to the shaft with a set screw. Move the synchronizer to the neutral position.

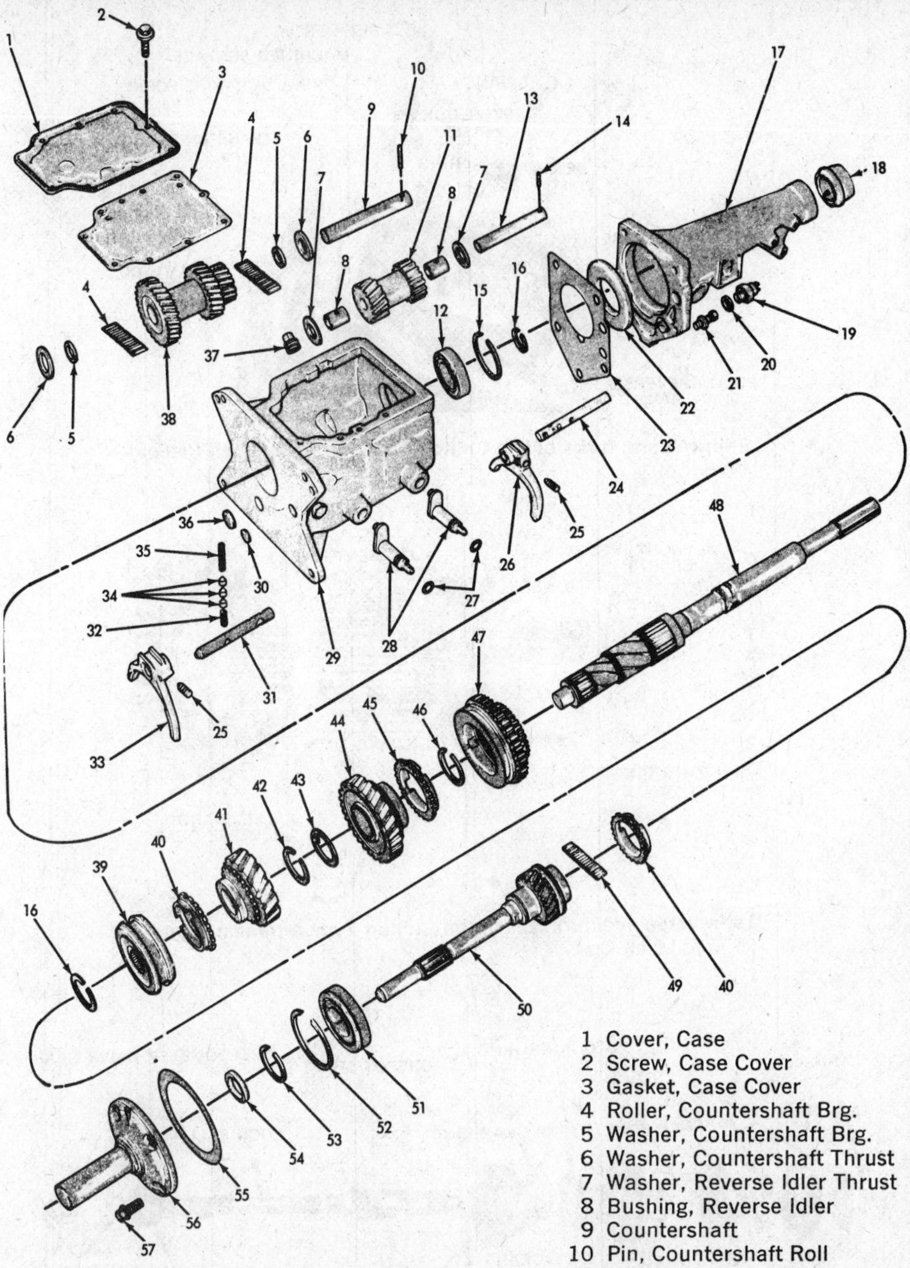

11 Gear, Reverse Idler
12 Bearing, Output Shaft
13 Shaft, Reverse Idler
14 Pin, Reverse Idler Stop
15 Snap Ring, Output Shaft Brg.Outer
16 Snap Ring, Output Shaft, Inner
17 Extension
18 Seal, Extension
19 Switch, Back-Up Lamp
20 Gasket, Back-Up Lamp Switch
21 Screw, Extension
   Lockwasher, Extension Screw
22 Retainer, Output Shaft Brg.
23 Gasket, Extension
24 Rail, Gearshift First and Reverse
25 Screw, Fork Set
26 Fork, Gearshift First and Reverse
27 Seal, Gearshift Lever Shaft Oil
28 Lever, Gearshift
29 Case
30 Plug
31 Rail, Gearshift Second and Third
32 Spring, Gearshift Detent Pin
33 Fork, Gearshift Second and Third
34 Pin, Gearshift Detent
35 Spring, Gearshift Detent Pin
36 Plug
37 Plug, Case Filler
38 Gear, Countershaft
39 Synchronizer Assy., Second and
   Third
40 Ring, Synchronizer Second and
   Third Stop
41 Gear, Second Speed
42 Snap Ring, Low Speed Gear
   Thrust Washer
43 Washer, Low Speed Gear Thrust
44 Gear, Low Speed
45 Ring, Synchronizer Low Stop
46 Snap Ring, Synchronizer Low and
   Reverse Clutch Gear
47 Synchronizer Assy., Low and
   Reverse
48 Shaft, Output
49 Roller, Output Shaft Pilot
50 Shaft, Input
51 Bearing, Input Shaft
52 Snap Ring, Bearing, Outer
53 Snap Ring, Bearing, Inner
54 Seal, Bearing Retainer Oil
55 Gasket, Bearing Retainer
56 Retainer, Bearing
57 Screw, Bearing Retainer

1 Cover, Case
2 Screw, Case Cover
3 Gasket, Case Cover
4 Roller, Countershaft Brg.
5 Washer, Countershaft Brg.
6 Washer, Countershaft Thrust
7 Washer, Reverse Idler Thrust
8 Bushing, Reverse Idler
9 Countershaft
10 Pin, Countershaft Roll

Exploded view of a Chilton Type 4 transmission—Chrysler A-390 version shown (© Chrysler Corp.)

14. Install the interlock pin in the case.

15. Place 1st-reverse shift fork in the groove of the 1st-reverse synchronizer. Rotate the fork into position and install the 1st-reverse shift rail. Move the rail inward until the center notch is aligned with the detent bore. Secure the fork to the shaft with a set screw.

16. Install a new expansion plug in the case front.

17. Install the input shaft and gear in the front of the case.

18. Place front bearing retainer (with new gasket in place) on the case with the oil return groove at the bottom. Torque attaching screws to 30 ft. lbs.

19. Install the large snap-ring on the rear

bearing. Place the bearing on the output shaft, with the snap-ring end toward the rear of the shaft. Press bearing into place and secure with a snap-ring.

20. Hold the speedometer drive gear lock ball in the detent and slide the speedometer gear into place. Secure the gear with a snap-ring.

21. Lift the countershaft gear cluster up into place, and, by entering the countershaft at the rear of the case, push the dummy shaft out of the gear and transmission case. Before the countershaft is completely in place, align the roll pin hole in the shaft with the hole in the case.

NOTE: On all eight cylinder vehicles

and Ford six cylinder models, the countershaft is a press fit in the case. On Ford six cylinder models with RAN transmission, there is a radial clearance of 0.020 in. at front bore and 0.010 in. at rear.

22. Working through the filler hole, install a roll pin into the case and countershaft.

23. Install filler and drain plugs in the case.

24. Coat a new extension housing gasket with sealer and install it on the case.

25. Apply sealer to attaching screws and secure extension housing to the case by torquing the screws 42–50 ft. lbs.

26. With transmission in gear, pour lubricant over the entire gear train while ro-

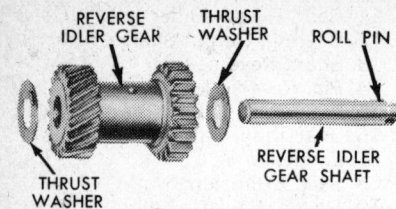

Reverse idler shaft of the Chilton Type 4 transmission (© Ford Motor Co.)

tating the input or output shaft.

27. Install the transmission cover, with a new sealer-coated gasket in place, and torque the nine attaching screws to 14–19 ft. lbs.

28. Check operation of transmission in all of the gear positions.

CHILTON TYPE 5

Transmission Disassembly

1. Remove the clutch release bearing and lever and detach the clutch housing.

2. Drain the lubricant and remove the cover and gasket from the case.

3. Remove the threaded plug, spring and shift rail detent plunger from the front of the case.

4. Drive the access plug from the rear of the case. Drive the interlock retaining pin from the case and remove the interlock plate.

5. Remove the roll pin from the selector lever arm.

6. Tap the front end of the shift rail, to displace the plug at the rear of the extension housing. Remove the shift rail from the rear of the extension housing.

7. Remove the selector arm and shift forks from the case.

8. Remove the extension housing attaching bolts. Loosen the extension housing and rotate the housing to align the countershaft with the cutaway in the extension housing flange.

9. Drive the countershaft rearward until the shaft clears the front of the case. Install a dummy shaft in the case and gear until the countershaft gear can be lowered to the bottom of the case. Remove the countershaft.

10. Lift the extension housing and mainshaft from the case as an assembly.

11. Remove the input shaft bearing retainer attaching bolts. Remove the input shaft and bearing retainer from the case as an assembly.

12. Remove the reverse idler gear and shaft from the rear of the case.

13. Remove the bearing retainers, bearings, and dummy shaft from the countershaft gear.

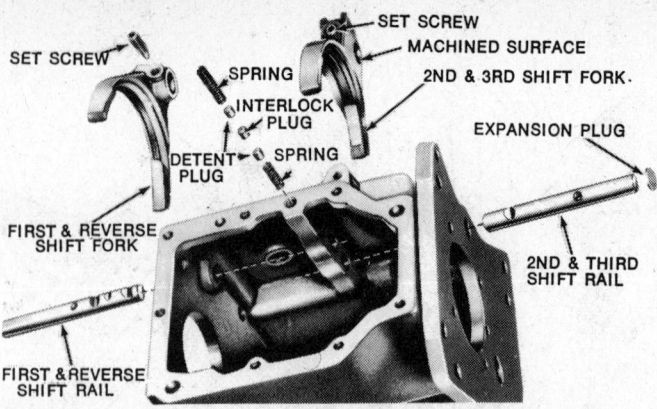

Shift rail and forks of the Chilton Type 4 transmission (© Ford Motor Co.)

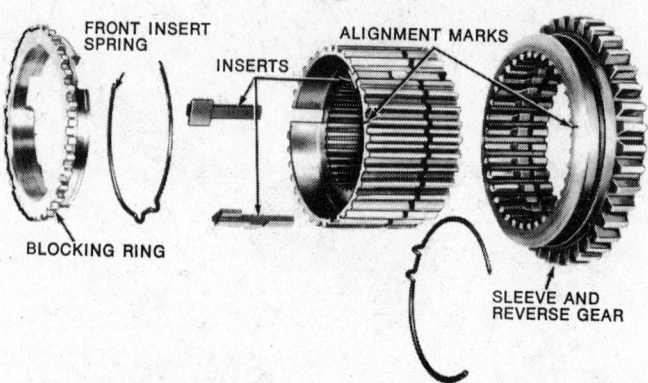

1st-reverse synchronizer of the Chilton Type 4 transmission (© Ford Motor Co.)

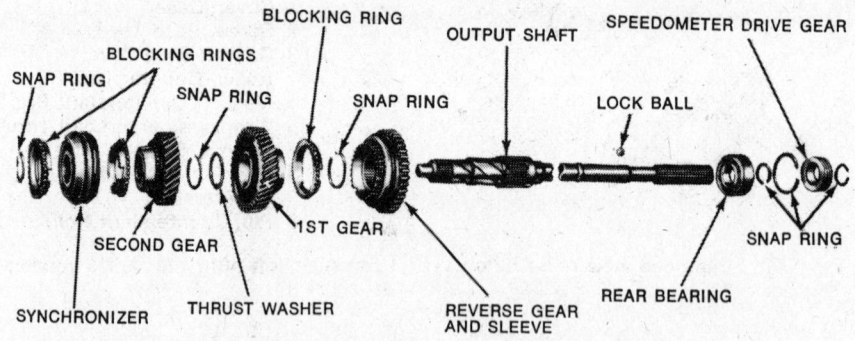

Output shaft of the Chilton Type 4 transmission (© Ford Motor Co.)

14. Remove the pilot bearing and bearing retainer from the input shaft gear.

15. Do not remove the ball bearing from the input shaft unless replacement is necessary. To remove it, take off the snap-ring and press the bearing off the shaft.

16. Pry the input shaft seal out of the bearing retainer.

17. Lift the 4th speed gear blocker ring from the front of the output shaft.

18. Remove the snap-ring from the forward end of the output shaft.

19. Support 3rd speed gear on press plates and place the output shaft and extension housing in a press. Push the output shaft out of the 3rd-4th synchronizer and 3rd speed gear, while supporting the extension housing and output shaft from beneath. Remove the snap-ring and washer and remove 2nd speed gear and the blocker ring from the output shaft.

20. Disassemble the synchronizer assembly by pulling the sleeve from the hub and removing the inserts and spring.

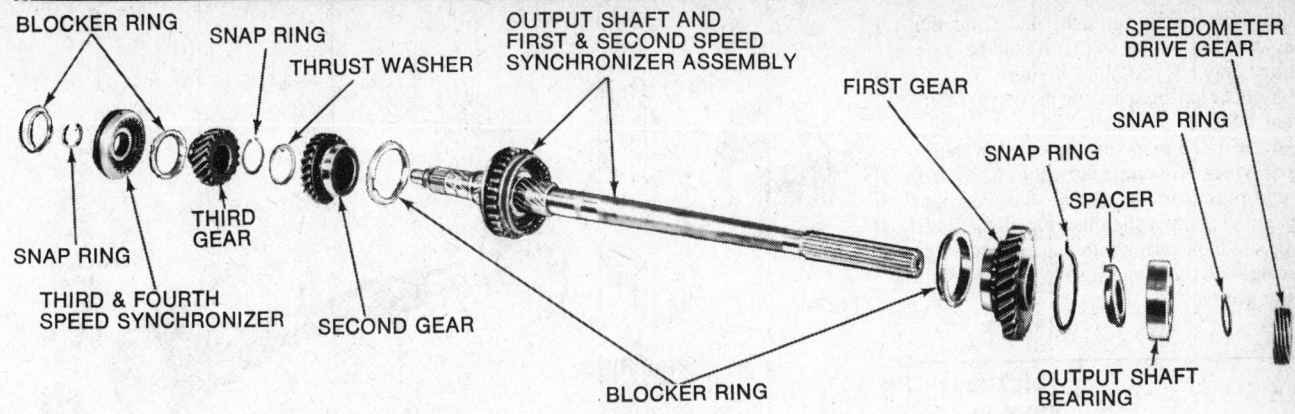

Output shaft and related components—Chilton Type 5 transmission (© Ford Motor Co.)

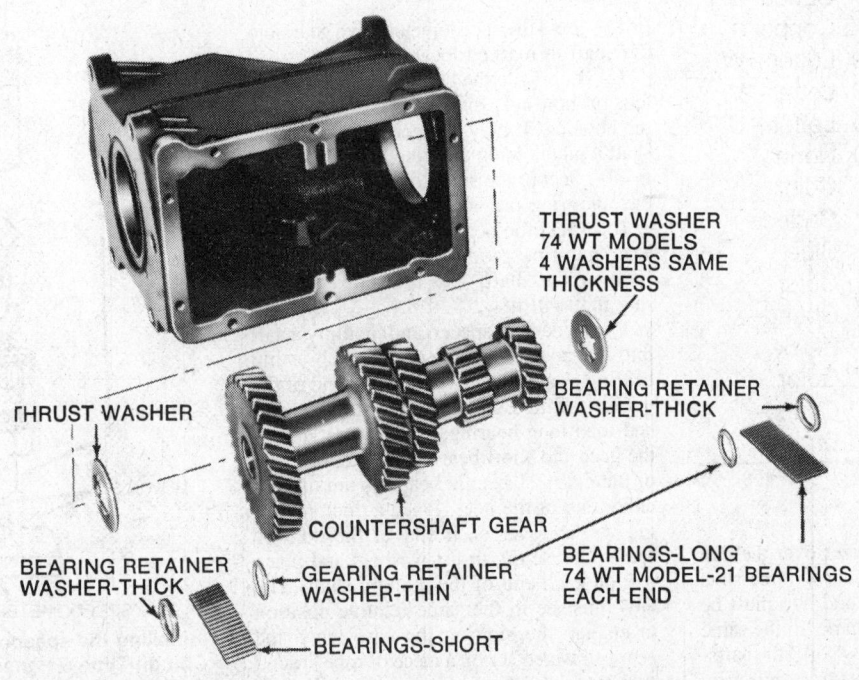

Countershaft and related components—Chilton Type 5 transmission (© Ford Motor Co.)

21. Remove the snap-ring which retains the output shaft bearing to the extension housing.

22. Use a plastic hammer and tap the output shaft assembly from the extension housing.

23. Measure or scribe the speedometer gear location on the output shaft and press the gear off.

24. Position press plates behind 1st speed gear and place the assembly in a press. The 1st-2nd synchronizer are serviced as an assembly. No attempt should be made to separate the hub from the shaft. The only serviceable parts are the springs and inserts. If the hub or sleeve is worn, the shaft and synchronizer must be replaced as an assembly.

25. Drive the shift rail bushing from the rear of the extension housing, using a 9/16 in. socket. Do not remove serviceable bushings.

26. Pry the shift rail seal from the rear of the case.

27. Remove the remaining shift linkage from the case.

Transmission Assembly

1. Install a new shift rail seal in the rear of the case.

2. If the shift rail bushing was removed, drive a new one into position with a 9/16 in. socket.

3. Slide the synchronizer hub over the shaft, making sure that the shift fork groove is toward the front of the shaft. The sleeve and hub are select fit and must be assembled with the etch marks in the same relative locations. Locate an insert in each of three slots in the hub. Oil all parts, and install an insert spring inside the sleeve. The spring tab must locate in a U-section of an insert. Fit the other spring to the opposite face, making sure that the tab locates in the same insert. Both springs should be in the same rotational direction. The tab end of one spring should be aligned with the tab of the spring on the opposite side.

4. Assemble a blocker ring on the 1st gear side of the 1st-2nd synchronizer. Lubricate the cone surface of 1st gear and all

output shaft gear journals, and slide the cone onto the output shaft, so that the cone surface engages the blocker ring.

5. Position the spacer on the output shaft, larger diameter rearward.

6. Install a snap-ring (selected from the chart) which will come closest to removing all end-play from the output shaft bearing. Position the output shaft bearing on the shaft and press the bearing into place. Secure the bearing with the thickest snap-ring that will fit the groove.

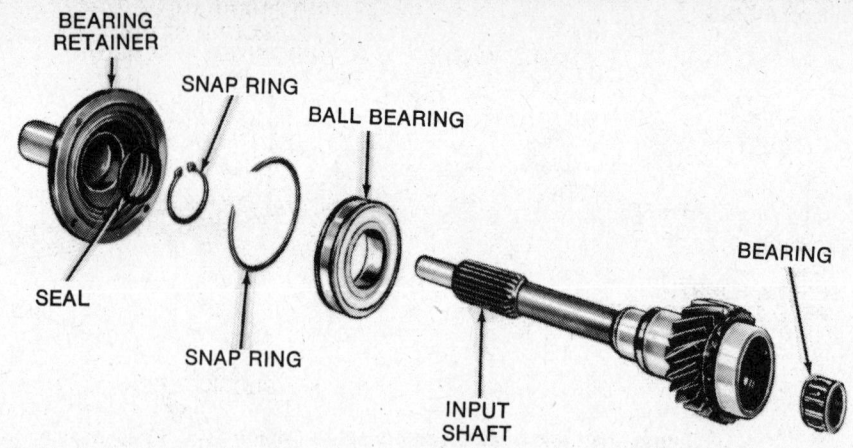

Input shaft and related components—Chilton Type 5 transmission (© Ford Motor Co.)

Part No.		Thickness Identifi-cation
D1FZ-7030-A	0.0679	Color Coded—Copper
D1FZ-7030-B	0.0689	Letter—W
D1FZ-7030-C	0.0699	Letter—V
D1FZ-7030-D	0.0709	Letter—U
D1FZ-7030-E	0.0719	None
DIFZ-7030-F	0.0728	Color Coded—Blue
DIFZ-7030-G	0.0738	Color Coded—Black
DIFZ-7030-H	0.0748	Color Coded—Brown

7. Slide the synchronizer over the hub and locate an insert in each of three slots in the sleeve. The sleeve and hub must be assembled with the etch marks in the same relative locations. Lightly oil all parts. Complete assembly of the synchronizer by following directions in previous Step 3.

8. Position 2nd speed gear and the blocker ring on the output shaft, dog teeth facing rearward. Install the washer and snap-ring. Position 3rd speed gear on the output shaft, dog teeth forward. Lubricate the gear cones and assemble a blocker ring on 3rd gear cone.

9. Position the 3rd-4th synchronizer assembly on the output shaft, hub boss facing forward.

10. Install press plates against the boss on the synchronizer hub.

11. Place the entire unit in a press, extension end up, and press the synchronizer assembly onto the output shaft as far as possible.

12. Retain the 3rd-4th synchronizer assembly to the output shaft with a snap-ring. Pull up on the synchronizer so that the snap-ring is tight in the groove.

13. Lubricate the gear cone and place the blocker ring on the input shaft gear cone.

14. Press the speedometer drive gear onto the shaft to marked location.

15. Lubricate the bearing bore of the extension housing. Install the output shaft in the housing. It may be necessary to tap the shaft while holding the synchronizer sleeves firmly. Secure the shaft to the housing with the snap-ring previously installed.

16. Press the bearing on the input shaft. The snap-ring groove must be toward the front of the shaft. Use the thickest snap-ring that will fit.

17. Slide the spacer and dummy shaft into the countershaft gear. Position a thin bearing retaining washer on each end of the dummy shaft. Lubricate the roller bearings and load long bearings in the small end of the gear and short bearings in the long end of the gear. 21 needle bearings are used at either end of the gear. Place a thick retaining washer over each end of the dummy shaft. Grease the thrust washers and place one on each end of the dummy shaft. The tabs must be in the same relative position to engage the slots in the case when the gear is lowered. Loop a piece of rope around each end of the gear and carefully install the gear and rope through the rear of the case. Lower the gear in place.

18. Lubricate the reverse idler gear shaft. Position the selector lever relay on the pivot pin. Secure with a spring clip. Hold the gear in the lever, long hub toward the rear of the case, and slide the reverse idler shaft into place. Seat the shaft in the case with a brass hammer.

19. Install a new seal in the input shaft bearing retainer. Install the input shaft in the case with a new bearing retainer O-ring. Tap on the outer race of the bearing to seat the outer snap-ring.

— **CAUTION** —
Use a soft hammer and do not tap on the input shaft itself.

20. Carefully slide the 3rd-4th synchronizer sleeve into 4th speed position.

21. Place a new gasket on the extension housing.

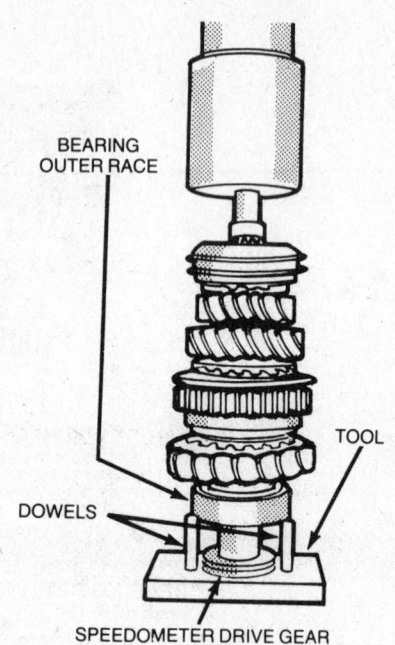

Installing the speedometer driven gear—Chilton Type 5 transmission

22. Lubricate and install the input shaft pilot bearing on the shaft. Slide the extension housing and output shaft into place, being careful not to disturb the 3rd-4th synchronizer.

23. Align the cutaway in the extension housing flange with the countershaft bore in the rear of the case.

24. Lift the countershaft gear into place and install the countershaft, making sure that the thrust washers remain in place. The flat on the countershaft should be parallel to the top of the case. Tap the shaft with a brass hammer until the front of the shaft is flush with the case.

25. Rotate the extension housing to align the bolt holes and loosely install the attaching bolts. Make sure that the rail slides freely in its bore. Binding is remedied by slightly rotating the extension housing to free the rail, then pushing the housing into the case. Apply sealer to the attaching bolts

and torque to 33–36 ft. lbs. Place the shift forks in the synchronizer sleeves. Install the interlock lever and new retaining pin. Lubricate the shift rail oil seal and slide the shift rail through the extension housing, case and second and 1st speed shift fork. Position the selector arm on the rail and slide the rail through the 3rd-4th shift fork. Slide the shift rail through the front of the case until the center detent bore is aligned with the detent plunger bore. Install a new retaining pin in the selector arm.

26. Install the detent plunger, spring and plug with sealer.

27. Install a new access plug in the rear of the case.

28. Position a new oil seal with tension spring and lip facing in the direction of the case.

29. Drive the seal in until it bottoms.

30. Position a new O-ring in the groove in the case. Position the input shaft bearing retainer with the groove in the retainer aligned with the oil passage in the case. Install the retaining bolts finger-tight.

31. Install the flywheel housing and tighten the retaining bolts and the front bearing retainer attaching bolts. Coat the retainer with grease.

32. Install the clutch release arm and bearing.

33. Install a new extension housing plug, using sealer.

34. Install a new cover gasket and cover, with the vent to the rear. Apply sealer to the left front cover attaching bolt. Torque to 8–10 ft. lbs.

CHILTON TYPE 6

Transmission Disassembly

1. Drain the lubricant by removing the lower extension housing bolt.

2. Drive the access plug from the rear of the extension housing. Remove the nut and washer securing the offset lever assembly. Remove the offset lever assembly.

3. Remove the remaining extension housing bolts and washers. Remove the extension from the case and discard the old gasket.

4. Remove the cap screws retaining the cover to the case. Remove the cover, shifter fork, shift rod assembly, and discard the old cover gasket.

5. Remove the bolts and washers attaching the front bearing retainer to the case. Remove the front bearing retainer and gasket.

6. Remove the spring clip retaining the reverse lever assembly to the pivot bolt. Remove the pivot and the reverse lever assembly.

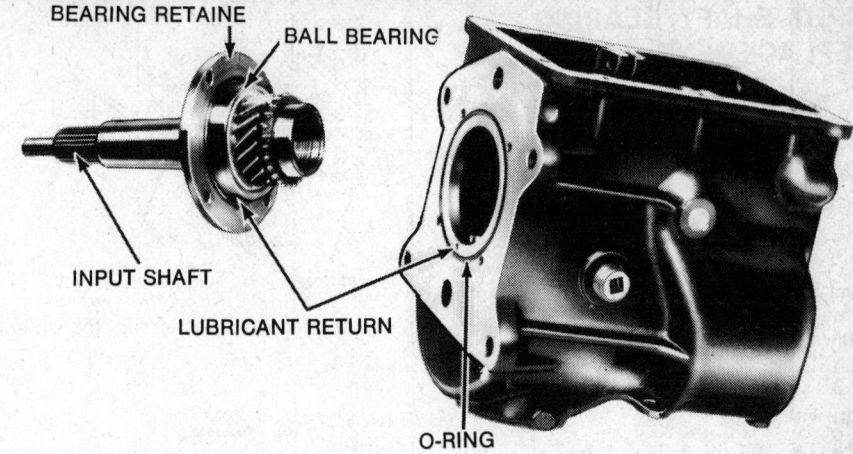

Installing the input shaft gear—Chilton Type 5 transmission (© Ford Motor Co.)

7. Remove the snap-ring holding the input bearing to the input shaft. Remove the outer snap-ring from the input bearing. Pull the bearing out.

8. Remove the snap-ring securing the speedometer drive gear on the output shaft. Slide the gear off and remove the lock ball from the shaft.

9. Remove the snap-ring retaining the output shaft bearing on the shaft. Use the outer snap-ring to pull the output shaft bearing from the shaft and case, then remove the snap-ring from the bearing.

10. Remove the input shaft through the front bearing hole in the case. Carefully lift the output shaft and gear train from the top of the case. Slide out the reverse idler gear shaft through the rear of the case and remove reverse gear.

11. Insert a dummy shaft from the front of the case to drive the countershaft out of the rear of the case. Lift out the countershaft gear, thrust washers, and dummy shaft through the top of the case.

12. Remove the cluster gear and dummy shaft assembly from the bottom of the case. Remove the cluster gear thrust washers.

13. Clean and inspect all parts. If the back-up light switch was damaged, remove it at this time.

Component Disassembly

COVER ASSEMBLY

1. Remove the detent screw, spring and plunger.

2. Pull the shifter shaft rod rearward, rotating it counterclockwise.

3. Remove the spring pin retaining the manual selector and interlock to the shifter shaft.

4. Remove the shifter shaft from the cover taking care not to tramage the seal.

5. Remove the manual selector and interlock plate.

6. Remove the first and second speed shifter fork. Remove the third and fourth speed shifter fork.

7. Clean and inspect all parts. Replace the shifter shaft seal and welch plug, if damaged.

OUTPUT SHAFT

1. Scribe alignment marks on the synchronizer and blocker rings. Remove the snap-ring from the front of the output shaft. Slide the 3rd-4th synchronizer assembly, blocker rings and 3rd gear off the shaft.

2. Remove the next snap-ring and the 2nd speed gear thrust washer from the shaft. Slide 2nd speed gear and the blocker ring off the shaft, taking care not to lose the sliding gear from the 1st-2nd synchronizer assembly. The 1st-2nd synchronizer hub cannot be removed from the output shaft.

3. Remove the 1st gear thrust washer (oil slinger) from the rear of the output shaft. Remove the spring pin retaining 1st speed gear onto the shaft.

4. Slide 1st speed gear off the output shaft, and remove the blocker ring. Take care not to lose the sliding gear from the 1st-2nd synchronizer assembly.

5. Clean and inspect all parts.

COUNTERSHAFT GEAR BEARING REPLACEMENT

1. Remove the dummy shaft, bearing retainer washers and needle bearings from the countershaft gear. Clean and inspect the parts.

2. Coat the bore at each end of the countershaft gear with grease to retain the needle bearings.

3. While holding the dummy shaft in the gear, install the needle bearings and retainer washers in each end of the gear.

INPUT SHAFT BEARING REPLACEMENT

1. Remove the roller bearings from the input shaft.

2. Remove the snap-ring retaining the input shaft bearing. Press the input shaft out of the bearing. Clean and inspect all parts.

3. Press the input shaft bearing onto the input shaft, making sure that the snap-ring groove faces the front of the shaft. Install a new snap-ring to retain the bearing on the shaft.

4. Lightly coat the bore of the input shaft with grease.

NOTE: If a thick film of grease, such as wheel bearing grease, is applied to the shaft, the lubrication holes may become clogged, thereby preventing transmission oil from reaching the bearings, possibly resulting in premature bearing failure.

5. Install the roller bearings in the bore.

SYNCHRONIZER REPLACEMENT

1. Scribe alignment marks on the hub and sleeve of the synchronizer.

2. Push the synchronizer sleeve from each synchronizer hub.

NOTE: The 1st-2nd synchronizer hub cannot be removed from the output shaft.

3. Separate the inserts and insert springs from the hubs, taking care not to mix the parts of the 1st-2nd synchronizer with that of the 3rd-4th synchronizer. Clean and inspect all parts.

4. Position the sleeve on the hub, making sure that the alignment marks scribed prior to disassembly are aligned.

5. Position the 3 inserts on the hub. Install the insert springs, taking care to seat the bent tab in one of the inserts. The springs must face in opposite directions.

NOTE: Some 1982 and all 1983 AMC's use a press fit 3rd-4th synchronizer.

Component Assembly

OUTPUT SHAFT

1. Place a blocker ring on the cone of 1st speed gear, and slide the gear and ring assembly onto the output shaft. Make sure that the inserts in the synchronizer engage in the blocker ring notches.

2. Install the spring pin retaining 1st speed gear to the output shaft.

3. Install a blocker ring on the cone of the 2nd speed gear, and slide the gear and ring assembly onto the output shaft. Make sure that the inserts in the synchronizer engage in the blocker ring notches.

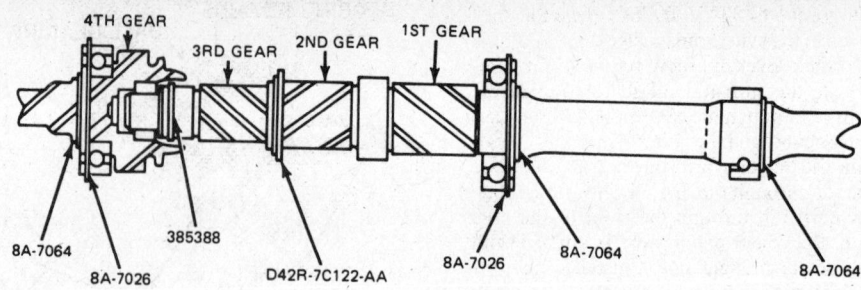

Mainshaft snap-ring locations of the Chilton Type 6 transmission (© Ford Motor Co.)

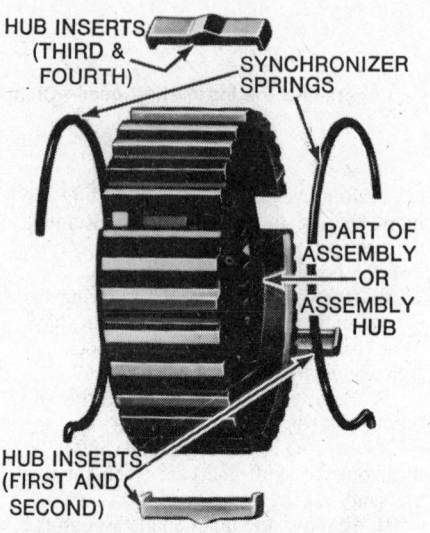

Synchronizer spring installation—Chilton Type 6 transmission (© Ford Motor Co.)

4. Install the 2nd speed gear thrust washer and new snap-ring on the shaft.

5. Install a blocker ring on the cone of the 3rd speed gear, and slide the gear and ring assembly onto the output shaft. Install the 3rd-4th synchronizer. Make sure that the inserts in the synchronizer engage in the blocker ring notches.

6. Install a new 3rd-4th synchronizer snap-ring.

7. Place the 1st gear thrust washer (oil slinger) on the shaft and on the spring pin retaining 1st gear.

————— CAUTION —————
The oil grooves must be positioned against the gear.

COVER ASSEMBLY

1. Assemble the two plastic inserts to each shift fork; the two projections on the inside of the inserts fit into the blind holes in the ends of the shift forks. Insert the selector arm plates into the shift forks.

2. Install the 3rd-4th shifter fork into the cover.

3. Install the 1st-2nd shifter fork into the cover. Lubricate the shifter shaft bore with grease.

4. Install the manual selector arm through the interlock plate, and position the two pieces into the cover, with the wide leg of the interlock plate towards the inside of the transmission case.

5. Align the shifter shaft in the cover, and insert the shaft through the shifter forks and manual selector. Coat the shifter shaft with a light coating of grease. Make sure the detent grooves face the plunger side of the cover.

6. Align the pin holes in the manual selector arm and shifter shaft. Install the spring pin flush with the surface of the selector arm.

7. Install the detent plunger, spring, and plug. Tighten the plug to 8–12 ft. lbs.

8. Check the operation of the shift forks in each gear position.

Transmission Assembly

1. Position the reverse idler gear and shaft in place.

2. Coat the surfaces of the countershaft thrust washers with a thin film of grease and position the case. The plastic washer goes in front, the bronze one at the rear. Position the cluster gear assembly in the bottom of the case.

3. Place the transmission in the vertical position. Align the countershaft gear bore and thrust washers with the bore in the case. Install the countershaft from the rear of the case. Return the transmission to the horizontal position.

4. Position the output shaft assembly into the case through the cover opening. With the snap-ring groove facing rearward, place the rear bearing on the output shaft. Place the transmission in the vertical position and install the bearing. Position the 1st gear thrust washer on the roll pin carefully, holding it tightly during bearing installation. Install the rear bearing snap-rings.

5. Install the input shaft and blocker ring through the front of case. Make sure that the blocker ring notches engage the synchronizer insert.

6. Install the front bearing retainer using a new gasket. Apply gasket sealer to the bolt threads and tighten to 11–15 ft. lbs.

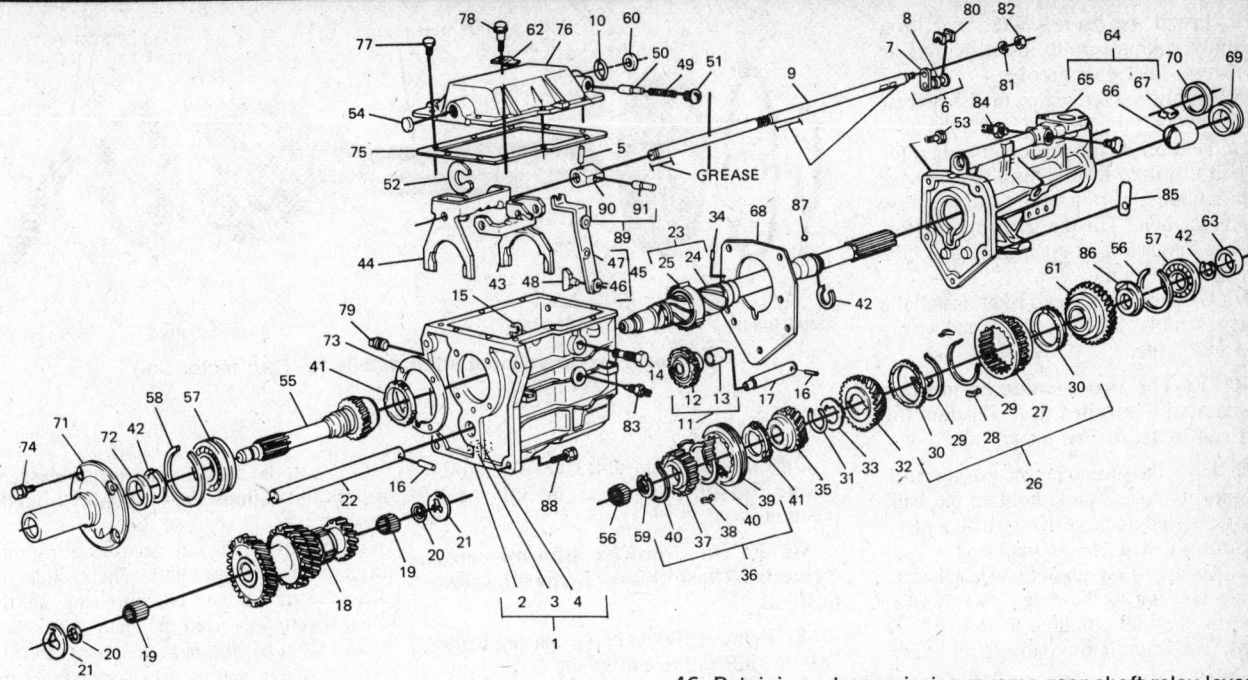

1 Case assembly—transmission
2 Case—transmission
3 Magnet—transmission case chip
4 Nut spring 9/64
5 Pin—3/16 diameter x 13/16 rolled spring
6 Lever assembly—transmission gearshift shaft offset
7 Lever transmission gearshift shaft offset
8 Pin—transmission gearshift shaft offset lever
9 Shaft—transmission shifter
10 Seal—O-ring
11 Gear & bush assembly—transmission reverse idler sliding
12 Gear—transmission reverse idler sliding
13 Bushing—transmission reverse idler gear
14 Pin—transmission reverse gear selector fork pivot
15 Ring—7/16 retaining
16 Pin—1/4 x 1 spring
17 Shaft—transmission reverse idler gear
18 Gear—transmission countershaft
19 Roller—transmission countershaft bearing
20 Washer—208/.918 flat
21 Washer—transmission countershaft gear thrust
22 Countershaft—transmission
23 Shaft assembly—transmission output
24 Shaft—transmission output
25 Hub—transmission synchronizer 1st & 2nd gear cluster
26 Shaft and gear assembly—transmission output
27 Gear—transmission reverse sliding
28 Insert—transmission synchronizer hub
29 Spring—transmission synchronizer retaining
30 Ring—transmission synchronizer blocking
31 Ring—transmission 2nd speed gear retaining snap
32 Gear—transmission 2nd speed
33 Washer—transmission 2nd speed gear thrust
34 Pin—1/8 x 1/4 rolled spring
35 Gear—transmission 3rd speed
36 Synchronizer assembly—3rd & 4th speed
37 Hub—transmission synchronizer
38 Insert—transmission synchronizer hub
39 Sleeve—transmission 3rd & 4th gear clutch hub
40 Spring—transmission synchronizer retaining
41 Ring—transmission synchronizer blocking
42 Ring—transmission m/d gear bearing shaft snap
43 Fork—transmission 1st & 2nd gear shift
44 Fork—transmission 3rd & 4th gear shift
45 Lever assembly—transmission reverse gear shaft relay

46 Retaining—transmission reverse gear shaft relay lever
47 Lever—transmission reverse gear shaft relay
48 Fork—transmission reverse gear shift
49 Spring—transmission shifter interlock
50 Plunger—transmission meshlock
51 Screw—m12 x 10 round head flat
52 Plate—transmission gear selector interlock
53 Screw & washer assembly—m10 x 30 hex head
54 Plug—3/4 diameter welch type
55 Shaft—transmission input
56 Roller—transmission mainshaft bearing
57 Bearing assembly—transmission m/d gear ball
58 Ring—m/d gear bearing retaining snap
59 Ring—1.00 retaining
60 Seal—transmission shift shaft
61 Gear—transmission 1st speed
62 Clip—spark control switch wire retaining
63 Gear—speedometer drive
64 Extension assembly—transmission
65 Extension—transmission
66 Bushing—transmission extension
67 Stop—transmission gear shift lever reverse
68 Gasket—transmission extension
69 Seal assembly—transmission extension oil
70 Plug—transmission extension
71 Retainer—transmission input shaft gear bearing
72 Seal assembly—transmission input shaft oil
73 Gasket—transmission input shaft bearing retainer
74 Bolt—M8 x 20 hex head-lock
75 Gasket—transmission case cover
76 Cover—transmission case
77 Screw—m6 x 20 hex head
78 Bolt—m6 x 32 hex washer HD shoulder
79 Plug—1/2-14 pipe (filler)
80 Bushing—transmission gear shift damper
81 Washer—spring lock
82 Nut—hexagon
83 Switch assembly—back-up lamp
84 Switch assembly—transmission seat belt warning sensor
85 Tag—transmission service identification
86 Washer—transmission 1st gear thrust
87 Ball—.25 diameter
88 Screw & lockwasher assembly—m12 x 40
89 Arm assembly—transmission control selector
90 Arm—transmission control selector
91 Pin—transmission gear shift

Exploded view of a Chilton Type 6 transmission—Ford version (RAD) shown, SR4 similar (© Ford Motor Co.)

7. Install the reverse idler gear lever assembly, taking care to insert the fork in the reverse idler gear groove.

8. Apply gasket sealer to the reverse lever pivot bolt threads and install the bolt. Align the lever on the pivot bolt and torque the bolt to 15–25 ft. lbs. Install the reverse lever retaining spring clip to the reverse gear pivot bolt. Tilt the transmission forward and pour a light coating of gear lube over the gear train.

9. Using a new cover gasket, install the cover assembly. Install the bolts and wiring clips and tighten.

NOTE: The two shouldered locating bolts must be installed first. Position the shift rail in 1st or 3rd gear.

10. Insert the speedometer drive gear lock ball into its hole. While holding the ball, slide the speedometer drive gear into place and secure it with a new snap-ring.

11. Using a new gasket, install the extension housing to the case. Using gasket sealer on the bolts, tighten them to 18–27 ft. lbs. Take care not to damage the extension yoke seal.

12. Install the offset lever assembly onto the shift shaft, securing the assembly with a nut and flat washer. Use sealer on the shift shaft threads. Tighten to 8–12 ft. lbs.

13. Insert the gearshift lever into place. Check its operation in each gear position.

14. Install the access plug into the rear of the extension housing, using a soft mallet.

CHILTON TYPE 7

Transmission Disassembly

1. Remove retaining clips and flat washers from the shift rods at the levers.

2. Remove shift linkage control bracket attaching screws and remove shift linkage and control brackets.

3. Remove cover attaching screws. Then lift cover and gasket from the case. Remove the long spring that holds the detent plug in the case. Remove the plug with a magnet.

4. Remove extension housing attaching screws. Then remove extension housing and gasket.

5. Remove input shaft bearing retainer attaching screws. Then slide retainer from the input shaft.

6. Working a dummy shaft in from the front of the case, drive the countershaft out the rear of the case. Let the countergear assembly lie in the bottom of the case. Remove the set screw from the 1st-2nd shift fork. Slide the 1st-2nd shift rail out the rear of the case. Use a magnet to remove the interlock detent from between the 1st-2nd and 3rd-4th shift rails.

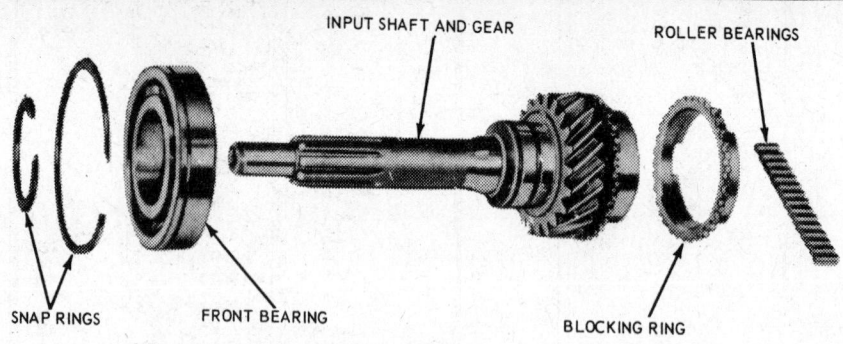

4-Speed overdrive input shaft details (© Ford Motor Co.)

7. Locate 1st-2nd shift lever in neutral. Locate 3rd-4th shift lever in 3rd speed position.

NOTE: On overdrive transmissions, locate 3rd-4th shift lever in the 4th speed position.

8. Remove the lockbolt that holds the 3rd-4th shift rail detent spring and plug in the left side of the case. Remove spring and plug with a magnet.

9. Remove the detent mechanism set screw from top of case. Then, remove the detent spring and plug with a small magnet.

10. Remove attaching screw from the 3rd-4th shift fork. Tap lightly on the inner end of the shift rail to remove the expansion plug from front of case. Then, withdraw the 3rd-4th shift rail from the front (do not lose the interlock pin from rail).

11. Remove attaching screw from the 1st-2nd shift fork. Slide the 1st-2nd shift rail from the rear of case.

12. Remove the interlock and detent plugs from the top of the case with a magnet.

13. Remove the snap-ring or disengage retainer that holds the speedometer drive gear to the output shaft, then remove speedometer gear drive ball.

14. Remove the snap-ring used to hold the output shaft bearing to the shaft. Pull out the output shaft bearing.

15. Remove the input shaft bearing snap-rings. Use a press to remove the input shaft bearing. Remove the input shaft and blocking ring from the front of the case.

16. Move output shaft to the right side of case. Then, maneuver the forks to permit lifting them from the case.

17. Support the thrust washer and 1st speed gear to prevent sliding from the shaft, then lift output shaft from the case.

18. Remove reverse gear shift fork attaching screw. Rotate the reverse shift rail 90°, then slide the shift rail out the rear of the case. Lift out the reverse shift fork.

19. Remove reverse detent plug and spring from the case with a magnet.

20. Using a dummy shaft, remove the reverse idler shaft from the case.

21. Lift reverse idler gear and thrust washers from the case. Be careful not to drop the bearing rollers or the dummy shaft from the gear.

22. Lift the countergear, thrust washers, rollers and dummy shaft assembly from the case.

23. Remove the next snap-ring from the front of the output shaft. Then, slide the 3rd-4th synchronizer blocking ring and the third-speed gear from the shaft.

24. Remove the next snap-ring and the second-speed gear thrust washer from the shaft. Slide the 2nd speed gear and the blocking ring from the shaft.

25. Remove the snap-ring, then slide the 1st-2nd synchronizer, blocking ring and the 1st speed gear from the shaft.

26. Remove the thrust washer from rear of the shaft.

Unit Repairs

CAM AND SHAFT SEALS

1. Remove attaching nut and washers from each shift lever, then remove the three levers.

2. Remove the three cams and shafts from inside the case.

3. Replace the old O-rings with new ones that have been well-lubricated.

4. Slide each cam and shaft into its respective bore in the transmission.

5. Install the levers and secure them with their respective washers and nuts.

SYNCHRONIZERS

1. Push the synchronizer hub from each synchronizer sleeve.

2. Separate the inserts and springs from the hubs. Do not mix parts of the 1st-2nd with parts of 3rd-4th synchronizers.

3. To assemble, position the hub in the sleeve. Be sure the alignment marks are properly indexed.

4. Place the three inserts into place on the hub. Install the insert springs so that the irregular surface (hump) is seated in one of the inserts. Do not stagger the spring.

COUNTERSHAFT GEAR

1. Dismantle the countershaft gear assembly.

2. Assemble the gear by coating each end of the countershaft gear bore with grease.

3. Install dummy shaft in the gear. Then install 21 bearing rollers and a retainer washer in each end of the gear.

REVERSE IDLER GEAR

1. Dismantle reverse idler gear.

2. Assemble reverse idler gear by coating the bore in each end of reverse idler gear with grease.

3. Hold the dummy shaft in the gear and install the 22 bearing rollers and the retainer washer into each end of the gear.

4. Install the reverse idler sliding gear on the splines of the reverse idler gear. Be sure the shift fork groove is toward the front.

INPUT SHAFT SEAL

1. Remove the seal from the input shaft bearing retainer.

2. Coat the sealing surface of a new seal with lubricant, then press the new seal into the input shaft bearing retainer.

Transmission Assembly

1. Grease the countershaft gear thrust surfaces in the case. Then, position a thrust washer at each end of the case.

2. Position the countershaft gear, dummy shaft, and roller bearings in the case.

3. Align the gear bore and thrust washers with the bores in the case. Install the countershaft.

4. With the case in a horizontal position, countershaft gear end-play should be from 0.004–0.018 in. Use thrust washers to obtain play within these limits.

5. After establishing correct end–play, place the dummy shaft in the countershaft gear and allow the gear assembly to remain on the bottom of the case.

6. Grease the reverse idler gear thrust surfaces in the case, and position the two thrust washers.

7. Position the reverse idler gear, sliding gear, dummy, etc. in place. Make sure that the shift fork groove in the sliding gear is toward the front.

8. Align the gear bore and thrust washers with the case bores and install the reverse idler shaft.

9. Reverse idler gear end-play should be 0.004–0.018 in. Use selective thrust washers to obtain play within these limits.

10. Position reverse gear shift rail detent spring and detent plug in the case. Hold the reverse shift fork in place on the reverse idler sliding gear and install the shift rail from the rear of the case. Lock the fork to the rail with the Allen head set screws.

11. Install the 1st-2nd synchronizer onto the output shaft. The first and reverse synchronizer hub are a press fit and should be

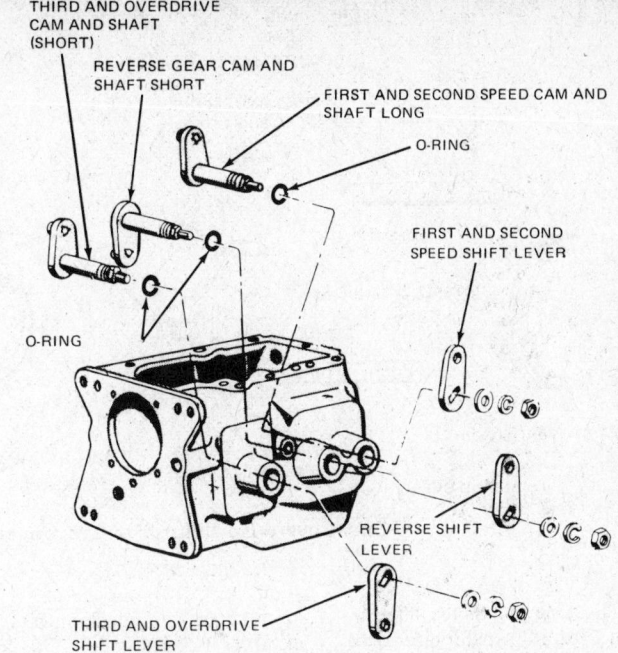

4-Speed overdrive cams and shift levers (© Ford Motor Co.)

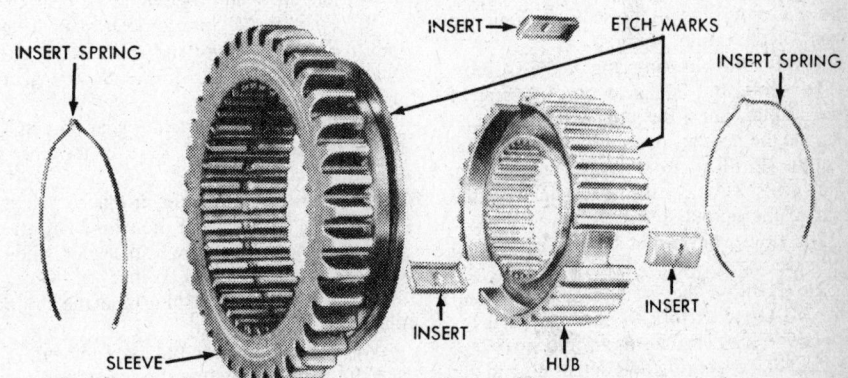

FIRST AND SECOND SPEED SYNCHRONIZER

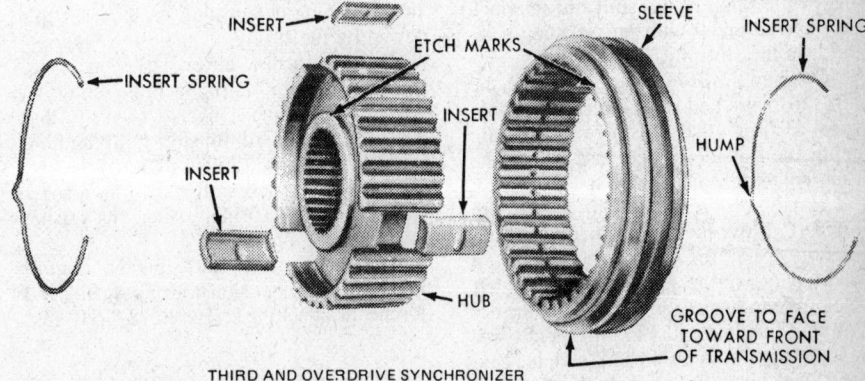

4-Speed overdrive synchronizer assembly (© Ford Motor Co.)

installed with gear teeth facing the rear of the shaft.

NOTE: On overdrive transmissions, the 1st-reverse synchronizer hub is a slip fit.

12. Place the blocking ring on 2nd gear.

Slide 2nd speed gear onto the front of the shaft with the synchronizer coned surface toward the rear.

13. Install the 2nd speed gear thrust washer and snap-ring.

14. Slide the fourth gear onto the shaft with the synchronizer coned surface front.

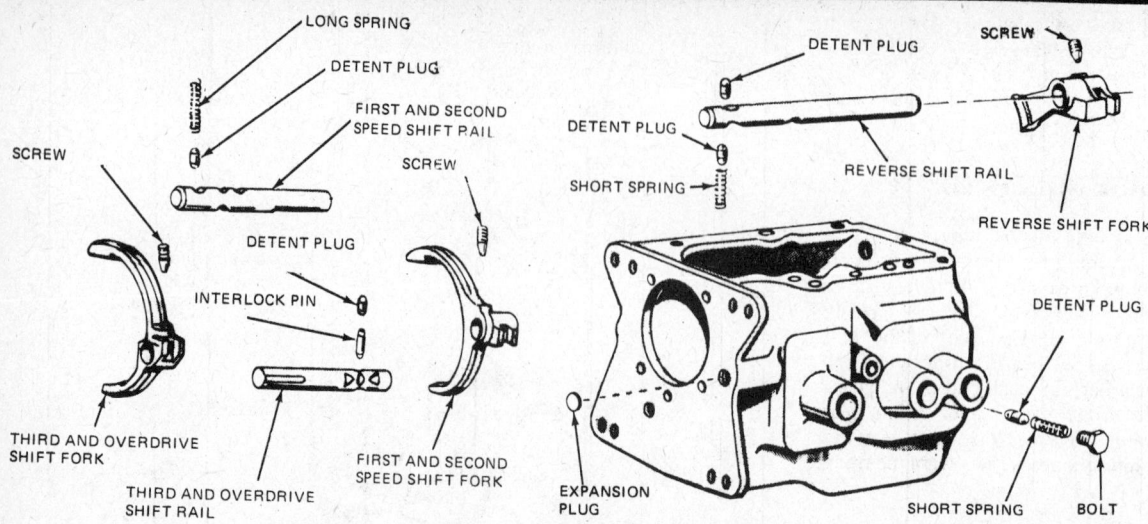

4-Speed overdrive shift rail and fork details (© Ford Motor Co.)

15. Place a blocking ring on the 4th gear.
16. Slide the 3rd-4th synchronizer onto the shaft. Be sure that the inserts in the synchronizer engage the notches in the blocking ring. Install the snap-ring onto the front of the output shaft.
17. Put the blocking ring on the 1st gear.
18. Slide the first gear onto the rear of the output shaft. Be sure that the inserts engage the notches in the blocking ring and that the shift fork groove is toward the rear.
19. Install heavy thrust washer onto the rear of the output shaft.
20. Lower the output shaft assembly into the case.
21. Position the 1st-2nd shift fork and the 3rd-4th shift fork in place on their respective gears. Rotate them into place.
22. Place a spring and detent plug in the detent bore. Place the reverse shift rail into neutral position.
23. Coat the 3rd-4th shift rail interlock pin (tapered ends) with grease, then position it in the shift rail.
24. Align the 3rd-4th shift fork with the shift rail bores and slide the shift rail into place. Be sure that the three detents are facing the outside of the case. Place the front synchronizer into 4th speed position and install the set screw into the 3rd-4th shift fork. Move the synchronizer to neutral position. Install the 3rd-4th speed shift rail detent plug, spring and bolt into the left side of the transmission case. Place the detent plug (tapered ends) in the detent bore.
25. Align 1st-2nd shift fork with the case bores and slide the shift rail into place. Lock the fork with the set screw.
26. Coat the input gear bore with a small amount of grease. Then install the 15 bearing rollers.
27. Put the blocking ring in the 3rd-4th synchronizer. Place the input shaft gear in the case. Be sure that the output shaft pilot enters the roller bearing of the input shaft gear.
28. With a new gasket on the input bear-

ing retainer, dip attaching bolts in sealer, install bolts and torque to 30–36 ft. lbs.
29. Press on the output shaft bearing, then install the snap-ring to hold the bearing.
30. Position the speedometer gear drive ball in the output shaft and slide the speedometer drive gear into place. Secure gear with snap-ring.
31. Align the countershaft gear bore and thrust washers with the bore in the case. Install the countershaft.
32. With a new gasket in place, install and secure the extension housing. Dip the extension housing screws in sealer, then torque screws to 42–50 ft. lbs.
33. Install the filler plug and the drain plug.
34. Pour E.P. gear oil over the entire gear train while rotating the input shaft.
35. Place each shift fork in all positions to make sure they function properly. Install the remaining detent plug in the case, followed by the spring.
36. With a new cover gasket in place, install the cover. Dip attaching screws in sealer, then torque screws to 14–19 ft. lbs.
37. Coat the 3rd-4th shift rail plug bore with sealer. Install a new plug.
38. Secure each shift rod to its respective lever with a spring washer, flat washer and retaining pin.
39. Position the shift linkage control bracket to the extension housing. Install and torque the attaching screws to 12–15 ft. lbs.

CHILTON TYPE 8

Transmission Disassembly

1. Remove the lower extension housing bolt to drain the transmission.

2. Remove the cover screws; remove the cover and discard the gasket.
3. Remove the screw, detent spring and plug from the case; a magnetized rod will aid in removal.
4. Drive the roll pin from the shifter shaft.
5. Remove the backup lamp switch, snap ring, and the dust cover from the rear of the extension housing.
6. Remove the shifter shaft from the turret assembly.
7. Remove the extension housing bolts and housing; discard the gasket.
8. Remove the speedometer gear snap ring; slide the gear from the shaft and remove the drive ball.
9. Remove the output shaft bearing snap ring. Remove the bearing.
10. Use a dummy shaft to push the countershaft out of the rear of the case. Lower the countershaft gear to the bottom of the case.
11. Remove the input shaft bearing retainer attaching bolts and slide the retainer and gasket from the input shaft; discard the gasket.
12. Remove the input shaft bearing snap ring; remove the bearing.
13. Remove the input shaft and blocking ring (including roller bearings) from the case.
14. Remove the overdrive shift pawl, gear selector and interlock plate. Remove the 1st-2nd gearshift selector arm plate. Remove the roll pin from the 3rd-overdrive shift fork.
15. Drive the 3rd–overdrive shift rail and expansion plug from the rear of the case. Remove the mainshaft.
16. Remove the 1st–2nd gear shift fork; remove the 3rd–overdrive shift fork.
17. Remove the countershaft gear and thrust washers from the case.
18. Remove the snap ring from the front of the output shaft. Slide the 3rd gear and O.D. synchronizer, blocking ring, and gear from the shaft.

19. Remove the next snap–ring and washer; remove 2nd speed gear. Remove next snap ring and remove the 1st–2nd synchronizer. Slide the 1st gear and blocking ring from the rear of the shaft.

20. Remove the roll pin from the reverse fork, slide the reverse shifter rail through the rear of the case, and remove the reverse gearshift fork and spacer.

21. Drive the reverse gear shaft out the rear of the case.

22. Remove the reverse idler gear, thrust washers and roller bearings.

23. Remove the retaining clip, reverse gearshift relay lever and reverse gear selector fork pivot pin. Remove the O.D. shift control link assembly. Remove the shift shaft seal from the rear of the case; remove the expansion plug from the front of the case.

Transmission Assembly

Assembly is the reverse of the disassembly procedure. Tighten the extension housing bolts in a criss-cross pattern to 42–50 ft. lbs. The bearing rollers, extension housing bushing, shifter shaft and gear shift damper bushing are to be lubricated with grease before assembly (Ford #ESW-M1C109-A or the equivalent). The gear shaft shaft sleeve and the turret cover assembly should be coated with sealer prior to installation. The intermediate and high rail welch plug must be seated firmly; it must not protrude above the front face of the case, nor seat below 0.6 in. below the front face.

With the 1st gear thrust washer clamped tightly against the output shaft shoulder, 1st gear end–play must be 0.005–0.024 in. 2nd gear end–play must be 0.003–0.021 in. O.D. end–play must be 0.009–0.023 in. Countershaft gear end–play, checked after installation between the thrust washers, must be 0.004–0.018 in.

When the gearshift selector arm plate is seated in the 1st–2nd shift fork plate slot, the shifter shafter must pass freely through the bore without binding.

CHILTON TYPE 9

Transmission Disassembly

1. Using a 10mm wrench, remove the ten attaching bolts and lift off the transmission case cover.

2. Drain the lubricant from the transmission case.

3. Using a pencil size magnet, remove the shift rail detent plug, spring and plunger from the upper left side of the case.

4. Working through the shift turret

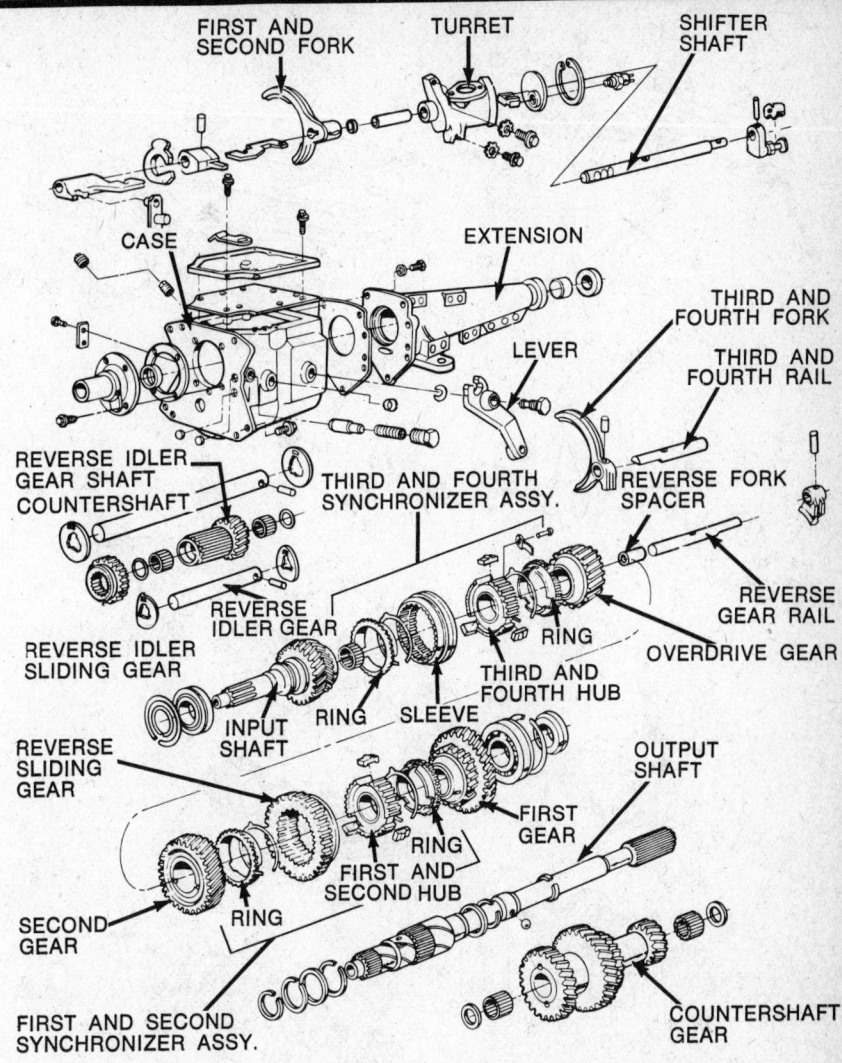

Exploded view of the Ford single rail 4-speed overdrive (© Ford Motor Co.)

opening in the extension housing, remove the access plug from the rear of the housing.

5. After shifting the transmission into reverse gear, remove the roll pin from the gear shift shaft offset lever, then slide the offset lever and bushing off the shaft.

6. Remove the 5th-speed interlock pilot bolt from the front top of the extension housing.

7. Remove the six extension housing attaching bolts, then slide the housing and gasket off the output shaft.

8. Remove the snap ring, speedometer drive gear and drive ball from the output shaft.

9. Remove the 5th gear synchronizer retaining snap ring from the output shaft, then slide the retaining spacer from the output shaft.

10. Shift the transmission into 1st gear. Using a hammer and a punch, drive out the roll pin located inside the transmission case, which secures the 1st, 2nd, 3rd, 4th and reverse selector pin. Remove the selector pin.

11. Slide the shifter shaft, 5th speed shift fork and 5th speed synchronizer from the output shaft as an assembly.

12. Remove the interlock sleeve bolt from the right side of the transmission case.

13. Lift the interlock sleeve, 3rd–4th speed shift fork, and the 1st–2nd speed shift fork from the case.

14. Working from inside the transmission case, remove the C-clip from the reverse gear selector fork pivot pin. Remove the pivot pin, then lift the reverse gear selector fork relay lever, the spring and the reverse gearshift fork from the transmission case.

15. Slide the 5th-speed maindrive gear off the output shaft.

16. Remove the piece snap ring located at the rear of the 5th-speed cluster gear.

17. Using a puller, remove the 5th speed cluster gear.

18. Remove the snap ring from the output shaft rear bearing and remove the bearing cup from the transmission.

19. Remove the bearing retainer and seal,

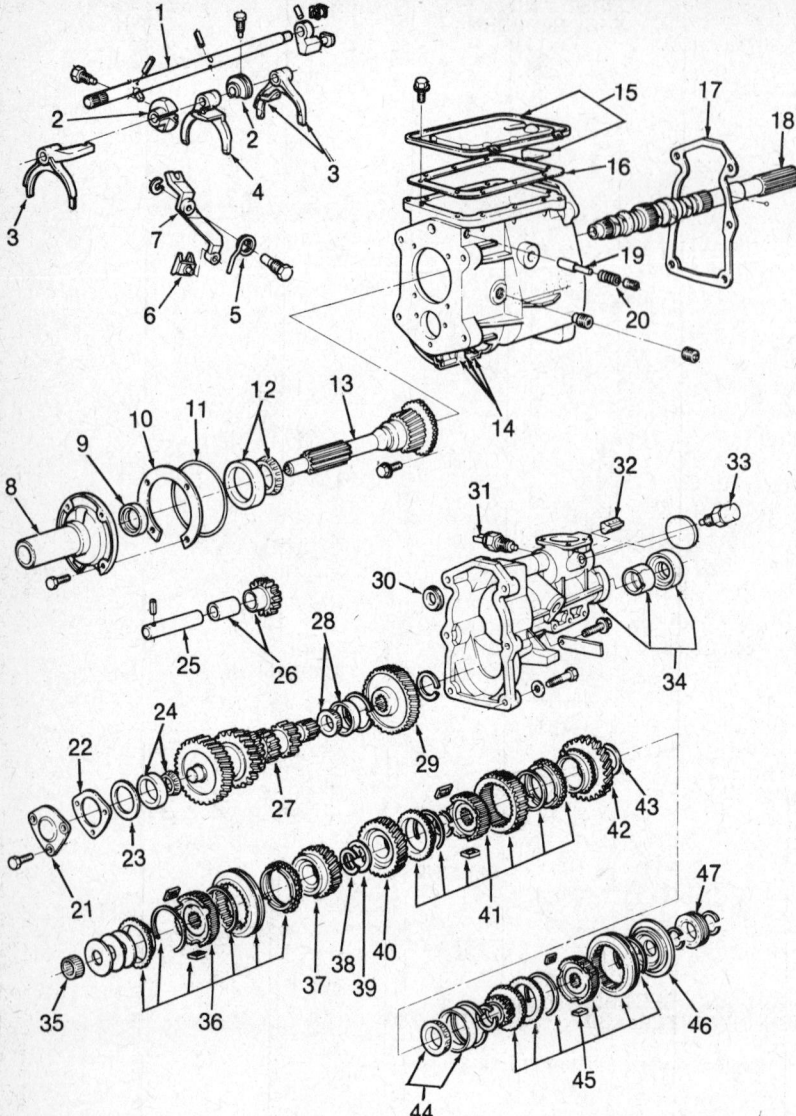

the case by removing the three attaching bolts.

24. Lift the countershaft gear out through the top of the transmission case.

25. Remove the reverse idler gear and shaft by removing the roll pin that secures the shaft to the case.

Component Disassembly

OUTPUT SHAFT

1. Slide the 3rd–4th speed synchronizer off the front end of the output shaft.

2. Slide the 3rd speed gear off the front end of the output shaft.

3. Remove the snap ring and the 2nd speed gear thrust washer from the output shaft. Slide the 2nd speed gear and the synchronizer blocking ring from the output shaft.

4. Remove the snap ring that retains the 1st–2nd speed synchronizer on the output shaft, then press the synchronizer off the output shaft.

5. Remove the snap ring from the rear of the output shaft. Place the output shaft in a press, and remove the 1st speed gear, thrust washer and output shaft rear bearing.

INPUT SHAFT

1. If not previously removed, remove the roller bearings from the input shaft.

2. Place the input gear in a press and press the input gear from the bearing.

COUNTERSHAFT GEAR

1. Place the countershaft gear in a press, and remove the rear bearing.

2. Place the countershaft in a vise protected with wood blocks and pry the front bearing from the countershaft.

INPUT SHAFT GEAR BEARING RETAINER

1. Place the bearing retainer in a vise.

2. Using a slide impact-type puller, remove the seal from the bearing retainer.

EXTENSION HOUSING

1. Carefully remove the seal from the extension housing.

2. Using a suitable driver, remove the bushing.

Component Assembly

EXTENSION HOUSING

1. Install the bushing and the seal using a suitable driver.

1. Shifter shaft
2. Gear selector interlock
3. 3rd/4th shifter fork
4. 1st/2nd shifter fork
5. Shift lever return spring
6. Reverse shifter fork
7. Reverse shift lever
8. Bearing retainer
9. Input shaft oil seal
10. Input shaft front bearing shim
11. Bearing retainer seal
12. Input shaft bearing assembly
13. Input shaft
14. Case assy.
15. Cover assy.
16. Cover gasket
17. Extension gasket
18. Output shaft
19. Meshlock plunger
20. Interlock shifter spring
21. Countershaft gear front retainer
22. Retainer gasket
23. Front bearing shim
24. Front bearing assy.
25. Reverse idler gear shaft
26. Reverse idler gear and bushing
27. Countershaft cluster gear
28. Rear bearing assy.
29. 5th speed cluster gear
30. Shifter shaft seal
31. Back-up switch
32. Lever reverse stop
33. 5th speed inhibitor plunger
34. Extension housing assy.
35. Mainshaft roller bearing
36. 3rd/4th synchronizer assy.
37. 3rd speed gear
38. Snap ring
39. Thrust washer
40. 2nd speed gear
41. 1st/2nd synchronizer assy.
42. 1st speed gear
43. Thrust washer
44. Output shaft bearing assy.
45. 5th speed synchronizer assy.
46. Retaining spacer
47. Speedometer drive gear

Ford RAP five speed overdrive transmission (© Ford Motor Co.)

the shim and the O-ring from the case by removing the four input shaft bearing retainer bolts.

20. Without loosing the roller bearings, the thrust washers and the thrust bearing, rotate the input shaft so that the teeth recess toward the countershaft gear to provide clearance. Then lift the input gear from the case.

21. Lift the output shaft assembly out through the top of the transmission case.

22. Remove the snap ring from the rear of the transmission case and remove the countershaft gear rear bearing cup from the case.

23. Remove the bearing retainer, the gasket, shim and the front bearing cup from

INPUT SHAFT GEAR BEARING RETAINER

1. Install the seal in the retainer with the lip facing forward toward the transmission case mounting surface. Make sure the seal is bottomed in the retainer.

COUNTERSHAFT GEAR

1. With the taper facing outward, exert pressure on the inner race of the front bearing and press the bearing until it is bottomed on the gear.

2. Install the rear bearing in the same matter.

INPUT SHAFT

1. With the taper toward the front of the gear, apply pressure on the inner race and press the bearing onto the input gear until it is bottomed.

2. Apply a heavy coat of polyethylene on the inner bearing surface of the gear. Load the 15 roller bearings into the gear.

OUTPUT SHAFT

1. Position the 1st gear thrust washer and the bearing on the rear of the output shaft. Apply pressure on the bearing inner race until the bearing is bottomed on the spacer and shaft.

2. Select a snap ring that will not allow any clearance between the bearing race and the ring groove. Then press the 1st–2nd gear synchronizer and the reverse sliding gear into place and secure with the snap ring.

3. Slide the 2nd gear and the thrust washer into position and secure with the snap ring.

4. Slide the 3rd gear and the 3rd–4th synchronizer into place. Make sure the thrust surface of the synchronizer hub is facing toward the front of the shaft.

Transmission Assembly

NOTE: Coat all bolts and plugs used throughout the case with a thread sealant to prevent leakage.

1. Hold the reverse idler gear into position with the long end of the hub facing to the rear of the transmission case. Slide the idler gear shaft into the case and gear and align the roll pin holes. Secure the shaft with the roll pin.

2. Lower the countershaft and bearings into place, and install the rear bearing cup. Secure with the snap ring.

3. Position the front bearing cup, the shim, a new gasket and the bearing retainer to the front of the transmission case. Install the bearing retainer cap screws and tighten to 7–10 ft. lbs. while rotating the gear. If

the gear rotating effort increases while tightening the bearing retainer, replace the shim with a thinner one.

4. Correct end-play is 0.001–0.005 inch. Decrease the shim thickness to increase the end-play and increase the shim thickness to reduce end play.

5. Lower the main shaft into the transmission case through the case cover opening.

6. Apply a coat of polyethylene grease to the thrust washers and the thrust bearing. Place the thrust washer on the 3rd–4th speed synchronization thrust surface. Place the thrust bearing and the remaining thrust washer on the 3rd–4th speed synchronizer.

7. Without disturbing the roller bearings, carefully install the input shaft assembly in the transmission case with the blank portion of the teeth toward the countershaft gear to provide the proper clearance.

8. Coat a new input shaft O-ring with polyethylene grease and position it in the bearing retainer groove.

9. Install the output shaft bearing cup and snap ring in the rear of the transmission case.

10. Position the shim and bearing retainer to the transmission case. Install the bearing retainer cap screws and tighten to 8–10 ft. lbs. while rotating the input shaft. If the input shaft turning effort increases when tightening the bearing retainer bolts, replace the shim with a thicker one.

11. Install a dial indicator on the transmission case. Pry the output shaft toward the dial indicator and zero the indicator. Pry the output shaft in the opposite direction. End-play should be between 0.001–0.005 inch. Decrease shim thickness to decrease end-play or increase shim thickness to increase end-play. Remove the dial indicator.

12. Install the spring and reverse fork on the relay lever. Position the relay lever assembly in the transmission case and install the pivot pin in the case and lever assembly. Secure the lever with a C-clip.

13. Install the 5th speed cluster gear and secure with a snap ring.

14. Slide the 5th speed main drive gear onto the output shaft. Coat the blocker ring with polyethylene grease and position it on the main drive gear.

15. Position the 1st–2nd and 3rd–4th shift forks on the main shaft assembly.

16. Place the interlock gear selector sleeve between the two shifter forks and install the interlock pilot bolt in the right side of the transmission case.

17. With the synchronizer thrust surface facing toward the rear of the output shaft, install the shifter shaft, the 5th speed shift fork and the 5th speed synchronizer as an assembly.

18. Working through the cover opening in the transmission case, install the gearshift selector pin in the shifter shaft and secure with a rollpin.

19. Slide the 5th speed synchronizer retaining plate onto the output shaft and secure it with a snap ring.

20. Secure the speedometer drive gear ball to the output shaft with polyethylene grease then slide the speedometer drive gear onto the shaft over the ball and secure with a snap ring.

21. Using a new gasket, position the extension housing on the transmission case. Install the two pilot bolts, one in the upper left side of the housing and the other in the lower right corner. Install the four remaining bolts and tighten to 40–60 ft. lbs.

22. Install the 5th gear pilot bolt in the top of the extension housing.

23. Shift the transmission into reverse gear. Install the offset lever on the rear of the shifter shaft and secure the lever with a roll pin.

24. Install the detent plunger, the spring and the plug in the upper right side of the transmission case. Tighten the plug to 12–14 ft. lbs.

25. Install the access plug in the rear of the extension housing.

26. Using a new gasket place the cover on the transmission case and tighten the attaching bolts to 8–10 ft. lbs.

CHILTON TYPE 10

Transmission Disassembly

1. Remove side cover assembly and shift forks.

2. Remove clutch gear bearing retainer.

3. Remove clutch gear bearing to gear stem snap-ring. Pull clutch gear outward until a screwdriver can be inserted between bearing and case. Remove clutch gear bearing.

4. Remove speedometer driven gear and extension bolts.

5. Remove reverse idler shaft snap-ring.

6. Remove mainshaft and extension assembly through the rear of the case.

7. Remove clutch gear and third speed blocker ring from inside case. Remove 14 roller bearings from clutch gear.

8. Expand the snap-ring which retains the mainshaft rear bearing. Remove the extension.

9. Using a dummy shaft, drive the countershaft and key out the rear of the case. Remove the gear, two tanged thrust washers, and dummy shaft. Remove bearing washer and 27 roller bearings from each end of countergear.

10. Use a long drift to drive the reverse idler shaft and key through the rear of the case.

11. Remove reverse idler gear and tanged steel thrust washer.

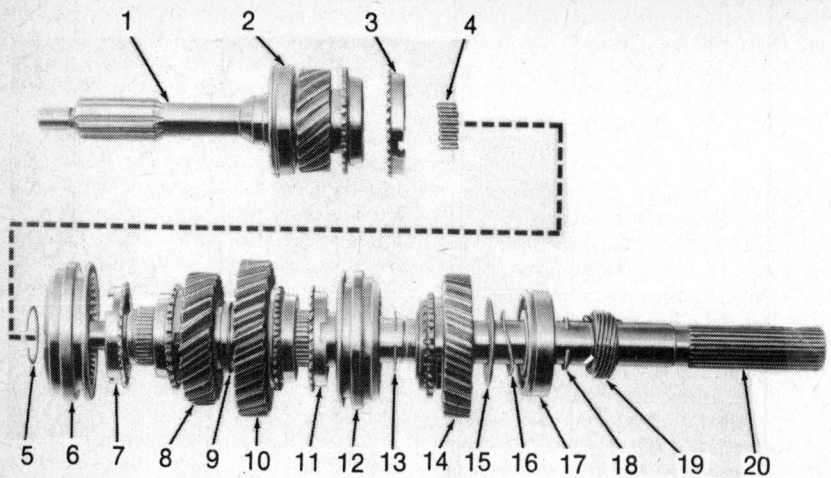

1 Clutch gear
2 Clutch gear bearing
3 3rd speed blocker ring
4 Mainshaft pilot bearings (14)
5 Snap ring
6 2-3 synchronizer assembly
7 2nd speed blocker ring
8 2nd speed gear
9 Shoulder (part of main shaft)
10 1st speed gear
11 1st speed blocker ring
12 1st speed synchronizer assembly
13 Snap ring
14 Reverse gear
15 Reverse gear thrust washer
16 Spring washer
17 Rear bearing
18 Snap ring
19 Speedo drive gear and clip
20 Mainshaft

Clutch gear and mainshaft assembly—Saginaw 3 speed (Chilton Type 10) transmission (© GM Corp.)

MAINSHAFT DISASSEMBLY

1. Remove 2nd–3rd speed sliding clutch hub snap-ring from mainshaft. Remove clutch assembly, 2nd speed blocker ring, and 2nd gear from front of mainshaft.
2. Depress speedometer drive gear retaining clip. Remove gear. Some units have a metal speedometer driver gear which must be pulled off.
3. Remove rear bearing snap-ring.
4. Support reverse gear. Press on rear of mainshaft. Remove reverse gear, thrust washer, spring washer, rear bearing, and snap-ring. When pressing off the rear bearing, be careful not to cock the bearing on the shaft.
5. Remove first and reverse sliding clutch hub snap-ring. Remove clutch assembly, first speed blocker ring, and first gear. Sometimes the synchronizer hub and gear must be pressed off.

REPAIR

Clutch Keys And Springs

Keys and springs may be replaced if worn or broken, but the hubs and sleeves are matched pairs and must be kept together.
1. Mark hub and sleeve for reassembly.
2. Push hub from sleeve. Remove keys and springs.
3. Place three keys and two springs, one on each side of hub, in position, so all three keys are engaged by both springs. The tanged end of the springs should not be installed into the same key.
4. Slide the sleeve onto the hub, aligning the marks.

NOTE: A groove around the outside of the synchronizer hub marks the end that must be opposite the fork slot in the sleeve when assembled.

Extension Oil Seal And Bushing

1. Remove seal.
2. Using bushing remover and installer tool, drive bushing into extension housing.
3. Drive new bushing in from the rear. Lubricate inside of bushing and seal. Install new oil seal with extension seal installer tool or other suitable tool.

Clutch Bearing Retainer Oil Seal

1. Pry old seal out.
2. Install new seal using seal installer. Seat seal in bore.

MAINSHAFT ASSEMBLY

1. Turn front of mainshaft up.
2. Install 2nd gear with clutching teeth up; the rear face of the gear butts against the flange on the mainshaft.
3. Install a blocker ring with clutching teeth down. All three blocker rings are the same.
4. Install 2nd–3rd speed synchronizer assembly with fork slot down. Press it onto mainshaft splines. Both synchronizer assemblies are the same. Be sure that blocker ring notches align with synchronizer assembly keys.
5. Install synchronizer snap-ring. Both synchronizer snap-rings are the same.
6. Turn rear of shaft up.
7. Install 1st gear with clutching teeth

up; the front face of the gear butts against the flange on the mainshaft.
8. Install a blocker ring with clutching teeth down.
9. Install the 1st–reverse synchronizer assembly with fork slot down. Press it onto mainshaft splines. Be sure blocker ring notches align with synchronizer assembly keys.
10. Install snap-ring.
11. Install reverse gear with clutching teeth down.
12. Install steel reverse gear thrust washer and spring washer.
13. Press rear ball bearing onto shaft with snap-ring slot down.
14. Install snap-ring.
15. Install speedometer drive gear and retaining clip. Press on metal speedometer drive gear.

Transmission Assembly

1. Using dummy shaft, load a row of 27 roller bearings and a thrust washer at each end of countergear. Hold in place with grease.
2. Place countergear assembly into case through rear. Place a tanged thrust washer, tang away from gear, at each end. Install countershaft and key, making sure that tangs align with notches in case.
3. Install reverse idler gear thrust washer, gear, and shaft with key from rear of case. Be sure thrust washer is between gear and rear of case with tang toward notch in case.
4. Expand snap-ring in extension. Assemble extension over rear of mainshaft and onto rear bearing. Seat snap-ring in rear bearing groove.
5. Install 14 mainshaft pilot bearings into clutch gear cavity. Assemble 3rd speed blocker ring onto clutch gear clutching surface with teeth toward gear.
6. Place clutch gear, pilot bearings, and 3rd speed blocker ring assembly over front of mainshaft assembly. Be sure blocker rings align with keys in 2nd–3rd synchronizer assembly.
7. Stick extension gasket to case with grease. Install clutch gear, mainshaft, and extension together. Be sure clutch gear engages teeth of countergear anti-lash plate. Torque extension bolts to 45 ft. lbs.
8. Place bearing over stem of clutch gear and into front case bore. Install front bearing to clutch gear snap-ring.
9. Install clutch gear bearing retainer and gasket. The retainer oil return hole must be at the bottom. Torque retainer bolts to 10 ft. lbs.
10. Install reverse idler gear shaft E-ring.
11. Shift synchronizer sleeves to neutral positions. Install cover, gasket, and forks, aligning forks with synchronizer sleeve grooves. Torque side cover bolts to 10 ft. lbs.
12. Install speedometer driven gear.

1 Synchronizer retainer ring
2 Synchronizer blocking ring
3 Synchronizer assembly
4 Second speed gear
5 Main shaft
6 Synchronizer assembly
7 Gear assembly
8 Thrust washer
9 Retainer clip

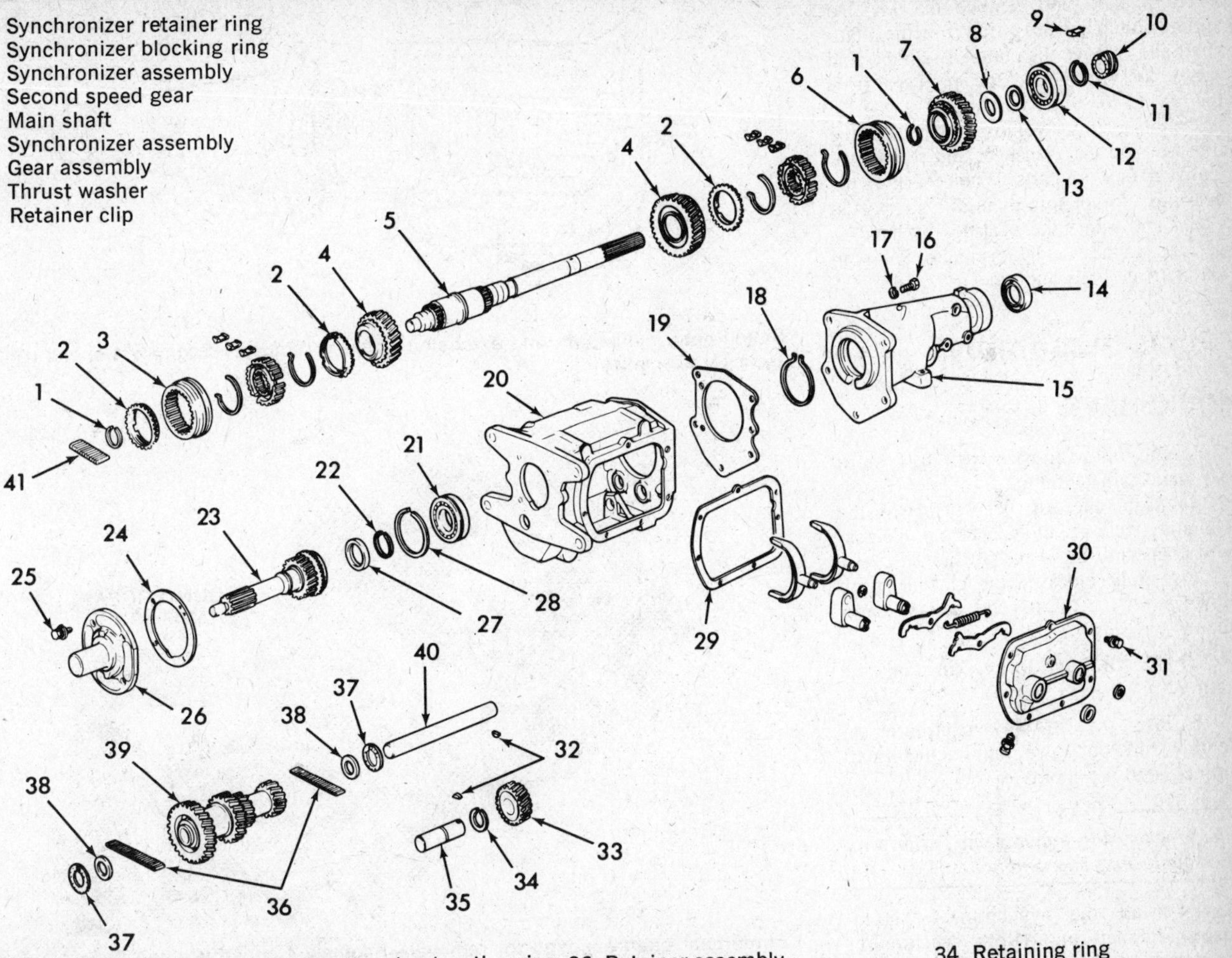

10 Speedometer drive gear	18 Rear bearing location ring	26 Retainer assembly
11 Ring	19 Gasket	27 Ring
12 Mainshaft bearing	20 Case	28 Clutch gear bearing locating ring
13 Washer	21 Bearing assembly	29 Cover gasket
14 Seal	22 Ring	30 Cover assembly
15 Extension housing	23 Clutch gear	31 Bolt and lockwasher
16 Bolt	24 Gasket	32 Woodruff keys
17 Washer	25 Bolt and lockwasher	33 Gear assembly

34 Retaining ring
35 Shaft
36 Roller
37 Washer
38 Washer
39 Gear assembly
40 Counter gear shaft
41 Mainshaft bearing roller

Exploded view of the Saginaw 3 speed (Chilton Type 10) transmission (© GM Corp.)

CHILTON TYPE 11

Transmission Disassembly

1. Remove the side cover and shift forks after draining the transmission.

2. Remove the clutch gear bearing retainer. Remove the bearing-to-gear stem snap-ring and pull out on the clutch gear until a screwdriver can be inserted between the bearing, large snap-ring, and case to pry the bearing off.

NOTE: The clutch gear bearing is a slip-fit on the gear and in the case. Removal of the bearing will provide clearance for clutch gear and mainshaft removal.

3. Remove the rear extension attaching bolts and remove the clutch gear, mainshaft, and extension as an assembly.

4. Spread the snap-ring which holds the mainshaft rear bearing and remove the extension case.

5. Remove the countershaft and its woodruff key by driving out of the rear of the case with a pipe or an old countershaft. Remove the countergear assembly and bearings.

6. Using a long drift, drive the reverse idler shaft and woodruff key through the rear of the case.

7. Expand and remove the 3rd–4th speed sliding clutch hub snap-ring from the mainshaft. Remove the clutch assembly, 3rd gear blocker ring, and 3rd speed gear from the front of the mainshaft.

8. Press in the speedometer gear retaining clip and slide the gear off the mainshaft. Remove the rear bearing snap-ring from its groove in the mainshaft.

9. With 1st gear supported on press plates, press first gear, thrust washer, spring washer, rear bearing, and snap-ring from the rear of the mainshaft.

CAUTION

Be careful to center the gear, washers, bearings, and snap-ring when pressing the rear bearing.

10. Expand and remove the 1st–2nd sliding clutch hub snap-ring from the mainshaft and remove the clutch assembly, 2nd speed blocker ring, and 2nd speed gear from the rear of the mainshaft.

After thoroughly cleaning all parts and the transmission case, inspect and replace all damaged or worn parts. When checking the bearings, do not spin them at high speeds. Clean and rotate the bearings by hand to detect roughness and unevenness. Spinning can damage balls and races.

Assembly

MAINSHAFT

Install the following parts with the front of the mainshaft facing up:

1. Install the 3rd speed gear with the clutching teeth up; the rear face of the gear will abut with the mainshaft flange.

2. Install a blocking ring, clutching teeth down, over the third-speed gear synchronizing surface.

NOTE: All four blocker rings are the same.

3. Press the 3rd–4th synchronizer assembly, fork slot down, onto the mainshaft splines until it bottoms.

—— **CAUTION** ——
The blocker ring notches must align with the synchronizer assembly keys.

4. Install the synchronizer hub-to-mainshaft snap-ring. (Both synchronizer snap-rings are the same.)
Install the following parts with the rear of the mainshaft up:

5. Install the 2nd speed gear with the clutching teeth up; the front face of the gear will abut with the flange on the mainshaft.

6. Install a blocking ring, clutching teeth down, over the 2nd speed gear synchronizing surface.

7. Press the 1st–2nd synchronizer assembly, fork slot down, onto the mainshaft.

—— **CAUTION** ——
The blocker ring notches must align with the synchronizer assembly keys.

8. Install the synchronizer hub-to-mainshaft snap-ring.

9. Install a blocking ring with the notches down so they align with the 1st–2nd synchronizer assembly keys.

10. Install 1st gear with the clutching teeth down. Install the 1st gear thrust washer and spring washer.

11. Press the rear ball bearing and snap-ring, slot down, onto the mainshaft. Install the snap-ring. Install the speedometer gear and clip.

TRANSMISSION

1. Using a dummy countergear shaft,

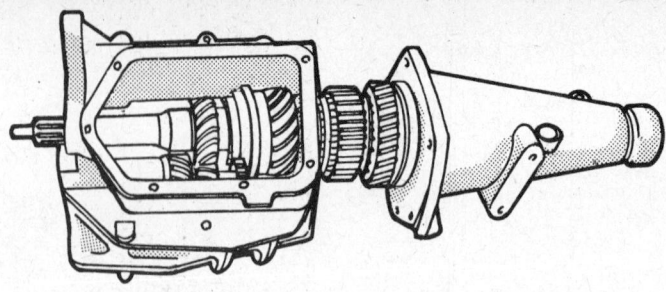

Clutch gear, mainshaft, and extension housing removal—Saginaw 4 speed (Chilton Type 11) transmission

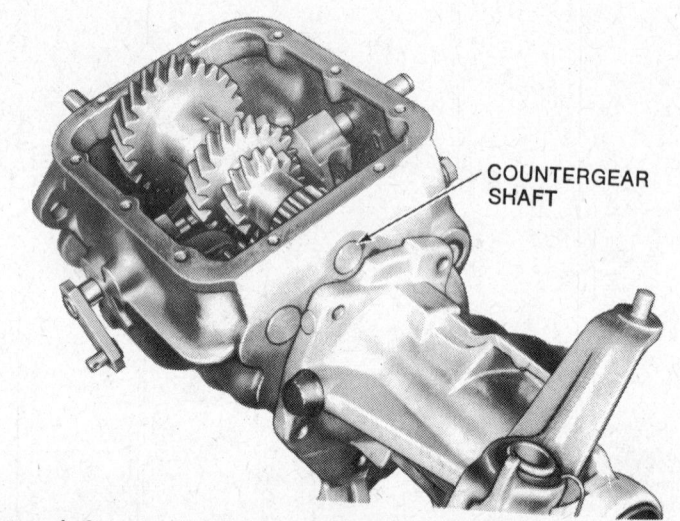

COUNTERGEAR SHAFT

Countergear shaft exposed for removal—Saginaw 4 speed (Chilton Type 11) transmission (© GM Corp.)

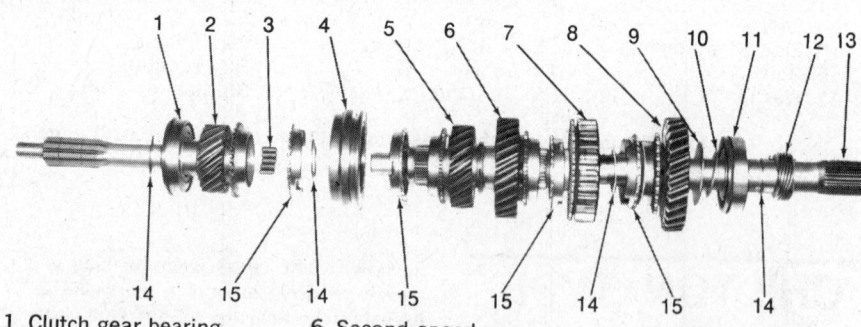

1 Clutch gear bearing	6 Second speed gear
2 Clutch gear	7 1-2 synchronizer and reverse gear assembly
3 Mainshaft pilot bearings	8 First speed gear
4 3-4 synchronizer assembly	9 Thrust washer
5 Third speed gear	10 Spring washer
	11 Rear bearing
	12 Speedo drive gear
	13 Mainshaft
	14 Snap-ring
	15 Synchronizing "blocker" ring

Clutch gear and mainshaft components—Saginaw 4 speed (Chilton Type 11) transmission (© GM Corp.)

load a row of roller bearings (27) and bearing thrust washers at each end of the countergear. Grease can be used to hold the bearings in place.

2. Position the countergear assembly into the case through the rear opening. Place a tanged thrust washer at each end of the countergear.

3. Install the countergear shaft and woodruff key from the rear of the case. Make sure that the shaft engages both thrust washers and that the tangs align with their

1 Clip
2 Speedometer drive gear
3 Snap ring
4 Mainshaft rear bearing
5 Washer (wavy)
6 Washer (wavy)
7 First speed gear
8 Blocking ring
9 Retaining ring
10 Synchronizer assembly

11 Spring
12 Synchronizer key
13 Synchronizer hub
15 Second speed gear
16 Main shaft
17 Third speed gear
18 Synchronizer assembly
19 Mainshaft bearing rollers
20 Extension housing oil seal
21 Extension housing

22 Bolt
23 Washer
24 Rear bearing ring
25 Gasket
26 Case assembly
27 Drain plug

28 Bearing assembly
29 Retainer ring
30 Locating ring
31 Seal

32 Main drive gear
33 Gasket
34 Retainer assembly
35 Bolt
36 Shifter shaft seal

37 Shifter shaft seal
38 Bolt
39 Cover
40 Dowel pin
41 Spring
42 Bearing
43 Shaft assembly
44 Retainer
45 Pin
46 Cam
47 Spring
48 Cam
49 Shaft assembly

50 Shaft assembly
51 Fork
52 Fork
53 Gasket
54 Woodruff key
55 Counter shaft
56 Gear assembly
57 Counter shaft gear
58 Gear thrust washer
59 Bearing thrust washer
60 Counter shaft rollers
61 Extension bushing
62 Reverse idle gear shaft

Exploded view of the Saginaw 4 speed (Chilton Type 11) transmission (© GM Corp.)

notches in the case.

4. Install the reverse idler gear and shaft and the woodruff key. Install the extension-to-rear bearing snap-ring. Assemble the extension housing over the rear of the mainshaft and onto the rear bearing.

5. Install the fourteen mainshaft pilot bearings into the clutch opening and install the 4th speed blocker ring onto the clutching surface of the clutch gear (clutching teeth toward the gear).

6. Assemble the clutch gear, pilot bearings, and 4th speed blocker ring unit over the front of the mainshaft. Do not assemble the bearing to the gear at this point.

— CAUTION —

Be sure that the blocker ring notches line up with the 3rd–4th synchronizer assembly keys.

7. Install the extension-to-case gasket and secure it with grease. Insert the clutch gear, mainshaft, and extension into the case as a unit. Install the extension-to-case bolts (apply sealer to the bottom bolt) and torque to 45 ft. lbs.

8. Install the outer snap-ring on the front bearing and place the bearing over the stem of the clutch gear and into the case bore.

9. Install the snap-ring to the clutch gear stem. Install the clutch gear bearing retainer and gasket to the case, with the retainer oil return hole at the bottom.

10. Place the synchronizer sleeves into neutral positions and install the cover, gasket, and fork assemblies to the case. Be sure the forks align with their synchronizer sleeve grooves. Torque the cover bolts to 22 ft. lbs.

CHILTON TYPE 12

Transmission Disassembly

1. Place the transmission so that it is resting on the bellhousing.

2. Drive the spring pin from the shifter shaft arm assembly and shifter shaft, then remove the shifter shaft arm assembly.

3. Remove the five bolts holding the extension housing to the transmission case and remove the extension.

4. Press down on the speedometer gear retainer and remove the gear and retainer from the mainshaft.

5. Remove the snap rings from the shifter shaft and remove the reverse shifter shaft cover, shifter shaft detent cap, the spring and ball, and the interlock lock pin.

6. Pull the reverse lever shaft outward to disengage the reverse idler; remove the idler shaft with the gear attached.

7. Remove the snap ring on the reverse gear and reverse countershaft gear; when finished remove the gears.

8. Turn the transmission on its side and remove the clutch gear bearing retainer bolts, the retainer and gasket.

9. Remove the snap-ring holding the clutch gear ball bearing to the bell housing; remove the bolts holding the bell housing to the case.

10. Turn the transmission so that it rests on the bell housing again and expand the snap-ring in the mainshaft bearing opening. Remove the case by lifting it off the mainshaft. Make sure that the mainshaft assembly, the countergear, and shifter shaft assembly stay with the bell housing.

11. Lift the entire mainshaft assembly complete with shifter forks and countergear from the bell housing.

MAINSHAFT

12. Separate the shift shaft assembly and countergear from the mainshaft.

13. Remove the clutch gear and blocker ring from the mainshaft. When doing this, make sure you don't lose any of the clutch gear roller bearings.

14. Remove the snap ring in front of third-fourth gear synchronizer hub and remove the hub, using an arbor press if necessary.

15. Remove the blocker ring and the third speed gear, then using press plates, remove the ball bearing from the rear of the mainshaft. Remove the remaining parts from the mainshaft keeping them in order for later reassembly.

Assembly

SYNCHRONIZER KEYS AND SPRINGS

1. The synchronizer hubs and sliding sleeves are an assembly and should be kept together as originally assembled; the keys and springs can be replaced.

2. Mark the position of the hub and sleeve for reassembly.

3. Push the hub from the sliding sleeve; the keys will fall out and the springs can be easily removed.

4. Place the new springs in position with one on each side of the hub so that the three keys are engaged by both springs.

5. Place the keys in position and while holding them in position, slide the sleeve

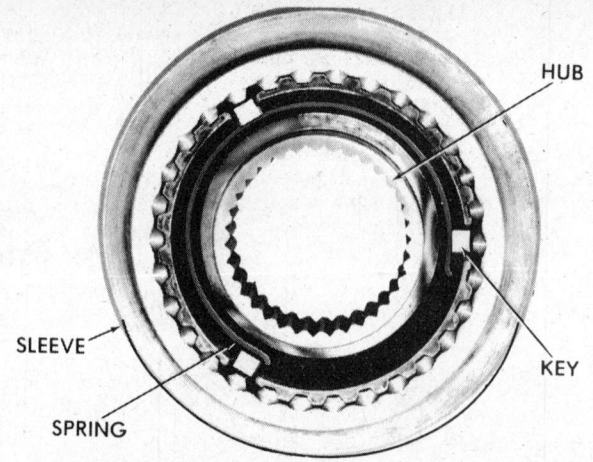

GM 70 mm. synchronizer assembly (© G.M. Corp.)

GM 70 mm. countergear and mainshaft assembled to the bellhousing
(© G.M. Corp.)

into the hub aligning the marks made during disassembly.

EXTENSION OIL SEAL

6. Pry the old seal from rear of the extension, then drive the bushing from the rear of the extension housing.

7. Coat the inside diameter of the seal and bushing with transmission fluid and install them.

DRIVE GEAR BEARING OIL SEAL

8. Pry out the old seal, and install a new one making sure that it bottoms properly in its bore.

MAINSHAFT

9. With the rear of the mainshaft turned up, install the 2nd speed gear with the clutching teeth upward; the rear face of the

gear will butt against the flange of the mainshaft.

10. Install a blocker ring with the clutching teeth down over the second speed gear.

11. Install the 1st–2nd synchronizer assembly with the fork slot down; press it on the splines on the mainshaft until it bottoms. Make sure the notches of the blocker ring align with the keys of the synchronizer assembly.

12. Install the synchronizer hub to the mainshaft snap-ring, then install a blocker ring with the notches down so that they align with the keys of the 1st–2nd gear synchronizer assembly.

13. Install the 1st speed gear with the clutching teeth down; install the rear ball bearing with the snap-ring groove down and press into place on the mainshaft.

14. Turn the mainshaft up and install the 3rd speed gear with the clutching teeth going up; the front face of the gear will butt against the flange on the mainshaft.

15. Install a blocker ring with the clutching teeth down, over the synchronizer surface of the 3rd speed gear.

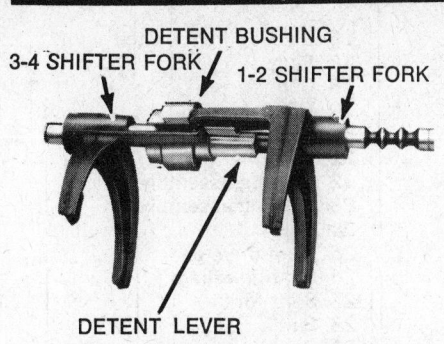

GM 70 mm. shift forks assembled
(© G.M. Corp.)

16. Install the 3rd–4th gear synchronizer assembly with the fork slot down; make sure the notches of the blocker ring align with the keys of the synchronizer assembly.

17. Install the synchronizer hub to mainshaft snap-ring; install a blocker ring with the notches down so that they align with the keys of the 3rd–4th gear synchronizer assembly.

COMPONENTS TO TRANSMISSION CASE

18. Using a press, install the shielded ball bearing to the clutch gear shaft with the snap-ring groove up.

19. Install the snap-ring on the clutch gear shaft; place the pilot bearings into the clutch gear cavity, using heavy grease to hold them in place.

20. Assemble the clutch gear to the mainshaft and then install the detent lever to the shift shaft with the roll pin.

21. Slide the 1st–2nd gear shifter so that it engages the detent lever.

22. Assemble the 3rd–4th gear shifter fork to the detent bushing and slide the assembly on the shift shaft to place it below the first and second shifter fork arm.

23. Install the shifter assembly to the synchronizer sleeve grooves on the mainshaft.

24. With the front of the bell housing resting on wooden blocks, place a thrust washer over the hole for the countergear shaft. The thrust washer must be placed in the holes in the bellhousing.

25. Mesh the countershaft gears to the mainshaft gears and install this assembly into the bellhousing.

26. Turn the bellhousing on its side, and install the snap-ring to the ball bearing on the clutch gear; then install the bearing retainer to the bellhousing. Make sure you use sealant on the four retaining bolts.

27. Turn the bellhousing so that it is resting on the blocks again, and install the reverse lever to the case using grease to hold it in place. When the reverse lever is installed, the screwdriver slot should be parallel to the front of the case.

28. Install the reverse lever snap-ring; install the roller bearing to the countergear opening with the snap ring groove inside of the case.

29. Install the gasket on the bellhousing with rubber cement. Before installing the case, make sure the synchronizers are in the neutral position, the detent bushing slot is facing outward, and the reverse lever is flush with the inside wall of the case.

30. Expand the snap-ring in the opening of the mainshaft case and let it slide over the bearing.

31. Install the interlock lock pin with locking compound to hold the shifter shaft in place; install the idler shaft so it will engage with the reverse lever inside the shaft.

32. Install the cover over the screwdriver arm to hold the reverse lever in place.

33. Install the detent ball, spring and cap in the transmission case, then install the reverse gear with the chamfer on the gear teeth up. Push the reverse gear on the splines and hold it there with a snap-ring.

34. Install the smaller reverse gear on the countergear shaft with the shoulder resting against the countergear bearing and hold it there with a snap-ring.

35. Install the snap-ring, thrust washer and reverse idler gear with the chamfer of the gear teeth facing down, to the idler shaft. Hold it there with the thrust washer and snap-ring.

36. Install the snap-rings on the shifter shaft and engage the speedometer gear retainer in the hole in the mainshaft with the retainer loop toward the front; slide the speedometer gear over the mainshaft and into position. Heat the gear to 175°F before installation; use an oven or heat lamp, not a torch.

37. Place the extension housing and gasket on the transmission case and loosely install two pilot bolts (one in the top right hand corner; the other in the bottom left hand corner) and then the other three bolts. The pilot bolts *must* be installed in the right holes to prevent splitting the transmission case.

38. Assemble the shifter shaft arm over the shifter shaft to a position aligned with the drilled hole near the end of the shaft; drive spring pin into shifter shaft arm and shaft to hold these parts.

39. Turn the transmission on its side and loosely install two pilot bolts through the bell housing, and then the four retaining bolts.

CHILTON TYPE 13

Transmission Disassembly

1. Remove cover, front bearing cap,

gasket, and two front bearing snap-rings.

2. Align notch in clutch shaft third bear with countergear. Remove clutch shaft and front bearing. A puller may be needed.

3. Pull off front bearing.

4. Remove extension housing and gasket. Using oil seal remover and slide hammer, remove extension housing oil seal. Remove extension housing bushing. Install new bushing, aligning oil groove with housing slot.

5. Remove snap-ring, speedometer drive gear, and locating ball.

6. Remove two rear bearing snap-rings and pull off rear bearing.

7. Move mainshaft aside. Remove both shift forks.

8. Push front synchronizer toward rear. Tilt front of mainshaft up and out through top of case.

9. If necessary, remove the transmission controlled spark switch assembly.

10. Drive out roll pins. Push shift shafts into case. Remove shift shafts and detent assembly.

11. Tap reverse idler shaft and countershaft rearward. Remove shaft lockplate. Drive reverse idler shaft from case. Use dummy shaft to drive out countershaft.

MAINSHAFT DISASSEMBLY

1. From front of shaft, remove front snap-ring, 2nd-3rd synchro-clutch assembly, and 2nd gear.

2. From rear of shaft, remove reverse gear, rear snap-ring rear synchro-clutch assembly, and low gear.

MAINSHAFT ASSEMBLY

1. Install low gear and friction ring; friction ring hub to the rear.

2. Install low synchro-gear into synchro-collar so deep end of gear faces low gear. Install synchro-plates (dogs) and retainer ring with large end of plates toward low gear.

3. Place synchro-clutch assembly on mainshaft with synchro-collar groove toward low gear. Install the thickest snap-ring that will fit in groove.

4. Measure clearance between first gear and collar on mainshaft. The clearance should be 0.003–0.012 in. for the T-14; 0.003–0.014 in. for the T-15.

5. Place 2nd gear and the friction ring on the front of the mainshaft with the gear hub and ring forward. Place 2nd synchrogear into synchro-collar with deep end of gear facing rear of shaft.

6. Hold synchro-clutch assembly with one synchro-plate, or dog, in 12 o'clock position. Install tang of retainer ring into the dog at 12 o'clock and install ring clockwise. On opposite side, start with the same dog and install ring clockwise.

7. Place 2nd synchro assembly on shaft with deep end to rear. Install the thickest snap-ring that will fit into the groove.

1 Bolt
2 Bearing retainer
3 Seal assembly
4 Gasket
5 Clutch housing
6 Wire assembly
7 Switch assembly (TCS)
8 Gasket assembly
9 Case assembly
10 Spring
11 Cap
12 Ball
13 Gasket
14 Cap
15 Retainer
16 Back-up light switch
17 Plug
18 Cap
19 Bolt
20 Retaining ring
21 Locating ring
22 Bearing assembly
23 Bearing assembly
24 Bolt
25 Main drive gear
26 Bearing rollers
27 Shift fork
28 Pin
29 Bushing
30 Detent lever
31 Shift fork
32 Shift shaft
33 Pin
34 Lock ring
35 Extension assembly
36 Gasket
37 Arm assembly
38 Pin
39 Bushing
40 Seal
41 Reverse shaft and lever
42 Lock ring
43 Clip
44 Retaining ring
45 Synchronizer assembly
46 Mainshaft
47 Second speed gear
48 Synchronizer assembly
49 Synchronizer blocking ring
50 Synchronizer spring
51 Synchronizer key
52 Third speed gear
53 First speed gear
54 Locating ring
55 Mainshaft rear bearing
56 Reverse gear
57 Retaining ring
58 Speedometer drive gear
59 Retainer ring
60 Thrust washer
61 Countershaft gear
62 Locating ring
63 Bearing race
64 Bearing assembly
65 Countershaft reverse gear
66 Reverse idler shaft
67 Retainer ring
68 Thrust washer
69 Reverse idler gear

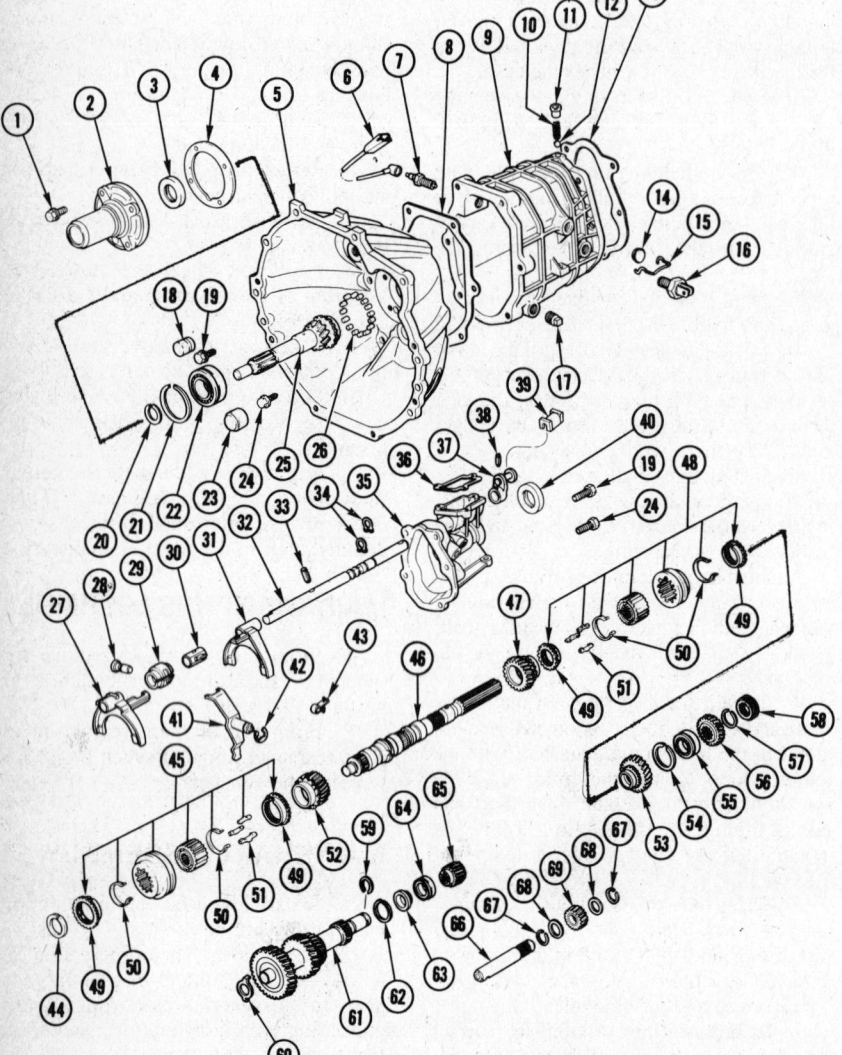

Exploded view of GM 70 mm. transmission (© G.M. Corp.)

8. Measure clearance between second gear and collar on mainshaft. It must be 0.003–0.018 in.

9. Install reverse gear on rear of mainshaft.

Transmission Assembly

1. Install dummy shaft in countergear. Install spacer washers and roller bearings.

2. Place countergear in case. Align thrust washers at each end. Insert countershaft.

3. Install rollers in reverse idler gear. Hold rollers with petroleum jelly. Place gear in case. Position thrust washers. Insert shaft. Install shaft lockplate.

4. Insert shifter shafts in case. Position low-reverse lever to inside of case. Locate notches on top of levers to rear of case stud. Align shift detent assembly with shifter shafts and case stud. Push detent assembly and shifter shafts into place. Install shaft roll pins.

5. If removed, install the transmission controlled spark switch.

6. Place front synchronizer in second shift position. Place mainshaft assembly in case to one side.

7. Pull detent levers up. Place shift forks in shifting assembly.

8. Install mainshaft pilot end support in case. Install front bearing cap. Drive rear bearing on thickest rear bearing snap-ring with a 1¼ × 17 in. pipe. Install support and bearing cap.

9. Install locating ball, speedometer drive gear, and snap-ring.

10. Press front bearing onto clutch shaft.

11. Place rollers in clutch shaft. Hold with petroleum jelly.

12. Place friction ring on mainshaft. Slide clutch shaft into position from front.

13. Install thickest front bearing snap-ring that will fit in groove, gasket and cap. Align cap lubrication hole with hole in case.

14. Install extension housing. Install oil seal. Install shift lever, gaskets, and cover.

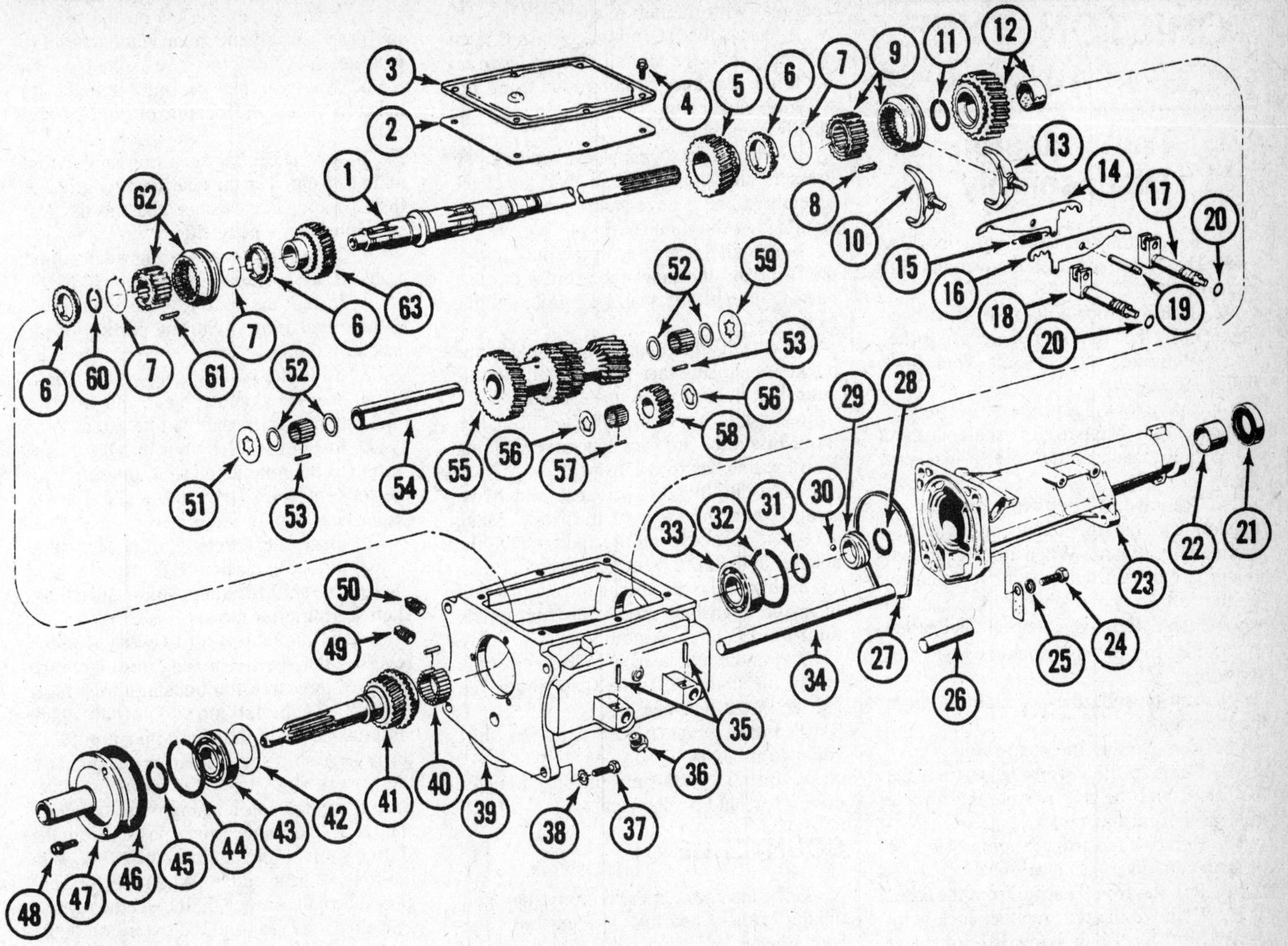

1. Spline Shaft
2. Gasket
3. Case Cover
4. Bolt
5. First Gear
6. Clutch Friction Ring Set
7. Shaft Plate Retaining Spring
8. Clutch Shaft First and Reverse Plate
9. First and Reverse Clutch Assembly
10. Shifter Second and High Fork
11. Clutch First and Reverse Gear Snap Ring
12. Reverse Gear
13. Shifter First and Reverse R Fork
14. Shifter Interlock First and Reverse Lever
15. Speed Finder Interlock Poppet Spring
16. Shifter Interlock Second and Third Lever
17. Shifter Fork First and Reverse Shaft
18. Shifter Fork Second and Third Shaft
19. Shifter Fork Interlock Lever Pivot Pin

20. Shifter Fork Shaft Seal
21. Rear Bearing Cap Oil Seal
22. Rear Bearing Cap Bushing
23. Rear Bearing Cap
24. Bolt
25. Lock Washer
26. Idler Gear Shaft
27. Rear Bearing Cap Gasket
28. Speedometer Drive Gear Ring
29. Speedometer Drive Gear
30. Speedometer Drive Gear Ball
31. Rear Ball Bearing Lockring
32. Rear Ball Bearing Lockring
33. Rear Ball Bearing
34. Countershaft
35. Shifter Fork Retaining Pin
36. Solenoid Control Switch
37. Bolt
38. Lock Washer
39. Case
40. Spline Shaft Pilot Bearing Roller
41. Clutch Shaft
42. Front Ball Bearing Washer
43. Front Ball Bearing
44. Front Ball Bearing Lockring
45. Front Ball Bearing Snap Ring
46. Gasket

47. Front Bearing Cap
48. Bolt
49. Drain Plug
50. Filler Pipe Plug
51. Front Countershaft Gear Thrust Washer
52. Countershaft Gear Bearing Roller Washer
53. Countershaft Gear Bearing Roller
54. Countershaft Gear Roller Bearing Spacer
55. Countershaft Gear
56. Reverse Idler Gear Bearing Roller Washer
57. Reverse Idler Gear Bearing Roller
58. Reverse Idler Gear
59. Rear Countershaft Thrust Washer (Less Lip)
60. Clutch Second and Third Snap Ring
61. Clutch Shaft Second and Third Plate
62. Second and Third Clutch Assembly
63. Second Gear

Exploded view of the Warner T-14 (Chilton Type 13) transmission (© AMC)

CHILTON TYPE 14

Transmission Disassembly

1. Drain transmission, shift into 2nd gear. Then remove the side cover and shift controls.

2. Remove four bolts from front bearing retainer, then remove retainer and gasket.

3. Remove output shaft companion flange, if any.

4. Drive lock-pin up from reverse shifter lever boss, then pull shift-shaft out about ⅛ in. to disengage shifter fork from reverse gear.

5. Remove five bolts from the case extension and tap the extension (with soft hammer) rearward. When idler gear shaft is out as far as it will go, move extension to the left so the reverse fork clears the reverse gear. Remove extension and gasket.

6. Remove the speedometer gear outer snap-ring.

7. Tap or slide the speedometer from the mainshaft.

8. Remove the 2nd snap-ring.

9. Remove the reverse gear from the mainshaft and the rear part of the reverse idler gear from the case.

10. Remove the front bearing selective fit snap-ring and spacer washer.

11. Pull the front bearing from the case.

12. Remove the rear retainer lock bolt.

13. Shift the 1st-2nd and 3rd-4th clutch sliding sleeves forward for clearance.

14. Remove the mainshaft and rear bearing retainer assembly from the case.

15. Take the front reverse idler gear and thrust washer from the case. Note that the gear teeth face the front.

16. With a dummy shaft, drive the countergear shaft out. Take the countergear and tanged thrust washers out.

MAINSHAFT

17. With snap-ring pliers, remove the 3rd-4th clutch assembly retaining ring from the front of the mainshaft. Take off the washer, synchronizer and clutch assembly, synchronizer ring, and third gear.

18. Spread the rear bearing retainer snapring and slide the retainer off. Remove the rear bearing to mainshaft snap-ring.

19. Support 2nd gear and press the mainshaft out, removing the rear bearing, 1st gear and sleeve, 1st-2nd clutch and synchronizer assembly, and 2nd gear.

Assembly

MAINSHAFT

1. From the rear of the shaft, install

2nd gear with the hub to the rear.

2. Install the 1st-2nd synchronizer clutch assembly with the sliding clutch sleeve taper to the rear and the hub to the front. Put a synchronizer ring on both sides of the clutch assemblies.

3. Place the 1st gear sleeve on the shaft. Press the sleeve on until 2nd gear, the clutch assembly, and sleeve bottom against the shoulder of the mainshaft.

4. Install 1st gear with the hub toward the front and the inner race. Press the rear bearing on with the snap-ring groove to the front.

5. Install the spacer and select the thickest snap-ring that can be fitted into the mainshaft behind the rear bearing.

6. Install 3rd gear with the hub to the front. Install the 3rd gear synchronizing ring with the notches to the front.

7. Install the 3rd-4th gear clutch assembly with the taper to the front. Make sure that the keys in the hub match the notches in the third gear synchronizing ring.

8. Install the thickest snap-ring that will fit in the mainshaft groove in front of the third-fourth clutch assembly.

9. Put the rear bearing retainer over the end of the shaft. Place the snap-ring in the groove in the rear bearing.

10. Install reverse gear with the shift collar to the rear.

11. Install a snap-ring, the speedometer drive gear, and a snap-ring.

COUNTERGEAR

1. Install countergear dummy shaft and tubular roller bearing spacer into the countergear.

2. Using heavy grease to hold the rollers, install 20 bearing rollers in either end of the countergear, two spacers, 20 more rollers, then one spacer. Install the same combination of rollers and spacers in the other end of the countergear.

3. Set the countergear assembly in the bottom of the transmission case, be sure the tanged thrust washers are in their proper position.

TRANSMISSION

1. Place the case on its side. Install the countergear tanged washers with the tangs in the thrust face notches, holding them with grease.

2. Install the countergear and dummy shaft. Push the countergear shaft in from the rear, forcing the dummy shaft out the front. Install the shaft key and tap the shaft in until it is flush with the rear face of the case.

3. Install the front reverse idler gear with the teeth forward. Use grease to hold the thrust washer in place.

4. Use heavy grease to hold the 16 roller bearings and the washer in the main drive gear. Mate the main drive gear with the mainshaft. Hold them together by moving the 3rd-4th clutch sliding sleeve forward.

5. Place a new gasket on the rear of the case. Install the mainshaft and drive gear assembly into the case.

6. Align the rear bearing retainer with the case. Install the locating pin and locking bolt.

7. Put the bearing snap-ring on the front main bearing. Tap the bearing into the case. Install the spacer washer and the thickest snap-ring that can be fitted.

8. Install the front bearing retainer and a gasket. Use a sealer on the bolts.

9. Install the rear reverse idler gear. Engage the splines with the portion of the gear in the case.

10. Slide the reverse gear on the shaft. Install the speedometer gear and the two thickest snap-rings that can be fitted.

11. Install the idler shaft into the extension until the hole in the shaft lines up with the lockpin hole. Drive the lockpin and a sealer coated plug into place.

12. Place the reverse shifter shaft and detent into the extension. Use grease to hold the reverse shift fork in position. Install the shaft O-ring after the shaft is in place.

13. Put the tanged thrust washer on the reverse idler shaft. The tang must be in the notch of the extension housing thrust face.

14. Place the 1st-2nd and 3rd-4th clutch sliding sleeves in the neutral position. Pull the reverse shift shaft part-way out and push the reverse shift fork in as far as possible. Start the extension housing onto the mainshaft. At the same time, push in on the shifter shaft to engage the shift fork with the reverse gear collar. When the fork engages, turn the shifter shaft to let the reverse gear go to the rear and the extension housing to fit in place.

15. Install the reverse shift shaft lockpin.

16. Install the extension housing bolts, making sure to use sealer on the upper left-side bolt.

17. Position the 1st-2nd clutch sliding sleeve into 2nd gear and the 3rd-4th clutch sliding sleeve into neutral. Position the forward shift forks in the sliding sleeves.

18. Place the 1st-2nd shifter shaft and detent plate into 2nd gear position. Install the side cover gasket, with sealer.

CHILTON TYPE 15

Transmission Disassembly

1. Thoroughly clean the exterior of the transmission assemblies.

2. Remove the (7) bolts attaching the overdrive unit to the reverse housing and then separate the two transmission units.

3. Remove the drain plug from the lower right side of the case and drain the lubricant from the transmission.

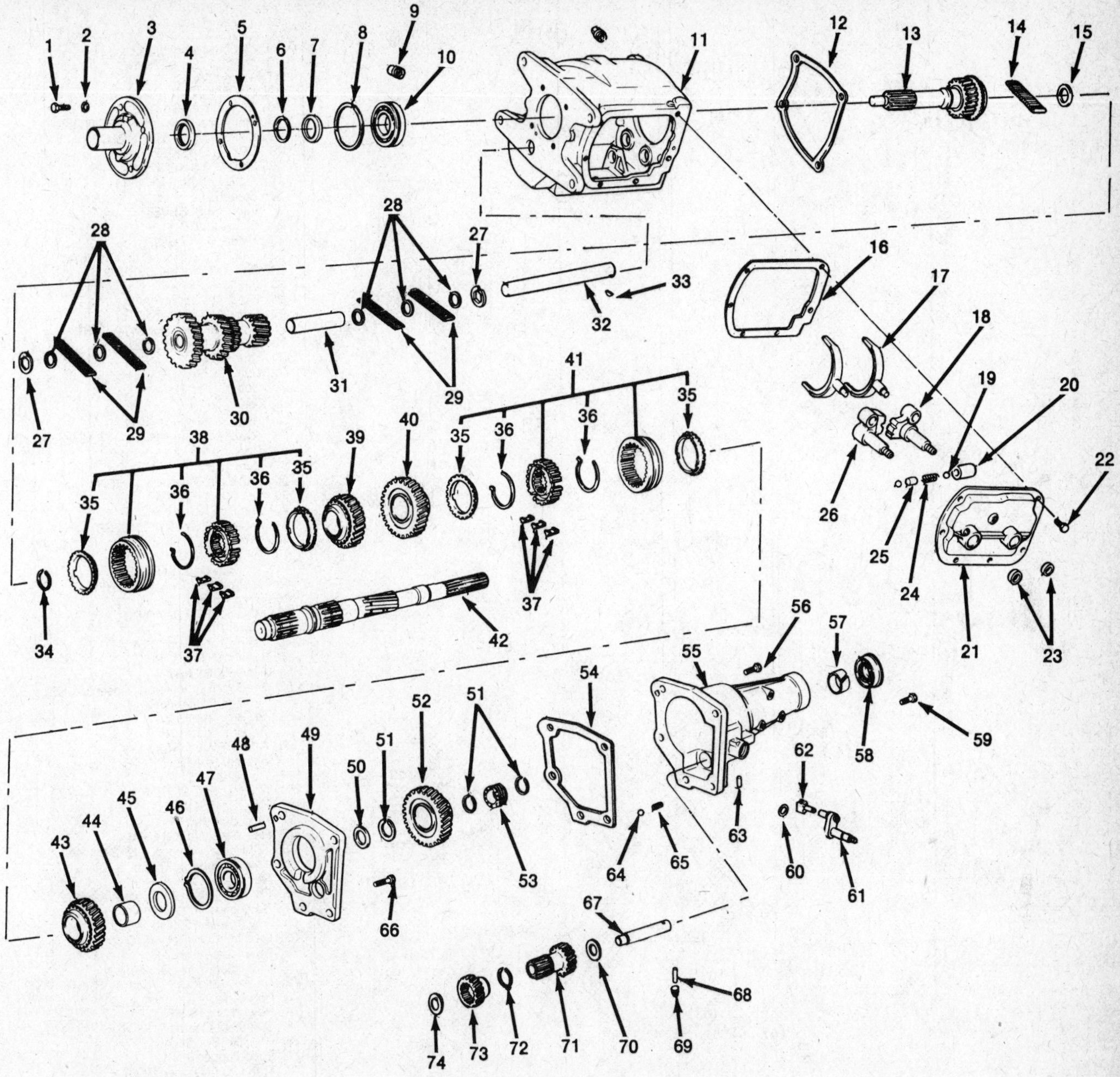

1. Bolt	20. Interlock sleeve
2. Lock washer	21. Transmission cover
3. Bearing retainer	22. Bolt
4. Seal	23. Shifter shaft seal
5. Gasket	24. Rev. lever poppet spring
6. Snap ring	25. Interlock pin
7. Ring	26. 3rd and 4th shaft assy.
8. Snap ring	27. Washer
9. Drain plug	28. Countershaft bearing washer
10. Bearing	29. Roller
11. Transmission case	30. Countershaft gear
12. Front gasket	31. Spacer
13. Clutch gear	32. Counter shaft
14. Roller	33. Key (1/8″ × 5/8″)
15. Spacer	34. Clutch hub retainer ring
16. Side gasket	35. Blocking ring
17. 1st, 2nd, 3rd and 4th fork	36. Synchronizer spring
18. 1st and 2nd shaft assy.	37. Shifting key
19. Balls	38. 3rd and 4th synchronizer

39. 3rd speed gear	57. Extension bushing
40. 2nd speed gear	58. Extension seal
41. 1st and 2nd synchronizer	59. Bolt
42. Transmission main shaft	60. Shifter shaft oil seal
43. 1st speed gear	61. Reverse shifter shaft
44. 1st speed sleeve	62. Reverse fork
45. 1st speed thrust washer	63. Lock pin
46. Snap ring	64. Lever poppet spring
47. Main shaft rear bearing	65. Ball
48. Pin	66. Bolt
49. Retainer assy.	67. Shaft
50. Ring	68. Pin
51. Retainer ring	69. Plug
52. Reverse gear	70. Rev. idler gear washer
53. Speedometer drive gear	71. Reverse idler gear
54. Gasket	72. Front ring
55. Extension assy.	73. Rev. idler gear (front)
56. Bolt	74. Washer

Borg Warner 4-speed transmission (© Chevrolet Motor Division)

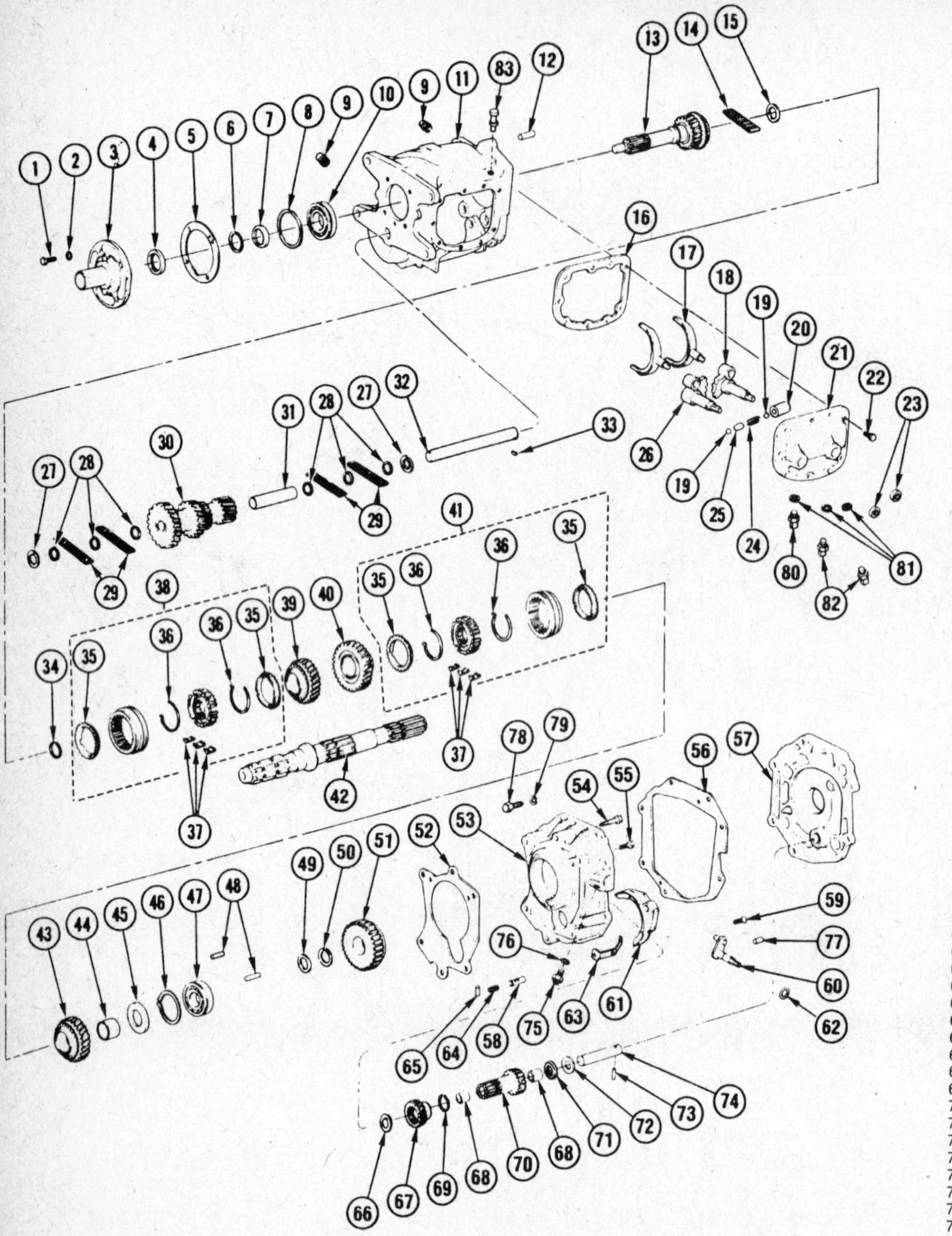

9. Drain (Magnetic) PLUG
10. Main Dr. Gr. BEARING
11. Trans. CASE
12. Dowel PIN
13. Main Drive GEAR
14. Main Dr. Gr. Pilot Rr. ROLLER
15. Main Shf. Pilot Brg. SPACER
16. Si. Cvr. GASKET
17. Shift (1-2 3-4) FORK
18. 1st & 2nd Shift SHAFT
19. Steel BALL
20. Interlock SLEEVE
21. Side COVER
22. Trans. Cover BOLT
23. Shft. Lvr. Shf. Oil (1-2 3-4) SEAL
24. Shft. Lvr. Poppet SPRING
25. Interlock PIN
26. 3rd & 4th Shift SHAFT
27. Cntr. Gr. Rr. WASHER
28. Cntr. Shf. Brg. Roller WASHER
29. Cntr. Gr. Brg. ROLLER
30. Cntr. GEAR
31. Cntr. Gr. Brg. SPACER
32. Cntr. Gr. SHAFT
33. Woodruff KEY
34. Snap Main Shf. RING
35. Sync. Blocking RING
36. Sync. SPRING
37. Sync. KEY
38. 3rd & 4th SYNCHRONIZER
39. 3rd Spd. GEAR
40. 2nd Spd. GEAR
41. 1st & 2nd SYNCHRONIZER
42. Main SHAFT
43. 1st Spd. GEAR
44. 1st Spd. Gear SLEEVE
45. 1st Spd. Gr. Thrust WASHER
46. Snap Rr. Brg. Loc. RING
47. Main Shf. Rr. BEARING
48. Dowel PIN
49. Main Dr. Gr. Brg. SPACER
50. Main Shf. RING, Snap
51. Reverse GEAR
52. Rr. Brg. Ret. to Trans. Case GASKET
53. Rr. Brg. RETAINER
54. Rr. Brg. Ret. BOLT
55. Rr. Brg. Ret. BOLT
56. Adapt. Plate GASKET
57. Adapter PLATE
58. Rev. Detent PIN
59. Rr. Brg. Ret. SCREW
60. Rev. Shift SHAFT
61. Rev. Shift FORK
62. Rev. Shft. Shf. Oil SEAL
63. TBI Harness Clip BRACKET
64. Rev. Detent Pin Poppet SPRING
65. Rev. Detent Spr. PIN
66. Frt. Rev. Idler Gr. Thrust WASHER
67. Rev. Idler Frt. GEAR
68. Rev. Idler BUSHING
69. Rev. Idler Gr. Ret. RING
70. Rev. Idler Rr. GEAR
71. Rev. Idler Thrust BEARING
72. Rr. Rev. Idler Gr. Thrust WASHER
73. Spr. PIN
74. Rev. Idler SHAFT
75. Overdrive Override Rev. Gear SWITCH
76. Rev. Gr. Sw. SEAL
77. Solid Tapper PIN
78. Trans. to Overdrive BOLT
79. Trans. to Overdrive Bolt Lk. WASHER
80. Overdrive Override (3-4) SWITCH
81. Overdrive Override Sw. SEAL
82. Overdrive Override (1-2) SWITCH
83. Trans. VENTILATOR

1. Hex BOLT
2. Ext. Lock WASHER
3. Main Dr. Gr. Brg. Frt. RETAINER
4. Main Dr. Gr. Brg. Frt. Oil SEAL
5. Main Dr. Gr. Brg. Ret. GASKET
6. Main Dr. Gr. Brg. Ret. RING Snap
7. Main Dr. G. Brg. SPACER
8. Main Dr. Gr. Brg. Loc. RING

Exploded view of the 83mm 4 speed transmission (Chilton Type 15)

4. Shift the transmission into second gear. Remove the shift cover attaching bolts, cover, gasket and both shift forks from the transmission.

5. Remove the backup switch from the reverse housing.

6. Rotate the reverse shifter shaft and remove the shift fork and gear from the mainshaft.

7. Remove the lock pin from the reverse shift lever boss and pull the shaft from the housing.

8. Remove the drive gear bearing retainer bolts, retainer and gasket from the front of the transmission.

9. Remove front bearing snap ring, selective fit snap ring and spacer washer.

10. Using Tool J-6654-01 and J-8433-1, pull the drive gear bearing from the transmission.

11. Remove the (6) bolts attaching the reverse housing to the case. Using a small drift and a hammer, tap the locating pin for the reverse housing into the case.

12. Rotate the reverse housing on the mainshaft until the hole for the reverse idler gear shaft in the housing lines up with the countergear shaft.

13. Using Tool J-24658 or a dummy shaft, drive the countergear shaft rearward

out of the gear and through the reverse housing. The countergear will drop to the bottom of the case allowing clearance for the removal of the mainshaft.

14. Remove the mainshaft with the reverse housing and drive gear from the transmission case.

15. Remove the front reverse idler gear and thrust washer from the case.

16. Remove the countergear and two tanged thrust washers from the transmission case. Check the bottom of the transmission case for loose pilot bearings. Remove the locating pin for the reverse housing and any other loose components.

MAINSHAFT

Disassembly

1. Using snap ring pliers, remove 3-4 synchronizer assembly retaining ring at front of mainshaft. Slide washer, synchronizer assembly, synchronizer ring 3rd speed gear from mainshaft.

2. Spread rear bearing retainer snap ring and slide retainer from mainshaft.

3. Remove rear bearing-to-mainshaft snap ring.

4. Support mainshaft under 2nd gear and press mainshaft from rear bearing, 1st gear and sleeve, 1-2 synchronizer assembly, and the second gear.

COUNTERGEAR

Disassembly

1. Remove Tool J-24658 from the countergear.

2. Tip the countergear on end and let the (6) spacers, (112) rollers and roller sleeve slide out from the gear.

Cleaning and Inspection

TRANSMISSION CASE

1. Wash the transmission thoroughly inside and outside with cleaning solvent, then inspect the case for cracks.

2. Check the front and rear faces for burrs, and if present, dress them off with a fine mill file.

ROLLER BEARINGS AND SPACERS

All main drive gear and countergear bearing rollers should be inspected closely and replaced if they show wear. Inspect countershaft and reverse idler shaft at the same time. Replace if necessary. Replace all worn spacers.

GEARS

1. Inspect all gears for excessive wear, chips or cracks and replace any that are worn or damaged.

2. Inspect reverse gear bushing and if worn or damaged, replace the entire gear (reverse gear bushing is not serviced separately).

3. Check both synchronizer sleeves to see that they slide freely on their hubs.

FRONT AND REAR BEARINGS

1. Wash the front and rear ball bearings thoroughly in a cleaning solvent.

2. Blow out bearing with compressed air.

NOTE: Do not allow the bearing to spin. Turn them slowly by hand. Spinning bearings may damage the race and balls.

SYNCHRONIZER KEYS AND SPRINGS

Replacement

The synchronizer hubs and sliding sleeves are a selected assembly and should be kept together as originally assembled, but the keys and two springs may be replaced if worn or broken.

1. If relation of hub and sleeve are not already marked, mark for assembly purposes.

2. Push the hub from the sliding sleeve, the keys will fall free and the springs may be easily removed.

3. Place the two springs in position (one on each side of hub) so all three keys are engaged by both springs.

Place the keys in position and while holding them in place, slide the sleeve onto the hub, aligning the marks made before disassembly.

DRIVE GEAR BEARING RETAINER OIL SEAL

Replacement

1. Pry out old seal.

2. Using a new seal, install new seal into retainer using Tool J-23096 until it bottoms in bore. Lubricate I.D. of seal with transmission lubricant.

REVERSE SHIFTER SHAFT AND/OR SEAL

Replacement

1. With the reverse housing removed from transmission, the reverse shifter shaft lock pin will already be removed.

2. Carefully drive shifter shaft into the reverse housing allowing ball detent to drop into case. Remove shaft and ball detent spring. Remove O-ring seal from shaft.

3. Place ball detent spring into detent spring hole and start reverse shifter shaft into hole in boss.

4. Place detent ball on spring and while holding ball down, push the shifter shaft into place and turn until the ball drops into place in detent on the shaft detent plate.

5. Install O-ring seal on shaft.

6. Install shift fork. Do not drive the shifter shaft lock pin into place until the reverse housing has been installed on the transmission case.

REVERSE IDLER SHAFT

Replacement

1. Place a small punch into hole in front cover of the overdrive unit and drive the pin into the shaft until the shaft can be pulled from front cover.

2. Insert new idler shaft into cover until hole in shaft lines up with hole in boss.

3. Insert roll pin into boss opening and drive the pin into the cover until the shaft is securely locked in place.

TRANSMISSION SIDE COVER

Although service of the side cover is covered here, the transmission does not have to be removed to perform these operations. To remove the side cover in-the-vehicle, simply drain the transmission, disconnect electrical leads at the side cover switches, disconnect the 1st/2nd and 3rd/4th linkage and remove the attaching bolts.

1. Remove the outer shifter lever nuts and lockwasher and pull levers from shafts.

2. Carefully push the shifter shafts into cover, allowing the detent balls to fall free, then remove both shifter shafts.

3. Remove interlock sleeve, interlock pin and poppet spring.

4. Replace necessary parts and assembly by reversing Steps 1-3.

COUNTERGEAR

Assembly

1. Install roller spacer in countergear (if removed).

2. Insert a dummy shaft or loading Tool J-24658 into countergear.

3. Using heavy grease to retain rollers, install spacer, 28 rollers, spacer, 28 rollers, and spacer in either end of countergear. Repeat in other end of countergear.

CHECKING COUNTERGEAR END PLAY

1. Rest the transmission case on its side with the side cover opening toward the assembler. Put countergear tanged thrust washers in place, retaining them with heavy grease, making sure the tangs are resting in the notches of the case.

2. Set countergear in place in bottom of transmission case, making sure that tanged thrust washers are not knocked out of place.

3. Position the transmission case resting on its front face.

4. Lubricate and insert countergear (pushing loading Tool J-24658 out front of case) until woodruff key slot is in its relative installed position (do not install key).

5. Attach a dial indicator and check end play of the countergear. If end-play is greater than 0.025 in., a new thrust washer must be installed.

MAINSHAFT

Assembly

1. From rear of mainshaft, assemble the 2nd speed gear (with hub of gear toward rear of shaft).

2. Install 1st-2nd synchronizer assembly (sliding synchronizer sleeve taper toward rear, hub to front) on the mainshaft together with a synchronizer ring on both sides of the synchronizer assemblies.

3. Position the 1st gear sleeve on the shaft and press the sleeve onto the mainshaft until the 2nd gear, synchronizer assembly and sleeve bottom against the

shoulder of the mainshaft.

4. Install 1st speed gear (with hub toward front) and supporting inner race, press the rear bearing onto the mainshaft with the snap ring groove toward front of the transmission.

5. Install spacer and new correct selective fit (thickest that will assemble) snap ring in mainshaft behind rear bearing.

6. Install the 3rd speed gear (hub to front of transmission) and the 3rd speed gear synchronizing ring (notches to front of transmission).

7. Install the 3rd and 4th speed gear synchronizer assembly (hub and sliding sleeve) with taper toward the front making sure that the keys in hub correspond to the notches in the 3rd speed gear synchronizing ring.

8. Install new selective fit snap ring (thickest that will install) in the groove in mainshaft in front of the 3rd and 4th speed synchronizer assembly.

9. Install the rear bearing retainer (reverse housing) over end of mainshaft. Spread the snap ring to drop around the rear bearing. Release snap ring when it aligns with groove in rear bearing.

Transmission Assembly

1. Place the transmission case on its side with the shift cover opening toward the assembler. Position the countergear tanged washers in place, using a heavy grease to retain them.

NOTE: Be sure the tangs are in the notches of the thrust face.

2. Position the countergear in the bottom of the case.

3. Install front reverse idler gear (teeth forward) and thrust washer in case. Use a heavy grease to hold thrust washer in position.

4. Using a heavy grease, install sixteen (16) roller bearings and washer into main drive gear. Mate main drive gear with mainshaft assembly. Position 3rd-4th synchronizer sliding sleeve forward. This will provide clearance for installation as well as hold the assembly together.

5. Position a new reverse housing to case gasket on the rear of the case.

6. Install the mainshaft and drive gear assembly into the case.

7. Place bearing snap ring on front main bearing. Position front main bearing to case opening and with a hollow shaft, or Tool J-5590, tap bearing into case. Install spacer washer and selective fit snap ring to secure main drive bearing.

8. Raise the countergear in the case, aligning the holes in the case with the center of the gear. With the thrust washers in place, slide the counter shaft through the rear of the case. Install the woodruff key and tap the shaft into the case, until flush with the rear face of the transmission case.

9. Align the reverse housing and gasket to the transmission case. Install the locating pin for the reverse housing. Tap the pin in until flush with housing.

10. Install the (6) bolts attaching the reverse housing to the case. Torque bolts to specifications.

11. Install the reverse shift shaft and O-ring into the housing. Install retaining pin.

12. Install the reverse gear and shift fork. Slide the gear and fork forward on the mainshaft until shift fork and shifter shaft can be indexed into position.

13. Position the drive gear bearing retainer and gasket to the front of the case. Apply sealer to the bolts. Install bolts and torque to specifications.

14. Install the rear reverse idler gear. Align the splines on the rear gear with the front gear and slide together.

15. Assemble the overdrive unit to the reverse housing. Guide the idler shaft on the O/D unit into the idler gears and align the splines on the mainshaft with the splines in the input sun gear. Slide the units together and install the retaining bolts. Torque the bolts to specifications.

16. Slide the 1-2 synchronizer forward into second gear. Install the shift forks into the grooves of the synchronizers. Place the side cover with a gasket on the transmission. Guide the shift forks into the cover and install the retaining bolts. Torque the bolts to specifications.

17. Check operation of transmission by manually shifting the transmission into all gears.

Overdrive Unit— Disassembly

Cleanliness is an important factor in the overhaul of the transmission. Before attempting any disassembly operation, the exterior of the transmission should be thoroughly cleaned to prevent the possibility of dirt entering the transmission internal mechanism. During inspection and reassembly, all parts should be thoroughly cleaned with cleaning fluid and then air dried. Wiping cloths or rags should not be used to dry parts. Do not use solvents on neoprene seals, composition-faced clutch plates

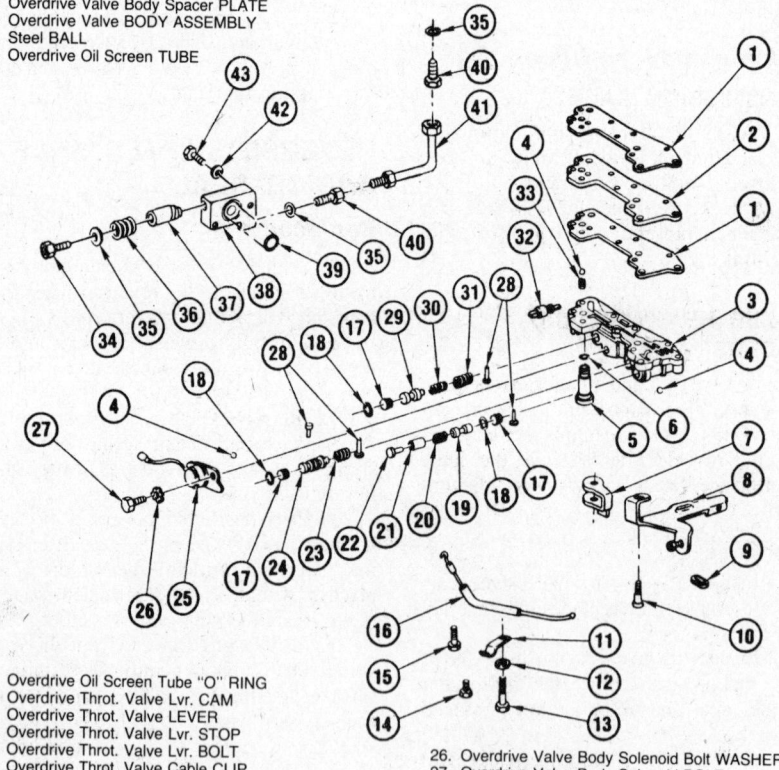

1. Overdrive Valve Body GASKET
2. Overdrive Valve Body Spacer PLATE
3. Overdrive Valve BODY ASSEMBLY
4. Steel BALL
5. Overdrive Oil Screen TUBE

6. Overdrive Oil Screen Tube "O" RING
7. Overdrive Throt. Valve Lvr. CAM
8. Overdrive Throt. Valve LEVER
9. Overdrive Throt. Valve Lvr. STOP
10. Overdrive Throt. Valve Lvr. BOLT
11. Overdrive Throt. Valve Cable CLIP
12. Overdrive Throt. Valve Lvr. Stop WASHER
13. Overdrive Valve Body BOLT
14. Hex BOLT
15. Hex BOLT
    Hex BOLT
16. Overdrive Valve Body Throt. Valve CABLE
17. End PLUG
18. Overdrive Oil Pump "O" RING
19. Modulator SPOOL
20. Modulator SPRING
21. Piston BUSHING
22. Modulator PISTON
23. Shift SPRING
24. Shift SPOOL
25. Overdrive Valve Body SOLENOID

26. Overdrive Valve Body Solenoid Bolt WASHER
27. Overdrive Valve Body Solenoid BOLT
28. PIN
29. Relief SPOOL
30. Inner Relief SPRING
31. Outer Relief SPRING
32. Press Overdrive Valve Body SWITCH
33. Overdrive Piston Exh. Chk. Valve Ball SPRING
34. Overdrive Oil Cooler By-Pass CONNECTOR
35. Overdrive Oil Cooler Valve Conn. "O" RING
36. Overdrive Oil Cooler Chk. Valve SPRING
37. Cooler Valve SPOOL
38. Overdrive Oil Cooler VALVE
39. Overdrive Oil Cooler Valve "O" RING
40. Oil Cooler FITTING
41. Overdrive Oil Cooler TUBE
42. Overdrive Oil Cooler Valve Bolt Lk. WASHER
43. Overdrive Oil Cooler Valve BOLT

Disassembled view of valve body

or thrust washers. All oil passages should be blown out and check to make sure that they are not obstructed. Small passages should be checked with tag wire. All parts should be inspected to determine which parts are to be replaced.

1. Remove the fill plug and drain oil from the case.

2. Remove the retaining bolt and bracket for the speedometer sensor and driven gear. Remove the sensor and gear.

3. Remove (3) $\frac{1}{8}$ in. pipe plugs from the rear of the unit.

4. Install the (3) pressure plate retaining bolts (J-34681) until flush with the case. Turn bolts (2) additional turns, by rotating each bolt one turn at a time.

NOTE: This sequence must be followed in order to prevent the pressure plate from cocking and causing damage to the unit.

5. Remove the (4) Allen head bolts retaining the adapter plate to the case.

6. Remove the adapter plate, using a hammer (plastic) and screwdriver. Tap adapter plate to separate from case.

NOTE: Do not pry between the case and adapter plate, damage to the sealing surfaces could occur.

7. Bolt the overdrive unit to J-34162. Mount the holding fixture to the base plate J-3389-20.

8. Remove the large snap ring from the O/D unit forward of the accumulator piston.

CAUTION

If pressure is felt at snap ring, do not remove. Check to insure the (3) pressure plate retaining bolts (J-34681) are installed. If the bolts are installed, tighten each bolt one additional turn until pressure is relieved. The pressure plate is under a 1200 lb. spring load. If the (3) retaining bolts (J-34681) are not installed, personal injury could occur.

9. Remove the piston/accumulator assembly. Using an Allen wrench, pry the assembly up evenly by lifting under the flange. Do not pry at or near seal surface.

10. Remove the carrier and bearing assembly (includes input sun and pinion gears) as an assembly.

11. Remove the finger pressure plate.

12. Remove the overdrive clutches, ((4) composition, (4) steel and (1) clutch stop plate).

13. Remove the direct clutch plates, ((5) composition (5) steel and (1) steel bearing plate). Measure each selective clutch plate in the direct clutch pack and record the readings. The selective clutch plates are used to control the clutch pack clearance. When replacing the clutch plates, replace each selective clutch plate with one of the same size.

Inspect the overdrive and direct clutch plates as follows:

a. Compositioned Plates—Dry plates and inspect for pitting, flaking wear, glazing, cracking, charring and chips or metal particles imbedded in lining. If a compositioned plate shows any of the above conditions, replacement is required.

b. Steel Plates—Wipe plates dry and check for discoloration. If the surface is smooth and even color smear is indicated, the plate should be reused. If severe heat spot discoloration or surface scuffing is indicated, the plate must be replaced.

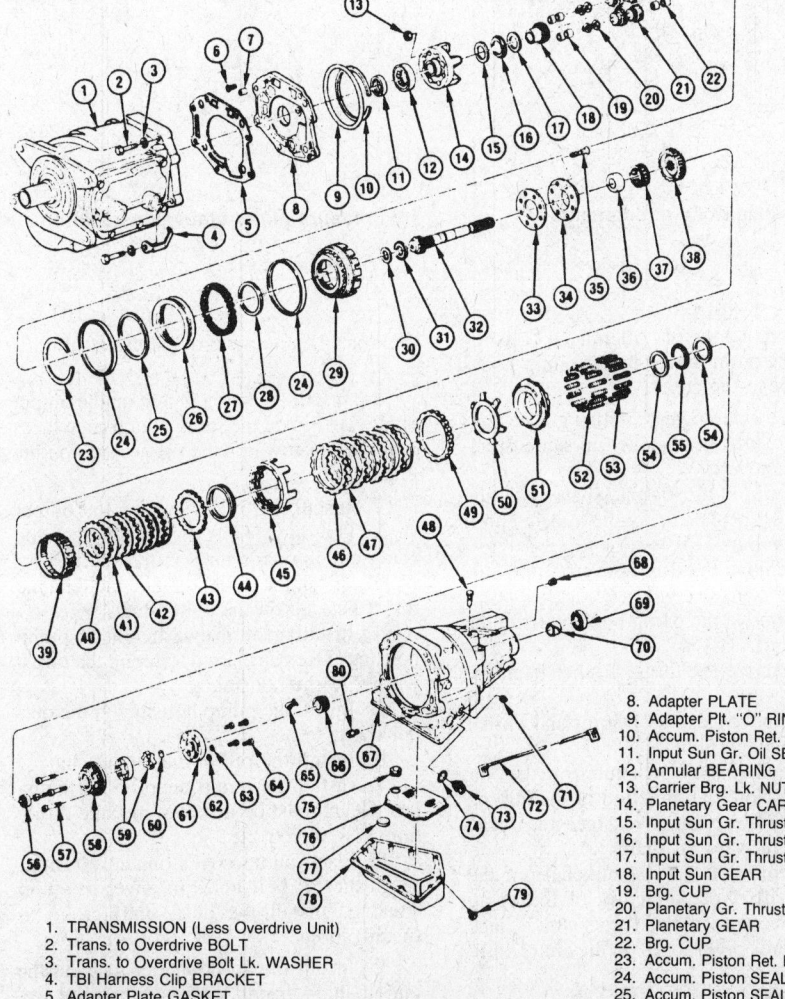

1. TRANSMISSION (Less Overdrive Unit)
2. Trans. to Overdrive BOLT
3. Trans. to Overdrive Bolt Lk. WASHER
4. TBI Harness Clip BRACKET
5. Adapter Plate GASKET
6. Adapter Plate SCREW
7. Dowel PIN
8. Adapter PLATE
9. Adapter Plt. "O" RING
10. Accum. Piston Ret. RING
11. Input Sun Gr. Oil SEAL
12. Annular BEARING
13. Carrier Brg. Lk. NUT
14. Planetary Gear CARRIER
15. Input Sun Gr. Thrust WASHER
16. Input Sun Gr. Thrust BEARING
17. Input Sun Gr. Thrust WASHER
18. Input Sun GEAR
19. Brg. CUP
20. Planetary Gr. Thrust WASHER
21. Planetary GEAR
22. Brg. CUP
23. Accum. Piston Ret. RING
24. Accum. Piston SEAL
25. Accum. Piston SEAL
26. Accum. Cushion PISTON

27. Accum. Piston SPRING
28. Accum. Piston SEAL
29. Accum. PISTON
30. Otpt. Shf. Thrust WASHER
31. Otpt. Shf. Thrust BEARING
32. Otpt. SHAFT
33. Planetary Gear Thrust PLATE
34. Clu. Drum PLATE
35. Clu. Drum BOLT
36. Inner RACE
37. Dir. Clu. SPRAG
38. Dir. Clu. HUB
39. Dir. Clu. DRUM
40. Dir. Clu. Inr. Driven PLATE
41. Dir. Clu. PLATE
42. Dir. Clu. Driven PLATE
43. Dir. Clu. Press PLATE
44. Dir. Clu. BEARING
45. Overdrive Clu. PISTON
46. Overdrive Clu. Driven PLATE
47. Overdrive Clu. PLATE
48. Overdrive Vent TUBE
49. Overdrive Clu. Press PLATE
50. Dir. Clu. Thrust WASHER
51. Overdrive Dir. Clu. PISTON
52. Overdrive Dir. Clu. Otr. SPRING
53. Overdrive Dir. Clu. Inr. SPRING
54. Overdrive Dir. Clu. Hub Thrust WASHER
55. Overdrive Dir. Clu. Hub Thrust BEARING
56. Pump Brg. CUP
57. Overdrive Pump & Otpt. Shf. SCREW
58. W/Brg. Overdrive Pump (Gerotor) HOUSING
59. Overdrive Oil (Gerotor) PUMP
60. Oil Pump Drive PIN
61. Pump (Gerotor) SPOOL
62. Overdrive Oil Pump "O" RING
63. Overdrive Oil Pump "O" RING
64. Overdrive Pump Spool (Gerotor) SCREW
65. Speedo Drive Gr. CLIP
66. Speedo Drive GEAR
67. Overdrive CASE
68. Headless Slotted PLUG
69. Overdrive Otpt. Shf. Oil SEAL
70. Case BUSHING
71. Overdrive Vlv. Body Press Sw. WIRE
72. Sq. Hd. Filler PLUG
73. Overdrive Sol. Elec. CONNECTOR
74. Overdrive Sol. Elec. Conn. "O" RING
75. Overdrive Oil Screen Tube GROMMET
76. Overdrive Oil SCREEN
77. Overdrive Oil Pan MAGNET
78. Overdrive Oil PAN
79. Overdrive Oil Pan BOLT
80. Oil Cooler FITTING

Exploded view of the 83mm 4 speed transmission overdrive unit (Chilton Type 15)

14. Remove thrust washer and bearing from the output sun gear. Thrust washer may stick to the input sun gear hub.

15. Remove (4) Allen head pump housing retaining bolts by rotating the hub to gain access to the bolts.

16. Remove the output shaft assembly (Inc. output sun gear, spag clutch, clutch hub, gerotor pump and speedometer drive gear).

17. Remove the pressure plate and springs by positioning J-21420-2 on the pressure plate with the bolt from J-23327 through the center of the plate. Next position J-23327 on the rear of the case and install the retaining nut. Remove the (3) retaining bolts, J-34681, from the rear of the case. Loosen the retaining nut on J-23327 bolt to relieve the spring pressure.

18. Remove the cooler valve assembly by loosening the (2) nuts on the tube and then remove the (2) bolts holding the valve to the case.

19. Remove the (12) oil pan retaining bolts and then pry the pan from the case.

20. Remove the oil filter and tube from the valve body.

21. Disconnect the T.V. cable from the lever. Remove the cable retaining bolt and remove the cable assembly.

22. Remove the T.V. lever retaining bolt and then lever from the valve body.

23. Remove the remaining valve body bolts and then remove the valve body with the spacer plate.

NOTE: There are (2) check balls, one on each side of spacer plate. One ball is located in the case and the other is spring loaded in the valve body.

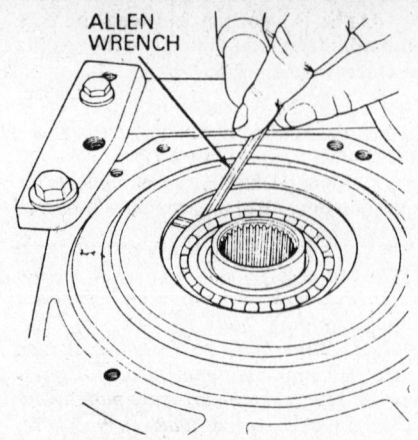

Piston/accumulator removal

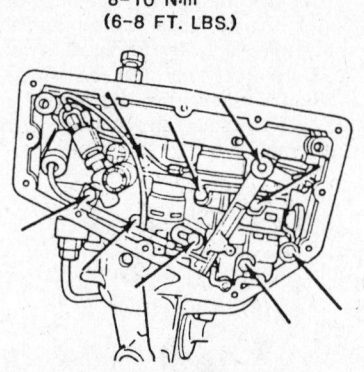

8–10 N·m
(6–8 FT. LBS.)

Valve body attachments

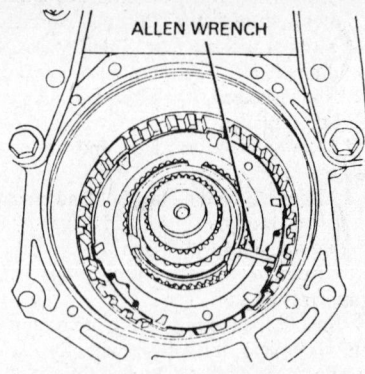

Pump retaining bolts

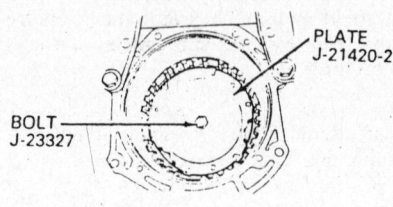

PLATE
J-21420-2

BOLT
J-23327

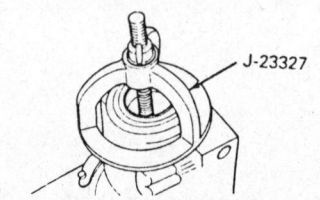

J-23327

Pressure plate removal/installation

VALVE BODY

Disassembly

1. Using J-34529 relieves the pressure on the shift valve. Remove the pin, spring and valve.

2. Using J-34529 relieves the pressure on pressure relief valve. Remove the pin, spring and valve.

3. Using J-34529 relieves the pressure on the accumulator valve. Remove the pin, spring, valve, plug, sleeve and plunger.

4. Disconnect the solenoid electrical lead at the pressure switch. Remove the solenoid attaching bolts. Remove the solenoid and check ball.

5. Disconnect the other electrical lead at the pressure switch. Remove the switch from the valve body.

6. To assemble, reverse the removal procedures. Coat all the components with clean Dexron® II automatic transmission fluid before assembling.

OUTPUT SHAFT

Disassembly

1. Remove the speedometer gear retaining clip and gear.

2. Remove the (4) Allen head bolts retaining the pump cover to the pump housing. Remove the cover.

3. Mark pump gears with a grease pencil. Gears must be installed in same direction as removed.

4. Position the output shaft with the splies down. Rotate the pump housing until gears slide out.

5. Remove the drive pin from the output shaft.

6. Remove the pump housing from output shaft.

7. Remove the thrust washer from pump housing.

8. Remove the thrust bearing and washer from the clutch hub.

9. Remove the clutch hub from the output shaft. Note the direction of the hub on the shaft. The oil grooves face the sprag clutch or forward on shaft.

10. Remove the sprag clutch from the output shaft. Note direction of the sprag clutch. The lip on the sprag clutch cage goes towards oil grooves on the clutch hub.

Assembly

Coat all parts before assembling with clean Dexron® II automatic transmission fluid.

1. Install the sprag clutch on the output shaft. The lip on the sprag clutch cage faces rearward or towards the oil grooves on the clutch hub.

2. Install the clutch hub on the output shaft. The oil grooves on the hub face the sprag clutch or forward on the shaft.

3. Install the thrust washer and then the thrust bearing on the clutch hub.

4. Install the thrust washer on the pump housing. Use petrolatum to retain the thrust washer to the housing.

5. Install the pump housing on the output shaft.

6. Install the pin in the output shaft.

7. Install the pump gears in the housing. Gears must be installed in same direction as removed.

8. Place pump cover on the housing. Align the (4) bolt holes in cover to pump housing. Install the bolts and torque to specifications.

9. Install the speedometer gear on the output shaft. Install the retaining clip.

10. Install new O-rings on pump. Use petrolatum to retain the O-rings to the cover.

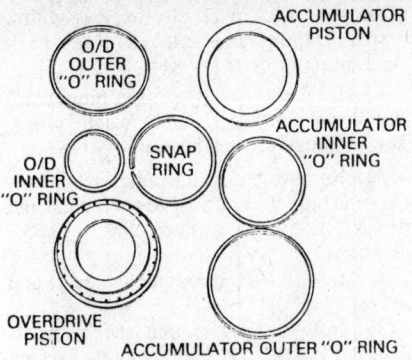

Piston/accumulator assembly

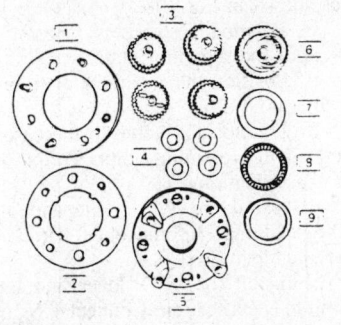

1 CARRIER BASE
2 THRUST PLATE
3 PINION GEARS (4)
4 PINION THRUST WASHERS (4)
5 CARRIER COVER
6 INPUT SUN GEAR
7 SELECTIVE THRUST WASHER
8 THRUST BEARING
9 THRUST WASHER

Carrier assembly

CARRIER ASSEMBLY

Disassembly

1. Remove the (4) nuts retaining the carrier cover. Remove the cover.

2. Remove the thrust washer, thrust bearing, selective washer and input sun gear.

3. Remove the (4) pinion gears.

4. Remove the steel thrust plate from the carrier.

5. Clean and inspect parts. Replace any parts that are cracked, chipped or show excessive wear. The carrier assembly must be reassembled in the transmission case.

PISTON/ACCUMULATOR ASSEMBLY

Disassembly

1. Remove the snap ring retaining the accumulator to the piston.

2. Remove the accumulator and (24) springs from the piston.

3. Remove the (2) O-rings from the accumulator.

4. Remove the (2) O-rings from the piston.

5. To assemble, reverse the removal procedures. Coat O-rings with clean Dexron® II automatic transmission fluid before installing.

Overdrive Unit— Assembly

1. Install the pressure plate springs into the pockets of the transmission case.

2. Place the pressure plate on top of the springs. Seat the springs into the pockets of pressure plate.

3. Position plate J-21420-2 on top of the pressure plate with the bolt from J-23327 through the center of the plate. Next position J-23327 on the rear of the case and install the retaining nut. Tighten the nut until the pressure plate is drawn approximately $\frac{1}{8}$ in. below the step for the overdrive clutch plates. Install the (3) pressure plate retaining bolts (J-34681). Remove tools J-21420-2 and J-23327 for the case.

4. Install the output shaft assembly into the transmission case. Be sure the O-rings are positioned properly on pump cover before installing the output shaft assembly. Install the (4) pump retaining bolts and torque to specifications.

5. Install the thrust bearing on the output sun gear.

6. Install the tanged direct clutch thrust washer with the tabs facing pressure plate.

7. Install the direct clutch thrust bearing.

8. Install the direct clutch thrust washer. The thrust washer will have a tooth missing from its outer edge. The side of the thrust washer with the circular grind pattern must face the thrust bearing. The side with the grind pattern can be identified by the notch ground into the tooth.

9. Install one composition clutch disc and then install a selective clutch plate. The selective clutch plates come in (5) sizes (0.080-0.120 in.) and is used to control clutch pack clearance. A 0.050-0.070 in. clearance must be maintained in the direct clutch pack. Excessive or insufficient amount of clutch travel will cause failure to the clutch plates and discs.

10. Alternate the remaining clutch discs and plates until all (5) plates and discs are installed.

11. Install the lower half of the carrier assembly onto the direct clutch pack. Index the carrier until all clutch plates are engaged.

12. Install the steel overdrive stop clutch plate and then alternate with a disc and plate until all (4) plates and disc are installed.

13. Install the finger pressure plate.

14. Install the carrier thrust plate with tabs facing the sprag clutch.

15. Install (2) pinion gears with the index mark on the gears facing inward or towards each other. Install the other (2) pinion gears with the index mark 90° off from the first (2) gears.

16. Install the thrust washer for the output sun into the rear of the input sun gear. Use petrolatum to retain the thrust washer to the input sun gear.

17. Install the input sun gear. If the input sun gear spreads the pinion gears when installing, the pinion gears are not indexed properly.

18. Install the selective thrust washer with the oil grooves on washer facing input sun gear.

19. Install the thrust bearing on the input sun gear.

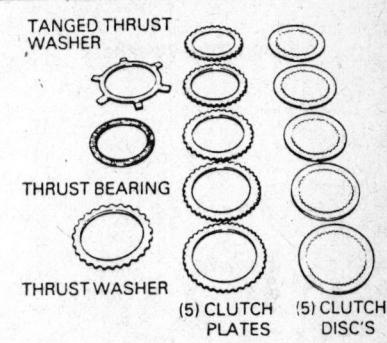

CIRCULAR GROUND SIDE OF WASHER HAS A NOTCH IN TOOTH

THRUST WASHER IDENTIFICATION TOOTH MISSING FROM OUTER EDGE

TANGED THRUST WASHER

THRUST BEARING

THRUST WASHER

(5) CLUTCH PLATES

(5) CLUTCH DISC'S

Direct clutch pack

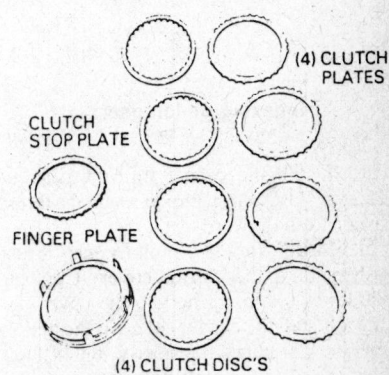

(4) CLUTCH PLATES

CLUTCH STOP PLATE

FINGER PLATE

(4) CLUTCH DISC'S

Overdrive clutch pack

X = DOUBLE SPRINGS
O = SINGLE SPRINGS

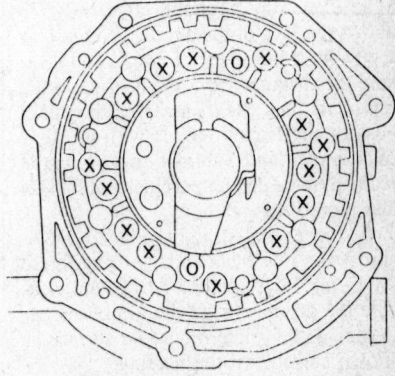

Pressure plate spring installation

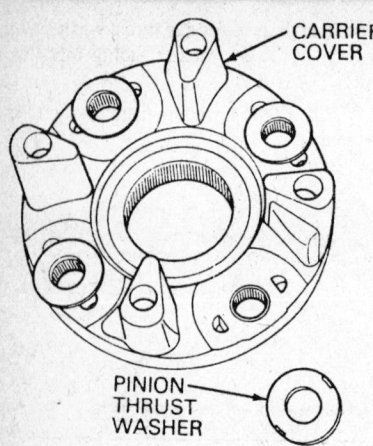

Pinion thrust washers

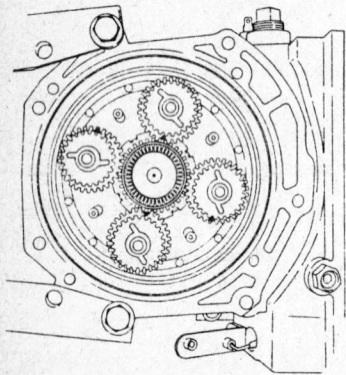

Indexing pinion gears

20. Install the carrier thrust washer to the cover. Use petrolatum to retain the thrust washer to the cover.

21. Install the (4) pinion gear thrust washers onto the carrier cover. Use petrolatum to retain washers to the cover.

22. Install the carrier cover. If the pinion gears are not indexed properly, the (4) bolt holes in the cover will not align with the bolts in lower half of the carrier.

23. Install (4) new retaining nuts and torque to specifications.

24. Measure the end play for the overdrive unit as follows.

a. Place the straight edge J-34673 across the face of the overdrive unit. Use the Depth Micrometer J-34672 and measure the distance from the bearing to the top of the bar. Next, measure the thickness of the bar (J-34673) with a 0 to 1 micrometer and subtract this from the reading of the depth micrometer (J-34672) and record this reading.

b. Place the straight edge J-34673 across the rear of the adapter plate. Use the Depth Micrometer J-34672 and measure the distance from the top of the bar to the adapter plate mounting surface as shown and record the reading.

c. Next measure the distance from the top of the bar to the bearing seat in the

adapter plate as shown and record the reading.

d. Subtract the reading from Step (c) from Step (b) and record the difference.

e. Next, subtract the difference from step (d) from step (a). The difference will be the end-play (Specification is 0 ± 0.003 in.). If the results of your measurements are not within the specifications, it will be necessary to remove the carrier cover and change the input sun selective thrust washer. The selective thrust washers are available in (8) sizes. They are in 0.005 in. increments ranging from 0.123-0.158 in.

25. Install the accumulator and piston assembly. Coat the lips of the seals with clean Dexron® II automatic transmission fluid before installing.

26. Install the large snap ring that goes in the front of the overdrive unit. The snap ring must be installed.

27. Install a new seal in the adapter plate. Place the seal on tool J-34523 and install the seal from the front side of the adapter plate.

28. Place seal protector J-34621 on the input sun gear.

29. Install the adapter plate. Apply a light coating of R.T.V. Sealant #1052366 or equivalent around the heads of the adapter plate bolts. Install the (4) adapter plate bolts and tighten to specifications.

30. Remove the seal protector.

31. Remove the first $\frac{1}{8}$ in. pipe plug from the left side of the overdrive unit. Install air line fitting J-34742 into plug hole and tighten.

32. Measure the clutch pack clearance as follows:

a. Loosen the (3) pressure plate retaining bolts (J-34681) evenly until spring pressure is released.

b. Assemble J-8001 Dial Indicator to the rear of the overdrive unit.

c. Apply a minimum of 100 PSI to the air line fitting J-34742 and read the dial indicator (specification is 0.050-0.070 in.). If the reading does not fall within the specification, it will be necessary to disassemble the overdrive unit to change the direct clutch selective clutch plates. The selective clutch plates are available in (5) sizes. The are in 0.010 in. increments ranging from 0.080-0.120 in. If

the the clutch pack clearance is within specification, remove the (3) clutch pack retaining bolts (J-34681).

33. Coat the (3) $\frac{1}{8}$ in. pipe plugs with anti-sieze compound and install plugs. Torque plugs to specification.

34. Remove the air line adapter J-34742. Coat the plug with anti-sieze compound and install the plug. Torque plug to specifications.

35. Install the speedometer gear and sensor.

36. Install a new output seal using J-21426. Coat the lip of the seal with Dexron II transmission fluid.

37. Install the valve body as follows:

a. Install the check ball into the case as shown in Fig. 3lb.

b. Position (2) gaskets, one on each side of the separator plate.

c. Position the separator plate on the valve body.

d. Position the valve to the case and install the retaining bolts. Torque bolts to specifications.

e. Install the T.V. cable and install the retaining clip and bolt. Torque bolt to specifications.

f. Install the T.V. lever and torque bolt to specification. Connect T.V. cable to the lever.

g. Install tool J-34671-1 (Throttle Setting Gage) into the T.V. cable bore on the side of the case. Set the hook on the T.V. cable onto the high step of the gage. Place the cam stop on the valve body as close to the lever as possible and install the retaining bolt. Torque bolt to specifications.

h. Set the hook on the T.V. cable onto the lower step of the gage. Place tool J-34671-2 between the piston and the solenoid bracket. Adjust the screw/bolt on the T.V. lever until the bolt makes contact with the stop on the cam.

38. Install the pickup tube and oil filter on the valve body.

39. Apply a bead of R.T.V. Sealant #1052366 or equivalent to the oil pan flange and assemble wet. Install the magnet in the oil pan. The bead of R.T.V. should be applied around the inside of the bolt holes. Install the pan bolts and torque to specifications.

Torque Specifications

DRIVE GEAR BEARING RETAINER BOLTS	20-27 Nm	15-20 ft. lbs.
SIDE COVER TO CASE BOLTS	20-27 Nm	15-20 ft. lbs.
REVERSE GEAR HOUSING TO CASE (1) BOLT	40-54 Nm	30-40 ft. lbs.
REVERSE GEAR HOUSING TO CASE (2) BOLTS	54-67 Nm	40-50 ft. lbs.
REVERSE GEAR HOUSING TO CASE (3) BOLTS	47-61 Nm	35-45 ft. lbs.
DRAIN PLUG	20-33 Nm	15-25 ft. lbs.
FILLER PLUG	33-47 Nm	23-35 ft. lbs.
TRANSMISSION TO BELL HOUSING BOLTS	60-80 Nm	45-60 ft. lbs.

40. Assemble the overdrive unit to the reverse housing. Guide the idler shaft on the adapter plate into the idler gears and align the splines on the mainshaft with the splines in the input sun gear. Slide the units together and install the retaining bolts. Torque bolts to specifications.

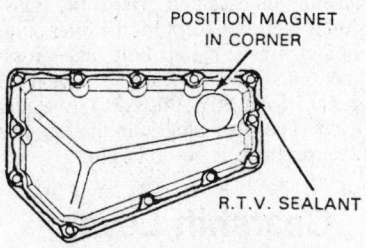

POSITION MAGNET IN CORNER

R.T.V. SEALANT

Magnet and RTV location

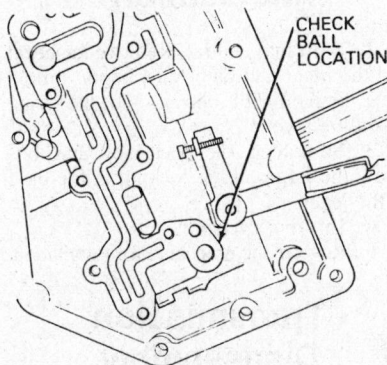

CHECK BALL LOCATION

Check ball location

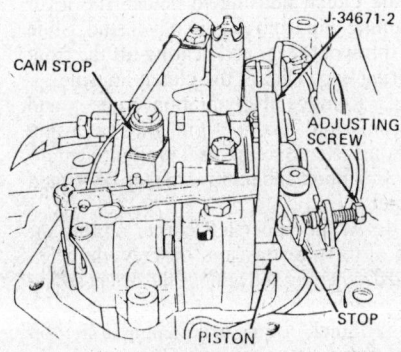

J-34671-2

CAM STOP

ADJUSTING SCREW

STOP

PISTON

T.V. lever adjustment

CHILTON TYPE 16

NOTE: Some small parts may or may not be installed in the transmission being serviced. Some are applicable only to certain car makes and models; some were installed in later production versions. Be sure to note these items during disassembly to avoid confusion later.

Disassembly

Drain the unit and remove it from the vehicle.

1. Remove the plug, poppet spring and mesh lock plunger. Remove the selector lever pivot.

2. Drive the spring pin from the shifter head and shift rail. You can leave the pin in place if you aren't disassembling the linkage.

3. Remove the six bolts which retain the transmission case and extension housing to the center support.

4. Slide the case forward from the transmission. Remove the needle thrust bearing and race from the input shaft or case. Remove the lipped thrust washer, if any.

5. Disassembly may be completed on a bench; however, a holding fixture will simplify the job by supporting the transmission.

6. Remove the extension housing by sliding it rearward. The shifter head, shift rail and selector are not fastened to the housing and should not be permitted to drop out and be damaged. The selector lever is held to the shift rail with a retaining clip and pin.

NOTE: The needle rollers are not always retained in the needle race. Catch loose needles as they fall out during disassembly so that they can be replaced in the mating race during assembly.

7. Remove the rail selector pin and the rail selector.

8. Press down on the speedometer gear retainer tab and remove the gear and retainer from the output shaft. Later speedometer gears are retained by a snap-ring and ball.

9. Remove the snap-ring, thrust washer, 1st speed gear, and blocking ring from the output shaft. The same snap-ring must be used on assembly, so mark it.

10. Remove the snap-ring from behind the synchronizer hub.

11. Move the shift rail to locate the pawl to permit removal of the first and reverse shift link.

12. Slide the 1st-reverse synchronizer, shift fork, and rail rearward from the transmission. Remove the reverse idler gear from the idler shaft, slide reverse gear off the output shaft.

13. Position the interlock pawl in a position to permit the 2nd-3rd speed shift link and shift fork to be removed.

14. Position the interlock pawl in an outboard position to permit the 4th-5th shift fork and link to be removed.

15. Remove the center support from the output shaft and cluster gear. Catch the center support roller bearings.

16. Remove the needle thrust race and bearing from the output shaft or center support. Remove the lipped thrust race, if any.

17. Remove the cluster gear from the remaining gears.

18. Remove the output shaft from the input shaft.

19. The remaining components may be removed one at a time from the output shaft.

SERVICE HINTS

1. The 2nd-3rd synchronizer must be installed with the large chamfer on the outside diameter to the front. If it is not, there will be interference between the sleeve and cluster gear in 2nd gear.

2. Lack of mainshaft end–play can be caused by bearing thrust plates or bearing spacers out of place. The 5th gear roller bearing front spacer can be dislodged and trapped between the 4th-5th synchronizer hub and mainshaft shoulder.

3. Some transmissions have an anti-rattle plate and spring at the front of the cluster gear. The purpose of this is to lessen gear rattle in neutral with the clutch engaged. In some cases, the anti-rattle plate causes a whine in 4th gear.

4. There are a number of possible causes for hard shifting in this transmission. Check for the shift handle retainer being misaligned. To adjust, loosen the bolts holding the handle and move the rear end of the retainer until shift lever movement is equal in all gears. A hard shift from 1st to 2nd can be caused by the lower end of the shift lever and the reverse inhibitor cam making contact. Incorrect installation of the interlock pawl retaining plate will cause hard shifting. The inside of the plate should be symmetrical about the interlock pawl and shift link slots. Vague shifting may be caused by side play of the shift lever. This can be the result of a loose roll pin in the upper shift rail at the shifter head. Use of a lubricant other than Dexron® II will cause shifting problems, especially when cold.

5. A grind in reverse can be caused by an improperly functioning reverse inhibitor mechanism or shift lever centering springs.

Assembly

1. Assemble the 3rd speed gear over the output shaft with the coned end toward the front and against the shaft shoulder.

NOTE: Synchronizer assemblies are similar except hub splines differ. The hub and sleeve are a selective fit to obtain a free sliding fit with 0.002 inch maximum backlash. Keep mated parts together to insure correct sliding fit and backlash.

2. Assemble the blocker rings with the slots aligned with the shift keys of the 2nd-3rd synchronizer assembly.

3. Assemble the synchronizer and blocker rings, with the chamfer on the sleeve toward the front of the shaft, over the output shaft and position them on the face of the third speed gear.

4. Assemble a snap-ring in the shaft groove ahead of the synchronizer hub.

ONE END OF EACH SPRING TO BE ASSEMBLED IN STRUT SLOT AS SHOWN IN OPPOSITE DIRECTION.

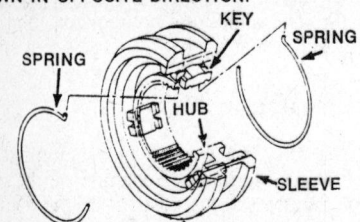

T50 5 speed synchronizer details
(© Pontiac Div., G.M. Corp.)

5. Assemble the 2nd gear, coned end in, against the blocker ring.

6. Assemble a thrust washer on the face of the 2nd speed gear.

7. Assemble a snap-ring in the shaft groove in front of the thrust washer.

8. Assemble the 5th gear over the output shaft against the thrust washer. Assemble one needle spacer over the shaft and into the gear bore. Follow the spacer with a row of needles, a second spacer, a second row of needles, and a third spacer. Use petroleum jelly to retain these parts as they are assembled. One needle space in each row should not be used.

NOTE: Make sure you are using the correct needle bearings. Other bearings in the transmission are the same length, but a different diameter.

9. Assemble the blocker rings with the slots aligned to the shift keys on the 4th-5th synchronizer assembly. Install the assembly on the output shaft with the chamfered edge of the sleeve toward the front.

10. Install the needle thrust bearing on the end of the 4th-5th synchronizer assembly.

11. Assemble 19 needle rollers into the second step of the input shaft bore and carefully lower the shaft with needles over the end of the output shaft. Petroleum jelly or low melting point grease should hold needles in position.

12. Assemble a needle thrust washer and thrust plate over the output shaft against the shaft shoulder. Some models will also have a lipped thrust washer.

13. Install the output shaft, mainshaft, and countergear into the center support.

14. Install the reverse gear and bushing assembly over the output shaft and against the center support.

15. Install the reverse idler gear and bushing assembly over the reverse idler shaft to mesh with the reverse gear.

NOTE: If the rubber O-ring on the reverse idler gear shaft is loose or damaged, it should be replaced. Not all models have the O-ring.

16. Put the 4th-5th shift fork on the 4th-5th synchronizer sliding sleeve. Locate the interlock pawl to let the shift link be put through the center slot in the center tsupport.

Install the 4th-5th shift link through the slot and engage it with the shift fork.

17. Locate the interlock pawl to let the 1st-reverse shift link be installed in the inboard slot of the center support. Install the link into the shift fork.

18. If the selector arm was removed, install it over the shift rail, aligning the holes. Drive the spring pin into place.

19. Install the shift rail through the shift fork from front to rear with the notches at the rear.

20. Engage the shift fork with the 1st-reverse synchronizer sleeve. Slide the synchronizer hub over the output shaft, with the chamfered edge of the sleeve to the front.

21. Guide the shift rail through the interlock pawl, 2nd-3rd fork, and 4th-5th fork. Be sure the selector arm is aligned with the notch in the shift link.

22. Install a snap-ring in the output shaft groove. Put a blocker ring and 1st gear over the shaft, behind the 1st-reverse synchronizer assembly. Align the notches in the blocker ring with those in the synchronizer hub.

23. Install a thrust washer and snap-ring behind the 1st gear.

24. Put the speedometer gear retainer in the hole in the output shaft with the loop forward. Slide on the speedometer gear until the retainer locks it.

25. Slide the rail selector onto the shift with the loop forward. Slide on the speedometer gear until the retainer locks it.

26. Slide the rail selector onto the shift rail with the ball inward and drive the spring pin in. Install the selector lever and shift rail into the hole in the extension housing. Install the shifter head on the rail, but don't put in the pin yet.

27. Put a bead of silicone on the case and extension housing. Make sure the needle rollers in the extension housing stay in place. Install the extension housing over the output shaft and guide the selector lever to engage the rail selector.

28. Install the lipped needle thrust race, if any, needle thrust bearing, and flat race over the input shaft.

29. Bolt the cases to the center support. Torque the bolts to 35 ft. lbs. If there is binding, check to see if a 5th gear spacer might have fallen between the 5th gear and the synchronizer.

30. Drive the pin into the shifter head and shift rail. Install the mesh lock plunger, spring, and threaded plug. Use thread locking compound on the plug. Align the holes in the selector lever and the extension housing and install the selector lever pivot, tightening to 28 ft. lbs.

31. Fill the transmission with about 3½ pts. of Dexron® II automatic transmission fluid.

32. After the transmission is installed, place the transmission and shift lever in neutral. Apply silicone sealant inside the bolt pattern and bolt the shift lever and cover down.

CHILTON TYPE 17

The HR-1 transmission has an identification tag under the lower left extension housing to transmission case bolt. The entire transmission is metric, except for the filler plug, speedometer gear clamp bolt, and crossmember bolts. The lubricant fill capacity is 2.4 pts. of SAE 80W-90, API GL-4 gear lubricant. The filler plug is in the left side of the case; there is no drain plug.

Gearshift Lever Removal And Installation

1. Shift into neutral. Remove the bezel and the inner and outer dust boots.

2. Pull off the E-clip and slide the spring up on the lever.

3. Straighten the lock-tabs and unscrew the large plastic locknut at the base of the lever.

4. Lift the lever out.

5. Reverse the procedure for installation.

Transmission Disassembly

CASE

1. Pull the throwout lever straight out of the clutch housing to detach the lever retaining clip from the pivot ball stud. Slide the throwout lever and bearing off the front bearing cap. Unbolt the clutch housing.

2. Remove the vibration damper and transmission mount from the extension housing. Remove the backup light switch.

3. Unbolt and remove the top cover and gasket.

4. At the upper left corner on the left side of the transmission, unscrew the allen head detent plug and remove the detent spring and plunger.

5. Punch out the access plug at the top right rear face of the case. Insert a 5/16 in. diameter rod and drive out the interlock plate retaining pin.

6. Drive out the selector arm roll pin with a 5/32 in. punch.

7. Tap the shift rail back until it pushes out the large plug at the rear of the extension housing and pull it out. Now you can remove the selector arm, interlock plate, and shift forks.

NOTE: Make a note of the arrangement of the shift mechanism before removing it.

8. Unbolt and remove the front bearing cap and O-ring. The O-ring and cap oil seal should be replaced.

1. Oil seal
2. Bushing
3. Pin
4. Shifter head
5. Threaded plug
6. Poppet spring
7. Mesh lock plunger
8. Breather
9. Selector lever pivot
10. Wiring harness clip*
11. Name plate
12. Back-up light bracket*
13. Cup plug
14. Extension housing
15. Switch
16. 3/8-16 x 3-1/4 hex head bolt
17. Switch
18. Needle bearing
19. Shift Rail
20. Spring pin
21. Rail selector end
22. First & reverse shift fork
23. Shift fork pad
24. First & reverse shift link
25. Gasket
26. 9/16-18 plug
27. Speedometer gear
28. Speedometer gear retaining clip
29. Snap ring
30. Thrust-washer
31. 1st speed gear
32. Snap ring
33. Blocking ring
34. Synchronizer spring
35. Shift plate
36. Clutch hub
37. Clutch sleeve
38. Reverse gear & bushing assembly
39. Bushing
40. Selector arm
41. Spring pin
42. Interlock pawl
43. Selector arm retaining screw
44. 1/4-20 x 3/4 hex head self tapping screw
45. Reverse idler gear & bushing
46. Bushing
47. Spring pin
48. Reverse idler shaft
49. Dowel pin
50. Center support
51. Magnet
52. Needle bearing
53. Shift rail
54. Pin
55. Retaining clip
56. Selector lever
57. Needle bearing
58. Thrust washer
59. Needle thrust bearing
60. Needle thrust race*
61. Output shaft
62. 3rd speed gear
63. Blocking ring
64. Synchronizer spring
65. Synchronizer shift plate
66. Clutch hub
67. Clutch sleeve
68. Snap ring

69. Synchronizer blocking ring
70. 2nd speed gear
71. Thrust washer
72. Snap ring
73. Spacer
74. 5th speed gear
75. 2nd & 3rd shift link
76. 2nd & 3rd shift fork
77. 4th & 5th shift link
78. 4th & 5th shift fork
79. Needle rollers
80. Spacer

81. Synchronizer blocking ring
82. Synchronizer spring
83. Shift plate
84. Clutch hub
85. Clutch sleeve
86. Synchronizer blocking ring
87. Needle thrust bearing
88. Needle rollers
89. Input drive gear
90. Needle thrust plate*
91. Needle thrust bearing
92. Thrust washer
93. Needle bearing

94. Oil seal
95. Cluster gear
96. Spring*
97. Spring pin*
98. Gear damper*
99. Snap ring
100. Thrust washer*
101. Needle bearing
102. 1/2 inch pipe plug
103. Transmission case sleeve
104. Transmission case

* Not used in all transmissions

Exploded view of the T-50 5-speed (© G.M. Corp.)

9. Remove the front bearing retaining and locating snap-rings. Remove the bearing with a puller.

10. Unbolt the extension housing. Tap it with a soft hammer to break it loose. Remove the clutch (input) shaft from the front of the case, and the extension housing and output shaft gear train from the rear of the case.

— **CAUTION** —

Don't let the 3rd-4th synchronizer sleeve separate from the hub.

11. Pry the shift rail oil seal out of the case at the top rear.

12. Remove the roller bearing from the inner end of the clutch shaft or from the front end of the mainshaft.

13. Screw a slide hammer into the reverse idler gear shaft and remove it. Re-

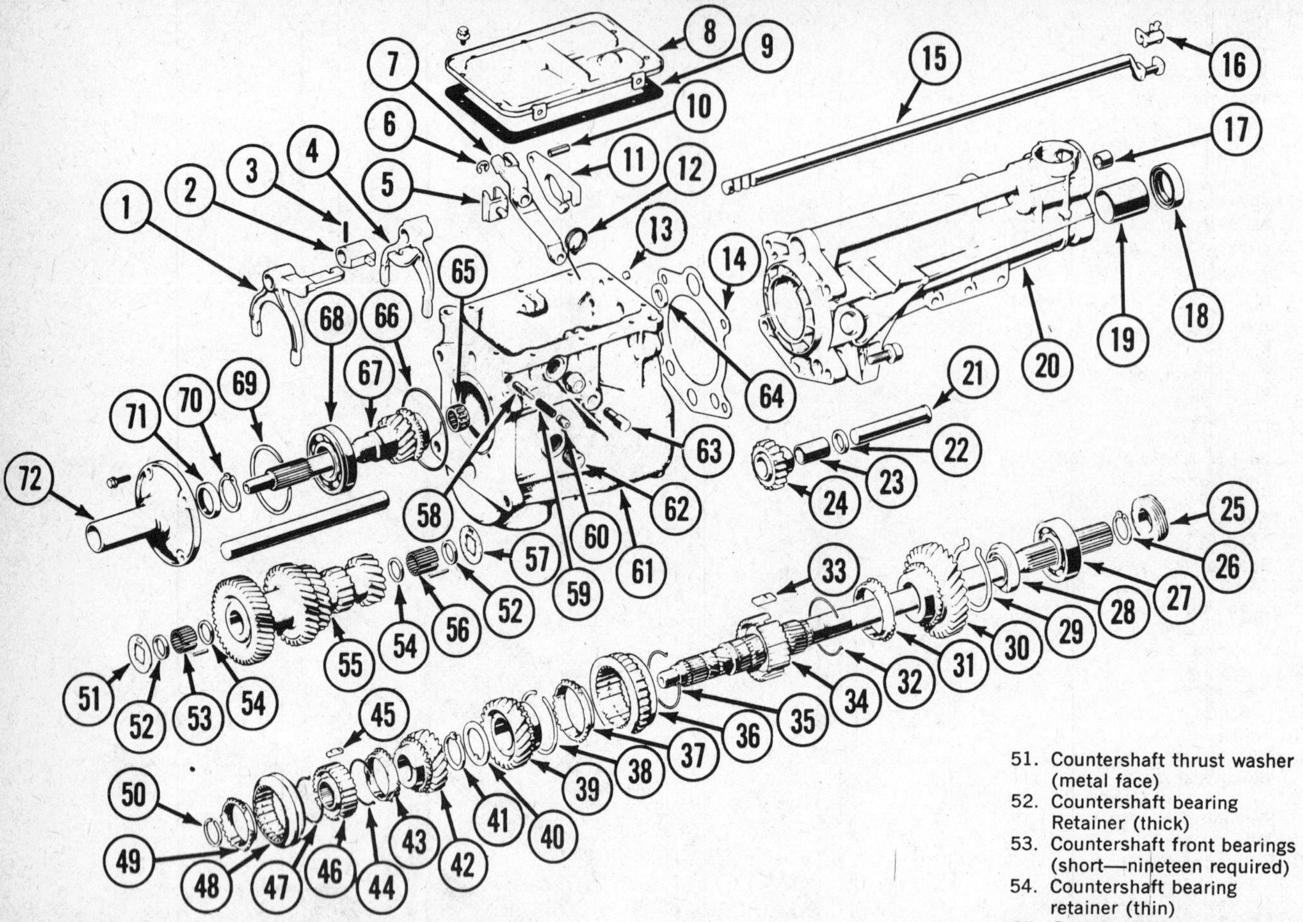

AMC HR-1 4-Speed details (© AMC Corp.)

1. Third-fourth shift fork
2. Selector arm
3. Selector arm roll pin
4. First-second shift fork
5. Reverse level shift fork
6. Reverse lever spring clip
7. Reverse lever
8. Top cover
9. Top cover gasket
10. Interlock plate retaining pin
11. Interlock plate
12. Reverse lever spring
13. Interlock retaining pin access plug
14. Extension housing gasket
15. Shift rail
16. Shift rail insert
17. Shift rail bushing (nylon)
18. Extension housing seal
19. Extension housing bushing (Serviced as a part of housing)

20. Extension housing
21. Reverse idler gear shaft
22. Reverse idler gear spacer
23. Reverse idler gear bushing (Serviced as part of gear)
24. Reverse idler gear
25. Speedometer gear
26. Rear bearing snap ring
27. Rear bearing
28. Oil slinger/spacer
29. Output shaft rear snap ring
30. First gear
31. First gear blocking ring
32. First-second synchronizer insert spring
33. First-second synchronizer insert (3)
34. Output shaft and first-second synchronizer hub assembly (Serviced as assembly only)
35. First-second synchronizer insert spring

36. First-second synchronizer sleeve
37. Second gear blocking ring
38. Second gear stop ring (Installed on gear)
39. Second gear
40. Second gear spacer
41. Second gear snap ring
42. Third gear
43. Third gear blocking ring
44. Third-fourth synchronizer insert spring
45. Third-fourth synchronizer insert (3)
46. Third-fourth synchronizer hub
47. Third-fourth synchronizer insert spring
48. Third-fourth synchronizer sleeve
49. Fourth gear blocking ring
50. Output shaft front snap ring

51. Countershaft thrust washer (metal face)
52. Countershaft bearing Retainer (thick)
53. Countershaft front bearings (short—nineteen required)
54. Countershaft bearing retainer (thin)
55. Countershaft gear
56. Countershaft rear bearings (long—nineteen required)
57. Countershaft thrust washer (metal face)
58. Detent plunger
59. Detent spring
60. Detent plug
61. Transmission case
62. Fill plug
63. Reverse level pivot (Serviced as part of case)
64. Shift rail oil seal
65. Clutch shaft roller bearing
66. Front bearing cap O-ring
67. Clutch shaft
68. Front bearing
69. Front bearing locating snap ring
70. Front bearing retaining snap ring
71. Front bearing cap oil seal
72. Front bearing cap

move the reverse idler gear and spacer, noting their positions.

14. Push the countershaft out the back of the case. Use a dummy shaft inserted from the front end of the case to push it out and keep all the bearings in place.

15. Remove the shift fork from the reverse lever. Remove the spring clip holding the reverse lever on the lever pivot shaft; remove the reverse lever and lever spring.

NOTE: Make a note of the arrangement of the reverse shift mechanism before removing it.

16. Remove the countershaft gear along with the dummy shaft. Separate the 38 needle bearings and 4 retainers. Note the location of the bearing retainers; there are thick and thin ones. There are also short and long needle bearings. Remove the countershaft gear thrust washers.

OUTPUT SHAFT GEAR TRAIN

1. Remove the 4th gear blocking ring from the 3rd-4th synchronizer at the front of the shaft.

2. At the front of the extension housing, compress the snap-ring and slide it forward. Separate the shaft from the extension housing by tapping it out with a soft hammer.

3. Remove the snap-ring at the front of the shaft. It should not be reused.

4. Remove the 3rd-4th synchronizer. Mark the hub and sleeve for reassembly. Separate the sleeve and hub, remove the synchronizer inserts and springs.

5. Remove 3rd gear and the blocking ring. Remove the 2nd gear snap-ring, take off 2nd gear and the blocking ring.

6. Remove the gear bearing snap-ring toward the speedometer gear.

7. Press off 1st gear, the 1st gear spacer, the rear bearing, and the speedometer gear as an assembly.

8. Remove the 1st gear blocking ring.

9. Mark the 1st-2nd synchronizer sleeve and hub for reassembly. Remove the sleeve, inserts, and springs.

--- CAUTION ---

Do not try to remove the 1st-2nd synchronizer hub from the shaft.

10. Remove the extension housing oil seal. The best way is to use a slide hammer seal puller.

Transmission Assembly

NOTE: Lubricate all thrust washers, needle and roller bearings, and gear tapered surfaces with petroleum jelly. Lubricate all other components with SAE 80W-90 gear lubricant.

OUTPUT SHAFT GEAR TRAIN

1. Seat the rear bearing in the extension housing, using a soft hammer.

2. The output shaft gear snap-ring is available in several sizes; select the thickest one that will fit in the groove in the extension housing, then remove it.

3. Remove the rear bearing from the extension housing, using a long punch or a socket drive extension.

4. Lubricate the output shaft, synchronizers, and gear bores with transmission lubricant; lubricate the tapered blocking ring gear surfaces with petroleum jelly.

5. Install the synchronizer spring and inserts in the 1st-2nd hub, install the synchronizer sleeve over the hub and inserts, using the alignment marks made on disassembly. Engage the tang end of each insert spring in the same synchronizer insert, but position them so that the open ends of each spring face away from each other.

6. Install the blocking ring on the tapered surface of 2nd gear; install the ring and gear on the shaft. Make sure the synchronizer inserts engage in the blocking ring notches.

7. Install the 2nd gear thrust washer and snap-ring on the output shaft. Make sure the tabbed end of the snap-ring is seated in the shaft groove. 2nd gear end play, measured with feeler gauges, must be 0.004–

0.014 in. If it is excessive, replace the thrust washer, snap-ring, and gear to correct.

8. Install the 1st gear blocking ring on the tapered gear surface; install the ring and gear on the shaft. Make sure that the tapered gear surface faces the first-second synchronizer hub and that the synchronizer inserts engage in the blocking ring notches.

9. Put the oil slinger/spacer on the shaft. The grooves must be toward first gear and the flat surface must be away from it.

10. Place the output shaft rear snap-ring, selected in Step 2, on the shaft over the slinger/spacer and against first gear.

11. Drive or press the rear bearing on the output shaft. Use force only on the inner race. Make sure the bearing seats against the slinger/spacer and that first gear seats in the 1st-2nd synchronizer hub.

12. Install the thickest possible rear bearing snap-ring in the shaft groove, making sure it is completely seated.

13. Press the speedometer gear into place. Do not press it down all the way against the bearing; there is a special AMC positioning gauge, J-26832, designed for this job.

14. Install 3rd gear on the output shaft; install the blocking ring on the tapered gear surface.

15. Assemble the 3rd-4th synchronizer hub, sleeve, inserts, and springs, using the hub to sleeve alignment marks made on disassembly. Engage the tang ends of each insert spring in the same insert, but face the open ends away from each other.

16. Install the 3rd-4th synchronizer assembly on the output shaft and install the front snap-ring. Check synchronizer end play with feeler gauges; it should be 0.004–0.014 in. If it is excessive, replace the snap-ring, synchronizer hub, and sleeve to correct.

17. Insert the output shaft and gear train assembly into the extension housing. Tap the front end of the shaft with a soft hammer to seat the rear bearing.

18. Compress the output shaft rear snap-ring and install it in the housing groove. Make sure it is fully seated.

CASE

1. Insert the dummy shaft into the countershaft gear. Coat the needle bearings and retainers with petroleum jelly. Install a thin bearing retainer in the needle bearing bores in each end of the gear. Install the long needle bearings in the bore at the rear of the gear. Install the short needle bearings in the bore at the front of the gear. Install a thick bearing retainer in each gear bore over the ends of the needle bearings. Coat the replacement thrust washers with petroleum jelly. Position a thrust washer over the bearing bore at the front of the countershaft gear. Push the dummy shaft through far enough to hold the washer in place.

2. Align the front thrust washer locating tab with the notch in the case. Place the gear in the case. Push the dummy shaft through

far forward enough to hold the thrust washer and countershaft gear in place. Stand the front case on its end. Align the locating tab on the rear thrust washer with the notch in the case and install it between the gear and case.

3. Install the countershaft, making sure that the step in the rear end of the shaft is horizontal, with the lower step down.

4. Check the countershaft gear end play with feeler gauges. It should be 0.006–0.018 in. If it is excessive, replace the thrust washers.

5. Install the reverse lever fork in the reverse lever. Install the reverse lever and spring on the pivot shaft in the case and install the spring clip.

6. Place the reverse idler gear and spacer in the case. Make sure the spacer is between the idler gear and the rear of the case. Make sure the reverse lever fork engages the idler gear.

7. Install the reverse idler shaft from the rear of the case. Make sure the reverse lever fork stays engaged with the gear.

8. Use a socket to drive a new shift rail oil seal into the back of the case.

9. Coat the output shaft pilot bearing with petroleum jelly and install it into the clutch (input) shaft bore.

10. Install the blocking ring on the tapered surface of the clutch shaft. Place the shaft in the case.

11. Install a new gasket on the extension housing. Insert the output shaft into the case and install the clutch shaft on the output shaft. Make sure the two shafts are fully engaged.

12. Make sure that the notch in the end of the countershaft is aligned with the extension housing recess. If you don't do this, you will likely crack the case.

13. Coat the extension housing bolts with non-hardening sealer and install them finger tight.

14. Install the front bearing on the clutch shaft and into the case, driving on the inner race only. Install the front bearing retaining and locating snap-rings.

15. Install the front bearing cap with a new oil seal and O-ring.

16. Install the shift forks in the synchronizer sleeves. Position the interlock plate and its new retaining pin in the case. Lubricate the shift rail with transmission lube and install it into the case through the 1st-2nd shift fork and the interlock plate. Place the selector arm on the shift rail and slide it through the 3rd-4th shift fork and into the front of the case. Install the selector arm roll pin, making sure it is in flush.

17. Install the detent plunger, spring, and plug in the case.

18. Tighten the extension housing bolts to 34 ft. lbs.

19. Install replacement access plugs in the extension housing shift rail bore and in the interlock plate retaining pin access hole.

20. Install a new extension housing oil seal.

21. Fill the case with SAE 80W-90, API

GL-4 lubricant (2.4 pts.) to the edge of the filler plug hole. Install the top cover.

22. Replace the vibration damper and transmission mount on the extension housing.

23. Install the clutch housing, throwout lever, and throwout bearing. Tighten the clutch housing to transmission case bolts to 54 ft. lbs.

CHILTON TYPE 18

Transaxle Disassembly

NOTE: Final mainshaft adjustment requires a measurement made with a special tool. Check Step 16 of the assembly procedure before disassembly.

1. Remove the clutch pushrod, being careful not to bend it.

2. Unscrew the selector shaft plug from the case. Remove the detent spring assembly and rubber boot. Tap out the selector shaft and pry out the oil seal.

3. Pry out the two mainshaft bearing retaining nut rubber plugs using a suitable tool.

4. Take off the clutch release bearing end cover by removing the four bolts. Hold the clutch release lever upwards while removing the cover to avoid loading or damage to the case threads. Take out the release bearing and plastic sleeve.

5. Use two screwdrivers to push the circlip off the clutch torque shaft. Pull the torque shaft out of the case and remove the pedal return spring and release lever. Pry out the torque shaft oil seal.

6. Remove the three mainshaft bearing retainer nuts. Two of them were under the rubber covers removed earlier and the third is inside the clutch release housing. The three studs and clips will drop into the case. Remove the reverse idler set screw (bolt) and the backup light switch.

7. Remove the ten case attaching bolts and four stud nuts. Remove the transmission case. The factory uses a special tool to do this—it pushes against the end of the mainshaft. Make sure to tag all shims for reuse.

8. Remove the two bolts and take out the reverse shift fork and supports.

9. Remove the snap-ring from the end of the pinion shaft.

10. Pull off the bearing and 4th gear from the end of the mainshaft. Take the needle bearing for the 4th gear off, too.

11. Pry off the two shift rail E-clips with a screwdriver. Remove the shift forks assembly.

12. Lift the mainshaft assembly out. It can be fully disassembled by removing snap-rings and components. The clutch pushrod

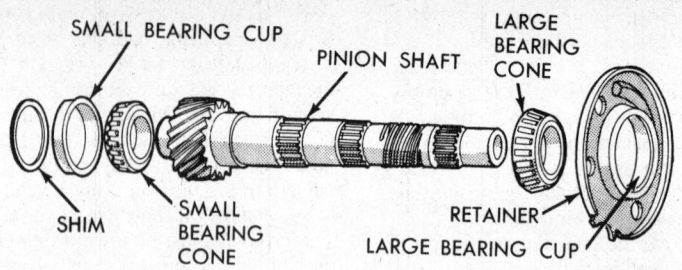

Pinion shaft and related components—Chrysler A-412 (Chilton Type 18) transaxle (© Chrysler Corp.)

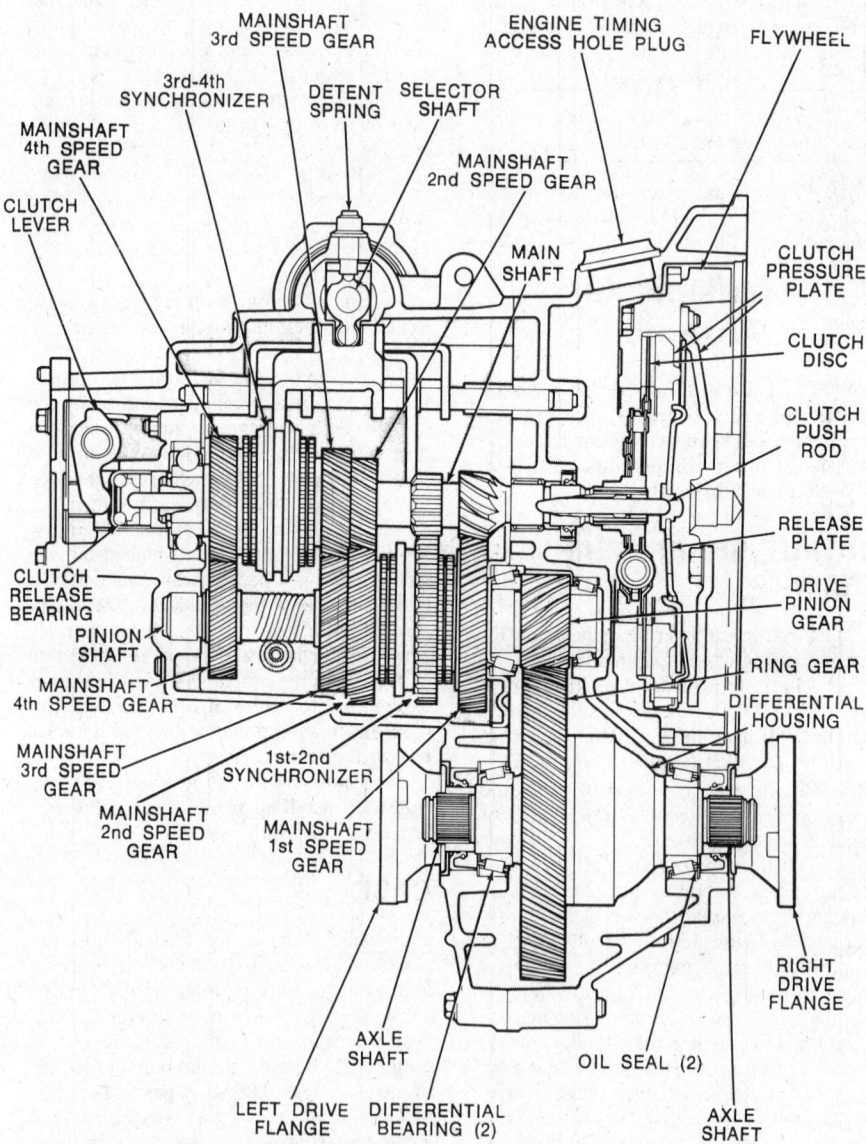

Cutaway view of the Chrysler A-412 (Chilton Type 18) transaxle (© Chrysler Corp.)

seal and bushing assembly can be driven out of the shaft with a ⅜ in. diameter brass rod. Replace it by driving with a plastic hammer.

13. Remove the fitted snap-ring from the pinion shaft and lift off the 3rd gear. Lift off the 2nd gear and its needle bearing.

14. Pry or pull out the reverse idler gear shaft.

15. Pull (with a puller) off the 1st gear and 1st-2nd synchronizer assembly from the pinion shaft.

NOTE: The inner sleeve for 2nd gear and the 1st gear are removed together.

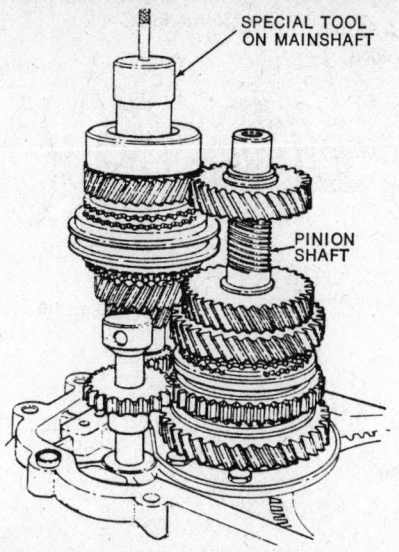

Special tool used to determine mainshaft bearing shim thickness—Chrysler A-412 (Chilton Type 18) transaxle (© Chrysler Corp.)

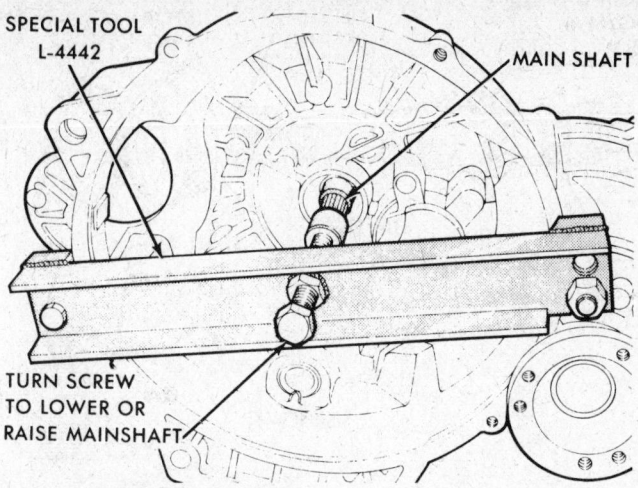

Adjusting the mainshaft gear clearance—Chrysler A-412 (Chilton Type 18) transaxle (© Chrysler Corp.)

16. Take off the 1st gear needle bearing. Scribe a mark across the 1st-2nd synchronizer for reassembly.

17. Remove the four pinion shaft retainer bolts, lift off the retainer, the thrust washer (the flat side goes up), and remove the pinion shaft.

Transaxle Assembly

1. The pinion shaft bearing preload must be adjusted. Place a 0.65mm shim in the bearing housing and press the small bearing cup into the clutch housing. Install the pinion up and down, measuring the end play with a dial indicator.

NOTE: Do not rotate the shaft while moving it up and down.

2. The correct preload is determined by adding 0.20mm to the measured reading obtained from the dial indicator in Step 1, along with the shim thickness, 0.65mm. For example if the measurement was 0.30mm, the correct shim to use would be 1.15mm (0.65 + 0.03 + 0.20 = 1.15). Remove the pinion shaft ball bearing retainer and the pinion shaft. Remove the small bearing cup and the 0.65mm shim, and install the correct shim.

3. If you have installed new bearings on the pinion shaft, lubricate them with transmission oil, install the shaft, and check the shaft turning torque with a torque wrench. It should be 4.4–13.1 inch lbs. If it isn't, reset the preload.

4. Install the pinion shaft. Place the first gear thrust washer over the shaft with the flat side up (toward the gear). Install the pinion shaft retainer and tighten the bolts to 29 ft. lbs.

5. Install the needle bearing, the 1st gear, and the 1st gear synchronizer stop ring over the shaft.

NOTE: The wear limit for spacing between the synchronizer teeth on the 1st gear and those on the stop-ring is 0.019 in. There is one tooth missing from the 1st gear stop-ring on early models. 1st gear will grind if this ring isn't used. Later models have three teeth missing in three places, 120° apart.

6. Align the marks on the 1st-2nd synchronizer hub and sleeve, made on disassembly. Install the synchronizer, driving it into place.

7. Drive the 2nd gear needle bearing inner race into place over the shaft.

8. Drive the reverse idler gear shaft into place. Make sure that the threaded hole in the top of the shaft is centered pointing out between the two nearest case edge bolt holes.

9. Put the 2nd gear needle bearing over the pinion shaft. Put the 2nd gear stop ring, 2nd gear, and 3rd gear onto the shaft. Make sure that third gear has the thrust face down.

10. Install the snap-ring to hold third gear. Measure end play between third gear and the snap-ring with a feeler gauge; it should be 0.004–0.004 in., as little as possible. Snap-rings are available in thicknesses from 0.098–0.118 in. for adjustment. Replace the snap-ring with the one selected.

11. Install the mainshaft assembly.

12. Install the shift forks assembly and install the E-clips.

13. Install the fourth gear needle bearing over the mainshaft. Put the fourth gear synchronizer stop ring in place. Install the fourth gear and the snap-ring.

14. Install the reverse shift fork and the support brackets, tightening the bolts to 105 inch lbs.

15. Use a feeler gauge to measure the clearance between the top of the pinion shaft second gear and the bottom of the mainshaft third gear. Ideal clearance should be 0.039 in. The clearance is adjusted by forcing the mainshaft up or down in relation to the clutch case. The factory has a special tool to do this from the clutch end.

16. The next step is to determine the thickness of the shim or shims to be placed between the mainshaft roller bearing and the transmission case. The factory does this by inserting a special tool of the same thickness as the bearing in the case, installing the case, and measuring up and down movement of the special tool with a dial indicator. Shims are available in 0.012 and 0.024 in. sizes.

Up and down movement	Shim size needed
0.000–0.018 in.	none
0.019–0.029 in.	0.012 in.
0.030–0.041 in.	0.024 in.
0.042–0.57 in.	0.035 in.

17. After the selected shim is installed behind the bearing, tighten the bearing retainer clamp bolts to 155 inch lbs. Install the transmission case to the clutch housing, using the guide pin for alignment. Tighten the stud nuts and bolts to 250 inch lbs.

CHILTON TYPE 19

Transaxle Disassembly

The Chrysler designed and built A-460, A-465, and A-525 "fully-synchronized" manual transaxles combine gear reduction, ratio selection, and differential functions in one unit housed in a die-cast aluminum case. The A-460 is a four-speed while both the A-465 and A-525 are five-speeds. The A-525 has a close-ratio gearset with different 2nd, 3rd, and 4th-gear ratios than the

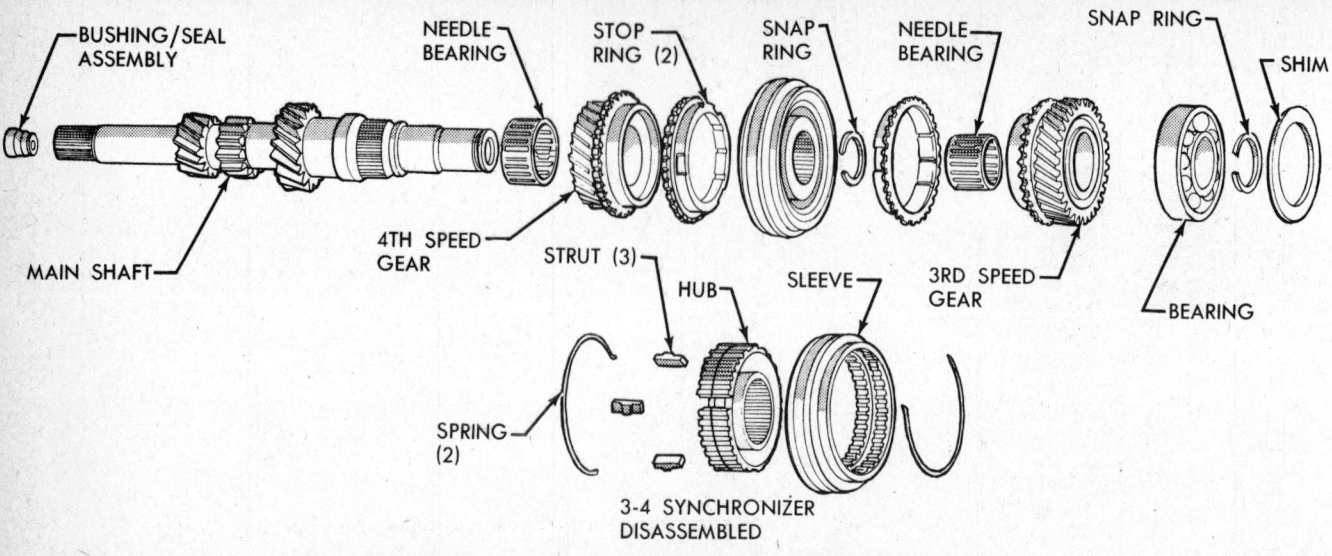

Mainshaft details—Chrysler A-412 (Chilton Type 18) transaxle (© Chrysler Corp.)

A-465, to provide better performance through the gears, while 1st and 5th gear ratios are the same as the A-465 to maintain the same launch and top-gear characteristics.

1. With the transaxle removed from the vehicle, remove the eight differential cover bolts and the two stud nuts and remove the cover.

2. Remove the differential bearing retainer bolts.

3. Using tool L-4435 or equivalent, rotate the differential bearing retainer to remove it.

4. Remove the extension housing bolts, then remove the differential assembly and extension housing.

5. Remove the selector shaft housing bolts, then remove the selector shaft housing.

6. Remove the stud nuts and the bolts from the rear end cover, then using a suitable tool in the notch pry off the rear end cover.

7. Using snap ring pliers, remove the large snap ring from the intermediate shaft rear ball bearing.

8. Remove the bearing retainer plate by tapping it with a plastic hammer.

9. Remove the 3rd–4th shift fork rail.

10. Remove the reverse idler gear shaft and gear.

11. Remove the input shaft gear assembly and the intermediate shaft gear assembly.

12. To remove the clutch release bearing remove the E-clips from the clutch release shaft, then disassemble the clutch shaft components.

13. To remove the input shaft oil seal remove the three bolts from the input shaft seal retainer. Remove the seal and retainer assembly and the select shim.

14. To remove the input shaft front bearing cup from the transaxle case you will need special tools C-4171, C-4656 and an arbor press to press the cup from the case.

15. To remove the intermediate shaft front bearing, remove the two bolts from the bearing retaining strap, then using special tool C-4660 remove the bearing.

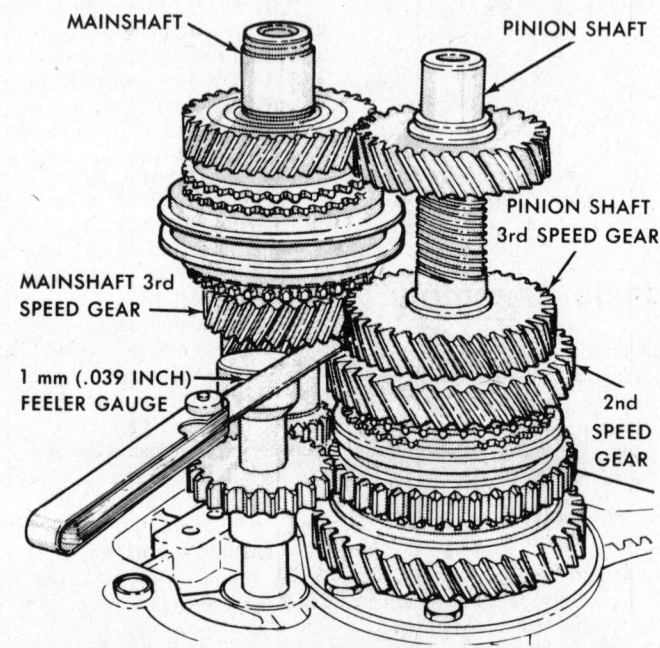

Measuring gear clearance—Chrysler A-412 (Chilton Type 18) transaxle (© Chrysler Corp.)

NOTE: If your vehicle is equipped with a 5 speed transaxle the following procedures are used in conjunction with the previous ones:

1. Remove the 5th speed shifter pin.

2. Remove the 5th speed detent ball and spring.

3. Remove the 5th speed synchronizer strut retainer plate snap ring.

4. Remove the 5th speed synchronizer strut retainer plate.

5. Remove the 5th speed synchronizer assembly and shift fork with shift rail.

6. Remove the intermediate shaft 5th speed gear.

7. Remove the input shaft 5th speed gear snap ring.

8. Remove the input shaft 5th speed gear.

9. Remove the bearing support plate bolts.

10. Pry off the bearing support plate.

INTERMEDIATE SHAFT DISASSEMBLY

NOTE: The 1st–2nd and 3rd–4th shift forks and the synchronizer stop rings are interchangeable. However, if parts are to be reused reassemble in original position.

1. Remove the intermediate shaft rear bearing snap ring.

2. Using special tool C-4693 (puller) or equivalent, remove the intermediate shaft rear bearing.

3. Using snap ring pliers, remove the 3rd–4th synchronizer hub snap ring.

4. Using special tool L-4534 (puller) or equivalent, remove the 3rd–4th synchronizer hub and the 3rd speed gear.

5. Remove the retaining ring, split thrust washer, 2nd speed gear and the synchronizer stop ring.

6. Using snap ring pliers, remove the 1st–2nd synchronizer hub snap ring.

7. Remove the 1st speed gear, stop ring and 1st–2nd synchronizer assembly.

8. Remove the 1st speed gear thrust washer and anti-spin pin.

INTERMEDIATE SHAFT ASSEMBLY

Assembly of the intermediate shaft is the reverse of disassembly; however, please note the following: When assembling the intermediate shaft, make sure all speed gears turn freely and have a minimum of 0.003 in. end play. When installing the 1st speed gear thrust washer make sure the chamfered edge is toward the pinion gear. When installing the 1st–2nd synchronizer make sure the relief faces the 2nd speed gear. Use an arbor press to install the intermediate shaft rear bearing and the 3rd–4th synchronizer hub and 3rd speed gear.

Transaxle Assembly

Assembly of the transaxle is the reverse of disassembly; however, please note the following: When installing the intermediate shaft front bearing special tools C-4657, C-4171 and an arbor press will be needed. The input shaft front bearing cup is installed with the same tools used for removal. Determining shim thickness for correct bearing endplay need only be done if any of the following parts are replaced: transaxle case, input shaft seal retainer, bearing retainer plate, rear end cover, input shaft or input shaft bearings. To determine proper shim thickness refer to the Input Shaft Bearing Endplay Adjustment at the end of this section. To install the input shaft oil seal use special tool C-4674 or equivalent and a plastic hammer. Use a 1/16 inch bead of R.T.V. sealant around the edge of the input shaft seal retainer and make sure the drain hole of the retainer is facing downward. The differential bearing retainer is installed with the same special tool used for removal. The rear end cover, selector shaft housing and the differential cover are all sealed with R.T.V. sealant.

Input Shaft Bearing End–play Adjustment

1. Press the input shaft front bearing cup slightly forward in the case using special tool L-4656 with handle C-4171. Then,

1. 5th gear
2. 5th speed stop ring
3. 5th speed synchronizer
4. 5th speed synchronizer retainer plate
5. 3rd gear
6. 4th speed stop ring
7. 3rd & 4th synchronizer
8. 4th speed gear
9. Interm. shaft rear bearing
10. 1st & 2nd stop ring
11. 1st & 2nd synchronizer
12. 2nd gear
13. Thrust washer
14. Retaining ring
15. Oil feeder
16. Inter. shaft roller bearing
17. Intermediate shaft
18. Low gear thrust washer
19. 1st gear
20. Input shaft front bearing cup
21. Input shaft front bearing
22. Input shaft
23. Input shaft rear bearing
24. Input shaft rear bearing cup
25. 5th gear input shaft

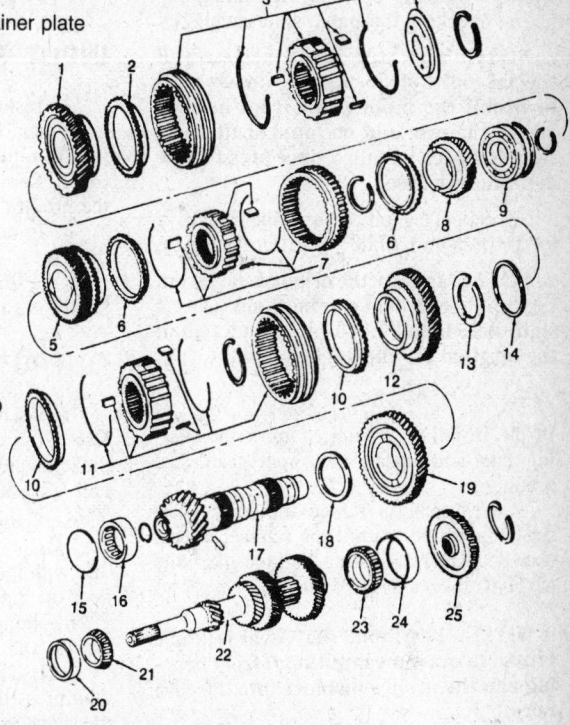

Chrysler A460, A465, and A525 transaxle gear train

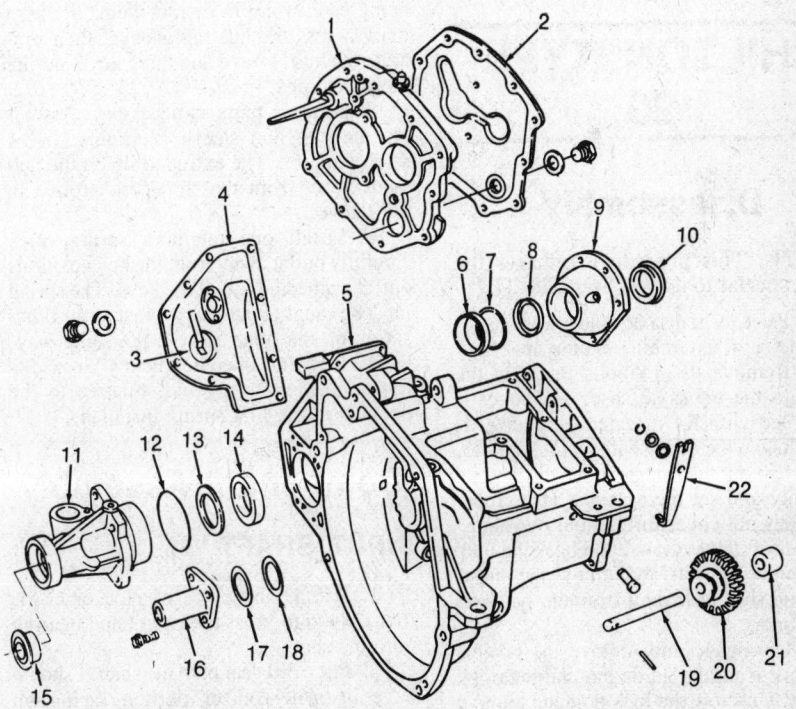

1. Bearing retainer plate	9. Differential bearing retainer
2. Rear cover	10. Bearing retainer seal
3. Magnet	11. Extension
4. Oil pan	12. Extension O-ring
5. Transaxle case	13. Retainer
6. Cup (bearing)	14. Bearing cup
7. Spacer	15. Extension seal
8. Oil feed baffle	16. Bearing retainer

17. Input shaft seal
18. Input shaft spacer
19. Reverse idler shaft
20. Reverse idler gear
21. Reverse idler spacer
22. Reverse gearshift lever

Chrysler A460, A465, A525 transaxle case (Chilton Type 19)

using tool L-4655 with handle C-4171, press the bearing cup back into the case, from front, to properly position the bearing cup before checking the input shaft endplay.

NOTE: This step is not necessary if special tool L-4655 was previously used to install the input shaft front bearing cup in the case and no input shaft select shim has been installed since pressing the cup into the case.

2. Select a gaging shim which will give 0.025–0.254mm (0.001–0.010 in.) endplay.

NOTE: Measure the original shim from the input shaft seal retainer and select a shim 0.254mm (0.010 in.) thinner than the original for the gaging shim.

3. Install the gaging shim on the bearing cup and install the input shaft seal retainer.

4. Alternately tighten the input shaft seal retainer bolts until the retainer is bottomed against the case. Tighten the bolts to 21 ft. lbs.

NOTE: The input shaft seal retainer is used to draw the input shaft front bearing cup the proper distance into the case bore.

CHILTON TYPE 20

Disassembly

NOTE: This procedure requires the use of special tools; see Steps 28–34.

1. Place the transaxle onto a work stand, with the shaft assemblies facing up.

2. Remove the 15 bolts retaining the clutch to the transaxle case. The cover is assembled with RTV sealer; if removal is difficult, rap the cover with a soft hammer.

3. Lift out the ring gear and differential assembly and set them aside. This procedure does not cover differential overhaul.

4. Shift to Neutral. Bend back the lock tab, remove the bolt, and remove the shifter shaft and shift fork shaft from the synchronizer forks.

5. Disengage and remove the reverse shift fork from the guide pin and interlock bracket. Unscrew the lock bolt and remove the reverse idler gear shaft, gear, and spacer assembly.

6. Remove the detent shift lever and interlock assembly, but leave the shift forks engaged with the synchronizers.

7. Lift the input and output shafts from the case as an assembly. Note the location and installed position of the shift forks, then remove them from the shafts.

Component Disassembly

INPUT SHAFT

1. Install support plates under fourth gear, then press the gear and left hand bearing from the shaft.

2. Remove the brass blocker ring and the 3rd-4th synchronizer snap ring.

3. Install support plates behind 3rd gear, then press 3rd gear and the synchronizer from the shaft. Press the right hand bearing from the shaft.

OUTPUT SHAFT

4. Install support plates behind 4th gear. Use a rod or pilot which will fit through the left hand bearing to press off the bearing and 4th gear.

5. Remove the 3rd gear snap ring. Slide the 1st-2nd synchronizer into 1st. Support 2nd with the plates, then press 2nd and 3rd gear off the output shaft.

6. Remove the brass blocker ring and the 1st-2nd synchronizer snap ring.

7. Use press plates to support 1st gear, then press the gear and synchronizer from the shaft. Press the right hand bearing from the shaft.

8. Pry out the synchronizer springs, being careful not to distort them. Scribe a mark across the hub and sleeve, then separate the hub, sleeve and three keys, noting their locations.

9. Replace parts as necessary. Assemble the hub and sleeve according to the scribed marks. The extruded lip on the hub faces away from the shift fork groove in the sleeve.

10. Install one retaining spring, then carefully pull it away from the key positions one at a time and install the keys. The spring must be caught on the keys. Install the other spring on the other side in the same way, but be sure the open segment is in a different position (staggered) relative to the opening in the first spring installed.

Component Assembly

INPUT SHAFT

1. Use a long piece of pipe or G.M. tool J28406 to press the right hand bearing onto the shaft.

2. Place 3rd gear onto the shaft. I should have its synchronizer portion facing up towards the 3rd-4th synchronizer. Install the brass blocker ring onto the gear, then press the 3rd-4th gear synchronizer into place. Use a piece of pipe which will contact the synchronizer hub near the shaft. Do not press on the outside of the hub. Install the snap ring with the beveled edges away from the synchronizer.

3. Install the brass blocker ring. Press 4th gear onto the shaft with its synchronizer portion facing the synchronizer. Press the left hand bearing into place.

OUTPUT SHAFT

4. Press the right hand bearing into place. Place 1st gear onto the shaft, then install its brass blocker ring into place. Press the 1st-2nd synchronizer into place, using a long pipe which will press on the hub near the shaft. Do not press on the outer edges of the hub or the sleeve.

5. Install the snap ring and brass blocker ring over the synchronizer.

6. Place 2nd gear onto the shaft. Press 3rd gear into place, with its hub away from 2nd gear; press on the gear close to the shaft—do not press on its outer edges. Install the 3rd gear snap ring.

7. Press 4th gear into place, with its hub facing 3rd gear. Press the left hand bearing into place.

Case Overhaul

1. Remove the reverse inhibitor fitting from the outside of the case, and the spring and pilot/spacer from the inside.

2. A puller is necessary to remove the input and output shaft bearing cups. The oil slingers can be slipped out.

3. Check the interlock bracket and reverse shift fork guide pins, and the case magnet for wear or damage. Clean the sealant from the case.

4. Preload shims must be selected before final assembly. The three left hand bearing cups must be installed into the case. Install the input and output shaft assemblies and the differential assembly into position in the case. Install the three right hand bearing cups onto their bearings.

5. Place G.M. gauge J-26935-2 on the input bearing, J-26935-4 on the output bearing, and J-26935-3 on the differential bearing. The gauges must fit smoothly and completely over the bearings.

6. Install the metal oil shield retainer over tool J-26935-4 on the output shaft.

7. Install the seven spacers supplied with the spacer kit around the perimeter of the transaxle case. Carefully install the clutch cover over the gauges and spacers. Install the seven long bolts provided and tighten evenly and in rotation to 10 ft. lbs.

8. Rotate each gauge to seat the bearings. Rotate the differential case through three revolutions in each direction.

9. The gap between the outer sleeve and the base pad is the correct thickness for the preload shim at each location. The largest shim which can be placed in the gap and drawn through without binding is the correct one for assembly.

10. Remove the clutch cover, spacers and gauges. Place the selected shims in their respective bores in the clutch cover, add the metal shield, then install the bearing cups.

1. Case assembly
2. Axle shaft seal assembly
3. Case locating pin
4. Chip collecting magnet
5. Vent assembly
6. Synchronizer key
7. Oil shield
8. Bearing assembly
9. 4th speed input gear
10. Blocking ring
11. Synchronizer spring
12. Synchronizer assembly
13. 3rd speed input gear
14. Oil shield sleeve
15. Input cluster gear
16. Input gear bearing
17. Input gear seal
18. Input gear retainer assembly
19. Retainer seal
20. Throwout bearing assembly
21. Reverse idler shaft
22. Reverse idler shaft
23. Reverse idler shaft gear
24. Reverse inhibitor spring seat
25. Reverse inhibitor spring
26. Reverse inhibitor spring pin
27. Reverse shift lever
28. Detent lever assembly
29. Detent spring
30. Shift shaft
31. Shift shaft seal assembly
32. Shift interlock
33. 3rd-4th shift fork
34. 1st-2nd shift fork
35. Shift fork shaft
36. Oil guide
37. Clutch fork shaft seal assembly
38. Clutch fork shaft bearing
39. Clutch fork shaft assembly
40. Clutch and differential housing assembly
41. Speedometer driven gear sleeve
42. Speedometer driven gear sleeve seal
43. Speedometer driven gear
44. Case bearing oil shield
45. Case bearing assembly
46. 4th speed gear
47. 3rd speed output gear
48. 2nd speed output gear
49. Synchronizer blocking ring
50. Synchronizer spring
51. Synchronizer key
52. 1st-2nd synchronizer assembly
53. 1st speed output gear
54. Oil shield sleeve
55. Output gear
56. Output bearing assembly
57. Output gear bearing shim
58. Output gear bearing oil shield
59. Output gear bearing oil shield retainer
60. Differential assembly
61. Differential ring gear
62. Differential bearing assembly
63. Differential case
64. Differential pinion shaft
65. Speedometer drive gear
66. Differential bearing assembly
67. Housing bearing shim
68. Side gear thrust washer
69. Differential side gear
70. Pinion thrust washer
71. Differential pinion gear

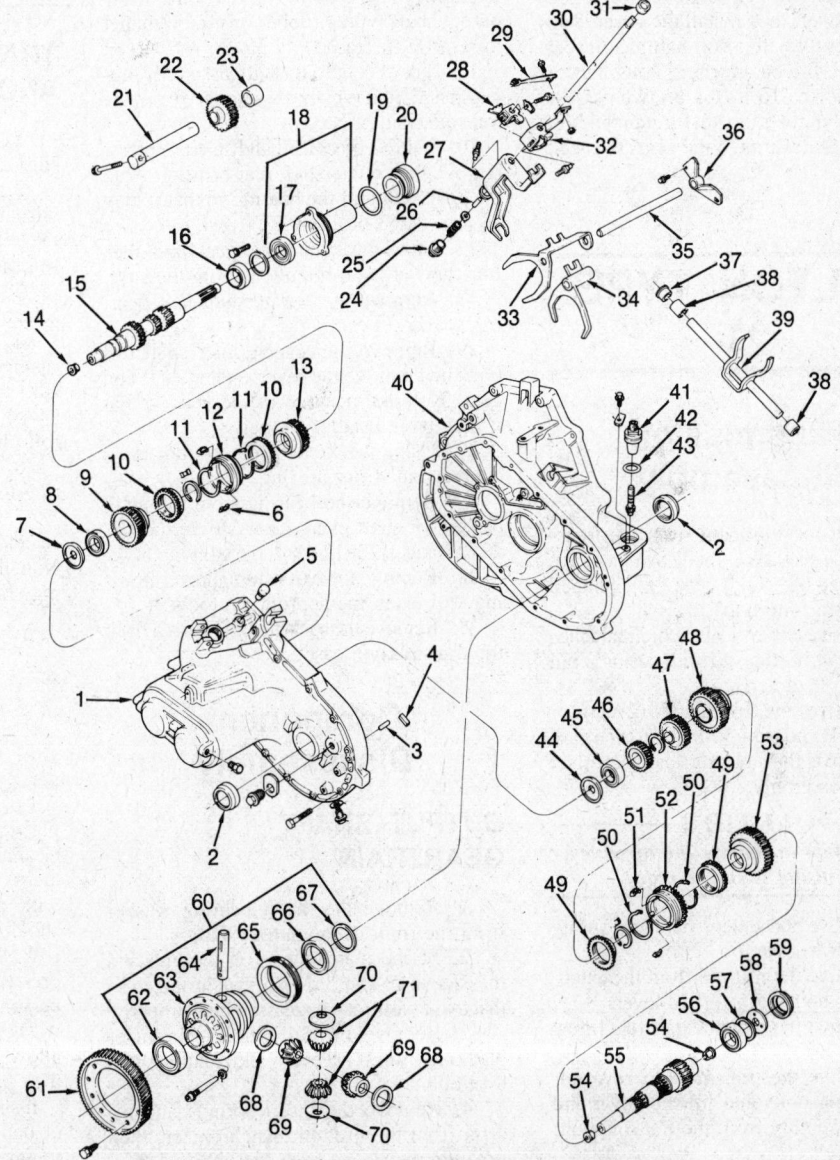

Exploded view of the G.M. 125-4 4-speed transaxle

Transmission Assembly

1. Place the input and output shafts together on the workbench. Install the two shift forks onto the shafts. Pick up the shafts and carefully lower them into the case as an assembly.

2. Place the interlock bracket onto a dummy shaft, making sure the bracket engages the shift fork fingers. Place the detent shift lever into the interlock.

3. Install the shifter shaft through the interlock bracket and the detent shift lever, but do not push through any farther. Install the reverse shift fork onto the dummy shaft, engaging the reverse shift fork with the interlock bracket.

4. Install the reverse idler gear and its shaft. The long end of the shaft points upward; the large chamfered ends of the idler gear teeth should also be facing up. Install the spacer. The flat on the reverse idler shaft should be facing the input shaft.

5. Push the shifter shaft through the reverse shift fork until it fits into the inhibitor spring spacer. Remove the dummy shaft. Shift to Neutral and install the shifter shaft bolt and lock through the detent shift lever. Bend the lock tab over the bolt head.

6. Install the fork shaft through the synchronizer forks and into the case bore.

7. Carefully install the ring gear and differential case assembly.

8. Install the magnet into the case. Apply a thin bead of RTV silicone sealer to the clutch cover, then install the cover. Tap the cover gently with a soft hammer to seat it. Install the fifteen attaching bolts, torquing in rotation to 16 ft. lbs. in two passes.

9. Tighten the idler shaft retaining bolt to 7 ft. lbs. Shift through the gears to check operation.

CHILTON TYPE 21

Transmission Disassembly

1. Drain the lubricant from the transmission. Note that 2WD models do not have a drain plug; the fluid must be siphoned from these transmissions.

2. Remove the roll pin which attaches the offset lever to the shift rail, using a pin punch and a hammer.

3. Remove the extension (2WD) or adapter (4WD) housing-to-transmission case bolts. Remove the housing and the offset lever as an assembly.

─────── CAUTION ───────
Do not attempt to remove the offset lever while the housing is still in place.

4. Remove the detent ball and spring from the offset lever.

5. Remove the roll pin from the extension/adapter housing or offset lever.

6. Remove the countershaft rear thrust bearing and race.

7. Remove the transmission cover-to-case attaching bolts and lift the cover and shift fork assembly from the transmission.

NOTE: Two of the transmission cover bolts are alignment-type dowel bolts. Note their location so that they may be reinstalled in their original locations.

8. Remove the C-clip which attaches the reverse lever to the reverse lever pivot bolt.

9. Remove the reverse lever pivot bolt, then remove the reverse lever and the reverse lever fork as an assembly.

10. Mark the position of the front bearing cap in relation to the transmission case. Remove the bearing cap bolts and the cap.

11. Remove the front bearing race and the end-play shims from the bearing cap. Pry the oil seal out of the bearing cap using an appropriate tool.

12. Rotate the main drive gear shaft until the flat portion of the gear faces the countershaft, then remove the main drive gear shaft assembly.

13. Remove the thrust bearing and the 15 roller bearings from the clutch shaft.

14. Remove the output shaft bearing race. If the race is stubborn, tap the front of the output shaft with a rubber or plastic mallet to remove the race.

15. Tilt the output shaft assembly upward and remove the assembly from the transmission case.

16. Using a brass drift and an arbor press, remove the countershaft rear bearing. Note the positioning of the bearing so that it may be reinstalled properly.

17. Move the countershaft rearward, then tilt it upward and remove it from the case.

18. Remove the countershaft rear bearing spacer.

19. Remove the reverse idler shaft roll pin, then remove the reverse idler shaft and gear. Note the position of the gear so that it may be reinstalled properly.

20. Using an arbor press, remove the countershaft front bearing.

21. Remove the bearing from the main drive gear shaft using Kent-Moore tools J-29721 and J-22912 (or their equivalents).

22. Remove the extension/adapter housing seal using the appropriate tools.

23. Remove the back-up light switch from the transmission case.

Component Disassembly

OUTPUT SHAFT GEARTRAIN

1. Remove the thrust bearing washer from the front of the output shaft.

2. Scribe matchmarks on the hub and the sleeve of the 3rd–4th synchronizer so that these parts may be reassembled properly.

3. Remove the 3rd–4th synchronizer blocking ring, sleeve, and hub as an assembly.

4. Remove the insert springs and inserts from the 3rd–4th synchronizer, then separate the sleeve from the hub.

5. Remove the 3rd speed gear from the shaft.

6. Remove the snap-ring which attaches the 2nd speed gear to the output shaft. Remove the tabbed 2nd gear thrust washer and the 2nd speed gear.

7. Remove the output shaft bearing using Kent-Moore puller set J-29721 and adapters 293-39 (or their equivalents).

8. Remove the 1st gear thrust washer, roll pin, 1st speed gear, and the blocking ring. Diagonal cutters may be used CAREFULLY to remove the roll pin.

9. Scribe matchmarks on the 1st–2nd synchronizer sleeve and the output shaft in the same manner as in step 2.

10. Remove the insert spring and the inserts from the 1st–reverse sliding gear. Remove the gear from the output hub.

─────── CAUTION ───────
Do not attempt to remove the 1st-2nd-reverse hub from the output shaft. The shaft and hub are machined and assembled as a matched set during manufacture.

TRANSMISSION COVER AND SHIFT FORKS

1. Place the selector arm plates and the shift rail in the Neutral position (centered).

2. Rotate the shift rail counterclockwise until the selector arm disengages from the selector arm plates. The selector arm roll pin should now be accessible.

3. Pull the shift rail rearward until the selector contacts the 1st-2nd shift fork.

4. Remove the selector arm roll pin (using a 3/16 in. pin punch) and remove the shift rail.

5. Remove the shift forks, selector arm, roll pin, and the interlock plate.

6. Remove the shift rail oil seal and O-ring using an appropriate tool.

7. Remove the nylon inserts and the selector arm plates from the shift forks. Note the position of these parts so that they may be reinstalled properly.

Cleaning and Inspection

All parts (except those which are nylon or plastic) should be thoroughly cleaned in cleaning solvent. Nylon or plastic parts which are to be reused should just be wiped clean with a cloth. Assembled roller bearings should be dried with compressed air, but DO NOT spin the bearings with the compressed air as they could shatter and cause personal injury. Individual bearing rollers, washers, thrust bearings, etc., should be allowed to air dry after cleaning, though they may be wiped with a clean cloth.

Inspect all parts for excessive wear and/or damage such as scoring, cracks, nicks, rough edges, etc. Replace any defective parts. To check the condition of the assembled bearings, first clean and dry them, then coat the bearings with light engine oil. Slowly spin the bearings by hand and check for any signs of roughness. If the bearing does not feel perfectly smooth, it should be replaced.

NOTE: AMC recommends that if any gear of the mainshaft must be replaced, the countershaft gear should also be replaced to avoid noisy operation and maintain proper gear mesh.

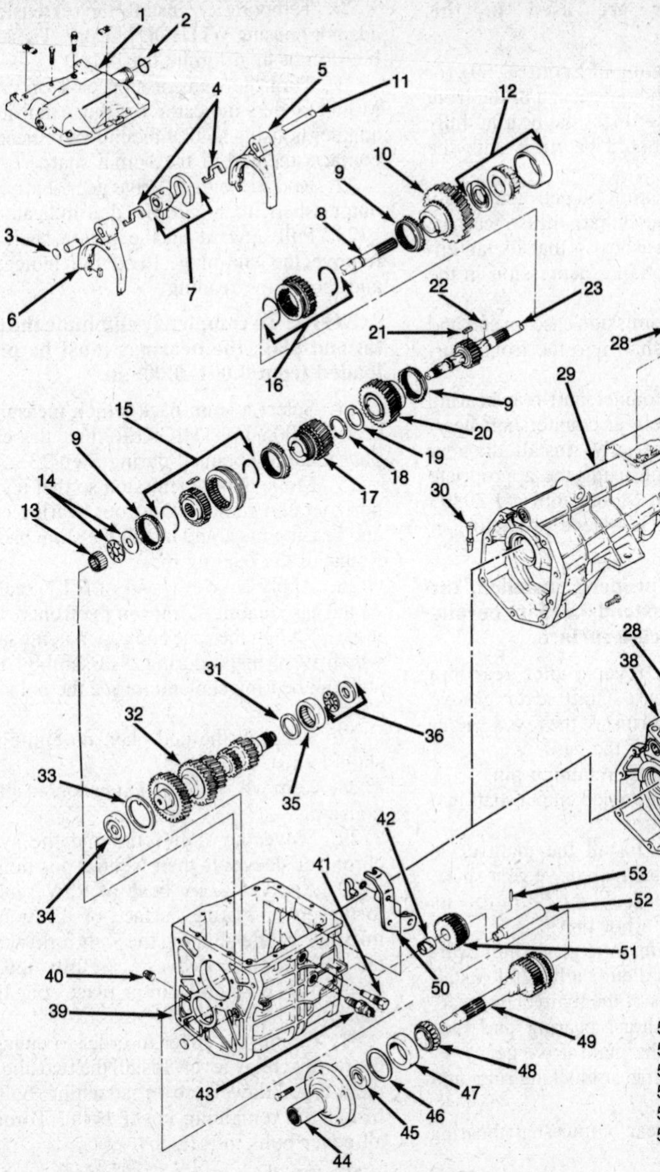

1. Transmission cover
2. O-ring
3. Plug
4. Selector plate
5. 1st-2nd shift fork
6. 3rd-4th shift fork
7. Selector arm interlock plate and pin
8. Mainshaft
9. Blocking ring
10. 1st speed gear
11. Shift rail
12. Thrust washer, rear bearing and cup
13. Clutch shaft needle bearings
14. Needle thrust bearing and race
15. 3rd-4th synchronizer assembly
16. Reverse sliding gear and insert springs
17. 3rd speed gear
18. Snap-ring
19. Thrust washer
20. 2nd speed gear
21. Synchronizer insert
22. Roll pin
23. Mainshaft
24. Roll pin
25. Damper sleeve
26. Offset lever
27. Detent spring
28. Detent ball
29. Extension housing (2WD)
30. Breather
31. Rear countershaft spacer
32. Countershaft gear unit
33. Front countershaft thrust washer
34. Front countershaft bearing
35. Rear countershaft bearing
36. Needle thrust bearing and race
37. Bushing and oil seal
38. Adapter housing (4WD)
39. Transmission case
40. Plug
41. Reverse lever pivot bolt
42. Reverse idler bushing
43. Back-up lamp switch
44. Front bearing cap
45. Oil seal
46. Shim
47. Front bearing cup
48. Front bearing (main)
49. Main drive gear and shaft
50. Reverse lever

51. Reverse idler gear
52. Reverse idler shaft
54. Roll pin
54. Breather
55. Seal
56. I.D. tag

Exploded view of the AMC T4 (Chilton Type 21) transmission

While the transmission is out of the vehicle, it is good practice to check the condition of the clutch assembly and the throwout bearing. Also, replace all transmission gaskets, seals, etc. during assembly of the transmission.

Component Assembly

TRANSMISSION COVER

1. Attach the nylon inserts to, and the selector arm plates through the shift forks.
2. If removed previously, coat the edges of the shift rail plug with sealer and install the plug.
3. Coat the shift rail and rail bores with petroleum jelly and slide the shift rail into the cover until the end of the rail is flush with the inside edge of the cover.
4. Position the 1st–2nd shift fork into the cover, with the offset of the shift fork facing the rear of the cover. Push the shift rail through the fork. Note that the 1st–2nd fork is the larger of the two forks.
5. Position the selector arm and the C-shaped interlock plate into the cover and push the shift rail through the arm. Note that the widest portion of the interlock plate must face away from the cover, and that the selector arm roll pin must face downward and towards the rear of the cover.
6. Position the 3rd–4th shift fork into the cover, with the fork offset facing the rear of the cover.

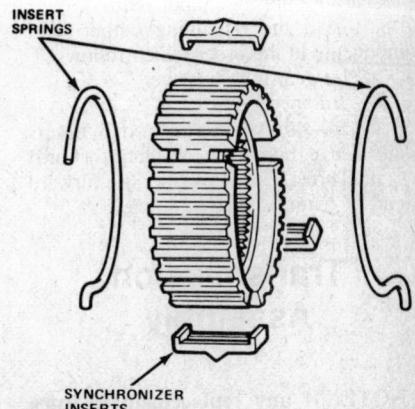

Synchronizer insert spring and insert installation (© AMC)

NOTE: The 3rd–4th shift fork selector arm plate must be positioned UNDER the 1st–2nd shift fork selector arm plate.

7. Push the shift rail through the 3rd–4th shift fork and into the front rail bore of the cover.

8. Rotate the shift rail until the forward selector arm plate faces away from, but is parallel to the cover.

9. Align the roll pin holes of the selector arm and the shift rail. Install the roll pin, noting that it must be installed flush with the surface of the selector arm to prevent selector arm plate-to-pin interference.

10. Install the O-ring into the groove of the shift rail oil seal, then install the oil seal assembly as follows:

a. Install an oil seal protector (Kent-Moore tool #J-26628-2 or its equivalent) over the threaded end of the shift rail.

b. Lubricate the lip of the oil seal with petroleum jelly. Slide the seal over the protector and onto the shift rail.

c. Seat the oil seal into the cover, using an appropriate tool.

OUTPUT SHAFT GEARTRAIN

1. Coat the output shaft and gear bores with transmission lubricant.

2. Using the matchmarks made during disassembly, align and install the 1st–2nd synchronizer sleeve on the output shaft hub.

3. Install the three inserts and two springs into the 1st-reverse synchronizer sleeve. Note that the tanged end of each spring should be positioned on the same insert but that the open face of each spring should be opposite the other.

4. Install the blocking ring and the 2nd speed gear onto the output shaft.

5. Install the tabbed thrust washer and the 2nd gear snap-ring on the output shaft. Be sure that the tab of the washer is properly seated in the notch of the output shaft.

6. Install the blocking ring and the 1st speed gear onto the output shaft, then install the 1st gear roll pin.

7. Using an arbor press and Kent-Moore tool #J-2995 (or its equivalent), install the rear bearing onto the output shaft.

8. Install the remaining output shaft components in the order which follows:

a. 1st gear thrust washer

b. 3rd speed gear

c. 3rd–4th synchronizer hub inserts and sleeve (hub offset must face forward)

d. Thrust bearing washer (on forward end of output shaft)

Transmission Assembly

NOTE: If any replacement fastener must be used, be absolutely sure that it matches the original EXACTLY. Many metric fasteners are used in this transmission.

1. Apply a coating of Loctite® 601 (or its equivalent) to the outer cage of the front countershaft bearing. Press the bearing fully into its bore; it should be flush with the transmission case.

2. Apply a coating of petroleum jelly to the tabbed countershaft thrust washer. Install the thrust washer so that its tab engages the corresponding depression in the transmission case.

3. Tip the transmission case on end and install the countershaft into the front bearing bore.

4. Install the countershaft rear bearing spacer and coat the rear countershaft bearing with petroleum jelly. Install the rear countershaft bearing using the appropriate special tools (Kent-Moore tool #J-29895 installer and J-33032 sleeve protector, or their equivalents).

NOTE: When properly installed, the rear bearing will extend 0.125 in. beyond the transmission case surface.

5. Position the reverse idler gear into the transmission case (shift lever groove facing rearward) and install the reverse idler shaft from the rear of the case.

6. Install the shaft retaining pin.

7. Install the assembled output shaft into the transmission case.

8. If removed, install the main drive gear bearing onto the main drive gear shaft, using Kent-Moore tool #J-2995 (or its equivalent) and an arbor press.

9. Coat the main drive gear roller bearings (15) with petroleum jelly and install them into the recess of the main drive gear.

10. Install the thrust bearing and race into the recess of the main drive gear.

11. Install the 4th gear blocking ring onto the output shaft.

12. Install the rear output shaft bearing race.

13. Install the main drive gear assembly into the transmission case, engaging the 3rd–4th synchronizer blocking ring.

14. Evenly and carefully tap a new front bearing cap seal into place.

15. Install a new oil seal into the adapter housing (4WD) in the same manner as in Step 14.

16. Install the front bearing race into the front bearing cap. Do not yet install the front bearing cap shims.

17. Temporarily install the front bearing cap WITHOUT sealer.

18. Install the reverse lever, pivot pin (coat the threads with non-hardening sealer), and the retaining C-clip.

NOTE: Be sure that the reverse lever fork is engaged with the reverse idler gear.

19. Coat the countershaft rear bearing race and the thrust bearing with petroleum jelly. Install these parts into the extension/adapter housing.

20. Temporarily install the extension/adaptor housing WITHOUT sealer. Tighten, but do not final torque the bolts.

21. Turn the transmission case on end. Mount a dial indicator on the extension/adapter housing so that the indicator needle contacts the end of the output shaft.

22. Rotate the main drive gear shaft and output shaft, then zero the dial indicator.

23. Pull upward on the output shaft to remove the end-play. Read the indicator and record the reading.

NOTE: To completely eliminate the total end-play, the bearings must be preloaded from 0.001–0.005 in.

24. Select a shim pack which measures 0.001–0.005 in. THICKER than the end play reading obtained during Step 23.

25. Move the transmission so that it sits horizontally, remove the front bearing cap and bearing race, and install the shim pack. Reinstall the bearing race.

26. Apply a ⅛ in. bead of RTV sealer on the case mating surface of the front bearing cap. Align the case and cap matchmarks which were made during disassembly. Install the bearing cap and torque the bolts to 15 ft. lbs.

27. Recheck the end-play; no end-play should exist.

28. Remove the extension/adapter housing.

29. Move the shift forks and the synchronizer sleeves to their Neutral positions.

30. Apply a ⅛ in. bead of RTV sealer to the cover mating surface of the transmission. While aligning the shift forks with the synchronizer sleeves, carefully lower the cover assembly into place on the transmission.

31. Center the cover in order to engage the reverse relay lever. Install the two alignment-type (dowel) cover attaching bolts. Install the remaining cover bolts. Torque all cover bolts to 9 ft. lbs.

NOTE: The offset lever-to-shift rail roll pin hole must be positioned vertically; if it is not, repeat Steps 29–31

32. Apply a ⅛ in. bead of RTV sealer to the extension/adapter housing mating surface of the transmission and install the housing over the output shaft.

NOTE: The shift rail must be positioned so that it just enters the shift cover opening.

33. Install the detent spring into the offset lever and place the steel ball into the neutral guide plate detent. Apply pressure to the steel ball with the detent spring and the offset lever, then slide the offset lever on the shift rail and seat the extension/adapter housing against the transmission case. Tighten the housing retaining bolts to 25 ft. lbs.

34. Install the roll pin into the offset lever and shift rail.

35. Install the damper sleeve in the offset lever. Coat the back-up lamp switch threads with RTV sealer and install the switch

into the transmission case. Torque the switch to 15 ft. lbs.

CHILTON TYPE 22

Transmission Disassembly

NOTE: Many special tools and an arbor press are required to properly disassemble and assemble this transmission. Read the entire procedure carefully BEFORE starting the job.

1. Remove the transmission from the vehicle as outlined in the appropriate car section, then drain the lubricant from the transmission. On AMC Spirit and Concord models, the fluid must be siphoned from the transmission, as these models are not equipped with drain plugs.

2. Using a pin punch and a hammer, carefully remove the roll pin which attaches the offset lever to the shift rail.

3. Remove the extension or adapter (AMC 4WD) housing-to-case bolts. Remove the housing and offset lever as an assembly.

─── **CAUTION** ───
DO NOT attempt to remove the housing with the offset lever still in place.

4. Remove the detent ball and spring from the offset lever. Remove the roll pin from the extension housing or offset lever.

5. Remove the plastic funnel, thrust bearing race, and thrust bearing from the rear of the countershaft.

NOTE: The funnel and race may be found inside the extension.

6. Remove the transmission cover-to-case bolts and lift the cover assembly off of the case.

NOTE: Two of the cover bolts are alignment-type dowel bolts. Note the location of these bolts so that they may be reinstalled in their original locations.

7. Place a wooden block under the 5th gear shift fork and drive the roll pin from the fork. The wood must be used to prevent damage to the shift rail.

8. Remove the following items from the rear of the countershaft:
   a. 5th gear synchronizer snap-ring
   b. Shift fork
   c. 5th gear synchronizer sleeve
   d. Blocking ring
   e. 5th speed drive gear

9. Remove the 5th gear synchronizer springs and inserts from the sleeve and hub. Mark the sleeve and hub so that they may be properly reassembled.

10. Remove the snap-ring from the 5th speed driven gear. The driven gear may be removed with a puller (Kent-Moore tool #J-25215).

11. Mark the front bearing cap and case so that the cap may be reinstalled in its proper position. Remove the front bearing cap.

12. Remove the front bearing race and end-play shim(s) from the bearing cap. Carefully pry the oil seal from the cap using an appropriate tool.

13. Rotate the clutch shaft until the flat surface on the main drive gear faces the countershaft. Remove the clutch shaft/main gear unit from the transmission case.

NOTE: The clutch shaft bearing is pressed on. An arbor press must be used to replace the bearing if the bearing is rough.

14. Remove the mainshaft rear bearing race and tilt the shaft upward. Remove the output shaft assembly from the case.

15. On AMC models, unhook the overcenter spring from the rear of the case, using a piece of welding rod bent into a hook to grab and pull the spring. On the Chevette, unhook the overcenter spring from the front of the transmission case.

16. Remove the reverse lever C-clip (all models) and the pivot bolt (Chevette).

17. Rotate the 5th-reverse shift rail clockwise to disengage it from the reverse lever. Remove the rail from the rear of the transmission case.

18. On AMC models, remove the reverse lever pivot pin and detach the lever from the reverse idler gear. On all models, remove the reverse lever and fork assembly from the transmission case.

19. On Chevette models, drive the roll pin from the forward end of the reverse idler shaft. Remove the reverse idler shaft, rubber O-ring and the gear from the transmission.

20. Remove the gear countershaft snap-ring and spacer.

21. Insert a brass drift through the main drive gear opening in the front of the case so that it contacts the countershaft gear assembly. Using an arbor press positioned at the other end of the drift, carefully press the countershaft gear rearward just enough to remove the countershaft rear bearing.

NOTE: During assembly, note that the bearing identification numbers should face outward.

22. Move the countershaft assembly rearward, tilt it upward, then remove the assembly from the case. Note the position of the front countershaft thrust washer so that it may be reinstalled properly, then remove the washer from the case.

23. Remove the countershaft rear bearing spacer.

24. Drive the roll pin from the front of the reverse idler shaft and remove the shaft and gear from the case. Note the position

of the gear so that it may be reinstalled properly.

25. Using an arbor press, remove the countershaft front bearing from the transmission case.

26. Remove the clutch shaft front bearing, using the proper pulling tools.

27. Using a flat drift and a hammer, carefully tap out the rear extension/adapter housing seal.

Component Disassembly

MAINSHAFT

AMC Models

1. Remove the thrust bearing and the washer from the front of the mainshaft.

2. Scribe matchmarks on the 3rd–4th synchronizer hub and the sleeve to indicate their relationship for proper reassembly.

3. Remove the 3rd–4th synchronizer blocking ring, sleeve, and hub from the mainshaft as an assembly. Note the positions of these items so that they may be properly reassembled.

4. Remove the 3rd–4th synchronizer insert springs. Remove the synchronizer inserts and the sleeve from the hub.

5. Remove the 3rd speed gear from the mainshaft.

6. Remove the 2nd gear snap-ring and tabbed thrust washer. Remove the 2nd speed gear from the mainshaft.

7. Using the appropriate special tools, remove the rear mainshaft bearing.

8. Remove the 1st gear thrust washer, roll pin (using diagonal cutters carefully), 1st speed gear, and the blocking ring.

9. Scribe matchmarks on the 1st–2nd sychronizer sleeve and the mainshaft shaft to indicate their relationship for proper reassembly.

10. Remove the insert spring and inserts from the 1st-reverse sliding gear. Remove the gear from the mainshaft hub.

─── **CAUTION** ───
DO NOT attempt to remove the 1st-2nd-reverse hub from the mainshaft as these parts are machined as a matched set from the factory.

Chevette

1. Follow Steps 1-3 of the previous AMC procedure.

2. Remove the snap ring, tabbed thrust washer, and second gear from the mainshaft.

3. Using an arbor press and the appropriate special tool, remove the 5th speed gear from the mainshaft.

4. Slide the rear mainshaft bearing off of the mainshaft.

5. Remove the 1st gear thrust washer, roll pin, 1st speed gear, and the blocking ring.

6. Scribe matchmarks on the 1st–2nd

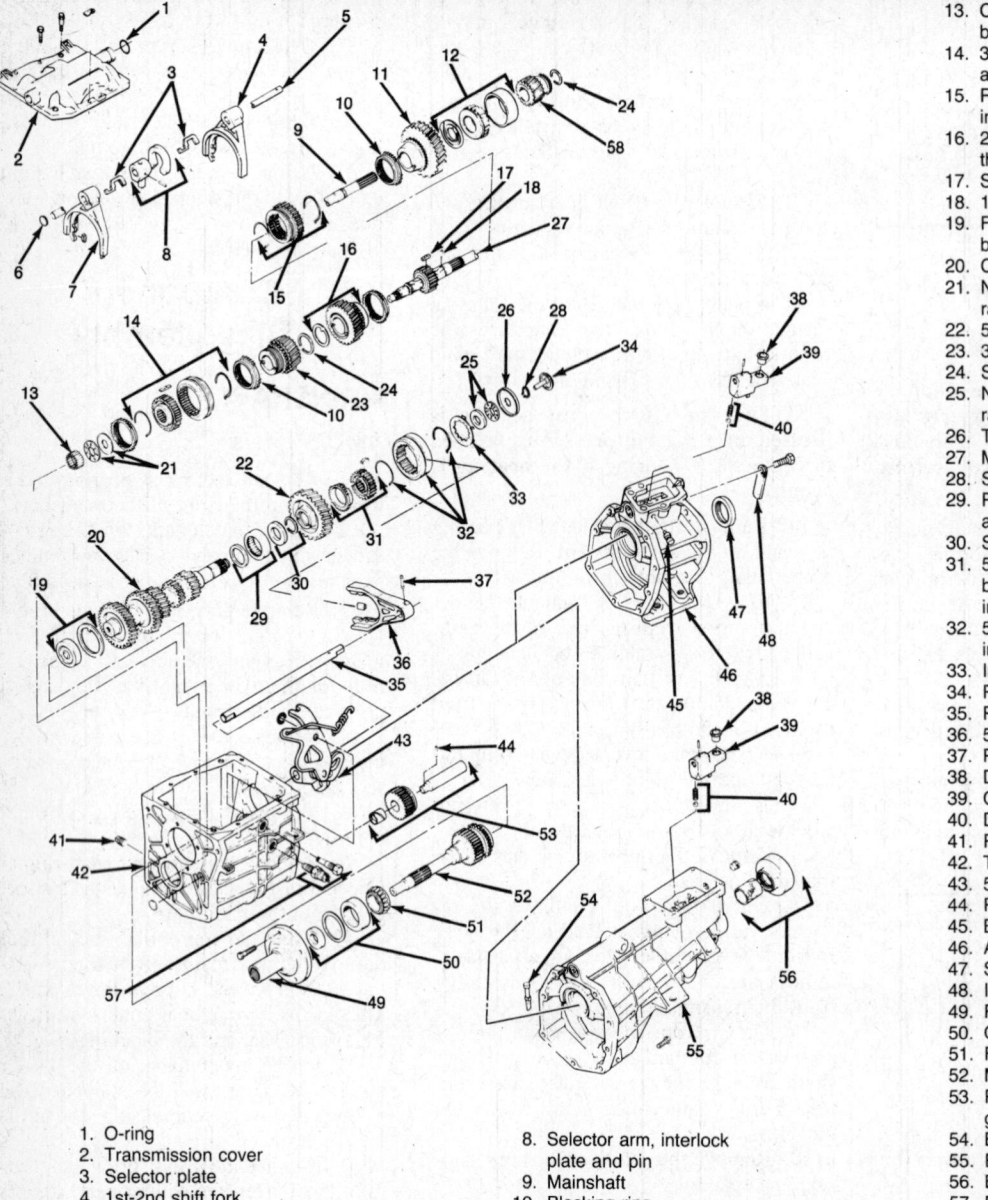

13. Clutch shaft needle bearing
14. 3rd-4th synchronizer assembly
15. Reverse sliding gear and insert springs
16. 2nd speed gear and thrust washer
17. Synchronizer insert
18. 1st gear roll pin
19. Front countershaft bearing and thrust washer
20. Countershaft gear unit
21. Needle thrust bearing and race
22. 5th speed gear
23. 3rd speed gear
24. Snap-ring
25. Needle thrust bearing and race
26. Thrust race
27. Mainshaft
28. Snap-ring
29. Rear countershaft bearing and spacer
30. Snap-ring and spacer
31. 5th gear synchronizer blocking ring, hub and insert
32. 5th gear synchronizer insert springs and sleeve
33. Insert retainer
34. Plastic funnel
35. Reverse seal
36. 5th speed shift fork
37. Roll pin
38. Damper sleeve
39. Offset lever
40. Detent spring and ball
41. Plug
42. Transmission case
43. 5th-reverse shift lever
44. Roll pin
45. Breather
46. Adapter housing (4WD)
47. Seal
48. I.D. tag
49. Front bearing cap
50. Oil seal, shim and cup
51. Front bearing
52. Main drive gear and shaft
53. Reverse idler bushing, gear and shaft
54. Breather
55. Extension housing (2WD)
56. Bushing and oil seal
57. Back-up lamp switch and 5th-reverse lever pivot bolt
58. Fifth speed driven gear

1. O-ring
2. Transmission cover
3. Selector plate
4. 1st-2nd shift fork
5. Shift rail
6. Plug
7. 3rd-4th shift fork

8. Selector arm, interlock plate and pin
9. Mainshaft
10. Blocking ring
11. 1st speed gear
12. Thrust washer, rear bearing and clip

Exploded view of the AMC T5 (Chilton Type 22) transmission

synchronizer hub and sleeve for reassembly purposes.

7. Remove the insert spring and inserts from the 1st-reverse sliding gear. Remove the gear from the mainshaft.

— CAUTION —

DO NOT attempt to remove the 1st-2nd-reverse hub from the mainshaft as these parts are machined as a matched set from the factory.

TRANSMISSION COVER

1. Place the selector arm plates and shift rail in the Neutral position (centered).

2. Rotate the shift rail counterclockwise until the selector arm disengages from the selector arm plates. The selector arm roll pin will now be accessible.

3. On AMC models, pull the selector arm rearward until the arm contacts the 1st-2nd shift fork.

4. Carefully drive out the selector arm roll pin using a 3/16 in. pin punch and a hammer. Remove the shift rail.

5. Remove the shift forks, selector arm plates, selector arm, roll pin and interlock plate.

6. Remove the nylon inserts and the selector arm plates from the shift forks. Note the positions of the inserts and plates

so that they may be properly reinstalled.

Cleaning and Inspection

All parts (except those which are nylon or plastic) should be thoroughly cleaned in cleaning solvent. Nylon or plastic parts which are to be reused should just be wiped clean with a cloth. Assembled roller bearings should be dried with compressed air, but DO NOT spin the bearings with the compressed air as they could shatter and cause personal injury. Individual bearing rollers,

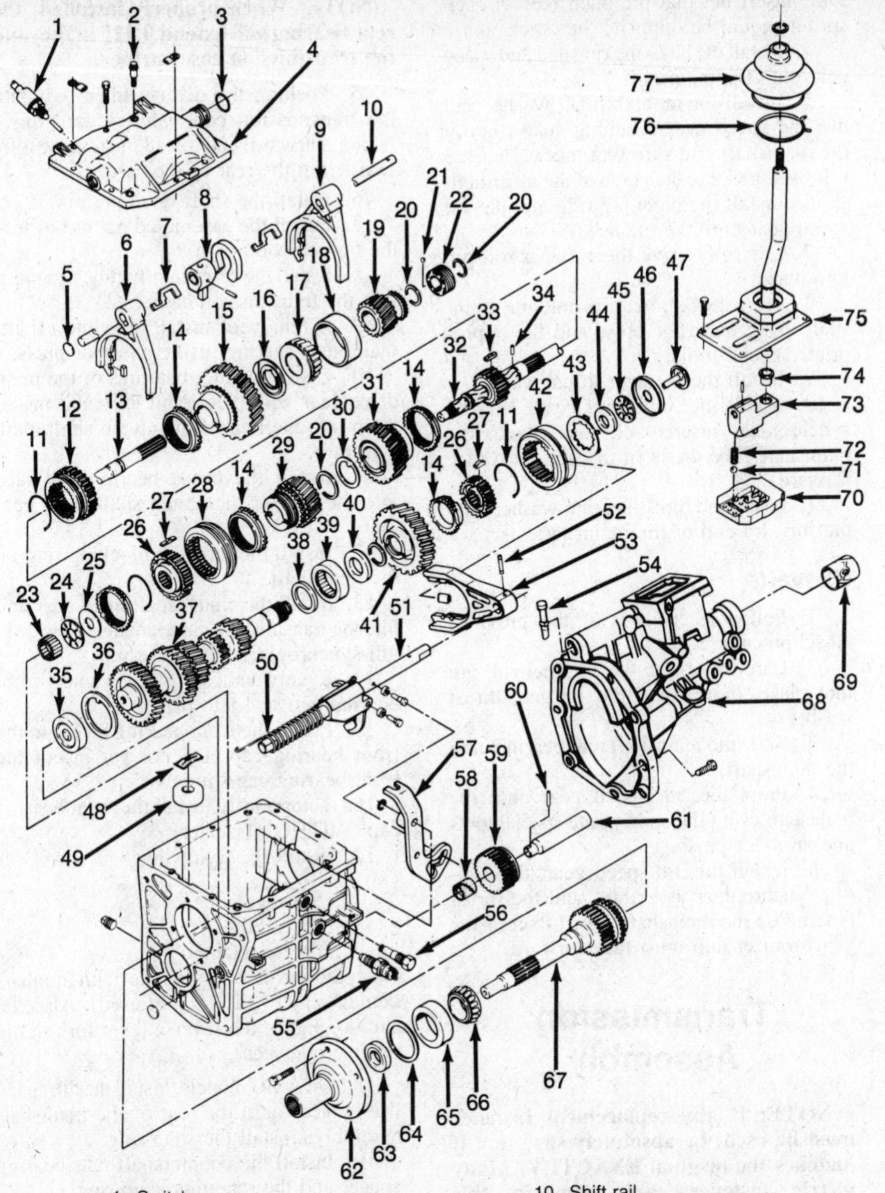

20. Snap-ring
21. Ball
22. Speedometer drive gear
23. Clutch shaft needle bearing
24. Needle thrust bearing
25. Thrust bearing race
26. 3rd-4th synchronizer hub
27. Synchronizer insert
28. 3rd-4th synchronizer sleeve
29. 3rd speed gear
30. Thrust washer
31. 2nd speed gear
32. Mainshaft
33. Insert
34. Roll pin
35. Front countershaft thrust bearing
36. Thrust washer
37. Countergear unit
38. Bearing spacer
39. Rear countershaft bearing
40. Spacer
41. 5th speed gear
42. 5th synchronizer sleeve
43. Thrust washer
44. Bearing race
45. Needle thrust bearing
46. Thrust race
47. Plastic funnel
48. Retainer
49. Magnet
50. Overcenter spring
51. 5th-reverse shift rail
52. Roll pin
53. 5th-reverse shift fork
54. Breather
55. Back-up lamp switch
56. Reverse lever pivot bolt
57. Reverse lever
58. Reverse idler gear bushing
59. Reverse idler gear
60. Roll pin
61. Reverse idler shaft
62. Front bearing cap
63. Oil seal
64. Shim
65. Front bearing cup
66. Front bearing
67. Main drive gear and shaft unit
68. Extension housing
69. Bushing
70. Detent plate
71. Detent ball
72. Spring
73. Offset lever
74. Bushing
75. Lever assembly
76. Retainer
77. Boot

1. Switch
2. Alignment (dowel) bolt
3. O-ring
4. Transmission cover
5. Plug
6. 3rd-4th shift fork
7. Selector plate
8. Selector arm and interlock plate
9. 1st-2nd shift fork
10. Shift rail
11. Synchronizer insert spring
12. Reverse sliding gear
13. Mainshaft
14. Blocking ring
15. 1st speed gear
16. Thrust washer
17. Rear bearing
18. Bearing cup
19. 5th speed driven gear

Exploded view of the Chilton Type 22 transmission used in the Chevette

washers, thrust bearings, etc., should be allowed to air dry after cleaning, though they may be wiped with a clean cloth.

Inspect all parts for excessive wear and/or damage such as scoring, cracks, nicks, rough edges, etc. Replace any defective parts. To check the condition of the assembled bearings, first clean and dry them, then coat the bearings with light engine oil. Slowly spin the bearings by hand and check for any signs of roughness. If the bearing does not

feel perfectly smooth, it should be replaced.

NOTE: AMC recommends that if any gear of the mainshaft must be replaced, the countershaft gear should also be replaced to avoid noisy operation and maintain proper gear mesh.

While the transmission is out of the vehicle, it is good practice to check the condition of the clutch assembly and the throwout bearing. Also, replace all transmission

gaskets, seals, etc. during assembly of the transmission.

Component Assembly

NOTE: Coat all bearings, gear teeth, washers, etc., with light engine oil during assembly unless stated otherwise within the procedures.

TRANSMISSION COVER

1. Attach the nylon inserts to the shift forks and install the selector arm plates into the shift forks.

2. If removed, apply sealer to the edges of the shift rail plug then carefully tap the plug into place.

3. Coat the shift rail and rail bores with petroleum jelly then slide the shift rail into the cover until the end of the rail is flush with the inside edge of the cover.

4. With the offset of the 1st–2nd shift fork facing the rear of the cover, install the fork into the cover and push the shift rail through the fork. Note that the 1st–2nd fork is the larger of the two forks.

5. Place the selector arm and C-shaped interlock plate into the cover and insert the shift rail through the arm. Note that the widest part of the interlock plate must face away from the cover and that the selector arm roll pin hole must face downward and toward the rear of the cover.

6. With the offset of the 3rd–4th shift fork facing the rear of the cover, install the fork into the cover. The 3rd–4th shift fork selector arm plate must be positioned under the 1st–2nd arm plate. Push the shift rail completely forward, through the 3rd–4th fork and into the cover bore.

7. Rotate the shift rail so that the forward selector arm plate faces away from, but is parallel to the cover.

8. After aligning the holes, install the selector arm-to-shift rail roll pin.

NOTE: To prevent the roll pin from contacting the selector arm plates when shifting, the roll pin must be installed flush with the surface of the selector arm.

9. Install the O-ring into the groove of the shift rail oil seal.

10. Installation of the shift rail oil seal should be performed as follows, using the appropriate special tools:

 a. Install Kent-Moore tool #J-26628-2 (or its equivalent) over the threaded end of the shift rail.

 b. Lubricate the lip of the oil seal with petroleum jelly.

 c. Slide the seal over the special tool (protector) and onto the shift rail.

 d. Using Kent-Moore tool #J-26628-1 (seal installer), seat the seal in the cover.

MAINSHAFT

AMC Models

1. Lubricate the mainshaft and gear bores with a liberal coating of transmission lubricant.

2. Align then install the 1st–2nd synchronizer sleeve on the mainshaft, using the matchmarks made during disassembly as an alignment guide.

3. If removed, install the synchronizer inserts and springs into the 1st–2nd synchronizer sleeve. Note that the tanged end of each spring should be positioned on the

same insert but that the open face of each spring should be opposite the other.

4. Install the blocking ring and 2nd speed gear onto the mainshaft.

5. Install the tabbed thrust washer and the 2nd speed gear retaining snap-ring on the mainshaft. Be sure that the washer tab is fully seated into the notch of the mainshaft.

6. Install the blocking ring and the 1st speed gear onto the mainshaft.

7. Carefully drive the 1st gear roll pin into place.

8. Press the rear bearing onto the mainshaft using an arbor press and the appropriate special tools.

9. Install the 1st gear thrust washer.

10. Install the 3rd speed gear, 3rd–4th synchronizer inserts and sleeve onto the mainshaft. The offset of the hub must face forward.

11. Install the thrust bearing washer onto the forward end of the mainshaft.

Chevette

1. Follow Steps 1-6 of the previous AMC procedure.

2. Carefully drive the 1st gear roll pin into place, then install the 1st gear thrust washer.

3. Slide the mainshaft rear bearing onto the mainshaft.

4. Press the 5th speed gear onto the mainshaft using the appropriate special tools and an arbor press.

5. Install the 3rd speed gear, the 3rd–4th synchronizer assembly, and the thrust bearing on the mainshaft. The offset of the synchronizer hub must face forward.

Transmission Assembly

NOTE: If any replacement fastener must be used, be absolutely sure that it matches the original EXACTLY. Many metric fasteners are used in this transmission.

1. Apply a coating of Loctite® 601 (or its equivalent) to the outer cage of the front countershaft bearing. Press the bearing fully into its bore; it should be flush with the transmission case.

2. Apply a coating of petroleum jelly to the tabbed countershaft thrust washer. Install the thrust washer so that its tab engages the corresponding depression in the transmission case.

3. Tip the transmission case on end and install the countershaft into the front bearing bore.

4. Install the countershaft rear bearing spacer and coat the rear countershaft bearing with petroleum jelly. Install the rear countershaft bearing using the appropriate special tools (Kent-Moore tool #J-29895 installer and J-33032 sleeve protector, or their equivalents).

NOTE: When properly installed, the rear bearing will extend 0.125 in. beyond the transmission case surface.

5. Position the reverse idler gear into the transmission case (shift lever groove facing rearward) and install the reverse idler shaft from the rear of the case.

6. Install the shaft retaining pin.

7. Install the assembled mainshaft into the transmission case.

8. Install the rear mainshaft bearing race into the transmission case.

9. If removed, install the clutch shaft/main gear bearing, using an arbor press.

10. Coat the roller bearings of the main drive gear with petroleum jelly and install them into the rear of the clutch shaft/main gear unit.

11. Install the thrust bearing and race into the rear of the clutch shaft/main gear unit.

12. Install the 4th gear blocking ring on the mainshaft.

13. Install the clutch shaft/main gear unit into the transmission case, engaging the 3rd–4th synchronizer blocking ring.

14. Evenly and carefully tap a new front bearing cap seal into place.

15. Install the front bearing race into the front bearing cap. Do not yet install the front bearing cap shims.

16. Temporarily install the front bearing cap, WITHOUT sealer.

17. Install the following:

 a. 5th-reverse lever
 b. Pivot bolt
 c. C-clip retainer

Coat the pivot bolt threads with nonhardening sealer (RTV is preferred). Also, be sure to engage the reverse lever fork in the reverse idler gear.

18. On AMC models, install the 5th speed driven gear onto the rear of the mainshaft assembly. Install the snap-ring.

19. Install the countershaft rear bearing spacer and the retaining snap-ring.

20. Install the 5th speed gear onto the mainshaft.

21. Install the 5th-reverse rail through the rear transmission case opening and install it into the 5th-reverse lever. Rotate the rail to engage it with the lever.

22. On AMC models only:

 a. Install the overcenter spring.

 b. Assemble the 5th gear synchronizer sleeve, insert springs and insert retainer. use the matchmarks made during disassembly to align.

 c. Install the plastic inserts on the fifth speed shift fork.

23. Position the 5th speed synchronizer assembly on the 5th speed shift fork and slide onto countershaft and 5th-reverse rail. Note that the 5th-reverse rail roll pin hole must be aligned with the hole of the 5th speed shift fork.

24. Support the 5th speed shift fork rail and fork with a block of wood and drive the roll pin into place.

25. Install the:

a. Thrust race against the 5th speed synchronizer hub and retain with the snapring.

b. Needle-type thrust bearing against the thrust race on the countershaft (coat the bearing and race with petroleum jelly).

c. Lipped thrust race over the needle-type thrust bearing.

d. Plastic funnel into the hole in the end of the countershaft gear.

26. Temporarily install the extension/adapter housing and the attaching bolts.

27. Turn the transmission case on end. Mount a dial indicator on the extension/adapter housing so that the indicator needle contacts the end of the mainshaft. Zero the indicator needle.

28. Pull upward fully on the mainshaft to remove the end-play. Read the indicator and record the reading.

29. Select a shim pack which measures 0.001-0.005 in. THICKER than the end play reading obtained during Step 28.

30. Move the transmission so that it sits horizontally, remove the front bearing cap and bearing race, and install the shim pack. Reinstall the bearing race.

31. Apply a ⅛ in. bead of RTV sealer on the case mating surface of the front bearing cap. Align the case and cap matchmarks which were made during disassembly. Install the bearing cap and torque the bolts to 15 ft. lbs.

32. Recheck the end-play. No play should be evident.

33. Remove the extension/adapter housing and carefully drive a new housing seal into place.

34. Move the shift forks of the transmission cover and the synchronizer sleeves of the transmission to their Neutral positions.

35. Apply a ⅛ in. bead of RTV sealer to the cover mating surface of the transmission. While aligning the shift forks with the synchronizer sleeves, carefully lower the cover assembly into place on the transmission.

36. Center the cover in order to engage the reverse relay lever. Install the two alignment-type (dowel) cover attaching bolts. Install the remaining cover bolts. Torque all cover bolts to 10 ft. lbs.

NOTE: The offset lever-to-shift rail roll pin hole must be positioned vertically; if it is not, repeat Steps 34, 35 and 36.

37. Apply a ⅛ in. bead of RTV sealer to the extension/adapter housing mating surface of the transmission and install the housing over the mainshaft.

NOTE: The shift rail must be positioned so that it just enters the shift cover opening.

38. Install the detent spring into the offset lever and place the steel ball into the neutral guide plate detent. Apply pressure on the steel ball with the detent spring and offset lever, then slide the offset lever on

the shift rail and seat the extension/adapter against the transmission case.

39. Install the extension/adapter housing retaining bolts and torque the bolts to 25 ft. lbs.

40. Install the roll pin into the offset lever and shift rail.

41. Install the damper sleeve in the offset lever. Coat the back-up lamp switch threads with RTV sealer and install the switch into the transmission case. Torque the switch to 15 ft. lbs.

CHILTON TYPE 23

Transmission Disassembly

NOTE: The use of an arbor press is required to properly disassemble and assemble this transmission. Read the entire procedure carefully before starting the job.

1. Remove the transmission plug and allow the lubricant to drain from the transmission.

2. Remove the throwout bearing and fork from the transmission as outlined in the appropriate car section.

3. Remove the drive gear bearing retainer. If damaged, remove the ball stud.

4. Remove the Belleville spring from the front of the drive gear bearing.

5. Remove the bolt, retainer, and speedometer driven gear from the side of the transmission.

6. Remove the shift lever quadrant from the extension housing.

7. Remove the back-up light switch.

8. Remove the extension housing bolts and the extension housing.

9. Remove the snap-rings, speedometer drive gear, spacer, and bearing from the mainshaft.

10. Remove the snap-ring, then the thrust washer and lock ball from the driveshaft.

11. Remove the large snap-ring from the main drive gear bearing.

12. Remove the following components from the case as an assembly:

a. Center support

b. Mainshaft

c. Countergear

d. Drive gear

13. Using a drift punch and a hammer, carefully drive the roll pins from the 1st-2nd, 3rd-4th, and 5th-reverse shift forks. Support the shaft ends with a bar or a block of wood to prevent damage to these components.

14. Remove the detent spring plate mounting bolts, detent spring plate, and the three springs and balls from the center support.

15. Remove the shifter shafts from the center support, then remove the shift forks from the shafts. Remove the interlock pins from the center support.

16. Move the 1st-2nd synchronizer sleeve to the 1st gear position, and the 3rd-4th synchronizer sleeve to the 3rd gear position.

17. Install a holding fixture (Kent-Moore tool #J-29768 or its equivalent) on the end of the drive gear shaft and countergear. Remove the countergear retaining nut and the washer.

18. Using an appropriate puller, remove the ball bearing and 5th speed gear from the counter shaft.

19. Remove the 5th gear, blocking ring, and the needle bearing from the mainshaft.

20. Remove the self-locking nut from the reverse idler gear shaft.

21. Remove the thrust washers and the reverse idler gear from the reverse idler gear shaft.

22. Bend the locking retainer of the mainshaft nut away from the nut. Remove the mainshaft nut using the appropriate tool.

23. Remove the 5th-reverse synchronizer locking retainer, 5th-reverse synchronizer assembly, reverse gear, needle bearing, collar, and the thrust washer from the mainshaft.

24. Remove the reverse gear from the countergear and remove the holding fixture installed during Step 17.

25. Move the sychronizer sleeves back to their Neutral positions.

26. Expand the countergear bearing snapring (using snap-ring pliers) and gently tap on the front of the center support. Expand the mainshaft bearing snap-ring and move the mainshaft inward. Remove the countergear and mainshaft.

27. Remove the drive gear, needle bearing, and the blocking ring from the end of the mainshaft.

Mainshaft

1. Remove the mainshaft rear bearing using an arbor press and Kent-Moore tool #J-22912-01 (or its equivalent).

2. Remove the thrust washer, 1st speed gear, needle bearings, and the spacer.

3. Remove the 1st-2nd synchronizer assembly, the 2nd speed gear, and the needle bearings.

4. Remove the snap-ring from in front of the 3rd-4th synchronizer and slide the synchronizer off of the mainshaft.

REMOVAL & INSTALLATION
Drive Gear Bearing

1. Remove the snap-ring from the drive gear shaft.

2. Install Kent-Moore tool #J-22912-01 (or its equivalent) under the drive gear bearing and press the drive gear shaft through the bearing (an arbor press must be used).

3. Installation is performed in the reverse of the previous steps.

Countergear Bearing

The bearing is removed in the same manner as the drive gear bearing, using the same special tool and an arbor press. Note that the groove on the bearing is installed towards the rear of the transmission.

Extension Housing or Drive Gear Retainer Seals

The seals are removed by prying them out with an appropriate tool. Install the new seals by carefully tapping them into place.

Mainshaft Assembly

1. Install the third speed gear (with needle bearings) onto the front of the mainshaft. Note that the coned side of the gear is installed toward the front of the mainshaft.

2. Install the 3rd-4th sychronizer assembly onto the mainshaft, with the large chamfered end toward the front of the transmission. Retain the synchronizer the snapring.

3. Install the 2nd speed gear (with needle bearings) onto the rear of the mainshaft. Note that the coned side of the gear is installed toward the rear of the mainshaft.

4. Install the 1st-2nd synchronizer assembly onto the mainshaft, with the large champfered end toward the rear of the transmission.

5. Install the 1st speed gear (with spacer and needle bearings), with the coned end facing the front of the transmission.

6. Install the 1st gear thrust washer, with the slots of the washer facing the gear.

7. Press the rear bearing onto the mainshaft according to the previous procedure under ''Removal and Installation''.

Transmission Assembly

1. If removed, install the countergear and mainshaft snap-rings into the center support. Also install the reverse idler shaft into the center support.

2. Install the drive gear onto the front of the mainshaft and engage it with the countergear.

3. Install the holding fixture in the same manner as Disassembly, Step 17.

4. With the mainshaft and countergears meshed together, slide the center support onto the mainshaft. Expand the mainshaft snap-ring and continue to push the center support on until the mainshaft bearing groove aligns with the snap-ring. Release the mainshaft snap-ring to lock the mainshaft bearing into place. Repeat the same procedure to seat the countergear snap-ring.

5. Move the synchronizer sleeves to engage both 1st and third gear ranges in order to lock the gears.

6. Install the reverse gear onto the countergear.

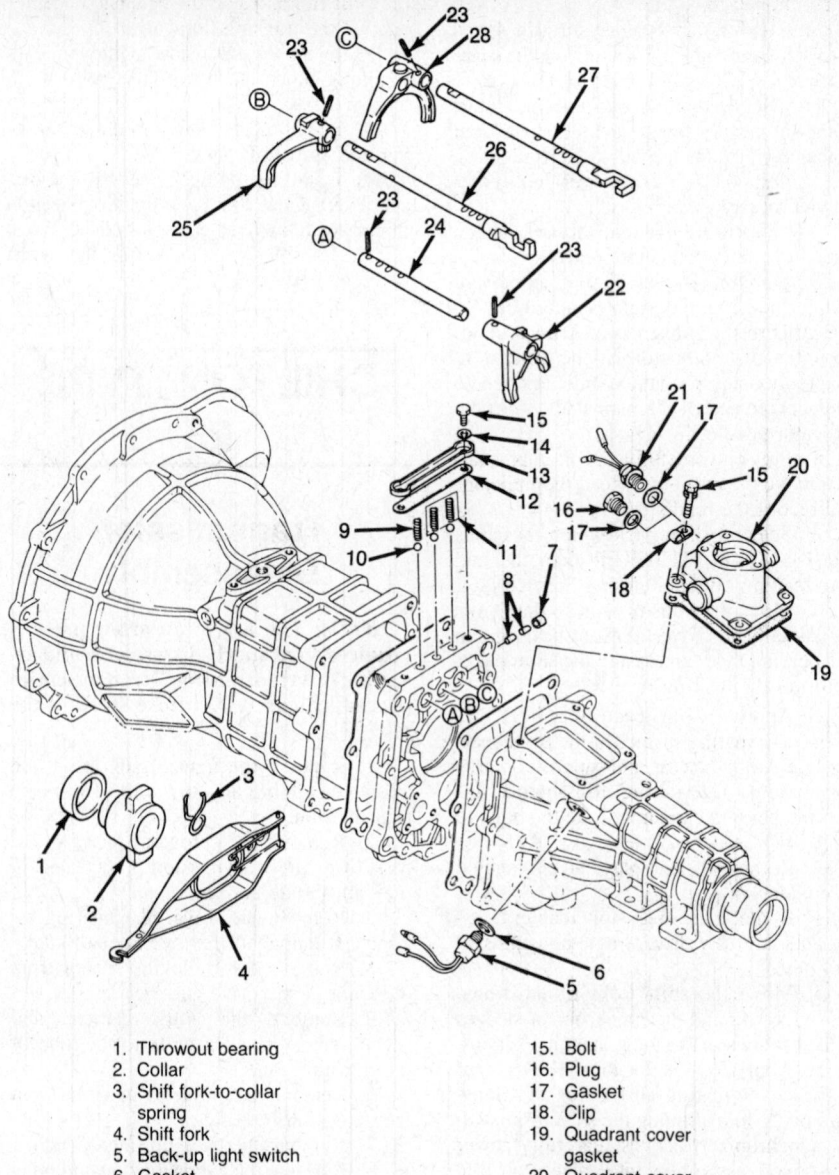

1. Throwout bearing	15. Bolt
2. Collar	16. Plug
3. Shift fork-to-collar spring	17. Gasket
4. Shift fork	18. Clip
5. Back-up light switch	19. Quadrant cover gasket
6. Gasket	20. Quadrant cover
7. Interlock spring	21. Neutral switch
8. Interlock pin	22. Reverse shift fork
9. Reverse detent spring	23. Roll pin
10. Reverse detent ball	24. Reverse shifter shaft
11. Detent springs	25. 3rd-4th shift fork
12. Detent spring plate gasket	26. 3rd-4th shifter shaft
13. Detent spring plate	27. 1st-2nd shifter shaft
14. Washer	28. 1st-2nd shift fork

Shift components of the Chilton Type 23 transmission

7. Install the thrust washer on the mainshaft (oil groove toward the rear), then install the collar, needle bearing, and reverse gear onto the mainshaft.

8. Install the 5th-reverse sychronizer, with the face of the higher clutch hub boss facing the reverse gears.

9. Install the locking retainer and the mainshaft nut onto the mainshaft. Torque the mainshaft nut to 94 ft. lbs., then bend the locking retainer tabs in order to lock the nut.

10. Install the thrust washers and the reverse idler gear on the reverse idler gear shaft. Thread a NEW self-locking nut onto the reverse idler shaft and torque the nut to 80 ft. lbs.

NOTE: The flange of the plate-side thrust washer must be fitted to the center support.

11. Install the synchronizer blocking ring and the 5th speed gear (with needle bearings) onto the mainshaft.

12. Install the fifth speed gear (of the countergear), ball bearing, washer, and a NEW self-locking nut onto the rear of the countergear. Torque the nut to 80 ft. lbs.

13. Remove the holding fixture and move the synchronizer sleeves back to their Neutral positions.

14. Grease the interlock pins and install them into the center support.

15. Place the shift forks into position on the synchronizer sleeves. Install the shifter shafts through their respective forks from the rear of the center support, except the 5th-reverse shaft, which is installed from the front of the support.

16. Install the detent balls (3), springs, detent plate gasket, and the detent plate. Torque the detent plate bolts to 14 ft. lbs.

17. Using a drift punch and a hammer, carefully install the retaining pins into the shift forks. Remember to support the shafts with a bar or a block of wood to prevent damage.

18. If removed, lubricate the countergear needle bearing and install it into the front of the case. The bearing should be driven into place while a socket is positioned on the outer bearing race.

19. Install a NEW center support-to-transmission case gasket on the transmission case and install the center support/mainshaft/countergear/drive gear assembly into the case.

20. Install the large snap-ring onto the shaft of the drive gear bearing.

21. Install the lock ball, thrust water, and the retaining snap-ring onto the mainshaft.

22. Using a feeler gauge, check the clearance between the 5th speed gear (of the mainshaft) and its thrust washer. The clearance should be 0.010–0.016 in. If necessary, adjust the clearance by purchasing a thrust washer of the correct thickness which will replace the existing washer. Thrust washers are available in thickness ranging from 0.307–0.327 in. in 0.003 in. increments.

NOTE: Use care when removing/installing the snap-ring; it must be replaced if it becomes distorted.

23. Install these parts on the mainshaft behind the 5th gear snap-ring (in this order):
 a. Ball bearing
 b. Snap-ring
 c. Speedometer gear clip
 d. Speedometer drive gear

24. Attach the extension housing to the center support, using a NEW gasket. Torque the bolts to 27 ft. lbs.

25. Install the shift lever quadrant onto the extension housing, using a NEW gasket. Torque the bolts to 14 ft. lbs.

26. Install the speedometer driven gear and torque the bolt to 14 ft. lbs.

27. Install the back-up light switch into the extension housing.

28. Install the belleville washer in front of the drive gear bearing, noting that the

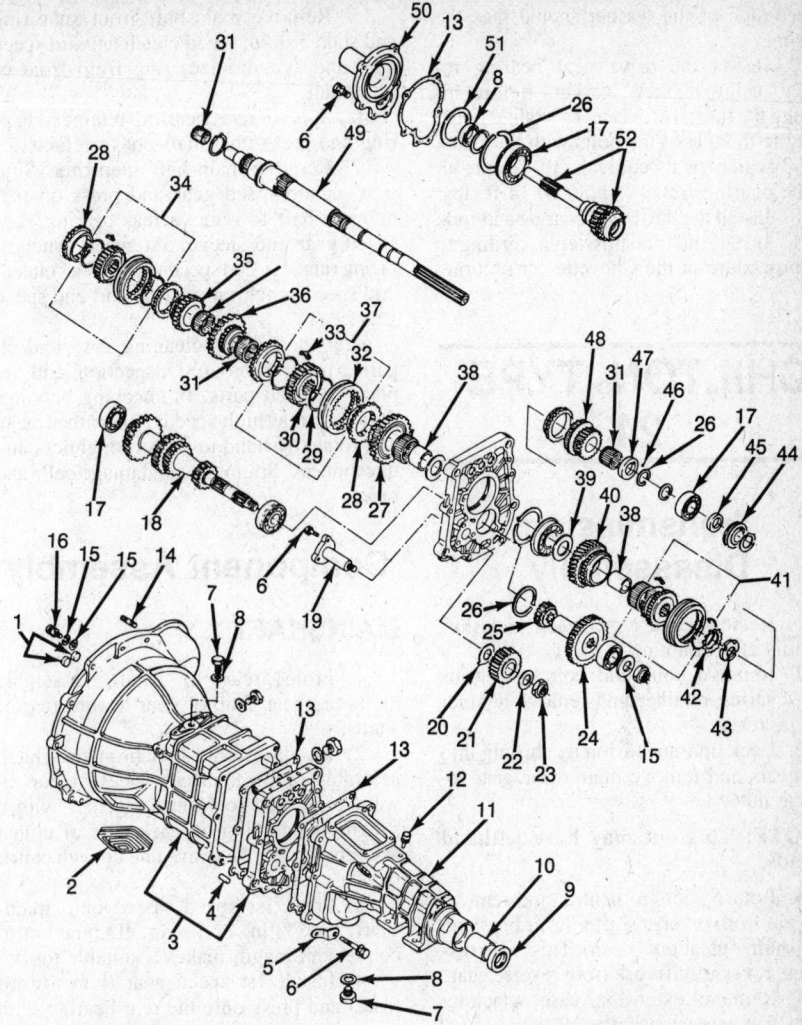

1. Shift rod plug
2. Dust cover
3. Case with center support
4. Pin
5. Return spring bracket
6. Bolt
7. Plug
8. Seal
9. Seal
10. Bushing
11. Extension
12. Ventilator
13. Gasket
14. Starter locating stud
15. Washer
16. Shift fork support
17. Ball bearing assembly
18. Countergear
19. Reverse idler shaft
20. Reverse idler front thrust washer
21. Reverse idler gear
22. Reverse idler rear thrust washer
23. Self-locking nut
24. 5th speed gear
25. Reverse gear
26. Snap-ring
27. 1st speed gear assembly
28. Blocking ring
29. Synchronizer insert spring
30. Synchronizer hub
31. Needle bearing
32. Synchronizer sleeve
33. Synchronizer insert (key)
34. 3rd-4th synchronizer assembly
35. 3rd gear assembly
36. 2nd gear assembly
37. 1st-2nd synchronizer assembly
38. Collar
39. Thrust washer
40. Reverse gear (mainshaft)
41. 5th-reverse synchronizer assembly
42. Mainshaft lockwasher
43. Mainshaft nut
44. Speedometer drive gear
45. Spacer
46. Ball
47. Selective thrust washer
48. 5th speed gear (mainshaft)
49. Mainshaft
50. Drive gear bearing retainer
51. Belleville spring
52. Main drive gear and shaft assembly

Transmission case and geartrain components of the Chilton Type 23 transmission

dished side of the washer should face the bearing.

29. Install the drive gear bearing retainer, using a NEW gasket. Before installing the three lower bearing retainer bolts, coat the threads of the bolts with Permatex No. 2 sealer (or its equivalent). Torque all of the bearings retainer bolts to 14 ft. lbs.

30. Install the throw-out bearing and fork.

31. Install the transmission according to the procedure in the Chevette car section.

CHILTON TYPE 24

Transmission Disassembly

1. Remove side covers and and shift controls after draining.

2. Remove bolts and bolt lock strips from bearing retainer and remove retainer and gasket.

3. Lock up transmission by shifting into two gears and remove main drive gear retaining nut.

NOTE: This nut may have lefthand threads.

4. Return gears to neutral and remove lock pin from reverse shifter lever boss and pull shaft out about ⅛ in. This will disengage reverse shift fork from reverse gear.

5. Remove extension case attaching bolts. Tap extension with soft hammer toward rear. When idler shaft is out as far as it will go, move extension to left so reverse fork clears gear and remove extension and gasket.

6. Remove reverse idler gear, flat washer, shaft and roll spring pin.

7. Remove speedometer and reverse gears.

NOTE: Slide 3rd-4th synchronizer clutch sleeve to 4th speed gear position (forward) before trying to remove mainshaft assembly from case.

8. Remove rear bearing retainer and mainshaft assembly from case by tapping bearing retainer with soft hammer.

9. Unload bearing rollers from main drive gear and remove fourth-speed synchronizer blocking ring.

10. Lift front half of reverse idler gear with tanged thrust washer from case.

11. Press main drive gear down from bearing.

12. Tap front bearing and snap-ring from case.

13. From front of case , press out countershaft. Then, remove the countershaft gear and both tanged washers.

14. Remove the rollers (112), six spacers and roller spacer from countergear.

15. Remove mainshaft front snap-ring and slide 3rd-4th speed clutch and 3rd speed gear and synchronizer ring from front of mainshaft.

16. Spread rear bearing retainer snap-ring and press mainshaft out of retainer.

17. Remove mainshaft snap-ring. Support second-speed gear and press on rear of mainshaft to remove rear bearing, 1st-speed gear and sleeve, 1st-speed synchronizing ring, 1st-2nd speed sychronizer clutch, 2nd speed synchronizer ring and 2nd speed gear.

After thoroughly cleaning case and all parts, make thorough inspection and replace required parts. In checking bearings do not spin at high speeds, but rather clean and rotate by hand to detect roughness and unevenness. Spinning can damage balls and races.

Component Assembly

MAINSHAFT

1. From rear of shaft, assemble 2ndspeed gear (hub of gear toward rear of shaft).

2. Install 1st-2nd synchronizer clutch assembly onto mainshaft (sleeve taper toward rear, hub to front): together with a synchronizing ring on each side of clutch assembly so that keyways line up with clutch keys.

3. Press 1st speed sleeve onto mainshaft. (A 1¾ in. or 1⅝ in. ID pipe cut to convenient length makes a suitable tool).

4. Install 1st speed gear (hub toward front) and press onto the rear bearing with snap-ring grooves toward front of transmission. Be sure bearing is firmly seated.

5. Choose selective fit snap-ring (0.087, 0.090, 0.093 or 0.096 in.) and install it into groove in mainshaft behind rear bearing. Maximum clearance of snap-ring and rear face should be between 0 and 0.005 in.

NOTE: Always use new snap-ring.

6. Install 3rd-speed gear (hub to front of transmission) and third-speed gear synchronizing ring (notches to front).

7. Install 3rd-4th-speed gear clutch assembly with both sleeve taper and hub toward front.

8. Install snap-ring into mainshaft in front of 3rd-4th-speed clutch, with ends of snap-ring seated behind spline teeth.

9. Install rear bearing retainer. Spread snap-ring in plate, to allow ring to drop around rear bearing, and press on the end of mainshaft until snap-ring engages the groove in rear bearing.

10. Install reverse gear (shift collar to rear).

11. Install speedometer drive gear.

COUNTERGEAR

1. Install roller spacer into countergear.

2. With heavy grease to assist, install a spacer in either end of countergear, 28 roller bearings, then a spacer and 28 more rollers. Then, install another spacer. In the other end of the countergear, do the same.

3. Insert dummy shaft into countergear.

Transmission Assembly

1. Rest case on side with cover opening toward mechanic. Install countergear tanged thrust washers in place, holding with heavy grease. Make sure tangs are in proper notches.

2. Set countergear in place. Use care not to disturb tanged washers.

3. Position transmission case so that it rests on front face.

4. Lubricate and insert countershaft in rear. Turn countershaft so flat on end of shaft is horizontal and facing bottom of case.

NOTE: The flat of shaft must be horizontal and toward bottom to mate with rear bearing retainer when installed.

5. Align countergear with shaft in rear and hole in front of case (pushing dummy shaft out front of case) until flat of shaft is flush with rear of case. Be sure thrust washers remain in place.

6. Check end-play in countergear (dial indicator should be used). If end-play is more than 0.025 in. install new thrust washer.

7. Install cage and 17 roller bearings into main drive gear. Use heavy grease to hold bearings.

8. Install main drive gear with bearings through side opening of case and into position in front bore.

9. Place gasket in position on rear bearing retainer.

10. Install 4th-speed synchronizing ring onto main drive gear (notches toward rear).

11. Position tanged thrust washer for reverse idler on machined face. Position front of reverse idler gear next to thrust washer (hub facing toward rear of case).

─── **CAUTION** ───
Before attempting to install mainshaft to case, slide the 3rd-4th synchronizer clutch sleeve forward into 4th-speed detent position.

12. Lower mainshaft assembly into case. Be sure notches on fourth-speed synchronizer ring correspond to keys in clutch assembly.

13. With guide pin in rear bearing retainer aligned with hole in rear of case, tap rear bearing retainer into position with soft hammer.

14. From rear of case, insert reverse idler gear, engaging splines with portion of front gear in case.

15. Place gasket in position on rear face of bearing retainer.

16. Install remaining flat washer on reverse idler shaft.

17. Install reverse idler shaft, roll pin, and thrust washer into gears and front boss of case. Make sure to pick up front tanged thrust washer.

18. Pull reverse shifter shaft to left side of extension and rotate shaft to bring reverse shift fork forward in extension (reverse detent position). Start extension onto transmission case, while slowly pushing in on shifter shaft to engage the shift fork with the reverse gear shift collar. Then, pilot the reverse idler shaft into the extension housing, permitting the extension to slide into the transmission case.

19. Install extension and retainer-to-case attaching bolts.

20. Push or pull reverse shifter shaft to line up grooves in the shaft with the holes in the boss and drive in the lockpin. Install shift lever.

21. Press bearing onto main drive gear (snap-ring groove in front), and into case until several main drive gear retaining nut threads are exposed.

22. Lock transmission by shifting into two gears. Install main drive gear retaining nut onto the gear shaft and draw it up tight. Be sure bearing is completely seated against shoulder. Torque retaining nut to 40 ft. lbs. and lock in place by staking into main drive gear shaft hold with punch. Do not damage shaft threads.

23. Install main drive gear bearing retainer, gasket attaching bolts and boltlock retainers. Use a suitable seal on bolts. Tighten to 20 ft. lbs.

24. Shift mainshaft 3rd-4th sliding clutch sleeve into neutral position and 1st-2nd sliding clutch into 2nd gear (forward) detent position. Shift side cover 3rd-4th shift lever into neutral detent and 1st-2nd shift lever into 2nd gear detent position.

25. Install side cover, with gasket, and carefully position in place. A dowel pin provides proper alignment position. Install bolts and tighten evenly to avoid distortion. Torque to 20 ft. lbs.

CHILTON TYPE 25

Transaxle Disassembly

1. Remove the clutch release bearing. Attach the transaxle to transaxle holding fixture J-33366 or its equal.

2. Remove the seven bolts from the rear cover and remove the cover.

3. Remove the control box assembly together with four bolts from the transaxle case.

4. Shift the transaxle into gear. Remove the fifth speed drive and driven gear

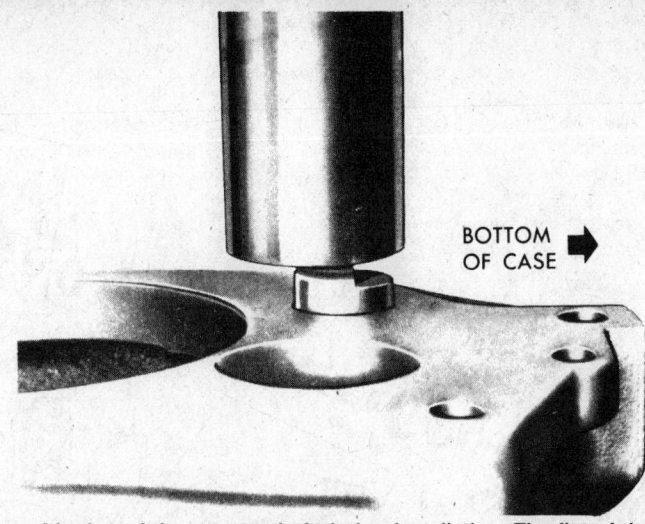

Proper positioning of the countershaft during installation. The flat of the shaft must face toward the bottom of the transmission case.

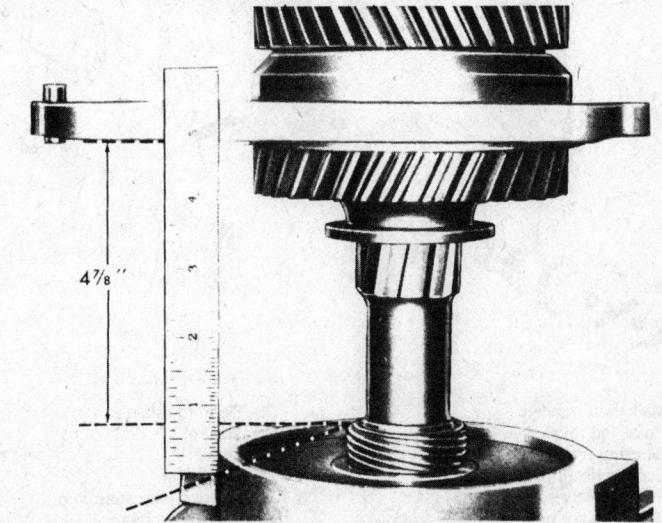

Installation of the speedometer drive gear. The gear must be positioned as shown.

retaining nuts from the input and output shaft. Shift the transaxle back into neutral, aligning the detents on the shift rails.

5. Remove the detent spring retaining bolts for 1st/2nd, 3rd/4th, reverse and 5th speeds. Remove the detent springs and detent balls. Remove the reverse detent spring retaining bolts, spring and detent.

6. Place 5th speed synchronizer in neutral and remove the roll pin at the 5th gear shift fork. Remove 5th gear synchronizer hub, sleeve, roller bearing and gear. Remove the shift fork as an assembly from the output shaft. Remove the 5th speed gear from the input shaft.

7. Remove the torx screws from the bearing retainer. Remove the bearing retainer and shims from the input and output shafts.

8. Remove the bolt used to retain the reverse idler shaft at the transaxle case.

9. Remove the collar and thrust washer from the output shaft using tool J-22888

and J-22888-30 or their equal.

10. Remove the bolts retaining the transaxle case and separate the transaxle case from the clutch housing.

11. Remove the reverse idler gear, reverse idler shaft.

12. Lift the 5th gear shaft. With the detent aligned facing the same way, remove the 5th and reverse shafts at the same time.

13. Use a punch and hammer to remove the roll pin from the 1-2 shift fork. Slide this shaft upward to clear the housing and remove the fork and shaft from the case.

14. Remove the cotter pin, then remove the pin and reverse shift lever.

15. Remove input and output shafts with 3-4 shift fork and shaft as an assembly.

16. Remove differential case assembly.

17. Remove the reverse shift bracket together with four bolts. Take out three interlock pins.

18. Remove the rear bearing outer race from the transaxle case. Remove the input shaft race.

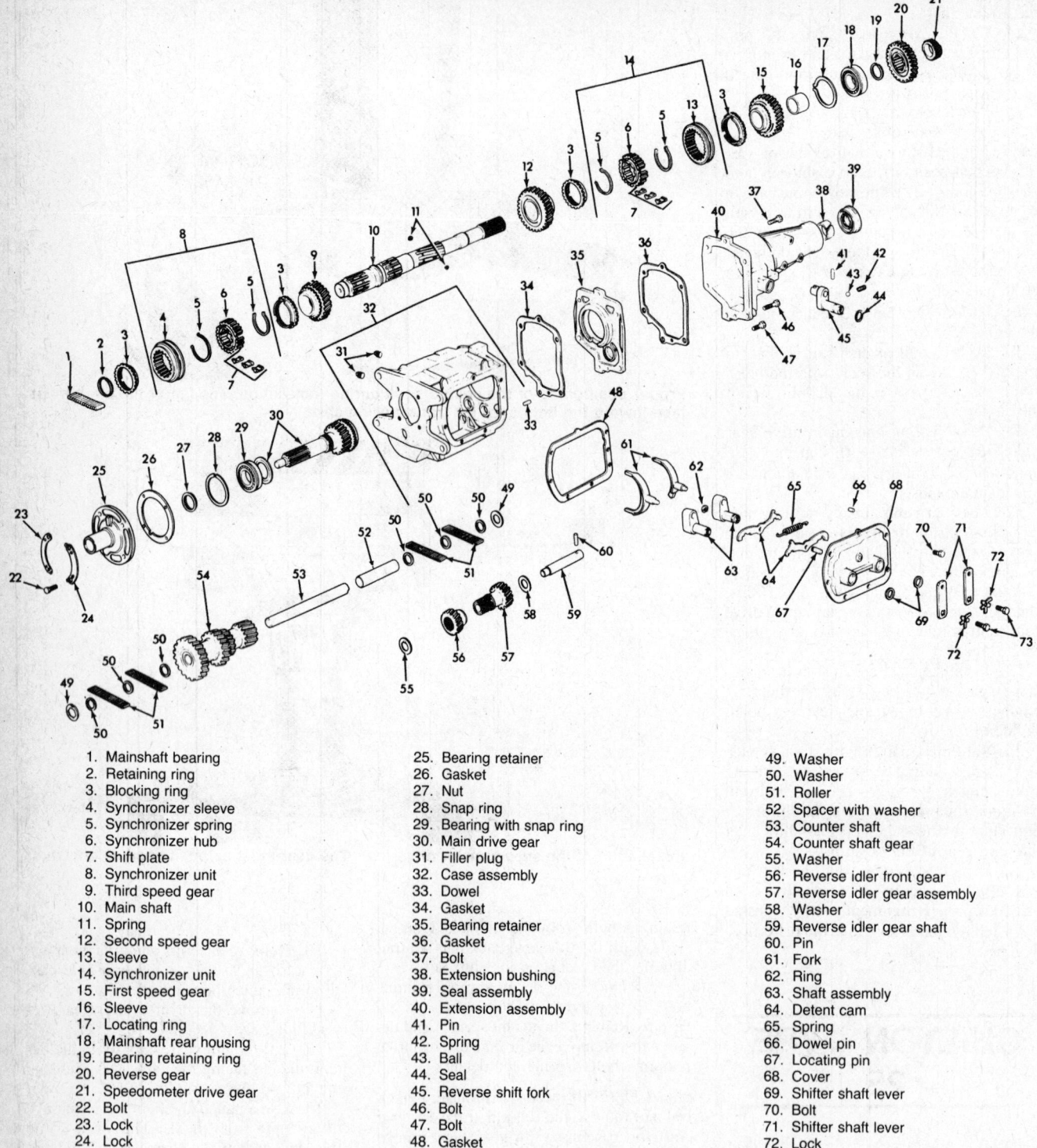

Exploded view of a Muncie 4 speed (Chilton Type 24) transmission

1. Mainshaft bearing
2. Retaining ring
3. Blocking ring
4. Synchronizer sleeve
5. Synchronizer spring
6. Synchronizer hub
7. Shift plate
8. Synchronizer unit
9. Third speed gear
10. Main shaft
11. Spring
12. Second speed gear
13. Sleeve
14. Synchronizer unit
15. First speed gear
16. Sleeve
17. Locating ring
18. Mainshaft rear housing
19. Bearing retaining ring
20. Reverse gear
21. Speedometer drive gear
22. Bolt
23. Lock
24. Lock

25. Bearing retainer
26. Gasket
27. Nut
28. Snap ring
29. Bearing with snap ring
30. Main drive gear
31. Filler plug
32. Case assembly
33. Dowel
34. Gasket
35. Bearing retainer
36. Gasket
37. Bolt
38. Extension bushing
39. Seal assembly
40. Extension assembly
41. Pin
42. Spring
43. Ball
44. Seal
45. Reverse shift fork
46. Bolt
47. Bolt
48. Gasket

49. Washer
50. Washer
51. Roller
52. Spacer with washer
53. Counter shaft
54. Counter shaft gear
55. Washer
56. Reverse idler front gear
57. Reverse idler gear assembly
58. Washer
59. Reverse idler gear shaft
60. Pin
61. Fork
62. Ring
63. Shaft assembly
64. Detent cam
65. Spring
66. Dowel pin
67. Locating pin
68. Cover
69. Shifter shaft lever
70. Bolt
71. Shifter shaft lever
72. Lock
73. Bolt

19. Remove the outer races from the input shaft front bearing, output shaft front and differential side bearings.

20. Remove the input shaft seal from the housing. Remove the clutch shaft seal only when replacement is required.

21. Drive the bushing toward the inside of the housing. Remove the fork assembly only when replacing the clutch fork assembly.

INPUT SHAFT DISASSEMBLY

1. Remove the front bearing using tool J-22912-01 or its equal, in addition to a press.

2. Pull out the rear bearing 4th gear, 3rd/4th synchronizer assembly and 3rd gear as an assembly.

NOTE: This procedure requires a press and special tool J22912-01 or its equal.

1. CLUTCH AND DIFF. HOUSING
2. CLUTCH SHAFT BUSHING
3. INPUT SHAFT OIL SEAL
4. DRIVE SHAFT OIL SEAL
5. STRAIGHT KNOCK PIN
6. TRANSAXLE CASE
7. DRAIN PLUG
8. GASKET
9. MAGNET
10. BEARING RETAINER
11. REAR COVER
12. GASKET
13. INPUT SHAFT
14. INPUT SHAFT FRONT BEARING
15. 3RD GEAR ASSEMBLY
16. 3RD/4TH SYNCHRONIZER ASM.
17. SYNCHRONIZER SLEEVE
18. CLUTCH HUB
19. INSERT
20. INSERT SPRING
21. 3RD/4TH BLOCKER RING
22. 4TH GEAR ASSEMBLY
23. 3RD NEEDLE BEARING
24. 4TH NEEDLE BEARING
25. 4TH COLLAR
26. 4TH GEAR THRUST WASHER
27. INPUT SHAFT REAR BEARING
28. 5TH GEAR
29. INPUT SHAFT END NUT
30. OUTPUT SHAFT
31. OUTPUT SHAFT FRONT BEARING
32. 1ST GEAR ASSEMBLY
33. 1ST/2ND SYNCHRONIZER ASSEMBLY
34. REVERSE GEAR
35. CLUTCH HUB
36. INSERT
37. INSERT SPRING
38. 1ST/2ND BLOCKER RING
39. 2ND GEAR ASSEMBLY
40. 1ST NEEDLE BEARING
41. 2ND NEEDLE BEARING
42. 2ND COLLAR
43. 3RD/4TH OUTPUT GEAR
44. KEY
45. OUTPUT SHAFT REAR BEARING
46. INPUT SHAFT BEARING SHIM
47. OUTPUT SHAFT BEARING SHIM
48. 5TH GEAR THRUST WASHER
49. 5TH NEEDLE BEARING
50. 5TH COLLAR
51. 5TH GEAR ASSEMBLY
52. 5TH SYNCHRONIZER ASSEMBLY
53. SYNCHRONIZER SLEEVE
54. CLUTCH HUB
55. INSERT
56. INSERT SPRING
57. 5TH BLOCKER RING
58. INSERT STOPPER PLATE
59. OUTPUT SHAFT END NUT
60. REVERSE IDLER GEAR ASM.
61. REVERSE IDLER SHAFT

62. STRAIGHT PIN
63. REVERSE IDLER SHAFT BOLT
64. GASKET
65. CLUTCH FORK SHAFT ASM.
66. CLUTCH RELEASE BEARING

67. RELEASE BEARING SPRING
68. CLUTCH SHAFT BUSHING
69. CLUTCH SHAFT SEAL
70. CLUTCH PRESSURE PLATE ASM.
71. CLUTCH DISK ASSEMBLY

5 speed transaxle—exploded view (Chilton Type 25)

OUTPUT SHAFT DISASSEMBLY

3. Remove other parts from the input shaft.

1. Remove the front bearing using tool J-22227-A or its equal along with a press.
2. Remove the rear bearing and 3rd/4th gear as an assembly using J-22912-01 and a press.
3. Remove the key, 2nd gear, needle bearing and blocker ring.
4. Remove the collar, reverse gear assembly and 1st gear as an assembly, using a press.

Transaxle Assembly

Before reassembly, attach the clutch housing to the transaxle holding fixture if removed.

1. Install input shaft seal.
2. Install the front outer bearing races for the input shaft, output shaft and differential into the clutch housing. Press the input, output and differential races into the housing.

3. Apply grease to three interlock pins, and install them on the clutch housing.
4. Install the reverse shift bracket on the clutch housing. Use 3rd/4th shift rod to align bracket to housing. Install retaining bolts and torque to specification. Make sure rod operates smoothly after installation.
5. Install the differential assembly first, then install the input and output shaft with

b. Place seven spacers provided with J-33373 evenly around the perimeter of the clutch housing.

c. Install bearing and shim retainer on transaxle case. Torque screws to 11-16 ft. lbs. (15-22 Nm).

d. Carefully position the transaxle case over the gauges and on the spacers. Install the seven bolts provided with the tool kit and tighten bolts alternately until case is seated on spacers. Torque bolts to 10 ft. lbs. (15 Nm).

e. Rotate each gauge to seat the bearings. Rotate the differential case through three revolutions in each direction.

f. With the three gauges compressed, measure the gap between the outer sleeve and the base pad using available shim sizes. Use the largest shim that can be placed into the gap and drawn through without binding. This will be the correct shim for the bearing being measured.

g. When each of the three shims have been selected, remove the transaxle case, seven spacers and three gauges.

12. Position the shim selected for the input, output and differential into the bearing race bores in the transaxle case.

13. Install the rear input shaft bearing race using J-24256-A with J-8092 or its equal and a press. Press bearing until seated in its bore.

14. Install the rear output shaft bearing race using J-33370 with J-8092 and a press. Press bearing until seated in its bore.

15. Install the rear differential case bearing race using J-8611-01 with J-8092 or its equal and a press. Press bearing until seated in its bore.

into the transaxle case. Torque the bolt to 22-33 ft. lbs. (30-45 Nm).

19. Install 14 case bolts. Torque bolts to 22-33 ft. lbs. (30-45 Nm) in a diagonal sequence.

20. Install drive axle seals.

21. Install the thrust washer and collar to the output shaft.

22. Install the 5th gear to the input shaft. Install the needle bearing, 5th gear, blocker ring, hub/sleeve assembly with shift fork in its groove and back plate on the output shaft. Align shift fork on shifter shaft and install roll pin.

23. Install the detent balls and detent springs for the reverse, 1st/2nd, 3rd/4th and 5th speeds. Install retaining bolts and torque to 15-21 ft. lbs. (21-29 Nm).

24. Apply Loctite® 262 or equivalent to the threads of the input and output shafts. Install new retaining nuts and torque to 87-101 ft. lbs. (118-137 Nm). Stake nuts after reaching final torque.

25. Install the gasket and control box assembly on the transaxle case, and torque four bolts to 11-16 ft. lbs. (15-22 Nm). Make sure transaxle shifts properly before installing rear cover.

26. Install the gasket and rear cover with seven bolts, and torque the bolts to 11-16 ft. lbs. (15-22 Nm).

27. Install the clutch fork assembly if it has been removed. Install the bushing into the upper hole using J-28412 or its equal. Install the oil seal. Before installing the bushing, apply grease to both the interior and exterior.

28. Install the clutch release bearing.

the 3rd/4th shift fork and shaft together as an assembly into the clutch housing.

NOTE: Make sure interlock pin is in the 3rd/4th shifter shaft before installing.

6. The 3rd/4th shift shaft is installed into the raised collar of reverse shift lever bracket.

7. Install the 1-2 shift fork onto the synchronizer sleeve and insert the shifter shaft into the reverse shift lever bracket. Align hole in fork with the shaft and install roll pin.

8. Install reverse lever on shift bracket.

9. Install reverse and 5th gear shifter shaft and at the same time, engage reverse shaft with reverse shift lever. Make sure interlock pin is in the 5th gear shifter shaft before installing.

10. Install the reverse idler shaft together with the gear into the clutch housing. Make sure reverse lever is engaged in collar of gear.

11. Measure and determine shim size using J-33373 or its equal.

a. Position the outer bearing races on the input, output and differential bearings. Position the shim selection gauges on the bearing races. The 3 gauges are identified: Input, Output and Differential.

16. Apply a 1/8 in. bead of Loctite® #514 or equivalent to the mating surfaces of the clutch housing and transaxle case.

17. Be sure magnet is installed in transaxle case.

18. Install the transaxle case on the clutch housing. Install the reverse idle shaft bolt

Automatic Transmissions

TRANSMISSION IDENTIFICATION BY PAN GASKET

AMC
TORQUE COMMAND 727
CHRYSLER
TORQUEFLITE 727

AMC
TORQUE COMMAND 904, 998
CHRYSLER
TORQUEFLITE 904

CHRYSLER
TORQUEFLITE
TRANSAXLE

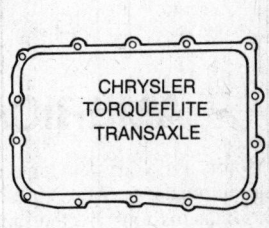

FORD FMX

FORD C3

FORD C4, C5

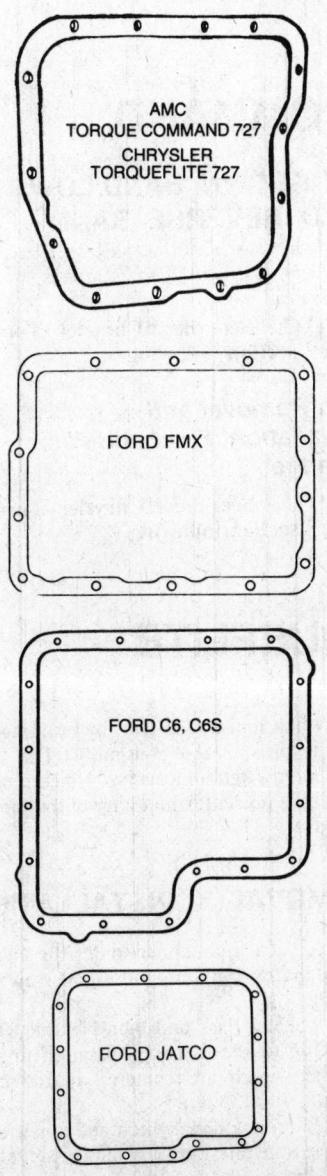

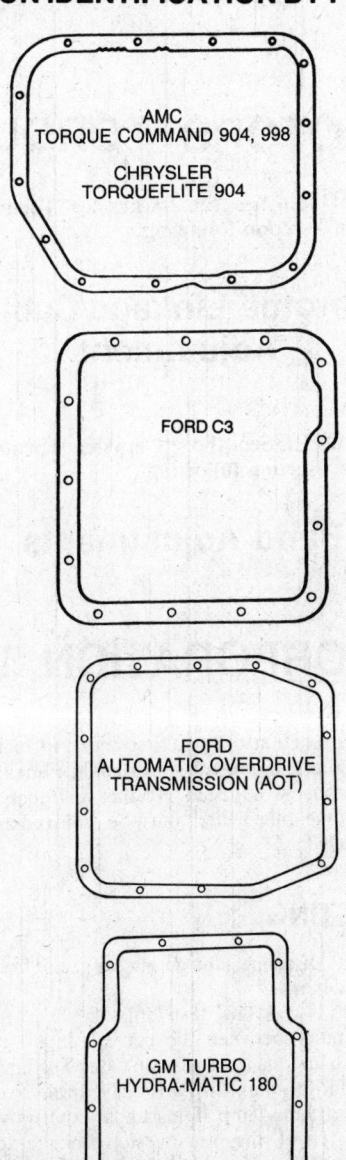

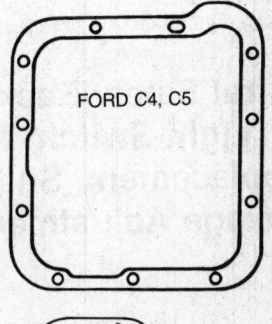

FORD C6, C6S

FORD
AUTOMATIC OVERDRIVE
TRANSMISSION (AOT)

FORD
AUTOMATIC
TRANSAXLE (ATX)

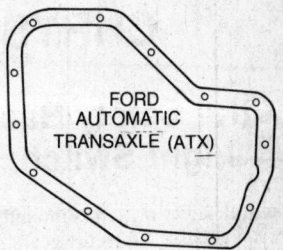

FORD JATCO

GM TURBO
HYDRA-MATIC 180

GM TURBO
HYDRA-MATIC 200

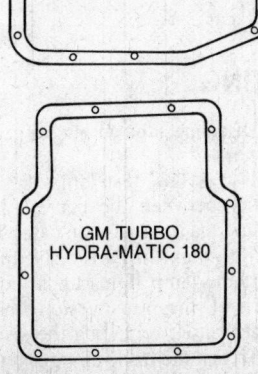

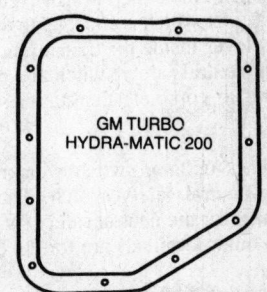

GM TURBO HYDRA-MATIC 250, 350, 375B

GM TURBO HYDRA-MATIC 400

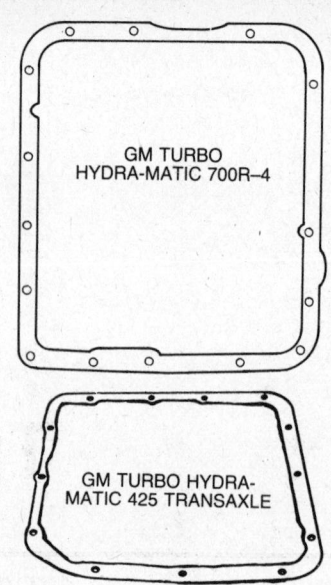

GM TURBO HYDRA-MATIC 700R–4

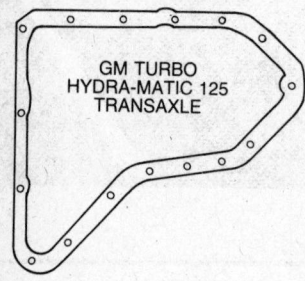

GM TURBO HYDRA-MATIC 125 TRANSAXLE

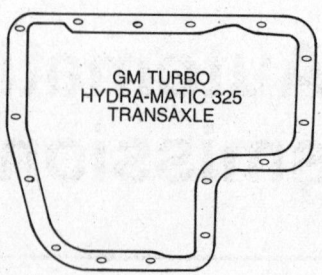

GM TURBO HYDRA-MATIC 325 TRANSAXLE

GM TURBO HYDRA-MATIC 425 TRANSAXLE

AMERICAN MOTORS TORQUE COMMAND

Amercan Motors uses Chrysler Corporation TorqueFlite automatic transmissions in all cars. These transmissions are the same as the equivalent Chrysler units, the only differences being in case designs required by the difference in American Motors' bell housing configurations and driveshafts.

Neutral Safety/Backup Light Switch Replacement, Shift Linkage Adjustment

NOTE: See the "Chrysler Torque-Flite" section following.

Throttle Linkage/Cable Adjustment

NOTE: See the "Chrysler Torque-Flite" section following.

Band Adjustments

KICKDOWN BAND/LOW AND REVERSE BAND

NOTE: See the "Chrysler Torque-Flite" section following.

Pan Removal and Installation, Fluid and Filter Change

NOTE: See the "Chrysler Torque-Flite" section following.

CHRYSLER CORPORATION TORQUEFLITE

Neutral Safety/Backup Light Switch

The neutral safety switch is mounted in the transmission case. When the gearshift lever is placed in either the Park of Neutral position, a cam, which is attached to the transmission lever inside the transmission, contacts the neutral safety switch and provides a ground to complete the starter solenoid circuit.

The back-up lamp switch is incorporated into the neutral safety switch. The center terminal is for the neutral safety switch and the two outer terminals are for the back-up lamps.

There is no adjustment for the switch. If

a malfunction occurs, first check to make sure that the transmission gearshift linkage is properly adjusted. If the malfunction continues, the switch must be removed and replaced.

TESTING

1. Disconnect the wiring connector from the switch.
2. Use a 12V test lamp to check for continuity between the center pin of the switch and the transmission case. The lamp should only light in Park or Neutral.
3. If the lamp lights up in other positions, check the transmission linkage adjustments before replacing the switch.
4. To test the back-up light function of

the switch repeat step two, by bridging the outside pins to test continuity. The light should only light in Reverse. No continuity should be present from either of the pins to the case.

REMOVAL & INSTALLATION

1. Place a container under the switch to catch transmission fluid. Unscrew the switch.
2. Select Park and then Neutral while checking to see that the operation fingers for the switch are centered in the case opening.
3. Screw a new switch and a *new* seal into the transmission. Tighten the switch to 24 ft. lbs.

4. Retest continuity. Replenish the transmission fluid, as required.

Adjustments

THROTTLE LINKAGE

Throttle linkage adjustment is important to proper operation of this transmission. This adjustment positions a valve which controls shift speed, shift quality and downshift sensitivity at part throttle. If the setting is too short, early shifts and slippage between shifts may occur. If the linkage setting is too long, shifts may be delayed and part throttle downshifts may be very sensitive. This adjustment is so critical that the use of a throttle lever holding spring is advised to remove slack in the linkage during adjustment.

1. Disconnect carburetor return spring at the carburetor.

2. Block the choke open and set the carburetor throttle off the fast idle cam.

3. Raise and safely support vehicle.

4. Use a spare carb return spring to hold the transmission throttle control lever fully forward against the stop. Do this by hooking one end of the spring on the throttle control lever and the other end at a convenient location, such as the bellcrank bracket on the converter housing.

NOTE: On some carburetors with a throttle operated solenoid valve, it will be necessary to turn the ignition to the "ON" position to energize the solenoid. Then open the throttle so that the solenoid can lock, and return the carb to the idle position.

5. Loosen the bolt on the throttle adjusting link. It is not necessary to remove it.

6. Pull on the end of the adjusting link to eliminate slack, then tighten retaining bolt.

7. Remove the spring put on the transmission throttle lever.

THROTTLE CABLE

4 Cylinder Engine

1. Remove air cleaner.

2. Remove spark plug wire separator from throttle cable bracket and move separator and wires aside.

3. Raise automobile.

4. Remove strut rod bushing heat shield to gain access to transmission throttle control lever.

5. Hold throttle lever rearward against its stop. Use spare spring to hold lever. Hook one end of spring to lever and hook opposite end of spring to convenient attachment point.

6. Lower automobile.

7. Block choke open and set carburetor linkage completely off fast idle cam.

8. On four cylinder automobiles without air conditioning, turn ignition key to On position to energize throttle stop solenoid.

9. Unlock throttle control cable by releasing T-shaped cable adjuster clamp. Release clamp by lifting upward with small screwdriver.

10. Grasp cable outer sheath and move cable and sheath forward to remove any cable load on throttle bellcrank.

NOTE: The bellcrank is part of the carburetor throttle linkage.

11. Adjust cable by moving cable and sheath rearward until there is zero lash between plastic cable end and bellcrank ball.

12. When zero lash between cable end and bellcrank is achieved, lock cable by pressing T-shaped cable adjuster clamp downward until clamp snaps into place.

13. Turn ignition off. Install spark plug wires and separator, connect throttle stop solenoid on air conditioned automobiles and install air cleaner.

14. Remove holding spring from transmision throttle control lever, install strut rod bushing heat shield and lower automobile.

15. Road test automobile and check transmission operation. Readjust throttle cable if necessary.

NOTE: Some V-8 cars use a slightly different arrangement, in that the adjusting link is pushed instead of pulled to remove the slack. However, the end result should be the same, and no slack or lash should be permitted. Too, many Chrysler Corp. vehicles use a lower bellcrank with a short throttle rod and adjustable swivel to hook up to the transmission throttle lever. In these cases, make sure the swivel is free to slide along the throttle rod so that the small pre-load spring action is not impaired. If necessary, clean and lightly lubricate. Again, the throttle lever must be held firmly forward against its internal stop. In this case, the linkage slack, or backlash was automatically removed by the small pre-load spring.

GEAR SHIFT LINKAGE

The gear shift linkage adjustment is important because the linkage positions the manual valve in the valve body. Incorrect adjustment will result in creeping in Neutral, premature clutch wear, delayed engagement in any gear or a no-start in Park or Neutral condition.

Proper operation of the neutral start switch will provide a quick check of linkage adjustment as follows:

1. Turn key to "ON" to unlock column and shift lever.

2. Move shift lever slowly until it clicks into the Park detent. Try to start engine. If starter does operatore, Park position is correct.

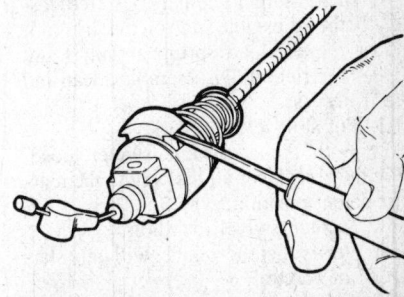

Throttle cable used with the AMC 151 engine. The snap-lock is shown in the raised (unlocked) position.

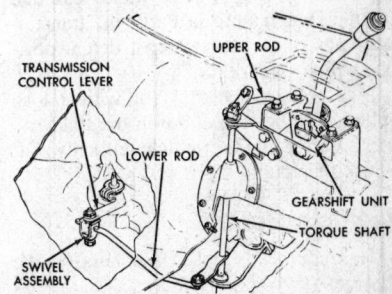

Typical automatic console shift linkage
(© Chrysler Corp)

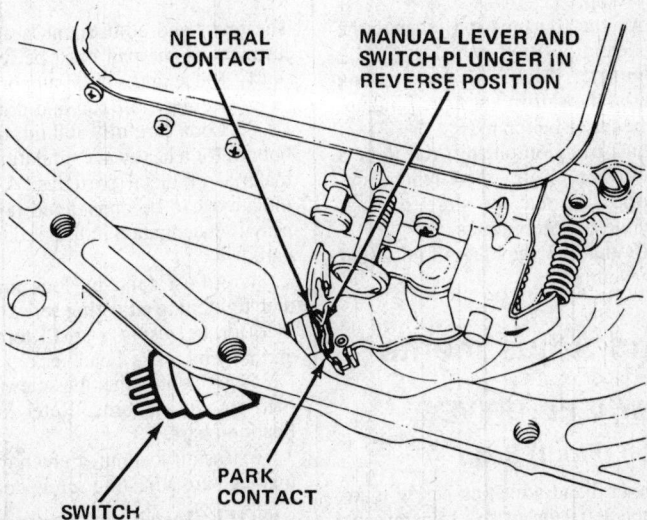

Torque-Command and TorqueFlite neutral start and backup light switch; pan removed, looking up (© American Motors Corp.)

3. Stop engine. Repeat, only this time moving lever to Neutral. Try to start engine. If starter does operate, Neutral position is correct and linkage is properly adjusted.

To adjust the linkage follow procedure below.

Chrysler Corporation

NOTE: Chrysler recommends that when it is necessary to disassemble linkage rods from their levers which use plastic grommets for retainers, the grommets should be replaced with new ones.

COLUMN SHIFT:

1. Make sure all linkage is free, especially the adjustable slide on the shift rod, so that the pre-load spring action is not reduced by friction. Disassemble, clean and lube if necessary.

2. Put shift lever in Park.

3. With the adjustable swivel loose, move the shift lever all the way to the rear-most detent position, which is Park.

4. Tighten swivel lock bolt.

5. Verify that the vehicle will only start in Park or Neutral.

CONSOLE SHIFT:

1. Adjustment is similar to above, but no pre-load spring is used. Make sure that with the shift handle in Park, the transmission lever is in the rear-most detent position, which is Park.

2. Tighten swivel lock bolt with no load applied in either direction on the linkage.

3. Verify that the vehicle will only start in Park or Neutral.

American Motors

1. Under car, loosen the nuts on the trunnions (swivels).

2. Disengage trunnion and shift rod at the bellcrank.

3. Place shift lever in Park and lock steering column.

4. Move the transmission lever to the rear-most detent position, which is Park.

5. Eliminate backlash by pulling downward on the shiftrod and pressing upward on the outer bellcrank.

6. Adjust trunnion on shift rod to be a free fit into bellcrank arm, then tighten jamnuts, making sure that the shift rod does not turn while tightening nuts.

7. Verify that the vehicle will only start in Park or Neutral.

Band Adjustments

REAR WHEEL DRIVE

Kickdown (Front) Band

The kickdown band adjusting screw is located on the left side of the transmission case above the throttle and shift linkage levers.

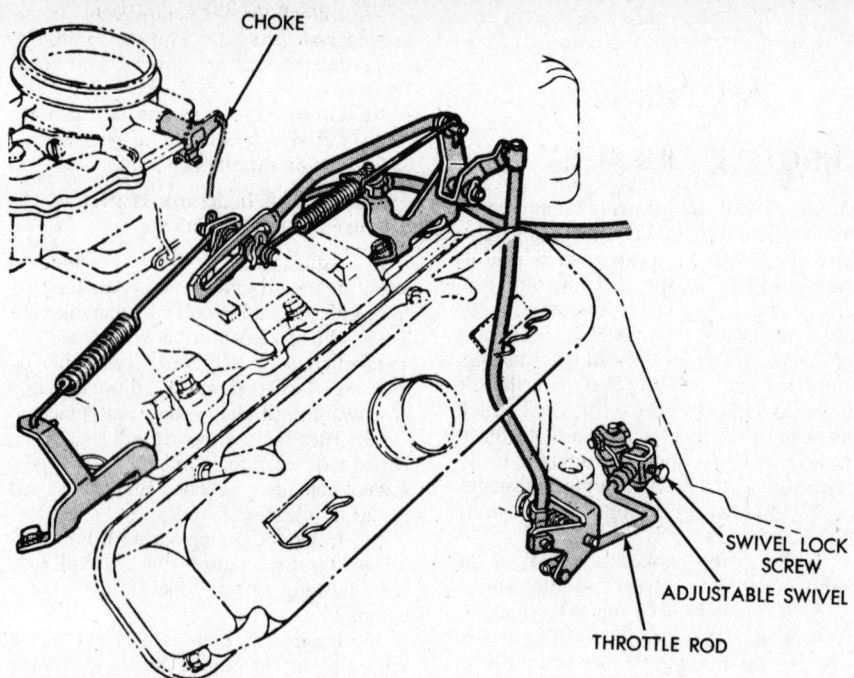

V8 throttle rod adjustment—6 cyl. similar (© Chrysler Corp.)

NOTE: On 4WD AMC models, it may be necessary to remove the front axle driveshaft to gain proper access to the adjusting screw and locknut.

1. Raise and safely support the front of the vehicle. Loosen the locknut and back off about five turns. Be sure the adjusting screw is free in the case.

2. Use a torque wrench and 5/16 inch square socket, to tighten the adjusting screw to exactly 72 inch lbs.

3. Back off the adjusting screw exactly to specification. Hold the adjusting screw so that it does not turn and tighten the locknut to 35 ft. lbs.

Rear Band

The rear band adjustment is an inside adjustment so the pan must be removed.

1. Raise and safely support car.

2. Remove oil pan and drain fluid.

3. Look carefully at fluid, filter and pan bottom for a heavy accumulation of friction material or metal particles. A little accumulation can be considered normal, but a heavy concentration indicates damaged worn parts.

4. Adjust band by loosening locknut, then tightening adjusting screw to the specified torque, using a small torque wrench and a 1/4 inch hex head socket.

5. Back off adjusting screw to the specified amount of turns. Refer to the specification chart.

6. Install locknut, tighten to 35 ft. lbs. making sure adjusting screw does not turn.

NOTE: Install a new transmission filter. Torque the three screws to 35 inch pounds.

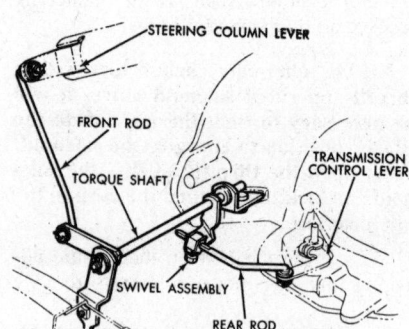

Typical automatic column shift linkage (© Chrysler Corp)

7. Using a new gasket on the pan, install and torque bolts evenly to 150 inch pounds.

8. Lower car and fill transmission with specified amount of Dexron® type fluid.

FRONT WHEEL DRIVE

Kickdown (Front) Band
A-404

The kickdown band (front band) has its adjusting screw located on the top front (left side) of the transaxle case. Adjustment is as follows:

1. Loosen the locknut and back off about five turns.

2. Tighten the adjusting screw to 72 inch pounds.

3. Back off adjusting screw 3½ turns for 1978–79 models and 3 turns for 1980 and later models, from the 72 inch pound torque, then hold this position and tighten the lock nut to 35 ft. lbs.

BAND ADJUSTMENT SPECIFICATIONS
American Motors Corporation Torque Command

		2L 904	2.5L 904	232 CID 904	258 CID Std-904	H/D-727③	998	304 CID Std-998	H/D-727③	360 CID Std-727	H/D-727③	401 CID Std-727	H/D-727③
'78	Front Band①	2	—	2	2	2.5	—	2	2.5	2.5	2	—	—
	Rear Band①	7②	—	7②	7②	2	—	4	2	2	2	—	—
'79	Front Band①	2	—	2	2	—	—	2	—	—	—	—	—
	Rear Band①	7②	—	7②	7②	—	—	4	—	—	—	—	—
'80	Front Band①	—	2	—	2	—	2	—	—	—	—	—	—
	Rear Band①	—	7②	—	7②	—	4	—	—	—	—	—	—
'81	Front Band①	—	2.5	—	2.5	—	2.5	—	—	—	—	—	—
	Rear Band①	—	7②	—	7	—	4	—	—	—	—	—	—
'82 and Later	Front Band①	—	2.5	—	2.5	—	2.5	—	—	—	—	—	—
	Rear Band①	—	7②	—	7	—	4	—	—	—	—	—	—

NOTE: Numbers represent back-off turns from specified torque. Torque lock-nut to 35 ft. lbs when adjustment is completed.
①Backed off from 72 inch pounds
②Backed off from 41 inch pounds
③H/D = Fleet usage only

BAND ADJUSTMENT SPECIFICATIONS
Chrysler Corporation TorqueFlite

		A904	A904-LA			A727					
		225	225	318	360-2 BBL 360-4 BBL	225	318	360-2 BBL 360-4 BBL	360-HP	400-2 BBL	440-4 BBL
'78	Front Band①	2	—	2	2	2.5	2.5	2.5	2.5	2.5	2.5③
	Rear Band①	7②	—	4	4	2	2	2	2	2	2
'79	Front Band①	2	—	2	2	—	2.5	2.5	2.5⑤	—	—
	Rear Band①	7②	—	4	4	—	2	2	2	—	—
'80	Front Band①	2	2⑥	2.5⑥	2.5⑥	—	2.5	2.5	2.5	—	—
	Rear Band①	7②	4⑥	4⑥	4⑥	—	2	2	2	—	—
'81 and Later	Front Band①	2.5⑥	—	2.5⑥	—	—	2.5	—	—	—	—
	Rear Band①	7②⑥	—	4⑥	—	—	2	—	—	—	—

①Backed off from 72 inch pounds torque
②Backed off from 41 inch pounds torque
③440-4 BBL dual exhaust - two turns off
④Not used
⑤4 BBL
⑥With wide ratio gears, all '84 and later

A-413, A-415 AND A-470

The kickdown band (front) has its adjusting screw located on the front left top of the transaxle case, in the same location as the A-404 transaxle. The adjustment is as follows:

1. Loosen the locknut and back off approximately five turns.
2. Tighten the band adjusting screw to 72 inch lbs.
3. Back off the adjusting screw the correct number of turns as shown on chart.
4. Hold this position on the adjusting screw and tighten the lock nut to 35 ft. lbs.

Low-Reverse (Rear) Band
A-404

The low-reverse band (rear band) is not adjustable in this unit. The band lining itself needs to be inspected to determine the need for replacement. The grooves must be no less than 0.008 in. (0.2mm) deep at any point to still be usable. With a 100 pound force applied to band around drum, the end gap must not be less than 0.020 in. (0.5mm).

A-413, A-415 AND A-470

The low-reverse band (rear) is not adjustable on A-415 model. On A-413 and A-

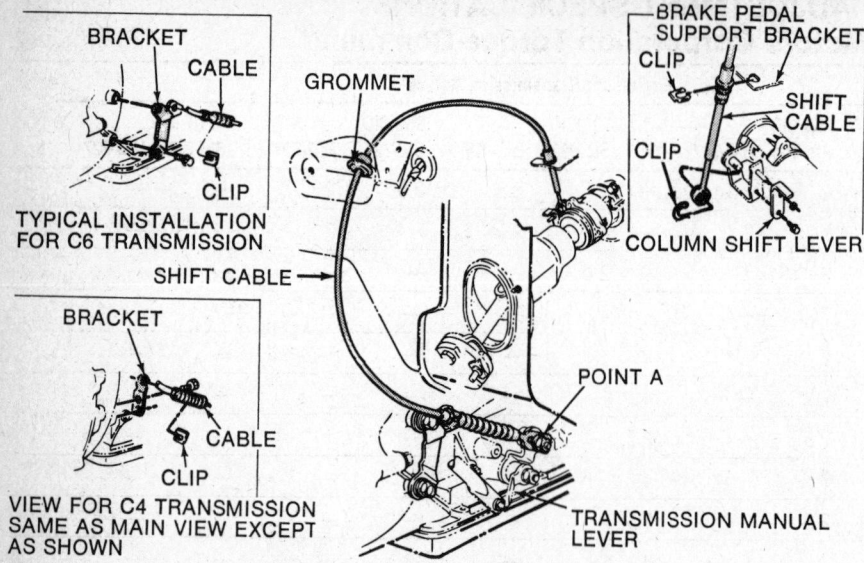

BRACKET
CABLE
GROMMET
CLIP

TYPICAL INSTALLATION
FOR C6 TRANSMISSION

SHIFT CABLE

BRACKET

CABLE

CLIP

VIEW FOR C4 TRANSMISSION
SAME AS MAIN VIEW EXCEPT
AS SHOWN

BRAKE PEDAL
SUPPORT BRACKET
CLIP
SHIFT
CABLE
CLIP
COLUMN SHIFT LEVER

POINT A

TRANSMISSION MANUAL
LEVER

Typical cable-type column shift mechanism (© Ford Motor Co.)

1. Raise vehicle on hoist or jackstands.
2. Place drain pan under transmission.
3. Loosen transmission pan attaching bolts to drain fluid above pan level.
4. When the fluid has drained to the level of the pan mounting flange, remove the attaching bolts beginning at the rear of the pan. Gradually drop the pan and drain slowly.
5. After draining the fluid, remove and thoroughly clean the transmission pan. Discard the filter, valve body to filter gasket, and transmission pan gasket.
6. Install new filter and filter to valve body gasket do not attempt to clean and reuse the old filter.
7. Using a new gasket, install the pan on the transmission.
8. Add three quarts of the specified fluid Ford CJ or Dexron® II, through the fill tube.
9. Check and adjust the fluid level as necessary.

FMX Transmission

ADJUSTMENTS

Vacuum Diaphragm

The vacuum diaphragms used in production are nonadjustable. Adjustable units are available for installation in the transmission, allowing changes in the control pressures.

An adjusting screw is located in the vacuum nipple of the diaphragm and is accessible after removing the vacuum supply line from the diaphragm. Using a small screwdrive and turning the screw clockwise will

2. Attach a 0-100 psi pressure gauge to the TV Port on the transmission.

3. Operate engine until normal operating temperature is reached and throttle lever is off fast idle.

4. Verify that the throttle lever is at its idle stop. Place a .063 gauge (use ¹⁄₁₆ in. or 1.6mm drill) between the linkage lever adjustment screw and the throttle lever. With engine operating at idle and in Neutral TV pressure msut be below 5 psi. If TV pressure is greater than 5 psi, the TV control linkage is set too long.

5. Place a 0.313 in. gauge (use ⁵⁄₁₆ in. or 8mm drill) between the linkage lever adjustment screw and the throttle lever. With the engine operating at idle and in Neutral, the TV pressure must be at least 22 psi. A low reading indicates that the linkage is set short.

6. Correct a long setting by backing out the linkage lever adjustment screw. Turn in the adjusting screw for a short rod condition. If insufficient adjusting capacity is available, the TV control rod length must be reset using the procedure described in "Linkage Adjustment at Transmission".

7. If the limits specified cannot be obtained, diagnosis of the transmission control pressure system is required.

Idle Speed

Whenever it is required to adjust idle speed by more than 50 rpm, the adjustment screw on the linkage lever at the carburetor should also be readjusted as shown in following chart.

After making any idle speed adjustments, always verify the linkage lever and throttle lever are in contact with the throttle lever at its idle stop and the shift lever is in Neutral.

Manual Linkage

1. Loose the linkage adjustment screw located in the engine compartment of Ford/Mercury full size and Lincoln/Mark VI, and under the car on Cougar/Thunderbird models.

2. Move the shift selector *firmly* against the overdrive gate stop. (Hang a weight on the lever to hold it in place.)

3. Locate the overdrive detent in the transmission, third from the front.

4. Tighten the adjustment screw. Recheck the adjustment before driving the vehicle.

Neutral Safety Switch

The neutral safety switch in the transmission is merely an on-off switch actuated by the manual linkage detent mechanism within the transmission. The switch is replaceable if defective, but is *non-adjustable*.

OIL PAN

Draining, Removal and Installation

It is not necessary, under normal operating conditions, to periodically change the transmission fluid. Only under severe conditions (police or taxi) or in the case of a major overhaul is it recommended that the fluid be changed.

When the reason for a fluid change is internal transmission damage, it is necessary to also flush the transmission cooler and cooler lines to remove any traces of abrasive matter from the system.

— CAUTION —
When flushing torque converters, use only professional equipment designed for this purpose. Traces of solvent in the converter could cause severe transmission damage in the future.

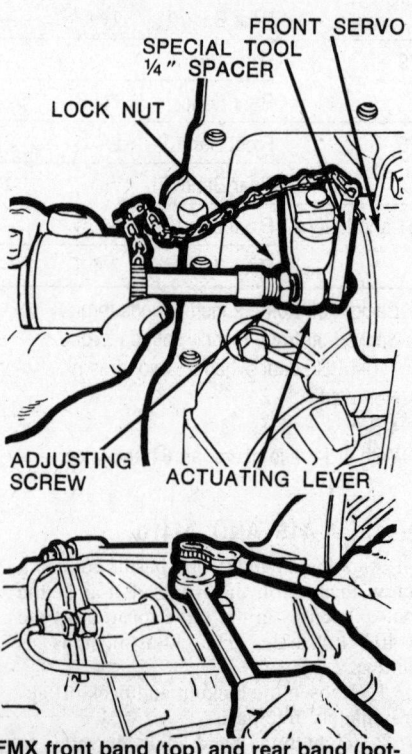

FRONT SERVO
SPECIAL TOOL
¼" SPACER
LOCK NUT

ADJUSTING
SCREW

ACTUATING LEVER

FMX front band (top) and rear band (bottom) adjustments

increase the control pressure, while turning the screw counter-clockwise will decrease the control pressure. One complete turn of the adjusting screw will change the control pressure approximately 2–3 psi.

NOTE: The diaphragm should not be adjusted to provide pressures below the specified ranges to change shift engagement feel, as soft or slipping shift points could result and damage to the transmission could occur.

Throttle Linkage

1. Position the carburetor in the wide open throttle position (W.O.T.).

2. Hold the kickdown rod downward with a 4½ pound weight against the through detent stop.

3. Adjust the kickdown adjusting screw to obtain 0.01–0.08 in. clearance between the screw and the throttle arm.

4. Return the system to idle.

Band

The only adjustments that are needed on the FMX automatic transmission are the front and rear bands.

To prevent damage to the transmission and to assure proper band adjustment, it is essential that the proper tools and procedures are used whenever the bands are adjusted.

FRONT BAND

1. Raise the vehicle and support on jackstands. Drain the transmission fluid from the transmission unit.

2. Remove the transmission pan, then remove the fluid screen and clip from the transmission. Remove all gasket material from the transmission pan and pan mounting surface of the transmission case.

3. Loosen the front servo adjusting rod, and insert the ¼ in. spacer between the adjusting screw and the servo piston stem.

Tighten the adjusting screw to 10 inch pounds. Remove the spacer and tighten the adjusting screw an additional ¾ turn. Hold the adjusting screw stationary and tighten the locknut. Torque the locknut 20–25 ft. lbs.

5. Install the transmission fluid screen and clip. Install a new transmission pan gasket on the transmission pan. Mate the transmission pan to the transmission case and install the pan bolts.

6. Refill the transmission with the proper grade and type automatic transmission fluid.

7. Lower the vehicle. Start the engine and check for leaks. Correct as necessary.

REAR BAND

1. Raise the vehicle and support on jackstand. Remove all dirt and foreign material away from the adjusting screw threads. Oil the threads.

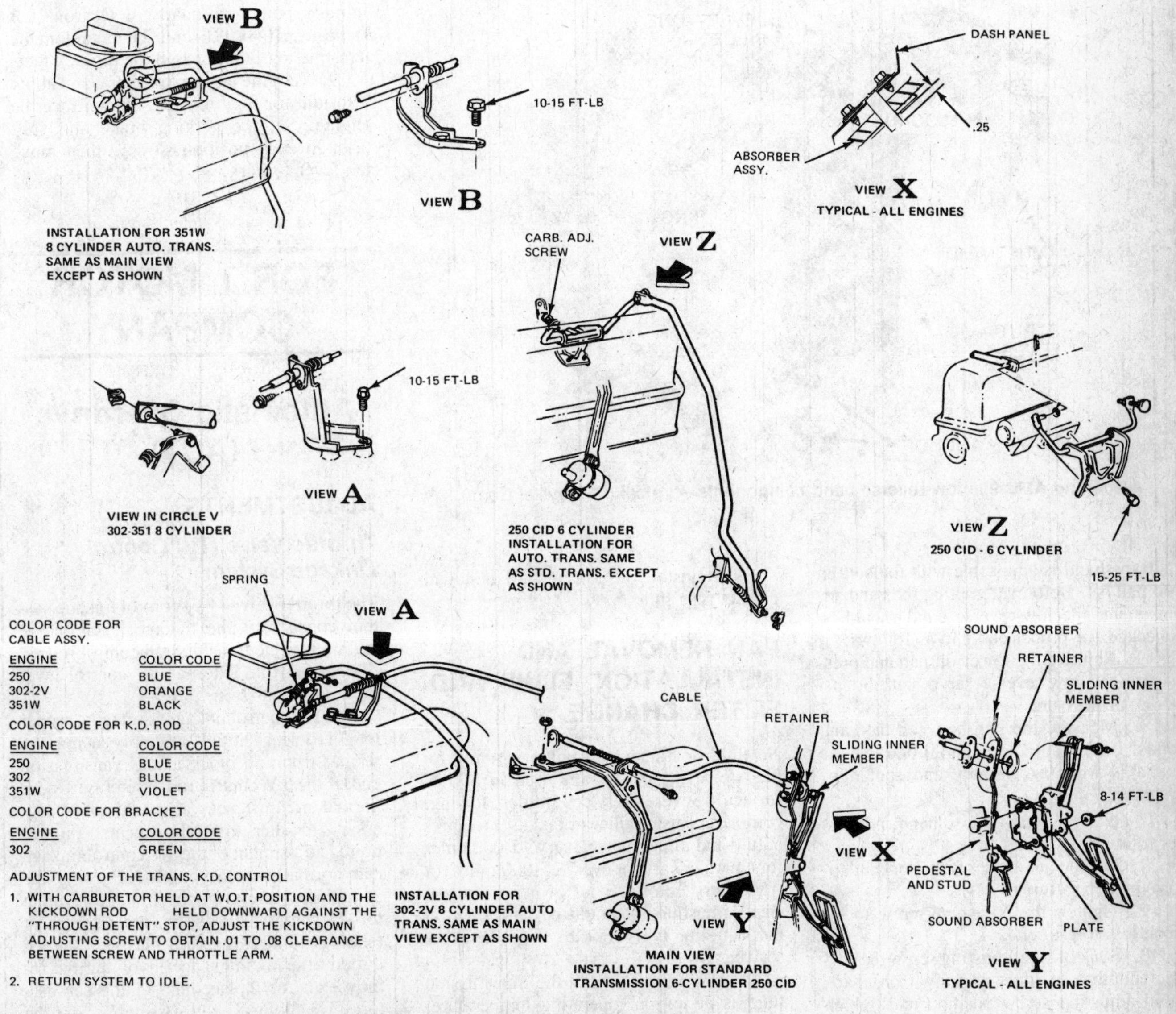

VIEW **B**

10-15 FT-LB

VIEW **B**

INSTALLATION FOR 351W
8 CYLINDER AUTO. TRANS.
SAME AS MAIN VIEW
EXCEPT AS SHOWN

CARB. ADJ. SCREW

VIEW **Z**

DASH PANEL

.25

ABSORBER ASSY.

VIEW **X**
TYPICAL - ALL ENGINES

10-15 FT-LB

VIEW **A**

VIEW IN CIRCLE V
302-351 8 CYLINDER

250 CID 6 CYLINDER
INSTALLATION FOR
AUTO. TRANS. SAME
AS STD. TRANS. EXCEPT
AS SHOWN

VIEW **Z**
250 CID - 6 CYLINDER

15-25 FT-LB

SPRING

VIEW **A**

COLOR CODE FOR CABLE ASSY.	
ENGINE	COLOR CODE
250	BLUE
302-2V	ORANGE
351W	BLACK

COLOR CODE FOR K.D. ROD	
ENGINE	COLOR CODE
250	BLUE
302	BLUE
351W	VIOLET

COLOR CODE FOR BRACKET	
ENGINE	COLOR CODE
302	GREEN

ADJUSTMENT OF THE TRANS. K.D. CONTROL

1. WITH CARBURETOR HELD AT W.O.T. POSITION AND THE KICKDOWN ROD HELD DOWNWARD AGAINST THE "THROUGH DETENT" STOP, ADJUST THE KICKDOWN ADJUSTING SCREW TO OBTAIN .01 TO .08 CLEARANCE BETWEEN SCREW AND THROTTLE ARM.

2. RETURN SYSTEM TO IDLE.

CABLE

RETAINER

SLIDING INNER MEMBER

VIEW **X**

INSTALLATION FOR
302-2V 8 CYLINDER AUTO
TRANS. SAME AS MAIN
VIEW EXCEPT AS SHOWN

VIEW **Y**

MAIN VIEW
INSTALLATION FOR STANDARD
TRANSMISSION 6-CYLINDER 250 CID

SOUND ABSORBER

RETAINER

SLIDING INNER MEMBER

8-14 FT-LB

PEDESTAL AND STUD

SOUND ABSORBER

PLATE

VIEW **Y**
TYPICAL - ALL ENGINES

Typical throttle and downshift linkage—except ATX (© Ford Motor Co.)

BAND ADJUSTMENT SPECIFICATIONS
Chrysler Corporation Transaxle

| | | Engine and Transmission Models | | | | |
| | | A-404 | | | A-413, A-470 | |
		1.7L	2.2L	2.6L	2.2L	2.6L
'78–'80	Front Band	3②	2.75②	—	—	—
	Rear Band	①	3.5③	—	—	—
'81–'83	Front Band	3②	3.0②	3.0②	2.0②	2.0②
	Rear Band	①	①	①	3.5③	3.5③
'84 and Later	Front Band	—	—	—	2.5②④	2.5②④
	Rear Band	—	—	—	3.5③④	3.5③④

① Not adjustable
② Backed off from 72 inch pounds torque
③ Backed off from 41 inch pounds torque
④ 1.6L engine w/A415: 3.0
   Rear Band: Non-adjustable

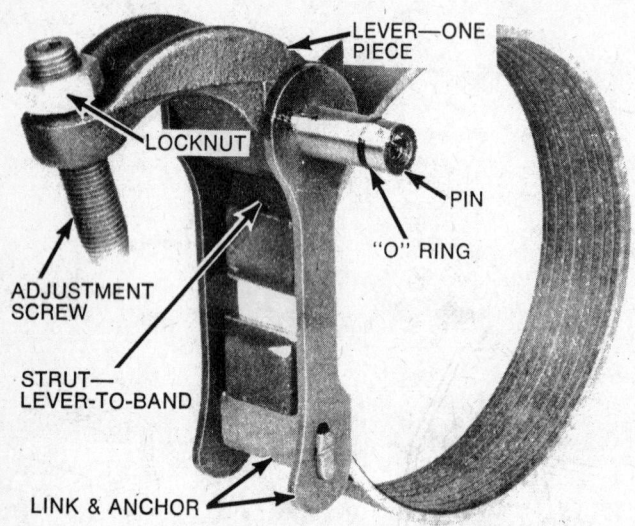

A-904 and AMC 998 low-reverse band components—typical (© Chrysler Corp.)

470 the band is adjustable with the bottom oil pan off. Before attempting the band adjustment, the low-reverse band should be checked for proper end gap as follows:

1. Remove the lower oil pan and pressurize the low-reverse servo with 30 psi shop air pressure.

2. Measure the gap between the band ends. If the gap is less than 0.080 in., the band is worn excessively and should be replaced.

To adjust the low-reverse band, proceed as follows:

1. Loosen and back off the locknut approximately 5 turns.

2. Tighten the adjusting screw to 41 inch lbs. true torque.

3. Back off the adjusting screw the correct number of turns as shown on chart, hold adjusting screw position and tighten the locknut to 10 ft. lbs.

4. Reinstall oil pan and fill unit with correct type fluid.

PAN REMOVAL AND INSTALLATION, FLUID AND FILTER CHANGE

No fluid or filter changes are required for the life of the car if it is used in normal service. Severe service (trailer towing, commercial use, police or taxi use) requires a fluid and filter change every 15,000 miles for Chrysler cars, or every 25,000 miles for AMC cars (refer to your owners manual). Band adjustments should be performed at the same intervals for cars used in severe service.

1. Drive the car until the transmission fluid is at normal operating temperature. Raise and safely support the vehicle.

2. Unbolt the pan. Be ready with a large container to catch the fluid.

NOTE: If the fluid smells burnt or is discolored, serious transmission troubles, probably due to oveheating, should be suspected.

3. When the fluid is drained, remove the pan.

4. Unscrew and discard the filter.

5. Install a new filter. The proper torque is 28 in. lbs., AMC, or 35 in. lbs., Chrysler.

6. Clean out the pan, being extremely careful not to leave any lint from rags inside.

7. Replace the pan, using a new gasket. On most front wheel drive models, RTV silicone sealer is used instead of a gasket. Peel off the old sealer and apply a ⅛ in. bead of silicone sealer to the pan flange. Run the bead around the inside of the bolt holes. Tighten the pan bolts to 10–12 ft. lbs. in a criss-cross pattern.

8. It is a good idea to measure the amount of fluid drained from the transmission, because some fluid will remain inside. Initially pour four quarts of Dexron® (or Dexron® II—1981 and later) automatic transmission fluid through the dipstick tube.

9. Start the engine in Neutral and allow it to idle for two minutes. Do not race the engine. Set the parking brake and shift through each position slowly, then move the lever to Park.

FORD MOTOR COMPANY

Automatic Overdrive (AOT)

ADJUSTMENTS

Throttle Valve (TV) Control Linkage System

The throttle valve (TV) control linkage system consists of the linkage lever on the carburetor, the transmission control rod assembly and the external TV control lever on the transmission.

The TV control linkage is set to its proper length during initial assembly using the sliding trunnion block at the transmission end of the TV control rod assembly. Under normal circumstances, it should not be necessary to alter this adjustment. Any required adjustment of the TV control linkage can normally be accomplished using the adjustment screw on the linkage lever at the carburetor. Major linkage adjustment (sliding trunnion on rod) may only be required after maintenance involving the removal and/or replacement of the carburetor, TV control rod assembly or the transmission. Minor linkage adjustment

(adjustment screw on linkage lever) may be required after idle speed adjustments greater than 50 rpm and to correct complaints of poor transmission shift quality.

When the linkage is properly adjusted, the TV control lever on the transmission will be at its internal idle stop position (lever up as far as it will travel) when the carburetor is at its hot idle stop with the engine off. There will be a light contact force between the throttle lever and end of the linkage lever adjustment screw. Due to flexibility in the linkage system, the linkage lever adjustment screw would have to be backed out approximately three turns before a gap between the screw and throttle lever could be detected.

At wide open throttle, the TV control lever on the transmission may or may not be at its wide open stop. The wide open throttle position must not be used as the reference point in adjusting the linkage.

Linkage Adjustment at Carburetor

The TV control linkage may be adjusted at the carburetor using the following procedure.

1. De-cam the fast idle cam on the carburetor so that the throttle lever is at its idle stop. Place shift lever in Neutral and set parking brake. Engine off.

2. Back out linkage lever adjusting screw all the way (screw end is flush with lever face).

3. Turn in adjusting screw until a thin shim (0.005 in. max) or piece of writing paper fits snug between end of screw and throttle lever. To eliminate the effect of friction, push the linkage lever forward (tending to close gap). Release it before checking clearance between the end of the screw and the throttle lever. Do not apply any load on the levers with tools or hands while checking gap.

4. Turn in adjusting screw an additional three turns. (Three turns are preferred. One turn minimum is permissible if screw travel is limited.)

5. If it is not possible to turn in adjusting screw at least one additional turn or if there was insufficient screw adjusting capacity to obtain an initial gap in Step 2, refer to "Linkage Adjustment at Transmission."

Linkage Adjustment at Transmission

The linkage lever adjustment screw has a limited adjustment capability. If it is not possible to adjust the TV linkage using this screw, the length of the TV control rod assembly must be readjusted using the following procedure. This procedure must also be followed whenever a new TV control rod assembly is installed.

1. Set the engine curb idle speed to specification.

2. With engine off, de-cam the fast idle cam on the carburetor so that the throttle lever is against the idle stop. Place shift

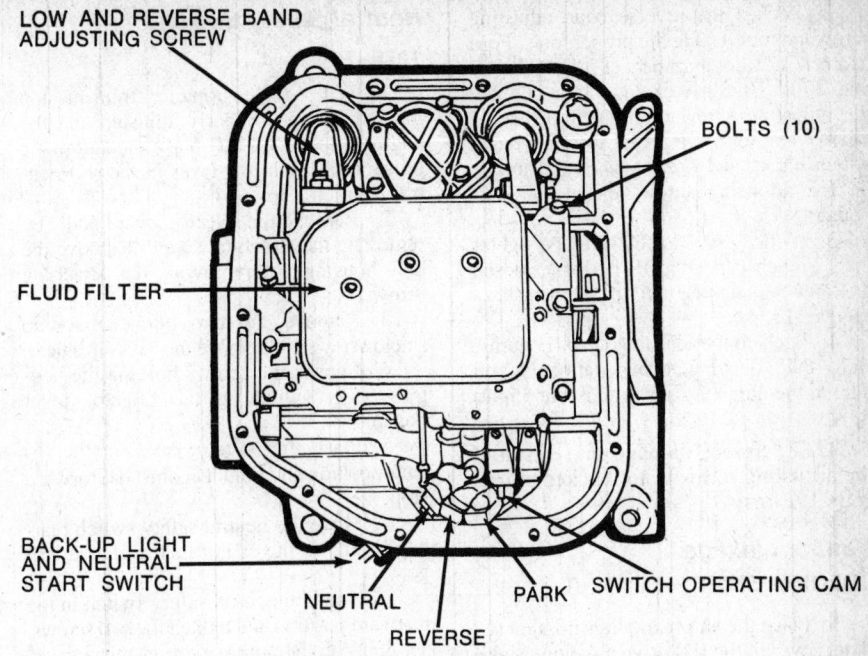

Low and reverse band adjusting screw location

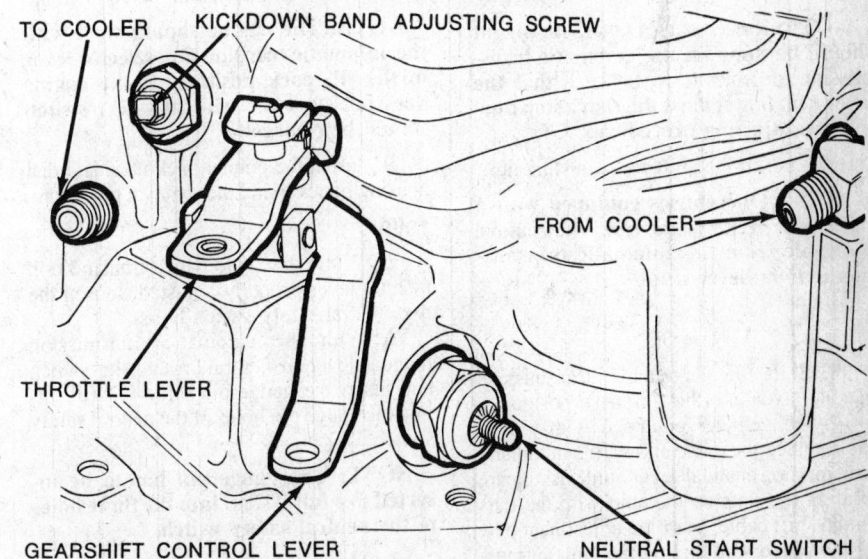

Torque-Command and TorqueFlite external adjustments and controls

lever in Neutral and set parking brake. Engine off.

3. Set the linkage lever adjustment screw at approximately mid-range.

4. If a new TV control rod assembly is being installed, connect the rod to the linkage lever at the carburetor.

5. Loosen the bolt on the sliding trunnion block on the TV control rod assembly. Remove any corrosion from the control rod and free-up the trunnion block so that it slides freely on the control rod.

6. Push up on the lower end of the control rod to insure that the linkage lever at carburetor is firmly against the throttle lever. Release force on rod. Rod must stay up.

7. Push the TV control lever on the transmission up against its internal stop with a firm force (approximately 5 pounds) and tighten the bolt on the trunnion block. Do not relax force on the lever until the bolt is tightened.

Linkage Adjustment Using TV Control Pressure

The following procedure may be used to check and/or adjust the TV control linkage using TV control pressure.

1. Place the shift selector lever in Neutral and disconnect the idle kicker solenoid. Set parking brake.

2. Loosen the reverse band adjusting screw locknut. Using the proper tools, Ford Motor Co. tool numbers T70O-7B200-B and T70P-7B200-A or equivalent, tighten the adjusting screw until the tool handle clicks. The tool is a preset torque wrench which clicks and breaks when the torque on the adjusting screw reaches 10 foot pounds.

3. If the screw is found to be tighter than wrench capacity (10 ft. lbs.), loosen the screw and tighten until the wrench clicks and breaks.

4. Back off the adjusting screw 1½ turns. Hold the adjusting screw stationary and tighten the adjusting screw lock nut 35–40 ft. lbs.

NOTE: Severe damage may result if the adjusting screw is not backed off exactly 1½ turns.

Manual Linkage
COLUMN SHIFT

1. Place the automatic transmission selector lever in the (D) drive position. Make sure that the lever is tight against the (D) drive stop.

NOTE: If necessary a 10–15 lb. weight should be hung on the automatic transmission shift lever to be sure that the lever remains against the Drive stop during the adjusting procedure.

2. Loosen the shift rod adjusting nut.

NOTE: On vehicles equipped with a shift cable, remove the nut, and remove the cable from the automatic transmission manual lever stud.

3. Shift the automatic transmission manual lever into the (D) drive position.

4. On vehicles equipped with a shift cable, place the cable end on the automatic transmission manual lever stud, using care to align the flats on the stud with the flats on the shift cable. Start the adjustment nut.

5. Make sure that the automatic transmission lever has not moved from the (D) drive stop. Torque the adjusting nut to 15 ft. lbs.

6. Check the tranmission operation for all selector lever detent positions.

FLOOR SHIFT

1. Position the automatic transmission selector lever in the (D) drive position against the rearward (D) drive stop.

2. Raise the vehicle and loosen the manual lever shift rod retaining nut. Move the automatic transmission manual lever to the (D) drive position.

3. With the automatic transmission selector lever and the manual lever in the (D) drive positions, torque the attaching nut to 15 ft. lbs.

4. Check the operation of the transmission in each selector lever Position. Lower the vehicle.

Neutral Safety Switch
1978–79

1. With the autmatic transmission manual linkage properly adjusted and the engine turned "OFF," place the automatic transmission selector lever in the (N) neutral position.

2. Remove the selector lever handle by removing the attaching screw. Remove the dial housing by removing the attaching screw.

3. Remove the two pointer back-up shield screws and remove the back-up shield.

4. Loosen the screws holding the neutral safety switch to the selector lever housing.

5. Place the selector lever in the (P) park position and hold it against the forward stop.

6. Move the neutral safety switch rearward as far to the end of its travel as it will go.

7. Hold the neutral safety switch in the rearward position and tighten the two screws.

8. With the automatic transmission selector lever in the (P) park position check the operation of the neutral safety switch.

NOTE: The engine should start with the automatic transmission selector lever in the (P) park position. If the engine does not start the neutral safety switch should be replaced.

9. Install the pointer back-up shield dial housing by reversing the removal procedure.

1980

1. With the automatic transmission manual lever properly adjusted, loosen the two neutral safety switch bolts.

2. With the automatic transmission manual lever in neutral, rotate the switch and insert the gauge pin (No. 43 drill bit) into the gauge pin holes of the neutral safety switch.

NOTE: The gauge pin has to be inserted to a full ³¹⁄₆₄ in. into the three holes of the neutral safety switch.

3. Torque the neutral safety switch bolts to 55–75 inch lbs. Remove the gauge pin from the neutral safety switch.

4. Check the operation of the neutral safety switch.

NOTE: The engine should start with the automatic transmission selector lever in (P) park or (N) neutral only.

VACUUM DIAPHRAGM
Removal & Installation

1. Raise the vehicle and support it safely on jackstands.

2. Disconnect the vacuum diaphragm hoses. Remove the vacuum unit with tool #S8696-A or equivalent.

3. Remove the vacuum unit control rod from the transmission case.

4. Place the vacuum control rod in the transmission case.

5. Thread the vacuum diaphragm unit into the transmission case using the special tool. Using a torque wrench, torque the unit to 15–23 ft. lbs.

6. Reinstall the vacuum hoses to their proper location. Lower the vehicle. Road test as requied and correct as necessary.

OIL PAN
Draining and Removal

1. Raise the vehicle and support it safely on jackstands. Place a drain pan under the transmission.

2. Loosen the automatic transmission oil pan bolts and drain the automatic transmission fluid from the unit.

3. When the transmission fluid has drained to the level of the oil pan flange, remove the rest of the transmission oil pan bolts working from the rear and both sides of the pan to allow the transmission pan to drop and the fluid to drain slowly.

4. After the fluid has stopped draining, remove the oil pan. Clean all the old gasket material from the pan and the transmission case. Thoroughly clean the inside of the transmission pan.

Installation

1. Install a new transmission pan gasket on the transmission pan and place it against the transmission case.

2. Install all the transmission oil pan bolts. Torque the bolts to 12–17 ft. lbs.

3. Install three quarts of automatic transmission fluid (Type "F") (converter not drained). Be sure to use the proper grade and type transmission fluid. Failure to do this could result in serious internal transmission damage.

4. When refilling a dry transmission and torque converter install five quarts of the proper grade and type automatic transmission fluid.

5. Start the engine and operate it at idle speed for approximately two minutes and then raise the engine speed to approximately 1200 rpm until the engine/transmission assembly reaches normal operating temperature.

NOTE: Do not overspeed the engine during warm-up.

6. Check the fluid level after moving the gear selector through all shift ranges. Correct the fluid level if necessary.

C3 Transmission

ADJUSTMENTS
Vacuum Diaphragm

The vacuum diaphragms used in production are nonadjustable. Adjustable type units are

available for installation in the transmission, allowing changes in the control pressures.

An adjusting screw is located in the vacuum nipple of the diaphragm and is accessible after removing the vacuum supply line from the diaphragm. Using a small screwdriver and turning the screw clockwise will increase the control pressure, while turning the screw counter-clockwise will decrease the control pressure. One complete turn of the adjusting screw will change the control pre-sure approximately 2–3 psi.

─── CAUTION ───

The diaphragm should not be adjusted to provide pressures below the specified ranges to change shift engagement feel, as soft or slipping shift points could result and damage to the transmission could occur.

Throttle Linkage

Throttle pressure control linkage is not used on the C-3 automatic transmission. A vacuum-operated diaphragm assembly is used to control and modulate the throttle pressure in proportion to the road speed, throttle opening and internal oil pressures.

A downshift control rod is used and is connected to the carburetor control linkage. Both linkages must be properly adjusted to actuate the downshift system.

ACCELERATOR AND DOWNSHIFT LINKAGE

1. With the engine off, fully depress the accelerator pedal and hold in place. Inspect the carburetor for wide open throttle plates and full accelerator linkage travel. Adjust as necessary.
2. With the accelerator fully depressed and adjusted, push the downshift control rod downward to its fully depressed position (downshift valve in the transmission fully depressed).
3. A clearance of .010–.080 in. between the tip of the kickdown adjusting screw and the throttle lever should exist. Adjust the screw as necessary.
4. Release the accelerator linkage. The linkage and the downshift control rod must return to their closed position by return spring tension.

Band

The intermediate band is the only adjustment needed during normal operation. The reverse band is adjusted internally during assembly or at times of overhaul.

INTERMEDIATE BAND

1. Locate the adjusting screw on the left side of the transmission case, in front of the manual control lever.
2. Remove the downshift control rod from the downshift control lever to gain access to the adjusting screw and locknut.
3. Clean the dirt and foreign material from the locknut area. Loosen, remove and discard the locknut from the adjusting screw.
4. Install a new locknut on the adjusting screw.

5. Tighten the adjusting screw to 10 ft. lbs. of torque.

NOTE: A special wrench with a present "click," "break" or "overrun," can be used to tighten the adjusting screw.

6. Back the adjusting screw *off* exactly 1½ turns, 2 turns for '84 and later models.
7. Hold the adjustment and tighten the locknut to 35–45 ft. lbs. torque.
8. Install the downshift control rod to the downshift control lever.

Manual Linkage
COLUMN SHIFT

1. Place the selector lever in the "D" position against the "D" stop of the shift gate.

NOTE: The selector lever should be held by hand or by a weight, against the "D" stop of the shift gate during any adjustments.

2. Loosen the shift rod adjusting nut.
3. Position the transmission manual lever in the "D" detent, which is third from the front.

NOTE: The control rod may have to be disconnected at the adjusting nut and bolt to properly engage the transmission detent.

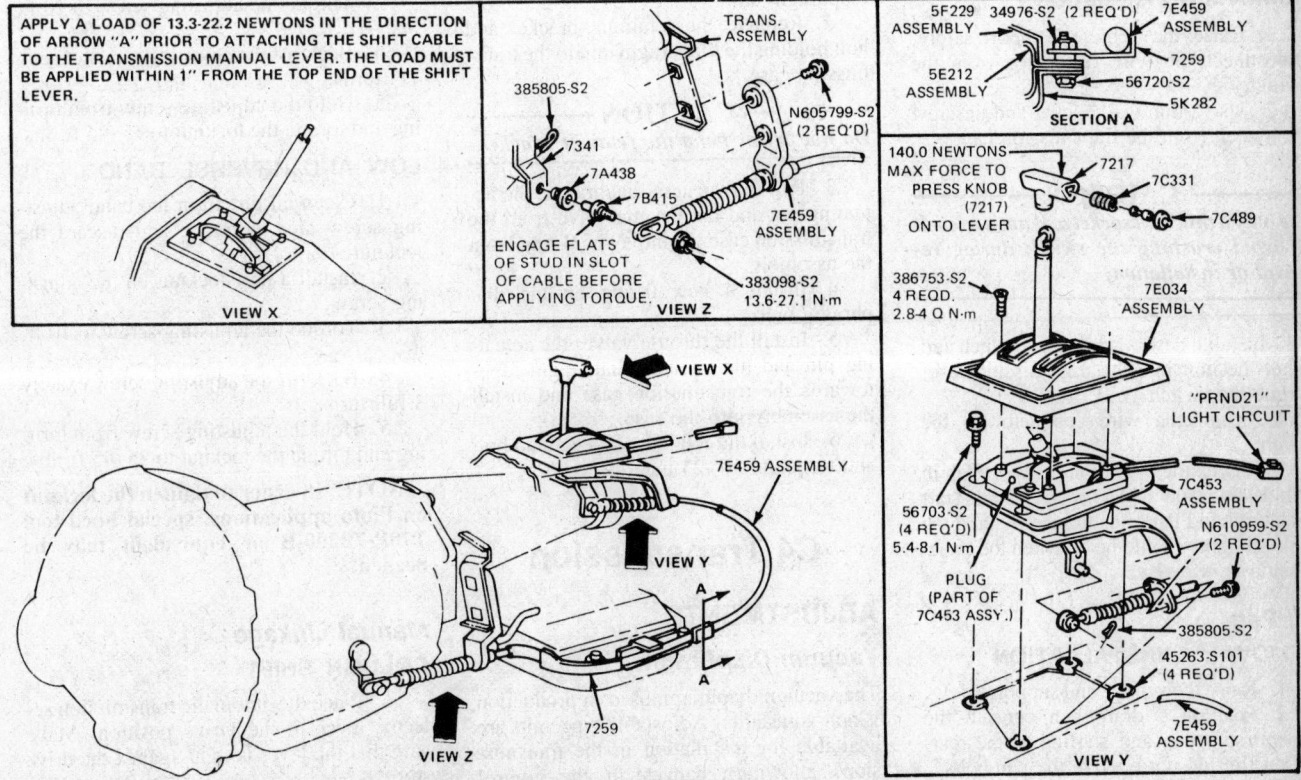

Typical cable-type floor shift mechanism (© Ford Motor Co.)

4. Recheck the selector lever so that it is against the "D" stop of the shift gate. Tighten the shift rod adjusting nut securely.

NOTE: Engage the flats of the stud in the control rod slot before tightening the nut, if equippe.

5. Operate the gear selector through the detents and check for proper alignment of the lever indicator to the shift detents. Readjust as necessary.

CONSOLE OR FLOOR SHIFT

1. Place the selector lever in the "D" position and against the rearward "D" stop of the shift gate. Hold in position while any adjustments are made.

2. Loosen the manual shift linkage adjusting nut and move the selector lever to the "D" position on the transmission (third position from the front).

3. With the selector lever and the manual lever in the "D" positions respectively, tighten the shift linkage adjusting nut to 10–15 ft. lbs.

NEUTRAL SAFETY SWITCH

The C-3 automatic transmission has a screw-type neutral start switch, located above the manual control lever on the transmission case. The internal shift detent operates the switch contacts to allow the engine to start in either Park or Neutral positions and to operate the back-up lights when the transmission is in the Reverse position.

Removal & Installation

1. Raise the vehicle, support safely. Disconnect the wire connector from the switch.

2. Use a thin wall socket and unscrew the switch from the transmission case.

—————— CAUTION ——————
Use only a thin wall socket and not a wrench to avoid crushing the switch during removal or installation.

3. Install a new 0-ring on the switch and install the unit into the transmission case. Torque the switch 12–15 ft. lbs.

4. Install the wire connector to the switch.

5. Check the operation of the switch in each detent position. The engine should start in Neutral and Park positions only, and the back-up lights should be on when the transmission is in reverse.

Oil Pan

REMOVAL & INSTALLATION

1. Raise the vehicle and support safely.

2. Position a drain pan beneath the transmission pan and starting at the rear, loosen, but do not remove the pan bolts.

3. Loosen the pan from the transmis-

sion case and allow the fluid to drain gradually.

4. Remove all pan bolts except two at the front of the pan and allow the fluid to continue draining.

5. Remove the pan; clean the old gasket from the pan and transmission case.

6. Install a new gasket on the pan and install it to the transmission case.

7. Install all pan bolts and torque to 12–17 ft. lbs.

8. Install three quarts of transmission fluid Type "F" prior to 1981. "CJ" or Dexron® II, 1981 and later into the filler tube (converter not drained).

When refilling a dry transmission and converter, install five quarts of fluid into the transmission.

9. Start the engine and operate the engine at idle speed for approximately two minutes. Then raise the engine speed to approximately 1200 rpm until the engine/transmission assembly reaches normal operating temperature.

—————— CAUTION ——————
Do not overspeed the engine during warmmp-up.

10. Check the fluid level after moving the gear selector through all ranges. Correct the fluid level as necessary.

VACUUM DIAPHRAGM

Removal & Installation

1. Raise the vehicle and support safely. Disconnect the vacuum hose(s) from the diaphragm unit.

2. Remove the retaining bracket and bolt holding the diaphragm unit to the transmission case.

—————— CAUTION ——————
Do not pry or bend the retainer bracket.

3. Pull the vacuum diaphragm, the actuating pin and the throttle valve from the transmission case. Remove the 0-ring from the assembly.

4. Install a new 0-ring on the diaphragm unit.

5. Install the throttle valve, the actuating pin and the vacuum diaphragm tubes towards the transmission case and install the assembly into the case.

6. Install the retaining bracket and bolt and torque to 15–23 inch lbs.

C4 Transmission

ADJUSTMENTS

Vacuum Diaphragm

The vacuum diaphragm used in production is non-adjustable. Adjustable type units are available for installation in the transmission, allowing changes in the control pressures.

An adjusting screw is located in the vacuum nipple of the diaphragm and is accessible after removing the vacuum supply line from the diaphragm. Using a small screwdriver and turning the screw clockwise will increase the control pressure, while turning the screw counter-clockwise will decrease the control pressure. One complete turn of the adjusting screw will change the control pressure approximately 2–3 psi.

After adjustments are made, reinstall the vacuum supply line.

NOTE: The diaphragm should not be adjusted to provide pressures below the specified ranges to change shift engagement feel, as soft or slipping shift points could result and damage to the transmission could occur.

Throttle Linkage

1. Hold the carburetor in the wide open throttle position (W.O.T.).

2. Hold the kickdown rod downward with the specified weight against the through detent stop.

3. Adjust the kickdown screw to obtain 0.01–0.08 in. clearance between the screw and the throttle arm.

4. Return the system to idle position.

Band

INTERMEDIATE BAND

1. Clean all dirt from the band adjusting screw area. Remove and discard the locknut.

2. Install a new locknut on the adjusting screw.

3. Torque the adjusting screw to 10 ft. lbs.

4. Back off the adjusting screw exactly 1¾ turns.

5. Hold the adjusting screw from turning and torque the locknut to 35–45 ft. lbs.

LOW AND REVERSE BAND

1. Clean all dirt from the band adjusting screw area. Remove and discard the locknut.

2. Install a new locknut on the adjusting screw.

3. Torque the adjusting screw to 10 ft. lbs.

4. Back off the adjusting screw exactly 3 full turns.

5. Hold the adjusting screw from turning and torque the locknut to 35–45 ft. lbs.

NOTE: In order to tighten the locknut on Pinto applications, special Ford tool T70P-7B200-B or equivalent may be needed.

Manual Linkage

COLUMN SHIFT

1. Place the automatic transmission selector lever in the Drive position. Make sure that the lever is tight against the drive stop.

2. Loosen the shift rod adjusting nut.

NOTE: On vehicles equipped with a shift cable, remove the nut, and remove the cable from the automatic transmission manual lever stud.

3. Shift the automatic transmission manual lever into the Drive position (at the transmission).

4. On vehicles equipped with a shift cable, place the cable end on the automatic transmission manual lever stud, using care to align the shift cable. Start the adjustment nut.

5. Make sure that the automatic transmission lever has not moved from the drive stop. Torque the adjusting nut to 15 ft. lbs.

6. Check the transmission operation for all selector lever detent positions.

FLOOR SHIFT

1. Position the automatic transmission lever in the Drive position against the drive stop.

2. Raise the vehicle and loosen the manual lever shift rod retaining nut. Move the automatic transmission manual lever to the Drive Position.

3. With the automatic transmission selector lever and the manual lever in the Drive positions, torque the attaching nut to 15 ft. lbs.

4. Check the operation of the transmission in each selector lever position.

Neutral Safety Switch
FLOOR SHIFT

1. With the manual linkage properly adjusted and the engine turned off, place the selector lever in the Neutral position.

2. Remove the selector lever handle attaching screw and remove the handle.

3. Remove the dial housing attaching screws and remove the housing.

4. Take out the two pointer backup shield attaching screws and remove the shield.

5. Loose the two screws securing the neutral start switch to the selector lever housing.

6. Place the selector lever in the Park position; hold it against the forward stop.

7. Move the switch rearward to the end of its travel.

8. Hold the switch in the rearward position and tighten the two attaching screws.

9. With the selector lever in the Park position, check the operation of the switch. The engine should start in the Park position. If the engine does not start replace the switch.

10. Install the pointer back-up shield, dial housing, and selector lever handle.

COLUMN SHIFT

In the column shift cars the switch is located on the transmission behind the manual lever.

1. With the automatic transmission manual lever properly adjusted, loosen the two neutral safety switch bolts.

2. Place the automatic transmission manual lever in neutral, rotate the switch

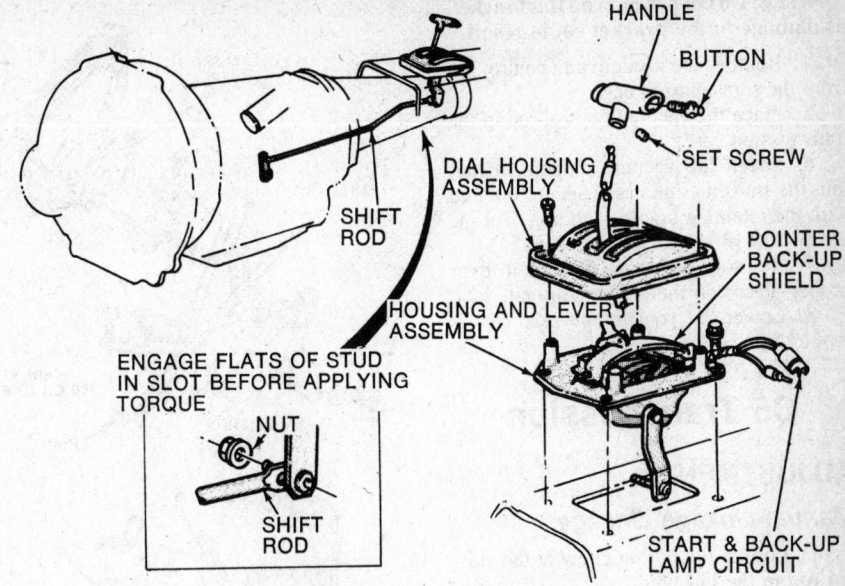

Typical linkage-type floor shift mechanism (© Ford Motor Co.)

and insert the gauge pin (no. 43 drill bit) into the gauge pin holes.

3. Be sure that the pin is through the switch and into the hole in the other wall.

4. Torque the neutral safety switch bolts to 55–75 inch lbs. and remove the gauge pin from the switch.

5. Check for engine starting in the Park and Neutral positions.

OIL PAN

Removal & Installation

1. Raise the vehicle and support it safely. Place a drain pan under the transmission.

2. Loosen the transmission oil pan bolts and drain the fluid from the unit.

3. When the fluid has drained to the level of the oil pan flange, remove the rest of the transmission pan bolts working from the rear and both sides of the pan to allow the transmission pan to drop and the fluid to drain slowly.

4. After the fluid has stopped draining, remove the oil pan. Clean all the old gasket material from the pan and the transmission case. Thoroughly clean the inside of the transmission pan and screen.

5. Install a new pan gasket on the transmission pan and place the pan against the case.

6. Install all of the transmission pan bolts. Torque the bolts to 12–17 ft. lbs.

7. If the converter has not been drained, Put three quarts of automatic transmission fluid in and run the transmission. Type "F" prior to 1980, "CJ" or Dexron® II, 1980 and later.

8. Check the fluid at normal operating temperature and add fluid if necessary.

9. When filling a dry transmission and torque converter install five quarts of the proper type and grade fluid into the

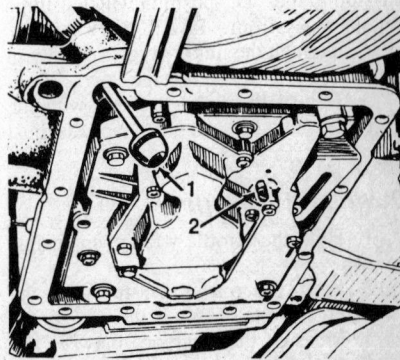

1. If found, this plug may be discarded (see text)
2. Throttle pressure limit valve and spring

View of C4 with transmission oil pan removed

transmission.

10. Start the engine and operate at idle speed for approximately two minutes and then raise the engine speed to approximately 1200 rpm until the engine and transmission assembly reaches normal operating temperature.

NOTE: Do not overspeed engine during warm-up.

11. Check the fluid level after moving the gear selector lever through all ranges. Correct the fluid level as necessary.

VACUUM DIAPHRAGM

Removal & Installation

1. Raise the vehicle and support on jackstands.

2. Disconnect the vacuum diaphragm hoses.

3. Remove the vacuum unit retaining bracket and bolt. Pull the vacuum diaphragm from the transmission case.

NOTE: Do not pry or bend this bracket, as damage to the bracket could result.

4. Remove the vacuum unit control rod from the transmission case.

5. Place the vacuum control rod in the transmission case.

6. Install the vacuum diaphragm unit into the transmission case. Secure the unit with the retaining bracket and bolt. Torque the bolt to 13–16 ft. lbs.

7. Reinstall the vacuum hoses to their proper places on the diaphragm unit.

8. Lower the vehicle and road test as required.

C5 Transmission

ADJUSTMENTS

Manual Linkage Linkage

1. Loosen the nut or screw at the slotted rod in the linkage.

2. Put the selector in the ''D'' position, firmly against the shift gate stop.

3. Shift the manual lever on the transmission to the ''D'' position which is three detents away from ''PARK.''

4. Tighten the nut or screw securely in the slotted rod of the linkage.

5. Repeat the linkage check with the shift lever and the shift gate stop. Readjust as required.

Downshift Linkage

1. Hold the throttle wide open against its stop.

2. Push the rod down to force the downshift valve to bottom in the valve body.

3. Measure the clearance between the tip of the adjusting screw and the throttle lever. The clearance should be 0.050–0.070 in.

4. Turn the adjusting screw to obtain the proper clearance.

Band (Both)

To adjust either band;

1. Remove the adjusting screw locknut and discard.

2. Install a new locknut on the adjusting screw, loosely.

3. Tighten the adjusting screw to 10 ft. lbs. torque, or until the adjusting tool overruns and clicks.

4. Back the adjusting screw off exactly the specified number of turns:
Intermediate band 4¼ turns
Low-reverse band 3 turns

5. Hold the adjustment screw at the specified back-off turns and tighten the new locknuts to 35–45 ft. lbs.

Neutral Start Switch

1. Place the selector in the ''NEUTRAL'' position and hold.

2. Loosen the switch bolts and insert a ³⁄₃₂ inch gauge pin or drill through the hole in the switch.

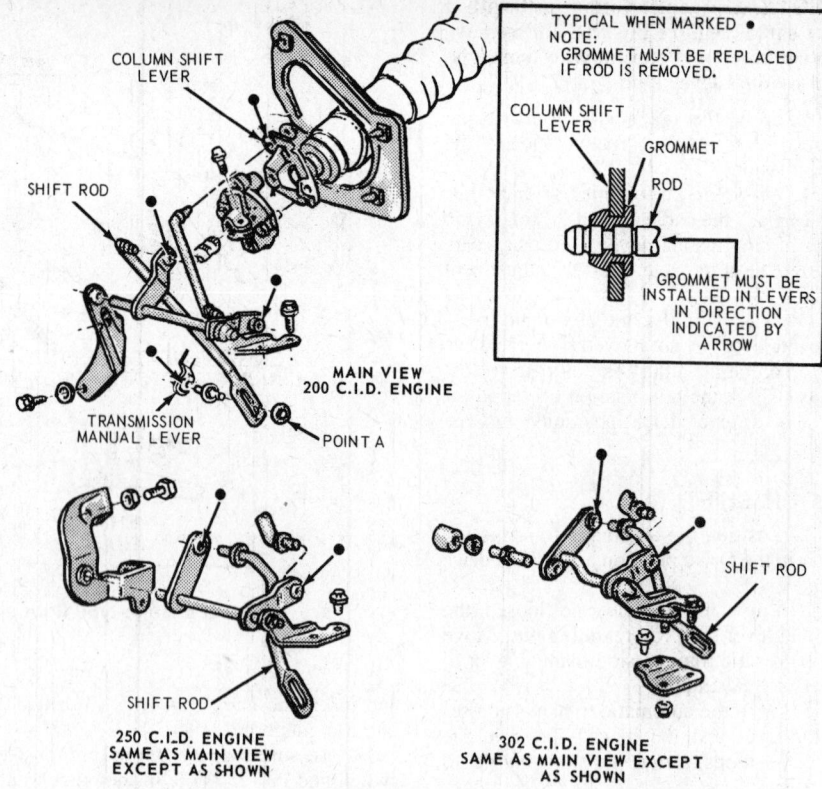

Typical linkage-type column shift mechanism (© Ford Motor Co.)

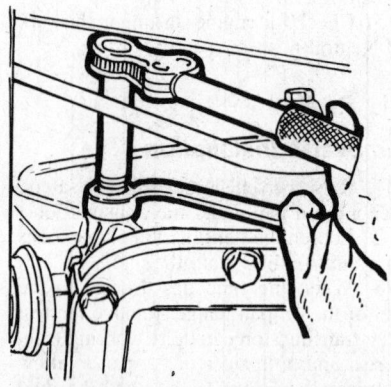

C4 and C5 low-reverse band adjustment

3. Wiggle the switch until the drill seats in the case.

4. Tighten the switch bolts to 55–75 inch lbs. torque and remove the drill.

Vacuum Diaphragm

Adjustment of the vacuum diaphragm is controlled by the installation of longer or shorter throttle valve rods to obtain the proper line pressure. Five selective rods are used.

Length	Color Code
1.5925–1.5875	Green
1.6075–1.6025	Blue
1.6225–1.6175	Orange
1.6375–1.6325	Black
1.6585–1.6535	Pink and White

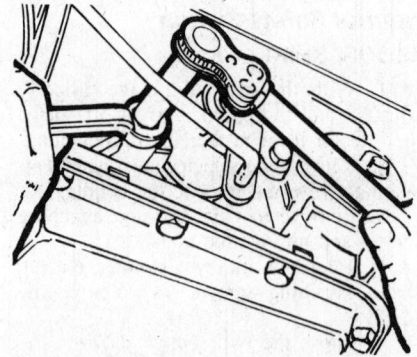

C4, C5 and C6 intermediate band adjustment

The following procedure will determine if a change in the length of the rod is required.

1. Attach a tachometer to the engine.

2. Attach a hand vacuum pump to the transmission vacuum diaphragm unit.

3. Attach a hydraulic pressure gauge to the control pressure outlet on the transmission.

4. Firmly apply the parking brake. On vehicles equipped with a vacuum brake release, apply the service brakes. Otherwise the parking brake will release when the selector is moved to Drive.

5. Start the engine, allow it to reach normal operating temperature.

6. Set the engine idle speed to the specified rpm.

7. Adjust engine speed to 1000 rpm and apply 10 inches of vacuum to vacuum

diaphragm unit. Read and record the control pressure in all selector positions.

8. Compare the pressure readings from Step 7 to the specified pressure in the line Pressure chart and Proceed as follows:

a. Pressure within specification no change required

b. Pressure below specification use the next longest rod

c. Pressure above specification use the next shortest rod

If the length of the rod is not known, it should be measured with a micrometer.

LINE PRESSURE CHART

Transmission Model		Range 10″ Vacuum
PEN-C,G,J,K	D	#90–101
PEM-AL,AM	2,1	123–136
	R	151–168
PEP-E,F,G,H,P,N	D	#87–97
	2,1	119–132
	R	145–162
PEP-B,D	D	#86–99
	2,1	120–132
	R	143–165

NOTE: Refer to the ID tag for the transmission model.

OIL PAN

Removal & Installation

1. Raise the vehicle and support safely.

2. Loosen the oil pan retaining bolts, removing only enough bolts to tilt the oil pan and drain the fluid.

3. Carefully remove the remaining bolts and the oil pan from the transmission. Pour out the remaining fluid from the oil pan.

NOTE: Discard the nylon shipping plug found in the bottom of the oil pan.

4. Thoroughly clean and remove all gasket material from the oil pan and the pan mounting surface of the transmission case.

5. Install new gasket and mount the pan to the transmission case.

6. Install the pan retaining bolts and torque to 12–16 ft. lbs.

7. Lower the vehicle and fill the transmission with fluid. Type "H" only. Start the engine and recheck the fluid level. Correct as required.

C6 Transmission

ADJUSTMENTS

Throttle Linkage

1. Position the carburetor in the wide open throttle position (W.O.T.).

2. Hold the kickdown rod downward

with a 4½ lb. weight against the through detent stop.

3. Adjust the kickdown adjusting screw to obtain 0.01–0.08 in. clearance between the screw and the throttle arm.

4. Return the system to idle.

Band

NOTE: The only adjustment that is needed on the C-6 automatic transmission is the intermediate band adjustment.

1. Raise the vehicle and support on jackstands.

2. Clean all the grease and dirt away from the band adjusting screw area. Remove and discard the locknut.

3. Install a new locknut and torque the adjusting screw to 10 ft. lbs. Back off the adjusting screw 1½ turns.

4. Hold the adjusting screw, so that it does not turn, and torque the locknut to 40 ft. lbs.

5. Lower the vehicle. Road test and correct as necessary.

Manual Linkage
COLUMN SHIFT

1. Place the transmission selector level in the (D) drive position. Make sure that the lever is tight against the (D) drive stop.

NOTE: If necessary a 10–15 lb. weight should be hung on the transmission shift lever to be sure that the lever remains against the Drive stop during the adjusting procedure.

2. Loosen the shift rod adjusting nut.

NOTE: On vehicles equipped with a shift cable, remove the nut, and remove the cable from the transmission manual lever stud.

3. Shift the transmission manual lever into the (D) drive position.

4. On vehicles equipped with a shift cable, place the cable end on the transmission manual lever stud, using care to align the flats on the stud with the flats on the shift cable. Start the adjustment nut.

5. Make sure that the transmission lever has not moved from the (D) drive stop. Torque the adjusting nut to 15 ft. lbs.

6. Check the transmission operation for all selector lever detent positions.

FLOOR SHIFT

1. Position the transmission selector lever in the (D) drive position against the rearward (D) drive stop.

2. Raise the vehicle and loosen the manual lever shift rod retaining nut. Move the transmission manual lever to the (D) drive position.

3. With the transmission selector lever and the manual lever in the (D) drive positions, torque the attaching nut to 15 ft. lbs.

4. Check the operation of the transmission in each selector lever position. Lower the vehicle.

Neutral Safety Switch
1978–79

1. With the transmission manual linkage properly adjusted and the engine turned OFF, place the automatic transmission selector lever in the (N) neutral position.

2. Remove the selector lever handle by removing the attaching screw. Remove the dial housing by removing the attaching screw.

3. Remove the two pointer back-up shield screws and remove the back-up shield.

4. Loosen the screws holding the neutral safety switch to the selector lever housing.

5. Place the selector lever in the (P) park position and hold it against the forward stop.

6. Move the neutral safety switch rearward as far to the end of its travel as it will go.

7. Hold the neutral switch in the rearward position and tighten the two screws.

8. With the transmission selector lever in the (P) park position check the operation of the neutral safety switch.

NOTE: The engine should start with the automatic transmission selector lever in the (P) park position. If the engine does not start the neutral safety switch should be replaced.

9. Install the pointer back-up shield dial housing by reversing the removal procedure.

1980 AND LATER

1. With the transmission manual lever properly adjusted, loosen the two neutral safety switch bolts.

2. With the transmission manual lever in neutral, rotate the switch and insert the gauge pin (No. 43 drill bit) into the gauge pin holes of the neutral safety switch.

NOTE: The gauge pin has to be inserted to a full 31/64 inch into the three holes of the neutral safety switch.

3. Torque the neutral safety switch bolts to 55–75 ft. lbs. Remove the gauge pin from the neutral safety switch.

4. Check the operation of the neutral safety switch.

NOTE: The engine should start with the transmission selector lever in (P) park or (N) neutral only.

Vacuum Diaphragm (Modulator)
ADJUSTABLE VACUUM DIAPHRAGM (MODULATOR)

1. Remove the vacuum hose from the vacuum nipple and insert a small screwdriver into the nipple end and engage the adjusting screw.

2. Adjust the pressure by turning the adjusting screw in to increase the pressure or by turning the adjusting screw out to decrease the pressure.

NOTE: One complete turn of the adjusting screw should change the pressure 2–3 psi, either higher or lower, dePending upon the direction of rotation.

NON-ADJUSTABLE VACUUM DIAPHRAGM (MODULATOR)

1. Remove the modulator assembly and measure the selective pushrod.

NOTE: The pushrods can be identified by length, color code or part numbers.

2. Install a longer push rod to increase the pressure or a shorter push rod to decrease the pressure.

3. Each selective push rod increment should change the pressure 5–6 psi.

OIL PAN

Removal & Installation

1. Raise the vehicle and support on jackstands. Place a drain pan under the transmission.

2. Loosen the automatic transmission oil pan bolts and drain the automatic transmission fluid from the unit.

3. When the transmission fluid has drained to the level of the oil pan flange, remove the rest of the transmission oil pan bolts working from the rear and both sides of the pan to allow the transmission pan to drop and the fluid to drain slowly.

4. When the fluid has drained to the level of the pan flange, remove the rest of the pan bolts. Work from the rear and both sides of the pan to allow it to drop and drain slowly.

5. Install a new transmission pan gasket on the transmission pan and place it against the transmission case.

6. Install all the transmission oil pan bolts. Torque the bolts to 12–17 ft. lbs.

7. Install three quarts of automatic transmission fluid (converter not drained). Be sure to use the proper grade and type transmission fluid; failure to do this could result in serious internal transmission damage. Use "CJ" or Dexron® II fluid.

8. When refilling a dry transmission and torque converter install five quarts of the proper grade and type automatic transmission fluid into the transmission.

9. Start the engine and operate the engine at idle speed for approximately two minutes and then raise the engine speed to approximately 1200 rpm until the engine/transmission assembly reaches normal operating temperature.

NOTE: Do not overspeed the engine during warm-up.

10. Check the fluid level after moving the gear selector through all ranges. Correct the fluid level as necessary.

VACUUM DIAPHRAGM

Removal & Installation

1. Raise the vehicle and support on jackstands.

2. Disconnect the vacuum diaphragm hoses.

3. Remove the vacuum unit retaining bracket and bolt. Pull the vacuum diaphragm from the transmission case.

NOTE: Do not pry or bend this bracket, as damage to the bracket could result.

4. Remove the vacuum unit control rod from the transmission case.

5. Place the vacuum control rod in the transmission case.

6. Install the vacuum diaphragm unit into the transmission case. Secure the unit with the retaining bracket and bolt. Torque the bolt (12–16 ft. lbs.).

7. Reinstall the vacuum hoses to their proper places on the diaphragm unit.

8. Lower the vehicle and road test as required.

JATCO Transmission

ADJUSTMENT

Manual Linkage

The manual control linkage adjustment should be performed in the order listed. Idle speed should be properly adjusted before manual linkage is set.

1. Place the transmission selector in the "N" position.

2. Raise the vehicle and disconnect the clevis from the lower end of the selector lever operating arm.

3. Move the transmission manual lever to the neutral position, third detent position from the back of the transmission.

4. Loosen the two clevis retaining nuts and adjust the clevis so that it freely enters the selector lever operating arm hole. Tighten the clevis retaining nuts to secure the adjustment.

5. Connect the clevis to the lever and secure it with the spring washer, flat washer and retaining clip.

6. Lower the vehicle and check the operation of the transmission in each selector lever position.

Band Servo

1. Raise the vehicle.

2. Remove the servo cover attaching bolts and take off the servo cover.

3. Loosen the band adjusting screw lock nut and tighten the adjusting screw to 9–11 ft. lbs. torque.

4. Back off the adjusting screw two turns. Hold the adjusting screw stationary and tighten the adjusting screw locknut to 22–29 ft. lbs. torque.

5. Lower the vehicle and check the transmission fluid level.

Neutral Safety Switch

1. With the manual linkage properly adjusted, place the transmission manual lever in the "N" position, third detent from the back of the transmission.

2. Remove the transmission manual lever retaining nut and lever.

3. Loosen the two neutral safety switch attaching bolts. Remove the screw from the alignment pin hole at the bottom of the switch.

4. Rotate the switch and insert a 0.079 in. diameter alignment pin through the alignment pin hole into the hole in the internal switch.

5. Tighten the two attaching bolts and remove the alignment pin.

6. Reinstall the alignment pin hole screw in the switch body.

7. Position the transmission manual lever on the manual lever shaft and secure it with the flat washer and nut.

8. Check the operation of the switch. The engine should start only with selector lever in Neutral or Park.

Vacuum Diaphragm

The vacuum diaphragms used in production are nonadjustable. If the adjustable type is on the transmission and is in need of adjustment follow the normal adjusting procedures.

An adjusting screw is located in the vacuum nipple of the diaphragm and is accessible after removing the vacuum supply line from the diaphragm. Using a small screwdriver and turning the screw clockwise will increase the control pressure, while turning the screw counterclockwise will decrease the control pressure. One complete turn of the adjusting screw changes the control pressure approximately 2–3 psi.

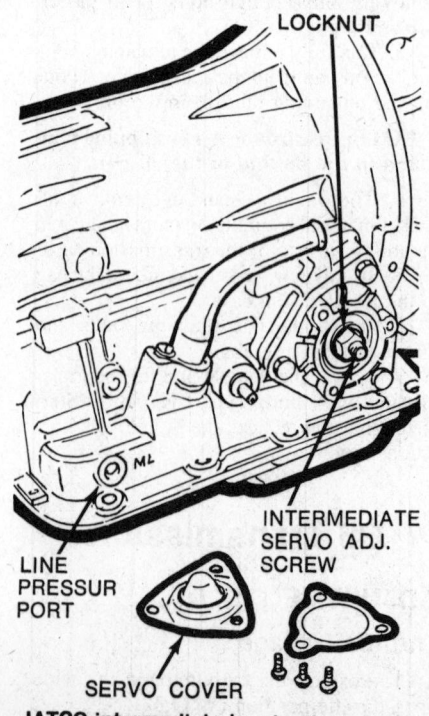

JATCO intermediate band adjustment

—— CAUTION ——

The diaphragm should not be adjusted to provide pressures below the specified ranges to change shift engagement fell, as soft or slipping shift points could result in damage to the transmission.

Downshift (Kickdown Switch)

1. Move the ignition switch to the ON position.

2. Loosen the kickdown switch to engage when the accelerator pedal is between ⅞-¹⁵⁄₁₆ of full travel. The downshift solenoid will click when the switch engages.

3. Tighten the attaching nut and check for proper switch operation.

OIL PAN

Draining, Removal & Installation

1. Raise the vehicle and support safely.

2. Position a drain pan beneath the transmission pan and starting at the rear, loosen, but do not remove the pan bolts.

3. Loosen the pan from the transmission case and allow the fluid to drain gradually.

4. Remove all pan bolts except two at the front of the pan and allow the fluid to continue draining.

5. Remove the pan. Clean the remains of the old gasket from the pan and transmission case.

6. Install a new gasket on the pan and install it to the transmission case.

7. Install all pan bolts and torque to 4–5 ft. lbs.

8. Install three quarts of transmission fluid. "CJ" or Dexron® II, into the filler tube (converter not drained).

9. Start the engine and operate the engine at idle speed for approximately two minutes. Then raise the engine speed to approximately 1200 rpm until the engine and transmission reach operating temperature.

—— CAUTION ——

Do not overspeed the engine during warm-up.

10. Check the fluid level after moving the gear selector through all ranges. Correct the fluid as necessary.

VACUUM DIAPHRAGM

Removal & Installation

1. Raise the vehicle and support safely. Disconnect the vacuum hose(s) from the diaphragm unit.

2. Turn the threaded diaphragm unit to remove it from the transmission case.

3. Pull the actuating pin and the throttle valve from the transmission case.

4. Remove the O-ring from the assembly.

5. Install a new O-ring on the diaphragm unit.

6. Install the throttle valve, the actuating pin and the vacuum diaphragm tubes toward the transmission case and install the assembly into the case.

7. Install and tighten the vacuum diaphragm, connect vacuum hose(s).

Automatic Transaxle (ATX)

ADJUSTMENTS
Manual Linkage

This is a critical adjustment. Be sure the "D" detent in the transaxle corresponds exactly with the stop in the console.

1. Raise and support the vehicle safely. Position the selector lever in the drive position, against the rearward stop. Hold in position while the adjustment is being done.

2. Loosen the manual lever to control cable retaining nut and move the transmission manual lever to the Drive position, second detent from the most rearward position.

3. Having both the transaxle detent and the shift stop in the console correspond, tighten the retaining nut 10–15 ft. lbs.

4. Lower the vehicle and verify the adjustment. Be sure the park mechanism and the neutral start switch function properly.

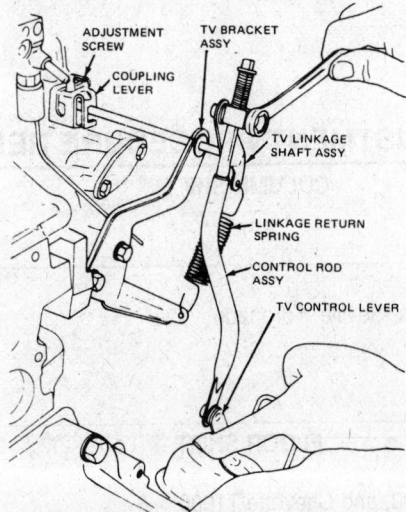

Throttle linkage adjustment—all models with an ATX (© Ford Motor Co.)

Throttle Linkage
MANUAL

The TV control linkage must be adjusted at the TV control rod assembly sliding trunnion block using the following procedure.

1. Set the engine curb idle speed to specification.

2. After the curb idle check, turn the engine off and insure that the carburetor throttle lever is against the hot engine curb idle stop. (The choke must be off.)

NOTE: The linkage cannot be properly set if the choke is allowed to cool and the throttle lever allowed to be on the choke fast idle cam.

3. Set the coupling lever adjustment screw at its approximate mid-range. Insure that the TV linkage shaft assembly is fully seated upward into the coupling lever.

4. Loosen the bolt on the sliding trunnion block on the TV control rod assembly one turn minimum.

—— CAUTION ——

The following steps involve working in proximity to the EGR system. Allow the EGR system to cool before proceeding.

5. Free-up the trunnion block so that it slides freely on the control rod.

6. Rotate the transaxle TV control lever up using one finger and a light force, approximately 5 pounds. to insure that the TV control lever is against its internal idle stop. Without relaxing the force on the TV control lever, tighten the bolt on the trunnion block to specification.

7. Verify that the carburetor throttle lever is still against the hot engine curb idle stop.

USING LINE PRESSURE

The following procedure may be used to check and/or adjust the TV control linkage using a line pressure gauge.

1. Place the shift selector lever in the Park position.

2. Apply the emergency brake.

3. Attach a 0-300 psi pressure gauge to the line press port on the transaxle with sufficient flexible hose to make gauge accessible while operating engine.

4. Operate the engine until normal operating temperature is reached and the throttle lever is against the hot engine curb idle stop (with A/C off, if so equipped).

5. Verify that the coupling lever adjusting screw is in contact with the TV linkage shaft assembly. If not, then the linkage must first be readjusted.

6. Verify that the carburetor throttle lever is against its hot engine curb idle stop. With the engine operating at idle and in Park, line pressure must be 43–59 psi. If line pressure is greater than 59 psi, the TV control linkage is set too long.

7. Place a 4mm drill (a ⁵⁄₃₂ in. drill or 0.157 gauge pin) between the coupling lever adjustment screw and the TV linkage shaft. With the engine operating at idle and in Park, the line pressure must be 72–88 psi. A low reading indicates linkage is set short. A high reading indicates linkage is set too long.

8. Correct a long setting by backing out (CCW) the coupling lever adjustment screw. Turn in (CW) the adjustment screw for a short rod condition. This adjusting screw will change line pressure by approximately 2 psi per turn. If insufficient adjusting capacity is available, the TV control rod length must be reset.

LINE PRESSURE①

Range	Pressure (At Idle)	Pressure (WOT Stall)
D-2-1	43–5 psi	105–127 psi
R	70–105 psi	230–285 psi
P-N	43–58 psi	②

①Governor pressure is at zero (vehicle stationary). Transaxle is at operating temperature.
②Not available.

Neutral Safety Switch

1. Loosen the two switch retaining bolts and place the manual lever in the "Neutral" position.
2. Insert a ³⁄₃₂inch drill bit through the hole in the neutral start switch.
3. Move the neutral switch until the drill seats in the case.
4. Torque the neutral start switch retaining bolts to 7–9 ft. lbs.
5. Remove the drill from the switch.

Band

The band adjustment is done during a transaxle overhaul with the use of special tools. Selective sized servo pistons are used to correctly position the band for its application.

OIL PAN AND FILTER

Removal & Installation

1. Raise the vehicle and support on jack stands.
2. Place a drain pan under the transaxle.
3. Loosen the pan attaching bolts and drain the fluid from transaxle.
4. When the fluid has drained to the level of the pan flange, remove the rest of the pan bolts. Work from the rear and both sides of the to allow it to drop and drain slowly.
5. When all fluid has drained from transaxle, remove and thoroughly clean the pan. Discard the gasket.
6. Remove the three retaining bolts and remove the filter. Discard the seal.
7. Install a new oil filter and seal. Tighten the bolts 7–9 ft. lbs.
8. Place a new gasket on the oil pan and install the oil pan on the transaxle case. Tighten the retaining bolts to 15–19 ft. lbs.
9. Fill the transaxle to the correct level with Dexron® II automatic transmission fluid.

NEUTRAL START SWITCH

Removal & Installation

1. Disconnect the battery.
2. Remove the two managed air valve supply rear hoses and all vacuum lines from the managed air valve.
3. Remove the managed air valve supply hose band to intermediate shift control bracket attaching screw.
4. Remove the air cleaner.
5. Disconnect the neutral start switch connector.
6. Remove the two neutral start switch attaching bolts.
7. Remove the neutral start switch.
8. Install the neutral start switch on the manual shaft.
9. Loosely install the two neutral start switch attaching bolts and washers.
10. Using a No. 43 drill (0.089 in.), set the neutral start switch.
11. Tighten the attaching bolts to 7–9 ft. lbs.
12. Connect the neutral start switch connector.
13. Install the managed air valve supply hose band to intermediate shift control bracket attaching screw.
14. Connect the two managed air valve supply rear hoses and all vacuum hoses to the managed air valve.
15. Install the air cleaner.
16. Connect the battery.
17. Start the engine in both Park and Neutral.

LINKAGE ADJUSTMENT PROCEDURE REFERENCE

COLUMN SHIFT	
Rear Wheel Drive Models	
All	Procedure 1
Front Wheel Drive Models	
Except Eldorado, Riviera, Seville, Toronado	Procedure 2
78 Eldorado, Toronado	Procedure 3
w/shift linkage①	—
w/shift cable②	—

FLOOR SHIFT	
Rear Wheel Drive Models	
Except Corvette w/TH400, and Chevette/T1000	Procedure 4
Corvette w/TH400	Procedure 6
Chevette/T1000	Procedure 5
Front Wheel Drive Models	
All w/TH125 and TH125C	Procedure 2

① Procedure 1 may be used, but note that the adjusting clamp location is different than that of the rear wheel drive cars.
② Not adjustable.

GENERAL MOTORS CORPORATION

NOTE: To identify the transmission used in your vehicle, refer to the transmission oil pan outlines at the beginning of this section.

Shift Linkage/Cable Adjustment

NOTE: Refer to the accompanying Linkage Adjustment Reference Chart to determine the procedure which must be used for your vehicle.

PROCEDURE 1

1. Loosen the screw on the shift linkage clamp.

2. Set the lever on the transmission into Neutral by moving it counterclockwise to the L1 detent, then clockwise three detent positions to Neutral.

3. Place the transmission selector lever (in the car) in Neutral as determined by the stop in the steering column. Don't use the indicator pointer for reference.

4. Tighten the shift linkage screw.

5. Check that the key cannot be removed and the steering wheel is not locked with the key in Run and the transmission in Reverse. Check that the key can be removed and that the steering wheel and transmission linkage is locked when the key is in Lock and the transmission is in Park. Be sure that the car will start only in Park and Neutral. If it starts in any gear, the neutral start switch must be adjusted. Start the engine and check for proper shifting into all ranges.

PROCEDURE 2

1. Place the shift selector in Neutral.

2. From under the hood, remove the nut which attaches the shift cable end to the transmission lever pin.

3. Place the transmission lever in Neutral. The Neutral position is the second detent FROM the Park (fully counterclockwise) position.

4. With both the shift selector and transmission levers in Neutral, assemble the shift cable to the transmission lever pin and tighten to 15 ft. lbs.

--- CAUTION ---

Hold the transmission lever stationary while tightening the nut or an incorrect adjustment will result.

5. Check for proper operation.

PROCEDURE 3

1. Pull the relay rod fully upward (Park), then push the rod down to the third detent (Neutral) position. The rod should be centered in this position.

2. Loosen the adjustment screw of the relay lever rod clamp.

3. Position the shift selector lever in Neutral.

4. Tighten the clamp adjusting screw to 20 ft. lbs. Refer to the Caution which follows Step 4 of the previous procedure.

5. Check for proper operation.

PROCEDURE 4

All models in this group use a cable operated shift selector control. Some models also use an adjustable vertical linkage rod which is used for the steering column interlock.

Models With an Interlock Rod

1. Place the shift selector lever in the park position.

2. Loosen the cable pin nut at the transmission lever. The pin must be able to slide freely within the slot of the lever.

3. Loosen the swivel clamp (bolt) of the column interlock rod. The rod must be able to slide freely within the clamp.

4. Push the transmission lever fully into the Park detent, then tighten the cable pin nut.

5. Lightly pull the interlock rod downward against the stop, then tighten the swivel clamp bolt. Refer to the Caution following Step 4 of "Procedure 2."

6. Check for proper operation.

Models Without an Interlock Rod

1. Place the shift selector in the Neutral position.

2. Loosen the cable pin nut at the transmission lever. The pin must be able to slide freely within the slot of the lever.

3. Verify that the transmission lever is in the Neutral position by turning the lever fully clockwise, then bring it back 2 detents counterclockwise.

4. Tighten the cable pin nut and check the operation of the shifter mechanism.

1. Lever
2. Nut (⅜"–16)
3. Equalizer shaft assembly
4. Anti-rattle spring
5. Flat washer
6. Pivot bushing
7. Shaft-to-frame bracket
8. Screw (⁵⁄₁₆"–12)
9. Screw (⁵⁄₁₆"–18 × ½")
10. Washer
11. Swivel clamp
12. Gearshift control rod
13. Retainer
14. Control rod sleeve
15. Bushing

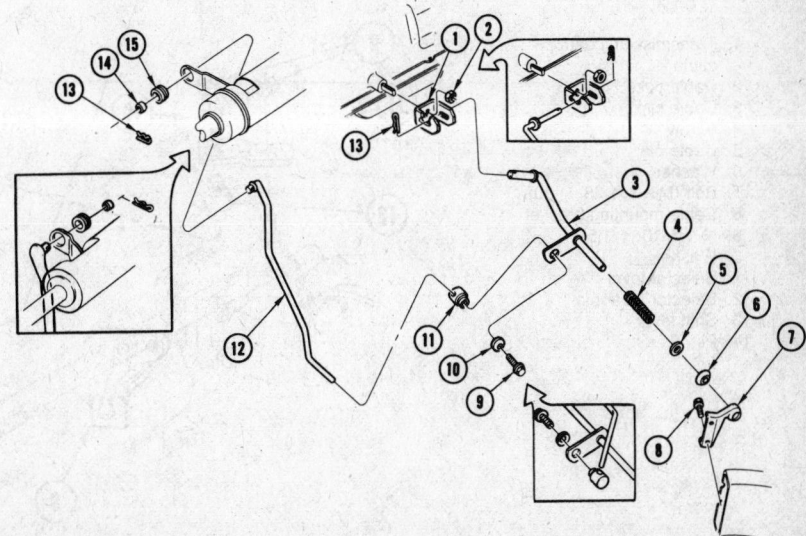

Typical rear wheel drive column shift linkage. Note that the location of the swivel clamp (11) may differ slightly between models. (© GM Corp.)

1. Transmission control cable
2. Bracket
3. Cable pin
4. Washer
5. Nut
6. Lever pin
7. Washer
8. Nut (M10P × 1.50)
9. Cable spring
10. Cable retaining yoke
11. Washer
12. Washer
13. Bolt
14. Cable pin
15. Bracket
16. Screw (¼″–14 × ¾″)
17. Heat shield
18. Heat shield brace
19. Bolt (⅜″–16 × ¾″)

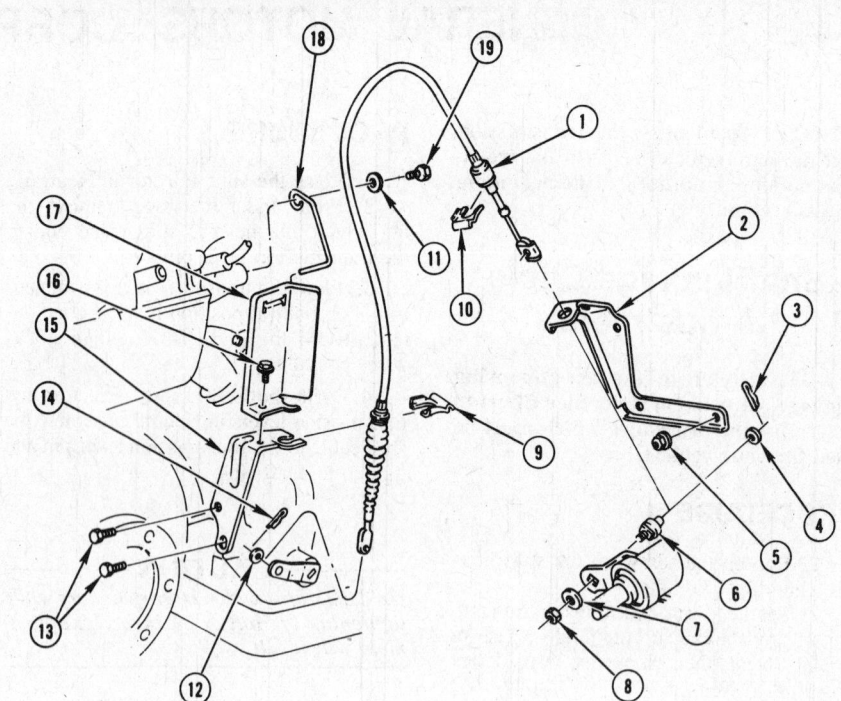

Column shift cable and related components—front wheel drive Eldorado, Riviera, Seville, and Toronado (© Oldsmobile Div., GM)

1. Transmission control cable
2. Cable yoke
3. Cable clip
4. Screw
5. Cable pin
6. Washer
7. Bolt (M8 × 1.25 × 20)
8. Cable mounting bracket
9. Nut (M10 × 1.5)
10. Washer
11. Selector lever
12. Selector lever pin
13. Shift lever
14. Pin

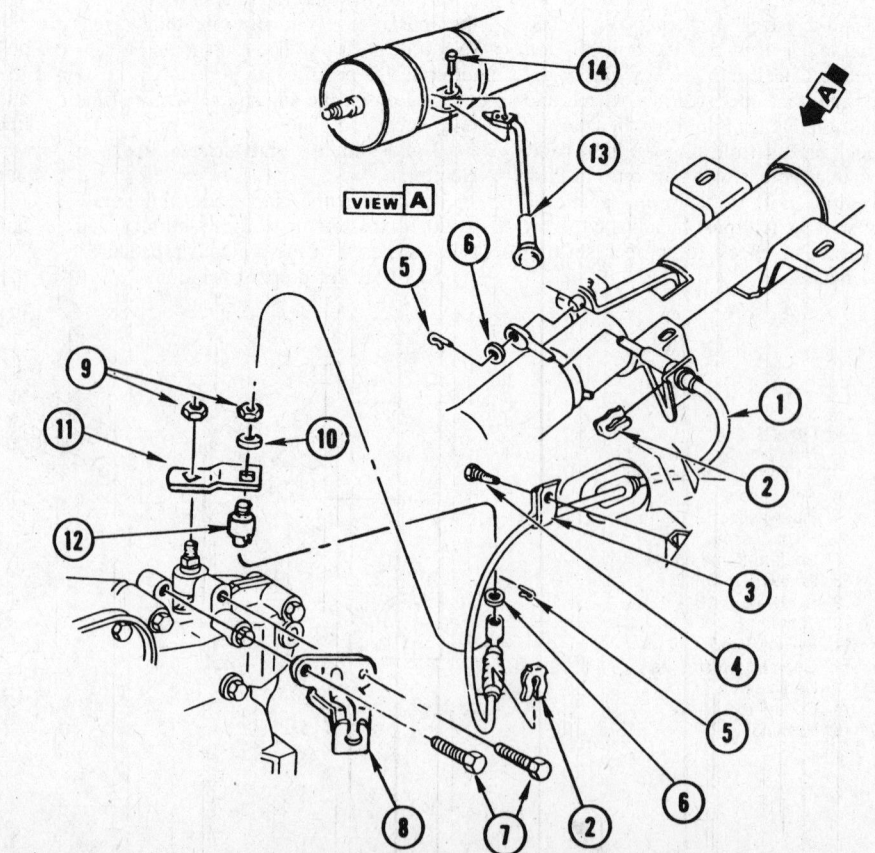

Typical front wheel drive column shift cable and related components—except Eldorado, Riviera, Seville, and Toronado. Note that the cable attachment at the transaxle is the same for floor shift models. (© GM Corp.)

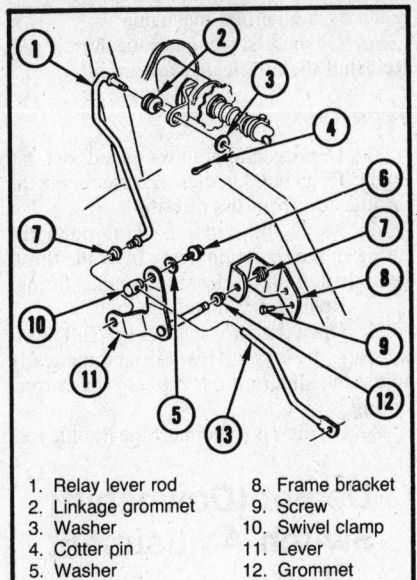

1. Relay lever rod
2. Linkage grommet
3. Washer
4. Cotter pin
5. Washer
6. Screw
7. Grommet
8. Frame bracket
9. Screw
10. Swivel clamp
11. Lever
12. Grommet
13. Rod

Column shift linkage—typical of Eldorado and Toronado front wheel drive 1978 models

PROCEDURE 5

The shifter assembly and linkage is basically the same on all models, though the point of adjustment is different between the THM180 and THM200 transmissions.

1. Place the shift selector lever in Neutral.

2. Disconnect the threaded end of the shift selector rod from either the transmission lever (THM180's) or the shifter lever (THM200's).

3. Rotate the transmission lever fully clockwise (Park), then bring it back (counterclockwise) 2 detents, to Neutral.

4. The shift selector rod link (THM180's) or the clevis (THM200's) should align with its respective mating part. If necessary, turn the link (THM180's) or clevis (THM200's) to lengthen or shorten the selector rod as required.

5. Connect the rod after the proper alignment is obtained.

6. Check for proper operation.

PROCEDURE 6

1. Loosen the nut on the transmission lever so that the pin can move in the slot. Remove the console cover.

2. Move the transmission lever counterclockwise to the L1 position and then clockwise five detents to Park.

3. Place the shift lever in Park and insert a 0.40 in. spacer in front of the pawl.

4. Tighten the nut on the transmission lever to 20 ft. lbs.

5. Turn the ignition switch to Lock with the shift lever in Park.

6. Remove the cotter pin and washer from the backdrive cable at the column lever. Disconnect the cable.

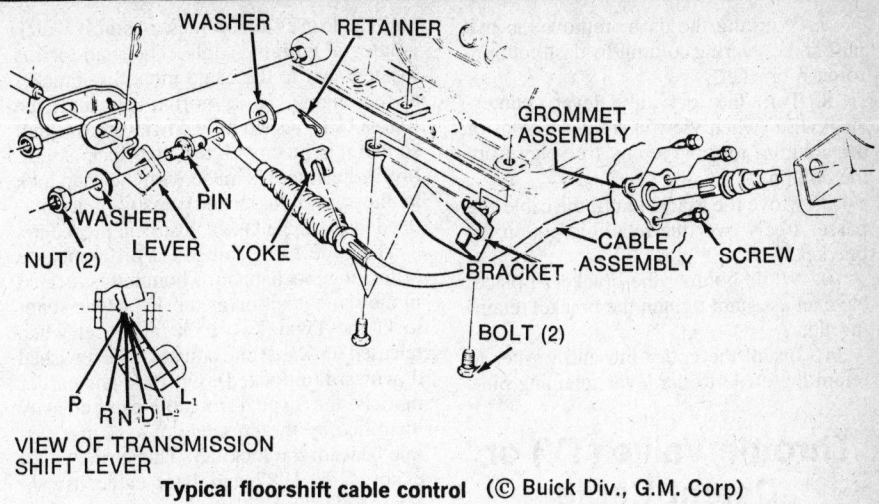

VIEW OF TRANSMISSION SHIFT LEVER

Typical floorshift cable control (© Buick Div., G.M. Corp)

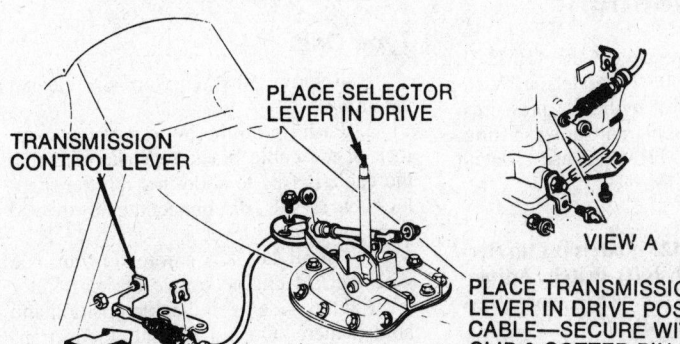

Typical Corvette shift cable adjustment (© Chevrolet Motor Div., GM)

1. Swivel clamp
2. Equalizer shaft assembly
3. Retainer
4. Bushing
5. Grommet

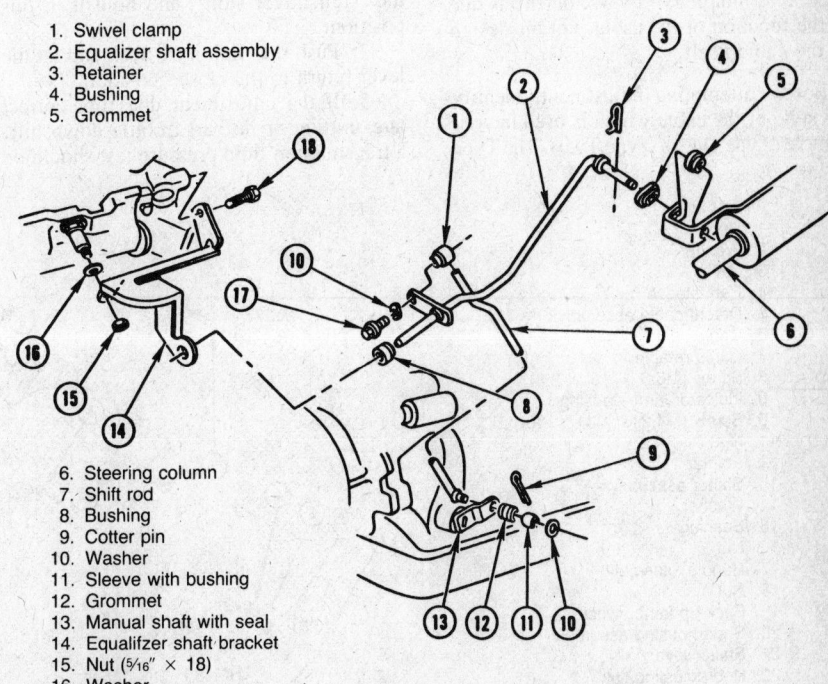

6. Steering column
7. Shift rod
8. Bushing
9. Cotter pin
10. Washer
11. Sleeve with bushing
12. Grommet
13. Manual shaft with seal
14. Equalizer shaft bracket
15. Nut (5/16" × 18)
16. Washer
17. Screw (M8 × 1.25 × 13.5)
18. Bolt (3/8"–16 × 3/4")

Column shift linkage of the front wheel drive Eldorado, Riviera, Seville, and Toronado (© Oldsmobile Div., GM)

7. Working the dash, remove the two nuts at the steering column-to-dash column-to-dash bracket.

8. Turn the lock tube lever counterclockwise (when viewed from the front of the column) to remove any free-play from the column.

9. Move the bracket until the cable eye passes freely over the retaining pin on the bracket.

10. While holding the bracket in place, have an assistant tighten the bracket retaining nuts.

11. Install the cotter pin and washer to retain the cable to the lever retaining pin.

Throttle Valve (TV) or Detent Cable Adjustment

On all transmissions except the THM250, THM350 and TH400/425 models, a TV cable is used to control hydraulic pressures, shift points, shift feel, and downshifting. The THM250 and THM350 use a detent cable.

NOTE: TH400/425 models use an electrical detent (downshift) switch. Adjustment of this switch is covered separately, after cable adjustment.

Though the detent cable is virtually identical in appearance to the TV cable, the detent cable controls only the downshift functions of the transmission. The difference in terminology (TV vs. detent) is due to the function of the cable, not the design of the cable itself.

Before attempting adjustment, identify the style of the cable which is used in your vehicle (Type One or Type Two). The Type One cable uses a snap-lock assembly which is integral with the cable. The snap-lock is located next to the cable mounting bracket at the engine. In its normal position, the snap-lock is pushed fully downward (locked) so that it is flush with the snap-lock assembly. Adjustment is made with the snap lock in the raised (unlocked) position, as outlined in the Type One adjustment procedure.

The Type Two cable uses a different type of locking mechanism. Though it is located in the same position as the Type One snap-lock, the Type Two lock tab is set when released (upward) and adjusted when pushed downward (unlocked). On 1981 and earlier models, the Type Two cable can be easily identified by the presence of a spring, visible beneath the lock tab. The spring is not exposed on 1982 and later cable assemblies. Refer to the Type Two adjusting procedure to adjust the cable.

Type One

1. Remove the engine air cleaner assembly.

2. Push up on the bottom of the snap-lock at the cable bracket. Make sure that the cable is free to slide through the snap-lock. On diesels, disconnect the throttle rod from the throttle lever.

3. On all but 125 automatic transaxle with the L-4 engine, move the carburetor lever to the wide open throttle position and hold it there. On the 125 automatic transaxle with the L-4 engine, rotate the carburetor idler lever to "full travel stop" (carburetor open) and hold it in this position. On diesels, rotate the throttle lever to the "full travel stop" and hold it in this position.

4. Push the snap-lock flush and let the lever return to the closed position.

5. If the adjustment does not correct late shifting or no part throttle downshift, a transmission fluid pressure test should be made by a qualified mechanic.

6. On diesels, reconnect the throttle rod. Reinstall the air cleaner assembly.

Type Two

1. Depress and hold the metal lock tab on the TV cable. On diesels, disconnect the throttle rod from the throttle lever.

2. Move the slider back through the fitting in the direction away from the throttle body until the slider stops against fitting.

3. Release the metal lock tab.

4. Open the throttle lever to "full throttle stop" position. This will automatically adjust the slider on the cable to the correct setting.

5. On diesels, reconnect the throttle rod.

Detent (Downshift) Switch Adjustment

TURBO HYDRA-MATIC® 400/425

All General Motors divisions, except Cadillac, use the same detent switch on TH400 and TH425 equipped models. The switch is mounted on the accelerator pedal bracket and is for all intents and purposes, self-adjusting. If a new switch is installed, a preliminary adjustment should be performed according to the accompanying illustration.

Cadillac has used two different types of switches: the majority use a switch mounted at the throttle linkage, next to the carburetor or throttle body (fuel injected models); the other switch is mounted at the accelerator pedal bracket, but is different than the switch used by the other GM divisions. Both types of Cadillac switches are adjusted in basically the same manner, as outlined in the following procedure:

1. Retainer
2. Washer
3. Lever
4. Park sleeve
5. Detent cable assembly
6. Cable seal
7. Cable retainer
8. Screw (M6.3 × 16 × 9.8)
9. Indicator lamp housing
10. Screw (M4.2 × 1.41 × 10)
11. Nut
12. Pointer
13. Shifter assembly
14. Washer
15. Bushing
16. Nut
17. Handle assembly
18. Nut
19. Back-up lamp switch
20. Shaft housing assembly
21. Shifter lever
22. Rod adjusting link
23. Shift selector rod assembly
24. Nut (M10 × 1.5)
25. Shift selector rod clevis pin
26. Shift selector rod clevis

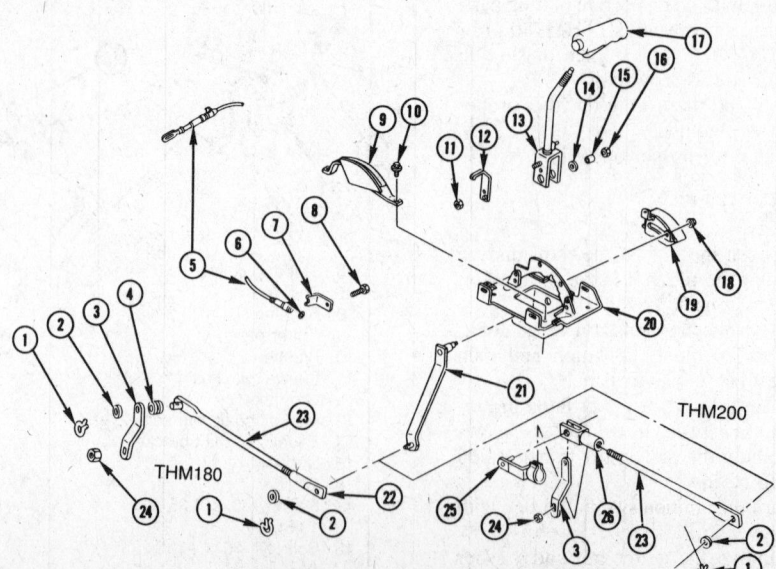

Chevette and T1000 floor shift linkage. Note the difference between the THM180 and THM200 linkage (© GM Corp.)

1. Remove the air cleaner assembly.
2. Make sure that the throttle linkage is in the low idle position, and that the idle speed is set to specifications.
3. Loosen the detent switch mounting screws and insert a .094 in. wire gauge into the hole located below the lower terminal of the switch.
4. For switches mounted at the engine, adjust the position of the switch so that the switch lever just touches the throttle linkage arm. If the switch is mounted at the accelerator pedal, adjust the switch position so that the switch lever just touches the accelerator relay rod. In either case, the downshift switch should make contact above 60° of throttle opening.
5. Tighten the switch mounting screws and remove the gauge.
6. Reinstall the air cleaner assembly.

Diesel Engine Transmission Linkage Adjustments

These adjustments are for all GM cars with the V6 and V8 engines. Only the TV cable is adjustable on the diesel Chevette.

NOTE: Before making any linkage adjustments, check the injection timing, and adjust if necessary. Also note that these adjustments should be performed together. The vacuum valve adjustment (THM350's only) on 1979 and later models requires the use of several special tools. If you do not have these tools at your disposal, refer the adjustment to a qualified, professional technician.

THROTTLE ROD ADJUSTMENT

1. If equipped with cruise control, remove the clip from the control rod, then remove the rod from the bellcrank.
2. Remove the throttle valve cable (THM125, 200, 325) or detent cable (THM350) from the bellcrank.
3. Loosen the locknut on the throttle rod, then shorten the rod several turns.
4. Rotate the bellcrank to the full throttle stop, then lengthen the throttle rod until the injection pump lever contacts the injection pump full throttle stop. Release the bellcrank.
5. Tighten the throttle rod locknut.
6. Connect the throttle valve or detent cable and cruise control rod to the bellcrank. Adjust if necessary.

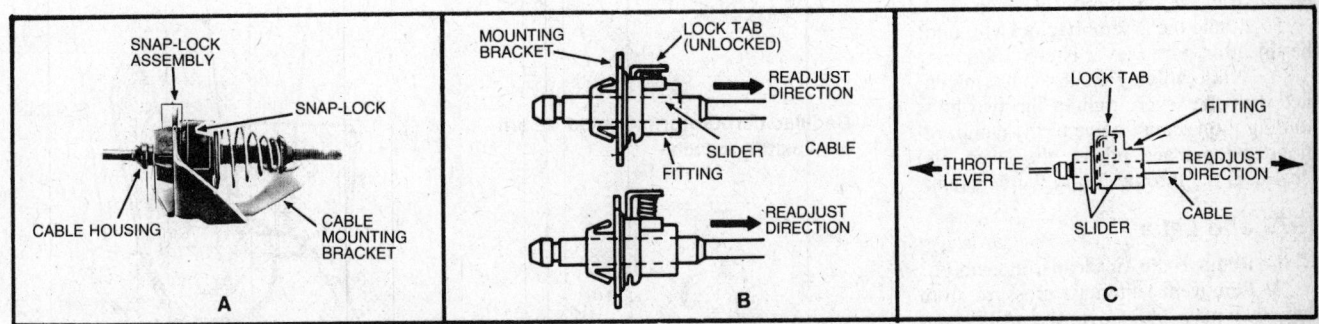

TV/detent cables used with GM automatic transmissions: A. type one; B. type two ('81 and earlier); C. type two ('82 and later).

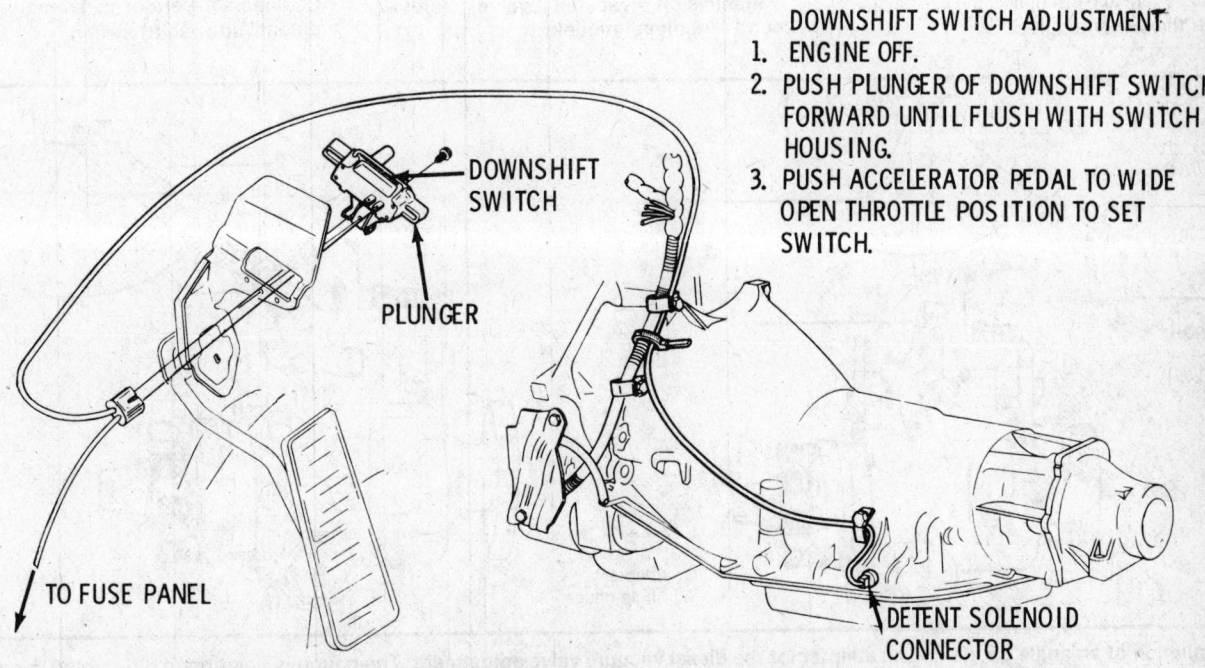

DOWNSHIFT SWITCH ADJUSTMENT
1. ENGINE OFF.
2. PUSH PLUNGER OF DOWNSHIFT SWITCH FORWARD UNTIL FLUSH WITH SWITCH HOUSING.
3. PUSH ACCELERATOR PEDAL TO WIDE OPEN THROTTLE POSITION TO SET SWITCH.

Detent (downshift) switch adjustment—except Cadillac (© GM Corp.)

U417

THROTTLE VALVE (TV) OR DETENT CABLE ADJUSTMENT

Refer to the previous cable adjustment procedures for gas engines. Adjust according to the style of cable which is used.

TRANSMISSION VACUUM VALVE ADJUSTMENT

1978

1. Remove the throttle rod from the bellcrank.
2. Loosen the transmission vacuum valve attaching bolts just enough to disengage the valve from the injection pump shaft.
3. Hold the injection pump lever against the full throttle stop.
4. Rotate the valve to the full throttle position, then insert a 0.09 in. pin to hold the valve in the full throttle position.
5. Rotate the assembly clockwise until the injection pump lever is contacted.
6. While holding the assembly in contact with the lever, tighten the two bolts holding the vacuum valve to the pump, remove the pin and release the lever, and reconnect the throttle rod to the bellcrank.

1979 and Later

1. Remove the air cleaner assembly.
2. Remove the air intake crossover from the intake manifold. Cover the intake manifold passages to prevent foreign material from entering the engine.
3. Disconnect the throttle rod from the injection pump throttle lever.
4. Loosen the transmission vacuum valve-to-injection pump bolts.
5. Mark and disconnect the vacuum lines from the vacuum valve.

6. Attach a carburetor angle gauge adapter (Kent-Moore tool J-26701-15 or its equivalent) to the injection pump throttle lever. Attach an angle gauge (J-26701 or its equivalent) to the gauge adapter.

NOTE: To service the V6 diesel, it may be necessary to file the gauge adapter in order for it to fit the thicker throttle lever of the V6 injection pump.

7. Turn the throttle lever to the wide open throttle position. Set the angle gauge to zero degrees.

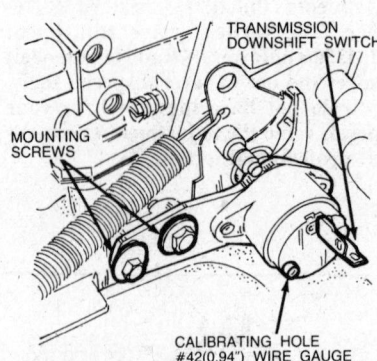

Cadillac carburetor-mounted detent (downshift) switch

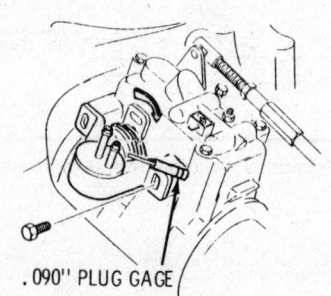

Transmission vacuum valve adjustment—'78 diesel models

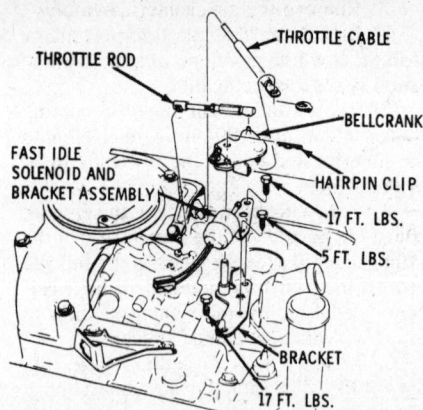

GM diesel throttle linkage—typical, except Chevette (© Oldsmobile Div., GM)

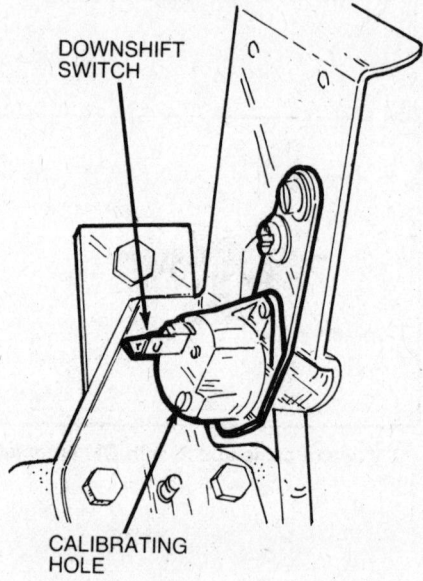

Cadillac accelerator pedal-mounted detent (downshift) switch

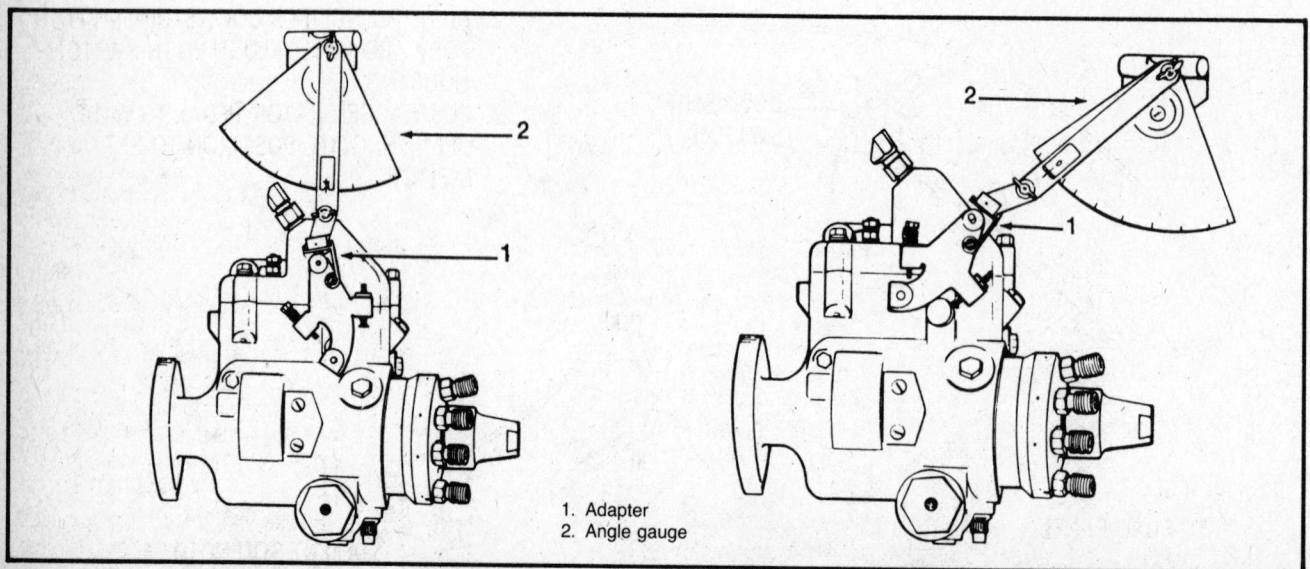

1. Adapter
2. Angle gauge

Installation of an angle gauge and an adapter for the diesel vacuum valve adjustment. The gauge is positioned differently, depending upon the type of throttle lever which is used.

8. Center the bubble in the gauge level.

9. Set the angle gauge to one of the following settings, according to the year and type of engine:

Year	Engine	Setting
All	V	49°
1979	V8	49°
1980	V8	49–50°
1981	V8—Calif.	49–50°
1981	V8—non-Calif.	58°
1982 and later	V8	58°

10. Attach a vacuum gauge to port 2 and a vacuum source (e.g., hand-held vacuum pump) to port 1 of the vacuum valve (as illustrated).

11. Apply 18–22 in. of vacuum to the valve. Slowly rotate the valve until the vacuum reading drops to one of the following values:

Year	In. Hg.
1979	8½—9
1980	7
1981 Calif.	7–8
1981 non-Calif.	8½—9
1982 and later	10½

12. Tighten the vacuum valve retaining bolts.

13. Reconnect the original vacuum lines to the vacuum valve.

14. Remove the angle gauge and adapter.

15. Connect the throttle rod to the throttle lever.

16. Install the air intake crossover, using new gaskets.

17. Install the air cleaner assembly.

Band Adjustments

Only the THM250 has an externally adjustable band. Band adjustments are not externally possible on other transmissions.

INTERMEDIATE BAND— TURBO HYDRAMATIC® 250

The intermediate band must be adjusted with every required fluid change or whenever there is slippage.

1. Position the shift lever in Neutral.

2. Loosen the locknut on the right side of the transmission. Tighten the adjusting screw to 30 inch lbs.

3. Back the screw out three turns and then tighten the locknut to 15 ft. lbs.

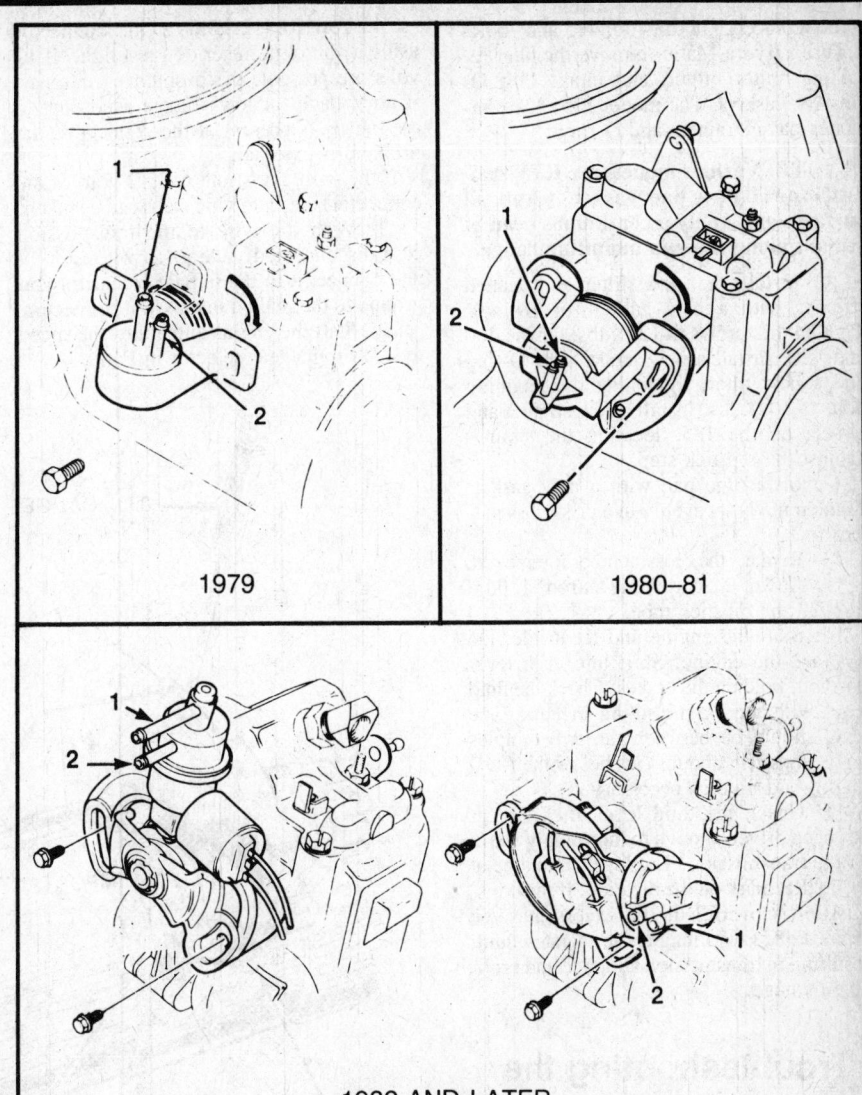

1979
1980–81
1982 AND LATER

1. Attach vacuum source here
2. Attach vacuum gauge here

Transmission vacuum valve adjustment—'79 and later diesel models

Pan Removal, Fluid and Filter Change

The fluid should be changed with the engine and transmission at normal operating temperature. If the car is raised, the transmission should be level. Be careful when draining, because the fluid will be hot.

1. Raise and safely support the vehicle.

2. On some models, it may be necessary to remove the transmission supporting crossmember in order to gain access to all of the pan bolts. Support the transmission with a jack before removing the crossmember.

3. Place a large pan underneath the transmission to catch the fluid. Loosen all the pan screws, then pull down one corner to drain most of the fluid. Be careful; the fluid will be hot. Do not pry between the pan and the transmission with a screwdriver or the like to remove the pan, as this will damage the mating surfaces. The pan can be tapped with a rubber mallet to loosen its grip.

4. Remove the pan screws and empty out the pan. The pan can be cleaned with solvent but it must be air dried thoroughly before replacement. Be very careful not to leave any lint or threads from rags in the pan.

NOTE: It is normal to find a SMALL amount of metal shavings in the pan. An excessive amount of metal shavings indicates transmission damage which must be professionaly investigated.

5. Remove the filter or strainer retaining bolt (two on the Turbo Hydra-Matic 180, 200, 250 and 350). A reuseable strainer is used on the Turbo Hydra-Matic 180, 200 and 250. The strainer may be cleaned in solvent and thoroughly air dried. Filters are

to be replaced. On the 400, 425 and 700R-4 Turbo Hydra-Matic, remove the filter retaining bolt(s), filter, and intake Pipe O-ring (or gasket). The model 125, 325 transaxles have strainers and O-rings.

NOTE: Various models use RTV sealant instead of a pan gasket. Clean all surfaces and apply a continuous bead of sealant along the pan mounting flange.

6. Install the new filter or cleaned strainer with a new gasket (or O-ring). Tighten the screws to 12 ft. lbs. On the 400 and 425, install a new intake pipe O-ring and a new filter, tightening the retaining bolts to 10 ft. lbs. Install a new strainer and O-ring on the 125, locating the strainer against the dipstick stop.

7. Install the pan with a new gasket. Tighten the bolts evenly in a crisscross pattern to 12 ft. lbs.

8. Replace the crossmember if removed.

9. Lower the car. Add Dexron® II fluid through the dipstick tube.

10. Start the engine and let it idle. Do not race the engine. Shift into each lever position, holding the brakes. Check the fluid level with the engine idling in Park. The level should be between the two dimples on the dipstick, about ¼ in. below the ADD mark. Add fluid as necessary.

11. Check the fluid level after the car has been driven enough to thoroughly warm up the transmission. The level should be at the FULL mark on the dipstick. If the transmission is overfilled, the excess must be drained off. Overfilling causes aerated fluid, resulting in transmission slippage and probable damage.

Troubleshooting the Torque Converter Clutch (TCC)

G.M. TURBO HYDRAMATIC

Before diagnosing the TCC system as being at fault in the case of rough shifting or other malfunctions, make sure that the engine is in at least a reasonable state of tune. Also, the following points should be checked:

1. Check the transmission fluid level and correct as necessary.

2. Check the manual linkage adjustment and correct as necessary.

3. Road test the vehicle to verify the complaint. Make sure that the vehicle is at normal operating temperature.

If it has been determined that there is a problem with the TCC system, the next step is to determine if the problem is internal or external. The following procedure can be used:

1. Disconnect the electrical connector at the transmission case.

2. Raise and safely support vehicle.

3. Start engine and adjust the speed to 2000 rpm, gear selector in Neutral.

4. Test for 12 volts at the connector using a volt/ohm meter or a test light. If 12 volts are present, the problem is internal. If no voltage (or low voltage according to the meter) is present at the connector, the problem is external.

If the problem is internal (12 volts at the connector) the following steps can be taken:

1. With the wire to the transmission case disconnected, take a 12 volt test light and connect it to the female connector and ground to the male transmission connector.

2. Start the engine and adjust the speed to 2000 rpm, gear selector in Park.

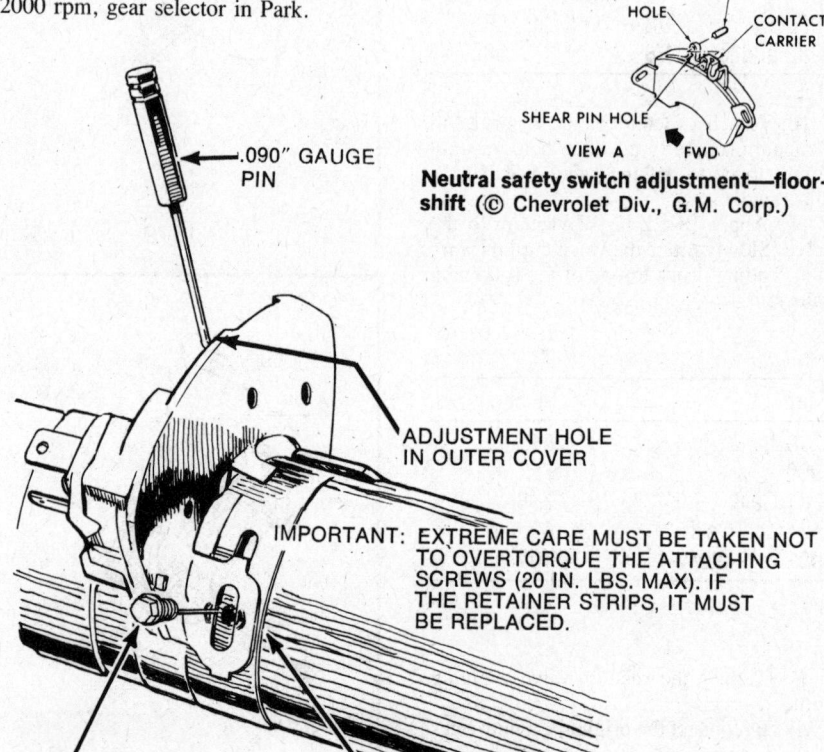

Neutral safety switch adjustment—floorshift (© Chevrolet Div., G.M. Corp.)

Neutral safety switch adjustment—column shift (© Pontiac Div., G.M. Corp.)

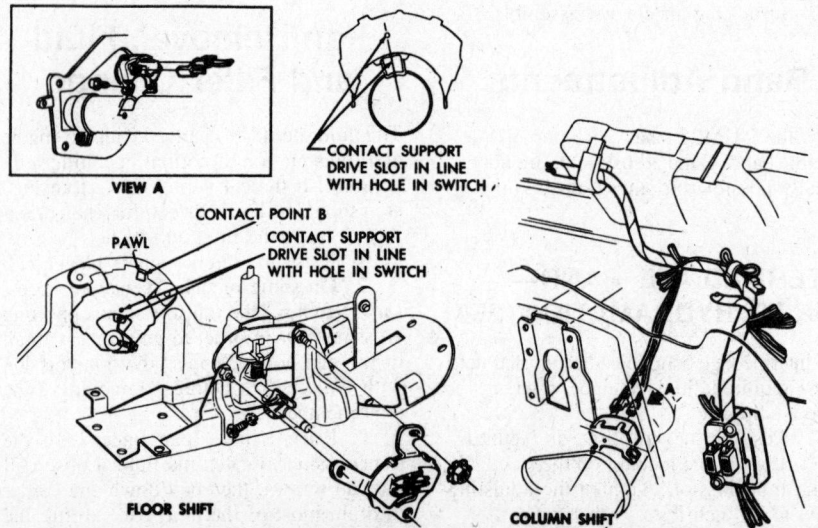

Typical neutral safety switch installation (© Chevrolet Div., G.M. Corp.)

3. If the test light comes on, the governor switch or the internal wiring is shorted to ground. The oil pan will have to be removed, the wiring checked and/or the governor switch replaced.

4. If the test light now comes on, the internal hydraulic/mechanical controls will have to be checked. Refer to the Hydraulic/Mechanical Controls section.

5. If the test light still does not light, there is a problem with the solenoid or governor switch.

To test for solenoid or governor switch electrical malfunction, the following steps can be used:

1. Drain the transmission fluid and remove the oil pan.

2. Using an external 12 volt source, (self--powered test light or small lantern battery, etc.) connect a positive lead to the case connector. Remove the lead wire from the governor pressure switch and connect it to the ground lead of the external 12 volt source.

—————— CAUTION ——————

Do not reverse the leads or the solenoid diode will be destroyed by the reverse voltage. Do not use an automobile battery for this test. A self-powered test light is best for these tests.

3. If the solenoid clicks, it can be considered serviceable; replace the governor switch.

4. If the solenoid does not click, check the wiring. If the wiring appears to be good, replace the solenoid and recheck.

Internal Hydraulic/Mechanical Controls Check

Since part of these checks involves the governor system, obtain, if possible, a test governor of the same type used in the transmission being serviced. Cut two pieces of 5/32 in. O.D. rubber vacuum hose to 3/8 in. long. Put one piece of the cut-off hose under each weight of the governor. Remove

the engine vacuum switch electrical connector. The vacuum switch should be mounted on an inner fender wall. Using a jumper wire, connect both terminals of the connector together. As a check that the proper connection has been made, turn the ignition to ON, raise the vehicle and check for 12 volts at the transmission case female connector. There should be 12 volts on a voltmeter. Then, proceed as follows:

1. Remove the transmission governor and replace with the test governor.

2. With the vehicle's wheels off the ground, apply the parking brake. The rear wheels must not be able to turn.

3. Start the engine, selector in Park, and allow to idle.

4. Step on the brake pedal. This will interrupt the flow of current to the transmission.

5. Place the selector in Drive. The transmission should automatically shift into 3rd gear because the test governor is causing high governor pressure.

6. Release the service brakes and the engine should stall immediately. If the engine stalls, the converter clutch and the internal hydraulic and mechanical controls are operating properly.

If the engine does not stall, check the following:

1. Missing or damaged O-ring at the end of the turbine shaft.

2. Missing check ball or O-ring at the solenoid.

3. Loose solenoid bolts.

4. Converter clutch apply passages in the pump blocked or restricted.

5. Defective converter.

NOTE: After the test has been completed remove the test governor and replace it with the original governor. If the original governor was used for the test, remove the rubber bushings that were installed and be sure the weight springs are in the correct position before reinstalling.

External Controls Check

1. Turn the ignition switch to the ON position.

2. Check the vacuum switch connector for 12 volts.

3. If no voltage is present at the vacuum switch, check the fuse block for a blown fuse, the brake switch and the wiring to the vacuum switch.

4. If there is a reading of 12 volts at the switch, reconnect the electrical connector to the vacuum switch. Using a hand vacuum pump with a gauge, apply 2.5–7 in. of vacuum to the vacuum switch.

5. With the ignition switch in the ON position, check for 12 volts at the female end of the transmission connector.

6. If no or low (as read on a voltmeter) voltage is present, look for a break in the wire between the vacuum switch and the transmission. Further vacuum switch checks are given below.

Vacuum Switch Check

1. Disconnect the vacuum hose and the electrical connector from the vacuum switch.

2. Attach one lead of a test light to either one of the terminals of the vacuum switch. Ground the other vacuum switch terminal.

3. Apply 12 volts to the other test light lead.

4. Attach the hand vacuum pump and gauge to the vacuum switch port.

5. Turn the ignition switch to the ON position.

6. The test light should be off. Apply vacuum with the hand pump until the gauge reads 2.45–7 in. of vacuum. The light should come on.

7. Bleed off some vacuum slowly. The light should remain on until the vacuum drops to 1.5–2.5 in. of vacuum.

8. If the vacuum switch does not turn the test light on and off at the specified vacuum readings, the switch is bad and should be replaced.

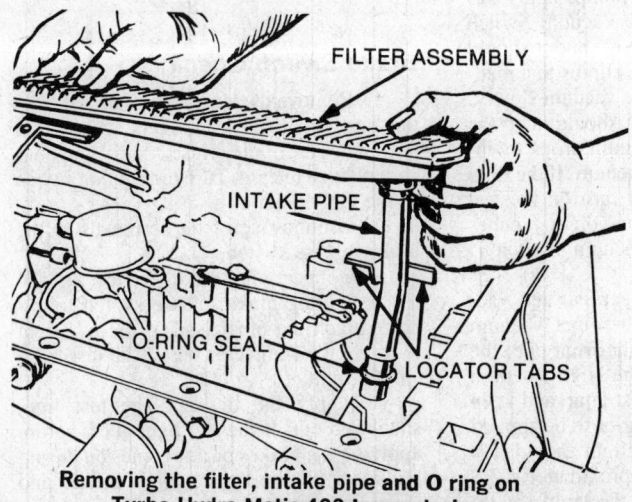

Removing the filter, intake pipe and O ring on Turbo Hydra-Matic 400 transmission

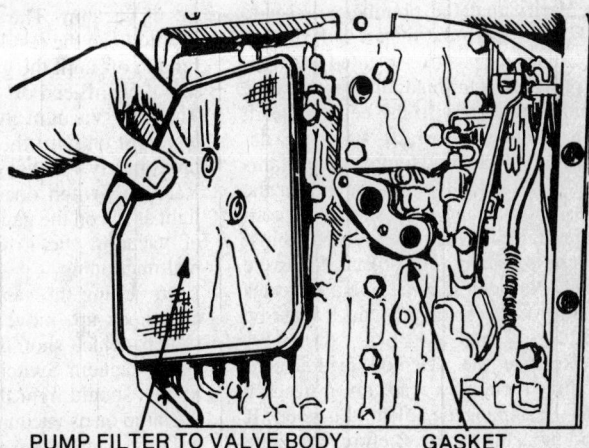

Removing the filter and gasket on a Turbo Hydra-Matic 200, 350, or 375B

NOTE: The high vacuum limit, which is the point where the test light goes out, and the low vacuum limit, which is the point at which the test light comes back on, must have at least 4 in. of vacuum difference.

If the above checks of the vacuum switch verify the proper operation of the switch, then the trouble is elsewhere, possibly at the thermal vacuum valve.

Thermal Vacuum Valve Check

1. Disconnect the vacuum hose at the vacuum switch and install a vacuum gauge to the hose.

2. Start the engine and check the vacuum reading, gear selector in Park. With the engine cold (coolant temperature below 130°F.), vacuum at idle should be zero. Adjust engine speed to 200 rpm. The vacuum should still be zero.

3. With the engine warm, after about five minutes running at fast idle, the coolant temperature should be above 130°F. The vacuum at idle should still be zero while the vacuum at 2000 rpm should be 10 in. of vacuum minimum.

Solenoid Diode Check

----- **CAUTION** -----
Do not use an automotive battery for troubleshooting solenoids. Solenoids must not be bench tested by touching the leads of an automotive battery. The internal diode will be destroyed when the leads are reversed, as they must be to check the diode.

Remember that a diode allows electricity to flow freely in one direction, and prevents or at least restricts the flow of current in the opposite direction.

To check the solenoid diode, an ohmmeter should be used. Use only a meter reading type of ohmmeter since electronic digital-type will often give a false indication. Use the X1 scale on the ohmmeter, and use the following procedure:

1. Verify that the ohmmeter is set to the X1 scale. Zero the meter.

2. Attach the positive solenoid lead (red) to the positive meter lead, and the negative solenoid lead (black) to the negative lead. The meter should read 20–40 ohms, depending on the solenoid temperature. If this reading is obtained, neither the coil or the diode is shorted and they should be considered useable. If the meter reads 0 ohms, then there is a short. The solenoid must be replaced. An open reading again indicates a bad coil in the solenoid, and it must be replaced.

3. Reverse the solenoid lead attachment. If the meter now reads lower (usually reads 2–15 ohms), the solenoid is good. If the reading is the same as before, the diode is bad and the solenoid will have to be replaced.

NOTE: On the Turbo-Hydra-Matic 250/350 transmissions, the solenoid is mounted on the valve body and the removal and replacement includes only R&R of the oil pan and the solenoid. However, on the Turbo Hydra-Matic 200 transmissions, the solenoid is mounted on the inside face of the oil pump. Therefore solenoid replacement for this model transmission will require the removal of the entire transmission, the torque converter and the oil pump. Be careful when diagnosing the solenoid so as not to burn out a good one

Transmissions using the TCC system are also used in vehicles equipped with diesel engines. Due to the different vacuum characteristics of a diesel engine, a slightly different control system is used. Incorporated into the diesel system are a Low and a High Vacuum Switch. These are usually mounted on the engine, just above the right-hand valve cover. These switches can also be checked with a 12 volt test light and a hand vacuum pump.

Low and High Vacuum Switch Check Diesel

1. Disconnect the vacuum hose and the electrical connector from the switch. The test is run on both switches, but in this procedure, start with the Low Vacuum Switch. The Low Vacuum Switch should be at the rearmost of the two, with the High Vacuum Switch to the front.

2. Attach one lead of a test light to either one of the terminals of the Low Vacuum Switch and ground the remaining terminal of the vacuum switch.

3. Attach the remaining lead of the test light to the hot (+ 12 volt) side of the vacuum switch connector. Attach the hand vacuum pump and gauge to the vacuum port of the vacuum switch.

4. Turn the ignition switch to the ON position. If using a self-powered test light, the ignition does not have to be turned on.

5. With the vacuum pump, apply 5.5 in. of vacuum. The Low Vacuum Switch should keep the test light off, and it should remain off until the gauge climbs to a reading of 5.5. Bleed off some vacuum slowly. The Low Vacuum Switch should keep the test light on until the vacuum drops to approximately 4 inches of vacuum. If the Low Vacuum Switch does not turn on the test light at 5.5 on the gauge, and off at 4 inches of vacuum, the Low Vacuum Switch is malfunctioning.

6. Using the same electrical and vacuum hook-up, move to the other vacuum switch, which should be the front one, the High Vacuum Switch. The High Vacuum Switch should light the test lamp and keep the lamp on as vacuum begins to be applied with the hand pump. The light should stay on until the gauge reads approximately 12.5 in. of vacuum, and then the lamp should

go out. Bleed the vacuum slowly. The lamp should come back on at 12.5 in. of vacuum. If the High Vacuum Switch does not turn on at 12.5 in. of vacuum and off as the vacuum goes higher, the High Vacuum Switch is malfunctioning.

High Vacuum Switch Adjustment Diesel

The High Vacuum Switch on the diesel engine must be adjusted anytime the throttle rod, transmission vacuum valve or high idle speed adjustments are altered. The following steps can be used for adjustment:

1. Disconnect the electrical connector from the High Vacuum Switch. This should be the front switch of the two. It has an adjustment port opposite the electrical connector.

2. Using a self-powered test light, connect one lead to either one of the terminals on the switch and connect the probe of the test light to the other switch terminal.

3. Start the engine and allow to run at high idle speed. To do this, actuate the fast idle solenoid. A pink and green wire connector goes to the coolant switch located on the left rear of the engine on the intake manifold, and this connector should be pulled off the coolant switch to produce the fast idle.

4. Remove the small dust cap from the back of the High Vacuum Switch.

5. The High Vacuum Switch must be closed before making the adjustment. This means that the test light should be on. If the test light is off, the contacts are open. Take a 5/64 in. Allen wrench and turn the adjustment screw clockwise until the contacts close and the test light comes on.

6. Adjust the vacuum switch by turning the adjustment screw *slowly* counterclockwise until the switch contacts just open and the test light goes off. Turn the screw slowly so that the screw is not turned past this position.

7. Put the dust cap back on, reconnect the High Vacuum Switch electrical connector, and reconnect the coolant switch connector.

Brake Switch Check

1. Remove the electrical connector from the rear of the brake switch. These rear terminals are for the cruise control and converter clutch release. Turn the ignition switch to the ON position.

2. Ground one of the terminals of the brake release switch.

3. Connect one lead of the test light to the remaining brake release switch terminal. Attach the other lead of the test light to the brake connector wire. The test lamp should light.

4. Apply the brakes. The test light should go out. If the test light is off before applying the brakes or if it comes on during brake application, the switch is bad and should be replaced.

Transfer Cases

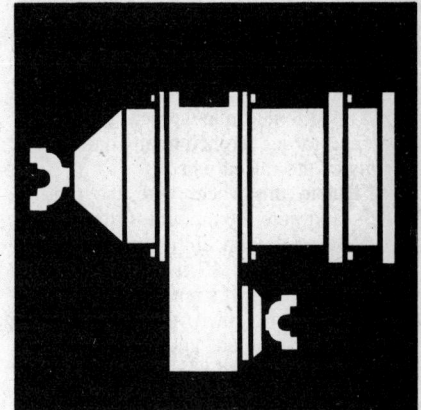

AMC Eagle

Two different models of transfer cases have been used in 4WD American Motors passenger cars. All 1980–81 vehicles use the model 119 transfer case; later vehicles use the model 129 unit with the Select Drive 4WD system. Parts usage and operation are basically the same for both units, though the 129 is equipped for use in the 2WD mode. Minor differences between the two transfer cases will be noted as necessary throughout the section.

NOTE: Refer to the AMC car section for services not listed here.

Lubrication

The lubricant capacities and types are as follows:

1980 model 119—3 pints of 10W-30 engine oil

1981 model 119—4 pints of 10W-30 engine oil

1982 and later model 129—7 pints of Dexron® II

NOTE: Lubricant capacities for 1982 and later transfer cases were increased from 6 to 7 pints as per an AMC service bulletin dated 5-84.

———— CAUTION ————
DO NOT use any type of lubricant additive in AMC transfer cases, as their use could cause transfer case damage.

TROUBLESHOOTING

VEHICLE WANDERS OR PULLS FROM A STRAIGHT-AHEAD POSITION

1. *Check the tire pressures (tires cold).*

The pressures must be within specification and must not vary more than 1 psi between sides.

2. *Check that the tires are all of the same size and type.* Replace the tire(s) if necessary until all are matched properly.

3. *Check that the lubricant in the transfer case is of the correct type.* Drain and refill the transfer case with the correct lubricant, if necessary.

SEVERE LOW SPEED SHUDDER

1. *Low level of viscous silicone fluid in the viscous coupling.* First, perform the in-car Torque Bias Test as outlined later. Follow the instructions with that procedure to remedy the problem. Check the transfer case fluid; if it is contaminated with viscous fluid, the transfer case must be completely disassembled for inspection. While the unit is disassembled, check for a cracked viscous coupling and/or damaged seal. Replace damaged parts as required.

2. *Check that the front and rear axles are of the same gear ratio.* Mismatched differential ratios can cause failure of the viscous coupling. Replace one of the gear sets in order to match the other.

NOISY OPERATION

NOTE: Do not compare the noise of a 4WD vehicle to that of a 2WD vehicle, as 4WD is inherently noisier due to the use of additional drive line components.

1. *Check that the lubricant in the transfer case is of the correct type and quantity.* Drain and refill, or add fluid as required. Check for fluid leakage.

2. *Check the tire pressures, sizes, and styles as mentioned previously.* Adjust the tire pressures or replace the tires as required.

In-Vehicle Services

LUBRICANT CHANGE

1. Raise the vehicle and support it safely with jackstands.

2. Place a drain pan beneath the transfer case.

3. Remove both the drain and fill plugs and allow the lubricant to drain completely.

4. Install the drain plug and tighten it to 18 ft. lbs.

5. Fill the transfer case with the correct type of lubricant (10W-30 engine oil—119 unit; Dexron® II automatic transmission fluid—129 unit). The lubricant level should be up to the lower edge of the fill plug hole. Install the fill plug.

6. Drive the vehicle 8-10 miles to circulate the fluid throughout the transfer case.

7. Remove the fill plug and top off transfer case to the bottom edge of the fill plughole.

8. Install the fill plug and tighten it to 18 ft. lbs. (1980-81), 25 ft. lbs. (1982 and later).

9. Remove the drain pan from beneath the vehicle.

10. Remove the jackstands and lower the vehicle.

TORQUE BIAS TEST

This test may be performed to determine the condition of the viscous coupling, which is the ''heart'' of the AMC transfer case. Note that if a malfunction in the coupling is observed, the coupling cannot be repaired in any way—it must be replaced if defective. The following procedure is an in-vehicle test. If the transfer case is to be disassembled, test the coupling as outlined within the overhaul procedure (bench test).

1. Drive the vehicle onto a level surface, turn the engine OFF, and place the

transmission shift lever in Neutral. On 1982 and later models, place the Select Drive lever in the 4WD position.

2. Raise one of the front wheels off of the floor, then remove the wheel cover from the raised wheel.

3. Attach a socket (of the same size as the lug nuts) to a torque wrench. Install the socket and torque wrench to any one of the lug nuts of the raised wheel.

4. Rotate the wheel with the torque wrench, and note the amount of torque required to turn the wheel.

5. A reading of 45 ft. lbs. minimum should be obtained. If a reading of less than 45 ft. lbs. was obtained, the transfer case must be disassembled, and the bench test of the coupling should be performed. If the reading was 45 ft. lbs. or more, the coupling is operating properly.

6. Remove the torque wrench and socket, then install the wheel cover and lower the vehicle.

PARTS REPLACEMENT

18. Remove the drive chain from the front output shaft and sprocket

19. Remove the driven sprocket-to-front output shaft snap-ring. Mark the sprocket and shaft so they may be reassembled properly, then remove the sprocket from the shaft.

20. Remove the mainshaft, side gear, clutch gear, drive sprocket and spline gear as as assembly. Set the assembly aside until disassembly of the front case has been completed.

3. Matchmark the propeller shafts and their respective yokes so that these parts may be properly aligned during assembly.

4. Disconnect the propeller shafts from the yokes, then tie the shafts out of the way.

5. Remove the speedometer cable and adapter from the rear retainer.

NOTE: Discard the adapter seal. Use a NEW seal during assembly.

6. Support the engine and transmission using a small hydraulic jack with a block of wood placed between the jack and the transmission.

7. Remove the rear crossmember attaching nuts. Carefully lower the transfer case, just enough to gain access to the rear bearing retainer bolts.

8. Matchmark the retainer and the case so that the retainer may be properly reinstalled. Remove the rear yoke nut and seal washer.

9. Remove the rear yoke.

NOTE: If necessary, the front yoke may be removed in the same manner as the rear yoke.

10. Remove the rear retainer bolts. Tap the retainer lightly to loosen and remove it.

11. Remove the differential shim(s) and the speedometer gear from the rear output shaft.

12. If so equipped, remove the output bearing snap-ring. Remove the output bearing from the retainer.

13. Remove the yoke seal from the retainer. Clean the retainer thoroughly and remove the old sealant from the retainer and case mating surfaces.

Assemble the components in the following manner:

1. Install the output bearing into the retainer, making sure that the shielded side of the bearing faces the interior of the transfer case.

2. If so equipped, install the bearing retaining snap-ring.

3. Install a new yoke seal (or both seals, if removed), using Kent-Moore tool J-29162 or its equivalent.

4. Install the speedometer gear and differential shim(s).

5. Coat the mating surface of the retainer and the retainer bolt threads with sealer (Loctite® 515 is recommended) and install the retainer. Be sure to align the matchmarks made during disassembly to locate the retainer.

6. Install and tighten the retainer bolts to 23 ft. lbs.

7. Install the yoke(s), new sealing washer(s), and new yoke nut(s). Torque the yoke nut(s) to 120 ft. lbs.

—— CAUTION ——
NEVER reuse the old yoke nuts.

8. Align the front propeller shaft and yoke matchmarks (which were made during disassembly) and attach the propeller shaft to the yoke. Torque the clamp strap bolts to 15 ft. lbs.

9. Install the transfer case drain plug and add the proper amount and type of lubricant to the transfer case.

10. Install the fill plug. Both of the plugs should be torqued to 18 ft. lbs.

11. Raise the transmission, transfer case, and rear crossmember enough to install the crossmember attaching nuts.

12. Install the crossmember attaching nuts and torque them to 30 ft. lbs.

13. Remove the hydraulic jack and wood block.

14. Align the matchmarks, then attach the rear propeller shaft to the yoke. Torque the clamp bolts to 15 ft. lbs.

15. Install a NEW O-ring seal on the speedometer adapter. Do not reuse the old seal. Install the adapter and cable into the rear retainer.

16. Install the transfer case skid plate.

17. Lower the vehicle.

Transfer Case Disassembly

1. Remove the transfer case as outlined in the appropriate car section.

2. Remove the drain plug and drain the lubricant from the transfer case.

3. On 1982 and later models only, remove the nut and bolt which attaches the shift motor bracket to the transfer case. Remove the motor and bracket as an assembly.

4. Remove the nuts which attach the yokes. Discard the sealing washers. Remove the yokes.

5. Mount the transfer case on wood blocks which have V-notches cut into them to clear the front transfer case mounting studs.

6. Mark the relationship between the rear retainer and the case. Remove the retainer attaching bolts.

7. Pry the retainer off of the case using two screwdrivers placed into the two slots provided in the retainer for this purpose.

8. Remove the differential shim(s) and the speedometer gear from the rear output shaft.

9. Remove the front case-to-rear case bolts, then pry the cases apart with two screwdrivers.

—— CAUTION ——
*Screwdriver slots are provided at each end of the rear case for this purpose. **DO NOT** attempt to wedge the two halves apart.*

10. Remove the thrust bearing and races from the front output shaft. Note their relationships so that these parts may be reinstalled properly.

11. Remove the oil pump from the rear output shaft, noting its position for reassembly.

12. Remove the rear output shaft from the viscous coupling.

13. Remove the pilot bearing rollers from the shaft coupling. Set the rollers aside in a group.

14. Remove the mainshaft O-ring from the end of the shaft.

15. Remove the viscous coupling from the mainshaft and side gear.

16. Lift the front output shaft, sprocket, and chain upward, then tilt the front output shaft toward the mainshaft. Slide the chain off of the mainshaft drive sprocket and remove the assembly.

17. Remove the front thrust bearing assembly. The bearing will be positioned on either the front output shaft or the case.

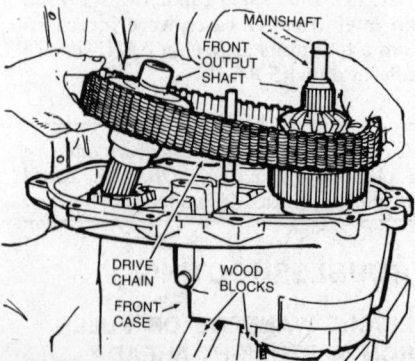

Removing the front output shaft, driven sprocket, and drive chain

18. Remove the drive chain from the front output shaft and sprocket

19. Remove the driven sprocket-to-front output shaft snap-ring. Mark the sprocket and shaft so they may be reassembled properly, then remove the sprocket from the shaft.

20. Remove the mainshaft, side gear, clutch gear, drive sprocket and spline gear as as assembly. Set the assembly aside until disassembly of the front case has been completed.

21. Remove the range fork, rail and clutch sleeve as an assembly. Mark the sleeve and fork so that they may be reassembled properly, then remove the sleeve from the fork.

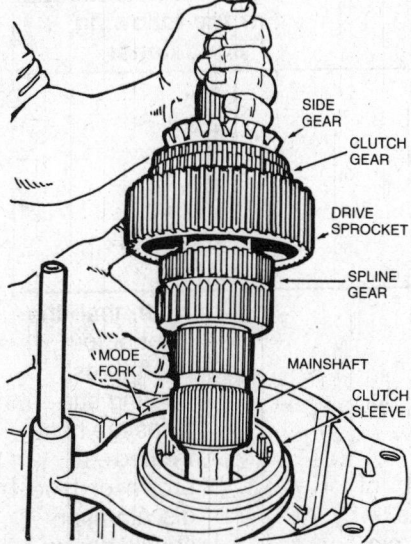

Removing the mainshaft and related components as an assembly

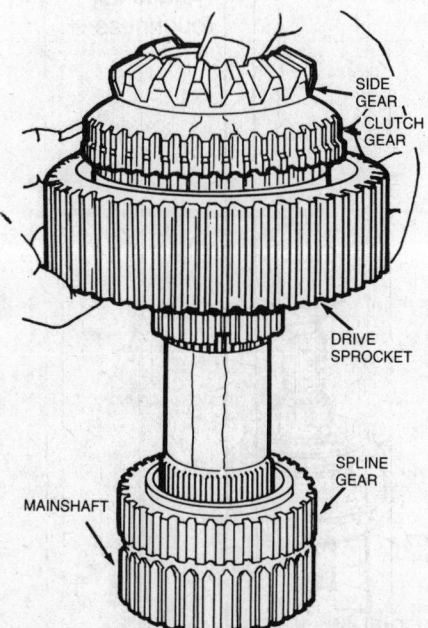

Removing the drive sprocket, clutch gear, side gear, and sprocket carrier

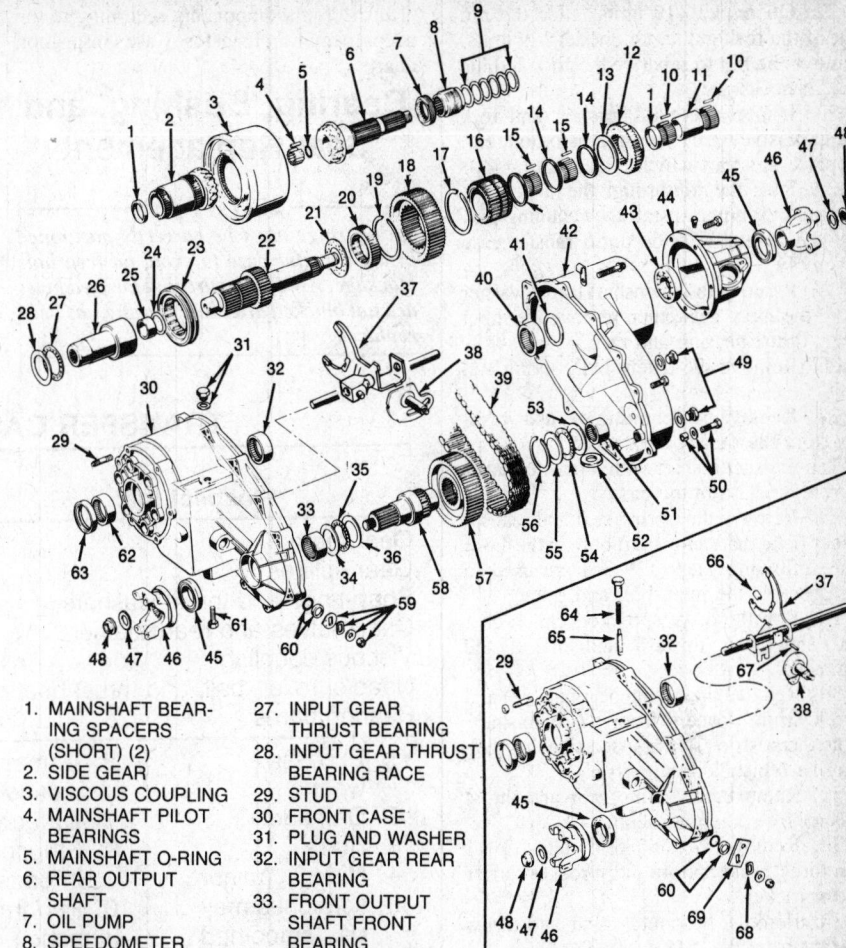

1. MAINSHAFT BEARING SPACERS (SHORT) (2)
2. SIDE GEAR
3. VISCOUS COUPLING
4. MAINSHAFT PILOT BEARINGS
5. MAINSHAFT O-RING
6. REAR OUTPUT SHAFT
7. OIL PUMP
8. SPEEDOMETER DRIVE GEAR
9. DIFFERENTIAL SHIMS
10. MAINSHAFT NEEDLE BEARINGS (82)
11. MAINSHAFT NEEDLE BEARING SPACER (LONG) (1)
12. CLUTCH GEAR
13. CLUTCH GEAR THRUST WASHER
14. SPROCKET CARRIER NEEDLE BEARING SPACER (3)
15. SPROCKET CARRIER NEEDLE BEARINGS (120)
16. SPROCKET CARRIER
17. SPROCKET CARRIER SNAP RING
18. DRIVE SPROCKET
19. SPROCKET CARRIER SNAP RING
20. SPLINE GEAR
21. MAINSHAFT THRUST WASHER
22. MAINSHAFT
23. CLUTCH SLEEVE
24. MAINSHAFT THRUST WASHER
25. MAINSHAFT BUSHING
26. INPUT GEAR
27. INPUT GEAR THRUST BEARING
28. INPUT GEAR THRUST BEARING RACE
29. STUD
30. FRONT CASE
31. PLUG AND WASHER
32. INPUT GEAR REAR BEARING
33. FRONT OUTPUT SHAFT FRONT BEARING
34. FRONT OUTPUT SHAFT FRONT THRUST BEARING RACE (THICK)
35. FRONT OUTPUT SHAFT FRONT THRUST BEARING
36. FRONT OUTPUT SHAFT FRONT THRUST BEARING RACE (THIN)
37. RANGE FORK AND RAIL
38. RANGE SECTOR
39. DRIVE CHAIN
40. REAR OUTPUT SHAFT BEARING
41. REAR OUTPUT SHAFT BEARING SEAL
42. REAR CASE
43. REAR OUTPUT BEARING
44. REAR RETAINER
45. YOKE SEAL
46. YOKE
47. SEAL WASHER
48. YOKE NUT
49. FILL AND DRAIN PLUGS
50. ALIGNMENT DOWEL, WASHER AND BOLT
51. FRONT OUTPUT SHAFT REAR BEARING
52. MAGNET
53. FRONT OUTPUT SHAFT REAR THRUST BEARING RACE (THICK)
54. FRONT OUTPUT SHAFT REAR THRUST BEARING
55. FRONT OUTPUT SHAFT REAR THRUST BEARING RACE (THIN)
56. DRIVEN SPROCKET RETAINING SNAP RING
57. DRIVEN SPROCKET
57. DRIVEN SPROCKET
58. FRONT OUTPUT SHAFT
59. RANGE SECTOR SHAFT RETAINING LOCKNUT AND WASHERS
60. RANGE SECTOR SHAFT SEAL AND RETAINER
61. POSITIVE LOCK DETENT BOLT
62. INPUT GEAR FRONT BEARING
63. INPUT GEAR SEAL
64. SPRING
65. PLUNGER
66. SHIFT FORK PAD
67. PIN
68. RANGE LEVER COLLAR
69. RANGE LEVER

Exploded view of the AMC 4WD transfer case. Note the minor differences in parts usage for the model 129 unit (shown in inset).

22. On model 119 units, slide the rail out of the fork guide. On model 129 units, remove the pin to separate the fork and the rail, if necessary.

23. Inspect the rail, bracket, and fork for excessive wear, scoring, distortion, etc. Replace any part which is damaged.

24. Slide the rail through the range fork, and on 129 units, install the retaining pin. Set the assembly aside until transfer case assembly.

25. Remove the mainshaft thrust washer from the input gear, then remove the input gear, thrust bearing and race.

26. Remove the detent ball, spring and bolt.

27. Remove the retaining nut and washers from the range sector shaft.

Tap the sector shaft with a plastic mallet to remove it from the case.

28. Remove the O-ring seal and seal retainer from the sector shaft bore in the case. The following Steps (29–35) are used to disassemble the mainshaft and gears.

29. Pull the drive sprocket, clutch gear and side gear upward and off of the mainshaft.

30. Remove the needle bearings (82) and two bearing spacers from the mainshaft. Note the position of the spacers so that they may be reinstalled properly.

31. Remove the spline gear and thrust washer from the mainshaft.

32. Remove the side gear, clutch gear and thrust washer from the sprocket carrier and sprocket.

33. Remove the clutch gear and thrust washer from the side gear.

34. Remove the sprocket carrier snap-ring, then remove the drive sprocket from the carrier. Mark the sprocket and the carrier so that they may be reassembled in their proper relationship.

35. Remove the bearing spacers (3) and the sprocket carrier needle bearings (120) from the carrier.

——— CAUTION ———
DO NOT intermix the mainshaft needle bearings (Step 30) with the sprocket carrier needle bearings, as they are of different sizes.

36. Remove the rear output bearing and rear yoke seal from the rear retainer. Note that one side of the bearing is shielded—the bearing must be reinstalled in the same direction.

37. Remove the input gear and yoke seals from the front case.

Cleaning

All parts must be thoroughly washed with clean solvent. Be sure that all of the old lubricant and foreign matter has been removed from all transfer case parts. Verify that the oil feed ports and channels of both case halves are clear by flowing compressed air through them.

Inspect all components according to the accompanying Transfer Case Inspection chart.

Bearing, Bushing, and Seal Replacement

——— CAUTION ———
All bearings must be correctly positioned in the transfer case to avoid oil feed hole blockage. Always be sure that the feed holes are not blocked after any bearing has been replaced.

TRANSFER CASE INSPECTION

Inspect the:	For the following conditions:
Gear teeth	1,2
Gear splines	1,2,3,4
Snap-rings and thrust washers	1,2,5
Case halves and rear retainer	5,6,7,8,9
Viscous coupling	10,11,12
Needle, roller, ball, and thrust bearings	1,2,6,13,14
Bearing bores	1,2,5,6

1. Excessive wear
2. Damage
3. Burrs
4. Nicks (minor scratches may be smoothed with an oil-stone)
5. Distortion
6. Cracks
7. Porosity
8. Damaged mating surfaces
9. Stripped bolt threads
10. Perform bench-test of torque-bias
11. Damaged pinions and/or carrier
12. Fluid leakage
13. Note that the front output shaft thrust bearing surfaces are heat-treated—a brown or blue discoloration should be considered NORMAL.
14. Rotational roughness

FRONT OUTPUT SHAFT— FRONT BEARING

This bearing may be removed and installed with a bearing driver. Be sure that the driver contacts the bearings squarely, then check that the oil feed hole is not blocked after the bearing is in place.

FRONT OUTPUT SHAFT— REAR BEARING

Replacement is performed in the same manner as the "Front Output Shaft—Front Bearing." Be sure that the bearing is seated flush with the edge of the bore in the case to allow room for the thrust bearing.

INPUT GEAR FRONT AND REAR BEARINGS

1. Drive both bearings out at the same time, using an appropriate bearing driver.

REAR OUTPUT SHAFT BEARING RACE

1. Pull the race from the transfer case bore using a slide hammer and an appropriate adapter.

2. Using a small screwdriver, carefully pry out the rear output lip seal.

3. Install a new output lip seal.

4. Carefully drive a new bearing race into place, using a bearing driver.

5. Remove the tool, then check to make sure that the oil feed hole is clear.

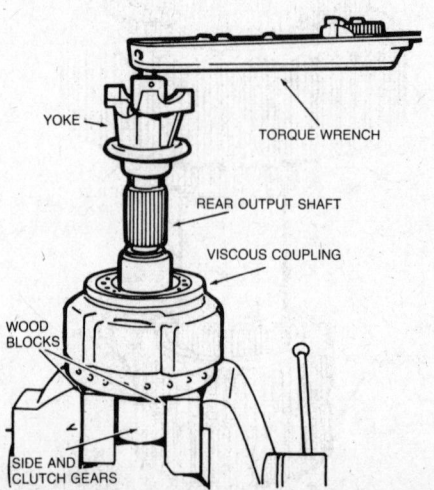

YOKE

TORQUE WRENCH

REAR OUTPUT SHAFT

VISCOUS COUPLING

WOOD BLOCKS

SIDE AND CLUTCH GEARS

Bench-testing the torque bias of the viscous coupling

2. Drive the new bearings into place one at a time (rear bearing first).

3. After installation, check that the oil feed holes are not blocked, and that the bearings are flush with the case bore surface.

4. Carefully drive a new oil seal into place.

MAINSHAFT PILOT BUSHING

1. Position the input gear on an opened vise (bushing facing downward). The vise must be opened enough for the bushing to be clear of the vise jaws when pulled downward.

2. Using a slide hammer-type bushing puller, remove the bushing.

3. Drive the new bushing into place, making sure that the oil feed hole is properly aligned

REAR RETAINER BEARING AND SEAL

1. Remove the bearing using a brass drift and a hammer. The seal is removed in the same manner.

2. Drive the new bearing into place, making sure that the shielded side of the bearing faces the interior of the transfer case.

3. Carefully drive a new seal into the retainer.

Bench-Testing the Viscous Coupling

This torque bias test should be performed while the transfer case is disassembled for any reason, as the viscous coupling is the key to the operation of the AMC 4WD system. If a viscous coupling problem was previously diagnosed by the in-vehicle torque bias test, the coupling should again be tested according to the following procedure, for fault verification purposes.

1. Install the clutch gear onto the side gear.

2. Install the clutch gear/side gear assembly into the viscous coupling.

3. Mount the coupling and gear assembly in a vise, with wood blocks between the side gear and the vise jaws. Clamp the side gear firmly.

4. Make sure that the clutch gear is firmly engaged in the coupling, then install the rear output shaft in the viscous coupling.

5. Install the yoke on the rear output shaft and attach with the retaining nut.

6. Attach a socket (of the same size as the yoke nut) to a torque wrench. With the socket engaged to the yoke nut, rotate the rear output shaft and note the torque reading obtained with the torque wrench. The minimum acceptable rotational torque reading is 25 ft. lbs. If the reading is at or above

25 ft. lbs., the coupling is okay. If a lower torque reading is obtained, the coupling is defective and must be replaced.

7. Remove the yoke nut and yoke from the rear output shaft, then remove the coupling assembly from the vise.

Transfer Case Assembly

NOTE: All parts should be lubricated prior to assembly, with either the specified lubricant (10W-30 engine oil for the model 119 unit; Dexron® II automatic transmission fluid for the 129), or petroleum jelly if stated within the procedure DO NOT use any type of heavy grease (e.g.—chassis lubricant) during assembly of the transfer case, as lubricants of this nature can block the oil passages.

1. Install new yoke oil seals.

2. Install a new O-ring and retainer into the range sector shaft bore of the case.

3. Install the range sector. On model 119 units, install the washers and locknut on the sector shaft. On model 129 units, install the O-ring seal, retainer, range lever, washer, and locknut on the sector shaft.

4. Torque the sector shaft locknut to 17 ft. lbs.

5. Install the thrust bearing and race on the input gear. Install the gear into the front of the case.

6. Install the mainshaft thrust washer into the input gear.

7. Assemble the range fork, rail, and clutch sleeve, then install the assembly into the case. Make sure that the rail is fully seated in the case bore.

NOTE: The rail bore of the front case must be perfectly dry. A small amount of oil in the bore will prevent proper seating of the rail

8. Install a thrust washer and a new O-ring on the mainshaft.

9. Coat the mainshaft needle bearing surface with petroleum jelly, then install the needle bearings and spacers in the following order:

   a. Install the short bearing spacer on the shaft.

   b. Install the first 41 needle bearings.

   c. Install the long bearing spacer.

   d. Install the remaining 41 needle bearings.

   e. Install the remaining short spacer. When installing the spacers, be careful not to disturb the needle bearings. If necessary, use additional petroleum jelly to hold the bearings in place.

10. Install the splined gear on the mainshaft, being careful not to disturb the bearings.

11. Install the sprocket carrier in the drive sprocket, being sure to align the carrier-to-sprocket reference marks made during disassembly.

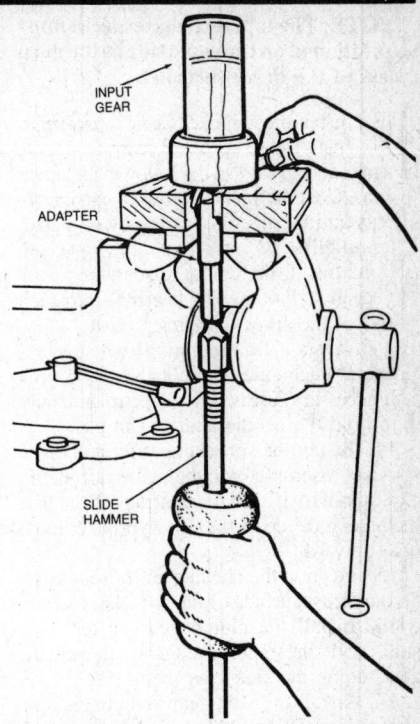

Removing the mainshaft pilot bushing

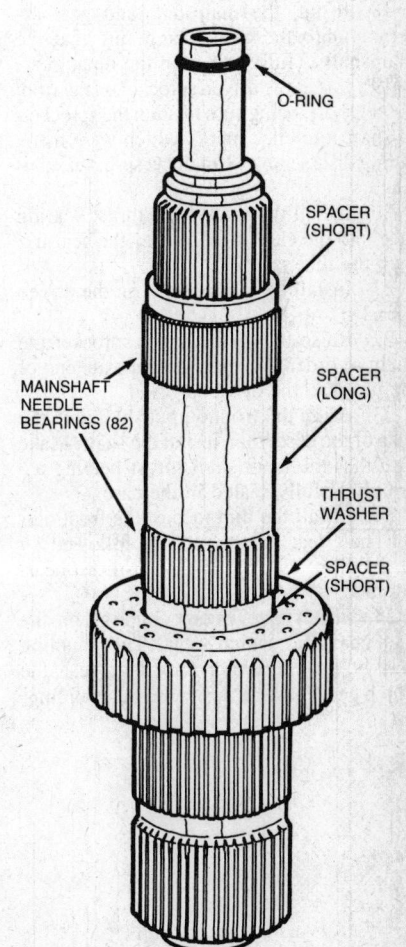

Proper arrangement of the mainshaft needle bearings and spacers

NOTE: The tapered carrier teeth must be positioned on the same side as the deep recess of the drive sprocket.

12. Install the sprocket carrier snap-rings.

13. Install the sprocket carrier needle bearings and spacers in the following manner:

   a. Coat both the sprocket carrier recess and the needle bearings with petroleum jelly.

   b. Install the center spacer.

   c. Install 60 needle bearings into each end of the sprocket carrier.

   d. Install the remaining two spacers, one at each side of the carrier.

If necessary, use additional petroleum jelly to hold the needle bearings in place.

14. Install the sprocket carrier and drive sprocket assembly onto the mainshaft, being careful not to disturb the bearings. Note that the recessed side of the drive sprocket must face upward.

15. Position the clutch gear thrust washer on the thrust surface of the sprocket carrier.

16. Install the clutch gear on the gear side, with the tapered edge of the clutch gear facing the side gear teeth.

17. Install the side gear and clutch gear assembly onto the mainshaft, being careful not to disturb the bearings. The side gear must be fully seated in the sprocket carrier.

18. Install the mainshaft and gear assembly into the case, being sure that the mainshaft is fully seated in the input gear.

19. Install the driven sprocket on the front output shaft, being sure to align the sprocket-to-shaft reference marks which were made during disassembly. Install the sprocket snap-ring.

20. Install the thick front thrust bearing race into the case, followed by the bearing, then the thin race.

21. Install the drive chain on the driven sprocket.

22. Raise and tilt the driven sprocket and chain in order to attach the opposite end of the chain to the drive sprocket.

23. Align the front output shaft with the bore of the case, then install the shaft. Make sure that the front shaft thrust bearing assembly is fully seated in the case.

24. Install the thin race of the front output shaft rear thrust bearing, followed by the bearing, then the thick rear thrust bearing race.

25. Install the viscous coupling on the side gear and clutch gear. The coupling must be fully seated on the clutch gear, the clutch gear must be flush with the coupling,

and the gear teeth should not be visible.

26. Coat the pilot bearing surface of the mainshaft and all of the pilot roller bearings with petroleum jelly. Install the pilot roller bearings on the shaft, using additional petroleum jelly to hold the bearings in place, if necessary.

27. Install the rear output shaft on the mainshaft, then into the viscous coupling. Be careful not to disturb the bearings during shaft installation. The shaft must be fully seated in the coupling; if necessary, tap the shaft with the plastic mallet to seat it.

28. Install the oil pump on the rear output shaft.

29. Install a new rear output shaft bearing oil seal.

30. Apply a bead of sealer (Loctite® 515 is recommended) to the mating surface of the rear case. If removed, reinstall the case magnet.

31. Install the front case to the rear case, being sure to align the dowels at the front case with the bolt holes of the rear case. Seat the rear case onto the front case.

NOTE: If the rear case will not seat completely into the front case, check for the following conditions:

   a. Oil present in the range fork rail bore.

   b. Rear thrust bearing assembly of the front output shaft is not aligned with the rear case.

   c. Mainshaft not completely seated.

   d. Rear case not aligned with the oil pump.

32. Install the rear case-to-front case bolts. Be sure to use flat washers on the bolts at the case ends where the alignment dowels are located. Torque the bolts to 23 ft. lbs.

33. Install the speedometer drive gear and the differential shims on the rear output shaft.

34. Align and temporarily install the rear retainer. Tighten, but do not "final-torque" the bolts.

35. Install the front and rear output shaft yokes. Install the *original* yoke nuts, then finger-tighten them only.

36. Mount a dial indicator on the rear retainer so that the indicator stylus contacts the rear yoke nut. The stylus must be in-line with the rear output shaft.

37. Rotate the front output shaft 10–12 revolutions. Zero the dial indicator and rotate the front shaft one more full revolution.

Note the dial indicator reading, which should be 0.002–0.010 in. If the end-play is okay, proceed to the next step. If the end-play is not within specifications, remove the rear retainer and add or subtract differential shims as required. Reinstall the rear retainer, yoke, and nut, then recheck the end play. Repeat if necessary until the end play is correct.

38. Remove the front and rear yokes, then discard the original yoke nuts.

39. Remove the rear retainer. Apply sealer (Loctite® 515 is recommended) to the retainer mating surface and all of the retainer bolt threads. Install the retainer and the bolts. Torque the retainer bolts to 23 ft. lbs.

40. Install the front and rear yokes, using new sealing washers and yoke nuts. Tighten the yoke nuts to 120 ft. lbs.

41. Install the detent ball, spring, and bolt. Apply sealer to the bolt threads and tighten the bolt to 23 ft. lbs.

42. Install the drain plug and washer.

43. Fill the transfer case with the proper types and amount of lubricant (see "Lubrication" at the beginning of this section).

44. Install the fill plug and washer, then tighten both the drain and fill plugs to 18 ft. lbs. (1980-81) 25 ft. lbs. (1982 and later).

45. If removed, install the plug and washer in the front case. Tighten to 18 ft. lbs.

46. On 1982 and later models, install the shift motor and bracket.

47. Reinstall the transfer case according to the procedure in the appropriate car section.

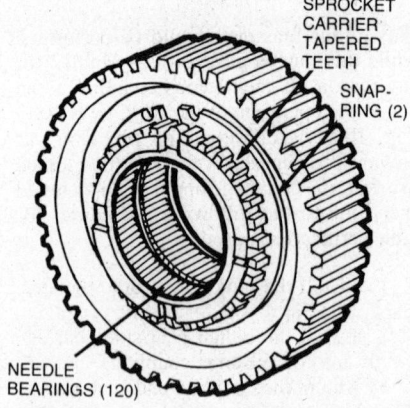

Sprocket carrier and drive sprocket assembly

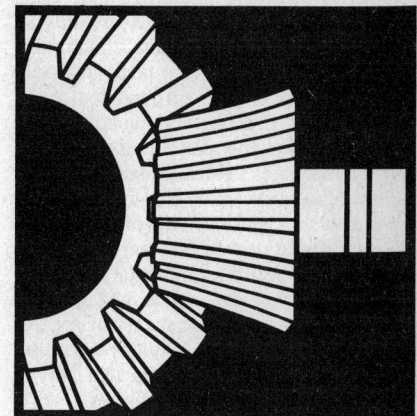

Drive Axles

DRIVE AXLES

FRONT WHEEL DRIVE

Front wheel drive cars do not have conventional rear axles or drive shafts. Instead, power is transmitted from the engine to a transaxle, or a combination of transmission and drive axle, in one unit. Both the transmission and drive axle accomplish the same function as their counterparts in a front-engine/rear-drive axle design. The difference is in the location of the components.

In place of a conventional driveshaft, a front-wheel-drive design uses two driveshafts, sometimes called halfshafts, which couple the drive axle portion of the transaxle to the wheels. Universal joints or constant velocity joints are used just as they would in a rear-wheel drive design.

See the General Troubleshooting and Diagnosis section in Unit Repair.

REAR WHEEL DRIVE

The rear axle must transmit power through 90°. To accomplish this, straight cut bevel gears or spiral bevel gears were used. This type of gear is satisfactory for differential side gears, but since the centerline of the gears must intersect, they rapidly became unsuited for ring and pinion gears. The lowering of the driveshaft brought about a variation of the bevel gear, which is called the hypoid gear. This type of gear does not require a metting of the gear centerlines and can therefore be underslung, relative to the centerline of the ring gear.

Gear Ratios

The drive axle of a vehicle is said to have a certain axle ratio. This number (usually a whole number and a decimal fraction) is actually a comparison of the number of gear teeth on the ring gear and the pinion gear.

For example, a 4.11 rear means that theoretically, there are 4.11 teeth on the ring gear and one tooth on the pinion. Actually, on a 4.11 rear, there are 37 teeth on the ring gear and nine teeth on the pinion gear. By dividing the number of teeth on the pinion gear into the number of teeth on the ring gear, the numerical axle ratio (4.11) is obtained. This also provides a good method of ascertaining exactly which axle ratio one is dealing with.

Differential Operation

The differential is an arrangement of gears that permits the rear wheels to turn at different speeds when cornering and divides the torque between the axle shafts. The differential gears are mounted on a pinion shaft and the gears are free to rotate on this shaft. The pinion shaft is fitted in a bore in the differential case and is at right angles to the axle shafts.

Power flow through the differential is as follows. The drive pinion, which is turned by the driveshaft, turns the ring gear. The ring gear, which is bolted to the differential case, rotates the case. The differential pinion forces the pinion gears against the side gears. In cases where both wheels have equal traction, the pinion gears do not rotate on the pinion shaft, because the input force of the pinion gear is divided equally between the two side gears. Consequently the pinion gears revolve with the pinion shaft, although they do not revolve on the pinion shaft itself. The side gears, which are splined to the axle shafts, and meshed with the pinion gears, rotate the axle shafts.

When it becomes necessary to turn a corner, the differential becomes effective and allows the axle shafts to rotate at different speeds. As the inner wheel slows down, the side gear splined to the inner wheel axle

shaft also slows down. The pinion gears act as balancing levers by maintaining equal tooth loads to both gears while allowing unequal speeds of rotation at the axle shafts. If the vehicle speed remains constant, and the inner wheel slows down to 90 percent of vehicle speeds, the outer wheel will speed up to 110 percent.

Limited-Slip Differential Operation

Limited-slip differentials provide driving force to the wheel with the best traction before the other wheel begins to spin. This is accomplished through clutch plates or cones. The clutch plates or cones are located between the side gears and inner wall of the differential case. When they are squeezed together through spring tension and outward force from the side gears, three reactions occur. Resistance on the side gears causes more torque to be exerted on the clutch packs or clutch cones. Rapid one-wheel spin cannot occur, because the side gear is forced to turn at the same speed as the case. Most important, with the side gear and the differential case turning at the same speed, the other wheel is forced to rotate in the same direction and at the same speed as the differential case. Thus driving force is applied to the wheel with the better traction.

DIFFERENTIAL DIAGNOSIS

The most essential part of rear axle service is proper diagnosis of the problem. Bent or broken axle shafts or broken gears pose little problem, but isolating an axle noise and correctly interpreting the problem can be extremely difficult, even for an experienced mechanic.

Any gear driven unit will produce a certain amount of noise, therefore, a specific diagnosis for each individual unit is the best practice. Acceptable or normal noise can be classified as a slight noise heard only at certain speeds or under unusual conditions. This noise tends to reach a peak at 40–60 mph, depending on the road condition, load, gear ratio and tire size. Frequently, other noises are mistakenly diagnosed as coming from the rear axle. Vehicle noises from tires, transmission, driveshaft, U-joints and front and rear wheel bearings will often be mistaken as emanating from the rear axle. Raising the tire pressure to eliminate tire noise (although this will not silence mud or snow treads), listening for noise at varying speeds and road conditions and listening for noise at drive and coast conditions will aid in diagnosing alleged rear axle noises.

External Noise Elimination

It is advisable to make a thorough road test to determine whether the noise originates in the rear axle or whether it originates from the tires, engine transmission, wheel bearings or road surface. Noise originating from other places cannot be corrected by overhauling the rear axle.

Road Noise

Brick roads or rough surfaced concrete, may cause a noise which can be mistaken as coming from the rear axle. Driving on a different type of road (smooth asphalt or dirt) will determine whether the road is the cause of the noise. Road noise is usually the same on drive or coast conditions.

Tire Noise

Tire noise can be mistaken as rear axle noises, even though the tires on the front are at fault. Snow tread and mud tread tires or tires worn unevenly will frequently cause vibrations which seem to originate elsewhere; *temporarily, and for test purposes only,* inflate the tires to 40–50 lbs. This will significantly alter the noise produced by the tires, but will not alter noise from the rear axle. Noises from the rear axle will normally cease at speeds below 30 mph on coast, while tire noise will continue at lower tone as car speed is decreased. The rear axle noise will usually change from drive conditions to coast conditions, while tire noise will not. Do not forget to lower the tire pressure to normal after the test is complete.

Engine and Transmission Noise

Engine and transmission noises also seem to originate in the rear axle. Road test the vehicle and determine at which speeds the noise is most pronounced. Stop the car in a quiet place to avoid interfering noises. With the transmission in neutral, run the engine slowly through the engine speeds corresponding to the car speed at which the noise was most noticeable. If a similar noise was produced with the car standing still,

the noise is not in the rear axle, but somewhere in the engine or transmission.

Front Wheel Bearing Noise

Front wheel bearing noises, sometimes confused with rear axle noises, will not change when comparing drive and coast conditions. While holding the car speed steady, lightly apply the footbrake. This will often cause wheel bearing noise to lessen, as some of the weight is taken off the bearing. Front wheel bearings are easily checked by jacking up the wheels and spinning the wheels. Shaking the wheels will also determine if the wheel bearings are excessively loose.

Rear Axle Noises

If a logical test of the vehicle shows that the noise is not caused by external items, it can be assumed that the noise originates from the rear axle. The rear axle should be tested on a smooth level road to avoid road noise. It is not advisable to test the axle by jacking up the rear wheels and running the car.

True rear axle noises generally fall into two classes—gear noise and bearing noises, and can be caused by a faulty driveshaft, faulty wheel bearings, worn differential or pinion shaft bearings, U-joint misalignment, worn differential side gears and pinions, or mismatched, improperly adjusted, or scored ring and pinion gears.

REAR WHEEL BEARING NOISE

A rough rear wheel bearing causes a vibration or growl which will continue with the car coasting or in neutral. A brinelled rear wheel bearing will also cause a knock or click approximately every two revolutions of the rear wheel, due to the fact that the bearing rollers do not travel at the same speed as the rear wheel and axle. Jack up the rear wheels and spin the wheel slowly, listening for signs of a rough or brinelled wheel bearing.

DIFFERENTIAL SIDE GEAR AND PINION NOISE

Differential side gears and pinions seldom cause noise since their movement is relatively slight on straight ahead driving. Noise produced by these gears will be more noticeable on turns.

PINION BEARING NOISE

Pinion bearing failures can be distinguished by their speed of rotation, which is higher than side bearings or axle bearings. Rough or brinelled pinion bearings cause a continuous low pitch whirring or scraping noise beginning at low speeds.

SIDE BEARING NOISE

Side bearings produce a constant rough noise, which is slower than the pinion bearing noise. Side bearing noise may also fluctuate in the above rear wheel bearing test.

GEAR NOISE

Two basic types of gear noise exist. First

is the type produced by bent or broken gear teeth which have been forcibly damaged. The noise from this type of damage is audible over the entire speed range. Scoring or damage to the hypoid gear teeth generally results from insufficient lubricant, improper lubricant, improper breakin, insufficient gear backlash, improper ring and pinion gear alignment or loss of torque on the drive pinion nut. If not corrected, the scoring will lead to eventual erosion or fracture of the gear teeth. Hypoid gear tooth fracture can also be caused by extended overloading of the gear set (fatigue fracture) or by shock overloading (sudden failure). Differential and side gears rarely give trouble, but common causes of differential failure are shock loading, extended overloading and differential pinion seizure at the cross-shaft, resulting from excessive wheel spin and consequent lubricant breakdown.

The second type of gear noise pertains to the mesh pattern between the ring and pinion gears. This type of abnormal gear noise can be recognized as a cycling pitch or whine audible in either drive, float or coast conditions. Gear noises can be recognized as they tend to peak out in a narrow speed range and remain constant in pitch, whereas bearing noises tend to vary in pitch with vehicle speeds. Noises produced by the ring and pinion gears will generally follow the pattern below.

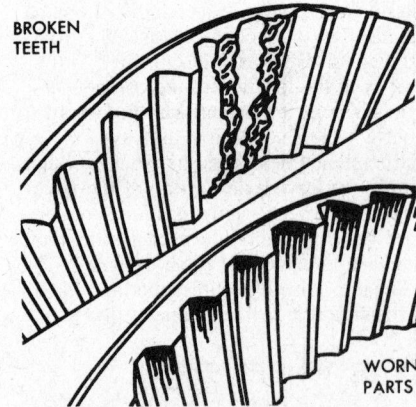

BROKEN TEETH

WORN PARTS

Two types of damage which cause gear noise
(© Chevrolet Div., G.M. Corp)

A. Drive Noise:	Produced under vehicle acceleration.
B. Coast Noise:	Produced while the car coasts with a closed throttle.
C. Float Noise:	Occurs while maintaining constant car speed (just enough to keep speed constant) on a level road.
D. Drive, Coast and Float Noise:	These noises will vary in tone with speed and be very rough or irregular if the differential or pinion shaft bearings are worn.

Bearing Diagnosis

This section will help in the diagnosis of bearing failure and the causes. Bearing diagnosis can be very helpful in determining the cause of rear axle failure.

When disassembling a rear axle, the general condition of all bearings should be noted and classified where possible. Proper recognition of the cause will help in correcting the problem and avoiding a repetition of the failure.

Some of the common causes of bearing failure are:

    a. Abuse during assembly or disassembly.

    b. Improper assembly methods.

    c. Improper or inadequate lubrication.

    d. Bearing contact with dirt or water.

    e. Wear caused by dirt or metal chips.

    f. Corrosion or rust.

    g. Seizing due to overloading.

    h. Overheating.

    i. Frettage of the bearing seats.

    j. Brinelling from impact or shock loading.

    k. Manufacturing defects.

    l. Pitting due to fatigue.

To avoid damage to the bearing from improper handling, it is best to treat a used bearing the same as a new bearing. Always work in a clean area with clean tools. Remove all outside dirt from the housing before exposing a bearing and clean all bearing seats before installing a bearing.

——————— CAUTION ———————
Never spin a bearing, either by hand or with compressed air, as this will lead to almost certain bearing failure.

LIMITED-SLIP DIFFERENTIAL DIAGNOSIS

Lubrication

The use of proper lubricant is very important in limited-slip type drive axles. The forces applied when cornering tend to apply the clutch pack or clutch cones. The use of the wrong lubricant can cause the clutch surfaces to grab and chatter while turning. Always follow the manufacturer's recommendations regarding drive axle lubrication. When chatter is encountered, the differential lubricant should be drained and refilled with the specified lubricant.

Testing

The clutch operation on all limited-slip type axles can be tested as follows. Refer to the manufacturer in question.

AMERICAN MOTORS "TWIN-GRIP"

1. With the engine off and the transmission in neutral, jack up one rear wheel.

2. Block the other wheel to prevent it from moving.

3. With a socket and torque wrench on the axle shaft nut, turn the raised wheel forward.

4. The torque required to move the wheel should be 70–100 ft lbs for 8⅞ in. axles or 80–120 ft lbs for 7⁹⁄₁₆ in. axles.

5. A breakaway torque which is less than the specified figure, indicates a need for repair or replacement.

CADILLAC CONTROLLED DIFFERENTIAL

This unit should not be serviced. If a malfunction exists that cannot be cured by changing the fluid, remove the unit and install a new one.

CHRYSLER CORP. SURE-GRIP

1. Place the vehicle on a hoist with the engine off and the automatic transmission in Park (manual transmission in low gear).

2. Attempt to rotate the wheel by hand, by gripping the tire.

3. If it is extremely difficult, if not impossible, to rotate either wheel the Sure-Grip differential can be assumed to be performing satisfactorily.

4. If it is relatively easy to continuously turn either rear wheel, the unit should be removed and replaced.

——————— CAUTION ———————
The Sure-Grip differential is serviced as a unit only. Under no circumstances should the unit be disassembled and reinstalled.

FORD MOTOR COMPANY EQUA-LOK

1. Jack up one rear wheel and remove the wheel cover.

2. Block the other wheel front and rear to prevent the car from moving.

3. Using a 200 ft lbs capacity torque wrench on one of the wheel lug nuts, measure the torque required to continuously rotate the wheel. The breakaway torque reading can be disregarded. The minimum torque to continuously rotate the wheel should be as follows.

All axles except integral carrier type: 75 ft lbs.

Integral carrier type axles: 50 ft lbs.

4. If the minimum torque is not as specified, the differential should be checked for improper assembly.

FORD MOTOR COMPANY TRACTION-LOK

1. Follow the procedure for the Ford Motor Company Equa-Lok rear. The minimum torque to continuously rotate the wheel (disregarding the breakaway torque) should be at least 40 ft lbs through 1979 and 30 ft lbs for 1980 and later.

GENERAL MOTORS CORP. (EXCEPT CADILLAC) POSITRACTION

1. Place the transmission in neutral.

2. Raise one rear wheel off the floor and block the other rear wheel (front and rear) to prevent the car from moving.

3. Install a torque wrench and extension on the lug nut and note the torque required to continuously rotate one rear wheel. Disregard the breakaway torque figure, as this may be a great deal higher.

4. The minimum torque to continuously rotate the rear wheel should be at least 35 ft lbs. If it is not, the rear axle is in need of service.

General Diagnosis

Improper operation of a limited-slip type rear axle is generally indicated by clutch slippage or grabbing, which will sometimes produce a whirring or chatter sound. Occasionally, this condition is induced by improper lubrication. Check the unit for the wrong type of lubricant or lubricant which has broken down or become contaminated. Replace the lubricant with the type specified by the manufacturer.

During normal operation, i.e., straight-ahead driving, both wheels are rotating at equal speeds, and the driving force is distributed equally between both wheels. When cornering, the inside wheel delivers extra driving force, causing slippage in both clutch packs. Therefore, if the wheel rotation of both rear wheels is not equal, the unit will constantly be functioning as if the car were cornering. This will cause constant slippage and lead to eventual failure of the unit. It is important that there be no excessive differences in wheel and tire size, wear pattern, or tire pressures between both rear wheels. Swerving on acceleration is an indication of one or more of the above conditions. Before attempting an overhaul or replacement operation, check both rear wheels for identical tire sizes, tire pressure, tire tread depth, and wear pattern.

DRIVE AXLE DISASSEMBLY ANALYSIS

Testing the Gear Tooth Contact Pattern

Once it has been established that the differential is indeed in need of service, the worst procedure is to simply plunge ahead and remove the differential and disassemble the parts. Prior to disassembly, a tooth contact pattern test should be made. However, it is worthwhile to first know the nomenclature associated with hypoid gear teeth.

The thick end of the tooth is called the heel and the thin end of the tooth is called the toe. The base half of the tooth is called the flank and the other end of the tooth is known as the face. The imaginary line at the halfway point between the face and flank is known as the pitch line. The space between the meshed pinion and ring gear tooth is known as backlash.

A gear tooth contact pattern can be made with the carrier in or out of the housing depending on the type of carrier. On inte-

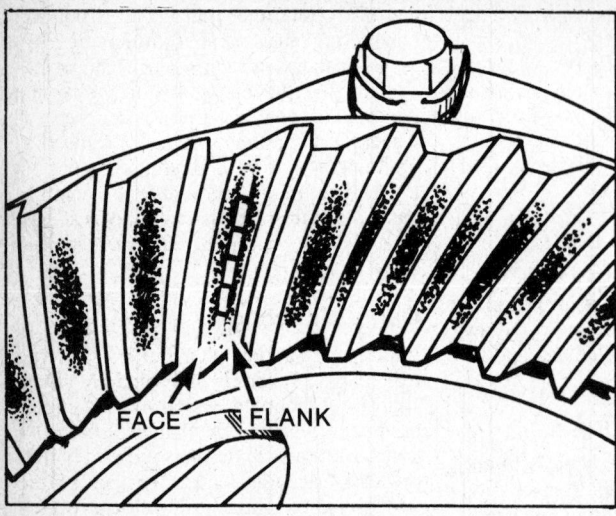

Gear tooth face and flank showing oval gear tooth contact pattern

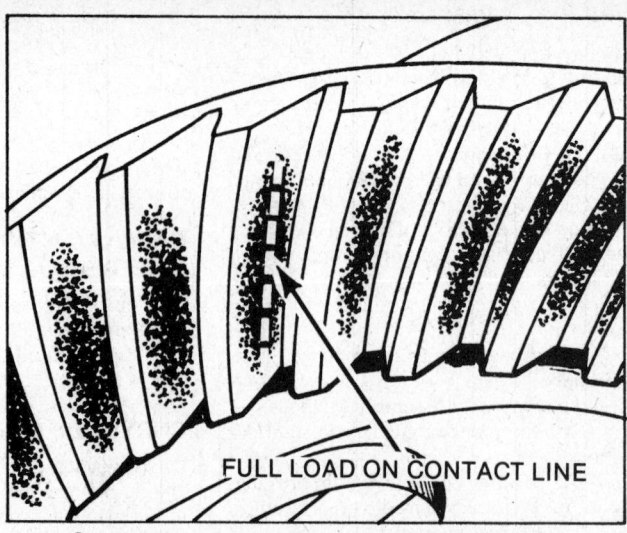

FULL LOAD ON CONTACT LINE

Gear tooth contact pattern showing load centered on gear tooth

gral carrier models, the lubricant must be drained and the rear cover removed. The ring gear will now be exposed and the test can be made with the carrier still in the housing. On removable carrier models, drain the lubricant and remove the carrier from the housing. The test can be made on the bench.

Unlike simple spur gears, hypoid gear teeth leave a complex pattern on the ring gear. When hypoid gears turn, the line contact between pinion and ring gear teeth has the same wiping motion as with spur gear teeth. Because of the complicated movement of hypoid gear teeth, the contact area takes an oval shape as opposed to the rectangular shape left by spur gear teeth. Actually, the tooth contact test shows where each gear tooth has been wiped by the movement of the contact line, so that you can tell whether the gears are set correctly. With a properly adjusted ring and pinion (with properly adjusted pinion depth and backlash) the tooth contact will be close to center. In this case, the load is borne by the strongest part of the tooth. If the gear

setting is off, the contact line may reach any part of the edge of a tooth, and the metal will be overloaded at that point. When overload occurs, rapid deterioration of the gears will follow.

PREPARING THE TEST

Coat the drive gear teeth with a metallic base artists' oil color such as zinc white or titanium white. The tooth coating material must be smooth and firm enough to spread without running. A consistency somewhat like toothpaste works well. If it is necessary to thicken the material, add a small amount of cup grease.

NOTE: Prussian blue dye does not work well, since the blue tends to smear the pattern.

Thoroughly clean the ring gear and pinion before applying the testing material. Any gear lube left on the teeth will make the pattern quite unreadable. Coat the drive and coast sides of all the ring gear teeth, but leave the pinion gear teeth clean. Do

not apply the coating too thickly as the pattern will be smeared.

Because the axle gears are normally easy to rotate, turning resistance must be applied to produce pressure between the pinion and ring gear teeth to make a legible pattern. On a removable carrier type axle, insert a large screwdriver between the carrier housing and the differential case rim. Apply the load squarely against the case rim while prying out against the upper or lower section of the carrier housing. On integral carrier models, apply the parking brake to a point where it requires approximately 50 ft lbs to turn the pinion with a torque wrench. Since the shape and position of the contact pattern will vary, depending on the load, try to use the same load for each test or the results can be misleading. This is especially true when testing after an overhaul.

Once the gears have a load applied, obtain a tooth contact pattern by rotating the ring gear and pinion one complete turn in each direction. This will produce a constant pattern on the coast and drive side of each tooth. Do not rotate the ring gear more than

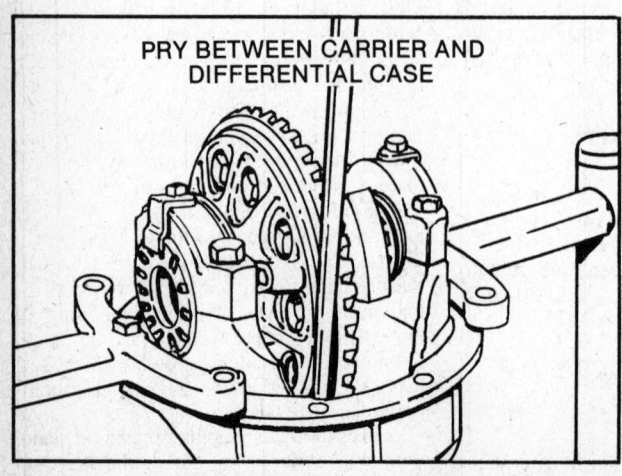

PRY BETWEEN CARRIER AND DIFFERENTIAL CASE

Applying a load to the differential case

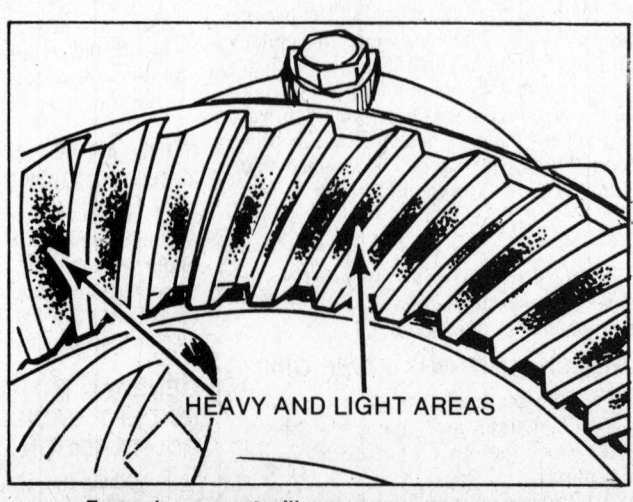

HEAVY AND LIGHT AREAS

Excessive run-out will cause an uneven pattern

THICKER SPACER NEEDED

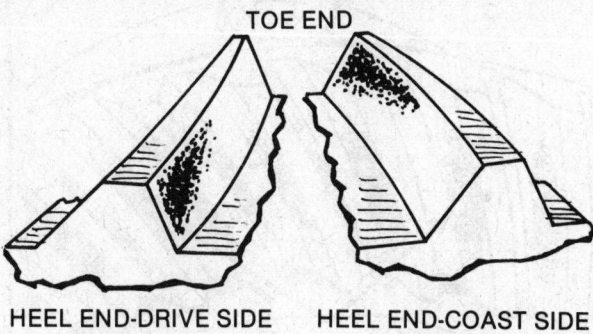

TOE END

HEEL END-DRIVE SIDE
(CONVEX)
HEEL END-COAST SIDE
(CONCAVE)

Tooth contact patterns high on the tooth side

THINNER SPACER NEEDED

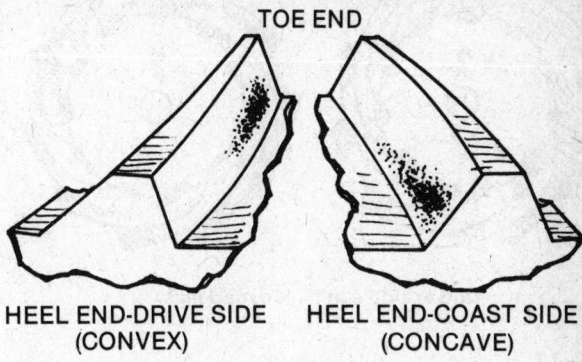

TOE END

HEEL END-DRIVE SIDE
(CONVEX)
HEEL END-COAST SIDE
(CONCAVE)

Gear contact pattern low on tooth side

one revolution in each direction as this will tend to obscure the pattern.

NOTE: If the pattern does not look right on the first try, try again.

Making a good gear tooth test takes a little practice; so if it is not right, try again.

INTERPRETING GEAR TOOTH CONTACT PATTERNS

The tooth contact pattern should be the same on every tooth. If the pattern shows heavy and light areas on different teeth, check the ring gear and differential case for excessive run-out.

. **NOTE: Run-out can be cured in many cases by removing the ring gear from the case, rotating it 90° or 180°, and remounting it.**

Since you can only apply test load pressure to the gears, the contact pattern will be less distinct toward the tooth ends. But, when the ring gear and pinion are under operating loads in the vehicle, the tooth contact area spreads out, especially towards the heel end of the tooth. For this reason, do not try to "get by" with a tooth contact pattern that is centered, but favors the heel end of the teeth. This will only lead to overloading at the heel ends of the gear teeth. On the other hand, a contact pattern which is reasonably centered, but favors the toe end of the teeth, is acceptable.

Assuming that the tooth contact pattern is even on all teeth, the main problems is to get the most distinct part of the pattern centered on both the teeth. The contact patterns should be nearly opposite each other on both sides of each tooth. In some cases, the pattern will be centered on the drive side and off center on the coast side, or vice versa. The off center pattern can be moved to a more acceptable position by slightly altering the backlash. This procedure will not seriously affect the other pattern. More often, however, the pattern will be off center on both sides of the teeth. The basic cause of this condition is an improperly adjusted pinion.

ADJUSTING PINION DEPTH

It is necessary to understand that an incorrect pinion depth setting moves the contact pattern away from the center on both sides of the tooth in opposite directions. This means that when you install a thicker or thinner washer under the pinion head you bring the pattern into the center of the tooth from opposite ends.

When the contact pattern is high on the heel end of the drive side and low on the toe end of the coast side, a thicker washer is needed to bring the pinion in, toward the

center of the drive gear. Increasing the thickness of the spacer washer will bring the pattern in, toward the center of the drive gear teeth, and also will move the pattern down from the tooth face. However, this movement is less than the in-or-out movement.

When tooth contact is low on the toe end of the drive side and high on the heel end of the coast side, the pinion must be moved out, by installing a thinner washer under the pinion head. This will move the pattern inward toward the center, and will also result in slight movement of the pattern up from the tooth flank.

A factory service facility will use special tools and gauge blocks to determine the thickness of the spacer under the pinion head. In the absence of such specialized equipment, the following procedure may be used. Bear in mind that with the "hit-or-miss" method, each time you are wrong with the pinion depth, the unit must be disassembled, the spacer thickness changed, and the unit must be completely set up again.

Gather a handful of spacers to cover any thickness and several collapsible pinion spacers (if the unit uses them). Assemble the unit. If the original gear set is being reused, and the tooth contact pattern is reasonably correct, install a new spacer of the same thickness as the old one. This will

PATTERN MOVES TOWARD CENTER AND DOWN

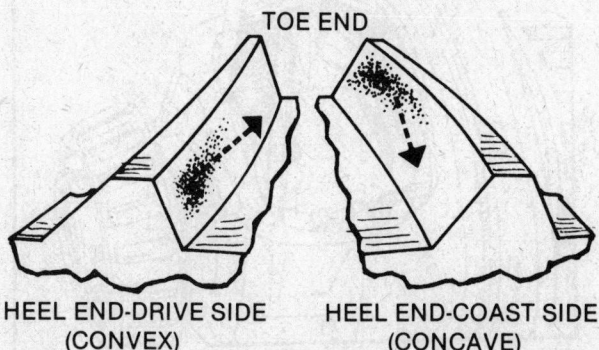

TOE END

HEEL END-DRIVE SIDE
(CONVEX)
HEEL END-COAST SIDE
(CONCAVE)

A thicker spacer moves the pattern in and down

PATTERN MOVES INWARD AND UP

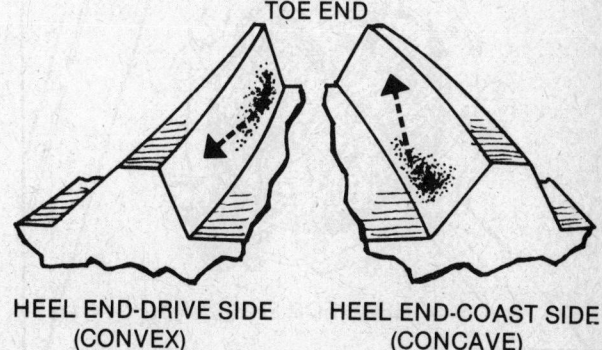

TOE END

HEEL END-DRIVE SIDE
(CONVEX)
HEEL END-COAST SIDE
(CONCAVE)

A thinner spacer will move the pattern up and inward

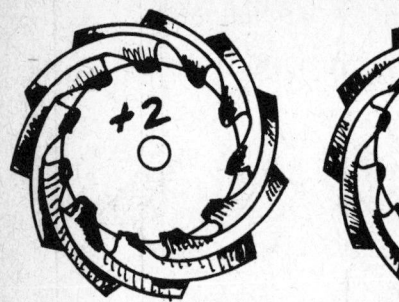

One example of pinion markings

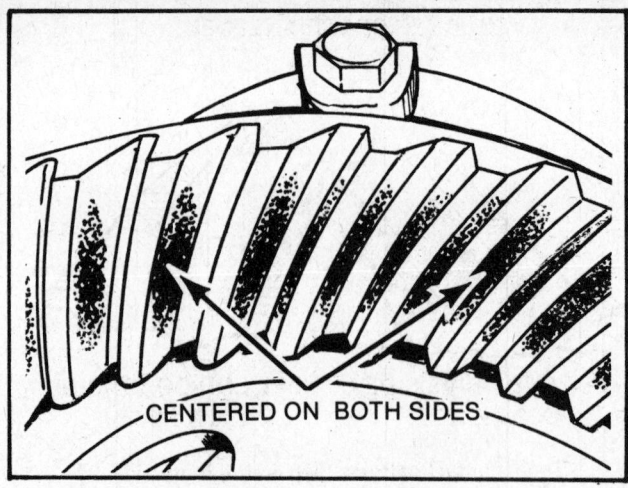

Gear tooth contact pattern showing load centered
on gear tooth

provide a reasonable starting point. If the gear contact pattern test indicates a need for movement of the pinion, use a new spacer 0.001–0.002 in. thicker or thinner, depending on the direction the pinion must go. If a new gear set is being used, the thickness of the spacer will have to be determined in the following manner. Compare the markings on the old and new pinion. It will usually be marked with a number preceded by a plus (+) or minus (−) sign. This number indicates the production deviation from the nominal pinion, which are known as "zero pinions." In service, zero pinions are rare. Assume that the old pinion is marked with a plus two (+2). Assume that the new pinion is marked with a +3. By comparing the pinion markings, find the numerical difference between the two pinions, in this case +1. With a micrometer, measure the thickness of the original spacer. We will assume that the old spacer is 0.030 in. thick. If the numerical difference between pinions is a positive number (+1) the spacer should be 0.001 in. thinner than the original spacer, or 0.029 in. total. If the numerical difference is a negative number (say, −1) then the spacer should be increased by 0.001 in., to 0.031 in. total. This will only provide a reasonable beginning point.

It is rare that this method works out the first time. Assemble the pinion, differential, and ring gear with the spacer of calculated thickness. The side bearing preload, backlash, pinion nut torque, and pinion rotating torque must all be set correctly. Obtain a gear tooth pattern on the ring gear teeth and analyze the results. Small deviations from the acceptable pattern can usually be made by varying the backlash within the limits of specifications. If the gear tooth contact pattern is off, the unit must be disassembled and another spacer installed. This spacer must be of suitable thickness to compensate for the contact pattern test.

NOTE: Without special tools, there is absolutely no way of determining exactly how much to increase or decrease the thickness of the pinion shim; it must be estimated.

After estimating the thickness of the new shim, assemble the unit again, setting all preloads and backlash. Check the contact pattern again and act accordingly. If the unit uses a collapsible spacer, be sure a new one is installed each time it is disassembled. Crushed spacers can not be used again. It is well to note that the unit may have to be assembled and disassembled several times before an acceptable contact pattern is obtained.

Adjusting Backlash

The tooth contact pattern can be altered slightly, by varying the backlash adjustment within the limits of the specifications. The backlash adjustment can be used to alter a pattern which is slightly off center on either side of the tooth, but should not be used as a substitute for pinion depth adjustment. This adjustment must always be made after the pinion depth has been adjusted.

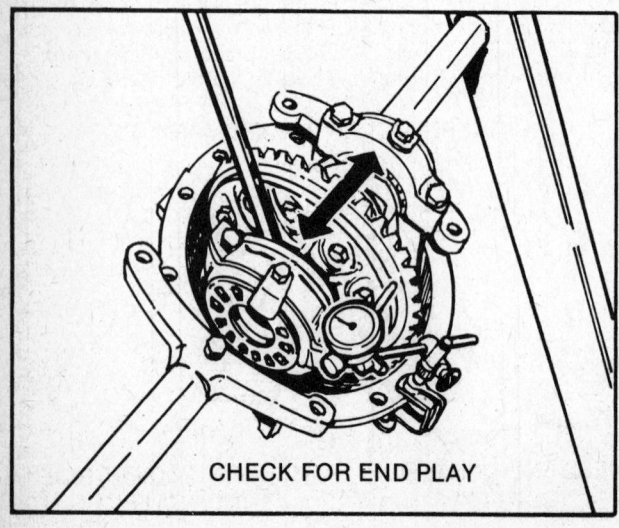

CHECK FOR END PLAY

Checking differential bearing end-play

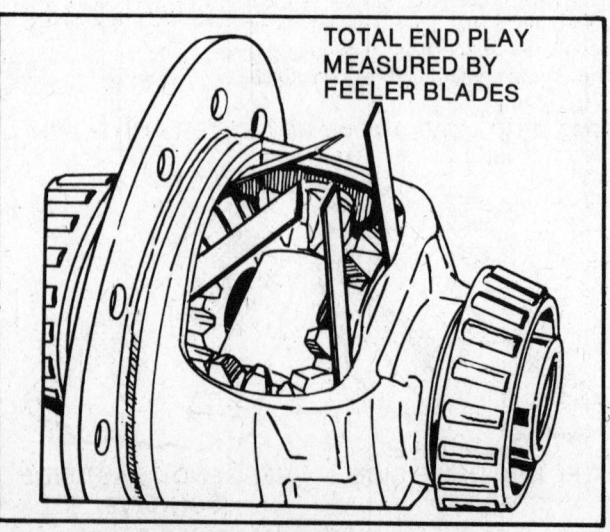

TOTAL END PLAY
MEASURED BY
FEELER BLADES

Checking total differential end-play

U-Joint/CV-Joint Overhaul

UNIVERSAL JOINTS

U-joint is mechanic's jargon for universal joint. U-joints should not be confused with U-bolts, which are U-shaped bolts used to connect U-joints to the differential pinion flange.

Universal joints provide flexibility between the driveshaft and axle housing to accommodate changes in the angle between them. (Changes of length are accommodated by the sliding splined yoke between the driveshaft and transmission.) The engine and transmission are mounted rigidly on the car frame, while the driving wheels are free to move up and down in relation to the frame. The angles between the transmission, driveshaft and axle change constantly as the car responds to various road conditions.

To give flexibility and still transmit power as smoothly as possible, several types of universal joints are used.

The most common type of universal joint is the cross and yoke type. Yokes are used on the ends of the driveshaft with the yoke arms opposite each other. Another yoke is used opposite the driveshaft and when placed together, both yokes engage a center member, or cross, with four arms spaced 90° apart. (The U-joint cross is alternately referred to as a spider, and the arms are called trunnions.) A bearing cup (or cap) is used on each arm of the cross to accommodate movement as the driveshaft rotates. The bearings used are needle bearings.

A conventional universal joint will cause the driveshaft to speed up and slow down through each revolution and cause a corresponding change in the velocity of the driven shaft. This change in speed causes

natural vibrations to occur through the driveline, necessitating a third type of universal joint: the constant velocity joint. A rolling ball moves in a curved groove, located between two yoke-and-cross universal joints, connected to each other by a coupling yoke. The result is a uniform motion as the driveshaft rotates, avoiding the fluctuations in driveshaft speed. This type of joint is found in cars with sharp driveline angles, or where the extra measure of isolation is desirable.

CROSS AND YOKE U-JOINT OVERHAUL

There are two types of cross and yoke U-joints. One type retains the cross within the

yoke with C-shaped snap rings. This type is found on all American Motors, Chrysler, and Ford cars. GM cars generally use the second type of joint, which is held together by injection molded plastic retainer rings. The second type cannot be reassembled with the same parts, once disassembled. However, repair kits are available.

Snap-Ring Type

1. Remove the driveshaft. For the correct procedure, see the car section for the model you are working on.

2. If the front yoke is to be disassembled, matchmark the driveshaft and sliding splined yoke (transmission yoke) so that driveline balance is preserved upon reassembly. Remove the snap rings which retain the bearing caps.

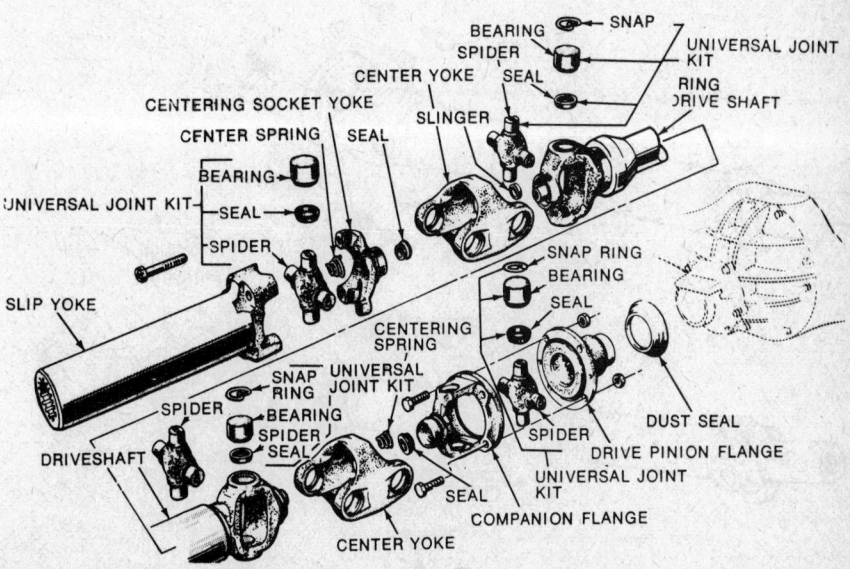

Typical driveshaft with cardan type U–joints

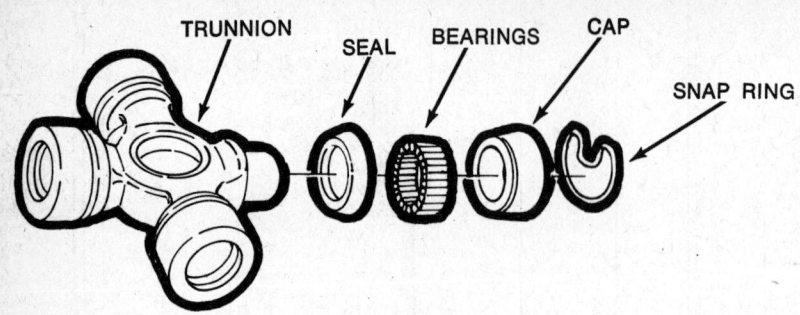

TRUNNION SEAL BEARINGS CAP SNAP RING

Snap ring type universal joint

3. Select two sockets, one small enough to pass through the yoke holes for the bearing caps, the other large enough to receive the bearing cap.

4. Using a vise or a press, position the small and large sockets on either side of the U-joint. Press in on the smaller socket so that it presses the opposite bearing cap out of the yoke and into the larger socket. If the cap does not come all the way out, grasp it with a pair of pliers and work it out.

5. Reverse the position of the sockets so that the smaller socket presses on the cross. Press the other bearing cap out of the yoke.

6. Repeat the procedure on the other bearings.

7. To install, grease the bearing caps and needles thoroughly if they are not pregreased. Start a new bearing cap into one side of the yoke. Position the cross in the yoke.

8. Select two sockets small enough to pass through the yoke holes. Put the sockets against the cross and the cap, and press the bearing cap ¼ inch below the surface of the yoke. If there is a sudden increase in the force needed to press the cap into place, or if the cross starts to bind, the bearings are cocked. They must be removed and restarted in the yoke. Failure to do so will greatly reduce the life of the bearing.

9. Install a new snap ring.

10. Start a new bearing into the opposite side. Place a socket on it and press in until the opposite bearing contacts the snap ring.

11. Install a new snap ring. It may be necessary to grind the facing surface of the snap ring slightly to permit easier installation.

12. Install the other bearings in the same manner.

13. Check the joint for free movement. If binding exists, smack the yoke ears with a brass or plastic faced hammer to seat the bearing needles. Do not strike the bearings,

and support the shaft firmly. Do not install the driveshaft until free movement exists at all joints.

Plastic Retainer Type

Remove and install the bearing caps and trunnion (cross) as described for the snapring type universal joints. On an original universal joint, however, the bearing caps will be secured in the yokes with injected plastic. The plastic will shear when the bearing caps are pressed. Service snap-rings are installed in the groove on the inside (of hoke) of the installed caps.

NOTE: The plastic which retains the bearing will be sheared when the bearing cup is pressed out. Be sure to remove the remains of the plastic retainer from the ears of the yoke. It is easier to remove the remains if a small pin or punch is first driven through the injection holes in the yoke. Failure to remove all of the plastic remains may prevent the bearing cups from being pressed into place and the bearing retainers from being properly seated.

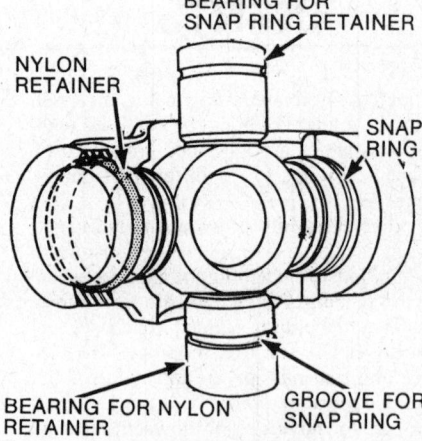

BEARING FOR SNAP RING RETAINER
NYLON RETAINER
SNAP RING
BEARING FOR NYLON RETAINER
GROOVE FOR SNAP RING

U-joint locking methods
(© Pontiac Div., G.M. Corp)

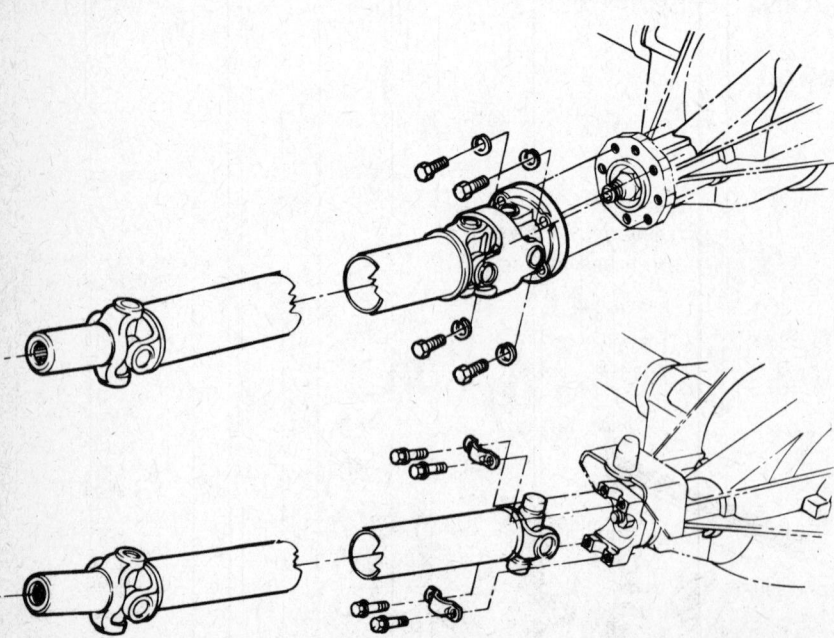

The driveshaft may be retained to the differential pinion by a flange (top) or by U-bolts or straps (bottom) (© Pontiac Div., G.M. Corp.)

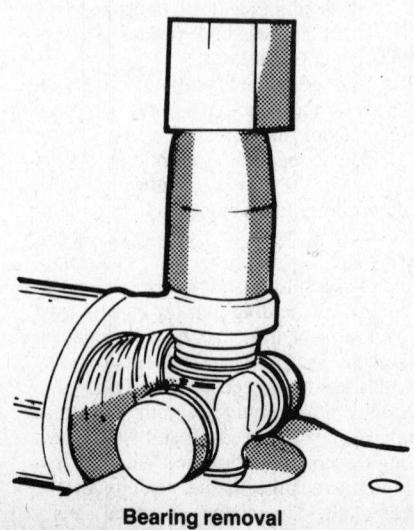

Bearing removal

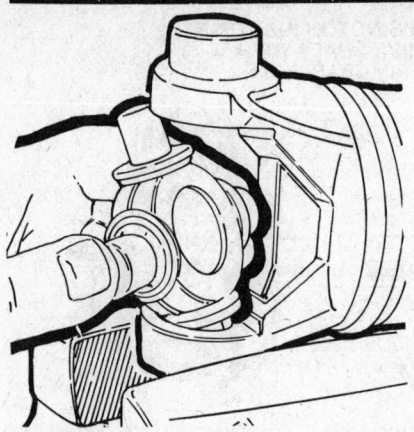

Press a bearing cap into the yoke, then install the cross

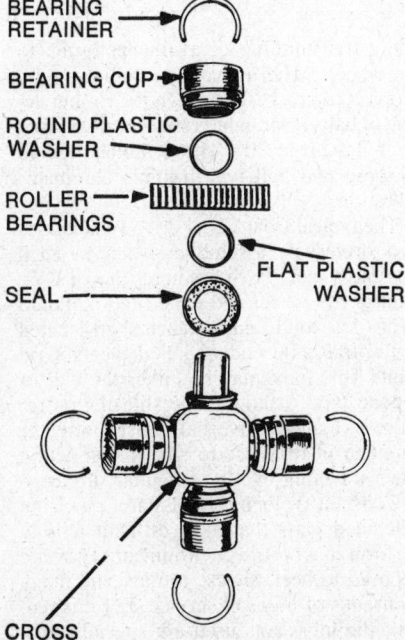

Plastic retainer U-joint repair kit components

CARDAN TYPE U-JOINT OVERHAUL

Ford and Chrysler products with Cardan type U-joints use snap rings to retain the bearing cups in the yokes. Most GM cars have plastic retainers. Be sure to obtain the correct rebuilding kit.

1. Use a punch to mark the coupling yoke and the adjoining yokes before disassembly, to ensure proper reassembly and driveline balance.

2. It is easiest to remove the bearings from the coupling yoke first. Follow the order indicated in the illustration.

3. Support the driveshaft horizontally on a press stand, or on the workbench if a vise is being used.

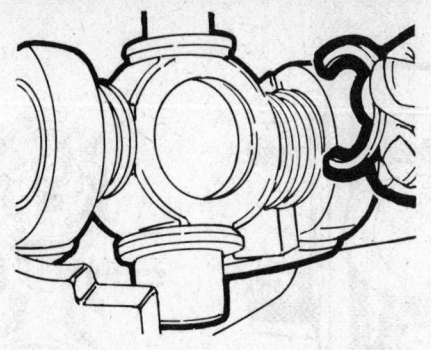

Service snap rings are installed inside the yoke

4. If snap rings are used to retain the bearing cups, remove them. Place the rear ear of the coupling yoke over a socket large enough to receive the cup. Place a smaller socket, or a cross press made for the purpose, over the opposite cup. Press the bearing cup out of the coupling yoke ear. If the cup is not completely removed, insert a spacer and complete the operation, or grasp the cup with a pair of slip joint pliers and work it out. If the cups are retained by plastic, this will shear the retainers. Remove any bits of plastic.

5. Rotate the driveshaft and repeat the operation on the opposite cup.

6. Disengage the trunnions of the spider, still attached to the flanged yoke, from the coupling yoke, and pull the flanged yoke and spider from the center ball on the ball support tube yoke.

NOTE: The joint between the shaft and coupling yoke can be serviced without disassembly of the joint between the coupling yoke and flanged yoke.

7. Pry the seal from the ball cavity,

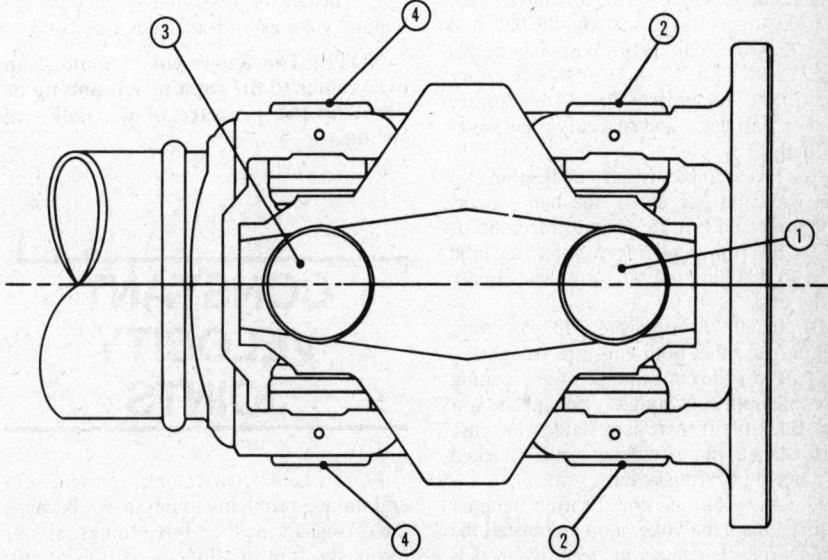

Cardan joint disassembly sequence

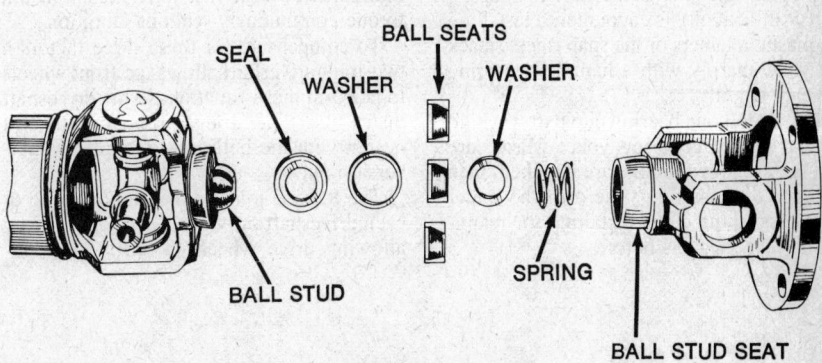

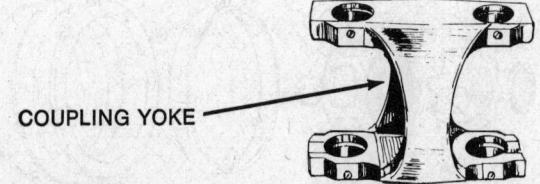

Cardan type joint

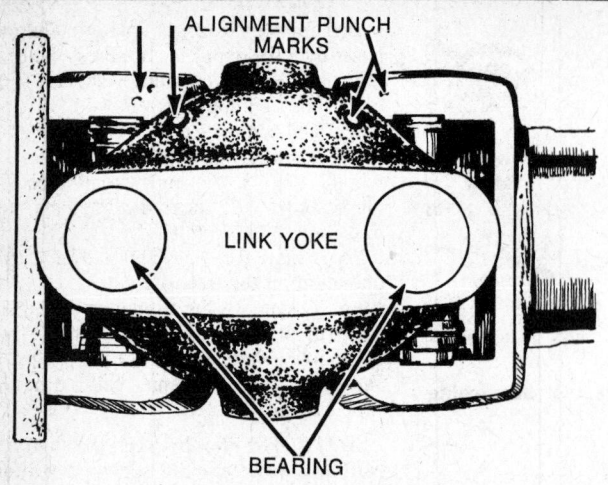

ALIGNMENT PUNCH MARKS

LINK YOKE

BEARING

Match marks for double cardan joint

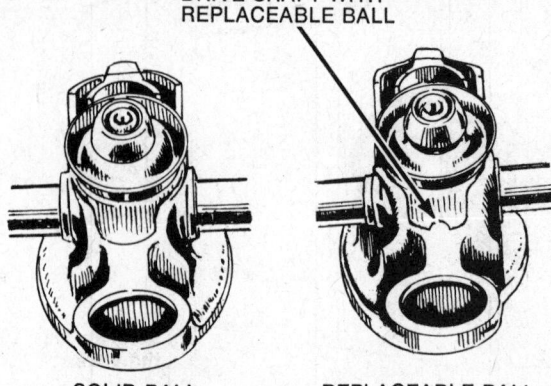

THIS NOTCH IDENTIFIES DRIVE SHAFT WITH REPLACEABLE BALL

SOLID BALL   REPLACEABLE BALL

Solid and replaceable U-Joint balls

remove the washers, spring and three seats. Examine the ball stud seat and the ball stud for scores or wear. Worn parts can be replaced with a kit. Clean the ball seat cavity and fill it with grease. Install the spring, washer, ball seats, and spacer (washer) over the ball.

8. To assemble, insert one bearing cup part way into one ear of the ball support tube yoke and turn this cup to the bottom.

9. Insert the spider (cross) into the tube yoke so that the trunnion (arm) seats freely in the cup.

10. Install the opposite cup part way, making sure that both cups are straight.

11. Press the cups into position, making sure that both cups squarely engage the spider. Back off if there is a sudden increase in resistance, indicating that a cup is cocked or a needle bearing is out of place.

12. As soon as one bearing retainer groove clears the yoke, stop and install the retainer (plastic retainer models). On models with snap rings, press the cups into place, then install the snap rings over the cups.

13. If difficulty is encountered installing the plastic retainers or the snap rings, smack the yoke sharply with a hammer to spring the ears slightly.

14. Install one bearing cup part way into the ear of the coupling yoke. Make sure that the alignment marks are matched, then engaged the coupling yoke over the spider and press in the cups, installing the retainers or snap rings as before.

15. Install the cups and spider into the flanged yoke as with the previous yoke.

NOTE: The flange yoke should snap over center to the right or left and up or down by the pressure of the ball seat spring.

CONSTANT VELOCITY JOINTS

Front wheel drive vehicles present several unique problems to engineers because the driveshaft must do three things, simultaneously. It must allow the wheels to turn for steering, telescope to compensate for road surface vibrations, and it must transmit torque continuously without vibration.

To compensate for these three factors a two-joint driveshaft allows the front wheels to perform these functions. This driveshaft mates disc type straight groove ball joint design with the bell type Rzeppa CV universal joint.

The Rzeppa joint on the outboard end of each driveshaft provides steering ability by allowing drive wheels to steer up to 43°

while transmitting all available torque to the wheels. The inboard joint allows telescoping (up to 1½″) through the rolling action of balls in straight grooves and operates at angles up to 20°. The combined action of these two ball type u-joints eliminates vibration.

The typical front wheel drive vehicle uses two driveshaft assemblies—one to each driving wheel. Each assembly has a CV-joint at the wheel end called the outboard joint. A second joint on each shaft located at the transaxle end is called the inboard joint. This joint may be either the ball or tripode type. It allows the slip motion required when the driveshaft must shorten or lengthen in response to suspension action when traveling over an irregular surface.

Constant velocity joints are precision machined parts that have difficult jobs to perform in a hostile environment. They are exposed to heat, shock, torque, and many thousands of miles of service. For this reason, the lubricants used are specially formulated to be compatible with the rubber boot and give proper lubrication. Most CV-joint repair kits have this special lubricant included.

NOTE: Wear pattern in a used ball or tripode CV-joint are impossible to match during reassembly. If there are any signs of wear, abnormal operating noise, corrosion, heat discoloration, the joint must be replaced.

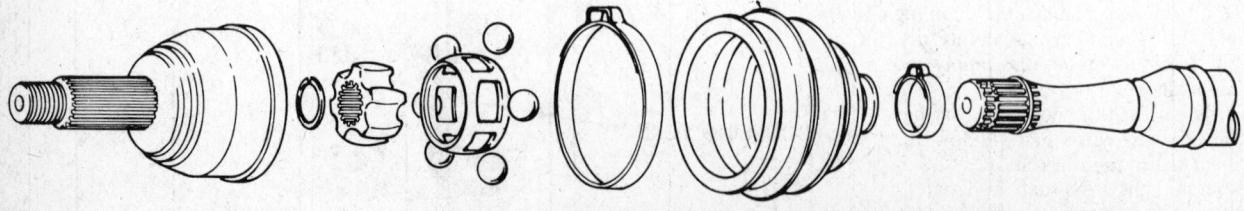

Fixed CV joint

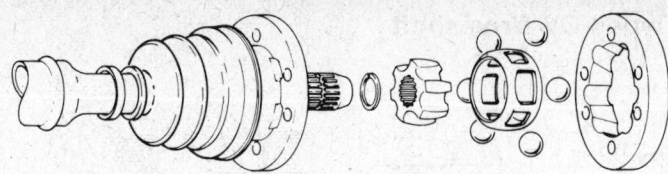

Ball style (Rzeppa) plunging CV–joint

TROUBLESHOOTING

Noises from the engine, drive axles, suspension and steering in the front drive cars can be misleading to the untrained ear. Ideally a smooth road serves best for detecting operating condition(s) that cause noise.

• A humming noise could indicate that early stage of insufficient or incorrect lubricant.

• Worn driveshaft joints will cause a continuous knock at low speeds.

• A popping or clicking sound on sharp turns indicates trouble in the outer or wheel end joint.

• The clunk noise at acceleration from coasting or deceleration from a load pull indicates two possibilities—damaged inner or transaxle joint or differential problem(s).

• An inner joint will create a vibration during acceleration due to plunging action hanging up and releasing repeatedly. Probable cause would be foreign particles or lack of lubrication, or improper assembly.

• Remember that tires, suspension, engine, and exhaust system are all up front to add their noises.

• Make a check with front wheels elevated off ground. Spin the wheels by hand to determine if wheel bearing could be noisy or if out of round tires are causing vibration. Many wheel bearings are prelubed and sealed at the factory.

CAUTION

Personal injury can occur from spinning wheels by engine power. Spinning a wheel at excess speed may cause damage to CV-joints that could be operating at angles too steep when wheels are allowed to hang. Over speeding might also cause damage to tires and the differential.

SHAFT REMOVAL

1. Remove the hub nut and discard it.
2. Drain the lubricant from the transaxle. Remove the differential cover (Chrysler only).

CAUTION

The lubricant may be hot.

3. The speedometer pinion gear assembly must be removed before the right drive shaft can be removed. (Automatic transaxles only).
4. Rotate the driveshaft to view the circlip.
5. Compress the circlip tangs with needle nose pliers as you pry into the side gear. This compresses the circlip in position for shaft removal later. Keep an awl between the differential pinion shaft and the end face of the shaft to prevent circlip reentry to the groove.

NOTE: This applies to Chrysler cars only.

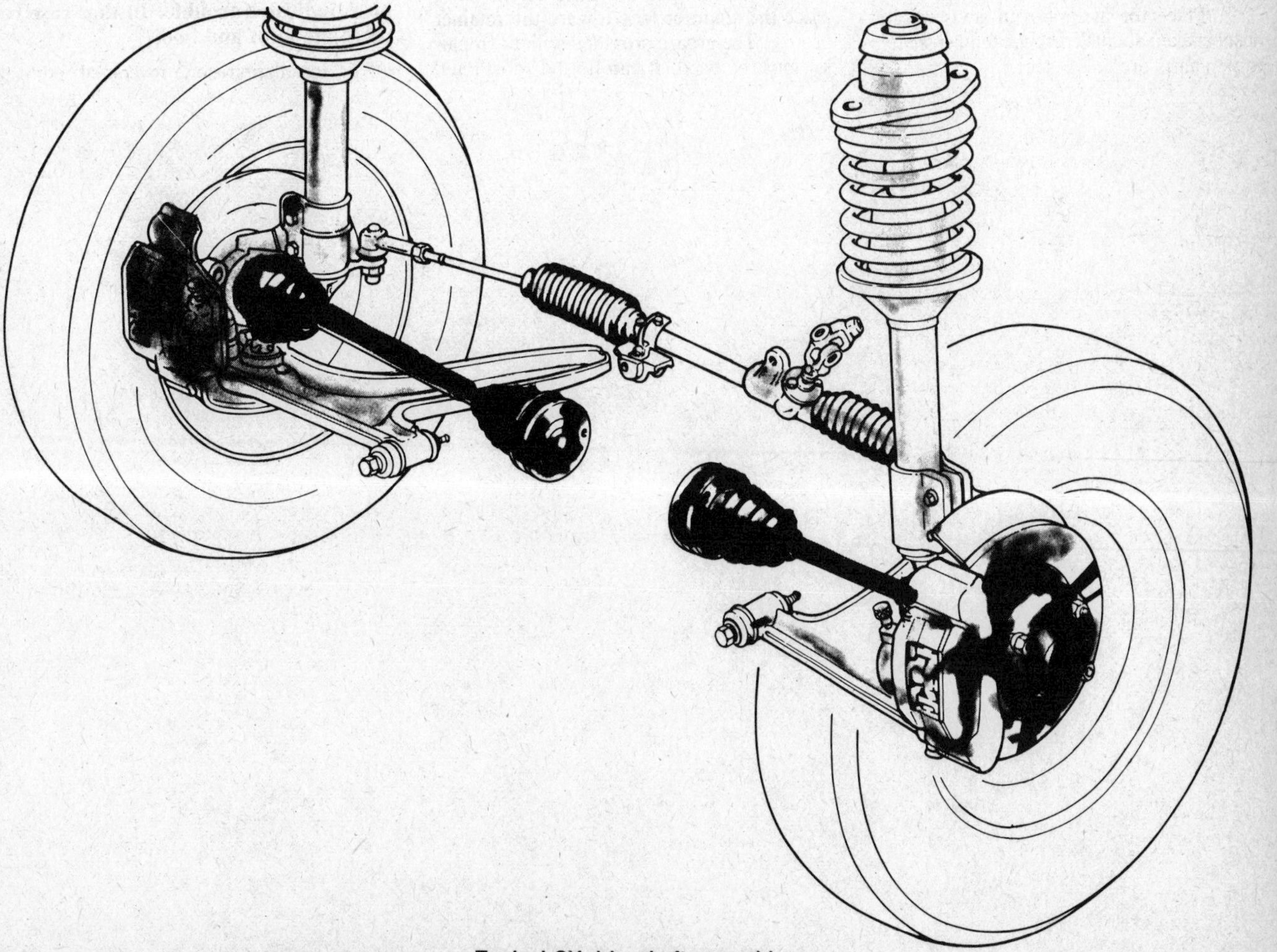

Typical CV driveshaft assembly

Tripode Types CV Driveshaft

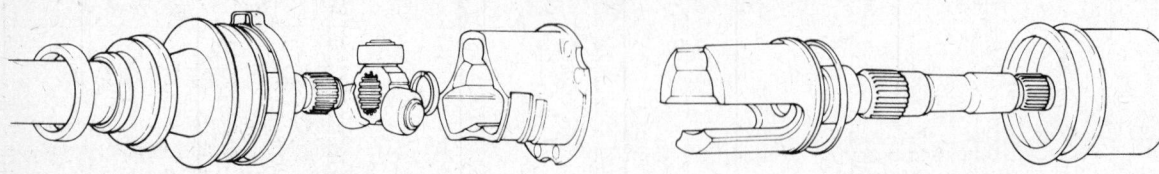

Closed tulip plunging CV–joint   **Open tulip plunging CV–joint**

6. Remove the ball joint clamp bolt. Drop the lower arm too allow clearance. This will permit the front wheel to swing free.

7. Pull the outer splined shaft from the wheel hub, when swinging wheel hub away. Do not pull on the shaft. Grasp the joint housing.

8. Remove the inner joint by pulling outward on the inner joint housing. Do not pull the shaft.

NOTE: Do not allow the assembly to hang at either end. This can jam the CV-joint and cause vibration during operation. If necessary, support the shaft at either end by rope or wire.

INNER JOINT/BOOT

9. Place the assembly in a vise. Care must be taken not the crush the tubular shafts. Some shafts are solid steel.

10. If the inner joint needs replacement, cut the small rubber clamp, large metal clamp, and remove the rubber boot. These items must be discarded.

11. Inspect for internal wear and/or damage.

12. Clean the grease by hand from inside the joint housing and around the 3 ball trunnion assembly to inspect. Mark the tripod and housing for proper reassembly, if it is to be reinstalled.

13. To replace the boot, CV-joint, or both, remove the snap ring from the groove and tap the trunnion lightly with a brass drift pin. Leave the tripode bearings on the trunnion. Care must be taken to support the bearings as they may fall off.

14. Installation is the reverse of removal with the following recommendations.
When reinstalling the tripode on the shaft place the chamfer face toward the retainer groove. The grease provided with the repair kit must be used. It can not be substituted

with any other type grease.

OUTER JOINT/BOOT

1. Place the shaft in a vise. Be careful not to over tighten the vise thereby damaging the shaft.

2. Remove the boot and clamps. Discard these parts.

3. Using a soft hammer rap sharply on the housing. This forces the inner race over the internal circlip. Never remove the slinger from the housing.

4. Remove and discard the circlip. A new one is included with the boot kit. Leave the lock ring in place.

NOTE: Never disassemble the cage and balls from the housing. Reuse the joint assembly with a new boot kit, unless the grease is contaminated and prior diagnosis indicated trouble. In that case replace the joint and boot.

5. Installation is the reverse of removal.

Gauges and Indicators

There are various systems used to indicate values of heat, pressure, vacuum, current flow, and fuel supply. The following are the more popular systems used.

Bourdon Tube

This gauge consists of a flattened tube that is bent to form a curve. The curve tends to straighten under internal pressure caused by engine oil pressure. The curved tube is geared or linked to an indicator needle which may be read on a calibrated scale.

Bourdon tube oil pressure gauges are used on some Corvettes and the optional instrument panels on some Chevrolet sport models. This type of gauge may be easily distinguished from the electrical type by the small copper or nylon tube running from the gauge to the engine.

Bi-Metallic or Thermal

This gauge is activated by the difference in the expansion factors of a bi-metal bar. A sending unit, consisting of a variable resistance conductor, influences current flow to a voltage limiter, or directly to a heating element coiled around a bi-metal bar in the gauge. A bi-metallic gauge pointer will move slowly to its gauging position.

Magnetic

In this system, the indicator needle is moved by changing the balance between the magnetic pull of two coils built in the gauge. When the ignition switch is in the "off" position, the pointer may rest any place on the gauge dial. Balance is controlled by the action of a sending unit or a tank unit containing a rheostat, the value of which varies with temperature, pressure or movement of a float arm. A magnetic gauge will snap to its position when turned on.

Vacuum Gauges

The gauge operates by monitoring engine

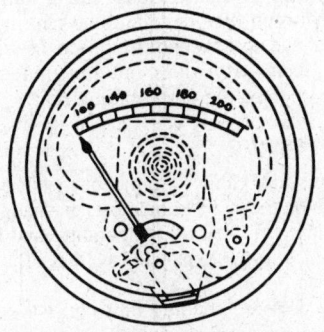

Bourdon tube gauge

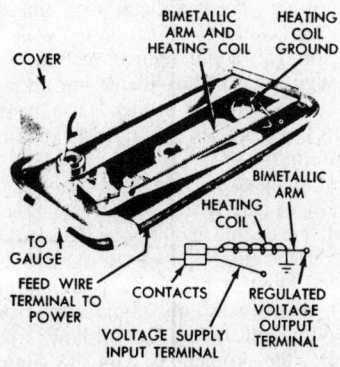

Constant voltage regulator

vacuum. High engine vacuum draws the needle to the high side of the gauge against internal spring tension. As engine vacuum decreases, the spring tension overcomes the vacuum pull and the needle moves to the low side of the gauge.

Warning Lights

This system is quite popular and may be used to indicate heat, low pressure or as a battery discharge indicator. General Motors uses a two-light temperature indicator version of this unit in some models.

Electronic Instruments

These systems use vacuum fluorescent displays to replace the conventional indicator needle type gauge. Typical instrumentation of this type is used for the chronometer, odometer, speedometer, temperature, and fuel gauges. These systems vary, and both digital and graphic displays are used. They are often connected to a microcomputer and used to "call up" additional information. Display information may be shown in English or Metric.

SECTION 1
BOURDON TUBE

Oil Pressure

The gauge is the pressure expansion type and is activated by oil pressure developed by the oil pump, acting directly on the mechanism of the gauge. The gauge is connected by a small tube to the main oil passage in the engine oiling system. This design registers the full pressure of the oil pump.

TESTING

A gauge pointer that flutters is usually an indicator that oil has entered the gauge tube. The tube should contain trapped air to cushion the pulsations of the oil pump and relief valve. Oil can work up into the gauge lines as a result of a gauge or tube leak or improper installation. To correct this condition, renew the unit or correct the leak; then, with the gauge line disconnected at both ends, blow the line clear. Connect line at gauge first and then at the engine.

If the gauge reads too low or reads no pressure, test for a possible obstruction by disconnecting the line at the gauge. Hold the end of the line over an empty container, then start the engine. After a few bubbles, oil should flow steadily.

If oil does not flow satisfactorily, first make sure that the oil level is correct and that the oil pump is functioning. Should the engine oil system be operating correctly, the problem is either with the gauge or the line. Check the line for kinks, leaks, or blockage which would prevent oil from reaching the gauge. If the line is unobstructed, remove the gauge unit from the instrument panel. Check to make sure that the hole leading to the Bourdon tube is clear and be sure that the lever linkage and pointer gears operate freely. If none of these points is at fault, the Bourdon tube itself is defective and the gauge must be replaced.

SECTION 2
BI-METAL

Fuel

Bi-metal or thermal type gauges operate on the principle of constant applied voltage and are sensitive only to changes originating at the sending unit.

The fuel gauge system consists of a sending unit, located in the fuel tank, and a registering unit mounted in the instrument cluster. The sending unit is a rheostat that varies its resistance depending on the amount of fuel in the tank.

TESTING THE DASH GAUGE

— **CAUTION** —

Gauge systems using constant voltage regulators should not be grounded while testing. An excess of 5 volts is likely to burn out the unit.

To safely test this type of voltage regulated system:

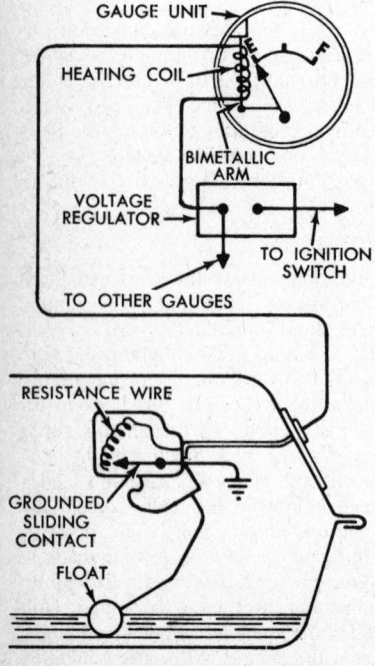

Bi-metallic fuel gauge system

1. Have the ignition switch in the "off" position.

2. Connect the terminals of four, series-connected. D-type flashlight batteries (total of six volts) to the terminals of the gauge to be tested. Three volts should cause the gauge to read approximately half-scale.

If the gauge reads half-full and was not working properly before, the sending unit in the tank is probably defective.

If the gauge is inaccurate or does not register, replace it.

If both the fuel gauge and temperature gauge are in error, in the same manner, the constant voltage regulator is probably at fault.

While working under the dash, be careful not to ground any of the gauges. A full flow of current through the regulator to ground is likely to burn out the regulator.

TESTING THE SENDING UNIT

If the dash gauge test shows that unit to be satisfactory, the sending unit or gauge system wiring is faulty. Substitute a jumper wire between the gauge and the tank unit. If the gauge now functions, replace the wire. If the gauge still does not function correctly, replace the tank sending unit.

Oil Pressure

Oil pressure gauges of the bi-metal type operate on the same principle as gas gauges. They are activated by temperature and the difference in the expansion factors of a bi-metal bar.

The pressure sending unit consists of a pressure-activated variable resistor. This sealed unit is usually screwed into the engine oil pressure circuit. As pressure is applied to one side of a diaphragm, linkage advances a contact arm across the coils of a resistor. This action reduces resistance in the gauge circuit, thus increasing current flow and heat to the bi-metal arm in the gauge. The gauge is calibrated to read oil pressure in psi.

Run the engine and have an assistant watch the dash gauge. If the gauge reads zero, turn off the engine and remove the sending unit from the engine block. Restart the engine and allow it to idle for a minute. If there is oil pressure, oil should surge from the sending unit hole. If no oil flows from the hole, the problem is with the engine lubricating system. If oil flows, the fault lies with the sending unit, the wiring, or the dash gauge.

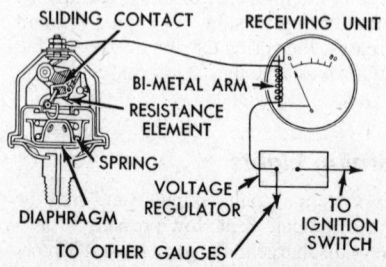

Bi-metallic oil gauge circuit

Check the gauge by grounding the connecting wire for an instant with the ignition switch turned on. A good gauge will go to the top of its scale.

— **CAUTION** —

Grounding the connecting wire for any longer than a moment will damage the dash units.

If the gauge did not move when grounded, check the wiring to the dash unit for continuity. If the wiring is not faulty and the gauge doesn't register when grounded, replace the gauge. If the gauge functions when grounded, replace the sending unit.

Temperature

The temperature gauge consists of a sending unit, mounted in the cylinder head or block, and a remote resistor unit (temperature gauge) mounted on the instrument panel. The principle of operation is essentially the same as the bi-metallic fuel gauge, the exception being that the resistance of the sending unit is influenced by engine temperature instead of tank fuel level, as with the fuel gauge.

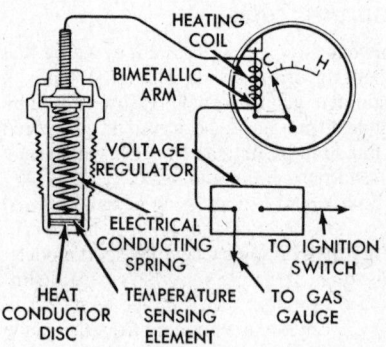

Bi-metallic temperature gauge circuit

The temperature sending unit is constructed with a coil spring and sensing disc. Current passing through this coil encounters increased resistance, proportional to an increase in temperature. The gauge registers this resistance change and is calibrated to indicate the temperature.

TESTING THE DASH GAUGE

Connect four D-cells (total of 6 volts) in series with the dash gauge, with the ignition switched off. A good gauge will register ½ on the scale. Replace the gauge if it does not move.

TESTING THE SENDING UNIT

Bring the engine to normal operating temperature (check with a thermometer). If the gauge doesn't register, disconnect the connecting wire from the engine sending unit and ground the connecting wire for an instant and have an assistant observe the gauge.

— **CAUTION** —

Grounding the wire for any longer than a moment will damage the dash units.

If the gauge shows no reading, replace the connecting wire. If the gauge registers when grounded, replace the sending unit.

SECTION 3
MAGNETIC

Fuel

The magnetic fuel gauge consists of two units, the dash unit and the sending unit in the fuel tank. One terminal of the dash unit is connected to the ignition switch so that the system is active only when the ignition is on. With the ignition off, the pointer may come to rest at any position on the dial.

The gauge pointer is moved by varying the magnetic pull of two coils in the unit. The magnetic pull is controlled by the action of the tank unit which contains a variable rheostat, the value of which varies with movement of a float and arm.

When the ignition switch is on and the tank unit arm is in the full position, the current flow to ground is through the resistor, battery coil and the ground coil. Because the ground coil has more windings than the battery coil, it builds up a stronger magnetic field and the pointer is pulled to the full position.

When the tank unit arm is in the empty position, the current flow is through the resistor, the battery coil and the wire to ground at the tank unit. The pointer is thus pulled to the empty position. The resistor in series with the battery coil balances resistance between the two coils in the dash unit.

TESTING THE DASH GAUGE

Disconnect the wire from the tank unit. Using a tank unit of known accuracy, clip a test wire from the body of the test unit to ground. Clip another test wire from the connector of the test unit to the tank unit wire. With the ignition on, moving the float arm through its entire range should cause the gauge to respond proportionally. If the dash gauge does not correspond to the movement of the test unit and the wiring to the gauge is OK, the dash unit is bad.

TESTING THE TANK UNIT

If tests indicate that the trouble lies in the tank unit, remove the unit and check for mechanical failure. The unit may have either a ruptured or binding float.

An electrical check for circuit continuity may be made throughout the unit's range.

Temperature

The temperature gauge system consists of a magnetic dash unit and a resistance-type sending unit screwed into the water jacket of the cylinder head or the engine block.

The dash unit has two magnetic poles. One of the windings is connected to the ignition switch and ground. This electromagnet exerts a steady pull to hold the gauge pointer to the left or "cold" position when the ignition is on.

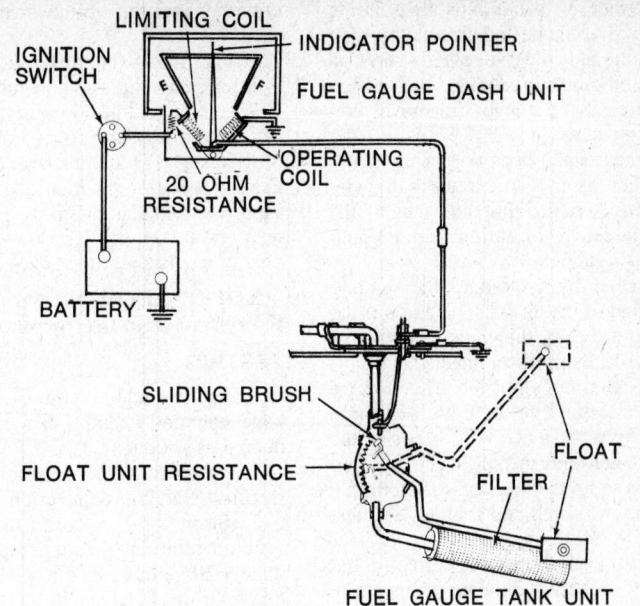

Magnetic fuel gauge circuit

The other winding in the dash unit connects to a ground through the engine sending unit. This electromagnet exerts a steady pull on the gauge pointer toward the right, or "hot" side of the gauge. The strength of this pull is dependent upon the current allowed to pass through the engine unit (sending unit) resistor.

The sending unit, located in the engine cooling system, contains a flat disc (thermistor) that changes resistance as its temperature varies.

NOTE: This sending unit, while similar in appearance, is different and is not interchangeable with the unit used in systems using bi-metal or thermal dash gauges. The resistance of the thermistor disc is maximum when the temperature is cold and minimum when hot. The decrease in resistance allows more current to flow through the electromagnet connected to the engine unit. The resulting increase in magnetic pull causes the gauge pointer to move to the right, or "hot" side.

TESTS

1. Disconnect the wire at the sending unit and turn on the ignition switch. The gauge hand should stay against the cold side stop pin.

2. Ground the wire disconnected from the sending unit. With the ignition switch still on, the gauge hand should swing across the dial to the hot stop pin.

CORRECTIVE MEASURES

If the gauge hand does not stay to the left, either the wire is grounded between the dash unit and the engine unit or the dash unit is defective.

Test further by disconnecting the sending unit wire at the gauge. Turn on the ignition. If the gauge hand stays on the left-hand stop pin, replace the disconnected wire. If the gauge still moves, replace the gauge.

If the gauge hand does not swing across the dial, there is an open circuit in the wire between the sending unit and gauge, the gauge is defective, or current is not reaching the dash gauge.

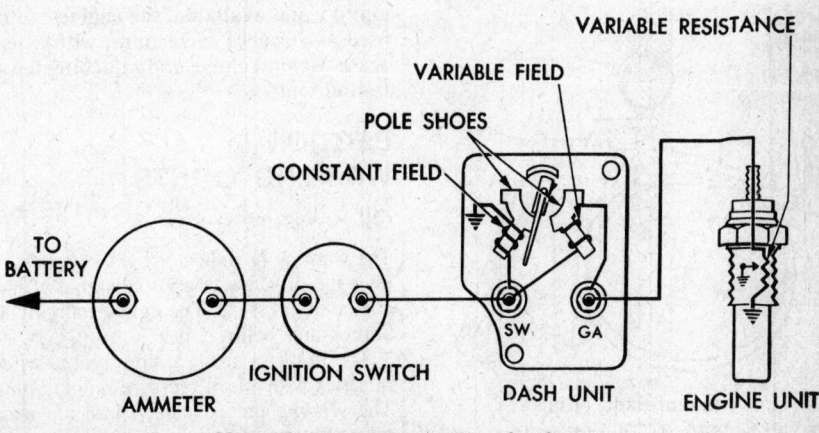

Magnetic temperature gauge circuit

Test further by grounding the sending unit terminal of the dash gauge and turning on the ignition. If the gauge hand stays on the left-hand stop pin, replace the disconnected wire. If the gauge still moves, replace the gauge.

If the gauge hand does not swing across the dial, there is an open circuit in the wire between the sending unit and gauge, the gauge is defective, or current is not reaching the dash gauge.

Test further by grounding the sending unit terminal of the dash gauge and turning on the ignition. If the gauge hand now moves, replace the disconnected wire. If the gauge hand does not move, connect a test lamp into the circuit. If the test lamp does not light, test the wire between the ignition switch and the dash unit by connecting the lamp to the accessory terminal at the ignition switch and ground. The test lamp should light.

If the gauge hand operates correctly, but the gauge does not indicate temperature correctly, either the sending unit is defective or the dash gauge is out of calibration. Replace sending unit with one of known accuracy. If gauge reading is still incorrect, replace the gauge.

If the gauge hand is at maximum at all times, and tests 1 and 2 indicate that the wiring and the dash unit are good, the sending unit must be replaced.

If the gauge hand will not move, the dash unit is bad, or incorrectly installed. Correct the installation or replace the gauge.

SECTION 4
VACUUM AND ECONOMY GAUGES

The fuel economy gauge indicates engine manifold vacuum, as a function of throttle position and engine load. The face of the gauge dial is divided into three segments; Poor (low vacuum), Good (normal vacuum for cruise), and Decelerate (high vacuum). Although the gauge is not intended as a close tolerance vacuum indicator, it may be assumed that a gauge reading continuously below the Good band (normal cruise or idle) may mean poor engine performance due to

improper ignition timing or manifold vacuum leakage.

A manifold vacuum pulsation restrictor is inserted in the vacuum tube at the end closest to the manifold vacuum connection. This enables the inside area of the vacuum hose to serve as a small vacuum reservoir, thereby reducing the manifold vacuum pulsations and to also damp the gauge reading restriction against sudden accelerator operation.

NOTE: Some manufacturers do not use the restrictor in the vacuum line.

TESTING

A standard vacuum system test, using a hand operated vacuum test pump, is conducted as follows:

1. Disconnect the vacuum tube at the manifold vacuum connection.

2. Insert the tester into the end of the vacuum tube and hand pump to approximately 20 inches vacuum. Observe the test gauge for loss in vacuum.

   a. If the tester vacuum gauge indicates a loss in vacuum, remove the vacuum tube connector from the threaded vacuum connector on the back of the gauge. Apply a short length of teflon tape around the threads of the vacuum connection and reinstall the vacuum tube connector on the threaded vacuum connection. Recheck the gauge with the hand vacuum pump. If the tester gauge still indicates a loss in vacuum, replace the gauge assembly.

   b. If the vacuum reading remains steady, the vacuum tube and gauge are OK. Check the end of the tube to be sure the pulsation restrictor is installed; then reconnect the manifold vacuum connection.

Connect the vacuum tube of the test pump directly to the economy gauge tube connector. Pump the tester to approximately 20 inches vacuum and observe the tester gauge for a loss in vacuum.

If the tester gauge indicates a loss in vacuum, replace the economy gauge assembly.

If the tester gauge reading remains steady, the hose to the engine manifold vacuum port must be repaired or replaced.

NOTE: If a hand operated vacuum pump is not available, the engine can be used as a source of vacuum, with a separate vacuum gauge and attaching tee as testing tools.

SECTION 5
WARNING LIGHTS

Oil Pressure

The warning or indicator light system supplies the driver with a visual signal of low engine oil pressure. The light usually lights at pressures below 5 psi.

The low pressure warning light is wired in series with an oil pressure sending unit. The sending unit is tapped into the main oil gallery and is sensitive to oil pressure.

The unit contains a diaphragm, spring linkage and electrical contacts. When the ignition switch is on, the warning light circuit is energized and the circuit is completed through the closed contacts in the sending unit. When the engine starts, oil pressure will compress the diaphragm, opening the contact points and breaking the circuit.

TESTS

The light should light when the engine is not running and the ignition switch is turned on. If the light does not go on, first substitute a new bulb. If there is still no light, check the wire from the light to the switch. If the wire is not at fault, disconnect the wire at the sending unit and ground it. Replace the sending unit if the light now lights.

Temperature

This system employs a heat sending unit with either one or two sets of contacts. Some systems use a green light to indicate subnormal, and a red light to warn of abnormal heat. The more common system, however, uses a simple make-and-break heat-sensitive sending unit screwed into the engine cooling system, and wired in series with the hot indicator light in the instrument panel.

The two-light system uses a bi-metal element mounted between two signal circuits. Normal operating temperature (somewhere between 120°F. and 250°F.) will cause the bi-metal bar to assume a position of no contact between the low and the high temperature circuit. When the ignition switch is turned on, with a cold engine, the cold (green) circuit is complete. If the engine becomes hot enough to move the bi-metal bar so that it touches the contacts of the hot circuit, the hot (red) light comes on. This hot signal indicates that temperatures are in the area of 250°F. in the sealed cooling system.

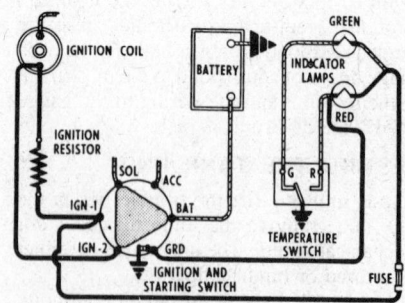

Cold and hot temperature indicator circuit

TESTS

Use the same testing procedure given for oil pressure.

Charge Indicator

A light is used to indicate general charging system operation. When output is below battery potential, a red light is shown. When output is above battery potential, other factors (wiring, voltage regulator, etc.) being

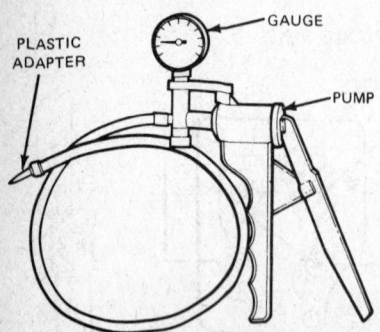

Vacuum hand pump
(© Ford Motor Company)

normal, the light is out.

The charge indicator bulb is connected to the charging circuit, obtaining its ground through the voltage regulator. When the output rises above battery potential, the current flow causes the light to go out.

When an alternator is used, it is necessary to supply a small amount of excitation current to the alternator field, due to the small amount of residual magnetism. Current can be supplied from the battery, through the indicator light, and to the regulator terminal on the alternator. This current has a value of about 12 volts at .25 amperes and will cause the indicator light to come on. Most systems have a resistor in parallel with the bulb to provide excitation if the bulb burns out and to prevent the light from glowing dimly during normal operation.

When the alternator starts to supply current, an output voltage is developed at the regulator terminal. When this voltage exceeds the battery voltage, current will pass from the alternator to the battery and to the system. This current is flowing in the reverse direction of the voltage supplied by the battery. The current flow coming from the alternator exceeds the battery current by a regulated 1 or 2 volts. This is not enough to light the indicator light, therefore, the light will go out when the alternator is supplying sufficient current.

If the alternator output current should drop below battery voltage, current will begin to flow in the opposite direction. If it exceeds 2 or 3 volts, the light will glow indicating that the alternator is not operating properly.

Coolant Level Indicator

Some GM models have a warning light which comes on if the coolant level in the radiator drops below a predetermined level. The coolant level indicator consists of three units; a sending unit which is threaded into the side tank of the radiator, a module which is mounted behind the instrument cluster, and a warning light. As a bulb test, the light is wired so that it comes on when the key is turned to the "START" position.

LIGHT DOESN'T COME ON

Perform the following checks if the warning light won't come on when the key is turned to the "START" position:

1. With the ignition switch in the "ON" position, unfasten the lead from the coolant level sending unit. If the light comes on replace the sending unit.

2. If the light didn't come on in step 1, check the light in the indicator and replace it, if necessary.

3. If the bulb is OK, check the wiring between the sending unit and module, and then between the module and light. If the wiring is not "open," replace the module.

LIGHT WON'T GO OUT

Perform the following checks if the light won't go out when the coolant is at the specified level:

1. Detach the lead from the coolant level

sending unit and ground the lead connector with a jumper wire. Turn the ignition switch to the "ON" position.

2. If the light doesn't come on, replace the sending unit. If the light remains on

disconnect the jumper wire and proceed with the next step.

3. Check for a short in the sending unit-to-module wiring. If there is no short, replace the module.

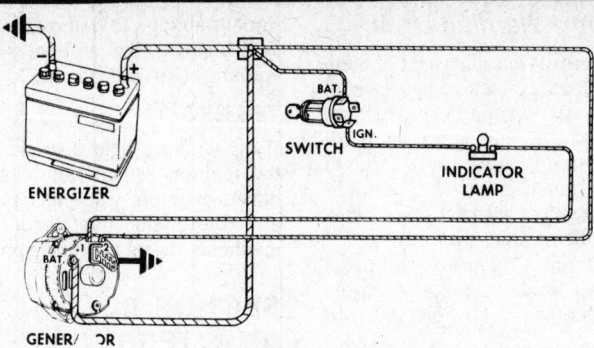

Charging indicator light circuit

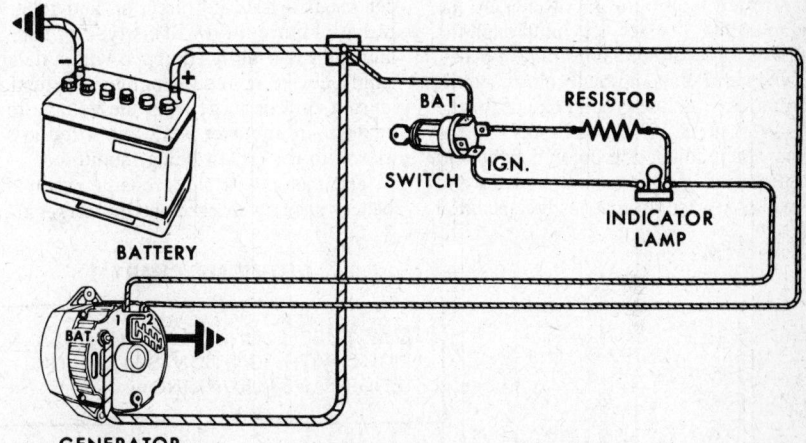

Simplified view of a typical charging system schematic showing the resistor wire in parallel with the charge indicator lamp (© Cadillac Div., G.M. Corp.)

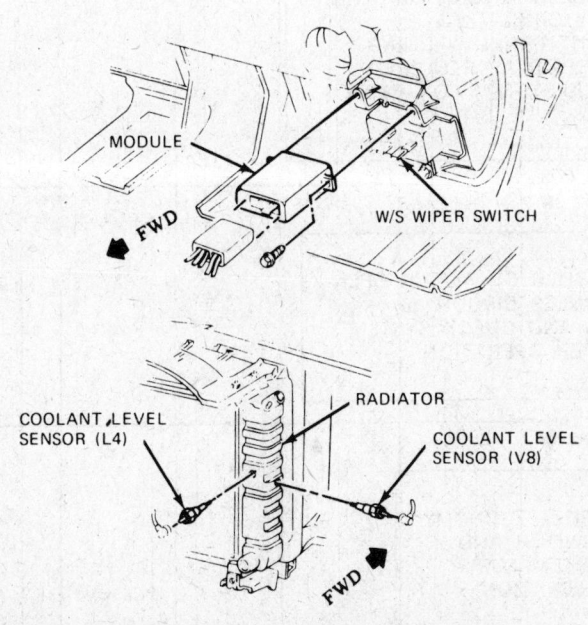

Coolant level sending unit and module

Fuel Economy Warning Light

The fuel economy warning light system consists of a normally closed vacuum switch, an instrument panel warning light, vacuum hose, wire harness, and attaching hardware. Its operation is similar in function to that of the oil pressure (switch type) indicating system, except the switch opens when vacuum is applied, rather than pressure.

A warning light in the instrument panel warns the driver when the engine manifold vacuum has dropped below the specified limit.

Electrical Circuit

The warning light bulb is powered by the ignition switch accessory circuit through the printed circuit board of the instrument panel. The wire harness and normally closed switch assembly provide the ground circuit for the bulb. With the ignition switch ON and the engine not running, the colored light will be illuminated. As the engine is started and the manifold vacuum reaches the specified

limit of about 4 to 6 in. of hg., the vacuum switch opens the ground circuit and the warning light will go out.

TESTING

If the warning light does not operate with the ignition switch on, (engine not running), or if the warning light remains on after the engine has started, refer to the diagnosis charts for repair procedures.

SECTION 6 AMMETERS

The automotive ammeter is a gauge or meter used to indicate direction and relative value of current flow. This type of charge indicator is usually equipped with a dampening device to reduce pointer fluctuation during current surge from the voltage regulator. An ammeter is always wired in series with the circuit being monitored.

The meter will show charge when the battery is being charged and discharge when

the battery is being discharged. It merely gives an indication of the state of charge of the battery, since it shows a relatively high charging rate when the battery is low, and a low charging rate when the battery is near full charge. An ammeter does not give a complete report of battery condition, whereas a voltmeter does. Just after cranking the engine, the meter will swing toward the charge side for a short time, if lights and accessories are turned off. As the energy spent in cranking is restored to the battery, the pointer will gradually move back toward center but should stay on the charge side. If the battery charge is low, however, the indicator will show a high charging rate for an indeterminate length of time.

The ammeter does not show the charging rate of the alternator.

At speeds above 30–35 mph, with all lights and accessories on, the indicator should show a reading somewhere on the charge side, depending on the state of the battery. Above this speed, the indicator should never show a discharge reading; if it does, the

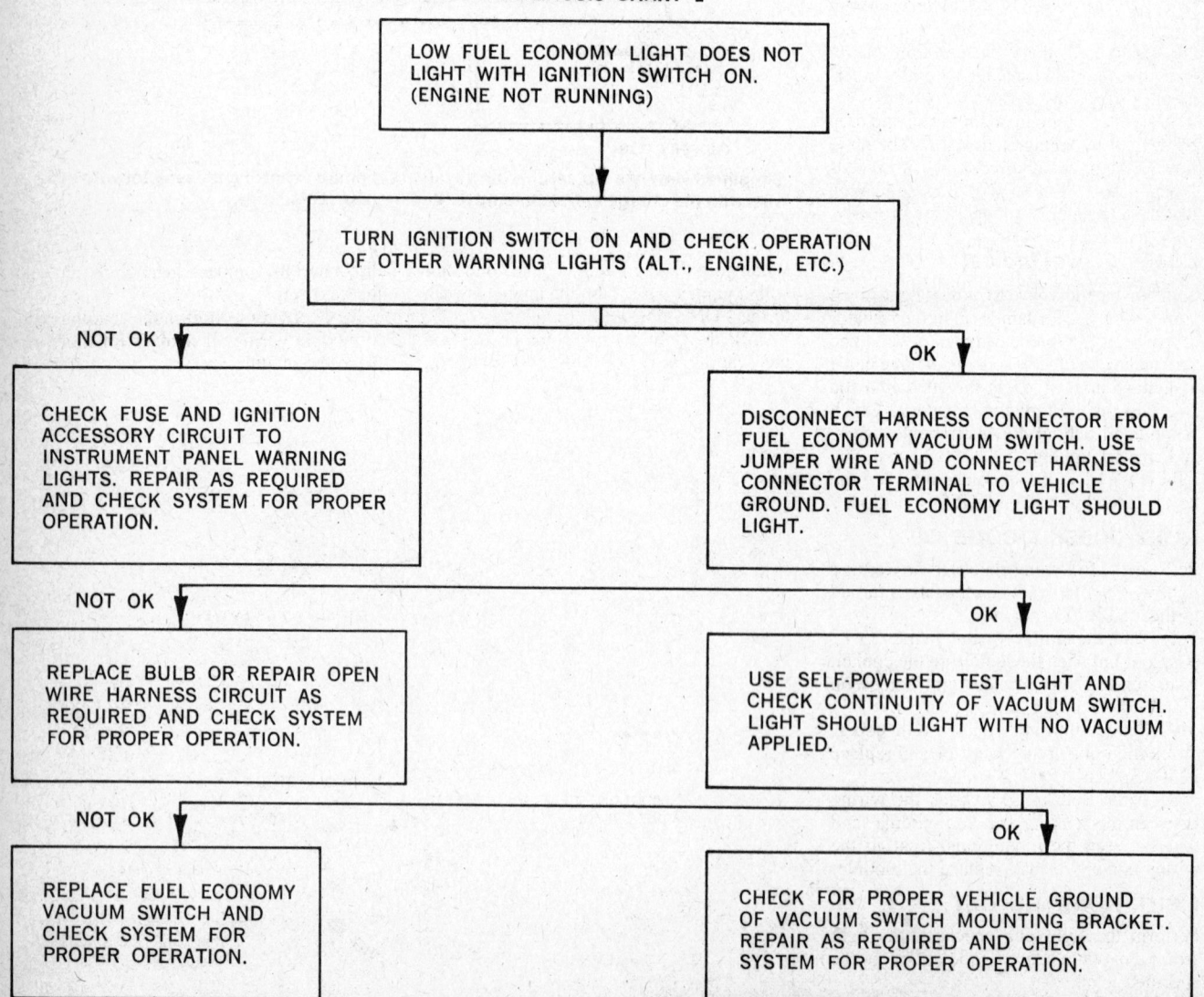

DIAGNOSIS CHART 1

LOW FUEL ECONOMY LIGHT DOES NOT LIGHT WITH IGNITION SWITCH ON. (ENGINE NOT RUNNING)

TURN IGNITION SWITCH ON AND CHECK OPERATION OF OTHER WARNING LIGHTS (ALT., ENGINE, ETC.)

NOT OK

OK

CHECK FUSE AND IGNITION ACCESSORY CIRCUIT TO INSTRUMENT PANEL WARNING LIGHTS. REPAIR AS REQUIRED AND CHECK SYSTEM FOR PROPER OPERATION.

DISCONNECT HARNESS CONNECTOR FROM FUEL ECONOMY VACUUM SWITCH. USE JUMPER WIRE AND CONNECT HARNESS CONNECTOR TERMINAL TO VEHICLE GROUND. FUEL ECONOMY LIGHT SHOULD LIGHT.

NOT OK

OK

REPLACE BULB OR REPAIR OPEN WIRE HARNESS CIRCUIT AS REQUIRED AND CHECK SYSTEM FOR PROPER OPERATION.

USE SELF-POWERED TEST LIGHT AND CHECK CONTINUITY OF VACUUM SWITCH. LIGHT SHOULD LIGHT WITH NO VACUUM APPLIED.

NOT OK

OK

REPLACE FUEL ECONOMY VACUUM SWITCH AND CHECK SYSTEM FOR PROPER OPERATION.

CHECK FOR PROPER VEHICLE GROUND OF VACUUM SWITCH MOUNTING BRACKET. REPAIR AS REQUIRED AND CHECK SYSTEM FOR PROPER OPERATION.

DIAGNOSIS CHART 2

> LOW FUEL ECONOMY LIGHT DOES NOT GO OUT WITH ENGINE RUNNING.

> START ENGINE. ALLOW TO WARM UP AND RUN AT IDLE. FUEL ECONOMY LIGHT SHOULD BE ON.

> IF LOW FUEL ECONOMY LIGHT STAYS ON, DISCONNECT WIRE HARNESS CONNECTOR TO FUEL ECONOMY VACUUM SWITCH. LIGHT SHOULD GO OUT.

NOT OK

> CHECK WIRE HARNESS CIRCUIT FOR GROUND OR SHORT. REPAIR AS REQUIRED AND CHECK SYSTEM FOR PROPER OPERATION.

OK

> CHECK VACUUM HOSE TO VACUUM SWITCH FOR LEAK. PINCHED OR PLUGGED CONDITION.

NOT OK

> REPAIR OR REPLACE VACUUM HOSE AS REQUIRED AND CHECK SYSTEM FOR PROPER OPERATION.

OK

> USE HAND VACUUM PUMP AND CHECK VACUUM SWITCH FOR PROPER OPERATION. REPLACE SWITCH, IF REQUIRED, AND CHECK SYSTEM FOR PROPER OPERATION.

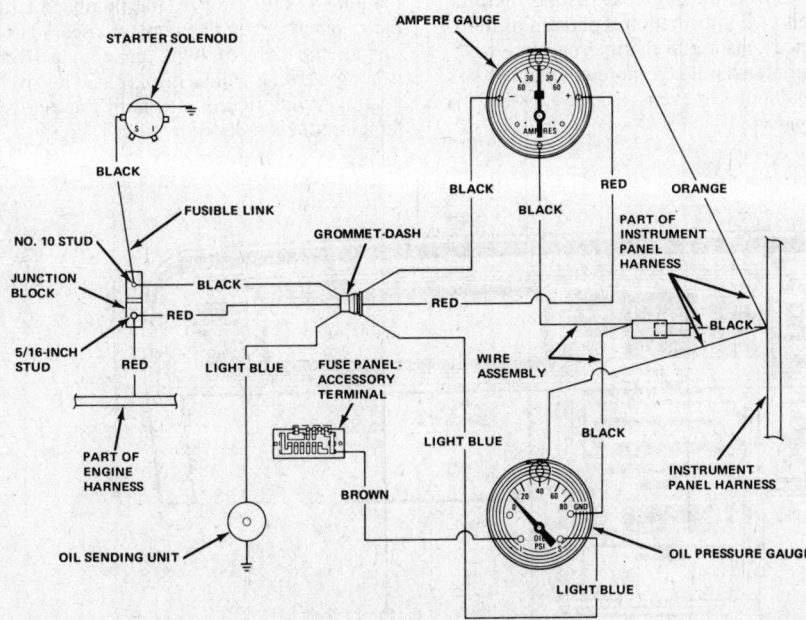

Typical ammeter and oil pressure gauge wiring (© American Motors Corp.)

alternator and regulator should be tested. See "Charging and Starting Systems" for troubleshooting.

SECTION 7
VOLTMETERS

A voltmeter is used on some cars, instead of an ammeter. The voltmeter indicates regulated voltage, which shows the charging system's ability to keep the battery charged. A voltmeter is always wired in parallel with the circuit being monitored. Voltmeter readings that are continuously high or low, may indicate a defective regulator, broken or slipping alternator drivebelt, a faulty alternator, or a defective battery. For testing and service of these items, see "Charging and Starting Systems."

If a faulty voltmeter is suspected, check the voltage regulator output with a test voltmeter of known accuracy (See "Charging and Starting Systems"). If the voltage indicated on the test instrument is within specifications, and disagrees with the car's

AMMETER DIAGNOSIS

```
TURN HEADLAMPS ON (DO NOT START
ENGINE. MAKE SURE LIGHTS ARE ON)
```

AMMETER SHOWS CHARGE	AMMETER NEEDLE DOES NOT MOVE	AMMETER SHOWS DISCHARGE
CONNECTIONS REVERSED ON AMMETER	CHECK AMMETER TERMINALS FOR LOOSE CONNECTIONS	AMMETER OK
	CHECK WIRING AND CONNECTIONS	
	FAULTY AMMETER	

voltmeter reading, replace the car's voltmeter.

SECTION 8
ELECTRONIC
INSTRUMENTS

Electronic Chronometer

Digital chronometers may be capable of displaying the time of day, month, the day of the month, and on some models an elapsed time function is built-in.

Electronic Digital Speedometer

Digital speedometers are as easy to read as a digital clock, with vehicle speed shown clearly in large numbers. On some models a mode selection may be made to display either miles or kilometers per hour.

Electronic Odometer

Vehicle and trip distance, or kilometers and average speed, are available at the touch of a button from the odometer display on some models. All information is derived from the distance sensor and the internal time base. Accumulated mileage stored in the memory is maintained even if the battery is disconnected.

Electonic Fuel Gauge or Display

The electronic fuel gauge is a bar graph with a row of bar segments. The fuel level is indicated by the number of lit bars. The bars individually turn off as the fuel is consumed.

The electronic fuel display on some models offers multiple functions. In addition to fuel remaining in the tank it may also measure fuel comsumption for range, present fuel efficiency, and trip fuel efficiency. Also a mode selection may be made to display either gallons or liters.

Electronic Temperature Gauge

The electronic temperature gauge is a bar graph with a row of bar segments. The temperature is indicated by the number of lit bars. When the engine coolant rises, causing all the bars to light, an engine over heating warning will be displayed. This over heating symbol continues until the engine temperature is reduced to the normal range.

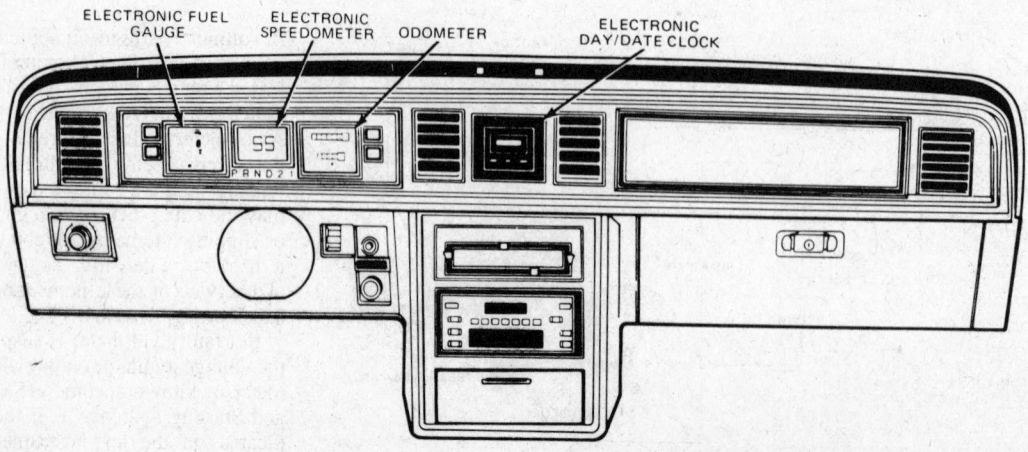

Typical electronic instrument cluster (© Ford Motor Co.)

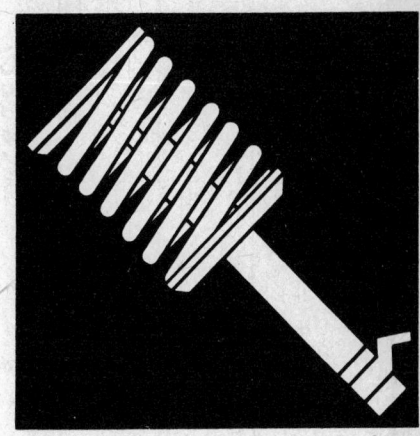

Strut Overhaul

STRUT SERVICE AND REPAIR

MacPherson struts are appearing on the front (and rear) wheels of more and more cars. The strut design takes up less room in the engine compartment, compared to a conventional upper and lower arm with shock absorber arrangement. The trend toward smaller, lighter and more efficient packaging mandates the use of a strut suspension to permit more room for engine accessories and front wheel drive components.

Strut Suspension Design

In a conventional front suspension, the wheel is attached to a spindle, which is in turn, connected to upper and lower control arms through upper and lower ball joints. A coil spring between the control arms (sometimes on top of the upper arm) supports the weight of the vehicle and a shock absorber controls rebound and dampens oscillations.

In a strut type suspension, the strut performs a shock dampening function, like a shock absorber, but unlike a conventional shock absorber, the strut is a structural part of the vehicle's suspension.

The strut assembly usually contains a spring seat to retain the coil spring that supports the vehicle's weight. The shock absorber is built into the body of the strut housing. The strut is normally attached at the bottom to the lower control arm and at the top to the car body. The upper mount usually features a bearing that permits the

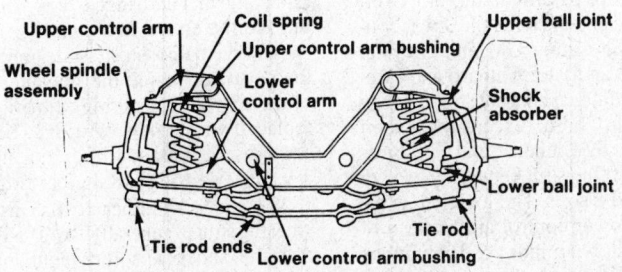

Conventional upper and lower arm suspension

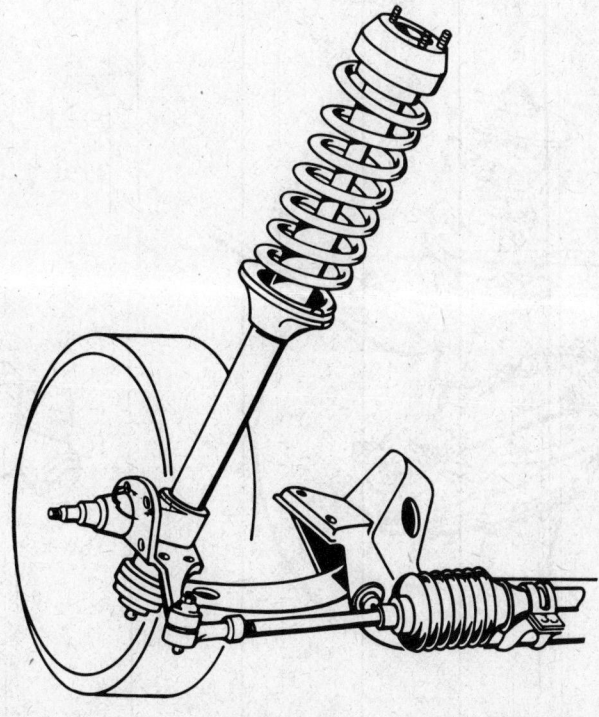

Strut with concentric coil spring (rear wheel drive)

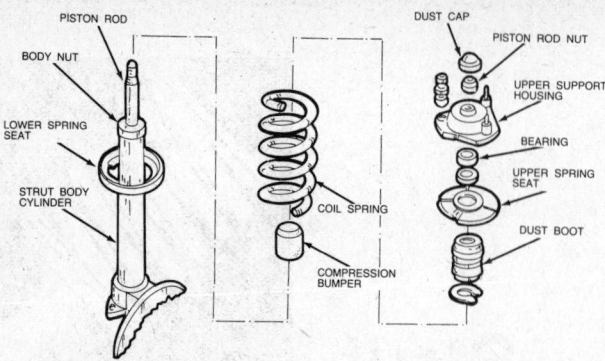

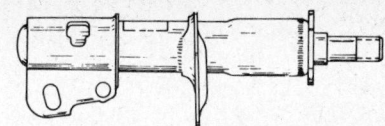

A sealed strut has no body nut and is serviceable by replacement

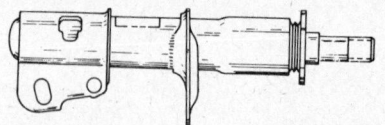

Serviceable struts have a removeable body nut to allow replacement of the strut cartridge

Exploded view of a typical strut

coil spring to rotate as the wheels turn for smoother steering. The entire design eliminates the need for the upper control arm, upper ball joint and many of the conventional suspension bushings. The lower ball joint is no longer a load carrying unit, because it is isolated from the weight of the vehicle.

Domestic struts have taken 2 forms—a concentric coil spring around the strut itself and a spring located between the lower control arm and the frame. GM and Chrysler (except for '82 and later Camaro and Firebird) use the traditional concentric coil spring around the strut. Ford (except the Escort and Lynx) and '82 Camaros and Fire-birds use the spring off the strut between the lower control arm and frame. The location of the spring on the lower control arm instead of on the strut, allows minor road vibrations to be absorbed through the chassis rather than be fed back to the driver through the steering system.

Serviceability

Struts fall into 2 broad categories—serviceable and sealed units. A sealed strut is designed so that the top closure of the strut assembly is permanently sealed. There is no access to the shock absorber cartridge inside the strut housing and no means of replacing the cartridge. It is necessary to replace the entire strut unit.

A serviceable strut is designed so that the cartridge inside the housing, that provides the shock absorbing function, can be replaced with a new cartridge. Serviceable struts use a threaded body nut in place of a sealed cap to retain the cartridge.

The shock absorber device inside a serviceable strut is generally "wet". This means that the shock absorber contains oil that contacts and lubricates the inner wall of the strut body. The oil is sealed inside the strut by the body nut, O-ring and piston rod seal.

Servicing a "wet" strut with the equivalent components involves a thorough cleaning of the inside of the strut body, absolute cleanliness and great care in reassembly.

Cartridge inserts were developed to simplify servicing "wet" struts. The insert is a factory sealed replacement for the strut shock absorber. The replacement cartridge is simply substituted for the original shock absorber cartridge and retained with the body nut, avoiding the near laboratory-like conditions required to service a "wet" strut with "wet" service components.

Most OEM domestic struts are serviced by replacement of the entire unit. There is no strut cartridge to replace. Exceptions to this general rule are the struts used on GM front wheel drive J-cars and A-cars, which feature an internally threaded housing, accessible by removing the OEM cap from the housing. Once the old cartridge is removed, a new cartridge can be threaded

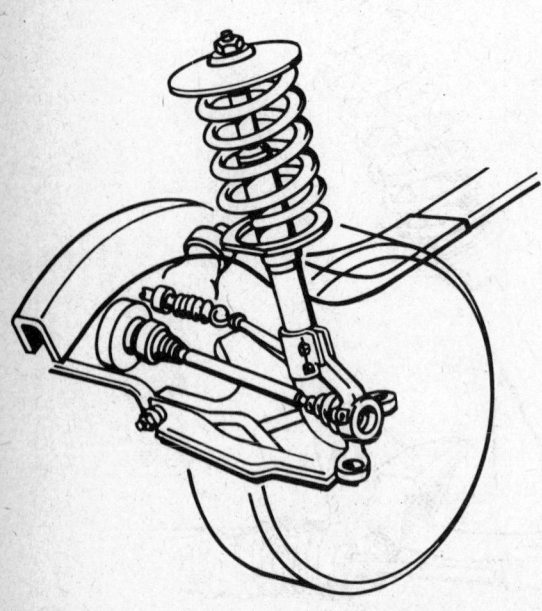

Strut with concentric coil spring (front wheel drive)

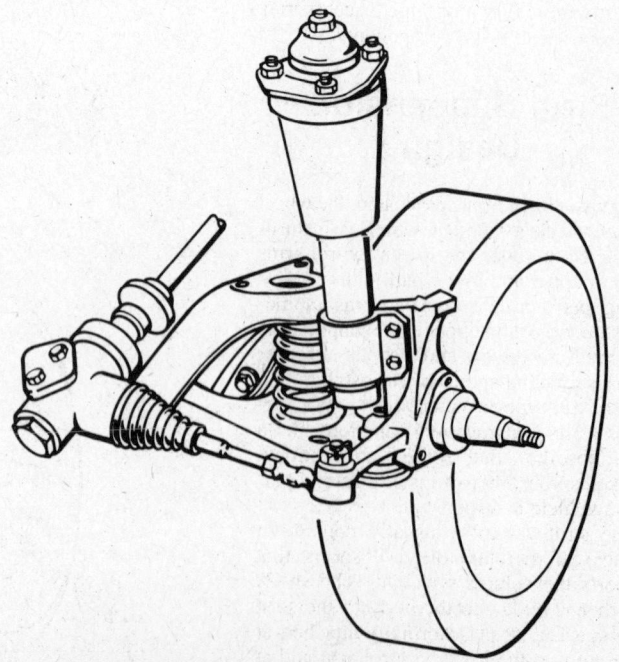

Modified MacPherson strut design with coil spring on the lower arm

into the housing.

Sealed, OEM units can also be serviced by replacement with an aftermarket unit, that will permit future servicing by cartridge replacement.

WHEEL ALIGNMENT

It is not always necessary to re-align the wheels after struts are serviced. If care is taken matchmarking affected components and in reassembling, alignment may be unaffected. However, if wheels were not in proper alignment prior to service, or if the entire strut assembly was replaced, a wheel alignment check should be made. Generally, only camber is adjustable, and then only within a narrow range.

Do not attempt to bend components to correct wheel alignment.

Since the majority of OEM struts are serviced by replacement, most manufacturers recommend wheel alignment following strut replacement.

Tools

Without the right tools, a strut job will take longer than necessary and can be dangerous.

A normal selection of hand tools such as open end and box wrenches, sockets, pliers, screwdrivers and hammers are necessary to work on struts. Extensions and universal joints will help reach tight spots. Be sure to have both metric and inch-sized wrenches on hand. Two big time-savers are "crowsfeet" and ratcheting box wrenches in assorted sizes. Torx fasteners are also showing up more and more in chassis fasteners.

In addition to the normal handtools, some sort of spanner is necessary to remove the body nut on serviceable struts. Sometimes a pipe wrench can be used successfully.

Strut and cartridge replacement requires a spring compressor.

Makeshift tools for compressing coil springs—threaded rod, chains, wire or other methods—should never be used. The coil spring is under tremendous compression and can fly off causing personal injury and damage to equipment. Use only a good quality spring compressor such as described below.

Economy, or manual, spring compressors are the least expensive but more time consuming to use. Angle hooks grasp the spring coils and must be compressed with a wrench. For those who service struts infrequently, this is probably the wisest investment for purchase.

Other manual spring compressors (jaws type) are faster to operate, have a more positive gripping action and can be used on or off the car. These types are probably not cost effective for the do-it-yourselfer, but can be rented from auto supply stores for single-time use.

For volume work, compressors that are pneumatically or hydraulically operated are

MAINTAINING WHEEL ALIGNMENT

The location and method of adjusting wheel alignment determines the components that must be match-marked to maintain wheel alignment. There are 4 basic methods of adjusting wheel alignment. Almost all cars use one of these or a slight variation.

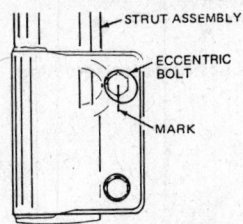

Mark the eccentric (camber adjusting bolt) relative to the clevis mounting bracket.

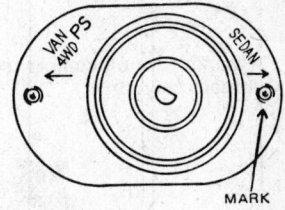

Mark the mounting stud that faces the front of the vehicle. This type of bracket is reversible for varying applications.

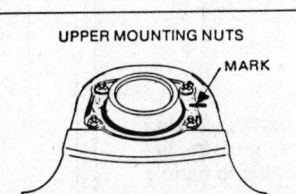

Mark the upper support housing relative to the inner fender before removing the strut from the upper mount.

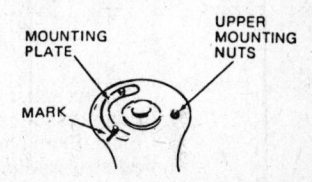

Mark the location of the mounting plate relative to the location on the inner fender.

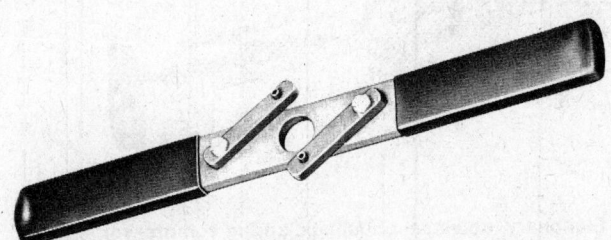

A simple spanner wrench designed for use with body nuts equipped with recessed lugs. A pipe wrench is a frequent substitute

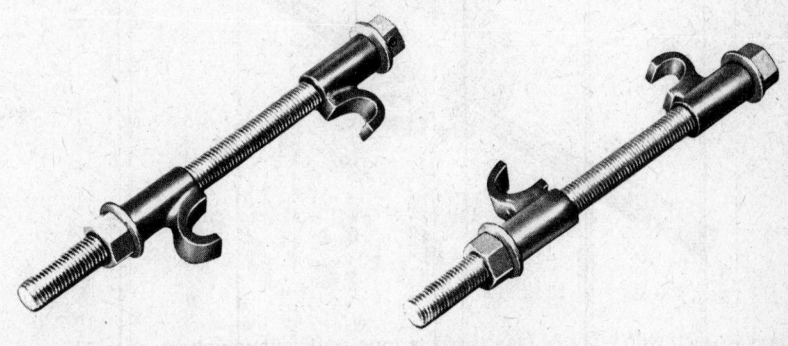

An economical manual spring compressor

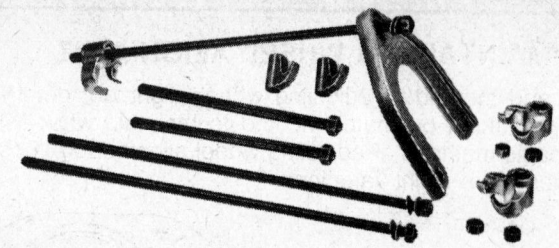

A manual spring compressor with plates or hooks for servicing virtually any strut

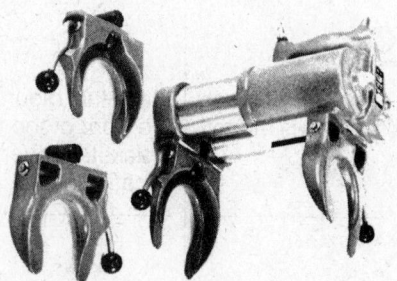

Lightweight, air operated, portable spring compressor can be used on or off the vehicle. Extra shoes are available to handle all strut applications

Stationary, universal pneumatic spring compressor

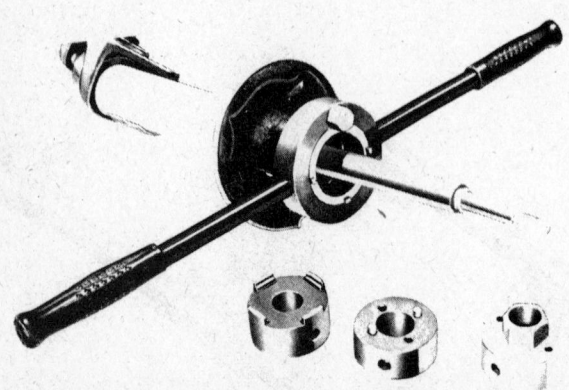

Spanner wrench with adaptor inserts for various applications of body nuts. This type of spanner can be used with a torque wrench for retorqueing the body nut

best. Air operated compressors are suitable for all types of struts (through use of adaptors), are lightweight and can be used on or off the vehicle. Bench mounted hydraulically operated units are probably the safest, but are also the most expensive and require that the strut be removed from the vehicle, which means separating brake lines and other connections which can be time consuming.

There are also universal kits that fit all struts in either the manual or air operated types.

Regardless of what type of spring compressor you're using, GM front wheel drive A-, J-, and X-cars as well as Chrysler Corp. Omni, Horizon and K-cars, require the use of a special spring compressor with self-leveling plates to grasp the spring seats as the spring is compressed. Likewise, the portable, pneumatic units have extra wide shoe sets suitable for these cars. The shoes are also epoxy coated to avoid scratching the coated springs on these models.

GM front wheel drive A-, J- and X-cars also make use of a camber assist tool, that makes camber adjustment a one man job.

A tube cutter is necessary on GM J-cars to cut the welded top from the strut housing for cartridge replacement.

"Jaws" type spring compressor

Spring compressor for GM and Chrysler product applications

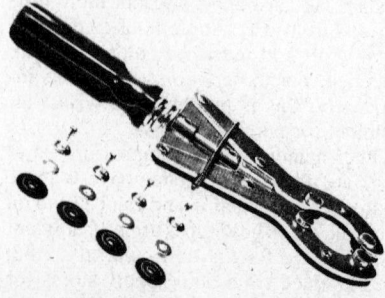

A tube cutter allows opening of the GM J-car struts for cartridge replacement

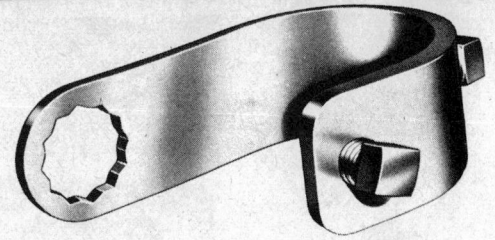

A camber assist tool makes GM cars a one-man job

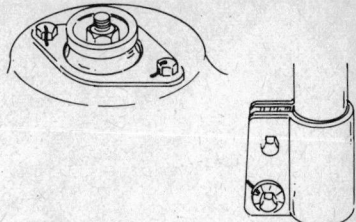

Mark the position of the attachments that control wheel alignment. See Maintaining Wheel Alignment earlier in this section

Repair Tips

1. Make sure you have all the tools you'll need. NEVER IMPROVISE A SPRING COMPRESSOR.

2. Normally both front struts should be repaired or replaced at the same time.

3. The easiest way to work on most struts is to remove the entire unit from the vehicle, unless you have access to an air operated spring compressor. Some struts, however, can, and should, be repaired while installed on the vehicle.

4. Always read the instructions packaged with any replacement parts. In particular, note whether the body nut is supplied new or re-used.

5. Mark the position(s) of any bearing plate nuts or cam bolts to assure proper alignment after installation.

6. Be sure to protect the rubber boot on the drive axle of front wheel drive cars.

7. If necessary to remove the brake caliper, do not let the caliper hang by the brake hose. Suspend the caliper from a wire hook or rope.

8. Be careful in clamping a strut in a vise. Special fixtures are available to hold struts in a vise, but are not necessary if care is used to be sure the housing is not crushed or dented. A block of soft wood on either side of the housing will prevent most damage.

9. Use a spring compressor to relieve tension from the spring. Be sure to clean and lubricate the screw threads, particularly on hand operated (manual) spring compressors.

Some springs have a special coating that should not be scuffed.

10. If you are replacing the strut cartridge, clean the inside of the strut housing and the body nut threads before replacing the oil and installing a new cartridge.

11. Be sure to use OEM quality fasteners any time a fastener is replaced.

STRUT OVERHAUL (OFF-CAR)

Following is a typical overhaul procedure of a serviceable MacPherson strut, after having removed the strut from the vehicle. The vehicle should be firmly supported. If it is necessary, to separate the brake line from the strut for strut removal, the brakes will have to be bled after reinstallation. See the manufacturer's car section for specific MacPherson strut removal and installation procedures.

Photos Courtesy Gabriel Div., Maremont Corp.

Step 1. Examine the strut assembly for damage, dented strut body, spring seat, broken or missing strut mounting parts. Any of these will require replacement of the complete assembly. Also inspect other suspension components for wear or damage

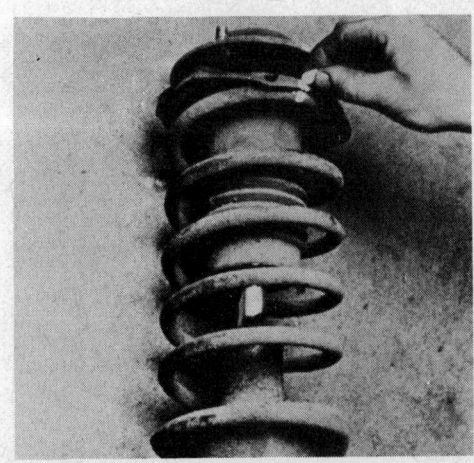

Step 2. Matchmark the upper end of the coil spring and bearing plate to avoid confusion during reassembly

STRUT OVERHAUL

Step 3. To make servicing easier, clamp the strut in a strut vise. The strut vise is designed to clamp the strut tight without damage to strut cylinder. It is very handy for strut work and can be used in your shop vise or mounted to any bench

Step 4. Before using the manual spring compressor, lubricate both sides of the thrust washers and the threads with a light coat of grease

Step 5. Install the compressor hooks on opposite sides of the coil spring with the hooks attached to the upper-most and lower-most spring coils. To avoid possible slippage, use tape or small hose clamps on either side of the compressor hooks

Step 6. Alternately tighten the bolts a few turns at a time until all tension is removed from the spring seat

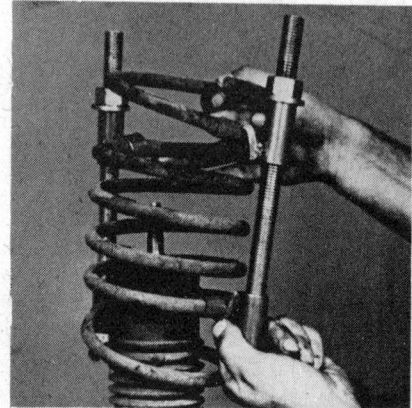

Step 7. Remove the piston rod nut and disassemble the upper mounting parts, keeping them in order for reassembly. Remove the coil spring. There is no need to remove the compressor from the coil spring

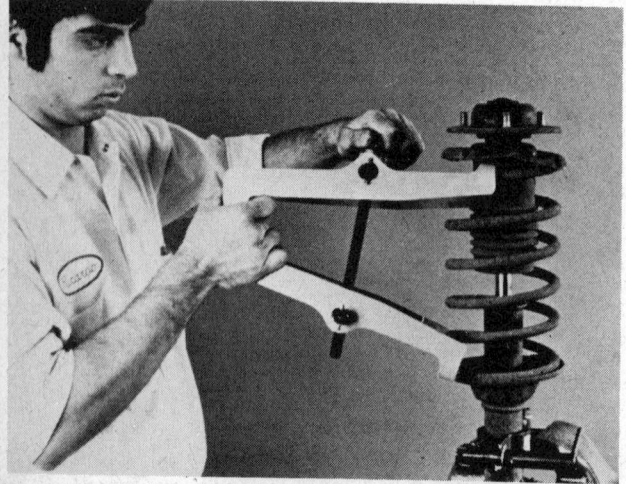

Step 8. An alternative to the manual compressor is the "jaws" type. Turn the load screw to open or close the compressor until the maximum number of spring coils can be engaged

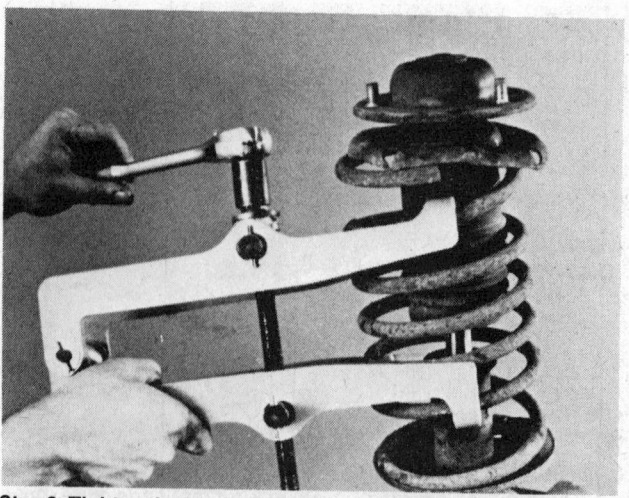

Step 9. Tighten the load screw until the coil spring is loose from the spring seats. There is no need to compress the spring any further

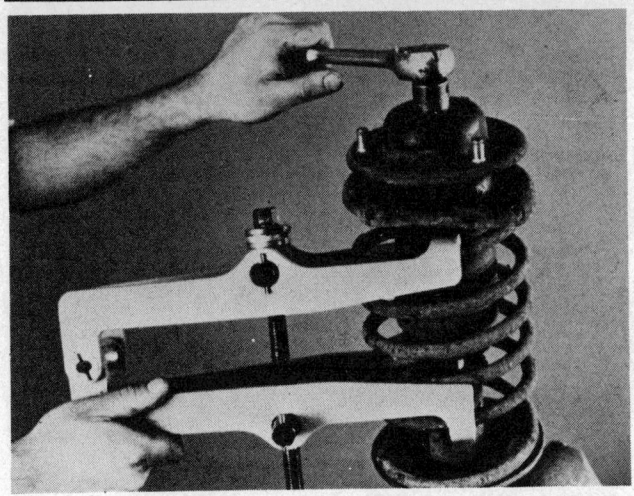

Step 10. Remove the piston rod nut and disassemble the upper mounting parts

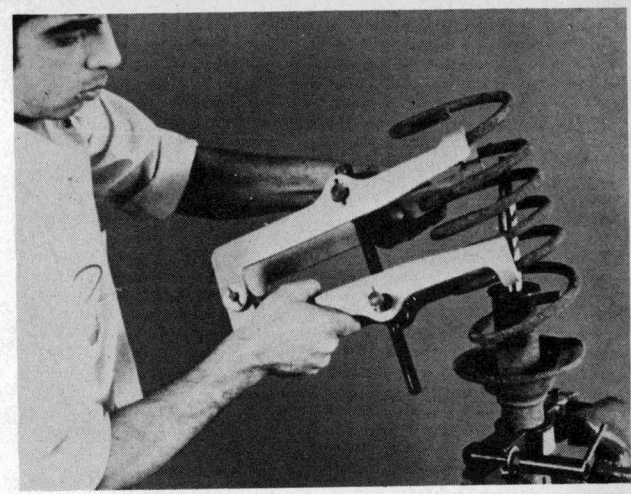

Step 11. Like the manual compressor, there is no need to remove the compressor from the coil spring. Remove the coil spring and compressor

Step 12. Keep the upper mounting parts in order of their removal. They'll be re-assembled in reverse order

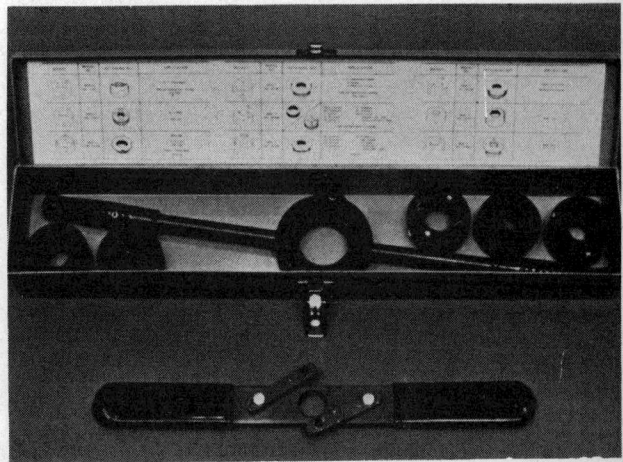

Step 13. A spanner wrench is necessary to remove body nuts, although a pipe wrench will do the job

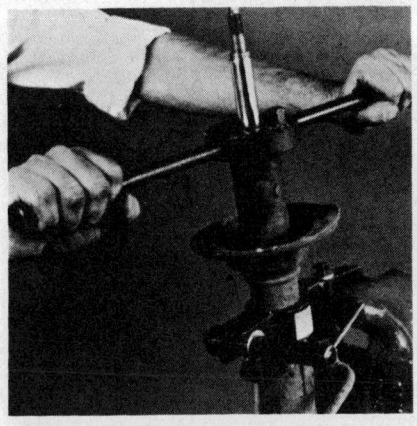

Step 14. Use the spanner wrench or pipe wrench to loosen the body nut

Step 15. Remove the body nut and discard if a new body nut came with the replacement cartridge. If not, save the body nut

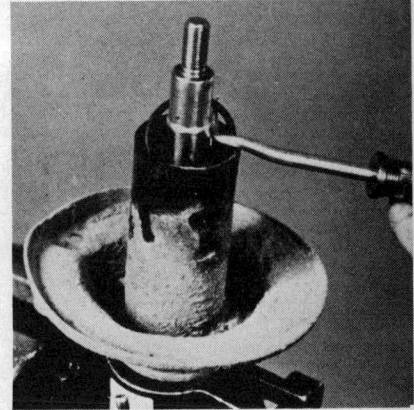

Step 16. Use a scribe or suitable tool to remove the O-ring from the top of the housing

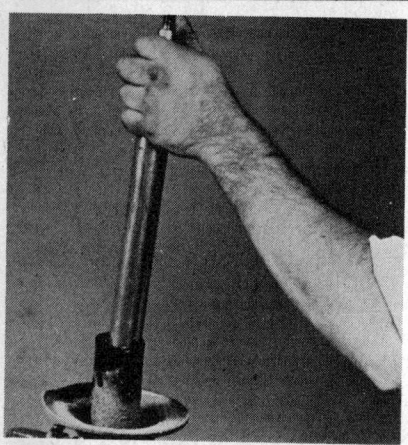

Step 17. Grasp the piston rod and pull cartridge out of the housing. Remove it slowly to avoid splashing oil. Be sure all pieces come out of the housing

Step 18. Pour all of the strut fluid into a suitable container, clean the inside of the strut cylinder, and inspect the cylinder for dents and to insure that all loose parts have been removed from inside of strut body

Step 19. Refill the cylinder with one ounce (a shot glass) of the original oil or fresh oil. The oil helps dissipate internal cartridge heat during operation and results in a cooler running, longer lasting unit. Do not put too much oil in—otherwise the oil may leak at the body nut after it expands when heated

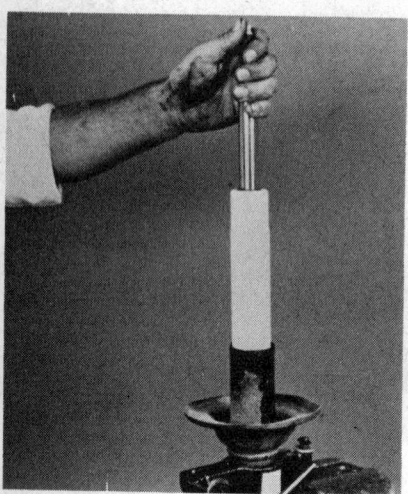

Step 20. Insert the new replacement cartridge into the strut body

Step 21. Push the piston rod *all* the way down, to avoid damage to the piston rod if the spaner wrench slips, and start the body nut by hand. Be sure it is not cross-threaded

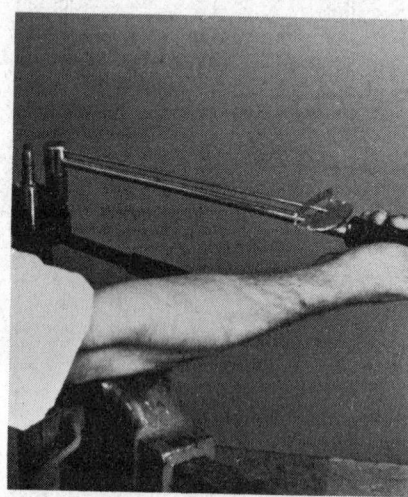

Step 22. Tighten the body nut securely

Step 23. Inspect the loose parts prior to re-assembly. Note the chalk mark location for proper seating of the upper spring seat

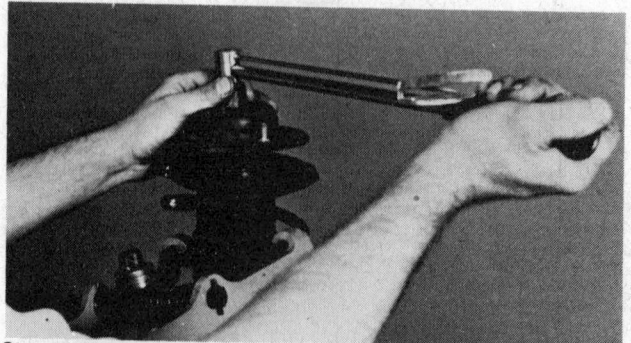

Step 24. Re-assemble the coil spring and upper mounting parts in reverse order. Tighten the piston rod nut and remove the spring compressor. Install the dust cap. Install the strut in the vehicle. See the car section for details

STRUT OVERHAUL

Most domestic car OEM MacPherson struts are sealed units and not repairable. The exceptions are GM front wheel drive A- and J-cars, which use replaceable cartridges. All other cars must use aftermarket struts to be serviceable at a future date. The following procedures cover disassembly of the strut, installation of a serviceable strut, reassembly and cartridge replacement on GM front wheel drive A- and J-models. Consult the applicable manufacturer's car section for removal and installation procedures.

Photos Courtesy Gabriel Div., Maremont Corp.

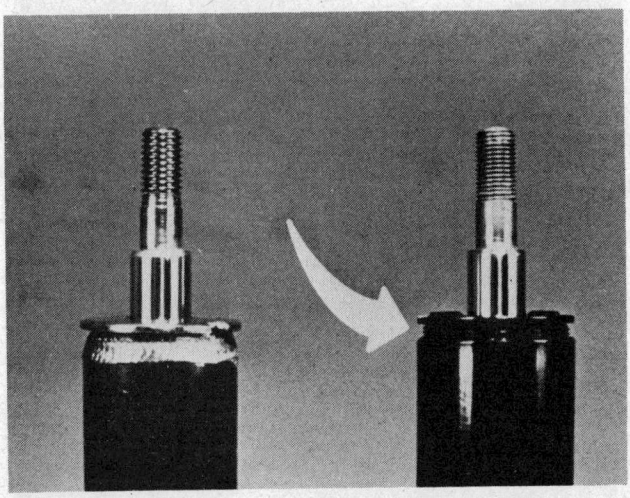

Step 1. Most domestic cars are serviced initially by replacing the entire strut rather than by using a replacement cartridge. This is necessary because the original equipment struts are sealed shut and cannot be serviced with a replacement cartridge. After-market struts are designed with serviceable threaded body nuts which means they can be serviced in the future by installing a replacement cartridge, using normal cartridge service methods, rather than by replacing the entire strut

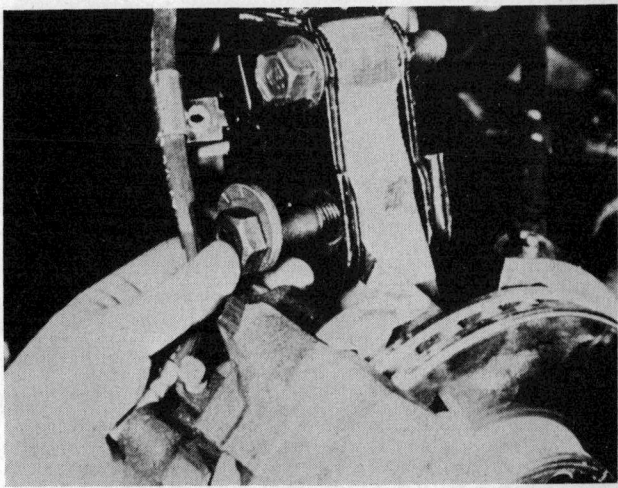

Step 2. An X-car is shown, but the lower mount on the Citation is typical of many vehicles. They all have two bolt clevis mounts and the position of the strut determines the camber adjustment. This means that if you are replacing a sealed strut, front end alignment is necessary because the original alignment is eliminated when you change the strut. If the car has a serviceable strut, you can retain the alignment by marking the position of the mounting bolt relative to the strut. GM has made a running change on the lower mount of their X-Car. The earlier type had an eccentric bolt for camber adjustment. Camber on the latest type is adjusted by pushing or pulling on the wheel with the bolts loosened slightly, but the eccentric can be installed on later cars

Step 3. A special type spring compressor is required for the GM cars and Chrysler K and L cars. A compressor should be used that does not damage the protective coating on the coil spring. Virtually any compressor can be used on other car lines/models

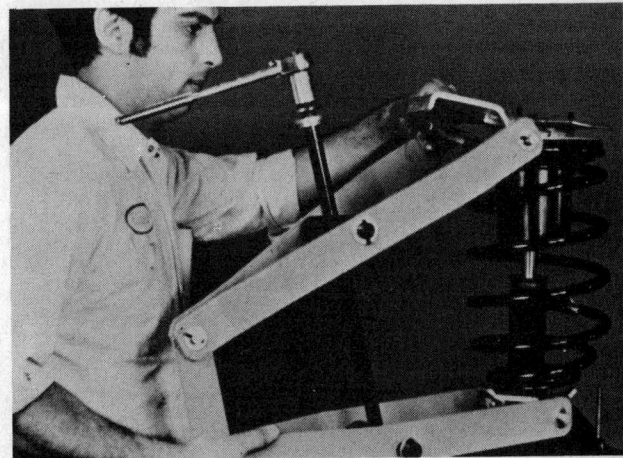

Step 4. Secure the strut in the strut vise; turn the load screw counter-clockwise until the lower plate can be fitted under the lower spring seat and the upper plate can be fitted between the upper spring seat and support housing

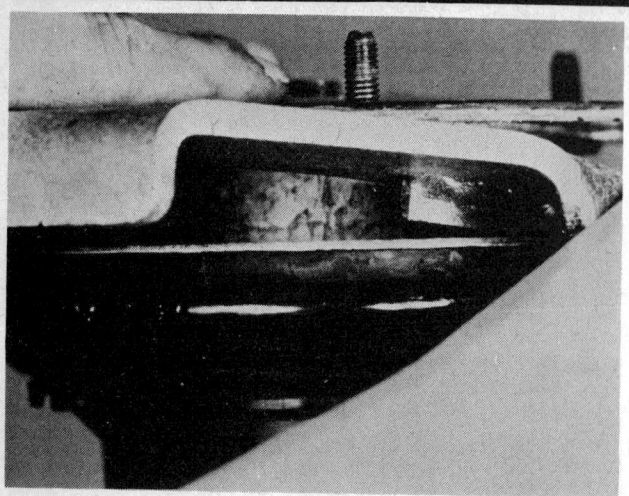

Step 5. Make sure that the crescent shaped bars on the upper compression plate are located inside the upper spring seat

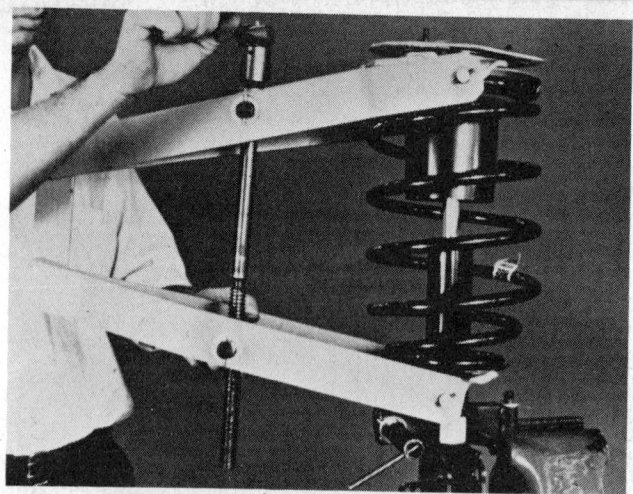

Step 6. Turn the load screw clockwise enough to tighten the compression plates on the spring seats. Stop and make sure that the coil spring will not arch, and that the pivot points are aligned with the center-line of the coil spring

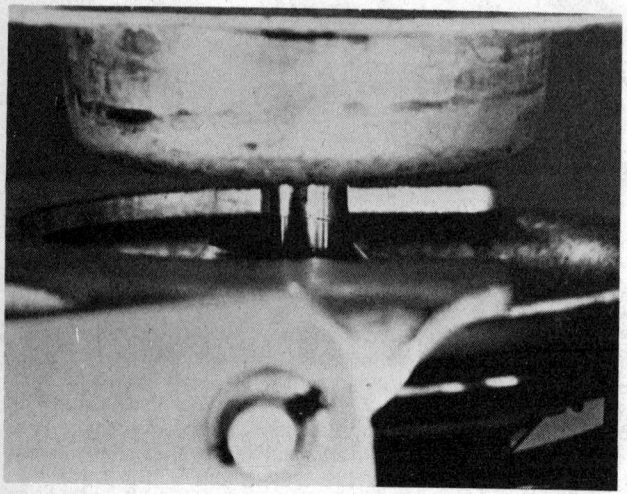

Step 7. Continue to tighten the load screw until the upper support housing can be pulled up to expose about ½ inch of piston rod. This assures that the spring load has been removed from upper spring seat

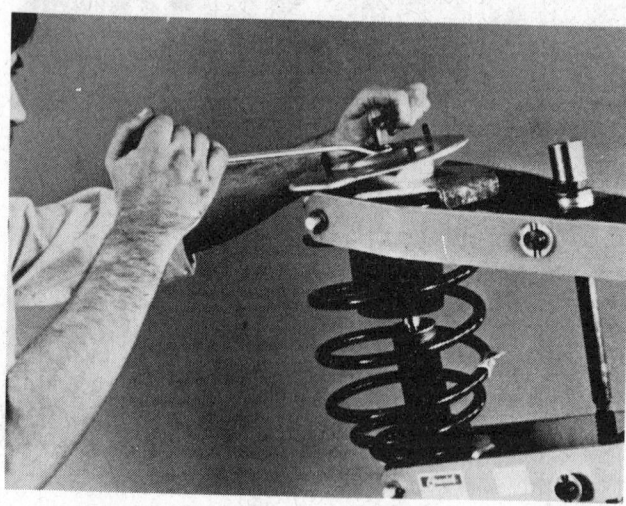

Step 8. Remove the piston rod nut with the aid of a wrench to keep the piston rod from turning and remove upper support housing

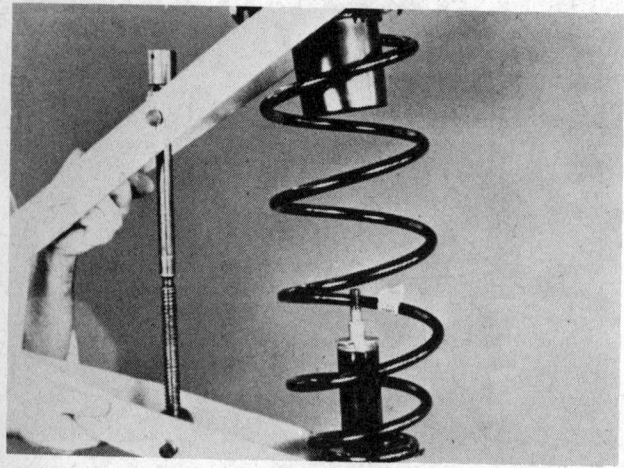

Step 9. Turn the load screw counter-clockwise until the spring tension is completely relieved. Remove the compressor, coil spring and upper support housing from the strut.

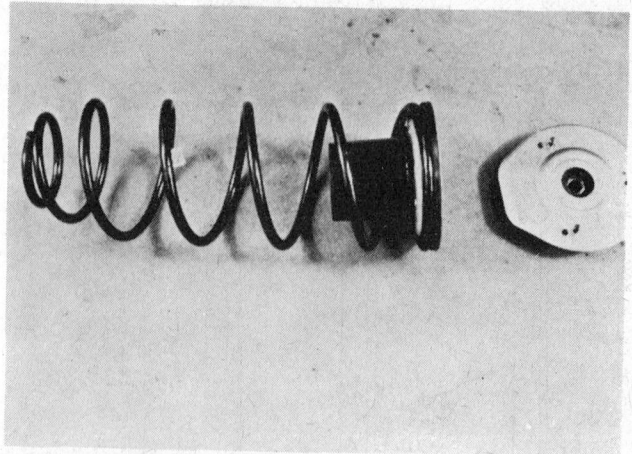

Step 10 Assemble the upper mounting parts in order of their removal. They'll be re-assembled in reverse order

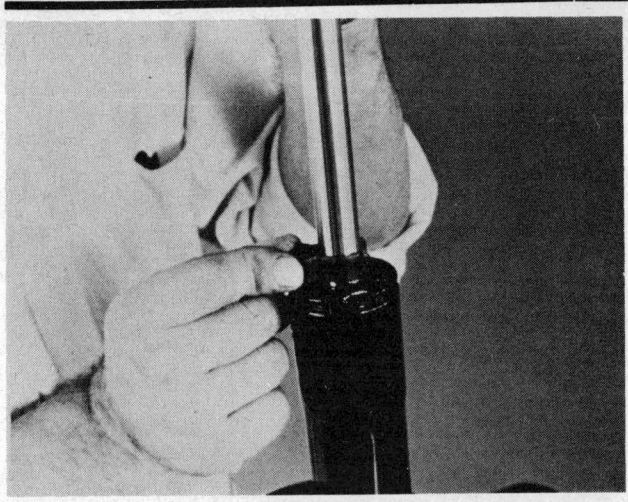

Step 11. Place the new strut in the vise and extend piston rod fully and install clip (spring type clothes pin will do) as shown. This keeps the piston rod extended while assembling the spring and upper mounting parts.

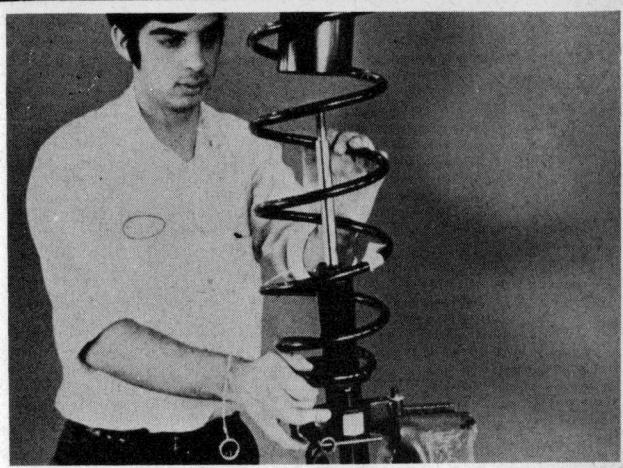

Step 12. Install the coil spring and upper spring seat on the new strut

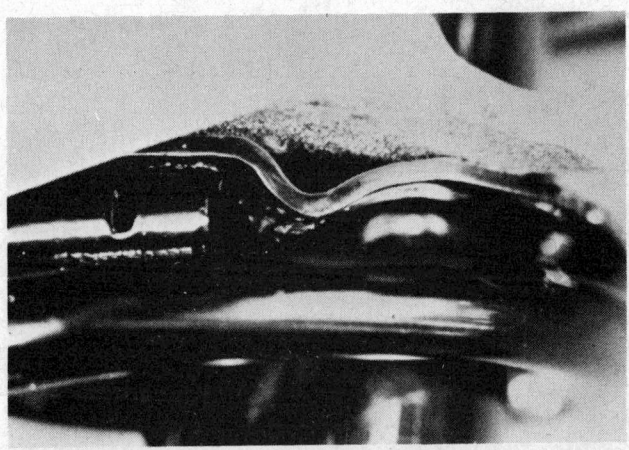

Step 13. Make sure that the spring helix is aligned with the lower spring seat

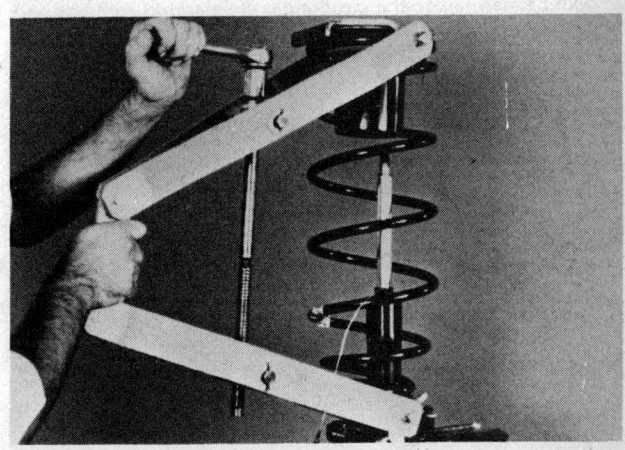

Step 14. Locate upper and lower compression plates on spring seat

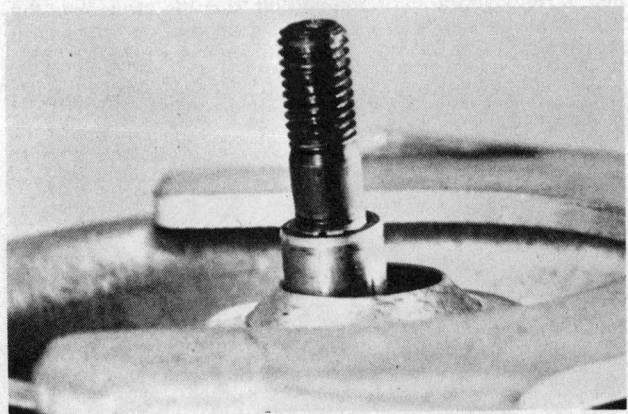

Step 15. Make sure that the crescent shaped bars on the upper compression plate are located on the upper spring seat as shown. Turn the load screw clockwise enough to tighten the compression plates on the upper and lower spring seats. Stop. Again, to assure that the coil spring will not arch, make sure that the pivot points are aligned with the centerline of the coil spring. Then continue turning the load screw clockwise until about 1½ inches of piston rod is showing above the upper spring seat

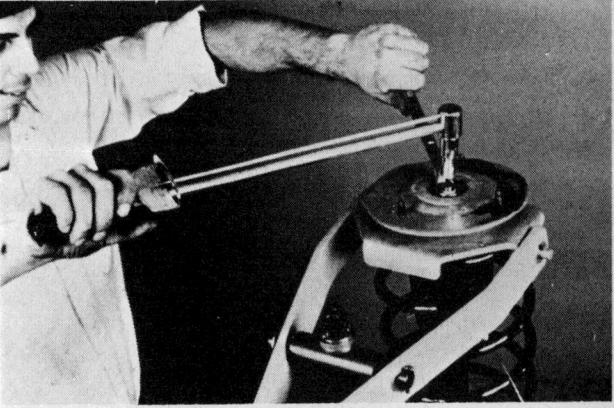

Step 16. Install upper support housing on piston rod. Tighten the piston rod nut and remove the compressor from the strut and the strut from the vise. Install the strut. See the car section for details

GM J- AND A-CARS ONLY

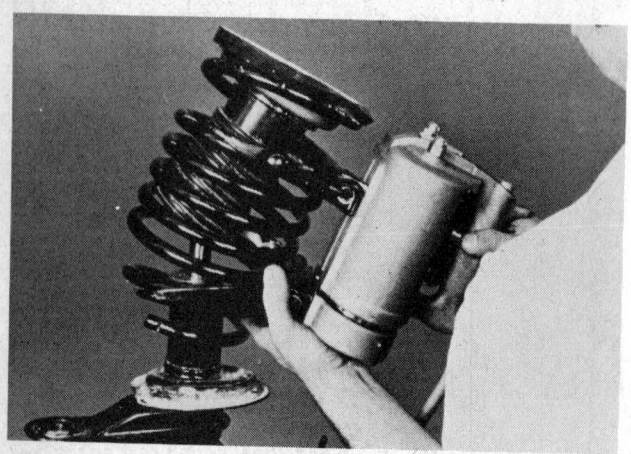

Step 1. Place the strut assembly in a vise, and compress the coil spring. Remove the piston rod, upper support housing, spring seat and coil spring. If the universal pneumatic spring compressor is used, an adaptor provided with the compressor should be fastened to the strut under the steering arm. The ears of the adaptor should be aligned with steering arm. The adaptor provides a square seating surface for the strut while it is being compressed

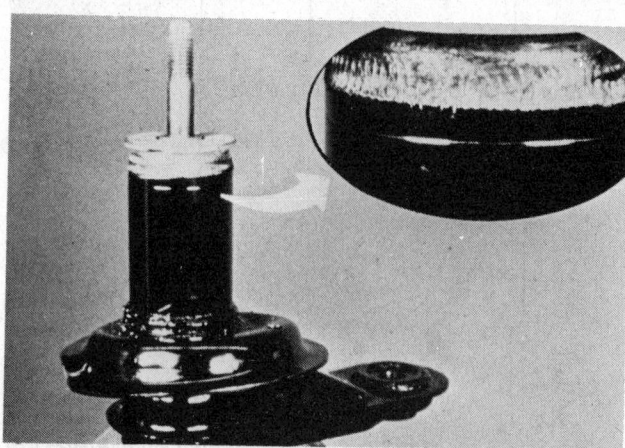

Step 2. J and A–car struts have a welded upper closure, but the strut is designed so the damping mechanism can be replaced with a cartridge insert. Just below the spin weld there is a cut-line scribed in the strut body

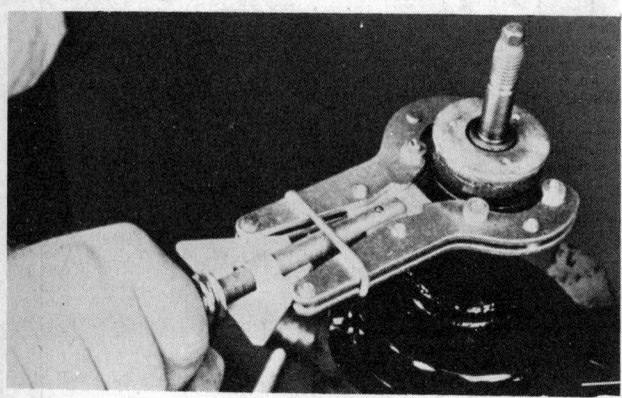

Step 3. Using a pipe cutter, cut open the strut body at the scribed line. (Note: *It is important that the cut be made on the cut-line*)

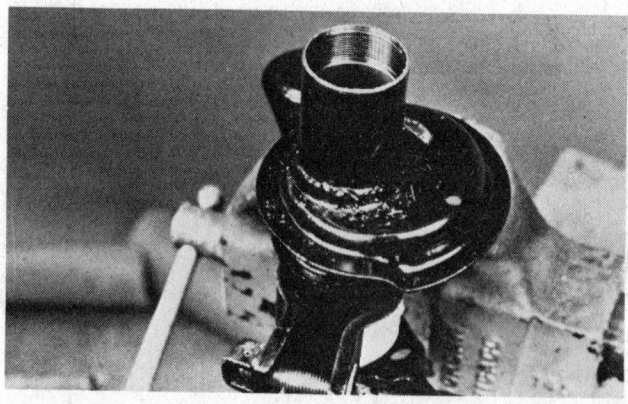

Step 4. Remove the cartridge and oil from the strut. Note the threads on the inside of the strut. Deburr the top of the strut body if necessary

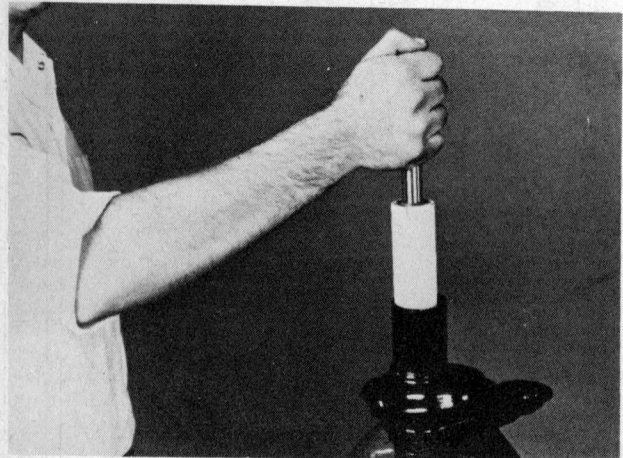

Step 5. Pour about one ounce of oil into the strut body and insert the replacement cartridge. Push the piston rod down and start the body nut by hand. Tighten the nut securely

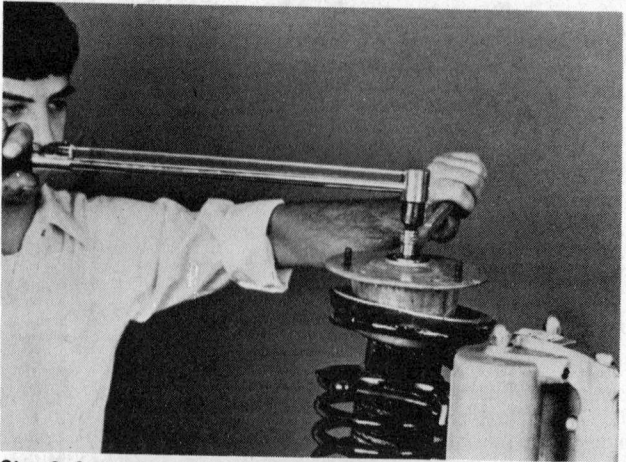

Step 6. Assemble spring, upper spring seat, and upper support housing on the strut, and tighten the new piston rod nut. The renewed strut is now ready to install on the vehicle. Release the spring tension

— MACPHERSON STRUT PROBLEM DIAGNOSIS —

Problems with MacPherson struts generally fall into 3 main categories: suspension, tire wear and steering. In general, the symptoms encountered are not significantly different from those encountered on conventional suspensions.

Suspension

Sag

Vehicle "sag" is a visible tilt of the car from one side to the other or one end to the other while parked on a level surface.

Weak or damaged strut springs could cause this condition and should be repaired immediately.

Sag will also cause steering and tire wear problems to be more pronounced and vehicle instability on rough roads. Front wheel alignment will not solve the problem.

Weak strut springs increase vehicle sag. See "Tire Cupping".

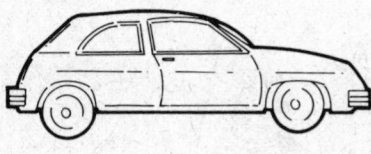

Cartridge Leaks

Strut cartridge leaks (not seepage) indicate the need for cartridge or strut replacement. Be sure the leakage is coming from the strut, and not from elsewhere on the vehicle.

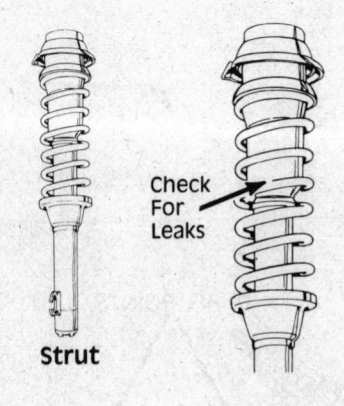

Check For Leaks

Strut

Abnormal Tire Wear

Wear on One Side

One sided tire wear indicates incorrect camber. Check the causes in the accompanying illustration and be sure the wheel alignment is correct.

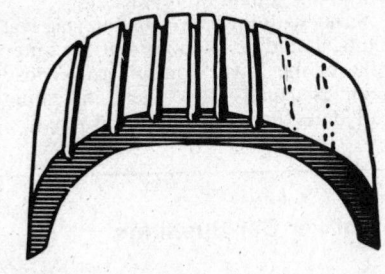

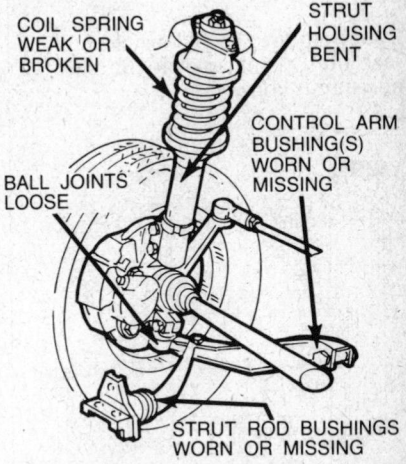

COIL SPRING WEAK OR BROKEN

STRUT HOUSING BENT

CONTROL ARM BUSHING(S) WORN OR MISSING

BALL JOINTS LOOSE

STRUT ROD BUSHINGS WORN OR MISSING

Tire "Cupping"

Cupped tires indicate any or all of the following problems.

1. A weak strut cartridge can be verified by bouncing each corner of the car vigorously and letting go. The car should not bounce more than once, if the shock absorber cartridges are good.
2. Weak strut springs allow sag to increase with only a slight amount of downward pressure. A visual inspection will reveal any broken springs or shiny spots.
3. Check for loose or worn wheel bearings with the weight of the car off of the wheel.
4. Check the wheel balance.

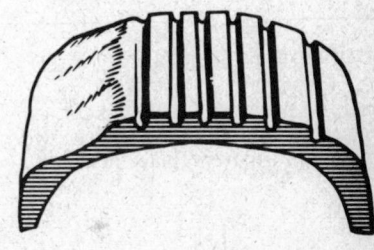

Tread Edge Wear

Wear along tread edges (feathering) indicates a suspension or steering system problem.

1. Strut rod bushings are worn or missing.
2. Tie rod end wear can be determined by grabbing the tie rod end firmly and forcing it up, down or sideways to check for lost motion.

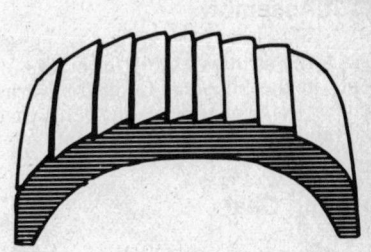

MACPHERSON STRUT PROBLEM DIAGNOSIS

Problems with MacPherson struts generally fall into 3 main categories: suspension, tire wear and steering. In general, the symptoms encountered are not significantly different from those encountered on conventional suspensions.

Tires

Both front tires should match and both rear tires should match. Be sure air pressure is correct.

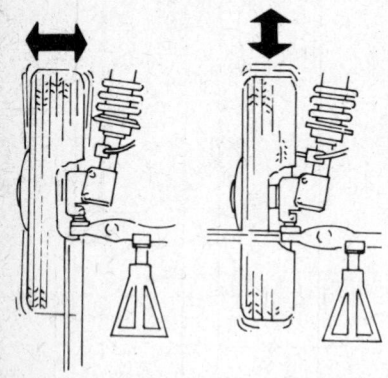

Strut Rod Bushings

Grasp the strut rod and shake it. Any noticeable play indicates excessive wear and need for parts replacement.

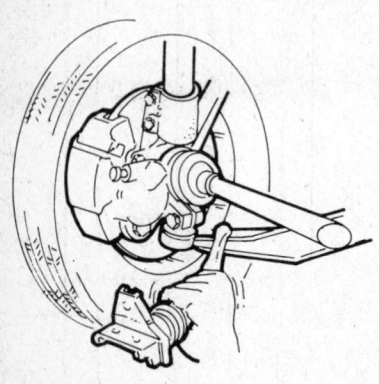

Steering

Ball Joints

Support the car under the frame or crossmember so that the jack does not interfere with the control arm. Rock the tire in and out and up and down. Excessive movement means that both ball joints should be replaced.

Struts with lower weight-carrying ball joints should be supported at the outer edge of the lower control arm. These vehicles usually have wear indicating ball joints that can be checked visually.

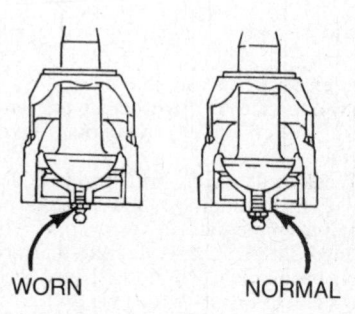

WORN   NORMAL

Stabilizer Bar Bushings

Check for worn bushings or lost motion with the vehicle level and the weight evenly distributed on all wheels.

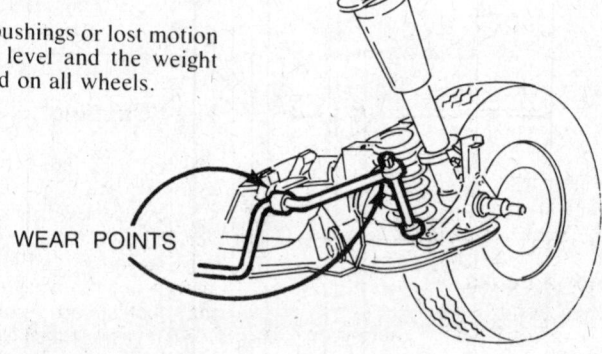

WEAR POINTS

Control Arm Bushings

Support the car under the frame or body and remove the weight from the wheel and control arm. Check for free-play in the bushings at the pivot point, using a pry bar.

NOTE: Some control arm bushings are serviceable only by replacing the entire arm.

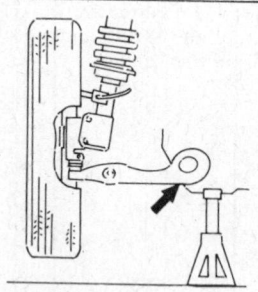

Strut Assembly

Check the strut assembly for cracks or dents in the housing. Look for worn, bent or loose piston rods or dents that will inhibit piston rod movement.

Steering Gear

Check for worn steering gear or loose or worn mounting bolts and bushings.

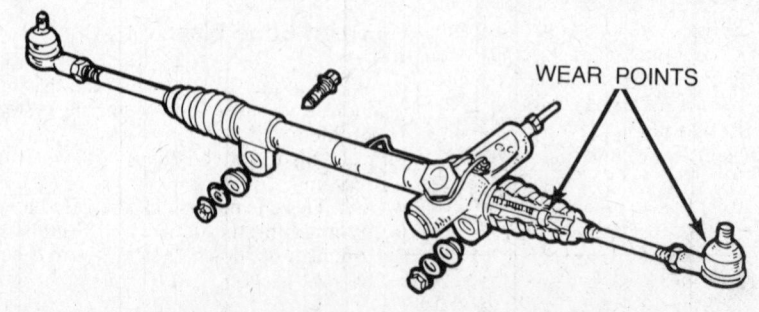

WEAR POINTS

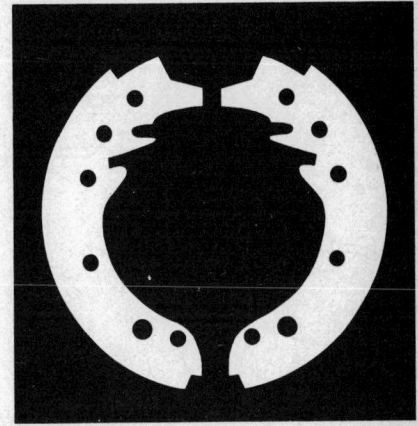

Brakes

HYDRAULIC BRAKE COMPONENT SERVICE

Understanding the Hydraulic Brake System

BASIC OPERATING PRINCIPLES

The hydraulic brake system transports the power required to force the frictional surfaces of the braking system together from the pedal to the individual brake units at each wheel. A hydraulic system is used for two reasons. First, fluid under pressure can be carried to all parts of an automobile by small hoses—some of which are flexible—without taking up a significant amount of room or posing routing problems. Second, a great mechanical advantage can be given to the brake pedal end of the system, and the foot pressure required to actuate the brakes can be reduced by making the surface area of the master cylinder pistons smaller than that of any of the pistons in the wheel cylinders or calipers.

The master cylinder consists of a double reservoir and piston assembly as well as other springs, fittings etc. Double (dual) master cylinders are designed to separate two wheels from the others. The standard approach has been have separate circuits for the front and rear wheels. Newer car models may have a diagonally split system; i.e. one front wheel and the opposite side rear wheel are in a separate circuit from the other front and rear wheel.

Steel lines carry the brake fluid to a point on the car's frame near each wheel. A flexible hose usually carries the fluid to the disc caliper or wheel cylinder. The flexible line allows for suspension and steering movements.

The rear wheel cylinders contain two pistons each, one at either end, which push outward in opposite directions. The brake calipers usually contain one piston, however in some cases they contain four.

All pistons employ some type of seal, usually made of rubber, to minimize fluid leakage. A rubber dust boot seals the outer end of the cylinder against dust and dirt. The boot fits around the outer end of the piston on disc brake calipers, and around the brake actuating rod on wheel cylinders.

The hydraulic system operates as follows: When at rest, the entire system, from the piston(s) in the master cylinder to those in the wheel cylinders or calipers, is full of brake fluid. Upon application of the brake pedal, fluid trapped in front of the master cylinder piston(s) is forced through the lines to the wheel cylinders and calipers. Here, it forces the pistons outward, in the case of drum brakes, and inward toward the disc, in the case of disc brakes. The motion of the pistons is opposed by return springs mounted outside the cylinders in drum brakes, and by internal springs or spring seals, in disc brakes.

Upon release of the brake pedal, a spring located inside the master cylinder immediately returns the master cylinder pistons to the normal position. The pistons contain check valves and the master cylinder has compensating ports drilled in it. These are uncovered as the pistons reach their normal position. The piston check valves allow fluid to flow toward the wheel cylinders or calipers as the pistons withdraw. Then, as the rubber boot/seal or return springs force the

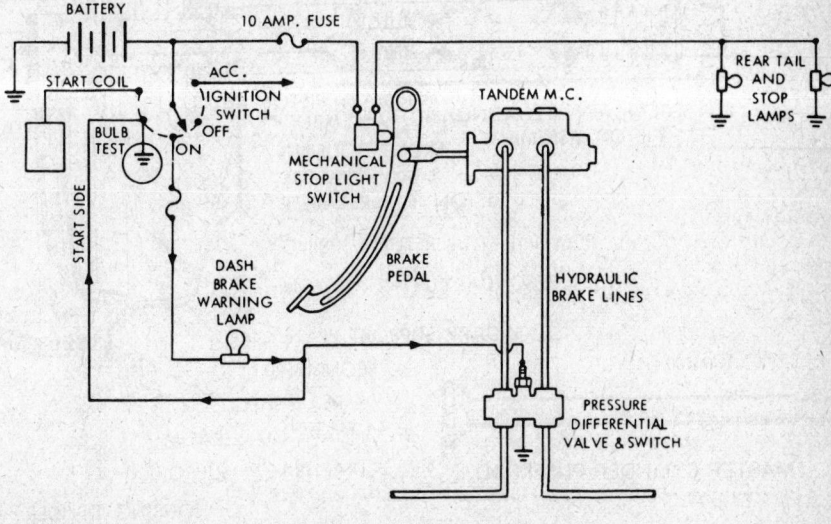

Typical dual brake system

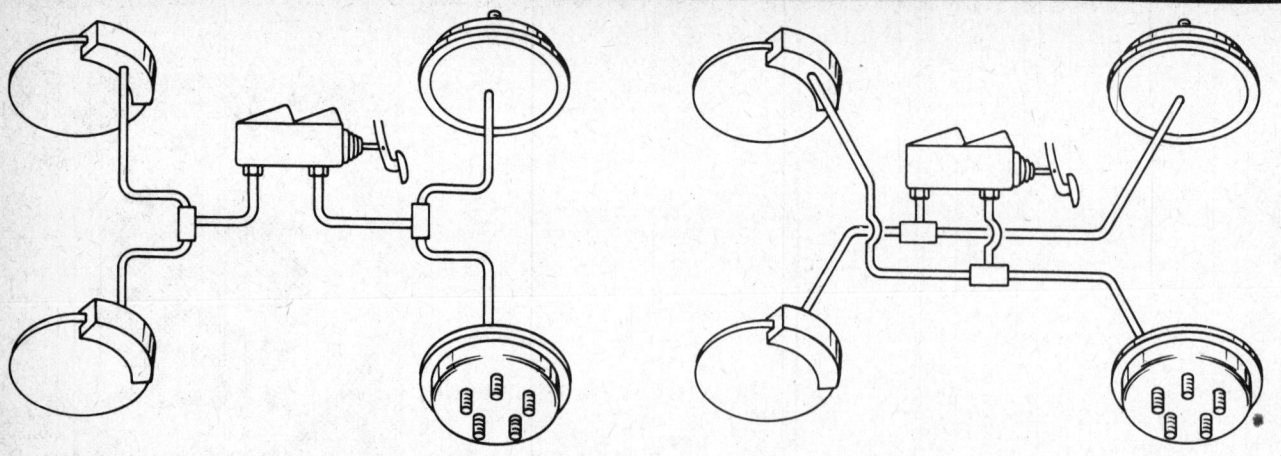

Typical front/rear split hydraulic brake system

Typical diagonally split hydraulic brake system

brake pads or shoes into the released position, the excess fluid returns to the reservoir through the compensating ports.

The dual master cylinder has two pistons, located one behind the other. The primary piston is actuated directly by mechanical linkage from the brake pedal. The secondary piston is actuated by fluid trapped between the two pistons. If a leak develops in front of the secondary piston, it moves forward until it bottoms against the front

of the master cylinder. The fluid trapped between the pistons will operate one side of the split system. If the other side of the system develops a leak, the primary piston will move forward until direct contact with the secondary piston takes place, and it will force the secondary piston to acuate the other side of the split system. In either case the brake pedal drops closer to the floor board and less braking power is available.

The brake system uses a switch to warn

the driver when only half of the brake system is operational. This switch is usually located in a valve body which is mounted on the firewall or the frame below the master cylinder. A hydraulic piston receives pressure from both circuits, each circuit's pressure being applied to one end of the piston. When the pressures are in balance, the piston remains stationary. When one circuit has a leak, however, the greater pressure in that circuit during brake appli-

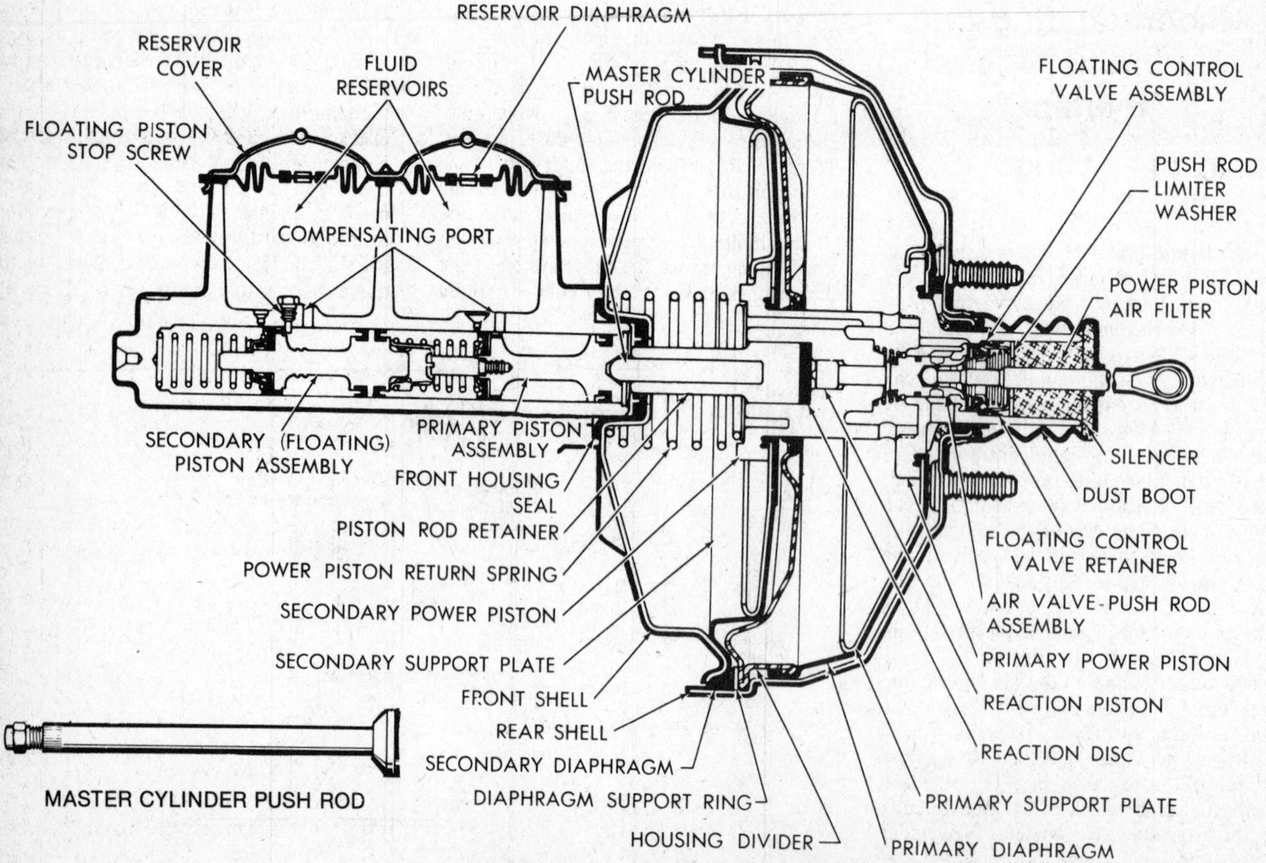

RESERVOIR DIAPHRAGM

RESERVOIR COVER

FLUID RESERVOIRS

MASTER CYLINDER PUSH ROD

FLOATING CONTROL VALVE ASSEMBLY

FLOATING PISTON STOP SCREW

PUSH ROD LIMITER WASHER

COMPENSATING PORT

POWER PISTON AIR FILTER

SECONDARY (FLOATING) PISTON ASSEMBLY

PRIMARY PISTON ASSEMBLY

FRONT HOUSING SEAL

PISTON ROD RETAINER

POWER PISTON RETURN SPRING

SECONDARY POWER PISTON

SECONDARY SUPPORT PLATE

FRONT SHELL

REAR SHELL

SECONDARY DIAPHRAGM

DIAPHRAGM SUPPORT RING

HOUSING DIVIDER

SILENCER

DUST BOOT

FLOATING CONTROL VALVE RETAINER

AIR VALVE-PUSH ROD ASSEMBLY

PRIMARY POWER PISTON

REACTION PISTON

REACTION DISC

PRIMARY SUPPORT PLATE

PRIMARY DIAPHRAGM

MASTER CYLINDER PUSH ROD

Typical dual master cylinder

cation will push the piston to one side, closing the switch and activating the brake warning light.

In disc brake systems, this valve body contains a metering valve and, in some cases, a proportioning valve or valves. The metering valve keeps pressure from traveling to the disc brakes on the front wheels until the brake shoes on the rear wheels have contacted the drums, ensuring that the front brakes will never be used alone. The proportioning valve controls the pressure to the rear brakes to avoid rear wheel lock-up during very hard braking.

Warning lights may be tested by depressing the brake pedal and holding it while opening one of the wheel cylinder bleeder screws. If this does not cause the light to go on, substitute a new lamp, make continuity checks, and, finally, replace the switch as necessary.

The hydraulic system may be checked for leaks by applying pressure to the pedal gradually and steadily. If the pedal sinks very slowly to the floor, the system has a leak. This is not to be confused with a springy or spongy feel due to the compression of air within the lines. If the system leaks, there will be a gradual change in the position of the pedal with a constant pressure.

Check for leaks along all lines and at wheel cylinders or calipers. If no external leaks are apparent, the problem is inside the master cylinder.

DISC BRAKES

Basic Operating Principles

Instead of the traditional expanding brakes that press outward against a circular drum, disc brake systems utilize a disc (rotor) with brake pads positioned on either side of it. Braking effect is achieved in a manner similar to the way you would squeeze a spinning phonograph record between your fingers. The disc (rotor) is a casting which may be equipped with cooling fins between the two braking surfaces. The fins (if equipped) enable air to circulate between the braking surfaces making them less sensitive to heat buildup and more resistant to fade. Dirt and water do not affect braking action since contaminants are thrown off by the centrifugal action of the rotor or scraped off by the pads. Also, the equal clamping action of the two brake pads tends to ensure uniform, straightline stops. Disc brakes are inherently self-adjusting.

DRUM BRAKES (REAR)

Basic Operating Principles

Drum brakes employ two brake shoes mounted on a stationary backing plate. These shoes are positioned inside a circular drum which rotates with the wheel assembly. The shoes are held in place by springs; this allows them to slide toward the drums (when they are applied) while keeping the linings and drums in alignment. The shoes are ac-

tuated by a wheel cylinder which is mounted at the top of the backing plate. When the brakes are applied, hydraulic pressure forces the wheel cylinder's actuating links outward. Since these links bear directly against the top of the brake shoes, the tops of the shoes are then forced against the inner side of the drum. This action forces the bottoms of the two shoes to contact the brake drum by rotating the entire assembly slightly (known as servo action). When pressure within the wheel cylinder is relaxed, return springs pull the shoes back away from the drum.

Rear drum brakes are (in most cases) designed to self-adjust themselves during application. Motion causes both shoes to rotate very slightly with the drum, rocking an adjusting lever, thereby causing rotation of the adjusting screw or lever.

POWER BRAKE SYSTEM

Power brakes operate just as standard brake systems except in the actuation of the master cylinder pistons. A vacuum diaphragm is located on the front of the master cylinder and assists the driver in applying the brakes, reducing both the effort and travel he must put into moving the brake pedal.

The vacuum diaphragm housing is connected to the intake manifold by a vacuum hose. A check valve is placed at the point where the hose enters the diaphragm housing, so that during periods of low manifold vacuum brake assist vacuum will not be lost.

Depressing the brake pedal closes off the vacuum source and allows atmospheric pressure to enter on one side of the diaphragm. This causes the master cylinder pistons to move and apply the brakes. When the brake pedal is released, vacuum is applied to both sides of the diaphragm, and return springs return the diaphragm and master cylinder pistons to the released position. If the vacuum fails, the brake pedal rod will butt against the end of the master cylinder actuating rod, and direct mechanical application will occur as the pedal is depressed.

HYDRAULIC CYLINDERS AND VALVES

Master Cylinders

CAUTION

The master cylinder unit is a highly calibrated unit specifically designed for the car it is on. Although the cylinders may look alike there are many differences in calibration. If replacement is necessary, make sure the replacement unit is the one specified for the car.

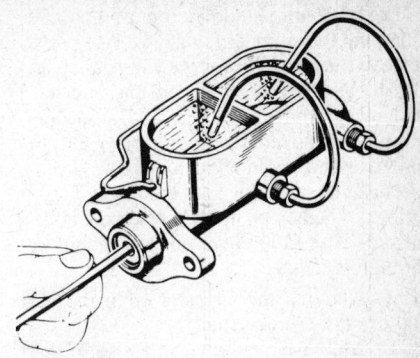

Pre-bleeding master cylinder

NOTE: Some 1981 and later G.M. cars are equipped with "Quick Take-Up" master cylinders which provide a large volume of fluid to the wheels brakes at low pressure when the brake pedal is initially applied. This large volume of fluid is needed because of the new self retracting piston seals at the front disc brake calipers which pull the pistons into the calipers after the brakes are released, thereby preventing the brake pads from causing a drag on the rotors.

The "Quick Take-Up" master cylinder has a hydraulically operated brake warning light switch incorporated in the master cylinder body. The piston is accessible by removing the large plug at the front of the master cylinder body. Only remove the plug when overhauling the cylinder, as brake fluid will escape.

Overhaul procedures on these new type master cylinders are basically the same as those on conventional master cylinder. Make sure you buy a "Quick Take-Up" master cylinder rebuild kit.

SERVICING MASTER CYLINDERS

NOTE: Plastic reservoirs need to be removed only for the following reasons:
1. Reservoir is damaged or the rubber grommet(s) between the reservoir and bore is leaking.
2. Removal of stop pin from Chrysler style plastic reservoir master cylinder to allow removal of pistons. Pin is located underneath front reservoir nipple.
3. Service "Quick Take-up" valve on GM quick take-up master cylinders.

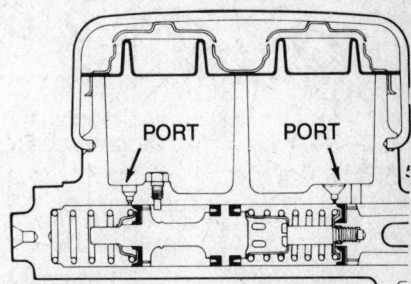

Feed and return ports

The reservoir should be removed by first clamping the cylinder flange in a vice. Next remove the reservoir for the Chrysler style. Grasp the reservoir base on one end and pull away from the body. GM reservoirs must be removed by prying between the reservoir and casting with a pry bar. Grommets can be reused if they are in good condition. Whether or not the reservoir is removed, it and the cover or caps should be throughly cleaned.

1. Remove the cylinder from the car and drain the brake fluid.

2. Mount the cylinder in a vise so that the outlets are up and remove the rubber boot seal from the hub.

3. Remove the stop pin or screw from the bottom of the front reservoir, if present.

4. Remove the snap-ring from the front of the bore and remove the primary piston assembly.

5. Remove the secondary piston assembly using compressed air or a piece of wire.

6. Clean metal parts in brake fluid and discard rubber parts.

7. Inspect the bore for damage or wear, and check pistons for damage and proper clearance in the bore.

—————— CAUTION ——————
Aluminum cylinder bores cannot be honed. The cylinder must be replaced if the bore is scored.

8. If the bore is only slightly scored or pitted it may be honed. (See CAUTION). Always use hones that are in good condition and completely clean the cylinder with brake fluid when honing is completed. If any sign of wear or corrosion is apparent on "Quick Take-Up" master cylinder bores, the master cylinder must be replaced; it cannot be honed. If any evidence of contamination exists in the master cylinder the entire hydraulic system should be flushed and refilled with clean brake fluid. Blow out passages with compressed air.

NOTE: Most rebuilding kits provide a primary and secondary piston assembly. If the kit you are using only provides seals—see Steps 9–13.

9. Install new secondary seals in the two grooves in the flat end of the front piston. The lips of the seals will be facing away from each other.

10. Install a new primary seal and the seal protector on opposite end of the front piston with the lips of the seal facing outward.

11. Coat the seals with brake fluid. Install the spring on the front piston with the spring retainer in the primary seal.

12. Insert the piston assembly, spring end first, into the bore and use a wooden rod to seat it.

13. Coat the rear piston seals with brake fluid and install them into the piston grooves with the lips facing the spring end.

14. Assemble the spring onto the piston and install the assembly into the bore spring first. Install the snap-ring.

15. Hold the piston at the bottom of the bore and install the stop screw.

16. On G.M. models with the hydraulic brake warning light switch ("Quick Take-Up" units), remove the allen head plug and remove the switch assembly with needle nose pliers. Remove the O-rings and retainers from the piston. Install new O-rings and retainers, fit the piston back into the master cylinder after lubricating with brake fluid.

NOTE: If any corrosion is present in the switch piston bore the master cylinder must be replaced: do not attempt to hone the bore.

17. Fit a new O-ring on the allen head plug and install the plug and tighten.

18. On all master cylinders, install a new seal in the hub, if equipped, then either bench bleed or bleed the cylinder on the car. Some master cylinders have bleed screws on the outlet flanges and may be bled without disturbing the wheel cylinders and calipers.

MASTER CYLINDER PUSH ROD ADJUSTMENT

Models Equipped with Adjustable Push Rod

After assembly of the master cylinder to the power section, the piston cup in the hydraulic cylinder should just clear the compensating port hole when the brake pedal is fully released. If the push rod is too long, it will hold the piston over the port.

A push rod that is too short, will give too much loose travel (excessive pedal play).

Apply the brakes and release the pedal all the way observing the brake fluid flow back into the master cylinder.

A full flow indicates the piston is coming back far enough to release the fluid.

A slow return of the fluid indicates the piston is not coming back far enough to clear the ports. The push rod adjustment is too tight, and should be shortened.

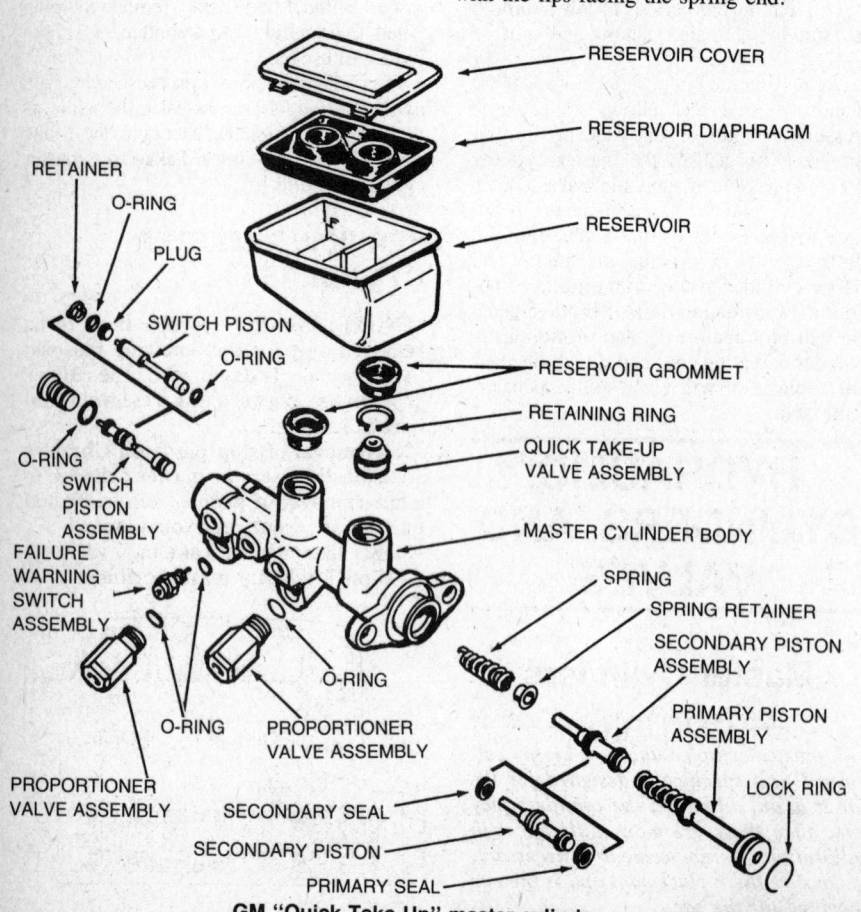

GM "Quick Take Up" master cylinder

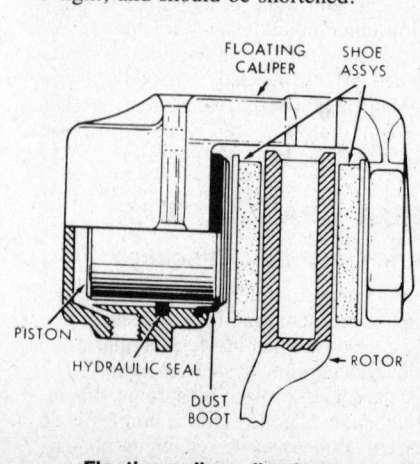

Floating caliper disc brake

Disc Brake Calipers

Caliper disc brakes can be divided into three types: the four-piston, fixed-caliper type; the single-piston, floating-caliper type, and the single-piston sliding-caliper type. Refer to the Brake Specifications Chart for applications.

In the four piston type (two in each side of the caliper) braking effect is achieved by hydraulically pushing both shoes against the disc sides.

With the single piston floating-caliper type the inboard shoe is pushed hydraulically into contact with the disc, while the reaction force thus generated is used to pull the outboard shoe into frictional contact (made possible by letting the caliper move slightly along the axle centerline).

In the sliding caliper (single piston) type, the caliper assembly slides along the machined surfaces of the anchor plate. A steel key located between the machined surfaces of the caliper and the machined surfaces of the anchor plate is held in place with either a retaining screw or two cotter pins. The caliper is held in place against the anchor plate with one or two support springs.

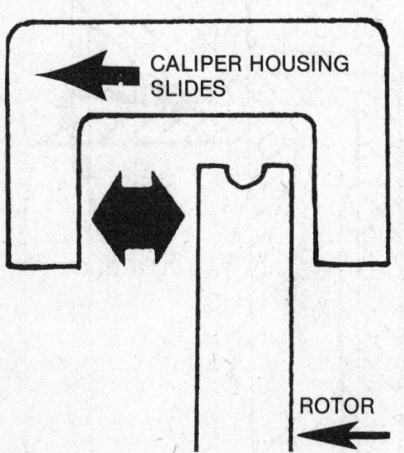

Floating (or sliding) caliper type

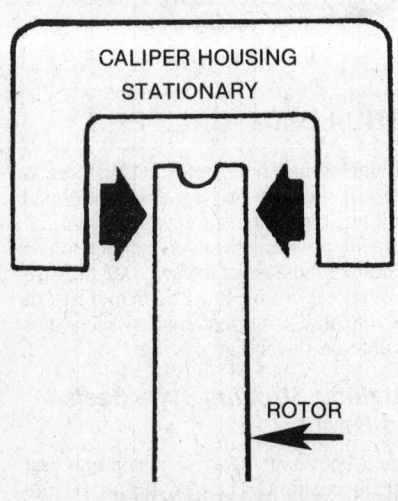

Fixed caliper type

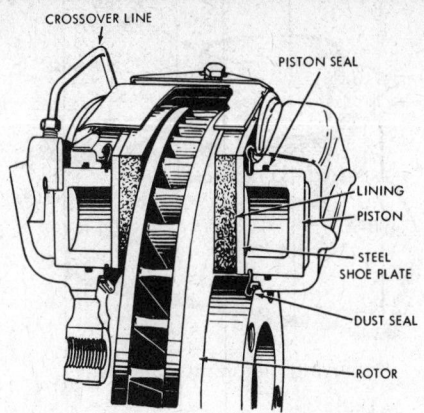

Fixed caliper disc brake

SERVICING THE CALIPER ASSEMBLY

NOTE: The following is a general caliper service procedure. Before proceeding, check under the individual disc brake section for your car (Delco Moraine, Bendix, etc.) for any special servicing procedures.

1. Raise the vehicle and safety support it on jackstands. Remove the front wheels.
2. Working on one side at a time only, disconnect the hydraulic inlet line from the caliper and plug the end. Remove the caliper mounting bolts or pins, and shims (if used) and slide the caliper off the disc.
3. Remove the disc pads from the caliper or mounting adapter. If the old ones are to be reused, mark them so that they can be reinstalled in their original positions.
4. Open the caliper bleed screw and drain the fluid. Clean the outside of the caliper and mount it in a vise with padded jaws.

─────── **CAUTION** ───────
When cleaning any brake components, use only brake fluid or denatured (Isopropyl) alcohol. Never use a mineral-based solvent, such as gasoline or paint thinner, since it will swell and quickly deteriorate rubber parts.

5. Remove the bridge bolts (fixed type), separate the caliper halves, and remove the two O-ring seals from the transfer holes.
6. Pry the lip on (each) piston dust boot from its groove and remove the piston assemblies and spring(s) from the bore(s). If necessary, air pressure may be used to force the piston(s) out of the bore(s), using care to prevent the piston from popping out of control.
7. Remove the boot(s) and seal(s) from the piston(s) and clean the piston(s) in brake fluid. Blow out the caliper passages with an air hose.
8. Inspect the cylinder bore(s) for scoring, pitting, or corrosion. Corrosion is a pitted or rough condition not to be confused with staining. Light rough spots may be removed by rotating crocus cloth, using fin-

Replacing disc brake bleeder screw

ger pressure, in the bores. Do not polish with an in and out motion or use any other abrasive.

9. If the piston(s) are pitted, scored, or worn, they must be replaced. A corroded or deeply scored caliper should also be replaced.
10. Check the clearance of the piston(s) in the bores using a feeler gauge. Clearance should be 0.002–0.006 in. If there is excessive clearance the caliper must be replaced.
11. Replace all rubber parts and lubricate with brake fluid. Install the seals (or square cut rings) and boots in the grooves in each piston. The seal should be installed in the groove closest to the closed end of the piston with the seal lips facing the closed end. The lip on the boot should be facing the seal.
12. Lubricate the piston and bore with brake fluid. Position the piston return spring (if so equipped), large coil first, in the piston bore.

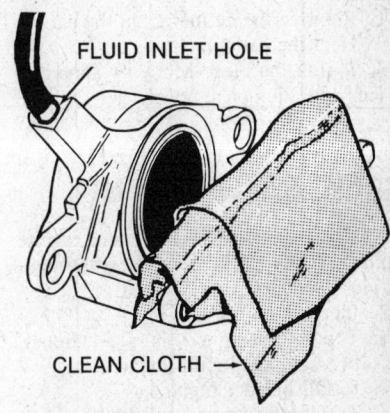

Removing piston hydraulically

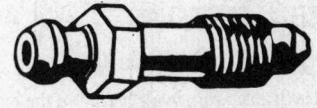

Bleed screw

13. Install the piston in the bore, taking great care to avoid damaging the seal lip as it passes the edge of the cylinder bore.

14. Compress the lip on the dust boot into the groove in the caliper. Be sure the boot is fully seated in the groove, as poor sealing will allow contaminants to ruin the bore.

15. On fixed calipers: Position the O-rings in the cavities around the caliper transfer holes, and fit the caliper halves together. Install the bridge bolts (lubricated with brake fluid) and be sure to torque to specification.

16. Install the disc pads in the caliper or adapter and remount the caliper on the hub (see "Disc Pad Replacement"). Connect the brake line to the caliper and bleed the brakes (see "Brake Bleeding"). Replace the wheels. Recheck the brake fluid level, check the brake pedal travel, and road test the vehicle.

Overhaul Notes

Field reports indicate that two factors determine whether to replace or rebuild calipers:

1. Can the piston or pistons be removed?
2. Will the bleed screw break off when removal is attempted? (Rebuilders will not accept a caliper with a broken bleed screw.)

Since there is no way to predict how a bleed screw will react, follow this procedure to attempt removal.

1. Insert a drill shank into the bleed screw hole (snug fit).
2. Tap the screw on all sides.
3. With a six point wrench apply pressure gently while working the drill up and down slightly.
4. If the drill starts to bind, the screw is beginning to collapse and cannot be removed intact.

Heating the caliper is another successful, but time consuming, bleed screw removal technique.

1. Remove the caliper from the car.
2. Heat the caliper.
3. Shrink the bleed screw by applying dry ice, and attempt removal.

DISC BRAKE BLEEDER SCREW REPLACEMENT

1. Using existing hole in bleed screw for pilot drill ¼ in. hole completely through existing bleeder.
2. Increase hole to ⁷⁄₁₆ in.
3. Tap hole using a ¼ in. (18-national pipe tap) ½ in. deep-(full thread.)
4. Install bleeder repair kit.
5. Test for leaks and full brake pedal pressure.

FROZEN PISTONS

Sliding or Floating Caliper

1. Hydraulic removal: Remove the caliper assembly from the rotor.

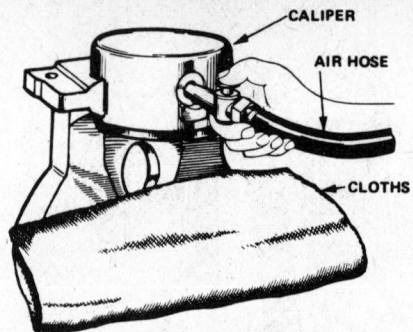

Removing piston pneumatically

2. Remove brake pads and dust seal.

With brake flexible line connected and bleed screw closed apply enough pedal pressure to move the piston most of the way out of the bore (brake fluid will begin to ooze past the piston inner seal).

3. Pneumatic removal: Remove the caliper from the car.
4. With the bleed screw closed apply air pressure to force the piston out.

Hydraulic and pneumatic methods of piston removal should be done carefully to prevent personal injury or piston damage.

Fixed Caliper

NOTE: The hydraulic or pneumatic methods which apply to the single piston type caliper will not work on the multiple piston type brake caliper.

1. Remove the caliper from the car with the two halves separated.
2. Mount in a vise and use a piston puller (many types available) to remove the pistons.

CALIPER CLEANING

NOTE: Castings may be cleaned with any type cleaning fluid after all rubber seals have been removed.

——— CAUTION ———

It is important that all traces of cleaning fluid be completely removed from the caliper casting. Rubber components are compatible with alcohol and/or brake fluid.

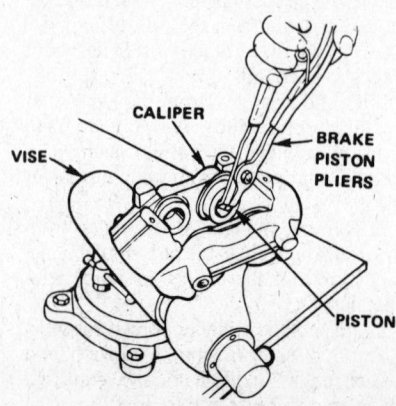

Removing pistons

Use a lint free wiping cloth to clean the caliper and parts. Black stains on pistons or walls, caused by the seals, will not do harm; however, extreme cleanliness is essential. Blow out passages with compressed air. A fine grade of crocus cloth may be used to correct minor imperfections in the cylinder bore. Slide crocus cloth with finger pressure in a circular rather than a lengthwise motion. Do not use any form of abrasive on a plated piston. Discard a piston which is pitted or has signs of plating wear.

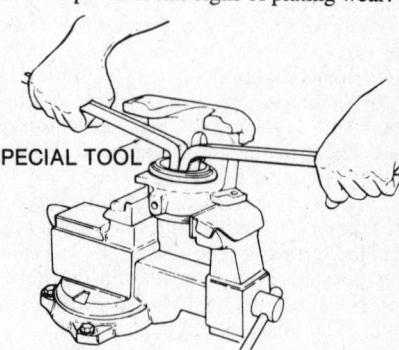

Removing hollow end piston

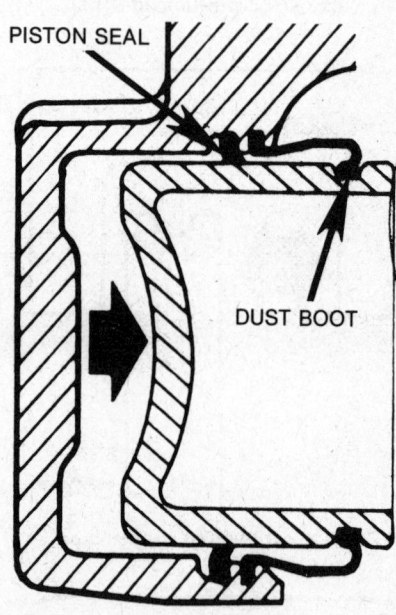

Brake applied

REBUILDING CALIPERS

If a fine stone honing of a caliper bore is necessary it should be done with skill and caution. Some cars can develop 800 p.s.i. hydraulic pressure on severe application so the honing must never exceed .003 in. Also the dust seal groove must be free of rust or nicks so that a perfect mating surface is possible on piston and casting.

Installing Stroking Type Seals and Boots

Stretch boot and seal over piston and seat them in position. The seal lip on Bendix and Delco makes faces toward hydraulic

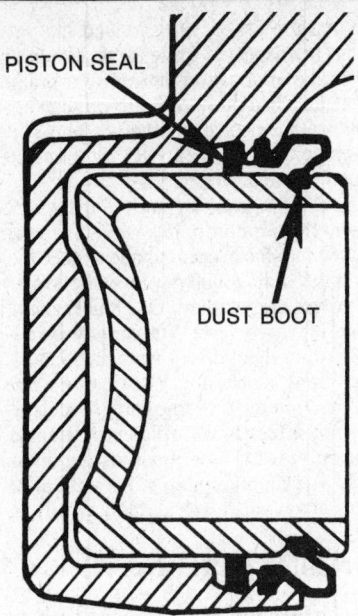

Brake released

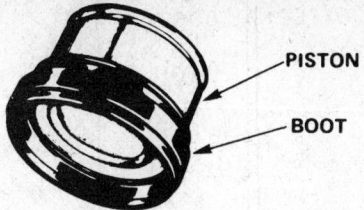

Assembling boot on piston

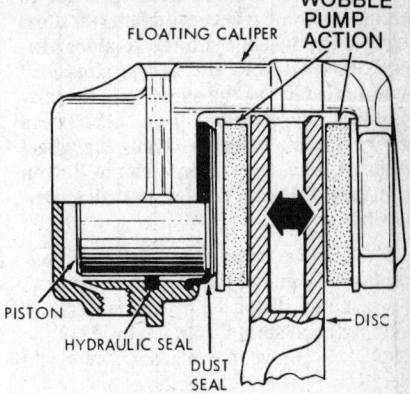

Wobble pump action

pressure; boot lips face toward the brake shoe. Locate return spring, if used, in the cylinder and carefully start the piston into the cylinder to avoid nicking the seal. Alignment tools are available for inserting lip cup seals. Fully depress the piston into the bore in order to fasten the boot lip to the caliper housing. On Delco makes, use a wooden drift or a special seating tool to seat the boot ring in the caliper counterbore. It must be flush or below the caliper machined surface.

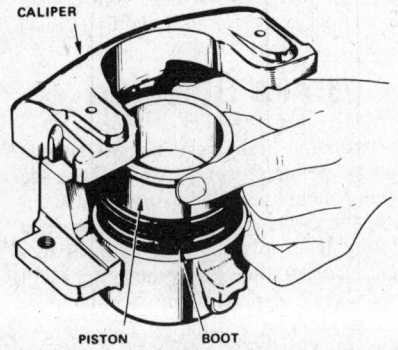

Installing piston

Installing Fixed Position (Rectangular Ring) Seals and Boots

Insert rectangular ring seal into bore and, at any location, push the ring into the seal groove. From this area, with a finger, gently work around the bore until the ring is seated in this channel. Be sure the ring does not twist or roll in the groove. When the boot lip is retained inside the cylinder bore, insert the boot in the same manner. Then work the inside of the boot over the pressure end of the piston, stretching the boot with a small plastic tool, and press the piston through the seal, straight in, until it bot-

toms. The inside of the boot should slide on the piston and come to rest in the boot groove. If the boot lip is retained outside of the cylinder bore, first stretch boot over the piston and seat it in its groove, then press the piston through the seal. Fully depress the piston, 50–100 pounds force will be required, in order to fasten the boot lip in place. On Delco-Moraine makes, use a wooden drift or a special seating tool to seat the metal boot ring in the caliper counterbore below the face of the caliper.

Installing Fixed-Caliper Bridge Bolts

If the caliper contains internal fluid crossover passages, be sure to install new O-ring seals at joints. Mate the caliper halves and install in-tensile strength bridge bolts. Never replace bridge bolts with ordinary standard hardware bolts.

Wheel Cylinders

Wheel cylinders contain a pair of opposed pistons fitted with rubber cups, compression spring and sometimes expander washers to keep the cups tight against the pistons.

SERVICING WHEEL CYLINDERS

1. Raise the car and safely support it on jackstands. Remove the wheel and drum from the side to be serviced.
2. Remove the brake shoes and clean the backing plate and wheel cylinder. Re-

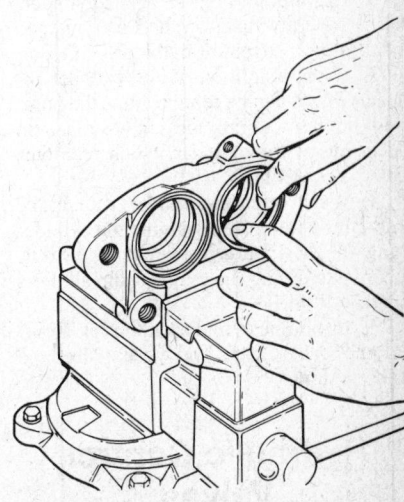

Installing fixed position rectangular ring seal (seal lip toward pressure side)

building can be done on the car, depending on the design of the brake backing plate. If the backing plate is recessed to the point that it is impossible to get a hone into the cylinder, the cylinder has to be removed.

3. To remove the cylinder; disconnect the brake line from the rear of the cylinder, remove the mounting bolts or retainers and remove the cylinder.

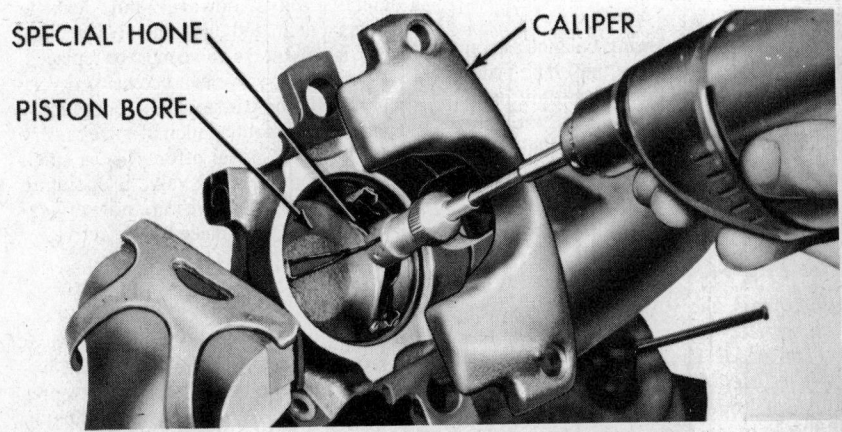

Honing cylinder bore

NOTE: On some models, in order to remove the rear wheel cylinders you must remove the wheel cylinder retainer. Insert two awls into the access slots and bend both tabs at the same time thereby releasing the cylinder. You must use a new retainer when reinstalling the wheel cylinder. The new retainer can be driven on using an 1⅛ in. socket with an extension bar.

4. Remove the rubber boots (dust covers) from the ends of the cylinder. Remove the pistons, piston cups (expanders, if equipped) and spring from the inside of the cylinder. Remove the bleeder screw and make sure it is not clogged.

5. Discard all of the parts that the rebuilding kit will replace.

6. Examine the inside of the cylinder. If it is severely rusted, pitted or scratched install a new or rebuilt cylinder.

7. If the condition of the cylinder indicates that it can be rebuilt, hone the bore. Light honing will provide a new surface on the inside of the cylinder which promotes better cup sealing.

8. Wash out the cylinder with brake fluid after honing. Reassemble the cylinder using the new parts provided in the kit. When assembling the cylinder dip all parts in brake fluid.

9. Install the cylinder on the car. Reinstall the brakes, drum and wheel. Bleed the brake system.

Hydraulic Control Valves

PRESSURE DIFFERENTIAL VALVE

The pressure differential valve activates a dash panel warning light if pressure loss in the brake system occurs. If pressure loss occurs in one half of the split system the other system's normal pressure causes the piston in the switch to compress a spring until it touches an electrical contact. This turns the warning lamp on the dash panel to light, thus warning the driver of possible brake failure.

On some cars the spring balance piston automatically recenters as the brake pedal is released warning the driver only upon brake application. On other cars, the light remains on until manually cancelled.

Valves may be located separately, as part of a combination valve, or incorporated into the master cylinder.

Re-setting Valves

On some cars, the valve piston(s) remain off center after failure until necessary repairs are made. The valve will automatically reset itself (after repairs) when pressure is equal on both sides of the system.

If the light does not go out, bleed the brake system that is opposite the failed system.

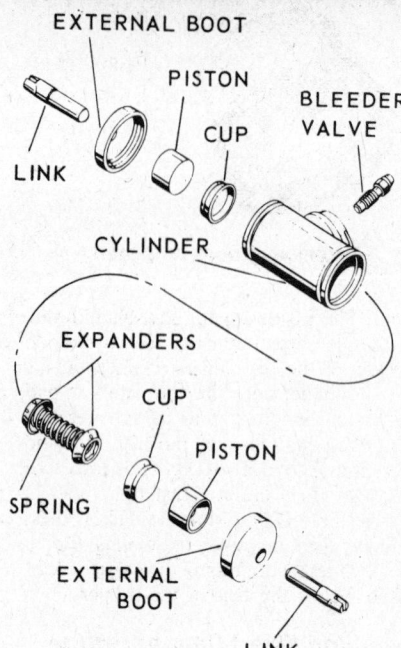

Wheel cylinder components

tem. If front brakes failed, bleed the rear brakes, this should force the light control piston toward center.

If this fails, remove the terminal switch. If brake fluid is present in the electrical area, the seals are gone, replace the complete valve assembly.

METERING VALVE

The metering valve's function is to improve braking balance between the front disc and rear drum brakes, especially during light brake application.

The metering valve prevents application of the front disc brakes until the rear brakes overcome the return spring pressure. Thus, when the front disc pads contact the rotor, the rear shoes will contact the brake drum at the same time.

Inspect the metering valve each time the brakes are serviced. A slight amount of moisture inside the boot does not indicate a defective valve, however, fluid leakage indicates a damaged or worn valve. If fluid leakage is present the valve must be replaced.

The metering valve can be checked very simply. With the car stopped, gently apply the brakes. At about an inch of travel a very small change in pedal effort (like a small bump) will be felt if the valve is operating properly. Metering valves are not serviceable, and must be replaced if defective.

PROPORTIONING VALVE

The proportioning (pressure control) valve is used, on some cars, to reduce the hydraulic pressure to the rear wheels to prevent skid during heavy brake application and to provide better brake balance. It is usually mounted in line to the rear wheels.

When the brakes are serviced the valve should be inspected for leakage. Premature rear brake application during light braking can mean a bad proportioning valve. Repair is by replacement of the valve. Make sure the valve port marked "R" is connected toward the rear wheels.

On GM "Quick Take-Up" master cylinders, the proportioning valve(s) is (are) screwed into the master cylinder. Since these cars have a diagonally split brake system, two valves are required. One rear brake line screws into each valve. The early type valves (GM front wheel drive) were steel and silver colored, a occasional "clunking" noise was encountered on some early models, but does not affect brake efficiency. Replacement valves are now made of aluminum. Never mix an aluminum valve with a steel valve, always use two aluminum valves.

COMBINATION VALVE

The combination valve may perform two or three functions. They are; metering, proportioning and brake failure warning.

Variations of the two-way combination valve are: proportioning and brake failure warning or metering and brake failure warning.

A three-way combination valve directs the brake fluid to the appropriate wheel, performs necessary valving and contains a brake failure warning.

The combination valve is usually mounted under the hood close to the master cylinder, where the brake lines can easily be connected and routed to the front or rear wheels.

The combination valve is non-serviceable and must be replaced if malfunctioning.

Brake Bleeding

The hydraulic brake system must be free of air to operate properly. Air can enter the system when hydraulic parts are disconnected for servicing or replacement, or when the fluid level in the master cylinder reservoirs is very low. Air in the system will give the brake pedal a spongy feeling upon application.

The quickest and easiest of the two ways for system bleeding is the pressure method, but special equipment is needed to externally pressurize the hydraulic system. The other, more commonly used method of brake bleeding is done manually.

BLEEDING SEQUENCE

Bleeding may be required at only one or two wheels or at the master cylinder, depending upon what point the system was opened to air. If after bleeding the cylinder caliper that was rebuilt or replaced and the pedal still has a spongy feeling upon application, it will be necessary to bleed the entire system.

Bleed the system in the following order:

1. **Master cylinder.** If the cylinder is not equipped with bleeder screws, open the

brake line(s) to the wheels slightly while pressure is applied to the brake pedal. Be sure to tighten the line before the brake pedal is released. The procedure for bench bleeding the master cylinder is in the following section.

2. **Power Brake Booster:** If the unit is equipped with bleeder screws, it should be bled after the master cylinder. The car engine should be off and the brake pedal applied several times to exhaust any vacuum in the booster. If the unit is equipped with two bleeder screws, always bleed the higher one first.

3. **Combination Valve:** If equipped with a bleeder screw.

4. **Front/Back Split Systems:** Start with the wheel farthest away from the master cylinder, usually the right rear wheel. Bleed the other rear wheel then the right front and left front.

NOTE: If you are unsuccessful in bleeding the front wheels, it may be necessary to deactivate the metering valve. This is accomplished by either pushing in, or pulling out a button or stem on the valve. The valve may be held by hand, with a special tool or taped, it should remain deactivated while the front brakes are bled.

5. **Diagonally Split System:** Start with the right rear then the left front. The left rear then the right front (refer to the following ''GM Quick Take-Up Master Cylinder'' section).

6. **Rear Disc Brakes:** If the car is equipped with rear disc brakes and the calipers have two bleeder screws, bleed the inner first then the outer.

CAUTION

Do not allow brake fluid to spill on the car's finish, it will remove the paint. Flush the area with water.

MANUAL BLEEDING

1. Clean the bleed screw at each wheel.
2. Start with the wheel farthest from the master cylinder (right rear).
3. Attach a small rubber hose to the bleed screw and place the end in a clear container of brake fluid.
4. Fill the master cylinder with brake fluid. (Check often during bleeding). Have an assistant slowly pump up the brake pedal and hold pressure.
5. Open the bleed screw about one-quarter turn, press the brake pedal to the floor, close the bleed screw and slowly release the pedal. Continue until no more air bubbles are forced from the cylinder on application of the brake pedal.
6. Repeat procedure on remaining wheel cylinders and calipers, still working from cylinder/caliper farthest from the master cylinder.

Master cylinders equipped with bleed screws may be bled independently. When bleeding the Bendix-type dual master cylinder it is necessary to solidly cap one res-

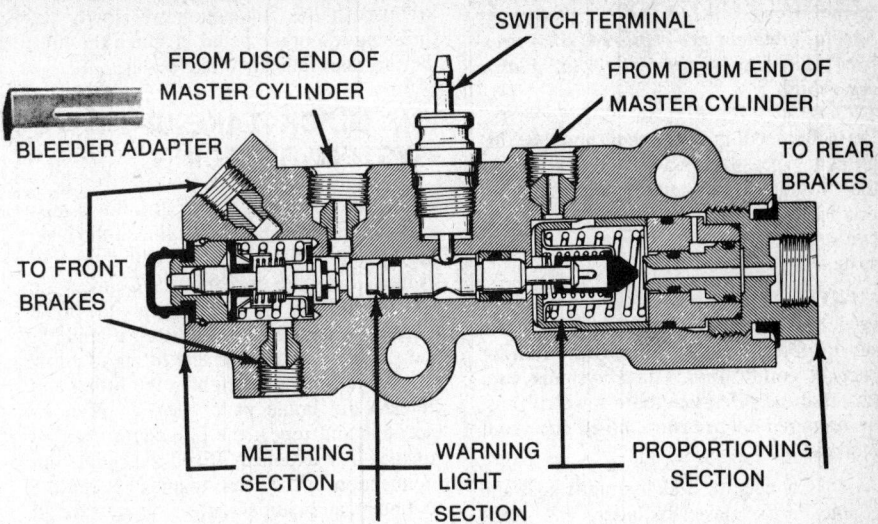

Push valve in when pressure bleeding-not necessary when using pedal bleed method

ervoir section while bleeding the other to prevent pressure loss through the cap vent hole.

NOTE: The disc should be rotated to make sure that the piston has returned to the unapplied position when bleeding is completed and the bleed screw closed.

CAUTION

The bleeder valve at the wheel cylinder must be closed at the end of each stroke, and before the brake pedal is released, to insure that no air can enter the system. It is also important that the brake pedal be returned to the full up position so the piston in the master cylinder moves back enough to clear the bypass outlets.

PRESSURE BLEEDING DISC BRAKES

Pressure bleeding disc brakes will close the metering valve and the front brakes will not bleed. For this reason it is necessary to manually hold the metering valve open during pressure bleeding. Never use a block or clamp to hold the valve open, and never force the valve stem beyond its normal position. Two different types of valves are used. The most common type requires the valve stem to be held in while bleeding the brakes, while the second type requires the valve stem to be heldout (.060 in. minimum travel). Determine the type of visual inspection.

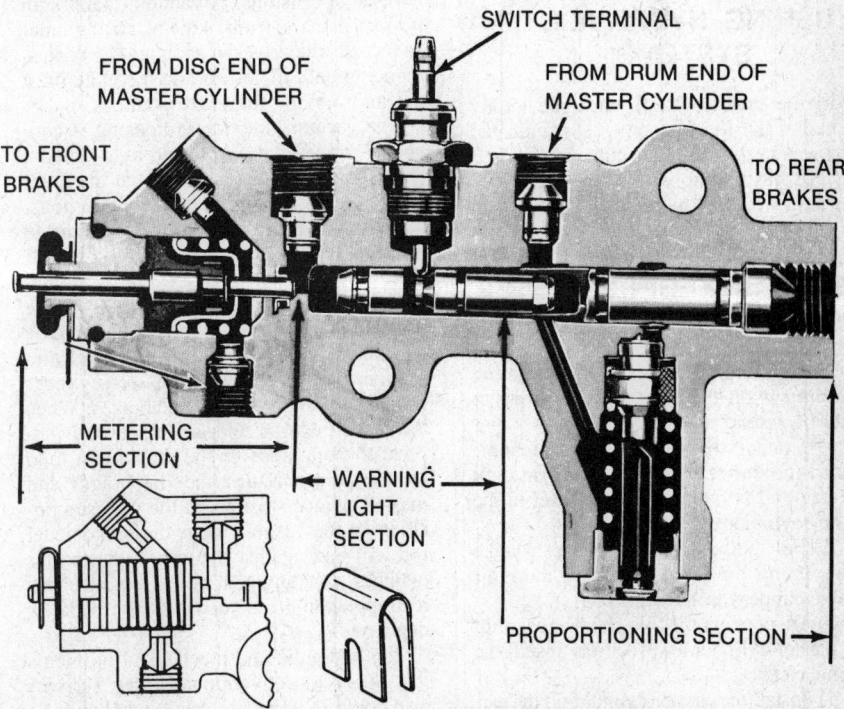

Hold valve out .060 in pressure bleed only-not necessary when using pedal bleed method

CAUTION

Special adapters are required when pressure bleeding cylinders with plastic reservoirs.

Pressure bleeding equipment should be diaphragm type; placing a diaphragm between the pressurized air supply and the brake fluid. This prevents moisture and other contaminants from entering the hydraulic system.

NOTE: Front disc/rear drum equipped vehicles use a metering valve which closes off pressure to the front brakes under certain conditions. These systems contain manual release actuators which must be engaged to pressure bleed the front brakes.

1. Connect the tank hydraulic hose and adapter to the master cylinder.
2. Close hydraulic valve on the bleeder equipment.
3. Apply air pressure to the bleeder equipment.

CAUTION

Follow equipment manufacturer's recommendations for correct air pressure.

4. Open the valve to bleed air out of the pressure hose to the master cylinder.

NOTE: Never bleed this system using the secondary piston stopscrew on the bottom of many master cylinders.

5. Open the hydraulic valve and bleed each wheel cylinder and caliper. Bleed rear brake system first when bleeding both front and rear systems.

FLUSHING HYDRAULIC BRAKE SYSTEMS

Hydraulic brake systems must be totally flushed if the fluid becomes contaminated with water, dirt or other corrosive chemicals. To flush, simply bleed the entire system until *all* fluid has been replaced with the correct type of new fluid.

BENCH BLEEDING MASTER CYLINDER

Bench bleeding the master cylinder before installing it on the car reduces the possibility of getting air into the lines.

1. Connect two short pieces of brake line to the outlet fittings, bend them until the free end is below the fluid level in the master cylinder reservoirs.
2. Fill the reservoirs with fresh brake fluid. Pump the piston until no more air bubbles appear in the reservoir(s).
3. Disconnect the two short lines, refill the master cylinder and securely install the cylinder cap(s).
4. Install the master cylinder on the car. Attach the lines but do not completely tighten them. Force any air that might have been trapped in the connection by slowly depressing the brake pedal. Tighten the lines before releasing the brake pedal.

GM QUICK TAKE-UP SYSTEM BLEEDING

Bleed the master cylinder as follows; disconnect the left front brake line at the master cylinder. Fill the cylinder with fluid until it flows from the opened port. Connect the line and tighten the fitting. Apply the brake pedal slowly one time and keep it applied. Loosen the same brake line fitting to allow any air to escape. Retighten the fitting and release the brake pedal slowly. Wait 15 seconds and repeat the procedure until all of the air is expelled. Bleed the right front connection in the same manner. Bleed the cylinders and calipers after you are sure all the air is out of the master cylinder.

CAUTION

Rapid pumping will move the secondary piston down the bore and make it difficult to bleed the system. Always apply slow pedal pressure.

POWER BRAKES

Vacuum Operated Booster

Power brakes operate just as standard brake systems except in the actuation of the master cylinder pistons. A vacuum diaphragm is located on the front of the master cylinder and assists the driver in applying the brakes, reducing both the effort and travel he must put into moving the brake pedal.

The vacuum diaphragm housing is connected to the intake manifold by a vacuum hose. A check valve is placed at the point where the hose enters the diaphragm housing, so that during periods of low manifold vacuum brake assist vacuum will not be lost.

Depressing the brake pedal closes off the vacuum source and allows atmospheric pressure to enter on one side of the diaphragm. This causes the master cylinder pistons to move and apply the brakes. When the brake pedal is released, vacuum is applied to both sides of the diaphragm, and return springs return the diaphragm and master cylinder pistons to the released position. If the vacuum fails, the brake pedal rod will butt against the end of the master cylinder actuating rod, and direct mechanical application will occur as the pedal is depressed.

The hydraulic and mechanical problems that apply to conventional brake systems also apply to power brakes, and should be checked for if the tests and chart below do not reveal the problem.

Tests for a system vacuum leak as described below:

1. Operate the engine at idle with the transmission in Neutral without touching the brake pedal for at least one minute.
2. Turn off the engine, and wait one minute.
3. Test for the presence of assist vacuum by depressing the brake pedal and releasing it several times. Light application will produce less and less pedal travel, if vacuum was present. If there is no vacuum, air is leaking into the system somewhere. Test for system operation as follows:

1. Pump the brake pedal (with engine off) until the supply vacuum is entirely gone.
2. Put a light, steady pressure on the pedal.
3. Start the engine, and operate it at idle with the transmission in Neutral. If the system is operating, the brake pedal should fall toward the floor if constant pressure is maintained on the pedal.

Power brake systems may be tested for hydraulic leaks just as ordinary systems are tested, except that the engine should be idling with the transmission in Neutral throughout the test.

POWER BRAKE BOOSTER TROUBLESHOOTING CHART

The following items are in addition to those listed in the "General Troubleshooting" section. Check those items first.

Hard Pedal

1. Faulty vacuum check valve.
2. Vacuum hose kinked, collapsed, plugged. leaky, or improperly connected.
3. Internal leak in unit.
4. Damaged vacuum cylinder.
5. Damaged valve plunger.
6. Broken or faulty springs.
7. Broken plunger stem.

Grabbing Brakes

1. Damaged vacuum cylinder.
2. Faulty vacuum check valve.
3. Vacuum hose leaky or improperly connected.
4. Broken plunger stem.

Pedal Goes to Floor

Generally, when this problem occurs, it is not caused by the power brake booster. In rare cases, a broken plunger stem may be at fault.

Overhaul

Most power brake boosters are serviced by replacement only. In many cases, repair parts are not available. A good many special tools are required for rebuilding these units. For these reasons, it would be most practical to replace a failed booster with a new or remanufactured unit.

Hydro-Boost, Hydro-Boost II

Hydro-Boost differs from conventional power brake systems, in that it operates from power steering pump fluid pressure, rather than intake manifold vacuum.

The Hydro-Boost unit contains a spool valve with an open center which controls the strength of pump pressure when braking occurs. A lever assembly controls the valve's position. A boost piston provides the force necessary to operate the conventional master cylinder on the front of the booster.

A reserve of at least two assisted brake applications is supplied by an accumulator which is spring loaded on earlier and pneumatic on later models. The accumulator is an integral part of the Hydro-Boost II unit. The brakes can be applied manually if the reserve system is depleted.

All system checks, tests and troubleshooting procedure are the same for the two systems.

HYDRO-BOOST SYSTEM CHECKS

1. A defective Hydro-Boost cannot cause any of the following conditions:
   a. Noisy brakes
   b. Fading pedal
   c. Pulling brakes
   If any of these occur, check elsewhere in the brake system.
2. Check the fluid level in the master cylinder. It should be within ¼ in. of the top. If it isn't, add only DOT-3 or DOT-4 brake fluid until the correct level is reached.
3. Check the fluid level in the power steering pump. The engines should be at normal running temperature and stopped. The level should register on the pump dipstick. Add power steering fluid to bring the reservoir up to the correct level. Low fluid level will result in both poor steering and stopping ability.

——— CAUTION ———
The brake hydraulic system uses brake fluid only, while the power steering and Hydro-Boost systems use power steering fluid only. Don't mix the two.

4. Check the power steering pump belt tension, and inspect all of the power steering/Hydro-Boost hoses for kinks or leaks.
5. Check and adjust the engine idle speed, as necessary.
6. Check the power steering pump fluid for bubbles. If air bubbles are present in the fluid, bleed the system:
   a. Fill the power steering pump reservoir to specifications with the engine at normal operating temperature.
   b. With the engine running, rotate the steering wheel through its normal travel 3 or 4 times, without holding the wheel against the stops.
   c. Check the fluid level again.

7. If the problem still exists, go on to the Hydro-Boost test sections and troubleshooting chart.

HYDRO-BOOST TESTS

Functional Test

1. Check the brake system for leaks or low fluid level. Correct as necessary.
2. Place the transmission in Neutral and stop the engine. Apply the brakes 4 or 5 times to empty the accumulator.
3. Keep the pedal depressed with moderate (25–40 lbs.) pressure and start the engine.
4. The brake pedal should fall slightly and then push back up against your foot. If no movement is felt, the Hydro-Boost system is not working.

ACCUMULATOR LEAK TEST

1. Run the engine at normal idle. Turn the steering wheel against one of the stops; hold it there for no longer than 5 seconds. Center the steering wheel and stop the engine.
2. Keep applying the brakes until a "hard" pedal is obtained. There should be a minimum of 2 power (1-Hydro-Boost II) assisted brake applications when pedal pressure of 20–25 lbs. is applied.
3. Start the engine and allow it to idle. Rotate the steering wheel against the stop. Listen for a light "hissing" sound; this is the accumulator being charged. Center the steering wheel and stop the engine.
4. Wait one hour and apply the brakes without starting the engine. As in step 2, there should be at least 2 (1-Hydro-Boost II) stops with power assist. If not, the accumulator is defective and must be replaced.

Hydro-Boost System Bleeding

The system should be bled whenever the booster is removed and installed.
1. Fill the power steering pump until the fluid level is at the base of the pump reservoir neck. Disconnect the battery lead from the distributor.

NOTE: On diesel engines remove the electrical lead to the fuel solenoid terminal on the injection pump before cranking the engine.

2. Jack up the front of the car, turn the wheels all the way to the left, and crank the engine for a few seconds.
3. Check steering pump fluid level. If necessary, add fluid to the "Add" mark on the dipstick.
4. Lower the car, connect the battery lead, and start the engine. Check fluid level and add fluid to the "Add" mark if necessary.
With the engine running, turn the wheels from side to side to bleed air from the sys-

tem. Make sure that the fluid level stays above the internal pump casting.
5. The Hydro-Boost system should now be fully bled. If the fluid is foaming after bleeding, stop the engine, let the system set for one hour, then repeat the second part of step 4.

The preceding procedures should be effective in removing excess air from the system, however sometimes air may still remain trapped. When this happens the booster may make a "gulping" noise when the brake is applied. Lightly pumping the brake pedal with the engine running should cause this noise to disappear. After the noise stops, check the pump fluid level and add as necessary.

HYDRO-BOOST TROUBLESHOOTING CHART

High Pedal and Steering Effort (Idle)

1. Loose/broken power steering pump belt
2. Low power steering fluid level
3. Leaking hoses or fittings
4. Low idle speed
5. Hose restriction
6. Defective power steering pump

High Pedal Effort (Idle)

1. Binding pedal/linkage
2. Fluid contamination
3. Defective Hydro-Boost unit

Poor Pedal Return

1. Binding pedal linkage
2. Restricted booster return line
3. Internal return system restriction

Pedal Chatter/Pulsation

1. Power steering/pump drivebelt slipping
2. Low power steering fluid level
3. Defective power steering pump
4. Defective Hydro-Boost unit

Brakes Oversensitive

1. Binding pedal/linkage
2. Defective Hydro-Boost unit

Noise

1. Low power steering fluid level
2. Air in the power steering fluid
3. Loose power steering pump drivebelt
4. Hose restrictions

OVERHAUL

Ford Motor Company services the Hydro-Boost unit with a replacement new or rebuilt unit only. No provisions are made for overhaul of the unit. GM Hydro-Boost units may be overhauled by qualified mechanics.

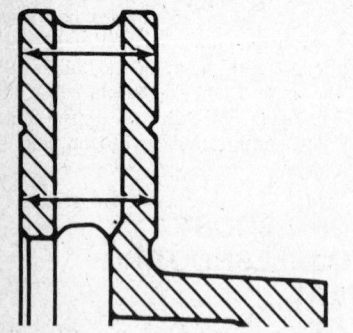

Taper variation not to exceed .003 in.

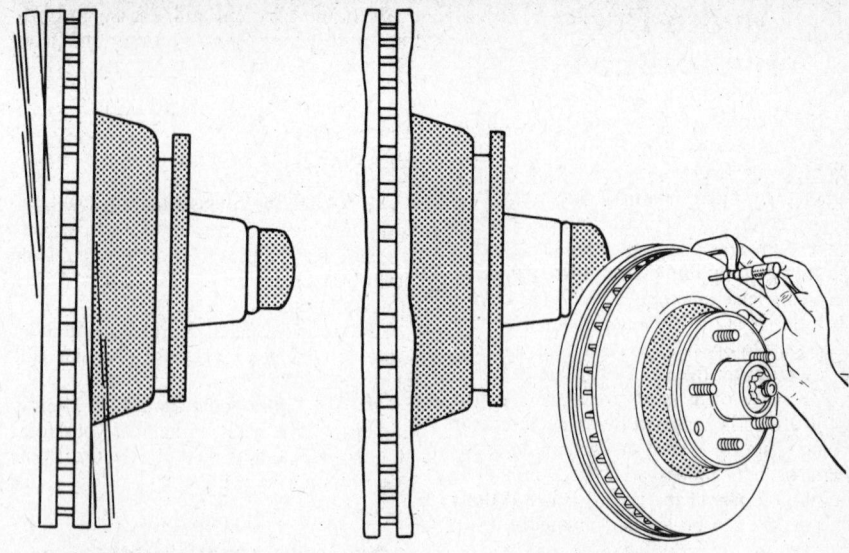

Excessive runout

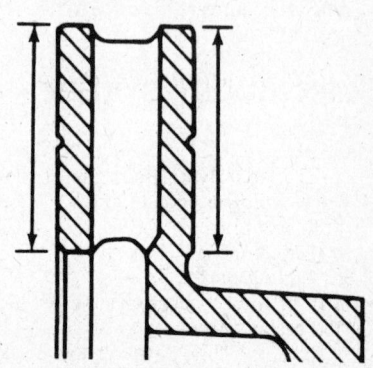

Parallelism

Disc Brake Rotors

RUNOUT

Manufacturers differ widely on permissible runout, but too much can sometimes be felt as a pulsation at the brake pedal. A wobble pump effect is created when a rotor is not perfectly smooth and the pad hits the high spots forcing fluid back into the master cylinder. This alternating pressure causes a pulsating feeling which can be felt at the pedal when the brakes are applied. This excessive runout also causes the brakes to be out of adjustment because disc brakes are self-adjusting; they are designed so that the pads drag on the rotor at all times and therefore automatically compensate for wear.

To check the actual runout of the rotor, first tighten the wheel spindle nut to a snug bearing adjustment, end-play removed.

Fasten a dial indicator on the suspension at a convenient place so that the indicator stylus contacts the rotor face approximately one inch from its outer edge. Set the dial at zero. Check the total indicator reading while turning the rotor one full revolution. If the rotor is warped beyond the runout specification, it is likely that it can be successfully remachined.

"Lateral Runout": A wobbly movement of the rotor from side to side as it rotates. Excessive lateral runout causes the rotor faces to knock back the disc pads and can result in chatter, excessive pedal travel, pumping or fighting pedal and vibration during the breaking action.

"Parallelism" (lack of): Refers to the amount of variation in the thickness of the rotor. Excessive variation can cause pedal vibration or fight, front end vibrations and possible "grab" during the braking action; a condition comparable to an "out-of-round brake drum." Check parallelism with a mi-

These surfaces to be flat and within .002 in.

crometer. "Mike" the thickness at eight or more equally spaced points, equally distant from the outer edge of the rotor, preferably at mid-points of the braking surface. Parallelism then is the amount of variation between maximum and minimum measurements.

"Surface or Micro-inch finish, flatness, smoothness": Different from parallelism, these terms refer to the degree of perfection of the flat surface on each side of the rotor; that is, the minute hills, valleys and swirls inherent in machining the surface. In a visual inspection, the remachined surface should have a fine ground polish with, at most, only a faint trace of nondirectional swirls.

SERVICING THE DISC ROTOR

Disc Replacement

1. Raise the vehicle and safely support on jackstands. Remove the wheel.
2. Remove the caliper mounting bolts. Slide the caliper away from the disc and suspend it using a wire loop. On some cars, it is advisable to install a cardboard spacer between the pads to prevent the piston from coming out of its cylinder.

Ideal rotor surface condition

DISC BRAKE APPLICATION CHART & SPECIFICATIONS

Make/ Model	Year	Text Reference Type	Caliper Style	Manufacturer	Anchor Bolt (ft lbs)	Bridge, Pin or Key Bolts (ft lbs)	Wheel Lugs (ft lbs)	Minimum Thickness Normal Standard	Machine To	Discard At	Rotor Parallel Variation	Max. Runout
AMERICAN MOTORS												
Eagle	'82–'85	1	Sliding	Bendix	100	30	75	.880	.815	.810	.0005	.003
Concord, Spirit	'82–'83	1	Sliding	Bendix	85	30	75	.880	.815	.810	.0005	.003
Except Matador	'78–'81	1	Sliding	Bendix	80	15	75	.880	.815	.810	.0005	.003
Matador	'78	1	Sliding	Bendix	80	15	75–90	—	—	1.210	.0005	.003
CHRYSLER CORPORATION (Front Wheel Drive)												
Aries, Reliant LeBaron, Dodge 400, 600 without H.D brakes	'83–'85	12 or 14	Floating	ATE	70–100	18–22	80	.935	.912	.882	.0005	.004
H.D. brakes	'83–'85	12 or 14	Floating	K/H	70–100	25–35	80	.935	.912	.882	.0005	.004
E Class, New Yorker, Town & Country, Daytona, Laser	'83–85	12 or 14	Floating	ATE or K/H	70–100	ATE: 18–22 K/H: 25–35	80	.935	.912	.882	.0005	.004
Omni, Horizon, Charger, Turismo	'83–'85	11	Floating	K/H	70–100	25–40	80	.500	.461	.431	.0005	.004
Aries, Reliant, LeBaron, Dodge 400	'81–'82	12	Floating	ATE	70–100	18–22	85	.935	.912	.882	.0005	.004
Omni, Horizon	'78–'82	11	Floating	K/H	70–100	25–40	85	.500	.461	.431	.0005	.004
CHRYSLER CORPORATION (Rear Wheel Drive)												
Cordoba, Diplomat, Gran Fury, Mirada, New Yorker, Imperial	'79–'85	6	Sliding	Chrysler	95–125	15–20	85	1.010	.955	.940	.0005	.004
Full Size	'78	6	Sliding	Chrysler	95–125	15	85	1.240	1.195	1.180	.0005	.004
Intermediate	'78	6	Sliding	Chrysler	95–125	15	85	1.010	.955	.940	.0005	.004
	'78	5	Floating	K/H	95–125	25–40	85	1.010	.955	.940	.0005	.004
FORD MOTOR CO. (Front Wheel Drive)												
Escort, Lynx, LN7, EXP, Tempo, Topaz	'81–'85	10	Sliding	Ford	—	18–25	80–105	.945	—	.882	.0005	.003
FORD MOTOR CO. (Rear Wheel Drive)												
Lincoln Continental, Mark VII-Front	'82–'85	13	Sliding	Ford	—	40–60	80–105	1.030	—	.972	.0005	.003
Rear	'82–'85	7	Sliding	K/H	85–115	15–20	80–105	.945	—	.895	.0004	.004
Lincoln Town Car, Crown Victoria, Grand Marquis	'83–'85	13	Sliding	Ford	—	40–60	80–105	1.030	—	.972	.0005	.003
Ford, Mercury, Lincoln ('80)	'79–'82	13	Sliding	Ford	—	40–60	80–105	1.030	—	.972	.0005	.003
Ford, Mercury, Lincoln ('79)	'78	1	Sliding	K/H	90–120	12–16	70–115	1.180	—	1.120	.0005	.003
All models, except noted	'79–'85	13	Sliding	Ford	—	30–40	80–105	.870	—	.810	.0005	.003
Granada, Monarch Versailles	'78–'80	1	Sliding	K/H	105U-65L	12–16	80–105	.870	—	.810	.0005	.003

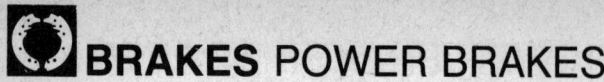

DISC BRAKE APPLICATION CHART & SPECIFICATIONS

Make/ Model	Year	Text Reference Type	Caliper Style	Manu-facturer	Anchor Bolt (ft lbs)	Bridge, Pin or Key Bolts (ft lbs)	Wheel Lugs (ft lbs)	Minimum Thickness			Rotor Parallel Varia-tion	Max. Run-out
								Normal Standard	Machine To	Discard At		
LTD II, Elite, Torino, Ranchero, Ranch Wagon, Squire, Cougar, XR7, Montego	'78–'79	1	Sliding	K/H	90–120	12–16	80–105	1.180	—	1.120	.0005	.003
Mustang, Capri	'78	1	Sliding	K/H	105U-65L	12–16	80–105	.870	—	.810	.0005	.003
Pinto, Bobcat	'78–'80	1	Sliding	K/H	105U-65L	12–16	80–105	.870	—	.810	.0005	.003
Rear Disc Brakes	'78–'82	7	Sliding	K/H	85–115	15–20	80–105	.945	—	.895	.0004	.003
GENERAL MOTORS—BUICK												
Electra Limited, Park Ave (Front Wheel Drive)	'85	2	Floating	Delco	—	35	70	1.043	.972	.957	.0005	.002
Electra, Estate Wagon (Rear Wheel Drive)	'78–'84	2	Floating	Delco	—	35	80①	1.037	.980	.965	.0005	.004
Riviera Front:	'78–'85	2	Floating	Delco	—	35	100	1.037	.980	.965	.0005	.004
Rear:	'79–'85	9	Floating	Delco	35	30	100	—	.980	.965	.0005	.004
Century w/H.D.	'83–'85	2	Floating	Delco	—	28	100	—	.972	.957	.0005	.002
exc. H.D	'82–'85	2	Floating	Delco	—	28	100	—	.830	.815	.0005	.002
Skyhawk w/vented disc	'82–'85	2	Floating	Delco	—	28	100	—	.830	.815	.0005	.002
w/solid disc	'82	2	Floating	Delco	—	28	100	—	.444	.429	.0005	.002
	'78–'80	3	Floating	Delco	—	—	80	.885	.830	.815	.0005	.005
Regal, LeSabre,	'82–'85	2	Floating	Delco	—	35	70–80	—	.980	.965	.0005	.004
Skylark	'80–'85	2	Floating	Delco	—	21–35	102	.885	.830	.815	.0005	.003
	'78–'79	2	Floating	Delco	—	35	80	1.037	.980	.965	.0005	.004
Century, Regal, LeSabre	'78–'81	2	Floating	Delco	—	35	80	—	.980	.965	.0005	.004
GENERAL MOTORS—CADILLAC												
Cimarron	'82–'85	2	Floating	Delco	—	28	100	.885	.830	.815	.0005	.004
Fleetwood, DeVille (Front Wheel Drive)	'85	2	Floating	Delco	—	35	70	1.043	.972	.957	.0005	.002
Fleetwood, DeVille, (Rear Wheel Drive) Front	'78–'84	2	Floating	Delco	—	30	100	1.037⑥	.980	.965	.0005	.004
Rear	'78–'84	9	Floating	Delco	35	30	100	.974⑤	.910	.905	.0005	.003
CC, Limousine	'78–'85	2	Floating	Delco	—	30	100	1.285⑤	1.230	1.215	.0005	.004
Eldorado, Seville ('80–'85) Front	'79–'85	2	Floating	Delco	—	28	100	1.000	.980	.965	.0005	.004
Front	'78	2	Floating	Delco	—	30	130	1.036	—	.965	.0005	.008
Seville—Front	'78–'79	2	Floating	Delco	—	30	100	1.037	.980	.965	.0005	.004
Eldorado, Seville Rear	'78–'85	9	Floating	Delco	35	30	100	.974	.910	.905	.0005	.004
GENERAL MOTORS—CHEVROLET												
Full Size	'78–'85	2	Floating	Delco	—	35	80②	1.030	.980	.965	.0005	.004

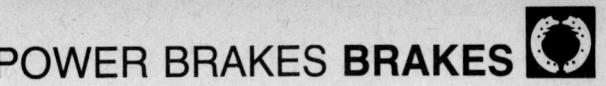
DISC BRAKE APPLICATION CHART & SPECIFICATIONS

Make/ Model	Year	Text Reference Type	Caliper Style	Manu-facturer	Anchor Bolt (ft lbs)	Bridge, Pin or Key Bolts (ft lbs)	Wheel Lugs (ft lbs)	Minimum Thickness Normal Standard	Machine To	Discard At	Rotor Parallel Variation	Max. Run-out
Malibu, Monte Carlo,	'78–'85	2	Floating	Delco	—	35	80③	1.030	.980	.965	.0005	.004
Camaro—Front	'78–'85	2	Floating	Delco	—	21–35	80	1.030	.980	.965	.0005	.004
Rear	'78–'85	9	Floating	Delco	—	30–45	80	1.030	.980	.965	.0005	.004
Corvette—Front	'78–'82	4	Fixed	Delco	70	130	70④	1.285	1.230	1.215	.0005	.004
Rear	'78–'82	4	Fixed	Delco	70	60	70④	1.285	1.230	1.215	.0005	.004
Front	'84	16	Floating	Girlock	70	24	100	—	.724	—	.0005	.006
Rear	'84	16	Floating	Girlock	44	24	100	—	.724	—	.0005	.006
Celebrity, Cavalier	'82–'85	2	Floating	Delco	—	28	100	Vented .885, Solid .490	Vented .830, Solid .444	.815, .429	.0005	.004
Citation	'80–'85	2	Floating	Delco	—	28	102	.885	.830	.815	.0005	.003
Nova	'78–'79	2	Floating	Delco	—	35	80	1.037	.980	.965	.0005	.004
Monza	'78–'80	3	Floating	Delco	—	—	80③	.885	.830	.815	.0005	.005
Chevette	'78–'82	8	Floating	Delco	70	28	70	.440	.390	.374	.0005	.005
	'83–'85	2	Floating	Delco	—	21–25	70	—	.390	.374	.0005	.005
GENERAL MOTORS—OLDSMOBILE												
98 Regency, Brougham (Front Wheel Drive)	'85	2	Floating	Delco	—	35	70	1.043	.972	.957	.0005	.002
Full Size	'78–'84	2	Floating	Delco	—	35	80①	1.040	.980	.965	.0005	.005
Toronado—Front	'79–'84	2	Floating	Delco	—	35	100	1.040⑦	.980	.965	.0005	.004
Rear	'79–'84	9	Floating	Delco	32	30	100	1.040⑦	.980	.965	.0005	.004
	'78	2	Floating	Delco	—	35–40	130		1.185	1.170	.0005	.004
Cutlass Supreme, Cutlass	'78–'84	2	Floating	Delco	—	35	80	1.040	.980	.965	.0005	.005
Ciera, Firenza	'82–'84	2	Floating	Delco	—	28	100	Vented .885, Solid .490	Vented .830, Solid .444	.815, .429	.0005	.004
Omega	'80–'84	2	Floating	Delco	—	28	103	.885	.830	.815	.0005	.003
	'78–'79	2	Floating	Delco	—	35	80	1.040	.980	.965	.0005	.005
Starfire	'78–'80	3	Floating	Delco	—	—	80	.880	.830	.815	.0005	.003
GENERAL MOTORS—PONTIAC												
Full Size	'78–'85	2	Floating	Delco	—	35	80①	1.040	.980	.965	.0005	.004
Grand Prix, Grand Am, LeMans	'78–'85	2	Floating	Delco	—	35	80	1.030	.980	.965	.0005	.004
Firebird—Front	'78–'85	2	Floating	Delco	—	21–35	80	1.030	.980	.965	.0005	.004
Rear	'78–'85	9	Floating	Delco	—	30–45	80	1.030	.980	.965	.0005	.004
6000, J2000	'82–'85	2	Floating	Delco	—	28	100	Vented .885, Solid .490	Vented .830, Solid .444	.815, .429	.0005	.004
Phoenix, Ventura	'80–'85	2	Floating	Delco	—	28	103	.885	.830	.815	.0005	.003
	'78–'79	2	Floating	Delco	—	35	80	1.037	.980	.965	.0005	.005

DISC BRAKE APPLICATION CHART & SPECIFICATIONS

Make/ Model	Year	Text Reference Type	Caliper Style	Manu-facturer	Anchor Bolt (ft lbs)	Bridge, Pin or Key Bolts (ft lbs)	Wheel Lugs (ft lbs)	Minimum Thickness			Rotor Parallel Varia-tion	Max. Run-out
								Normal Standard	Machine To	Discard At		
Sunbird	'78–'80	3	Floating	Delco	—	—	80	.885	.830	.815	.0005	.005
T1000	'81–'82	8	Floating	Delco	70	28	70	.440	.390	.374	.0005	.005
	'83–'85	2	Floating	Delco	—	21–25	70	—	.390	.374	.0005	.005
Fiero												
Front	'84–'85	2	Floating	Delco	—	35	81	—	.444	.390	.0005	.004
Rear	'84–'85	15	Floating	Delco	—	35	81	—	.444	.390	.0005	.004

① 100 with ½ in. studs
② 100 on s/w
③ 90 with aluminum wheels
④ 80 with aluminum wheels
⑤ 1980 and later is 1.250
⑥ 1980 and later is 1.000

3. Remove the wheel bearing nut from the spindle and remove the outer wheel bearing roller assembly from the hub.

On Ford sliding caliper brakes, remove the wheel bearing adjusting nut and pull the hub and disc assembly outward enough to loosen the washer and outer wheel bearing. Push the assembly back onto the spindle and remove the washer and outer wheel bearing from the spindle.

4. Remove the hub and disc assembly from the spindle.

5. Installation of hub and disc is in reverse order of removal.

NOTE: The disc is removable from the hub on the Eldorado, Toronado, and Corvette (rear only).

To separate the rear disc and hub on a Corvette the three hub-to-disc attaching rivets must be drilled out. This can be done with the hub and rotor mounted on the car.

It is not necessary to install new rivets when the disc is installed.

SERVICING FRONT DISC BRAKES

INSPECTION

Disc pads (lining and shoe assemblies) should be replaced in axle sets (both wheels) when the lining on any pad is worn to 1/16 in. at any point. *If lining is allowed to wear past 1/16 in. minimum thickness severe damage to disc may result.*

NOTE: State inspection specifications take precedence over these general recommendations.

Note that disc pads in floating caliper type brakes may wear at an angle, and measurement should be made at the narrow end of the taper. Tapered linings should be replaced if the taper exceeds 1/8 in. from end to end (the difference between the thickest and thinnest points).

——— CAUTION ———

To prevent costly paint damage, remove some brake fluid (don't re-use) from the reservoir and install the reservoir cover before replacing the disc pads. When replacing the pads, the piston is depressed and fluid is forced back through the lines to squirt out of the fluid reservoir.

When the caliper is unbolted from the hub do not let it dangle by the brake hose; it can be rested on a suspension member or wired onto the frame. All disc brake systems are self-adjusting and have no provision for manual adjustment.

Type One: Kelsey–Hayes or Bendix Sliding Caliper Disc Brakes (Single Piston)

PAD REMOVAL

1. Remove half of the brake fluid from the master cylinder.

2. Remove the retaining screw holding the caliper support key.

3. Use a hammer and drift to drive the caliper retaining key and support spring out of the anchor plate.

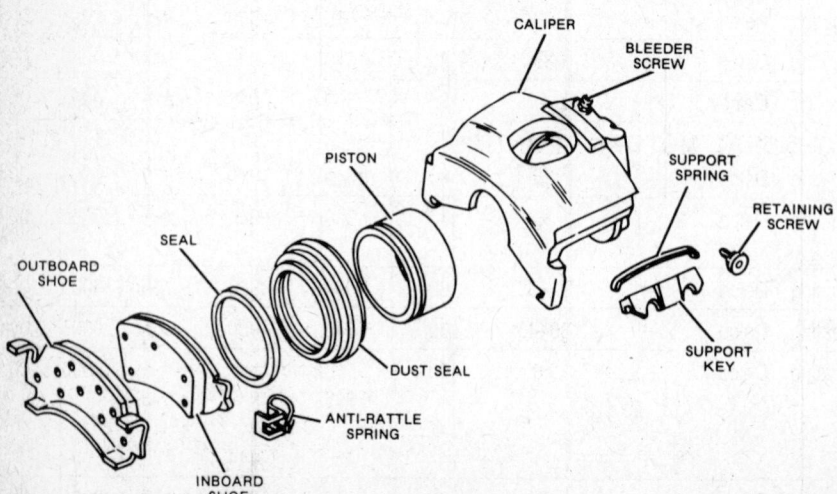

Type one Bendix floating caliper disc brakes (single Piston)

4. Lift the caliper off of the rotor.

5. Support caliper so it doesn't hang by the brake hose.

6. Use a large C-clamp to force the piston back into its bore, being careful not to scratch the piston or bore, and being careful not to cut or tear the dust boot.

7. Remove the inboard pad and anti-rattle spring from the caliper support adapter.

8. Remove the outboard pad from the caliper. Check the condition of the rotor. If rotor run out exceeds manufacturer's specifications or has deep scratches, re-machine the rotor.

9. Clean all sliding surfaces on the adapter and caliper.

PAD INSTALLATION

1. Position the inboard brake pad and anti-rattle spring in the caliper support adapter.

2. Position the outboard brake pad in the caliper. Bend ears if necessary to provide slight interference fit in caliper.

3. Position the caliper over the rotor take care not to damage the caliper piston dust boot.

4. Position the caliper support spring and support key into the slot and drive them into the opening between the lower end of the caliper and the lower anchor plate abutment.

5. Install and tighten the key retaining screw.

6. Fill the master cylinder with brake fluid. Bleed the system if necessary.

Type Two: Delco Floating Caliper (Single Piston)

PAD REMOVAL

1. Remove half of the brake fluid from the master cylinder.

2. Position a large C-clamp over the

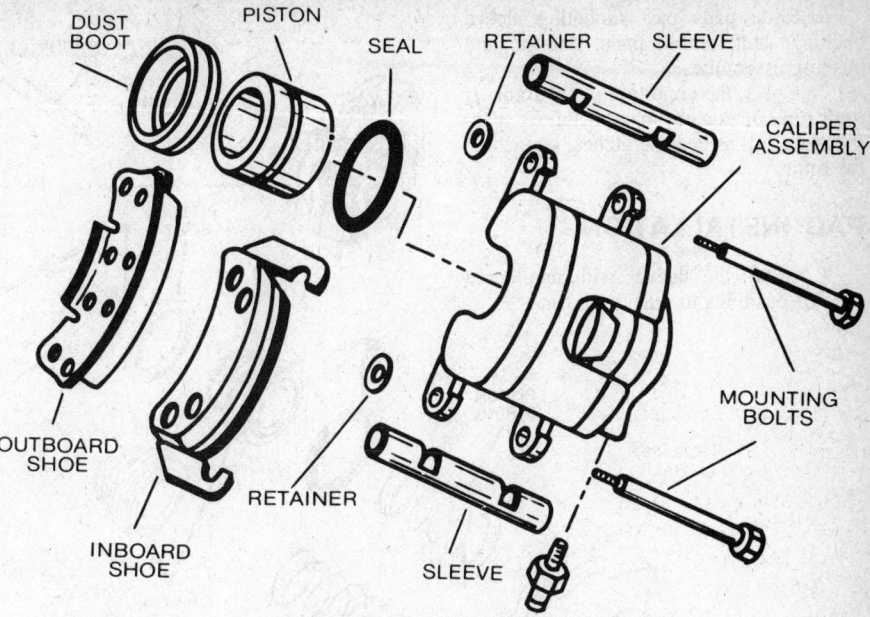

Type three-Disc floating caliper (single piston)

caliper with the screw end against the outboard brake pad. Tighten the clamp until the caliper is pushed out enough to bottom the piston.

3. Remove the C-clamp. Remove the two caliper guide pin mounts and lift the caliper off of the rotor.

4. Support the caliper so there is no strain on the brake hose.

5. Press the outboard pad inward, then lift from the caliper.

6. Press the inboard pad outward, then lift from the caliper.

7. Remove and discard the four O-ring bushings and steel sleeves if new ones are to be installed. Check the condition of the rotor. If rotor run out exceeds manufacturer's specifications or has deep scratches, re-machine the rotor.

PAD INSTALLATION

1. Lubricate and install the four O-ring

bushings, install the sleeves, pressing them through the O-rings until the sleeve end on the pad side is flush with caliper ear. Position the inboard pad so the pad contacts the piston and the two support spring ends. Note that the inboard and outboard pads are similar but not interchangeable.

2. Press down on the ears at the top of the inboard pad until the pad lies flat and the spring ends are just inside the lower edge of the pad.

3. Position the outboard pad with the ears toward the positioning pin holes and the tab on the inner edge of the pad resting in the notch in the edge of the caliper. Bend ears if necessary to provide slight interference fit in caliper.

4. Press the outboard pad tightly into position and use a pair of pliers to clinch the ears of the outboard pad over the outboard caliper half.

5. Position the caliper over the rotor.

6. Install the caliper mounting bolts and tighten to specification.

7. Fill the master cylinder with brake fluid.

Type Three: Delco Floating Caliper (Sleeve Type)

PAD REMOVAL

1. Remove half of the brake fluid from the master cylinder.

2. Remove two stamped nuts from the mounting pins and remove pins.

3. Lift the caliper off the rotor.

4. Support the caliper so there is no strain on the brake hose.

5. Use large C-clamp to force the piston back into its bore, being careful not to cut or tear the dust boot.

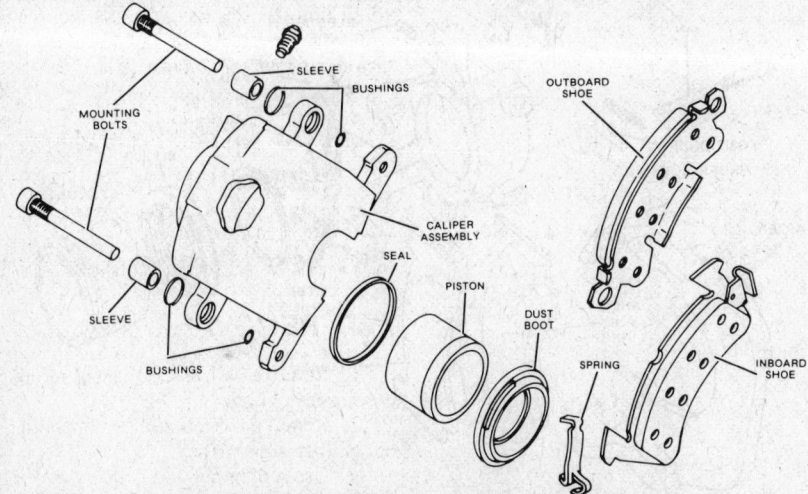

Type two Delco floating disc brakes (single piston)

6. Slide pads past mounting sleeve openings and remove pads, sleeves, and bushing assemblies.

7. Check the condition of the rotor. If rotor run out exceeds manufacturer's specifications or has deep scratches, remachine the rotor.

PAD INSTALLATION

1. Install the sleeves with shouldered ends of bushings to outside of car.

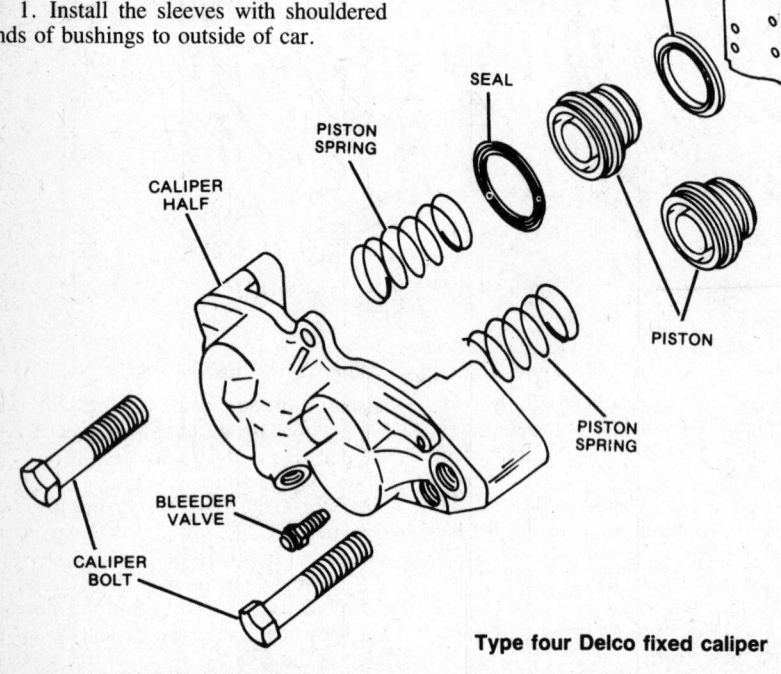

Type four Delco fixed caliper

2. Install pads in caliper with ears over sleeve.

3. Position the caliper on the rotor.

4. Install mounting pins.

5. Install stamped nuts on mounting pins using small socket to press on as far as possible.

6. Fill the master cylinder with fluid.

Type Four: Delco Fixed Caliper (Four Pistons)

PAD REMOVAL AND INSTALLATION

1. Remove half of the brake fluid from the master cylinder.

2. Remove the brake pad retaining pins.

3. Pry the pistons back into their bores (being careful to pry both pistons at once so as not to force one out of its bore) and lift out one pad by tipping it down at the rear and up at the front.

4. Hold the rear piston in and slide the rear end of the new pad into place, being careful not to force out the front piston.

5. Check the condition of the rotor. If rotor run out exceeds .003 thousands, or has deep scratches, re-machine the rotor.

6. Now push the front piston back into its bore and slide the front of the new pad into position.

7. Change the other pad in the same manner.

8. Reinstall the retaining pin through the caliper holes and through the holes in the pads.

9. Fill the master cylinder with fresh brake fluid.

Type Five: Kelsey–Hayes Floating Caliper (Single Piston)

PAD REMOVAL

1. Remove half of the brake fluid from the master cylinder.

2. Remove the caliper guide pins and positioners and anti-rattle spring.

3. Lift the caliper off of the rotor.

4. Support the caliper so there is no strain on the brake hose.

5. Pry the piston back into its bore, being careful not to scratch the pistons or bores, and being careful not to cut or tear the dust boots.

6. Lift the brake pads out of the caliper.

7. Check the condition of the rotor. If rotor run out exceeds manufacturer's specifications or has deep scratches, re-machine the rotor.

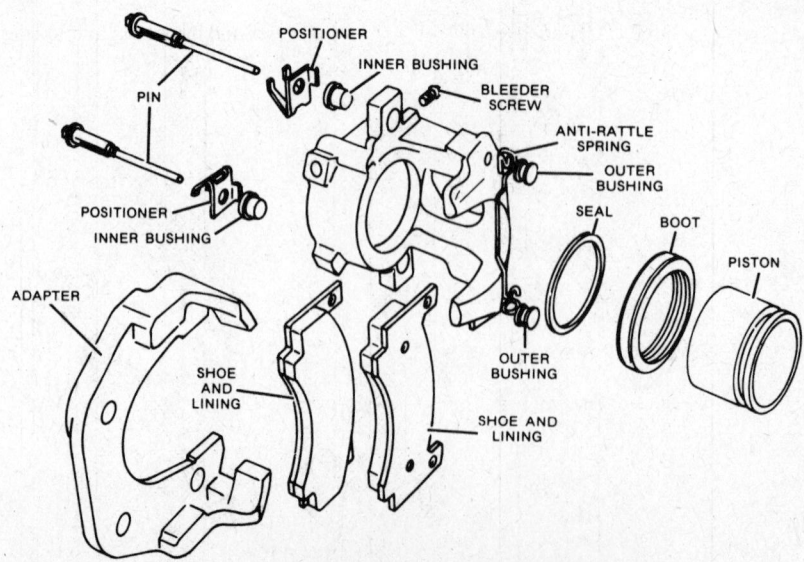

Type five-Kelsey Hayes floating caliper (single piston)

PAD INSTALLATION

1. Clean and lubricate (with light waterproof grease) caliper guide pins and guide surfaces.

2. Position the new pads in the caliper. The inboard and outboard pads are identical and interchangeable.

3. Position the caliper on the rotor.

4. Align the guide pin holes of the adapter and the caliper, and install new positioners over the guide pins, with the open ends facing toward the outside. Tighten the pins to proper specification.

5. Install the anti-rattle spring.

6. Fill the master cylinder with fluid.

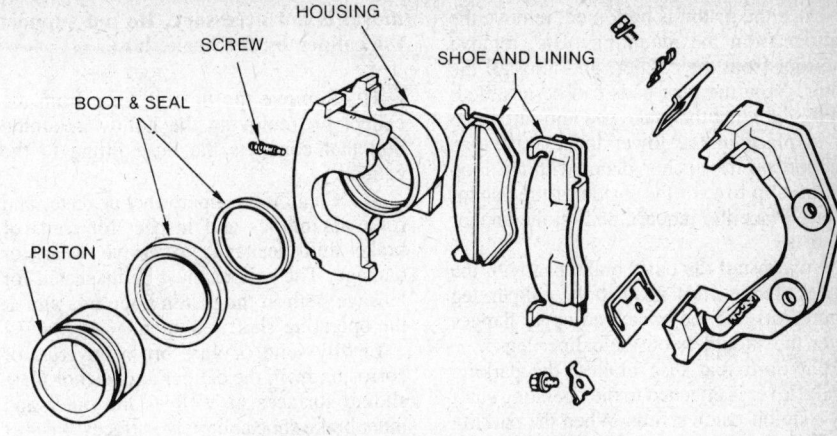

Type six Kelsey Hayes sliding caliper

Type Six: Kelsey–Hayes/Chrysler Sliding Caliper

PAD REMOVAL

1. Remove half of the brake fluid from the master cylinder.

2. Remove caliper retaining clips and anti-rattle springs.

3. Lift the caliper off of the rotor.

4. Support the caliper so there is no strain on the brake hose.

5. Use a large C-clamp to force the piston back into its bore, being careful not to scratch the piston or bore, and being careful not to cut or tear the dust boot.

6. Pry the outboard pad from caliper.

7. Remove inboard pad from the adapter.

8. Check the condition of the rotor. If rotor run out exceeds manufacturer's specifications or has deep scratches, re-machine the rotor.

PAD INSTALLATION

1. Adjust ears of outboard pad to provide tight fit and install pad in caliper recess.

2. Install inboard pad with flanges inserted in adapter ''ways.''

3. Position the caliper on the rotor with the caliper engaging the adapter ''ways.''

4. Install anti-rattle springs and caliper retaining clips and torque retaining screws to 180 inch lbs. (15 ft. lbs.)

5. Fill the master cylinder with brake fluid.

Type Seven: Ford Rear Sliding Caliper

PAD INSTALLATION

Except Mark VII Continental

The recommended procedure for this operation calls for removing the rotor from the car and mounting the caliper in position in the anchor plate with the key only. A special tool is needed to screw the piston back into its bore. While holding the shaft, rotate the tool handle counterclockwise until the tool is seated firmly against the piston. Now loosen the handle about a quarter turn. While holding the handle, rotate the tool shaft clockwise until the piston is fully bottomed in its bore.

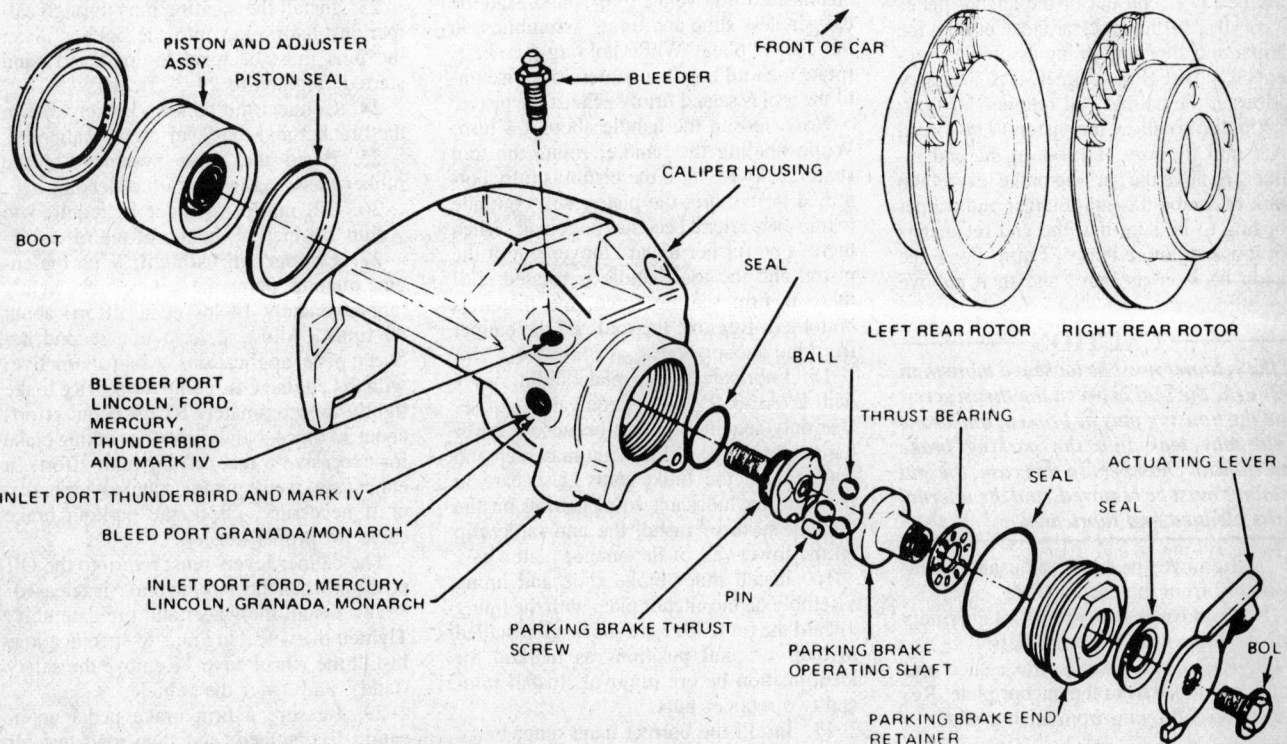

Type seven—Ford optional rear disc brakes

Once the piston is bottomed, remove the caliper from the mounting plate, remove the tool from the caliper, and reinstall the rotor. Now the new pads can be installed. Make sure that the brake pad anti-rattle clip is in place in the lower inner brake pad support on the anchor plate, with the loop of the clip toward the inside of the anchor plate. Place the inboard pad on the anchor plate.

Now install the outer brake pad with the lower flange ends against the caliper leg abutments and the brake pad upper flanges over the shoulders on the caliper legs.

On Ford rear disc brakes, the parking brake lever is attached to the operating shaft by a nylon-patch screw. When the parking brake is applied, the cable rotates the lever and operating shaft. The three steel balls, located in pockets on the opposing heads of the operating shaft and thrust screw, roll between ramps formed in these ball pockets. The balls force the thrust screw away from the operating shaft, driving the piston and pad against the rotor, creating the parking brake force.

Mark VII Continental

1. Raise the vehicle, and install safety stands. Block both front wheels.
2. Remove the wheel assemblies.
3. Disconnect the parking brake cable from the lever and bracket. Use care to avoid kinking or cutting the cable or return spring.
4. Remove the caliper locating pins.
5. Lift the caliper assembly away from the anchor plate by pushing the caliper upward toward the anchor plate, and then rotate the lower end out of the anchor plate.
6. If insufficient clearance between the caliper and shoe and lining assemblies prevents removal of the caliper, it is necessary to loosen the caliper end retainer 1/2 turn, maximum, to allow the piston to be forced back into its bore. To loosen the end retainer, remove the parking brake lever, then mark or scribe the end retainer and caliper housing to be sure that the end retainer is not loosened more than 1/2 turn. Force the piston back in its bore, and then remove the caliper.

—— CAUTION ——
If the retainer must be loosened more than 1/2 turn, the seal between the thrust screw and the housing may be broken, and brake fluid may leak into the parking brake mechanism chamber. In this case, the end retainer must be removed, and the internal parts cleaned and lubricated.

7. Remove the outer shoe and lining assembly from the anchor plate.
8. Remove the two rotor retainer nuts and the rotor from the axle shaft.
9. Remove the inner brake shoe and lining assembly from the anchor plate. Remove anti-rattle clip from anchor plate.

NOTE: If no further service than pad replacement is required, brake hose re-

moval is not necessary. Do not support the caliper by the brake hose.

10. Remove the flexible hose from the caliper by removing the hollow retaining bolt that connects the hose fitting to the caliper.
11. Clean the caliper, anchor plate, and rotor assemblies and inspect for signs of brake fluid leakage, excessive wear, or damage. The caliper must be inspected for leakage both in the piston boot area and at the operating shaft seal area.

Lightly sand or wire brush any rust or corrosion from the caliper and anchor plate sliding surfaces as well as the outer and inner brake shoe abutment surfaces. Inspect the brake shoes for wear. If either lining is worn to within 1/8 in. of the shoe surface, both shoe and lining assemblies must be replaced using the shoe and lining removal procedures.

12. If the end retainer has been loosened only 1/2 turn, reinstall the caliper in the anchor plate without shoe and lining assemblies. Tighten the end retainer to 75-96 ft. lbs.
13. Install the parking brake lever on its keyed spline. The lever arm must point down and rearward. The parking brake cable will then pass freely under the axle. Tighten the retainer screw to 16-22 ft. lbs. The parking brake lever must rotate freely after tightening the retainer screw. Remove the caliper from the anchor plate.
14. If new shoe and lining assemblies are to be installed, the piston must be screwed back into the caliper bore, using Tool T75P-2588-B or equivalent to provide installation clearance. Remove the rotor, and install the caliper, less shoe and lining assemblies, in the anchor plate. While holding the shaft, rotate the tool handle counterclockwise until the tool is seated firmly against the piston.

Now, loosen the handle about 1/4 turn. While holding the handle, rotate the tool shaft clockwise until the piston is fully bottomed in its bore; the piston will continue to turn even after it becomes bottomed. When there is no further inward movement of the piston and the tool handle is rotated until there is firm seating force, the piston is bottomed. Remove the tool and the caliper from the anchor plate.

15. Lubricate anchor plate sliding ways with D7AE-019590-A or equivalent grease. Use only specified grease because a lower temperature type of lubricant may melt and contaminate the brake pads. Use care to prevent any lubricant from getting on the braking surface. Install the anti-rattle clip on the lower rail of the anchor plate.
16. Install inner brake shoe and lining assembly on the anchor plate with the lining toward the rotor. Be sure shoes are installed in their original positions as marked for identification before removal. Install rotor and two retainer nuts.
17. Install the correct hand outer brake shoe and lining assembly on the anchor plate with the lining toward the rotor and wear

indicator toward the upper portion of the brake.

18. Install the flexible hose by placing a new washer on each side of the fitting outlet and inserting the attaching bolt through the washers and fitting. Tighten to 20-30 ft. lbs.
19. Position the upper tab of the caliper housing on the anchor plate upper abutment surface.
20. Rotate the caliper housing until it is completely over the rotor. Use care so that the piston dust boot is not damaged.
21. **Piston Position Adjustment:** Pull the caliper outboard until the inner shoe and lining is firmly seated against the rotor, and measure the clearance between the outer shoe and caliper. The clearance must be 1/32-3/32 in. If it is not, remove the caliper, then readjust the piston to obtain required gap. Follow the procedure given in Step 14, and rotate the shaft counterclockwise to narrow gap and clockwise to widen gap (1/4 turn of the piston moves it approximately 1/16 in.).

—— CAUTION ——
A clearance greater than 3/32 in. may allow the adjuster to be pulled out of the piston when the service brake is applied. This will cause the parking brake mechanism to fail to adjust. It is then necessary to replace the piston/adjuster assembly.

22. Lubricate locating pins and inside of insulator with D7AZ-19A331-A or equivalent silicone grease. Add one drop of Loctite® E0AC-19554-A or equivalent to locating pin threads.
23. Install the locating pins through caliper insulators and into the anchor plate; the pins must be hand inserted and hand started. Tighten to 29-37 ft. lbs.
24. Connect the parking brake cable to the bracket and the lever on the caliper.
25. Bleed the brake system. Replace rubber bleed screw cap after bleeding.
26. Fill master cylinder as required to within 1/8-inch of the top of the reservoir.
27. **Caliper Adjustment:** With the engine running, pump the service brake lightly (approximately 14 lbs pedal effort) about 40 times. Allow at least one second between pedal applications. As an alternative, with the engine Off, pump the service brake lightly (approximately 87 lbs pedal effort) about 30 times. Now check the parking brake for excessive travel or very light effort. In either case, repeat pumping the service brake, or if necessary, check the parking brake cable for proper tension.

The caliper levers must return to the Off position when the parking brake is released.

28. Install the wheel and tire assembly. Tighten the wheel lug nuts to specification. Install the wheel cover. Remove the safety stands, and lower the vehicle.
29. Be sure a firm brake pedal application is obtained, and then road test for proper brake operation, including parking brakes.

Type Eight: Chevette/T1000 Disc Brake

PAD REMOVAL

1. Remove half of the brake fluid from the master cylinder.

2. Use a large C-clamp to force the piston back into its bore, being careful not to scratch the piston or bore, and being careful not to cut or tear the dust boot.

3. Remove the two hex head bolts that attach the caliper mounting bracket to the steering knuckle.

4. Support the caliper so there is no strain on the brake hose.

NOTE: Do not remove the socket head retainer bolt.

5. Remove the old shoe and lining assemblies. If the retaining spring does not come out with the inboard shoe, remove the spring from the piston.

6. Check the condition of the rotor. If rotor run out exceeds manufacturer's specifications or has deep scratches, re-machine the rotor.

PAD INSTALLATION

1. Before installing the inboard shoe, make sure that the shoe retaining spring is properly installed. Push the tab on the single-leg end of the spring down into the shoe hole, then snap the other two legs over the edge of the shoe notch.

2. Position the caliper over the rotor, lining up the bracket mounting holes. Install the mounting bolts.

3. Clinch the outboard shoe to the caliper. After clinching, radial and end play of the outboard shoe should be zero to 0.127 nm (zero to 0.005 inch).

Type Nine: GM Rear Disc Brake

PAD REMOVAL

NOTE: Calipers must be removed to replace linings.

1. Remove two-thirds of the fluid in the front master cylinder.

2. Remove wheel and tire assembly, and reinstall one wheel mounting nut, flat side toward rotor, to prevent rotor from falling when caliper is removed.

3. Loosen tension on the parking brake cable at equalizer, and remove the cable from the parking brake lever at the caliper.

4. Remove return spring, lock nut, lever, lever seal and anti-friction washer. (Lever must be held in place while removing nut.)

5. Using a C-clamp with the solid end of the lever stop and the screw end of the

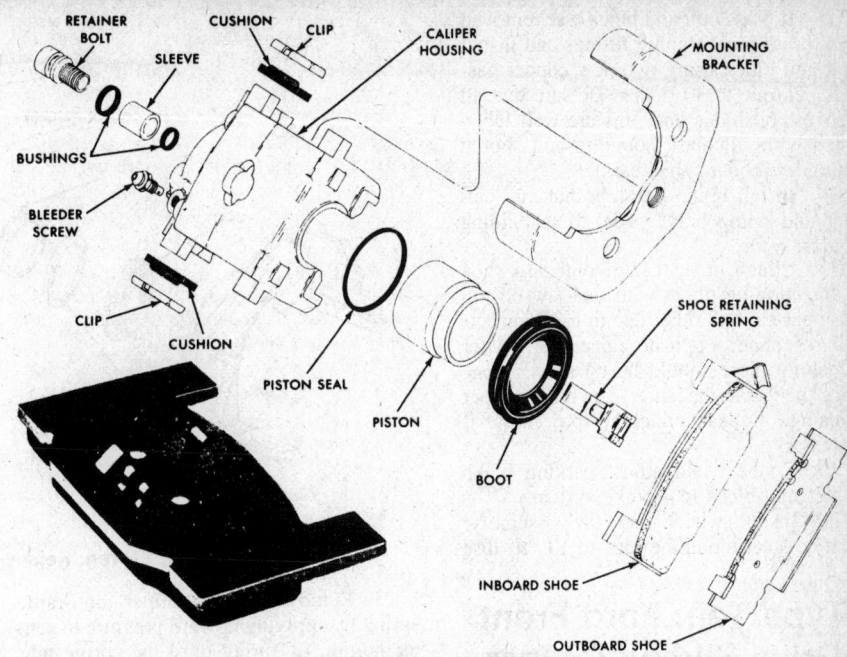

Type eight—Chevette/T1000

back of the outboard lining assembly, tighten clamp until piston bottoms in the caliper.

NOTE: Do not position C-clamp on actuator screw.

6. Before removing the clamp lube the caliper housing surface (under the lever seal) with silicone.

7. Install new anti-friction washer, new lever seal and lever. Be certain to install lever on hex with arm pointing downward.

8. Rotate lever toward front of car and while holding in this position install nut and torque to 25 ft. lbs. Rotate lever back to stop.

9. Install lever return spring, and remove C-clamp. Springs are color coded, red for right side caliper and black for left.

10. Remove brake line from caliper and plug openings to retain fluid.

NOTE: If brake line nut is seized, brass bolt and block on caliper can be removed with brake line attached by removing bolt and block copper washers after removing caliper mounting bolts.

11. Remove caliper mounting bolts and remove caliper and brake shoes.

12. Remove two caliper mounting sleeves and four bushings, and install new parts using a silicone lubricant (sleeves are installed in inner bushings).

13. Position new inboard shoe assembly on piston. D shaped tab must fit in the indentation provided in the piston.

14. Install new outboard shoe assembly.

15. To reinstall caliper replace any corroded caliper mounting bolts with new parts. Wire brushing or sanding will damage the bolt plating.

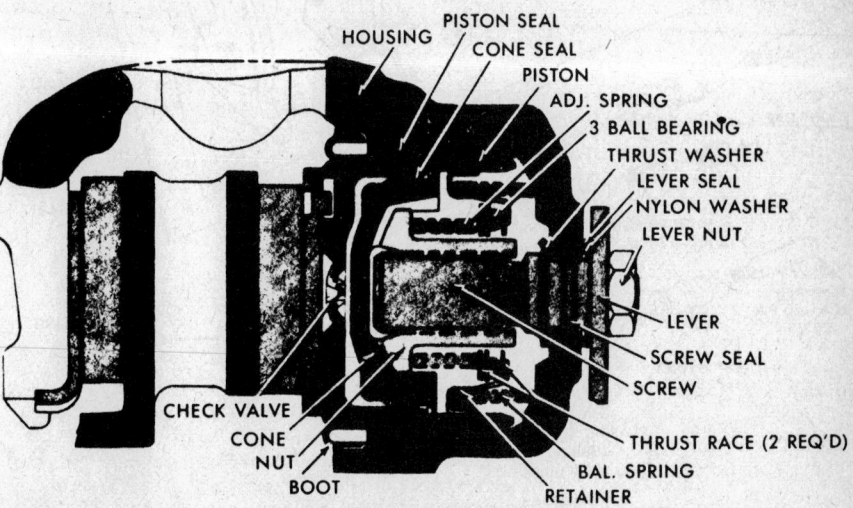

Type nine—GM rear disc brake

16. If brass bolt and block was removed with brass pipe, unplug fittings and install bolt and block using two new copper gaskets. Torque to 30 ft. lbs. Be sure that all sleeves, bushings and pins are well lubricated with silicone (mounting bolt should go under inboard shoe ears).

17. Install brake line tube nut into caliper and pump brake pedal to seat lining against rotor.

18. Clinch upper ear of outboard shoe by positioning pliers with one jaw on top of upper ear and other jaw in notch or bottom of shoe, opposite upper ear. After clinching there should be no radial clearance between the shoe ears and caliper housing. Repeat clinching procedure if necessary.

19. Connect and adjust parking brake cables and bleed rear brake system.

20. Install wheel and tire assembly. Torque steel mounting nuts to 130 ft. lbs.

Type Ten: Ford Front Drive Sliding Caliper

PAD REMOVAL

1. Remove master cylinder cap and check fluid level in reservoirs. Remove brake fluid until each reservoir is half full. Discard the removed fluid.

2. Remove wheel and tire assembly from rotor mounting face. Use care to avoid damage or interference with the caliper splash shield or bleeder screw fitting.

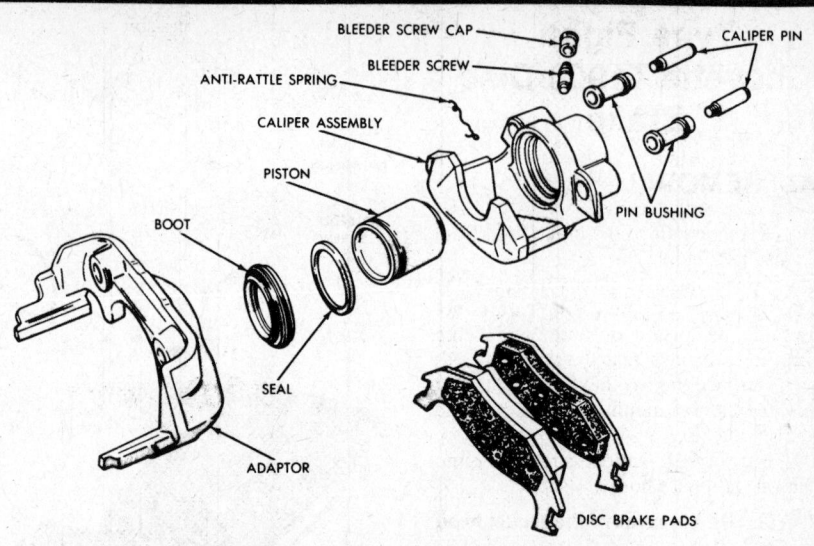

Type Eleven; Kelsey-Hayes Floating Caliper

3. Remove brake caliper anti-rattle spring by applying upward pressure to center portion of spring until the spring tabs are free of the caliper holes.

4. Back out the caliper locating pins. Do not remove pins completely unless new bushings are to be installed. Reinstalling pins after complete removal can be difficult.

5. Lift caliper assembly from integral knuckle and anchor plate and rotor. Remove outer shoe and lining assembly from caliper assembly.

6. Remove inner shoe and lining assembly and inspect both rotor braking surfaces. Minor scoring or build-up of lining material does not require machining or replacement of the rotor.

7. Suspend caliper inside the fender housing. Use care not to damage caliper or stretch the brake hose.

PAD INSTALLATION

1. Use a 4-inch C-clamp and a block of wood 2¾ inch × 1 inch and approximately ¾-inch thick to seat the caliper hydraulic piston in its bore. This must be done to provide clearance for the caliper assembly to fit over the rotor during installation. Extra care must be taken during this procedure to prevent damage to the aluminum piston. Metal or sharp objects cannot come into direct contact with the piston surface or damage will result.

2. Install the correct inner shoe and lining assembly in caliper piston(s). Do not bend shoe clips during installation in the piston or distortion and rattles can occur.

3. Install the correct outer shoe and lining assembly making sure clips are properly seated. Replace caliper anti-rattle spring. Refill master cylinder to at least ¼ in. from the top in both reservoirs.

4. Install the wheel and tire assembly. Tighten wheel nuts to 80–105 ft. lbs. (109–142 Nm).

5. Pump the brake pedal prior to moving the vehicle to position brake linings.

6. Road test the vehicle.

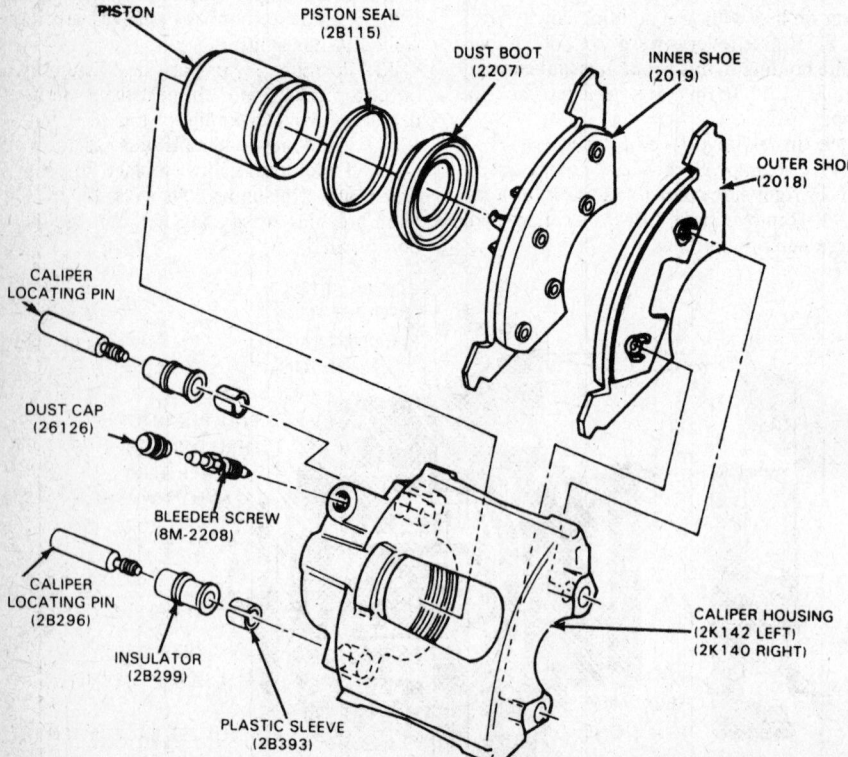

Type Ten; Ford Front Drive Caliper

Type Eleven: Kelsey-Hayes Floating Caliper

PAD REMOVAL

1. Remove half of the brake fluid from each master cylinder reservoir.

2. Remove the caliper guide pins, positioners and anti-rattle spring.

3. Lift the caliper from the rotor and support to prevent strain on the brake hose.

4. Pry the caliper piston back into the bore. Use a C-clamp if necessary.

5. Remove the brake pads from the caliper adaptor. Remove and discard the four bushings if they are to be replaced.

PAD INSTALLATION

1. Clean and lubricate the caliper guide pins and guide mounting surfaces. Install new guide bushings.

2. Position the new brake pads in the caliper adaptor.

3. Carefully lower the caliper over the adaptor. Install the guide pins and anti-rattle spring. The anti-rattle spring is installed with the end loop inboard on the caliper lug.

4. Fill the master cylinder with new fluid. Bleed the brakes if necessary.

Type Twelve: ATE Floating Caliper

PAD REMOVAL

1. Remove the guide pin(s) and anti-rattle clips or springs.

2. Remove the caliper from the rotor by slowly sliding it up and away. Support the caliper so there is no strain on the brake hose. Late model calipers may be pivoted on the anchor bolt.

3. Remove the pads from the adaptor or caliper. In some cases the rotor must be removed to replace the inboard pad.

4. Push the caliper piston back into its bore.

PAD INSTALLATION

1. Install the pads and hardware into the adapter or caliper.

2. Position the caliper over the rotor and install the guide pin(s), anti-rattle springs or clips. Fill the master cylinder with new brake fluid. Bleed the brake system if necessary.

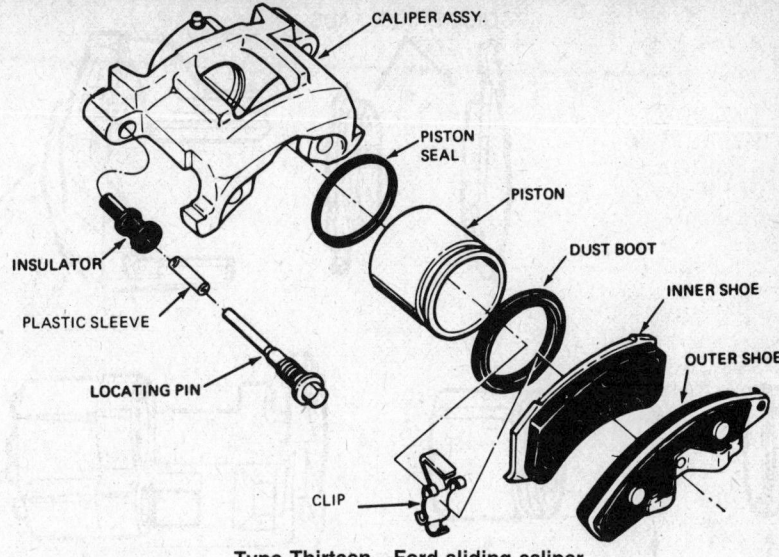
Type Thirteen—Ford sliding caliper

Type Thirteen: Ford Sliding Caliper

PAD REMOVAL

1. Remove half of the brake fluid from the master cylinder reservoirs.

2. Remove the caliper guide pins.

3. Lift the caliper assembly from the rotor. Support the caliper so there is no strain on the brake hose.

4. Remove the outboard pad from the caliper. Remove the inboard pad from the piston.

NOTE: Step six can now be accomplished by using a C-clamp against the inboard pad.

5. Remove the insulators and inserts from the guide pin holes if they are to be replaced.

6. Push the caliper piston back into it's bore.

PAD INSTALLATION

1. Install new guide bushings and insulators if they are to be replaced.

2. Install the inboard pad into the piston. Install the outboard making sure the buttons are seated into the caliper body. The wear indicator faces toward the front of the car.

3. Lower the caliper assembly onto the anchor plate and slide the guide pins through the holes in the caliper. When the guide pins reach the rubber insulators, they will require more pressure. After the pins bottom thread them into the hole.

—————— **CAUTION** ——————
Take care not to cross thread the guide pins.

4. Refill the master cylinder with new brake fluid. Bleed the brake system if necessary.

Type Fourteen: Kelsey–Hayes Floating Caliper

PAD REMOVAL

1. Remove half of the brake fluid from the master cylinder reservoir.

2. Remove caliper guide pin, slide caliper up and away from the rotor and secure out of the way with wire. Avoid strain on the brake hose.

3. Remove outboard pad from the caliper adapter.

NOTE: There are three retaining springs used. One spring is located at the top of the outboard caliper adapter, one at the bottom of the outboard pad and the last on the top of the inboard pad. Pay attention to the shape and location of these springs.

4. Remove the disc brake rotor by sliding from the hub. Remove inboard pad.

5. Push the caliper piston back into the caliper bore.

Type Twelve; ATE Floating Caliper

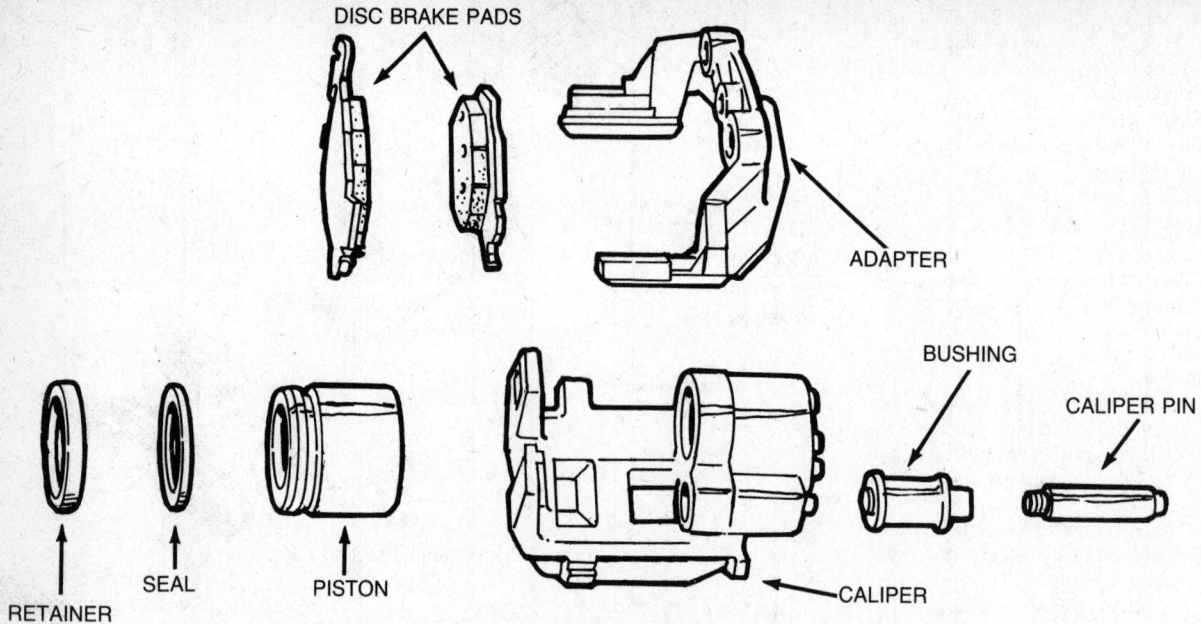

DISC BRAKE PADS

ADAPTER

BUSHING

CALIPER PIN

RETAINER SEAL PISTON CALIPER

Type fourteen—Kelsey–Hayes floating caliper

PAD INSTALLATION

1. Slide the inboard pad into position with spring on the adapter.

2. Install disc brake rotor. Slide the outboard pad and springs into position.

3. Lower caliper down over rotor and pad adapter.

4. Install guide pin by pressing in and turning to engage the threads.

5. Refill the master cylinder with new fluid. Pump the brake pedal several times to position the pads. Bleed system if necessary.

Type Fifteen: Delco Floating Rear Brake Caliper

PAD REMOVAL

1. Remove ⅔ of the brake fluid from the master cylinder.

2. Loosen the rear wheel lugs. Raise and support the rear of the vehicle on jackstands.

3. Mark the wheel and axle lug for same reinstallment location and remove the wheel assemblies.

4. Reinstall two lug nuts to retain the brake rotor.

5. Loosen the tension on the parking brake cable by backing off the equalizer.

6. After cable tension has been released, remove the cable end from the apply lever at the caliper.

7. Hold the apply lever in position and remove the retaining nut.

8. Remove the lever, lever seal and anti-friction washer.

NOTE: If the parking brake levers are not disconnected from the caliper during pad removal and installation, damage to the piston assembly will occur when it is moved back in the caliper bore.

9. Position a C-clamp over the caliper and tighten until the piston bottoms in the caliper bore. Take care not to allow the C-clamp to contact the actuator screw on the caliper. Reinstall anti-friction washer, seal and lever.

10. If caliper service is required, disconnect the brake line. Plug all openings.

11. Remove the caliper mounting bolts using a ⅜ in. Allen head socket or wrench.

12. Remove the caliper by lifting up and off the rotor. Do not permit the caliper to be suspended by the brake hose.

13. Remove the pads from the caliper. A suitable tool is required to pry the outboard pad from the caliper since it is retained by a spring button.

14. Remove the pin bushings and sleeves from the caliper ears.

PAD INSTALLATION

1. Install new sleeves and bushings after lubricating them. Insure that the sleeve is flush with the pad side of the caliper ear.

2. Install the inboard pad. Make sure that the D shaped retainer on the pad engages the D shaped slot in the caliper piston. Turn piston if necessary for correct alignment.

3. Be sure that the wear indicator is mounted on the leading edge of the pad for forward rotation of the wheel.

4. Slide the edge of the metal shoe under the ends of the dampening spring and snap the pad into position flat against the caliper piston.

5. Mount the outboard pad in position. Be sure it snaps into the caliper recess.

6. Install the caliper over the disc rotor in the reverse order of removal. Apply the brakes several times to seat the linings, after filling the master cylinder. Bleed brakes if necessary.

Type Sixteen Girlock Floating Front and Rear Calipers

PAD REMOVAL

1. Remove ⅔ of the brake fluid from the master cylinder.

2. Loosen the rear lugs and raise the rear of the vehicle. Support the vehicle on jackstands.

3. Remove the wheel assemblies. Install two lug nuts to hold the brake disc rotor in position.

4. Position a C-clamp over the caliper, one end on the outboard pad, the other on the inlet fitting bolt head.

5. Tighten the clamp to push the caliper piston until it bottoms in the bore.

6. Remove and discard the upper caliper self-locking bolt. Rotate the caliper on the lower bolt to expose the brake pads.

7. Remove the inner and outer pads from the caliper.

8. Clean the pad mounting frame on the caliper. Inspect the caliper for signs of fluid leakage. Remove and service caliper if necessary.

1. NUT
2. LEVER
3. RETURN SPRING
4. BOLT
5. BRACKET
6. LEVER SEAL
7. ANTI-FRICTION WASHER
8. MOUNTING BOLT
9. SLEEVE
10. BOLT BOOT
11. BUSHING
12. OUTBOARD SHOE & LINING
13. INBOARD SHOE & LINING
14. SHOE DAMPENING SPRING
15. CALIPER BOOT
16. TWO WAY CHECK VALVE
17. PISTON ASSEMBLY
18. PISTON SEAL
19. ACTUATOR SCREW
20. BALANCE SPRING
21. THRUST WASHER
22. SHAFT SEAL
23. PROTECTOR
24. BLEEDER VALVE
25. CALIPER HOUSING
26. WEAR SENSOR

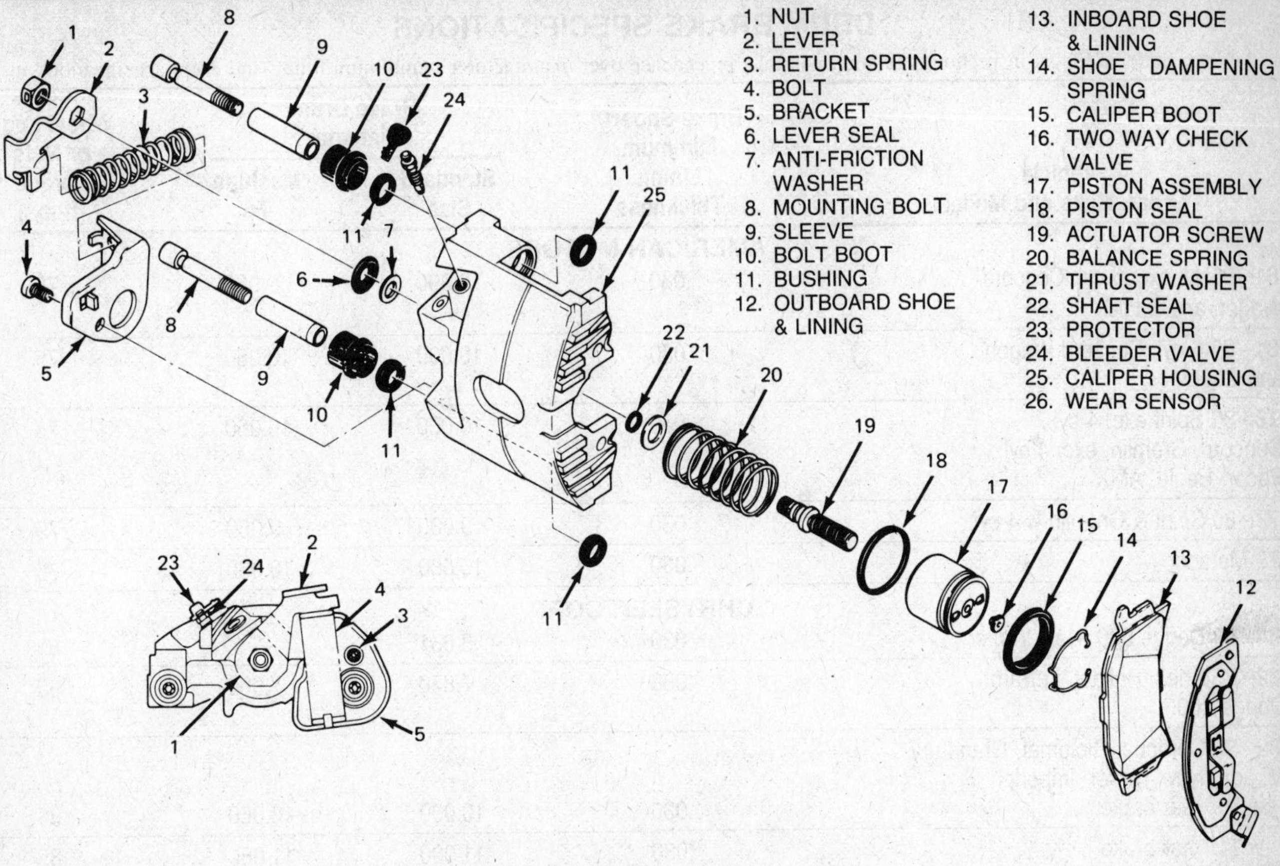

Type Fifteen—Delco floating rear brake caliper

PAD INSTALLATION

1. Install the new inner and outer pad in position on the caliper.

2. Rotate the caliper back into position over the disc brake rotor.

3. Install a new self-locking bolt and tighten to 22–25 ft. lbs.

4. Install wheel assemblies and lower vehicle.

5. Fill the master cylinder and pump the brake pedal several times to seat the pads. Bleed the brakes if necessary.

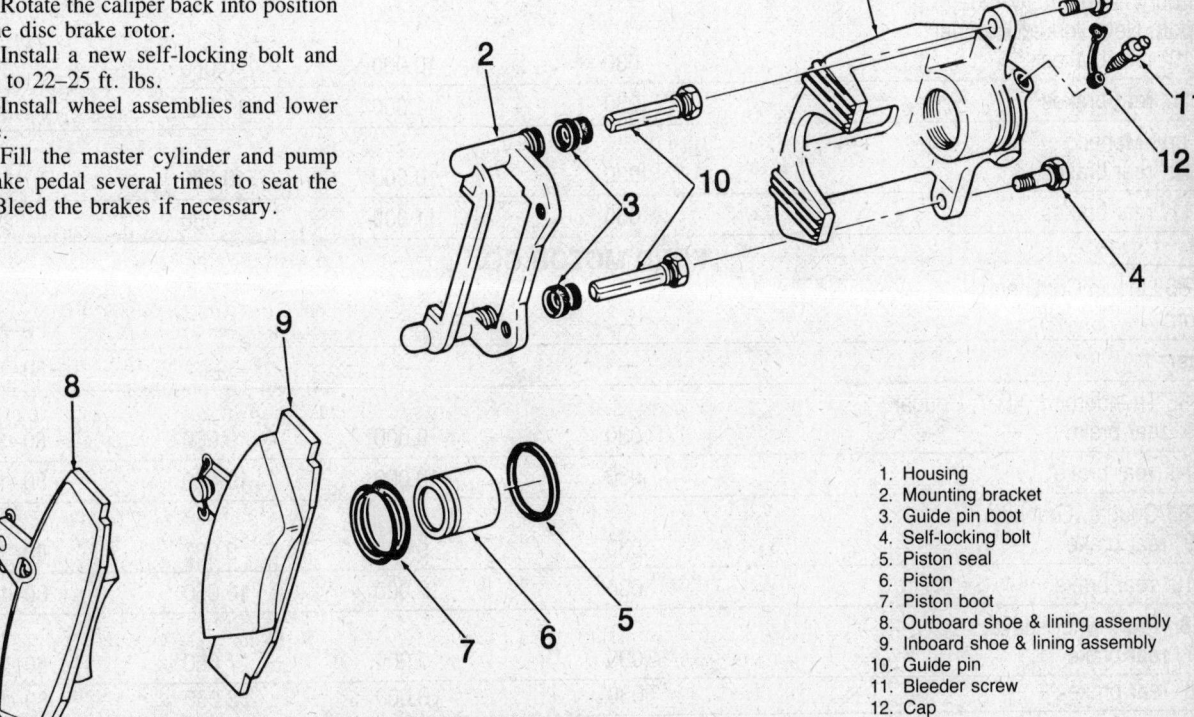

1. Housing
2. Mounting bracket
3. Guide pin boot
4. Self-locking bolt
5. Piston seal
6. Piston
7. Piston boot
8. Outboard shoe & lining assembly
9. Inboard shoe & lining assembly
10. Guide pin
11. Bleeder screw
12. Cap

Type Sixteen—Girlock front and rear brake caliper

DRUM BRAKE SPECIFICATIONS

(Note: State and local inspection regulation will take precedence over manufacturer's minimum lining and drum specifications.)

Vehicle Year, Make and Model	Brake Shoe ① Minimum Lining Thickness	Brake Drum Diameter		Wheel Lugs or Nuts Torque (ft-lbs)
		Standard Size	Machine To	
AMERICAN MOTORS				
'81–'85 All exc. 6 cyl. Concord Wagon and Eagle	.030	9.000	9.060	75
'81–'85 6 cyl. Concord Wagon and Eagle	.030	10.000	10.060	75
'78–'80 Spirit exc. 4 cyl., Concord, Gremlin, exc. 4 cyl.; Pacer, Eagle, AMX	.030	10.000	10.060	75
'78–'80 Spirit & Gremlin w/4 cyl.	.030	9.000	9.060	75
'78 Matador	.030	10.000	10.060	75
CHRYSLER CORP.				
'84–'85 Dodge 600, New Yorker	.030	8.661	—	85
'82–'85 Aries, Reliant, LeBaron Dodge 400	.030	7.870	7.900	85
'82–'85 Cordoba, Diplomat, Gran Fury, Mirada, New Yorker, Imperial				
w/10″ rear brake	.030	10.000	10.060	85
w/11″ rear brake	.030	11.000	11.060	85
'78–'85 Omni, Horizon	.030	7.870	7.900	85
'81 Aries, Reliant	.030	7.870	7.900	85
'78–'81 Aspen, Volare, LeBaron, Diplomat, St. Regis, Cordoba, Gran Fury, Magnum, Mirada, Newport, New Yorker, Imperial				
w/10″ rear brakes	.030	10.000	10.060	85
w/11″ rear brakes	.030	11.000	11.060	85
'78 Fury, Monaco				
w/10″ rear brakes	.030	10.000	10.060	85
w/11″ rear brakes	.030	11.000	11.060	85
FORD MOTOR CO.				
'82–'85 Lincoln Continental				
Front	—	—	—	80–105
Rear	—	—	—	80–105
'81–'85 Thunderbird, XR-7, Cougar				
w/9″ rear brake	.030	9.000	9.060	80–105
w/10″ rear brake	.030	10.000	10.060	80–105
'81–'83 Cougar, Granada				
w/9″ rear brake	.030	9.000	9.060	80–105
w/10″ rear brake	.030	10.000	10.060	80–105
'81–'85 Front wheel drive,				
w/7″ rear brake	.030	7.000	7.060	80–105
w/8″ rear brake	.030	8.000	8.060	80–105

DRUM BRAKE SPECIFICATIONS

(Note: State and local inspection regulation will take precedence over manufacturer's minimum lining and drum specifications.)

Vehicle Year, Make and Model	Brake Shoe ① Minimum Lining Thickness	Brake Drum Diameter		Wheel Lugs or Nuts Torque (ft-lbs)
		Standard Size	Machine To	
'78–'85 Mustang, Capri, Fairmont, Zephyr w/9″ rear brake	.030	9.000	9.060	80–105
w/10″ rear brake	.030	10.000	10.060	80–105
'79–'85 Lincoln Town Car, Mark VI, LTD, Marquis w/10″ rear brakes	.030	10.000	10.060	80–105
w/11″ rear brakes	.030	11.030	11.090	80–105
'80 Thunderbird, Cougar	.030	9.000	9.060	80–105
'79–'80 Granada, Monarch, Versailles w/o rear disc brakes	.030	10.000	10.060	80–105
w/rear disc brakes	—	—	—	80–105
'78–'79 Pinto, Bobcat, Mustang II	.030	9.000	9.060	80–105
'79 LTD II, Thunderbird, Cougar	.030	11.030	11.090	80–105
'78–'79 Mark V w/o rear disc brakes	.030	11.030	11.090	80–105
w/rear disc brakes	—	—	—	80–105
'78 Ford, Lincoln, Mercury, Custom 500, LTD II, Cougar, Ranchero II, Squire, Thunderbird	.030	11.030	11.090	70–115
'78 Fairmont, Zephyr exc. Wagon	.030	9.000	9.060	70–115
Wagon	.030	10.000	10.060	70–115
'78 Maverick, Comet, Granada Monarch, Versailles	.030	10.000	10.060	70–115
'78 LTD II, Thunderbird, Cougar	.030	11.030	11.090	70–115
GENERAL MOTORS CORP—BUICK				
'82–'85 Century, Skyhawk	①	7.880	7.899	100
'82–'85 Regal, LeSabre	①	9.500	9.560	80③
'79–'85 Riviera w/o rear disc brakes	①	9.500	9.560	100
w/rear disc brakes	—	—	—	100
'79–'84 Electra, Estate Wagon	①	11.000	11.060	100
'80–'85 Skylark	①	7.880	7.899	103
'79–'81 Century, Regal, LeSabre	①	9.500	9.560	80③
'78–'80 Skyhawk	①	9.500	9.560	80
'79 Skylark	①	9.500	9.560	80
'78 Electra, Estate Wagon, Riviera	①	11.000	11.060	80②
'78 Century, LeSabre, Regal, Skylark	①	9.500	9.560	80③
GENERAL MOTORS CORP.—CADILLAC				
'82–'85 Cimarron	.030	7.880	7.899	100
'82–'84 Fleetwood	.030	11.000	11.060	100

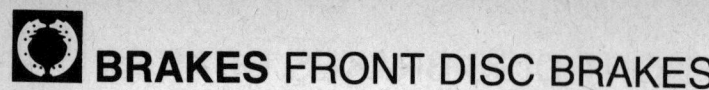

DRUM BRAKE SPECIFICATIONS

(Note: State and local inspection regulation will take precedence over manufacturer's minimum lining and drum specifications.)

Vehicle Year, Make and Model	Brake Shoe① Minimum Lining Thickness	Brake Drum Diameter		Wheel Lugs or Nuts Torque (ft-lbs)
		Standard Size	Machine To	
'82–'85 Eldorado, Seville				
Front	—	—	—	100
Rear	—	—	—	100
'78–'85 Fleetwood Limo, Commercial Chassis	①	12.000	12.060	100
'79–'81 Fleetwood, Brougham, DeVille, Seville, (RWD)				
w/o rear disc brakes	①	11.000	11.060	100
w/rear disc brakes (1979)	—	—	—	100
'79–'81 Eldorado, Seville (FWD)				
Front Disc	—	—	—	100
Rear Disc	—	—	—	100
'78 DeVille	①	11.000	11.060	100
'78 Brougham, Seville;				
Front	—	—	—	100
Rear	—	—	—	100
'78 Eldorado				
Front	—	—	—	130
Rear	—	—	—	130
GENERAL MOTORS CORP.—CHEVROLET				
'82–'85 Celebrity, Cavalier	①	7.880	7.899	100
'82–'85 Camaro				
w/rear drum brakes	①	9.500	9.560	80†
w/rear disc brakes	—	—	—	80†
'82–'85 Malibu, Monte Carlo, El Camino	①	9.500	9.560	80†
'80–'85 Citation	①	7.880	7.899	103
'79–'85 Impala, Caprice				
w/9½″ rear brakes	①	9.500	9.560	80
w/11″ rear brakes	①	11.000	11.060	100
'78–'85 Chevette	①	7.874	7.899	70
'78–'85 Corvette				
Front	—	—	—	70④
Rear	—	—	—	70④
'79–'81 Malibu, Camaro, Nova, Monte Carlo, El Camino	①	9.500	9.560	80④
'78–'80 Monza	①	9.500	9.560	80④
'78 Caprice, Camaro, Impala, Nova				
exc. Wagon	①	9.500	9.560	80†
Wagon	①	11.000	11.060	100
'78 Malibu, Monte Carlo El Camino	①	11.000	11.060	80

DRUM BRAKE SPECIFICATIONS

(Note: State and local inspection regulation will take precedence over manufacturer's minimum lining and drum specifications.)

Vehicle Year, Make and Model	Brake Shoe① Minimum Lining Thickness	Brake Drum Diameter		Wheel Lugs or Nuts Torque (ft-lbs)
		Standard Size	Machine To	
GENERAL MOTORS CORP.—OLDSMOBILE				
'82–'85 Ciera, Firenza	①	7.880	7.899	100
'82–'85 Cutlass Supreme, 88	①	9.500	9.560	100⑤
'80–'84 Omega	①	7.880	7.899	103
'79–'84 Toronado w/o rear disc	①	9.500	9.560	100
w/rear disc	—	—	—	100
'78–'84 Custom Cruiser, 88 (w/403), 98 w/9.5″ rear brake	①	9.500	9.560	100
w/11″ rear brake	①	11.000	11.060	100
'78–'81 Cutlass, 88 (w/o 403)	①	9.500	9.560	80
'78–'80 Starfire	①	9.500	9.560	80
'78–'79 Omega w/5 Speed	①	11.000	11.060	80
'78 Omega w/o 5 Speed	①	9.500	9.560	80
'78 Toronado	①	11.000	11.060	130
GENERAL MOTORS CORP.—PONTIAC				
'82–'85 A6000, J2000	①	7.880	7.899	100
'82–'85 Firebird w/rear drum brakes	①	9.500	9.560	80④
w/rear disc brakes	—	—	—	80④
'81–'85 T 1000	①	7.874	7.899	70
'80–'85 Phoenix (F.W.D.)	—	7.880	7.899	103
'78–'84 Bonneville, Catalina, LeMans, Grand Prix, Grand Am, Safari w/9.5″ rear brakes	①	9.500	9.560	80
w/11″ rear brakes	①	11.000	11.060	80⑥
'78–'79 Firebird, Ventura, Phoenix (R.W.D.)	①	9.500	9.560	80
w/rear disc (1981–79)	—	—	—	80
'78–'80 Sunbird, Astre	①	9.500	9.560	80

① .030″ over rivet head, if bonded lining use .062″
② w/½″ stud 100 ft/lbs.
③ w/Aluminum whls. LeSabre 90 ft/lbs., Regal 100 ft/lbs.
④ Aluminum whls; Corvette 80, Camaro 105, others 90.
⑤ 88 w/7/16″ stud; 80 ft/lbs.
⑥ ½″ stud 100 ft/lbs.

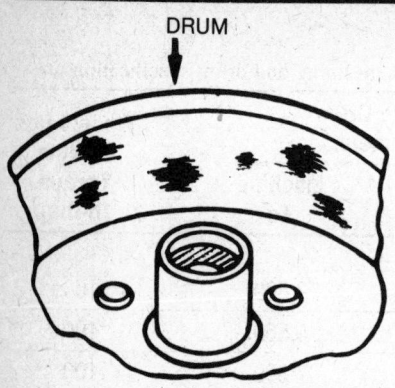

Hard or Chill Spots

LOOK HERE FOR TURNED DRUM TOOL MARK RIDGE

0.60"

Oversize drum

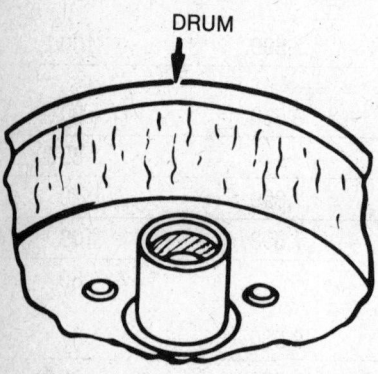

Heat checks

DRUM BRAKES

CAUTION

The asbestos dust thrown off from the brake linings or disc pads may be dangerous to your health if inhaled. Never use compressed air or your own breath to blow the dust from the brake assembly. Use a damp rag or a well filtered vacuum cleaner. Dispose of the rag or cleaner bag properly.

Brake Drums

BRAKE DRUM TYPES

The FULL-CAST drum has a cast iron web (back) of 3/16–1/4 in. thickness (passenger car sizes) whereas the COMPOSITE drum has a steel web approximately 1/8 inch thick. These two types of drums, with few exceptions are not interchangeable.

BRAKE DRUM DEPTH

Rest a straight edge across the drum diameter on the open side. The actual drum depth then is the measurement at a right angle from the straight edge to that part of the web which mates against the hub mounting flange.

ALUMINUM DRUMS

When repaced by other types, aluminum drums must be replaced in pairs.

METALLIC BRAKES

Drums designed for use with standard brake linings should not be used with metallic brakes.

REMOVING TIGHT DRUMS

Difficulty removing a brake drum can be caused by shoes which are expanded beyond the drum's inner ridge, or shoes which have cut into, and ridged the drum. In either case back off the adjuster to obtain sufficient clearance for removal.

BRAKE DRUM INSPECTION

The condition of the brake drum surface is just as important as the surface to the brake

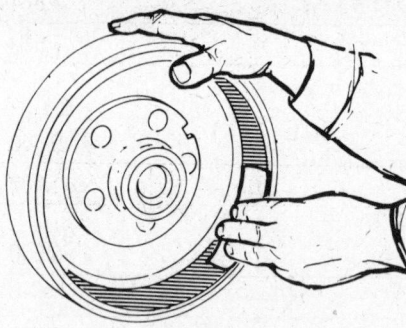

Sanding brake drums

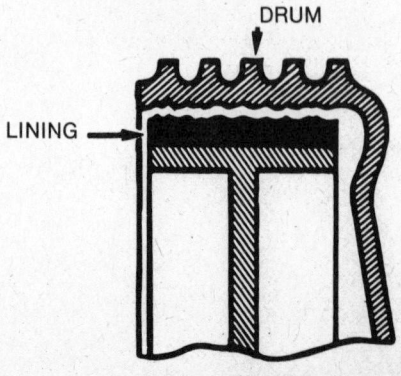

Scored drum surface

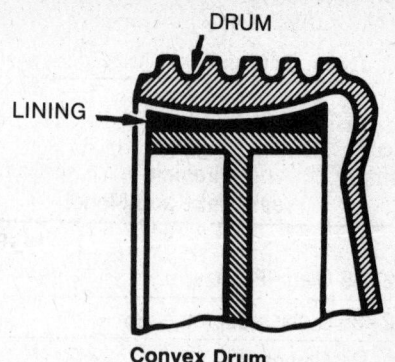

Convex Drum

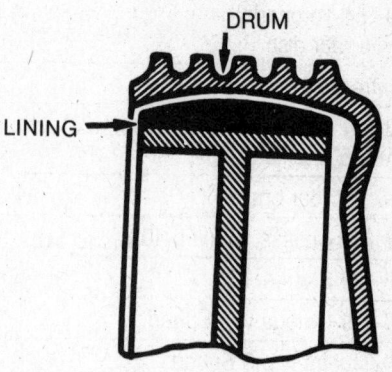

Concave Drum

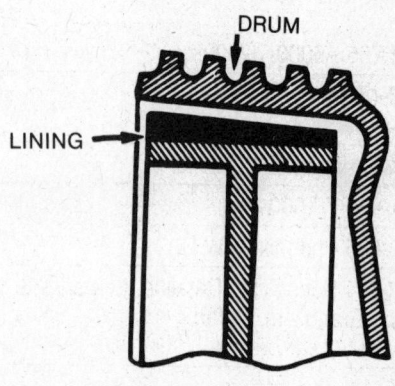

Bellmouth Drum

lining. All drum surfaces should be clean, smooth, free from hard spots, heat checks, score marks and foreign matter imbedded in the drum surface. They should not be out of round, bell-mouthed or barrel shaped. It is recommended that all drums be first checked with a drum micrometer to see if they are within oversize limits. If drum is within safe limits, even though the surface appears smooth, it should be turned not only to assure a true drum surface but also to remove any possible contamination in the surface from previous brake linings, road dusts, etc. Too much metal removed from a drum is unsafe and may result in:

1. Brake to fade due to the thin drum being unable to absorb the heat generated.

2. Poor and erratic brake due to distortion of drums.

3. Noise due to possible vibration caused by thin drums.

4. A cracked or broken drum on a severe or very hard brake application.

Brake drum run-out should not exceed .005 in. Drums turned to more than .060 in. oversize are unsafe and should be replaced with new drums, except for some heavy ribbed drums which have an .080 in. limit. It is recommended that the diameters of the left and right drums on any one axle be within .010 in. of each other. In order to avoid erratic brake action when replacing drums, it is always good to replace the drums on both wheels at the same time.

If the drums are true, smooth up any slight scores by polishing with fine emery cloth. If deep scores or grooves are present, which cannot be removed by this method, then the drum must be turned.

DUO-SERVO BRAKE

Refer to the Drum Brake Application Chart for adjuster applications.

In the Duo-Servo design, the force which the wheel cylinder applies to the shoes is supplemented by the tendency of the shoes to wrap or twist into the drum during braking. Thus two braking forces are applied at each drum every time the brakes are activated.

Star and Screw Adjuster

The duo-servo brake, with star and screw type self-adjusters, is used on most late-model American cars. The same basic brake unit has been used on all cars. General Motors cars use a rod-operated lever to turn the star-wheel, while all others use a cable-operated lever. This is the only difference, other than size, among units used on different models.

ADJUSTMENT

The drum brakes, used on today's cars, are usually self-adjusting. They require manual adjustment only when the shoes have been replaced or when the star and screw adjuster has been disturbed.

DRUM BRAKE APPLICATION CHART

Car and Years	Brake Type	Self-Adjuster Type
American Motors 1978–85 all models	Duo-Servo	Star & Screw
Chrysler Corp. 1978–85 all models①	Duo-Servo	Star & Screw
Ford Motor Co. 1978–85 all models except below	Duo-Servo	Star & Screw
1981–85 Front Wheel Drive (Ford)		Star & Screw (8 in. brake)
	Non-Servo	Strut & Pin (7 in. brake)
General Motors Corp. 1978–85 all models except below	Duo-Servo	Star & Screw
1978–79 Chevette	Duo-Servo	Pin and Slot

①The rear drum brakes on Chrysler front wheel drive cars, through 1982, are not automatically adjusted.

NOTE: The drum brakes on most cars can be initially adjusted by removing the brake drum, measuring its internal diameter, then adjusting the shoes to that measurement and installing the drum. Use a vernier gauge to make the measurements. This method can be used on all models, and may be preferable to punching out the covering over the access hole in the backing plate or brake drum edge.

1. Remove the access slot plug from the backing plate or front of drum. On some cars no access slot in the backing plate or in the front of the drums is provided. Some have been filled in and must be punched out to gain access to the adjuster. Complete the adjustment and cover the hole with a plug to prevent entrance of dirt and water.

2. Using a brake adjusting spoon or screwdriver, pry downward on the end of the tool (starwheel teeth moving up) to tighten the brakes, or upward on the end of the tool (starwheel teeth moving down) to loosen the brakes.

NOTE: It will be necessary to use a small rod or suitable tool to hold the adjusting lever away from the starwheel. Be careful not to bend the adjusting lever.

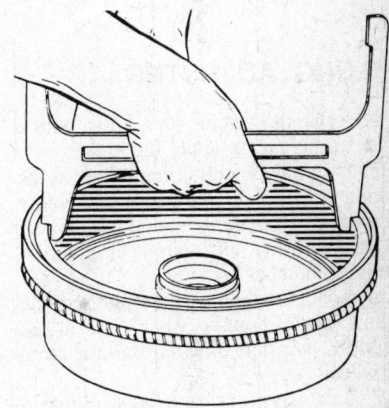

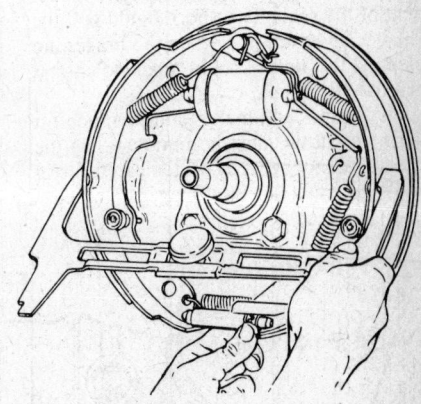

Brake drum guage

3. When the brakes are tight almost to the point of being locked, back off on the starwheel until the wheel is able to rotate freely. The starwheel on each set of brakes (front or rear) must be backed off the same number of turns to prevent brake pull from side to side.

4. After adjustment, check brake pedal

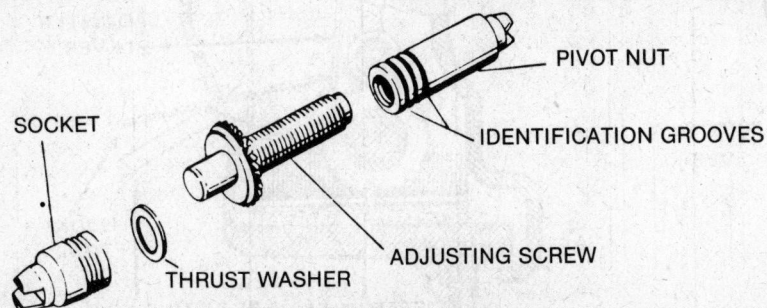

SOCKET
PIVOT NUT
IDENTIFICATION GROOVES
THRUST WASHER
ADJUSTING SCREW

Adjusting screw assembly

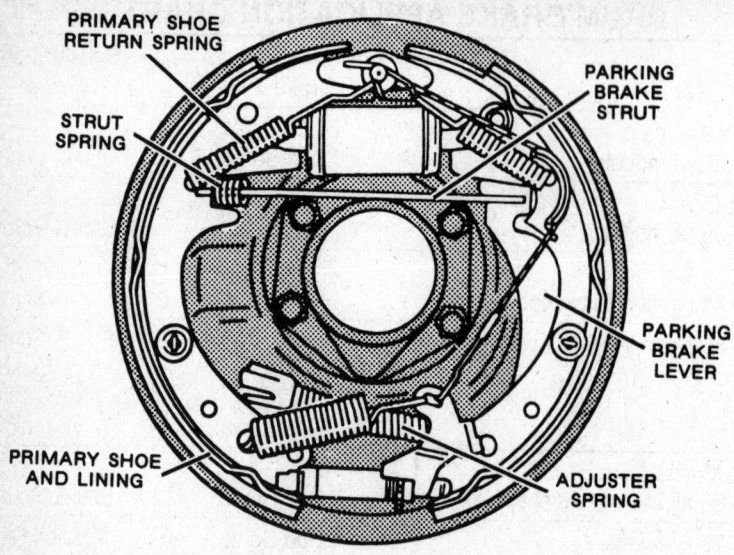

PRIMARY SHOE
RETURN SPRING

STRUT
SPRING

PARKING
BRAKE
STRUT

PARKING
BRAKE
LEVER

PRIMARY SHOE
AND LINING

ADJUSTER
SPRING

AMC, Ford type rear drum brake assembly

travel and then make several stops, while backing the car up, to equalize both wheel systems.

TESTING ADJUSTER

1. Raise the vehicle on a hoist, with a helper in the car, to apply the brakes.
2. On models with access plugs in the backing plate, loosen the brakes by holding the adjuster lever away from the starwheel and backing off the starwheel approximately 30 notches.

On models without access plugs in the backing plate, remove wheel and drum, loosen the adjuster, then reinstall the drum and wheel.

3. Spin the wheel and brake drum in reverse and apply the brakes. The movement of the secondary shoe should pull the adjuster lever up, and when the brakes are released the lever should snap down and turn the starwheel.

4. If the automatic adjuster doesn't work, the drum must be removed and the adjuster components inspected carefully for breakage, wear, or improper installation.

BRAKE SHOE REMOVAL

NOTE: If you are not thoroughly familiar with the procedures involved in brake replacement, disassemble and assemble one side at a time, leaving the other wheel intact, as a reference.

1. Remove the brake drum.
2. Place the hollow end of a brake spring service tool on the brake shoe anchor pin and twist it to disengage one of the brake shoe return springs. Repeat this operation to remove the other return spring.

—— CAUTION ——
Be careful that the springs do not slip off the tool during removal, as the spring could break loose and cause personal injury.

3. Reach behind the brake backing plate and place a finger on the end of one of the brake holddown mounting pins. Using a pair of pliers or special brake pin retainer tool, grasp the washer on the top of the hold-down spring that corresponds to the pin that you are holding. Push down on the pliers and turn them 90° to align the slot in

the washer with the head on the spring mounting pin. Remove the spring and washer and repeat this operation on the holddown spring of the other brake shoe.

4. Step 4 varies according to manufacturer:

On Ford and American Motors cars, place the tip of a screwdriver on the top of the brake adjusting screw and move the screwdriver upward to lift up on the brake adjusting lever. When there is enough slack in the automatic adjuster cable, disconnect the loop on the top of the cable from the anchor. Back off the adjusting screw while holding the adjustment lever away from the screw. Grasp the top of each brake shoe and move them outward to disengage from the wheel cylinder and parking brake link. When the brake shoes are clear, lift them from the backing plate. Twist the shoes slightly and the automatic adjuster assembly will disassemble itself.

On GM cars, remove the automatic adjuster link. Remove the automatic adjuster lever, pivot, and override spring from the secondary spring as an assembly. Move the top of each brake shoe outward to clear the wheel cylinder pins and parking brake link (rear brakes). Lift the brakes from the backing plate and remove the adjusting screw.

On Chrysler cars, (except some front wheeldrive models), slide the automatic adjuster cable from the anchor pin and disengage it from the adjusting lever. Remove the cable, overload spring, and cable guide. Disconnect the automatic adjuster lever return spring and remove the spring and lever. Move the top of the brake shoes outward to clear the wheel cylinder pins and parking brake link (rear brakes). Lift the brakes from the backing plate and remove the adjusting screw.

5. Grasp the end of the brake cable spring with a pair of pliers and, using the brake lever as a fulcrum, pull the end of the spring away from the lever. Disengage the cable from the brake lever.

BRAKE SHOE INSTALLATION

1. The brake cable must be connected to the secondary brake shoe before the shoe

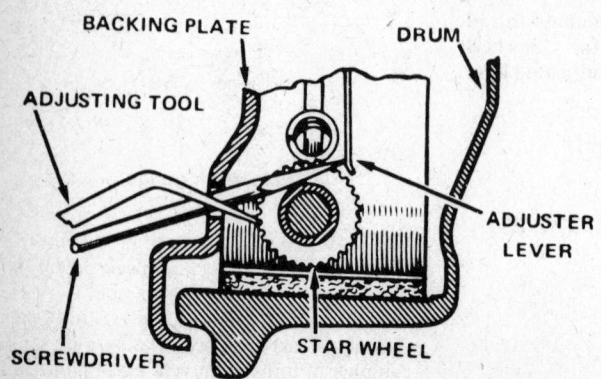

BACKING PLATE

DRUM

ADJUSTING TOOL

ADJUSTER
LEVER

SCREWDRIVER

STAR WHEEL

All cars except Chrysler and GM "H" body (Chevette)

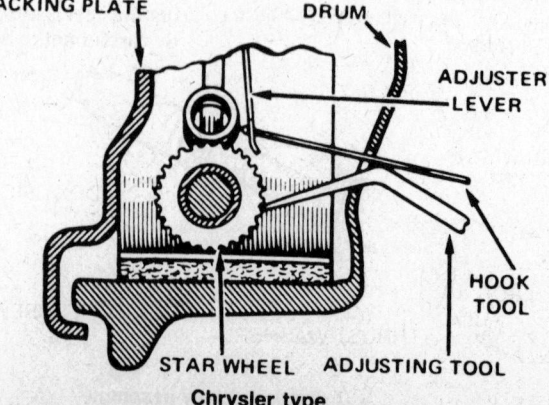

BACKING PLATE

DRUM

ADJUSTER
LEVER

HOOK
TOOL

STAR WHEEL   ADJUSTING TOOL

Chrysler type

is installed on the backing plate. To do this, transfer the parking brake lever from the old secondary shoe to the new one. This is accomplished by spreading the bottom of the horseshoe clip and disengaging the lever. Position the lever on the new secondary shoe and install the spring washer and the horseshoe clip. Close the bottom of the clip after installing it. Grasp the metal tip of the parking brake cable with a pair of pliers. Position a pair of side cutters on the end of the cable coil spring and, using the pliers as a fulcrum, pull the coil spring back with the side cutters. Position the cable in the parking brake lever.

2. Apply a light coating of high-temperature grease to the brake shoe contact points on the backing plate. Position the primary brake shoe on the front of the backing plate and install the hold-down spring and washer over the mounting pin. Install the secondary shoe on the rear of the backing plate.

3. If working on rear brakes, install the parking brake link between the primary brake shoe and the secondary brake shoe.

4. Step 4 varies according to manufacturer:

On Ford and American Motors cars, install the automatic adjuster cable loop end on the anchor pin. Make sure that the crimped side of the loop faces the backing plate.

On GM cars, assemble the automatic adjuster lever, pivot, and override spring and install to the secondary springs as an assembly.

On Chrysler, (except some front wheel-drive models) install the automatic adjuster lever and return spring. Install the adjuster overload spring and cable. One end of the cable engages with the adjusting lever while the other slips over the anchor pin underneath the primary and secondary return springs.

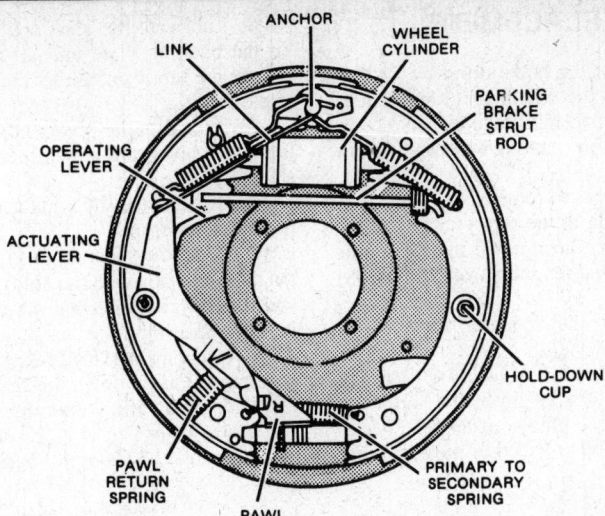

GM type rear drum brake assembly

5. Install the return spring in the primary brake shoe and, using the tapered end of a brake spring service tool, slide the top of the spring onto the anchor pin.

------------ CAUTION ------------
Be careful to make sure that the spring does not slip off the tool during installation, as the spring could break loose and cause personal injury.

6. Install the automatic adjuster cable guide in the secondary brake shoe, making sure that the flared hole in the cable guide is inside the hole in the brake shoe. Fit the cable into the groove in the top of the cable guide.

7. Install the secondary shoe return return spring through the hole in the cable guide and the brake shoe. Using the brake spring tool, slide the top of the spring onto the anchor pin.

8. Clean the threads on the adjusting screw and apply a *light* coating of high-temperature grease to the threads. Screw the adjuster closed, then open it one-half turn.

9. Install the adjusting screw between the brake shoes with the star wheel nearest to the secondary shoe. Make sure that the star wheel is in a position that is accessible from the adjusting slot in the backing plate.

10. Install the short, hooked end of the automatic adjuster spring in the proper hole in the primary brake shoe.

11. Connect the hooked end of the automatic adjuster cable and the free end of the automatic adjuster spring in the slot in the top of the automatic adjuster lever.

12. Pull the automatic adjuster lever (the lever will pull the cable and spring with it) downward and to the left, and engage the pivot hook of the lever in the hole in the secondary brake shoe.

13. Check the entire brake assembly to make sure everything is installed properly. Make sure that the shoes engage the wheel cylinder properly and are flush on the anchor pin. Make sure that the automatic adjuster cable is flush on the anchor pin and in the slot on the block of cable guide. Make sure that the adjusting lever rests on the adjusting screw star wheel. Pull upward on the adjusting cable until the adjusting lever is free of the star wheel, then release the cable. The adjusting lever should snap back into place on the adjusting screw star wheel and turn the wheel one tooth.

14. Expand the brake adjusting screw until the brake drum will just fit over the brake shoes.

15. Install the wheel and drum and adjust the brakes. (See ''Brake Adjustment.'')

Pin and Slot Adjuster

The duo-servo brake with pin and slot adjusters is used on the early model Chevette. 1980 and later Chevettes use star and screw adjusters.

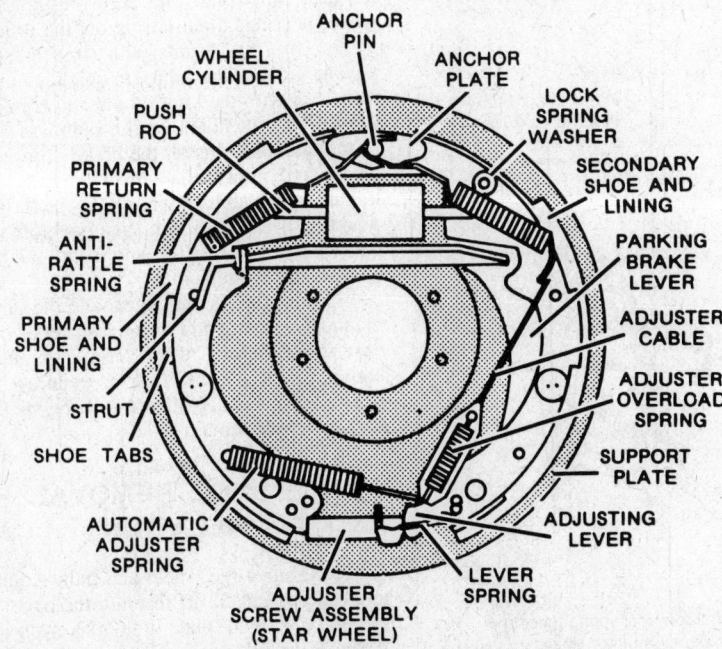

Chrysler type rear drum brake assembly

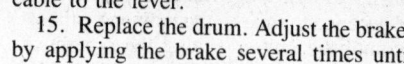

SHOE REPLACEMENT

1. Remove the brake drum.
2. Loosen the equalizer to let all tension from the parking brake cable.
3. Unhook the parking brake cable from the lever.
4. Use pliers to remove the long shoe pull back spring at the top.
5. Use pliers to remove the shoe hold down springs and retainers from the middle of each shoe.
6. Separate the shoes at the top and remove them.
7. Check that the adjusters work properly; it should take 29–36 ft. lbs. torque to turn the adjusters. The adjusters and backing plate must be replaced as an assembly.

8. Lubricate the shoe contact surfaces on the backing plate and all pivot points with brake lubricant. Lubricate the parking brake cable.
9. Lubricate the pivot end of the parking brake lever and attach the lever to the shoe.
10. Connect the shoes at the bottom with the retaining spring.
11. Place the shoes in position and fasten the front shoe with the hold down spring and retainer. Be sure that the adjuster peg is in the shoe slot.
12. Install the parking brake lever to front shoe strut. Fasten down the rear shoe with the hold down spring and retainer. Be sure that the adjuster peg is in the shoe slot.
13. Install the shoe pull back spring.

14. Attach the end of the parking brake cable to the lever.
15. Replace the drum. Adjust the brakes by applying the brake several times until the pedal is firm. Check the fluid level frequently. Adjust the parking brake.

NON-SERVO BRAKES

On the non-servo brake each brake shoe is separately anchored and their action is not compounded. The leading shoe does the majority of the work, stopping forward motion. The trailing shoe works in the same manner for rearward motion. Non-servo brakes may or may not be equipped with self-adjusters.

Ford Non-Servo Brakes

The star and screw adjuster is used on models with 8 in. diameter brake drums while the strut and pin adjuster is used on 7 in. diameter drums.

ADJUSTMENTS

Normal shoe adjustments are automatic, however, when the shoes have been replaced or the adjuster has been disturbed, the shoes should be initially adjusted by hand.

1. Raise the rear of the car and remove the wheels and drums. Drums are removed by releasing the parking brake, removing the dust cap, cotter pin, adjusting nut and wheel bearing, then pulling off the drum.
2. On 7 in. drums with strut and pin adjuster, pivot the adjuster quadrant until it meshes with the knurled pin and is in the third or fourth notch of the outboard end of the quadrant. Install the brake drum and wheel and adjust the wheel bearings by tightening the adjusting nut to 17–25 ft. lbs. while rotating the drum, then back off the adjusting nut about 100° and install the nut retainer and cotter pin.
3. 8 in. drums are adjusted in the same manner as the star and screw adjuster drums described under "Duo-Servo" brakes, above. See that section for procedure.
4. Complete adjustment by applying the brakes several times.

BRAKE SHOE REMOVAL AND INSTALLATION

1. Remove the wheel and hub. Adjusters can be backed off through the back of the brake backing plate with a screwdriver if the drum will not come off.
2. Remove the holddown springs and

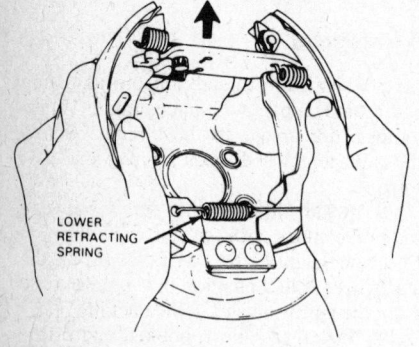

STEP 1

a. Remove holddown springs and pins.
b. Lift assembly off backing plate.
c. Disengage parking brake cable.
d. Remove lower retracting spring.

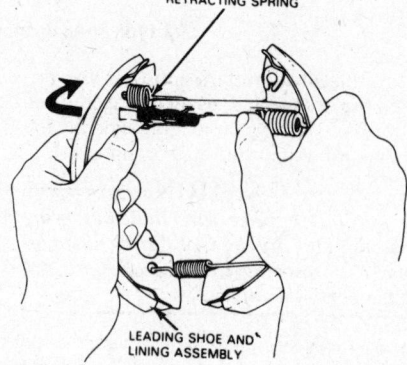

STEP 2

Remove leading shoe retracting spring by rotating shoe as shown to release spring tension. Do not pry spring off shoe.

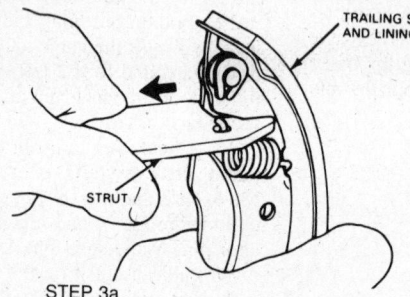

STEP 3a

Remove strut to trailing shoe and lining assembly by pulling strut away from shoe and . . .

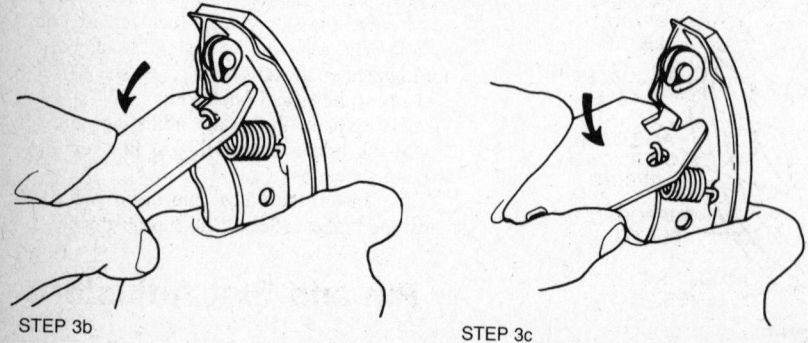

STEP 3b

. . . twisting strut downward

STEP 3c

. . . toward technician until spring tension is released. Remove spring from slots.

Non-servo; 7 in. Ford rear brakes

INSTALLATION PROCEDURE

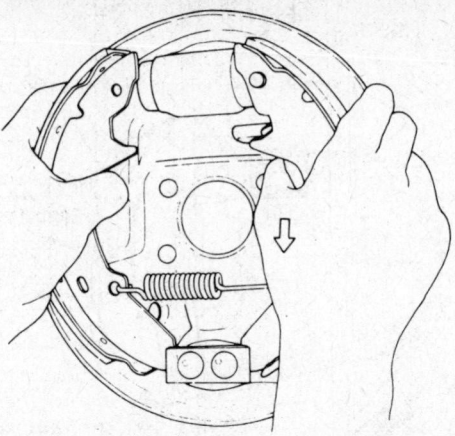

STEP 1

a. Assemble parking brake cable to trailing shoe and parking brake lever.

b. Install lower retracting spring to leading-trailing shoes.

c. Install this assembly to backing plate.

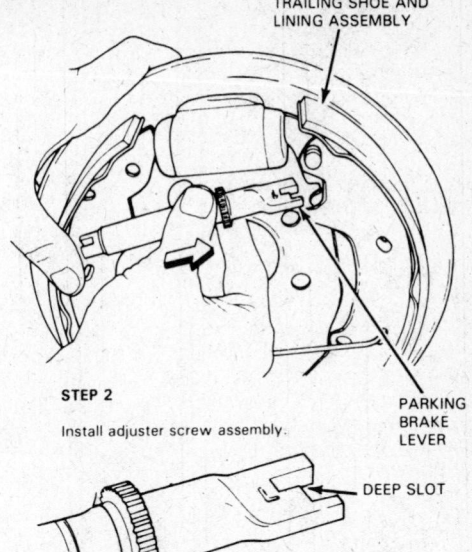

TRAILING SHOE AND LINING ASSEMBLY

PARKING BRAKE LEVER

STEP 2

Install adjuster screw assembly.

DEEP SLOT

NOTE: Socket Blade marked R and L. Install letter in upright position to insure proper slot engagement to parking brake lever.

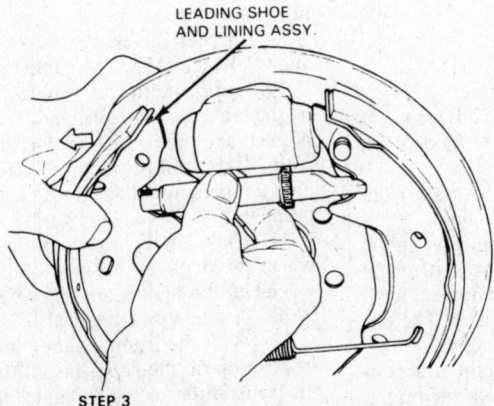

LEADING SHOE AND LINING ASSY.

STEP 3

Install adjuster screw to leading shoe and lining assembly.

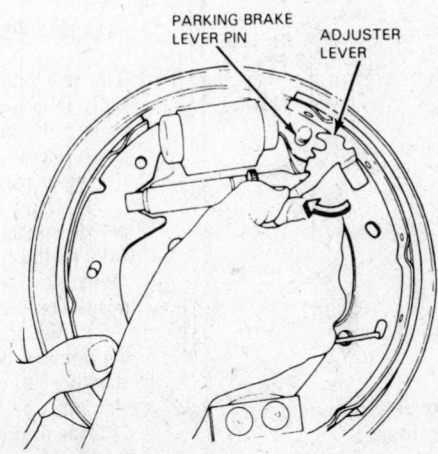

PARKING BRAKE LEVER PIN

ADJUSTER LEVER

STEP 4

Install the adjuster lever in groove of parking brake lever pin.

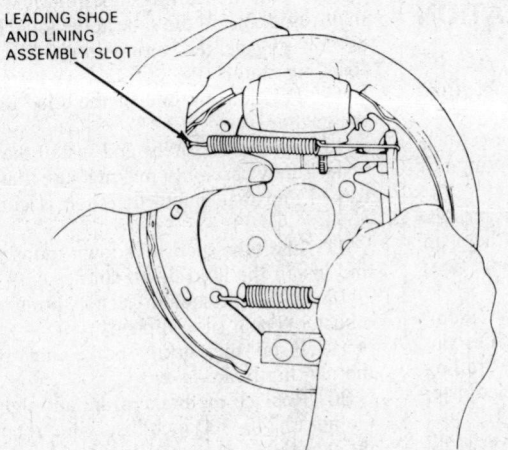

LEADING SHOE AND LINING ASSEMBLY SLOT

STEP 5

a. Install shoe holddown springs and pins.

b. Install upper retracting spring to leading shoe slot — stretch spring to install to trailing shoe. If adjuster lever does not contact star wheel after spring installation check adjuster socket installation.

Rear drum brakes

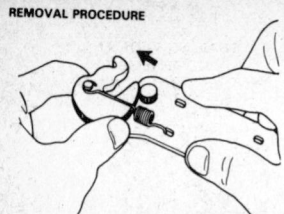

1. PULL QUADRANT AWAY FROM KNURLED PIN THE STRUT

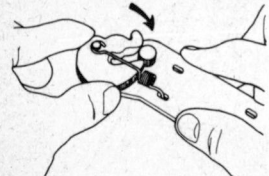

2. ROTATE QUADRANT UNTIL TEETH ARE NO LONGER MESHED WITH PIN.

3. REMOVE THE SPRING AND SLIDE QUADRANT OUT OF STRUT—BE CAREFUL NOT TO OVERSTRESS SPRING. INSTALL ADJUSTER QUADRANT PIN INTO SLOT IN STRUT. TURN ASSEMBLY OVER AND INSTALL SPRING

INSTALLATION PROCEDURE

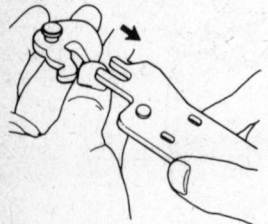

Quadrant removal and installation; 7 in. Ford non-servo brakes

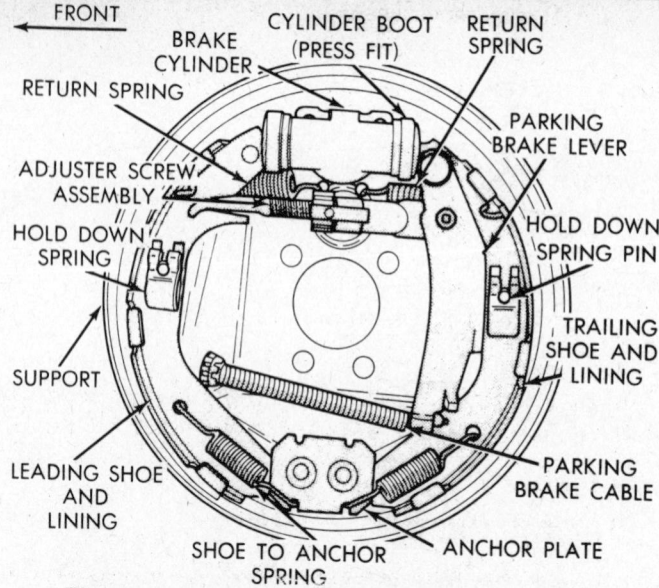

Chrysler non-servo rear brakes (non-self-adjusting)

pins. Lift the assembly off the brake backing plate and disengage the parking brake cable.

3. On 7 in. drums, remove the lower retracting spring. On 8 in. drums, remove all retracting springs and the adjuster lever.

4. The following removal procedures are for 7 in. drums only:

  a. Remove the leading shoe retracting spring by rotating shoe to release spring tension. Do not pry the spring off the shoe.

  b. Remove the strut to trailing shoe assembly by pulling the strut away from the shoe and twisting the shoe downward until spring tension is released. Remove the spring from the slots.

5. Installation is the reverse of removal. See adjustment procedure, above, for special information on initial adjustment techniques. Wheel bearings on 8 in. drums are adjusted in the same manner as 7 in. drums. See Step 2 of Adjustment Procedure.

Chrysler Non-Servo Brakes

ADJUSTMENTS

The rear brakes through 1982 were manually adjusted. 1983 and later models are equipped with self-adjusters.

1. Remove the access slot plug from the upper part of the backing plate.

2. Using a thin brake adjusting spoon pry downward (left side) or upward (right side) on the end of the tool (starwheel teeth moving up) to tighten the brakes. The opposite applies to loosen the brakes.

3. When the brakes are tight almost to the point of being locked, back off on the starwheel 10 clicks. The starwheel on each side must be backed off the same number of turns to provide for even braking.

REMOVAL & INSTALLATION

1. Remove the brake drum.

2. Unhook the parking brake cable from the secondary (trailing) shoe.

3. Remove the shoe-to-anchor retracting spring(s) and the upper spring (if equipped).

4. Remove the shoe hold down springs: compress them slightly and slide them off of the hold down pins or push in and twist them from the mount pin.

5. Remove the adjuster screw assembly by spreading the shoes apart. Disconnect the adjuster spring from the trailing shoes on self-adjuster models. The adjuster nut must be fully backed off.

6. Raise the parking brake lever. Pull the secondary (trailing) shoe away from the backing plate so pull-back spring tension is released.

7. Remove the secondary (trailing) shoe and disengage the spring end from the backing plate.

8. Raise the primary (leading) shoe to release spring tension. Remove the shoe and disengage the spring end from the backing plate.

9. Inspect the brakes (see procedures under ''Brake Drum Inspection'').

10. Lubricate the six shoe contact areas on the brake backing plate and the web end of the brake shoe which contacts the anchor plate. Use a multi-purpose lubricant or a high temperature brake grease made for the purpose.

11. Chrysler recommends that the rear wheel bearings be cleaned and repacked whenever the brakes are renewed. Be sure to install a new bearing seal.

12. With the leading shoe return spring in position on the shoe, install the shoe at the same time as you engage the return spring in the end support.

13. Position the end of the shoe under the anchor.

14. With the trailing shoe return spring in position, install the shoe at the same time as you engage the spring in the support (backing plate).

15. Position the end of the shoe under the anchor.

16. Spread the shoes and install the adjuster screw assembly making sure that the forked end that enters the shoe is curved down.

17. Insert the shoe hold down spring pins and install the hold down springs.

18. Install the shoe-to-anchor springs and adjuster spring (if equipped).

19. Install the parking brake cable onto the parking brake lever.

20. Replace the brake drum and tighten the nut to 240–300 inch lbs. while rotating the wheel.

21. Back off the nut enough to release the bearing preload and position the locknut with one pair of slots aligned with the cotter pin hole.

22. Install the cotter pin. The end play should be 0.001–0.003 in.

23. Install the grease cap.

Front End Alignment

SERVICE PROCEDURE INDEX
(Numbers refer to types in text)

Manufacturer/Car	Year	Caster, Camber, and Toe in
AMERICAN MOTORS		
American Motors (All Except Pacer)	'78-'85	3
Pacer	'78-'80	9
CHRYSLER CORPORATION		
All Front Wheel Drive	'78-'85	4
All Rear Wheel Drive	'78-'85	5
FORD MOTOR COMPANY	'78-'85	8
Ford Fairmont, Mustang; Mercury Capri, Zephyr, '80-'85 Cougar, '82-'85 Lincoln Continental, '80-'85 Thunderbird, '81-'83 Granada; '82-'85 LTD; '82-'85 Marquis, Mark VII		
Ford Pinto, Mustang II; Mercury Bobcat	'78-'80	8
Ford Torino, LTD II, Mercury Montego	'78-'79	7
Ford Elite, Mercury Cougar	'78-'79	7
Ford Granada; Mercury Monarch, Lincoln Versailles	'78-'80	3
Ford (Full Size), Mercury (Full Size)	'78-'85	7
Ford Thunderbird (Through 1979), Lincoln Mk IV, Mk V, Mk VI	'78-'83	7
Lincoln Continental (Through 1980), Town Car	'78-'85	7
All Front Wheel Drive	'81-'85	8

Manufacturer/Car	Year	Caster, Camber, and Toe in
GENERAL MOTORS		
Chevrolet Chevette, Pontiac 1000 (GM T-Body)	'78-'85	6
Chevrolet Vega, Monza, Pontiac Astre, Sunbird, Oldsmobile Starfire, Buick Skyhawk (GM H-Body)	'78-'85	9
Chevrolet Camaro, Pontiac Firebird	'82-'85	13
Pontiac Fiero	'84-'85	6
All rear wheel drive (Except GM T Body, GM H Body, Pontiac Fiero, 1982-'85 Camaro and Firebird	'78-'85	1
Chevrolet Citation, Celebrity, Buick Skylark, Century (FWD), Oldsmobile Omega, Ciera, Pontiac Phoenix, 6000	'80-'85	11
Chevrolet Cavalier, Pontiac 2000, Cadillac Cimarron, Oldsmobile Firenza	'82-'85	12
Oldsmobile Toronado, Buick Riviera, Cadillac Eldorado, Seville (Front Wheel Drive)	'78-'85	10
Buick Electra, Cadillac Fleetwood and Deville, Oldsmobile 98 (Front Wheel Drive)	'85	2
Buick Somerset, Oldsmobile Calais, Pontiac Grand Am	'85	12

Wheel Alignment

Front wheel alignment is the position of the front wheels relative to each other and to the vehicle. This preset relationship provides safe, accurate steering, directional stability, and minimum tire wear. Many factors are involved in wheel alignment, and adjustments are provided to return those that might change due to normal wear to their original value. The factors which determine wheel alignment are dependent on one another; therefore, when one of the factors is adjusted, the others must be adjusted to compensate.

Descriptions of these factors and their effects on the car are provided below. Adjustment specifications for each model year are given at the beginning of each Car Section.

Camber

Camber angle is the number of degrees that the centerline of the wheel is inclined from the vertical when viewed from the front. A small degree of positive camber reduces loading of the outer wheel bearing, and allows for easier steering.

Caster

Caster angle is the number of degrees that a line drawn through the steering knuckle pivots is inclined from the vertical, toward the front or rear of the car. A small degree of positive caster improves directional stability and increases resistance to cross winds or road surface deviations.

Steering Axis Inclincation

Steering axis inclination is the number of degrees that a line drawn through the steering knuckle pivots is inclined to the vertical, when viewed from the front of the car. This, in combination with caster, is responsible for directional stability and self-centering of the steering. As the steering knuckle swings from lock to lock, the spindle generates an arc (see illustration), the high point being the straight ahead position of the wheel. Due to his arc, as the wheel turns, the front of the car is raised. The weight of the car acts against this lift, and attempts to return the spindle to the high point of the arc, resulting in self-centering when the steering wheel is released, and straight line stability.

Included Angle

Included angle is the sum of the camber angle and the steering axis inclination. This angle is determined by the design of the steering knuckle forging and must remain constant. Therefore, if a different camber angle is necessary to make the included angle on both sides identical, a bent spindle or steering knuckle is indicated. If so, the damaged suspension member must be replaced to permit accurate front wheel alignment. Since steering knuckle damage is most commonly due to impact on the lower portion of the wheel (i.e., hitting curb), the side with the greater included angle (camber angle same on each side) will often be found to have a bent spindle.

Toe

Toe is the difference of the distance between the centers of the front and rear of the front wheels, measured at spindle height. It is most commonly measured in inches, but is occasionally referred to as an angle between the wheels. Toe-in means the front of the tires are closer together than the rear; toe-out is the opposite condition. Toe-in compensates for the tendency of the wheels to deflect out while in motion. Due to this tendency, the wheels of a car with properly adjusted toe-in are traveling straight forward when the car itself is moving straight forward, resulting in directional stability and minimum tire wear. Front wheel drive and four wheel drive cars are often set with toe-out, to compensate for the drive axles' tendency to pull the front wheels together.

Steering wheel spoke misalignment is often an indication of incorrect front end alignment. Care should be exercised when aligning the front end to maintain steering wheel spoke position. When adjusting the tie rod ends, adjust each an equal amount (in the opposite direction) to increase or decrease toe. If, following toe adjustment, further adjustments are necessary to center the steering wheel spokes, adjust the tie rod ends an equal amount in the same direction.

Steering Radius

When a car is negotiating a turn, the outer wheel follows the path of a circle of a larger radius than the inner wheel. For this reason, the inner wheel must be steered to a somewhat larger angle than the outer wheel. This value (known as the Ackerman effect) is designed into the steering linkage; therefore, if alignment is adjusted properly, and the steering radius (or toe-out on turns) appears to be incorrect, the steering arms or the linkage is bent.

Tracking

Tracking is the relationship between the paths traveled by the front and rear wheels when the vehicle is traveling in a straight line. When a car is tracking correctly, the path of the rear wheels will duplicate, or evenly straddle the path of the front wheels. Observing the car from the rear as it is driven away in a straight line will often make incorrect tracking evident.

If incorrect tracking is indicated, check as follows: Drop a plumb line from each lower ball joint, and from a point at each end of the rear axle, and mark the points on the ground with chalk. Measure these points from front to rear and diagonally. If the diagonal measurements are different (a tolerance of + ¼ in. is acceptable), but the longitudinal measurements are the same, the frame is swayed (diamond shaped). If the diagonal and longitudinal measurements are both different, the rear axle is misaligned. If both diagonal and longitudinal measurements are different, but the car does not appear to be tracking incorrectly, a kneeback condition is indicated. Kneeback implies that one side of the front suspension is bent or pushed back. It is possible to align the front end to specifications, and, if kneeback exists, have very poor handling characteristics.

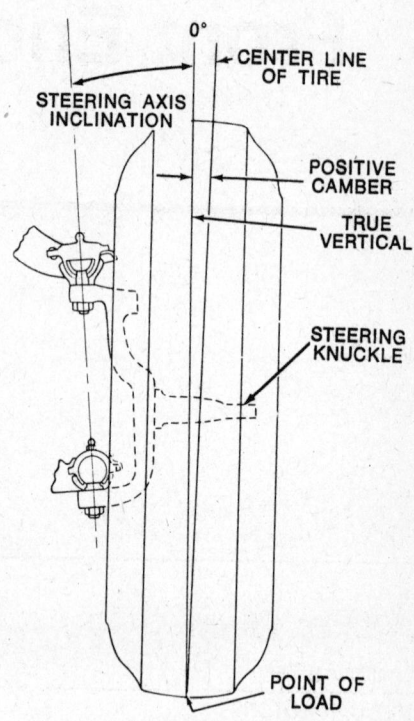

Camber and steering axis inclination angles

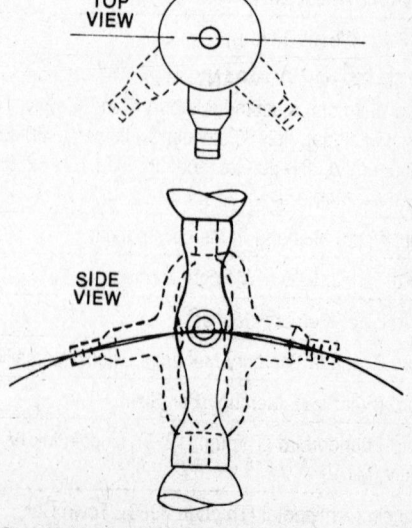

Arc generated by the spindle as the steering knuckle turns

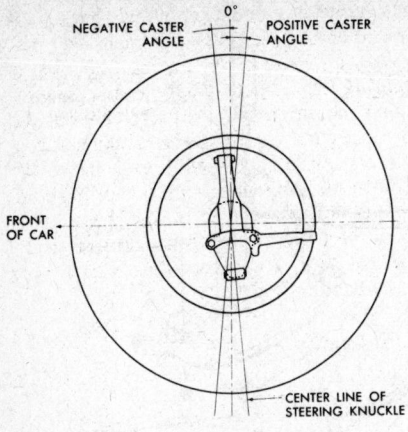

Caster angle

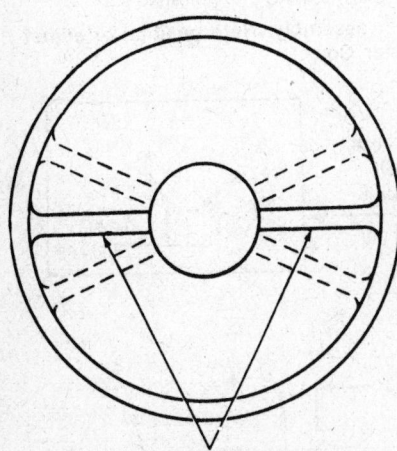

ADJUST BOTH RODS EQUALLY TO
MAINTAIN NORMAL SPOKE POSITION

Steering wheel spoke alignment

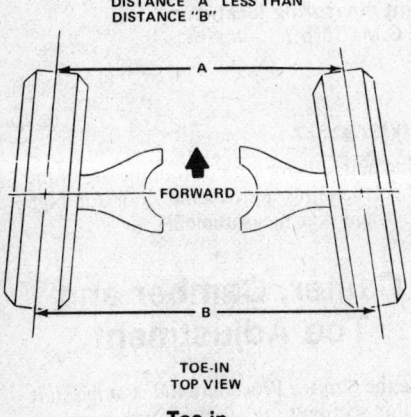

TOE-IN
TOP VIEW

Toe-in

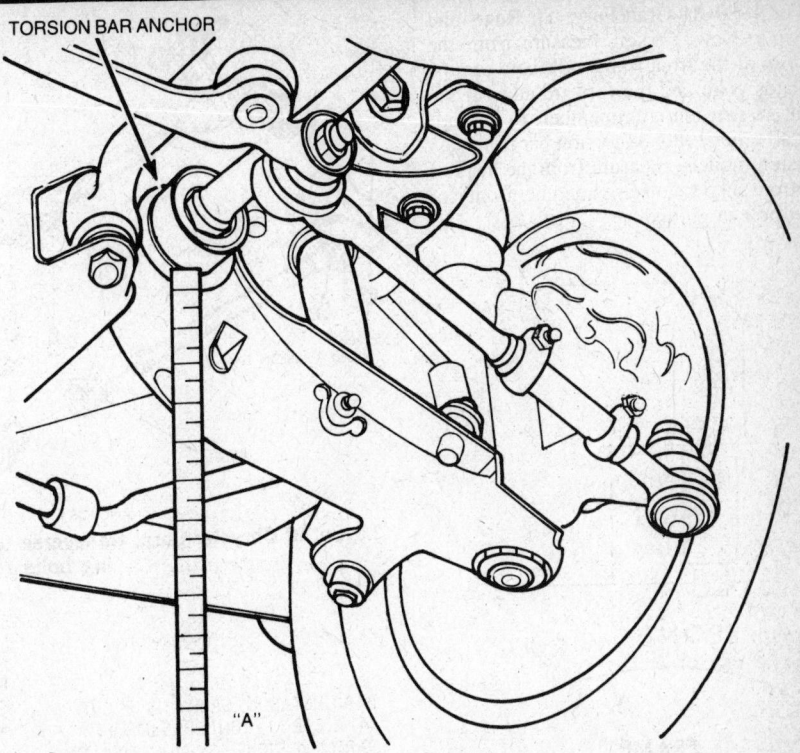

Measuring points for 1977–79 Chrysler Corp. cars with longitudinal tortion bars

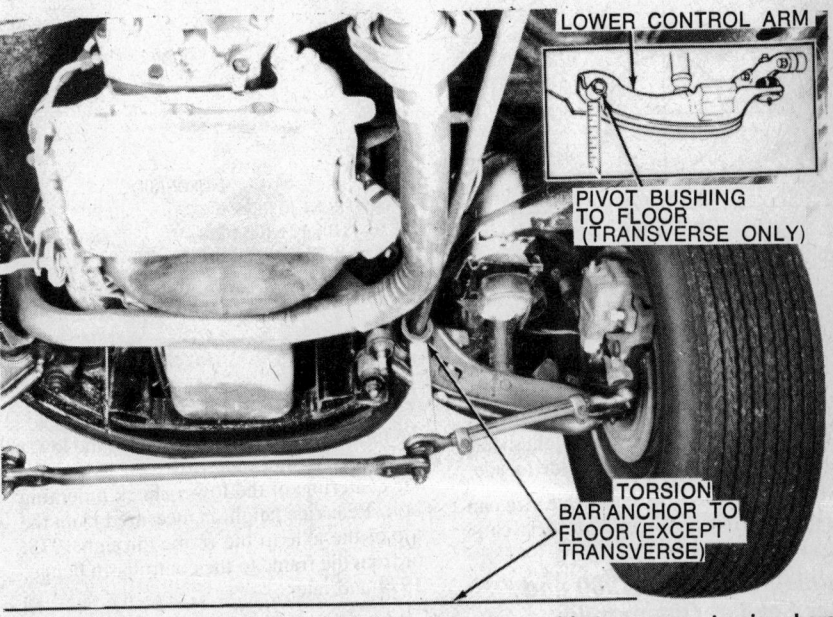

Height measuring location for Chrysler Corp. cars with transverse torsion bars
(© Chrysler Corp.)

Ride Height Adjustment

This adjustment is required before adjusting front end alignment on cars with torsion bar front suspension.

NOTE: The car must be on a level floor with the gas tank full and the tires properly inflated. There should be no unusual loads in the car. On all models, check the measurements against those given with the front end. Alignment specifications in the car sections.

Chrysler Corporation

Rock the car at the centers of the front and rear bumpers five times and allow it to settle.

For 1978–79 models with longitudinal (front to rear) torsion bars, measure from the lowest point of the lower control arm torsion bar anchor (''A''), at a point one inch forward of the rear face of the anchor, to the ground. On models with transverse (across the chassis) torsion bars, measure from the lowest point of the lower control arm inner pivot bushing to the floor.

U501

FRONT END ALIGNMENT

For 1980–81 Gran Fury, St. Regis and Newport/New Yorker, measure from the bottom of the front frame rail, between the radiator yoke and the forward edge of the front suspension crossmember, to ground. For all other 1980–83 torsion bar front suspension models, measure from the head of the front suspension crossmember front isolator bolt to ground.

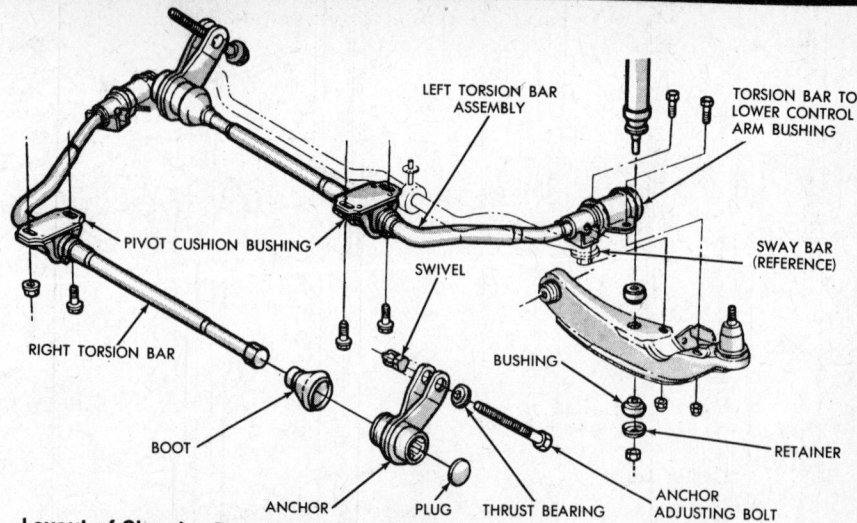

Layout of Chrysler Corp. transverse torsion bar assembly. Note position of adjusting bolts (© Chrysler Corp.)

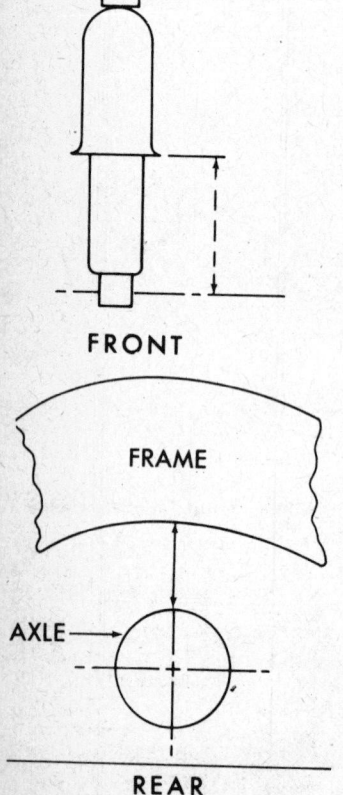

Cadillac Eldorado and 1980-81 Seville ride height measuring locations (© Cadillac Div., G.M. Corp.)

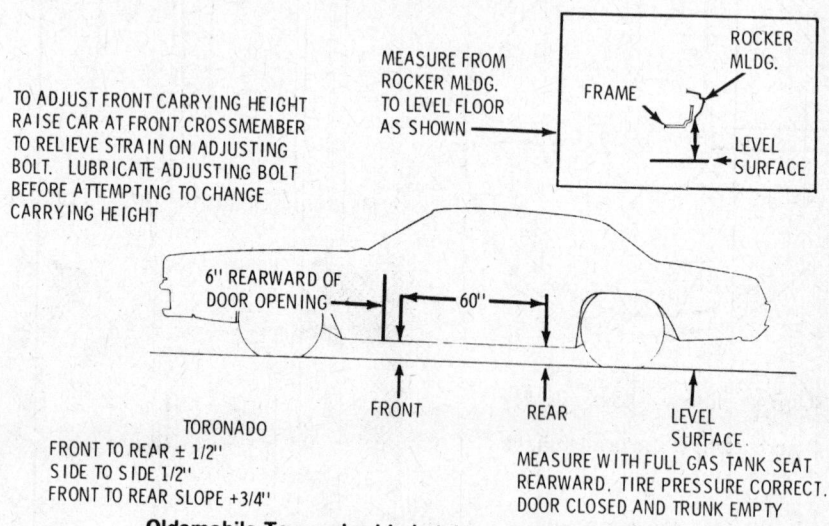

TO ADJUST FRONT CARRYING HEIGHT RAISE CAR AT FRONT CROSSMEMBER TO RELIEVE STRAIN ON ADJUSTING BOLT. LUBRICATE ADJUSTING BOLT BEFORE ATTEMPTING TO CHANGE CARRYING HEIGHT

TORONADO
FRONT TO REAR ± 1/2''
SIDE TO SIDE 1/2''
FRONT TO REAR SLOPE +3/4''

MEASURE WITH FULL GAS TANK SEAT REARWARD. TIRE PRESSURE CORRECT. DOOR CLOSED AND TRUNK EMPTY

Oldsmobile Toronado ride height measuring locations (© Oldsmobile Div., G.M. Corp.)

Adjust the height by turning the torsion bar adjusting bolt clockwise to raise or counterclockwise to lower. The height should not vary more than ¼ in. from side to side.

NOTE: A change of front tire size can change the front end height on these cars.

Cadillac Eldorado, 1980 and Later Seville, Oldsmobile Toronado, 1979 and Later Riviera

Front ride height is controlled by the settings of the torsion bar adjusting bolts. The height is adjusted by turning the adjusting bolt clockwise to raise, and counterclockwise to lower. Rear ride height can only be corrected by spring replacement or shimming through 1978. 1979 and later models have electronic level control. 1980–83 are the only model Sevilles equipped with torsion bar front suspension.

Cadillac Eldorado, Seville

Front ride height is measured from the lower edge of the shock absorber dust cover to the centerline of the lower shock mounting bolt. Rear ride height is measured from the top of the axle to the frame through 1978, or from the frame to the control arm flange, 1979 and later.

Oldsmobile Toronado

The front height is measured from the rocker panel moulding lower edge, 6 inches rearward of the forward edge of the door opening, to the floor through 1978. 1979 and later models should be measured directly below the door opening, from the rocker moulding to the floor. The rear height is measured from the rocker panel moulding lower edge, 60 inches back from the front height measuring point on models through 1978, or 71 inches back on 1979 and later models, to the floor.

Riviera

Ride height is measured from the top of the wheel opening arch to the floor for both front and rear measurements.

Caster, Camber and Toe Adjustment

Use the Service Procedure Index at the start of this section to relate these type numbers to makes and models.

NOTE: The car must be on a level floor with the gas tank full and the tires properly inflated. There should be no unusual loads in the vehicle. In order to settle the suspension before checking alignment, grasp the front bumper in the center and rock the car up and down several times. Repeat the procedure on the rear bumper.

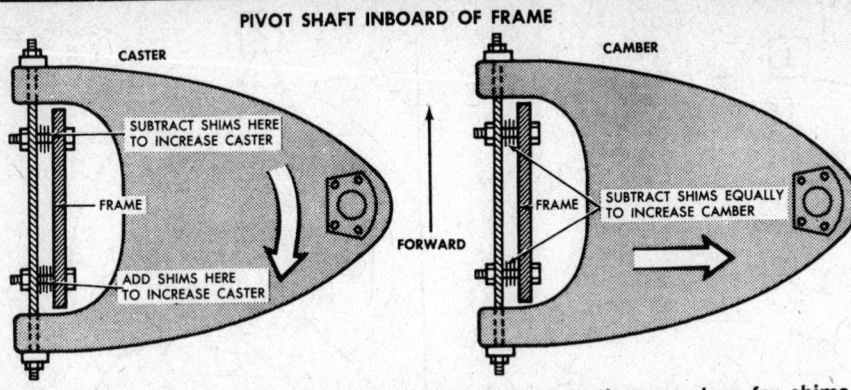

PIVOT SHAFT INBOARD OF FRAME

Typical caster and camber adjustment, Type 1 (reverse the procedure for shims on the opposite side of the frame) (© Chevrolet Div., G.M. Corp.)

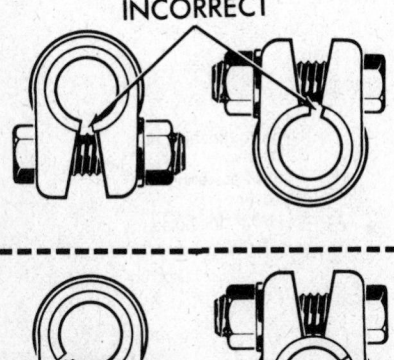

INCORRECT

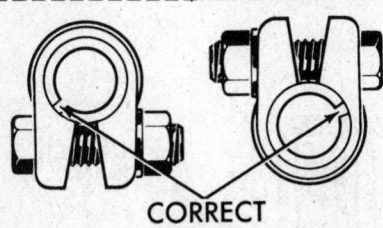

CORRECT

Typical tie rod clamp to sleeve position (© Cadillac Div, G.M. Corp.)

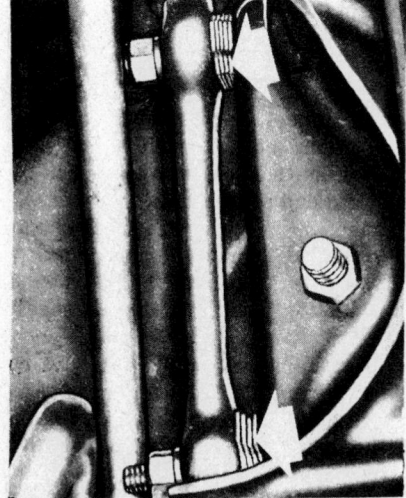

Typical Type 1 caster and camber adjusting shim location (© Chevrolet Div., G.M. Corp.)

TYPE 1

Caster and camber are controlled by shims between the frame bracket and the upper suspension arm pivot shaft.

To adjust caster, remove shims from the front bolt and replace them at the rear bolt, or vice versa. To adjust camber, add or remove the same number of shims from each bolt.

Keep in mind when loosening the bolts that the upper suspension arm is supporting the weight of the vehicle. Loosen the bolts only a sufficient amount to remove the shims.

Adjust toe-in by loosening the clamps on the sleeves at the outer ends of the tie-rod, and turning the sleeves an equal amount in the opposite direction, to maintain steering wheel spoke alignment while adjusting toe-in.

TYPE 2

To adjust camber on these models loosen both strut-to-knuckle nuts. Attach camber

adjusting tool No. J-29862 and set camber to specifications. Retighten both strut-to-knuckle nuts to 144 ft. lbs. To adjust caster loosen, but do not remove, two of the top three strut attaching nuts covering the slotted mounting holes. Remove the nut over the remaining oval strut mounting hole, then move the washer away from the oval strut mounting hole. Lift the front of the car by the body to separate the strut from the inner wheel house. Drill 11/32 in. holes at the front and rear of the oval strut mounting hole and file the excess metal. Lower the front of the car and reinstall the washer and nut.

Caster adjustment is made by moving the top of the strut forward or rearward to specifications. Tighten the strut attaching nuts to 18 ft. lbs.

Front toe is adjusted by loosening the locknut on both inner tie-rods then turning the inner tie-rod to specifications. Tighten the locknut on the inner tie-rods to 50 ft. lbs.

TYPE 3

Caster is adjusted by lengthening or shortening the struts at the frame crossmember. To adjust, turn both nuts an equal number of turns in the same direction. Caster adjustments should be within ¼° of the opposing side of the car.

To adjust camber, loosen the lower control arm pivot bolt and rotate the eccentrics.

Adjust toe-in by loosening the clamp bolts, and turning the adjuster sleeves at the outer ends of the tie-rod. Turn each sleeve an equal amount in the opposite direction, in order to maintain steering wheel spoke alignment.

TYPE 4

Ride height should be checked before front end alignment. Ride height is not adjustable on front wheel drive models.

Caster and camber are controlled by eccentric (cam) bolts; only camber is adjustable on the front wheel drive models. The cam bolts are located at the ends of the upper control arm shafts on all models except with front wheel drive. There is only one eccentric cam for each side of the front wheel drive models, on the top bolt connecting the strut to the steering knuckle. To adjust the caster, loosen the eccentric (cam) bolt nuts and turn either of the eccentric bolts. Camber is adjusted by turning both eccentrics an equal amount, except on the front wheel drive models. For those models, loosen the cam and through bolts, and rotate the upper cam bolt to move the knuckle and wheel in or out to specification. Recheck caster after setting camber. Torque the eccentric (cam) bolts to 90 ft. lbs. on the front wheel drive models, and 65–70 ft. lbs. on all others.

To adjust toe-in (toe-out on the front wheel drive models), loosen the tie-rod clamp bolts (jam nuts on the front wheel drive models) and turn the adjuster sleeves (tie-rods on the front wheel drive models) at the outer ends of the tie-rod an equal amount in opposite directions so that steering wheel spoke alignment is maintained.

TYPE 5

Ride height should be checked before front end alignment.

Caster and camber are controlled by the positioning of the upper control arm pivot bar adjusting bolts. To adjust caster, loosen one of the pivot bar adjusting bolts or nuts and slide one end of the bar either inboard or outboard in its elongated mounting hole in the crossmember. Camber is adjusted by loosening both the pivot bar adjusting bolts or nuts and sliding both ends of the bar an equal amount.

NOTE: Chrysler recommends the use of a special pry bar no. C-4196 through 1976, C-4387 1977–78, or C-4576, 1979 and later for the adjusting operation on the upper control arm pivot bar.

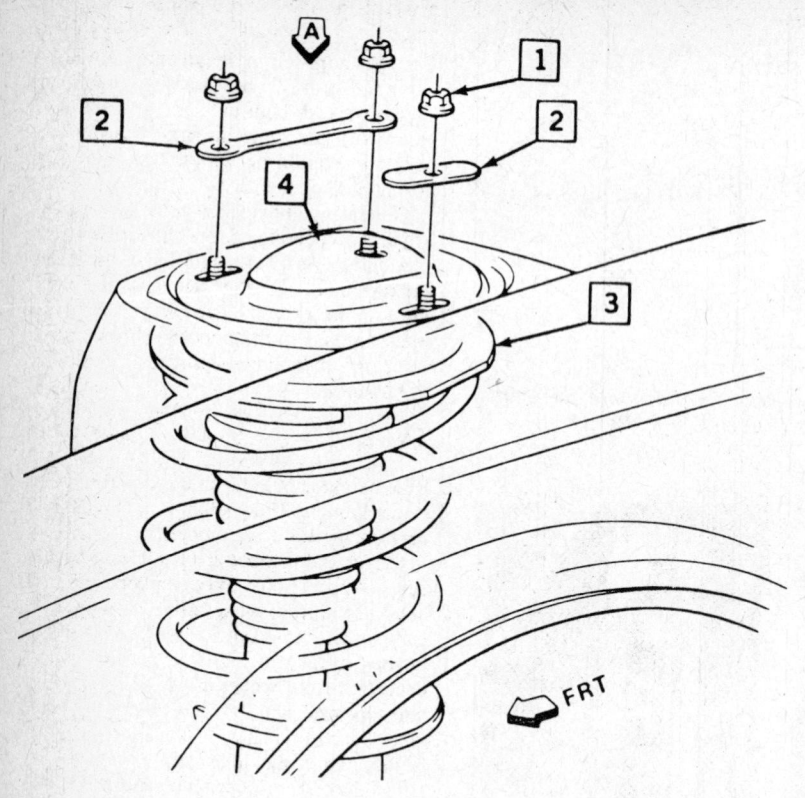

Caster adjustment—Type 2

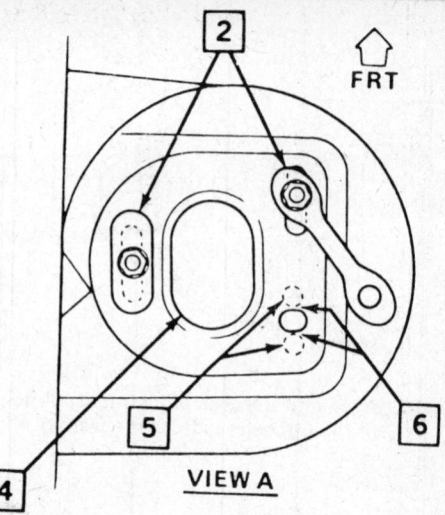

VIEW A

1. Strut attaching nuts
2. Washer
3. Strut assembly
4. Cover
5. 11/32" drill holes
6. File here

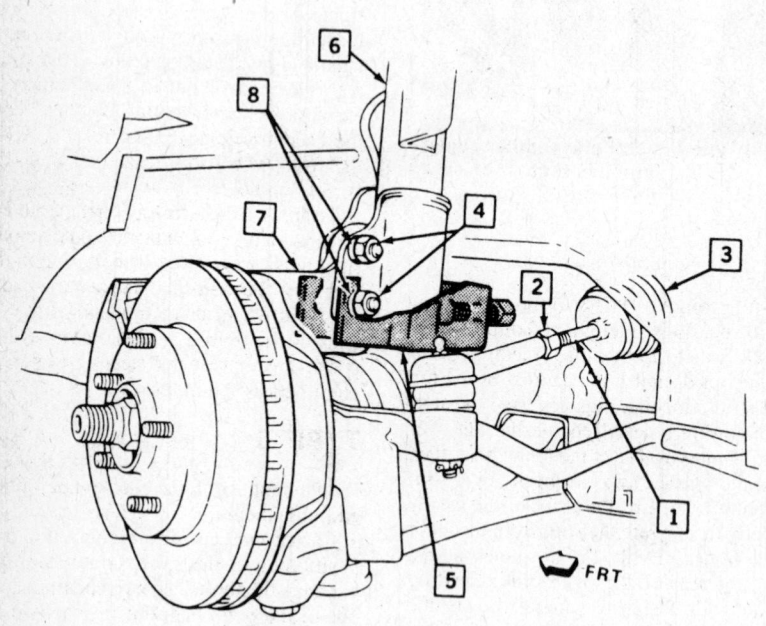

1. Inner tie-rod
2. Inner tie-rod lock nut (50 ft. lbs.)
3. Boot
4. Strut-to-knuckle nuts (144 ft. lbs.)
5. Camber adjusting tool No. J-29862
6. Strut assembly
7. Knuckle
8. Washer

Camber and toe adjustment—Type 2

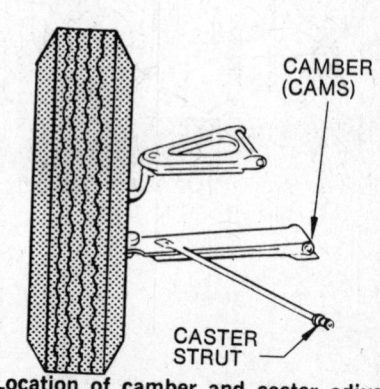

CAMBER (CAMS)

CASTER STRUT

Location of camber and caster adjustments for Type 3
(© Snap-On Tools Corp.)

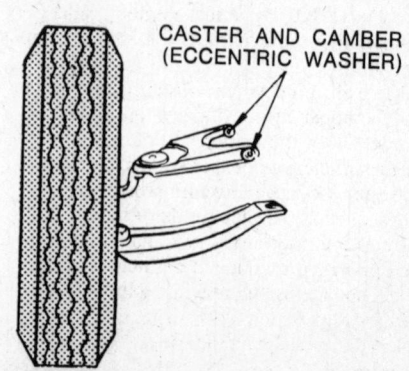

CASTER AND CAMBER (ECCENTRIC WASHER)

Location of caster and camber adjustments for Type 4 (except Imperial and Omni/Horizon) (© Snap-On Tools Corp.)

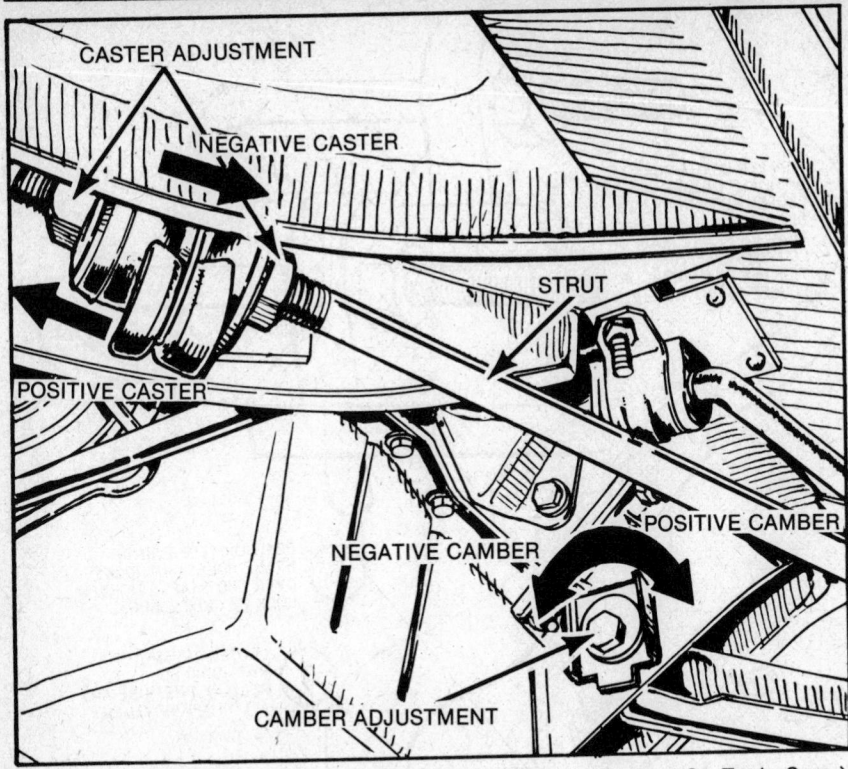

Location of caster and camber adjustments for Type 3 (© Snap-On Tools Corp.)

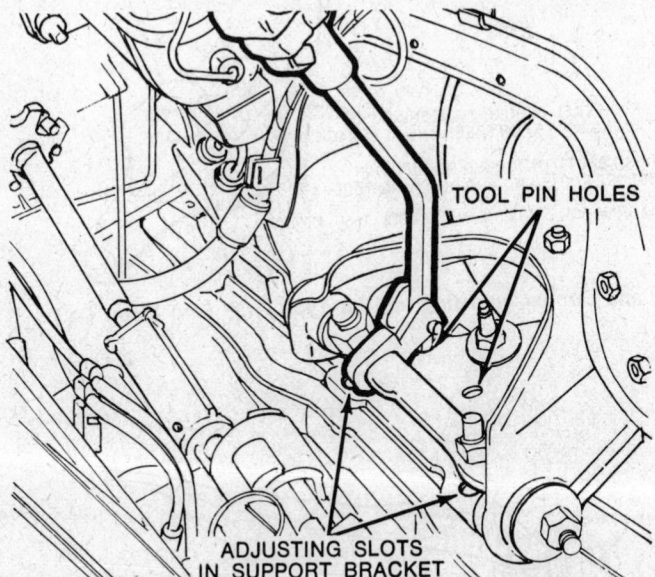

Type 5 upper control arm showing location of pivot bar adjusting nuts and bolts with adjusting pry bar in place.

Recheck caster after setting camber. Torque the pivot bar adjusting bolts or nuts to 160 ft. lbs.

To adjust toe-in, loosen the tie-rod clamp bolts and turn the adjuster sleeves at the outer ends of the tie-rod an equal amount in opposite directions, so that steering wheel spoke alignment is maintained.

TYPE 6

Caster and camber are not fully adjustable, but they may be corrected. Camber can be increased by approximately one degree by removing the upper ball joint, turning it around, and reinstalling it with the flat on the upper flange on the inboard side of the control arm. Caster can be changed one degree by changing the position of the washers between the legs of the upper control arm. Placing the thinner washer in front will increase caster, while placing it at the back will reduce caster.

Toe-in is adjusted by loosening the nuts at the steering knuckle end of each tie-rod and the rubber cover at the other end, then turning the rod.

TYPE 7

Install Ford tool T69P-3000-A (through 1979), or T79P-3000-A (1980 and later) or its equivalent on the frame rail, position the hooks around the upper control arm pivot shaft, and tighten the adjusting nuts of the tool slightly. Loosen the pivot shaft retaining bolts to permit adjustment.

To adjust caster, loosen or tighten either the front or rear adjusting nut. After adjusting caster, adjust camber by loosening or tightening both nuts an equal amount. Tighten the shaft retaining bolts to specifications, remove the tool, and recheck the adjustments.

Adjust toe-in by loosening the clamp bolts, and turning the adjuster sleeves at the outer ends of the tie-rod. Turn the sleeves an equal amount in the opposite direction, to maintain steering wheel alignment.

TYPE 8

NOTE: Camber and caster on the Fairmont, Zephry, Capri, 1979 and later Mustang, 1980 and later Cougar and Thunderbird, 1981-82 Granada, and Monarch, 1982-84 Lincoln Continental and all FWD models is permanently set at the factory. Only toe-in can be adjusted.

Position one Ford tool T74P-3000 or its equivalent at each end of the upper control arm, pivot shaft with the leg of the tools through the holes in the sheet metal (see illustration). Turn the adjusting bolts until they are solidly contacting sheet metal, and loosen the pivot shaft retaining bolts.

Caster is adjusted by turning the front and rear adjusting bolts in the opposite direction. Camber is adjusted by turning both bolts an equal amount in the same direction. Following the adjustments, tighten the pivot shaft retaining bolts, remove the adjusting tools, and recheck caster and camber.

Prior to adjusting toe-in, align the straight ahead marks at the base of the steering wheel and the head of the steering column. Loosen both the clamp at the outer end of the rack bellows and the tie-rod jam nuts. Turn the inner tie-rod shafts to adjust toe-in. Turn the shafts an equal amount in the opposite direction, to maintain steering wheel spoke alignment. Following the adjustment, hold the inner shafts with pliers, and tighten the jam nuts to 35–50 ft. lbs.

Camber and caster are adjusted using eccentrics on the lower control arm pivot bolts. Camber is adjusted first, by loosening the front pivot nut and rotating the eccentric. Tighten the front, and loosen the rear pivot nuts. Adjust caster by rotating the rear eccentric, and tighten the rear pivot nut while holding the bolt in position. Recheck camber and caster.

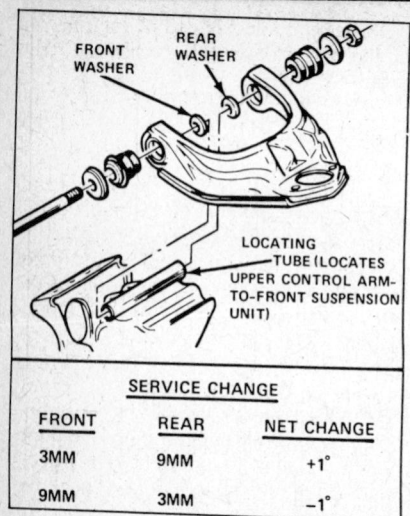

SERVICE CHANGE		
FRONT	REAR	NET CHANGE
3MM	9MM	+1°
9MM	3MM	−1°

Type 6 caster adjustment
(© Chevrolet Div., G.M. Corp.)

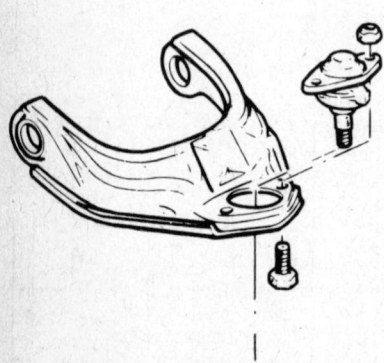

NOTE: TO INCREASE CAMBER, DISCONNECT UPPER BALL JOINT, ROTATE 180° TO POSITION "FLAT" OF FLANGE INBOARD, THEN RECONNECT BALLJOINT.

Type 6 camber adjustment
(© Chevrolet Div., G.M. Corp.)

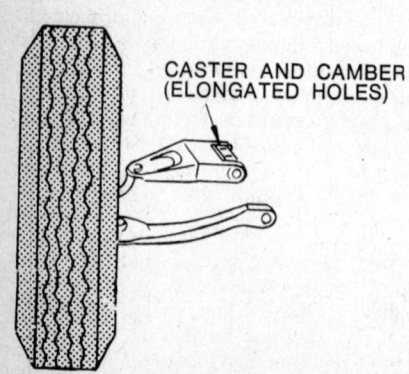

CASTER AND CAMBER (ELONGATED HOLES)

Location of caster and camber adjustments for Type 7
(© Snap-On Tools Corp.)

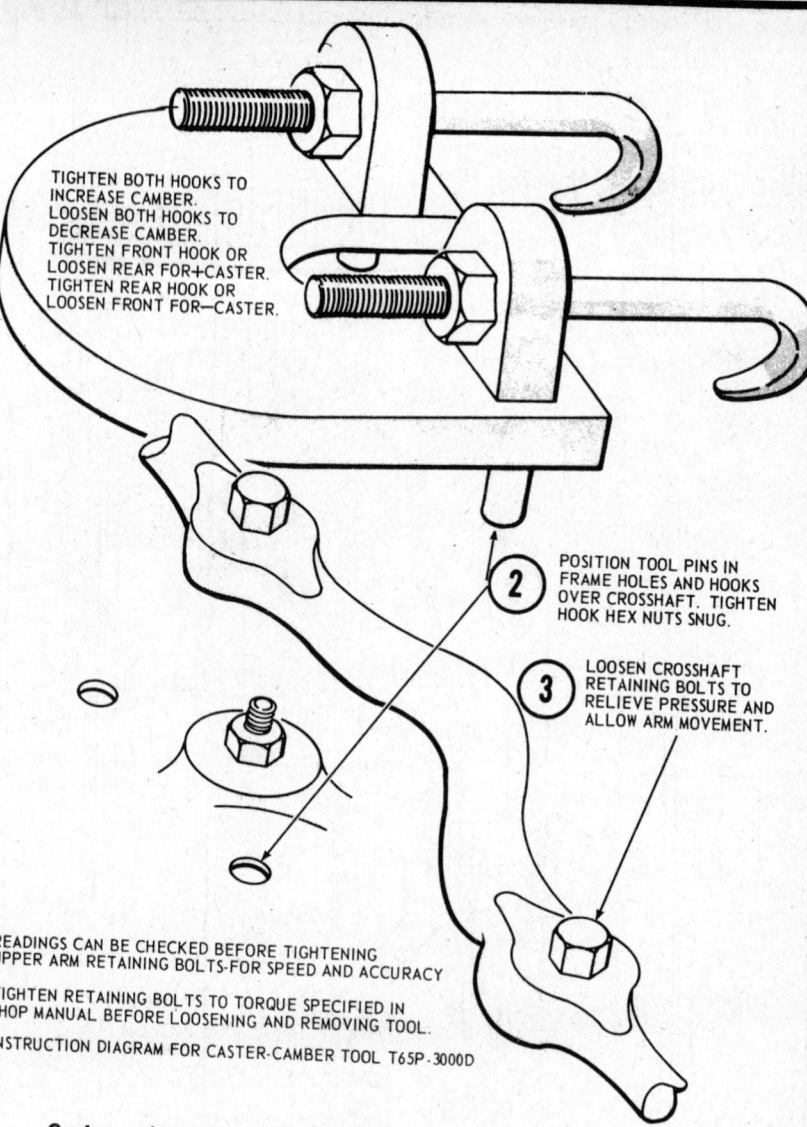

TIGHTEN BOTH HOOKS TO INCREASE CAMBER. LOOSEN BOTH HOOKS TO DECREASE CAMBER. TIGHTEN FRONT HOOK OR LOOSEN REAR FOR+CASTER. TIGHTEN REAR HOOK OR LOOSEN FRONT FOR—CASTER.

② POSITION TOOL PINS IN FRAME HOLES AND HOOKS OVER CROSSHAFT. TIGHTEN HOOK HEX NUTS SNUG.

③ LOOSEN CROSSHAFT RETAINING BOLTS TO RELIEVE PRESSURE AND ALLOW ARM MOVEMENT.

READINGS CAN BE CHECKED BEFORE TIGHTENING UPPER ARM RETAINING BOLTS-FOR SPEED AND ACCURACY

TIGHTEN RETAINING BOLTS TO TORQUE SPECIFIED IN SHOP MANUAL BEFORE LOOSENING AND REMOVING TOOL.

INSTRUCTION DIAGRAM FOR CASTER-CAMBER TOOL T65P-3000D

Caster and camber adjusting tool for Type 7 (© Ford Motor Co.)

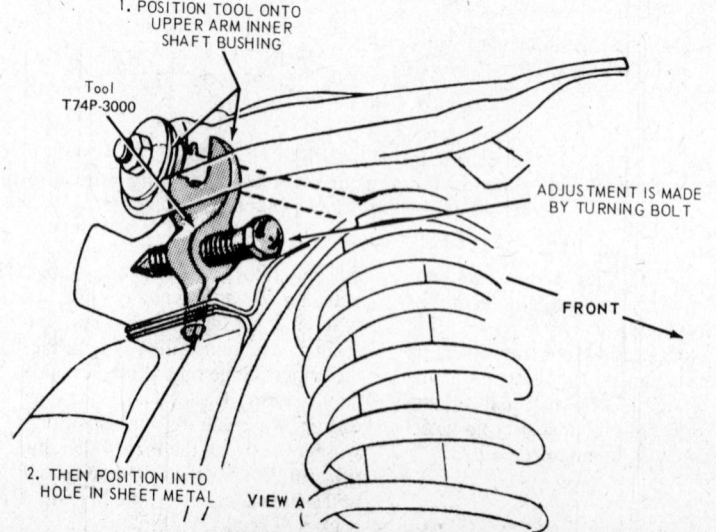

1. POSITION TOOL ONTO UPPER ARM INNER SHAFT BUSHING

Tool T74P-3000

ADJUSTMENT IS MADE BY TURNING BOLT

FRONT

2. THEN POSITION INTO HOLE IN SHEET METAL   VIEW A

Type 8 caster and camber adjusting tool installation (© Ford Motor Co.)

Type 9 camber (left) and caster (right) adjustments
(© Chevrolet Div, G.M. Corp)

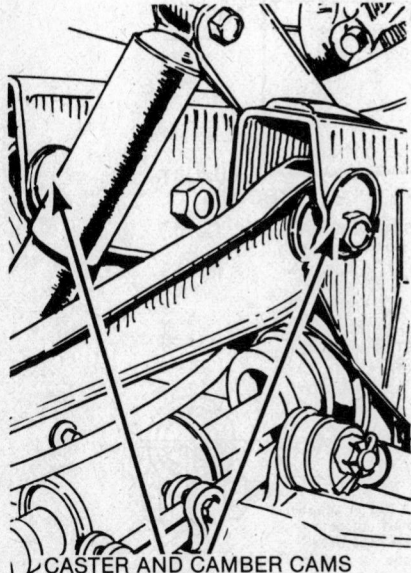

Typical caster and camber cam locations for Type 10

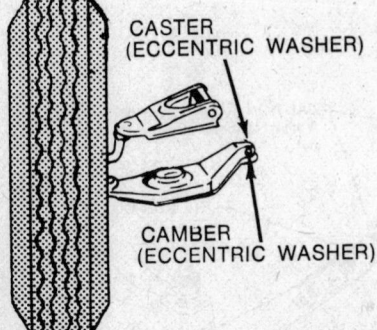

Location of caster and camber adjustments for Type 9
(© Snap-On Tools Corp.)

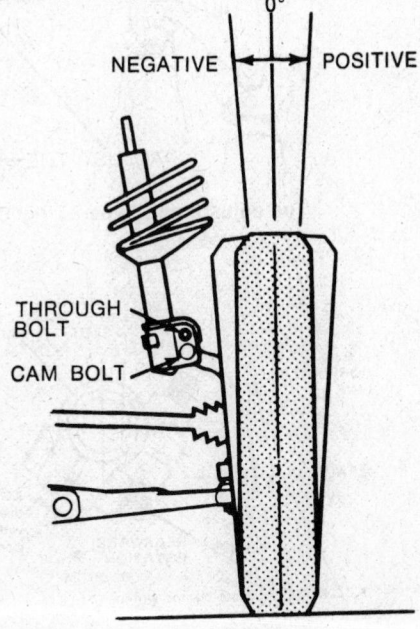

Location of camber adjusting bolts on Type 11 (© Oldsmobile Div., G.M. Corp.)

To adjust toe-in, loosen the clamps on the adjusting sleeves at the outer ends of the tie-rod, and turn each sleeve an equal amount in the opposite direction, to maintain steering wheel spoke alignment while adjusting toe-in.

TYPE 10

Ride height should be checked and corrected before front end alignment. Caster and camber are adjusted by eccentric cam bolts on the frame end of the upper control

arms. Loosen the cam bolt nuts to permit adjustment.

Adjust camber by turning the front cam bolt to make half the necessary correction. Turn the rear cam bolt in the same direction for the other half of the correction.

Adjust caster by turning the front cam bolt to make a quarter of the necessary correction. Turn the rear cam bolt to bring the camber back to the correct setting. The caster should now be correct.

Tighten the cam bolts to 95 ft. lbs. 110 for 1978 Toronado and 80 ft. lbs. for 1979 and later Toronado. Hold the bolts when tightening the nuts to prevent the settings from changing.

Adjust toe-out by centering the steering wheel, loosening the tie-rod sleeve clamps, and turning the adjusting sleeves. Turn the sleeves an equal amount in opposite directions to maintain steering wheel alignment. Position the sleeve clamps up to avoid linkage interference. Tighten the clamps to 15 ft. lbs.

TYPE 11

Camber is adjusted by loosening the cam and through bolts on the MacPherson strut-to-knuckle bolts and rotating the cam bolt to move the upper knuckle and wheel in or out. Tighten the bolts to 140 ft. lbs. after adjustment and check that the cam is seated between the inner and outer guide surfaces.

NOTE: It may be necessary to apply only partial torque because of inaccessibility to the bolts. Torque just enough to hold the correct camber position, then remove the wheel and tire and apply final torque.

Caster is not adjustable.

Toe is adjusted with the steering linkage tie-rods. Loosen the jamnuts at the steering knuckle end of the tie-rods, and remove the boot clamps. Rotate the tie-rods to align the toe. Tighten the jamnuts to 40 ft. lbs., and replace the boot clamps.

TYPE 12

NOTE: Before the camber can be adjusted the strut must be modified by filing the holes in the outer flanges to enlarge the bottom holes until they match the slots in the inner flanges. This can be accomplished by disconnecting the strut from the knuckle.

Camber is adjusted by reaching around both sides of the tire and loosening both strut-to-knuckle bolts just enough to allow movement between the strut and the knuckle. Grasp the top of the tire firmly, and move the tire in or out until the correct camber reading is obtained. Carefully reach around the tire and tighten both bolts enough to hold the correct camber, then remove the wheel and tire and torque both bolts to 140 ft. lbs. Reinstall the tire and wheel.

Caster is not adjustable.

Toe is controlled by the tie-rod position. To adjust toe setting, loosen the clamp bolts at the outer end of the tie-rod, rotate the adjuster to toe specifications, then tighten the clamp bolts to 15 ft. lbs.

TYPE 13

Caster and camber is adjusted by moving the position of the upper strut mount assembly forward/rearward for caster or inboard/outboard for camber.

The position of the mount can be changed by removing the dust cap and loosening the three upper mount attaching nuts. The weight of the vehicle will normally cause the strut assembly to move to fill the inboard position. A special tool No. J-29724 is available which is attached to a fender bolt and hooked to the upper mount assembly. By tightening the turnbuckle on the tool the proper camber can be obtained. If a caster adjustment is necessary the mount can be tapped forward or rearward with a rubber mallet. Tighten the three nuts to 20 ft. lbs. after adjustment.

Toe-in can be increased or decreased by turning the tie-rod adjusting sleeves after loosening the clamp bolts. When adjusting has been completed, check to see that there are an equal number of threads showing on each end of the sleeve and that the tie-rod end housings are at the right angles to the steering arm. Position the tie-rod clamps and sleeves according to the illustration. Torque the nuts to 15 ft. lbs.

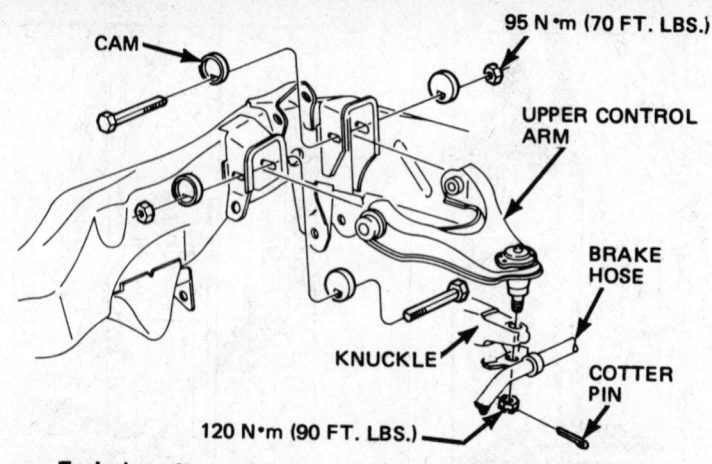

Typical caster and camber cam locations for Type 10

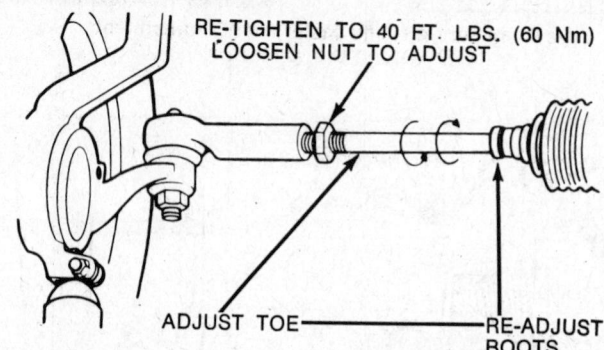

Toe adjustment, Type 11 (© Oldsmobile Div., G.M. Corp.)

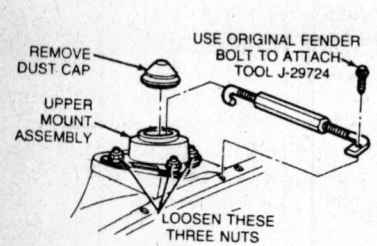

Camber adjusting tool - Type 13

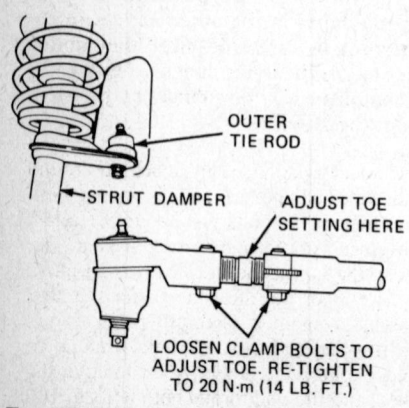

Toe adjustment, Type 12 (© Pontiac Div., G.M. Corp.)

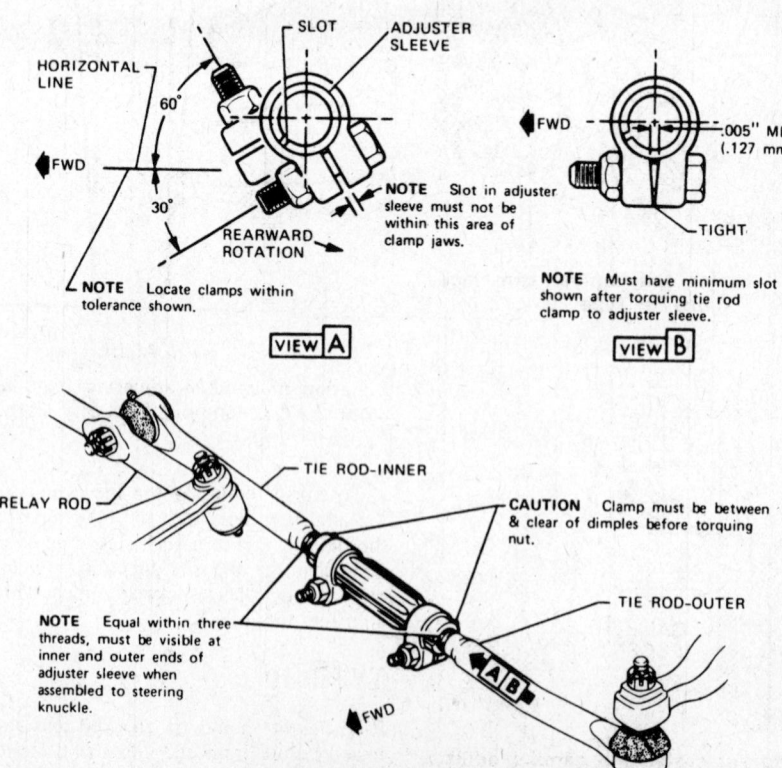

Tie rod clamp and sleeve positioning - Type 13

Troubleshooting and Diagnosis

This section is arranged so that following each test, instructions are given to proceed to another, until a problem is diagnosed.

SECTION 1—BATTERY

Test and Procedure	Results and Indications	Proceed to
1.1 Inspect the battery visually for case condition (corrosion, cracks) and water level.	If case is cracked, replace battery.	**1.4**
	If the case is intact, remove corrosion with a solution of baking soda and water. **(CAUTION: Do not get the solution into the battery).** Fill with water.	**1.2**
1.2 Check the battery cable connections: Insert a screwdriver between the battery post and the cable clamp. Turn the headlights on high beam, and observe them as the screwdriver is gently twisted to ensure good metal to metal contact.	If the lights brighten, remove and clean the clamp and post; coat the post with petroleum jelly, install and tighten the clamp.	**1.4**
	If no improvement is noted	**1.3**
1.3 Test the state of charge of the battery using an individual cell tester or hydrometer.	If indicated, charge the battery. **NOTE: If no obvious reason exists for the low state of charge (i.e., battery age, prolonged storage), proceed to:**	**1.4**

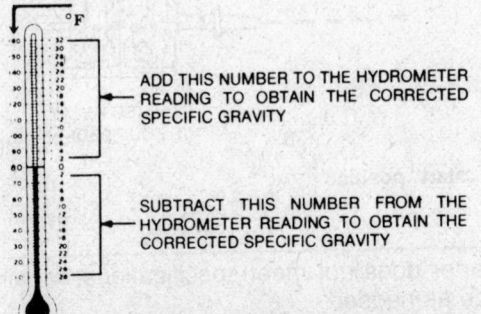

TESTING BATTERY CABLE CONNECTIONS USING A SCREWDRIVER

ADD THIS NUMBER TO THE HYDROMETER READING TO OBTAIN THE CORRECTED SPECIFIC GRAVITY

SUBTRACT THIS NUMBER FROM THE HYDROMETER READING TO OBTAIN THE CORRECTED SPECIFIC GRAVITY

Specific Gravity (@ 80° F.)

Minimum	Battery Charge
1.260	100% Charged
1.230	75% Charged
1.200	50% Charged
1.170	25% Charged
1.140	Very Little Power Left
1.110	Completely Discharged

The effects of temperature on battery specific gravity (left) and amount of battery charge in relation to specific gravity (right)

Test and Procedure	Results and Indications	Proceed To
1.4 Visually inspect battery cables for cracking, bad connection to ground, or bad connection to starter.	If necessary, tighten connections or replace the cables.	2.1

SECTION 2—STARTING SYSTEM

Test and Procedure	Results and Indications	Proceed to
Note: Tests in Group 2 are performed with coil high tension lead disconnected to prevent accidental starting.		
2.1 Test the starter motor and solenoid: Connect a jumper from the battery post of the solenoid (or relay) to the starter post of the solenoid (or relay).	If starter turns the engine normally	2.2
	If the starter buzzes, or turns the engine very slowly	2.4
	If no response, replace the solenoid (or relay).	3.1
	If the starter turns, but the engine doesn't, ensure that the flywheel ring gear is intact. If the gear is undamaged, replace the starter drive.	3.1
2.2 Determine whether ignition override switches are functioning properly (clutch start switch, neutral safety switch), by connecting a jumper across the switch(es), and turning the ignition switch to "start".	If starter operates, adjust or replace switch.	3.1
	If the starter doesn't operate	2.3
2.3 Check the ignition switch "start" position: Connect a 12V test lamp or voltmeter between the starter post of the solenoid (or relay) and ground. Turn the ignition switch to the "start" position, and jiggle the key.	If the lamp doesn't light or the meter needle doesn't move when the switch is turned, check the ignition switch for loose connections, cracked insulation, or broken wires. Repair or replace as necessary.	3.1
	If the lamp flickers or needle moves when the key is jiggled, replace the ignition switch.	3.3

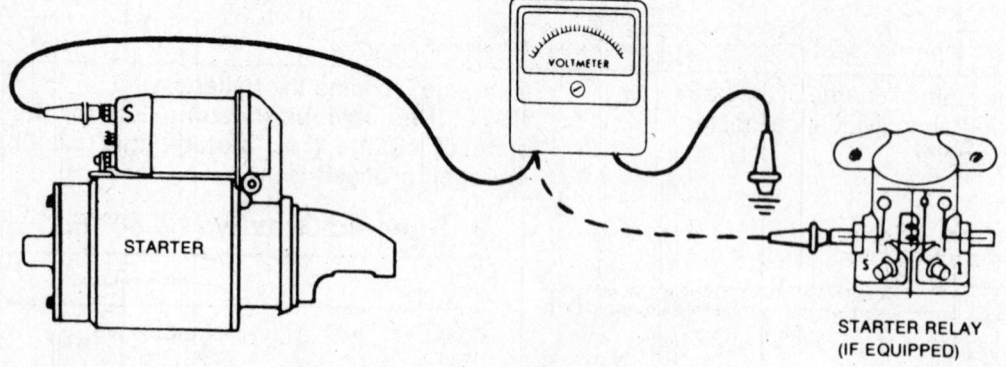

Checking the ignition switch "start" position

Test and Procedure	Results and Indications	Proceed to
2.4 Remove and bench test the starter, according to specifications in the car section.	If the starter does not meet specifications, repair or replace as needed	3.1
	If the starter is operating properly	2.5

Test and Procedure	Results and Indications	Proceed To
2.5 Determine whether the engine can turn freely: Remove the spark plugs, and check for water in the cylinders. Check for water on the dipstick, or oil in the radiator. Attempt to turn the engine using an 18″ flex drive and socket on the crankshaft pulley nut or bolt.	If the engine will turn freely only with the spark plugs out, and hydrostatic lock (water in the cylinders) is ruled out, check valve timing.	9.2
	If engine will not turn freely, and it is known that the clutch and transmission are free, the engine must be disassembled for further evaluation.	See Car Section

SECTION 3—PRIMARY ELECTRICAL SYSTEM

Test and Procedure	Results and Indications	Proceed to
3.1 Check the ignition switch "on" position: Connect a jumper wire between the distributor side of the coil and ground, and a 12V test lamp between the switch side of the coil and ground. Remove the high tension lead from the coil. Turn the ignition switch on and jiggle the key.  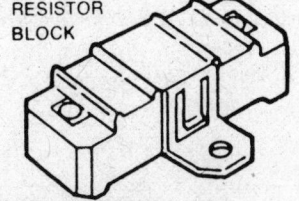 **Checking the ignition switch "on" position**	If the lamp lights	3.2
	If the lamp flickers when the key is jiggled, replace the ignition switch.	3.3
	If the lamp doesn't light, check for loose or open connections. If none are found, remove the ignition switch and check for continuity. If the switch is faulty, replace it.	3.3
3.2 Check the ballast resistor or resistance wire for an open circuit, using an ohmmeter. RESISTOR BLOCK / CALIBRATED RESISTANCE LEAD / **Two types of resistors**	Replace the resistor or resistance wire if the resistance is zero. **NOTE: Some ignition systems have no ballast resistor.**	3.3
3.3 On point-type ignition systems, visually inspect the breaker points for burning, pitting or excessive wear. Gray coloring of the point contact surfaces is normal. Rotate the crankshaft until the contact heel rests on a high point of the distributor cam and adjust the point gap to specifications. On electronic ignition models, remove the distributor cap and visually inspect the armature. Ensure that the armature pin is in place, and that the armature is on tight and rotates when the engine is cranked. Make sure there are no cracks, chips or rounded edges on the armature.	If the breaker points are intact, clean the contact surfaces with fine emery cloth, and adjust the point gap to specifications. If the points are worn, replace them. On electronic systems, replace any parts which appear defective. If condition persists	3.4

Test and Procedure	Results and Indications	Proceed To
3.4 On point-type ignition systems, connect a dwell-meter between the distributor primary lead and ground. Crank the engine and observe the point dwell angle. On electronic ignition systems, conduct a stator (magnetic pickup assembly) test. See Electronic Ignition Unit Repair Section.	On point-type systems, adjust the dwell angle if necessary. **NOTE: Increasing the point gap decreases the dwell angle and vice-versa.**	3.6
	If the dwell meter shows little or no reading	3.5
	On electronic ignition systems, if the stator is bad, replace the stator. If the stator is good, proceed to the other tests in The Electronic Ignition Unit Repair Section.	

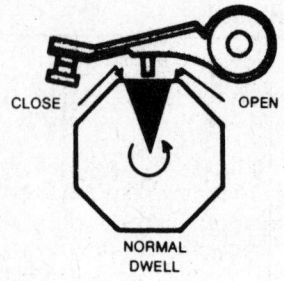 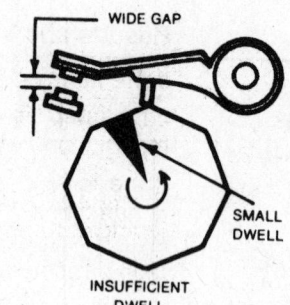 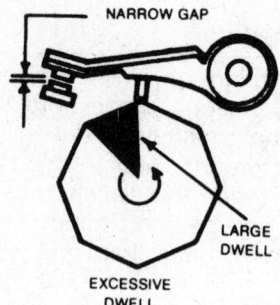

CLOSE — OPEN

NORMAL DWELL

WIDE GAP

SMALL DWELL

INSUFFICIENT DWELL

NARROW GAP

LARGE DWELL

EXCESSIVE DWELL

Dwell is a function of point gap

3.5 On the point-type ignition systems, check the condenser for short: connect an ohmeter across the condenser body and the pigtail lead.	If any reading other than infinite is noted, replace the condenser	3.6

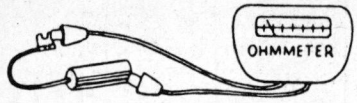

OHMMETER

Checking the condenser for short

3.6 Test the coil primary resistance: On point-type ignition systems, connect an ohmmeter across the coil primary terminals, and read the resistance on the low scale. Note whether an external ballast resistor or resistance wire is used. On electronic ignition systems, test the coil primary resistance.	Point-type ignition coils utilizing ballast resistors or resistance wires should have approximately 1.0 ohms resistance. Coils with internal resistors should have approximately 4.0 ohms resistance. If values far from the above are noted, replace the coil.	4.1

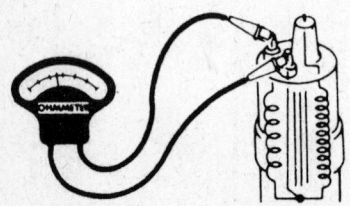

Checking the coil primary resistance

SECTION 4—SECONDARY ELECTRICAL SYSTEM

Test and Procedure	Results and Indications	Proceed to
4.1 Check for spark: Hold each spark plug wire approximately ¼″ from ground with gloves or heavy, dry rag. Crank the engine, and observe the spark.	If no spark is evident	4.2
	If spark is good in some cylinders	4.3
	If spark is good in all cylinders	4.6

Check for spark at the plugs

Test and Procedure	Results and Indications	Proceed to
4.2 Check for spark at the coil high tension lead: Remove the coil high tension lead from the distributor and position it approximately ¼″ from ground. Crank the engine and observe spark. **CAUTION: This test should not be performed on engines equipped with electronic ignition.**	If the spark is good and consistent	4.3
	If the spark is good but intermittent, test the primary electrical system starting at 3.3.	3.3
	If the spark is weak or non-existent, replace the coil high tension lead, clean and tighten all connections and retest. If no improvement is noted	4.4

Test and Procedure	Results and Indications	Proceed to
4.3 Visually inspect the distributor cap and rotor for burned or corroded contacts, cracks, carbon tracks, or moisture. Also check the fit of the rotor on the distributor shaft (where applicable).	If moisture is present, dry thoroughly, and retest per 4.1.	4.1
	If burned or excessively corroded contacts, cracks, or carbon tracks are noted, replace the defective part(s) and retest per 4.1.	4.1
	If the rotor and cap appear intact, or are only slightly corroded, clean the contacts thoroughly (including the cap towers and spark plug wire ends) and retest per 4.1.	
	If the spark is good in all cases	4.6
	If the spark is poor in all cases	4.5

CORRODED OR LOOSE WIRE

HIGH RESISTANCE CARBON

EXCESSIVE WEAR OF BUTTON

ROTOR TIP BURNED AWAY

Inspect the distributor cap and rotor

Test and Procedure	Results and Indications
4.4 Check the coil secondary resistance: On point-type systems connect an ohmmeter across the distributor side of the coil and the coil tower. Read the resistance on the high scale of the ohmmeter. On electronic ignition systems, see The Electronic Ignition Unit Repair Section for specific tests.	The resistance of a satisfactory coil should be between 4,000 and 10,000 ohms. If resistance is considerably higher (i.e., 40,000 ohms) replace the coil and retest per 4.1. **NOTE: This does not apply to high performance coils.**

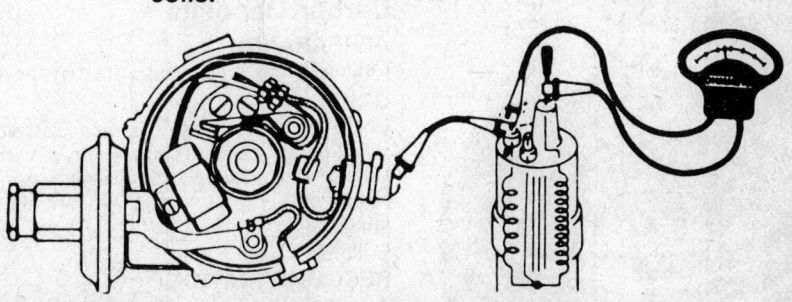

Testing the coil secondary resistance

Spark Plug Analysis

Normal

APPEARANCE

This plug is typical of one operating normally. The insulator nose varies from a light tan to grayish color with slight electrode wear. The presence of slight deposits is normal on used plugs and will have no adverse effect on engine performance. The spark plug heat range is correct for the engine and the engine is running normally.

CAUSE

Properly running engine

RECOMMENDATION

Before reinstalling this plug, the electrodes should be cleaned and filed square. Set the gap to specifications. If the plug has been in service for more than 10–12,000 miles, the entire set should probably be replaced with a fresh set of the same heat range.

Incorrect Heat Range

APPEARANCE

The effects of high temperature on a spark plug are indicated by clean white, often blistered insulator. This can also be accompanied by excessive wear of the electrode, and the absence of deposits.

CAUSE

Check for the correct spark plug heat range. A plug which is too hot for the engine can result in overheating. A car operated mostly at high speeds may require a colder plug. Also check ignition timing, cooling system level, fuel mixture and leaking intake manifold.

RECOMMENDATION

If all ignition and engine adjustments are known to be correct, and no other malfunction exists, install spark plugs one heat range colder.

Oil Deposits

APPEARANCE

The firing end of the plug is covered with a wet, oily coating.

CAUSE

The problem is poor oil control. On high mileage engines, oil is leaking past the rings or valve guides into the combustion chamber. A common cause is also a plugged PCV valve, and a ruptured fuel pump diaphragm can also cause this condition. Oil fouled plugs such as these are often found in new or recently overhauled engines, before normal oil control is achieved, and can be cleaned and reinstalled.

RECOMMENDATION

A hotter spark plug may temporarily relieve the problem, but the engine is probably in need of engine work.

Carbon Deposits

APPEARANCE

Carbon fouling is easily identified by the presence of dry, soft, black, sooty deposits.

CAUSE

Changing the heat range can often lead to carbon fouling, as can prolonged slow, stop-and-start driving. If the heat range is correct, carbon fouling can be attributed to a rich fuel mixture, sticking choke, clogged air cleaner, worn breaker points, retarded timing or low compression. If only one or two plugs are carbon fouled, check for corroded or cracked wires on the affected plugs. Also look for cracks in the distributor cap between the towers of affected cylinders.

RECOMMENDATION

After the problem is corrected, these plugs can be cleaned and reinstalled if not worn severely.

Ash Deposits

APPEARANCE

Ash deposits are characterized by light brown or white colored deposits crusted on the side or center electrodes. In some cases it may give the plug a rusty appearance.

CAUSE

Ash deposits are normally derived from oil or fuel additives burned during normal combustion. Normally they are harmless, though excessive amounts can cause misfiring. If deposits are excessive in short mileage, the valve guides may be worn. Reddish or rusty deposits are caused by manganese, an anti-knock compound replacing lead in unleaded gas. No engine malfunction is indicated.

RECOMMENDATION

Ash-fouled plugs can be cleaned, gapped and reinstalled.

Splash Deposits

APPEARANCE

Splash deposits occur in varying degrees as spotty deposits on the insulator.

CAUSE

These usually occur after a long delayed tune-up. By-products of combustion have accumulated on pistons and valves because of a delayed tune-up. Following tune-up or during hard acceleration, the deposits loosen and are thrown against the hot surface of the plug. If the deposits accumulate sufficiently, misfiring can occur.

RECOMMENDATION

These plugs can be cleaned, gapped and reinstalled.

High Speed Glazing

APPEARANCE

Glazing appears as shiny coating on the plug, either yellow or tan in color.

CAUSE

During hard, fast acceleration, plug temperatures rise suddenly. Deposits from normal combustion have no chance to fluff-off; instead, they melt on the insulator forming an electrically conductive coating which causes misfiring.

RECOMMENDATION

Glazed plugs are not easily cleaned. They should be replaced with a fresh set of plugs of the correct heat range. If the condition recurs, using plugs with a heat range one step colder may cure the problem.

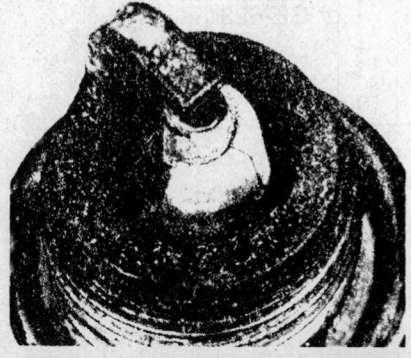

Detonation

APPEARANCE

Detonation is usually characterized by a broken plug insulator.

CAUSE

A portion of the fuel charge will begin to burn spontaneously, from the increased heat following ignition. The explosion that results applies extreme pressure to engine components, frequently damaging spark plugs and pistons.

Detonation can result by over-advanced ignition timing, inferior gasoline (low octane) lean air fuel mixture, poor carburetion, engine lugging or an increase in compression ratio due to combustion chamber deposits or engine modification.

RECOMMENDATION

Replace the plugs after correcting the problem.

Test and Procedure	Results and Indications	Proceed To
4.5 Visually inspect the spark plug wires for cracking or brittleness. Ensure that no two wires are positioned so as to cause induction firing (adjacent and parallel). Remove each wire, one by one, and check resistance with an ohmmeter.	Replace any cracked or brittle wires. If any of the wires are defective, replace the entire set. Replace any wires with excessive resistance (over 8000 Ω per foot for suppression wire), and separate any wires that might cause induction firing.	4.6

Misfiring can be the result of spark plug leads to adjacent, consecutively firing cylinders running parallel and too close together

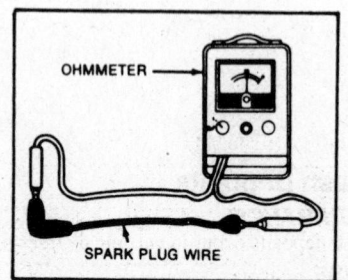

On point-type ignition systems, check the spark plug wires as shown. On electronic ignitions, do not remove the wire from the distributor cap terminal; instead, test through the cap

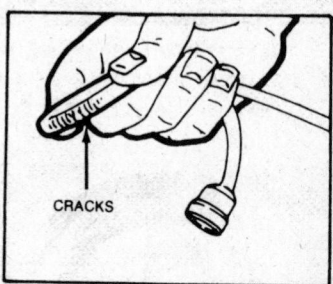

Spark plugs wires can be checked visually by bending them in a loop over your finger. This will reveal any cracks, burned or broken insulation. Any wire with cracked insulation should be replaced

Test and Procedure	Results and Indications	Proceed To
4.6 Remove the spark plugs, noting the cylinders from which they were removed, and evaluate according to the chart in this section.	See chart.	See Chart
4.7 Reinstall the spark plugs.		4.8

4.7 Reinstall the spark plugs.
NOTE: Modern electronic ignition systems generate extremely high voltages and high heats. The spark plug boots can soften and actually fuse to the ceramic insulator of the spark plugs after long exposures to high temperature and voltage. If this happens, the boot (and possibly the wire) must be replaced.

To help alleviate this condition, many manufacturers are recommending new silicone compounds to slow the deterioration. The compounds are generally nonconductive, protective lubricants that will not dry out, harden, or melt away. They form a weather-tight seal between rubber or plastic and metal and are found in several typical locations: Inside the insulating boots of spark plug wires, inside primary ignition circuit cable connectors, on distributor and rotor cap electrodes, and under the GM HEI control module.

Application Point	Silicone Compound
GENERAL MOTORS: Under HEI module	Supplied with new module, or use GE-642 or DC-340
FORD MOTOR COMPANY: Inside spark plug boots, on end of cable when installing new boot, and on rotor and cap electrodes	Ford part number D7AZ-19A331-A or use GE-627 or DC-111
CHRYSLER CORPORATION: ¼" deep within spark control computer connector cavity coating rotor electrode	Use Mopar part number 2932524 or NLGI Grade 2 EP (not a silicone) supplied with new rotor, or use GE-628 or DC-111
AMERICAN MOTORS (Prestolite system): Distributor primary connector—coat male terminal, fill female ¼ full	AMC part number 8127445 or GE-623

GE: General Electric
DC: Dow Corning

Test and Procedure	Results and Indications	Proceed To
4.9 Determine the static ignition timing. Using the crankshaft pulley timing marks as a guide, locate top dead center on the compression stroke of the number one cylinder.	The rotor should be pointing toward the No. 1 tower in the distributor cap, and, on electronic ignitions, the armature spoke for that cylinder should be lined up with the stator.	4.10
4.10 Check coil polarity: Connect a voltmeter negative lead to the coil high tension lead, and the positive lead to ground. **NOTE: Reverse the hook-up for positive ground systems.** Crank the engine momentarily.	If the voltmeter reads up-scale, the polarity is correct.	5.1
	If the voltmeter reads down-scale, reverse the coil polarity (switch the primary leads).	5.1

Checking coil polarity

SECTION 5—FUEL SYSTEM

Test and Procedure	Results and Indications	Proceed to
5.1 Determine that the air filter is functioning efficiently: Hold paper elements up to a strong light, and attempt to see light through the filter.	Clean permanent air filters in solvent (or manufacturer's recommendation), and allow to dry. Replace paper elements through which light cannot be seen.	5.2
5.2 Determine whether a flooding condition exists: Flooding is identified by a strong gasoline odor, and excessive gasoline present in the throttle bore(s) of the carburetor.	If flooding is not evident	5.3
	If flooding is evident, permit the gasoline to dry for a few moments and restart.	
	If flooding doesn't recur	5.7
	If flooding is persistent	5.5

If the engine floods repeatedly, check the choke butterfly flap

Test and Procedure	Results and Indications	Proceed to
5.3 Check that fuel is reaching the carburetor: Detach the fuel line at the carburetor inlet. Hold the end of the line in a cup (not styrofoam), and crank the engine.	If fuel flows smoothly	5.7
	If fuel doesn't flow	5.4
	If fuel flows erratically.	
	NOTE: Make sure that there is fuel in the tank	

Check the fuel pump by disconnecting the output line (fuel pump-to-carburetor) at the carburetor and operating the starter briefly

Test and Procedure	Results and Indications	Proceed To
5.4 Test the fuel pump: Disconnect all fuel lines from the fuel pump. Hold a finger over the input fitting, crank the engine (with electric pump, turn the ignition or pump on); and feel for suction.	If suction is evident, blow out the fuel line to the tank with low pressure compressed air until bubbling is heard from the fuel filler neck. Also blow out the carburetor fuel line (both ends disconnected).	5.7
	If no suction is evident, replace or repair the fuel pump. **NOTE: Repeated oil fouling of the spark plugs, or a no-start condition, could be the result of a ruptured vacuum booster pump diaphragm, through which oil or gasoline is being drawn into the intake manifold (where applicable).**	5.7
5.5 Occasionally, small specks of dirt will clog the small jets and orifices in the carburetor. With the engine cold, hold a flat piece of wood or similar material over the carburetor, where possible, and crank the engine.	If the engine starts, but runs roughly the engine is probably not run enough.	
	If the engine won't start.	5.9
5.6 Check the needle and seat: Tap the carburetor in the area of the needle and seat.	If flooding stops, a gasoline additive (e.g., Gumout) will often cure the problem.	5.7
	If flooding continues, check the fuel pump for excessive pressure at the carburetor (according to specifications). If the pressure is normal, the needle and seat must be removed and checked, and/or the float level adjusted.	5.7
5.7 Test the accelerator pump by looking into the throttle bores while operating the throttle.	If the accelerator pump appears to be operating normally	5.8
	If the accelerator pump is not operating, the pump must be reconditioned. Where possible, service the pump with the carburetor(s) installed on the engine. If necessary, remove the carburetor. Prior to removal	5.8
5.8 Determine whether the carburetor main fuel system is functioning: Spray a commercial starting fluid into the carburetor while attempting to start the engine.	If the engine starts, runs for a few seconds, and dies	5.9
	If the engine doesn't start	6.1
5.9 Uncommon fuel system malfunctions: See below:	If the problem is solved	6.1
	If the problem remains, remove and recondition the carburetor.	

Check for gas at the carburetor by looking down the carburetor throat while someone moves the accelerator

Condition	Indication	Test	Prevailing Weather Conditions	Remedy
Vapor lock	Engine will not re-start shortly after running.	Cool the components of the fuel system until the engine starts. Vapor lock can be cured faster by draping a wet cloth over a mechanical fuel pump.	Hot to very hot	Ensure that the exhaust manifold heat control valve is operating. Check with the vehicle manufacturer for the recommended solution to vapor lock on the model in question.
Carburetor icing	Engine will not idle, stalls at low speeds.	Visually inspect the throttle plate area of the throttle bores for frost.	High humidity, 32–40° F.	Ensure that the exhaust manifold heat control valve is operating, and that the intake manifold heat riser is not blocked.
Water in the fuel	Engine sputters and stalls; may not start.	Pump a small amount of fuel into a glass jar. Allow to stand, and inspect for droplets of a layer of water.	High humidity, extreme temperature changes.	For droplets, use one or two cans of commercial gas line anti-freeze. For a layer of water, the tank must be drained, and the fuel lines blown out with compressed air.

SECTION 6—ENGINE COMPRESSION

Test and Procedure	Results and Indications	Proceed to
6.1 Test engine compression: Remove all spark plugs. Block the throttle wide open. Insert a compression gauge into a spark plug port, crank the engine to obtain the maximum reading, and record.	If compression is within limits on all cylinders	7.1
	If gauge reading is extremely low on all cylinders	6.2
	If gauge reading is low on one or two cylinders: (If gauge readings are identical and low on two or more adjacent cylinders, the head gasket must be replaced.)	6.2

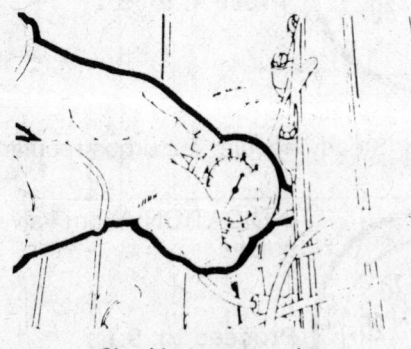

Checking compression

6.2 Test engine compression (wet): Squirt approximately 30 cc. of engine oil into each cylinder, and re-test per 6.1.	If the readings improve, worn or cracked rings or broken pistons are indicated:	See Car Section
	If the readings do not improve, burned or excessively carboned valves or a jumped timing chain are indicated.	7.1
	NOTE: A jumped timing chain is often indicated by difficult cranking.	

SECTION 7—ENGINE VACUUM

Test and Procedure	Results and Indications	Proceed to
7.1 Attach a vacuum gauge to the intake manifold beyond the throttle plate. Start the engine, and observe the action of the needle over the range of engine speeds.	See below.	**See below**

Normal engine

Gauge reading: Steady, from 17–22 in./Hg.

INDICATION: Normal engine in good condition

Proceed to: 8.1

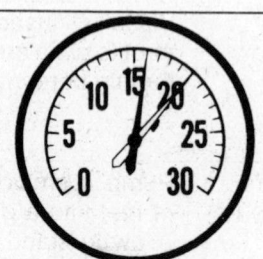

Sticking valves

Gauge reading: Intermittent fluctuation at idle

INDICATION: Sticking valves or ignition miss

Proceed to: 9.1, 8.3

Incorrect valve timing

Gauge reading: Low (10–15 in./Hg) but steady

INDICATION: Late ignition or valve timing, low compression, stuck throttle valve, leaking carburetor or manifold gasket

Proceed to: 6.1

Carburetor requires adjustment

Gauge reading: Drifting needle

INDICATION: Improper carburetor adjustment or minor intake leak.

Proceed to: 7.2

Blown head gasket

Gauge reading: Needle fluctuates as engine speed increases

INDICATION: Ignition miss, blown cylinder head gasket, leaking valve or weak valve spring

Proceed to: 8.3, 6.1

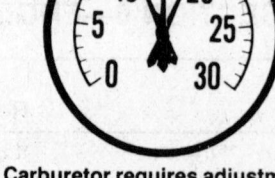

Burnt or leaking valves

Gauge reading: Steady needle, but drops regularly

INDICATION: Burnt valve or faulty valve clearance: Needle will fall when defective valve operates

Proceed to: 9.1

Clogged exhaust system

Gauge reading: Gradual drop in reading at idle

INDICATION: Choked muffler, excessive back pressure in system

Proceed to: 10.1

Worn valve guides

Gauge reading: Needle vibrates excessively at idle, but steadies as engine speed increases

INDICATION: Worn valve guides

Proceed to: 9.1

White pointer = steady gauge hand

Black pointer = fluctuating gauge hand

Test and Procedure	Results and Indications	Proceed To
7.2 Attach a vacuum gauge per 7.1, and test for an intake manifold leak. Squirt a small amount of oil around the intake manifold gaskets, carburetor gaskets, plugs and fittings. Observe the action of the vacuum gauge.	If the reading improves, replace the indicated gasket, or seal the indicated fitting or plug:	8.1
	If the reading remains low:	7.3
7.3 Test all vacuum hoses and accessories for leaks as described in 7.2. Also check the carburetor body (dashpots, automatic choke mechanism, throttle shafts) for leaks in the same manner.	If the reading improves, service or replace the offending part(s):	8.1
	If the reading remains low:	6.1

SECTION 8—SECONDARY ELECTRICAL SYSTEM

Test and Procedure	Results and Indications	Proceed to
8.1 Remove the distributor cap and check to make sure that the rotor turns when the engine is cranked. Visually inspect the distributor components.	Clean, tighten or replace any components which appear defective.	8.2
8.2 Connect a timing light (per manufacturer's recommendation) and check the dynamic ignition timing. Disconnect and plug the vacuum hose(s) to the distributor if specified, start the engine, and observe the timing marks at the specified engine speed.	If the timing is not correct, adjust to specifications by rotating the distributor in the engine: (Advance timing by rotating distributor opposite normal direction of rotor rotation, retard timing by rotating distributor in same direction as rotor rotation.)	8.3
8.3 Check the operation of the distributor advance mechanism(s): To test the mechanical advance, disconnect the vacuum lines from the distributor advance unit and observe the timing marks with a timing light as the engine speed is increased from idle. If the mark moves smoothly, without hesitation, it may be assumed that the mechanical advance is functioning properly. To test vacuum advance and/or retard systems, alternately crimp and release the vacuum line, and observe the timing mark for movement. If movement is noted, the system is operating.	If the systems are functioning	8.4
	If the systems are not functioning, remove the distributor, and test on a distributor tester.	8.4
8.4 Locate an ignition miss: With the engine running, remove each spark plug wire, one at a time, until one is found that doesn't cause the engine to roughen and slow down. **CAUTION: Do not pull on the wire to remove the boot from the plug. Be sure your hand is insulated from the wire.**	When the missing cylinder is identified	4.1

SECTION 9—VALVE TRAIN

Test and Procedure	Results and Indications	Proceed to
9.1 Evaluate the valve train: Remove the valve cover, and ensure that the valves are adjusted to specifications. A mechanic's stethoscope may be used to aid in the diagnosis of the valve train. By pushing the probe on or near push rods or rockers, valve noise often can be isolated. A timing light also may be used to diagnose valve problems. Connect the light according to manufacturer's recommendations, and start the engine. Vary the firing moment of the light by increasing the engine speed (and therefore the ignition advance), and moving the trigger from cylinder to cylinder. Observe the movement of each valve.	Sticking valves or erratic valve train motion can be observed with the timing light. The cylinder head must be disassembled for repairs.	**See Car Section**
9.2 Check the valve timing: Locate top dead center of the No. 1 piston, and install a degree wheel or tape on the crankshaft pulley or damper with zero corresponding to an index mark on the engine. Rotate the crankshaft in its direction of rotation, and observe the opening of the No. 1 cylinder intake valve. The opening should correspond with the correct mark on the degree wheel according to specifications.	If the timing is not correct, the timing cover must be removed for further investigation.	**See Car Section**

SECTION 10—EXHAUST SYSTEM

Test and Procedure	Results and Indications	Proceed to
10.1 Determine whether the exhaust manifold heat control valve is operating: Operate the valve by hand to determine whether it is free to move. If the valve is free, run the engine to operating temperature and observe the action of the valve, to ensure that it is opening.	If the valve sticks, spray it with a suitable solvent, open and close the valve to free it, and retest. If the valve functions properly If the valve does not free, or does not operate, replace the valve.	**10.2** **10.2**
10.2 Ensure that there are no exhaust restrictions: Visually inspect the exhaust system for kinks, dents, or crushing. Also note that gases are flowing freely from the tailpipe at all engine speeds, indicating no restriction in the muffler or resonator.	Replace any damaged portion of the system.	**11.1**

SECTION 11—COOLING SYSTEM

Test and Procedure	Results and Indications	Proceed to
11.1 Visually inspect the fan belt for glazing, cracks, and fraying, and replace if necessary. Tighten the belt so that the longest span has approximately ½″ play at its midpoint under thumb pressure (see Maintenance Section).	Replace or tighten the fan belt as necessary.	**11.2**

Checking belt tension

Test and Procedure	Results and Indications	Proceed to
11.2 Check the fluid level of the cooling system.	If full or slightly low, fill as necessary.	**11.5**
	If extremely low	**11.3**
11.3 Visually inspect the external portions of the cooling system (radiator, radiator hoses, thermostat elbow, water pump seals, heater hoses, etc.) for leaks. If none are found, pressurize the cooling system to 14–15 psi.	If cooling system holds the pressure	**11.5**
	If cooling system loses pressure rapidly, reinspect external parts of the system for leaks under pressure. If none are found, check dipstick for coolant in crankcase. If no coolant is present, but pressure loss continues	**11.4**
	If coolant is evident in crankcase, remove cylinder head(s), and check gasket(s). If gaskets are intact, block and cylinder head(s) should be checked for cracks or holes.	
	If the gasket(s) is blown, replace, and purge the crankcase of coolant.	**12.6**
	NOTE: Occasionally, due to atmospheric and driving conditions, condensation of water can occur in the crankcase. This causes the oil to appear milky white. To remedy, run the engine until hot, and change the oil and oil filter.	
11.4 Check for combustion leaks into the cooling system: Pressurize the cooling system as above. Start the engine, and observe the pressure gauge. If the needle fluctuates, remove each spark plug wire, one at a time, noting which cylinder(s) reduce or eliminate the fluctuation.	Cylinders which reduce or eliminate the fluctuation, when the spark plug wire is removed, are leaking into the cooling system. Replace the head gasket on the affected cylinder bank(s).	**See Car Section**

Pressurizing the cooling system

Test and Procedure	Results and Indications	Proceed To
11.5 Check the radiator pressure cap: Attach a radiator pressure tester to the radiator cap (wet the seal prior to installation). Quickly pump up the pressure, noting the point at which the cap releases.	If the cap releases within ±1 psi of the specified rating, it is operating properly.	**11.6**
	If the cap releases at more than ±1 psi of the specified rating, it should be replaced.	**11.6**

Checking radiator pressure cap

Test and Procedure	Results and Indications	Proceed To
11.6 Test the thermostat: Start the engine cold, remove the radiator cap, and insert a thermometer into the radiator. Allow the engine to idle. After a short while, there will be a sudden, rapid increase in coolant temperature. The temperature at which this sharp rise stops is the thermostat opening temperature.	If the thermostat opens at or about the specified temperature	**11.7**
	If the temperature doesn't increase (If the temperature increases slowly and gradually, replace the thermostat.)	**11.7**
11.7 Check the water pump: Remove the thermostat elbow and the thermostat, disconnect the coil high tension lead (to prevent starting), and crank the engine momentarily.	If coolant flows, replace the thermostat and retest per 11.6.	**11.6**
	If coolant doesn't flow, reverse flush the cooling system to alleviate any blockage that might exist. If system is not blocked, and coolant will not flow, replace the water pump.	**See Car Section**

FAN CLUTCH DIAGNOSIS

Air conditioned vehicles originally come equipped from the factory with either a thermostatically controlled fan clutch bolted to a rigid fan or a flexible fan with no fan clutch. If your vehicle is equipped with a fan clutch and any of the following circumstances exist, the fan clutch should probably be replaced.

1. If the engine is overheating and the fan spins freely or does not engage.

2. Manually move the fan back and forth. If there is excessive fan clutch play of more than a ¼ inch the clutch bearing is probably worn.

3. Fluid leakage or greasy dirt build-up around the outer seal at the center of the thermostat spring.

4. A hot engine in the "off" position which allows easy revolving of the fan manually, from 1-1½ revolutions indicates a weak clutch.

5. If the fan is frozen and cannot be rotated by hand, or if hand rotation makes a harsh, rumbling noise, the bearing is defective.

6. The fan clutch is mounted on the water pump between the water pump shaft and the fan. Any vibration can mean a worn bearing in the water pump or fan clutch. Since the fan clutch and the water pump have about the same life span, it generally makes good sense to replace both at the same time.

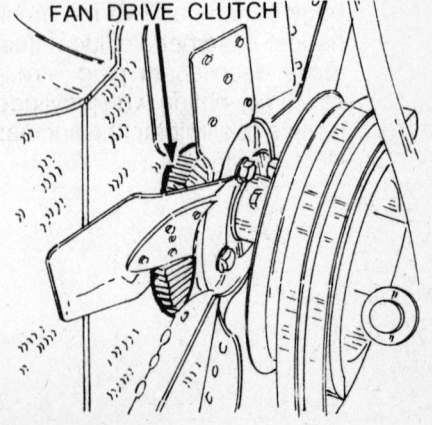

FAN DRIVE CLUTCH

GENERAL CONVERSION TABLE

Multiply By	To Convert	To	—
Length			**—**
2.54	Inches	Centimeters	.3937
25.4	Inches	Millimeters	.03937
30.48	Feet	Centimeters	.0328
.304	Feet	Meters	3.28
.914	Yards	Meters	1.094
1.609	Miles	Kilometers	.621
Volume			
.473	Pints	Liters	2.11
.946	Quarts	Liters	1.06
3.785	Gallons	Liters	.264
.016	Cubic inches	Liters	61.02
16.39	Cubic inches	Cubic cms.	.061
28.3	Cubic feet	Liters	.0353
Mass (Weight)			
28.35	Ounces	Grams	.035
.4536	Pounds	Kilograms	2.20
Area			
.645	Square inches	Square cms.	.155
.836	Square yds.	Square meters	1.196
Force			
4.448	Pounds	Newtons	.225
.138	Ft./lbs.	Kilogram/meters	7.23
1.36	Ft./lbs.	Newton-meters	.737
.112	In./lbs.	Newton-meters	8.844
Pressure			
.068	Psi	Atmospheres	14.7
6.89	Psi	Kilopascals	.145
Other			
1.104	Horsepower (DIN)	Horsepower (SAE)	.9861
.746	Horsepower (SAE)	Kilowatts (KW)	1.34
1.60	Mph	Km/h	.625
.425	Mpg	Km/1	2.35
—	**To obtain**	**From**	**Multiply by**

TAP DRILL SIZES

NATIONAL COARSE OR U.S.S.				NATIONAL FINE OR S.A.E.			
Screw & Tap Size	Threads Per Inch	Use Drill Number		Screw & Tap Size	Threads Per Inch	Use Drill Number	
No. 5	40	39		No. 5	44	37	
No. 6	32	36		No. 6	40	33	
No. 8	32	29		No. 8	36	29	
No. 10	24	25		No. 10	32	21	
No. 12	24	17		No. 12	28	15	
1/4	20	8		1/4	28	3	
5/16	18	F		5/16	24	1	
3/8	16	5/16		3/8	24	Q	
7/16	14	U		7/16	20	W	
1/2	13	27/64		1/2	20	29/64	
9/16	12	31/64		9/16	18	33/64	
5/8	11	17/32		5/8	18	37/64	
3/4	10	21/32		3/4	16	11/16	
7/8	9	49/64		7/8	14	13/16	
1	8	7/8		1 1/8	12	1 3/64	
1 1/8	7	63/64		1 1/4	12	1 11/64	
1 1/4	7	1 7/64		1 1/2	12	1 27/64	
1 1/2	6	1 11/32					

MECHANIC'S DATA

DRILL SIZES IN DECIMAL EQUIVALENTS

Inch	Decimal	Wire	mm
1/64	.0156		.39
	.0157		.4
	.0160	78	
	.0165		.42
	.0173		.44
	.0177		.45
	.0180	77	
	.0181		.46
	.0189		.48
	.0197		.5
	.0200	76	
	.0210	75	
	.0217		.55
	.0225	74	
	.0236		.6
	.0240	73	
	.0250	72	
	.0256		.65
	.0260	71	
	.0276		.7
	.0280	70	
	.0292	69	
	.0295		.75
	.0310	68	
1/32	.0312		.79
	.0315		.8
	.0320	67	
	.0330	66	
	.0335		.85
	.0350	65	
	.0354		.9
	.0360	64	
	.0370	63	
	.0374		.95
	.0380	62	
	.0390	61	
	.0394		1.0
	.0400	60	
	.0410	59	
	.0413		1.05
	.0420	58	
	.0430	57	
	.0433		1.1
	.0453		1.15
	.0465	56	
3/64	.0469		1.19
	.0472		1.2
	.0492		1.25
	.0512		1.3
	.0520	55	
	.0531		1.35
	.0550	54	
	.0551		1.4
	.0571		1.45
	.0591		1.5
	.0595	53	

Inch	Decimal	Wire	mm
	.0610		1.55
1/16	.0625		1.59
	.0630		1.6
	.0635	52	
	.0650		1.65
	.0669		1.7
	.0670	51	
	.0689		1.75
	.0700	50	
	.0709		1.8
	.0728		1.85
	.0730	49	
	.0748		1.9
	.0760	48	
	.0768		1.95
5/64	.0781		1.98
	.0785	47	
	.0787		2.0
	.0807		2.05
	.0810	46	
	.0820	45	
	.0827		2.1
	.0846		2.15
	.0860	44	
	.0866		2.2
	.0886		2.25
	.0890	43	
	.0906		2.3
	.0925		2.35
3/32	.0935	42	
	.0938		2.38
	.0945		2.4
	.0960	41	
	.0965		2.45
	.0980	40	
	.0981		2.5
	.0995	39	
	.1015	38	
	.1024		2.6
	.1040	37	
	.1063		2.7
	.1065	36	
	.1083		2.75
7/64	.1094		2.77
	.1100	35	
	.1102		2.8
	.1110	34	
	.1130	33	
	.1142		2.9
	.1160	32	
	.1181		3.0
	.1200	31	
	.1220		3.1
1/8	.1250		3.17
	.1260		3.2
	.1280		3.25

Inch	Decimal	Wire	mm
	.1285	30	
	.1299		3.3
	.1339		3.4
	.1360	29	
	.1378		3.5
	.1405	28	
9/64	.1406		3.57
	.1417		3.6
	.1440	27	
	.1457		3.7
	.1470	26	
	.1476		3.75
	.1495	25	
	.1496		3.8
	.1520	24	
	.1535		3.9
	.1540	23	
5/32	.1562		3.96
	.1570	22	
	.1575		4.0
	.1590	21	
	.1610	20	
	.1614		4.1
	.1654		4.2
	.1660	19	
	.1673		4.25
	.1693		4.3
	.1695	18	
11/64	.1719		4.36
	.1730	17	
	.1732		4.4
	.1770	16	
	.1772		4.5
	.1800	15	
	.1811		4.6
	.1820	14	
	.1850	13	
	.1850		4.7
	.1870		4.75
3/16	.1875		4.76
	.1890		4.8
	.1890	12	
	.1910	11	
	.1929		4.9
	.1935	10	
	.1960	9	
	.1969		5.0
	.1990	8	
	.2008		5.1
	.2010	7	
13/64	.2031		5.16
	.2040	6	
	.2047		5.2
	.2055	5	
	.2067		5.25
	.2087		5.3

Inch	Decimal	Wire & Letter	mm
	.2090	4	
	.2126		5.4
	.2130	3	
	.2165		5.5
7/32	.2188		5.55
	.2205		5.6
	.2210	2	
	.2244		5.7
	.2264		5.75
	.2280	1	
	.2283		5.8
	.2323		5.9
	.2340	A	
15/64	.2344		5.95
	.2362		6.0
	.2380	B	
	.2402		6.1
	.2420	C	
	.2441		6.2
	.2460	D	
	.2461		6.25
	.2480		6.3
1/4	.2500	E	6.35
	.2520		6.4
	.2559		6.5
	.2570	F	
	.2598		6.6
	.2610	G	
	.2638		6.7
17/64	.2656		6.74
	.2657		6.75
	.2660	H	
	.2677		6.8
	.2717		6.9
	.2720	I	
	.2756		7.0
	.2770	J	
	.2795		7.1
	.2810	K	
9/32	.2812		7.14
	.2835		7.2
	.2854		7.25
	.2874		7.3
	.2900	L	
	.2913		7.4
	.2950	M	
	.2953		7.5
19/64	.2969		7.54
	.2992		7.6
	.3020	N	
	.3031		7.7
	.3051		7.75
	.3071		7.8
	.3110		7.9
5/16	.3125		7.93
	.3150		8.0

Inch	Decimal	Letter	mm
	.3160	O	
	.3189		8.1
	.3228		8.2
	.3230	P	
	.3248		8.25
	.3268		8.3
21/64	.3281		8.33
	.3307		8.4
	.3320	Q	
	.3346		8.5
	.3386		8.6
	.3390	R	
	.3425		8.7
11/32	.3438		8.73
	.3445		8.75
	.3465		8.8
	.3480	S	
	.3504		8.9
	.3543		9.0
	.3580	T	
	.3583		9.1
	.3594		9.12
23/64	.3622		9.2
	.3642		9.25
	.3661		9.3
	.3680	U	
	.3701		9.4
	.3740		9.5
3/8	.3750		9.52
	.3770	V	
	.3780		9.6
	.3819		9.7
	.3839		9.75
	.3858		9.8
	.3860	W	
	.3898		9.9
25/64	.3906		9.92
	.3937		10.0
	.3970	X	
	.4040	Y	
13/32	.4062		10.31
	.4130	Z	
	.4134		10.5
27/64	.4219		10.71
	.4331		11.0
7/16	.4375		11.11
	.4528		11.5
29/64	.4531		11.51
15/32	.4688		11.90
	.4724		12.0
31/64	.4844		12.30
	.4921		12.5
1/2	.5000		12.70
	.5118		13.0
33/64	.5156		13.09
17/32	.5312		13.49

Inch	Decimal	mm
	.5315	13.5
35/64	.5469	13.89
	.5512	14.0
9/16	.5625	14.28
	.5709	14.5
37/64	.5781	14.68
	.5906	15.0
19/32	.5938	15.08
	.6094	15.47
	.6102	15.5
5/8	.6250	15.87
	.6299	16.0
41/64	.6406	16.27
	.6496	16.5
21/32	.6562	16.66
	.6693	17.0
43/64	.6719	17.06
11/16	.6875	17.46
	.6890	17.5
45/64	.7031	17.85
	.7087	18.0
23/32	.7188	18.25
	.7283	18.5
47/64	.7344	18.65
	.7480	19.0
3/4	.7500	19.05
49/64	.7656	19.44
	.7677	19.5
25/32	.7812	19.84
	.7874	20.0
51/64	.7969	20.24
	.8071	20.5
13/16	.8125	20.63
	.8268	21.0
53/64	.8281	21.03
27/32	.8438	21.43
	.8465	21.5
55/64	.8594	21.82
	.8661	22.0
7/8	.8750	22.22
	.8858	22.5
57/64	.8906	22.62
	.9055	23.0
29/32	.9062	23.01
59/64	.9219	23.41
	.9252	23.5
15/16	.9375	23.81
	.9449	24.0
61/64	.9531	24.2
	.9646	24.5
31/32	.9688	24.6
	.9843	25.0
63/64	.9844	25.0
1	1.0000	25.4